The Making, Shaping and Treating of Steel

EDITED BY

HAROLD E. McGANNON

UNITED STATES STEEL

Eighth Edition

vi

PREFACE

Since 1920, "The Making, Shaping and Treating of Steel" has provided steel makers and users, manufacturers and suppliers of steel-plant equipment, educators and students, and others, with a source of facts relating to the raw materials, processes and products of iron- and steelmaking. The ever-broadening scope of ferrous metallurgy and the rapid technological changes of the recent past made this Eighth Edition necessary.

Preparation of the new edition was under the direction of Messrs. S. M. Jenks, Executive Vice President—Engineering and Research, and J. B. Austin, Administrative Vice President—Research and Technology.

Many United States Steel personnel cooperated in the work. Manuscripts for the individual chapters were checked for completeness and accuracy by the following individuals and their associates: Messrs. W. J. Bates, P. W. Chase, J. A. Eckel, W. Foster, G. H. Gaynor, C. J. Hunter, M. W. Lightner, O. T. Marzke, W. H. Mayo, and E. L. Tindall. This work was coordinated by R. F. Miller.

Collection of information and illustrations, writing of new material and updating of former chapters involved major contributions by Messrs. J. C. Agarwal, J. S. Alter, S. Arnold 3rd, J. J. Beinlich, J. Bigos, A. L. Billeter, C. A. Bishop, J. J. Bosley, W. A. Cureton, W. S. Debenham, F. A. Dudderar, J. R. England, D. O. Gittings, D. T. Goettge, G. J. Haddad, H. W. Hannigan, J. J. Heger, J. M. Hodge, C. G. Hogberg, F. P. Hubbell, W. R. Huber, G. J. Hurlston, G. T. Jones, B. J. Kelly, W. L. Kerlie, R. J. King, G. D. Lawrence, R. R. Leo, J. W. Levergood, H. S. Link, R. L. Livingston, R. M. Lloyd, R. W. Marsden, D. L. McBride, M. P. McDermitt, G. A. McGrann, R. B. Mears, A. Montgomery, Jr., R. C. Myers, R. A. Neish, W. F. Nicoden, D. O. Northrup, W. I. Ong, M. A. Orehoski, R. I. Packer, H. A. Parker, E. H. Phelps, F. O. Phillips, O. Richmond, D. Max Seeley, J. F. Sigh, R. W. Simon, J. M. Stapleton, H. A. Starr, S. H. Steffey, R. L. Stephenson, H. G. Stout, A. M. Tohir, D. A. Toland, W. R. Trognitz, E. T. Turkdogan, H. L. von Ende, A. V. Wiebel and J. H. Zorn. The majority of the art work was executed by Miss M. H. Snyder. Miss H. E. Kaiser assisted with proofreading.

The assistance of everyone who contributed in any way to the completion of this edition is duly acknowledged, for without the help of each participant, the preparation of a timely and accurate volume would have been impossible.

The Editor

Pittsburgh, Pa.

August, 1964

TABLE OF CONTENTS

THE MAKING, SHAPING
AND
TREATING OF STEEL

CHAPTER 1

Evolution Of Iron- And Steelmaking

SECTION 1

FERROUS METALS IN ANTIQUITY

Prehistoric and Ancient Use of Iron—The antiquity of man's use of iron is attested by references to that metal both in fragmentary writings and in inscriptions on monuments, palaces and tombs that survived the collapse of such ancient civilizations as those of Assyria, Babylonia, Egypt, China, India, Greece and Rome. In addition to these written records, archeologists have unearthed actual iron tools, weapons and ornaments used by many of these historic ancient peoples, as well as some implements and jewelry of iron in sites in many parts of the world that were occupied by prehistoric peoples who left no written records. The chemical composition and the properties of the metals in these specimens vary widely. Some closely resemble modern wrought iron; some are more nearly like steel as it is known today. For the sake of simplicity, all of the ancient ferrous metals discussed in this section will be referred to as "iron." In later sections the modern meanings of "iron," "steel," "wrought iron," etc., will be clearly defined and the words used in their proper, more exact sense.

Meteoric Iron—Mere mention of the use of iron in the oral traditions or writings of primitive or prehistoric peoples does not necessarily mean that they knew how to produce iron by extracting it from ore. Actually, there is evidence that most of the iron used in earliest times was not man-made, but was obtained from fragments of meteorites. This belief in the origin of the iron used by very ancient peoples is based on three facts. In the first place, practically all of their names for iron, when translated, mean **"stone (or hard substance or metal) from heaven," "star metal"** or have similar meanings that suggest that the metal they used came from outside the earth. Secondly, chemical analysis of numerous archeological specimens has established that they contain considerable quantities of nickel which likewise is found in similar quantities (usually 7 to 15 per cent, but sometimes as high as 30 per cent) in the iron of meteorites. The third instance supporting this belief is that many primitive peoples of relatively recent times used iron from meteorites to make useful implements. In several historical cases, the main masses of huge meteorites from which the natives had laboriously severed bits of the metal were still in existence in the places where they had fallen and still served as sources of supply.

Telluric (Native) Iron—Gold, silver, copper and some other metals known to the ancients often are found on or near the surface of the ground in a fairly pure metallic condition, in the form of nuggets or rough masses. Being bright in appearance, such native metals are noticed readily and, as they are capable of being shaped by hammering without heating, they were put to eventual use by primitive peoples. The softness of gold and silver made them useless for ordinary tools and weapons, and their ultimate chief use was for vessels and ornament. The metal copper, however, can be hardened appreciably by hammering it without previous heating, and the very hammering required to shape a tool from native copper makes it sufficiently hard to be useful for many purposes.

Iron, however, is very rarely found in the native state. One of the few known occurrences of native iron is in Northwestern Greenland; the iron occurs as grains or nodules in basalt (an iron-bearing igneous rock) that erupted through beds of coal. Mention might be made of two very rare natural nickel-iron alloys, given the mineralogical names of **awaruite** ($FeNi_2$) and **josephinite** (Fe_3Ni_5), that have been found in the form of granules and small bean-shaped pebbles. It is improbable, therefore, that primitive man could have found any useful quantity of naturally occurring metallic iron, certainly not enough to account for the widespread distribution of iron artifacts that have been discovered by archeologists.

Man-Made Iron—From the foregoing it may be deduced that iron must have been a rare metal for many centuries and that any specimens of it would be highly prized by the possessor. It was not until man learned how to extract iron from its ores that it could have become a common metal.

Archeological evidence seems to indicate that a knowledge of how to obtain copper from its ores existed long before iron was intentionally made by man. Mixtures (alloys) of copper and tin that formed **bronze,** and of copper and zinc that formed **brass,** provided the ancients with metals that found widespread usage. In a book such as this, devoted to a discussion of iron and steel, space limitations permit only brief mention of these non-ferrous metals. It should be remembered, however, that for many years after man learned how to extract iron from its ores, the product probably was so relatively soft and unpredictable, and undoubtedly hard to work, that bronze in particular continued to be preferred for many tools and weapons. Eventually, iron supplanted the nonferrous metals for these purposes when men learned how to master the difficult arts of smelting, forging and hardening iron.

The origin of the methods used by early man for extracting iron from its ores is unknown. The rocky, granular or earthy ores gave little promise or outward indication of their valuable content. Some have suggested that men learned the method accidentally, when they built fires by chance on crude hearths built of iron-bearing rock in a location where a strong, natural draft caused the fire to burn fiercely. This is a possibility, since what could happen under such circumstances would meet the conditions now known to be required for extracting iron from its ores. These conditions are that the **iron-bearing ore should be heated strongly in contact with hot carbon out of contact with air.** Small lumps of ore on a hearth, surrounded completely by hot coals, might meet these requirements. The important iron ores consist mostly of combinations of iron with oxygen. The process just outlined causes the oxygen of the iron oxide to combine with the hot carbon, leaving metallic iron; in modern language, the iron is said to have been **reduced** from its oxides, and the process whereby the reduction is effected is called **smelting.** Some of the early smelting processes are described in Sections 2 and 3 of this chapter.

It may be assumed that such chance production of iron occurred often enough in the experience of one individual or tribe to attract attention and eventually to excite a desire to reproduce the process deliberately, whenever desired. It should be remembered, however, that the high melting point of iron kept it from ever becoming fluid under such conditions. Copper, on the other hand, could be obtained in the fluid state from the smelting operation, and was quite obviously a desirable product that could be shaped either by casting directly into molds or by hammering a solidified lump. Bronze and brass also could be melted in the furnaces available to the ancient metallurgist. The iron reduced in smelting, however, would collect in a loosely coherent mass or "sponge" of metallic granules that would contain much slag in its pores. There would be nothing in its appearance to indicate the potential value of the crude, sponge-like mass. The key step probably occurred when some early man first discovered that if this unattractive mass was hammered while still hot, slag would be forced out and a lump of reasonably sound metal would result. Repeated heating and hammering would eventually be found to further improve the product, since such operations were necessary to the shaping of the lump into a useful implement.

The manufacture of iron on a relatively large scale could be undertaken once the smelting process was established and its limitations, as outlined above, were understood. Some ancient peoples mastered the principles and practices of smelting iron much earlier than others, and many instances in history point to the rapid rise and eventual ascendancy of the iron-producing nations over their backward neighbors. It is not known definitely whether the knowledge of ironmaking spread from a single point of original discovery or whether it was developed independently in several widely separated localities.

Archeological Evidence—Some of the oldest known iron objects found in various localities include one piece found in the Great Pyramid (built about 2900 B.C.) and another in a grave at Abydos (from about 2600 B.C.), both in Egypt. A cube of iron was found in an 1800 B.C. grave at Knossos in Crete. Tombs at Pylos in the Peloponnesian peninsula of Greece contained iron finger rings dating from around 1550 B.C. What was probably an iron dagger was found at the site of Ur of the Chaldees and is believed to date from 3100 B.C. None of the foregoing are believed to have been fashioned from man-made iron. Tools and weapons of man-made iron were discovered at Gerar, near Gaza in Biblical Palestine, and some of the iron knives found there are believed to go back to 1350 B.C.; remains of iron-working furnaces from about 1200 B.C. were also unearthed at this site. The dates given here are only relative, since archeological research is continually turning up new evidence that necessitates frequent revision of chronology.

References made to iron in very ancient writings from China and India suggest that the metal was used in those areas at least as early as 2000 B.C., but there is nothing to indicate that the iron was man-made. Some authorities ascribe the original discovery of practical iron smelting to peoples in India at a very early date.

On the basis of existing evidence, the deliberate smelting of ore to produce iron seems to have begun to be practiced to an ever-increasing extent over a relatively wide geographic area in the ancient world between 1350 B.C. and 1100 B.C. After the latter date, the art of iron-making seems to have become generally practiced, at least by the more advanced peoples.

There is little doubt of some use of iron by the ancient Hebrews, by the Assyrians (about 1400 B.C.), and by the Greeks. The metalworking activities of the Greeks involved little iron, while the Romans became somewhat proficient in its metallurgy. The Romans through their conquests—the success of which they no doubt owed to a considerable extent to the use of metals in making their engines of war—spread the art of extracting and fashioning iron throughout Europe. Some knowledge of the metal had preceded them, however, for Julius Caesar found it in use by the native Britons when he crossed the English Channel and invaded their country (55 and 54 B.C.).

It must not be inferred that the peoples of all areas advanced the art of smelting iron to the same degree over the same period of time; isolated peoples in India, Africa, and Malaya, for example, still employ crude iron-smelting processes not unlike those of other more advanced peoples of 3000 years ago. Neither must it be assumed that, as soon as man-made iron became available, iron at once supplanted stone, bronze, brass, and other materials in tools and weapons. In some localities, tools and weapons of both stone and metals were in simultaneous use for some time until the metals completely took the place of stone. Iron gradually and eventually replaced bronze, brass and the other then-known metals wherever the superior properties of iron made it desirable. The properties of bronze and brass, which could be melted readily and cast into shape, depended largely on their chemical composition. The properties of objects made from iron, however, were more dependent upon the care and skill expended in smelting, forging and hardening, as described below.

Products of Ancient Iron Smelting—According to the usual manner in which early smelting processes probably were carried out, the product would be soft, malleable, wrought iron. If the temperature was high enough and the lump of reduced iron, intentionally or unintentionally, was kept long enough in contact with hot charcoal, away from contact with air, the pasty sponge of iron could be made to absorb carbon from the fuel. Absorption of moderate amounts of carbon (up to, say, one per cent) would cause the metal to become capable of being made very hard by cooling rapidly from a high temperature, in a manner comparable to modern steels. "Soft" wrought iron, containing only very small amounts of carbon, cannot be hardened appreciably by such treatment. Carbon might similarly be absorbed during repeated heating of the metal in charcoal forge fires prior to hammering to make a tool or weapon. Carbon could also be added to iron by variations of the crucible and cementation processes discussed in Section 5 of this chapter.

The metal now called "steel," in its simplest form, is essentially an alloy of pure iron with less than 2 per cent carbon. As mentioned above, one of the important properties of iron alloyed with moderate amounts of carbon is its ability to become very hard by rapidly cooling (**quenching**) it from a high temperature, providing that it contains sufficient carbon. This effect evidently was known at an early date. It also was known that the quenched metal, which was very hard and somewhat brittle, could be reheated to a relatively low temperature after quenching to make it less brittle without too drastically lessening the hardness obtained by quenching. This latter process is now known as **tempering.**

Judgment and skill of the operator were the only means of control of any of the early smelting or hardening methods, since nothing was known of the metallurgical principles which governed them. In smelting, the metal was not predictably uniform from one operation to the next, and a large part of the iron in the ore was lost to the slag. This lack of uniformity in the product of the smelting operation made it impossible to use other than "rule-of-thumb" methods for carrying out the hardening treatment, and failure to obtain the desired results was probably common. In some areas, the iron ores also contained some other metals beneficial to the properties of the iron with which they became alloyed during smelting (manganese, for instance), and the metals produced from such ores were so superior as to become justly celebrated, although the reason for the superiority was not then known.

Early Cast Iron—The more carbon an alloy of iron with carbon contains, up to something over 4 per cent carbon, the lower the melting point of the alloy will be. As mentioned earlier, iron reduced from ore in the smelting process could absorb carbon from the fuel in the hearth or furnace if the spongy metal was kept surrounded by the hot charcoal in a location where it was protected from contact with air. It was even possible for at least parts of the "sponge" to absorb enough carbon (say, 2.5 to 3 per cent) so that the melting point of those parts of the metal was lowered to such a degree that molten high-carbon iron was produced. In most cases, the lumps that formed when the liquid metal solidified were thrown away by the early smelters as worthless, since they were not malleable even when heated. Eventually, it was learned how to produce such molten iron deliberately in special types of furnaces, from which it was poured into molds of the desired shapes to make useful articles. Specimens of cast-iron utensils are extant, notably in China, dating back to at least 200 B.C. As larger and larger smelting furnaces were used (see Section 3 of this chapter), molten high-carbon iron eventually came to be the chief product of smelting. The molten iron might be run directly from the furnace into molds to produce castings. Alternatively, the iron might be run into channels where it solidified into pieces of convenient size. Subsequently, this iron could be remelted as desired for casting into molds, or could be treated by various processes to make wrought iron and steel. Details of wrought-iron manufacture by direct and indirect processes, respectively, are given in Sections 2 and 4 of this chapter; some early steelmaking processes are described in Section 5.

SECTION 2

DIRECT PROCESSES FOR MAKING WROUGHT IRON

Historical Background of Direct Processes—From about 1350 B.C. to 1300 A.D. all of the iron wrought into tools and weapons was produced directly from ore. Reduction of iron ore was carried out in a relatively simple manner using charcoal as fuel. In the earliest times the operation was carried out in crude hearths which eventually were superseded by furnaces of various designs having a strong family resemblance.

In the first smelting hearths or furnaces, natural draft alone supplied the air for combustion. Later, it seems to have been the practice to construct the hearth on a hillside or at the base of a cliff facing in

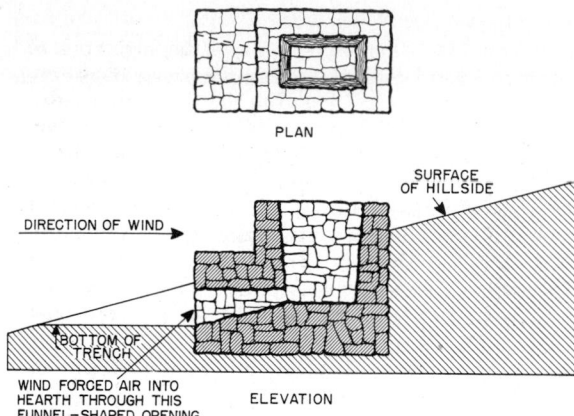

FIG. 1—1. Schematic representation of an early smelting furnace, built on a hillside to take advantage of the direction of prevailing winds to supply a gentle blast. Actual discovered remains of similar furnaces indicate that the hearth of such furnaces may have been relatively shallower and greater in area in proportion to their height.

the direction of a prevailing wind (Figure 1—1). A wind of suitable direction and velocity could be led into the burning fuel bed through an opening in the hearth or furnace wall to provide the air blast required to produce strong combustion of the charcoal fuel. Still later, devices for blowing air into the fuel bed were developed to make the process independent of wind and weather. These devices ranged all the way from mouth-blown hollow reeds, through foot-operated bladders of animal skins, foot-operated bellows, hand-operated bellows, and air-blowing devices operated by treadmills and water wheels. Another device somewhat widely used was the **trompe,** which made use of the aspirating effect of a falling column of water inside a tube, to draw air in through holes in the sides of the tube near its top, and expel the air into a closed chamber at the bottom; the air was piped from this chamber to the furnace (see Figure 1—2).

In view of the many centuries in which the direct process was used, it is to be expected that many different methods and types of apparatus would have been developed. Little is known of the furnaces in use prior to the eighteenth century, but the majority were of the hearth type, while the remainder were of the shaft type and may be compared to small blast furnaces, as will be discussed later. While these furnaces might, and did, differ widely as to form, size, and materials of construction, the fundamental metallurgical principles were the same in all. Charcoal was the only fuel used: it served the triple purpose of (1) a fuel to supply heat, (2) a reducing agent, and (3) a protector to shield the hot reduced metal from the oxidizing influences of the air.

The Catalan Process—The **Catalan hearth,** as the furnace used in this process was called, was anywhere from 20 inches square and 16 inches deep to around 30 inches by 40 inches and something over two feet deep. The **nozzle** or **tuyere,** through which the blast

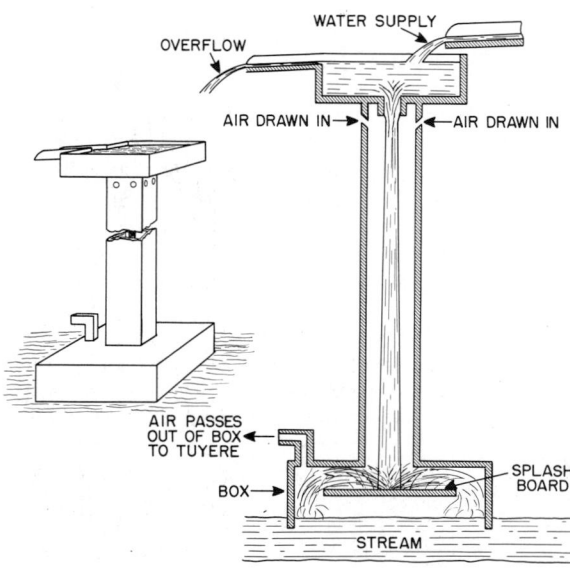

FIG. 1—2. (Right) Schematic representation of the operation of the trompe for utilizing the principle of aspiration to provide air blast for smelting furnaces. (Left) Sketch of external appearance of a trompe. The cross-section of the vertical column was more commonly round than square.

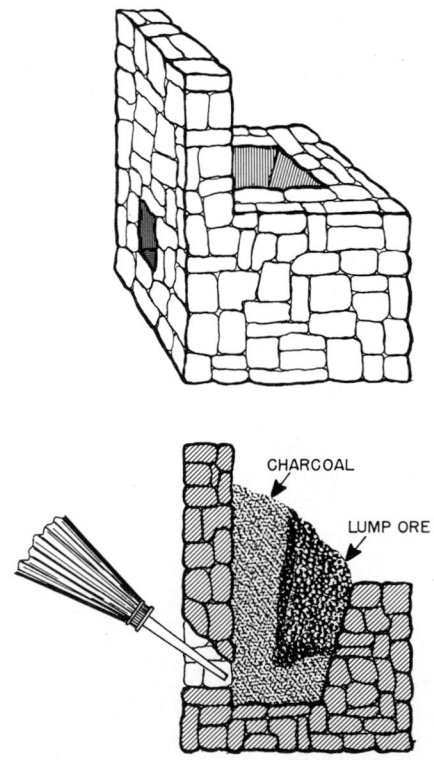

FIG. 1—3. (Above) Representation of a Catalan hearth or forge used for smelting iron ore up until relatively recent times. (Below) Cross section showing method of charging fuel and ore in the Catalan hearth, and approximate position of the nozzle supplied with air by a bellows.

was blown into the furnace, was placed about 9 inches from the bottom in the smaller hearths and about 15 inches from the bottom in the larger hearths. The hearth was filled to the level of the tuyere with charcoal, on which was piled lump ore together with charcoal. These materials were placed so as to form two separate columns, the charcoal against the tuyere side of the hearth, and the ore against the other side (Figure 1—3). A gentle blast of air was applied at first and carbon monoxide, formed by combustion of the charcoal, passed preferentially through the open pile of lump ore. The ore was reduced to metallic iron when the oxygen in the iron oxide of the ore combined with some of the carbon monoxide to form carbon dioxide. The waste gases escaped at the top of the charge. Charcoal (along with fine ore) was added at regular intervals to replace that consumed in combustion. After about two hours, the lump-ore column was gradually pushed downwards and the temperature of the hearth was raised by increasing the blast. As successive portions of the ore became reduced, they were pushed nearer the tuyere where the hearth was hottest. By the time the ore had reached the hotter regions, it was largely reduced to the metallic state.

The unreduced portion of the lump ore, along with part of the fine ore added periodically with charcoal, formed a siliceous slag of high iron content with the **gangue** (waste material). The metallic iron resulting from reduction of the ore became pasty at the temperatures existing near the tuyere, to form a coherent **loup** or **bloom.** After as much as possible of the ore had been reduced, the bloom was pried out of the hearth and hammered into bar form.

The American Bloomery—Among the variations of the process just described was the **American Bloomery Process** which was very similar to the Catalan process, differing from it chiefly in the fact that ore in a fine state, instead of in lumps, was mixed with charcoal to form the charge. The American bloomery represented the highest development in the simple hearth type of furnace for producing wrought iron. The bellows supplying the blast was operated by a water wheel or steam engine. The hearth was provided with a water-cooled metal bottom-plate, and cast-iron plates lined the sides. These hearths, rectangular in shape, were about 2 feet deep and 3 feet wide, and were surmounted by a tall chimney in the form of a truncated pyramid for carrying off the hot waste gases. The blast was heated (to save fuel) by passing the air through cast iron pipes around which the hot waste gases passed on their way from the furnace to the opening of the stack. Usually, bloomeries were open in front like an open fireplace, with the tuyere placed either at one side or at the back, about 20 inches above the bottom. Charcoal was first put into the hearth, the blast turned on, and when the fire was burning well, some ore was spread on the charcoal. Thereafter, charcoal and ore were added alternately until a sufficient amount of metal had collected upon the bottom. Then the iron, in a pasty mass and mixed with much slag, was removed from beneath the fuel bed with bars and tongs and hammered into a bloom. The last wrought iron to be produced by the bloomeries in this country was made in 1901.

SECTION 3

DEVELOPMENT OF THE BLAST FURNACE

It may be said in general that the blast furnace for producing molten high-carbon iron developed gradually from the early hearths in which only wrought iron was produced. The development consisted in gradually increasing the height of the furnace and introducing the charge at intervals through the top. These higher furnaces, distinguished as a class from the Catalan type of hearth or bloomery, were termed **shaft furnaces.** Originally developed by ironmakers of Central Europe, the new type of furnace was built of masonry that enclosed a vertical chamber in the form of two truncated cones placed base to base—in a crude way resembling the lines of a modern blast furnace (see Figure 1—4). The iron ore, flux and charcoal were charged into the top of the shaft, while air under relatively low pressure was blown into the furnace through a **tuyere** or tuyeres near the bottom of the structure.

Early Shaft-Type Furnaces—The **stuckofen** or **old high bloomery,** variations of which appear to have been called **salamander furnace, wolf furnace, wolf oven, wulf's oven** and **luppenofen** or **loup furnace,** evolved as described above from the Catalan type of hearth furnace. The earliest recorded sites of such shaft-type furnaces were in territories included in pre-World War II Germany (in Nassau, Siegen, and Saxony) and in parts of Austria, Belgium, and the Netherlands.

The stuckofen, in the state of development described around 1350 A.D., was a furnace 10 to 16 feet high; having a round, elliptical or rectangular shaft cross-section (greatest cross-sectional dimension about 3 to 4 feet).

One or two tuyeres supplied the blast, which entered the stuckofen somewhat over a foot above the hearth. Fuel and ore were charged into the top of the furnace, being replenished from time to time as smelting proceeded. A drawing hole was provided in the wall at the bottom of the shaft for extracting the blooms. This hole was closed by brick or stone work that was torn out each time a bloom was removed, after which the hole was again closed. Charcoal was the only fuel used.

The furnace called the wolf oven has been de-

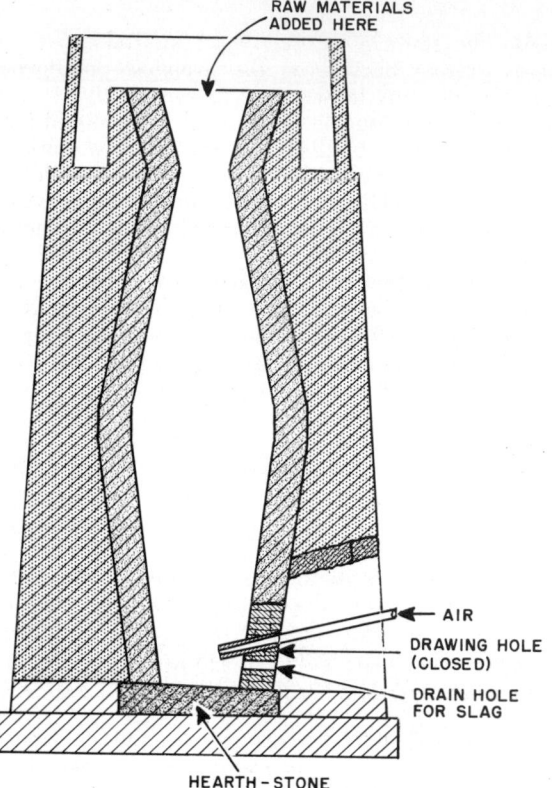

RAW MATERIALS
ADDED HERE

AIR

DRAWING HOLE
(CLOSED)

DRAIN HOLE
FOR SLAG

HEARTH-STONE

Fig. 1—4. Schematic cross-section of a stuckofen, equipped with a drawing hole for the extraction of the blooms. (After Percy.)

scribed as lower than the stuckofen, perhaps 6 to 7 feet in average height. Intermediate in size, between the wolf oven and the stuckofen, are the **blasofen** and **bauernofen**. The bauernofen corresponds to the **osmund furnace** (about 8 feet high) used in Sweden (a similar type was used in India). A type of furnace which originally resembled and was operated like the stuckofen, and was later adapted to produce either blooms of low-carbon wrought iron or molten, high-carbon iron, resembled a crude blast furnace and was termed **blauofen, blau furnace** or **blue furnace**.

The stuckofen may be considered as the forerunner of the modern blast furnace which produces only liquid, high-carbon iron. Liquid high-carbon iron often was produced in the stuckofen, intentionally or otherwise. This occurred when the reduced iron was in contact with hot fuel away from the blast long enough to absorb sufficient carbon to reduce its melting point to where it would become liquid. The height of the furnace made this possible, especially if the operating temperature was high enough. A **flussofen** was strictly a primitive blast furnace intended only to produce molten, high-carbon iron. The modern blast furnace, then, is a shaft furnace, gradually evolved from the stuckofen and flussofen. In its early days it was called a **high furnace**, from its German name, **hochofen** (French: **haut fourneaux**). It is designed solely to produce molten iron and operates continuously, in that the solid raw materials (ore, coke and limestone) are charged at the top at regular short intervals, and the molten iron and slag which collect in the hearth are tapped out at longer intervals.

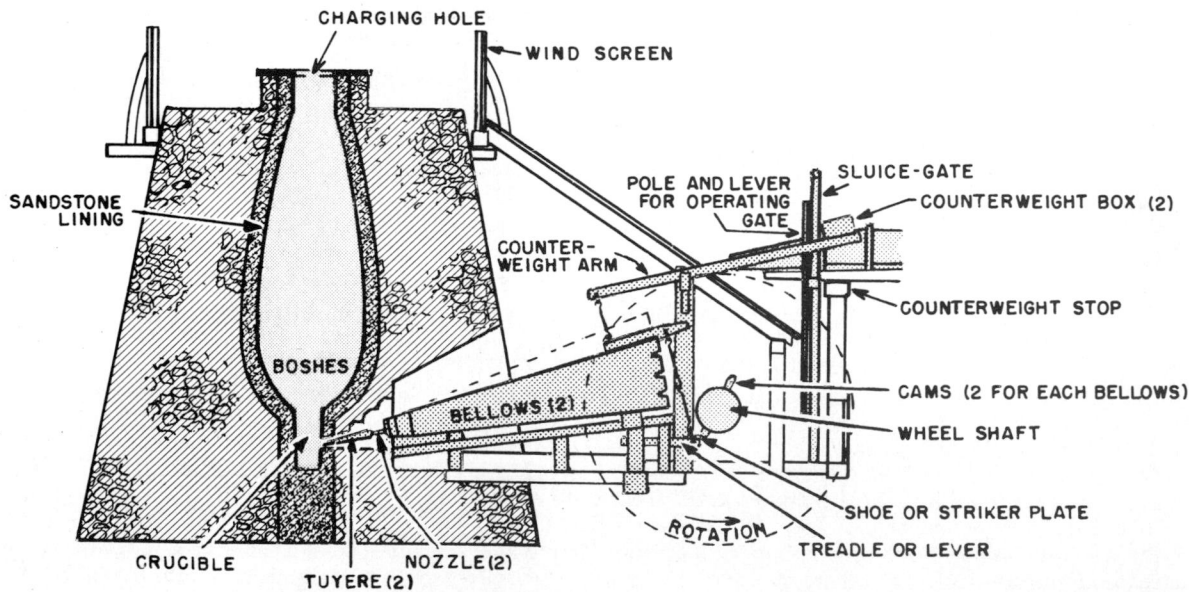

CHARGING HOLE

WIND SCREEN

SANDSTONE
LINING

POLE AND LEVER
FOR OPERATING
GATE

SLUICE-GATE

COUNTERWEIGHT BOX (2)

COUNTER-
WEIGHT ARM

COUNTERWEIGHT STOP

BOSHES

BELLOWS (2)

COUNTERWEIGHT STOP

CAMS (2 FOR EACH BELLOWS)

WHEEL SHAFT

SHOE OR STRIKER PLATE

ROTATION

TREADLE OR LEVER

CRUCIBLE

NOZZLE (2)

TUYERE (2)

Fig. 1—5. Schematic cross-section of the Hammersmith furnace near Saugus, Massachusetts, restored by the American Iron and Steel Institute. Water from the sluice turned the overshot water wheel. Cams on the axle of the wheel engaged the treadle or lever and exerted a squeezing force on the bellows that compressed the air for the blast. The raw materials were dumped into the charge hole at the top of the stack, and molten iron was run from the furnace through an opening in the wall of the crucible. This opening was near the bottom of the crucible on the side facing the reader, and was kept plugged except when molten iron was run. (See also Figure 1—8.)

The blast furnace was introduced into England about 1500 A.D. Coke was first used as a blast-furnace fuel in England in 1619. About 200 years later—again in England—the principle of heating the air before it was blown into the furnace was introduced: air so heated is referred to as **hot blast.**

In America, an iron works was established in Virginia on the James River about 1619; this was destroyed in an Indian raid in 1622 and never rebuilt. The Hammersmith (now Saugus), Massachusetts iron works was begun in 1645 and was the first successful iron works in what is now the United States, not being abandoned until 1675.

It is an interesting fact that the principal development connected with the blast furnace for over 400 years after its inception was the spread of its use to new localities. There was a strong family resemblance among all of the furnaces built during this period, although there were variations in size and in the design of machinery for supplying the blast, etc. For this reason, the Hammersmith furnace shown schematically in Figure 1—5 can serve as typical of American blast furnaces of as recently as 100 years ago.

The American furnaces of the middle Nineteenth Century now would be called very crude affairs. They were usually in the form of a truncated cone or pyramid, twenty to thirty feet high, and constructed of stonework which enclosed a shaft about four feet across at the top and eight feet at the bosh. The hearth was either round or square in cross section. The capacity ranged from one to six tons a day. In 1850, for example, the production of iron in the United States was reported to be 563,755 tons, produced by 377 establishments.

Rods and bands of wrought iron were employed in the construction of some of the larger furnaces to in- crease the stability of the stack, but the expansive forces present burst even the strongest practicable ties. The obvious answer was to completely enclose the stack in a "shell" constructed of wrought-iron plates: a furnace built at Port Henry, New York in 1854 was said to be the first to be enclosed completely in an iron shell. The shell type of construction gave to such furnaces the name of "cupola blast furnaces" (Figure 1—6).

The top of the early furnaces was open and the escaping gases burnt in the air above the furnace. Eventually, attempts were made to use the heat of the burning gases to preheat the blast air. The first devices for heating air were mounted on top of the stacks. A later development was the adoption of the closed top, that involved the invention of a bell-and-hopper arrangement that kept the top closed except when the bell was lowered to charge materials into the furnace. One of the first American furnaces to adopt the closed top was the Fletcherville charcoal blast furnace near Mineville, New York about 1870. This principle was later extended to the use of a double bell and hopper (1883) that made it possible to charge materials without ever completely opening the furnace top (Figure 1—7): this is the present usual closure.

As early as 1859 in this country (earlier abroad) attempts were made to collect the gases at the top of the furnace before they burned, and lead them through suitable piping to ground level, where they could be burned in special structures called "stoves" in which the blast air could be heated before it was blown into the furnace through the tuyeres. Stoves of both recuperative and regenerative types were developed: only the regenerative type is employed at present.

The development of better machinery for com-

FIG. 1—6. The Isabella Furnaces, constructed in 1871–72. These were both open-top furnaces originally. A third furnace was added to the plant a few years later. These furnaces are typical of the design referred to as cupola-type blast furnaces.

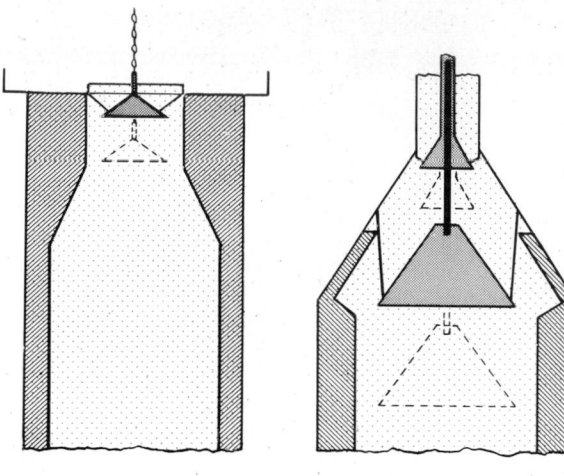

EARLY SINGLE BELL   MODERN DOUBLE BELL

FIG. 1—7. Schematic representation of the principle of operation of the single and double bell methods for effecting closure of a blast-furnace top. The distance the bells are lowered (as indicated by the dotted outlines) has been exaggerated for clarity.

pressing the blast air kept pace with—or even preceded—the construction of taller and larger furnaces. The water wheel that operated bellows or wooden cylinder-type blowing tubs was first replaced by the steam engine. Soon, steam-driven blowing engines of high capacity were developed and became standard for the larger furnaces about 1880. In the United States, the first gas-driven blowing engines were installed in 1903: these were internal-combustion engines that used cleaned blast-furnace gas as fuel. The most recent development for generation of the air blast is the turboblower, first used in 1910 and now the accepted means for the purpose. Some recently installed turboblowers have a capacity of 140,000 cubic feet per minute at a pressure of 40 lb. per sq. in.

The ore, fuel and flux for many of the early furnaces were brought to the charging hole atop the stack in barrows or wheeled carts that passed over a bridge leading from an adjacent elevation to the furnace (Figure 1—8). As furnaces grew taller, vertical hoists similar to elevators were employed to raise the barrows loaded at ground level to the top of the furnace (Figure 1—9). The men called "top fillers" then wheeled the materials to the charging position and dumped them onto the bell. As furnace capacity increased, it was impractical to handle the huge quantities of raw materials by manual methods. In 1883, the first inclined skip hoist (in conjunction with the first double bell and hopper) was installed on an American furnace to raise the raw materials in a skip car to the top of the furnace and automatically dump the contents of the car into a hopper above the small bell. The fact that a skip car always dumped its load in the same location interfered with the proper distribution of materials that was essential to smooth furnace operation, so that various means had to be developed to mechanically distribute the charge over the top bell: one of these consisted of a rotating hopper over the small bell that, with modifications, is generally employed on modern furnaces. Another method em-

FIG. 1—8. Exterior view of the restored Hammersmith furnace. Raw materials were brought to the charge hole at the top of the stone stack over the bridge in the upper left. The wooden wall surrounding the top of the stack served as a windbreak. The shed in the right foreground protected the area in front of the tap hole from which molten iron was run from the furnace. See also Figure 1—5. (Courtesy, M. H. Snyder.)

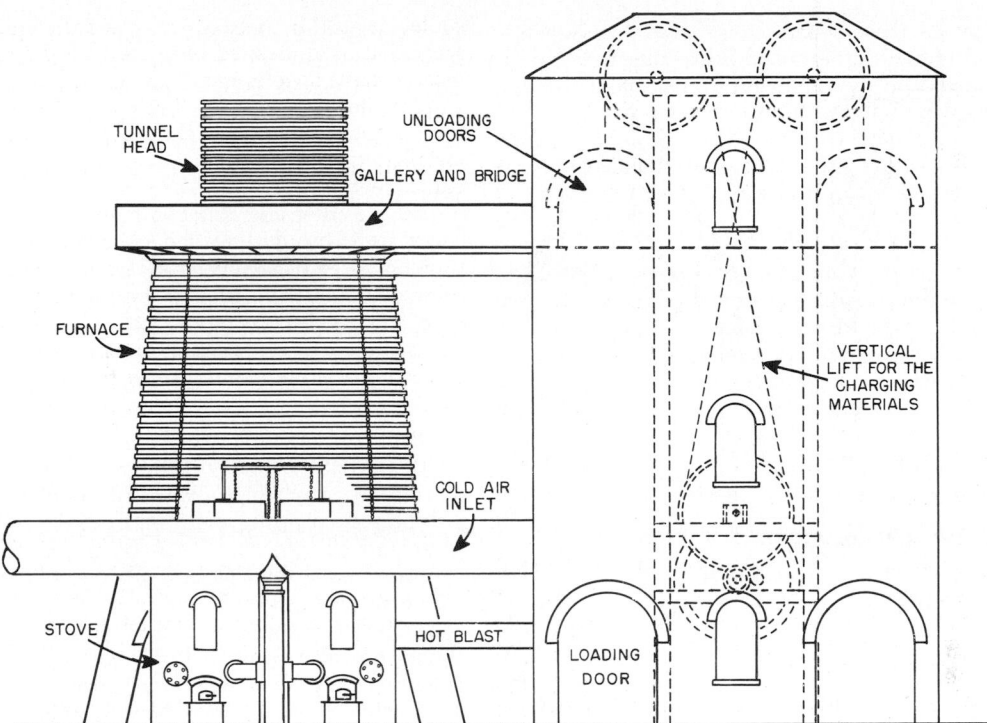

FIG. 1—9. An early blast-furnace plant, showing the vertical hoist (structure at the right) for lifting raw materials to the filling platform atop the stack. (After Percy.)

ployed a charging bucket that was rotated after filling in the stockhouse before delivering to the furnace top.

Increased production rates also forced the adoption of mechanical handling methods for handling and stocking raw materials before they were charged into the furnace skip car or bucket. Prior to 1890, raw materials were dumped from railroad cars run onto an elevated trestle, and manually moved to the stockhouse where the skip car or bucket was filled. In 1895, construction of the blast-furnace plant at Du-

quesne, Pa., included an ore yard with a stocking-bridge system similar to that employed in present-day blast-furnace plants: this was such a radically new principle that it was referred to as the "Duquesne revolution." The success of the new method led to its general adoption by the industry. This brief resume describes only some of the principal ideas and inventions that led, step-by-step, to the designs employed in contemporary blast-furnace plants. A detailed description of a modern plant is given in Chapter **14.**

SECTION 4

INDIRECT PROCESSES FOR MAKING WROUGHT IRON

After furnaces which produced molten high-carbon iron became commonly employed in Europe, part of their product was used to produce iron castings by pouring the liquid metal into molds of the desired shape. Such cast iron had limited usefulness, since it was inherently hard and brittle due to its high-carbon content and the presence of other elements that entered the iron during reduction of the iron ore. It was not malleable, that is, it could not be shaped at any temperature below its melting point by either hammering or rolling.

In order to utilize the high-carbon product of these

furnaces for making forged or wrought articles, it was necessary to develop purifying processes that would remove the excess carbon, manganese, silicon, etc., from the impure iron to produce relatively soft, malleable wrought iron that would have the same general composition and characteristics as the iron formerly produced directly from the ore in the Catalan and similar processes. As might be expected, a very great number of methods were developed in different localities. Two types of processes eventually became prominent: the **charcoal-hearth processes** and the **puddling process.** Since the production of wrought iron from ore by any of these processes involved two separate steps: (1) reducing the ore to make pig iron and (2) remelting and purifying the pig iron to make wrought iron, they were referred to as **indirect processes.**

Some of the most widely used charcoal-hearth processes for purifying pig iron are described below (the Walloon, South Wales and Lancashire processes).

WALLOON PROCESS

Just how, when, where, and by whom wrought iron was first produced from pig iron is unknown, though it is probable the process originated in Belgium. The first attempts were, no doubt, made in the forge or on a hearth such as those already described for the production of iron directly from the ore. Here the action of the air from the blast (by that time in general use) would, if the iron were handled properly during melting, result in the oxidation of the silicon and the greater portion of the manganese and carbon, giving a ductile and workable product. The first reference to the process in written records appeared about 1620, but by that time the process had reached a stage of considerable development. Previous to that date, the Walloons of Flanders had gone to Sweden, where they had introduced the process, since known as the Walloon process. In this process a rather deep hearth with one or two tuyeres was used (Figure 1—10). With the hearth filled with charcoal and heated to a high temperature, the pig iron, in the form of long pigs, was fed into the fire so that the lower end of the pig would be gradually melted, and the molten metal would trickle to the bottom directly in front of the blast. The metal, desiliconized and decarburized by the oxygen in the air blast, would collect as a pasty mass upon the bottom, being worked vigorously as it collected. The ball of pasty metal was then separated into lumps that were raised above tuyere level and remelted. The new ball formed on the bottom was then

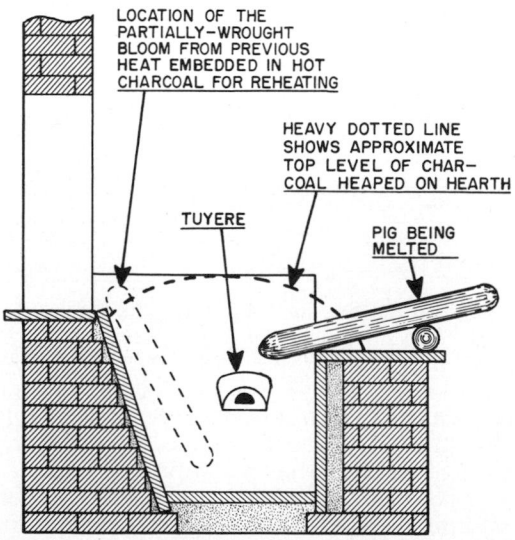

FIG. 1—10. General arrangement of a Walloon hearth used for purifying pig iron to make wrought iron.

removed from the hearth and hammered into a bloom. The second melting freed the metal from much of its entrapped slag. The pig used in Sweden, since it was reduced from the famous Dannemora ore in charcoal furnaces, was exceptionally low in silicon, sulphur and phosphorus, hence was especially adapted to this process.

SOUTH WALES PROCESS

Few districts outside of Dannemora are favored with ore so free from phosphorus, or were able to continue using charcoal for fuel for such a period of many years. The use of coke in the blast furnace leaves no alternative but the production of high-silicon iron, if the sulphur content is to be kept suitably within limits. At the lower temperatures necessary to produce low-silicon iron, more of the sulphur content of the coke will be picked up by the iron. Such iron, high in sulphur and silicon, could not be purified in a single operation, as in the Walloon process, where the purification was carried on in the combustion chamber with the metal and slag in contact with the fuel. It was found, however, that this iron could be purified and converted into wrought iron very readily in two stages. The South Wales process (sometimes confused with the Lancashire process) was a typical two-stage process. For the first stage, a small, rectangular, water-cooled hearth, surmounted by a stack and provided with a number of tuyeres, was used. In some cases, this hearth was a separate structure; in other cases this hearth for melting the pig iron formed part of a two-hearth furnace in which the melting hearth was slightly above the second hearth where final refining took place. When a separate melting hearth was employed, coke was used as fuel to melt the pig iron; for refining the melted iron, the second hearth was fired with charcoal. When the two hearths were incorporated into one furnace structure, charcoal was used as fuel in both. Sometimes two charcoal hearths were served by one melting hearth that tapped directly into them. The hearths were known by various names. The melting hearth, when separate, was called the **refinery,** or **refinery fire,** if the metal tapped was allowed to partially or completely solidify before being transferred to the second hearth. If the metal was allowed to flow directly from the refinery into the second hearth or hearths, as in the two-hearth furnace, the melting hearth was known as the **melting finery** or **running-out fire.** In both cases, the second hearth was known as the **finery, charcoal finery** or, more often, **knobbling fire.**

With a good fire burning upon the melting hearth, alternate charges of coke and pig iron were made upon it. As the metal melted, it would collect upon the bottom of the melting hearth where the blast from the tuyeres impinged upon it, oxidizing the silicon and some of the phosphorus along with a part of the iron. Assuming that the melting hearth in this case was a separate unit, when a sufficient quantity of partially purified and partially solidified metal had collected, it was transferred to the second hearth from the melting hearth, being piled in front of the tuyere and completely remelted while exposed to the blast. During the remelting, the metal was worked constantly and repeatedly raised slightly off the bottom, which treatment promoted the oxidation of the carbon. As the carbon was being removed, the metal gradually assumed a pasty condition, when it was worked into a ball, taken from the furnace, and hammered.

LANCASHIRE PROCESS

The Lancashire process differed essentially from the South Wales process, to which its name was sometimes loosely given, in that the pig iron was both melted and refined in a single hearth using charcoal as fuel. With some of the slag left from the previous operation to cover the bottom, the hearth was piled with charcoal up to above the tuyeres. The pig iron in lumps was placed on top of the charcoal pile, covered with more charcoal, and the blast turned on. The pig iron melted in drops which became partially decarburized in passing through the tuyere area and collected on the bottom. When all of the pig was melted, it was worked with bars to mix it with the slag and become thoroughly purified. As purification proceeded the metal became stiff and pasty, and when purification was completed the pasty mass was raised above the tuyeres and melted down again to free it from the intermingled slag. The pasty lump resulting from the remelting process was then taken from the furnace and hammered into a bloom.

These three are only a few of the many types of charcoal-hearth indirect processes developed for purification of pig iron to produce wrought iron.

HAND PUDDLING PROCESSES

About 1613, Rovenson invented the reverberatory furnace, which he described as a bloomery, finery or chaffery "in which the material to be melted or wrought may be kept divided from the touch of the fuel," but it was not employed for purifying pig iron until 1766, when the Cranege brothers received a British patent on a process which later came to be known as **puddling.** With careful manipulation of a reverberatory furnace, they were able to convert "white iron," or pig iron from which most of the silicon and phosphorus had been removed in a refinery, as described under the "South Wales Process," into a good malleable form of iron by the use of raw coal alone for fuel. In 1784, Henry Cort hollowed out the bottom of the furnace so as to contain the metal in the molten state, then by agitating this "puddle" or bath of metal with an iron bar or paddle he was able to convert white or partially-refined pig iron into a malleable form (wrought iron), the carbon being burned out by the oxidizing gases of the furnace atmosphere.

As the furnace bottom was made up of sand, it was rapidly fluxed away by the iron oxide formed. Besides, the process consumed much time and was wasteful of iron, the yield being less than 70 per cent of the metal charged. These objectionable features were largely overcome by Joseph Hall, who, in 1830, substituted old bottom material for the sand, thus introducing the iron oxide bottom, which adapted the process to any grade of iron, shortened the time of the heats, and increased the yield to about 90 per cent. On account of the boiling action of the bath caused by the rapid oxidation of the carbon by the oxides on the bottom, Hall's process came to be known as the **pig boiling** process. Later, this process became the leading method for the production of wrought iron.

The original method was designated as **dry puddling** because of the small quantity of slag formed, the slag-forming impurities having been removed in the refinery (see "South Wales Process," above). Hall, or his associates, also introduced the use of air-cooled iron plates for supporting the bottom and sides, which materially increased the life of the furnace. During the next 30 years, few changes were made in the process, for the new process was so far superior to previous ones that there was left little incentive for improvement. This attitude was changed, however, with the introduction of the pneumatic, or Bessemer, process in 1856. Then, in order to overcome competition of the Bessemer steel, and incidentally lessen the labor of puddling, which, like all its predecessors, was very arduous, hundreds of attempts were made to improve and cheapen the process (as shown under "Mechanical Puddling"). Few of these attempts were successful, and even the most promising of the successful ones, for various reasons, failed of universal adoption.

Between the years 1920 and 1930, however, hand puddling was almost entirely abandoned to be supplanted by the Ely mechanical puddler and the Aston process, the former duplicating conditions of hand puddling as closely as possible and the latter employing radically different principles and methods to obtain a similar but more uniform product. These three methods are briefly described in the following sections not only because they will help to define wrought iron and illustrate different methods of producing it, but also because they supply some fundamental knowledge as an introduction to the study of steelmaking processes.

Construction of the Hand Puddling Furnace—Although various modifications were introduced in the construction of puddling furnaces, affecting both size and design, the tendency was to adhere to the smaller and simpler types, such as the one shown in Figure 1—11. This type was known as a single furnace, had

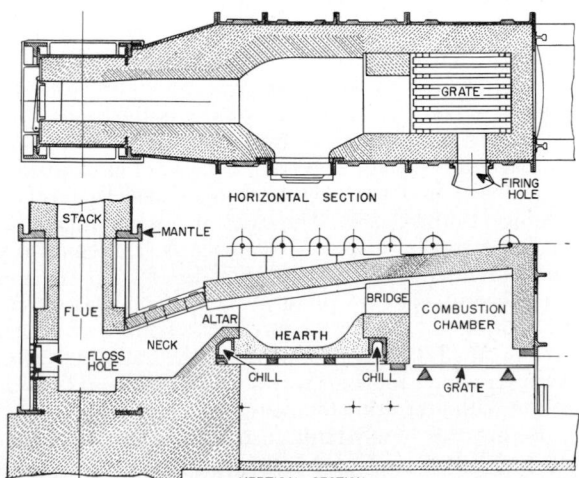

FIG. 1—11. Diagrammatic sections of a hand puddling furnace of the simple design known as a single furnace.

a capacity rating of 500 pounds per heat, and was coal-fired. The furnace was made up of the following parts: the **grate**, or fireplace, located at one end of the furnace; the **neck**, at the opposite end, leading to the **flue** that connected to the **stack**; and the **hearth**, or **puddling basin**, centrally located between the grate and the neck. The furnace was constructed entirely of brick, but was encased on the sides by a shell of iron plates held in place by tie rods. As the furnace was of the reverberatory type, all these parts were covered by an arched roof which sloped down from the fireplace to the uptake flue at an angle of 8 to 10 degrees. The roof over the fireplace was built of firebrick, but usually silica brick were used over the hearth and neck. The fireplace, which measured about 3½ feet in length, 2¾ feet in width, and 3¼ feet in height at the rear, was enclosed on each side by 12-inch firebrick walls and at the rear by a 9-inch wall of the same material. To support the fire bed the space over the ash pit was bridged with iron bars. About 16 inches above the bars a 10-inch square hole in the firebox on the front side of the furnace was provided for firing. The neck, at the other end of the furnace, was an inclined firebrick flue, frequently lined with a course of best-quality silica brick. The neck terminated in a short uptake, or vertical flue, that led to the stack, which was independently supported upon a **mantle.** At the base of the uptake, directly opposite the neck, was an opening or door, called the **floss hole,** which was provided primarily for the removal of the cinder that was carried, or overflowed, from the puddling basin.

The hearth, or puddling basin, was the most vital part of the furnace. Externally, the bottom of this basin consisted of three iron plates, 1 inch thick, which were supported upon four heavy bearer bars laid transversely across the space between the side walls of the furnace. This construction provided all the benefits of air cooling. A low brick wall, laid across the furnace and known as the **bridge,** separated the hearth from the fireplace and also served as a backing for one end of the basin. At the opposite end of the hearth, a somewhat lighter and lower wall, known as the **breast wall** or **altar,** separated the basin from the neck. Imbedded in each of these walls next to the lining, was a hollow iron casting, called a **chill,** through which air or water was circulated to keep these parts cool. The other two sides of the basin were supported by the walls of the furnace itself, and were similarly air-cooled. The back wall was built up solid to the roof, but the front wall contained the arched opening to the hearth. The sides of this opening were made of specially formed silica brick, known as the **jambs,** while its bottom was made of a heavy iron plate called the **fore plate.** This opening was closed by a brick-lined sliding door, in the bottom of which was a small U-shaped opening, the **rabbling hole,** through which tools for working the heat could be inserted without raising the door.

Before the newly-built furnace was put into productive operation, a smooth one-piece working bottom or basin was built up in the hearth. The details of this operation were varied considerably with equally good results. In general, the bottom was com-posed of a refractory fettling consisting mainly of the ferrosoferric oxide of iron (Fe_3O_4). Certain grades of ore or of heating-furnace cinder were frequently used, but more often the bottom was made by applying, oxidizing, and fritting in successive layers of fine iron cuttings (such as thread cuttings from a pipe mill) known as swarf.

Operation of the Hand Puddling Furnace—With the hearth properly built up or repaired and the furnace in good working order and at a proper temperature, about 500 pounds of pig iron were charged by hand through the door. Following this operation, occupying 2 to 3 minutes, the purification of the pig iron and the process of puddling advanced by stages, known as **melting, clearing, boiling, balling** and **drawing.** To achieve quick melting, the door and other openings were closed, the furnace was fired vigorously, and the pigs turned once or twice by the puddler or his helper. In this way the charge was usually melted within 20 to 25 minutes after charging. The molten metal, covered with a thin layer of slag, was then stirred or rabbled by the puddler to hasten the oxidation of the silicon, the manganese, and a part of the phosphorus, an operation known as clearing and requiring 8 to 10 minutes. As soon as the metal had cleared, as revealed by a change in its appearance, the puddler endeavored to bring on the boil by raising the temperature of the furnace, charging some dry roll scale (iron-oxide scale detached from bars in rolling), and stirring the bath vigorously. After some 8 to 10 minutes of strenuous effort, the oxidation of the silicon and manganese was brought to a point where the carbon could also be oxidized.

As the product of this reaction was the gas, CO, and since the slag was somewhat viscous, the action caused the latter to foam or boil and rise in the furnace. At this point the slag was permitted to flow from the furnace freely unless it was desired to hold the phosphorus high in the iron, when a little coal was added from time to time and as much of the slag as possible was held in the furnace. As the elimination of carbon became more rapid, the gas would escape in larger bubbles and burst into flame at the surface of the slag to form small flames called **puddler's candles.** With the disappearance of the candles, the puddler increased the stirring of the bath during the **lowering of the heat** until the metal in terms of the puddler, would **come to nature.** In this phenomenon, most characteristic of puddling, the metal appeared in small globules, like butter in churned milk, each globule representing a portion of the iron that had become decarburized. As this reaction neared completion, the bath became pasty and very hard to work. This change occurred because the high-carbon pig iron, which was molten at that temperature, was converted to low-carbon iron, which is solid (though pasty) at the same temperature. The change progressed rapidly, lasting only 6 to 8 minutes, so that in some 30 to 35 minutes after clearing the metal was ready for balling.

The globules agglomerated by the rabbling tended to collect in sponge-like clusters on the bottom; these clusters had to be raised constantly and exposed to the heat to prevent them from freezing to the bottom.

FIG. 1—12. Puddler removing a ball from a puddling furnace for transfer to the squeezer. This photograph, taken in 1949, shows one of the last puddling furnaces still in operation in the United States. (Courtesy, Lockhart Iron & Steel Company.)

So the temperature of the furnace was raised as high as possible, and the metal was worked into a mass which was next separated into three parts or balls of about 150 pounds each, a size convenient for handling with tongs. This operation required about 15 minutes. Each ball in turn was then grasped by the tongs supported from the trolley (Figure 1—12) and drawn through the door. After the last ball was removed, the furnace was permitted to cool to some extent, and the bridge and breast were covered with a special ore mix. Any necessary patching of the bottom was done, and another charge of metal was placed on the hearth for the next heat. These operations required about 2½ hours from heat to heat.

Rolling of Hand-Puddled Wrought Iron—At one time the balls were worked into the form of a rough bloom with a hammer, an operation called **shingling.** Later, hammering was superseded by the use of a device known as a **squeezer,** of which there were different types. One, known as the Burden squeezer, was most used (Figure 1—13). It was of the rotary

type and consisted essentially of a toothed cylinder mounted upon a vertical shaft so as to revolve within a section of a somewhat larger stationary cylinder set eccentrically to the revolving cylinder. Since the larger cylinder bore teeth or cogs on its inner surface and described only about three-fourths of a circumference, a ball placed in the larger opening between the cylinders was carried around the circumference by the smaller revolving cylinder to be compressed and discharged through the smaller opening in the form of a short round bloom. This action squeezed most of the excess slag out of the ball and compressed it into a form more suitable for rolling. As soon as the ball was delivered by the squeezer, it was grasped with tongs and at once delivered to the first pass of the rolling mill.

Rolling the Squeezed Ball—The **muck bar mill** for rolling the squeezed ball into muck bar was usually a 16- or 20-inch mill and consisted of a single stand or set of rolls, or of two stands in train; that is, end to end and coupled together. The first pass was of the open-box type* with large fillets at the corners in order to take the cylinder from the squeezer, while the second pass, generally an edging pass, was of similar design, thus working the metal into the form of a round-cornered square and squeezing out more of the slag at each pass. The remaining passes were all of the closed-box or tongue-and-groove type for rolling the bloom into flats called **muck bars,** with some open-box edging passes for use in producing the narrow widths. The size of the muck bars, of course, was regulated by the product to be made from them and the manner or system used in forming the product. For ordinary bar iron, which was the chief product, the

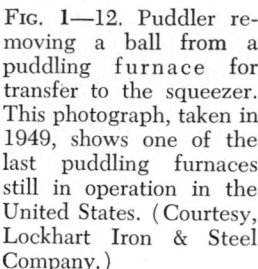

PUDDLE BALL

STATIONARY

ROTATING

SQUEEZED BLOOM

FIG. 1—13. Schematic representation of the path of a puddle ball passing through a Burden squeezer.

* See Part 1 of Chapter 20 on "Rolling Mill Rolls and Their Parts" for descriptions of the roll passes mentioned here.

muck bar was usually about ¾ inch thick and 2½ to 8 inches wide. Bars of these sizes required from 5 to 9 passes. On account of the rapid cooling of the bar in the rolls, it was not practicable to attempt to roll sizes smaller than these, as the slag was no longer fluid enough at this stage to be worked out of the bar. As slag was squeezed out of the bar at all passes in the mill, the muck bar had a very rough surface with some torn edges and was otherwise unfit to do service as a finished bar. Having been rolled to the size required, the muck bar was allowed to cool before being subjected to further treatment.

Variables in the Muck Bar—Owing to irregularities in the pig iron used, differences in manipulation by different puddlers, and in different plants, the small quantity of metal refined with each heat, and the fact that the metal solidified before purification was complete, muck bar was an exceedingly variable product. Since the retention of the characteristics of wrought iron did not permit melting, this variation had to be overcome through heat and mechanical treatments. To effect the necessary refinement, two methods were used, known as busheling and piling, followed by rolling.

Busheling—Obviously, the surest way to obtain a thorough mixing of the iron, was to shear the muck bars into small pieces—the smaller the better. These small pieces from the different muck bars were allowed to collect in a pile, or piles, from which portions weighing 180 to 600 pounds were removed with a scoop or fork and charged into a reheating furnace, called a **balling furnace,** where they were heated "white hot," or to a self-welding temperature. With a paddle, these pieces were then collected into a ball, similar to a puddle ball, which was squeezed or shingled, then rolled or hammered into a bloom, which was then reheated and worked into the form desired. This process, known as **busheling,** was used for working up muck bar only when iron of the highest quality was desired. The process was also used in working up small scrap. In this case there was no necessity for shearing, and the cost of the scrap was usually considerably less than the cost of muck bar, but unless the scrap was very carefully selected it was liable to contain much steel, in which case the iron produced was considered to be of inferior grade.

Piling—The more common practice, therefore, was to shear the muck bar into lengths of from 2 to 3 feet, then arrange these pieces in piles of from 5 to 7 or more each and bind the pieces together with wire or bands. The piles were carefully charged into a furnace and heated white hot. The high temperature caused the different bars to weld together, so that they could then be removed and rolled into bars. The first 2 or 3 passes squeezed out more and more of the liquid slag, but in the last passes the bar had cooled to a point where the slag was merely plastic and would not flow. Thus, a fairly smooth and uniform bar was produced, which would be sold as **merchant bar, single-rolled iron, single-refined iron,** or **No. 2 iron.** To attain the highest degree of uniformity, particularly with respect to distribution of slag fiber, the once-piled or so-called single-refined bars were in turn cut into short lengths, repiled and rerolled.

Double Refining—To further improve uniformity, then, merchant bar was cut up into short lengths, fagoted, reheated, and rerolled to produce the products known as **double-rolled iron, double-refined iron, best bar,** or **No. 3 bar.** The manner or **fagoting** (binding together into a bundle) or piling these bars varied in numerous ways, and depended only in part upon the use to which the iron was to be applied. Therefore, each manufacturer generally had his own methods of fagoting, which imparted to his iron an individuality detected by etching. Some of the more common methods of fagoting are illustrated by the accompanying sketches (Figure 1—14). When these

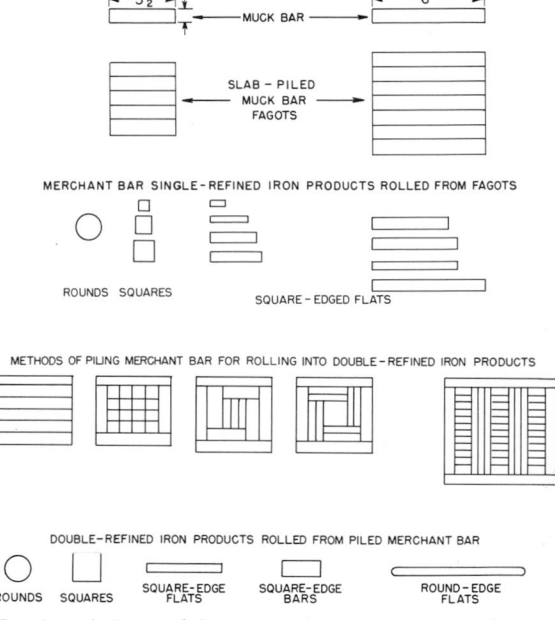

FIG. 1—14. Some of the more common methods of fagoting or binding together piles of single-refined wrought iron bars prior to heating for re-rolling to produce double-refined wrought iron bars.

fagots were heated and rolled into bars, more slag was expelled, the bar was made more uniform in composition, and the fibers were much elongated and reduced in size. As a result, the bars showed an improvement in mechanical properties, including both strength and ductility. There was a limit, in addition to the factor of cost, however, to the number of times the iron could be worked to advantage. After five or six workings its physical properties began to be lowered, and the bars decreased in strength and were less ductile. The cause, or causes, of this change was questionable; probably, it was due to the elimination of much of the silicate slag or possibly too much reheating and rerolling caused the ferrous silicate fibers to become oxidized to the ferric condition, thus destroying some of the characteristics of wrought iron. Wrought iron in this condition was often referred to as **dry iron.**

Reactions and Process Losses in Hand Puddling—The changes in composition of the pig iron during puddling involved the elimination, or oxidation, of silicon, manganese, phosphorus, and carbon about in the order mentioned. In these reactions, the oxidizing agents were FeO and Fe_3O_4. That Fe_2O_3 played little, if any, part in the reactions was evident from the fact that Fe_2O_3 decomposed at temperatures above $2010°$ F ($1100°$ C) to form Fe_3O_4. Also, it had been found that if hematite ore (Fe_2O_3) was used as the oxidizing medium, the boil came on very slowly; but if roll scale (Fe_3O_4 or $FeO \cdot Fe_3O_4$) were used, the reactions proceeded with much greater speed. Nearly all of the silicon and manganese and a part of the phosphorus were oxidized before the boil began, and at some period after melting and after the elimination of some of the silicon, the oxidation of all four elements, including carbon, might have proceeded simultaneously.

A study of the probable reactions that occurred in puddling indicates that a gain in weight of the puddled iron over the pig iron used could be expected, because iron was formed by reduction from the slag in the elimination of practically all impurities. By careful manipulation, furnaces could be operated to show a slight gain or a very slight loss. Nevertheless, in ordinary working, there was a loss of from 3 to 6 per cent, which was sometimes a little more, at other times a little less, than the total of the impurities present. If the heat were properly handled, the loss was largely due to oxidation of iron after solidification had begun in the after-part of the boil and during the balling stage. If the heat were not skillfully handled, a variable part of the loss may have been due to the escape of the metallic granules with the "boilings" before the "heat was lowered." In reheating and rolling the muck bar, there was a variable loss of from 10 to 20 per cent for each time the iron was worked depending upon the number of times it was worked, the manner of the working, and other factors incidental to the operations of heating and rolling. In general, these losses were due to surface oxidation of the metal in heating and rolling, expulsion of the slag, and cropping. Slag expulsion was the smallest item of loss, except in the case of muck bar, and depended mainly upon the number of times the iron was worked, but was also affected by the temperature at which the iron was worked, and the nature of the incorporated slag itself. The loss was a little greater on iron with a high phosphorus content than on iron low in phosphorus.

MECHANICAL PUDDLING

The never-ending competition in the iron and steel industry has been a constant spur to improve methods or lower costs of production. Just as the puddling process virtually eliminated the more primitive direct-reduction methods for the production of iron, so the Bessemer and open-hearth processes for the production of steel threatened the life of the wrought-iron industry. Even before the invention of these steel-making processes, much attention was given to improving the puddling process, because the process was costly and the labor arduous, and the furnace was wasteful of heat. With a reverberatory puddling furnace of the type described earlier, from 2000 to 2400 pounds of coal were required to produce one ton of muck bar. This consumption of fuel was reduced somewhat by the use of double furnaces with enlarged hearths, but, since the application of regenerative and recuperative furnaces appears to have been impracticable, efforts along this line failed to achieve much in the way of lowering costs. The installation of waste-heat boilers in the stacks effected marked economies, and their use became general. To overcome the high labor cost, many attempts were made to carry out the puddling operations mechanically. Such was the situation up to about 1880 when the Danks puddling furnace appeared. From this time up to 1925, wrought iron lost ground to steel in spite of several efforts to revive it. In the meantime, however, it came to be recognized as a product with characteristic properties unlike those of steel, and in 1925 attempts to revive the industry were noted. These endeavors advanced along two lines, the one mechanical and the other metallurgical, the former aiming to duplicate the process of hand-puddling as closely as possible and the latter aiming to produce a material having all the characteristics of wrought iron through the use of the same metallurgical principles but applied in a manner entirely different from that of hand puddling. These two lines of effort are described under the headings of mechanical puddling and the Aston process, the latter representing a successful and most revolutionary method of producing wrought iron by A. M. Byers Company.

Principles of Mechanical Puddling—At first these mechanical puddlers took the form of stirring or rabbling appliances that could be attached to the top of the ordinary furnace. Because of the great variety of motions necessary in the different operations of charging, raising and stirring the heat, balling the iron, and drawing the balls, none of these were successful. The more successful attempts at mechanical puddling have involved a complete change in the design of the furnace, and some changes also in the process. These attempts have been too numerous to warrant description here. The furnaces themselves may be classified as follows:

1. The rectangular furnace that oscillated about a horizontal axis of rotation.
2. The circular flat-bottom furnace that revolved about an axis slightly inclined to the vertical.
3. The circular furnace with flat or troughlike bottom that oscillated about a horizontal axis of rotation.
4. The cylindrical furnace that rotated about a horizontal axis coincident with the center.
5. The cylindrical furnace that oscillated about a horizontal axis coincident with the center, or both oscillated and rotated about such an axis.

Furnaces built on any of these plans were made to puddle iron successfully, but those of the fourth and fifth types were most successful, partly on account of the facilities they afford for controlling the agitation of the metal, and partly because of the simplicity of their construction. The **Danks furnace**, somewhat widely used in this country from 1868 to 1885, was of the fourth type, while the **Roe furnace**, built and successfully operated in 1905, is of the third type. **H. D. Hibbard's furnace,** first operated on a commercial scale in 1921, was somewhat similar to the Danks furnace. The **Ely furnace,** patented by W. C. Ely, was first designed for busheling scrap but was later (about 1920) applied to the puddling of iron. It represents the fifth type, and, along with the Roe furnace, survived until recent years as one of the two successful mechanical methods for making wrought iron.

THE ASTON PROCESS*

From the descriptions given in the preceding sections, it is apparent that the basis of wrought-iron manufacture consists in refining the base metal to a close approach to pure iron, and incorporating therein an iron-silicate slag of desirable chemical composition in proper amount and distribution. Obviously, as has been brought out previously, several correlated steps are involved, quite distinct in nature and capable of separation, but carried out in the usual methods for hand or mechanical puddling as one interconnected operation. Departing radically from these former methods is the Aston process developed and put into large scale operation by the A. M. Byers Company of Pittsburgh. In this process, metal refining, slag melting, and processing to form the slag-impregnated sponge ball are carried out as separate stages, each stage in a separate furnace or kind of equipment. The last stage is the crux of the process, and is based upon a positive and effective physico-chemical influence; namely, the change in gas solubility from a very high amount in molten iron to an

* Special acknowledgement is made of the assistance rendered by A. M. Byers Company, in the preparation of this section.

amount practically negligible on solidification. This stage of the Aston process is carried out by pouring the refined metal in a continuous stream into a large volume of molten slag. The slag acts as a heat absorbing agent which effects solidification of the metal with accompanying liberation of its dissolved gases, at a steady rate and with a force sufficient to disintegrate the plastic metal into a spongy mass, conforming in all particulars to the characteristics of high-quality wrought iron.

A large plant, with a daily capacity in excess of 1000 tons, is in operation in the Pittsburgh district. The essential features of the operation are illustrated in the accompanying Figures 1—15 to 1—20.

Three cupolas are operated to produce molten iron (hot metal) of Bessemer grade which is ladle desulphurized with caustic soda and subsequently further refined in acid-Bessemer converters (Figure 1—15).

The iron-silicate processing slag is melted to exacting chemical requirements in special furnaces, which are described later (see also Figure 1—16), and then transferred to the processing cups.

The molten desulphurized hot metal from the cupolas is "full-blown" in an acid-lined converter (Figure 1—17) and the highly refined, deoxidized metal is poured at a controlled uniform rate into a thimble holding molten iron-silicate slag (Figure 1—18). After the metal from the converter has been poured, the surplus slag is poured from the thimble, leaving the white hot sponge ball of wrought iron (Figure 1—19). This sponge iron is first pressed into a bloom of rectangular section (Figure 1—20) and is then rolled into slabs or billets.

Equipment for melting iron-silicate slag for the

PIG IRON, COKE AND LIMESTONE CHARGED BY BUCKET INTO CUPOLA

BUSTLE PIPE

SLAG NOTCH

RUNNER

TUYERES

Fig. 1—15. Hot metal tapped from these cupolas runs into a ladle where it is desulphurized and transferred to acid-Bessemer converters, one of which is shown in Figure 1—17. (Courtesy, A. M. Byers Company.)

Fig. 1—16. Molten iron silicate slag is tapped from rotary furnaces and transferred by ladle to replenish the slag in the processing ladles (processing cups) shown at lower level in Figure 1—18. (Courtesy, A. M. Byers Company.)

Fig. 1—18. At the processing floor, molten refined iron (2900° F.) is poured by processing machines into molten iron silicate (2500° F.) to form an iron sponge ball characteristic of the Aston process for making wrought iron. Processing machines, scale mounted, have traverse, oscillating, and tilting motions insuring distribution of the metal into the slag. (Courtesy, A. M. Byers Company.)

Fig. 1—17. Desulphurized hot metal is "full blown" in acid-Bessemer converters to refined iron, then deoxidized and transferred by ladle to the processing machine ladles shown at upper level in Figure 1—18. (Courtesy, A. M. Byers Company.)

Fig. 1—19. Empty processing ladle receives surplus decanted processing slag, is replenished if necessary, and returned by rail to processing floor for reuse. The welding-hot iron sponge ball, "wet" with molten iron silicate, is moved to the press by overhead traveling crane. (Courtesy, A. M. Byers Company.)

Fig. 1—20. The welding-hot sponge ball, "wet" with molten iron silicate retained in the processing ladle in which it was produced, is immediately transferred to and dumped on the press table, lowered between side and end rams, and pressed into a rectangular bloom prior to rolling. (Courtesy, A. M. Byers Company.)

processing operation (sponge-making), and for incorporating in the matrix of iron, consists of four rotary furnaces. These furnaces, which are fired with oil or powdered coal, have no refractory lining and are operated in such manner that the lining material is composed of the same silicate slag that is being melted. This eliminates all contamination which would occur with customary refractory linings and makes it possible to produce the iron-silicate slag for processing to a very exacting chemical composition.

The key operation is effected by pouring the molten refined and deoxidized metal in a steady stream into a "processing cup" or vessel containing molten slag as illustrated by Figure 1—18. The metal ladle is automatically oscillated and moved forward and backward, insuring uniform distribution of metal into the slag. As the stream of molten metal poured at the rate of a ton a minute disintegrates in the molten slag, solidifying droplets are formed which are burst apart by the liberated gas and the resulting shattered fragments settle to form a welding-hot spongy mass in the molten silicate. Individual iron sponge masses—"sponge balls"—varying in weight from three to four tons are produced.

These processing cups are on cars, so that the decanting of surplus slag and the dumping of the sponge ball (Figures 1—19 and 1—20) can be effected at a station remote from the pouring platform.

Pressing and rolling follow, using the original heat of the ball, to form intermediate products such as billets or slabs conforming to standard mill practice. Furnaces, mills, and auxiliary equipment, as well as man power, follow closely the standards of the mod-

ern rolling mill. In view of the large mass of the pressed bloom, most of the product—skelp, plate, etc.—is rolled from reheated solid sections, in marked contrast to older wrought-iron practice of building muck bar piles.

COMPOSITION, STRUCTURE AND PROPERTIES OF WROUGHT IRON

Chemical Composition of Wrought Iron—Chemical composition has a place in the determination of wrought-iron quality comparable with its importance in the steel industry. One must bear in mind, however, that the customary metalloids may be, in greater or lesser degree, alloyed with the base metal or associated as oxidized constituents with the intermingled slag. The commonly reported composition of wrought iron lists the carbon, manganese, phosphorus, sulphur and silicon of the composite mass. On the basis of analyses as commonly made, the following statements apply to wrought iron of high quality: Carbon seldom, if ever, exceeds 0.035 per cent in quality wrought iron. Silicon content is 0.075 to 0.150 per cent, normally almost negligible in alloyed association with the metal, and existing almost entirely as silicates in the slag. Sulphur is always undesirable, and in well-made wrought iron, it should be under 0.02 per cent. A sulphur content of 0.015 per cent or under is quite common in quality wrought iron. Phosphorus is almost invariably higher in wrought iron than in steel. It must be borne in mind that phosphorus is in part dissolved in the base metal, and in part associated with the slag. Good wrought iron may have a phosphorus content of from 0.10 per cent or less to 0.25 per cent or more, according to manufacturer's preference, nature of raw materials, or adaptability to service conditions. The lower order is advisable for materials subjected to shock, high temperature, or requiring higher ductility. Traditionally, the manganese content of hand-puddled or processed wrought iron (Aston process) is less than 0.10 per cent; British specifications generally have a 0.10 per cent maximum and in the United States most specifications carry a limit of 0.06 per cent. Low manganese in wrought iron has usually been an earmark of quality, although there is no logical ground for condemning an otherwise well-made product because of a relatively high manganese content.

Macroscopic Structure of Wrought Iron—In view of the composite nature of wrought iron, its quality is obviously affected by the nature of the association of base metal and slag. Methods of disclosing this internal structure have an importance greater even than the prominent place which the metallurgist assigns to them in the study of steel. Wrought iron exhibits a well-recognized fibrous fracture. The fracture test is a good over-all means for determining the general characteristics of wrought iron, but it should not be relied upon solely.

Macroscopic etching will reveal gross structure, reflecting such features of manufacture as methods of piling, and general slag distribution. Deep etching has a useful place but, like the fracture test, gives only a limited amount of information pertaining to the finer points of quality.

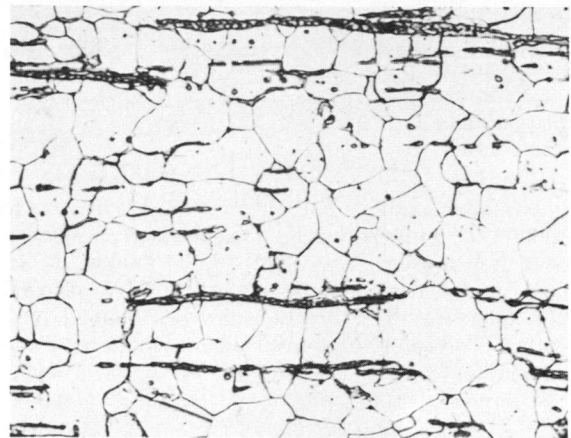

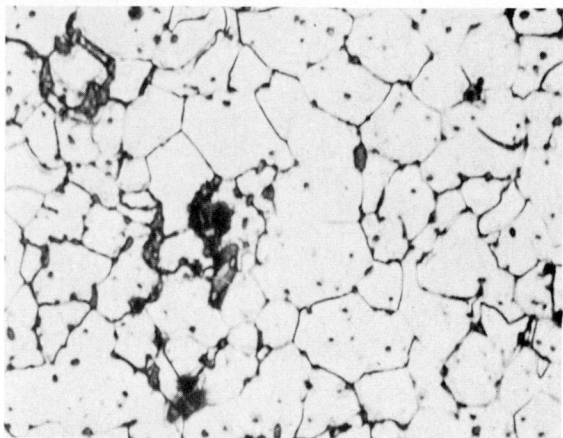

Fig. 1—21. Photomicrograph at 100X showing typical structure of wrought iron parallel to the direction of rolling. White areas are the highly refined iron matrix. Dark gray elongated lines are iron-silicate slag filaments. (Courtesy, A. M. Byers Company.)

Fig. 1—22. Photomicrograph at 100X showing typical structure of wrought iron perpendicular to the direction of rolling. White areas are the highly-refined iron matrix. Dark areas are cross-sections of iron-silicate slag filaments. (Courtesy, A. M. Byers Company.)

Microscopic Structure of Wrought Iron—Wrought iron consists essentially of a ferrite matrix, through which the slag is uniformly disseminated in the form of several hundred thousand filaments per square inch. Important disclosures of the microscope are:

a. **Grain Size**—Coarse grain, distortion, or lack of uniformity have a bearing upon quality in relation to mill history and use of product.

b. **Pearlitic areas** indicate the quantity and nature of distribution of the carbon, generally practically negligible or quite small in amount in real wrought iron.

c. **Slag—Type and Distribution**—Coarse, pocketed slag is undesirable. Finer textures result from progressive rolling reductions, and promote better mechanical properties, especially ductility.

d. **Chemical Composition**—The microscope is of no value in detection of alloying elements in solid solution in the base metal; for example, manganese, nickel, silicon, copper, etc.

Two photographs (Figures 1—21 and 1—22) illustrate typical structures and features related to the quality characteristics of wrought iron. These micrographs are of wrought iron produced by the A. M. Byers Company (Aston process), and show a typical longitudinal structure and a typical transverse structure.

Mechanical Properties of Wrought Iron—The mechanical properties of wrought iron are essentially those of pure iron, modified only slightly in general practice by metalloid content of the base metal and profoundly by the quantity and distribution of the incorporated slag. Up to certain limits, the ductility is increased by greater work in forge or mill, which causes a finer and more threadlike distribution of the slag. This is reflected in the common practice of the puddle mill of once or twice piling in products designated as "single" or "double-refined" iron. Obviously, a similar result will be achieved by rolling relatively large initial blooms into small final sections.

In comparison with steel or ingot iron, the longitudinal ductility of wrought iron is somewhat lowered, due to slag incorporation, while the transverse strength and ductility are markedly reduced. However, rolling history is an important factor with respect to quantity and direction of reduction.

The values below are representative of tensile properties for various wrought-iron products, compiled from standards of the American Society for Testing Materials. Because of the physical size of the products listed, only the longitudinal properties are reported, except for plate for which both longitudinal and transverse properties are given.

BAR IRON—SINGLE-REFINED
Under 1¼ Sq. In. Section

Tensile strength, lb. per sq. in.... 48,000 (minimum)
Yield point, tensile strength
    factor 0.6
Elongation in 8 in., per cent..... 25 (minimum)
Reduction of area, per cent..... 45 (minimum)

BAR IRON—DOUBLE-REFINED
Under 1¼ Sq. In. Section

Tensile strength, lb. per sq. in.... 48,000—52,000
Yield point, tensile strength
    factor 0.6
Elongation in 8 in., per cent..... 28 (minimum)
Reduction of area, per cent..... 48 (minimum)

The higher ductility accompanying greater work is reflected in the figures for double-refined material. For heavy sections, such as large diameter bars and forgings, strength and ductility requirements are somewhat lowered.

WELDED PIPE

Tensile strength, lb. per sq. in.... 40,000 (minimum)
Yield point, lb. per sq. in........ 24,000 (minimum)
Elongation in 8 in., per cent..... 12 (minimum)

Herein are reflected the effects of high temperatures in welding, and the lessened stretch in testing tubular sections. However, where special precautions are taken in the making of pipe for bending purposes, the ductility figures are bettered in practice by several per cent in the elongation obtained.

PLATE

Under normal rolling practice, plate exhibits the maximum of difference in longitudinal and transverse properties. The A.S.T.M. specifications for usual rolling require plate meeting the following tensile properties:

Tensile strength, lb. per sq. in.
 Longitudinal . . . . 48,000 (minimum)
Yield point, lb. per sq. in.
 Longitudinal . . . . 27,000 (minimum)
Elongation in 8 in., per cent:
 Longitudinal . . . . 14 (minimum)
 Transverse . . . . 2 (minimum)

By proper attention to rolling practice, it is feasible to equalize the properties, so that a specification requirement of a tensile strength of 39,000 lb. per sq. in. (minimum) and an elongation in 8 in. of 8 per cent (minimum) in either direction may be obtained. This feature is of great value in producing plate for flanging or other forming purposes.

SECTION 5

EARLY PROCESSES FOR CONVERSION OF IRON INTO STEEL

PROBABLE ANCIENT METHODS

It is probable that most of the steel produced in ancient times consisted of partially case-hardened wrought iron. Wrought iron, when heated and suddenly cooled by quenching in some liquid, will not harden because it does not contain enough carbon. By increasing the carbon content in the manner to be described, the outer portions and edges of a piece of wrought iron could be made to harden by heating and quenching.

The hardenable outer portion or "case" was produced by allowing a wrought-iron object to remain in a forge fire in contact with hot carbon, which completely surrounded it and protected it from oxidation. The carbon absorbed by the surface "layers" of the wrought iron would make it possible to obtain very hard surfaces and edges on a weapon, for example, by quenching the heated metal in a suitable liquid. The interior of the tool or weapon, of course, would remain relatively soft. Undoubtedly some steel was produced, intentionally or otherwise, when an imperfectly decarburized product was obtained from the South Wales, Lancashire, Walloon or similar processes. Another method, used in some of the Eastern countries to produce what very commonly is known as "Damascus steel," consisted of piling alternately pieces of soft iron on pieces of high-carbon iron and then heating, forging, fagoting and reforging the billets. The layering that resulted from incomplete diffusion of carbon from the high-carbon bars into the low-carbon iron resulted in the surface appearance called "watering," which was characteristic of the so-called Damascus steels.

It is difficult to say how or when the first processes for intentional making of steel were developed. Archeological specimens from as far back as 1000 B.C. exhibit evidences of having been deliberately treated (case-hardened) to produce points and edges that were hardened by rapidly quenching the heated steel. One example is a chisel with a hardened point, found in one of the ancient cities of Ceylon and believed to date back to about 500 B.C. Early writers mention steel razors, surgical instruments, files, chisels and stone-cutting implements as early as several hundred years before the Christian Era.

The steel called **wootz** was produced in India for many centuries. Its method of manufacture has been variously described. It is generally agreed that the first step consisted of heating pure ore with carbonaceous material such as charcoal or finely-chopped wood in closed crucibles. After heating at a high temperature for several hours, the ore was reduced to metallic iron and absorbed sufficient carbon from the excess of charcoal to have a low enough melting point to become fluid. The crucibles were allowed to cool and, when broken open, a small "button" of high-carbon steel was found at the bottom. Two methods have been recorded for lowering the carbon content of the buttons to give steel having the desired carbon content or "temper." One method consisted of repeatedly heating the buttons while they were covered with a layer of iron-oxide paste. The other recorded method comprised heating the buttons for several hours in a charcoal fire to a temperature not much below their melting point and turning them over in the path of the blast, so that the metal would be partially decarburized. In both cases, the partially decarburized buttons would then be heated to be welded together by hammering to form bars. Ambiguous records of various other processes for making steel by carburizing wrought iron appear in fragmentary literature from very early times.

In summary then, it may be said that prior to the invention of the Bessemer process for steelmaking in 1856 there were only two methods of making steel. One was the process of increasing the carbon content of wrought iron by heating it in contact with hot carbon away from air; this came to be called the **cementation process.** The other method, the **crucible process,** consisted of melting wrought iron in clay crucibles in which carbon had been added for the express purpose of increasing the carbon content of the iron. Both of these processes were certainly known to and practiced by the ancients.

During the Middle Ages both the cementation and crucible processes appear to have been lost to civilization. The cementation process was revived in Belgium about the year 1600 A.D. while the crucible process was rediscovered in England by Benjamin Huntsman in 1742. Both processes were practiced in secret for some time after their revival. Hence, little is known of their early history. The following brief descriptions will, therefore, be confined to practices in later years.

THE CEMENTATION PROCESS

The cementation process was highly developed and flourished in England during the 18th and 19th centuries and, though it has practically been replaced by other methods, is still practiced to a limited extent. The process depends upon the fact that when a low-carbon ferrous product, such as wrought iron, is heated to a red heat in contact with charcoal or other carbonaceous material, the metal absorbs carbon, which, up to the saturation point of less than 2.00 per cent (about 1.70 per cent), varies in amount according to the time the metal is in contact with the carbon and the temperature at which the process is conducted. For carrying on the process, a type of muffle-furnace or pot-furnace is used, and the iron and charcoal are packed in the pots in alternate layers.

The iron used was usually in the form of bars 2½ inches to 3 inches wide, ⅝ inch to ¾ inch thick, and 6 to 12 feet long. For the best grades of steel, only the best wrought iron was supposed to be used, though low-carbon steel made by the open-hearth process was later substituted. Charcoal, which had been passed over about a ¼-inch screen to remove fines, represented the favorite carburizing agent, though various other substances and mixtures had been tried and used. In charging the pots, their bottoms were first covered with a layer of charcoal 2 or 3 inches thick, then, in alternation, layers of bars and charcoal were added to each until the pots were full. The bars were laid flatwise and about ½ inch apart, between edges, so that each bar was completely surrounded by charcoal. After applying the final layer of charcoal the charge was covered with wheel swarf (refuse from the grindstones) and all openings to the pots were closed and made nearly as airtight as possible. A fire was next lighted in the furnace, and the charge, for the next 3 or 4 days, gradually heated to a full red heat—the actual temperature varied from 1470° F to 2010° F (800° C to 1100° C) and this temperature was then maintained for 7 to 12 days, depending upon the size of the bars used, the carbon content desired, and the temperatures attained and maintained. The degree of carburization, or the **temper** of the bars, was determined by fracture tests on test bars that were withdrawn from the pots through small openings or holes provided for the purpose. When the bars had reached the desired temper, i.e., had absorbed the desired amount of carbon, the fire was banked and the furnace allowed to cool slowly. When the contents of the furnace were cool enough to handle, the bars were removed from the pots.

If the original bars were of wrought iron, their surfaces were found to be covered with irregular elevations, known as **blisters** or **beads,** which resulted from the expansive force of the carbon monoxide formed by carbon reacting with the oxides of the incorporated slag. Hence, these bars were known as **blister steel.** If the original bars were of mild steel or remelted wrought iron, these blisters were absent. Both products were frequently referred to as **converted** or **cement steel.** If air had gained access to the bars during the process, their surfaces were covered with scale and almost decarburized. Such bars were known as **aired bars.** After sorting and reheating, the cement bars were hammered or rolled into what in England was called **spring plate** or **bar steel,** which formerly was used for springs, but later was used as raw material for crucible steel or for the production of shear steel. If for the latter, the bars were broken or sheared into short lengths, fagoted, sprinkled with a little borax, covered with clay, reheated to a welding temperature, and hammered into a bar, known as **single shear.** For purposes requiring a high grade, uniform steel, the single shear bars were again broken at their centers, the two halves of each laid together, and the fagot thus formed was reheated and hammered down to the required size. These bars were known as **double shear steel.** This steel was formerly used exclusively for the manufacture of cutlery, hence the name, shear steel.

This working was necessary to obtain the highly desirable homogeneity of the steel, and, prior to the revival of the crucible process, was the only method available to attain that end. Formerly, about seven grades or tempers of shear steel were produced. These varied in average carbon content from 0.50 per cent to 1.50 per cent. But as the carbon was absorbed from the surfaces of the bars, the carbon content of the blister steel bars progressively decreased to the center. In the softer grades the center portions of each bar remained unaltered, and this core was known as **sap.** In the harder grades the outside of the bar might show a carbon content of 1.50 to 2.00 per cent with a center of 0.85 to 1.10 per cent. It was this characteristic of cement steel that led Huntsman, who was a clockmaker, to seek a method for making a more uniform steel for his springs.

THE CRUCIBLE PROCESS

Realizing that the shortcomings of cement steel for springs lay in lack of homogeneity, Huntsman conceived the idea of melting it in crucibles, which melting he thought should make the steel perfectly homogeneous. Briefly, his method was as follows: First, cement bars were carefully selected that would give the exact temper, or carbon content, desired in the finished steel. These were cut or broken into small pieces. Then this steel was charged into large clay crucibles, which, after covering and luting the lids, were placed in a coke fire and heated until the contents were thoroughly fused. At this point the crucibles were withdrawn from the fire, and upon removing the cover and skimming off the small amount of slag formed on top, the molten metal was poured into a cast-iron mold, where it remained until solid. Finally, by the usual method of reheating and hammering then in use, the ingot was worked into the form desired. This method gave a steel that was not only homogeneous throughout, but was free from occluded slag and dirt, hence was so much superior to cement steel for many purposes that the method at once became the leader for the production of the finest steels. This position the process held for almost two hundred years, but today, at least in this country, it has been superseded for the making of special alloy steels and carbon tool steels by the electric-furnace process, including the high-frequency induction furnace. The electric-furnace process is cheaper, is capable of giving as good steel, and possesses many metallurgical advantages over the crucible method.

Although the principles and the general method of procedure remained the same, the crucible process was the subject of considerable experimentation after the time of Huntsman, and some changes in the material of the charge, in the manufacture of the crucibles, and in the furnace for melting the crucible charges were introduced, so that the details of standard practice for this now practically extinct process in different countries and localities varied somewhat.

Manufacture of the Crucibles—The **crucibles,** or **pots,** were a very important part of the equipment required in the manufacture of crucible steel. As they were costly to make and had a comparatively short life, they were a large item of expense. In England, they were frequently made of clay by the steel manufacturer himself, but in this country so-called graphite crucibles were almost universally used. These crucibles, with a capacity of 80 to 124 pounds, varied somewhat in form and thickness of wall. In general, they were barrel-like in shape, and varied in size from 13 to 18 inches in height and from 8 to 12½ inches in outside diameter at the bilge. As to wall thickness, they were somewhat thicker at the bottom than at the top, usually about 1½ inches at the bottom and about ¾ inch at the top.

The Crucible Melting Furnace—In this country, the crucible furnace was generally of the gas-fired regenerative type (Figure 1—23). It consisted of a number of combustion chambers or **melting holes** built in a row between two sets of checker chambers. Each melting hole, about three feet in depth and

otherwise large enough to hold 4 or 6 crucibles, was connected with the two sets of checkers by short flues leading upward from its bottom. If producer gas was used as fuel, the gas checkers were placed next to the line of melting holes with the air checkers extending along the outer walls of the furnace. This plan of construction readily permitted introducing the gas into the ports below the air, which was deflected downward by the roof, thus holding the flame near the bottom of the crucibles as it swept across the melting hole. In case natural gas, fuel oil, or powdered coal was used for fuel, both checkers would be used for air, or the furnace would be constructed with but one checker chamber on each side. The shop floor was on a level with the top of the melting hole, so that only the covers were visible from above. After moving these covers aside, the crucibles were lowered into and lifted out of the hole by tongs with broad jaws curved to fit the crucibles.

The bottoms of the melting holes were built of first-quality firebrick laid on plates, which were supported by beams, or cross bars, spanning the space between the two sets of checkers, thus forming a continuous cellar, or vault, that extended the full length of the furnace beneath the melting holes. A hole, some 4 or 5 inches in diameter, was provided in the center of the bottom of each melting hole, so that any refuse on the bottom of the melting hole could be poked into the vault below for cleaning. To protect the bottom in case of breakouts, it was covered to a depth of 6 to 8 inches with coke dust or crushed coke. This coke also gave some protection to the crucibles, as it helped to consume free oxygen not needed for combustion and to maintain a reducing atmosphere in the hole.

Charging the Crucibles—From what has already been said, it will be evident that, aside from the possible elimination of gases from the steel and the separation of slag and other non-metallic inclusions, the crucible process was not a purification process. Consequently, any elements capable of alloying with iron charged into the crucible were present also in the steel. On this account the greatest of care in the selection of the raw materials had to be exercised. And it was characteristic of the history of the process that, once a charge that produced the kind or grade of steel desired had been hit upon by any shop, that charge was strictly adhered to and could not be varied. For many years after the introduction of the process by Huntsman, cement steel or blister steel was the only raw material used. Eventually, attempts were made to eliminate the cementation step by the use of wrought iron with charcoal; and, provided Swedish iron, which was the purest wrought iron then made, was used, the steel produced was as good as that made from cement bars. In 1801 David Mushet introduced the use of manganese, by adding oxide of manganese with the charge, which practice was superseded some years later by the use of spiegel. It is interesting to note that the use of spiegel in Bessemer steel was patented in 1857 by a namesake, Robert Mushet (this method of adding manganese was an important factor in the early development of Bessemer steel). Then followed a great deal of unsuccessful experimental work, involving so many different

CRUCIBLES

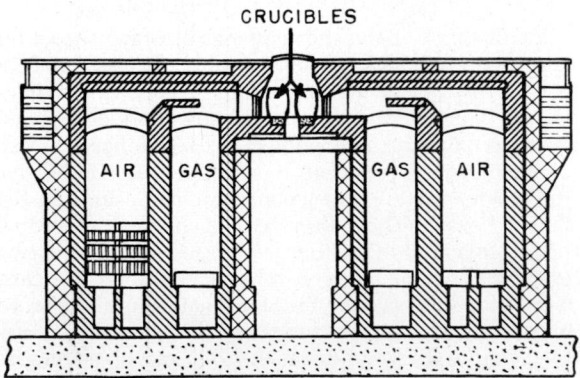

Fig. 1—23. Vertical section through checker chambers and one of the melting holes of a regenerative crucible furnace.

substances and mixtures that the stock house came to be known as the medicine house. Later, with the introduction of the Bessemer and acid open-hearth processes, efforts were made to reduce the cost by the substitution of soft-steel scrap for the Swedish wrought iron, but owing, perhaps, to the fact that miscellaneous scrap was used, which carried a higher content of manganese, phosphorus, and sulphur and was more variable in composition than the Swedish wrought iron, the steel was found to be of inferior quality. More recently, washed metal, that is semi-purified pig iron, freed from silicon, manganese, and phosphorus, had been used with excellent results to bring up the carbon of the wrought iron. Still more recently, owing to the introduction of the cheaper electric process and the difficulty of securing good wrought iron, recourse was had to the use of steel scrap, in part at least. With good basic or acid open-hearth mill scrap, the composition of which is more uniform than miscellaneous scrap and could be more readily controlled, steel of good quality could be made, provided proper care was taken to adjust the composition with the best wrought iron and washed metal.

All the practices just described had to do with carbon steels. Since the process had always been used in the production of the finest steels, especially tool steel, the introduction of alloy steels created the greatest diversity of practices. In making alloy steels, the old rule-of-thumb methods of charging had to be abandoned for other plans in which the composition of the charge could be accurately determined by chemical analysis. This applied particularly to high-speed tool steels, which, prior to the introduction of the electric process, could be made successfully only by the crucible process. At first, these steels were made from high-grade wrought iron or muck bar by the addition of the desired elements in the form of iron alloys, and the necessary recarburizer in the form of charcoal or washed metal. Later, tool scrap was used to make up a part of the charge, and much inspecting and many analyses were required to select the scrap and determine the proportions of the charge.

Stages of the Crucible Process—The materials for the charge, after they had been inspected and analyzed, were sheared or broken into small pieces, then carefully weighed out in proper proportions and amounts in the mixing house. These were carefully placed in the crucibles with the wrought iron or steel scrap on the bottom. The crucibles were then closed by snugly fitted covers and taken to the melting hole, into which they were lowered vertically by tongs in the hands of a workman. The gas and air were then regulated to melt the charge as rapidly as possible without injuring the crucibles. The time of melting varied from 2½ to 4 hours, according to the composition of the charge and the heating conditions of the furnace. Low-carbon heats required more time than high-carbon, and high-speed steel required the most time of all grades. As the charge melted, and for some time after melting, the metal evolved gases, which finally collected in fairly large bubbles and broke slowly on the surface of the metal, producing the spectacle known as **cat's eyes.** The melter, by tempo-

rarily removing the crucible cover, now watched each pot closely, and when the steel appeared to be **dead,** that is, free from gases and in a tranquil state, he signaled the puller-out, who grasped the crucible with the long broad tongs, lifted it out of the hole, and set it on the floor. The killing of the heat usually required 30 to 40 minutes, sometimes longer, and was an important part of the process, because the practice was necessary to give sound ingots. On the other hand, if the steel was kept in the furnace too long after it had reached the dead-melt stage, it would be damaged and might be ruined by absorption of too much carbon and silicon from the crucible. The temperature was also important; if the heat were pulled too cold, the steel would begin to solidify before it could be cast, and if it were cast too hot, the resulting ingot would not be sound. In some cases the pots were pulled before the steel was completely killed, and a little aluminum (not over 0.05 per cent) was added to the pot just before the steel was poured into the ingot mold. These methods of finishing affected the hardening properties of many of the steels made by this process.

Casting—The cover was then removed from the crucible and most of the slag was mopped or swabbed up by means of a ball of slag, on one end of an iron rod. The crucible then was grasped horizontally with a pair of tongs, and, by tilting the crucible, the steel was poured into a cast-iron mold. This pouring required strength and skill, for it had to be continuous, and the stream of metal could not be permitted to impinge upon the walls of the mold. Any slag that might remain on the surface of the liquid metal was held back, by a small iron bar, and prevented from flowing into the mold. The molds were closed at the bottom and to facilitate the removal of the ingots after casting, split molds were used. These molds were cast in two pieces or halves, which fitted together by rings and wedges, formed a mold of square section with the joint passing longitudinally through diagonally opposite corners. Usually, the capacity of the molds was but a single potful of steel, and their cross section was but 3 or 4 inches square; but occasionally larger ingots were required, in which case two pots might be poured at once by the use of a funnel or spout made from a worn-out crucible, or several pots might be poured into a steel ladle, and the steel teemed into the molds from it. The last plan was followed in the production of fine steel castings of a size requiring more than two pots of metal. As soon as the steel had been poured, the crucible was cleaned and carefully inspected for cracks, when, if found sound and in good condition, it was charged, as before, for another heat.

Stripping and Inspecting the Ingots—As soon as the steel had solidified in the molds, the wedges or keys were loosened, and the rings holding the two parts of the mold together were removed. In the case of lower carbon steels, the mold might be removed at once and the ingot cooled in air, but ingots of high-carbon and alloy steels had to be cooled slowly to prevent the formation of **clinks** or tiny cracks, due to non-uniform distribution of contraction and expansion forces. Such ingots were allowed to stand in their molds until solid, then removed and placed in dry lime or covered with ashes or hot, dry sand until cold. The ingots were then topped, that is, pieces of their tops were broken off until the fracture showed perfectly sound steel. From the fractures thus exposed, the temper or carbon content (except in the cases of certain alloy steels) was determined. Then they were inspected for surface defects, and carefully and slowly reheated to a forging temperature. They were next forged, or cogged, under a hammer and any cracks or defects that appeared during the forging were ground or chipped out. After being forged to the required section, usually 1 to 2½ inches square, the billets were inspected again. Any surface defects, such as rough spots, seams, or tiny cracks were ground out with emery wheels, and these billets were reheated and rolled or forged into the sections desired. All this work was done with the greatest care, and was so meticulous as compared with the attention given ordinary steel that it was termed **crucible practice.**

Without doubt, crucible practice played as important a part in the high quality of crucible steel as crucible melting.

Chemistry of the Crucible Process—From a chemical standpoint, at least, the crucible process was the simplest of all for making steel. In the beginning, the charge carried a small quantity of iron oxides in the form of rust and scale and an almost negligible quantity of free oxygen in the air trapped in the crucible. As the charge melted, these oxides at first formed an oxidizing and very basic slag, which was soon reduced to the ferrous condition by the carbon in the charge or the crucible. Some ferrous oxide dissolved in the metal, and the remainder reacted with clay of the crucible to form ferrous silicates and ferrous aluminum silicates, which, after the charge had all melted

and the temperature had been raised, absorbed more and more silica until the slag became very acid. In the meantime, the metal had been absorbing carbon, either from the crucible or the charcoal charged, and the conditions within the crucible now became strongly reducing. Any oxides dissolved or otherwise incorporated with the metal now reacted with carbon, forming carbon monoxide gas; and since the slag was very acid, silica was readily split off from the slag molecules and was at once reduced, forming silicon, which alloyed with the iron and entered the metal. The absorption of carbon and the reduction and absorption of silicon both progressed with time and temperature, and were more rapid in new crucibles than in crucibles that had been used. The presence of silicon in the metal had the effect of cleansing it of oxides, and, without doubt, it was a large factor in "killing" the steel; but after a content of 0.50 per cent was exceeded, it began to have a noticeable embrittling effect upon most steels. Silicon also affected the welding and certain other properties adversely, hence was positively undesirable in some steels, a difficulty overcome by partial substitution of aluminum. This change in the deoxidizer used sometimes was made for the purpose of controlling the hardening properties of the steel. Hence, the time of killing as well as the temperature had to be closely watched, but it is evident that close control of either of these factors was impossible, with the result that both the carbon and the silicon contents might vary over relatively wide limits.

To produce a large quantity of steel of uniform composition, say up to one ton, it was necessary to pour a number of these 100-lb. crucible melts into a ladle in such a manner that the metal would be thoroughly mixed.

SECTION 6

MODERN STEELMAKING PROCESSES

All of the steelmaking processes discussed in Section 5 of this chapter were destined eventually to be supplanted by entirely new methods. The first of the new techniques was the pneumatic or Bessemer process. Closely following the invention of the pneumatic process was the development of the regenerative-type furnace that, now known as the open-hearth furnace, became adapted to steelmaking and evolved into the principal means for producing steel throughout the world. The electric furnace is relatively a newcomer to the field of steelmaking and is gradually finding more and more applications in the quantity production of quality steels.

The most recently developed steelmaking method is a pneumatic process that involves blowing high-purity oxygen onto the surface of a bath of molten pig iron; a method known in this country as the basic oxygen steelmaking process.

There has been a recent revival of interest in processes for producing iron and steel by direct methods from ore, without the necessity for first reducing the ore in the blast furnace to make pig iron, and then purifying the pig iron in a second step. Some of these processes, generally referred to as "direct-reduction processes," are described in Chapter 13.

THE PNEUMATIC STEELMAKING PROCESSES

The Bottom-Blown Acid Process—The original pneumatic process, developed independently by William Kelly of Eddyville, Kentucky and Henry Bessemer of England, involved blowing air *through* a bath of molten pig iron contained in a bottom-blown vessel lined with acid (siliceous) refractories. The process was the first to provide a large-scale *direct* method whereby pig iron could rapidly and cheaply be refined and converted into liquid steel. Bessemer's American patent was issued in 1856; although Kelly did not apply for a patent until 1857, he was able to prove that he had worked on the idea as early as 1847. Thus, both men held rights to the process in this country; this led to considerable litigation and delay, as discussed later. Lacking financial means, Kelly was unable to perfect his invention and Bessemer, in the face of great difficulties and many failures, developed the process to a high degree of perfection and it came to be known as the acid Bessemer process, described in its modern form in Section 2 of Chapter 15.

The fundamental principle proposed by Bessemer and Kelly was that the oxidation of the major impurities in liquid blast-furnace iron (silicon, manganese and carbon) was preferential and occurred before the major oxidation of iron; the actual mechanism differs from this simple explanation, as outlined in the discussion of the physical chemistry of steelmaking in Chapter 12. Further, they discovered that sufficient heat was generated in the vessel by the chemical oxidation of the above elements in most types of pig iron to permit the simple blowing of cold air through molten pig iron to produce liquid steel without the need for an external source of heat. Because the process converted pig iron to steel, the vessel in which the operation was carried out came to be known as a converter. The principle of the bottom-blown converter is shown schematically in Figure 1—24.

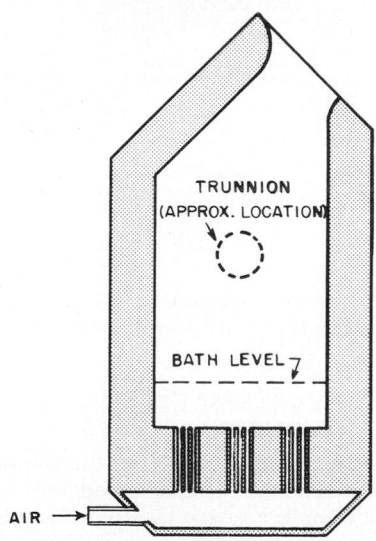

FIG. 1—24. Principle of the bottom-blown converter. The blast enters the wind box beneath the vessel through the pipe indicated by the arrow and passes into the vessel through holes in tuyeres set in the bottom of the converter.

At first, Bessemer produced satisfactory steel in a converter lined with siliceous (acid) refractories by refining pig iron that, smelted from Swedish ores, was low in phosphorus, high in manganese, and contained enough silicon to meet the thermal needs of the process. But, when applied to irons which were higher in phosphorus and low in silicon and manganese, the process did not produce satisfactory steel. In order to save his process in the face of opposition among steel-

makers, Bessemer built a steel works at Sheffield, England, and began to operate in 1860. Even when low-phosphorus Swedish pig iron was employed, the steels first produced there contained much more than the admissible amounts of oxygen, which made the steel "wild" in the molds. Difficulty also was experienced with sulphur which, introduced from the coke used as fuel in melting the iron in cupolas, contributed to "hot shortness" of the steel. These objections finally were overcome by the addition of manganese in the form of spiegeleisen to the steel after blowing was completed. The beneficial effects of manganese were disclosed in a patent by R. Mushet in 1856. The carbon and manganese in the spiegeleisen served the purpose of partially deoxidizing the steel, while part of the manganese combined chemically with some of the sulphur to form compounds that either floated out of the metal into the slag, or were comparatively harmless if they remained in the steel.

Because of trouble with tuyeres in the bottom, some early converters had tuyeres located in the side of the vessel but below the metal-bath surface. Many of the early converters were stationary and had to be tapped in a manner similar to the cupola or the open-hearth furnace; such converters were used for a considerable period in Sweden and Germany. However, the rotating or tilting type was favored in England and in the United States.

As stated earlier, Bessemer had obtained patents in England and in this country previous to Kelly's application; therefore, both men held rights to the process in the United States.

The Kelly Pneumatic Process Company had been formed in 1863 in an arrangement with William Kelly for the commercial production of steel by the new process. This association included the Cambria Iron Company; E. B. Ward; Park Brothers and Company; Lyon, Shord and Company; Z. S. Durfee and, later, Chouteau, Harrison and Vale. This company, in 1864, built the first commercial Bessemer plant in this country, consisting of a 2½ ton acid-lined vessel erected at the Wyandotte Iron Works, Wyandotte, Michigan, owned by Captain E. B. Ward. It may be mentioned that a Kelly converter was used experimentally at the Cambria Works, Johnstown, Pennsylvania as early as 1861.

As a result of the dual rights to the process a second group consisting of Messrs. John A. Griswold and John F. Winslow of Troy, New York and A. L. Holley formed another company under an arrangement with Bessemer in 1864. This group erected an experimental 2½-ton vessel at Troy, New York which commenced operations on February 16, 1865. The rival organizations, after much litigation had failed to gain for either sole control of the patents for the pneumatic process in America, decided to combine their respective interests early in 1866. This larger organization was then able to combine the best features covered by the Kelly and Bessemer patents, and the application of the process advanced rapidly.

By 1871, annual Bessemer steel production in this country had increased to 45,000 net tons, about 55 per cent of the total steel production of the country, which was produced by seven Bessemer plants.

A. L. Holley's contributions to the early development of the process were exceedingly important. He acted as consulting engineer on most of the plants erected in the first ten to fifteen years of the development of the process in the United States. Holley also greatly improved the design of the detachable bottom, originally developed by Bessemer in 1863; this permitted increased tonnage output because it permitted replacement of the bottom when repairs were necessary without excessive loss of production.

Another notable contribution to development of the pneumatic processes was made at a later date (1889) by William R. Jones of the Edgar Thomson Works of the Carnegie Steel Co., now a part of United States Steel Corporation, who conceived the idea of the hot-metal mixer. The purpose of the mixer and its construction are described in Section 2 of Chapter 15.

The Basic Bessemer or Thomas Process—The bottom-blown basic pneumatic process known by the several names of the **Thomas, Thomas-Gilchrist** or **basic Bessemer process,** was patented in 1879 by Sidney G. Thomas in England. The process, involving the use of a basic lining and a basic flux in the converter, made it possible to use the pneumatic method for refining pig irons smelted from the high-phosphorus ores common to many sections of Europe. It is described in Section 3 of Chapter 15. The process (never adopted in the United States) developed much more rapidly on the Continent than in Great Britain and, in 1890, Continental production was over 2 million tons as compared with 400,000 tons made in Great Britain.

The simultaneous development of the basic open-hearth process resulted in a decline of production of steel by the bottom-blown basic pneumatic process in Europe and, by 1904, production of basic open-hearth steel there exceeded that of basic pneumatic steel. From 1910 on, the bottom-blown basic pneumatic process declined continuously until World War II.

The Surface Side-Blown Acid Process—The side-blown acid pneumatic converter (Figure 1—25) is sometimes referred to as a surface-blown converter,

or as the Tropenas converter. There have been numerous variations of design of converters using the side-blowing technique, but all are characterized by having all of the tuyeres above the liquid level of the bath and entering through the side of the vessel. The majority of side-blown acid converters are of one-half to two ton capacity, although some larger vessels have been built. This type of converter finds its principal use in steel foundries. Its operating characteristics are described in Section 4 of Chapter 15.

The Basic Oxygen Steelmaking Process—In this process, oxygen of high purity is blown at high velocity onto the surface of the bath in a basic-lined vessel by a vertical pipe or lance inserted through the mouth of the vessel (Figure 1—26). Since this is a relatively

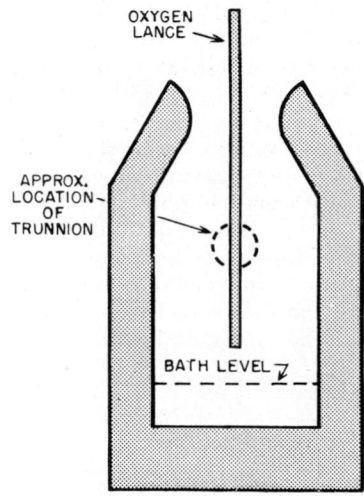

Fig. 1—26. Principle of the top-blown converter. Oxygen of commercial purity, at high pressure and velocity, is blown downward vertically onto surface of bath through a single water-cooled pipe or lance, indicated by arrow.

new process, its development is outlined in Section 5 of Chapter 15, where the process is described in detail.

THE OPEN-HEARTH STEELMAKING PROCESSES

Early History of the Process—The phenomenal success of the Bessemer process, coupled with the ever-increasing demand for steel, attracted many other inventors to the study of new and improved methods of steelmaking. Of all the methods which received attention, the only process which was destined to become a rival of the pneumatic process was developed through the invention of the regenerative principle by Karl Wilhelm Siemens who, although German-born, was a naturalized British citizen.

Siemens' early work with the regenerative principle as applied to steam engines showed that a very great saving of fuel and very high temperatures could be obtained by its use and, at the suggestion of his brother, Frederick, he turned his attention to the application of the principle for producing high temperatures in furnaces. The first experimental furnace was built in 1858, when it was discovered that, especially

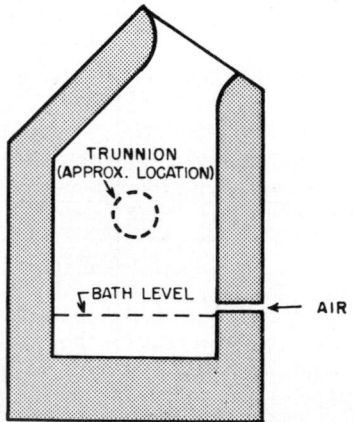

Fig. 1—25. Principle of the side-blown converter. The blast enters the vessel through tuyeres in its side, indicated by arrow. Angle at which centerline of tuyeres intersects horizontal surface of bath can be varied by tilting vessel.

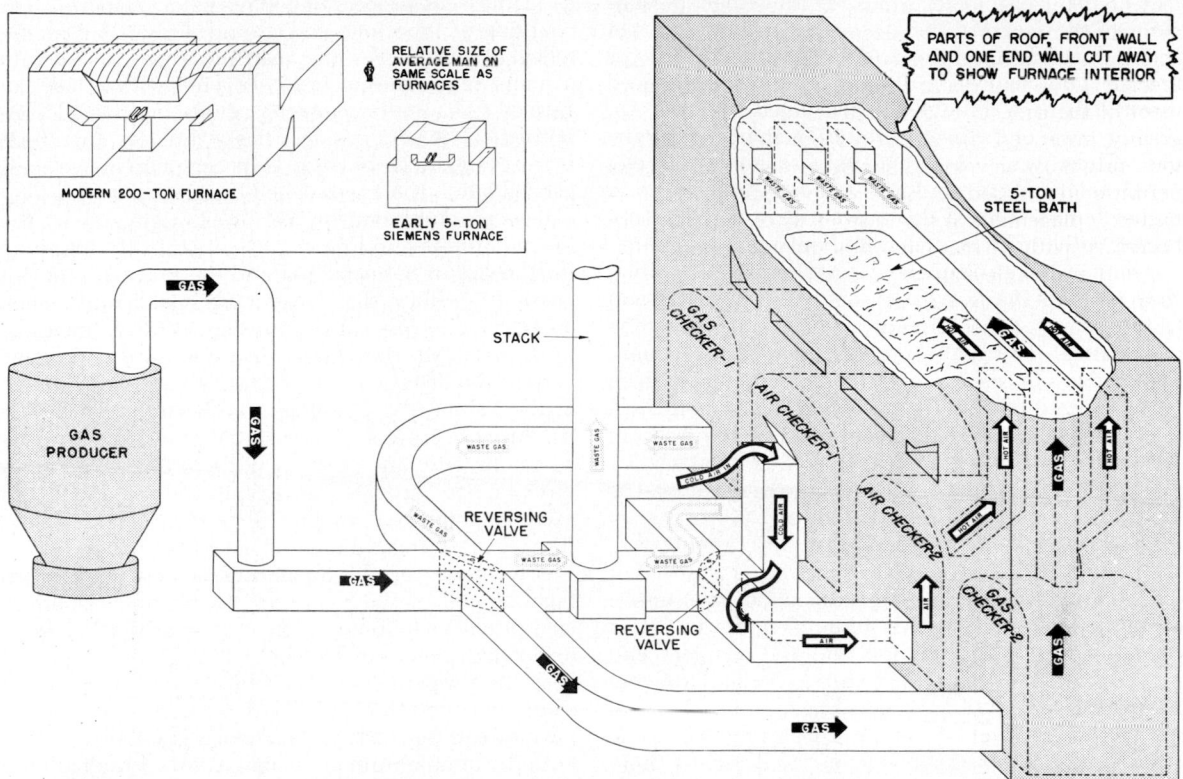

FIG. 1—27. Schematic arrangement of an early type of Siemens furnace with about a 5-ton capacity. The roof of this design (which was soon abandoned) dipped from the ends toward the center of the furnace to force the flame downward on the bath. Various different arrangements of gas and air ports were used in later furnaces. Note that in this design, the furnace proper was supported on the regenerator arches. Flow of gas, air and waste gases were reversed by reversing the position of the two reversing valves. The inset at the upper left compares the sizes of one of these early furnaces with a modern 200-ton open hearth.

with large furnaces using solid fuel, many difficulties were to be overcome if the full efficiency which the principle promised was to be realized.

After two years or more of experimentation, Siemens fell upon the plan of gasifying the fuel prior to burning it in the furnace, whereby he found that most of the difficulties could be overcome. Thus, a correlative development of the regenerative furnace was the **gas producer.** Siemens' patent covering the successful furnace design specifically mentioned the possibility of using the furnace for the production of steel. An early design of a Siemens steelmaking furnace, with gas producer, is shown schematically in Figure 1—27.

In the ferrous industry, some of the early uses Siemens made of the furnace were for puddling, reheating iron and steel for forging and rolling, and for melting crucible steel. Siemens next turned his attention to the manufacture of steel in his furnace and, though many trials were made at different works, he met with only indifferent success. Finally, like Bessemer, he found it necessary to erect a steel works of his own. These works were located in Birmingham, England, and were employed at first in a remelting process by which steel of the best quality was obtained from processing such scrap as old rails, plates, and so on.

In the meantime, Siemens was busy developing the idea that steel could be made from pig iron by oxidiz-

ing the carbon content of the latter with iron ore and, by the year 1868, proved that this method, which came to be known as the **pig and ore process,** could be employed successfully. He next turned his attention to evolving a method whereby steel could be produced directly from the ore, thus dispensing with the blast furnace. In this feat he actually succeeded, but the cost of production was many times that of producing steel from pig iron. Subsequent events have proved that it is more practical and economical to employ the blast furnace for the primary reduction of the iron ore to pig iron, and from this to make steel in the furnace which has been evolved from Siemens' original designs.

Principles of Siemens' Pig and Ore Process—Briefly, the method of Siemens was as follows: A rectangular covered hearth was used to contain the charge of pig iron or pig iron and scrap (see Figure 1—27). Most of the heat required to promote the chemical reactions necessary for purification of the charge was provided by passing burning fuel gas over the top of the materials. The fuel gas, with a quantity of air more than sufficient to burn it, was introduced through ports at each end of the furnace, alternately at one end and then the other. The products of combustion passed out of the port temporarily not used for entrance of gas and air, and entered chambers partly filled with brick checkerwork. This checkerwork, commonly called **checkers,** provided a multitude of passageways for the exit of the gases to the stack. During their passage through the checkers, the gases gave up a large part of their heat to the brickwork. After a short time, the gas and air were shut off at the one end and introduced into the furnace through the preheated checkers, absorbing some of the heat stored in these checkers. The gas and air were thus preheated to a somewhat elevated temperature, and consequently developed a higher temperature in combustion than could be obtained without preheating. In about twenty minutes, the flow of the gas and air was again reversed so that they entered the furnace through the checkers and port used first; and a series of such reversals, occurring every fifteen or twenty minutes was continued until the heat was finished. The elements in the bath which were oxidized both by the oxygen of the air in the furnace atmosphere and that contained in the iron ore fed to the bath, were carbon, silicon and manganese, all three of which could be reduced to as low a limit as was possible in the Bessemer process.

Thus, as in all other processes for purifying pig iron, the basic principle of the Siemens process was that of oxidation. However, in other respects, it was unlike any other process. True, it resembled the puddling process in both the method and the agencies employed, but the high temperatures attainable in the Siemens furnace made it possible to keep the final product molten and free of entrapped slag. The same primary result was obtained as in the Bessemer process, but by a different method and through different agencies, both of which imparted to steel made by the new process properties somewhat different from Bessemer steel, and gave the process itself certain metallurgical advantages over the older pneumatic process, as discussed later in this section.

Mechanical Changes and Improvements in the Siemens Process—As would be expected, many variations of the process, both mechanical and metallurgical, have been worked out since its original conception. Along mechanical lines, various improvements in the design, the size, and the arrangement of the parts of the furnace have been made. Early furnaces had capacities of only four or five tons, while modern furnaces range from 40 to 600 tons in capacity, with the majority having capacities between 200 and 300 tons.

The early development of the Siemens steelmaking process was retarded by the lack of refractory materials capable of withstanding the high temperatures and the chemical reactions of the process. Even in today's advanced stage of development of the process, it is recognized that additional production and improved steel quality may be possible of attainment if new or improved refractories eventually make feasible a sustained operation at higher temperatures.

The Siemens process now is known more generally, at least in this country, as the **open-hearth process.** The name "open hearth" was derived, probably, from the fact that the steel, while melted on a hearth under a roof, was accessible through the furnace doors for inspection, sampling, and testing. Modern open-hearth steelmaking practices are described in Chapter 16.

Metallurgical Improvements—The hearth of Siemens' furnace was of acid brick construction, on top of which the bottom was made up of sand—essentially as in the **acid process** of today. Later, to permit the charging of limestone and use of a basic slag for removal of phosphorus, the hearth was constructed with a lining of magnesite brick, covered with a layer of burned dolomite or magnesite, replacing the siliceous bottom of the acid furnace. These furnaces, therefore, were designated as basic furnaces, and the process carried out in them was called the **basic process.**

The **pig and scrap process** was originated by the Martin brothers, in France, who, by substituting scrap for the ore in Siemens' **pig and ore process,** found it possible to dilute the charge with steel scrap to such an extent that less oxidation was necessary. Since the time of the Martins, these processes have undergone various modifications, chief of which are those known as the **Talbot,** the **Campbell,** the **Bertrand-Thiel,** and the **Monell** process. These latter processes have become obsolete, and they did little to determine modern practice, except that Talbot and Campbell did exert an influence which still is reflected in tilting-furnace practice, as discussed in Chapter 16.

Advantages of the Siemens Process—The advantages offered by the Siemens process may be summarized briefly as follows: (1) By the use of iron ore as an oxidizing agent and by the external application of heat, the temperature of the bath is made independent of the purifying reactions, and the elimination of impurities can be made to take place gradually, so that both the temperature and composition of the bath are under much better control than in the Bessemer process. (2) For the same reasons, a greater variety of raw materials can be used (particularly scrap, not greatly consumable in the Bessemer converter) and a greater variety of products may be made by the open-hearth process than by the Bessemer process. (3) A very important advantage is the increased yield of finished steel from a given quantity of pig iron as compared to the Bessemer process, because of lower inherent sources of iron loss in the former, as well as because of recovery of the iron content of the ore used for oxidation in the open hearth. (4) Finally, with the development of the basic open-hearth process, the greatest advantage of the Siemens over the acid Bessemer process was made apparent, since the basic open-hearth process is capable of eliminating phosphorus from the bath. While this element can be removed also in the basic Bessemer (Thomas-Gilchrist) process, it is to be noted that, due to the different temperature conditions, phosphorus is eliminated before the carbon in the basic open-hearth process, whereas the major proportion of the phosphorus is not oxidized in the basic Bessemer process until after the carbon, in the period termed the afterblow. Hence, while the basic Bessemer process requires a pig iron with a phosphorus content of 2.00 per cent or more in order to maintain the temperature high enough for the afterblow, the basic open-hearth process permits the economical use of iron of any phosphorus content up to 1.00 per cent. In the United States, this fact is of importance since it makes available immense iron ore deposits which could not be utilized otherwise because of their phosphorus content, which is too high to permit their use in the acid Bessemer or acid open-hearth processes and too low for use in the basic Bessemer process. This is one of the important reasons why the basic open-hearth process has become the leading steelmaking method in this country: other reasons are discussed later.

The Open-Hearth Process in the United States—As early as 1868, a small open-hearth furnace was built at Trenton, New Jersey, but satisfactory steel at a reasonable cost did not result and the furnace was abandoned. Later, at Boston, Massachusetts, a successful furnace was designed and operated, beginning in 1870. Following this success, similar furnaces were built at Nashua, New Hampshire, and in Pittsburgh, Pennsylvania, the latter by Singer, Nimick and Company, in 1871. The Otis Iron and Steel Company constructed two 7-ton furnaces at their Lakeside plant in 1874. Two 15-ton furnaces were added to this plant in 1878, two more of the same size in 1881, and two more in 1887. All of these furnaces had acid linings, using a sand bottom for the hearths.

A furnace with a basic bottom, rammed from Austrian magnesite, produced basic steel at the Otis plant in January, 1886. Production rate on the basic furnace was so low compared to that normally achieved with an acid bottom that the basic bottom was torn out after four months, and replaced by an acid bottom. Following the Otis installation, the following companies also installed open-hearth furnaces: The Cleveland Rolling Mills (now part of the American Steel and Wire Division of United States Steel Corporation); The Pennsylvania Steel Company (later Bethlehem Steel Company); the Schoenberger Works (now dismantled, but formerly part of the American Steel and Wire Division); and Carnegie, Phipps and Company (now Homestead District Works of United States Steel Corporation).

It was in the last-named plant that the commercial production of steel by the basic process was achieved first, the initial heat being tapped March 28, 1888. By the close of 1890, there were 16 basic open-hearth furnaces operating. From 1890 to 1900, magnesite for the bottom began to be imported regularly and the manufacture of silica refractories for the roof was begun in American plants. For these last two reasons, the construction of basic furnaces advanced rapidly and, by 1900, furnaces larger than 50 tons were being planned.

While the Bessemer process could produce steel at a possibly lower cost above the cost of materials, it was restricted to ores of a limited phosphorus content and its use of scrap was also limited. The open hearth was not subject to these restrictions, so that the annual production of steel by the open-hearth process increased rapidly, and, in 1908, passed the total tonnage produced yearly by the Bessemer process. Total annual production of Bessemer steel has decreased rather steadily since 1908. In addition to the ability of the basic open-hearth furnace to utilize irons made from American ores, as discussed earlier, the main reasons were the flexibility of the open-hearth process, with respect to its ability to produce steels of many compositions, and its ability to use a large proportion of steel or iron scrap, if necessary. Also, steels made by any of the pneumatic processes that utilize air for blowing contain more nitrogen than open-hearth steels; this

higher nitrogen content makes Bessemer steel less desirable than open-hearth steel in some important applications.

ELECTRIC FURNACE STEELMAKING

It has been said that arc-type furnaces had their beginning in the discovery of the carbon arc by Sir Humphrey Davy in 1800, but it is more proper to say that their practical application began with the work of Sir William Siemens, who in 1878 constructed, operated and patented furnaces operating on both the direct-arc and indirect-arc principles.

At this early date, the availability of electric power was limited and its cost high; also, carbon electrodes of the quality required to carry sufficient current for steel melting had not been developed. Thus, the development of the electric melting furnace awaited the expansion of the electric-power industry and improvements in carbon electrodes.

Direct-Arc Furnaces—The first successful commercial direct-arc steelmaking furnace was placed in operation by Heroult in 1899, and the first shipment of electric steel was a carload of bars from Heroult's plant at La Praz to the firm of Schneider and Company at Creusot, France, on December 28, 1900. The Heroult patent, stated in simple terms, covered single-phase or multi-phase furnaces with the arcs in series through the metal bath. This type of furnace, utilizing three-phase power, has been the most successful of the electric furnaces in the production of steel. The design and operation of modern electric-arc furnaces are discussed in Sections 2, 3, and 4 of Chapter 17.

Simultaneous with and subsequent to Heroult's success with the direct-arc principle, many investigators abroad directed their attention to developing furnaces employing the same principle. However, in this country, there were no developments along arc-furnace lines until the first Heroult furnace was installed in the plant of the Halcomb Steel Company, Syracuse, New York, which made its first heat on April 5, 1906. This was a single-phase, two-electrode, rectangular furnace of four tons capacity. Two years later a similar but smaller furnace was installed at the Firth-Sterling Steel Company, McKeesport, Pennsylvania, and in 1909, a 15-ton, three-phase furnace was installed in the South Works of the Illinois Steel Company, now a part of the United States Steel Corporation, in Chicago, Illinois. The latter was, at that time, the largest electric steelmaking furnace in the world, and was the first round (instead of rectangular) furnace. It operated on 25-cycle power at 2200 volts and tapped the first heat on May 10, 1909.

The foregoing furnaces all were for making steel for ingots. The first electric furnace for the production of steel for commercial castings was that of the Treadwell Engineering Company, Easton, Pennsylvania. It was a single-phase, two-electrode furnace of two tons capacity, designed along the lines of the Halcomb and Firth-Sterling furnaces. It was operated first in August, 1911.

About the same time, the General Electric Company began to experiment with the design of direct-arc electric furnaces, with the view of developing a market for electrical equipment required for their operation, and built three or four units. Other furnace designs followed: the Snyder, Ludlum, Vom Baur, Booth-Hall, Moore, Green, Swindell, and Volta, the last-named being of Canadian origin.

Indirect-Arc Furnaces—The first work on indirect-arc furnaces was done by Stassano, in Italy. His design consisted of a vertical, cylindrical shell, with three electrodes spaced 120 degrees apart and entering the furnace just above the bath. A furnace of this design was installed in the plant of the Clark Equipment Company, Buchanan, Michigan, in 1911.

About the beginning of World War I, Rennerfelt of Sweden developed an indirect-arc furnace with two horizontal electrodes and one vertical electrode, so connected electrically that the arc was "blown" down on the charge or bath, and the horizontal electrodes were arranged to tilt downward so that they could arc directly on the bath.

None of the indirect-arc furnaces came into very great use because maintenance was difficult and power consumption was high.

The Induction Furnace—Another type of electric melting furnace, used to a certain extent for melting high-grade alloys, is the high-frequency coreless induction furnace described in Section 5 of Chapter 17, which gradually replaced the crucible process in the production of complex, high-quality alloys used as tool steels. It is used also for remelting scrap from fine steels produced in arc furnaces, melting chrome-nickel alloys, and high-manganese scrap.

The induction furnace had its inception abroad and first was patented by Ferranti in Italy in 1877. This was a low-frequency furnace. It had no commercial application until Kjellin installed and operated one in Sweden. The first large installation of this type was made in 1914 at the plant of the American Iron and Steel Company in Lebanon, Pennsylvania, but was not successful. Some other low-frequency furnaces, however, have operated successfully, especially in making stainless steel.

A successful development using higher-frequency current is the coreless high-frequency induction furnace. The first coreless induction furnaces were built and installed by the Ajax Electrothermic Corporation, who also initiated the original researches by E. F. Northrup leading to the development of the furnace. For this reason, the furnace is often referred to as the Ajax-Northrup furnace.

The first coreless induction furnaces for the production of steel on a commercial scale were installed at Sheffield, England, and began the regular production of steel in October, 1927.

The first commercial steel furnaces of this type in the United States were installed by the Heppenstall Forge and Knife Company, Pittsburgh, Pennsylvania, and were producing steel regularly in November, 1928. Each furnace had a holding capacity of 600 pounds and was served by a 150-kva motor-generator set transforming 60-cycle current to 960 cycles. The crucibles were monolithic, 6 inches in diameter, and 36 inches in depth. Time of an ordinary heat was 55 minutes. The coreless type of induction furnace normally operates on alternating current at a frequency of approximately 1000 cycles, produced by a motor-generator set of special design with the power transmitted over co-axial cables to the primary coil of the furnace. Recently, mercury-arc rectifiers, which have the advantage of higher efficiencies over motor-generator sets, have been developed to supply the high-frequency power.

Commercial use of the high-frequency furnace for melting is not extensive in the steel industry. Those in use are small in size, ranging in capacity from about 500 pounds to 2,000 pounds. The largest one in the United States reported to be operating in 1960 in a steel plant was of 3¼ tons capacity, although several 5-ton units had been installed for foundry service some years before.

Electric Reduction Furnaces—Electric reduction furnaces are used for smelting ores in the production of ferromanganese, ferrosilicon, ferrochromium, and so on. These furnaces differ from the steelmaking furnaces in that production is continuous, as in a blast furnace; the charge is placed in the furnace at the top and the molten product tapped near the bottom. They are either single-phase or three-phase units.

In the single-phase units, a single carbon electrode is suspended in the center of the furnace, with the carbon bottom of the furnace serving as the second electrode. This is an example of a furnace with a conducting bottom. In the three-phase furnaces, the three electrodes are spaced as in the arc furnace and are buried in the charge. These units normally have an open top, and the charge either is shoveled in or introduced by chutes. The electrical load on this type of furnace differs from that on the arc furnace used for steelmaking. Since charging is continuous, the load is fairly steady, and the power factor can be maintained around 90 per cent. The voltages used are lower than in the arc furnaces, and the current density greater. These requirements necessitate a careful design of the secondary circuits to keep reactance to a minimum. For some products, and on 25-cycle systems, units have electrical capacities up to 18,000 kva.

Electric Furnaces of Special Design—There have been other types of furnaces designed that are worthy of mention. The Hering furnace was a conventional unit except that the bath was deeper than usual and the hearth contained one or more resistance tubes at the bottom which served as water-cooled electrodes. Molten metal was required for the first charge, and only two-thirds of the heat was tapped. The effect of the current flowing through the molten metal in the resistor tubes was to pinch off the column of metal and eject it from the tube. The furnace had no commercial application.

Another furnace of European design was a combination of open-hearth and electric-arc furnace principles. Still another was a combination of low-frequency induction furnace and pneumatic converter, the tuyeres of the latter being equipped so that a reducing gas might be introduced into the furnace.

BIBLIOGRAPHY

Agricola, G., De re metallica. Translated from the first Latin edition of 1556 by Herbert Clark Hoover and Lou Henry Hoover. N. Y., Dover, 1950.

Aitchison, Leslie, A History of Metals. MacDonald &

(Continued on next page)

Evans, Ltd., Great Britain; published in the U. S. by Interscience Publishers, Inc., N. Y., 1960.

Biringuccio, V., Pirotechnia. Translated from the Italian by C. S. Smith and M. T. Gnudi (first edition 1540). N. Y., Am. Institute of Mining and Metallurgical Engineers, 1943.

Beck, L., Geschichte des Eisens. Braunschweig, Germany, Vieweg, 1891–1903. (5 vols.)

Forbes, R. J., Metallurgy in antiquity. Leiden, Netherlands, Brill, 1950.

Percy, John, Metallurgy. London, England, John Murray, 1864.

Petrie, W. M. F., Gerar. London, British School of Archaeology in Egypt, 1928.

Rickard, T. A., Iron in antiquity. Journal of the Iron and Steel Institute (London) **120**, 323–342 (1929).

CHAPTER 2

Refractories

SECTION 1

CLASSIFICATION OF REFRACTORIES

Refractories are the chief materials used in the steel industry in the construction of all furnaces and in the lining of ladles, hot-metal mixers and similar retaining vessels, as well as in the flues or stacks through which hot gases are conducted. At the risk of oversimplification, they may, therefore, be said to be materials of construction exposed to temperatures above a dull red. These materials are expensive, and any abrupt failure in the refractories results in a great loss of time, equipment and product. Therefore, the problems of obtaining refractories suitable for each branch of the industry and a refractory best suited to each specific purpose are of supreme importance. Economics figure largely in the solution of these problems, as a refractory best suited for an application is not necessarily the longest lived, but the one which provides the best balance between initial installed cost and service performance. These balances are never fixed, but are constantly shifting as a result of the introduction of new processes or new types of refractories. History reveals that refractory developments have occurred largely as the result of the pressure for improvement caused by the persistent search for superior metallurgical processes. The rapidity with which these ever-recurring refractory problems have been solved has been a large factor in the rate of advancement of the iron and steel industry. To discuss the many factors involved in these problems and to provide information helpful to their solution are the objectives of this chapter.

Refractories may be classified in a number of ways, no one of which is completely satisfactory. From the chemical standpoint, refractory substances, in common with matter in general, are of three classes; namely, acid, basic, and amphoteric or neutral. Theoretically, acid refractories should not be used in contact with basic slags, gases or fumes, while basic refractories should be exposed to no other conditions. Actually, for various reasons, these rules are continually violated. Also, the existence of a strictly neutral refractory may be doubted. Hence, the time-honored chemical classification is primarily academic, and of little value as a guide to actual service possibilities. Classifications by use, such as blast-furnace refractories or open-hearth refractories are generally too broad and are constantly subject to revision. Min-

eralogically, refractories may be classified two ways; namely, with reference to the raw materials, and with reference to the minerals predominating after processing for use. For the present purpose, the following raw-materials classification is believed to offer the best possibilities for a clear understanding of the origin and nature of steel-plant refractories.

A. SILICEOUS GROUP

Quartzite—Quartzite or **ganister** is the most commonly used, and the purest, of the siliceous raw materials. Massive rock forms analyzing over 98 per cent of SiO_2, such as have long been used for silica-brick manufacture, are found in Pennsylvania, Wisconsin, Alabama, Utah, and California. In recent years, as the result of persistent demands for silica brick of maximum purity for open-hearth roof service, these massive quartzites have given way to the still purer quartz pebbles and pebble conglomerates found in Ohio, Maryland, Pennsylvania, and Indiana. With proper selection and washing, these pebbles readily permit the manufacture of silica brick containing a total of less than 0.5 per cent of detrimental Al_2O_3 and alkalies. However, for coke-oven use, silica brick are still largely made from quartzite ganister.

Sandstone—Sandstone, or **firestone**, is a sedimentary rock consisting essentially of bonded sand grains, and usually analyzing 90 to 96 per cent SiO_2, 3 to 5 per cent Al_2O_3, and some iron oxide and lime. It is relatively soft and often striated, thus permitting easy cutting or splitting into blocks or shapes for use in the raw state for lining soaking pits or acid Bessemer converters.

Mica Schist—Mica schist is a highly laminated micaceous silica rock of composition similar to sandstone, but generally slightly lower in silica. Like sandstone it is readily cut and is also used in the raw state for hot metal ladle and mixer linings in addition to linings for soaking pits and converters.

Siliceous Fireclays—While the term **siliceous fireclays** might properly refer to clays having a rather wide range in silica content, reference here is to those clays with a minimum of 75 per cent SiO_2 which are employed in the manufacture of semi-silica brick, and are characterized by a very low percentage of impurities such as alkalies, alkaline earths and iron oxides. Somewhat less siliceous and often more impure clays are also widely used for mortars and daubing purposes with siliceous linings.

B. FIRECLAY GROUP

Chemically, clays are all hydrous silicates of alumina and occur widely distributed. They are identified as being plastic when in a wet and finely divided state (as obtained by pulverizing, wetting, and mixing), rigid when dried, and vitreous when heated to a sufficiently high temperature. Clays may be residual or sedimentary, and have been formed by the natural decomposition or weathering of feldspathic rock. Ordinary varieties contain high percentages of combined water and impurities that render them unfit for use as high-temperature refractories. Impurities include alkalies, titania, compounds of iron, calcium and magnesium, and organic matter from various sources. Even in small quantities the alkalies, and the compounds of iron, calcium and magnesium are important fluxes and have a pronounced effect on the refractory properties of the clay. The species used as a refractory is known as **fireclay**. Fireclays are of sedimentary origin, are usually associated with coal measures, and contain limited percentages of fluxing impurities. There are several varieties, namely:

Plastic Fireclay—A fireclay of sufficient natural plasticity to bond nonplastic materials.

Flint Fireclay—A hard or flint-like fireclay occurring as an unstratified massive rock, practically devoid of natural plasticity and showing a conchoidal fracture.

Nodular Fireclay—Also called **burley** or **burley flint** clay, nodular fireclay occurs in the form of a rock containing aluminous or ferruginous nodules, or both, bonded by fireclay.

Kaolins—While not fireclays, certain **kaolins** are highly refractory and are being increasingly employed in the manufacture of fire brick. Kaolins are both sedimentary and residual, and quite pure, generally closely approaching the theoretical clay composition represented by the formula $Al_2O_3 \cdot 2SiO_2 \cdot 2H_2O$.

C. HIGH-ALUMINA GROUP

This group includes those materials capable of serving for the production of refractories of higher alumina content than the maximum that can be provided by fireclays, namely, more than 47.5 per cent Al_2O_3. Occurring naturally are two classes of minerals, those which are combinations of Al_2O_3 and H_2O, typified by bauxite and diaspore, and those which are combinations of Al_2O_3 and SiO_2, typified by sillimanite, andalusite and kyanite.

Bauxite and Diaspore—Diaspore, $Al_2O_3 \cdot H_2O$, is found chiefly in Missouri where it occurs in lenses or pockets principally as diaspore clay, a rock consisting essentially of diaspore bonded by fireclay. For many years, diaspore was the principal raw material for high-alumina brick containing up to 80 per cent of Al_2O_3, but supplies have diminished, and now diaspore has been virtually replaced by bauxite for these products. **Bauxite**, $Al_2O_3 \cdot 3H_2O$ and $Al_2O_3 \cdot H_2O$, is found in Arkansas, Alabama, and South America.

Sillimanite, Andalusite, and Kyanite (Cyanite)—These minerals all have the formula $Al_2O_3 \cdot SiO_2$, and contain theoretically 62.9 per cent Al_2O_3 and 37.1 per cent SiO_2. On heating, all form **mullite** ($3Al_2O_3 \cdot 2SiO_2$) and a siliceous glass, but differ in the ease with which this decomposition takes place, kyanite being the easiest to convert (about 2415° F) and sillimanite the hardest (about 2785° F). These materials, and particularly Indian kyanite, were long the principal ingredient in the sillimanite or mullite type of high-alumina brick, but figure far less importantly today.

Tabular alumina, a high-temperature furnace product of nearly pure Al_2O_3, is being increasingly used in high-alumina refractories, either directly, or in combination with clay as synthetic mullite grain that is produced in a rotary kiln or electric furnace. It is widely used in many high-alumina products, particularly those containing over 80 per cent of Al_2O_3.

Fused alumina, an electric-furnace product, is used in some special high-alumina products containing usually over 90 per cent of Al_2O_3.

D. MAGNESIUM-SILICATE GROUP

This group includes the olivines and serpentines. **Olivines** have the general formula $2RO \cdot SiO_2$, in which the RO may be MgO, CaO, FeO, or MnO. The most common refractory olivine is a mixture of **forsterite** ($2MgO \cdot SiO_2$) and **fayalite** ($2FeO \cdot SiO_2$) and is found primarily in North Carolina. **Serpentines** are hydrous magnesium silicates of the general formula $3MgO \cdot 2SiO_2 \cdot 2H_2O$. Forsterite is the most desirable magnesium silicate for refractories, and is generally the end product aimed for in employing these minerals.

E. MAGNESIA-LIME GROUP

In this group have been classed all natural and synthetic magnesites, brucite, and dolomite. These constitute the most important group of refractories for basic steelmaking processes, as all are sources of magnesia, MgO, the best basic refractory known.

Natural magnesite, $MgCO_3$ is rarely found in a pure state, but contains varying percentages of silica, alumina, iron oxides and lime, so that on calcination the MgO content generally ranges from 80 to 85 per cent. Silica is the most objectionable impurity and varies from 4 to 10 per cent. Formerly, much magnesite was imported from Austria, but for several years, the steel industry has relied almost exclusively on sources in the state of Washington and in Canada.

Magnesia is derived synthetically from sea water brines, well brines, dolomite and brucite, or processes combining brines and dolomite. The production of magnesia or, more popularly, sea water magnesite or, more technically correct, periclase, by these means has increased rapidly in recent years, and this material is now used extensively in the manufacture of basic brick and granular refractories. With the rapid conversion from silica to basic roofs for open-hearth furnaces since 1958, demands for purer magnesite arose, just as previously there were demands for purer silica. As a result, synthetic magnesites containing as much as 98 per cent of MgO are now available.

Brucite is a hydrate of magnesia found chiefly in Nevada and is used largely in conjunction with dolomite in the manufacture of granular refractories.

Dolomite is a double carbonate ($CaCO_3 \cdot MgCO_3$), which calcines, evolving 47.8 per cent as CO_2 leaving 30.4 per cent CaO and 21.7 per cent MgO. Principal impurities are silica and alumina, but large deposits are found in several localities such as Illinois and Ohio, which closely approach the theoretical composition. Thus, for best refractory service, a dolomite should contain more than 21 per cent MgO, less than 1 per cent SiO_2 and less than 0.5 per cent Al_2O_3 in a crude state. From the standpoint of consumption, dolomite exceeds all other refractories, as in either the raw, calcined, or dead-burned state*, it is the chief mainstay in open-hearth-bottom maintenance.

F. CHROMITE GROUP

Chrome ores in general consist of a highly refractory spinel ($RO \cdot R_2O_3$) composed of FeO, MgO, Al_2O_3 and Cr_2O_3 in various proportions, and less refractory associated silicates. Chrome ores of widely different compositions are suitable for refractory purposes, the chief limitations being lime, iron oxide, and silica. Most of the suitable refractory grades are obtained from the Philippines, India, Russia, South Africa, Greece, and Turkey.

Until recently, only Philippine ore was used in American basic brick: with the approaching depletion of these ores, the Transvaal ores from South Africa are being used increasingly.

Chrome ore is used either alone or in various combinations with magnesia in brick manufacture, and as a granular or plastic refractory for a number of purposes.

G. CARBON GROUP

This group includes natural and artificial graphites, and various types of coal, coke, and tar.

Graphite deposits occur widely distributed, both in this country and abroad. It is often mixed with calcareous or siliceous rock and requires expensive purification. Flake graphite, as found in Ceylon, is preferred for crucible and stopper-head manufacture, in which the graphite is bonded with high percentages of clay. The amorphous graphites found in Mexico are sometimes used to enhance the slag-resistant properties of plastic-clay refractories.

Baking of molded coke and tar or coke and pitch mixtures will produce artificial graphite or carbon shapes, although much higher temperatures are required for graphitization. Carbon is used extensively as a refractory, and may be made from foundry coke, petroleum coke, or anthracite coal, bonded with pitch or tar of low moisture content. Such refractories are being used increasingly for blast-furnace refractories and other applications where reducing atmospheres prevail.

Typical chemical compositions and some typical physical and thermal properties of steelplant refractories of the various types discussed above are given in Tables 2—I, 2—II, and 2—III.

SECTION 2

PREPARATION OF REFRACTORIES

Steel-plant refractories are used in a wide variety of forms, the preparation of which may vary from little more than the operation of mining, to highly complex grinding, screening, molding, and firing procedures demanding precise control throughout. Hence their preparation will be discussed according to their use in the massive, granular, or finely-divided form, and according to whether these forms are in the raw, fired, or chemically-bonded state.

A. MASSIVE REFRACTORIES

Raw State—Sandstone and mica schist are invariably used in the form of large blocks sawed or split from the raw rock, and further shaped as needed on the job. To minimize spalling from heat, these blocks are laid flat, with laminated edges exposed to the heat. Chrome ore and olivine have been similarly used for open-hearth bridge walls, but their use in block form has practically ceased. A siliceous insulating brick, accurately cut to standard brick size from natural diatomaceous earth, is sometimes used to back up fireclay-brick walls. Such brick have superior insulating value as compared with brick made from the same material by conventional methods, although

that property will be greater with heat flow normal to the laminations.

Burned Products—Fired brick and shapes of all types of refractories constitute the bulk of refractories used in the massive form. The processes by which these brick and shapes are produced are basically similar although, as might be expected, the nature of the raw materials and the wide variety of properties desired in the final products have caused the adoption of a number of variations in these processes.

The first step is the mining of raw materials. **Mining methods** depend upon the location, size, and uniformity of the deposit. For the most part, deposits are underground, and mining methods are similar to those employed in the various types of underground mining and quarrying. However, large uniform deposits, such as are characteristic of some plastic clays and dolomites, are worked more economically by the open-pit method, even though this may involve stripping of many feet of overburden. More exacting refractory requirements and diminution of established sources of some materials are constantly forcing changes in methods of mining. For example, the quarrying of flow ganister on mountain sides for use in silica-brick manufacture has gradually given way to the mining of ledge rock in some localities in Pennsylvania.

Following the mining, some **purifying operations**

---

* See Section 2B, Granular Refractories—Fired Products for explanation of terms "calcined" and "dead burned."

Table 2—I. Typical Chemical Compositions of Steelplant Refractories

Refractory Type	SiO$_2$	Al$_2$O$_3$	Cr$_2$O$_3$	MgO	CaO	Fe$_2$O$_3$	TiO$_2$	Alkali	C
				Chemical Composition (Per Cent)					
Silica Brick									
High-Purity	96.4 to 97.4	0.1 to 0.4	—	0.1 to 0.2	2.2 to 3.4	0.3 to 2.1	<0.1	<0.1	—
Coke Oven	95.5 to 96.5	0.6 to 1.2	—	0.1 to 0.2	2.0 to 3.5	0.4 to 0.7	0.1	0.1 to 0.4	—
Sandstone	89.6 to 96.1	1.8 to 2.8	—	—	0.1 to 1.4	0.5 to 1.6	0.2 to 0.5	0.6 to 1.2	—
Semi-Silica Brick	69.6 to 79.0	18.0 to 26.9	—	0.1 to 0.4	0.1 to 0.4	0.6 to 2.0	0.8 to 1.6	0.2 to 0.4	—
Fireclay Brick or Shapes									
Stopper-Rod Sleeves	58.1 to 61.6	30.0 to 34.0	—	0.2 to 0.6	0.3 to 0.4	2.7 to 3.1	1.7 to 1.8	2.4 to 2.6	—
Steel-Teeming Nozzles	52.4 to 62.3	29.0 to 36.9	—	0.9 to 1.0	0.3	2.8 to 4.3	1.6 to 1.9	3.0 to 3.3	—
Ladle Brick; Bloating Type	60.0 to 61.3	28.0 to 30.8	—	0.5 to 0.8	0.2 to 0.5	2.3 to 5.3	1.3 to 1.5	3.6 to 4.2	—
Ladle Brick; Volume-Stable Type	53.4 to 61.0	30.6 to 40.6	—	0.4 to 0.6	0.2 to 0.4	1.1 to 2.7	1.4 to 2.4	0.9 to 4.2	—
Low Duty	53.0 to 69.0	25.0 to 34.0	—	0.4 to 0.6	0.3 to 0.6	2.3 to 3.4	1.0 to 2.0	1.8 to 2.9	—
Intermediate Duty	56.0 to 70.0	25.0 to 36.0	—	0.5 to 0.6	0.2 to 0.4	1.8 to 3.4	1.3 to 1.9	1.0 to 2.7	—
High Duty	51.0 to 59.0	35.0 to 40.0	—	—	0.3 to 0.5	1.6 to 2.5	2.0 to 3.0	1.5 to 2.6	—
Super Duty	51.0 to 54.0	40.0 to 43.0	—	—	0.2 to 0.5	1.4 to 2.3	2.1 to 2.5	0.8 to 1.4	—
High-Alumina Brick									
50% Al$_2$O$_3$	43.0 to 47.0	47.0 to 51.0	—	0.5 to 0.6	0.5 to 0.6	0.9 to 1.6	2.2 to 2.4	0.8 to 1.3	—
60% Al$_2$O$_3$	27.7 to 37.0	58.0 to 67.0	—	0.1 to 0.6	0.1 to 0.3	0.9 to 2.7	1.7 to 3.0	0.2 to 1.2	—
70% Al$_2$O$_3$	19.4 to 28.0	68.0 to 76.7	—	0.1 to 0.2	0.1 to 0.3	0.9 to 2.2	2.0 to 3.3	0.2 to 1.2	—
80% Al$_2$O$_3$	8.5 to 17.1	78.0 to 86.5	—	0.1 to 0.2	0.1 to 0.4	0.7 to 1.7	2.5 to 3.2	0.1 to 0.6	—
90% Al$_2$O$_3$	3.0 to 10.0	87.5 to 95.8	—	0.0 to 0.2	0.1 to 1.9	0.2 to 1.1	0.1 to 2.6	0.2 to 0.9	—
100% Al$_2$O$_3$	0.4 to 1.1	97.7 to 99.0	—	0.0 to 0.1	0.1 to 0.2	0.1 to 0.3	0.0 to 0.3	0.2 to 0.3	—
Mullite	12.4 to 29.3	67.5 to 86.5	—	0.0 to 0.1	0.1 to 0.4	0.1 to 1.4	0.1 to 2.8	0.2 to 0.6	—
Fireclay or High Alumina Monoliths									
Fireclay Plastics	50.0 to 55.0	40.0 to 45.0	—	—	0.2 to 0.5	1.0 to 2.5	2.0 to 3.0	0.5 to 1.6	—
2000° F Castables	44.0 to 74.0	20.0 to 40.0	—	—	5.4 to 16.5	3.1 to 6.8	1.4 to 2.8	0.6 to 2.0	—
2250° F Castables	38.0 to 46.0	30.0 to 40.0	—	—	7.6 to 14.0	2.1 to 5.2	1.5 to 2.1	0.6 to 1.5	—
2700° F Castables	39.0 to 45.0	40.0 to 52.0	—	—	4.2 to 6.5	0.5 to 3.6	1.6 to 2.6	0.6 to 1.2	—
3000° F Castables	2.0 to 32.0	54.0 to 96.0	—	—	2.5 to 5.9	0.1 to 1.3	0.1 to 2.6	0.1 to 0.4	—
60% Al$_2$O$_3$ Plastics or Ramming Mixes	28.1 to 41.3	54.1 to 66.0	—	0.1 to 0.4	0.1 to 0.3	0.3 to 2.1	0.7 to 2.8	0.2 to 1.7	—
70% Al$_2$O$_3$ Plastics or Ramming Mixes	5.8 to 26.2	66.0 to 75.5	—	0.1 to 0.3	0.1 to 0.4	0.9 to 2.4	1.6 to 4.1	0.2 to 2.6	—
80% Al$_2$O$_3$ Plastics or Ramming Mixes	7.2 to 17.2	75.8 to 85.1	—	0.0 to 1.3	0.3 to 2.8	0.3 to 2.8	1.6 to 3.1	0.0 to 1.2	—
90% Al$_2$O$_3$ Plastics or Ramming Mixes	0.0 to 11.0	72.3 to 95.0	—	0.0 to 0.2	0.0 to 5.4	0.0 to 0.9	0.2 to 2.5	0.1 to 0.8	—
100% Al$_2$O$_3$ Plastics or Ramming Mixes	0.0 to 0.3	97.7 to 99.8	—	—	—	0.1 to 0.5	—	0.0 to 0.3	—
Mullite Plastics or Ramming Mixes	23.8 to 36.4	59.7 to 72.9	—	0.1 to 0.3	0.1 to 0.2	0.5 to 1.2	0.2 to 2.4	0.2 to 1.7	—
Basic Brick									
Magnesite; Unburned or Fired	0.8 to 4.5	0.1 to 1.0	0.1 to 0.9	91.7 to 97.5	1.0 to 2.0	0.3 to 2.3			
Magnesite-Chrome; Unburned	1.8 to 8.3	5.5 to 14.1	6.1 to 15.0	49.5 to 82.0	0.8 to 1.8	2.3 to 8.4			
Magnesite-Chrome; Fired	1.8 to 4.4	2.5 to 10.0	6.7 to 17.1	60.8 to 80.7	1.0 to 1.5	2.3 to 11.5			
Chrome-Magnesite; Unburned	3.5 to 5.0	17.5 to 22.4	18.8 to 24.4	37.0 to 49.0	0.7 to 1.4	8.8 to 11.5			
Chrome-Magnesite; Fired	3.4 to 5.1	8.8 to 26.7	18.1 to 24.5	29.5 to 52.5	0.7 to 1.4	8.5 to 14.6			
Chrome; Fired	4.9 to 8.3	27.3 to 29.1	29.9 to 32.8	18.4 to 22.5	0.5 to 0.7	12.0 to 14.6			
Forsterite; Fired	31.0 to 35.2	1.0 to 1.7	1.0 to 1.7	53.0 to 60.0	1.2 to 1.6	8.6 to 9.3			
Spinel Bonded; Unburned or Fired	1.7 to 1.9	10.0 to 15.9	0.0 to 0.9	76.5 to 87.0	0.9 to 1.4	0.6 to 9.3			
Basic Monolithic Materials									
Dead-Burned Natural Magnesite	4.4 to 8.1	1.0 to 2.8	0.1 to 0.4	72.5 to 87.5	2.1 to 7.2	3.8 to 14.3			
Dead-Burned Dolomite	0.8 to 6.7	0.2 to 2.3	—	32.5 to 38.0	48.5 to 56.9	4.5 to 10.2			
Bottom Ramming Materials	2.0 to 3.2	0.2 to 1.4	0.0 to 0.8	92.1 to 95.3	1.1 to 12.4	0.4 to 0.9			
Bottom Patching Materials	4.3 to 13.2	0.5 to 8.4	0.1 to 7.8	47.0 to 88.5	0.8 to 42.4	1.3 to 13.0			
Plastic Chrome Ore	5.6 to 14.8	11.9 to 35.8	24.0 to 42.4	11.2 to 23.5	12.0 to 21.1	0.1 to 0.6			
Tar-Bonded Basic Refractories									
Stabilized Dolomite; Magnesite Type	4.8 to 6.0	1.0 to 1.5	0.5 to 0.8	40.0 to 45.0	28.0 to 42.0	7.0 to 8.0			3 to 5
Dolomite; Magnesite Type	1.3 to 4.0	0.4 to 0.8	0.0 to 0.3	60.0 to 66.0	26.0 to 34.0	2.5 to 3.0			3 to 5
Magnesite Type	0.8 to 6.4	0.2 to 1.4	0.0 to 1.4	74.0 to 91.0	8.0 to 13.0	0.2 to 13.0			3 to 5
Carbon Brick									
Graphite Base	1.0 to 2.5*								96 to 98
Anthracite Base	5.0 to 10.0*								88 to 94
Anthracite Base; Hot Pressed	15.0 to 20.0*								79 to 84

* Al$_2$O$_3$ plus SiO$_2$.

may be necessary. At present, these may be merely visual selection, weathering to remove soluble salts, or only a simple washing operation as employed with some flint clays and increasingly so with some quartzites. However, the employment of a flotation process for removal of lime and dolomite impurities from natural magnesites is indicative of the trend toward raw-material beneficiation.

The future will likely see the adoption of more ore-dressing practices by the refractory industry, although careful study will be required to determine which procedures are applicable and can be justified with each material.

The next step is one of crushing, grinding, screening, and mixing. These are important operations, as, in large measure, they control the density, porosity, strength, spalling resistance, and thermal characteristics of the brick, although there are no general rules for their control. The fineness of the **grinding** must be varied for different raw materials and different mixes, and with a given material the grinding to obtain a certain effect depends upon equipment available for subsequent operations. Formerly, no **screening** was done, but by 1930 it was being used as a means of controlling the particle size which, in turn, is one of the means of controlling the significant properties of porosity and bulk density of brick, and led to the important developments of super-duty fireclay brick and vastly-improved basic brick. **Mixing** may consist of adding fines to coarse material of the same kind to control the grain or particle size, or of adding one material to another; for example, lime to quartzite and plastic clay to flint clay to act as binders; burned clay or refractory to a plastic mix to control shrinkage; or magnesite to olivine, magnesite to chrome ore, bauxite to clay to change the composition and character of the brick.

Forming operations may be carried out by **hand molding, extrusion, extrusion and pressing, dry pressing, drop molding,** and **pneumatic ramming.** In 1905, all brick were formed by hand. The moist mix (15 to 20 per cent moisture) was tamped into forms set on pallets, the forms were removed, the pallet set upon a "hot floor" to "temper" and the tempered brick were repressed in a hand-operated press, thoroughly dried and then fired in a rectangular or round downdraft periodic kiln. By 1913, however, a goodly percentage of the brick was being formed by machine.

In the **stiff-mud process,** the wet clay mix, after tempering with 12 to 15 per cent moisture in a pug mill, is extruded through a die by a power-driven auger or plunger, and the column is cut with taut wires into the sizes desired. This may be the final processing before drying and firing, or the shapes may be given a final shaping and branding in a repress machine. This process is used almost exclusively for fireclay products.

A more universal forming method is **power pressing** or **dry pressing.** In this process, the refractory is thoroughly mixed with from 3 to 8 per cent moisture, and this relatively dry mixture is fed to steam-, electric-, or hydraulic-powered presses, where measured quantities are pressed in shape under pressures varying from 1,000 to more than 10,000 pounds per square inch. Dry-press products are generally more true to shape and more uniform in size than stiff-mud products. The density of the dry-press products may be greater or less, depending on the degree of particle-sizing control exercised and the pressure employed, but the cold strength is generally less than that of stiff-mud brick. Obviously, dry pressing lends itself to a wider range of refractories than extrusion processes, and fireclay, silica, and all types of basic brick are frequently made in this manner.

A measure employed to improve the bulk density of brick with either of the foregoing processes is **de-airing.** In the stiff-mud process, the auger chamber is evacuated. While the effectiveness varies with different clays, remarkable improvements in the properties of the clay column and the final product are often effected by this means. During pressing in the dry-press process, the mold box is evacuated of air through small holes in the pressing pads.

Drop molding is a process exclusive to the manufacture of silica brick, as the prepared mix has little or no plasticity. In this operation, the wet mixture of crushed ganister and about 2 per cent lime is elevated by bucket conveyor and dropped from a height of 15 to 20 feet into multiple molds below resting on pallets. The mold is struck off and removed, and the brick placed on dryer cars while still on pallets. Organic binders are often used to enhance the weak green strength of silica brick and thus minimize breakage.

Many large or special shapes of superior refractories which cannot be pressed in the usual way are produced by **pneumatic ramming** in steel molds or by special **vibrating** devices. The mix employed is very low in moisture and very carefully sized, as the aim is generally to obtain high density. The mix is fed in slowly and uniformly during ramming.

Refractories are burned or fired in either periodic kilns of the round down-draft or rectangular type, or in tunnel kilns. In **periodic firing,** the dried green brick are set in the kiln, the kiln is gradually brought to the required temperature, held at that temperature for the proper period of time, cooled and drawn. Total time for such a cycle will range from about two to four weeks, with a production of about 25,000 to over 50,000 nine-inch equivalent (cubical content of a standard 9 x 4½ x 2½-inch brick) per cycle. In **tunnel-kiln firing,** the green brick loaded on small cars are passed slowly through a long tunnel-shaped brick structure, divided successively into pre-heating, firing, and cooling zones, generally taking 3 to 5 days for the trip. Products of combustion from the fuel burned in the firing zone pass into the preheating zone (countercurrent to the direction of travel of the cars) and give up their heat to the oncoming loads of brick. Temperature of firing is important, because both the quality and properties of the brick may be affected. By maintaining an oxidizing or a reducing atmosphere, the subsequent behavior of most brick can be changed, and by controlling the rate of heating and the firing temperature, changes in the crystalline structure can be effected, which, in turn, may affect the service performance of the brick. In general, the objects in firing are: (a) to drive off hygroscopic and combined water; (b) to bring about desired chemical changes—drive off CO_2 and oxidize iron and sulphur compounds, organic matter, etc.; (c) to effect transformations of the mineral constituents and convert them to most desirable stable forms; and (d) to effect necessary combinations and vitrification of bonding agents.

By other developments in technique of manufacture, the porosity of fireclay and silica brick can be greatly increased, making the brick good insulators and considerably lighter in weight. Hence, they are designated as lightweight or insulating brick. Processes for making these brick aim for high porosity, preferably with fine pore structure. This is accomplished by mixing a bulky combustible substance, like sawdust or ground cork, or a volatile solid, such as naphthalene, with the wet batch, by forcing air into the wet plastic mass, or by mixing into the batch reagents which will react chemically to form a gas and a product not injurious to the brick.

Carbon refractories, as sometimes used in blast-furnace linings, are truly massive refractories, commonly being used in blocks 22 inches by 30 inches in cross section, up to 15 feet in length, and exceeding 6000 pounds in weight. As previously mentioned, these blocks are made of calcined anthracite coal and/or low-ash coke with a tar bond, and are formed by extrusion, after which they are baked in coke at a temperature of approximately 1800° F for long periods, seven weeks sometimes being required to complete a cycle. Smaller shapes and brick of standard size are likewise made and are replacing the larger blocks in many blast-furnace wall installations. In a recent development, such smaller shapes may be made by hot pressing, so that a finished "burned" brick is produced in a matter of seconds rather than weeks.

Chemically Bonded Products (Basic Brick)—Since their introduction about 1923, the manufacture of chemically-bonded basic brick has steadily increased, until today unburned basic brick constitute more than one-half of the total basic-brick production. In this process, a suitable chemical-bonding material is mixed with the raw materials and the brick are formed under pressures sometimes exceeding 10,000 pounds per square inch. Careful sizing of the raw materials and thorough mixing to insure uniform distribution of the bond are necessary. If the brick are to be metal encased, this process permits the pressing of the steel jacket onto the brick during the actual forming operation. After forming, all that is necessary is a thorough drying out at less than 500° F to develop maximum cold strength, which often exceeds that of burned basic brick.

Tar-Bonded Products—A variety of tar-bonded basic brick are now produced for linings for oxygen-steelmaking furnaces, and these are also finding some application in electric furnaces and even the open hearth. Such brick may be made from dead-burned dolomite, mixtures of dolomite and magnesite, or magnesite, by mixing the sized materials with approximately 6 per cent of tar or pitch at 250° to 300° F and pressing the hot mixture in a conventional brick press. The brick, particularly those containing high percentages of dolomite, are often cooled under controlled low-humidity conditions to prevent hydration. Some large blocks are made by vibration compaction and may be tar-dipped to provide protection from hydration.

Refractory Concrete Products—Refractory concrete is made of sized refractory aggregates, such as calcined flint clay, crushed fireclay brick bats, chrome ore, olivine, or magnesite, and a hydraulic bond, usually calcium aluminate cement. Aggregate-cement ratios may vary from 4 to 1 to 10 to 1. Calcium aluminate cements are employed because of their rapid setting and, more important, their ability to retain their water of hydration, and hence their bonding power, to considerably higher temperatures than Portland cement. Besides the use of such concretes for pouring refractory structures in place, they are often used to cast special shapes, such as burner blocks, on the job.

Electrocast Products—The electrocast process consists of mixing raw materials of high purity in proper proportions, heating them to complete fusion in an electric furnace, and casting in forms, very much as liquid iron or steel is cast. By 1935, many refractory bodies, consisting essentially of fused mullite, had been produced. Since that time, other products, consisting of various combinations of chrome, magnesia, alumina, and zirconia have also been produced. Advantages of the process are almost complete lack of voids, a narrow range of melting, and better control of chemical properties. Disadvantages, other than high cost, may be poor resistance to thermal shock and continued growth at high temperatures.

B. GRANULAR REFRACTORIES

Raw State—The chief refractories used in the raw state in granular form are clays, chrome ore, and dolomite. Clays coarse enough for this classification are seldom used without further reduction in size of granules on the job, blast-furnace-taphole clays being the principal application. Granular chrome ores are used in open-hearth front-wall maintenance as ground, or for reheating-furnace hearths and open-hearth doors when plasticized with clay and bonded with sodium silicate. Crushed raw dolomite is used extensively for open-hearth maintenance, principally for building up banks, where its consumption may vary from 10 to as much as 100 pounds per ton of steel produced.

Fired Products—Fired granular products include dolomite, magnesite, and other special basic refractories. Two types of dolomite are recognized in this category. Calcined dolomite, often called single burned, is produced in this country by heating the natural rock to a temperature somewhat above the decomposition temperature of the dolomite or generally to about 2000° F. This product consists of crushed porous granules which are very active chemically and tend to slake rapidly upon exposure to the atmosphere. Its use is decreasing. Dead-burned, or clinkered dolomite is a product made by calcining or dead-burning dolomite at temperatures of approximately 3000° F, usually in rotary kilns, using iron oxide as a dead-burning agent. The iron oxide forms calcium ferrites in the dead-burning operation. This has an important function in mineralizing and shrinking the refractory in the burning operation and in helping to coalesce the refractory into a monolithic mass in the open-hearth furnace. This is the most satisfactory form in which to use dolomite, but as it is also the most expensive, it is often used in combination with raw or single-burned dolomite.

Magnesite for making furnace bottoms, for furnace maintenance, and for brick making is always used in the dead-burned state, produced, like dolomite, by firing at high temperatures in rotary kilns. While it is the important refractory in making new open-hearth bottoms, its consumption per ton of steel, in contrast to dolomite, varies from about one to two pounds.

Special granular refractories are used principally for the basic ramming and patching materials which have been introduced since 1939. These are carefully-sized, chemically-bonded preparations composed of dead-burned magnesites or magnesia-dolomite mixtures. The latter generally contain a minimum of 60 per cent MgO, the balance being so proportioned between lime and silica as to form a predominance of dicalcium silicate when clinkered in a rotary kiln. To prevent the dusting (spontaneous transformation to a powder) of dicalcium silicate on cooling, it is necessary to prevent its sudden inversion from the beta to the gamma form. This is accomplished by stabilizing with small amounts of mineralizers such as Cr_2O_3, B_2O_3 and phosphates, or combinations of these. These special ramming mixtures are now widely used for open-hearth-bottom making, as they are quicker to install, provide more accurate contours, and generally are more uniform in composition, than burned-in magnesite bottoms. For new-bottom installations, the higher-purity sea-water-based materials containing over 90 per cent of MgO are usually used, the preparations having lower MgO content being generally employed for resurfacing and patching.

Another group of special granular refractories is the fireclay-base plastic refractories. These consist generally of sized mixtures of raw and calcined clays, often containing sodium silicate or organic bonds, which are shipped wet or dry for applications where a rammed refractory may substitute for brickwork. Such plastic refractories may also be made with super-duty clays, kyanite, or other high-alumina materials as additions. Some of the very-high-alumina types may contain little or no clay and employ phosphoric acid or other special chemical bonds.

The refractory concrete products referred to above are often made from dry, prepared mixtures called **castables**. As these are sold ready for mixing with water, they must be included as granular refractories.

C. FINELY DIVIDED OR PULVERIZED PRODUCTS

Raw State—Clays for brick laying and various bonding purposes are about the only refractory used in steel mills in the raw, finely-divided state. However, large tonnages of such clays covering a considerable range in refractoriness are employed.

Processed Products—These include the various heat-setting and air-setting cements and mortars. They are produced for laying every type of brick, and, hence, may have as many different base materials, the principal ones for steel-plant use being silica, fireclay, chrome, and magnesite. Silica cement, or silica fireclay, is usually made of finely-ground quartzite or sand to which is added about 10 per cent plastic clay and possibly an organic binder, although in a few superior grades, the undesirable introduction of alumina from the clay is avoided by using dolomite or lime bonds with other additions to provide the necessary workability for brick laying. Fireclay cements differ from plastic fireclay refractories chiefly in respect to fineness, as they also consist of mixtures of raw and calcined clays. The heat-setting varieties rely on vitrification for bonding, while the air-setting types usually contain liquid or dry sodium silicate and, hence, may be shipped wet or dry. Chrome and magnesite cements may contain small clay additions for workability, and like fireclay cements, may also contain sodium silicate or organic binders. All prepared cements generally are ground to completely pass a 30-mesh screen with substantial percentages passing a 100-mesh screen.

SECTION 3

PHYSICAL AND CHEMICAL CHARACTERISTICS OF REFRACTORIES AND THEIR APPLICATION TO MEET SERVICE CONDITIONS

The foregoing discussions have indicated that a wide variety of refractories, possessing nearly every extreme in characteristics normally used to differentiate between materials, have found a place among the requirements of steel-plant processes. Obviously, these requirements must be equally diversified. Analysis of service conditions in general shows that refractories are required to withstand:

(1) All ranges of temperature up to 3200° F.
(2) Sudden changes in temperature—"thermal shock."
(3) Stresses—mainly compressive, at both high and low temperatures.

(4) The action of slags, ranging from acid to basic in character.
(5) The action of molten metals, always at high temperatures and capable of exerting great pressures and buoyant forces.
(6) The action of gases, including SO_2, CO, Cl, CH_4, H_2O, and volatile oxides and salts of metals, even volatile metals. All are capable of penetrating and reacting with the brick. SO_2 may react with oxides in the brick to form easily-fused salts. CO, penetrating fireclay brick, breaks down to C and CO_2 in the presence of iron carbides, the carbon being deposited in the brick and causing its disintegra-

tion. Zinc in the vapor phase has a similar effect. At relatively low temperatures, steam and water vapor exert a slaking effect on dolomite and magnesite refractories. And nearly all refractories are apt to be subjected to, and adversely affected by, volatile iron and alkalies.

(7) The action of dust in gases, which may be fluxing or non-fluxing, and acid or basic.

(8) Impact and abrasive forces at both high and low temperatures, as those in the stack of a blast furnace.

At the same time a refractory is being subjected to one or more of the above conditions, it may be required to function as a storehouse for heat, as in checkers; as a conductor of heat, as in the walls of coking chambers; or as an insulator.

With such an array of service requirements it would be extremely helpful to have ways of predetermining the suitability of a refractory for a given application. However, it is difficult, or in many cases, impossible, to duplicate these widely variable service conditions in the laboratory. Even where this not the case, time and cost are effective barriers to the development of practical tests which will provide information necessary for positive selection of the proper refractory. Therefore, the standard tests which have been devised, generally within these limitations, primarily provide gages of performance which, while invaluable for quality control, must be judiciously correlated with additional fundamental knowledge of refractory behavior and with service observations before they can be effectively used by consumers. In many instances, information is not available to satisfactorily bridge the gap in this manner, and special tests must be devised.

Thus, by comparison with other materials of construction, refractories appear to suffer in the degree of precision with which they can be applied to fill a certain need. To appreciate this situation it is necessary to know something of the high-temperature behavior of refractories and to recognize that this behavior is the end result of a complex and inextricable combination of physical and chemical factors. Some of these factors are fixed, as they constitute the inherent properties of the materials employed, or of the products of their reaction with other materials in service. Others, mostly physical, may be varied within limits to produce certain desired behavior. In their combined effect on the cold and hot strength, resistance to spalling, resistance to deformation under hot load, permeability and other measured properties, these factors often oppose each other; hence a particular refractory may represent one or more compromises, with a sacrifice of excellence in one characteristic in order to achieve it in another more important for a given application. In the following discussion of refractory characteristics, these matters are emphasized rather than the details of the tests used in refractory evaluation.

Fusion or Softening Temperature—The fusion of most refractory materials is not clear cut, but a more or less gradual transition from solid to liquid. The amount of liquid that can be tolerated by a refractory

and still leave it in a serviceable condition is largely governed by the viscosity of the liquid and the type of crystallization of the solid phases present. For example, fireclay refractories may develop liquid and actually start to soften as low as 1800° F, but due to the high viscosity of the liquid their limiting service temperature may be several hundred degrees higher. An arbitrary procedure has, therefore, been established for gaging the refractoriness of such materials, and is called the **Pyrometric Cone Equivalent,** or **P.C.E. test,** in which the softening behavior of small cones of the refractory are compared with that of standard pyrometric cones of known time-temperature softening behavior. The P.C.E. is reported as the number of that standard cone whose tip touches the supporting plaque simultaneously with a cone of the refractory being investigated when tested in accordance with the Standard Method of Test for Pyrometric Cone Equivalent (A.S.T.M. Designation: C-24). The composition of the standard cones and the temperature range covered make the P.C.E. test most applicable to alumina-silica refractories. Figure 2—1 gives the P.C.E. of various refractories and the

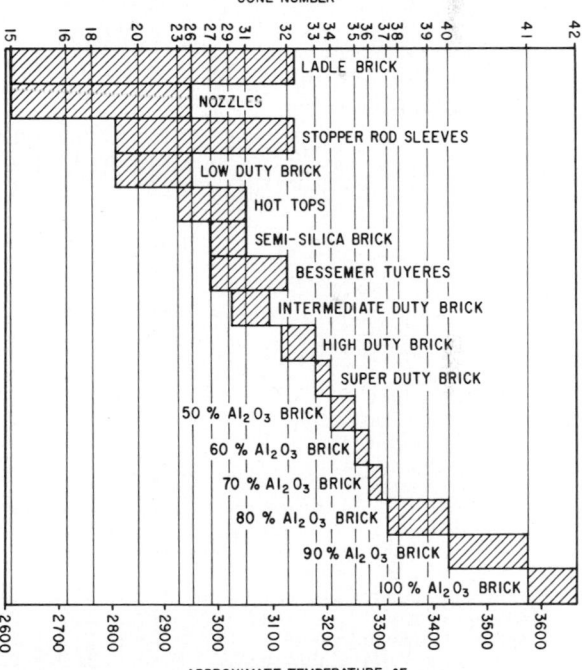

Fig. 2—1. Pyrometric cone equivalent (P.C.E.) of various alumina-silica refractories.

corresponding softening temperatures when heated under the test conditions. It must be recognized that the end points of pyrometric cones primarily reflect the influence of time and temperature, and hence are reproducible only under identical conditions. A cone used in a kiln fired for a week will soften completely at a temperature which would leave it unaffected in the short P.C.E. test. Fireclay refractories behave similarly, the influence of time being strikingly shown in the case of ladle brick. Normally, maximum service temperatures of fireclay brick are considerably below P.C.E. temperatures, but low-P.C.E. ladle brick are successfully used at temperatures 300° F above their P.C.E. temperatures because the duration of this exposure is seldom more than an hour at a time.

It is not particularly disturbing that the P.C.E. test is not equally satisfactory for silica and basic brick, as other tests provide a far more realistic appraisal of re-

fractoriness. The melting point of pure silica (3140° F) is certainly not impressive when compared to that of other materials, and yet silica brick, containing 95 to 98 per cent SiO_2, until recently, successfully resisted replacement by more refractory materials in open-hearth roofs attaining temperatures frequently exceeding 3000° F. This is because silica brick approach the sharp melting behavior of a pure compound, and,

Table 2—II. Some Typical Physical Properties of Steelplant Refractories

Refractory Type	Apparent Porosity (%)	Bulk Density (g. per cc.)	Bulk Density (lb. per cu. ft.)	Modulus of Rupture (lb. per sq. in.) At Room Temperature	Modulus of Rupture (lb. per sq. in.) At 2300° F
Silica Brick					
High-Purity	19.2 to 26.2	1.72 to 1.89	107 to 118	465 to 1085	—
Coke Oven	21.0 to 30.0	1.70 to 1.86	106 to 116	400 to 1500	—
Sandstone	5.5 to 22.9	2.04 to 2.48	127 to 155	600 to 1780	150 to 1780
Semi-Silica Brick	23.4 to 30.8	1.77 to 2.05	110 to 128	320 to 600	ND*
Fireclay Brick or Shapes					
Stopper-Rod Sleeves	15.7 to 21.5	2.06 to 2.20	129 to 137	1495 to 8765**	—
Steel-Teeming Nozzles	12.3 to 17.4	2.14 to 2.23	134 to 139	5850 to 16,000**	—
Ladle Brick; Bloating Type	9.1 to 17.7	2.14 to 2.39	134 to 149	1055 to 2750	—
Ladle Brick; Volume-Stable Type	9.3 to 19.9	2.13 to 2.27	133 to 142	905 to 3190	—
Low Duty	18.0 to 21.0	—	126 to 145	900 to 1500	—
Intermediate Duty	18.0 to 21.0	—	128 to 140	900 to 1600	—
High Duty	4.2 to 30.4	1.81 to 2.49	113 to 155	360 to 2920	—
Super Duty	5.3 to 21.5	2.06 to 2.43	129 to 152	345 to 3360	—
High-Alumina Brick					
50% Al_2O_3	20.0 to 24.0	2.00 to 2.16	125 to 135	1000 to 1500	—
60% Al_2O_3	15.2 to 28.4	2.07 to 2.56	129 to 160	570 to 2935	210 to >1600
70% Al_2O_3	14.6 to 28.6	2.25 to 2.79	140 to 174	845 to 3640	360 to 1365
80% Al_2O_3	14.3 to 28.7	2.45 to 2.97	153 to 185	675 to 4425	315 to >1600
90% Al_2O_3	15.5 to 26.8	2.67 to 3.00	167 to 187	1000 to 3790	450 to >1600
100% Al_2O_3	19.0 to 27.6	2.84 to 3.07	177 to 192	1185 to 3540	435 to >1600
Mullite	13.1 to 24.1	2.34 to 2.66	146 to 166	1185 to 3545	355 to >1600
Fireclay or High-Alumina Monoliths					
Fireclay Plastics	20.1 to 26.8	1.96 to 2.22	122 to 139	30 to 605	—
2000° F Castables	29.9 to 40.4	1.18 to 2.59	74 to 162	135 to 1290	—
2250° F Castables	27.6 to 37.5	1.66 to 2.06	104 to 129	210 to 925	—
2700° F Castables	28.4 to 37.8	1.71 to 2.15	107 to 134	180 to 1465	—
3000° F Castables	26.9 to 34.7	1.87 to 2.77	117 to 173	105 to 1315	—
High-Alumina Plastics or Ramming Mixes					
60% Al_2O_3	15.8 to 30.9	2.07 to 2.93	129 to 183	0 to 1080	245 to 1065
70% Al_2O_3	17.4 to 30.3	2.33 to 2.65	145 to 165	25 to 1175	55 to 1390
80% Al_2O_3	17.3 to 30.7	2.40 to 2.96	150 to 185	110 to 855	225 to 1390
90% Al_2O_3	12.7 to 30.4	2.68 to 3.09	167 to 193	65 to 2000	320 to 1645
100% Al_2O_3	14.8 to 23.8	2.14 to 3.02	134 to 189	0 to 2210	115 to 1555
Basic Brick					
Magnesite; Unburned or Fired	17.3 to 23.8	2.70 to 2.91	168 to 182	1575 to 3505	85 to 310
Magnesite-Chrome; Unburned	17.5 to 22.0	2.80 to 3.02	175 to 188	925 to 2335	140 to 440
Magnesite-Chrome; Fired	13.9 to 19.6	2.88 to 3.16	180 to 197	570 to 880	210 to >1600
Chrome-Magnesite; Unburned	18.8 to 21.0	2.97 to 3.15	185 to 197	1440 to 2055	245 to 300
Chrome-Magnesite; Fired	18.3 to 26.5	2.81 to 3.15	175 to 197	890 to 1450	420 to 1605
Chrome; Fired	16.6 to 18.5	3.16 to 3.40	197 to 212	1400 to 2425	65 to 160
Forsterite; Fired	18.0 to 27.0	2.46 to 2.53	154 to 164	450 to 800	200 to 400
Spinel Bonded; Unburned or Fired	15.3 to 21.5	2.74 to 2.97	171 to 185	1380 to 3070	330 to 920
Basic Monolithic Materials					
Bottom Ramming Materials	—	2.69 to 2.77	168 to 173	1105 to 1810	105 to 250
Bottom Patching Materials	3.7 to 21.7	2.72 to 3.08	170 to 192	—	—
Plastic Chrome Ore	17.8 to 24.1	2.75 to 3.13	172 to 195	140 to 1365	100 to 300
Tar-Bonded Basic Refractories					
Stab. Dolomite; Magnesite Type	13.0 to 17.0	2.75 to 2.90	172 to 181	1095 to 1300	350 to 550
Dolomite; Magnesite Type	13.6 to 16.5	2.65 to 2.83	165 to 176	1100 to 1900	380 to 550
Magnesite Type	13.9 to 16.6	2.70 to 2.81	168 to 175	1330 to 1780	380 to 715
Carbon Brick					
Graphite Base	15.0 to 17.0	1.65 to 1.72	103 to 107	3500 to 4000	—
Anthracite Base	19.0 to 23.0	1.50 to 1.55	94 to 97	1800 to 3100	—
Anthracite Base; Hot Pressed	20.0 to 22.0	1.64 to 1.68	102 to 105	1200 to 1500	—

*ND - Not determined.

**Compressive strength.

aided by a strong crystalline structure, remain rigid to within a few degrees of the temperature of complete fusion.

On the other hand, the main constituents of basic brick (magnesite, chrome, chrome-magnesite and forsterite) all melt at temperatures far above any encountered in steel plant service. Periclase (MgO) melts at 5070° F; chrome spinel, $(MgO,FeO) \cdot (Cr_2O_3,Al_2O_3,Fe_2O_3)$, above 3600° F; and forsterite $(2\ MgO \cdot SiO_2)$ at 3470° F. However, the raw materials for basic brick contain other minerals, considerably lower in refractoriness than the main constituents, which can form fluid liquids at temperatures as low as 2400° F and, as these materials are the matrix of most basic brick, they largely govern the melting behavior of the brick as a whole, particularly as the basic minerals lack the strong, interlocking crystalline structure of the silica and alumina-silica minerals. Fortunately, these low-refractory minerals are subject to control, so that their detrimental effects can be minimized or even eliminated by corrective additions, special firing treatments, and proper distribution.

Porosity and Permeability—Unless expensive measures are resorted to, all manufactured refractories will contain a certain amount of voids, the amount, size, and continuity of which have important influences on refractory behavior. The **apparent porosity** indicates the percent of the total volume which is open pore space, and hence is a measure of the area of surface available for reaction with slags and gases. The **total porosity** is the percentage of the total volume consisting of voids, whether open or closed, and thus, depending on the nature of the material, method of manufacture and degree of burn, may only slightly exceed the apparent porosity or be more than twice as great. The effect of porosity on various refractory properties will be discussed later, but in general, increasing the porosity adversely affects the cold strength, resistance to deformation under hot load, heat capacity, thermal conductivity and resistance to attack by gases and slags. Within limits, increasing porosity will improve spalling resistance, but as this can also be achieved in brick of low porosity, it is evident that as a general rule, far more can be gained in performance from refractories possessing the lowest possible porosity. The porosities typical of various kinds of refractories are given in Table 2—II.

Porosity bears but little relation to **permeability**, which is a measure of the rate of diffusion of liquids and gases through the refractory, and thus is governed by the size and number of connected pores or channels which are continuous from one side of the refractory to the other. Permeability to liquids will increase with increasing temperature as the viscosities of the liquids will decrease, while just the opposite is true of gases, whose viscosities increase at higher temperatures. While permeability is not commonly determined, and no standard tests exist in this country, it is undoubtedly important in such applications as blast-furnace linings where disintegration frequently occurs as a result of penetration by carbon monoxide and subsequent carbon deposition within the brick.

Bulk Density and True Specific Gravity—Like porosity, the **bulk density** of refractories is used as an indication of the voids/solids ratio, but is meaningless in this sense without reference to the **true specific gravity** of the refractory. Thus, the bulk density of a chrome brick having a true specific gravity of 4, but a porosity of 25 per cent is still much greater than that of a dense fireclay brick whose porosity is 10 per cent, but whose true specific gravity is only 2.6. Bulk density may be expressed in a number of ways, those most common being grams per cubic centimeter (**bulk specific gravity**), pounds per cubic foot, or ounces per cubic inch. Being thus the mass of refractory material in a given volume, an increase in the bulk density of a given refractory increases the strength, volume stability, heat capacity, resistance to slag penetration, and generally, resistance to structural spalling, or spalling resulting from vitrification caused by fluxing with dusts and slags.

The true specific gravity of a fired refractory may differ substantially from that of the raw materials from which it is made, owing to conversion of the mineral constituents. For example, quartzite with a specific gravity of 2.65 converts on heating to cristobalite and tridymite with specific gravities, respectively, of 2.32 and 2.26, so that the resultant specific gravity of fired silica brick reflects the degree of conversion, and is a most reliable test for adequacy of firing treatment. The conversion of kyanite to mullite is another example. Table 2—II shows typical bulk densities of various fireclay, high-alumina, basic, carbon and other refractories.

Thermal Expansion and Volume Changes—From the early steps in manufacture throughout their service life, refractories are subject to various types of volume changes. As these changes may affect product uniformity and service performance they are of concern to both manufacturer and user. Most familiar of these volume changes is the reversible **thermal expansion**, or **dilation** that is characteristic of practically all materials, manifested by an increase in volume on heating and a comparable decrease in volume, on cooling. Because of the difficulties involved in measuring actual increase in a three-dimensional volume, it is more practical to measure changes in one dimension: hence, **linear expansion** is taken as a measure of cubical expansion. Figure 2—2 shows typical

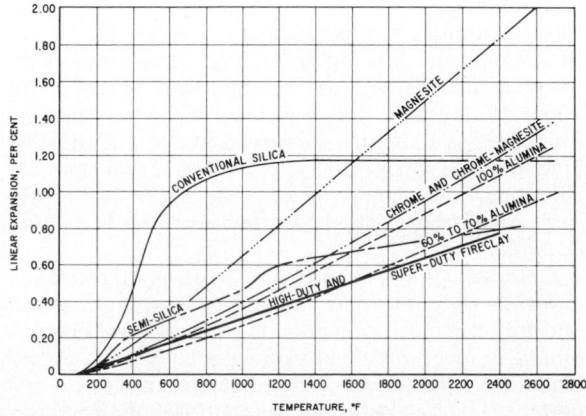

Fig. 2—2. Typical curves of linear expansion of various types of refractories.

curves of linear expansion for various types of refractories. Those which have a uniform expansion rate generally present the least difficulties when furnace temperatures fluctuate widely, and of these, those with the lowest total expansion, as a general rule, are less subject to thermal spalling. Such is the case with fireclay refractories. Silica brick, as previously mentioned, possess varying proportions of the silica minerals cristobalite, tridymite and unconverted quartz, depending on the heat treatment. As each of these silica forms has its own characteristic expansion with sudden changes accompanying inversions from low- to high-temperature forms, the curve for a silica brick will reflect its mineral composition to some extent. However, most of the expansion of silica brick from all sources takes place below 1060° F, hence, if care is taken in heating and cooling below dull-red heat, such brick behave admirably. In fact, one of the major problems in the application of basic brick to open-hearth roofs arises from the continuing high-temperature expansion of basic brick, which, while uniform, causes a "working" of such roofs with temperature changes in ranges that have no effect on silica roofs.

Permanent volume changes may be either expansion or contraction. The latter is first encountered in drying molded refractories, particularly clay brick, and must be accurately controlled to make a uniform product. Further shrinkage may take place on firing. Finally, if the refractory is used at temperatures above that at which it was fired, shrinkage may occur, or it may be caused by fluxing with dusts or slags and subsequent vitrification. Permanent expansion may also take place on firing refractories. Thus silica brick, because of the previously indicated decrease in specific gravities of the higher-temperature forms of silica, will expand about 13 per cent on firing. Some fireclay brick may also exhibit what has been termed **secondary expansion** on firing or reheating. This has been attributed to an exfoliation of the clay grains, and is to be distinguished from the "**bloating**" or vesicular structure development brought about by gas evolution and expansion in an overheated and hence pyro-plastic clay body. While generally indicative of misapplication of refractories, bloating is actually desired in ladle brick as it is conducive to the formation of a monolithic, steel-tight ladle lining. In service, refractories may also permanently expand. The action of alkalies on fireclay refractories to form alkali-alumina silicates with an accompanying expansion of about 12 per cent causes surface peeling of such refractories, as sometimes observed in open-hearth and blast-furnace-stove checkers. The expansion or "bursting" of some types of basic brick due to absorption of iron oxide at high temperatures is another example.

Cold Strength—The mechanical strength of refractories, as determined by modulus of rupture or cold crushing tests, is generally far more than that required to meet any dead loading encountered in construction. Nevertheless, adequate strength is an important characteristic of refractories. Refractories must be handled a great deal before they are finally put in service, and it is naturally desired that they survive this handling with a minimum of breakage, abrasion and lost corners. Soft-burned clay brick, particularly if dry pressed, may be very friable and easily broken but still possess a crushing strength above 1000 pounds per square inch. As cold strength reflects the heat treatment a refractory receives in manufacture, and as this heat treatment affects porosity, bulk density, refractoriness under load, and abrasion resistance, considerable general information on any specific burned refractory can be obtained from strength tests with sufficient correlation. For this reason, cold-strength requirements are often used in the specification of refractories. The ranges in crushing strength and modulus of rupture for various refractories are shown in Table 2—II.

Strength and Behavior Under Load at High Temperatures—The cold strength of refractories is governed mainly by the amount of glassy bond present, the hot strength by the changes brought about in that glassy bond by heat. Generally, with increasing temperature, the glass gradually becomes a viscous liquid, although the initial softening temperature and the temperature range of viscous flow may vary widely between different types of refractories. Thus, to different degrees, all refractories at some temperature exhibit plastic flow, and if subjected to pressure, the subsequent behavior will depend on the amount of pressure and the duration and rate of its application, on the amount and viscosity of the liquid present, and on the crystalline structure of the solids. Loaded heavily and rapidly as in normal compression testing, all refractories will fail in shear until temperatures are reached at which they contain so much liquid of such low viscosity that almost instant deformation occurs. Under such conditions, the compressive strength or modulus of rupture may not change materially below temperatures of initial liquid formation, but will decrease rapidly as these temperatures are exceeded by greater and greater amounts.

Of far more significance, however, is the behavior of refractories under light, sustained loads comparable to those encountered in service, and numerous tests have been devised to measure the amount or rate of deformation occurring under specified conditions of time, temperature and stress. While prolonged tests are especially informative to the refractory user, all standard tests are of relatively short duration, although increasing attention is being given to the longer tests, particularly those aimed at the determination of the almost imperceptible flow or "creep" of refractories at temperatures immediately below and above those of the initial liquid formation.

Fireclay refractories have the longest softening range and are most susceptible to plastic deformation. Under standard test conditions, consisting of heating a 9-inch brick on end under a 25-pound per square inch load in 4½ hours to the testing temperature (2460° F for high-duty brick; 2640° F for super-duty) and holding for 1½ hours, the temperature of initial deformation and the total amount of deformation will depend on the flux content, the degree of burn, and the porosity. Impurities such as lime, magnesia, iron oxides and alkalies, will lower the temperature of initial liquid formation and the viscosity of that liquid, and hence increase deformation. Hard-burned brick will show much better resistance to load than a soft-burned brick made of the same clays, due in part to greater mullite development, but primarily due to the fact that harder firing has developed a more refractory glassy phase which forms a liquid of initially higher viscosity at test temperatures. Increasing porosity decreases the ability of a particular brick

to resist deformation under load, as the voids provide opportunity for a brick to compress on itself and also decrease the amount of refractory available in a given volume to resist pressure. The temperature of initial deformation under load will vary widely for a given brick with deviations from standard test conditions. For example, a fireclay brick deforming initially at 2250° F in the standard test might not deform until

Table 2—III. Some Typical Thermal Properties of Steelplant Refractories

Refractory Type	Behavior Under 25 lb. per sq. in. Load			Percent Volume Change After Burning to Indicated Temperature		Spalling Loss After Indicated Preheat		Relative Spalling Resistance*
	After 1½ hr. at temp. °F	Deformation (%)	Temperature of Failure °F	temp. °F	Volume Change (%)	Preheat °F	Spalling loss (%)	
Silica Brick								Poor Below 1100° F; Good Above 1100° F.
High-Purity	—	—	3060 to 3090	—	—	—	—	
Coke Oven	—	—	2950 to 3020	—	—	—	—	
Sandstone	—	—	—	2460	+12.5 to +20.3	—	—	Poor
Semi-Silica Brick	2640	0.1 to 2.0	—	2700	−2.7 to +7.1	2700	0.0 to 9.8	Poor to Good
Fireclay Brick or Shapes								
Stopper-Rod Sleeves	—	—	—	2460	+0.3 to +10.7	—	—	Fair to Good
Steel-Teeming Nozzles	—	—	—	2460	+29.3 to +52.5	—	—	Fair
Ladle Brick; Bloating	—	—	—	2460	+5.8 to +32.8	—	—	Fair
Ladle Brick; Volume-Stable	—	—	—	2700	−1.2 to +6.2	—	—	Fair
Low Duty	2460	2.0 to 10.0	—	—	—	—	—	Poor to Fair
Intermediate	2460	2.0 to 6.0	—	—	—	—	—	Poor to Fair
High Duty	2640	0.5 to 15.0	—	—	—	2900	0.0 to 39.1	Poor to Good
Super Duty	2640	0.0 to 8.9	—	—	—	3000	0.0 to 32.9	Poor to Good
High-Alumina Brick								
50% Al₂O₃	2640	4.0 to 6.0	—	—	—	—	—	Poor to Good
60% Al₂O₃	2750	0.9 to 11.6	—	3000	−10.7 to +37.8	3000	0.2 to 33.4	Poor to Good
70% Al₂O₃	2750	0.5 to 7.5	—	3000	−4.7 to +33.9	3000	0.0 to 30.6	Poor to Good
80% Al₂O₃	2750	0.3 to 13.4	—	3100	−7.2 to +22.1	3100	0.0 to 28.7	Poor to Good
90% Al₂O₃	2900	0.0 to 16.0	—	3100	−7.0 to +4.9	3100	0.0 to 25.2	Poor to Good
100% Al₂O₃	2900	0.0 to 1.4	—	3100	−2.5 to +0.7	3100	0.0 to 30.0	Poor to Good
Mullite	2900	0.0 to 5.1	—	3100	−6.8 to +1.2	3100	0.0 to 31.9	Poor to Good
Fireclay or High-Alumina Monoliths								
Fireclay Plastics	2640	2.8 to Failure	—	2900	−0.3 to +57.8	3000	1.7 to 21.3	Poor to Good
2000° F Castables	—	—	—	—	—	—	—	Poor to Fair
2250° F Castables	—	—	—	2250	−1.6 to +0.2	—	—	Poor to Fair
2700° F Castables	2460	2.3 to Failure	—	2700	+0.3 to Fused	—	—	Poor to Fair
3000° F Castables	2640	3.0 to Failure	—	3000	+0.9 to Fused	—	—	Poor to Fair
High-Alumina Plastics or Ramming Mixes								
60% Al₂O₃	2750	0.9 to 15.7	—	3000	−9.2 to +24.4	3000	0.0 to 13.2	Poor to Good
70% Al₂O₃	2750	0.2 to 9.0	—	3000	−2.9 to +38.4	3000	0.0 to 26.6	Poor to Good
80% Al₂O₃	2750	0.0 to Failure	—	3100	−7.0 to +38.7	3100	0.0 to 19.9	Poor to Good
90% Al₂O₃	2900	0.2 to 8.6	—	3100	−5.4 to +23.7	3100	0.0 to 4.3	Poor to Good
100% Al₂O₃	2900	0.4 to Failure	—	3100	−4.7 to +1.6	3100	0.0 to 5.3	Poor to Good
Basic Brick								
Magnesite; Unburned or Fired	—	—	2910 to >3200	3100	−0.3 to −5.1	3100	0.0 to 35.7	Poor to Good
Magnesite-Chrome; Unburned	—	—	3000 to 3200	3100	−1.5 to −5.2	3100	0.0 to 2.0	Fair to Good
Magnesite-Chrome; Fired	—	—	3030 to >3200	3100	−2.3 to +1.8	3100	0.0 to 0.8	Poor to Good
Chrome-Magnesite; Unburned	—	—	3040 to 3100	3100	−3.2 to −5.7	3100	0.0 to 3.0	Fair to Good
Chrome-Magnesite; Fired	—	—	3025 to 3110	3100	−0.5 to −5.9	3100	0.5 to 37.9	Poor to Good
Chrome; Fired	—	—	2610 to 2995	3100	−1.7 to −5.6	3000	31.1 to 52.0	Poor to Fair
Forsterite; Fired	—	—	2980 to 3050	3100	−2.0 to −4.0	3100	4.2 to 28.0	Poor to Fair
Spinel Bonded; Unburned or Fired	—	—	3130 to >3180	3100	−1.0 to −7.1	3100	0.0 to 41.9	Poor to Good
Basic Monolithic Materials								
Bottom Ramming Materials	—	—	2920 to 2980	3100	−3.0 to −7.5	—	—	—
Bottom Patching Materials	—	—	2460 to 2810	3100	−14.6 to +2.0	—	—	—
Plastic Chrome Ore	—	—	—	2900	−8.6 to +34.6	—	—	—
Tar-Bonded Basic Refractories								
Stabilized Dolomite; Magnesite	—	—	—	—	—	—	—	Good
Dolomite; Magnesite	—	—	—	—	—	—	—	Good
Magnesite	—	—	—	—	—	—	—	Good
Carbon Brick								
Graphite Base	—	—	—	—	—	—	—	Good
Anthracite Base	—	—	—	—	—	—	—	Good
Anthracite Base; Hot Pressed	—	—	—	—	—	—	—	Good

*When used in normal temperature range for particular material.

2350° F with a lighter load or a faster heating rate, and conversely, might deform as low as 2000° F with a much heavier load or with that temperature maintained for several hours.

The behavior of high-alumina brick under load is similar to that of fireclay brick, although the temperature range of plastic deformation will be generally higher with greater alumina contents. The Al_2O_3 content of high-alumina brick, however, serves as only a very general indication of the properties of the brick because of similarities in the bonding phase in most of the alumina-brick classes. The properties of high-alumina brick, like fireclay brick, also vary widely with degree of burning.

Due to their strong, interlocking crystallization and purity, silica brick show little evidence of plastic deformation under load, remaining rigid under a load of 25 or even 50 pounds per square inch until they fail by shear at temperatures varying from 3000° F to 3100° F. The latter temperature, however, is attainable only by the purest types containing a maximum of 0.5 per cent of the impurities Al_2O_3, TiO_2, and alkalies. Because of their strong crystalline structure, silica brick may be more than 30 per cent molten at the temperature of failure.

The behavior of basic brick under high-temperature load will vary widely depending on the bond structure present. In brick made from chrome ore or impure magnesites, the formation of low-viscosity silicate liquids at temperatures from 2600° to 2800° F will cause failure by shearing. Magnesite brick having higher MgO contents (less impurities) and controlled CaO/SiO_2 ratios may withstand loads for long periods of time at temperatures up to 3200° F. The resistance to high-temperature load of refractories made from combinations of chrome ore and magnesite may also be quite good because of reaction of magnesia with gangue silicate to produce a bond of forsterite ($2MgO \cdot SiO_2$). Normally, the refractoriness under load of fired basic refractories made from chrome ore and magnesite will be somewhat better than unburned brick of similar composition because of the opportunity for more complete reaction of fired brick before high-temperature loads are encountered.

In recent years, increased emphasis has been placed on the modulus of rupture of basic brick measured at temperatures below that at which failure under high-temperature load occurs. This property is again characteristic of the bond structure in basic brick. As would be expected, with increasing temperature, unburned brick lose strength as the chemical bond is burned out; normally modulus-of-rupture values are 100 to 400 lb. per sq. in. at 2300° F. Fired basic brick, however, will vary in their modulus of rupture at 2300° F from 100 lb. per sq. in. to greater than 1600 lb. per sq. in. Normally, the higher strengths at temperature are associated with bonds other than the conventional silicate bonds, such as the spinel bonds formed from additions of Al_2O_3 or Cr_2O_3 to magnesia, or the direct magnesia-to-magnesia or magnesia-to-chrome spinel bonds produced by exceptional high-firing temperatures of selected compositions. As a result of the variations in bond structure produced, the long-time creep under load at higher temperature for current basic brick made from magnesite and chrome ore will vary from as little as 2 per cent deformation after 24 hours at 2900° F to failure after only one hour at temperatures as low as 2750° F.

Carbon refractories show little or no loss in strength and no deformation under load throughout the range of steel-plant temperatures.

Typical load-test data for various refractories are shown in Table 2—III.

Heat Capacity and Thermal Conductivity—The **heat capacity** of a refractory at a given temperature is a function of its bulk density and its specific heat at that temperature. The **thermal conductivity** is a measure of the rate of heat transmission through the refractory. Both properties are increased with increasing bulk density and hence decreased with increasing porosity. As refractories may be used to confine, store, or transmit heat, the thermal conductivity desired will vary widely with the application. While a wide range in conductivity is available in commercial refractories, if the insulating types are included, it is not always possible to use that refractory whose conductivity is best suited to the job. Thus in the majority of cases, it is desired to confine heat, but it was previously noted that in a majority of cases high bulk density was also desirable from a service standpoint. With refractories used for heat storage and transmission, such as checker brick, no conflict in properties exists, as high density is desired both for stability and increased heat storage and conductivity.

Typical thermal conductivity curves for general types of refractories are shown in Figure 2—3. It will be noted that at the temperatures common to steel-plant operations, the differences in conductivity found in these refractories at low temperatures are greatly reduced. The accuracy of these higher-temperature determinations is often questionable, although standardization of test methods in recent years has greatly improved the reproducibility of results from different laboratories. However, actual heat flow through furnace walls in service still may differ considerably from calculations. Thus the conductivity will change with the alterations in structure and composition of the hot face; the rate at which heat is carried away from the cold face affects the flow through the wall; and the gas pressure within the furnace has a great effect, not only on the heat flow but on refractory life as well, as positive pressures will drive heat in, increasing the depth of vitrification and fluxing.

Resistance to Thermal Shock (Spalling)—One of the major causes of refractory destruction is **spalling,** which is the breaking away of pieces of refractory from the hot face, thus exposing fresh surfaces. Spalling may result from too-rapid expansion or contraction of the hot face of the refractory with sudden temperature changes, called **thermal spalling.** Spalling also may result from changes in the hot face brought about by flux absorption or vitrification which set up zones in the brick which differ in expansion and sensitivity to thermal shock from the original brick, or shrinkage may occur, so that pieces

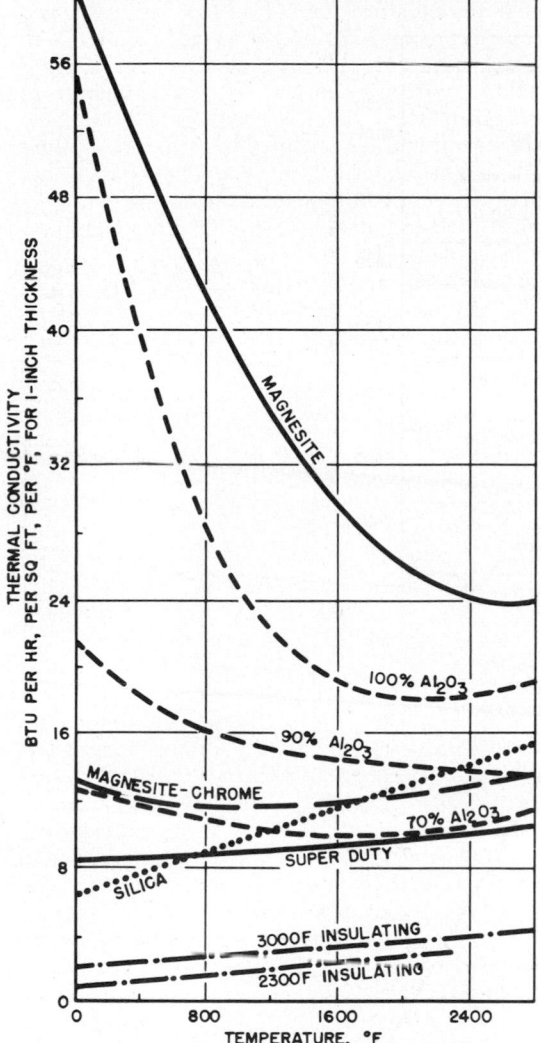

FIG. 2—3. Typical thermal conductivity curves for various refractory brick.

their resistance to spalling are thermal expansion, elasticity (ability to yield to stress without rupture), and strength. Because of their low thermal expansion, fireclay refractories as a class have the best spalling resistance, but since the elasticity and strength are strongly affected by the degree of burn, particle size and porosity, wide variations exist. Thus a soft-burned, coarse-grained, porous brick has higher elasticity and higher thermal-spalling resistance at low temperatures than a hard-burned dense brick, but may be expected to fail from structural spalling more readily at high temperature, due to greater shrinkage and flux absorption.

Basic refractories generally do not have the best resistance to thermal shock because of their high coefficients of thermal expansion. Chrome brick have poor to fair resistance to thermal spalling. Magnesite brick may have from poor to good resistance depending on their composition. Chemically-bonded brick made from combinations of magnesite and chrome ore ordinarily have improved resistance to thermal spalling over either chrome or magnesite brick; however, burned brick will vary widely in spalling resistance according to the bond structure present. Many special basic-brick compositions, such as the spinel-bonded magnesite brick, have spalling resistance equivalent to most fireclay or high-alumina brick.

As indicated earlier, the spalling resistance of silica brick varies from very poor to excellent, depending on whether they are subjected to temperature fluctuations below or above 1100° F, respectively.

Abrasion Resistance—The resistance of refractories to abrasion and erosion is primarily a function of the strength. As strength is governed by degree of burn, some correlation also exists between abrasion loss and porosity and bulk density. While no standard hot-abrasion test has been adopted, there are some indications that the strength-abrasion loss relationship holds at higher temperatures, in which case resistance to abrasion might not be expected to change appreciably below 2000° F, but to decrease at higher temperatures. Variations of the standard rattler test for paving brick are sometimes used in refractory testing, and more recently, an accelerated test employing a sand blast has been devised. For fireclay refractories, this test indicated a rapid decrease in abrasion loss with small increases in modulus of rupture to 1700 pounds per square inch, with further increases in strength being far less effective.

separate; this is termed **structural spalling**. A third type, **mechanical spalling**, may result from mechanical abuse, as in removing slag accumulations from refractory surfaces, or may be caused by shifting loads and stresses, particularly in arches, so that refractories are pinched and crack off.

The properties of refractories which most influence

SECTION 4

REACTIONS AT ELEVATED TEMPERATURES

Discussions of the high-temperature behavior of refractories thus far have tended to emphasize the influence of various physical factors, and have given but little indication that behavior also reflects the working of natural laws governing the high-temperature reactions occurring not only within the refractories themselves but between refractories and oxides encountered in service. Until comparatively recent

years, little was known of these reactions, and improvements in refractory products were slow, as they derived primarily from trial and error, and were generally physical in nature. Today there are available an ever-increasing number of phase-equilibrium diagrams which have proved invaluable guides to the production of superior refractories and to the correction of service difficulties. An indication of the

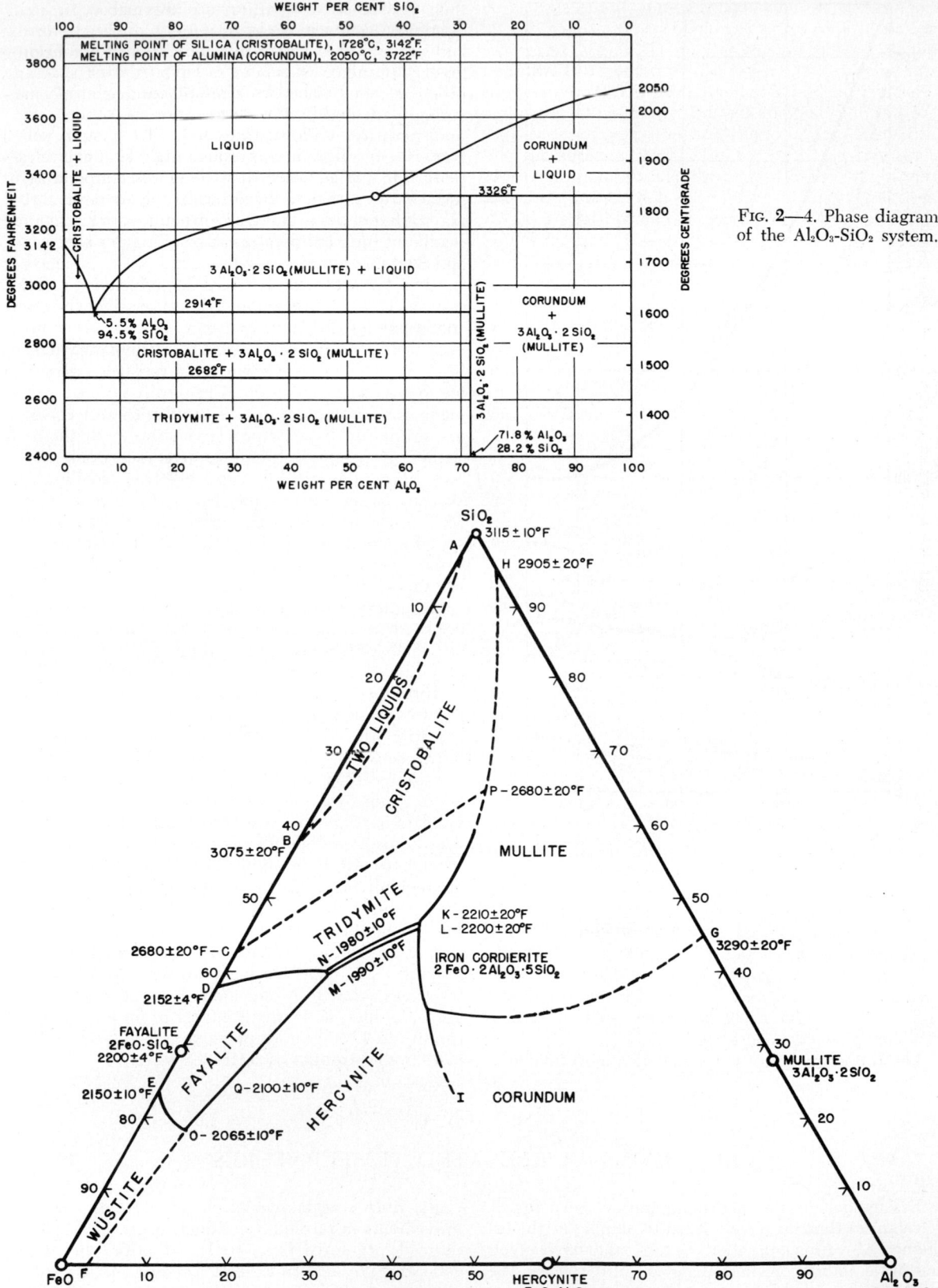

Fig. 2—4. Phase diagram of the Al₂O₃-SiO₂ system.

Fig. 2—5. The FeO–Al₂O₃–SiO₂ system.

importance of such data is found in the studies on the steel-plant refractory-oxide systems being carried out at the Pennsylvania State University under the sponsorship of the American Iron and Steel Institute. However, it should be recognized that these diagrams are not without limitations in their use to predict or explain refractory behavior. For example, the various systems have been explored with pure oxides and represent equilibrium conditions, while refractories are rarely pure and seldom in equilibrium, either as manufactured or in service. Because of this complex nature of refractories, information is often needed on reactions involving so many oxides that the usefulness of systems involving no more than three oxides is minimized. Finally, and most important, the diagrams give no information on such significant matters as viscosity of the liquids formed or the rate at which reactions proceed. Since it will be shown that under certain conditions many of the commonly-used refractories apparently can be liquefied to the point of

destruction at temperatures encountered in steel-plant service, we are often vitally concerned in the rate at which reactions progress toward equilibrium and failure. As excellent compilations of diagrams have been published (see references at end of chapter), only a few are reproduced here.

Figure 2—4 shows the Al_2O_3–SiO_2 system which applies to silica, fireclay, and high alumina refractories. It will be noted that the lowest temperature at which any liquid is developed in the system is 2914° F, while for those compositions more aluminous than mullite (3 Al_2O_3·2 SiO_2) or above 71.8 per cent Al_2O_3 no liquid is developed below 3326° F. A eutectic occurs at the composition 94.5 per cent SiO_2 and 5.5 per cent Al_2O_3. It is evident that if bonding and other manufacturing difficulties could be overcome, quite good refractories could be made of the pure oxides, even in the high-silica range. In fact, the semi-silica type brick containing about 80 per cent SiO_2 represent a practical approach to this condition. Such

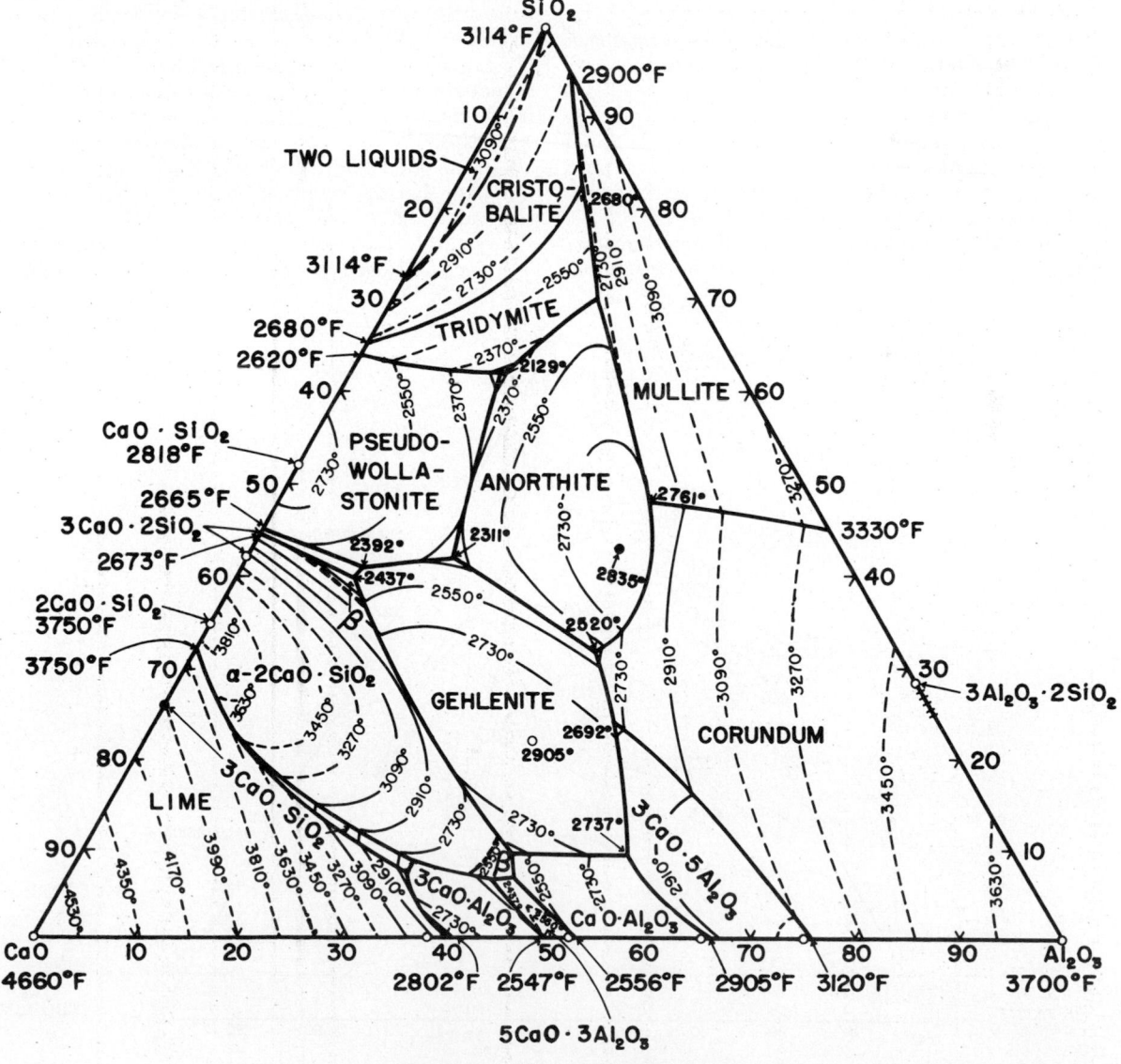

FIG. 2—6. The CaO–Al₂O₃–SiO₂ system.

brick, because of their low impurity content, are superior in load-carrying ability to many far more aluminous brick having a higher P. C. E. The pronounced effect of the impurities present in most commercial refractories in this system can be appreciated by comparing the temperatures at which they deform initially under load with the initial liquid temperatures of 2914° F or 3326° F indicated in the diagram. The oxide impurities largely responsible for lowering the refractoriness of fireclay refractories are CaO, MgO, FeO, Na_2O, and K_2O, and these are also encountered in service.

Figure 2—5 shows the $FeO-Al_2O_3-SiO_2$ system. Here it is seen that with unlimited amounts of iron oxide available for reaction with any but the purest end members of the $Al_2O_3-SiO_2$ series of refractories, the formation of some liquid can be expected even below 2000° F, and that very damaging amounts will be formed at the higher temperatures common to steel processes. This is particularly true as iron-oxide-bearing liquids are characteristically very fluid.

Figure 2—6 is the diagram of the $CaO-Al_2O_3-SiO_2$ system, which is most applicable to reactions of fireclay refractories with blast-furnace slags, but capable of supplying some information on other reactions involving refractories, as those occurring with the more complex open-hearth slags, or in the bond formed in magnesite brick. This system has also been useful in predicting behavior of silica brick, which will be discussed later.

The reactions of alkalies with alumina-silica refractories have recently been clarified by the publi-

cation of both the $Na_2O-Al_2O_3-SiO_2$ and the $K_2O-Al_2O_3-SiO_2$ systems by the Geophysical Laboratory. These systems are reproduced in Figures 2—7 and 2—8. It is evident that the refractoriness of alumina-silica refractories will be seriously affected by very small amounts of Na_2O, less than 1 per cent being sufficient to lower the temperature of initial liquid formation to less than 2000° F, while approximately 10 per cent is sufficient to completely liquefy the more siliceous alumina-silica compositions at 2200° F. K_2O has a similar effect in amounts up to 10 per cent, but whereas Na_2O continues to lower the melting point with greater additions, the reverse is true of K_2O additions in the range of 10 to 20 per cent.

Small percentages of impurities are far more critical in silica brick than fireclay brick, and alkalies are the worst offender, although fortunately they seldom occur in amounts greater than 0.3 per cent. The percentages of Na_2O, K_2O and Al_2O_3 required to lower the melting point of pure silica from 3140° F to 3050° F are, respectively 1.4, 1.9 and 3.1 per cent.

Another very serious fluxing agent for fireclay refractories is MnO, as can be seen in the diagram of the $MnO-Al_2O_3-SiO_2$ system in Figure 2—9. It will be noted that this system is quite similar to the $FeO-Al_2O_3-SiO_2$ system.

Because the raw materials for silica brick lack both a natural bond and a high melting point, care must be taken that the required bonding addition has the minimum effect on refractoriness. Figure 2—10 shows the $CaO-SiO_2$ system and explains why lime is universally used for this purpose. With additions

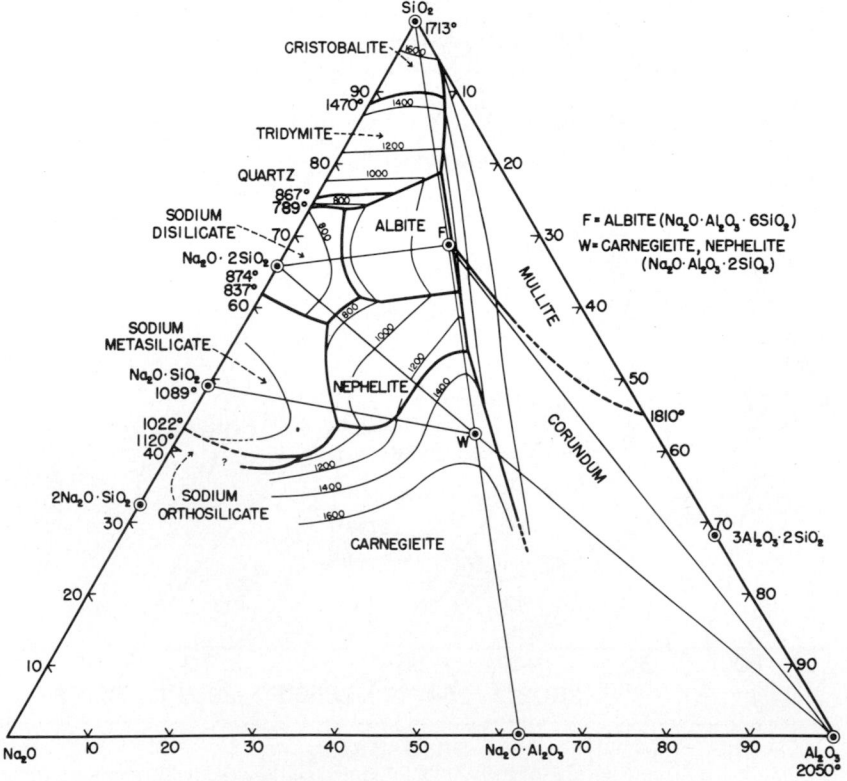

FIG. 2—7. The $Na_2O-Al_2O_3-SiO_2$ system.

of CaO to SiO_2, the melting temperature remains unchanged between 1 and 27.5 per cent CaO, due to the formation of two immiscible liquids. We have already seen that no such phenomenon occurs in the Al_2O_3–SiO_2 system, and by referring again to the CaO–Al_2O_3–SiO_2 system, we find that only a small amount of Al_2O_3 is required to destroy the CaO–SiO_2 immiscibility. In fact, the effect of minor increments of Al_2O_3 on the liquid development of silica brick is such that the temperature of failure under a load of 25 pounds per square inch will decrease approximately 10° F for each 0.1 per cent increase in Al_2O_3 in the 0.3 to 1.2 per cent range of Al_2O_3 between super duty and conventional silica brick. Figure 2—11 of the FeO–SiO_2 system shows that FeO, like CaO, also forms two immiscible liquids when added to SiO_2, thus greatly increasing the tolerance of silica brick for FeO. Furthermore, as with CaO, a small amount of Al_2O_3 can eliminate this immiscibility.

As atmospheric conditions in steel-plant furnaces may range from highly reducing to highly oxidizing, the form of iron oxides present may vary from FeO to Fe_2O_3. Accordingly, Figure 2—12, showing the system FeO–Fe_2O_3–SiO_2, as recently determined by Muan in the AISI-sponsored studies at Pennsylvania State University, is of considerable importance. Thus, it is seen that the lowest-melting liquids occur from reaction of FeO and SiO_2, and that at temperatures in the range of 2650° to 3030° F less liquid, and a less siliceous liquid, will be produced with either Fe_3O_4 or Fe_2O_3 than with FeO, due to the greater extent of the two-liquid region under oxidizing conditions. Hence, under oxidizing conditions, an open-hearth silica roof will have more tolerance for iron oxide, and therefore will be more durable.

The two principal refractory oxides considered as basic are magnesia (MgO) and lime (CaO). Magnesia is noted for its tolerance to iron oxides. As shown in Figure 2—13, MgO and FeO form a continuous series of solid solutions which have high refractoriness even with very high FeO contents. Under oxidizing conditions, magnesia is even more tolerant to iron oxide. Magnesia and iron oxide form the refractory compound magnesioferrite ($MgO \cdot Fe_2O_3$) which contains 80 per cent Fe_2O_3. Magnesioferrite forms solid solutions with magnetite ($FeO \cdot Fe_2O_3$) at higher iron-oxide contents and with magnesia at lower iron-oxide contents. On the other hand, lime is more reactive with iron oxide, forming low-melting calcium ferrites such as dicalcium-ferrite ($2CaO \cdot Fe_2O_3$) that melts incongruently at about 2620° F. Also, lime is subject to hydration and disruptive disintegration on exposure to atmospheric conditions and cannot be used in refractory shapes made by conventional procedures. It is evident, therefore, that magnesia is the more useful basic refractory oxide and forms the base for all types of basic refractories including those made from magnesite, olivine, dead-burned dolomite, and magnesite and chrome ore.

Magnesia-bearing refractories, regardless of type, contain accessory refractory oxides and encounter other refractory oxides in service which exert an important influence on their performance. Figure 2—14

Table 2—IV. Mineral Phases in Equilibrium with Periclase (MgO) in the MgO–CaO–SiO_2 System

Weight Ratio CaO/SiO_2	Minerals Present	Composition	Approximate Melting Temperature, °F
less than 0.93	Forsterite	$2MgO \cdot SiO_2$	3450
	Monticellite	$CaO \cdot MgO \cdot SiO_2$	2710*
0.93	Monticellite	$CaO \cdot MgO \cdot SiO_2$	2710*
0.93 to 1.40	Monticellite	$CaO \cdot MgO \cdot SiO_2$	2710*
	Merwinite	$3CaO \cdot MgO \cdot 2SiO_2$	2870*
1.40	Merwinite	$3CaO \cdot MgO \cdot 2SiO_2$	2870*
1.40 to 1.86	Merwinite	$3CaO \cdot MgO \cdot 2SiO_2$	2870*
	Dicalcium silicate	$2CaO \cdot SiO_2$	3865
1.86	Dicalcium silicate	$2CaO \cdot SiO_2$	3865
1.86 to 2.80	Dicalcium silicate	$2CaO \cdot SiO_2$	3865
	Tricalcium silicate	$3CaO \cdot SiO_2$	3450**
2.80	Tricalcium silicate	$3CaO \cdot SiO_2$	3450**
More than 2.80	Tricalcium silicate	$3CaO \cdot SiO_2$	3450**
	Lime	CaO	4650

* Incongruent melting.

** Stable only between 3450 and 2280° F. Dissociation below and above these temperatures into $2CaO \cdot SiO_2$ and CaO.

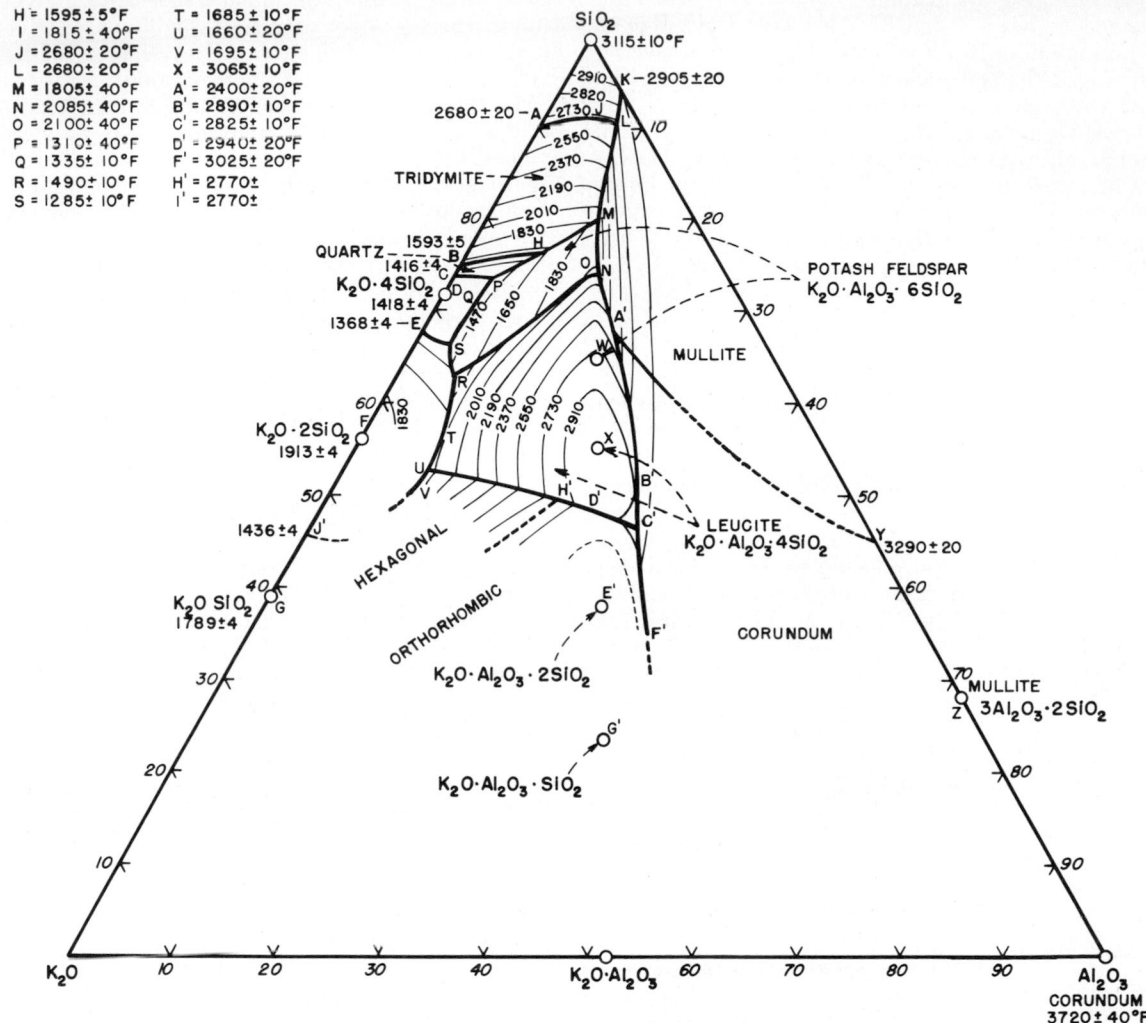

FIG. 2—8. The K₂O–Al₂O₃–SiO₂ system.

shows the reactions and phase assemblages in the MgO–CaO–SiO₂ system. In the high-MgO portion of this system, the principal mineral is of course always periclase. The accessory silicate bonding minerals, however, will vary considerably depending on the ratio of CaO to SiO₂. Table 2—IV presents a summary of the compounds present with periclase as affected by the CaO/SiO₂ weight ratio and their approximate melting points. While the type of refractory bonding preferred will depend on the intended application, the forsterite bond, which occurs at CaO/SiO₂ ratios less than 0.93, is generally desired in most basic brick to prevent excessive formation of monticellite and merwinite. These minerals form low-temperature liquids and therefore have poor high-temperature load-carrying ability. In recent years, in addition to the control of CaO/SiO₂ ratio, increased emphasis has been placed on decreasing the amounts of lime and silica present to obtain full advantages of the properties of almost pure magnesia. This has been accomplished largely through the use of the improved synthetic magnesites. Also, considerable effort has been devoted to developing

other bonds for magnesia such as the very refractory spinels, MgO·Al₂O₃ and MgO·Cr₂O₃. In these high-magnesia refractories, the addition of Al₂O₃ or Cr₂O₃ with sufficient temperature causes the formation of either spinel-to-magnesia or direct magnesia-to-magnesia bonds replacing the silicate bonds. These bonds offer not only excellent refractoriness-under-load, but also improved resistance to thermal spalling and higher modulus of rupture at elevated temperature. Figures 2—15A and 2—15B show photomicrographs of silicate and the above-type bonds.

For refractories with higher contents of lime, such as those produced from dead-burned dolomite or lime-containing magnesite, the CaO/SiO₂ ratio is normally such that calcium silicates are produced. The dicalcium silicate produced at high CaO/SiO₂ ratios has a high melting temperature, but must be stabilized against polymorphic inversion by additions of chrome oxide (Cr₂O₃) and/or boric acid (B₂O₃). The reaction of free lime with silica to form dicalcium silicate is one method of decreasing the hydration tendency of lime, but unfortunately does not overcome the poor resistance of such compositions to

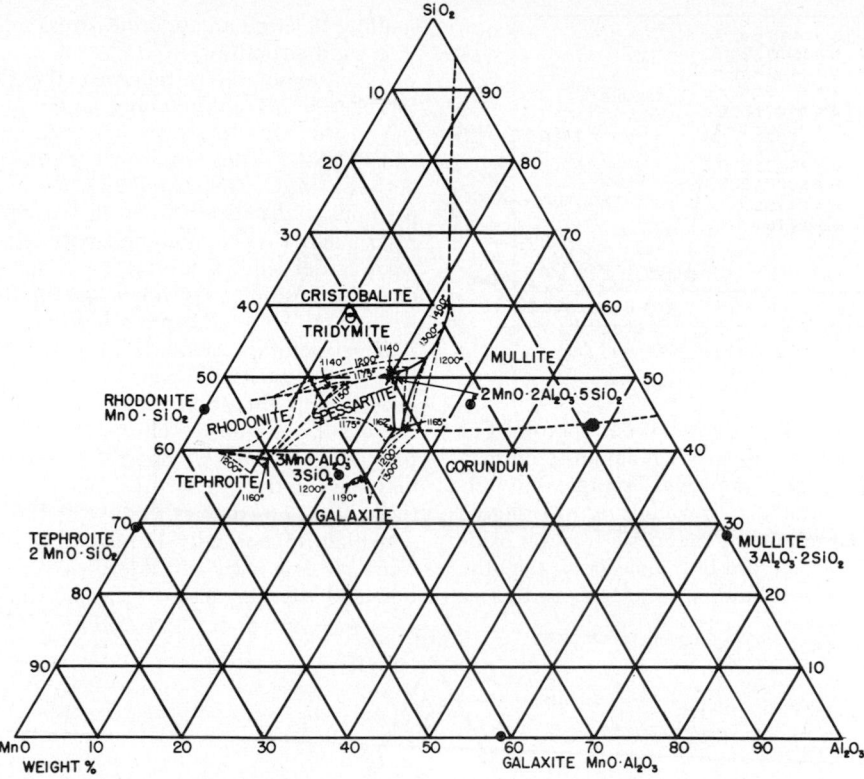

Fig. 2—9. The MnO–Al₂O₃–SiO₂ system.

iron oxides. Although used primarily in the past as granular hearth-maintenance materials, refractories made from combinations of lime-containing magnesites, dead-burned dolomite, and magnesia are now being produced with a protective bonding of coal-tar pitch for use in oxygen steelmaking vessels. In such refractories, the carbon, formed from coking the pitch, is the principal bond. It has been observed that the carbon bond inhibits much of the reaction and penetration of iron-oxide and lime-silicate liquids commonly associated with such refractories without the carbon bond.

The high-temperature reactions of refractories made from magnesia and chrome ore are under constant study. The properties of refractories made from these two raw materials are excellent because of the tendency of each to minimize the major weaknesses of the other constituent. Chrome ore consists of solid solution of chrome spinels $(Mg,Fe)O \cdot (Cr,Al,Fe)_2O_3$ with appreciable amounts of gangue silicates. At high temperatures, the gangue silicate in chrome ore is responsible for poor resistance to load deformation and the iron oxides may be alternately oxidized and reduced with an attendant expansion and contraction often causing disintegration. Also, chrome spinel shows considerable growth or bursting when in contact with iron oxide at high temperatures due to the formation of solid solutions of magnetite $(FeO \cdot Fe_2O_3)$ and other spinels. With additions of magnesia to chrome, however, the gangue silicates are converted on burning or in service to the more refractory forsterite, and the iron oxide to the spinel $MgO \cdot Fe_2O_3$ by co-diffusion of Fe_2O_3 and MgO between

the magnesia and chrome spinel. Magnesioferrite is more resistant to cyclic oxidizing-reducing conditions

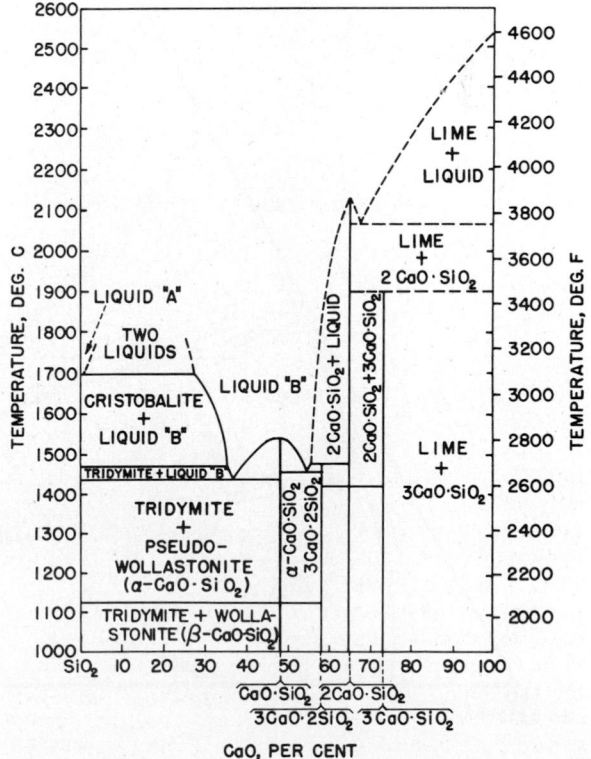

Fig. 2—10. The CaO–SiO₂ system.

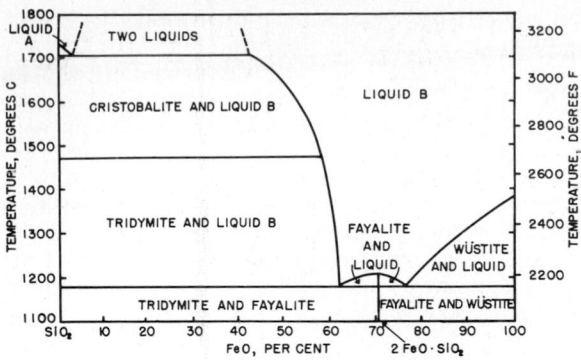

Fig. 2—11. The FeO–SiO₂ system.

spalling through an apparent stress relief in an otherwise rigid structure.

As in magnesia refractories, the CaO/SiO_2 ratio exerts an important influence on the phases present in composite refractories of magnesia and chrome ore. At CaO/SiO_2 ratios less than 1.86, the primary phases between MgO, CaO, and SiO_2 are the same as that previously discussed with the sesquioxides Cr_2O_3, Al_2O_3, and Fe_2O_3 combined with MgO and FeO to form spinel solid solutions. At higher CaO/SiO_2 ratios, the sesquioxides form low-melting compounds with CaO. Although such a high ratio is rare in original refractories made from periclase and chrome ore, such ratios will occur in many refractories after exposure to lime-rich basic slags in service. As in magnesia refractories, efforts have been made to replace the silicate-type bond in refractories made from magnesia and chrome ore. The most noteworthy of these efforts to date is the use of firing temperatures above those normally employed to produce a low-silica burned basic refractory with so-called "direct" bonds of the magnesia-to-chrome spinel, and magne-

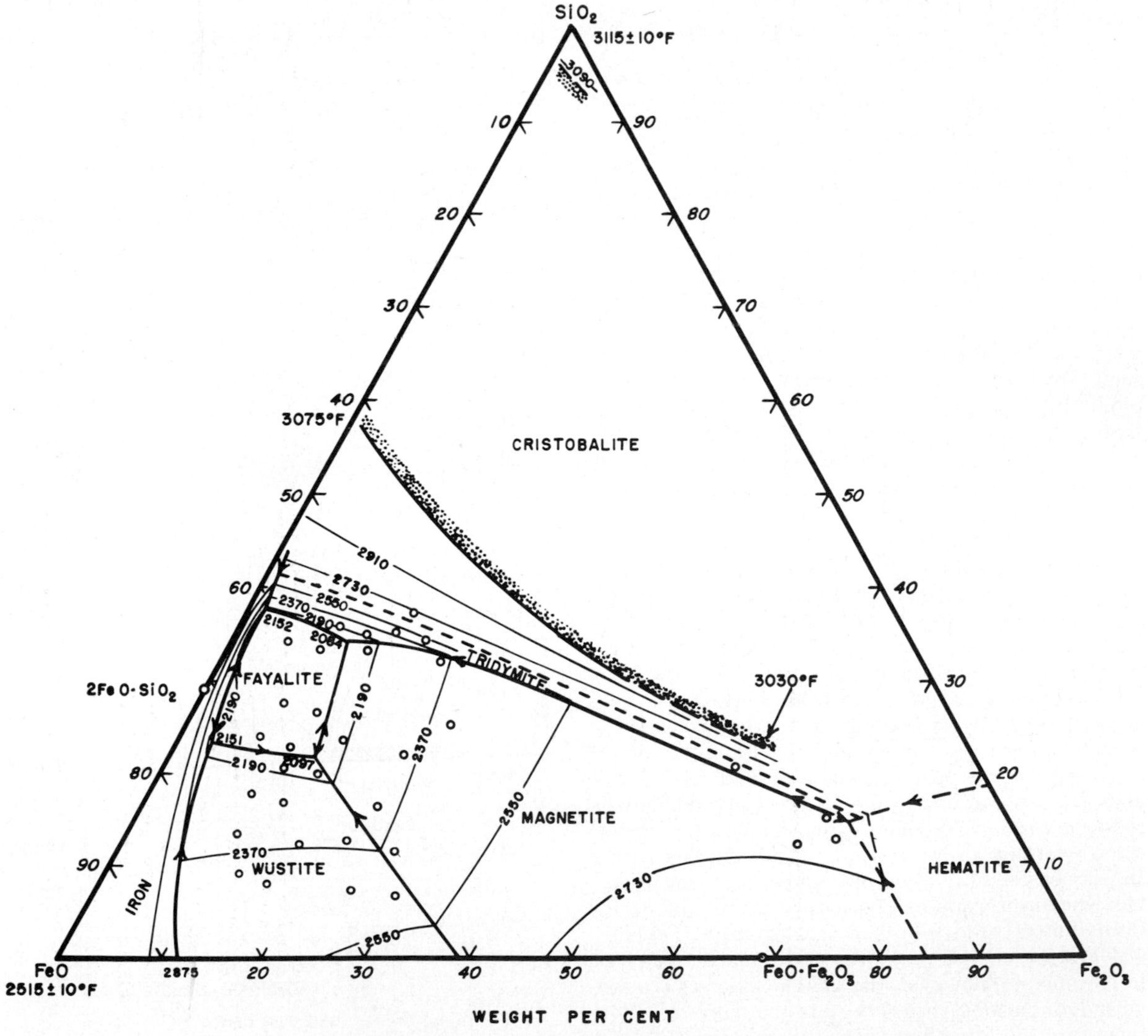

than the iron oxides in the original chrome ore. Further, the addition of still greater amounts of magnesia to chrome ore improves significantly the resistance of the refractory to iron-oxide bursting because of the great affinity of magnesia for iron oxide. The addition of chrome ore to magnesia on the other hand improves the resistance of magnesia to thermal

Fig. 2—12. The FeO–Fe₂O₃–SiO₂ system.

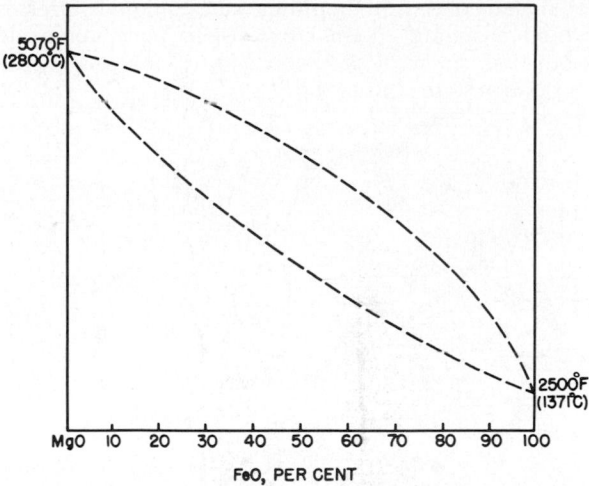

FIG. 2—13. The MgO–FeO system.

on the oxidation state of the iron present in various compositions including the oxides MgO, Cr_2O_3, Al_2O_3, FeO, and Fe_2O_3. It has been shown, for example, that in mixtures consisting originally of Fe_2O_3 and $MgO \cdot Fe_2O_3$, dissociation of the Fe_2O_3 is accompanied by solution of the dissociation product magnetite ($FeO \cdot Fe_2O_3$) in $MgO \cdot Fe_2O_3$ until a single spinel phase is formed. In this same region, it has been shown that the spinel-to-sesquioxide transition temperature decreases as the magnesia content increases, but at the same time magnesia stabilizes Fe_2O_3 at higher temperatures. Chrome oxide (Cr_2O_3) on the other hand, has an opposite effect to magnesia in that it increases the sesquioxide-to-spinel transition temperature and lowers the degree of dissociation of Fe_2O_3 at higher temperatures. In mixtures consisting initially of $MgO \cdot Fe_2O_3$ and MgO, dissociation of Fe_2O_3 proceeds with a decrease in the amount of spinel and solution of iron oxide in periclase. Further studies of this type involving all possible combinations of the main oxide components are in various stages of completion. The practical importance of such findings are extensive, but lie primarily in establishing the expansion-shrinkage characteristics associated with changes such as: (1) the solution and precipitation of magnesioferrite, (2) transformation from magnesioferrite to magnesiowüstite solid solution in periclase, and (3) the subsequent effects of the first two changes on the peeling or slabbing of basic brick in service un-

sia-to-magnesia, types. Figures 2—15C and 2—15D show photomicrographs of the conventional silicate and these unusual "direct" bonds, respectively. Direct-bonded brick are noted particularly for their high hot strengths which may be 2 to 8 times that of conventional brick of similar composition.

While the phase assemblages previously discussed indicate the general combinations of iron oxides in basic refractories, it is equally important to consider the influence of furnace temperature and atmosphere

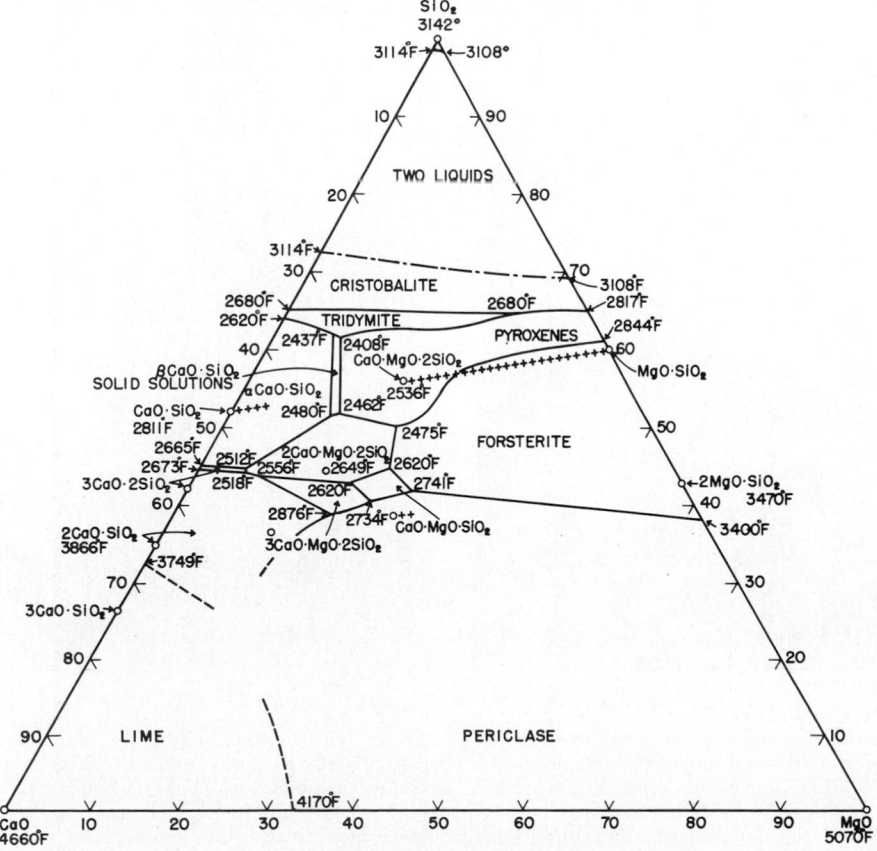

FIG. 2—14. The CaO–MgO–SiO₂ system.

der variable atmospheric and temperature conditions. Such information is necessary to fully define the causes of slabbing or peeling of basic refractories now believed related to various factors including migra-

tion and concentration of lime-silicate liquids, stresses from changing thermal expansions, and iron-oxide bursting, as well as the effects of changes in the oxidation state of iron oxide.

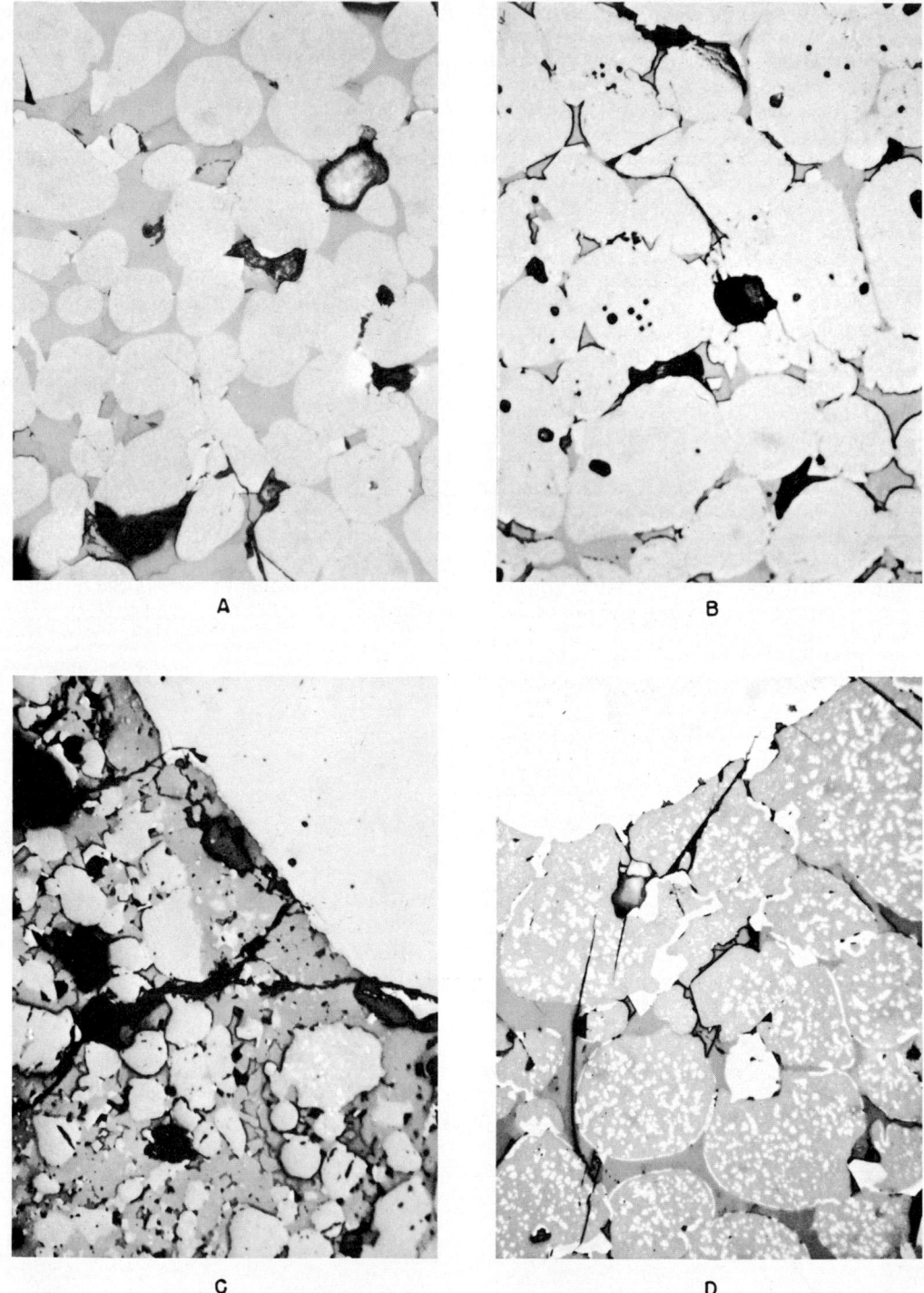

Fig. 2—15. Photomicrographs showing the structure of basic brick with various bonds. "A" shows a magnesite composition consisting of rounded gray magnesia crystals bonded principally by darker silicate. "B" is a magnesite composition having less silicate and bonded principally by spinel and direct magnesia-to-magnesia bonds. "C" shows a magnesite-chrome ore composition in which the bond between the large white chrome spinel grain and rounded magnesia crystals is principally the dark silicate. "D" shows a magnesite-chrome composition having less silicate and a direct bond between white chrome spinel and periclase (MgO) containing multiple white magnesioferrite inclusions. Reflected light, X200.

SECTION 5

SELECTION AND TESTING OF STEEL-PLANT REFRACTORIES

The ultimate goal in refractory selection is to achieve minimum overall operating costs per ton of steel. However, this is the universal endeavor of all phases of steel production, in some of which costs may be lowered only at the expense of refractories, as by harder driving of furnaces to increase the rate of production, or by a change to cheaper fuels which may increase refractory wear. Careful costs analyses may be required to determine which of the conflicting factors can best be sacrificed for maximum economy. Therefore, the specific aim of the refractories engineer is to obtain minimum refractory costs per ton of steel, but only those obtainable under operating conditions dictated by the above considerations. The successful selection of refractories requires a knowledge of refractory characteristics, a knowledge of service conditions and, based on experience, the ability to correlate the two in terms of performance. The importance of this work is attested by the fact that most steel companies now employ ceramic engineers and maintain laboratories devoted to quality control testing and research on refractories.

Information on refractory characteristics as revealed by standard A.S.T.M. tests is readily available from refractory suppliers or independent laboratories but, as indicated earlier, such data are often inadequate and even misleading if not used intelli-

gently. However, as it is always desired to establish correlations between performance in service and the simplest possible laboratory tests, the standard tests are an excellent starting point, and, because the range of variation in a given property is needed for proper correlation and quality control, the use of these tests in steel-plant laboratories is often the only means of determining such variations.

Obtaining information on service conditions is most important to the proper application of refractories. Systematic studies of used linings by chemical analysis, petrographic microscope, and various laboratory tests have clarified many of the mysteries as to the precise mechanism of failure of blast-furnace and open-hearth refractories, and have been responsible for some of the most significant advances in refractory practice and, also very important, in furnace design.

With information on refractory behavior and service conditions, much of the guesswork can be eliminated from service trials which, of course, provide the final answer on refractory suitability. When failures are encountered in such trials they are generally indicative of the need for more fundamental refractory research or, as often occurs, of changes in operating conditions from those on which the refractory selection was based.

SECTION 6

SPECIFIC USES OF REFRACTORIES IN STEEL PLANTS

BLAST FURNACES

For many years, blast furnaces were lined throughout with high-duty fireclay brick and, despite much recent experimentation with a number of special types of refractories, the high-duty brick still predominate. However, the present high-duty blast-furnace brick are greatly improved in strength, resistance to abrasion and disintegration by carbon monoxide, and in size uniformity, to those produced prior to 1950. While in some cases this type of brick may be used throughout the furnace lining, the more usual practice today is to employ "zoned" linings, in which various types of super-duty, high-alumina, or carbon brick are used in critical areas in an effort to achieve a better balance in lining wear. Thus, common types of "zoned" linings are constructed as follows:

Stack Lining—A 10-foot band of high-fired super-duty brick is often used immediately below the wearing plates to provide good resistance to the abrasive action of the charge. From this band to the mantle, high-duty brick or, less often, super-duty brick are used.

Bosh Lining—The majority of bosh linings are of the same high-duty brick used in the stack, laid in

the conventional banded bosh construction with copper cooling plates. In recent years, however, a number of carbon bosh linings have been installed in American furnaces: when this is done, a solid, welded bosh shell is used and the water cooling is external. This permits simpler brick construction and a smoother wearing bosh through the elimination of the corrugated pattern produced by the rows of coolers in a conventional bosh. However, some doubt exists as to the future of carbon in this application. Thus, while new types of anthracite-based carbon brick have shown substantial improvement with respect to deterioration by alkali attack, the problem of oxidation remains, and results have been such that some operators have abandoned carbon in any application above the tuyeres.

Hearth Walls—Carbon-brick linings laid tight against the shell are widely used from the top or centerline of the tuyeres, all the way down to the bottom of the stave coolers. While some wear is normal in the tuyere area, the durability of carbon hearth walls has been such that they have virtually eliminated breakouts in this zone. In some installations, composite walls of carbon faced with high-duty or super-duty fireclay brick are employed. With carbon hearth walls, as in the bosh, external water cooling is generally preferred to prevent any deteriorating effect of water leaking from internal cooling plates.

Hearth—Most American blast-furnace hearths are constructed of 18-inch by 9-inch by 4½-inch fireclay block laid within the outer carbon hearth wall. With this construction, the upper three or four rows (4½ to 6 feet) of hearth block are of hard-burned super-duty quality and the remainder of the courses are high-duty block. In some hearths, carbon is used throughout, in which case, large blocks several feet in length are employed to a depth of 4 to 8 feet. These are usually keyed together against flotation by molten iron. The relative merits and economics of the all-carbon construction versus the fireclay-block center "plug" construction has not been satisfactorily established.

While little use has yet been made of them, special refractories—particularly in high-alumina types—are being given increasing consideration for the trouble zones of the blast furnace, namely; below the wearing plates, the lower stack region, the bosh, and the upper hearth courses. While this is partially in anticipation of increased difficulties that may be related to changes in blast-furnace practices, the fact remains that blast-furnace lining life has steadily improved in recent years so that life in excess of 3,500,-000 tons per lining has become commonplace.

Hot-Blast Stoves—As with the blast-furnace linings, refractories for hot-blast stoves have gradually shifted from complete high-duty brick linings and checkers to a zoned construction. Thus, semi-silica brick, because of good hot-load-carrying ability and the characteristic of glazing in service without vitrification in depth, are widely used in combustion-chamber skin walls, the dome, upper ring walls, and even as checker brick in the upper middle zone of the setting. The remainder of the stoves, with the frequent exception of the use of super-duty checkers in the top 5 to 35 feet of the setting, is generally high-duty brick. In some cases, super-duty brick are used instead of semi-silica brick in the higher-temperature areas indicated above.

More recently, as beneficiated blast-furnace burdens and other improved practices have permitted or even necessitated substantial increases in hot-blast temperatures, considerable attention has been given to stove refractories. In cases where the increase in stove temperature is not expected to result in temperatures exceeding 2400° F at the dome, it has generally been concluded that the above-described refractory construction is adequate, provided that high-fired super-duty checkers are employed to a depth of approximately 35 feet. In other cases where higher temperatures are anticipated—as with small stoves with inadequate heating surface—high-alumina refractories, particularly of the mullite type, are being used in the combustion chamber, dome, upper ring walls, and the upper 20 to 30 feet of the checkers. Also, under both conditions, super-duty brick or mullite brick are being substituted for the semi-silica brick in the target area opposite the burner at the base of the combus-

tion chamber to prevent spalling attendant upon the use of burners of higher capacity.

BASIC OPEN-HEARTH FURNACES

The modern basic open-hearth furnace employs a wide variety of refractories. In the furnace itself, the types of brick that may be found include silica, semi-silica, all grades of fireclay, some grades of high-alumina, and nearly all kinds of basic brick. In granular or plastic form are found raw, calcined or clinkered dolomite; magnesite; special dolomite or magnesite patching or ramming mixtures; chrome ore; plastic chrome ore; and fireclay, silica, and basic mortars. With few exceptions, however, none of these refractories can be said to be securely established in a given application, as not only do requirements vary widely with different practices in different shops, but changes are constantly being brought about by improvements in refractories and changes in fuels and oxygen usage, with accompanying changes in design. The overall continuing trend in open-hearth refractories is toward increased use of basic refractories. Other trends and developments are revealed by a brief examination of refractories used in the various furnace parts and in accessory equipment in the shop.

Hearth—The time-honored practice of insulating open-hearth bottoms with insulating brick or insulating concrete and a layer of fireclay brick is gradually giving way to uninsulated bottoms, with the basic subhearth brick being laid directly on the steel pan. Also, more frequently, these basic brick are 90 per cent magnesite brick rather than chrome-magnesite or chrome brick. This basic-brick subhearth may be laid in horizontal courses to produce "stadium" construction, or as an inverted arch. In the latter case, a chrome castable is frequently used against the shell to contour the banks and ends. Above the subhearth, the working bottom is now generally installed by ramming 12 to 25 inches of a high-MgO bonded ramming mix, rather than by laboriously burning in layers of magnesite and slag as in years past. Very recently, a complete working hearth was installed by casting and vibrating a high-MgO mixture, using approximately 6 per cent moisture as against 3 per cent normally used in ramming. In a few instances, bottoms have been constructed almost entirely of magnesite brick, with only a 3-inch layer of granular-magnesite surfacing.

Front-, Back-, and Endwalls—Front- and back-walls were the first applications above the hearth to be converted from silica to basic refractories and these are now almost universally basic; of chrome-magnesite, magnesite-chrome or, more frequently, magnesite brick, either burned or unburned. Basic endwalls followed later. Steel-encased magnesite-chrome brick are most popular and these walls are generally constructed with steel tie plates every 2 to 4 courses, with the tie plates welded to the buckstays to prevent buckling.

In some cases, frontwall repairs are made with prefabricated basic-brick wall sections, set in place by the charging peel. Also, some experimentation has been done with cast frontwall sections made of high-MgO mixes of the types used in bottoms.

Port Sidewalls—Port sidewalls were one of the last

strongholds of silica brick, but are now generally basic and constructed of the same brick, and often in the same manner, as endwalls.

Doors—An important development in open-hearth refractories was the introduction of stud-type water-cooled doors with plastic basic-refractory linings, usually of chrome ore. Performance has generally more than justified the extra initial cost over brick-lined doors.

Roof—Despite many years of experimentation with basic roofs, it was not until late in 1957 that a sufficiently satisfactory solution to the problem of basic-roof design was found to eliminate the last doubt regarding the economic feasibility of basic roofs. From that time forward, the adoption of basic roofs on American furnaces was extremely rapid, the number of basic roofs increasing from about 15 in 1958 to over 300 by 1962, on furnaces accounting for about 75 per cent of the open-hearth steel produced. The design responsible for this conversion from silica to basic roofs was developed at the Fairless Works of United States Steel Corporation and consists of a rigidly held high arch sprung between fixed skewbacks, employing little or no expansion allowance. This design negates most prior theories that held that a successful roof design would have to provide compensation for the expansion and growth characteristics of basic brick.

The roof is built of steel-encased brick, held down by longitudinal I beams, and is supported by $3/16$-inch thick transverse plates inserted in the ring joints on 9- to 24-inch centers, the beams and plates being tied together and to the furnace superstructure so that the roof position is fixed. The support provided by the transverse plates results from the welding of the plates to the steel-jacketed brick by the heat developed at furnace operating temperatures. With this design, roof life of 400 to 600 heats is common on large furnaces, while on small, 150-ton furnaces not using oxygen lances, roof life exceeding 1000 heats has been obtained.

The basic roof brick used with this design originally were chemically bonded chrome-magnesite containing about 45 per cent of MgO. While such brick still are being used, the use of magnesite-chrome brick containing 60 to 70 per cent of MgO has become more common, particularly on furnaces using oxygen-lance practice, and there is evidence to indicate that brick containing yet higher amounts of MgO may be beneficial. Although unburned brick predominate, burned brick have been successful, and their use may increase. Experience has shown that the most important brick characteristics, regardless of MgO content, are low porosity, high strength at intermediate temperatures, and low SiO_2 content. All steel-encased roof brick are in key shape, rather than wedges, with a 3-inch by $4\frac{1}{2}$-inch cross-section with two internal steel plates, or a 3-inch by 3-inch cross-section with no internal plates. Roofs may be of uniform 9-inch, 12-inch, or 15-inch thickness or, more commonly, ribbed, with 12-inch valley sections and 15-inch ribs.

In plants where silica roofs are still in use, brick of highest purity are demanded to obtain the maximum refractoriness possible. Such silica brick are also used for the port roofs on many furnaces having basic main roofs, where experience has shown that the wear in these two sections can thus be kept in balance.

Uptakes—Uptake refractories have followed the general trend from silica to basic, so that nearly all furnaces with basic roofs have basic uptakes, at least on all vertical walls, many of which are of suspended construction. Both chrome-magnesite and magnesite-chrome brick are used. In the lower uptake zones, particularly on sloping suspended walls where conditions are less severe, basic brick increasingly have given way to high-alumina brick, generally of the 60 per cent Al_2O_3 type.

Slag Pockets, Checker Chambers, and Flues—Refractories for slag-pocket walls vary considerably, reflecting a wide range in service conditions. In many cases, silica brick are satisfactory: more rarely, fireclay brick faced with silica-brick false walls are used. Under more severe conditions of temperature and carryover, basic or high-alumina brick walls may be required.

Checkers and checker chambers are generally built of high-duty brick, although super-duty or 60 per cent alumina brick may be used in the hottest sections, as in the fantail, and semi-silica brick may be used in the checker-chamber roof. In a few cases, basic brick may be used in the upper courses of the checker setting, but dense, high-duty checker brick are more economical for most American furnaces. With the advent of oxygen-lance practice, regeneration has become less important than the maintenance of free drafting, so checker-flue openings have been increasing in size to minimize plugging of the setting.

Intermediate and low-duty brick may be used in the flues and stack.

BASIC ELECTRIC-STEELMAKING FURNACES

While electric-furnace refractories do not have to contend with the high-velocity gases common to the open hearth, they are often subjected to higher temperatures, and in the latter part of the heat, to reducing atmospheres. By far the greatest influence on electric-furnace refractory performance is the type of steel produced, as operating practices differ widely for different types of steel. Thus, refractory life in furnaces producing stainless steels is generally far better than in those producing low-carbon alloy-steel or oxygen-blown alloy-steel heats.

As in the open hearth, there is a definite trend away from silica brick in roofs but, in this case, to high-alumina brick rather than basic brick. The high-alumina brick may contain 60 to 80 per cent of Al_2O_3, with 70 per cent of Al_2O_3 most widely used, sometimes of the mullite type. High-alumina ramming mixes or castables are frequently used instead of brick in the delta section between the electrode rings.

Sidewalls are usually built of chrome-magnesite or magnesite-chrome steel-encased brick. In some furnaces, fused cast basic brick are used in the critical areas, such as the mast side and opposite to the electrodes. Recently, experimental sidewall installations have been made with tar-bonded magnesite or dolomite-magnesite brick or large blocks.

The developments in hearth refractories have paralleled those of the open hearth and most hearths are rammed, using high-MgO prepared mixes.

OXYGEN-STEELMAKING FURNACES

Traditionally, the linings of European basic steel converters such as used in the Thomas process have always been made of tar-bonded dolomite refractories, either rammed or brick. It was natural that, with the advent of top-blown oxygen steelmaking, these similar shaped furnaces would also be lined with this type of refractory, and experience in recent years has generally demonstrated the correctness of this choice. Thus, initial efforts to adopt many types of more conventional basic brick for such linings in American oxygen-steelmaking furnaces proved uneconomical because of higher initial cost and poorer performance, and now the tar-bonded products are universally used. However, much development work has been done on tar-bonded basic refractories and several types are now in use, mostly in brick form. These may be straight dolomite, dolomite and magnesite in various proportions, or straight magnesite, the latter ranging from 80 per cent MgO to over 90 per cent MgO content. The magnesite and the dolomite-magnesite brick are more widely used than the dolomite brick, not because of outstanding superiority in service, but primarily because of their greater resistance to deterioration by hydration that minimizes the storage problems so troublesome with dolomite brick.

In lining the furnace, a 4½-inch to 9-inch thick safety lining of burned-magnesite brick is laid against the steel shell. The working lining of tar-bonded brick, varying in thickness from 13½ inches to as much as 27 inches, is generally laid in a spiral manner, either directly against the safety lining or separated from it by a 2-inch to 4-inch rammed layer of magnesite-tar mixture. The safety and working linings of the bottom are generally the same as indicated above, but are laid as an inverted arch and without the rammed layer between. High-magnesia ramming mixes are commonly used to form the taphole. Lining life is quite variable, ranging from 200 to as much as 600 heats, being influenced by furnace size, blowing practice, charging practice, and metal composition.

POURING-PIT REFRACTORIES

These refractories—sleeves, nozzles, stopper heads, and ladle brick—must withstand severe thermal shock and corrosion by molten steel and slag. For many years, these requirements were most successfully met when all of these products except stopper heads were made of the lower grades of refractory clays, and this practice still predominates. There are two reasons for this apparent paradox, both based on the time factor. First, sleeves and nozzles are single-use refractories and seldom subjected to the service conditions mentioned above for more than an hour; and ladle linings are necessarily cooled between successive heats. Second, each of these refractories, and especially nozzles and ladle brick, during this short period should become pyroplastic to function to best advantage—nozzles to form a tight seal for the stopper, and ladle brick to seal and prevent accelerated wear of the brick

joints. Stopper heads obviously must remain hard and corrosion-resistant, and hence are made of refractory clay-graphite mixtures.

However, despite the proven acceptability of low refractoriness in pouring-pit refractories, there has been a trend toward increasing refractoriness in these products in recent years, largely as a result of increased heat size and the resultant increase in retention time of the steel in the ladle. Thus, the refractoriness of sleeves now in use in large ladles is rarely below Cone 28, and there has been considerable substitution of nozzles in the Cone 20 to Cone 23 range for those in the Cone 17 to Cone 19 range. Less deliberate changes have been made in ladle brick, although the increased use of circle brick, instead of arches and straights, with resultant fewer vertical joints, has minimized the difficulties associated with the use of more refractory, volume-stable ladle brick. A major requirement of either type, however, is low porosity and high density if an excessive rate of wear is to be avoided.

SOAKING PITS

Soaking-pit linings must possess good load-carrying ability, high resistance to abrasion, and resistance to iron-oxide attack, particularly at the slag line. Cover linings must be resistant to spalling, as must the top of the pit walls, or copings, although mechanical abuse in the latter zone is the main cause for deterioration. Several types of refractories for pit walls have been and are being used, with the siliceous types—sandstone, silica brick, and semi-silica brick—predominating. Fireclay brick generally have proven less satisfactory for this application, although super-duty fireclay plastics have gained some acceptance in recent years. This is particularly true for copings, where plastics and large fireclay block are widely used, as these materials are more resistant to thermal shock and are easier to maintain than the siliceous refractories. Basic brick predominate in the lower sidewalls, or slag line, but in many cases 70 per cent Al_2O_3 brick or 75 to 90 per cent Al_2O_3 plastics have provided at least comparable service, and the use of these latter materials is increasing.

Cover refractories vary widely, and are about evenly divided between fireclay brick, semi-silica brick, and monolithic refractories, with a much smaller percentage of insulating brick. The monolithic refractories are largely plastics, as these are now preferred to castables in most plants.

The bottoms of soaking pits are generally constructed of fireclay brick covered with approximately one foot of coke breeze. However, the use of so-called "dry bottoms" is increasing, in which case the coke breeze is eliminated in favor of a relatively thin layer of magnesite, dolomite, or chrome ore, and high-alumina or basic brick or monolithic refractories may be substituted for the fireclay brick.

The use of gunning refractories for pit maintenance is widespread. These may be siliceous or fireclay refractory material for the upper walls and high-alumina or basic material for the lower walls.

HEATING FURNACES

Heating furnaces include a wide variety of types

and service conditions, but refractory requirements generally are met by fireclay brick. Spalling resistance is needed in most furnaces, however, and recognition of this has led to greater use of super-duty and semi-silica brick in recent years, particularly in suspended and sprung-arch roofs and in the walls of heating zones of continuous slab-heating furnaces. More recently, these bricks have in turn been replaced with rammed plastic fireclay, and the use of these plastics has been extended, in many cases, to include the entire lining of a continuous slab-heating furnace. A number of refractories are used in the solid hearths of such furnaces, with a trend away from basic brick or plastics to high-alumina brick or plastics. Burner-block performance has been greatly improved through the use of super-duty, high-alumina, or mullite block, either prefired or rammed.

HEAT-TREATING FURNACES

In many low-temperature heat-treating furnaces, advantage can be taken of the low heat capacity and insulating value of lightweight fireclay brick or castables. Special insulating refractories of very low iron-oxide content are now available for use in controlled-atmosphere furnaces where iron oxide can interfere with dewpoint control.

Bibliography

Am. Ceramic Society, Phase diagrams for ceramists, 1956; Part II, 1959.

Am. Institute of Mining and Metallurgical Engineers, Iron and Steel Div., Committee on Physical Chemistry of Steelmaking, Basic open hearth steelmaking; 2nd ed. (Seeley W. Mudd series). N. Y., The Institute, 1951.
Chapter 3: Open-hearth refractories, by R. B. Sosman, pp. 59-80.

Am. Institute of Mining and Metallurgical Engineers, National Open Hearth Committee Proc., **27** (1944) —**44** (1961).

Am. Society for Testing Materials, Manual of ASTM standards on refractory materials (Committee C-8). Phila., The Society, 1957.

Chesters, J. H., Steelplant refractories; testing, research and development. Sheffield, Eng., United Steel Companies Ltd., 1945.

General Refractories Company, Refractories. Phila., The Company, 1949.

Harbison-Walker Refractories Company, Modern refractory practice; 3rd ed. Pgh., The Company, 1961.

Norton, F. H., Refractories; 3rd ed. N.Y., McGraw-Hill, 1949.

Osborn, E. F., Phase equilibrium studies of steel plant refractories systems. Am. Iron and Steel Institute, Regional Technical Meetings, 1954, pp. 145-177.

CHAPTER 3

Metallurgical Fuels and Fuel Economy

SECTION 1

FUELS, COMBUSTION AND HEAT FLOW

Any substance capable of producing heat by combustion may be termed a **fuel**. However, it is customary to rank as fuels only those which include carbon and hydrogen and their compounds. Wood was the earliest fuel used by man. Coal was known to exist in the fourth century B.C., and petroleum was used by the Persians in the days of Alexander. Prehistoric records of China and Japan are said to contain references to the use of natural gas for lighting and heating.

Heat generated by the combustion of fuel is utilized in industry directly as heat or is converted into mechanical or electrical energy. Fuel has become the major source of energy for manufacturing enterprises. In America, fuel has been produced and exploited to a greater extent than in any other country. The United States became the leading coal-producing country of the world in 1889, and in 1902 took the lead in crude-petroleum production from Russia. The United States is also the leading producer of natural gas.

Fuel enters significantly into manufacturing costs, and in some industries represents one of the largest items of expense. The steel industry is one of the major consumers of coal but, since coal is used so universally, consumes only about 15 per cent of the total produced. In periods of high production, the steel industry expends annually over a quarter of a billion dollars for coal. A modern fully-integrated steel plant consumes approximately a ton of coal for each ton of steel ingots produced. The steel industry also consumes large quantities of natural gas and petroleum: in some steel plants petroleum is the major fuel.

The enormous annual consumption of coal, petroleum, and natural gas in the United States has provoked interest in the natural resources of these materials. Our known resources are still the greatest in the world, but the best and most readily accessible petroleum and natural gas are said, by some authorities, to approach depletion, at the present high rates of consumption, before 2000 A.D. However, when the less desirable coal beds are included, the known coal reserves have been estimated to be sufficient to last anywhere from three hundred to two thousand years. Some industries are developing synthetic fuels, particularly liquid and gaseous fuels from lower-grade coal, in anticipation of the time when their use will be justified economically. Efficient fuel utilization has been intensified not only by the prospect of depletion, but also by rising costs of fuel production.

CLASSIFICATION OF FUELS

Fuels are classified usually into three general divisions; viz., **solid, liquid,** and **gaseous.** Fuels in each general division can be classified further as **natural, manufactured,** or **by-product.** Fuels found in nature sometimes are called **primary fuels;** those manufactured for a specific purpose or market, together with those which are the unavoidable by-product of some regular manufacturing process, are called **secondary fuels.** The primary fuels serve as the principal raw materials for the secondary fuels. Table 3—I gives a classified list of the important fuels. It also lists some interesting by-product fuels, many of which have been utilized by industry to conserve primary fuel.

Importance of Each Class—There has been a decline in the use of coal, and a proportional increase in petroleum and natural-gas consumption. Coal is still the major fuel of public utilities for the generation of power and is essential to the steel industry for the manufacture of coke. It has been supplanted to a large extent by liquid fuels for the generation of motive power by railroads. It is a major raw material in many chemical plants as a source of carbon, hydrogen, and their compounds.

The growth of petroleum consumption has been phenomenal in the past forty years due to the increasing demand for its distillation products. Gasoline, the most important product, is used as a motor fuel. Light oil is used for Diesel engines. Distillate and residual fuel oils, and some crude petroleums of too low commercial value for distillation, are used for industrial and domestic heating. Crude and refined petroleum of various grades are used for lubrication of all types of machinery and prime movers. Petroleum is the base for many synthetic products and is competitive with coal chemicals in a number of important applications.

The marketed production of natural gas increased fourfold in the twenty years prior to 1945, and the quantity used in that year was approximately 4,000 billion cubic feet (165,000,000 tons of coal equivalent, equal to about one-third the annual production of coal). During 1958, marketed production of natural gas was estimated to be 11,030 billion cubic feet (463,260,000 tons of coal equivalent). Natural gas has replaced coal to a considerable extent for domestic and industrial heating due to the installation of very large pipe lines from producing to consuming centers, the rise in the price of solid fuel, the relative level in

Table 3—I. Classification of Fuels

General Division	Primary Fuels	Secondary Fuels	
	Natural	Manufactured	By-Product
Solid	Anthracite coal Bituminous coal Lignite Peat Wood	Semi-coke (low-temperature 　　carbonization residue) Coke Charcoal Briquettes { Coal slack and culm 　　Lignite 　　Peat 　　Sawdust 　　Petroleum-refining 　　　residue Pulverized coal	Charcoal—low-temperature distillation of wood Wood refuse—shavings, trimmings, tan bark, 　　sawdust, etc. Bagasse—refuse sugar cane Anthracite culm—silt refuse of anthracite 　　screening Coke breeze { By-product coke—screenings 　　Petroleum coke— 　　　petroleum-refining residue Waste materials { Corn from grain { Barley 　　Wheat 　　Buckwheat 　　Sorghum
Liquid	Petroleum	Gasoline Kerosene Alcohol Colloidal fuels Fuel oil { Residual oils 　　Distillate oils 　　Crude petroleum Naphtha Vegetable oils { Palm 　　Cottonseed	Coal distillates { Tar 　　Naphthalene } —coke manu- 　　Pitch } facture 　　Benzol Acid sludge—petroleum-refining residue Pulp-mill waste
Gaseous	Natural Gas	Producer gas Water gas Carburetted water gas Coal gas Oil gas Reformed natural gas Butane[a] Propane[a] Acetylene Hydrogen	Blast-furnace gas—pig-iron manufacture Coke-oven gas[b]—coke manufacture Oil-refinery gas Sewage gas—sewage sludge

[a] Liquefiable heavier constituents of natural gas.
[b] Considered by-product of coke manufacture in steel industry but a manufactured fuel in the gas industry.

the price of natural gas over the intervening time, and its convenience, cleanliness, controllability and versatility as a fuel. The by-product gaseous fuels—coke-oven gas and blast-furnace gas—are major iron and steel industry fuels.

PRINCIPLES OF COMBUSTION

Fuels consist essentially of one, or a mixture of two or more, of four combustible constituents: (1) solid carbon, (2) hydrocarbons, (3) carbon monoxide, and (4) hydrogen. In addition to these combustible constituents, nearly all commercial fuels contain inert material, such as ash, nitrogen, carbon dioxide, and water. Bituminous coal is an example of a fuel which contains all four of the combustible constituents named above, and coke is an example of a fuel containing only one (solid carbon). The constituents which make up liquid fuels and many coals are quite complex, but since these complex constituents decom-

pose or volatilize into the four simpler constituents named above before actual combustion takes place, a knowledge of the combustion characteristics of these constituents is sufficient for nearly all practical applications. All of these four constituents of fuels except carbon are gases at the temperatures where combustion occurs. Combustion takes place by combining oxygen, a gas present in air, with the combustible constituents of a fuel. The complete combustion of all fuels generates gases. It is apparent, therefore, that a review of the properties, thermal values and chemical reactions of gases is necessary for an understanding of any class of fuel.

Since fuels are used to develop heat, a knowledge of heat terms and the principles of heat flow are essential for the efficient utilization of this heat. The combustion of fuels involves, besides combustion reactions, the factors and principles which influence speed of combustion, ignition temperature, flame luminosity, flame development, flame temperature and limits of flammability. The ensuing divisions of this section deal generally with these subjects. Sections 2, 3 and 4, respectively, deal specifically with the combustion of solid, liquid and gaseous fuels.

Calorific Value of Fuels—Heat is measured under the English system in terms of **British thermal units** (Btu); under the metric system the corresponding unit is the **calorie.** A Btu is defined as 1/180 of the amount of heat required to raise the temperature of a pound of water from 32° F to 212° F, or the average amount of heat per 1° F in this range. A **large calorie** is 1/100 of the heat required to raise the temperature of a kilogram of water from 0° C to 100° C or the average amount of heat per 1° C. The large calorie is equal to 1000 small calories and to 3.9683 Btu. The heat given up or absorbed by a body between two temperatures, providing no change of state or of allotropic form is involved, is known as **sensible heat.** The heat given up or absorbed by a body when a change of state takes place and no change of temperature is involved is known as **latent heat.** For example, a pound of water absorbs 180 Btu of sensible heat when being heated from 32° to 212° F, and absorbs 970.4 Btu of latent heat when one pound of water at 212° F is changed to steam at 212° F. Sensible heat and latent heat are used frequently in combustion calculations, particularly in problems dealing with flue-gas losses. Their significance is indicated in describing gross and net heating value of fuels.

The **gross heating value** of a fuel is the total heat developed by the combustion of a fuel at constant pressure after the products of combustion are cooled back to the starting point, assuming that all of the water vapor produced is condensed; that is, the gross heating value includes both sensible and latent heat.

The **net heating value** of a fuel is defined as the heat developed by the combustion of a fuel at constant pressure after the products of combustion are cooled back to the starting point, assuming that all of the water vapor remains uncondensed. Accordingly, the net heating value includes only sensible heat. The starting point usually is taken at either 32° F or 60° F. A starting point of 60° F has been used in all the tables and figures in this chapter, as it is generally the base for combustion calculations in the steel industry.

When a fuel contains neither hydrogen nor hydrocarbons, no water vapor is produced by combustion and the gross and net heating value will be the same, as in the case of burning carbon or carbon monoxide. The heating value or calorific value of a fuel may be determined on a dry or wet basis. The determination may be made by laboratory tests employing **calorimeters,** or by calculation. The process of determining the calorific value of solid and liquid fuels by a calorimeter consists in completely oxidizing the fuel in a space enclosed by a metal jacket (called the **bomb**) so immersed that the heat evolved is absorbed by a weighed portion of water contained in an insulated vessel. From the rise in temperature of the water, the heat liberated by one gram of the fuel is calculated. The best types of calorimeters for solid and liquid fuels are those called oxygen-bomb calorimeters in which the fuel is burned in the presence of compressed oxygen. Gas calorimeters are of different construction to permit volumetric measurement of the gas and its complete combustion under non-explosive conditions, as well as absorption of the heat produced in a water jacket. The Junkers-type continuous-flow calorimeter is a common type. The usual basis for reporting the calorific value of a gas is gross Btu per cubic foot of saturated gas measured at 60° F and 30

Table 3—II. Essential Gas Combustion Constants*
(60°F and 30 In. Hg, Dry Gases)**

| Gas | Formula | Molecular Wt. | Specific Gravity (Air = 1.0) | Heat of Combustion | | | | Cu. Ft. per Cu. Ft. of Combustible | | | | | |
| | | | | Btu per Cu. Ft. | | Btu per Lb. | | Required for Combustion | | | Flue Products | | |
				Gross	Net	Gross	Net	O_2	N_2	Air	CO_2	H_2O	N_2
Carbon............	C	12.01	....	....	......	14,093	14,093	...	......	......	......	......	......
Hydrogen.........	H_2	2.016	0.06959	324.9	274.9	60,991	51,605	0.5	1.882	2.382	....	1.0	1.882
Oxygen...........	O_2	32.000	1.1053	......	......	......	......	....	......	......	......	....	......
Nitrogen..........	N_2	28.016	0.9718	......	......	......	......	....	......	......	......	....	......
Carbon Monoxide...	CO	28.01	0.9672	321.6	321.6	4,347	4,347	0.5	1.882	2.382	1.0	....	1.882
Carbon Dioxide....	CO_2	44.01	1.5282	......	......	......	......	....	......	......	......	....	......
Methane..........	CH_4	16.041	0.5543	1014.6	914.5	23,896	21,537	2.0	7.528	9.528	1.0	2.0	7.528
Ethane...........	C_2H_6	30.067	1.04882	1789	1639	22,282	20,394	3.5	13.175	16.675	2.0	3.0	13.175
Ethylene..........	C_2H_4	28.052	0.9740	1514	1514	21,647	20,298	3.0	11.293	14.293	2.0	2.0	11.293
Propylene.........	C_3H_6	42.078	1.4504	2383	2233	21,464	20,115	4.5	16.939	21.439	3.0	3.0	16.939
Acetylene.........	C_2H_2	26.036	0.9107	1488	1438	21,344	20,617	2.5	9.411	11.911	2.0	1.0	9.411
Benzene..........	C_6H_6	78.180	2.6920	3930	3780	19,068	18,341	7.5	28.232	35.732	6.0	3.0	28.232
Hydrogen Sulphide..	H_2S	34.076	1.1898	647	596	7,100	6,545	1.5	5.646	7.146	$SO_2=1.0$	1.0	5.646
Sulphur Dioxide....	SO_2	64.06	2.264	......	......	......	......	....	......	......	......	....	......

*From "Gaseous Fuels," Second Edition (1954): published by American Gas Association, 420 Lexington Ave., New York.

**For gases saturated with water at 60°F, 1.74% of the Btu value must be deducted.

in. Hg. A **saturated gas** is one which contains the maximum amount of water vapor it can hold without any condensation of water taking place.

The heating value of a given fuel can be obtained by multiplying the calorific value of each gas by its percentage of the total fuel volume, and then totaling the individual Btu values of the separate constituents. The heat of combustion for various dry elementary gases may be found in Table 3—II. For instance, the gross heating value of dry blast-furnace gas is 92.58 Btu per cu. ft. for the composition given below, calculated as follows:

Composition of Gas	Composition by Volume (%)	Gross Heating Value Btu per cu. ft. each Component	Gross Heating Value of each Fraction
CO_2	12.76	0.0	0.0
CO	25.69	321.8	82.67
H_2	3.05	325.0	9.91
N_2	58.50	0.0	0.0
Total.....	....	....	92.58

In the calculation of the heating value of gases saturated with water vapor, the volume of water vapor must be deducted from the unit volume of gas. For instance, a cubic foot of dry CO gas has a heating value of 321.8 Btu, but when saturated with water vapor at 60° F and 30 in. Hg, a cubic foot has a heating value of only 316.2 Btu. The amount of water vapor present in saturated mixtures can be calculated from data in Table 3—III, as discussed later under "Gas Laws."

Thermal Capacity, Heat Capacity and Specific Heat—The **thermal capacity** or **heat capacity** of a substance is expressed as the amount of heat required to raise the temperature of a unit weight of the substance one degree. The British system uses Btu per lb. per °F, while the metric system uses cal. per gm. per °C. The **specific heat** of a substance is the ratio of the heat capacity of that substance to the heat capacity of water. Thus, specific heat is always a ratio, expressed as a number; for example, the specific heat of wrought iron is 0.115. There is no further designation, as this means that if it takes a certain number of Btu to heat a certain number of pounds of water a certain number of degrees F, it will take only 0.115 times as many Btu to heat the same number of pounds of wrought iron the same number of degrees F, and the same figure, 0.115, obviously applies if the metric system has been used. The amount of heat required to raise the temperature of equal masses of different substances to the same temperature level varies greatly; that is to say, the specific heat varies greatly; also the specific heat of the same substance varies at different temperatures. Usually, it is necessary to know the amount of heat required to raise the temperature of a substance some appreciable amount. For that purpose, formulae and tables are usually accessible in handbooks for supplying the mean specific heat be-

tween various temperature levels. Two values of specific heat for gases are usually given: (1) specific heat at constant pressure, and (2) specific heat at constant volume. The difference is due to the heat equivalent of the work of expansion caused by an increase of volume resulting from a temperature rise. Normal combustion practice with gases in steel plants deals with a constant pressure condition (or nearly so), and for this reason specific heat at constant pressure is used. The **mean specific heat** is the average value of the specific heat between two temperature levels. It is obtained by integrating the equations for instantaneous specific heat over the temperature limits desired, and dividing this quantity by the difference between the temperature limits.

The **heat content** is the heat contained at a specified temperature above some fixed temperature. It is calculated by multiplying the weight of a substance by the mean specific heat times the temperature difference, or H_t = weight × mean specific heat × $(T_2 - T_1)$. For convenience in calculations with gases, the unit weight of the volume of a cubic foot of gas is often used.

Gas Laws—The volume of a gas varies in direct proportion to its absolute temperature (**Charles' Law**) and inversely as its absolute pressure (**Boyle's Law**). Absolute temperature is the temperature above minus 459.6° F at 29.921 inches of mercury column in the English system, and the temperature above minus 273° C at 760 mm. of mercury in the metric system. In combustion calculations using the English system, 460° F and 30 in. Hg are assumed sufficiently accurate for all practical purposes. For instance, the volume of 40,000 cu. ft. of gas measured at 60° F and 30 in. Hg, when heated to 1800° F and 30 in. Hg, is equal to:

$$40,000 \times \frac{460 + 1800}{460 + 60} = 174,000 \text{ cu. ft.}$$

and the volume of 40,000 cu. ft. of fuel gas measured at 60° F and 8 in. Hg gage pressure* is equal to 31,579 cu. ft. at standard conditions (60° F and 30 in. Hg), calculated as follows:

$$40,000 \times \frac{30}{30 + 8} = 31,579 \text{ cu. ft.}$$

The total pressure of any gas mixture is equal to the sum of the pressures of each component. Each component produces a partial pressure proportional to its concentration in the mixture. Therefore, in a mixture of water vapor and any other gas, each exerts a pressure proportional to its percentage by volume, and since water has a definite vapor pressure at various temperatures, as shown in Table 3—III, the concentration of water vapor in a gas is limited. When this limit of water vapor is reached, the gas is said to be **saturated**. Any drop in temperature or increase in pressure from that point will cause condensation of the water vapor; for instance, the water vapor in 1000 cu. ft. of saturated fuel gas measured at 60° F and 30 in. Hg is calculated as follows:

* Gage pressure equals pressure above atmospheric pressure. Absolute pressure equals gage pressure plus atmospheric pressure.

$$1000 \times \frac{0.522}{30} = 17.40 \text{ cu. ft.}$$

(0.522 is the partial pressure of water vapor in a saturated mixture at 60° F and 30 in. Hg—Table 3—III). The amount of water vapor which will condense at various temperatures may be ascertained by the use of Table 3—IV.

In many combustion calculations it is necessary to convert volumes to weights and vice versa. Such conversions may be made very conveniently by using the molar units, pound-mol. (abbreviated lb.-mol.) or gram-mol. (abbreviated gm.-mol.) A lb.-mol. (or gm.-mol.) is that quantity whose weight in pounds (or grams) is the same number as the number of the molecular weight. Thus, the molecular weight of oxygen is 32, so that a lb.-mol. of oxygen is 32 lbs. of oxygen (or a gm.-mol. of oxygen is 32 gm. of oxygen). In the English system, a lb.-mol. of any gas theoretically occupies 359 cu. ft. at 32° F and 29.92 in. Hg; or at 60° F and 30 in. Hg, the usual reference points for combustion problems in the steel industry, a lb.-mol. occupies 378.4 cu. ft. Actually some gases deviate slightly from this figure, but for gases and air at pressures normally encountered in combustion practices, the ideal figure is entirely satisfactory. The simplicity of using the lb.-mol. for weight or volume conversions is shown by the following example. The weight of a cubic foot of dry air is:

0.21 (% vol. of O_2 in air) $\times$
        32 (molecular wt. of oxygen) = 6.72
0.79 (% vol. of N_2 in air) $\times$
        28 (molecular wt. of nitrogen) = 22.12
Weight in lbs. of a lb.-mol. of air   = 28.84

$$\frac{28.84}{378.4} = 0.076 \text{ lbs. (wt. per cu. ft. of dry air}$$
at 60° F and 30 in. Hg)

The volume of a pound of dry air at 60° F and 30 in. Hg is:

$$\frac{378.4}{28.84} = 13.1 \text{ cu. ft.}$$

The relation of an ideal gas to its volume and pressure is expressed by the formula:

$$PV = NRT$$
where:
    R = gas constant
    P = absolute pressure
    V = volume
    N = number of mols.
    T = absolute temperature of gas

The numerical value of R in the above equation depends upon what units (English or metric) are used to measure P, V, N and T. Values of R for various combinations of units for measuring the other quantities are as follows:

T	P	V	N	R
° F abs.	lb. per sq. in.	cu. ft.	lb.-mol.	10.72
° F abs.	inches of Hg	cu. ft.	lb.-mol.	21.85
° C abs.	mm. of Hg	liters	gram-mol.	62.37
° C abs.	atmospheres	liters	gram-mol.	0.08206

The application of the foregoing formula is shown by the following example. Calculate the volume occupied by 100 lbs. of natural gas having a composition of 80 per cent CH_4, 18 per cent C_2H_6 and 2 per cent N_2 by volume at a gage pressure of 8 in. Hg and a temperature of 100° F.

$$P = 30 + 8 = 38 \text{ in. Hg absolute}$$

The weight in lbs. of a lb.-mol. of the gas is:

$$CH_4 = 0.80 \times 16 = 12.8$$
$$C_2H_6 = 0.18 \times 30 = 5.4$$
$$N_2 = 0.02 \times 28 = 0.56$$
$$\overline{18.76}$$

$$N = \frac{100}{18.76} = 5.33$$

$$T = 100 + 460 = 560$$

Substituting these values in the equation for a perfect gas ($PV = NRT$):

Table 3—III. Water Vapor Pressure*

Temp. (°F)	Pressure (In. Hg)
32	0.1803
35	0.2035
40	0.2478
45	0.3004
50	0.3626
55	0.4359
60	0.5218
65	0.6222
70	0.7392
75	0.8750
80	1.0321
85	1.2133
90	1.4215
95	1.6600
100	1.9325
105	2.2429
110	2.5955
115	2.9948
120	3.4458
125	3.9539
130	4.5251
135	5.1653
140	5.8812
145	6.680
150	7.569
155	8.557
160	9.652
165	10.863
170	12.199
175	13.671
180	15.291
185	17.068
190	19.014
195	21.144
200	23.467
205	26.003
210	28.755
212	29.922

*From "Gaseous Fuels," Second Edition (1954): published by American Gas Association, 420 Lexington Ave., New York.

$$38 \ V = 5.33 \times 21.85 \times 560$$
$$V = 1716 \text{ cu. ft.}$$

Combustion Calculations — The combustion of fuels is carried out by chemical reaction with air, and occasionally with air enriched with oxygen, or with pure oxygen. **Dry air** is a mixture of the following gas volumes under average conditions:

$$
\begin{aligned}
N_2 &= 78.03\% \\
O_2 &= 20.99\% \\
Argon &= 0.94\% \\
CO_2 &= 0.03\% \\
H_2 &= 0.01\% \\
\hline
Total &= 100.00\%
\end{aligned}
$$

In combustion calculations it is customary to include all elements in dry air (other than oxygen) with the nitrogen, as shown below:

	% by Volume	% by Weight
Oxygen	20.99	23.11
Nitrogen	79.01	76.89

Only the oxygen in the air reacts with a fuel in combustion processes. The nitrogen acts as a diluent which must be heated up by the heat of the reaction between the oxygen and the fuel. It, therefore, reduces the temperature of the flame and reduces the velocity of combustion.

Water vapor which is present in air also acts as a diluent. The amount of moisture present in air is generally stated in terms of humidity. Air is capable of being saturated with water vapor the same as other gases as described under "Gas Laws." Air which is saturated completely with water vapor has a humidity of 100 per cent; if only 50 per cent saturated, it has a humidity of 50 per cent (Table 3—IV).

The principal **combustion reactions** are:

$$
\begin{aligned}
C + O_2 &= CO_2 \\
2CO + O_2 &= 2CO_2 \\
2H_2 + O_2 &= 2H_2O \\
CH_4 + 2O_2 &= CO_2 + 2H_2O \\
2C_2H_6 + 7O_2 &= 4CO_2 + 6H_2O \\
C_2H_4 + 3O_2 &= 2CO_2 + 2H_2O \\
2C_3H_6 + 9O_2 &= 6CO_2 + 6H_2O \\
2C_2H_2 + 5O_2 &= 4CO_2 + 2H_2O \\
2C_6H_6 + 15O_2 &= 12CO_2 + 6H_2O \\
2H_2S + 3O_2 &= 2SO_2 + 2H_2O
\end{aligned}
$$

The amount of oxygen required and consequently air, together with the amount of the resultant products of combustion, may be calculated by the use of molecular weights and the proper chemical equation. For instance, it will require $(32 \div 12)$ or 2.667 lbs. of O_2 to burn 1 lb. of C, and since dry air contains 23.11 per cent by weight of O_2, the weight of dry air required to burn one pound of carbon will be $(2.667 \div 0.2311)$ or 11.540 lbs. The product of combustion, CO_2, will amount to $[(12 + 32) \div 12] = 3.667$ lbs.

Combustion calculations using gases are more conveniently made in volumetric units. For instance, to burn a cubic foot of CO completely to CO_2 requires ½ cu. ft. of O_2 in accordance with the molecular relationship in the equation. The dry air required would be $(0.5 \div 0.209)$ or 2.382 cu. ft. For burning a cubic foot of methane, CH_4, to CO_2 and H_2O, the air required would be $(2.0 \div 0.209)$ or 9.528 cu. ft.

Table 3—IV. [1] **Properties of Air at Atmospheric Pressure**

Temp.	Volume of One Pound (Cu. Ft.)	Weight of One Cu. Ft.	Grains* of Water Vapor per Pound of Dry Air for Percentage Humidities of			
			25%	50%	75%	100%
32	12.36	0.0809	6.6	13.2	19.9	26.5
40	12.56	0.0796	9.1	18.2	27.3	36.4
45	12.69	0.0788	11.0	22.1	33.2	44.2
50	12.81	0.0781	13.4	26.7	40.1	53.5
55	12.94	0.0773	16.1	32.2	48.3	64.4
60	13.063	0.07655	19.3	38.6	58.0	77.3
65	13.19	0.0758	23.1	46.3	69.5	92.6
70	13.31	0.0752	27.6	55.2	82.9	110.5
75	13.44	0.0745	32.8	65.7	98.6	131.4
80	13.57	0.0737	38.9	77.9	116.9	155.8
85	13.69	0.0730	46.1	92.2	138.3	184.4
90	13.82	0.0724	54.4	108.8	163.2	217.6
95	13.94	0.0718	64.1	128.1	192.2	256.3
100	14.07	0.0711	75.3	150.6	226.0	301.3
105	14.19	0.0705	88.5	177.	265.	354.
110	14.32	0.0699	104.	208.	311.	415.
115	14.44	0.0693	121.	243.	365.	486.
120	14.57	0.0686	142.	285.	427.	569.
125	14.70	0.0680	167.	383.	500.	667.
150	15.32	0.0653	371.	742.	1113.	1485.
175	15.95	0.0627	927.	1851.	2777.	3703.
200	16.58	0.0603	4016.	8033.	12049.	16065.

[1] From "Combustion"—American Gas Association.   *7000 grains = 1 lb.

Table 3—V. Combustion Data* for Blast-Furnace, Coke-Oven and Natural Gas

BLAST FURNACE GAS (ALL VOLUMES AT 60°F AND 30" Hg).

Gas Comp.	% by Volume	Air Req'd Per Cu. Ft.	Air Req'd Each Component	No Excess Air CO₂	H₂O	SO₂	O₂	N₂	10% Excess Air CO₂	H₂O	SO₂	O₂	N₂	50% Excess Air CO₂	H₂O	SO₂	O₂	N₂
CO₂	11.5			.115					.115			.014†	.054†	.115			.071†	.269†
N₂	60.0							.600					.600					.600
CO	27.5	2.382	.655	.275				.517	.275				.517	.275				.517
H₂	1.0	2.382	.0238		.010			.019		.010			.019		.010			.019
Total	100.0		.679	.390	.010			1.136	.390	.010		.014	1.190	.390	.010		.071	1.405

COKE OVEN GAS (ALL VOLUMES AT 60°F AND 30" Hg).

Gas Comp.	% by Volume	Air Req'd Per Cu. Ft.	Air Req'd Each Component	No Excess Air CO₂	H₂O	SO₂	O₂	N₂	10% Excess Air CO₂	H₂O	SO₂	O₂	N₂	50% Excess Air CO₂	H₂O	SO₂	O₂	N₂
CO₂	1.4			.014					.014			.101†	.382†	.014			.507†	1.909†
H₂S	0.6	7.146	.0429		.006	.006		.034		.006	.006		.034		.006	.006		.034
O₂	0.4		−.0190					−.015					−.015					−.015
N₂	4.3							.043					.043					.043
CO	5.6	2.382	.1334	.056				.105	.056				.105	.056				.105
H₂	55.4	2.382	1.3196		.554			1.042		.554			1.042		.554			1.042
CH₄	28.4	9.528	2.7060	.284	.568			2.138	.284	.568			2.138	.284	.568			2.138
C₂H₄	2.5	14.293	.3573	.050	.050			.282	.050	.050			.282	.050	.050			.282
C₂H₆	0.8	16.675	.1334	.016	.024			.105	.016	.024			.105	.016	.024			.105
Ill.	0.6	26.208	.1572	.018	.018			.124	.018	.018			.124	.018	.018			.124
Total	100.0		4.831	.438	1.220	.006		3.858	.438	1.220	.006	.101	4.240	.438	1.220	.006	.507	5.767

NATURAL GAS (ALL VOLUMES AT 60°F AND 30" Hg).

Gas Comp.	% by Volume	Air Req'd Per Cu. Ft.	Air Req'd Each Component	No Excess Air CO₂	H₂O	SO₂	O₂	N₂	10% Excess Air CO₂	H₂O	SO₂	O₂	N₂	50% Excess Air CO₂	H₂O	SO₂	O₂	N₂
CO₂	0.08			.001					.001			.223†	.838†	.001			1.114†	4.191†
O₂	0.17		−.002					−.002					−.002					−.002
N₂	1.02							.010					.010					.010
CH₄	81.88	9.528	7.802	.819	1.638			6.164	.819	1.638			6.164	.819	1.638			6.164
C₂H₆	'16.85	16.675	2.810	.337	.506			2.220	.337	.506			2.220	.337	.506			2.220
Total	100.00		10.610	1.157	2.144			8.392	1.157	2.144		.223	9.230	1.157	2.144		1.114	12.583

*Dry Basis.   †From excess air.

Combustion calculations are necessary to determine the air requirements and the products of combustion for burning fuels of various compositions. The per cent of air used above theoretical requirements is called per cent **excess air;** the per cent below, the per cent **deficiency of air.** Typical combustion data on a dry basis for burning gaseous fuels of the compositions stated are shown in Table 3—V. In making calculations to include the water vapor which may be present in a saturated or partially saturated gas and in air, the same general method may be used by adding water vapor to the fuel-gas composition, and by adding the volume of water vapor which is introduced through air in the products of combustion column, headed H_2O.

In order to maintain combustion, a fuel must, after it has been ignited, be able to impart sufficient heat to its air-gas mixture so that it will not drop below **ignition temperature,** the minimum point of self-ignition. Too lean or too rich a mixture of a fuel with air is unable to support combustion. An **upper and lower limit of flammability** exists for all gases. The limits of flammability, as well as ignition temperatures, for a number of gases are shown in Table 3—VI.

In the design of burners or in the selection of fuel for a specific purpose, consideration of **velocity of combustion** is of major importance. Since gaseous fuels are composed usually of a mixture of combustible gases, a knowledge of the relative combustion speed of each elementary gas will provide means for evaluating this factor in any gaseous mixture. The **velocity of combustion,** or **rate of flame propagation,** of a given fuel, is influenced by three factors: (1) degree to which the air and gas are mixed, (2) temperature of the air-gas mixture, and (3) contact of the air-gas mixture with a hot surface (catalyst). By intimately mixing air and gas, combustion may be accelerated and a shorter, sharper flame developed. In the case of a gas containing large amounts of hydrogen, intimate mixing will provide a combustion reaction of ex-

plosive velocity relative to that of a gas containing large amounts of methane. Inert gases, such as carbon dioxide and nitrogen, present in fuel gases or in a gas-air mixture, reduce combustion velocity. The proportion of nitrogen in a fuel gas-air mixture may be reduced by oxygen enrichment of air for combustion, and combustion speed may, by this means, be accelerated many fold. Such measures also will raise the flame temperature. The use of preheated air for combustion also accelerates combustion of gases. In order to burn large volumes of fuel in a small space, a mixture of air and gas is sometimes directed against a hot, incandescent surface. By increasing the velocity of combustion, higher temperatures are localized close to the burner point. This condition is desirable for some processes and highly undesirable for others. For instance, the scarfing process requires a highly intensive localized heat, while the heating of steel for rolling requires a soft, even distribution of heat over the full surface of the pieces being heated. In order to reduce combustion speed of a gaseous fuel, the air and gas streams may be stratified to produce slow mixing. Such a method creates a **diffusion flame,** a long flame of relatively uniform temperature.

Theoretical flame temperature is the temperature which would be attained by the products of combustion if the combustion of a fuel took place instantaneously, and there were no loss of heat to the surroundings. Such a condition never exists, but theoretical flame temperature represents another measure for comparing fuels. Fuels which develop a high flame temperature by combustion are more capable of producing a higher thermal efficiency in practice than those which develop low flame temperatures. The efficiency of heat utilization is the relation of the total heat absorbed by a substance to the heat supplied. Since the temperature level at which waste gases leave a furnace is usually fixed within a relatively narrow range, the higher the flame temperature the higher the potentiality for heat absorption by the sub-

**Table 3—VI. Limits of Flammability and Ignition
Temperature for Simple Gases and Compounds**

Simple Gases and Compounds	Limits of Flammability*		Ignition Temperature** (°F)
	Lower % by Volume Gas in Air	Upper % by Volume Gas in Air	
H_2	4.0	75	1065
CO	12.5	74	1202–1211
CH_4	5.3	14	1200
C_2H_6	3.0	12.5	882–1000
C_3H_8	2.2	9.5	898–986
C_2H_4	3.1	32	1022
C_3H_6	2.4	10.3	986
C_4H_8	2.0	9.6	829
C_2H_2	2.5	81	581
C_6H_6	1.4	7.1	1078
C_7H_8	1.4	6.7	1026

* From U.S. Bureau of Mines Bulletin 503 (1952).
** From "Gaseous Fuels," Second Edition (1954): published by American Gas Association, 420 Lexington Ave., New York.

stance to be heated. The theoretical flame temperature of a fuel may be calculated by balancing the sum of the net heating value of a given quantity of fuel and the sensible heat of the air-gas mixture against the heat content of the products of combustion. Theoretical flame temperature so calculated should be corrected for **dissociation** of CO_2 and H_2O at temperatures in excess of 3000° F. The theoretical flame temperatures for a number of important gaseous fuels are given in Table 3—XVI. The reader is referred to "Gaseous Fuels" published by the American Gas Association and the books by Lewis and von Elbe and by Griswold and others listed in the bibliography at the end of this chapter for a full explanation of the calculation of theoretical flame temperatures and the dissociation of gases at elevated temperatures.

There are a number of factors which determine the character, size and shape of a gas flame. Gases burned at very high combustion velocity will produce very little or no luminosity regardless of the kind of gas. The velocity and volume with which the air-gas stream leaves a burner or furnace port, the fuel-air ratio, and the amount of non-combustible material in the fuel will influence the length and shape of a flame. The kind of gas to be burned has a very great effect upon the character of the flame. Carbon monoxide and hydrogen burn with an invisible to a clear blue flame, while the hydrocarbon gases, methane, ethane, etc., are capable of developing highly luminous flames. The principal reason that these gases burn with a luminous flame is due to the thermal breakdown of the hydrocarbons into carbon and hydrogen, and under combustion conditions which permit this, the carbon particles are heated to incandescence thereby giving the flame its luminous appearance. The luminosity of a flame may be decreased or increased by varying the supply of air. A deficiency of air below theoretical requirements will increase luminosity and it also usually will lengthen the flame. An excess of air will decrease luminosity and shorten the flame with most burners or furnace ports. Increasing the temperature of preheat of the air for combustion will reduce luminosity, as is also the case when water vapor (steam), which may be introduced with the gas, air, or for atomization of liquid fuels, is increased. A luminous flame has a number of desirable qualities, the principal one being its greater ability to transfer heat by radiation from a fixed temperature level. However, it should be noted that a luminous flame is obtained usually at a lower temperature level than when the same fuel is burned with a lower degree of luminosity.

HEAT FLOW

Heat flow is caused by a difference in temperature, and heat is transmitted in three ways, namely, by conduction, by convection, and by radiation.

Conduction is the transmission of heat through a solid body without visible motion of the body, as through a steel bar. The amount of heat transferred through a homogeneous solid by conduction is expressed by the formula:

$$Q = \frac{KA \triangle t}{L}$$

where Q = Btu transmitted per hour
K = conductivity, in Btu per hour per sq. ft. per °F per inch of thickness
A = area in sq. ft.
$\triangle t$ = temperature difference in °F
L = length of heat transfer path in inches.

The flow of heat through a non-homogeneous solid body by conduction is expressed by the formula:

$$Q = \frac{\triangle t}{\dfrac{L_1}{K_1 A_1} + \dfrac{L_2}{K_2 A_2} + \dfrac{L_n}{K_n A_n}}$$

where:

L_1, L_2 and L_n = the respective length of heat transfer path through the various resistances.

K_1, K_2 and K_n = the corresponding conductivity factors of the various resistances expressed in Btu per hr. per sq. ft. per °F per inch of thickness.

A_1, A_2 and A_n = the corresponding areas expressed in square feet.

Convection—When heat is transmitted by the mechanical motion of gas or water currents in contact with a solid, or by gas currents in contact with a liquid, the transfer of heat is by **convection**. In the transfer of heat by convection, it is necessary to conduct heat through the relatively stationary film between the moving and stationary bodies. This film becomes thinner as the velocity of the currents parallel to its surface increases. The transfer of heat by convection is expressed by the formula:

$$Q = a_c A \triangle t$$

where:

Q = Btu transmitted per hour

a_c = film coefficient (Btu per sq. ft. per °F per hr.) dependent upon the velocity, specific gravity and viscosity of the moving fluid, and the conductivity of the film.

A = area in sq. ft.

$\triangle t$ = temperature difference

Radiation refers to the transmission of heat through space without the help or intervention of matter. This is the means by which the heat of the sun reaches the earth, and by which much of the heat of combustion of fuels is utilized in high-temperature processes in the steel industry. When radiant energy strikes any body a certain proportion of the total is reflected, while that absorbed is reconverted to heat energy. A perfectly **black body** is one that will not reflect radiations falling upon it but absorbs them all. The **coefficient of reflectivity** of a body receiving radiation is equal to one minus its **black body coefficient**. **Emissivity** refers to the rate at which a body radiates heat, and this rate depends upon the temperature of the body and the nature of its surface. **Kirchoff's Law** shows that the **absorptivity** and **emissivity** of a given surface are numerically equal at the same temperature. The **Stefan-Boltzmann Law** states that the total energy of a black body is proportional to the fourth power of its absolute temperature. The net effect of heat transfer between two bodies is shown by the equation:

$$Q = 0.174 \, EA\left[\left(\frac{T_1}{100}\right)^4 - \left(\frac{T_2}{100}\right)^4\right]$$

where:

Q = Btu transmitted per hour
0.174 = radiation factor for a perfect black body
E = emissivity or "black body" factor
A = sq. ft. of surface
T_1 = temperature of body giving off heat, in °F absolute
T_2 = temperature of body receiving heat, in °F absolute

The emissivity factors for various materials at specified temperatures are shown in Table 3—VII.

In the generation of heat from fuels, the character of the flame and its proximity to the receptor of heat is particularly significant in the transfer of heat by radiation. The amount of heat transferred from a flame varies widely and in proportion to its degree of luminosity. The transfer of heat by radiation varies inversely with the square of the distance between the transmitter and receptor of radiant energy. For that reason, flames should be kept close to the substance to be heated where high heat transfer rates are desirable.

Table 3—VII. Emissivity Factors (A perfect absorber or radiator = 1)

Material	E
Polished aluminum at 445° F	0.039
Polished aluminum at 1075° F	0.056
Polished brass at 570° F	0.031
Polished nickel at 715° F	0.086
Polished nickel plated steel at 72° F	0.052
Bright tinned steel plate at 75° F	0.071
Polished mild steel	0.288
Cast iron—machined—at 72° F	0.437
Cast iron—liquid—at 2425° F	0.282
Cast iron—rough oxidized	0.97
Mild steel—dull oxidized—from 79° to 672° F	0.96
Firebrick glazed through use at 1830° F	0.75
Silica brick (rough)	0.81

SECTION 2

SOLID FUELS AND THEIR UTILIZATION

The solid fuels have played a significant role in the evolution of our modern, industrial civilization. Coal in particular has been of far-reaching importance in that it has provided the prodigious amount of energy essential to the development of the iron and steel industries. Vast quantities of this energy source remain to be exploited but the rate of utilization far exceeds the rate at which coal is being formed. It follows that the efficient use of the remaining supply is desirable. Toward this end, modern coal research is directed.

The earliest-formed coals thus far encountered occur in the Silurian strata of Bohemia. It is not until Lower Carboniferous time (see Table 3—VIII), however, that the source materials of coal began to accumulate in significant quantities. Every continent, including Antarctica, contains some coal and no system of rocks younger than the Silurian is devoid of this important substance. In North America major concentrations of source materials were accumulated during the Carboniferous, Cretaceous and Tertiary periods. A similar statement can be made for Europe but, in contrast, some of the most important Asiatic coals occur in Triassic and Jurassic rocks.

Coal Resources—The known coal deposits in the United States are greater than those of any other country. Based on U. S. Geological Survey estimates, the reserves of all grades of coal were about 1,900 billion net tons in 1953. This would be enough to supply requirements for a long period in the future if all present coal reserves were available economically and of acceptable quality. A considerable quantity of the reserves of better quality coking coal have been utilized in the past and it is apparent that in the future it will be necessary to use coals requiring efficient extraction, cleaning, and other processing to assure proper utilization.

For obvious reasons, the steel industry has been striving to use coals which would produce metallurgical coke of optimum quality with a minimum of processing. Concentrations of coals of this class are found chiefly in the Appalachian area, although isolated deposits also exist in some Central and Western states. The preponderance of total coal reserve in the United States is in the form of lower-rank coals in the Great Plains, the Rocky Mountains, the Pacific Coast states and the Gulf region (see Figure 3—1). The manner in which this material can be used most effectively remains to be determined.

Origin and Composition of Coal—Coal is known to be a complex mixture of plant substances which have been altered in varying degrees by physical and chemical processes. Ordinarily, plant material, upon death, fails to accumulate because micro-organisms induce complete decomposition. Under certain circumstances, notably those associated with forested freshwater swamps, the activities of bacteria and fungi are inhibited by antibiotic solutions which are common in this type of environment. As a result the rate of accumulation exceeds that of decomposition and dispersion. Under such conditions a brown fibrous deposit known as peat is formed. Peat is the first step in the formation of coal.

Peat deposits formed millions of years ago subsequently were submerged through vertical movements

Table 3—VIII. Geologic Time Divisions.

ERAS	PERIODS		EPOCHS	MILLIONS OF YEARS
Cenozoic	Quaternary		Recent	70
			Pleistocene	
	Tertiary		Pliocene	
			Miocene	
			Oligocene	
			Eocene	
Mesozoic	Cretaceous			200
	Jurassic			
	Triassic			
Paleozoic	Permian			500
	Carboniferous	Pennsylvanian (Upper Carboniferous)		
		Mississippian (Lower Carboniferous)		
	Devonian			
	Silurian			
	Ordovician			
	Cambrian			
Proterozoic	Algonkian	Keweenawan		3,000 +
		Huronian		
Archeozoic	Archean	Timiskamian		
		Keewatin		

of the earth's crust, in which position they became covered by deposits of sedimentary rocks. Later movements of the earth's crust raised many of these deposits to various heights above sea level. In the meantime, the peat had been changed, through agencies of biological action, pressure, and heat, into coal. The better ranks of coal in this country were formed during the Carboniferous period, the geologic period when conditions were most favorable for plant accumulation and decomposition. Included in the present deposits that originated in that period are the coal fields of the Appalachian and Central states.

The rate at which peat forms depends upon the rapidity of plant growth and the manner in which tissue increment is related to the rate of decomposition. It has been estimated that approximately one century is required to form a deposit of mature, compacted peat one foot in thickness. Certain studies of volatile matter relationships suggest that a three-foot-thick deposit of mature peat is required to produce a one-foot-thick layer of bituminous coal. These and other data indicate that a coal seam which is several feet thick may require a time span of thousands of years for its formation. If, in the course of time, the peat is subjected to the necessary conditions it becomes modified to **brown coal** and, when adequately consolidated, to **lignite**. From the lignitic stage, the material passes progressively through the **sub-bituminous, bituminous, semi-anthracite** and **anthracite** stages with a gradual change in the composition of the individual components of the complex mass. The elementary compositions of coal shown in Table 3—IX illustrate the gradual concentration of carbon and loss of oxygen in the various stages of coal formation.

Peat varies in appearance from a light, brown-colored, fibrous material to a very black and dense, muck-like sediment. Lignite is usually brown in color and commonly shows a woody texture. It contains a large amount of moisture and usually disintegrates or

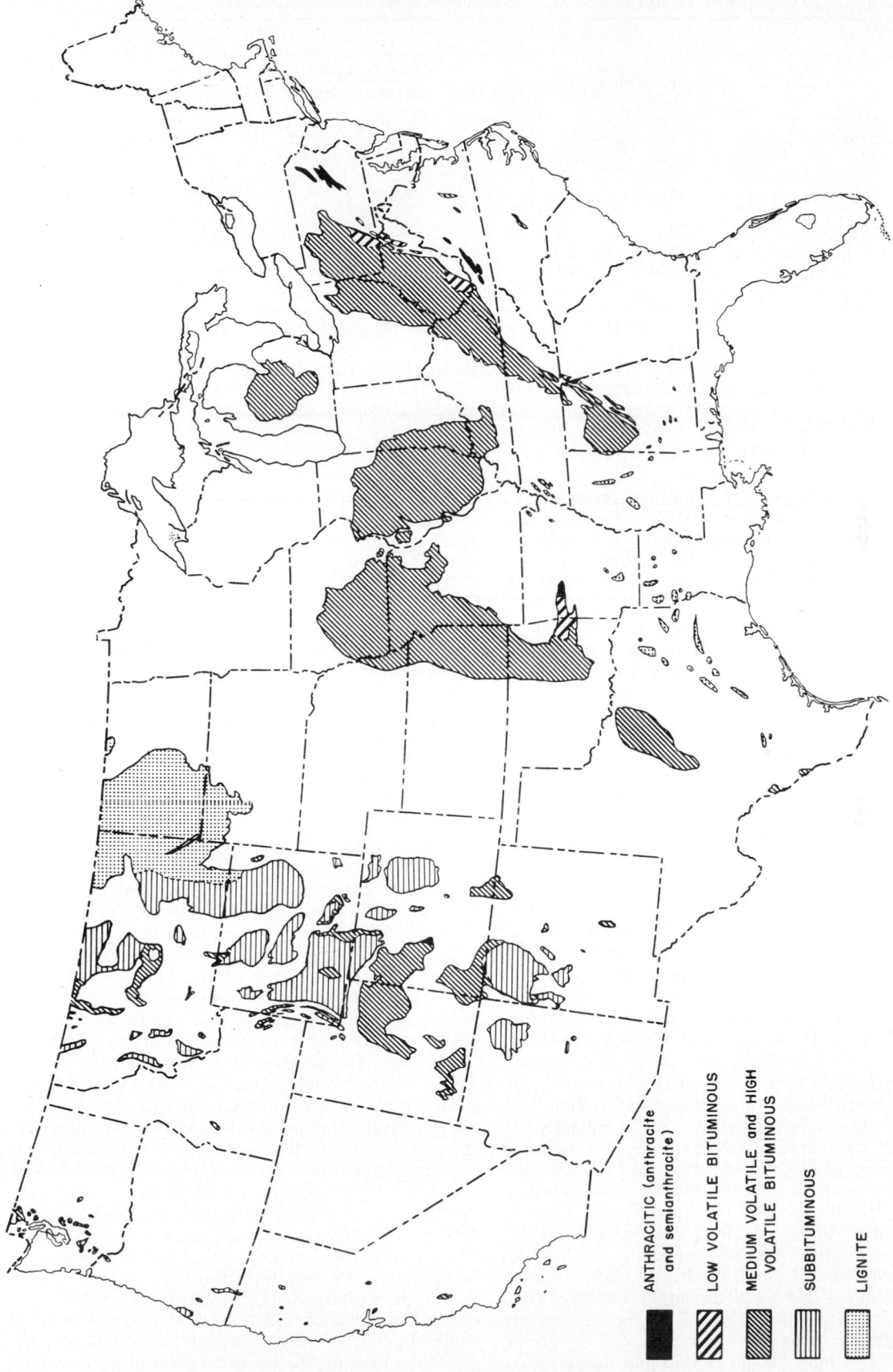

ANTHRACITIC (anthracite and semianthracite)

LOW VOLATILE BITUMINOUS

MEDIUM VOLATILE and HIGH VOLATILE BITUMINOUS

SUBBITUMINOUS

LIGNITE

FIG. 3—1. This map indicates the general location and extent of the important coal fields of the United States. (*Map prepared by United States Geological Survey.*)

Table 3—IX. Typical Elementary Compositions of Raw Solid Fuels (Per Cent)

	Moisture Content (Sample Taken at Tipple)	Elementary Composition (Dry Basis)					
		Carbon	Hydrogen	Oxygen	Nitrogen	Sulphur	Ash
Peat[1]	91.0	58.0	5.7	35.0	1.2	[3]	[3]
Lignite[2] .... (North Dakota)	40.0	65.6	4.5	20.2	1.1	1.0	7.6
Sub-Bituminous[2] ... (Wyoming)	17.1	73.8	5.1	15.2	1.6	1.0	3.3
Bituminous[2] .... (Low-volatile B)	2.5	78.3	4.1	1.7	1.3	3.2	11.4
Anthracite[1] .... (Northeastern Pa.)	5.5[4]	85.6	2.0	1.4	0.8	0.6	9.6

[1]Johnson, A. J. and Auth, G. H., Fuels and Combustion Handbook. McGraw-Hill Book Co., Inc., New York (1951).

[2]Aresco, S. J. and Haller, C. P., Analyses of Tipple and Delivered Samples of Coal. Bureau of Mines Report of Investigation 4972, October, 1953.

[3]Composition of peat reported on ash-, sulphur-, and moisture-free basis.

[4]Moisture content of anthracite coal reported as average of 4 to 7 per cent.

slacks into small pieces as it dries on exposure to air. Sub-bituminous coal varies in color from very dark brown to black and fractures irregularly. Bituminous coal is black in color and usually exhibits a banded structure due to the alternate dull and vitreous layers of varying thickness. Coals of the high-volatile bituminous rank commonly burn with a smoky, yellow flame. Anthracite coal is black, hard and brittle and has a high luster. It ignites less easily than bituminous coal and burns with a short bluish-yellow flame producing little smoke. The characteristics of semi-anthracite coal are intermediate between those of bituminous coal and anthracite.

All of the solid natural fuels contain both combustible and non-combustible materials. The combustible material is composed mainly of carbon, hydrogen and, to a lesser extent, sulphur. The non-combustible constituents are water, nitrogen and oxygen, and a variety of mineral materials usually referred to as **ash.**

The bituminous coals are of greatest interest in view of the fact that essentially all coking coals fall in this category. The lustrous black bands which are conspicuous in a lump of bituminous coal are generally referred to as **vitrain** although some American coal petrographers employ the term **anthraxylon** in preference. Following U. S. Bureau of Mines terminology, the anthraxylon is derived from woody plant tissues and is surrounded by a dull **ground mass** made up of **translucent attritus, opaque attritus** and **fusain.** The attrital portion is composed of finely comminuted fragments of altered plant materials. Fusain is a friable, charcoal-like substance derived from woody tissues and is a term used universally without modification.

In addition to the readily recognizable bands of vitrain and fusain, European and Asiatic coal investigators have found it useful to identify silky, minutely striated layers within a coal as **clarain.** Layers of dull, compact coal are called **durain.** Thus, coal seams can be thought of as being composed, usually, of various mixtures of **vitrain, fusain, clarain** and **durain,** each

occurring in the form of layers which are visually observable. Coals made up largely of vitrain and clarain are spoken of as **bright coals** whereas coals containing a high percentage of durain are called **splint coals.** Bright coals are generally better coking coals than splint coals, vitrain apparently playing an important part in the carbonization process. Fusain will not coke, but in small percentages it may actually increase coke strength. If present in concentrations greater than 18 to 20 per cent it begins to exert a deleterious effect. The fixed carbon content is higher and the volatile matter content is lower in fusain than in the other "banded ingredients."

Microscopic study has shown the banded components to be composed of identifiable plant entities called **phyterals,** but of greater significance is the fact that the vitrain, fusain, clarain and durain are made up of numerous components or **macerals** which can be defined by their physical and chemical properties. Durain, for example, may include several macerals (vitrinite, semi-fusinite, micrinite, cutinite, etc.) which are easily distinguished by their differing optical properties. It is probable that additional information regarding the nature and variability of these individual coal components will contribute materially to the effective and efficient utilization of all types of coal.

Chemical Composition and Coal Classification— There are two methods commonly employed to determine the chemical composition of coal; namely **ultimate analysis** and **proximate analysis.** An ultimate analysis determines the quantities of carbon, hydrogen, oxygen, nitrogen, sulphur, chlorine, phosphorus and ash in dry coal; a proximate analysis determines the fixed carbon, volatile matter, moisture and ash contents. The proximate analysis is used most commonly, since it furnishes most of the data required for normal commercial evaluations.

In order to provide a measure of the distillation products obtainable from coal used in coal-chemical and hydrogenation plants, another method of analysis called the **tube distillation assay test** (also called **pro-**

Table 3—X. Comparison of Results of Common Methods for Analyzing a High-Volatile Bituminous Coal

Proximate Analysis Dry Basis (%)		Progressive Distillation Dry Basis (%)		Ultimate Analysis Dry Basis (%)	
Ash...............	7.16	Coke[1]............	70.36	Ash...............	7.16
Fixed Carbon					
(by diff.)...........	59.98	Tar.................	5.02	C.................	79.41
Volatile Matter........	32.86				
Total.............	100.00	Total NH₃..........	0.32	H.................	5.14
		Water.............	4.76	N.................	1.46
Moisture...........	5.67	Volatile Sulphur......	0.31	O.................	5.81
		Light Oil..........	0.35	S.................	1.02
		Gas...............	18.88	P.................	0.005

[1]This comprises 63.20 per cent total carbonaceous residue containing a small amount (1.0 to 1.5 per cent) of non-volatilized volatile matter, and 7.16 per cent ash.

gressive distillation) is used. Table 3—X compares the composition of a bituminous coal as derived by the three methods mentioned.

Using data provided by chemical, physical or petrographic analyses, coals are classified according to **grade, rank** and **type.** The grade is determined by the amount, nature and fusibility of the ash and by the sulphur content. Classification according to rank is based upon the degree of metamorphism within the coal series from the level of lignite to that of anthracite coal. The American Society for Testing Materials ranks coals according to their fixed-carbon content on a dry basis, and the lower rank coals according to Btu content on a moist basis. The classification of coals by rank adopted by the American Society for Testing Materials (A.S.T.M. Specification D388-38), is shown in Table 3—XI.

In the United States, coals are also classified into **types** and such terms as **bright, semi-splint, splint, cannel** and **boghead coal** are applied. The data required are obtained from microscopic studies. The United States Bureau of Mines standards indicate that bright coal must have less than 20 per cent opaque matter, semi-splint must have between 20 and 30 per cent, and splint coal must be made up of more than 30 per cent of this ingredient. Cannel and boghead coals are **non-banded** and are characterized by a small percentage of anthraxylon (vitrain). Boghead possesses a high percentage of volatile oils and gases, and contains an abundance of algal material. Cannel, or candle coal, is so named because it can be ignited with a match or a candle flame and it burns with unusual brilliance. Cannel coal is non-coking, often contains large quantities of spore and pollen materials, and like boghead, has a high content of volatile oil and gas.

MINING OF COAL

It is found that seams of coals vary in thickness throughout the world from a fraction of an inch to over 250 feet. In this country the thickest seams are found in the sub-bituminous coals of the West, one of which approaches 100 feet. In the East, the Mammoth bed in the anthracite fields of Pennsylvania attains a thickness of 50 to 60 feet but is found to be quite variable when traced laterally. The Pittsburgh seam at the base of the Monongahela series in the Appalachian area is noteworthy because of its exceptionally uniform thickness (approximately 7 feet) over thousands of square miles. Figure 3—2 shows the western portion of Pennsylvania in such a manner as to make clear the areal extent as well as the sub-surface relations of the coal-bearing formations of this region. Data are provided as to thickness of seams and distance between coals.

Coal seams may dip gently as shown in Figure 3—2, or they may be horizontal, or they may exist almost vertical with respect to the Earth's surface. Mining problems are often complicated by the fact that seams seldom remain in the same plane throughout their extent. Under present conditions, a coal bed must be at least 30 inches to 36 inches thick to be profitable for mining. Figure 3—2 shows, also, that coal seams vary in their distance from the Earth's surface. U. S. Geological Survey estimates of coal reserves do not include coal seams deeper than 3,000 feet from the surface, although in Great Britain and Europe coal seams at greater depth at present are being mined economically.

The mining of coal is performed by either one of two methods: (1) **Open work** or **stripping,** also called **contour mining,** or (2) **underground** or **closed work.** The first method involves removing the formation (over-burden) above the seam by stripping with scrapers, bull-dozers, or mechanically operated shovels, followed by removing the exposed coal. Stripping is applied to coal seams which are relatively close to the surface, particularly to thick seams underlying overburden not over 75 feet deep, although the development of larger equipment and improved techniques in recent years has justified removal of thicker layers of overburden than this. Auger mining is being used extensively to recover coal where the overburden is too great for strip-mining practices to be employed. A large-diameter tube or drill with cutting bits on its end is propelled into the exposed edge of a coal seam. As the auger progresses into and along the seam, the broken coal is conveyed away from the face through the tube to the outside for transport away from the auger. Production by strip mining has increased greatly since World War I due to reduced labor and

Table 3—XI. Classification of Coals by Rank[a]*

Legend: F.C.—Fixed Carbon. V.M.—Volatile Matter. Btu.—British thermal units

Class	Group	Limits of Fixed Carbon or Btu. Mineral-Matter-Free Basis[g]	Requisite Physical Properties
I. Anthracitic	1. Meta-anthracite	Dry F.C., 98 per cent or more (Dry V.M., 2 per cent or less)	
	2. Anthracite	Dry F.C., 92 per cent or more and less than 98 per cent (Dry V.M., 8 per cent or less and more than 2 per cent)	
	3. Semianthracite	Dry F.C., 86 per cent or more and less than 92 per cent (Dry V.M., 14 per cent or less and more than 8 per cent)	Nonagglomerating[b]
II. Bituminous[d]	1. Low volatile bituminous coal	Dry F.C., 78 per cent or more and less than 86 per cent (Dry V.M., 22 per cent or less and more than 14 per cent)	
	2. Medium volatile bituminous coal	Dry F.C., 69 per cent or more and less than 78 per cent (Dry V.M., 31 per cent or less and more than 22 per cent)	
	3. High volatile A bituminous coal	Dry F.C., less than 69 per cent (Dry V.M., more than 31 per cent); and moist[e] Btu., 14,000[e] or more	
	4. High volatile B bituminous coal	Moist[e] Btu., 13,000 or more and less than 14,000[e]	
	5. High volatile C bituminous coal	Moist Btu., 11,000 or more and less than 13,000[e]	Either agglomerating or nonweathering[f]
III. Subbituminous	1. Subbituminous A coal	Moist Btu., 11,000 or more and less than 13,000[e]	Both weathering and non-agglomerating
	2. Subbituminous B coal	Moist Btu., 9500 or more and less than 11,000[e]	
	3. Subbituminous C coal	Moist Btu., 8300 or more and less than 9500[e]	
IV. Lignitic	1. Lignite	Moist Btu., less than 8300	Consolidated
	2. Brown coal	Moist Btu., less than 8300	Unconsolidated

[a] This classification does not include a few coals which have unusual physical and chemical properties and which come within the limits of fixed carbon or Btu. of the high-volatile bituminous and subbituminous ranks. All of these coals either contain less than 48 per cent dry, mineral-matter-free fixed carbon or have more than 15,500 moist, mineral-matter-free Btu.

[b] If agglomerating, classify in low-volatile group of the bituminous class.

[c] Moist Btu. refers to coal containing its natural bed moisture but not including visible water on the surface of the coal.

[d] It is recognized that there may be noncaking varieties in each group of the bituminous class.

[e] Coals having 69 per cent or more fixed carbon on the dry, mineral-matter-free basis shall be classified according to fixed carbon, regardless of Btu.

[f] There are three varieties of coal in the high-volatile C bituminous coal group, namely, Variety 1, agglomerating and nonweathering; Variety 2, agglomerating and weathering; Variety 3, nonagglomerating and nonweathering.

Computation of Mineral-Matter-Free Analyses

[g] Mineral matter was taken as 1.1 times the ash. The values for fixed carbon and Btu. as given in the charts were calculated as follows:

$$\text{Moist fixed carbon} \times \frac{100}{100 - (\text{moisture} + 1.1 \text{ Ash})} = \text{dry, mineral-matter-free fixed carbon}$$

$$\text{Moist Btu.} \times \frac{100}{100 - 1.1 \text{ Ash}} = \text{moist, mineral-matter-free Btu.}$$

Moist, as used in the formulas, refers to the coal containing its natural bed moisture but not including visible moisture on the surface of the coal. For more accurate formulas that apply corrections for the sulphur in the coal, reference should be made to those for fixed carbon and Btu. as given in A.S.T.M. Standards on Coal and Coke.

* From "ASTM Standards 1958," Part 8, Page 1078, with addition of method for computation of mineral-matter-free analyses.

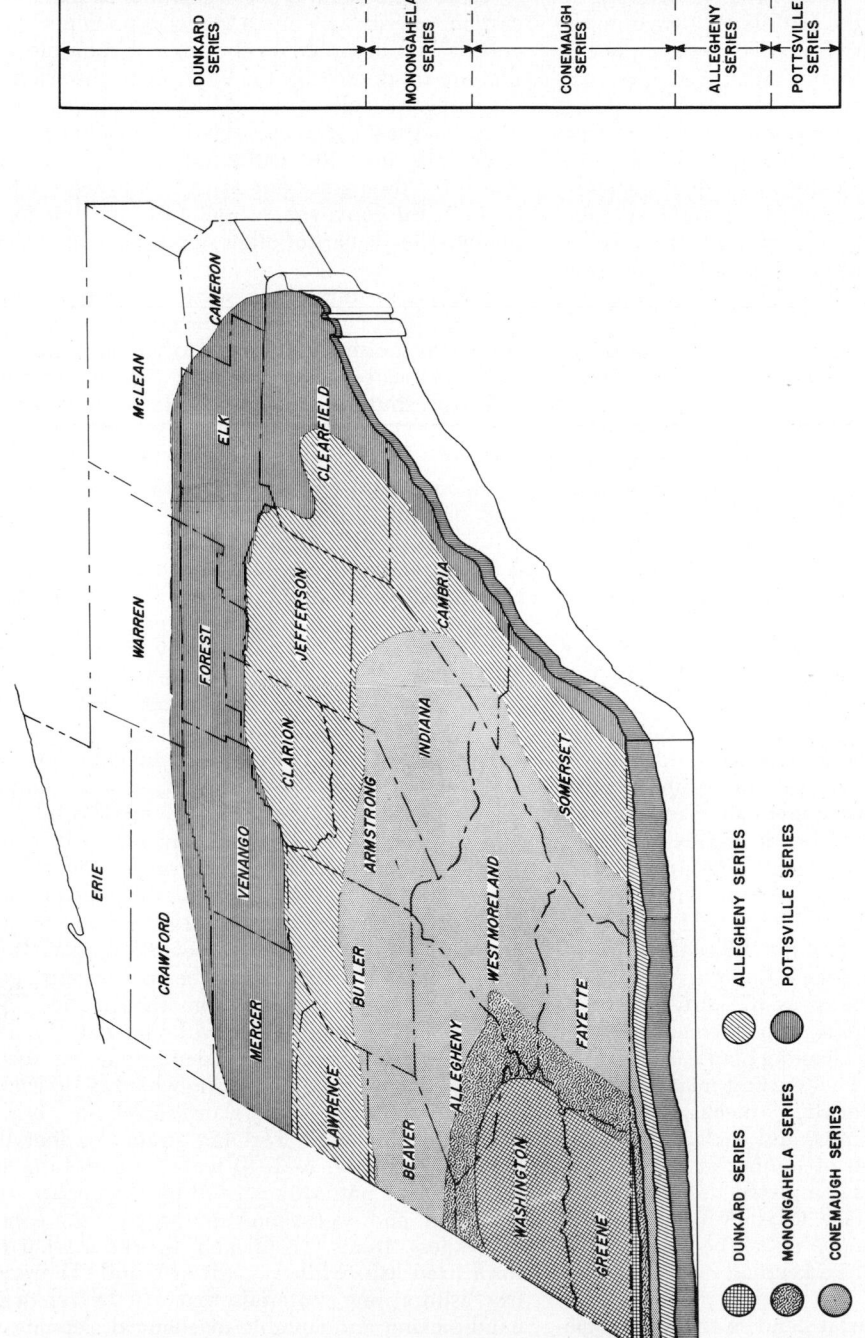

THICK-NESS	TOTALS FROM TOP
PROCTOR SANDSTONE 40 TO 40'	40'
WINDY GAP COAL 1/2' - 1'	180'
GILMORE COAL 1/2' - 1'	290'
NINEVEH "A" COAL 1/4' - 1'	455'
NINEVEH COAL 1/2' - 1'	505'
HOSTETTER COAL 1/2' - 1'	580'
FISH CREEK COAL 1/2' - 1'	675'
DUNKARD COAL 1/2' - 1'	740'
JOLLYTOWN COAL 1/2' - 1'	790'
HUNDRED COAL 1/4' - 1'	835'
WASHINGTON "A" COAL 1/2' - 1'	920'
WASHINGTON COAL 2' - 5'	1030'
LITTLE WASHINGTON COAL 15' - 2'	1054'
WAYNESBURG COAL 3' - 5'	1229'
UNIONTOWN COAL 0 - 1'	1285'
LOWER UNIONTOWN COAL 1' - 3'	1355'
SEWICKLEY COAL 3' - 5'	1485'
REDSTONE COAL 3' - 5'	1545'
PITTSBURGH COAL 5' - 8'	1590'
MORGANTOWN COAL 1' - 6'	1610'
LITTLE PITTSBURGH 1' - 6'	1665'
LITTLE CLARKSBURG 2' - 0	1740'
NORMANTOWN COAL 1' - 0	1790'
CLARYSVILLE COAL 1' - 0	1840'
ELK LICK COAL 2' - 4'	1940'
HARLEM COAL 1/2' - 4'	2040'
UPPER BAKERSTOWN 1/2' - 1'	2135'
BAKERSTOWN 2' - 5'	2140'
BRUSH CREEK COAL 0 - 6'	2345'
MAHONING COAL 1' - 6'	2339'
UPPER FREEPORT COAL 2' - 5'	2385'
LOWER FREEPORT COAL 1' - 3'	2465'
UPPER KITTANNING COAL 0 - 1'	2520'
MIDDLE KITTANNING COAL 3' - 8'	2545'
LOWER KITTANNING COAL 1' - 6'	2815'
CLARION COAL 1' - 4'	2720'
BROOKVILLE COAL 1' - 3'	2745'
MERCER COAL 0 - 2'	2800'

DUNKARD SERIES

MONONGAHELA SERIES

CONEMAUGH SERIES

ALLEGHENY SERIES

POTTSVILLE SERIES

IMPORTANT COALS OF THE NORTHERN PORTION OF THE APPALACHIAN COAL REGION

DISTRIBUTION OF COAL BEARING STRATA IN WESTERN PENNSYLVANIA

DUNKARD SERIES

MONONGAHELA SERIES

CONEMAUGH SERIES

ALLEGHENY SERIES

POTTSVILLE SERIES

FIG. 3—2. (Left) Distribution of coal-bearing strata in Western Pennsylvania. (Right) Important coals of the northern portion of the Appalachian coal region.

material costs and a quicker return on capital investment compared to underground mining. In the United States, strip-mining accounted for slightly over 25 per cent of the coal produced in 1957 and somewhat over 28 per cent in 1958.

Underground mining is performed by either the **room-and-pillar** or the **longwall** method. The room-and-pillar method is in more common use in the United States, accounting for approximately 90 per cent of present underground mining. The longwall method is particularly adaptable to mining seams up to about 4¼ feet thick under conditions where the roof may be permitted to settle. It is used more extensively in the mines of the Middle West than in the East. There are a number of modifications applicable to each method. The room-and-pillar system consists essentially of working out rooms, chambers, or breasts in the coal seam from passages (entries) driven from the mine entrance. Entrance to an underground mine is by drift, shaft or slope. The rooms vary in width from about 12 feet to 40 feet, and from 150 feet to 300 feet in length, depending on such factors as weight and character of the overlying and underlying structure and thickness of seam. Pillars separating the rooms vary in width from 6 feet to 100 feet, depending on conditions and mining practice. These pillars are sometimes removed by retreat mining and the coal recovered.

In the longwall method, a continuous mining face is maintained in the coal seam. After mining, the roof is permitted to settle, thirty or forty feet from the mine working face. Waste rock is used to support the roof for maintenance of haulage roadways, which include main roads running diagonally like the spokes of a wheel from a central shaft and auxiliary roads running through the intervening areas.

Prior to the advent of mechanical mining, undercutting of the coal seam preparatory to blasting was done manually. Production per man was low by this method and required a number of working faces in the mine to produce high mine tonnage. Hand loading of coal into mule-drawn cars was the prevailing practice for many years until development of machinery for both cutting and loading. Electric trolley-type locomotives capable of hauling longer underground trains of cars of increased capacity displaced mule-drawn trains as mine capacity increased.

In a modern underground mine the coal is emptied from the mine car by a rotary dumper which may have a capacity of as many as 37 cars. From the dumper the coal is fed by way of a conveyor or elevator to a shipping station or cleaning plant.

Continuous Mining—The cutting machines and loading machines characteristic of mechanical mining are both single-purpose units, and each performs essentially a single function of mining at the working face. After either unit has completed its work it must be withdrawn from the face to allow other units of the production setup to move up to the face to carry out succeeding functions. To keep all operating units working at full efficiency, it is necessary to have additional working places near at hand so that the single-purpose machines can enter the places in rotation and carry out their functions without interference.

To eliminate some of the difficulties attendant upon the addition of extra working places, multi-purpose machines known as **continuous miners** have been developed and the operation carried out by such machines has been given the name **continuous mining**. Continuous miners combine in a single unit the actions of dislodging the coal from the solid seam and loading it into some unit of a transportation system. Such machines, therefore, combine in one operation the separate steps of cutting, drilling, blasting and loading common to modern mechanical mining methods.

There are several types of continuous miners in operation, one of which is a ripper-type miner that has cutting bits mounted in the rims of multiple wheels that are rotated to rip the coal out of the seam while the ripper wheels are propelled into and up or down in the coal seam. The coal that is ripped loose from the seam falls into the gathering head of the loader, which has dual gathering arms that sweep the broken coal into the conveyor section of the machine for loading into shuttle cars or other suitable conveying equipment.

Continuous miners of some other types employ toothed-chain cutters to rip the coal from the face, or auger-type cutters that bore into the face, the cut coal in both cases being carried by a conveyor on the machine to a shuttle car or other means of transportation.

COAL PREPARATION

As one phase of coal preparation, the objective of **coal cleaning** (often called washing) is removal of solid foreign matter, such as rock and slate, from the coal prior to its use. Reduction of ash and sulphur contents; control of ash fusibility; increase of heating (calorific) value; and improvement of coking properties of the coal can be achieved by this practice. From a coal-cleaning standpoint, the impurities in coal are of two types; namely, those which cannot be separated from the coal, usually called **fixed impurities;** and those which can be removed, herein referred to as **free impurities** or **refuse.** Altogether, these impurities are of eight types, named as follows: (1) residual inorganic matter of the coal-forming plants from which the coal was derived; (2) mineral matter washed or blown into the coal-forming mass during the periods of its formation; (3) pyrites (FeS_2) formed by the reaction of iron sulphate with coal-forming matter; (4) sedimentary deposits during the coal-forming periods which appear as partings, sometimes called "bone," that usually must be mined with the coal; (5) massive deposits formed through deposition on bedding planes; (6) saline deposits, somewhat rare in coal beds of the United States; (7) slate, shale, clay, etc. from the underlying and overlying strata accidentally included in mining; and (8) water or moisture, which includes that naturally carried by the coal in air-dry condition, and excess moisture producing a condition of wetness. Items (1), (2) and, for the most part, (3) form **fixed** ash, while (4), (5), (6), and (7) are partly **free** ash-forming materials that can be removed by hand-picking and suitable mechanical cleaning treatments. Item (8) involves drying operations differing from those required to separate mineral impurities, which is the primary objective of cleaning. Mechanical cleaning is possible because of the difference in specific gravity between the free impurities and the coal, the density of the former being 1.7 to 4.9, while pure coal has a density of about 1.3. Sulphur is present as pyrites, organic compounds, and sulphates, and only part of the pyrites can be removed by cleaning. Phosphorus is usually associated more with bony and impure coal than with clean coal and is, therefore, reduced by washing. Salts, particularly the alkali chlorides, lower the fusion point of the ash, affect coke-oven linings and are troublesome in waste liquors from coking operations.

The preparation of coal starts at the production face in the mine. If loading is done by hand, the miner is required to discard all rock and slate over 3-in. size. If loading is done mechanically (according to the U. S. Bureau of Mines, about 85 per cent of the total bituminous coal mined underground in the United States is being loaded entirely by mechanical means as this is written) no attempt is made to prepare the coal at the face other than to control the tonnage from various sections of the mine if sulphur content of the coal is known to be high or variable.

The cleaning qualities of a particular coal are determined by the **float and sink test**. Fundamentally, this test effects a fractionation of the coal by specific gravity. This test consists in crushing coal to proper size and floating individual samples of it on liquids having densities of 1.30, 1.40, 1.50, 1.60, etc., to determine the weight and character of the material that floats and sinks in *each* liquid. The proportion of coal, and the ash and sulphur content of the different fractions, provides reasonably complete data on the washability characteristics of a tested coal.

There are two general types of coal cleaning processes: (1) gravity stratification, and (2) nongravity processes. Processes based upon the first type are generally used in this country; nongravity processes have been used extensively in Europe. The processes for cleaning coal may be classified as follows:

A. Gravity separation

    1. Wet processes
        a. Launder washers
        b. Jigs
        c. Rising-current classifiers
        d. Tables

    2. Dry processes
        a. Jigs
        b. Tables

B. Float-and-sink methods

    1. Fine-solids and water flotation
        a. Sand
        b. Magnetite and other materials

    2. Fine-solids and air flotation

C. Froth flotation

A complete description of each of the foregoing processes would be too lengthy for inclusion herein; hence only a brief review will be given of the principles of some of the more important types of processes in use at present. A reference list for further study of this subject is appended to this chapter.

Jigs were probably the earliest type of machine used in the mineral industry to separate materials of different densities. They consist essentially of a box with a perforated base into which the material is placed, and by alternate surges of water upward and downward through the perforations, materials of different specific gravities stratify. Materials having the highest specific gravities remain at the bottom while the lighter material rises. With proper mechanical facilities, a continuous separation is achieved. While jigs are not very efficient in cleaning a mixture of various sizes, they are capable of satisfying some market requirements, and capacities up to 500 tons per hour have been obtained.

The operating principle of a **launder** involves hydraulic stratification or the alluviation of materials of different gravity. The Rheolaveur launder consists of a downwardly inclined flume fitted with compartments spaced at intervals below the flume. Coal and flush water are fed at the high end, and the heavy-gravity material is withdrawn through the compartments. The water and coal having a top size not exceeding 6 inches are fed in at one end of the launder, the first section of which is steeply inclined to give the mixture a high initial velocity. This strong current causes the coal, middlings, and slate to stratify quickly, so that by the time the mixture reaches the flat section, the coal is carried forward while the refuse is definitely retarded. From this point the launder may again be steeply inclined to deliver the flow to a second flat section, finally to make an exit through a chute to dewatering screens. Successively, the heavy-gravity final rejects, including heavy and light middlings are withdrawn from the launder, the last two products being recirculated after withdrawal for the purpose of improving the washing efficiency. The end result is a refuse relatively free of recoverable coal and a coal relatively free of extraneous material. Where the coal has fallen into a middle-gravity classification due to its being laminated with slate or pyrites, it is drawn off, crushed, and freed of these impurities and then rewashed for recovery of the coal. The Rheolaveur launders are capable of cleaning coal of practically any size. Their capacity is variable depending upon the width of the launder and size of the coal to be cleaned. Coarse coal may be treated at rates ranging from 65 to 250 net tons an hour, and fine coal at rates as low as 20 net tons per hour.

With practically all wet-washing systems the water is recirculated. When the water passes through the dewatering screens it contains a considerable amount of small-size coal solids which must be recovered for efficiency reasons. Also, the circulating water must be clarified before it is returned to the cleaning unit. This clarification is accomplished in various ways, the most important being by the use of the Dorr-type thickener. Settling cones and settling tanks are also used for this purpose. Where the Dorr thickener and settling tanks are used, it is customary to draw off the settlings in the form of a slurry containing 40 per cent to 60 per cent of solids and to further separate the slurry in a vacuum-type filter. The filters deliver a product with approximately 20 per cent moisture.

Upward-current cleaners are somewhat similar to jigs except that a constant current of upward-flowing water carries the coal particles to the discharge, while the falling particles of refuse settle downward through the rising water stream and are removed at a lower level. They are used principally for cleaning anthracite coal and for cleaning a nearly uniform size coal in a single operation. They are capable of cleaning as much as 150 tons of the coarser sizes per hour.

In **dense-media classifiers,** only a part of the power for separating coal and refuse is supplied by the upward flow of liquid, this separating power being supplemented by using a liquid medium which is heavier than water. The medium employed is a mixture of water and some finely divided solid material, such as sand, magnetite, or barite, which can be separated readily from the washed coal and reused. In the **high-density suspension** process, the upward flow is discarded entirely, the liquid medium consisting of a mixture which is just dense enough so that the coal floats in it, and the impurities sink. The size of coal has less significance in the efficiency of this process than of those previously described, and material ranging from 1/16 inch to 10 inch can be cleaned in one operation. However, difficulty is encountered in separating the solid material from coal of fine size. Capacities up to 600 tons per hour have been obtained with bituminous coal. The **Chance** method, which uses a mixture of sand and water, is the most widely used of the heavy-media classifiers in the United States. The **Tromp** and **Barvoys** processes, using magnetite and barite respectively as the solid material in the mixture, are used extensively in Europe. In these processes, the specific gravity of the mixture of solid material and water can be varied by changing their proportions to suit the optimum conditions in cleaning. Agitation in the separating cone is supplied by an upward current of water and by mechanical stirring.

A number of **high-density solutions,** such as those made up of calcium chloride or halogenated hydrocarbons to give the desired specific gravity to the separating medium for cleaning coal, have been used, but to date their application has been limited to the coarser sizes of coal due to the expense of the solution and losses in recovery.

Coal is often cleaned on **table concentrators** similar to those used in ore dressing. Essentially these tables consist of a slightly inclined rectangular surface having a series of parallel grooves or cleats. The tables are mechanically agitated to permit stratification of the light and heavy material and to cause it to move with the long axis of the table. A current of water is introduced at one side of the table to wash the coal which has settled above the refuse to the discharge edge of the table. The refuse which settles underneath the coal moves longitudinally down the table and is discharged at the end. Tables have been used principally for cleaning coal of the smaller sizes, from 48-mesh up to about ½-inch.

The disadvantages of water retention associated with wet cleaning have been eliminated by the **pneumatic processes.** They are especially applicable to

cleaning a relatively dry coal. Tables, similar to those described for wet washing, are used where the sizes are under ¾-inch, except that air currents, rising through a perforated table, are used as the stratification agent rather than water. **Jigs** and **upward-flow** processes are also employed. The **Stump air-flow** cleaner uses air rather than water for classification of material in equipment operating much the same as a jig. A mixture of sand with air, rather than water, to produce a heavy medium for separation is used in some upward-current types of classifiers. In some cases combination wet and dry plants are used to advantage. The restrictions imposed for safety reasons by the U. S. Bureau of Mines, requiring the use of water at underground mining faces to allay coal dust, and the fact that many coals treated need to be cleaned at specific gravities lower than those obtainable by dry air processes, have retarded extensive development in the use of pneumatic methods.

Froth flotation of coal involves agitating fine coal with a mixture of water and a relatively small quantity of some frothing agent. In this process, coal is buoyed to the surface by the froth and removed while refuse settles. Its application has been increasing in this country.

The advent of full-seam mechanical coal mining and the increasing need for metallurgical coke of low and uniform ash and sulphur contents has focused attention on the needs for the most efficient types of washers, and also facilities for blending high and low quality coals to obtain the best over-all long-term results.

CARBONIZATION OF COAL

The most important use of coal in the modern steel industry is in the manufacture of metallurgical coke, which is discussed in detail in Chapter 4. About one-sixth of the total bituminous coal mined in the United States is converted into coke, either in beehive or by-product coke ovens. Of the 76.0 million tons of coke produced in 1957, 73.9 million was by-product and 2.1 million beehive. In 1958, there were 55 active by-product coke plants connected with iron furnaces out of a total of 77 plants, producing 46,462,512 net tons of coke, or 87.7 per cent of the total national by-product coke production.

In recent years, on the average, metallurgical coke produced in by-product ovens has shown an increase in ash and sulphur content above that of former years. An increase in ash and sulphur content of coke affects pig-iron production and economies. The penalties for high and variable ash and sulphur contents in coke in blast-furnace operations are additional slag volume, increased coke consumption, decreased production, and difficulty of furnace control. In addition to the importance of chemical properties, the structural properties (i.e., resistance to shatter, size, crushing strength and bulk density) and possibly the reactivity or combustibility of coke are of paramount importance in coke quality.

The carbonization of coal in by-product ovens entails the production of large amounts of coke-oven gas and tar, important fuels in the steel industry, as well as light oils and various coal chemicals. The yields of gas and tar are largely a matter of the kind of coal used and the temperatures employed in coke manufacture.

COMBUSTION OF SOLID FUELS

The principal combustion reactions of solid fuels have been given in Section 1 of this chapter, under "Principles of Combustion," and this present discussion will deal with operating factors pertinent to the combustion of solid fuels in steel plants.

The combustion of **coke** in blast furnaces has been studied by a number of investigators, each of whom has found that combustion takes place in a relatively small space directly in front of each tuyere, as discussed in Chapter 14 on "The Manufacture of Pig Iron."

Coke breeze, produced by screening coke at both the coke plant and blast furnaces, is utilized as a fuel in steel-plant boiler houses to generate steam and in ore-agglomerating plants. When used as boiler fuel, coke breeze is burned on **chain-grate stokers.** Of importance in the combustion of coke breeze on chain-grate stokers is the maintenance of a relatively uniform fuel bed on the grate, 8 to 12 inches thick, to prevent blowholes, and a balanced or slight positive pressure in the furnace at fuel-bed level. The operation of the grate should permit the normal combustion of about 30 pounds of coke breeze per square foot of effective grate area per hour. Chain-grate stokers are particularly adaptable to solid fuels with an ash of low fusion point. The design of front and back arches must take into consideration the fuel to be burned on chain-grate stokers. The arches are utilized to reflect heat and thereby aid ignition on the fuel bed. Use of coke breeze in ore agglomeration is discussed in Chapter 5 under "Sintering."

Stokers for firing coal have generally been used in steel-plant boilers on units whose capacity is under 100,000 pounds of steam per hour and for units using exclusively a solid fuel. They are often used on boilers to provide flexibility for the adjustment of boiler output to the steam load in plants where there is an insufficient or fluctuating supply of gaseous by-product fuels. The advantage of stokers lies in their ability to control easily the rate of combustion of a solid fuel with efficient use of air. The combustion process on stoker-fired boilers consists essentially in first driving the volatile matter from a continuous supply of fuel, and then oxidizing the carbon in the residue on the stoker. The combustion of the coke-like residue on the grate produces CO_2 and CO. The CO and volatile matter are burned over the grate by secondary air admitted over the fuel bed. The temperature of the fuel bed is affected by the rate of firing and, at the top or hottest part of the bed, varies from about 2250° F at low to 2750° F at high rates. The amount of primary air supplied determines the capacity of stoker-fired furnaces and the effective use of secondary air determines the efficiency of combustion. In well operated and carefully sealed boilers, approximately 20 to 30 per cent excess air will permit combustion of the gases within seven or eight feet above the grate.

Stokers are classified in general according to the travel of the fuel. In an **overfired stoker** the fuel is fed on top of the bed, and in an **underfired** or a **retort stoker** the fuel is fed at the bottom or side of the bed. A **traveling-grate stoker** carries the bed horizontally on the flat upper surface of a conveyor as in a chain-grate stoker. There are a number of modifications of these stoker types. While the fuel bed of a stoker-fired boiler is relatively thin, usually from 4 to 12 inches, compared to a gas-producer bed, similar zones of reaction occur. In over-fired stokers the ash zone is immediately above the grate, followed by the oxidation, reduction and distillation zones. In underfired or retort stokers the distillation of the volatile matter takes place in an oxidizing atmosphere and the volatile products pass through the incandescent residue from combustion rather than through green coal, as in the case of overfired stokers. The normal combustion rates on coal-fired stokers amounts to 30 to 60 pounds of coal per square foot of effective grate area per hour.

Pulverized Coal—The cement industry was the first to use pulverized ("powdered") coal extensively as a fuel. Public utilities and the steel industry began applying pulverized coal on an experimental basis as a boiler fuel about 1917, and by 1935 practically all large boilers (above 100,000 lbs. of steam per hour) in public-utility power stations used this fuel, except for those stations located in the vicinity of oil and natural-gas fields where local fuels were more competitive than coal. Large modern boiler installations in integrated steel plants generally use pulverized coal, either as a standby or as an auxiliary fuel in conjunction with blast-furnace gas for steam or power generation. Although pulverized coal has been used as a fuel for metallurgical purposes in steel plants, such as in open-hearth, reheating, forge and annealing furnaces, applications have been limited generally to periods of national fuel shortages, such as existed during the first and second World Wars, when the more desirable liquid or gaseous fuels were diverted to other uses and not available.

Pulverized coal offers important combustion advantages over solid fuels and an economic advantage over gaseous and liquid fuels in most sections of the country. Fine particles of coal burned in suspension are capable of developing a highly luminous, high-temperature flame. Coal in this form may be burned normally with less excess of air above theoretical requirements than with a solid fuel, and the rate of heat release from the combustion of pulverized coal is greater than that accomplished with the solid fuel. Coal, when pulverized to the degree common for boiler uses (70 per cent through a 200-mesh screen), has the control flexibility of gaseous and liquid fuels. Practically all ranks of coal, from anthracite to lignite, can be pulverized for combustion and each possesses specific combustion characteristics which largely influence the extent of pulverization.

The ash-disposal problem has been one of the principal deterrents to a more extended use of pulverized coal. In the cement kiln, coal ash is no problem as it is absorbed by the cement in the kiln without adverse effect on the final product. In boilers, the principal difficulty of clogged boiler tubes and deterioration of furnace walls has been overcome by the use of slagging-type furnaces in which the ash in molten form is granulated by water jets at the bottom of the furnace well. The introduction of the "cyclone furnace" over 15 years ago, which offered the removal of the ash as liquid slag, has further increased the application of pulverized-coal firing for steam and power generation. This equipment was developed to solve two major problems that beset the power engineer: (1) the increasing necessity to use low-quality, high-ash fuels for steam generation; and (2) the requirement that as much of the coal ash as possible be kept in the furnace and not permitted to go through the furnace and out of the stack.

The problem of ash contamination resulting from burning fine particles of coal in suspension above a metallic liquid bath or mass of hot steel, damage to refractories from the chemical or physical action of ash, and the clogging of furnace checkers or recuperators from ash accumulation, as well as the normal availability of other fuels, has prevented widespread use of the fuel for metallurgical purposes in steel plants.

Pulverized coal for firing boilers is relatively more modern than stokers. This fuel is used generally on boiler units having a capacity in excess of 100,000 lbs. of steam per hour, or on practically any size of boiler using combination firing with oil or gas. Pulverized coal offers high boiler efficiency, and means for quick regulation of boiler load. The rank of coal pulverized and the extent of pulverization particularly determine the speed of combustion. A high-volatile coal will burn faster than anthracite coal, also one with a lower

ash content will burn faster. The process of combustion with pulverized coal is similar to that of lump coal but is of much higher velocity due to the introduction of the particle in suspension in a high-temperature chamber, and the greater surface exposure relative to weight. The release of volatile matter in pulverized coal is practically instantaneous when blown into the furnace, and the speed of combustion of the resulting carbonized particle and volatile gases depends upon the thoroughness with which the pulverized coal has been mixed with air. High combustion temperatures, low ash losses, and low excess air needs (10–20 per cent), with resultant high boiler efficiencies (85 to 90 per cent with good practice), make pulverized coal an ideal boiler fuel. Air for combustion of pulverized fuel is generally preheated, with 10 to 50 per cent of that required introduced ahead of the pulverizer and the balance made up at a point near the burner. This method of introducing the air helps dry the coal and maintains a non-explosive mix in the pulverized-coal transmission system.

The combustion-chamber size for pulverized coal is generally proportioned for a heat-release range of from 20,000 to 100,000 Btu per cu. ft. of combustion space per hour. The difference in requirements is dependent upon whether pulverized coal is the sole fuel to be used in the chamber, the size of the coal particles, the rank of coal to be pulverized, the ash-slagging temperature of the coal, and the desired temperature for the combustion chamber.

SECTION 3

LIQUID FUELS AND THEIR UTILIZATION

Liquid fuels are essential to many parts of the American transportation system. The movement of passengers and freight by highway and air is dependent upon gasoline, a product of petroleum. The railways of the country have nearly all been equipped with Diesel locomotives powered by fuel oil. Nearly all ocean-going ships are driven by oil, as are the majority of lake and river craft. Liquid fuels have also become of major importance as a source of heat and power in manufacturing plants. The particular advantages of petroleum as a source of energy and the available supplies have brought about a phenomenal growth in the petroleum industry. In the period from 1918 to 1958 the consumption of all grades of oil in the United States rose from approximately 450 million to nearly

2,800 million barrels. In 1958, the United States produced 37 per cent of the world's supply of crude petroleum.

Fuel oil, tar, pitch and pitch-tar are the principal liquid fuels used in the steel industry. Table 3—XII shows the consumption of fuel oil, tar and pitch for the year 1960.

The liquid fuels consumed annually amount to over 4 million Btu per ton of steel ingots and castings produced. The largest share of this fuel is consumed in melting furnaces. Since melting furnaces require from 3 to 5 million Btu per ton of ingots produced, the significance of liquid fuels in open-hearth practice is apparent.

Tar and pitch are by-products of the manufacture

Table 3—XII. Consumption of Fuel Oil, Tar and Pitch in the Steel Industry (1960)[1]

Purpose	Fuel Oil (Gallons)	Tar and Pitch (Gallons)	Steel Ingots and Castings Produced (Net Tons)
Melting Furnaces...........	1,064,719,426	334,576,384	....
Heating and Annealing Furnaces................	367,053,035	5,162,590	....
All Other.................	267,227,776	25,394,356	....
Total for 1960.........	1,699,000,237	365,133,330	99,281,601

[1] From: Annual Statistical Report—1960; American Iron & Steel Institute.

of coke. The virgin tar as it comes from the ovens contains valuable tar-liquor oils which can be extracted and the residue pitch used as a fuel. It is customary to mix virgin tar with this highly viscous residue to provide fluidity for facilitating handling and burning, or to utilize tar in which only the lighter products have been removed by a topping process by which sufficient fluidity is retained. Pitch-tar mixtures and topped tar make available for use as a fuel 78 to 83 per cent of the heat in the virgin tar recovered in the distillation process. The virgin tar produced in the United States for the years 1957 and 1958 amounted to 873,474,352 and 669,316,299 gallons, respectively. Approximately 15 per cent of this (99,702,595 gallons) was used in the steel industry as a fuel in 1958.

The reserves of crude petroleum in this country were estimated at over 30,500,000,000 barrels as of January 1, 1959, and during the prior year (1958) the annual production was nearly 2,500,000,000 barrels.

Origin, Composition and Distribution of Petroleum —Classified according to their origins, three main types of rocks make up the outer crust of the earth: igneous, sedimentary and metamorphic rocks. **Igneous rocks** are formed from **magma**, a molten (liquid or pasty) rock material originating at high pressures and temperatures within the earth. Lava is magma that reaches the surface in the liquid or pasty state. Very commonly, the magma cools and solidifies before reaching the surface. In any case, when the molten material cools sufficiently to become solid, igneous rocks are the result. If cooling is slow, the rocks will be crystalline (granite, for example); but if the cooling is rapid, the rocks will not be crystalline but glassy in nature (obsidian, for example). Because of the nature of their origin and their usually dense, non-porous structures, igneous rocks are never hosts to petroleum deposits.

Sedimentary rocks are formed from eroded particles of rocks and soil, carried away by wind or water (and sometimes glacial action) and deposited in seas, lakes, valleys and deltas in relatively even, sometimes very thick, beds or strata (sandstones and shales are formed from deposits of this type). Other types of stratified deposits may be formed by evaporation of land-locked seas (beds of rock salt), by accumulation of the mineral remains of animals (composed chiefly of calcium carbonate, which is the principal constituent of limestone), or by chemical precipitation (gypsum and some limestones originate in this manner). The beds of sand, silt, clay, calcium carbonate or whatever eventually are covered by other sedimentary deposits, sometimes to very great depths. With the passage of long periods of time, pressure of the overlying strata, heat, cementation by chemical means, earth movements, or a combination of these or other agencies, the strata are consolidated into sedimentary rocks, typified by the few mentioned parenthetically earlier. *Petroleum occurs almost entirely in sedimentary rock formations*, principally sandstones and limestones, under certain ideal conditions to be described later.

Metamorphic rocks originally were sedimentary or igneous rocks. Their composition, constitution or structure have been changed through the single or combined action of natural forces such as heat, pressure, or other agencies. Marble, for example, is metamorphosed limestone.

The organic theory of the origin of petroleum, generally accepted by geologists, is that petroleum has been derived from either animal or vegetable matter, or both, by a process of slow distillation, after its burial under beds of sediments. There is evidence to indicate that the animal and vegetable matter was of marine origin; such evidence includes the association of brines with oil, the visible oily coating on seaweeds found in certain localities, and the optical phenomenon of light polarization by oils similar to that of substances found in certain plants and animals and which is not shown by inorganically synthesized petroleum. The accumulation of the matter from which petroleum has been derived, its burial by sedimentary material, and the action of pressure and heat to cause distillation, has resulted in petroleum formation in many parts of the world. Geological studies indicate that petroleum was not formed in the pools in which it is found, but that the action of water pressing against oil formations caused the petroleum to flow, over a period of many years, through porous beds or strata to points of accumulation. Pools of oil occur in "traps" in sedimentary rocks such as sandstone or limestone. These traps may be formed in various ways, a few of which are illustrated schematically in Figure 3—3. Essentially, such traps are formed by an impervious layer which prevents upward migration of the petroleum to any further extent. The oil is obtained by drilling wells into these zones of accumulation. The well is encased in a steel pipe through which it is often customary to run a number of smaller pipes to bring the product to the surface.

Crude petroleum is a liquid containing a complex mixture of solid, liquid and gaseous hydrocarbons. The solid hydrocarbons are in solution and the liquid is at least partly saturated with gases (methane, ethane, etc.). The elementary composition of American crude oils from representative fields covers the following ranges (in per cent):

Carbon	84 to 87
Hydrogen	11.5 to 14.0
Sulphur	0.05 to 1.75
Nitrogen	0.10 to 1.70

Ordinary crude petroleum is brownish-green to black in color with a specific gravity from about 0.810 to 0.985, and an ash content of 0.01 to 0.05 per cent.

The principal constituents in crude oil are the **paraffin** (C_nH_{2n+2}), **naphthene** (C_nH_{2n}), and **aromatic** (C_nH_{2n-x}) **series of hydrocarbons**, and **asphaltic compounds**. In **paraffin-base crudes**, such as found in Pennsylvania, the asphaltic content is low, only traces of sulphur and nitrogen are found, and the specific gravity averages about 0.810. In **mixed-base crudes** which have a lower content of paraffins and a higher content of naphthenes than the paraffin-base crudes, the content of asphaltic compounds is higher, the sulphur content usually is under 0.4 per cent and the paraffin-wax content is generally high. Mixed-base crudes occur in the mid-continent region. The **naphthene-base crudes** contain a high percentage of naph-

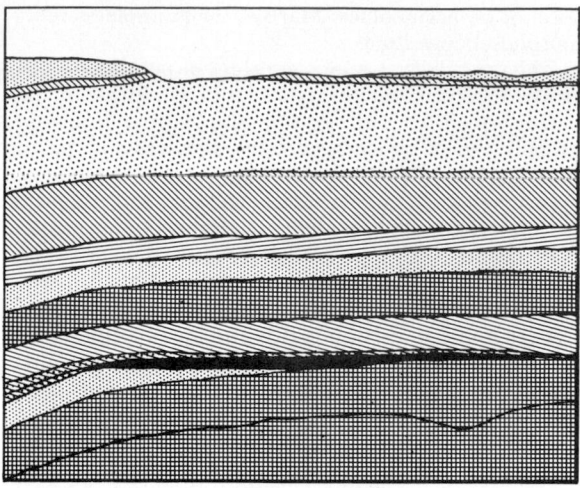

A. STRATIGRAPHIC TRAP.—In the stratigraphic trap, the producing formation gradually pinches out and disappears up the structure. An impervious layer is deposited on top of the sand, thus forming a cap rock. The solid black section represents petroleum accumulated below the cap rock.

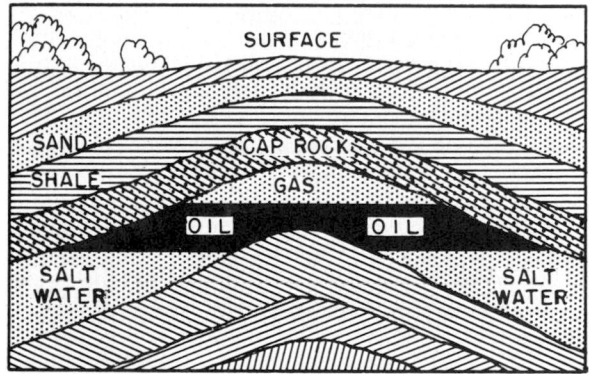

B. ANTICLINES.—In an anticlinal structure, the rocks comprising the crust of the earth are folded upward. The oil and gas are usually found on the crest of an anticlinal structure. An impervious cap rock must be present to seal the reservoir and prevent the escape of the gas and oil into higher layers. This cap rock, in one form or another, must be present in all reservoirs to contain the oil and gas within the structure.

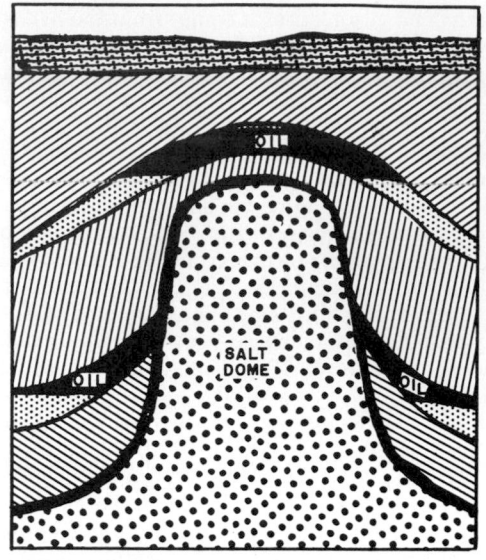

C. SALT DOMES.—The salt dome is believed to be the result of the intrusion of large masses of salt into the sediments where they are found. This intrusion creates an upward pressure and results in the doming of the overlying sedimentary rocks. In this type of structure, petroleum accumulates within the upturned porous beds about the summit and flanks of the salt core, as indicated by the solid black sections.

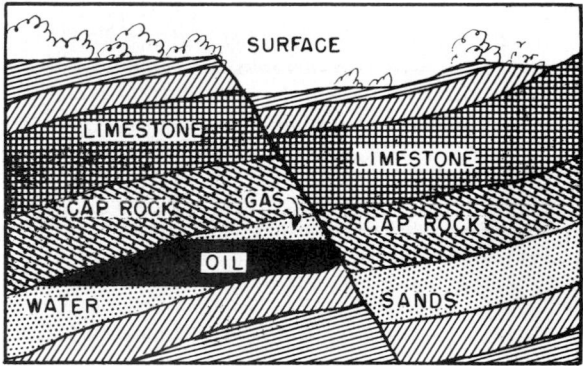

D. FAULTS.—A fault is a structural closure caused by the fracturing of the crustal rocks during earth movements. In the process of folding, a reservoir for oil may be formed when a porous rock is brought into contact with an impervious layer, thus forming a trap.

FIG. 3—3. Schematic representation of four geologic structures associated with the underground accumulation of petroleum through natural agencies. From "Fundamentals of Petroleum," NAVPERS 10883, Superintendent of Documents, U. S. Government Printing Office, Washington, D.C.

thenes, very little paraffin wax, and have a relatively high specific gravity. They occur in the central, south-central and south-western areas of the United States. Light naphthene-base crudes contain a low proportion of asphalt, compared to reverse proportions in heavy naphthene-base crudes. The sulphur content varies widely. The **aromatic crudes,** which occur chiefly in California, generally have a high asphaltic-compound content, sulphur content varying from 0.1 to 4.13 per cent and a relatively high nitrogen content. The specific gravity is often fairly low and the presence of

wax widespread, although some crudes of this class are free of wax.

Crude oil is delivered to the refineries by rail, inland and intercoastal waterways, in specially constructed tanks, and by pipeline. In 1915 there were less than 20,000 miles of crude-oil trunk lines, which had been expanded by 1959 to over 70,000 miles of crude-oil trunk lines and over 44,000 miles of pipelines for refined petroleum products.

Grades of Petroleum Used as Fuels—Fuel oils may be classified generally as: (1) **raw** or **natural crude**

petroleums, (2) **distillate fuel oils,** (3) **residual fuel oils,** and (4) **blended oils.** The increasing demand for gasoline and other petroleum products makes it very undesirable that crude petroleum as obtained from the wells be used for fuel. Besides, gasoline in a fuel oil is dangerous on account of the increased danger of explosions its presence entails. By the older methods of refining, the products from many of the oil refineries west of the Mississippi River were gasoline, naphtha, kerosene and fuel oil, while eastern refineries usually carried the fractionation of oil much further, their output being such products as gasoline, benzene, naphtha, kerosene, light machine oil, automobile oils, cylinder oils, paraffin wax and tar, pitch, or coke. Recent improvements in thermal cracking at both high and low pressure and the use of catalytic conversion processes have enabled refiners to convert more of the petroleum to gasoline and to produce lubricants from western petroleum relatively high in asphalt.

Distillate fuel oils consist of the fractions distilled intermediate between kerosene and lubricating oils. Residual fuel oils are the viscous residual products remaining after the more volatile hydrocarbons have been driven off in the refining process. Blended oils are mixtures of any or all of the three classes of fuel oils.

Properties and Specifications of Liquid Fuels—Before discussing the more important properties and specifications of fuel oil, some of the common terms will be reviewed.

Specific gravity is the ratio of the weight of a volume of a body to the weight of an equal volume of some standard substance. In the case of liquids, the standard is water. **Baumé gravity** is an arbitrary scale for measuring the density of a liquid, the unit being called "Baumé degree." Its relation to specific gravity is shown by the formula:

$$\text{Be}° = \frac{140}{\text{Sp. Gr.}} - 130 \text{ (for liquids lighter than water)}$$

For example, the Baumé hydrometer will read 10° Bé in pure water, when the specific gravity scale reads 1.000. The **American Petroleum Institute (API) Gravity** is a modification of the Baumé scale for light liquids. API gravities are always reported at 60° F. The relation between API gravity and specific gravity is:

$$°\text{API} = \frac{141.5}{\text{Sp. Gr.}} - 131.5$$

The greater the degrees Baumé or API, the lighter the fluid. There are about 90 API degrees between the heaviest and lightest oils which, therefore, makes this scale valuable for determining differences between the density of various oils.

Flash point is the lowest temperature at which, under definite specified conditions, a liquid fuel vaporizes rapidly enough to form above its surface an air and vapor mixture which gives a flash or slight explosion when ignited by a small flame. It is an indication of the ease of combustion or of the fire hazard in handling or using oil.

Pour point is the lowest temperature at which oil will pour or flow when chilled without disturbance under specified conditions.

Viscosity is the property of liquids that causes them to resist instantaneous change of shape or the arrangement of their parts due to internal friction. Since this property has a direct relation to resistance of flow in fuel-oil pipe systems and to atomization, it is an important specification. **Absolute viscosity** is a measure of internal fluid friction. It is expressed in the English system as pounds per second per foot and is the force which will move one square foot of a plane surface with a speed of one foot per second relative to another plane surface from which it is separated by a layer of the liquid one foot thick. The viscosity of a fluid relative to water at 68° F is the ratio of its absolute viscosity to that of water at 68° F (both absolute viscosities must be in the same units). This relation is called **relative viscosity.** The absolute viscosity of water at 68° F is 0.000672 lbs. per sec. per ft. or 0.0100 gms. per sec. per cm. which is equal to 0.0100 **poises** or 1.00 **centipoise.** The viscosity of all liquids decreases with increasing temperature and ASTM viscosity determinations are made at oil temperatures of 100° F, 122° F, 130° F and 210° F, and are often expressed as **Saybolt Universal** at 100° F or **Saybolt Furol** at 122° F. The terms "Saybolt Universal" and "Saybolt Furol" represent the type of instrument used in making the viscosity determinations. Viscosity measurements made by either may be interconverted by the use of tables.

Reid Vapor Pressure is a test for the vapor pressure of gasoline at 100° F. It shows the tendency of gasoline to generate vapor bubbles and is expressed in pounds per square inch absolute.

Octane number is the anti-knock rating of gasoline. The rating is made by matching the fuel in a test engine with a mixture of normal heptane, which detonates very easily and has an octane rating of zero, and iso-octane, which has exceptionally high anti-knock characteristics and is rated at 100. A fuel knock that matches a mixture of say 60 per cent octane and 40 per cent heptane would have an octane rating or number of 60. **Cetane number** is used to show the ignition quality of Diesel oils. The rating is based on a scale resembling those of octane numbers by matching the ignition delay of the fuel against blends of cetane, a fast-burning paraffin, and methyl naphthalene, a slow-burning aromatic material.

The A.S.T.M. has developed a table for grading fuel oils, consisting of six grades. According to this classification, heating oils generally used for domestic and small industrial heating furnaces comprise Grades 1, 2 and 3. Grades 5 and 6 correspond to **Bunker "B"** and **Bunker "C"** fuel oils, respectively, which are used extensively in the steel industry. Bunker "B" fuel oil is usually cracking-still tar and Grade 6, or Bunker "C" fuel oil, a straight-run or cracked residual, or a mixture of residual and cracking-still tar blended to reduce the viscosity to that required by the consumer.

All grades of fuel oil are normally sold to meet specifications mutually satisfactory to buyer and seller. A typical specification of Bunker "C" fuel oil for use in open-hearth furnaces is as follows:

Gravity—API (60° F) . . . . 13.0 to 16.0
Flash point (closed cup) . . . . 150° F minimum
Btu per gallon . . . . 150,000 minimum
Sulphur (%) . . . . 0.6 maximum
Viscosity at 122° F . . . . 100 secs. Saybolt
Furol
Water and sediment (% by vol.). . 1% maximum

The yield of tar produced in by-product coke ovens by high-temperature distillation between 1832 and 2012° F (1000 to 1100° C) differs within very wide limits according to the kind of bituminous coal coked, and to the temperature, coking time, and design of oven employed in the process. Virgin tar as produced in the by-product ovens consists essentially of tar acids, neutral oils which are principally aromatic hydrocarbons, and a residue pitch.

The residue pitch from the distillation of tar is highly viscous or brittle. Pitch contains a substantial percentage of free carbon and some high-boiling and complex organic chemicals. The properties of a typical pitch-tar mix and Bunker "C" fuel oil are shown in Table 3—XIII on the following page.

The viscosity of liquid fuels decreases with temperature increase. The range of typical samples of virgin tar, pitch-tar mixtures and topped tar is as follows:

Fuel	Test Temp. (°F)	Viscosity in Sec., Saybolt Universal
Virgin Tar	175	189.4 max. 73.3 min. 109.4 avg.
Pitch-Tar Mix	175	1940 max. 181 min. 946.1 avg.
Pitch-Tar Mix	210	687 max. 97 min. 561.7 avg.
Topped Tar	200	700 max. 550 min. 600 avg.

Combustion of Liquid Fuels—The combustion of liquid fuel usually is obtained by atomizing the fuel. Atomization breaks up the fuel into fine, mist-like globules, thus permitting an increased area for intimate contact between the air supplied for combustion and the fuel. The chemistry of combustion of liquid fuels is complex. The small particles of fuel either vaporize to form gaseous hydrocarbons which burn to CO_2 and H_2O through a chain of reactions, or the fuel cracks to form carbon (soot) and hydrogen which also burn with complete combustion to CO_2 and H_2O. Both of these conditions normally occur in the combustion of liquid fuels. The first condition predominates with good atomization and proper mixing with sufficient air. A deficiency of air or poor atomization will cause smoke. For large furnaces, such as open

hearths and heating furnaces, the atomizing agent is usually steam at a pressure anywhere between 60 and 125 pounds per square inch gage. The steam consumed in atomization varies from 0.3 to 0.7 pounds per pound of fuel. When liquid fuels are used in smaller furnaces, atomization usually is procured by compressed air or by mechanical action. The character of a liquid-fuel flame, that is, its shape, size and luminosity, may be altered with a fixed burner design by changing the degree of atomization which is controlled by the steam pressure. Liquid fuels normally are burned in steel plants to produce a highly luminous flame at an intensity of flame propagation intermediate between that generally secured with coke-oven gas and that with natural gas.

Liquid fuels usually are preferred above all other fuels for use in open-hearth furnaces because they permit better control of flame direction and, because of their high calorific value, control of flame temperature and luminosity.

The amount of air required to burn liquid fuels depends upon the chemical composition of the particular fuel. Bunker "C" fuel oil requires approximately 180 cu. ft. of dry air per pound of oil for perfect combustion, and tar-pitch approximately 158 cu. ft. From the ultimate analysis of a liquid fuel, the theoretical air requirements and products of combustion may be calculated, as explained in Section 1 under "Combustion Calculations." The composition and properties of tar-pitch are given in Table 3—XIII, shown later.

Liquid-Fuel Burners—There are many different designs of burners for liquid fuels. Burners designed for atomization by steam or air may be classified into two general types, the **inside mixing** and the **outside mixing**. In the inside-mixing type the fuel and atomizing agent are mixed inside the burner or burner system, while in the outside-mixing type the two fluids meet immediately outside the burner tip. In open-hearth furnaces and large reheating furnaces the inside-mixing type is used. The inside-mixing type is sometimes classified as an **emulsion type** or a **nozzle-mix type** of burner. In the emulsion type the mixing is performed at a point several feet from the burner tip, while in the nozzle-mix type the two fluids meet inside the burner but very close to the burner tip. In the latter type, mixing probably takes place both inside the burner and as the stream enters the furnace.

Liquid-fuel burners used in open-hearth furnaces are water cooled due to port end design; those in reheating, forge and annealing furnaces seldom require water cooling.

The handling of liquid fuels at consuming plants requires a system for their transportation, storage and conditioning. Where liquid fuels are received by tank car, a system of receiving basins, unloading pumps, strainers and storage tanks generally is required. The storage tanks must be of ample size to meet fuel demands between deliveries and should be provided with heaters to maintain proper fluidity for flow through pipe lines to the system pressure pumps. Pressure pumps are used to deliver the liquid fuel through a pipe system to the point of consumption. Where there are a number of consuming units being served from a common fuel-storage system, the pipe

Table 3—XIII. Properties of Typical Liquid Fuels

Fuel	Ultimate Analysis of Fuel (%)							
	H₂O	C	H₂	N₂	O₂	S	Ash	Undetermined
Pitch-Tar (Dry)...............	......	90.78	5.35	1.39	1.65	0.61	0.22	....
Pitch-Tar (Natural Basis)....	1.33	89.57	5.28	1.37	1.63	0.60	0.22	....
Bunker "C" Fuel Oil (Dry)*..	......	88.60	10.50	0.30	0.00	0.55	0.05	....

Fuel	Specific Gravity at 60° F.	Weight (Lbs./Gal.)	Calorific Value (Btu/Lb.)		Dry Air Required for Combustion (Cu. Ft./Lb.)	Theoretical Flame Temp. (°F)
			Gross	Net		
Pitch-Tar (Dry)..........	......	......	......	......	......	......
Pitch-Tar (Natural Basis).	1.199	9.9855	16,155	15,674	158.13	3495
Bunker "C" Fuel Oil (Dry)*...............	0.9529	7.935	18,890	17,820	180	3800±

* Courtesy of Sun Oil Co.—(Typical Analysis).

feeder line is designed in the form of a loop through which the fuel flows at constant pressure and temperature. The various units tap into this loop. The fuel-oil lines are lagged and provided with tracer steam lines to maintain uniform fluidity throughout the system and to provide fuel at the burners at the proper viscosity for atomization. The temperature at which liquid fuel is delivered to the burners varies with the character of the fuel and burner design. Where pitch is used, a temperature as high as 300° F in the lines is sometimes required. A temperature level usually somewhere between 200° F and 250° F is maintained for pitch-tar mixtures, and 150° F to 200° F for Bunker "C" fuel oil.

SECTION 4

GASEOUS FUELS AND THEIR UTILIZATION

The availability of **natural gas** in so many sections of this country has had a profound influence upon our industrial progress. It was first used as an illuminating gas at Fredonia, New York, in 1824. The discovery of new fields and the installation of pipe lines to consuming centers led to increasing demands, as the convenience, cleanliness, and general utility of this form of fuel became better known. The initial use of natural gas for steel manufacture was at a rolling mill plant at Leechburg, Pa., in 1874. A well in this area permitted exclusive use of natural gas for puddling, heating, and steam generation for a period of six months. Since 1932 there has been an accelerated demand for natural gas.

In 1958, for example, 11,787 billion cubic feet of natural gas were produced. To deliver this supply, the gas industry had installed some 540,800 miles of natural-gas pipe lines by the close of 1958.

Producer gas was the first gaseous fuel successfully utilized by the iron and steel industry. This gas permitted the early experimentation in regeneration, and the utilization of this principle started a new era of steel manufacturing. The advantages of preheated gas and air were so clearly indicated in 1861 that producer gas rapidly became the major fuel utilized by open-hearth furnaces and maintained its position for almost sixty years, or until about 1920, when by-product coke plants, supplying coke-oven gas and tar, began to challenge this leadership.

Blast-furnace gas utilization by the iron and steel industry probably should rank first historically, although its adoption by the industry was slower than in the case of producer gas. The sensible heat in the blast-furnace top gases was first utilized in 1832 to transfer heat to the cold blast. Originally, this heat exchanger was mounted on the furnace top. In 1845, the first attempts were made to make use of its heat of combustion, but history indicates that the burning of blast-furnace gas was not successful until 1857. It is probable that progress in the utilization of blast-furnace gas was delayed by its dust content, the problems of cleaning and handling, and the low cost of solid fuel. Increasing cost of other fuels and competition forced its use, and by the turn of this century, blast-furnace gas had become one of the major fuels of the iron and steel industry. In 1959, the blast-furnace gas produced and consumed amounted to nearly 24 million tons of coal equivalent.

The initial use of by-product **coke-oven gas** in the iron and steel industry was at the Cambria Steel Company, Johnstown, Pa., in 1894. This installation was followed by only a few by-product coke-plant additions until a shortage of transportation facilities and the rising price of coal and natural gas during the first

World War accelerated installations throughout the steel industry. The utilization of coke-oven gas has been very profitable as it reduced the purchase of outside fuels. It is estimated that plants operating steel-making furnaces used 750,170 million cubic feet of coke-oven gas as fuel in 1959.

NATURAL GAS

Natural gas and petroleum are related closely to each other in their chemical composition and in geographical distribution. Both are made up predominately of hydrocarbons. Petroleum rarely is free of natural gas, and the same fields usually produce both fuels. When natural gas exists indigenous to an oil stratum and its production is incidental to that of oil, it is called **casinghead gas.** Gas found in a field is usually under pressure which diminishes with extended use or, sometimes, from the presence of too many other wells. The life of a well varies from a few months to twenty years. Rocks bearing gas are sandstones, limestones, conglomerates, and shales—never igneous rocks. Natural gas is derived from the remains of marine animal and plant life—in theory, the same as described previously for petroleum.

Natural gas as found is usually of singular purity and is composed principally of the lower gaseous hydrocarbons of the paraffin series, methane and ethane, some of the heavier liquefiable hydrocarbons (which are recovered as **casinghead gasoline** or sold in bottled form as butane, propane, pentane, etc.) and a small amount of nitrogen or carbon dioxide. Some natural gases contain small quantities of helium. Occasionally, wells are found in which the gas contains hydrogen sulphide and organic sulphur vapors. **Sour gas** is defined as a natural gas which contains in excess of 1½ grains of hydrogen sulphide or 30 grains of total sulphur per 100 cu. ft. It is fortunate, however, that by far the greater part of natural gas available in this country is practically sulphur-free.

There are a number of great gas fields in this country; viz., the Appalachian, the Lima-Indiana, Illinois, Mid-Continent, Gulf, and California. Due to the increasing customer demand, exhaustion of wells, and the inability of the older local fields to adequately meet the demand, a number of the fields have been linked by pipe lines. Gas from the extensive Texas oil fields, which previously had been allowed to escape on account of lack of pipe lines to carry the excess to more distant consuming centers, now is being utilized.

The principal constituent of natural gas is methane, CH_4. Since natural gas contains from 60 to 100 per cent of CH_4 by volume, the characteristics of methane gas, which were shown in Section 1, largely dominate the parent gas. Comparing methane with the other principal combustible gases, it will be noted that it has a low rate of flame propagation, a high ignition temperature, and a narrow explosive range. Methane, as well as all other hydrocarbons (of which it is the lowest member), burns with a luminous flame.

Typical compositions of natural gas are presented in Table 3—XIV.

The iron and steel industry consumed 360,889 million cubic feet of natural gas in 1960, 317,051 million cubic feet in 1959, 278,700 million cubic feet in 1958, and 281,134 million cubic feet in 1957.

MANUFACTURED GASES

The four most important of the commercially used manufactured gases are **producer gas, water gas, oil gas,** and so-called **bottled gases.** Since none of these gases are used presently in steel manufacturing or processing in the United States, only a brief description of their manufacture and characteristics will be given here.

Manufacture of Producer Gas—Producer gas is manufactured by blowing an insufficient supply of air for complete combustion, with or without the admixture of steam, through a thick, hot, solid-fuel bed. A large proportion of the original heating value of the solid fuel is recovered in the potential heat of carbon monoxide, hydrogen, tarry vapors, and some hydrocarbons, and in the sensible heat of the composite gas which also contains carbon dioxide and nitrogen. When the gas is cleaned, the sensible heat of the gases and the potential heat of the tar vapors is lost.

Table 3—XIV. Typical Composition of Natural Gas in Various Districts

Constituents	Districts				
	Birmingham	Pittsburgh	So. California	Los Angeles	Kansas City
CO_2	....	....	0.7	6.5	0.8
O_2	....	....	....	....	....
N_2	5.0	0.8	0.5	....	8.4
CO	....	....	....	....	....
H_2	....	....	....	....	....
CH_4	90.0	83.4	84.0	77.5	84.1
C_2H_6	5.0	15.8	14.8	16.0	6.7
Total	100.0	100.0	100.0	100.0	100.0
Specific Gravity	0.60	0.61	0.64	0.70	0.63
Gross Heating Value— Btu/cu. ft.	1002	1129	1116	1073	974
Net Heating Value— Btu/cu. ft.	904	1021	1009	971	879

Table 3—XV. Composition of Clean Producer Gas [1]

Constituent	Anthracite Coal	Coke		Bituminous Coal	
		4 to 5" Lump	Breeze	A	B
CO_2	6.3%	9.2%	8.7%	3.4%	9.2%
Illuminants	0.0	0.1	0.0	0.8	0.4
O_2	0.0	0.0	0.0	0.0	0.0
CO	25.0	21.9	23.3	25.3	20.9
H_2	14.2	11.1	12.8	9.2	15.6
CH_4	0.5	0.2	0.4	3.1	1.9
N_2	54.0	57.5	54.8	58.2	52.0
Total	100.0%	100.0%	100.0%	100.0%	100.0%
Gross Heating Value, Btu per cu. ft	132	121	131	155	156

[1] U. S. Bureau of Mines, Bulletin 301.

The basic reactions in an air-blown producer are:

$$C + O_2 = CO_2 \text{ (exothermic)}$$
$$2C + O_2 = 2CO \text{ (exothermic)}$$
$$C + CO_2 = 2CO \text{ (endothermic)}$$

Theoretically, air-blown producers may have 70 per cent gasification efficiency if all the carbon is converted to carbon monoxide (CO). The other 30 per cent is lost when the hot gases are cooled. If all the carbon is converted to CO, the gas would have a heating value of 112 Btu per cu. ft. The introduction of steam with the air permits generating a gas of 130 to 190 Btu value, reduces the temperature of the hot zones in the producer on account of the endothermic reaction between steam and hot carbon, and reduces the temperature of the gases leaving the producer.

The thickness and temperature of the zones, the velocity at which the gases move through them, the relation of the volume and ratio of the air and steam in the blast to the coal consumed, gas channeling, and the character of the coal, determine the gas composition and the optimum producer efficiency.

Table 3—XV gives the composition of clean producer gas made from various fuels in a well-operated updraft producer.

The gross heating value of raw producer gas, including tar, made from a high-volatile coal, 8 per cent ash, is 170 to 190 Btu per cubic foot.

Producer gas has a very low rate of flame propagation due to the relatively large amount of inert gases, N_2 and CO_2, it contains. The hot gas, containing tar, burns with a luminous flame; the cold gas is only slightly luminous, while it is non-luminous if made from anthracite coal or coke. Producer gas is a relatively heavy gas and has a wide explosive range. The theoretical flame temperature is low, approximately 3175° F, and the gas generally was preheated when utilized in steel-plant processes.

Manufacture of Water Gas—Water gas or **blue gas** is generated by blowing steam through an incandes-

cent bed of carbon. The gas forming reactions are primarily:

$$C + H_2O = CO + H_2$$
$$C + 2H_2O = CO_2 + 2H_2$$

Since both of these reactions are endothermic, the temperature of the bed of carbon through which the steam is blown would be lowered quickly to a point where no reaction would occur, if proper control were not provided. The temperature of a bed of hot carbon may be increased by blowing air through it, causing the two basic exothermic reactions:

$$C + O_2 = CO_2$$
$$2C + O_2 = 2CO$$

By controlling the time during which air is blown, the temperature level of the bed can be controlled and the effect of the second reaction, which consumes more carbon and generates less heat, is minimized. The **air blow** raises the temperature level of the bed, and the gases formed during this part of the process pass through a stack to the outside air. The **steam run** lowers the temperature level of the bed and generates water gas which is collected by passing the gases through outlets to a gas holder, the reservoir for distribution.

During the air blow period of each cycle, a hot, lean producer gas is formed. A part of this gas sometimes is permitted to dilute the steam-run gas. The latter part of the air blow generates a gas generally high in CO, and is the most efficient period in which to collect this gas. Normally, however, all of the gas made during the air blow is passed through a separate chamber containing refractory checker work and the CO in the gas burned with air diverted from the generator to this chamber. The checkers absorb some of the heat of the spent gases as they pass to the stack. The down-run steam sometimes is passed through the checker chamber before entering the generator to recover the stored heat. Heat in a similar chamber is used for cracking fuel oil to form gases that are added to water gas to enrich it when **carburetted water gas** is made.

While coke generally is used as the fuel in the production of water gas because of its high carbon content and cleanliness, anthracite and bituminous coal and mixtures of coal and coke also have been used successfully, but with some sacrifice in over-all operating efficiency.

Water gas burns with a clear blue flame; hence, the name "blue gas." It is used in a number of chemical processes to supply a basic gas for synthetic processes, but it is not suitable for distribution as a domestic fuel unless it has been enriched with cracked fuel oil, when it is called carburetted water gas.

Water gas made from coke burns with a non-luminous flame. Carburetted water gas burns with a highly luminous flame. Both gases have a high rate of flame propagation. The speed of combustion for water gas exceeds that of any other extensively used fuel gas; that for carburetted water gas is practically the same as for coke-oven gas. Water gas has a slightly lower specific gravity than natural gas, but is somewhat heavier than coke-oven gas. Carburetted water gas is heavier than natural gas but lighter than producer gas. The theoretical flame temperature of both blue and carburetted water gas is very high, respectively about 3670 and 3725° F, exceeding that of all other industrial fuel gases commonly used. Both gases have a relatively wide explosive range.

Oil gas is a combination of cracked petroleum and water gas made by passing oil and steam through hot refractory checker work. Oil gas is commercially important in localities where coal or coke is expensive and oil cheap.

Bottled gases are liquefied petroleum gases. They have become commercially important because of the concentration of fuel energy in liquid form which may be converted easily into a gas. They are distributed for household use in steel cylinders called "bottles" and in tank cars or trucks for industrial purposes. They are sometimes sold under various trade names but are composed mainly of butane, propane, and pentane. A steel cylinder of propane as sold for domestic purposes contains approximately 21,640 Btu per pound of liquid gas.

Special Gas Processes—Studies and investigations in the art of gasification have been under way in the United States for a number of years. The German demand for self-sufficiency prior to and during the second World War led to developments of the water-gas machine which first made possible continuous gasification, and later the manufacture of a gas containing methane. Technical advances in the manufacture of cheap oxygen contributed largely to these developments. The first step towards improvements in fuel-gas manufacture eliminated the disadvantage of cyclic operation and the second, the necessity for carburetting water gas. Continuous gasification was accomplished in the **Winkler Process** by passing the proper mixture of steam and oxygen through a fuel bed to compensate for the endothermic reaction, $C + H_2O$, with the exothermic reaction, $C + O_2$, thereby maintaining a fixed temperature in the fuel bed.

The **Lurgi Process**, developed in 1936, produces a rich water gas containing CH_4. A mixture of steam and oxygen at 20 atmospheres pressure (steam at 900° F) is introduced through the hollow shaft of a rotating grate and passes through the ash bed into a fixed fuel bed, which is at a temperature of 2150° F, where the fuel is gasified. Fuel is charged intermittently into a hopper immediately above the generator proper. A foot valve between the hopper and generator locks the high pressure in the generator during charging. After filling the hopper, fuel is fed continuously into the generator chamber. A plow directs ash through the grate into a small compartment in the lower portion of the generator, and from there the ash is removed continuously by a revolving scraper into an outside ash hopper.

Slagging Gas Producers — Coal-gasification processes in which ash is removed as liquid slag have also been under development for many years, especially in Europe. The Ruhrgas and Rummel processes gasify coal in a vortex arrangement, and have been operated in large pilot plants.

At a new coking plant of the Netherlands State Mines, three slagging gas producers supply 700,000 cu. ft. per hr. of gas for underfiring the coke ovens. Gas with a gross heating value of 290 Btu per cu. ft. is produced from coke with a 50:50, steam-oxygen blast. Slag is tapped at about 2700–2750° F. Limestone and blast-furnace slag are added to the coke charge to maintain slag fluidity.

By-Product Gaseous Fuels—The two major by-product gaseous fuels are blast-furnace and coke-oven gases. A number of other unavoidable gaseous fuels are created by regular manufacturing processes. Some of these are of minor economic consequence, but the majority are useful and generally utilized at the plant where they are produced. An exception is oil-refinery gas which is sometimes piped and marketed to industries adjacent to refineries. The calorific value and flame characteristics of by-product gases have wide ranges. Blast-furnace gas has probably the lowest heat content of any, and oil refinery gas the highest, respectively 90 and 1850 Btu per cubic foot, although both vary from these values.

Blast-furnace gas is a by-product of the iron blast furnace. The paramount objective in blast-furnace operation is to produce iron of a specified quality, economically; the fact that usable gas issues from the top of the furnace is merely a fortunate attendant circumstance. When air enters the tuyeres (see Chapter 14 on "The Manufacture of Pig Iron") its oxygen reacts with the coke. The resulting gas passes up through the shaft of the furnace which has been charged with coke, ore, and limestone, and after a number of chemical reactions and a travel of some 80 feet, issues as a heated, dust-laden, lean, combustible gas. The annual volume production of this gas is greater than that of any other gaseous fuel. Four to five tons of blast-furnace gas are generated per ton of pig iron produced. While the purpose of the gases generated by the partial combustion of carbon is to reduce iron ore, the value of a blast furnace as a gas producer is evident from the relation just noted. The essential reactions by which blast-furnace gas is produced are shown in Chapter 12.

The percentage of CO and CO_2 in blast-furnace gas is directly related to the amount of carbon in the coke and the amount of CO_2 in the limestone charged per ton of iron produced. The rate of carbon consumption depends principally upon the kind of iron to be made, the physical and chemical characteristics of the charged material, the distribution of the material in the furnace stack, the furnace lines, and the temperature of the hot blast. The total $CO + CO_2$ content of the top gas is about 40 per cent by volume, and when producing ordinary grades of iron the ratio of CO to CO_2 will vary from 1.7 to 2.5, to 1. The hydrogen content of the gas varies from 3 to 4 per cent. The remaining percentage is made up of nitrogen, except for about 0.2 per cent CH_4. The efficiency of the blast furnace as a gas producer on a cold basis is a little less than 70 per cent; on a hot basis, about 90 per cent.

Blast-furnace gas leaves the furnace at a temperature of 250° to 700° F, and at a pressure of 15 to 60 inches w.g., carrying with it 10 to 50 grains of water vapor and 8 to 15 grains of dust per cubic foot. The particles of dust vary from ¼ to 0.00001 inch in diameter. In early days of blast-furnace operation, the gas was used as it came from the furnace without cleaning, causing a great deal of trouble with flues, combustion chambers, and stoves due to clogging. The gas now is cleaned almost universally, the degree depending upon the use.

The outstanding characteristics of blast-furnace gas as a fuel are: (1) very low calorific value—approximately 90 Btu per cu. ft., (2) low theoretical flame temperature—approximately 2650° F, (3) low rate of flame propagation—relatively lower than any other common gaseous fuel, (4) high specific gravity—highest of all common gaseous fuels, and (5) burns with a non-luminous flame.

Coke-Oven Gas—The steel industry, which uses about 85 per cent of the total coke-oven gas generated in the United States, generally classifies coke-oven gas as a by-product of coke manufacture. This undoubtedly is due to the former waste of coke-oven gas and other coal products for so many years in the beehive-coke process. Actually, the production of coke-oven gas and other coal chemicals is a part of an important manufacturing process in which large sums have been expended for their recovery, as they have a value almost equal to that of the coke. Coke-oven gas is produced during the carbonization or destructive distillation of bituminous coal in the absence of air, as described in Chapter 4.

The composition of coke-oven gas varies in accordance with grade and density of coal and operating practices. Typical ranges for the constituents of dry coke-oven gas by volume are as follows:

CO_2*	1.3 – 2.4
O_2	0.2 – 0.9
N_2	2.0 – 9.6
CO	4.5 – 6.9
H_2	46.5 –57.9
CH_4	26.7 –32.1
Illuminants	3.1 – 4.0
Specific Gravity	0.36–0.44
Heating Value, Btu per cu. ft. (gross)	537–580
Heating Value, Btu per cu. ft. (net) .	480–523
* Includes H_2S	

Coke-oven gas contains hydrogen sulphide, H_2S. About 40 per cent of the sulphur in coal, not removed in the washing process, is evolved with the distillation products. Much of this remains in the gas. Carbonization of coals containing 1.20 per cent sulphur evolves a gas containing about 424 grains of sulphur per 100 cu. ft., and those containing 1.60 per cent sulphur about 600 grains per 100 cu. ft. Commercial coals in the eastern part of the United States usually run from 0.5 to 1.5 per cent sulphur. Gases high in sulphur content are very undesirable for metallurgical purposes.

Coke-oven gas normally is saturated with water vapor. In distribution systems, means must be provided for draining off the condensation due to any temperature change.

Coke-oven gas burns with a non-luminous to semi-luminous flame, depending upon the degree of mixing air and gas. Its rate of flame propagation is high—considerably higher than natural, producer, or blast-furnace gas. It has a low specific gravity—lowest of any of the gaseous fuels commonly utilized by the steel industry. It has a high theoretical flame temperature—about 3600° F, a little higher than that of natural gas. The explosive range is about twice that of natural gas.

USE OF VARIOUS GASEOUS FUELS IN THE STEEL INDUSTRY

Gaseous fuels are ideal for many steel-plant applications. Below are the more important applications where gaseous fuels either must be used on account of the nature of the work or facility, or where they are preferred over a liquid or solid fuel:

> Coke-Oven Heating
> Blast-Furnace Stoves
> Gas Turbines for Power Generation
> Gas Engines for Blowing or Power Generation
> Soaking Pits
> Reheating Furnaces
> Forge and Blacksmith Furnaces
> Normalizing and Annealing Furnaces
> Controlled-Cooling Pits
> Foundry Core and Bessemer Bottom Ovens
> Blast Furnace and Steel Ladle Drying
> Drying of Blast-Furnace Runners and
>   Open-Hearth Tapping Spouts
> Hot-Top Drying

The choice of the most desirable fuel for each of the many facilities in a steel plant is not always possible, but by judicious planning the most efficient fuel or combination can be selected from those available. The general characteristics of each gas govern, wherever possible, its selection for a specific purpose in a steel plant. An outline of the important applications of the major gaseous fuels follows.

Uses for Blast-Furnace Gas—For many years, the use of blast-furnace gas for purposes other than for the firing of stoves and boilers was not economical. A number of factors have contributed, however, to the enlarged use of blast-furnace gas, the more important of which are: (1) rising cost of purchased fuel; (2) technical progress in gas cleaning, in the use of regeneration and recuperation, and in the mixing of gaseous fuels; (3) the economic advantage of using pulverized coal in boiler houses to substitute for blast-furnace gas, thereby permitting its substitution elsewhere for the more expensive liquid and gaseous fuels; and (4) seasonal shortages in the availability of purchased liquid and gaseous fuels.

In certain applications, in addition to preheating the air, the gas itself may be preheated to provide higher temperature potential. For the facilities listed below, blast-furnace gas may be utilized successfully without preheat:

> Blast Furnace Stoves
> Normalizing and Annealing Furnaces
> Foundry Core and Bessemer Bottom Ovens
> Gas Engines for Blowing or Power Generation
> Gas Turbines for Power Generation

The thermal advantage of using blast-furnace gas in gas engines for blowing and for electric-power generation must overcome the heavy investment and maintenance expense of this equipment. The modern boiler house utilizing high steam pressure and temperature with efficient turboblowers and generators has sufficiently reduced the thermal advantage of gas engines so that their use is difficult to justify. A relatively recent successful development has been the use of direct-connected gas turbines for driving generators, and jet engines for driving compressors.

Preheated blast-furnace gas burned with preheated air has been used successfully in the following:

> Coke-Oven Heating
> Soaking Pits
> Reheating Furnaces

When blast-furnace gas is preheated, it should have a minimum cleanliness of 0.01 grains per cu. ft.; and in all cases where this gas is used, extra precautions must be taken to prevent the escape of fuel or unburned gas into attendable surroundings since it contains a large percentage of toxic CO gas. Blast-furnace gas is used for many applications in the steel plant and, in addition, is used frequently for heating coke ovens and sometimes is mixed with other gases as an open-hearth fuel.

Use of Coke-Oven Gas—Coke-oven gas has had a more extended use than blast-furnace gas because of: (1) relatively low distribution costs due to its low specific gravity, high calorific value, and cleanliness; (2) its ability to develop extremely high temperatures by combustion; and (3) the high rate at which it can release heat, thereby eliminating excessively large combustion chambers. Important applications for coke-oven gas include open-hearth furnaces in addition to those previously listed for gaseous fuels. The low specific gravity of coke-oven gas is a disadvantage in the open hearth, and for this reason, it is supplemented wherever possible with a driven liquid fuel in this service. In addition, the sulphur (in the form of H_2S) present in coke-oven gas is a distinct disadvantage, particularly when used in making low-sulphur heats in the open hearth and in heating certain grades of alloy steel for rolling. Its presence also requires the use of materials resistant to sulphur attack in pipe lines, valves, and burners.

There are a number of fuel applications in a steel plant where neither blast-furnace gas nor coke-oven gas, when burned alone, develop the desired flame characteristics or temperature level for optimum results. By mixing two fuels of such great variance in characteristics, a more ideal fuel can be obtained for specific applications.

The speed of combustion is very high for coke-oven gas and very low for blast-furnace gas. The desired speed can be attained through the proper proportioning of the two fuels. The speed also can be modified to a limited extent when necessary by suitable combustion technique. Mixed blast-furnace and coke-oven gas is particularly suitable for application to soaking pits and reheating furnaces.

Use of Natural Gas—Due to plant balances requiring the purchase of outside gaseous fuels, mixtures of coke-oven gas and natural gas are often utilized. While the temperature-developing characteristics of these two gases are nearly identical, they have differences in other characteristics, notably in the rate of flame propagation and in luminosity. By proper proportioning, the advantage of a short, intensive cutting flame or a long, luminous, soft flame may be had to suit the applications.

Use of Producer Gas—Raw, hot, producer gas has been used extensively in steel-plant operations for open-hearth furnaces, soaking pits, and reheating furnaces. It has been customary to preheat this gas regeneratively when used in open hearths and soaking pits, and also in batch-type reheating furnaces. In continuous-type reheating furnaces, the fuel seldom is preheated. With good gas making, producer gas develops a soft, heavy, long, luminous flame desirable for reheating steel and in working an open-hearth heat. The use of this gas largely has been superseded in many plants by by-product gaseous and liquid fuels.

COMBUSTION OF VARIOUS GASEOUS FUELS

The major combustion reactions of the components of gaseous fuels with air and a table of essential gas combustion constants were given in Section 1 of this chapter. From chemical equations, the quantity of air required to provide perfect combustion and the resultant products may be calculated for any given gaseous fuel. Table 3—XVI shows the air requirements, products of combustion, and pertinent characteristics of several gaseous fuels. The degree of mixing of air with a gaseous fuel, and the degree of excess or deficiency of air to the theoretical requirements are pertinent combustion problems. The degree of mixing is controlled by burner design. Burners have been developed to produce short, intense flames or long, slow-burning flames. The short, intense flame is usually non-luminous or semi-luminous, while the long flame is luminous. This relation is not always the case, however, since a gas must contain hydrocarbons to develop luminosity. Burners capable of producing short, intense flames will liberate a large amount of heat in a small space. Some gases, due primarily to the constituents of which they are composed, are capable of a high rate of heat release; others, of a very low rate of heat release. The two extremes are evident in two common steel-plant fuels—coke-oven gas and blast-furnace

Table 3—XVI. Properties of Typical Gaseous Fuels[1]

Fuel Gas	Constituents of Fuel Gas Per Cent by Volume (Dry Basis)							Illuminants		Specific Gravity	Cu. Ft. of Air Required for Combustion of Cu. Ft. of Gas	Heating Value Btu per Cu. Ft. of Gas	
	CO_2	O_2	N_2	CO	H_2	CH_4	C_2H_6	C_2H_4	C_6H_6			Gross	Net
Natural Gas..........	.....	.....	0.8	.....	.....	83.4	15.8	.....	.....	0.61	10.58	1129	1021
Reformed Natural Gas.	1.4	0.2	2.9	9.7	46.6	37.1	.....	1.3	C_3H_6 0.8	0.41	5.22	599	536
Coke-Oven Gas.......	2.2	0.8	8.1	6.3	46.5	32.1	.....	3.5	0.5	0.44	4.99	574	514
Water Gas (Coke).....	5.4	0.7	8.3	37.0	47.3	1.3	.....	.....	.....	0.57	2.10	287	262
Carburetted Water Gas..............	3.0	0.5	2.9	34.0	40.5	10.2	.....	6.1	2.8	0.63	4.60	550	508
Oil Gas (Pacific Coast).	4.7	0.3	3.6	12.7	48.6	26.3	.....	2.7	1.1	0.47	4.73	551	496
Producer Gas (Bituminous Coal)..	4.5	0.6	50.9	27.0	14.0	3.0	.....	.....	.....	0.86	1.23	163	153
Blast Furnace Gas....	11.5	.....	60.0	27.5	1.0	.....	.....	.....	.....	1.02	0.68	92	92
Butane (Commercial)..	.....	.....	.....	(C_4H_{10}—93.0) (C_3H_8—7.0)				.....		1.95	30.47	3225	2977
Propane (Commercial).	.....	.....	.....	(C_3H_8—100.0)			.....	.....		1.52	23.82	2572	2371

Table 3—XVI. (Continued)

Fuel Gas	Products of Combustion in Cu. Ft. per Cu. Ft. of Fuel				Ultimate % CO_2	Net Btu per Cu. Ft. of Products of Combustion	Theor. Flame Temp. No Excess Air °F
	H_2O	CO_2	N_2	Total			
Natural Gas..........	2.22	1.15	8.37	11.73	12.1	87.0	3562
Reformed Natural Gas.	1.30	0.53	4.16	5.99	11.3	89.6	3615
Coke-Oven Gas.......	1.25	0.51	4.02	5.78	11.2	87.0	3610
Water Gas (Coke).....	0.53	0.44	1.74	2.71	20.1	96.6	3670
Carburetted Water Gas..............	0.87	0.76	3.66	5.29	17.2	96.2	3725
Oil Gas (Pacific Coast).	1.15	0.56	3.77	5.48	12.9	90.5	3630
Producer Gas (Bituminous Coal)..	0.23	0.35	1.48	2.06	18.9	74.6	3175
Blast Furnace Gas....	0.02	0.39	1.14	1.54	25.5	59.5	2650
Butane (Commercial)..	4.93	3.93	24.07	32.93	14.0	90.5	3640
Propane (Commercial).	4.17	3.00	18.82	25.99	13.7	91.2	3660

[1] From "Combustion"—American Gas Association.

gas. There is also a limit to the length of flame which can be produced. It is determined by the ability of the flame to provide enough heat to propagate itself. If the short, intense-flame type burner is used with coke-oven or natural gas, combustion will be so intense that no flame will be visible, and heat can be liberated at rates up to several million Btu per cubic foot of combustion space per hour; while the long, slow-burning-flame burner firing the same gases is capable of developing a visible flame twenty or thirty feet long with a heat liberation of 15,000 to 20,000 Btu per cu. ft. per hour. Both types of flames are desirable for specific steel-plant applications. It is obvious that burner selection based on degree of mixing is important. Carrying an excess or deficiency of air for combustion is practiced usually to control scale formation, but this is done sometimes in order to control flame characteristics. An excess of air tends to shorten, while a deficiency lengthens, a flame. An excess of air above theoretical requirements causes higher heat losses as any extra air absorbs its share of the heat of combustion. When there is a deficiency of air, potential heat is lost. In problems of design and fuel conservation, the air requirements and volume and constituents of the products of combustion must be known to effect a practical solution.

SECTION 5

FUEL ECONOMY

Since fuel represents the largest single item of expense in assembling raw materials for the manufacture of iron and steel, the subject of fuel economy is of consequence to both the producer and consumer of steel products. The steel industry consumes annually during normal times over 100 million net tons of fuel in coal equivalent. The efficient utilization of this large quantity of fuel is also pertinent to the conservation of our fuel resources. The history of the steel industry shows great progress has been made in reducing the amount of fuel required to produce a ton of steel. During the Revolutionary War, iron making required large quantities of charcoal, as the source of carbon, to reduce the ore. If a substitute had not been found for charcoal, our forests would have disappeared many years ago and our industrial progress arrested. In the past one hundred years, which really represents the modern era of steelmaking, a number of important developments have taken place to reduce the fuel requirements in producing steel. Some of these developments could be listed by historical sequence, while others are of such a nature that they cannot be designated by any period of time. The major contributions to fuel economy in steel plants have been:

(1) Development of the Bessemer converter.

(2) Development of the Siemens-Martin regenerator.

(3) Development of the hot blast.

(4) Utilization of blast-furnace gas.

(5) Installation of by-product coke plants and utilization of by-product fuels.

(6) Integration of steel plants.

(7) Electric drives for rolling mills.

(8) Improved efficiency of steam-generating equipment and steam prime movers.

(9) Large producing units.

(10) Balancing of producing units.

(11) Recovery of waste heat by recuperators, boilers and other forms of heat exchangers.

(12) Development and utilization of instruments and control equipment.

(13) Insulation of high-temperature facilities.

(14) Utilization of the optimum fuel for specific facilities.

(15) Improvements in manufacturing technique and production control.

(16) More highly skilled operators.

The results of the above contributions now have made it possible to produce a ton of steel ingots utilizing less than 1½ tons of coal (equivalent), instead of several tons as required a hundred years ago. The consumption of primary fuels in the iron and steel industry for some recent years is shown in Table 3—XVII.

In addition to these outstanding contributions to fuel economy in steel mills, the importance of the effect that rate of operations has on fuel economy should be stressed. Historically, the iron and steel industry follows the general business level maintained in the country, but its rate of operations often fluctuates more than that of many other industries. During peak production, optimum fuel economy is the natural result of operating the facilities which require fuel under the conditions for which they were designed to operate most economically. During periods of low production, fuel consumption undergoes a severe increase per unit of output; careful scheduling of production and facilities are required during this period to maintain minimum fuel losses.

The effectiveness with which by-product fuels are used in steel plants is of major significance in reducing the quantity of primary or purchased fuel required to produce a ton of steel. The consumption of by-product fuels (blast-furnace gas, coke-oven gas, pitch-tar and coke breeze) for five recent years is shown in Table 3—XVIII.

The efficiency of heat utilization by blast furnaces and their auxiliaries, by steelmaking furnaces, by soaking pits and by reheating furnaces is discussed in the chapters dealing with the design and operation of these units (Chapters 14 through 17 and Chapter 21).

Table 3—XVII. Primary Fuels Consumed by the Iron and Steel Industry[1]

| Year | Net Tons of Coal | | Net Tons of Coal Equivalent | | | Total Net Tons Coal Equivalent Consumed | Steel Production (Net Tons) | | Net Tons Coal Equivalent | |
	Anthracite	Bituminous	Fuel Oil*	Natural Gas**	Purchased Electric Power***		Ingots	Hot Rolled Product	Per Net Ton of Steel Ingots	Per Net Ton of Hot Rolled Steel
1960	771,457	77,934,530	10,194,001	15,157,338	8,370,450	112,427,776	99,281,601	76,446,483	1.132	1.471
1959	744,322	75,091,122	10,411,682	13,316,142	7,387,250	106,950,518	93,446,132	71,855,811	1.145	1.488
1958	727,008	73,999,511	9,644,937	11,705,400	7,090,630	103,167,486	85,254,885	65,105,455	1.210	1.585
1957	752,972	101,487,058	11,791,460	11,807,628	10,537,600	136,376,718	112,714,996	85,886,891	1.210	1.588
1956	700,980	97,023,169	13,569,773	11,915,568	10,810,385	134,019,785	115,216,149	89,284,317	1.163	1.501

[1]Based on statistics obtained from "Annual Statistical Reports"—American Iron & Steel Institute and "Minerals Yearbook"—Bureau of Mines.

Based on coal equivalents (ton of coal = 25,000,000 Btu) as follows:

* 1 Gallon of fuel oil = 0.006 tons of coal
** 1 Million cu. ft. of natural gas = 42 tons of coal
*** 1 Kwh. = 0.89 lbs. of coal (national utility average—1959)

Table 3—XVIII. By-Product Fuels Consumed by the Iron and Steel Industry[1]
(In Net Tons of Coal Equivalent)

Year	Blast-Furnace Gas[2]	Coke-Oven Gas[3]	Pitch-Tar[4]	Coke Breeze[5]	Total By-Product Fuels
1960	23,700,000	17,993,000	2,337,000	2,088,000	46,118,000
1959	21,400,000	15,003,000	2,064,000	1,841,000	40,308,000
1958	20,300,000	13,503,000	1,976,000	1,918,000	37,697,000
1957	27,900,000	18,583,000	2,872,000	2,311,000	51,666,000
1956	26,700,000	17,259,000	2,686,000	2,519,000	49,164,000

[1]Based on statistics obtained from "Annual Statistical Reports"—American Iron & Steel Institute, and "Minerals Yearbook"—U. S. Bureau of Mines.
[2]Based on 85 per cent utilization and 8,800,000 Btu in gas produced per net ton of pig iron.
[3]Based on 20 tons coal equivalent per million cubic feet of gas.
[4]Based on 0.0064 tons coal equivalent per gallon of pitch-tar.
[5]Based on the proportion of 10,500:12,500 to coal equivalent (0.840), and including only breeze reported as used in steam-generation and agglomerating plants.

MEANS EMPLOYED FOR HEAT CONSERVATION

The heat from the combustion of fuel which is not utilized in steel-plant metallurgical and service facilities represents an appreciable part of the total supplied. The amount lost differs with various processes. In general, the processes having the higher temperature levels have the greater thermal losses, and, therefore, offer the best opportunity for heat recovery. The largest losses usually are contained in the waste flue gases and in radiation from the furnace walls. The recovery of heat from waste flue gases of high-temperature processes has been practiced for nearly a hundred years. Since that time, improvements in design of the originally conceived regenerators, and the development and use of recuperators and waste-heat boilers, have made possible substantial recovery of heat losses. The reduction of radiation losses by the use of insulating material has been practiced in some processes for possibly fifty years; in others for relatively only a few years. The utilization of higher steam pressures and temperature and more efficient facilities for steam generation has progressed slowly but definitely in the past two decades.

Waste flue gases contain both sensible heat and the latent heat of vaporization of water and sometimes potential heat (unburned fuel gases). The recovery of the heat of vaporization of water is not practicable, and the elimination of potential heat in waste flue gas is controlled by providing sufficient air for combustion at the burners. The amount of sensible heat in waste flue gases is the product of the heat content per cubic foot or pound of gas, times the volume or weight of gases.

The total loss of heat in waste flue gases is minimized by providing only sufficient air for combustion, and by preventing air infiltration. The temperature of furnace exit gases is lowered by observance of heat-transfer principles. Waste flue-gas temperature is reduced and heat recovered by heat exchangers such as regenerators, recuperators and waste-heat boilers.

Fuel-Air Proportioning—In modern steel-plant furnaces, and in boilers, the amount of air supplied for combustion is maintained only a little above theoretical requirements by automatically controlling its flow in chosen proportion to the supply of fuel. In open-hearth and some other regenerative furnaces in earlier times, air for combustion was drawn into and through the regenerators solely by the draft created by the furnace stack. Crude attempts were made to control the supply of air by opening or closing the stack dampers. Where preheated gas was used as fuel, the problem was still more complicated.

In modern furnaces of this type, all possible points of leakage in the furnace system have been sealed to prevent air infiltration, and controlled quantities of air, in selected proportion to the amount of fuel supplied, are blown into and through the regenerators and thence into the furnace to mix with the fuel to provide the controlled combustion. In other types of furnaces, such as in heat-treating furnaces, special pressure regulators and valves accurately proportion the amounts of fuel and air fed to the burners and effect the same result.

Accurate and automatic proportioning of fuel and air has contributed to improvements in fuel economy, furnace efficiency and process control in the relatively recent past. The control of the rate of firing has also made important contributions and will be covered under "Automatic Temperature Control."

Oxygen Enrichment of Combustion Air—Air is composed of only about 20.9 per cent oxygen, with the remainder consisting of inert nitrogen plus a small amount of several other inert gases. When combustion takes place, the oxygen combines with the carbon and hydrogen of the fuel and liberates heat. The inert gases of the air absorb heat from the combustion and carry it out of the furnace, and it is lost so far as the furnace process is concerned. They reduce flame temperature by absorbing heat, thus reducing rate of heat transfer to the work.

It has been known for a long time that if the inert content of air could be diminished, much more efficient combustion could be attained. Recent technical developments that have lowered the production cost of oxygen of commercial purity have made large-scale use of this gas economical for some industrial processes. Consequently, many plants have experimented with the addition of oxygen to ordinary air used for combustion, with generally good results. In effect, increasing the oxygen content lowers the inert content of the air; consequently when a given amount of fuel is burned with oxygen-enriched air, the volume of waste gas is less than if ordinary air is used. If the temperature of the waste gas is not increased, the sensible heat loss in the flue gas will be decreased, due to the smaller heat capacity of the smaller volume. In furnaces operated at a high thermal head, a diminution of the inerts usually results in a decrease in waste-gas temperature. With the same fuel input, enriched air for combustion raises flame temperature of a given fuel, thereby improving heat-transfer rate and increasing production; alternatively, the fuel input may be decreased when enriched air is used, to maintain the same production rate as obtained with more fuel using ordinary air. Increased production rates almost always reduce the heat losses per ton of product in any furnace employing a high thermal head.

Furnace Pressure Control—If the pressure of the gases in the heating chamber of a furnace is below atmospheric, cold outside air will be drawn into the furnace through any openings that exist. If the interior pressure is above that of the outside air, the hot gases will be forced out of the furnace through these same openings, and if too much higher will, in addition, tend to penetrate the refractories with, in some cases, damaging effect. It is desirable generally to operate a furnace with a slight positive pressure in the heating chamber (i.e., furnace pressure slightly higher than atmospheric). It should be noted that the pressure from top to bottom of the heating chamber is not uniform, due to the **stack effect** of the hot gases. Control, therefore, is aimed at maintaining the desired pressure at hearth level.

Air drawn into a furnace operating under negative pressure upsets the fuel-air ratio which is controlled automatically or by valve settings. In some furnaces, such as reheating or heat treating, this air aggravates the problem of oxidation (or scaling) of the work because of the oxygen present.

If the pressure in the furnace at hearth level is equal to atmospheric or slightly positive, better heating conditions are obtained by improving heat transfer, and by better control of temperature uniformity. This is especially so in furnaces where most of the heating of the work takes place through heat transfer by radiation from the flame to the bath or work. The positive pressure must be controlled to prevent excessive **sting-out** of flame from furnace openings (a small pressure imparts a high velocity to hot gases), as well as to avoid the build-up of excessive back pressure that would interfere with the proper flow of fuel (if gaseous) and combustion air. Positive pressures maintained at hearth level in practical work are quite low, ranging only up to a few hundredths of an inch of water. Furnace pressure is controlled by adjusting the opening in the stack damper.

Positioning of the damper can be done manually, using the flame sting-out as an indication of the existence of a positive pressure, but it is difficult to adjust the opening for the frequent changes in furnace conditions. The development, about the year 1928, of industrial-type instruments with sufficient sensitivity to measure differential gas pressures with an accuracy of ± 0.0025 inch of water, made possible the use of automatic control of furnace pressure. Such instruments employ a diaphragm (or equivalent) to measure the difference between furnace and atmospheric pressure, and, through electrical relays or other devices that operate motors or by hydraulic systems, move the stack damper automatically to maintain the desired pressure in the furnace.

Automatic furnace-pressure control has been provided for the majority of steel-plant furnaces, and has been a principal factor in the improvements in fuel economy and efficiency of melting and reheating furnaces in the steel industry during the years following its adoption.

Automatic Temperature Control—By eliminating as nearly as possible human error in judging temperatures by senses, automatic instruments for measuring temperature have contributed largely to the improvement and economy of many steel-plant operations. The use of excessive amounts of fuel is wasteful of the fuel itself and results in high furnace exit gas temperatures and damage to refractories. In some processes, high fuel rates not only do not hasten transfer of heat to the material being processed, but also may cause actual damage to it. The use of insufficient fuel reduces the rate of heat transfer and prolongs process time, thereby increasing thermal losses. The optimum fuel rate for protection either of the material being heated or the furnace refractories, and often for control of heating or production rate, is maintained in many types of furnaces by automatic temperature-measuring instruments which control the fuel rate by actuating electrical relays or other units which control the operation of motors, hydraulic systems, or other means of regulating valves which control the fuel rate. It would be impossible within the scope of these pages to discuss even briefly the many types of instruments and auxiliaries used for the automatic control

of temperature; however, it may be stated that the instruments employed for measuring high temperatures in the steel industry operate on three main principles: (1) by measuring the intensity of radiation emitted by the hot furnace or object; (2) by measuring the minute electric current generated in a circuit composed of two wires of dissimilar metals, joined end to end, when one of the joints is heated (this is the principle of the thermocouple), and (3) by measuring the change in electrical resistance of conductors when heated to the temperature in question.

Regenerators and Recuperators—**Regenerators** are used alternately to absorb heat from one fluid and then transfer it to another fluid; **recuperators** are used to transfer heat continuously from one fluid to another. The fluids referred to in these two definitions are: (1) hot, gaseous products of combustion which give up heat during passage through the regenerator or recuperator and (2) fuel gas or air for combustion which undergo heating while passing through the regenerator or recuperator. Regenerators are applied usually to furnaces which can be fired alternately from the ends, the flow of gases through the furnace and regenerators being reversed by predetermined time and/or temperature cycles. Open-hearth furnaces, and many soaking-pit and batch-type reheating furnaces, are equipped with regenerators. Blast-furnace stoves also use the regenerative principle but operate over a much longer cycle and in a somewhat different manner than that practiced in other installations. In a blast-furnace stove, the checker brick is heated by burning a fuel exclusively for the purpose of heating the regenerator brick while in the open-hearth and other furnace installations the checkers are heated by waste gases. In both cases, the heat stored in the regenerators is used to preheat air for the combustion of fuel in the furnace they serve.

Recuperators have been applied in many cases to modern pit-, batch- and continuous-type reheating furnaces, and to steam boilers. When applied to steam boilers, they are commonly called "air preheaters." Recuperators are of three general types, classified according to the direction of flow of the waste gases and air, as follows:

1. Counter-flow
2. Parallel or co-current flow
3. Cross-flow

Counter-flow is used to attain maximum air-preheat temperatures; cross-current flow to secure optimum heat-transfer rates (Btu per sq. ft. of recuperator surface per degree F temperature difference per hour). Parallel flow is used where it is desirable, such as in metallic recuperators, to maintain the temperature of the division wall between the two fluids as uniform as possible throughout its length and to hold the temperature of the hot end to a minimum. Generally, a combination of the first and third types is applied to many steel-mill furnace applications where a refractory material is used to divide the two fluids. A combination of the two types is accomplished by baffling the flow of one of the fluids. In such designs, the general direction of flow of fluids exchanging heat is countercurrent and the flow in each baffled section is cross-current. Where the temperature of the waste gas from which heat is to be extracted is relatively low, say under 1800° F, metallic tubes (e.g., stainless steel) are generally used since they possess an advantage against leakage. High-temperature recuperators are generally constructed of a clay or silicon-carbide material.

Waste-Heat Boilers—These units are used to obtain heat recovery when the practical limit of recovery has been obtained by regenerators or recuperators and there is still sufficient heat left in the waste gases to justify expenditures for waste-heat boilers. In modern large, stationary open hearths, waste gases leave the regenerators at temperatures of approximately 1200° F, and from this level waste-heat boilers recover 30 to 33 per cent of the fuel used, converted into steam. Waste-heat boilers also are used sometimes in place of regenerators or recuperators, depending on conditions such as where preheated air is undesirable or where the generation of steam solves the problem of fuel conservation more satisfactorily.

Waste-heat boilers are most applicable to high-temperature, continuous processes and have been used principally in the steel plant in connection with open hearths and, to a lesser degree, with reheating furnaces and soaking pits. Fire-tube and water-tube boiler types have been installed, the former being the preferred type, generally of horizontal, single-pass design. Approximately 35 sq. ft. of boiler heating surface per ton of stationary open-hearth capacity, designed for high mass velocity of waste gases through the tubes to develop a scouring action for keeping the tubes clean and to provide high heat transfer, is used normally. Waste-heat boilers usually are provided with superheaters and sometimes with economizers.

Insulation—Thermal insulating materials have been used in steel plants for a great many years. There are many different kinds of insulating materials, each being most suitable for a specific temperature level and for the degree of insulation desired. Early applications were made to enable a facility to function more satisfactorily. Insulating material, such as **Kieselguhr,** was used to line the shell of a blast-furnace stove to aid in the retention of heat for later use by the blast furnace. Steam lines were covered with asbestos or other material to prevent condensation of steam and consequent loss of power or trouble with blowing or mill engines. The value of insulating material to conserve fuel, to afford safer and more comfortable working conditions, to protect materials susceptible to damage from heat and thermal strain, and to speed up furnace operations became evident and the progressive application of insulating material to practically all facilities which employ heat has proven beneficial to steel-plant economy. The high thermal heads at which many steel-plant operations are carried out are particularly conducive to the use of insulation for preventing large losses from radiation. In the modern steel plant, the use of insulation is justified in terms of fuel saved in boilers; stoves; open-hearth regenerators; reheating, pit, forge and annealing furnaces; steam, hot-blast and preheated-air lines; and many other miscellaneous facilities. In some operations, such as in the open hearth, the use of insulation is restricted by the temperature the refractories will stand;

consequently, radiation losses are still very high. Heat losses have been reduced in such cases by **sealing** cracks and openings in a furnace wall to prevent heat loss from radiation, exfiltration of gases and infiltration of cold air. Further progress in the development of high-temperature refractories will permit further insulation. The development of insulating firebrick in recent years is particularly significant to the fuel economy of furnaces which are operated intermittently. Many of the older furnaces are constructed of heavy refractory walls which must be heated up before the furnace is capable of producing at normal rates. These heavy furnace walls soak up considerable heat, which must be supplied by fuel. The replacement of these furnace walls with much lighter insulating firebrick permits heating up more rapidly because of less heat absorption, and permits increased production.

Instruments, for measuring temperature, pressure, volume, weight, electrical energy, etc., are used extensively in the steel industry as operating guides. They benefit fuel economy directly or indirectly.

Bibliography
(Published 1950 and later)

GENERAL

American Chemical Society, Progress in petroleum technology. Advances in Chemistry series, No. 5. The Society, 1951.

Campbell, J. R., Methods of analysis of fuels and oils. N. Y., Chemical Publishing Co., 1952.

Himus, Godfrey W., Fuel testing; laboratory methods in fuel technology; 3rd ed. London, Hill, Leonard, 1953.

Griswold, John, Fuels, combustion and furnaces. N. Y., McGraw-Hill Book Co., Inc., 1946.

Johnston, A. J. and Auth, G. H., Fuels and combustion handbook. N. Y., McGraw-Hill, 1951.

Lewis, B. and Pease, R. N., Combustion processes. Princeton University Press, 1956.

Lewis, B. and Von Elbe, G., Combustion, flames and explosions of gases. N. Y., Academic Press, 1951.

McCloud, L. W., Comparative costs of competitive fuels. University of West Virginia, Bureau of Business Research, 1951.

North American Manufacturing Co., North American combustion handbook. Cleveland, The Company, 1952.

Perry, J. H., ed., Chemical engineers' handbook. N. Y., McGraw-Hill Book Co., Inc., 1950.

Schmidt, A. X., Syllabus for fuels and lubricants; 2nd ed. N. Y. City College Press, 1950.

Smith, M. L. and Stinson, K. W., Fuels and combustion. N. Y. McGraw-Hill, 1952.

Symposium on combustion, 4th, Massachusetts Institute of Technology, 1952. Fourth symposium (international) on combustion (combustion and detonation waves). Baltimore, Williams and Wilkins, 1953.

Watkin's cyclopedia of the steel industry. Pittsburgh, Pa., Steel Publications, Inc., 1961.

STATISTICS

Keystone coal buyers manual. N. Y., McGraw-Hill Book Co., Inc., 1960.

Spiers, H. M., ed., Technical data on fuels; 5th ed. N. Y., American Society of Mechanical Engineers, 1950.

United Nations, Statistical office. World energy supplies in selected years 1929–1950. N. Y., Columbia University Press, 1952.

(Continued on next page)

COAL AND COKE—GENERAL

American Iron and Steel Institute and American Coke and Coal Chemical Institute, Coke evaluation project. Contributions to the metallurgy of steel, No. 43. N. Y., The Institute, 1952.

American Institute of Mining and Metallurgical Engineers, Gasification and liquefaction of coal. N. Y., The Institute, 1953.

Christopher, J. E. and Byron, T. H., Modern coking practice; 4th ed., 2 vols. London, Technical Press, 1952.

Coke oven managers association, Year-book, 1950. London, Benn, 1950.

———— same, 1951.

———— same, 1952.

Court, W. H. B., Coal (History of the Second World War, United Kingdom civil series) London, His Majesty's Stationery Office, 1951.

Glenn, R. A. and Rose, H. J., The metallurgical, chemical and other process uses of coal. Pittsburgh, Bituminous Coal Research, Inc., 1958.

Machin, R. E., Science in a coalfield; 2nd ed. Pitman, 1952.

Marshall, C. E., Coal petrology. Economic Geology, 50th Anniversary Volume, 1955.

Missouri, University of, School of mines and metallurgy. Process of underground electrocarbonization. The University, 1952.

Mitchell, D. R. ed., Coal preparation; 2nd ed. N. Y., A.I.M.M.E., 1950.

Pope, P. C., ed., Coal: production, distribution, utilization. London, Chapman, 1950.

Progress in coal science, ed. by D. H. Bangham. vol. 1. N. Y., Interscience, 1950. (Originally published in England).

Raistrick, A. and Marshall, C. E., Nature and origin of coal and coal seams. N. Y., British Book Centre, 1952.

United Nations, Economic Commission for Asia and the Far East, Coal and iron ore resources of Asia and the Far East, N. Y., Columbia Univ. Press, 1952.

Van Krevelen, D. W. and Schuyer, J., Coal Science. Elsevier Publishing Co., 1957.

Williams, A. W., Coal manual for industry. N. Y., Conover-Mast, 1952.

Wilson, P. J. and Wells, J. H., Coal, coke and coal chemicals. N. Y., McGraw-Hill, 1950.

COAL AND COKE—TESTING

American Society for Testing Materials, Coal and coke. Phila., The Society, 1961.

GASES

American Gas Association, Gaseous fuels. N. Y., the Association, 1954.

American Gas Association, Interchangeability of various fuel gases with manufactured gases. N. Y., The Assn., 1950.

American Society for Testing Materials. Gaseous fuels. Phila., The Society, 1953.

American Society for Testing Materials, Standards on gaseous fuels; 2nd ed. Phila., The Society, 1951.

Chapman, S. and Cowling, T. G., Mathematical theory of non-uniform gases; an account of the kinetic theory of viscosity, thermal conduction, and diffusion in gases; 2nd ed. London, Cambridge, 1952.

Cowling, T. G., Molecules in motion. N. Y., Longmans Green, 1950.

Foster, J. F. and Lund, R. J., eds., Economics of fuel gas from coal. N. Y., McGraw-Hill, 1950.

Franzen, H., Exercises in gas analysis. London, Blackie, 1951.

Gumz, W., Gas producers and blast furnaces. N. Y., Wiley, 1950.

Hoy, H. R. and Wilkins, D. M., Total gasification of coal. B.C.U.R.A. Monthly Bulletin 22, No. 2 (1958).

Jost, W., Diffusion in solids, liquids, gases. Academic Press, 1952.

Knudsen, M. H. C., Kinetic theory of gases; 3rd ed. N. Y., Wiley, 1950.

Lewis, B. and Von Elbe, G., Combustion, flames and explosions of gases. Academic Press, 1951.

Martin, G. and Francis, W., Volumes and weights of industrial gases; 2nd ed. London, Technical Press, 1953.

Physics of liquids and gases, by E. Kappler (and others); translated, edited and published in cooperation with the Office of Technical Services. Petersburg, N. Y. Leibiger Research Labs., 1951.

Ruhemann, M., Separation of gases; 2nd ed. N. Y., Oxford, 1950.

Sears, F. W., Introduction to thermodynamics, the kinetic theory of gases, and statistical mechanics. Cambridge, Mass., Addison-Wesley, 1950.

———— same. 2nd ed., 1953.

Sherwood, T. K. and Pigford, R. L., Absorption and extraction; 2nd ed. N. Y., McGraw-Hill, 1952.

CHAPTER 4

Metallurgical Coke and Coal Chemicals

SECTION 1

INTRODUCTORY

Although the oxides of iron may be reduced to metallic iron by many agents, carbon (directly or indirectly) is the reducing agent found to be best suited for the economical production of iron. Carbon of suitable reactivity and physical strength was at one time produced from wood by distillation, yielding wood charcoal; but for operation of a modern large blast furnace the carbon required for the smelting of iron is obtained from the destructive distillation of selected coking coals at 1650° F to 2000° F.

Chemical Nature of Coal—Coal is made up principally of the remains of vegetable matter which has been partially decomposed in the presence of moisture and the absence of air and subjected to variations in temperature and pressure by geologic action (see Chapter 3). It is a complex mixture of organic compounds, the principal elements of which are carbon and hydrogen with smaller amounts of oxygen, nitrogen, and sulphur. It also contains some non-combustible components called ash. The ash consists primarily of inorganic compounds which became imbedded in the coal matrix during the coalification process.

The chemical compounds making up coal, like most of those in animal and vegetable life, are unstable when subjected to a high degree of heat or thermal treatment. When heated to high temperatures, in the absence of air, the complex organic molecules break down to yield gases, organic compounds of lower molecular weight and a relatively non-volatile carbonaceous residue (coke).

Coke and Coal for Coking—Coke, then, is the residue from the destructive distillation of bituminous coal. Structurally it is a cellular, porous compound which is heterogeneous in both physical and chemical properties. The physical properties of metallurgical coke, as well as its composition, depend largely upon the coal used and the temperature at which it is carbonized. Not all bituminous coals will form coke, and not all coking coals will give the same firm, cellular mass characteristic of coke suitable for metallurgical purposes. Some coals will produce an acceptable coke without blending with other coals, while others are usable only as constituents of blends. Chapter 3 already has described how preparation of coals prior to coking is an important element in metallurgical-coke production. The type and method of operation of cok-

ing facilities also exert a profound influence on the quality and yield of coke for the blast furnaces.

Kinds of Coke—There are three principal kinds of coke, classified according to the methods by which they are manufactured: **low-, medium-** and **high-temperature coke.** All of the coke used for metallurgical purposes must be processed in the higher ranges of temperature if the product is to have satisfactory physical properties. Even with good coking coal, the product obtained by low-temperature carbonization (900° to 1400° F) is unacceptable for metallurgical purposes.

It is generally agreed that the most desirable blast-furnace coke is made from mixtures of high-volatile and low-volatile coals, pulverized and blended and then coked in ovens capable of heating the mass to a uniformly high temperature.

At the majority of coke plants, high-volatile coking coals are blended with low-volatile coals in varying percentages, depending on the particular coals, the purpose being to produce coke of high quality and yield. In the earlier days of the coke industry, some of the coking coals used were superior to those currently being carbonized. Some progress has been made in the utilization of coals which expand and exert pressures on oven walls during coking. In addition, it is generally conceded that higher ash and sulphur coals are acceptable currently for coking purposes than in use in former years. In all probability the practice of blending coals has been one of the greatest single factors in the extension of coal reserves usable for coking purposes. At present, laboratory scale tests are available which are capable of evaluating both the coking and expansion characteristics of individual coals or blends. A few plants retain the practice of using only a single coal for coking purposes while others use mixtures of high-, medium- and low-volatile coals for coke production. The practices followed in this respect are determined largely by economic considerations.

The acceptability of a coal for metallurgical-coke production depends on various factors relating to its chemical and physical characteristics as well as its economic availability. While laboratory tests can be used to develop data to permit evaluations in this respect, final appraisal can be determined best by actual full-scale plant test under exact conditions of their use.

Factors Controlling Properties of Metallurgical Coke—Coke for blast-furnace consumption must be sufficiently firm and strong to resist shattering by handling, and crushing by the pressure exerted by the heavy blast-furnace burden. It should be free of dust and fines, and in pieces not too large for optimum speed of combustion. With a good coking coal, these physical properties can be controlled only moderately by the coking process. As the coal is heated, it becomes plastic at 660° to 890° F, forming a fused mass irrespective of its form when charged into the retort. As bituminous coal is heated through this range of temperature, volatile matter is given off, rapidly at first, then more slowly up to about 1740° F. The coals making up a blend, so far as possible, should have about the same plastic range. Slow heating through the plastic range increases slightly the hardness of the coke. The size of the lumps of coke depends largely upon the thickness of the coal charge and whether or not it is heated from one or both sides. As to chemical composition, a good metallurgical coke will contain very little volatile matter—not over 2 per cent—and 85 to 90 per cent fixed carbon. The remainder is ash, sulphur and phosphorus. The phosphorus content, 0.018 to 0.040 per cent for making Bessemer iron, preferably should be low also for basic iron. Sulphur varies from 0.6 per cent to 1.5 per cent, but is desired as low as possible because coke is the chief source of sulphur in the pig iron produced. Standard specifications for foundry coke call for a volatile-matter content of 2 per cent, a maximum sulphur of 1 per cent, a maximum moisture of 3 per cent, and a minimum fixed carbon of 86 per cent. Shatter and tumbler tests are also specified, but no standard for combustibility has been adopted. These requirements are controlled through selection of the coal, which should be low in sulphur, free from slate or removable refuse, and give an ash which has a moderately-high fusion point in a reducing atmosphere. The question of why coals coke is not fully understood.

Methods of Manufacturing Metallurgical Coke—There are two methods for manufacturing metallurgical coke, known as the **beehive process,** and the **by-product** or **retort process.** In the beehive process, air is admitted to the coking chamber in controlled amounts for the purpose of burning therein the volatile products distilled from the coal to generate heat for further distillation. In the by-product method, air is excluded from the coking chambers, and the necessary heat for distillation is supplied from external combustion of some of the gas recovered from the coking process. With modern by-product ovens, properly operated, all the volatile products liberated during coking are recovered as gas and coal chemicals, and about 40 per cent of the gas produced is returned to the ovens for heating purposes. While the beehive process was the leading method for the manufacture of coke up to 1918, it now has been replaced largely by the by-product process. There are still places, however, where beehive ovens serve a useful purpose: the chief justification for their use is stated at the end of Section 2 of this chapter, under "Present Status of the Beehive Process." As far as can be determined, the processes of manufacture have little effect on the quality of the coke for blast-furnace use. There is a difference in coking temperature of the two processes, that of the by-product being somewhat lower than the beehive. Beehive coke is usually larger, though not as uniform in size. In general, properly carbonized beehive and by-product coke are silvery gray in appearance when quenched with fresh water.

Products of Coal Carbonization—The reactions occurring during the carbonization of coal for the production of metallurgical coke are complex. The process can be considered as taking place in three steps: (a) Primary breakdown of coal at temperatures below 1296° F (700° C), yields decomposition products some of which are water, oxides of carbon, hydrogen sulphide, hydroaromatic compounds, paraffins, olefins, phenolic, and nitrogen-containing compounds. (b) Secondary thermal reactions among these liberated primary products as they pass through hot coke, along hot oven walls and through highly-heated free space in the oven involve both synthesis and degradation. A large evolution of hydrogen and the formation of aromatic hydrocarbons and methane occur in the stage above 1296° F (700° C). Decomposition of the complex nitrogen-containing compounds produces ammonia, hydrogen cyanide, pyridine bases and nitrogen. (c) Progressive removal of hydrogen from the residue in the oven produces hard coke.

During carbonization, about twenty to thirty per cent by weight of the initial charge of coal is evolved as mixed gases and vapors which pass from the ovens into the collecting mains and are processed through the coal-chemical recovery section of the coke plant to produce coal chemicals. When the production of coke is accomplished in modern by-product coke ovens with equipment for recovering the coal chemicals, one net ton of coking coal in typical American practice yields about the following proportions of the several coal chemicals and coke, depending upon the type of coal carbonized, carbonization temperature and method of coal-chemical recovery:

Blast-Furnace Coke	1,200-1,400 lb.
Coke Breeze	100-200 lb.
Coke-Oven Gas	9,500-11,500 cu. ft.
Tar	8-12 gal.
Ammonium Sulphate	20-28 lb.
Ammonia Liquor	15-35 gal.
Light Oil	2.5-4 gal.

The **coke-oven gas** contains the **fixed gases** so classified because they are gases at 760 mm. pressure and 60° F (15.5° C). They are hydrogen, H_2; methane, CH_4; ethane, C_2H_6; carbon monoxide, CO; carbon dioxide, CO_2; illuminants which are essentially unsaturated hydrocarbons, such as ethylene, C_2H_4; propylene, C_3H_6; butylene, C_4H_8; and acetylene, C_2H_2. Other fixed gases present are hydrogen sulphide, H_2S; ammonia, NH_3; oxygen, O_2; and nitrogen, N_2.

Other substances in the raw gases and vapors leaving the ovens, which are **liquids** at ordinary temperatures, are:

(a) **Ammonia Liquor** (primarily the water condensing from the gas), an aqueous solution of ammonium salts of which there are two kinds—**free** and **fixed.** The free salts are those which are decomposed on boiling to liberate ammonia. The fixed salts are those which require boiling with an alkali such as lime to liberate the ammonia.

(b) **Tar,** the organic matter that separates by condensation from the gas in the collector mains. It is a black, viscous liquid, a little heavier than water. From it the following general classes of compounds may be recovered: pyridine, tar acids, naphthalene, creosote oil and pitch.

(c) **Light Oil,** a clear yellow-brown oil with a spe-

cific gravity of about 0.880. It contains varying amounts of coal-gas products with boiling points from about 40° C to 200° C and benzene, toluene, xylene and solvent naphthas are recovered from it.

In the recovery of coal chemicals (Figure 4—22), the first step is the recovery of the basic crude materials (coke-oven gas, ammonia liquor, tar and light oil) as a primary operation in accordance with commercial practice. Secondary operations consist of the processing of these primary products to separate them into their components. Coal-chemical recovery is discussed in Section 4 of this chapter.

SECTION 2

THE BEEHIVE PROCESS FOR CARBONIZING COAL

Construction of Ovens—As shown in Figure 4—1, the name beehive is literally descriptive of the form of the beehive coke oven. Beehive coke oven plants constructed in the past have followed three general arrangements, as follows: (1) the **bank system,** in which the ovens are built in single rows against a

bank of earth, natural or artificial, thus making it necessary to build but one retaining wall along the front of the ovens; (2) the **single-block system,** which consists of a single row of ovens with retaining walls at both the front and back; and (3) the **double-block system,** in which the ovens, in a double row, are built

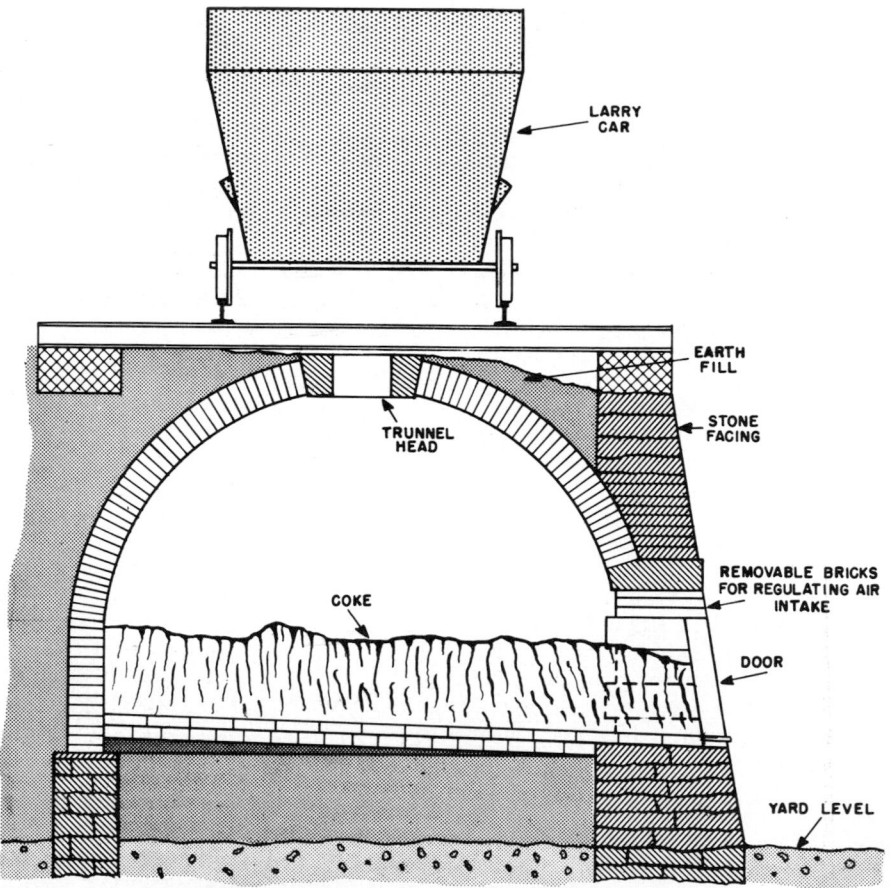

FIG. 4—1. Ideal section of beehive coke oven in a single-block battery, showing refractory brick lining, the clay and earth fill, the arched door through which the coke is watered and drawn, and the trunnel head at the top through which the coal is charged and the volatile products escape. Vertical lines in the coke bed indicate the fissures that develop during coking, giving beehive coke its characteristic columnar structure.

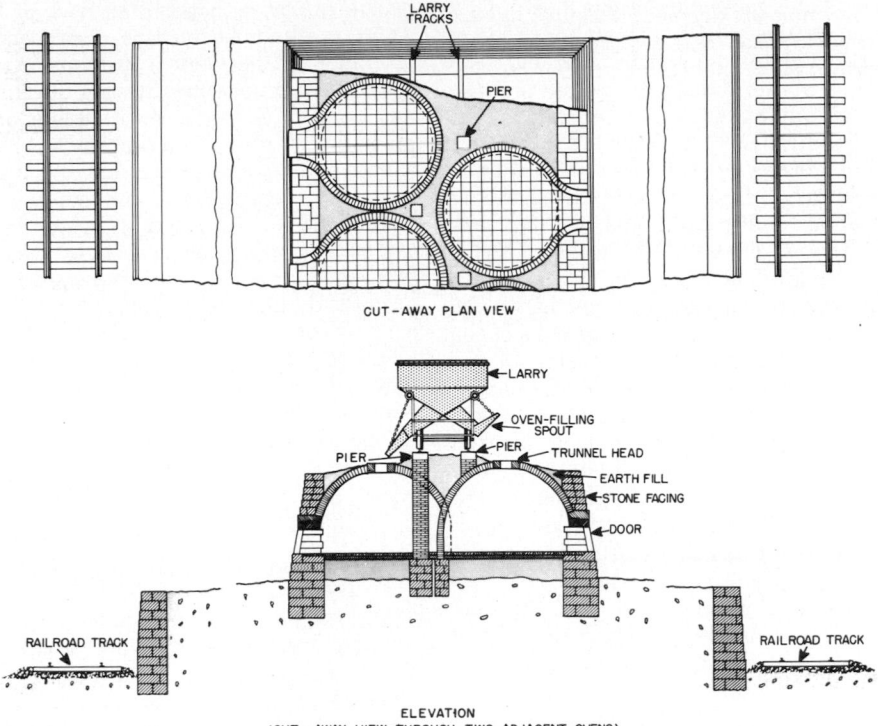

FIG. 4—2. Schematic diagram showing arrangement of beehive ovens built according to the double-block system.

back to back or staggered with a retaining wall extending along the front of each row. Figure 4—2 illustrates the double-block system.

Waste-Heat System—Early in this century, an occasional beehive coke-oven battery, usually of the banked ovens, was arranged for utilizing the waste heat from the products of combustion to generate steam. A large tunnel was constructed in the bank some 10 feet back of the ovens and parallel to the battery. This tunnel was connected to each oven by a flue which conducted the hot gases out of the oven from an opening sufficiently above the side wall to prevent its being closed by the largest charge of coal. Each flue was provided with a damper for closing off the draft during the period when the oven was being watered, drawn, and charged. From the battery, the tunnel passed to the boiler house, where branches conducted the hot gases through the fireboxes and flues of the boilers to a common stack. The stacks used were about 100 feet in height to produce proper draft. During the coking period, the coal-charging hole on the ovens necessarily was kept tightly closed. Owing to the increased draft, these ovens were inclined to run at a little higher temperature than ordinary beehive ovens, causing the temperature in the tunnel to be high, sometimes reaching 2730° F. A maximum of about 20 horsepower per oven was generated from the waste heat from a battery. This method did not achieve widespread popularity in this country and was used only at a few plants.

Charging—Beehive ovens are charged as soon as practicable after drawing, in order that stored-up heat from the previous charge will be sufficient to start

the coking process. New ovens must be heated up gradually to the coking temperature by wood and coal fires, after which small charges of coal are coked until the ovens reach normal working conditions. With the oven in readiness for charging, the door is partially bricked up and the charge is dropped through the **trunnel head** from the **larry car** above, leaving the coal in a cone-shaped pile in the oven. In order to secure uniform coking of the coal, this pile must be leveled so that the coal will lie in a bed of uniform depth over the entire bottom of the oven. This leveling may be done by machine or by hand. In works not equipped with a machine, the leveling is accomplished by a large long-handled scraper, operated through the door of the oven, which is purposely bricked up to only two-thirds of its height at the time of charging. After leveling the coal, the door opening is then bricked up to within about 1½ inches of the top.

Coking Process—The coking process begins very soon after leveling is completed, as the ovens retain enough heat in the brick of the walls and the loam backing to start liberation of the volatile matter from the coal. As more heat is absorbed by the coal charge, the temperature of the oven soon reaches the "kindling" (ignition) point of the combustible gases, which, in the presence of the air admitted to the oven, ignite with a slight explosion at first, and then continue to burn quietly in the crown of the ovens, or as small candlelike flames at the surface of the coking mass, thus supplying heat to continue the process. Coking proceeds from the top of the coal downward, so that the coking time depends mainly upon the depth of the coal. The generation of gas thus rapidly approaches a maximum, which is maintained for a period, then declines to practically nothing. The burning of volatile matter during this period must be regulated by gradually closing up the opening at the top of the door for admission of air. This regulation is necessary to maintain the temperature at a maximum, and conserve coke, as an excess of air at the beginning of the coking period tends to cool the oven, and later consumes the carbon of the coke. The yield is also reduced by improper leveling. If the coal is not of uniform depth in the oven, the thin portions coke through before the thick, and some of the coke of the thin sections is consumed while the coking of the thick portions is being completed. On the other hand, if the process is stopped when the thin areas have coked through, there will be a loss due to uncoked butts on the thick areas. In the coking of bituminous coals in beehive ovens, coking proceeds downward from the top of the charge in which the coal, at increasing depths, passes through a plastic state as the temperature rises. This produces expansion and contraction of the charge with the result that the cake is ramified by a great number of irregular vertical fissures, thus giving it a long columnar structure. These very irregular columns extend from the top to the bottom of the cake. This structure affords a means by which beehive coke can be distinguished from byproduct coke.

Watering and Drawing—At the end of the coking time, the brickwork closing the door is torn out, and the coke is **watered out.** Usually, this watering is accomplished by a self-propelled spraying device. It consists of a tube or pipe a few inches shorter than the diameter of the oven, pivoted at its center on a feed pipe and perforated by two rows of holes on opposite sides, starting from the center. The holes are arranged to throw jets of water horizontally, which causes the pipe to revolve. Where this device is not provided, the ovens are watered by spraying with a stream of water through the door of the oven. After watering, the coke may be drawn either by hand or machine. As the work is arduous, a machine known as the Covington coke-drawing machine is commonly employed. It is provided with a long arm fitted with a head, flat on the bottom, but inclined on the top, and a pair of hinged ears, or drawing lugs. Upon being pushed by motor into the oven, the head moves in advance of the drawing lugs, which lie flat, and raises the coke from the bottom of the oven. Upon the return, the lugs engage this loosened coke and force it through the door in advance of the head to fall upon a conveyor system that carries it to a screen, from which it passes to railroad cars. It is impossible to remove all the coke with the machine, and what remains must be drawn out by hand upon the conveyor. In straight hand-drawing, the coke is drawn out into the yard and forked into barrows, which are used to wheel the coke into railroad cars. The forking and screening leave the coke free of smaller particles called **breeze.**

Present Status of the Beehive Process—The beehive process still holds an advantage for certain peak requirements where the high investment cost of a by-product plant cannot be justified because of long inoperative periods. Beehive coke is usually made near a mine that supplies coal that can be coked successfully in this type of oven. Formerly, coals suitable for coking by the beehive process were relatively plentiful and accessible. The coal from any one source was seldom pre-treated or blended with other coals. Because of depletion of coals that have the rather limited range of individual properties that make them suitable for beehive coke making, it is possible that this method will find decreasing future use unless blended coals from more than one source can be used economically. If the beehive process could be modified to permit recovery of waste gases, this also might extend its use.

SECTION 3

THE BY-PRODUCT PROCESS FOR CARBONIZING COAL

The by-product process, being a true distillation process, involves the use of retort ovens. While there are many modifications, these ovens consist essentially of three main parts; namely, the **coking chambers,** the **heating chambers,** and the **regenerative chambers**—all constructed of refractory brick. The coking chambers are rectangular in section, varying in general from 30 to 42.6 feet in length, from 6 to 14 feet in height, and 12 to 22 inches in width. From 10 to 100 ovens constitute a **battery** of ovens, in which coking chambers alternate with heating chambers so that, in effect, there is a heating chamber on each side of each coking chamber. The regenerative chambers are underneath the heating and coking chambers. Separating walls between regenerators, also serve as foundation walls for the heating and coking chambers. The entire structure is supported either from the ground or by columns under a structural-steel base. The coal is charged through openings in the top of the oven, and the coke is pushed out from one end by a power-driven ram, or pusher, acting through the other end (Figure 4—3). All quenching or watering of hot coke is done outside of the oven. During the coking period, the ends of the oven are closed by refractory-lined doors, which must be constructed so as to effect complete sealing of the oven. The ovens first constructed in the industry provided a space between the door and the jamb which was filled with a special luting mixture prior to charging. Later several types of self-sealing doors were developed, which seal the opening when put in place and require no luting. To permit the escape of the volatile matter, which must undergo several different treatments to separate the various coal chemicals, an

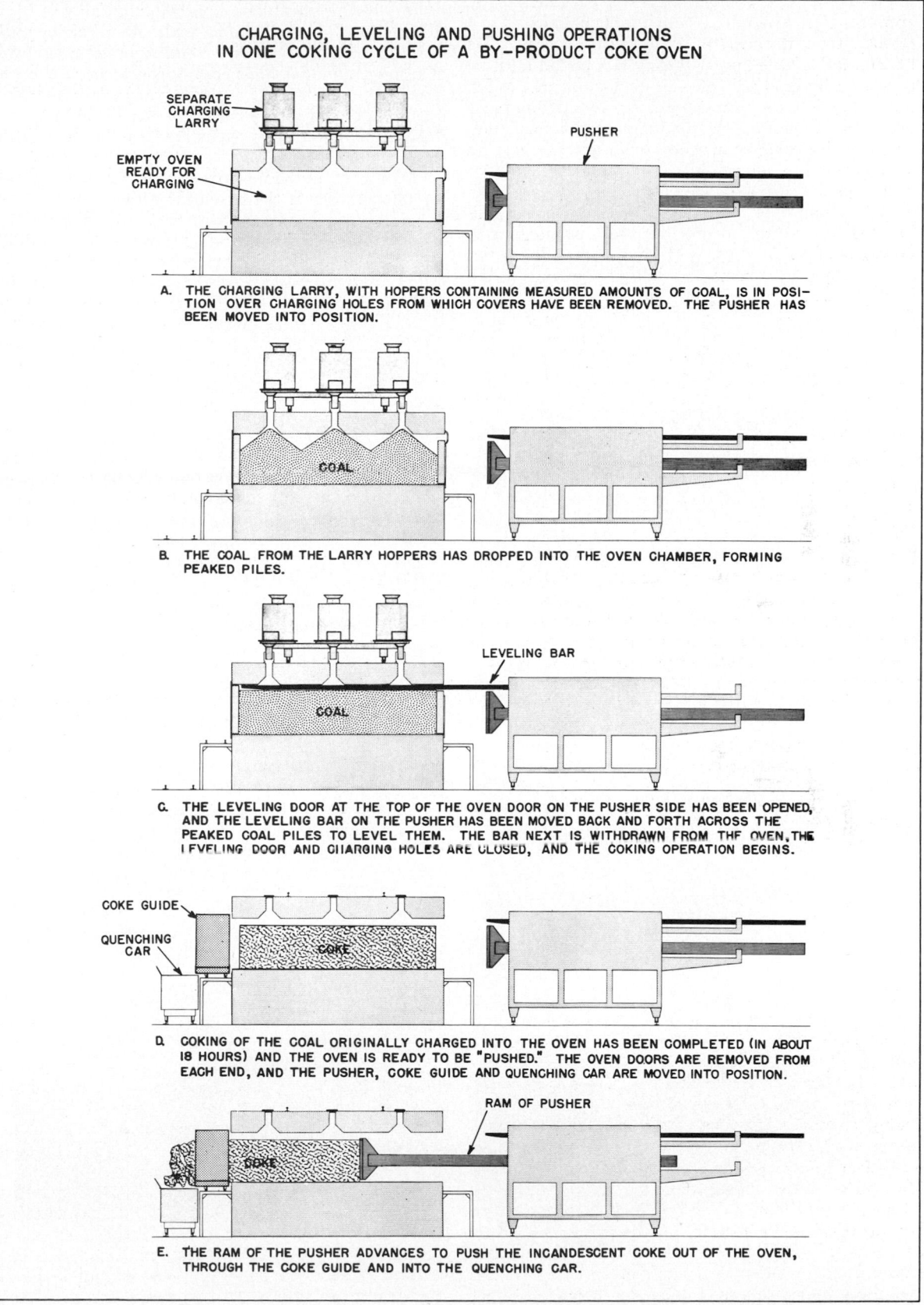

CHARGING, LEVELING AND PUSHING OPERATIONS
IN ONE COKING CYCLE OF A BY-PRODUCT COKE OVEN

SEPARATE CHARGING LARRY

EMPTY OVEN READY FOR CHARGING

PUSHER

A. THE CHARGING LARRY, WITH HOPPERS CONTAINING MEASURED AMOUNTS OF COAL, IS IN POSITION OVER CHARGING HOLES FROM WHICH COVERS HAVE BEEN REMOVED. THE PUSHER HAS BEEN MOVED INTO POSITION.

COAL

B. THE COAL FROM THE LARRY HOPPERS HAS DROPPED INTO THE OVEN CHAMBER, FORMING PEAKED PILES.

LEVELING BAR

COAL

C. THE LEVELING DOOR AT THE TOP OF THE OVEN DOOR ON THE PUSHER SIDE HAS BEEN OPENED, AND THE LEVELING BAR ON THE PUSHER HAS BEEN MOVED BACK AND FORTH ACROSS THE PEAKED COAL PILES TO LEVEL THEM. THE BAR NEXT IS WITHDRAWN FROM THE OVEN, THE LEVELING DOOR AND CHARGING HOLES ARE CLOSED, AND THE COKING OPERATION BEGINS.

COKE GUIDE

QUENCHING CAR

COKE

D. COKING OF THE COAL ORIGINALLY CHARGED INTO THE OVEN HAS BEEN COMPLETED (IN ABOUT 18 HOURS) AND THE OVEN IS READY TO BE "PUSHED." THE OVEN DOORS ARE REMOVED FROM EACH END, AND THE PUSHER, COKE GUIDE AND QUENCHING CAR ARE MOVED INTO POSITION.

RAM OF PUSHER

COKE

E. THE RAM OF THE PUSHER ADVANCES TO PUSH THE INCANDESCENT COKE OUT OF THE OVEN, THROUGH THE COKE GUIDE AND INTO THE QUENCHING CAR.

FIG. 4—3. Schematic representation of the sequence of operations involved in charging, leveling and pushing in one coking cycle of a by-product coke oven.

opening is provided through the top and at one or both ends of the oven. This opening is fitted with an offtake pipe, which in turn connects with the gas-collecting main for the battery.

The combustion chambers consist of a great number of flues in order to promote uniformity of heating throughout the entire length of the oven. Ovens with both horizontal and vertical heating flues have been built but the latter has largely replaced the former in present installations. While some of the older ovens employed the recuperative principle for preheating the air for combustion, modern practice demands the use of regenerative chambers, because the heat is better conserved and less gas is thereby required to heat the ovens. In the arrangement of these regenerators, two plans have been employed. By the first plan, the regenerative chambers, two in number, are placed longitudinally beneath a whole battery of ovens; with this arrangement, the ovens of a battery are at right angles to the regenerators. Each end of each oven is connected to one of the regenerators. The flow of gases, obviously, must be reversed simultaneously for all ovens in a battery when changing from one regenerator to the other. This precluded, to a great extent, precise heat regulation for an individual or selected group of ovens in a battery. This type oven did not achieve widespread popularity in this country. In the second plan, individual regenerators are placed under each oven. This plan permits control of the preheated-air supply for combustion to individual vertical heating flues, and makes closer control of heating possible to improve uniformity of heat distribution, in conjunction with other refinements made practicable by this system. Another advantage of using individual regenerators is that each oven is thus made more nearly an independent unit, and the operation of the whole battery is not liable to be influenced by one or two ovens that may be shut down for repair or other reasons.

Heating of individual ovens is controlled so that the temperature at the base of the flues in which gas is being burned does not exceed 2600° to 2700° F, which is considered the safe maximum temperature range to which coke-oven refractories should be subjected. With the flues operating within this temperature range, coking time depends upon the width of the oven, the nature of the coals being coked, and other factors. In general, a coking time is selected that will produce a uniform "skin temperature" of the block of coke in the oven of from 1900° to 2000° F at the time the charge has been coked all the way through to the center. The "skin temperature" referred to above applies to the coke adjacent to the walls of the oven. The time required for coking coal under the above operating conditions will vary from 16 to 20 hours, depending upon the factors already stated. Average time is about 17 to 18 hours.

MODERN TYPES OF BY-PRODUCT OVENS IN THE UNITED STATES

In the steel industry in the United States, the transition from beehive to by-product ovens was ac-

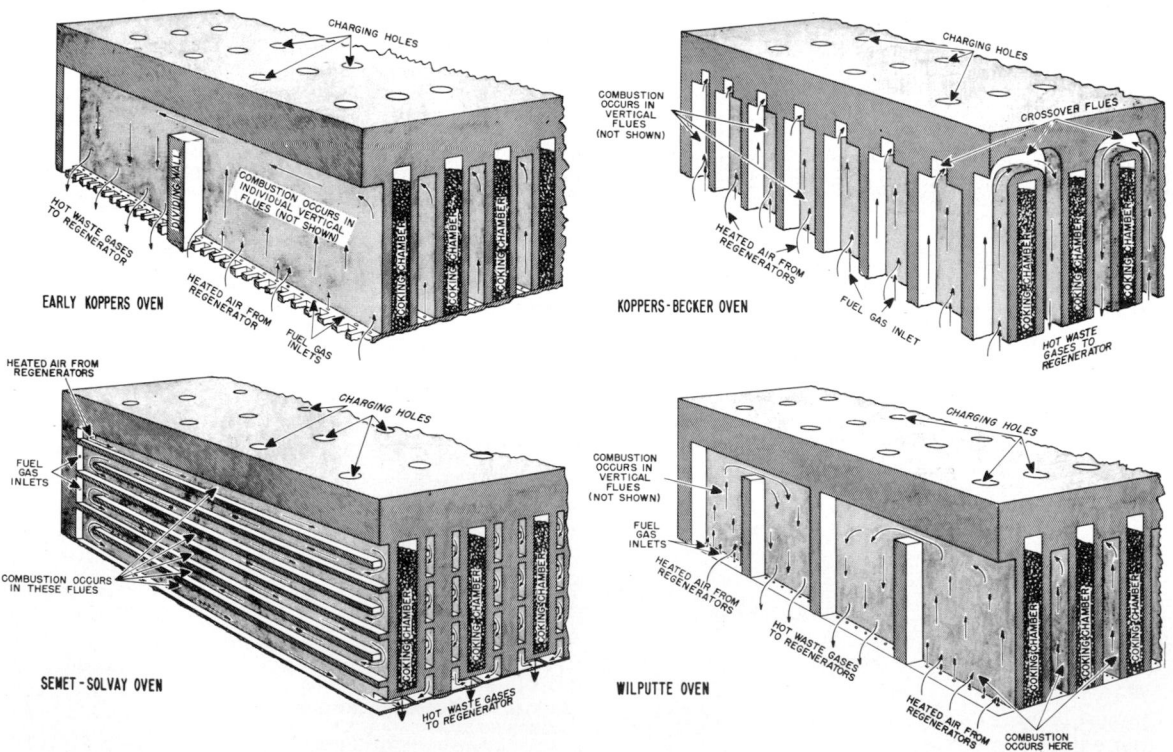

FIG. 4—4. Schematic representation of the differences in firing methods employed in the four most common types of coke ovens. Individual flues are not shown, except for the Semet-Solvay oven. The firing procedures shown are for a single phase of heating which is reversed at the end of a specified period.

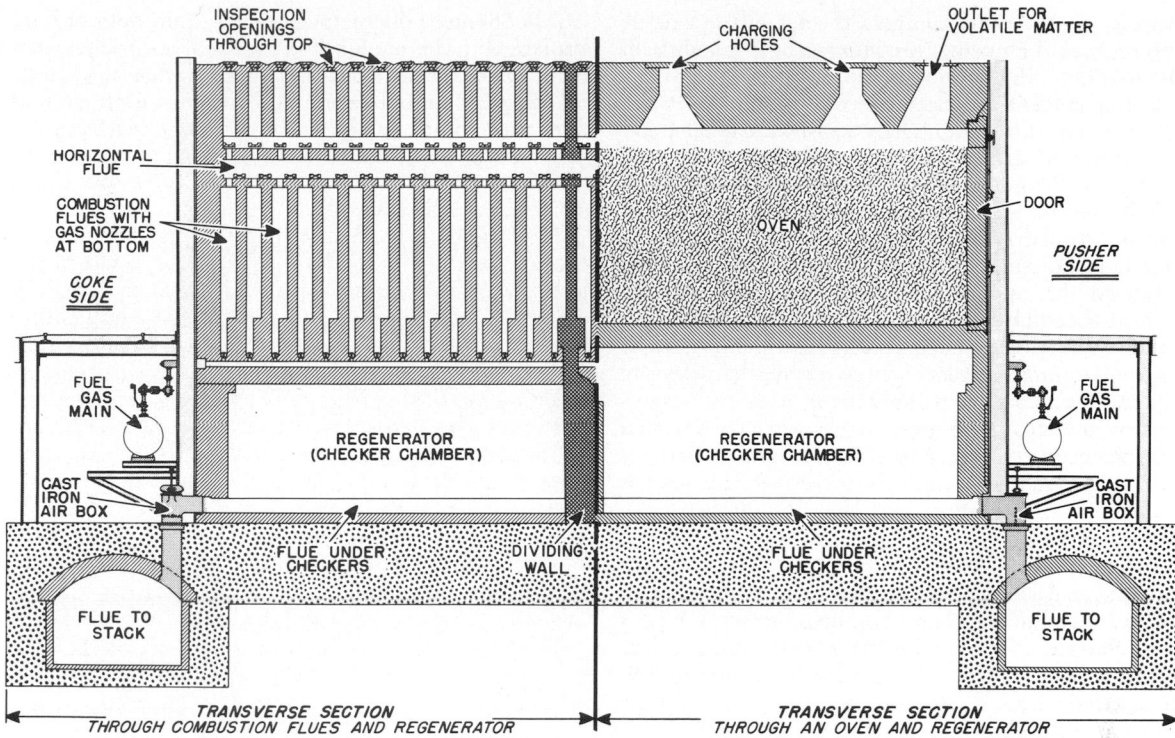

FIG. 4—5. Transverse and longitudinal sections of Koppers regenerative single-divided coke-oven battery. Left side of transverse section is through combustion chambers, that at right is through oven chamber. Left side of longitudinal section is through air ports: right side through gas nozzle brick. See also Figure 4—4. (Courtesy, Koppers Company, Inc.).

celerated with the start of World War I when the construction of by-product coke ovens was begun in many locations in the eastern and central states. While some of the ovens erected at that time are still in operation, a large number either have been rebuilt "in kind" or replaced with ovens of different design. The present popular designs in the United States, largely named after either the designer or builder, are the Koppers, Koppers-Becker, Wilputte and Semet-Solvay. The chief differences in design of these four types involve the heating systems employed. Figure 4—4 illustrates schematically, by simplified sketches, how each type is heated. More detail is given in the text and in subsequent illustrations. Ovens of these four designs comprise about 97 per cent of the by-product coking capacity in this country.

Metallurgical coke, while still the primary product, no longer commands the almost exclusive consideration in oven design as in former years since the coal chemicals recoverable in the by-product process are in constantly increasing demand.

The Koppers Oven—This type of by-product oven, more technically referred to as a regenerative, single-divided oven, was the most prominent around 1916 and many are still in operation. In a typical oven of this period (Figures 4—4 and 4—5), all parts except the foundation and battery top are constructed almost entirely of the best grade of silica brick.

The majority of ovens of this type initially constructed in the United States had a coking volume of 500 cubic feet. The dimensions of these ovens were: length, 37 feet from face to face of the doors; height, 9 feet, 10 inches from floor to roof; and width, tapering from 17 inches at the pusher end to 19½ inches at the discharge end. Usually four charging holes were provided in the top for admitting the coal charge, while a separate opening at one end provided an outlet for volatile matter. The oven is of the vertical-flue type with individual regenerative chambers (Figure 4—5). The heating chamber has a total of thirty vertical flues. They are provided with openings to the regenerative chambers, the fuel gas mains, and to a large horizontal flue on a level a little below the top of the coking chamber. A dividing wall near the middle of the oven separates the heating chamber, except the horizontal flue, into two parts with sixteen vertical flues on the narrower end of the oven and fourteen on the wider end. Each end, approximating half of the oven, may thus be heated alternately, and in practice the reversals are made automatically every half hour for each battery of ovens by a reversing mechanism controlled by an automatic timing device. Two large underground flues, one on each side, extending along both sides in front of, and parallel to, the battery and connected to the checker chambers by cast-iron air boxes, provide for escape of the products of combustion. These flues lead to a stack about 200 feet high at one end of each battery to furnish the draft necessary to draw the gases through the heating system. An idea of the magnitude of the structure may be gained from the fact that a single battery of sixty-four ovens contains the equivalent of about 2,500,000 nine-inch brick.

The Koppers-Becker Oven—The Koppers-Becker oven employs a different flue arrangement whereby the gas is burned on an entire wall simultaneously (both pusher and coke side). The products of combustion from groups of two or more vertical flues of the "on" walls in which fuel gas is burning enter short bus-flues and are thence conducted over the top of the oven through cross-over flues to a companion series of bus-flues whereby the vertical flues of the entire "off" wall are simultaneously conducting waste gas to the regenerators. On reversal, the opposite conditions obtain. Since the flues in each wall (coke side to pusher side) are connected only to the flues in its companion wall, there are no crossover flues over every other oven and the battery thus is limited to an uneven number of ovens (see Figures 4—6, 4—7 and 4—8).

The Wilputte Oven—The Wilputte oven is known as a double-divided oven, having two outer zones in the heating system and one double inner zone. In this oven, the gas is alternately burned upwards in the two outer zones with the products of combustion being carried down through the double inner zone and, on reversal, burned upwards in the double inner zone with the products of combustion being carried down through the two outer zones (Figures 4—4, 4—9 and 4—10).

The Semet-Solvay Oven—The Semet-Solvay installations have oven batteries employing horizontal heating flues (the other three types use vertical heating flues), wherein fuel gas is introduced at one end and waste gas drawn off at the other end, with regular reversal of flow (Figures 4—4 and 4—11).

CONSTRUCTION AND OPERATION OF BY-PRODUCT OVENS

For purposes of discussion, the different principal parts of a by-product oven will be considered in the following order; i.e., Coking Chamber, Heating System, Oven Doors, Gas-Collecting System, and Accessory Equipment.

Coking Chamber—The dimensions of the coking chamber are in each case a compromise of many correlated variables that will best suit the expected operations and produce the highest grade of product within practical limits. Past experience with coals of similar properties is the best guide, as there is no well defined academic method of arriving at definite oven dimensions for specific coals.

In general, the average dimensions of the present day oven are from 10 to 14 feet in height, 30 to 43 feet in length, and 15 to 19 inches in average width. The ovens are narrower on the pusher side and have a taper of from 2 to 4 inches, according to the expanding or contracting properties of the coals to be coked. The ends of the oven are closed with brick-lined re-

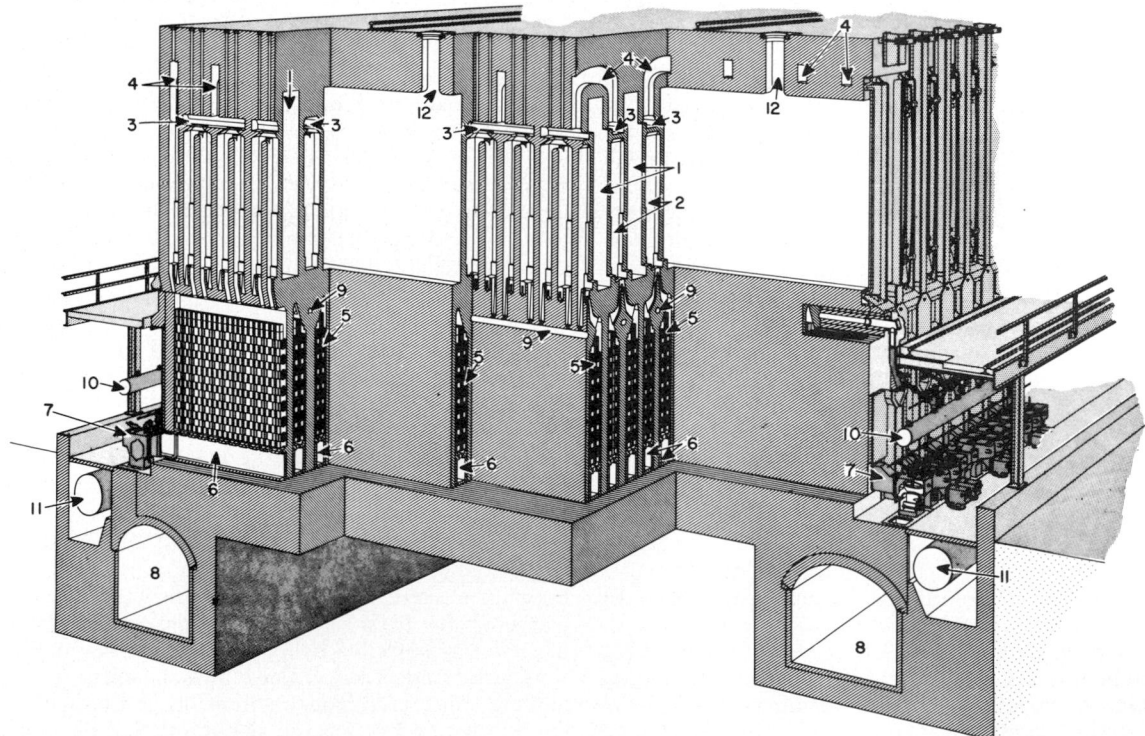

FIG. 4—6. General perspective cut-away section of Koppers-Becker combination ovens with gun-flue heating facilities (see Figure 4—8 for underjet-fired type). 1. Oven chamber. 2. Vertical combustion flues. 3. Horizontal flues. 4. Cross-over flues. 5. Regenerators. 6. Oven sole flues. 7. Gas and air connections to waste-gas flue. 8. Waste-gas flues. 9. Gas ducts for coke-oven gas. 10. Oven gas main. 11. Blast-furnace gas main. 12. Charging holes. (Courtesy, Koppers Company, Inc.).

movable doors. The side walls, or liners, are built of first-quality silica-brick shapes set in silica mortar that forms a ceramic bond at the higher temperatures. The oven floor may be of first-quality clay blocks, though silica bricks have been used for oven floors for many years.

Inasmuch as most of the heat for the coking process is conducted through the oven liners, the coking really starts at the side walls and progresses through to the center of the coal charge. There is no fusing together of the charge at the center as can be seen in Figure 4—12. This feature limits the length of any piece of coke to half the width of the oven minus any shrinkage. The structure of the coke mass at the end of the coking period is somewhat similar to two parallel slabs of irregularly interlaced pieces of coke that may be pushed from the oven by the pressure applied by the pushing ram with very little lateral pressure on the oven side walls. However, the walls must have sufficient structural strength to resist a high lateral pressure in case the interlaced structure of the coke mass is broken up for any reason during pushing. All modern ovens, from a structural point of view, also are designed to prevent, as far as possible, leakage of gases in either direction through the brickwork between the oven retort and the heating flues.

For a brief period after the establishment of the by-product coke oven in the United States, there was a trend toward using narrow ovens, but the modern trend for most plants is towards use of wider ovens. There is also a trend toward more taper, pusher to coke side, in the oven chambers. This increased taper permits the use of a wider range of coals of varying characteristics, allowing for greater flexibility in making up blends for charging ovens whenever changing blends becomes necessary to utilize coals other than those normally used. In this way irregular blends may be processed with less danger of damage to the ovens or excessive operating delays caused by stickers.

Stickers are ovens that cannot be pushed in the normal manner due to excessive expansion during the processing, or coke of insufficient structural strength to hold the interlaced mass during pushing, thereby developing a lateral component of the pushing force that greatly increases the side-wall friction.

The coal is charged into the oven through charging holes provided in the roof of the oven. The oven retort and the heating system are designed for a coal charge of definite volume, having a level top surface a definite distance below the oven roof, usually one foot. The number of charging holes and the physical characteristics of the coal have a definite bearing on the time required for charging the oven with coals. A minimum charging time is particularly desired for many reasons. To prevent escape of gases from the oven during charging, it has now become standard practice at most plants to **charge the oven on the main.** As charging on the main is accomplished by steam-jet aspiration, which puts the oven retort under suction during the charging and leveling period, it is impossible to prevent the introduction of some air into the gas recovery equipment.

Excessive leveling tends to pack the coal along the top of the coal charge, particularly under the charg-

ing holes thus increasing the bulk density and heat requirements at this area. This has particular significance when using expanding coals. Excessive leveling may also cause local erosion of the oven wall.

Heating System—The present-day heating systems of the more prominent ovens in this country fall into two general classes; the **gun-flue type,** shown in Figure 4—7, and the **underjet type,** shown in Figures 4—8 and 4—9. In the gun-flue type the gas is introduced through a horizontal gas-duct extending the length of each wall a little below the oven floor-line. Short connecting ducts lead vertically upward to a replaceable nozzle-brick at the bottom of each of the vertical flues. In the underjet type, the fuel gas is introduced into each flue from the gas distributing piping in the basement of the battery through a circular gas duct built integrally into the regenerator division and flue supporting walls. Each of these separate burner pipes is equipped with an orifice and metering pin to permit control of gas to each flue.

There are various designs of both general types, all attempting to heat the coal at a controlled rate and temperature, uniformly from end to end of oven, and from bottom to top of charge (with the exception of the top few inches which may be held slightly lower for the better control of coal-chemical recovery), and at the lowest rate of Btu's per pound of coal carbonized. In the Koppers oven of 1917, as previously described, the coke-oven gas, stripped of various coal chemicals, is burned in all flues on the pusher side at once, the products of combustion passing into the horizontal flue and then down through the coke-side flues and regenerators to the stack. On reversal, the air is preheated in the coke-side regenerators and burns the gas in the coke-side vertical flues. The products of combustion are conducted through the horizontal flue to the pusher-side flues where they are carried down through the pusher-side regenerators and to the stack. In the Koppers-Becker ovens the arrangement of the regenerators beneath the ovens, as shown in Figure 4—8, is such that the ovens under the cross-over ducts have alternately one wall with gas on and one with gas off, while the ovens not under cross-over ducts have alternately both walls with gas on, and then both with gas off. This regenerator arrangement is in the interest of having a minimum number of walls operating under high differential pressure. Considerable care is taken in design to have the lowest possible differential pressure between the flues and ovens and between adjacent regenerator walls in order to prevent cross flow of gases at these locations.

Another point of particular importance in flue design is the relative position of the gas inlet in the vertical flue in relation to the air port, and the manner in which the gas and preheated air are caused to be mixed. Excessive turbulence will result in too sharp combustion, and a short intense flame will cause local over-heating at the base of the vertical flue.

For many years, oven operators and designers have felt that control of the rate of flame propagation and flame length in the vertical flues was desirable. Many suggestions were considered, the principal one of which was waste-gas dilution. The difficulties and expense associated with the use of waste gas that had

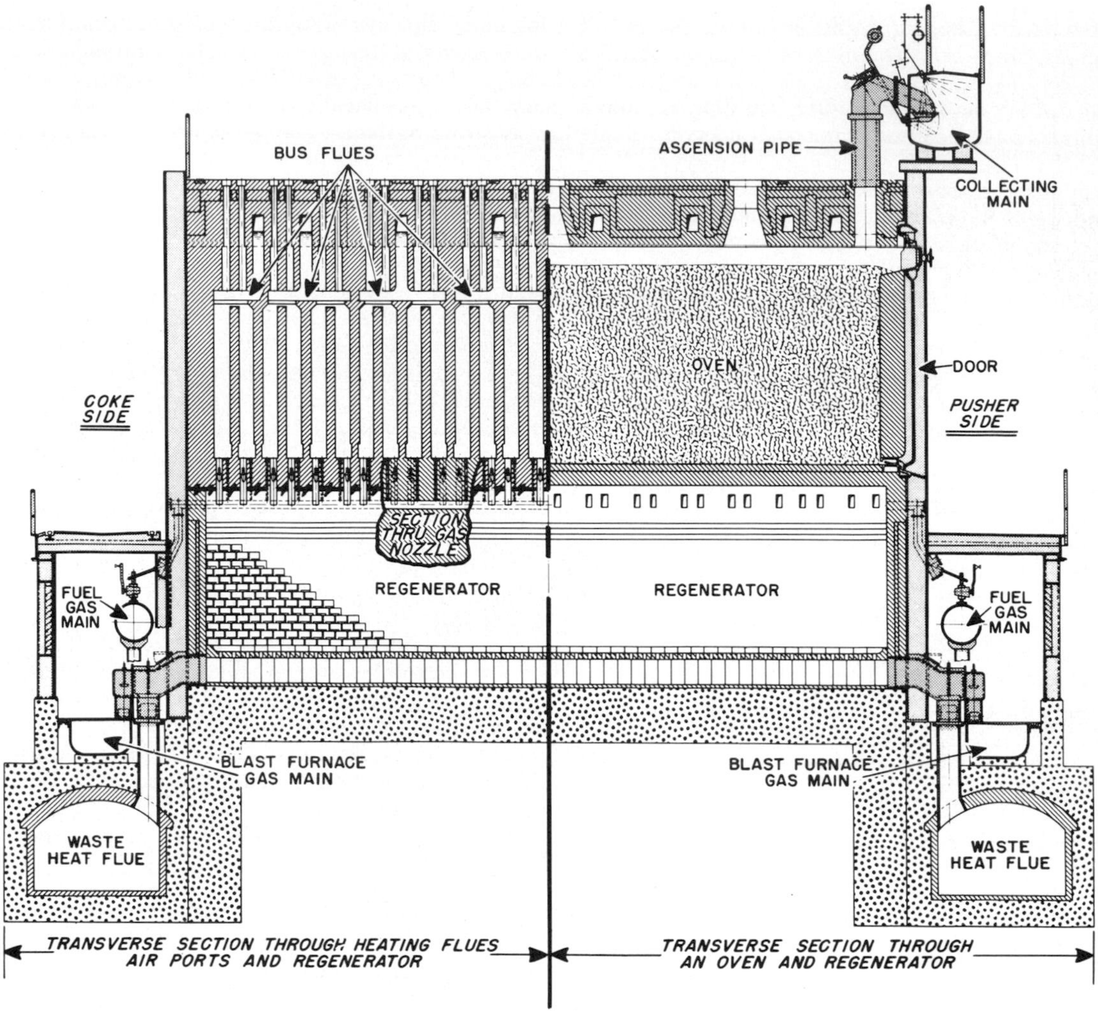

FIG. 4—7a. (Above) Transverse sections through a Koppers-Becker combination gun-flue type by-product coke-oven battery. (Courtesy, Koppers Company, Inc.).

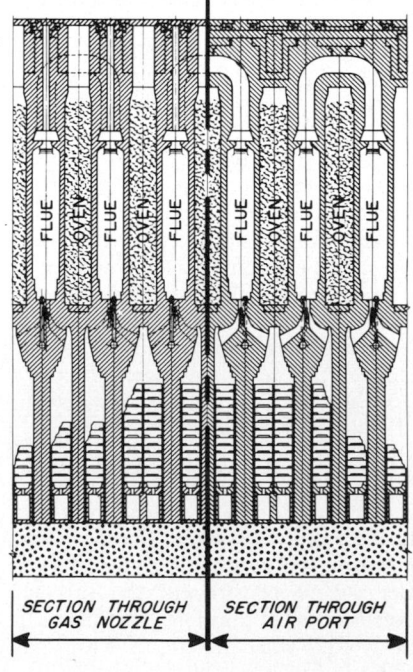

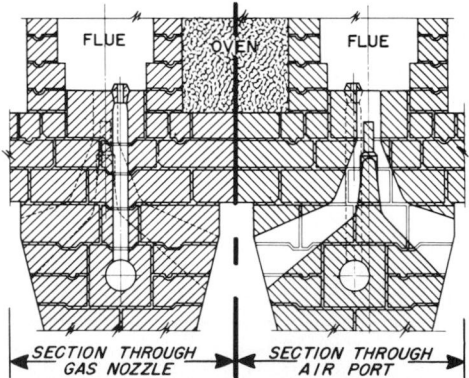

FIG. 4—7b. (Above) Enlarged sections through gas nozzles and air ports of a Koppers-Becker combination gun-flue type of by-product coke oven, showing detail of part of Figure 4—7c. (Courtesy, Koppers Company, Inc.).

FIG. 4—7c. (Left) Longitudinal section (left) through gas nozzles and (right) through air ports of a portion of a Koppers-Becker combination gun-flue type by-product coke-oven battery. (See Figure 4—8 for design of under-jet type of Koppers-Becker oven.)

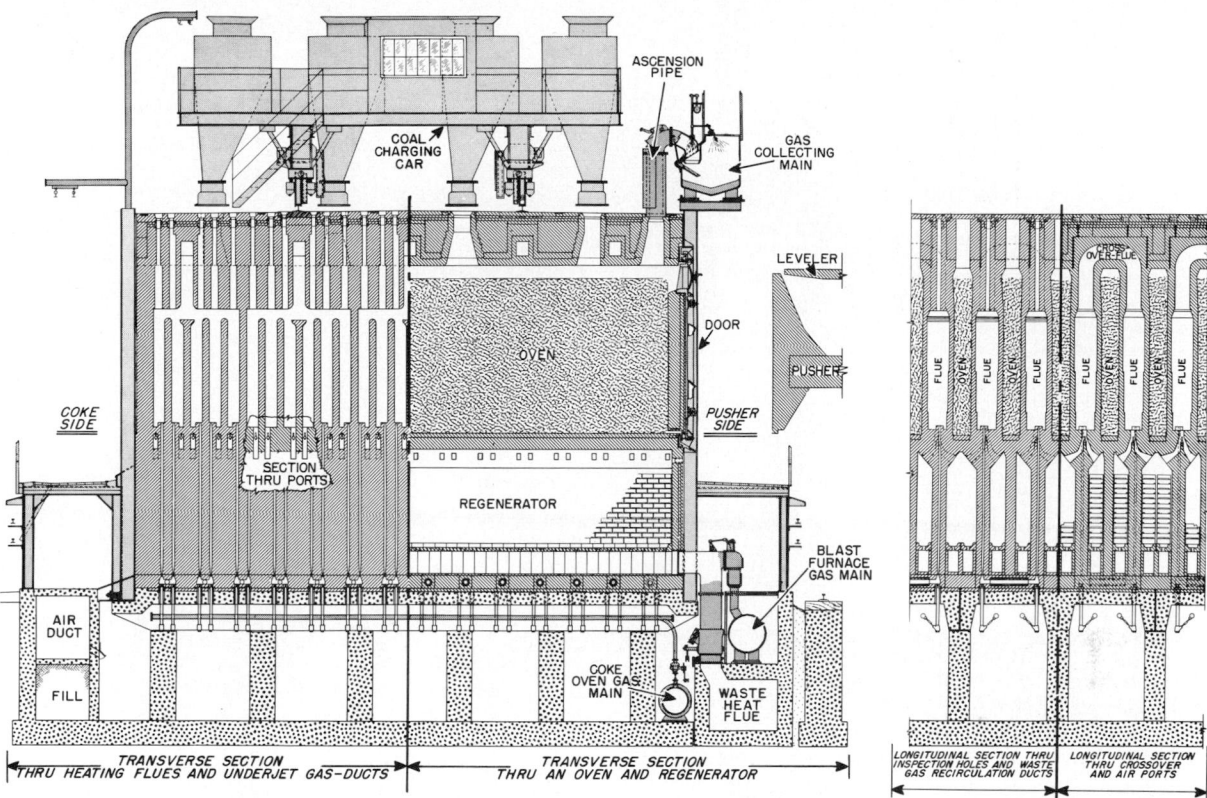

Fig. 4—8a. (Above) Transverse and longitudinal sections through Koppers-Becker underjet-fired low-differential combination by-product coke oven. See Figure 4—13 for enlarged section of waste-gas recirculation ducts seen in longitudinal section. (Courtesy, Koppers Company, Inc.)

Fig. 4—8b. (Right) Enlarged sections through underjet gas duct and air port of a Koppers-Becker underjet-fired low-differential combination by-product coke oven, showing detail of part of longitudinal section of Figure 4—8a. See also Figure 4—13. (Courtesy, Koppers Company, Inc.)

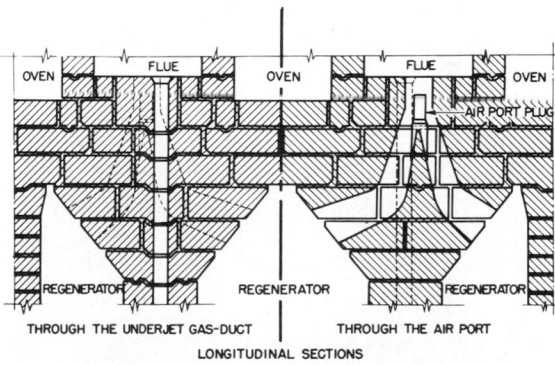

been permitted to cool below the dew point were prohibitive. A system of waste gas recirculation by jet aspiration has been used in the Koppers-Becker design (see Figure 4—13). By this device a fixed amount of hot, waste gas is mixed with the incoming gas. By this recirculation the flame length may be controlled without purification of the waste gas and without having to heat the diluent as would be required with external mixing. The ratio of recirculated waste-gas to oven gas is controlled by the orifice size and the fuel-gas pressure, and normally approximates a one-to-one mixture.

Waste-gas recirculation also prevents the accumula-

tion of carbon in the underjet gas-ducts, as the contained carbon dioxide and water vapor both tend to inhibit carbon deposition. In ovens not recirculating waste gas, air must be introduced into the gas ducts on the "gas off" periods for decarbonization.

A feature of the Wilputte oven, shown in Figures 4—9 and 4—10, especially those of over 10 feet in height, is the **high-low burner construction**. Low burners in alternating flues with adjacent high burners prevent overheating at the bottom of the flues and thus tend to give a better vertical distribution of heat.

In the gun-flue-type oven, the changes of the nozzle brick which regulate the gas flow to the various verti-

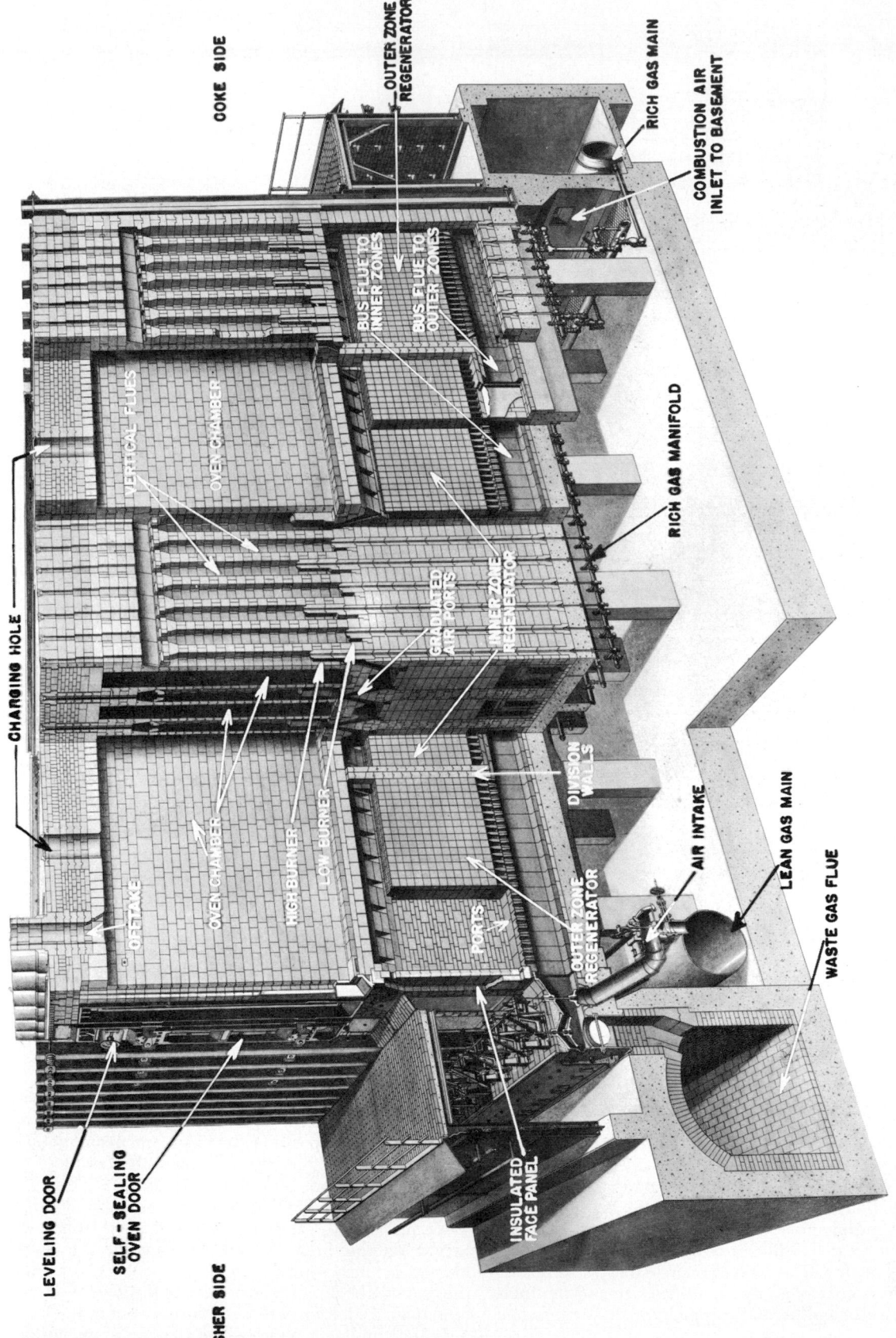

COKE SIDE

OUTER ZONE REGENERATOR

RICH GAS MAIN

COMBUSTION AIR INLET TO BASEMENT

BUS FLUE TO INNER ZONES

BUS FLUE TO OUTER ZONES

CHARGING HOLE

VERTICAL FLUES

OVEN CHAMBER

RICH GAS MANIFOLD

GRADUATED AIR PORTS

INNER ZONE REGENERATOR

DIVISION WALLS

OVEN CHAMBER

HIGH BURNER

LOW BURNER

AIR INTAKE

OFF-TAKE

PORTS

OUTER ZONE REGENERATOR

LEAN GAS MAIN

WASTE GAS FLUE

LEVELING DOOR

SELF-SEALING OVEN DOOR

PUSHER SIDE

INSULATED FACE PANEL

FIG. 4—9. General perspective "cut-away" drawing of a Wilputte combination underjet-fired by-product coke oven. The "rich" fuel gas referred to is coke-oven gas; the "lean" gas is blast-furnace gas. Compare with Figures 4—4 and 4—10 (Courtesy, Wilputte Coke Oven Division, Allied Chemical Corp).

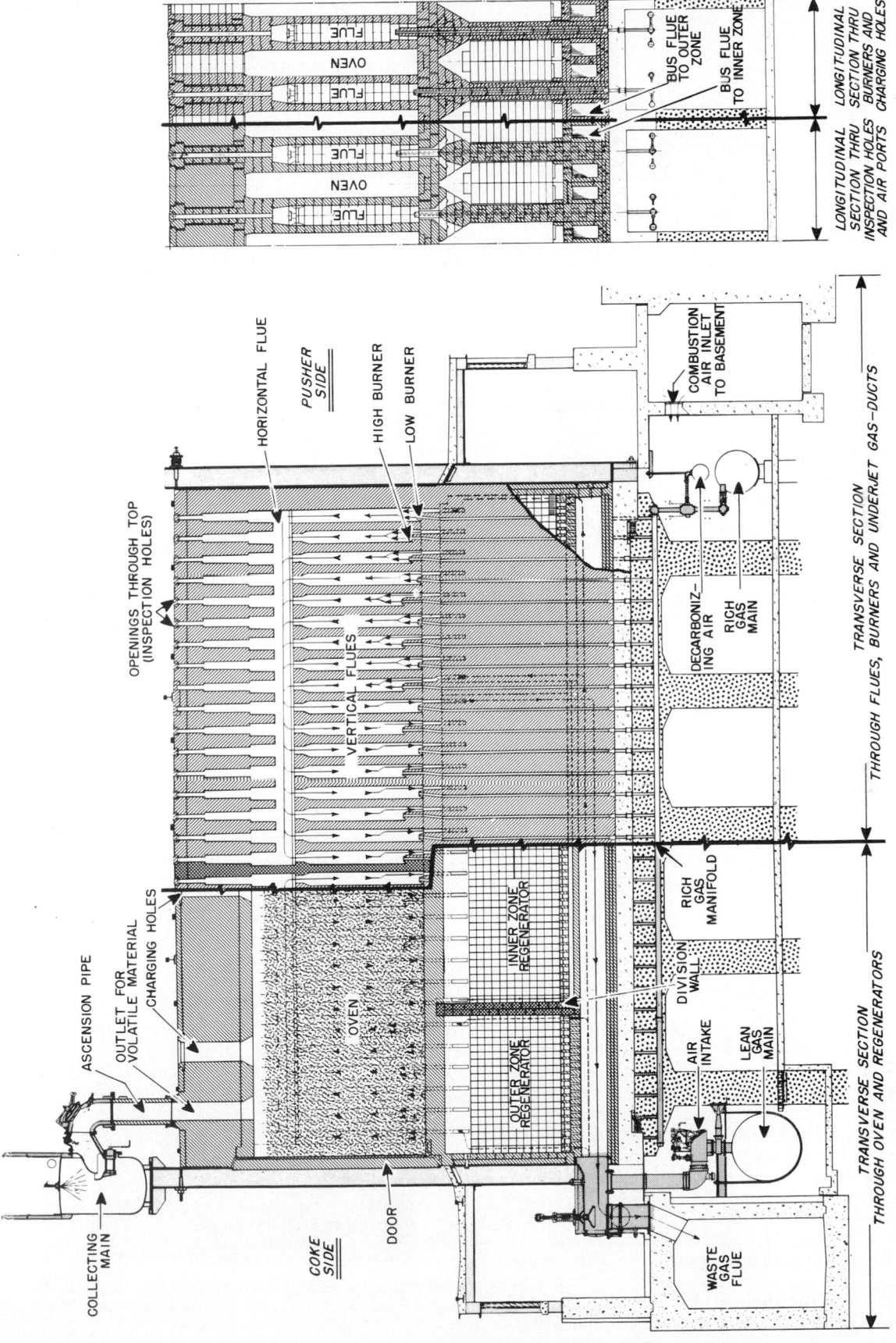

Fig. 4—10. Sections through a battery of Wilputte underjet, combination, by-product ovens, designated as "double-divided" ovens, having two outer zones and one double inner zone in the heating system. The rich gas and lean gas referred to on the drawing are coke-oven gas and blast-furnace gas, respectively. See also Figures 4—4 and 4—9. (Courtesy, Wilputte Coke Oven Division, Allied Chemical Corp.).

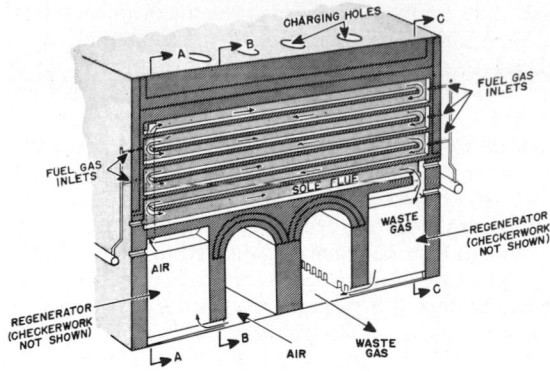

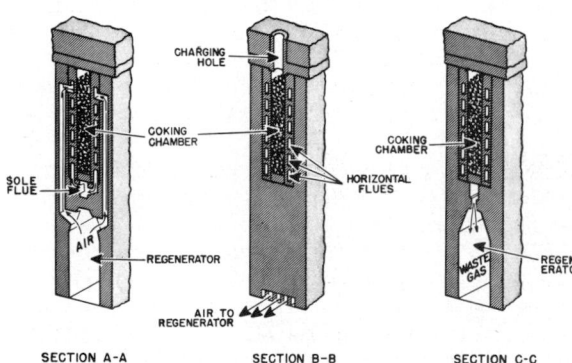

FIG. 4—11. Schematic sections showing paths of air, fuel gas and products of combustion in a Semet-Solvay coke oven. Upon reversal, the direction of the arrows in the upper drawing that indicate direction of flow of air and waste gas are reversed.

cal flues is done from the top of the battery. Immediately over each vertical flue, a duct is provided from the horizontal flue through the battery top and ending at a removable flue-inspection cap flush with the oven top. When necessary, the nozzles are removed and replaced through these ducts by long rods especially designed for this purpose. In the underjet-type oven, the same flue extensions are provided for flue inspection, but the gas flow is regulated by changing the orifice or metering pin in the accessible external fuel-gas piping in the oven basement.

Where blast-furnace gas or other lean gases are used for oven heating, the regenerator system must be designed so that both the air and gas are preheated. In the Koppers-Becker oven, the regenerator chambers are so arranged that the fuel gases and waste gases are not regenerated in adjacent chambers but are separated by an air-regenerating chamber. With this design, the effect of leakage across the high-differential-pressure wall is minimized, as the incoming air and gas are under the same pressure and traveling in the same direction, and the high-differential-pressure wall is between the incoming air and the outgoing waste-gas.

When a lean gas, such as blast-furnace gas or producer gas, is used for oven heating, supplementary

heating with a higher calorific value gas may be needed in order to maintain coke production at as high a rate per oven operating hour as when firing with straight high-Btu gas. It is not practical to do this mixing before regeneration of the gas as the rich component of the mixed gas will be partially cracked passing through the regenerators and will cause an objectionable deposition of carbon. To overcome this cracking tendency, the enriching gas is externally diluted to the desired degree with lean gas and introduced through the customary fuel system.

With the introduction of the underjet oven and the accurate proportioning of fuel gas necessary to each vertical flue, it is important that the reversing cocks, lines, and orifices or metering pins be clean at all times. This is accomplished by cleaning the fuel gas with electrical precipitators located at each battery of ovens.

After the electrical precipitators, and ahead of the battery fuel-gas mains, the gas is heated to assure its maintenance above the dew-point. On some of the older designs of the gun-flue type, the fuel-gas mains located in the alleys on both the pusher and coke side were insulated to limit the condensation in the headers and to keep the gas at a uniform temperature throughout the length of the header. This temperature control is important as temperature change affects the density and specific heat of the gas and influences the uniformity of battery heating.

Air for Combustion—In the gun-flue-type oven, the air required for combustion is taken into the sole flue at the base of the regenerator chambers through an air box equipped to regulate the amount of air

FIG. 4—12. View of coke being pushed from oven, showing central line of cleavage and block-like structure of the coke.

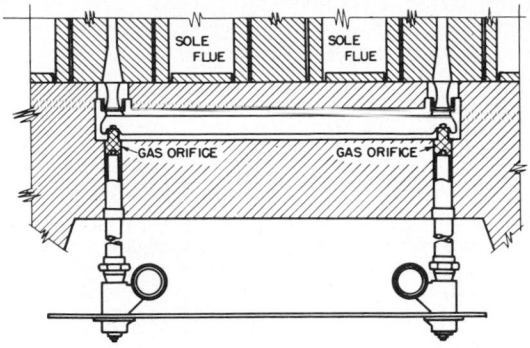

FIG. 4—13. Section through waste-gas recirculation duct of the Koppers-Becker by-product coke oven shown in Figure 4—8. (Courtesy, Koppers Company, Inc.).

taken from the alleys on both sides of the battery. In this arrangement the temperature, the velocity and direction of the wind have a marked effect on the heating and must be compensated for by the heater. In the underjet type, the air for combustion is taken from the enclosed basement and is independent of wind velocity, direction, and temperature.

In the Wilputte design of underjet ovens, the basements are sealed and kept at a constant air pressure (slightly above atmospheric) by sensitive controls, with only the air required for combustion entering the basement through a wind tunnel extending along the entire length of the battery. A fan of sufficient size delivers air to the wind tunnel. Spaced along the length of the basement are suitable openings equipped with regulating louvers to distribute the air uniformly throughout the basement. In this design, only the air required for combustion is available for basement cooling.

In Koppers-Becker underjet-type ovens of a recent design for large batteries, the air for combustion is introduced in much the same manner as that just described, with the exception that air in excess of the amount required for combustion is forced into the basement, the excess finding its way out through suitable openings around the buckstays on the pusher side (the wind tunnel being in the coke side of the basement). In this arrangement, from two to three times the air required for combustion is circulated through the basement for cooling. In still later designs of this type of oven, only the amount of air required for combustion is introduced into the basement.

Importance of Heat Control—The effects of faulty heating may be serious, not only to the quality and quantity of the coke and coal chemicals produced, but also to the ultimate life of the ovens. The most serious damage to the ovens is caused by fluxing or slagging of exposed brick surfaces due to local overheating beyond the critical temperature of the brick. This usually occurs in zones that are not readily accessible for repair. The advantages of an even and controlled heat throughout the oven cannot be overemphasized and remains a constant challenge.

When a new battery, or an old battery that has been allowed to go cold, is to be put into operation, great care must be taken in bringing the battery up to operating temperature. Since the major portion of the battery is of high-grade silica-brick construction, and silica brick has a high coefficient of thermal expansion at lower than operating temperature, it can readily be seen that the heating up must be slow enough to insure maximum temperature equalization throughout the entire battery structure. In actual practice, the heating up from cold to carbonizing temperature takes from five to seven weeks. This same practice obtains in reverse when it is desired to allow a battery of ovens to go out of operation and cold. The cooling of the battery is a project to be undertaken only after full appraisal of all alternatives.

The usual method of heating up a battery is first by installing a temporary brick door at each end of each oven and burning gas in a burner inserted in the oven through an opening provided in the temporary door. The products of combustion are allowed to enter the heating system at the horizontal or bus-flue elevation through suitable openings provided for this purpose, which are later plugged and sealed. The hot gases during the drying-out period are vented down through the vertical flues and regenerators to the stack flue and stack. When the flues become hot enough to ignite fuel gas on reversal, the gas is introduced through the normal channels. Where gas is not available for heating up, coal or coke may be used by substituting a brick bulkhead for the oven door, leaving openings for firing and ash removal. The same type of false hearth is used to protect the oven liner-brick. After heating up, the false hearth and bulkhead are removed, and the oven door is installed.

Many controls of the heating system are fixed in that they are built into the oven structure. The means of variable control are comparatively simple and to a great extent similar in all the modern ovens of the same type. In general, they consist of gas-pressure control in the headers; the selection of the proper size of nozzle, orifice, or metering pin used in the connections to the individual flues; stack-draft controls for the main stack-flue and for the individual ovens; combustion-air controls; various temperature controls and pyrometers.

Oven Doors—As has been mentioned, the ends of the oven are equipped with removable refractory-lined doors. After a coal charge is fully coked and the oven dampered off the main, suitable equipment on both the pusher and coke sides removes the doors and holds them during the pushing operation. After pushing, the doors are replaced and sealed preparatory to recharging the oven.

Until recent years, the method of sealing the doors was to trowel and smooth ground "mud" into a V-shaped opening between the door and the door jamb. In recent years there have been developed self-sealing doors that do not require luting. In principle, the self-sealing door has finally developed into a spring-loaded door that depends on a metal-to-metal contact between the door and the continuous machine-surfaced cast-iron jamb. The Wilputte design of self-sealing door is shown in Figure 4—14. The sealing edge of the door is carried by a flexible frame, and the door assembly is so designed that a powerful spring between each locking bar and the door forces

Fig. 4—14. Wilputte design of self-sealing coke-oven doors, showing spring-loaded bars that maintain metal-to-metal contact between the door and jamb. (Courtesy, Wilputte Coke Oven Division, Allied Chemical Corp.).

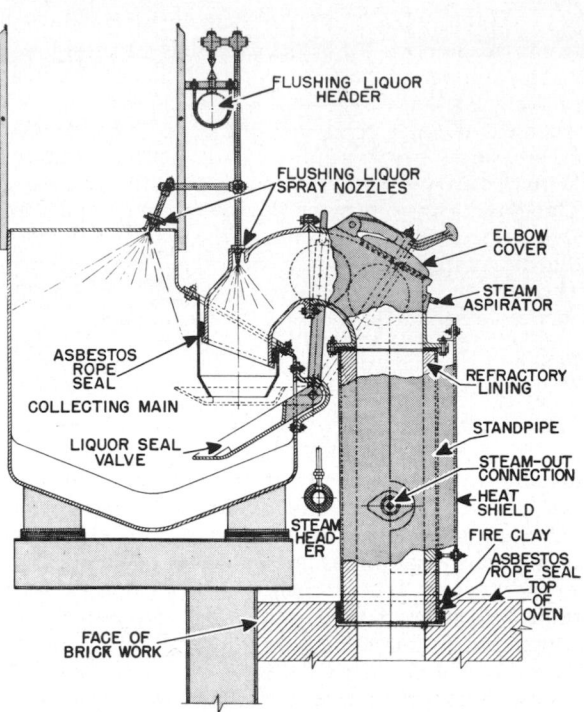

Fig. 4—15. Standpipe, liquid-sealed damper valve and collecting-main arrangement employed by Koppers Company, Inc., through whose courtesy this drawing is reproduced.

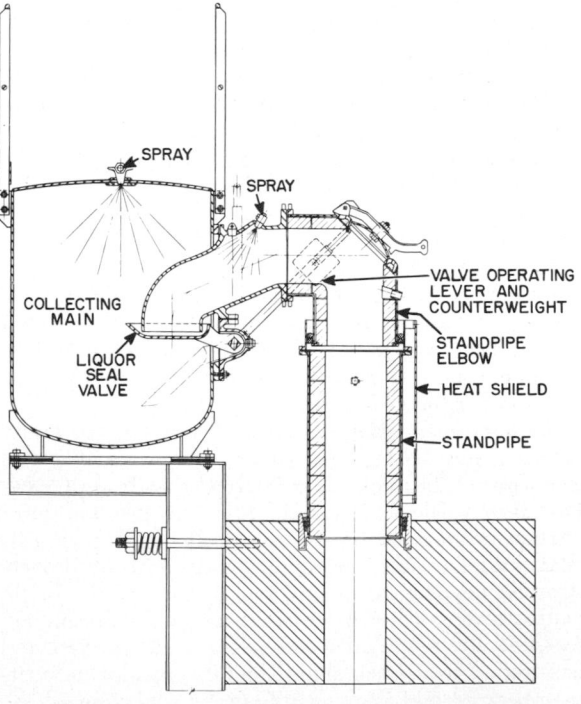

Fig. 4—16. Wilputte arrangement of standpipe, liquid-sealed damper valve, and collecting main. (Courtesy, Wilputte Coke Oven Division, Allied Chemical Corp.).

the sealing edge against the metal door jamb with considerable pressure, thus preventing the escape of volatile products from the oven. The pusher-side door is also equipped with a somewhat similar small self-sealing door to permit leveling of the coal as charged and removal of any excess coal.

Oven-door expense is a large factor in over-all oven repair and maintenance costs. This expense can be controlled by careful design of door-handling equipment and strict adherence to good operating practice. The lining of the door is usually sectionalized and made up of clay-brick shapes. In some plants the doors have a monolithic lining of lumnite cement made with an aggregate of various grades of crushed brick and ganister which give good service. The thickness of the lining, and the position of the inside face of the lining relative to the end vertical flue of the oven is important as it influences the heating of the ends of the coal charge.

Gas-Collecting System—The oven may be equipped with one or two offtakes to carry off the volatile products liberated in the coking process. Where one offtake is provided, it is through the roof of the oven at one end of the oven, and where two are provided, there is one at each end of the oven. The use of a double or single collecting main is still a question of no little debate among coke-plant operators, each system having its advantages. In either case the volatile products pass through the duct or ducts in the oven top and enter a refractory-lined standpipe (sometimes referred to as an "ascension pipe") which in turn is connected to a collecting main through a damper-valve (Figures 4—15 and 4—16).

Between the damper-valve and the oven the standpipe is equipped with a cap valve, or "elbow cover," which, when open, vents the oven to the atmosphere.

The damper valve is usually a liquid-sealed valve, so designed that the cooling spray furnishes the seal when the damper valve is in the closed position, the excess spray overflowing into the collecting main. With this arrangement, the cooling spray is always on. The liquid, called **flushing liquor,** used in damper box and collecting-main flushing, is the condensate from the volatile products driven off in the coking process. This flushing liquor is later processed by the coal-chemical division for the recovery of ammonia.

The standpipe and valve arrangement employed by Koppers is shown in Figure 4—15; that frequently installed by Wilputte is illustrated in Figure 4—16. In the Wilputte design, the standpipe and standpipe elbow are fabricated of welded steel plate lined with refractory brick. The valve body and valve pan are cast steel. The lined standpipe and elbow keep the crude gas coming from the oven hot with a minimum of deposits until the spray in the valve body cools the gas and flushes any deposits into the collecting main. The height of the elbow lid permits inspection of the inside of the elbow and the spray pattern when the oven is "off the main."

In addition to wet type dampers, two dry type dampers (not spray sealed) are in use at various plants; namely "dry butterfly" and "mushroom" valves.

All ovens of a battery are thus connected to a single or multiple pressure-equalized collecting main on either or both sides of the battery. The function of either the single or double collector main is not only to collect the gas from the ovens but also to maintain at all times an accurately-controlled pressure in the oven during the coking process. Pressure in the oven during coking has a pronounced effect on the coke and coal chemicals. The pressure in the collecting main is usually kept at a point that will give about 1 mm. water-gage pressure at the bottom of the oven at the end of the coking period. It should not vary over plus or minus 1 mm. of water-gage pressure. The pressure is controlled by a regulator, usually of the Smoot or Askania type, located in the connection between the collecting main and the suction main which carries the gas to the coal-chemical recovery units. The collection main also serves to transport to the tar decanters the products condensed from the gas by the flushing liquor.

Recent installations of Koppers-Becker underjet batteries have been designed for control of the temperature in the gas space above the coal charge. This has been accomplished by recirculating cooled raw coke-oven gas across the top of each oven above the coal charge by an artificially induced differential pressure between the pusher-side and coke-side gas-collecting mains. This differential pressure is provided by variable speed fans installed in the cross-over main connecting the two gas-collecting mains. On some predetermined cycle the differential pressure is reversed to keep the pusher-side and coke-side temperatures in the oven tops in proper balance.

The use of a patented principle, in which gas from newly charged ovens (in which a relatively high pressure exists) is drawn off and passed through the space above the charge in ovens nearing the end of their coking periods (in which pressures are lower than average), is incorporated in ovens of recent Wilputte design. It is applied to ovens with double collecting mains, one main being used alternately with the other as a compensating main. In effect, one main is employed as a suction main on one side of the battery, with the other acting as a connection between the ends of all of the ovens on the other side of the battery, to assist in equalizing pressures in the spaces above the charges. These functions are reversed periodically. In addition to aiding in control of pressure in the ovens throughout a battery, the system also affords control of temperature throughout the tops of the oven chambers to prevent overheating of the gas space. The alternate use of each main as a suction main makes it possible to cause gas flow in either direction through the ovens near the end of their coking cycle so as to prevent overcooling in any particular area. In general, this system provides the same benefits as that described in the preceding paragraph, but by a different method.

The gas, on entering the damper box, or, in the case of dry dampers, the collecting main, is shock cooled with a liquor spray which causes the first precipitation of tar from the gas. The amount of liquor sprayed is important, as it controls the temperature to which the gas is cooled. Too little cooling allows only the heavy tars to precipitate, which may cause pitch deposits in the damper box and collecting main. Too much cooling may throw down too much light tar, and may result in naphthalene stoppage in the primary coolers or difficulty in tar dehydration. Some plants are equipped to permit segregation of the tar condensed in the collecting and suction main as opposed to that condensed in the primary coolers.

ACCESSORY OVEN EQUIPMENT

Coal-Storage Bins and Charging Larries—To provide coal for the ovens, every modern plant has an overhead **coal bin** at the ovens of sufficient surge capacity to permit flexibility in coal preparation without interference to the scheduled uniform operation of the ovens. The number and size of bins required is determined for each individual plant. The location is determined from a study of each plant's layout of operating units.

All modern by-product coke ovens are designed to take a definite volume of coal per charge and are charged from a **larry car** operating between the overhead coal-storage bins and the ovens on a track supported by the battery top. Figure 4—17 is a view of a battery top, and shows a larry car.

The desired amount of coal for an oven charge is drawn from the storage bin, and is measured, usually by using either the track scales at the loading station, or by volumetric choke boxes on the larry car. Where track scales are used, the coal-bin gates over each hopper of the larry are usually hand operated. Where the separate hoppers of the larry, one for each charging hole, are equipped with volumetric choke boxes, the gates are usually linked together and power oper-

FIG. 4—17. Larry car equipped with screw conveyor for discharge of coal into ovens. The battery shown is fitted with double collector mains.

ated as all gates may be left open until the hoppers are full and the flow of coal is stopped by the choke boxes.

The larry car in principle is designed in connection with the number of charging holes per oven so that a predetermined quantity of coal is charged into the oven through each charging hole, the discharge from each hopper being independently operated, either manually or by power.

Improvements in larry cars, particularly the method of discharging coal, have been directed toward making possible better charging practices. The aim has been to reduce the charging time; to reduce the number of passes of the leveling bar necessary for leveling; to make a smokeless charge; to prevent hanging up of the coal in the larry hoppers; and to make a uniform charge as regards bulk density.

The gravity-discharge larry and the mechanically-unloaded larry are the two main types in use at the present time. The gravity-discharge larry is equipped with conical-shaped hoppers, shear gates and drop-sleeve mechanisms. Vibrators attached to the hoppers and stainless-steel liner plates may or may not be provided, depending upon the physical condition and flow characteristics of the coal. With this type, the coal charge flows by gravity into the ovens. There are

two designs of mechanically unloaded larry cars in use at present; namely, the "turntable" and "screw discharge" types. The turntable larry is equipped with a revolving table serving as the bottom of each hopper. The revolving table forces the coal through an opening in the side of the hopper leading to the shear gate and drop sleeve and thence to the oven. The screw-discharge larry is equipped with rectangular-shaped hoppers with the lower section tapering to a small opening directly over the screw trough. The trough contains the screw conveyor which forces the coal horizontally to the vertical drop sleeve and shear gate section. The hoppers are lined with stainless steel if adverse flow characteristics of the coal are encountered.

The screw-discharge larry gives a slightly better performance on wet or fine coal but considerable difficulty is encountered with any foreign matter in the coal, whereas the gravity-discharge larry and turn-table larry have less trouble with foreign matter in the coal. With fine or wet coal, the gravity-discharge larry gives slightly more trouble than either of the other two types.

Pusher-Side Equipment—The pusher-side equipment shown in Figure 4—18 is generally similar on all types of ovens. The pusher may be a combination of three machines, a **pusher,** a **leveler,** and a **door extractor,** so designed that it operates on a track parallel to, but independent of, the battery. In many plants, the door-handling equipment is a separate, self-propelled machine, operating on its own tracks.

The function of the door-extracting element of this machine is to remove and hold the pusher-side door during the pushing operation. It is either electrically and/or hydraulically operated from the elevated cab which contains all the machine controls. With self-sealing doors, an important feature of the door-extractor design is that its speed be relatively slow and easily controllable and the alignment be accurate to avoid damage to the sealing edges of the door. Contained in the head of the extractor is a mechanism for latching the door and for compressing the loading-springs.

The function of the pushing element (Figure 4—3, Diagram E and Figure 4—18) is to push the coke cake from the oven. This is done by an electrically-powered rack-and-pinion-operated ram, equipped with a suitable head that, when spotted immediately in front of the oven to be pushed, may be moved forward until all the coke has been pushed from the oven and through the coke guide into the quenching car.

The ram is equipped with a rider-shoe located about 5 feet behind the pushing head to support the ram during its passage through the oven. This rider-shoe is easily replaced as it is subject to considerable abrasion sliding over the brick floor of the oven, especially as there is always considerable coke breeze on the oven floor during the pushing and return. The ram is either a built-up box girder, "H" beam, or open-lattice electrically-welded structure. The open-lattice construction seems to be currently in favor as it is more easily repaired and resists the tendency to warp, due to more even cooling, regardless of wind direction. With the box-girder-type ram, it is necessary to have wind-and-rain guards for the ram in its retracted position. The pushing speed of the ram is about 60 feet per minute, and the maximum pressure exerted is controlled by overload relays to prevent damage to the oven brickwork.

The function of the leveling element (Figure 4—3, Diagrams B and C) is to level the coal charge in the oven, leaving a free-gas space below the roof of the charged oven. This is done by an electrically-operated leveling-bar carried by the pusher-machine structure in such a position that it may be introduced through a suitable opening in the top of the pusher-side door. The leveling-bar is a fabricated section consisting of two side-plates held apart by vertical plates spaced at from 2 to 4 feet which also serve as scrapers. When this bar is moved in and out of the oven, the scraper plates level the humps of coal into the valleys and, on removal from the oven, drag out

FIG. 4—18. Pusher-side equipment of a battery of by-product coke ovens, showing the machine which is equipped to level the coal charge in the oven and also push the finished coke out of the oven, as well as remove and replace oven doors before and after the pushing operation.

all excess coal into a chute discharging into a receiving bin carried by the pusher machine. This excess coal is periodically dropped into a ground-level hopper for return to the coal bunker. At some plants, the excess coal is returned by a conveyor to the next oven charged.

The various platforms, control rooms, and operating cab of the pusher machine should be designed to facilitate comfortable operation and accessibility for oiling, adjusting, and repair. Inasmuch as the three principal operations of the pusher machine always occur separately, one operator is all that is required. However, men known as door and jamb cleaners accompany the pusher and, in most cases, they also open and close the leveling door from the oven pusher-side bench and clean up any coal and coke spillage.

Where self-sealing doors are not used, it is necessary to provide equipment for the preparation of luting mud and for conveying the luting mud to the doors to be luted. The mud is usually prepared in the conventional-type wet pug mill from returned luting mud, coke breeze cleaned from the oven benches, and certain amounts of fresh clay. The mud buggies, or carriers for the pusher side, are usually electrically-operated and suspended from an overhead track, and are equipped with bins and platforms at two or three levels, according to the oven-door height, so that the luterman can easily trowel the mud required to seal the oven door.

With self-sealing doors a motorized buggy is sometimes provided to facilitate manual cleaning of doors and door jambs. Recently-developed buggies are equipped with elevators and heat shields.

The pusher side of the battery is equipped with a bench serving as a walkway along the entire length of the battery and as a working platform for men serving the pusher-side doors and jambs. Until recent years, the level of this bench was a few inches below the level of the oven floor and could not be protected by hand rails in any practical manner on account of clearance for the pusher ram. It is now general practice to lower the bench about 2½ to 3 feet below the oven-floor level so that the pusher ram may pass over the top of a railing. The benches are similarly lowered on the coke side.

The main operating units referred to above, and their functions, are illustrated schematically in Figure 4—3.

Coke-Side Equipment—The coke side of the bat-

FIG. 4—19. Door-extracting machine and coke guide operating on tracks on the coke-side bench of a coke-oven battery.

FIG. 4—20. Coke side of a battery of by-product coke ovens during the process of pushing the coke out of one of the ovens. The quenching car is self-propelled, and carries the coke to a quenching station where it is sprayed with, water before being dumped on the coke wharf.

tery is equipped with a **door-extracting machine, coke guide,** and, when using luted doors, a luting buggy. The coke-side equipment operates on a track integral with the coke-side bench, as shown in Figures 4—19 and 4—20.

The function of the door machine is to remove and hold the coke-side door during the pushing of an oven and to place an attached coke guide in the proper position to conduct the coke across the bench into a **quenching car** operating on a ground level track which is parallel with the battery.

The design and operation of the door extractor is generally similar to the door extractor of the pusher machine. Recent developments place the extracted door behind a heat shield and have details of design that facilitate door cleaning.

The coke guide is attached to the door-extractor machine by a disconnecting coupler. It is conducted along the coke-side bench. At modern plants, the coke guide is equipped with a movable lattice framework that is power-operated from the door machine. When spotted at the oven to be pushed, this movable framework is moved into the space between the buckstays and against the door jamb, thus preventing coke spillage at this point during pushing. As this part of the guide is subject to the greatest wear, it is designed for ease of replacement and is constructed of metal that will resist heat and wear.

On plants using luted doors, the coke side is pro-

vided with motorized luting buggies, generally similar in design and operation to the pusher-side luting buggies.

Quenching Station—There are two methods of quenching the hot coke that is pushed from ovens, namely, wet quenching and dry quenching, the latter being used more extensively in European countries than in the United States. All but one or two plants in the United States wet quench, principally for economic and operational reasons. In dry quenching, the sensible heat of the coke is used for the production of steam for general plant use; this will not be discussed here, except to state that it is accomplished by dumping the hot coke into a closed system where the recirculation of inert gas conducts the sensible heat from the coke to a low-pressure boiler until an equilibrium is reached within practical limits, and the coke is below the ignition point in air, at which time the coke is discharged for screening and loading.

Wet quenching in most modern plants is accomplished by receiving the charge of hot coke from the ovens in the quenching car, which is conducted to a quenching station by an electric locomotive, where the coke is quenched with water. The car is then taken to a coke wharf where the coke is discharged. The handling of the coke from the wharf will be discussed later.

The quenching car is designed so that by moving the car during the pushing operation the coke is caught in a relatively uniform bed about two feet thick on the sloping bottom of the car (Figure 4—20). The power-operated gates, either electric or air, at the low side of the sloping bottom are so designed and arranged that the quenching water not evaporated may readily drain from the car. When the charge of hot coke has arrived at the quenching station, it is spotted under a system of stationary sprays located in the quenching tower. The operator starts the quench by remote control. The purpose of quenching is obviously to rapidly cool the coke to stop any further combustion. However, it must be recognized that coke of low-moisture content is desired. This is accomplished by so arranging the sprays and the time of quench that sufficient heat will remain in the center of the individual coke lumps to dry excess surface water. The usual practice is to aim at 2½ per cent average moisture in the metallurgical coke after screening.

Most modern plants, of necessity, quench with contaminated water as there seems to be no other practical method of disposal of these waters. It is therefore necessary to design the quenching station in such a way that all such waters can be recirculated until evaporated. This is done by pumps delivering water from a contaminated water sump to the spray lines and returning the unevaporated water to the sump. Any makeup above the plant production of contaminated water is fresh water.

Instrumentation and Control—Most instrumentation around the ovens is confined to the heating facilities. As has been mentioned, the variable controls of individual ovens of a battery are so adjusted that master controls may be installed for each battery of ovens. In this manner, single machines, meters, gages, and other devices control the various functions of the battery heating system after the individual-oven controls have been adjusted and connected. Thus, the gas required for underfiring is metered in the battery header only. The choice of a flowmeter for this service will be influenced in large part by its accuracy over a wide range of flow. The meter should be recording, preferably one adapted to a uniform graduated chart for reasons of legibility and computation facility. It is also necessary to control accurately the pressure in the fuel-gas main with an instrument capable of close control at relatively low pressures. It may be desired to have a recording of these pressures. A recording thermometer is also installed in the fuel-gas header so that the gas quantities may be computed to standard conditions. The battery is also equipped with recording draft gages, waste-heat recording thermometers, and various indicating gages. Portable pressure gages, thermometers, and pyrometers are used in the setting of individual-oven controls. Another instrument used by the heaters is a portable pyrometer with which periodic temperature readings are taken of the flues and emerging coke. Probably the most widely accepted pyrometer is of the incandescent-filament type. Recording pressure and temperature gages are also installed in the gas-collecting mains.

The pressure in the collecting main is controlled by a back-pressure regulator located at the junction of the collecting main with the suction main: its function is to maintain a closely-controlled pressure in the ovens during coking. A draft regulator operates a butterfly valve to maintain a preset stack draft on the battery.

Many plants record the regularity of oven operation by some related activity, such as the time of pushing, by the peak-load recording of the pushing-power circuit, or by a recording of the time of quenching of each charge. All utilities have the usual types of instrumentation.

COKE SCREENING AND HANDLING

Coke Wharf — The coke wharf receives the quenched coke from the quenching car. The coke is spread out on the wharf in a thin bed for quick drying and visual inspection for the detection of unquenched coke. Manually directed streams of water are used to quench any still-hot coke detected on the wharf before the coke is conveyed on rubber-belt conveyors to the screens. Figure 4—21 shows a modern coke wharf. It is substantially a long, narrow inclined platform with the shorter dimension sloping away from the quenching-car track toward a conveyor belt that runs along the lower side of the structure. A properly designed wharf should be of such size that it will serve as a surge storage for quenched coke ahead of the screens so that short delays incidental to screening and loading operations will not interrupt the desired regularity in oven-pushing sequence. Most modern wharfs are paved with hard-burned clay brick, although some plants use cast-iron plates and even refractory concrete for the purpose.

The coke is retained on the wharf by a series of hand-operated gates which, when opened, permit the coke to slide down the wharf and onto the belt conveyor to be delivered to the screening station.

Fig. 4—21. General view of a coke wharf showing freshly quenched coke being discharged from the gates of the quenching car onto the brick-paved sloping wharf. When the wharf gates are opened, coke slides down the wharf as at the lower left onto a conveyor belt that carries it to the screening station.

Conveyor System for Coke—The transfer of coke from the wharf to the screening station is accomplished now almost universally by a system of rubber-belt conveyors and chutes.

Screening and Crushing—The purpose of coke screening and crushing is to provide a controlled size of coke for blast-furnace use from which fines, and, in some cases, pieces over a set maximum size, are removed. The latter are crushed and screened before use. The very small sizes, commonly called **coke breeze** are usually used in the coke plants as a boiler fuel, in sintering plants as sinter fuel, or screened for domestic trade.

Storage and Shipping—In the loading of furnace coke and the subsequent transportation to the blast furnaces, care must be taken to prevent additional breakage. For this reason, the coke is loaded into railroad cars and, where practical, is consigned directly to the blast furnaces, as additional handling into and out of stock results in inevitable coke degradation. Where the blast furnaces are located close to the coke plant, belt conveyors are often used to conduct the coke from the screening station to the blast-furnace stock-house bins.

LIMITATIONS AND FUTURE OF BY-PRODUCT COKING

Perhaps the most important over-all consideration that should be kept continually in mind in designing by-product coke ovens and the various auxiliary equipment is that the great majority of design features incorporated in the battery construction cannot be altered during the 20 to 30 years of battery life. It is, therefore, imperative that design as well as construction be of the highest quality. While theory must naturally play an important part in this design, it is well not to overlook the fact that, since the coking characteristics of the coals to be used have such a vital effect on oven design, empirical data developed from actual experience with similar coals is invaluable.

While it is true that the great majority of design work required for by-product coke-oven construction is necessarily carried on by the builders, the engineering work required of the operating company and plant organizations is of sizable amount and of tremendous importance. In the first place, the builders of coke ovens have always been extremely receptive to suggested improvements, and many have been incorporated in modern oven construction. Secondly, there is considerable latitude in the selection of type and size of ovens, in auxiliary equipment, and particularly in facility layout, all of which require intelligent action on the part of the operating company. And finally, the incentive to produce products of higher quality at reduced costs, coupled with the experience gained through actual operation, repair, and maintenance of the by-product coke-oven facilities, places the organizations of the operating companies in an increasingly important position in furthering the advancement of coke-plant design.

SECTION 4

RECOVERY OF COAL CHEMICALS

COLLECTION OF VOLATILE PRODUCTS FROM OVENS

Collecting Main and Suction Main—In the collection system for the recovery of the volatile products from coal, the first operation reduces the temperature of these products, which are generally referred to as **foul gas**. This takes place in a system of gas mains through which the foul gas passes.

The foul gas passes out of the oven chamber through a refractory-lined ascension pipe and into a gooseneck which connects into the **collecting main** through a damper valve. The collecting main serves an entire battery of ovens, running parallel with the battery and extending above it on one side or on both sides depending on whether it is a single or double collecting-main operation.

The gas and vapors ordinarily leave the oven at temperatures in the range 1100–1300° F (600–700° C), and are shock-cooled by spraying with flushing liquor in the goosenecks and further cooled by spraying again with flushing liquor at different points along the collecting main. The temperature of the gas and vapors at the point of exit from the collecting main is 295 to 420° F (145 to 215° C). The cooling is effected by the evaporation of a portion of the water from the flushing liquor which removes some of the sensible heat from the gas and condenses some of the vapors with the resultant condensation of heavy tar from the gas.

The gas and remaining vapors pass from the collecting main through one or more **cross-over mains** into the **suction main**. A pressure-regulating valve, automatically controlled, is located in each cross-over main. After the gas and vapors have passed this control valve their temperature drops to 175 to 212° F (80 to 100° C), as a result of atmospheric cooling and further evaporation of the flushing liquor.

The **flushing liquor,** used for cooling in the spray system, is liquor which has been condensed in the mains, collected and recirculated, amounting to 800 to 1,200 gallons per ton of coal carbonized on coke-oven batteries with a single collecting main and up to 2,000 gallons on those with two mains. The flushing liquor, which cools and condenses various vapors in the gas, provides a carrying medium for the condensable tars and other compounds formed in the operations. These liquid materials flow from the collecting main through a seal into a downcomer and are delivered through the return flushing liquor lines to a collecting unit customarily called a flushing-liquor decanter (Figures 4—22 and 4—23).

The uniform flow of gas and vapors into the system

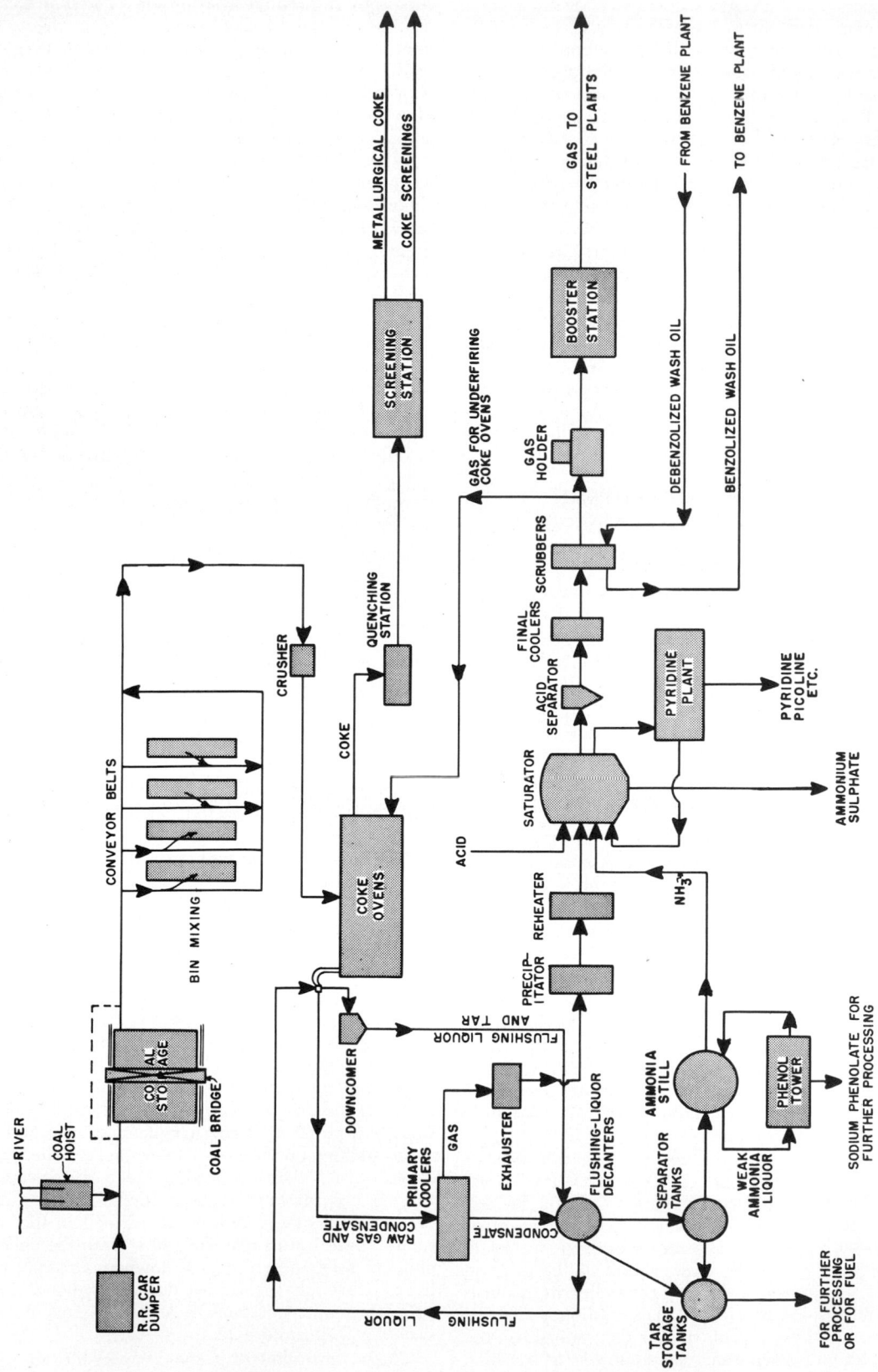

Fig. 4—22. Flow sheet showing the major steps involved in the carbonization of coal by the by-product process and the subsequent recovery of coal chemicals from the oven gases.

is accomplished by the charging of coal into the ovens at regularly prescribed intervals and the withdrawal of the evolved gases at a constant rate. This constant rate of removal of the gas is controlled by varying the speeds of the turbines and exhausters which pull the gas away from the ovens and by automatic pressure regulators in the cross-oven main. This pressure regulator provides a slight pressure of about one millimeter of water at the base of the oven prior to pushing. This control of pressure is for the purpose of eliminating the infiltration of atmospheric air or gases from the heating system into the oven, which would have a deleterious effect on the quality and quantity of the coke and coal chemicals.

As a consequence of this practice the pressure on the collecting main is about eight to twelve millimeters of water with a variable suction of about two to three hundred millimeters of water in the cross-over main after the regulating valve.

These pressure differentials are maintained by the use of either low speed positive turbo or centrifugal type exhausters designed to remove the gases and vapors at a controlled rate.

RECOVERY OF CRUDE COAL TAR

Flushing-Liquor Decanter Tank—The flushing-liquor decanter tank (Figure 4—23) serves a two-fold purpose in the processing of the liquid condensates and recirculating liquor in the primary liquid system:

(a) It provides a settling basin in which the velocity of the tar and liquor is reduced to permit separation of the tar and liquor by the difference in specific gravity.

(b) It serves as the first settling point for carbonaceous and other finely divided material that is carried along with tar and liquor from the collecting main.

The flushing-liquor decanter is a rectangular steel tank, inclined at one end to facilitate removal of solid accumulations. The tar and flushing liquor enter the decanter and flow into a trough which is designed to minimize agitation of the mixture in the decanter. The mixture overflows the trough into the main compartment, where the velocity is reduced to permit the

tar, which has a higher specific gravity than the flushing liquor, to settle to the bottom. The liquor flows over a fixed weir at the opposite end of the decanter and into the connecting lines to the flushing-liquor pumps. The tar leaves the bottom of the decanter through an adjustable seal, known as the decanter valve, which can be raised or lowered. Tar quality is controlled by adjusting this seal either upwards or downwards to regulate the retention time of the tar in the decanter. Carbonaceous deposits in the bottom of the decanter are continuously removed by scrapers dragged slowly along the bottom by two endless chains.

Normally, the tar recovered from the flushing liquor contains 2 to 5 per cent of water. When the water content of the tar is in excess of 5 per cent, further decantation or blending may be required to reduce the water content. This is usually accomplished by placing tar-receiving tanks and separating tanks in the process lineup prior to the tar-storage tanks. Tar-receiving tanks are simply intermediate storage tanks which receive the tar from the decanters prior to being pumped into the tar-storage tanks. Depending on the water content of the tar in a receiver, the tar may be pumped directly to storage, heated to lower the water content, or be pumped back into the decanter system.

Primary Cooler—The non-condensed gas and vapors leaving the collecting and suction mains at a temperature of 167–176° F (75–80° C) require further cooling to 95° F (35° C) to remove additional tar and a major portion of the water vapor and to reduce both the volume and temperature of the gas before its admission to the exhausters. This cooling may be conducted in either direct or indirect primary coolers.

The **direct primary cooler** (Figure 4—24) consists of a tall, cylindrical scrubbing tower fitted with hurdles or baffles usually constructed of wood. The top portion is equipped with a series of spray nozzles and the lower portion contains a chamber to collect the liquor and condensate.

The gas enters the bottom of the tower and the

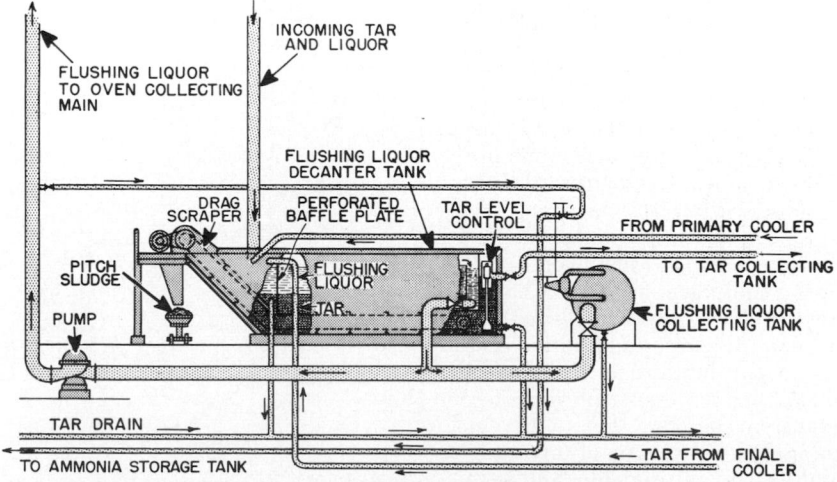

Fig. 4—23. Schematic representation of a flushing-liquor decanter tank or hot-tar drain tank.

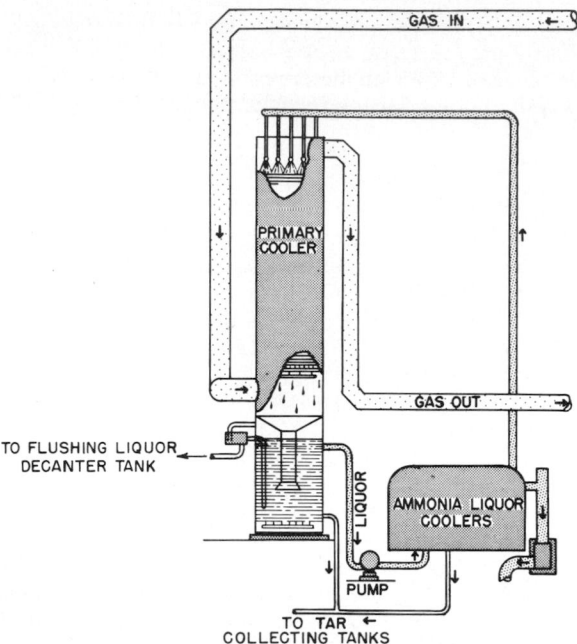

Fig. 4—24. Schematic diagram of a direct primary cooler. (Courtesy, Koppers Company, Inc.)

cooling liquor is pumped into the top of the tower through the spray system to provide a downward flow of cooling liquor in counter-current flow to the gas stream. This direct contact between the gas and liquor provides for exchange of heat which is transferred from the hot gas to the cold liquor. This heat is removed from the liquor by indirect heat exchange, through tubular heat exchangers, with circulating water. As a result of this cooling, 20 to 25 per cent of the total tar recovered is condensed along with a considerable quantity of weak liquor containing ammonia. These condensates are processed either separately or in conjunction with the tar and liquor condensates from the collecting main.

The **indirect primary cooler** used for cooling the gas is a heat exchanger, in which water is used for cooling by heat exchange through steel tubes. The water flows through the tubes and the gas around the tubes in counter-current directions.

Tar Extractor—The gas leaving the primary coolers still contains small amounts of tar that would cause difficulty in the operation of subsequent units in the recovery system. There are two methods available for removal of this entrained tar: (a) mechanical impingement and (b) electrostatic precipitation. In the case of operation by mechanical impingement, it is necessary to place the equipment after the exhausters, but the electrostatic precipitator may be placed before or after the exhausters. The preferred location is after compression to avoid any infiltration of air into the unit. The electrostatic type represents the modern concept of removing tar from gas.

The mechanical-impingement type of tar extractor was developed by Pelouze and Audouin, and is commonly referred to as the P & A tar extractor. The principle of operation is based on the fact that when

gas containing suspended solids is impinged (at high velocity) on a solid surface, deposition of the suspended particles takes place. This principle is made effective by forcing the gas through restricted spaces directly against a plate to develop a dispersion of the mass and effect a deposition of tar particles, which coalesce to form a liquid and flow to the bottom of the separator. The fixed gas then continues on through this unit for subsequent processing operations. The gas enters the bottom of the tar extractor and passes up through seven standpipes over each of which is suspended three concentric perforated steel shells. Each shell assembly is called a bell. The shells in each bell are arranged so that the perforations in successive shells are not aligned. The ascending gas enters the inside of each bell and passes through the perforations, impinging on the solid face of each succeeding shell to deposit the tar, and finally passes out of the top of the extractor.

The operation of this type of extractor requires the maintenance of a constant differential pressure of six to ten inches of water, regulated by the liquor seal.

The **electrostatic precipitator** has been found to be more efficient and is gradually replacing the mechanical impingement type of tar extractor. In the electrostatic precipitator (Figure 4—25) removal of tar fog from gas is achieved by passing the gas between electrodes having a high electrical potential. The discharge electrode is of small cross section, such as a wire or a series of points, in order to develop the high-intensity electrical field at its surface which is required for ionization of gas. The collecting electrode has a large cross section and serves as a collector for the suspended particles which are ionized and transferred to this electrode. In this operation, the electrostatic precipitator, in addition to its function as a collecting unit for dispersoids, also serves to catalyze the formation of vapor-phase gums formed by oxides of nitrogen and unsaturated hydrocarbons.

RECOVERY OF AMMONIA AS AMMONIUM SULPHATE

Ammonium sulphate is formed by the reaction between ammonia and sulphuric acid. The dry chemically pure salt is white in color and contains 25.78 per cent of ammonia. The commercial salt varies in color

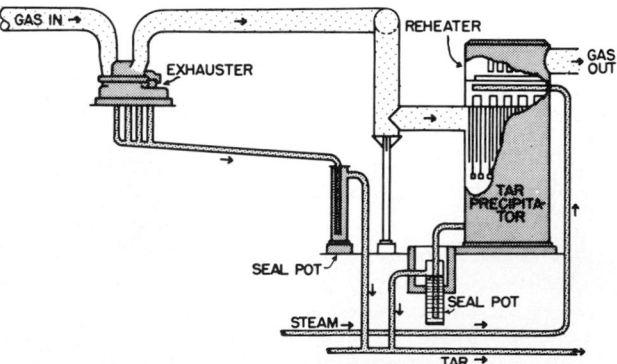

Fig. 4—25. Diagrammatic representation of an electrostatic precipitator for precipitation of tar from raw coke-oven gases. (Courtesy, Koppers Company, Inc.)

from white to grayish tan and contains from 25.0 to 25.7 per cent of ammonia.

The ammonia formed during coking exists in both the water and gas that form part of the volatile products. The recovery of this ammonia can be accomplished by three different methods: (a) the **direct process** in which the total vapor, after separation of condensed tar, is passed through a saturator containing a solution of sulphuric acid to absorb the ammonia; (b) the **indirect process** in which the ammonia is removed from the gas by scrubbing with water and then removed from the water by distillation and treatment with an alkali, after which the ammonia and steam are passed through the saturator and (c) the **semi-direct process** in which the ammonia in the liquor produced during carbonization is removed by distillation and alkali treatment and added to the gas stream, the gas containing all of the ammonia being then passed through an absorber containing dilute sulphuric acid for the extraction of ammonia.

Semi-Direct Process—Of these three processes, the semi-direct is most extensively used at the present time. The ammonia present in the weak liquor is in two forms classified as "free" and "fixed." The free ammonia is that which is readily dissociated by heat, such as the ammonium carbonates, sulphide, cyanide, etc., while the fixed ammonia is that which requires the presence of a strong alkali to effect displacement of the ammonia from the compound in which it is present, such as ammonium chloride, thiocyanate, ferrocyanide, sulphate, etc. The operation to recover this ammonia is carried out in an ammonia still.

Ammonia Still—In the processing of the liquor, a constant-head tank supplies a uniform flow of liquor, by gravity, to the top of the "free leg" of the ammonia still (Figure 4—26) and this liquor passes down the column over a series of plates equipped with bubble caps and overflow pipes. This liquor is heated by an upward flow of steam which vaporizes the ammonia and acidic gases. These vapors leave the top of the "free leg" at a temperature of 158–167° F (98 to 104° C), and pass into a dephlegmator to cool the vapors partially and remove excess water which is returned to the still. The vapor leaving the dephlegmator consists of ammonia which may vary between 10 to 25 per cent, depending upon the vapor temperature, with the balance consisting of water and some acidic gases and neutral oils.

The liquor leaving the base of the "free leg" passes into the "lime leg" where it is treated with "milk of lime" containing up to 40 grams of calcium hydroxide per liter. The calcium hydroxide reacts with the fixed ammonium salt of which ammonium chloride is the main constituent according to the following reaction:

$$2NH_4Cl + Ca(OH)_2 + Heat =$$
$$2NH_3 + 2H_2O + CaCl_2$$

The liquor then flows in to the "fixed leg" which consists of a series of plates equipped with bubble caps and overflow pipes to provide effective stripping of the ammonia by a countercurrent flow of steam. The steam pressure required at the base of the still is of the order of three to four pounds. This steam provides the heat for the operation of all three units of the still assembly.

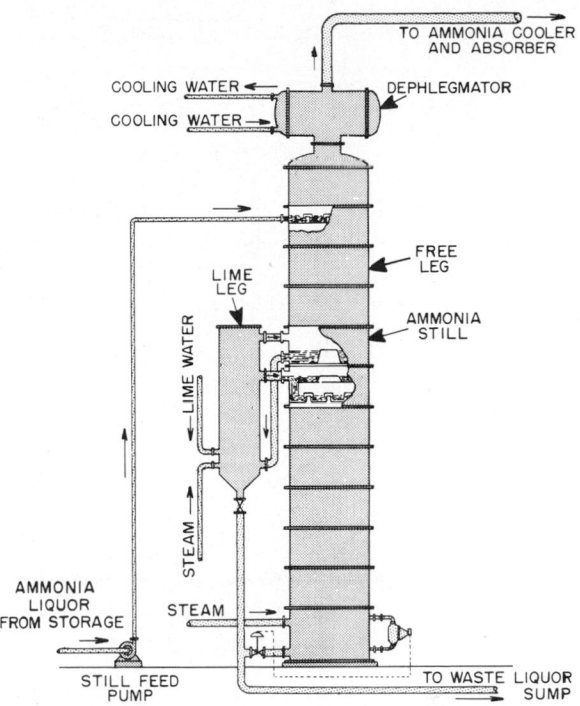

FIG. 4—26. Diagrammatic representation of the essential parts and operation of an ammonia still. (Courtesy, Koppers Company, Inc.)

The vapors leaving the ammonia still are added to the gas stream so that all of the ammonia can be recovered in the saturators or ammonia absorbers.

Reheater—The temperature of the gas after leaving the precipitators, is about 104–108° F (40–42° C) having been raised 9–13° F (5–7° C) by compression in the exhausters. The temperature is raised to about 130° F (55° C) by passing the gas through the reheaters which are cylindrical holders containing steel tubes. The gas passes through the tubes, around which direct steam is circulated. This reheating is necessary to prevent the condensation of water vapor in ammonia absorbing facilities.

Ammonia Absorber—In an Otto-type absorber, coke-oven gas enters the ammonia absorber (Figure 4—27) near the bottom and is sprayed with a dilute solution of sulphuric acid as it rises to the top of the absorber. Next the gas flows through a pyridine absorber where it is sprayed again with a more concentrated solution of sulphuric acid. The gas leaving the pyridine scrubbers is passed through the acid separator where entrained liquids are removed, after which the gas enters the final cooler.

As the dilute sulphuric acid sprays the gas rising through the ammonia absorber, the ammonia in the gas combines with the acid to form ammonium sulphate. The resulting solution drains to a crystallizer from which it is recirculated to the absorber. A constant flow of sulphuric acid is added to the ammonia absorber to replace the acid neutralized by the ammonia in the coke-oven gas. After the solution becomes super-saturated, crystals of ammonium sulphate are precipitated in the crystallizer and

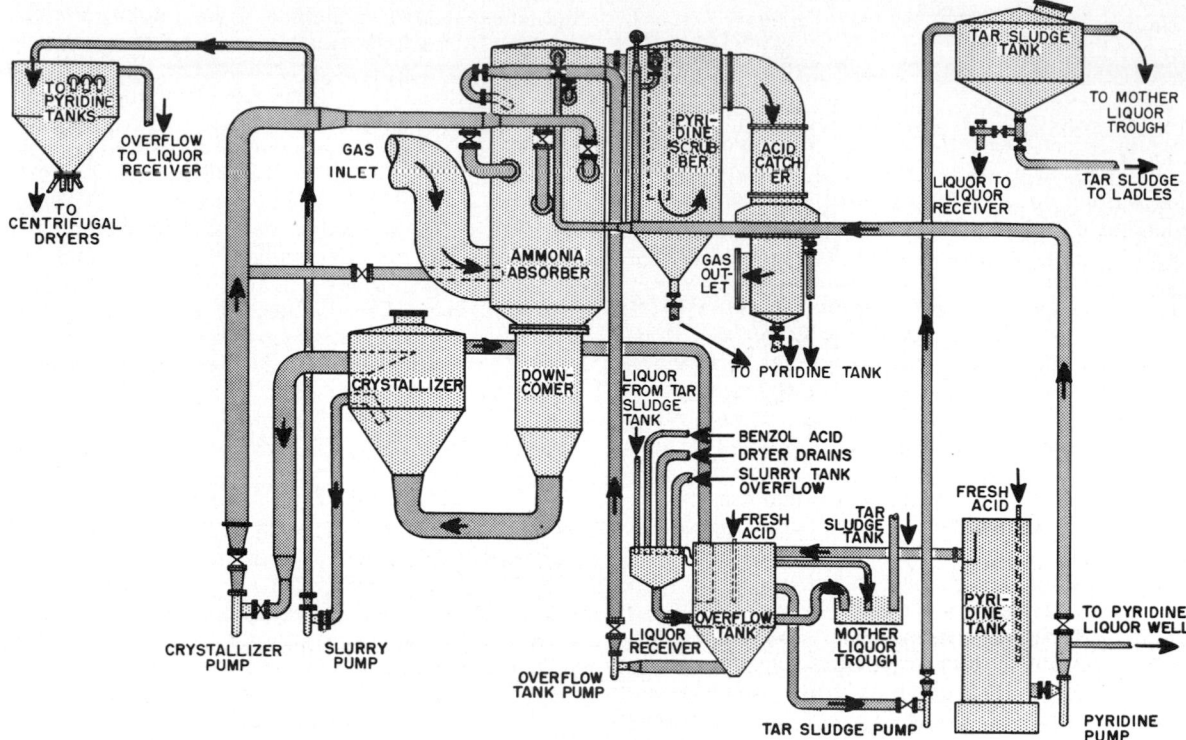

Fig. 4—27. Schematic flow sheet of the operation of an Otto spray-type saturator for the recovery of ammonia as ammonium sulphate. (Courtesy, Otto Construction Corporation).

accumulate as a slurry in the bottom. A portion of this slurry is removed from the crystallizer and is pumped to the slurry tank where the salt settles, the liquid overflows and returns to the ammonia absorber. The concentrated slurry is withdrawn from the bottom of the slurry tank and is fed continuously or in batches to the centrifugal dryers. These dryers currently are arranged to perform the following sequence of operations automatically: (a) rinse the dryer-basket screen with water; (b) feed the slurry into the basket; (c) neutralize the acid remaining in the salt with a dilute solution of aqueous ammonia; (d) rinse the salt with water to remove excess ammonia; (e) centrifuge the water from the salt in the basket; (f) remove the dried salt from the basket; and (g) discharge it onto a conveyor belt. The liquid portion of the slurry is recovered and returned to the ammonia absorbers. The partially-dried ammonium sulphate is conveyed to heated rotary-drum dryers for final drying to a content of approximately 0.1 per cent water.

Following the ammonia removal in the ammonia absorber, the gas comes in contact with more concentrated sulphuric acid in the pyridine scrubber which removes the tar bases (pyridines, picolines, etc.). Tar bases and sulphuric acid form a weak bond, therefore, the bases are the last to be removed from the gas and the first to be released at low acid concentrations. The tar-base sulphuric acid solution is continuously recirculated and portions are removed systematically for recovery of the tar bases by methods described later. The pyridine-free liquor is returned to the ammonia absorbers. The gas entrains some of the acid

solution in the pyridine scrubber, which is recovered by centrifugal force as it passes through the acid separator.

Another process for the recovery of ammonia is the Wilputte low-differential controlled-crystallization process for producing ammonium sulphate, the equipment for which is constructed of stainless steel throughout (Figure 4—28). In this process the gas is passed through a spray-type absorber over which is circulated a 6 per cent solution of sulphuric acid nearly saturated with ammonium sulphate. The acid-entrainment arrestor is an integral part of the absorber. Leaving the absorber, the solution is delivered to the solution-circulating system of a crystallizer in which crystallization takes place by the combined cooling and concentration effects of vacuum evaporation. By the variation of circulating rate and the degree of concentration, the size range of the product can be controlled closely within narrow limits. As the crystals grow in size, they settle or gravitate to the bottom of the suspension tank from which they are delivered to a slurry feed tank and from there to a continuous centrifuge or filter, followed in either case by a dryer. The accumulation of deposits of hard salt within the equipment is minimized and "killing" for removal of such deposits is very infrequent. The product can be made with a size consist favorable to almost any type of application.

Saturator—At coke plants built prior to about 1930, ammonia-absorbing facilities consist largely of devices often referred to as saturators. These facilities are large dome-shaped, cast iron, lead-lined vessels, sometimes operated in pairs. Gas is admitted to the saturator through a distributor called a "cracker pipe" which, in the older designs, runs completely around the inside circumference of the unit and has a cross section in the shape of an inverted U. The bottom of the pipe is open, but the gas is discharged from it through numerous vertical slots, located on each side of the pipe near the bottom. This arrangement was adopted to provide a large surface for direct contact between the ammonia and dilute acid, which react according to the following to form ammonium sulphate:

$$2NH_3 + H_2SO_4 = (NH_4)_2SO_4$$

The salt precipitates and settles to the bottom of the unit when the saturator bath becomes super-saturated. The salt is either siphoned through ejectors to elevated drain tables by means of compressed air, or removed from the base of the saturator by centrifugal pump. When the saturators are equipped with air ejectors, the salt is removed periodically from the elevated drain tables, placed in a pendulum-type centrifugal dryer, and centrifuged for about 5 minutes, which process removes nearly all the mother liquor. The ammonium sulphate is washed with hot water, to free the crystals of absorbed mother liquor, and centrifuged for about 10–12 minutes longer. It is then removed from the centrifugal basket by an unloader or plow and delivered to a belt conveyor, which carries it to a salt pit where any free acid is neutralized by spraying with concentrated ammonia liquid. The mother liquor derived from this operation, as well

as the wash water, flows back into the saturators. The acid concentration of the bath is held approximately constant by periodic addition of high-strength sulphuric acid.

Continued use of a saturator results in the accumulation of salt within the saturator, which interferes with the flow of gas. It is common practice to prevent such accumulations and to dissolve accumulated salt deposits by "killing" the bath periodically. "Killing" the bath is a term used to describe the method for rectifying this condition, whereby the height and acidity of a bath, prior to "killing," are allowed to decrease and the deficiency then made up by the addition of a definite quantity of acid, water and mother liquor. The bath then has a free sulphuric acid concentration of 12–14 per cent. These added materials reduce the saturation of ammonium sulphate in the total liquor and all deposits of salt are redissolved.

RECOVERY OF PHENOL

The water, i.e., weak ammonia liquor, recovered with the volatile products of coal carbonization contains 0.5 to 3.0 grams per liter of phenol (sometimes called carbolic acid) and its homologues. In order to recover this phenol, two processes are available—the vapor-recirculation process and the solvent extraction process. (Phenol is also recovered from coal tar, by processes described later in this chapter.)

Vapor-Recirculation Process—This process utilizes the vapor pressure of phenol and operates in conjunction with the ammonia still. The weak liquor first is

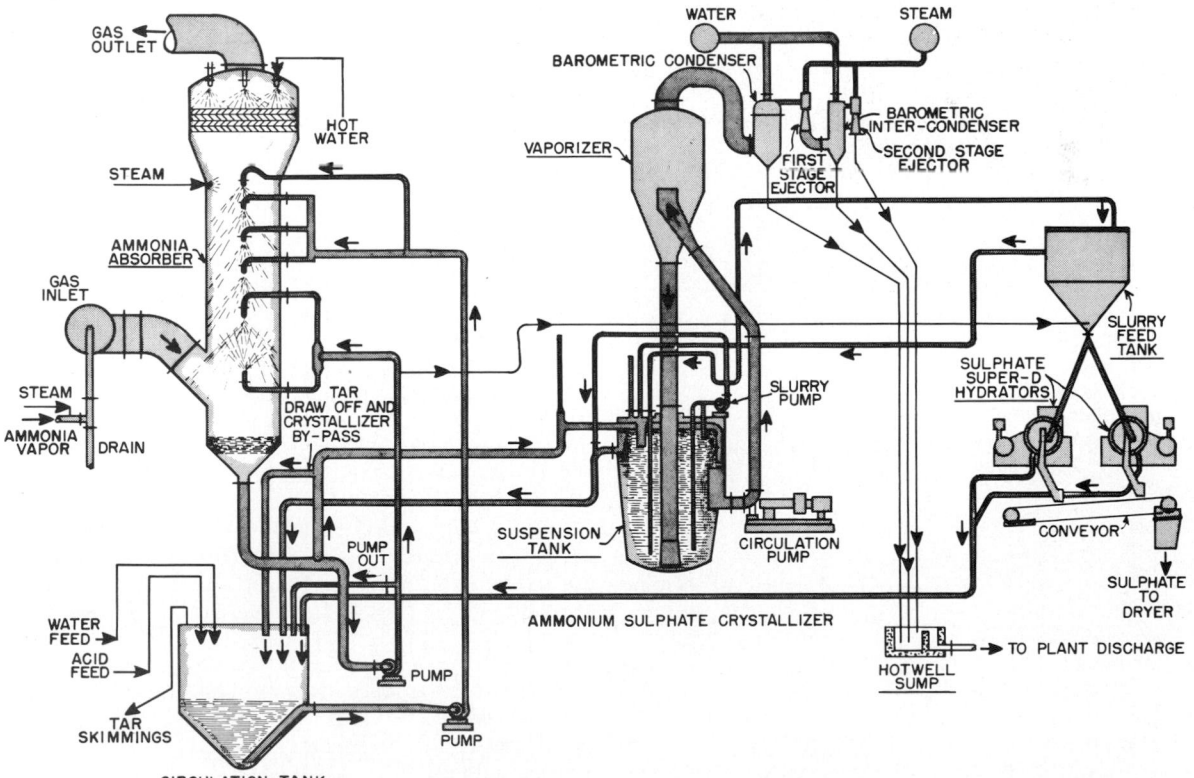

Fig. 4—28. Flow sheet of the Wilputte low-differential controlled-crystallization process for producing ammonium sulphate.

distilled in the free leg of the ammonia still in order to remove the maximum quantities of the acidic gases, H_2S, CO_2, and HCN, but the minimum amount of phenol.

The ammonia liquor leaving the base of the "free leg" is transferred to the dephenolizing unit, where the phenols are removed. The dephenolized liquor is returned to the "lime leg."

In the operation of the dephenolizing unit (Figure 4—29), the liquor is pumped into the top of a dephenolizing tower consisting of two main sections. In the upper section it passes downward over wooden hurdles and meets a countercurrent flow of steam which vaporizes the phenols. The liquor from the base of the upper section returns to the ammonia still. The phenol vapors and steam are carried into the bottom of the tower and travel upward through steel turnings where they meet a countercurrent flow of caustic soda which extracts the phenols and forms sodium phenolate.

This operation is conducted at 212° F (100° C). At this temperature, the equilibrium of the phenol-sodium phenolate reaction is such that a suitable balance between the utilization of sodium hydroxide and the loss of phenol results in the conversion of about 50 per cent of the available sodium hydroxide into sodium phenolate with a loss of about 5 per cent of the phenol.

Solvent Extraction Process—This method is based on the principle that the phenols are more soluble in benzene or light oil than in water and that the phenols can be extracted from benzene or light oil with caustic soda.

The process consists of treating weak liquor containing phenols with benzene or light oil in two or three stages by countercurrent flow. In the first stage of contact, the weak liquor from which the major part of the phenol has been extracted is treated with benzene or light oil from which the phenols have been removed. The solvent is then contacted with liquor that is richer in phenol. This operation may be carried to a third contact zone in order to increase the phenol content of the solvent.

The solvent is removed from the liquor system and treated with caustic soda in two or three steps in order to remove the phenol from the solvent and recover the phenol as sodium phenolate. The sodium phenolate is then boiled to remove the entrained solvent. It is then neutralized with sulphuric acid or carbon dioxide gas to liberate the crude phenol and phenol homologues.

RECOVERY AND REFINING OF PYRIDINE BASES

Among the products of carbonization of coal are the pyridine bases. Part of these bases dissolve in the

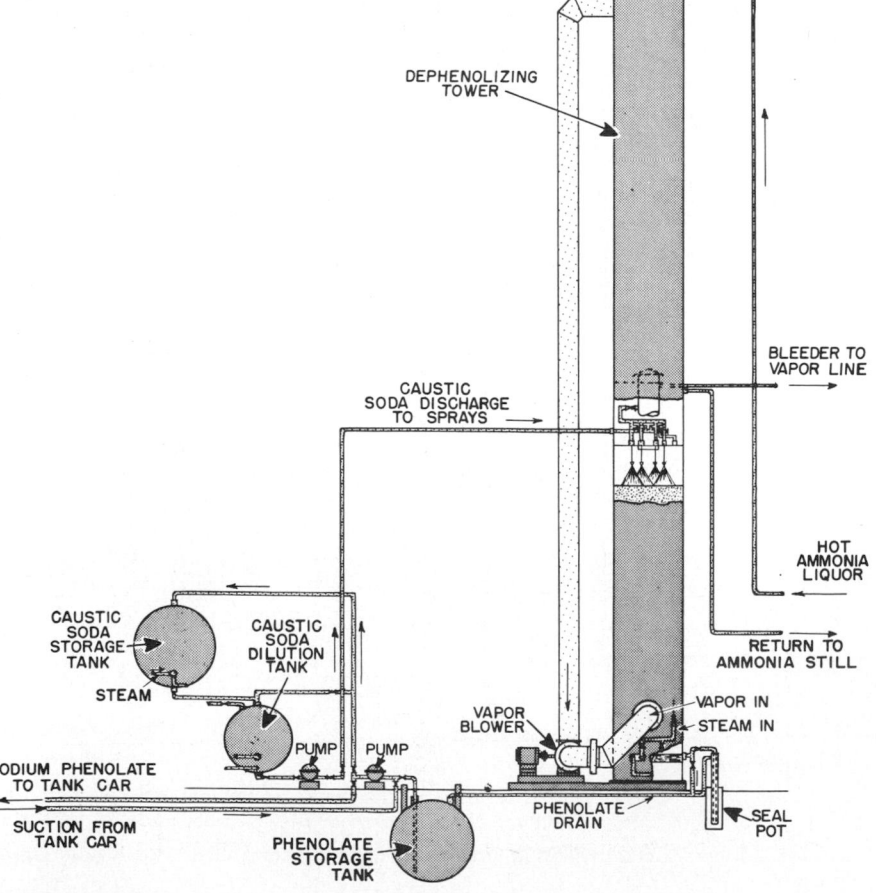

FIG. 4—29. Schematic representation of the steps in the vapor-recirculation process for the recovery of phenol from ammonia liquor. Side of column has been partially cut away to show spray arrangement. (Courtesy, Koppers Company, Inc.)

tar, while the remainder is present in the gas going to the saturators. The pyridine bases include pyridine, picolines (methyl pyridines), lutidines (dimethyl pyridines), etc. These compounds being basic in nature dissolve in the saturator liquor with the formation of pyridine sulphate. Where pyridine recovery operations are practical, the acidity of the saturator liquors must be carefully controlled. Two processes for the recovery of these bases from saturator liquors are described in the following. Recovery of pyridine bases from tar is described later in this chapter, when the refining of coal tar is discussed.

Saturator liquor is withdrawn continuously from the feed tank to the continuous dryers at a predetermined rate and conducted to a neutralizing still, where the neutralization of the saturator liquor and separation of the bases from the neutralized liquor are effected simultaneously. Ammonia vapors (containing carbon dioxide) are taken directly from the fixed leg of the ammonia stills, and conducted into the neutralizing still at a constant rate.

The neutralizing still is fitted with a dephlegmator which operates with top vapor temperature of from 185 to 195° F (85 to 90° C). Pyridine bases, ammonia, carbon dioxide, and water, distill overhead and are conducted to the separating unit, while the ammonium sulphate liquor is withdrawn continuously from the bottom of the still and returned to the saturator.

The vapors from the dephlegmator pass downward through a condenser and the condensate therefrom is conducted below the level of liquid in the separator. The ammonia, carbon dioxide, and water unite to form a solution of ammonium carbonate with a spe-

cific gravity of 1.07 to 1.08. The pyridine bases separate from this ammonium carbonate solution as a top liquid layer containing about 15 per cent water and are decanted continuously into a receiving tank. The ammonium carbonate solution is automatically maintained at a constant level, the excess being returned to the neutralizing still. This is done in order to maintain an equilibrium of ammonia and carbon dioxide in the system which results in a solution of the desired specific gravity in the separator.

In another method of continuous operation, the pyridine bases are completely condensed at the time of neutralization and separated from the saturator liquor by gravity.

Batch-Type Recovery Process for Pyridine Bases— Pyridine bases may be recovered by the intermittent removal of saturator liquor from the saturator and batch treatment of this liquor for the recovery of the pyridine bases (Figure 4—30).

The recovery equipment consists of a lead-lined tank which serves as a receiving tank and still. Its capacity is designed to hold the saturator liquors that will be removed from all saturators in 24 hours. It is equipped with a steam coil and an open pipe for the ammonia feed. A condenser is provided to condense the water and pyridine bases distilled over, along with a receiving tank for the wet product.

In the daily operation for the recovery of the bases 250–300 gallons of saturator liquor are removed from each saturator twice per 24 hours. The liquor is removed from the saturator or absorber and pumped to a pyridine-liquor well. This liquor, containing from 25 to 40 grams per liter of pyridine bases and 80 to 100 grams per liter of free acid, is transferred to the

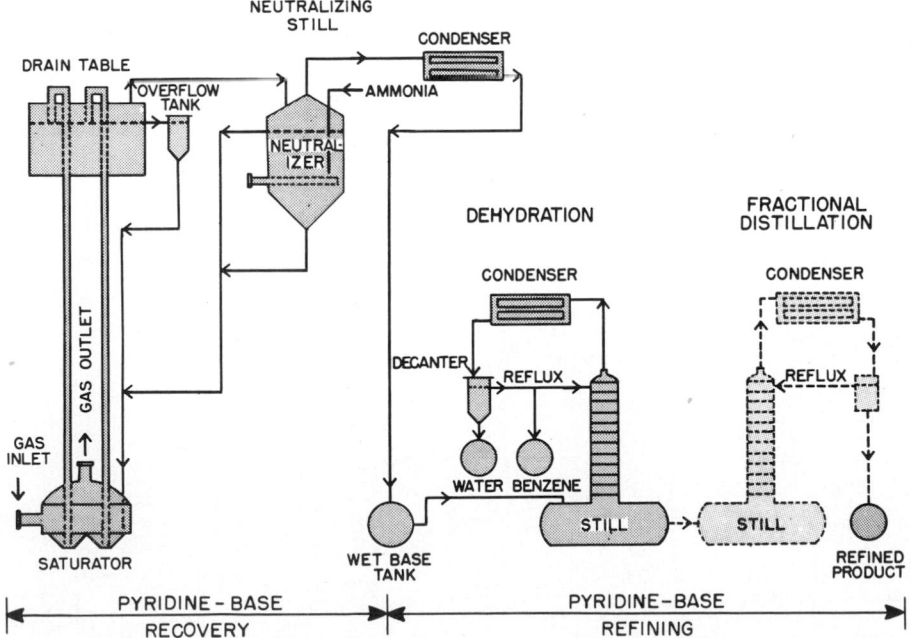

FIG. 4—30. Flow sheet of a batch-type plant for recovery and refining of pyridine bases. The equipment at the far right is shown dotted because the same still is used for both dehydration and fractional distillation, except that, in the latter case, the decanter is not employed.

neutralizing still or "rectifier," where it is first distilled to remove acidic gases and then treated with ammonia until the bases are liberated; this operation is called "springing." The liquor in this still is then heated and the bases are distilled off and condensed as a water solution containing 40 per cent of bases.

Refining of Pyridine Bases—The crude pyridine bases are first dehydrated by azeotropic distillation, using benzol as the entrainer.

The wet pyridine bases are charged to a still with a quantity of benzene. The quantity of benzene should be sufficient to form the azeotrope with water during distillation. The distillation is controlled by maintaining the vapor temperature at 157.1° F (69.5° C) until the water has been removed. The benzene and water are separated in a decanter tank where the water is sent to the waste disposal system and the benzene returned to the still.

After the water has been completely removed, the still is adjusted to provide a balance between the forward flow and reflux return to separate the benzene from the pyridine and then continued for the recovery of refined pyridine, picolines, and higher boiling point bases.

RECOVERY OF COKE-OVEN LIGHT OIL

Light Oil—The gas leaving the saturators contains light oil. This oil is a clear yellow-brown oil with a specific gravity of about 0.880. It is a mixture of all those condensable products of coal gas with boiling points up to 390° F (200° C), containing well over a hundred constituents (Table 4—I). Most of these are present in such low concentrations that their recovery is seldom practicable. Many of the constituents, such as olefin and diolefin hydrocarbons, some straight chain and cyclic paraffins, sulphur, nitrogen and oxygen compounds are present in small quantities. The principal usable constituents are benzene (60–85 per cent), toluene (6–17 per cent), xylene (1–7 per cent), and solvent naphtha (0.5–3 per cent). Light oil constitutes approximately one per cent of the coal carbonized.

Light-Oil Recovery Processes—The removal of light oil from coal gas is generally the last step in the coal-chemical recovery process.

There are three general methods used for the recovery of light oil:

(a) Refrigeration and compression involving temperatures below −70° C and pressures of 10 atmospheres.

(b) Adsorption by solid adsorbents involving the removal of light oil from the gas by passing it through a bed of activated carbon and recovering the light oil from the carbon by heating with direct or indirect steam.

(c) Absorption by solvents involving washing the coal gas with a petroleum wash oil, a coal-tar fraction, or other absorbent, followed by steam distillation of the enriched absorbent to recover the light oil. A process employing petroleum wash oil and another using a coal-tar fraction will be described here.

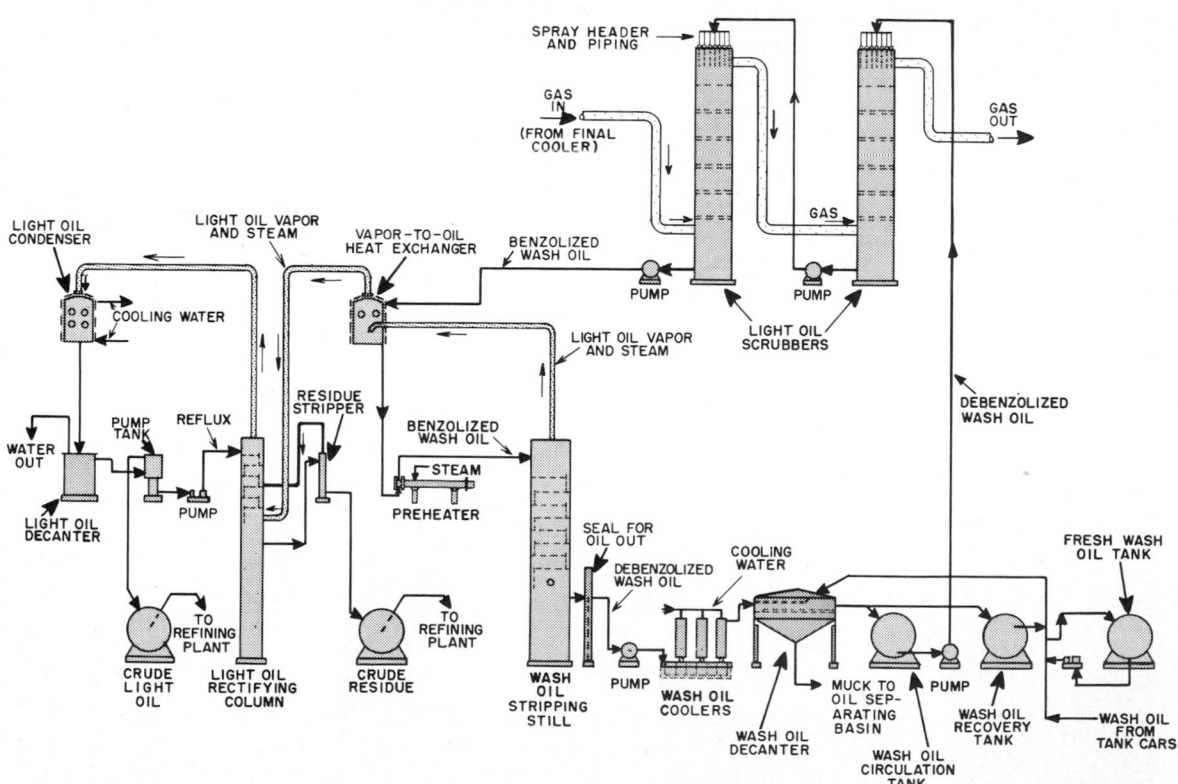

Fig. 4—31. Flow sheet of a light-oil recovery system. (Courtesy, Wilputte Coke Oven Division, Allied Chemical Corp.)

Table 4—I. Fractions of Coke-Oven Light Oil, and Boiling Points of Some of Their Constituents

CONSTITUENT GROUP	FORERUNNINGS (2% of Light Oil)	CRUDE BENZENE (60% of Light Oil)	CRUDE TOLUENE (18% of Light Oil)
AROMATICS	Traces of Benzene	Benzene C_6H_6 80.1° C.	Toluene $C_6H_5CH_3$ 110.6° C.
PARAFFINS	n-Pentane C_5H_{12} 36.1° C.	n-Hexene C_6H_{14} 68.8° C. 2-Methylhexane } C_7H_{16} 90.3° C. n-Heptane } 98.4° C.	n-Heptane C_7H_{16} 98.4° C. n-Octane C_8H_{18} 125.6° C.
CYCLOPARAFFINS NAPHTHENES	Cyclopentane C_5H_{10} 51.0° C.	Cyclohexane C_6H_{12} 80.8° C.	Methylcyclohexane $C_6H_{11}CH_3$ 100.3° C. Cycloheptane C_7H_{14} 120.3° C.
UNSATURATEDS (Olefins-Diolefins and Aromatic Hydrocarbons with Unsaturated Side Chains)	Butene-1 C_4H_8 −6.5° C. Pentene-1 } 30.1° C. Amylenes } C_5H_{10} 20 to 41.0° C. n-Hexylene C_6H_{12} 64.0° C. Cyclopentadiene-1, 3 C_5H_6 42.0° C. Butadiene-1, 3 C_4H_6 −5.0° C.	Hexene-2 } Hexadiene-1, 3 } C_7H_{14} 99.0° C. n-Heptylene } Cyclohexene } 85.0° C. Unidentified Compounds	Unidentified Compounds
SULPHUR COMPOUNDS	Carbon Disulphide CS_2 46.3° C. Hydrogen Sulphide H_2S −59.6° C. Hydrogen Cyanide HCN 26.0° C. Carbonyl Sulphide COS −50.2° C. Methyl Mercaptan CH_3SH 7.6° C. Ethyl Mercaptan C_2H_5SH 34.7° C. Dimethyl Sulphide $(CH_3)_2S$ 36.2° C.	Thiophene C_4H_4S 85.0° C. Diethyl Sulphide $(C_2H_5)_2S$ 91.6° C.	Methylthiophene C_5H_6S 112 to 115.0° C.
NITROGEN & OXYGEN COMPOUNDS			Pyridine C_5H_5N 115.3° C.

CONSTITUENT GROUP	CRUDE NO. 1 SOLVENT (8% of Light Oil)	CRUDE NO. 2 SOLVENT (6% of Light Oil)	CRUDE RESIDUE (6% of Light Oil)
AROMATICS	o-Xylene } 144.0° C. m-Xylene } $C_6H_4(CH_3)_2$ 139.1° C. p-Xylene } 138.4° C. Ethyl Benzene $C_6H_5C_2H_5$ 136.2° C.	n-Propyl Benzene } C_9H_{12} 158.6° C. Ethyl Toluenes } 161.2 to 164.9° C. Mesitylene } 164.6° C. Pseudocumene } $C_6H_3(CH_3)_3$ 169.2° C. Hemimellitene } 176.2° C. Cymenes $C_{10}H_{14}$ 175.5 to 177.3° C. Durenes $C_6H_2(CH_3)_4$ 196.0 to 198.0° C.	Wash Oil 275 to 360.° C. Naphthalene Solvents 218.° C. Pitch Residue Above 200.° C.
PARAFFINS	n-Octane C_8H_{18} 125.6° C. n-Nonane C_9H_{20} 150.7° C.	n-Decane $C_{10}H_{22}$ 174.0° C.	
CYCLOPARAFFINS NAPHTHENES	Cyclooctane C_8H_{16} 150.0° C.	Cyclononane C_9H_{18} 172.0° C.	
UNSATURATEDS (Olefins-Diolefins and Aromatic Hydrocarbons with Unsaturated Side Chains)	Octylene C_8H_{16} 126.0° C. Styrene C_8H_8 146.0° C. Unidentified Compounds	Coumarone C_8H_6O 175.0° C. Dicyclopentadiene $C_{10}H_{12}$ 170.0° C. Indene C_9H_8 182.0° C.	
SULPHUR COMPOUNDS	Thioxenes C_6H_8S 137 to 146.0° C.	Trimethylthiophene 160 to 163.0° C. Thiophenol 169.5° C. Tetramethylthiophene 182 to 184.0° C.	
NITROGEN & OXYGEN COMPOUNDS	Picolines C_5H_7N 131 to 143.0° C.	Cresols C_7H_8O 190 to 203.0° C. Dimethyl Pyridines C_7H_9N 143 to 164.0° C. Phenol C_6H_6O 182.0° C.	

Process Using Petroleum Wash Oil—The practice of using petroleum wash oil (Figure 4—31) is the one almost universally followed in the United States due to the availability and low cost of petroleum wash oil. The efficiency of recovery varies widely with the seasons since one of the major considerations is the temperature of the coal gas and wash oil entering the absorbing process. Another consideration is the ratio of wash oil to gas. The absorption equipment should be of reasonable design as to size and contact time. The oil-and-gas ratio varies depending on the equipment design and light-oil content of the gas prior to light-oil removal.

Typical operating conditions are as follows: the temperature of gas entering the absorption process is 59–86° F (15–30° C), the temperature of wash oil entering the process is 60–90° F (17–32° C) and the wash oil circulated per ton of coal carbonized is 150–200 gallons.

The boiling point of the wash oil should be well above 390° F (200° C) so as to permit an effective separation of light oil from wash oil in debenzolization. The oil should not thicken and should have a low viscosity to permit its distribution in the scrubbing towers. It should not deteriorate readily but maintain its initial properties as long as possible to keep makeup oil at a minimum. It must be especially stable with respect to the repeated heating which takes place in the recycling of the oil in the process. Its absorptive capacity should be very high and it should not react with or contaminate the coal gas. The specific gravity should be low enough to permit effective separation of wash oil and water in the processing and keep emulsification of the two to a minimum. The specific heat should be low because the oil is subjected to repeated heating and cooling as it is recycled in the process.

The petroleum wash oil normally used for this absorption process has a boiling range of 518–622° F (270–350° C). Other specifications which are general for a petroleum wash oil include a specific gravity of about 0.830, a viscosity of 45 seconds Saybolt at 100° F (38° C), a pour point of 35° F (2° C), an emulsification of 95 per cent separation in 50 seconds, a flash point of 300° F (150° C), fire point of 335° F (168° C), and a low residue under 0.10 per cent when heated for a period of five days at approximately 300° F (150° C).

Final Cooler— The first step in the recovery of light oil by absorption in a liquid medium is that of cooling the gas leaving the saturators at a temperature of 112–140° F (50–60° C) by direct contact with water in a tower scrubber called a final cooler. The facilities are so named since the gas is here given its final cooling in the coal-chemical processing. This is necessary to remove naphthalene from the gas and also cool the gas prior to its admission to the wash-oil scrubbers.

The tower consists of a tall cylindrical shell of steel approximately 10 to 15 feet in diameter and 50 to 75 feet in height filled with a suitable packing material, either metallic or wooden. The gas enters near the bottom of the tower and passes up through the packing material and out near the top. The cooling water enters the top of the tower through a spray system and the water passes down through the tower, coming in direct contact with the gas in a countercurrent manner. The water leaves the tower at the bottom through a sealed outlet pipe to prevent escape of any gas. The heat from the gas is transferred to the water, which in turn is cooled in an induced-draft water-cooling tower with air or in an atmospheric water-spray cooling operation. Cooling of the water depends upon air circulation and the vaporization of a part of the water in circulation, the latent heat of vaporization of the water being responsible for additional cooling. Operating practice is to cool the water, and in turn cool the gas, to as low a temperature as practicable, depending upon atmospheric temperature, since most effective absorption of light oil is obtained at low temperatures. Cooling is not carried below 60° F (15° C), since below that temperature petroleum absorbing oil becomes too viscous to flow freely.

This direct-cooling operation causes the condensation of a major portion of the naphthalene and any entrained tar and vapor-phase gums. The naphthalene is recovered in a sump operation and is either added to the tar or refined directly to provide a salable product.

In some of the more modern facilities, the lower part of the final-cooler tower is redesigned to permit the outlet water to come in direct contact with tar in order to dissolve the naphthalene as it is being removed from the gas.

Wash-Oil Scrubber—The second step in the recovery of light oil is its absorption in the liquid petroleum wash oil. The gas comes in direct contact with the wash oil in one or more tall scrubbing towers containing packing and interlocking sprays. The gas passes from the first tower to the last in series and the wash oil travels from the last tower to the first in reverse series. The flow of gas and wash oil is countercurrent in each tower. The steel towers are approximately 15 to 22 feet in diameter and 100 feet in height.

The wash oil is introduced through a number of sprays in the top of the tower and comes into direct contact with the gas, which flows from the bottom to the top. An oil-storage tank is provided in the base of the tower to receive the oil and maintain a surge capacity for pumping the oil away. The oil passes from the gas compartment to oil storage through a sealed pipe. It is pumped from the base of one tower to the spray system in the top of the next tower in the series. From the last tower the oil is pumped to the stripping stills for separation of light oil from wash oil. Wash oil prior to light-oil absorption is called debenzolized and, after absorption, benzolized. The benzolized wash oil contains 2 to 3 per cent light oil. The debenzolized wash oil is cooled in indirect coolers to a temperature several degrees higher than that of the gas entering the scrubbers, which is 60 to 75° F (15 to 25° C). This is to prevent condensation of water from the gas, which would form an emulsion with the oil, causing clogging of the free space in the packing of the tower. The rate requirement for the circulation of oil through the scrubbers is a function of the vapor-pressure distribution between the light oil dissolved in the absorbent oil and that remaining in the gas at the temperature of operation. From 90 to 95 per cent of the light-oil content of the gas is recovered in this operation. The wash oil, after being cooled, passes through a large decanting tank which acts as a settling compartment for the emulsified and resinous materials present in the wash oil. This material accumulates in the bottom of the tank, and the wash oil decants off at a higher level to a small receiving tank, from which it is pumped to the top of the first scrubbing tower in the series. Generally, two decanting and two receiving tanks are provided to permit cleaning the residue from the tanks periodically.

Recent designs of wash-oil scrubbers are not fitted with hurdles and packing used in the previous type. Contact between the gas and absorption oil is accomplished by the use of single conical sprays placed at three different elevations within the tower, as shown in Figure 4—32. Absorption oil pumped through the top pressure spray is collected by steel-plate umbrellas, and passed through second and third spray nozzles of the gravity-flow type. Baffles direct the flow of gas toward the spray in every pass and horizontal angles restore correct distribution above each umbrella collector. Restrictions to gas flow by accumulations of residues commonly found in packed scrubbers are minimized or eliminated in scrubbers of this design.

Debenzolization of Wash Oil—In the debenzolization step, the light oil (2 to 3 per cent) in the benzolized wash oil is separated by steam distillation. The carryover of absorbing oil into the light oil is kept to about 5 per cent and the debenzolized absorbing oil contains 0.2 per cent light oil.

In the straight steam-distillation process at atmospheric pressure, the benzolized wash oil is preheated to approximately 212° F (100° C) with a vapor-to-oil and an oil-to-oil heat exchanger. Heating is continued to 295° F (145° C) with an indirect preheater of the shell-and-tube type, with the oil flowing through the tubes, using steam as the heating medium on the shell side. The preheated oil is introduced near the top into a multi-plate bubble-cap fractionating column leaving several plates above the feed to keep entrainment of wash oil to a minimum. The benzolized wash oil flows down the column countercurrent to upward flow of live steam, which is introduced in the base of the still column. The debenzolized wash oil leaving the base of the column through a sealed outlet at a temperature of 290 to 300° F (145 to 150° C) passes through the oil-to-oil heat exchanger in which it is cooled to 212° F (100° C) giving up its heat to the incoming benzolized wash oil. Water separates out at this point and is drained off. The wash oil passes through a pumping tank and is pumped at 212° F (100° C) to cooling coils for cooling prior to being used again as an absorbent for the light oil in the scrubber towers.

The mixture of steam and light oil vapors leaving the top of the column flows through the tubular vapor-to-oil heat exchanger which recovers heat and also acts as a partial condenser. Sufficient heat is imparted to the incoming benzolized oil to raise its temperature 45° F (25° C) and, at the same time, the

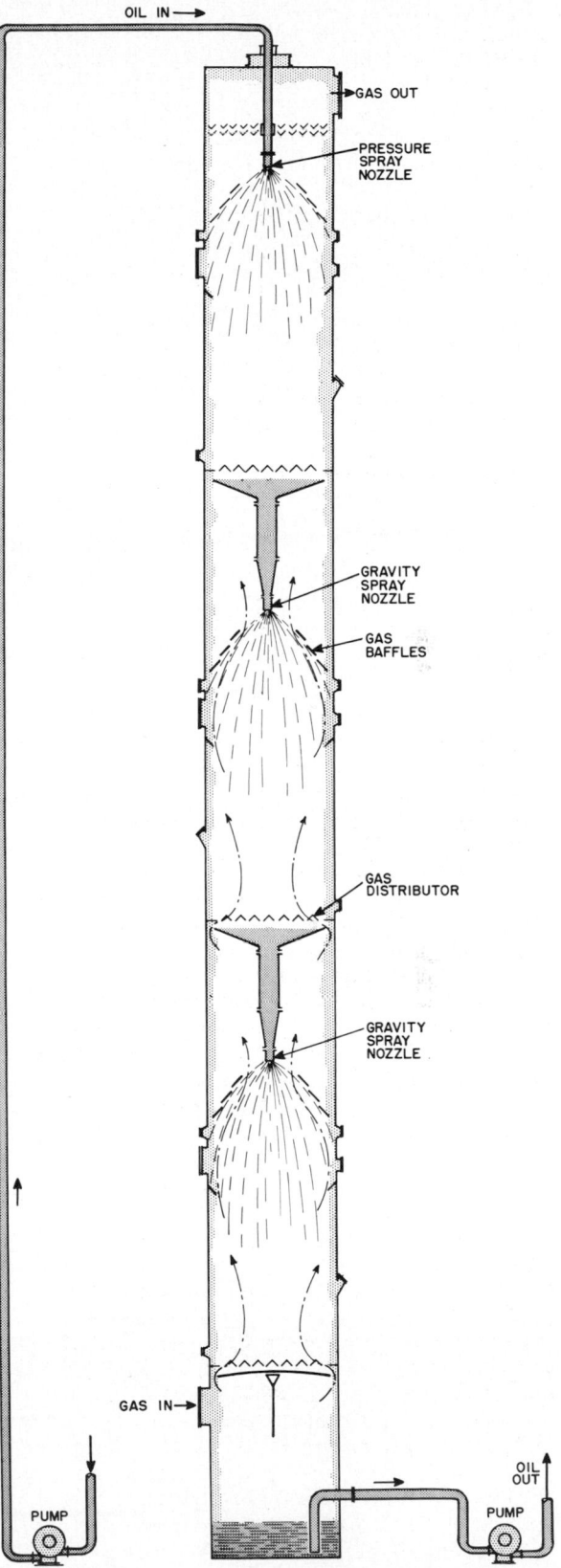

Fig. 4—32. Schematic representation of a spray-type wash-oil scrubber.

vapors are cooled to cause a portion of the steam and high-boiling constituents of light oil to condense (the condensate of which carries along some of the wash oil which was carried over the top of the column as entrainment). The mixture of oil and water is separated in a gravity separator tank, the water flowing to the sump system and the oil being returned to the debenzolized oil streams. The mixture of steam and light-oil vapors leaving the vapor-to-oil heat exchanger passes to a water-cooled condenser, which is of a multi-pass design, with the vapor and water flowing countercurrent to each other. The condensate flows to a gravity separator effecting a separation of the light oil and water, the light oil flowing to storage and the water to the sump system.

In some designs, an additional fractionating column is added to the debenzolization process for rectifying the light-oil vapors from the vapor-to-oil heat exchanger. In this case, the condensate of the vapor-to-oil heat exchanger, after separation of the water, is also introduced into the rectifying column. The mixture of steam and light-oil vapors enters the multiple-plate bubble-cap rectifying column near the middle section. The light oil is separated into two fractions: the distillate containing forerunnings, benzene, toluene, xylene, and low-boiling solvent; while the residual fraction contains an admixture of high-boiling

solvents, naphthalene and wash oil. A portion of the distillate is returned to the top of the column as reflux, the control point being the vapor temperature at the top of the column.

In the more modern debenzolization processes, the benzolized wash oil is processed at a temperature of 195 to 250° F (90 to 120° C) and this eliminates the need for an oil-to-oil heat exchanger in the process lineup.

Process Using Coal-Tar Fraction for Light-Oil Recovery—The light-oil recovery process at the Coke and Coal Chemical Division of Gary Steel Works of United States Steel Corporation is somewhat unique in the industry. A simplified flow diagram of the process is shown in Figure 4—33. The absorption oil used is a fraction of coal tar rather than the conventional petroleum wash oil used in most light-oil recovery processes. This oil has a lower molecular weight than petroleum wash oil, which allows a decrease in the volume of oil necessary to recover light oils from coal gas. Absorption oil distilled from tar is also more compatible with other coal-tar products, which reduces sludging.

Source of Absorption Oil—Approximately 8 to 12 per cent of the coal tar produced at Gary is recovered as absorption oil having a boiling range of 235° to 290° C (455° to 555° F). Other general characteristics

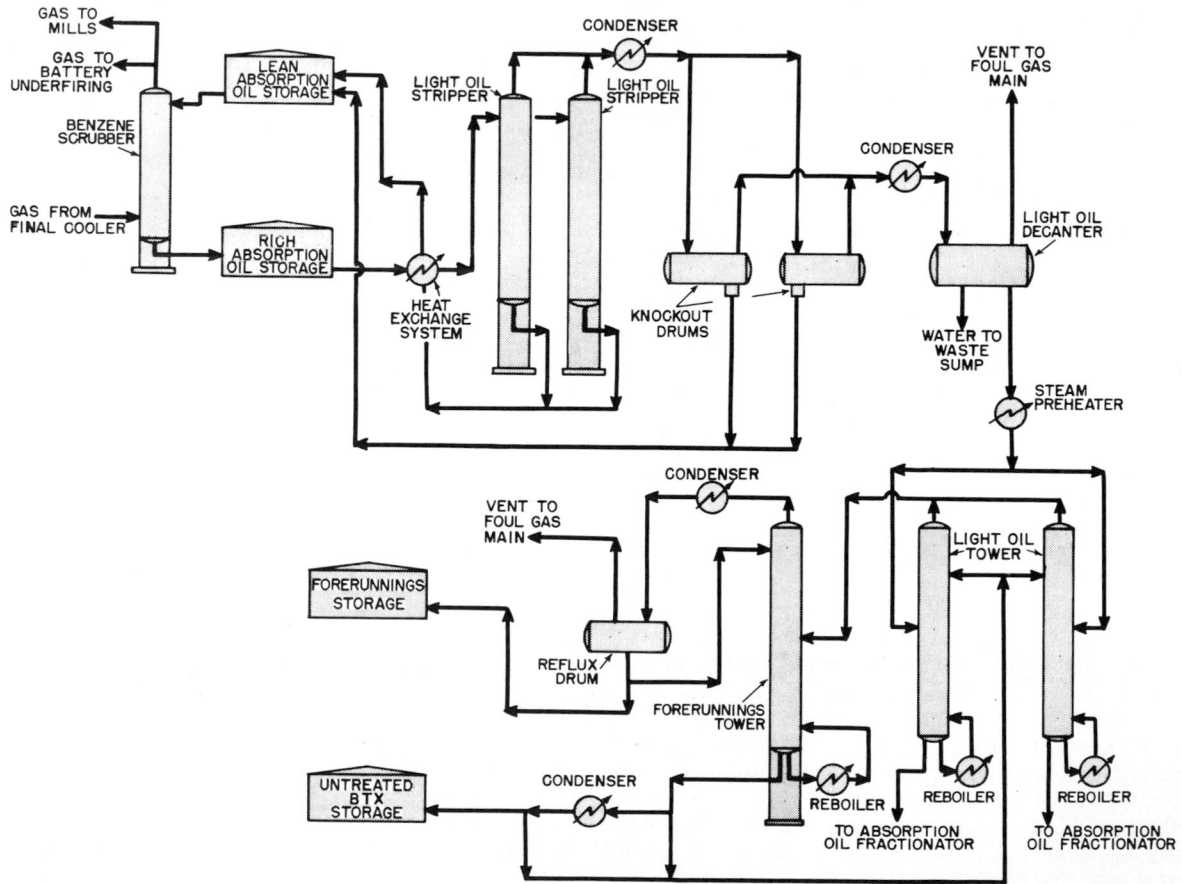

FIG. 4—33. Simplified flow diagram of a light-oil recovery process employing a coal-tar fraction as the absorption oil.

of the oil include: specific gravity, 1.05 to 1.08; viscosity, 30 to 50 Saybolt Universal seconds at 80° F; a limpid point of −10° to +10° C (15° to 50° F); flash point (Cleveland open cup), 200° to 230° F (85° to 110° C); and a tar-residue content of less than 2 per cent.

Benzene Scrubbers—The coal gas leaving the final coolers contains 1.2 to 1.5 mole per cent of light oils, the principal constituents being benzene, toluene, xylenes, and solvent naphtha. The total light oil in the gas represents about 3 to 3.5 gallons per ton of coal charged into the coke ovens, depending upon such variables as types of coal, coal mixtures, temperature of the coke ovens, and coking time. Recovery of these products is accomplished by scrubbing the coal gas with absorption oil in one or more cylindrical towers containing stainless-steel perforated trays. The absorption oil is sprayed into the top of the tower, flowing across each tray in turn, through the downcomer to the tray below. The gas enters the bottom of the tower and contacts the oil on each tray as it passes through the perforations and leaves the tower at the top, providing a countercurrent scrubbing of the gas. A unit located at the top of each benzene scrubber eliminates oil carried over with the gas: this unit is a conical device with vanes arranged to give the gas passing through the device a centrifugal motion, causing the oil droplets to separate out in troughs in the outer edge of the unit and flow back to the top tray of the benzene scrubber. The scrubbing operation is a continuous process, the gas entering the scrubbers at 27° to 32° C (80° to 90° F) and the oil entering at a temperature about 2° to 4° C higher than the gas to minimize the condensation of water from the gas.

The oil-circulation rate is usually expressed as gallons of oil circulated per minute per ton of coal charged, and in the recovery process at Gary this ratio is approximately 115 gallons of oil per ton of coal charged, depending upon the quality of the absorption oil and the light-oil content of the coal gas. Scrubbing efficiency of 90 to 95 per cent may be expected in a light-oil recovery process having perforated-tray type benzene scrubbers using the coal-tar fraction as absorption oil, depending upon the light-oil content of the lean absorption oil, oil-circulation rate, gas flow and velocity, temperature of the gas and oil, and the vapor-pressure distribution between the light oil dissolved in the absorption oil and that remaining in the gas. It may be noted that, at Gary, light-oil removal is accomplished at 8 to 10 lb. per sq. in. gage pressure.

Absorption-Oil Regeneration System—In the process of circulating the absorption oil over the benzene scrubbers, some heavy tar materials are picked up from the gas and build up in the absorption oil. As these materials build up in the oil, the molecular weight of the oil is increased and, consequently, a greater oil-circulation rate over the benzene scrubbers is required. These heavy components (with high boiling points) also tend to plug up the perforated trays in the benzene scrubbers and coat the tubes of the heat exchangers in the light-oil system, greatly reducing their efficiency. In order to remove these high-

boiling components, an absorption-oil regeneration system is necessary. A portion of the lean absorption oil is fed continuously to a flash system where the material boiling under 280° to 290° C (535° to 555° F) is flashed overhead to the absorption-oil tower where new absorption oil is produced and the bottoms from the flash system (material boiling above 280° to 290° C) is pumped to the creosote-fractionating tower where it goes as a bottoms stream to pitch creosote that is used as an open-hearth furnace fuel.

Light-Oil Stripping and Fractionation—The Gary Steel Works light-oil stripping facilities consist of two light-oil strippers that are 8 feet in diameter and 48 feet high, with 15 split-flow bubble-cap trays in each tower. Material used in construction of the shell of the strippers is Type 316 stainless steel: internal parts are constructed of Type 304 stainless steel. Each tower is capable of handling approximately 1100 gallons per minute of rich oil with an efficiency rating of 95 to 98 per cent. In the fractionating section of the light-oil recovery process, there are two light-oil towers, 5 feet in diameter and 27 feet high with 6 bubble-cap trays each; and a forerunnings tower, 5 feet in diameter and 73 feet high, with 30 bubble-cap trays.

The rich absorption oil containing 2.2 to 3.3 mole per cent of light oil is pumped continuously from storage to the light-oil strippers via a series of heat exchangers where the absorption oil is preheated to a temperature of 140° to 150° C (285° to 300° F) before it enters the light-oil strippers. At this point, live steam at 15 lb. per sq. in. gage pressure is introduced into the bottom of the strippers to strip the light oil from the absorption oil. As the light oils are stripped out, the lean absorption oil is pumped continuously as a bottom product to lean-oil storage from whence it is recirculated over the benzene scrubbers. In order to obtain maximum efficiency in the recovery of the light oils from the absorption oil, gas chromatographic analysis of the lean oil leaving the strippers is run on a daily basis to determine the amount of various light-oil fractions left in the lean oil, and adjustments are made in the process to obtain minimum light oil in the lean oil.

Light oils, water vapor from the stripping steam and entrained absorption oil go overhead on the light-oil strippers, where the vapors are partially condensed so as to drop out the entrained absorption oil in the absorption-oil knockout drums. The absorption oil dropped out at this point is pumped back into the lean-oil system, and the light-oil vapors and the water vapor go overhead in the knockout drums where they are condensed, collected in a decanter, and the water decanted off in the light-oil decanter.

The light oils are then pumped by way of a steam-heated preheater to the light-oil tower, where a separation is made to produce an overhead product with a dry point of 150° to 160° C (ASTM). The bottoms stream from this tower—which consists essentially of crude solvent naphtha, naphthalene, tar acids and absorption oil—flows by gravity back to the absorption-oil tower where it is recovered as crude acid oils (or carbolic oils) and absorption oil. Light-oil vapors which go overhead on the light-oil tower are fed as vapors to the forerunnings tower, where a separation is made to remove components from the light oil that have boiling points below that of benzene. These components include carbon disulphide, hydrogen sulphide, cyclopentadiene, and other constituents boiling below benzene that are taken overhead on the forerunnings tower, where the temperature of the condenser is controlled so as to condense the benzene and all the higher-boiling components that might go overhead, while allowing the lower-boiling components to be vented to a foul-gas main that ties into the under-firing system of the coke-oven batteries. Light oils are pumped from the bottom of the forerunnings tower, cooled, and stored as a raw BTX (benzene-toluene-xylene) fraction having a boiling point of 79° to 80° C (ASTM) and a dry point of 150° to 160° C (ASTM). At this point, the raw BTX is fed continuously to a 66° Bé sulphuric-acid wash system to remove constituents capable of reacting with the acid at approximately 40° C.

The major impurities removed from the light oil are olefins, diolefins, sulphur-containing constituents and substituted aromatics such as styrene, cyclopentadiene, thiophene, hexene, heptene and hexadienes. The reactions between sulphuric acid and the light oil impurities are varied and complex. Some of the constituents react to form sulphonic acids: some are oxidized; and others are polymerized to form gums and resins. Yields of benzene, toluene and xylene depend upon good temperature control. The greater the temperature, the greater the degree of aromatic sulphonation. This is reflected in higher sludge loss with

xylenes being affected to the greatest extent: toluene and benzene are affected to a lesser extent in that order. After the light oil is washed with sulphuric acid, it is washed with water, neutralized with caustic and then fed to a series of continuous stills, where it is processed to produce 1° benzene, 1° toluene, 10° xylene, and industrial xylene.

REFINING OF COKE-OVEN LIGHT-OIL

Light oil is separated into a number of marketable products by refining. The aromatic hydrocarbons in crude light oil, which are present in large quantities, are the principal source of the commercial products. These hydrocarbons are benzene, toluene, xylene, and solvent naphtha. The remaining substances, which are present in small quantities, are generally considered to be impurities. These consist of saturated straight-chain hydrocarbons or paraffins, saturated closed-chain or cylcoparaffin and naphthalene hydrocarbons, unsaturated hydrocarbon olefins and diolefins, sulphur compounds (carbon disulphide, thiophene and its homologues), nitrogen compounds (pyridine and its homologues), and oxygen compounds (phenol and its homologues).

Procedures for treatment of the light oil to obtain commercial products consist of a combination of a chemical treatment—acid washing—to remove certain impurities, plus fractional distillation to remove the refined products.

Acid Washing—Washing light-oil fractions with sulphuric acid removes impurities by chemical reac-

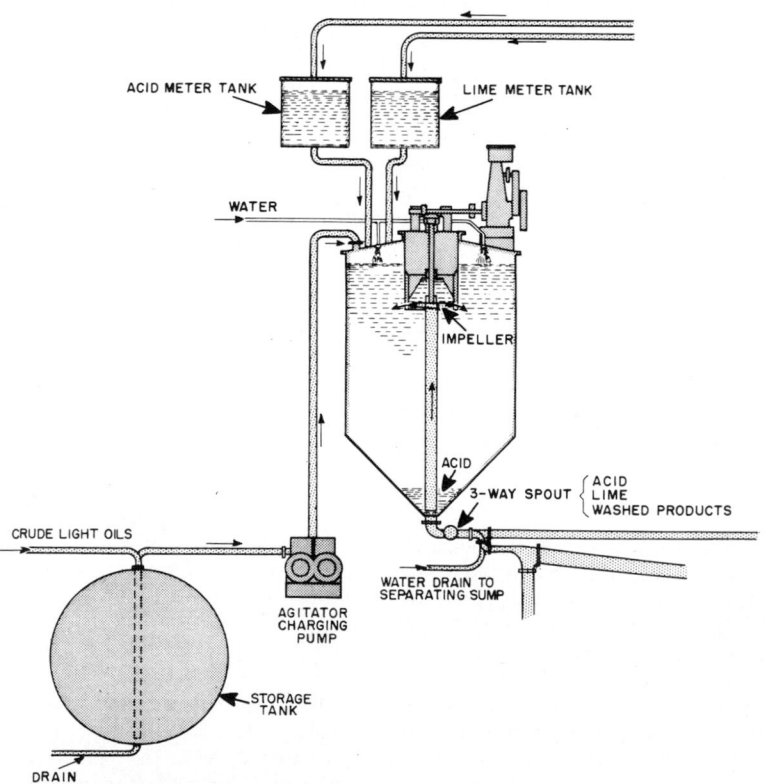

Fig. 4—34. Schematic representation of an acid washer. (Courtesy, Koppers Company, Inc.)

tion of the acid with the impurities (Figure 4—34). These particular impurities cannot be removed by fractional distillation. The chemical reactions involve oxidation, polymerization, sulphonation and other complex reactions with the unsaturated hydrocarbon olefins and diolefins, sulphur, nitrogen and oxygen compounds. Most reaction products remain in solution in the acid and are removed with it by gravity separation from the washed oil. The acid-washed oils are, after neutralization, separated into individual constituents by fractional distillation.

Fractional Distillation—Fractional distillation separates the principal aromatic components of light oil by repeated vaporization of a mixture of these compounds (which have different boiling points) followed by condensation of the vapors in such a way that the desired degree of separation of the components is obtained.

The following proportional distribution of the main constituents in light oil, based on distillation range, indicates the relationship of quantities involved:

Fraction	Distribution	Approx. Boiling Points
Forerunnings	1.5– 2.5%	77–158° F (25–70° C)
Pure Benzene	60.0–85.0%	176.2° F (80.1° C)
Pure Toluene	6.0–17.0%	231.1° F (110.6° C)
Pure Xylenes	1.0– 7.0%	275–293° F (135–145° C)
Heavy Solvents	0.5– 3.0%	338–392° F (170–200° C)
Residues	5.0–11.5%	392° F (Above 200° C)

The particular operating sequence in regard to chemical treatment and distillation varies, depending upon quality of the crude light oil, the equipment available, the chemical treatment employed, and the market demands. A complete examination is required in each plant to plan effectively the type of operation that will be most satisfactory.

In earlier distilling operations only batch stills were used, whereas modern refining techniques make use of continuous stills for a number of the separations.

Batch-Still Operation—A batch still consists of a kettle connected to a fractionating column by a vapor pipe that carries vapor to the column, and a liquid-sealed pipe that permits return flow of liquid to the kettle. The column contains thirty to forty plates which are fitted with bubble caps to bring ascending vapors into contact with descending condensate, and return flow lines to permit condensate to return to each succeeding lower plate. The actual number of plates, bubble caps, etc., must be determined from design characteristics dictated by the separation to be performed on the material to be distilled. The kettle is equipped with steam coils with sufficient surface for the available steam to supply the column with vapor at a predetermined rate. A vapor pipe conducts the vapors from the top of the column to a condenser which may also be equipped with an aftercooler. The condensate is collected in a receiving tank and a part returned to the top of the column to provide reflux for control of the temperature and efficient separation of the hydrocarbons. It is usually better practice to effect the reflux by pump flow, to provide positive control of this operation.

In the operation of a batch still, the kettle is filled to its designed capacity which leaves space in the up-

per section to receive the vapors, and the steam is turned into the heating coils. As the material reaches the boiling point, it is necessary to control the rate of steam flow by the pressure or temperature in the kettle. The vapors ascend the column, are condensed in the condenser, and a predetermined amount of condensate is returned to the column as reflux. It may all be returned for a while until the column is in product and temperature balance, at which time product may be removed and sent to storage. The vapors ascending into the fractionating column from the kettle pass through the bubble caps on each plate where they bubble through the reflux that is flowing downward. This contact provides a series of steps consisting of evaporation and condensation on each plate, and a temperature gradient is developed through the column, the lowest temperature at the top and the highest temperature at the bottom. This temperature gradient in a batch still column is in a constant state of change as the lower-boiling materials are first distilled over and replaced with the heavier fractions, but each plate maintains small temperature differentials between the plates above and below. During the progress of the distillation progressively higher-boiling materials are removed with consequent increase in the column and kettle temperatures. Intermediate fractions are always produced between the principal components, such as benzene and toluene. These intermediates are stored separately and re-run in the still to maintain the maximum recovery of finished products.

Continuous Still Operation—A continuous still (Figure 4—35) consists of a kettle or reboiler of considerably smaller capacity than that of the batch process, because the feed material is being constantly pumped into the unit and the residue pumped out of the reboiler. It is equipped with a fractionating column, a condenser, and reflux control. There are usually several still units in a group, with the hot residue from the first unit used as feed to the second unit, and this arrangement may be carried on with as many units as there are fractions to be recovered.

The feed to a continuous unit is pumped into the side of the fractionating column instead of into the kettle as in a batch still. In a batch still, a number of products are progressively removed from the top of the fractionating column, but in a continuous unit only one product is obtained from the top of a fractionating column, this product having the lowest boiling point of any component in the feed. Accordingly, there must be as many columns as there are products and intermediate off-grade fractions. The principles of fractional distillation apply to the operation of the column in regard to evaporation and condensation on each plate with a temperature gradient from top to bottom of the column. However, unlike the batch still, the conditions of temperature and pressure in the reboiler and column of a unit remain constant, and each plate operates at a constant temperature and pressure.

Control of Distillation Processes—The operations of batch and continuous distillation require control of various factors in the operating unit.

In batch-still operations, the principal control factors are the temperature of the vapor leaving the top of the column, rate of vaporization, and volume of re-

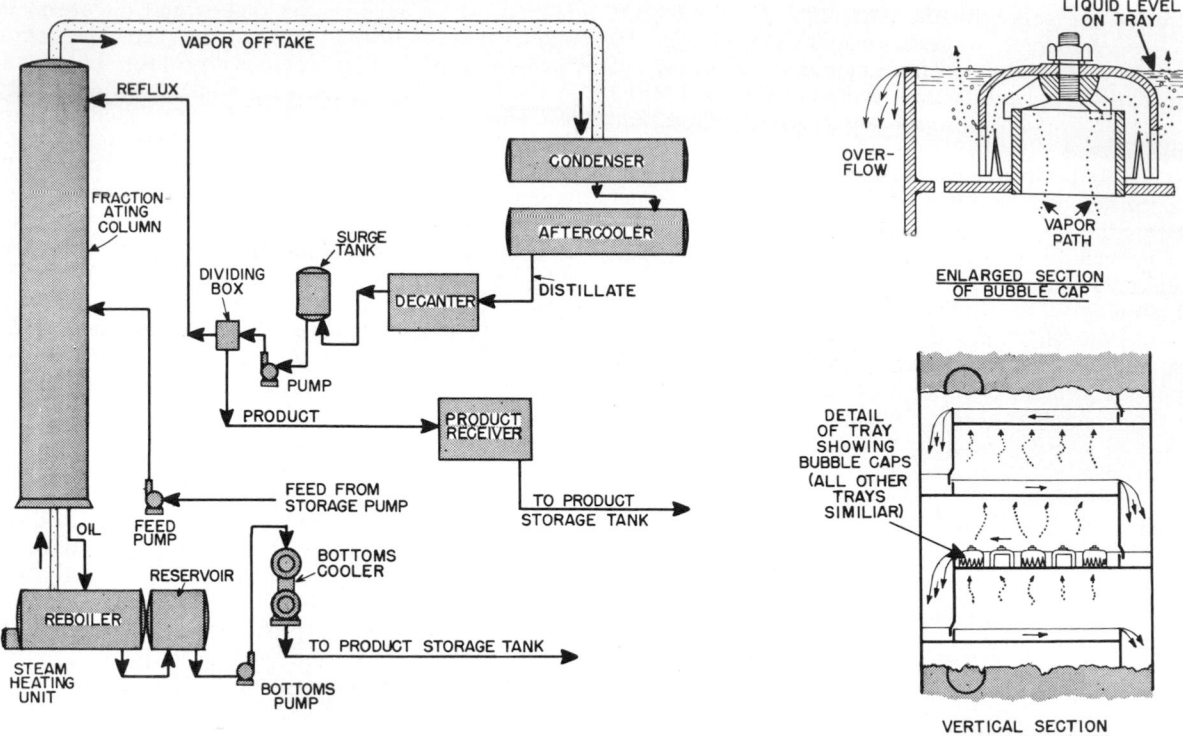

Fig. 4—35. (Left) Schematic diagram illustrating component parts and principle of operation of a modern continuous still. (Right) Schematic details of plates and bubble caps used in stills for fractional distillation. (Courtesy, Semet-Solvay Engineering Division, Allied Chemical Corporation).

flux pumped into the top of the column. The vaporization is controlled by the amount of steam introduced into the heating elements in the kettle, which can be done by hand operation of the steam valve or with a pressure controller actuated by the pressure in the kettle. The reflux provides a control of the temperature gradient in the column and makes it possible to remove in order the various components of the oil being fractionally distilled, the lowest-boiling fraction being the first removed. Other control factors are the level of oil in the kettle, rate of flow of product and reflux, temperature of condenser water in and out of the unit, and temperature of distillate.

Continuous distillation requires more control than batch in that all factors must be kept constant. A uniform feed of the light oil, which should be of constant composition, is maintained to the column by a flow controller. Continuous measurements of column temperatures—generally bottom of column, points below feed, above feed, and top of column, along with temperature of water in and out of the condenser, and temperature of distillate and bottom reboiler fractions—are taken. Liquid-level controllers are used to regulate pumping of the bottoms of one still to the next still and also pumping of the distillate as it flows from the condensers. The oil vaporization is controlled by a pressure regulator automatically operating the steam-header valve. Liquid levels in reboiler, surge, and receiving tanks are indicated by instruments. Volumes of oil flowing through pipe lines are indicated by rotameters, and steam flows are recorded.

Designs of plants for light-oil refining are classified as batch, semi-continuous and continuous, depending upon the types of distillation equipment employed. Of all the variables affecting the design of a plant, the size of the installation probably has the most bearing upon whether the process selected will be semi-continuous or continuous. It is not generally agreed just where the dividing point is. Small and medium-size plants usually are semi-continuous and larger plants are continuous.

Refining Heavy-Solvent-Free Light Oil—One of the most elementary light-oil refining processes is to acid-wash a crude light oil containing no heavy solvent, and to refine it into benzene, toluene, xylene, and pure still residue by either batch or continuous fractional distillation (Figures 4—36 and 4—37). Forerunnings, which are the lowest-boiling constituents of the light oil (including hydrogen sulphide, methyl mercaptan, butadiene, butylenes, amylenes, cyclopentadiene, carbon disulphide, and other compounds) may be removed in a stripper column prior to the acid-washing of the crude light oil. After removal of the forerunnings and acid-washing, the fraction containing the benzene, toluene and xylene is distilled for production of pure grades of these hydrocarbons.

In a refining operation of this character, the light oil, stripped of forerunnings, and acid-washed, is settled and stored in tanks from whence it is either charged to batch stills (Figure 4—36) or fed continuously to a series of pure continuous stills for production of the desired grades of pure substances.

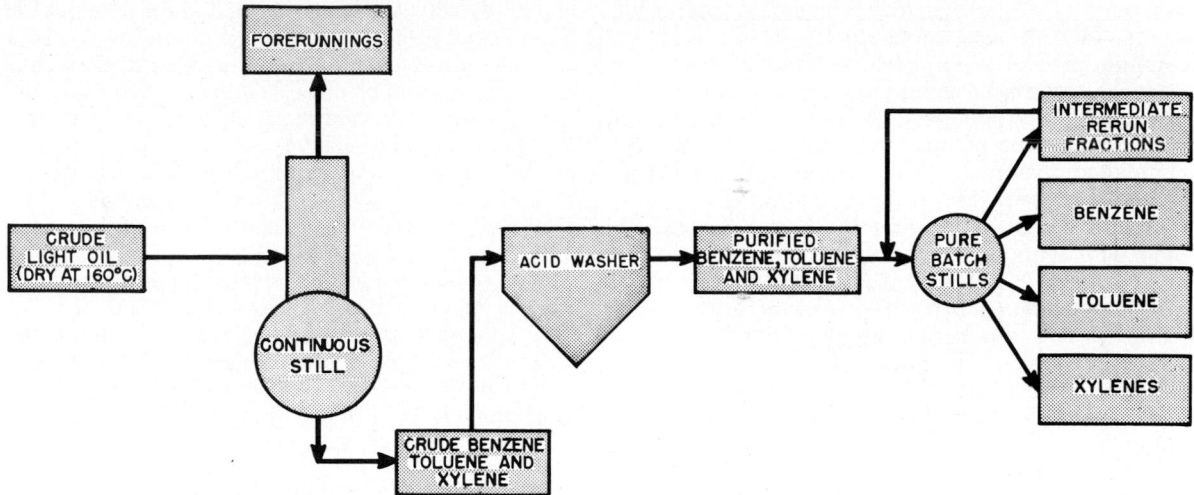

F<small>IG</small>. 4—36. Flow sheet illustrating combined use of a continuous still and batch-type stills for the semi-continuous recovery of the products shown in the boxes at the right.

In the latter case, the first continuous column, a residue remover, distills over the volatile compounds and retains acid-washing residue that has been dissolved in the washed light oil. Residue removal prior to distillation of the oil into its primary components eliminates impurities in the final products and the need for treatment of the still vapors or products with an aqueous solution of caustic soda. Otherwise, the continued heating of the residue as it passes through the still kettles would result in decomposition

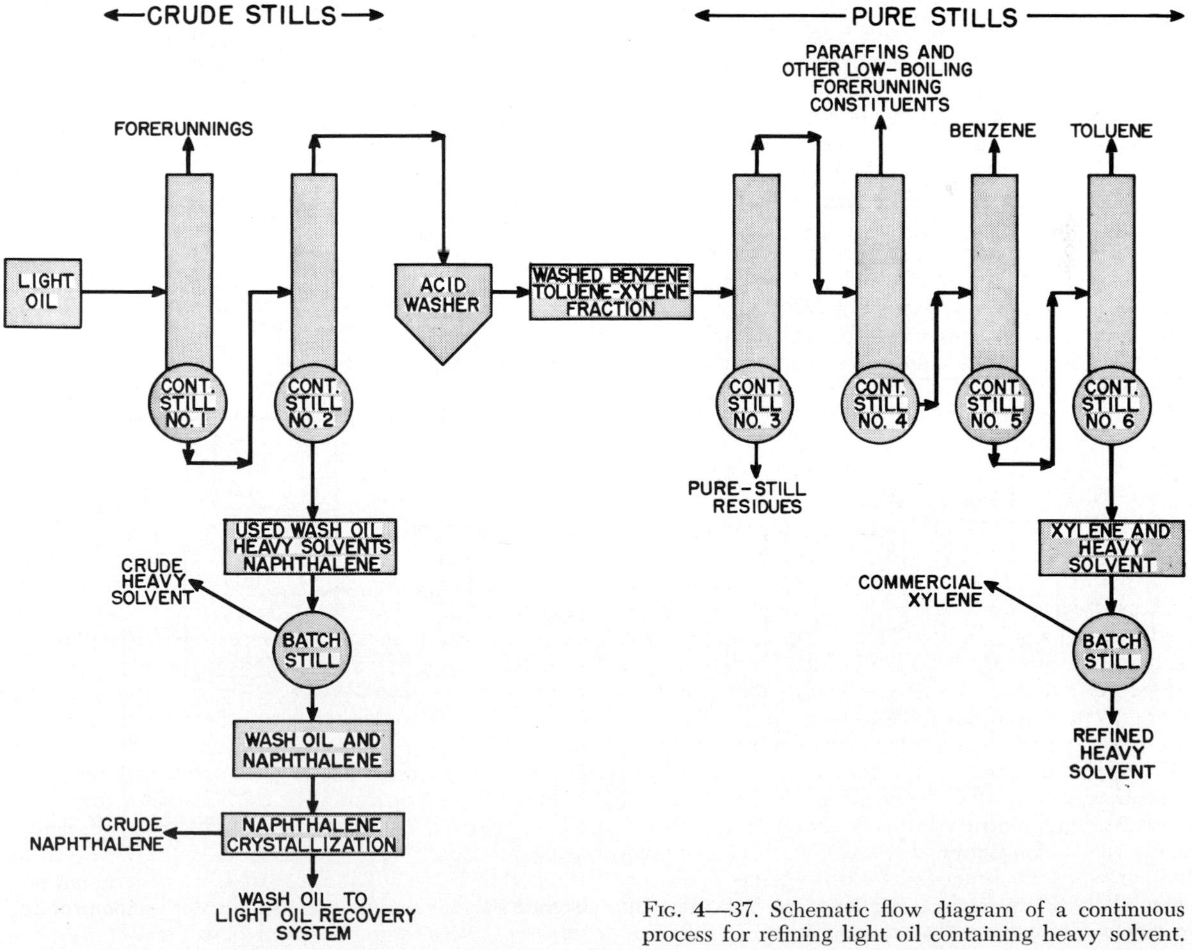

F<small>IG</small>. 4—37. Schematic flow diagram of a continuous process for refining light oil containing heavy solvent.

reactions of the polymerized materials, producing sulphur dioxide that would react with the hydrogen sulphide present to form free sulphur. After residue removal, a second column takes off benzene. A third column takes off toluene with xylene as a side cut, or the latter can be pumped from the reboiler and accumulated for batch distillation to separate xylene from the solvents with which it is associated.

Refining Light Oil Containing Heavy Solvent—If light oil containing heavy solvents and having a dry point of 390° F (200° C) is processed, an additional distillation column becomes necessary before acidwashing. This can be a continuous column (Figure 4—37). The overhead of this column would be a fraction consisting of benzene, toluene and xylene, which would be acid-washed. The bottoms of this column, crude residue consisting of used wash oil, solvents, and naphthalene, would be batch distilled to recover crude heavy solvent. The residue of this batch distillation, containing wash oil and naphthalene, would be processed in crystallizing pans for the recovery of crude naphthalene, while the used wash oil is returned to the wash-oil system.

Another technique used in the smaller installations is to have a batch still in addition to the continuous crude stills and operate it partly continuous with a final batch distillation. In this case, washed oil is fed to the column of the batch still and benzene is removed continuously, allowing the toluene and xylene to build up in the kettle. When the kettle becomes filled, the feed is discontinued and the unit is then operated as a batch still, with first the toluene distilled over, then the xylene.

In the continuous process for refining a light oil dry at 390° F (200° C) that is outlined in the flow sheet of Figure 4—37, the continuous crude unit would have two columns; the first for forerunnings and the second for producing the benzene, toluene, and xylene overhead for subsequent recovery of pure products after acid washing. The residue, consisting of used wash oil, heavy solvents and naphthalene, is batch distilled.

The continuous pure-still unit would consist of four columns, the first for removal of pure-still or acid-washing residues, the second for stripping the small volume of low-boiling forerunning constituents that are not removed in the acid-washing treatment. The third column produces benzene, and the fourth toluene, as a top product, and xylene with a small volume of heavy solvent as a bottom product. The bottom product is distilled in a batch operation to produce commercial xylenes and a refined heavy solvent.

For the production of additional grades of product, or to remove any intermediates between products, another column is required at the proper point in the layout, since each column produces an individual fraction or product.

REFINING OF COAL TAR

The volatile products resulting from the thermal decomposition of bituminous coal contain a yellow vapor as a finely divided suspensoid which, upon condensation, yields a black viscous material called coal tar. There are many types of coal tar produced, depending on the temperature and conditions of carbonization. The coal tar which has the most important commercial significance is that produced during the high-temperature carbonization of bituminous coal.

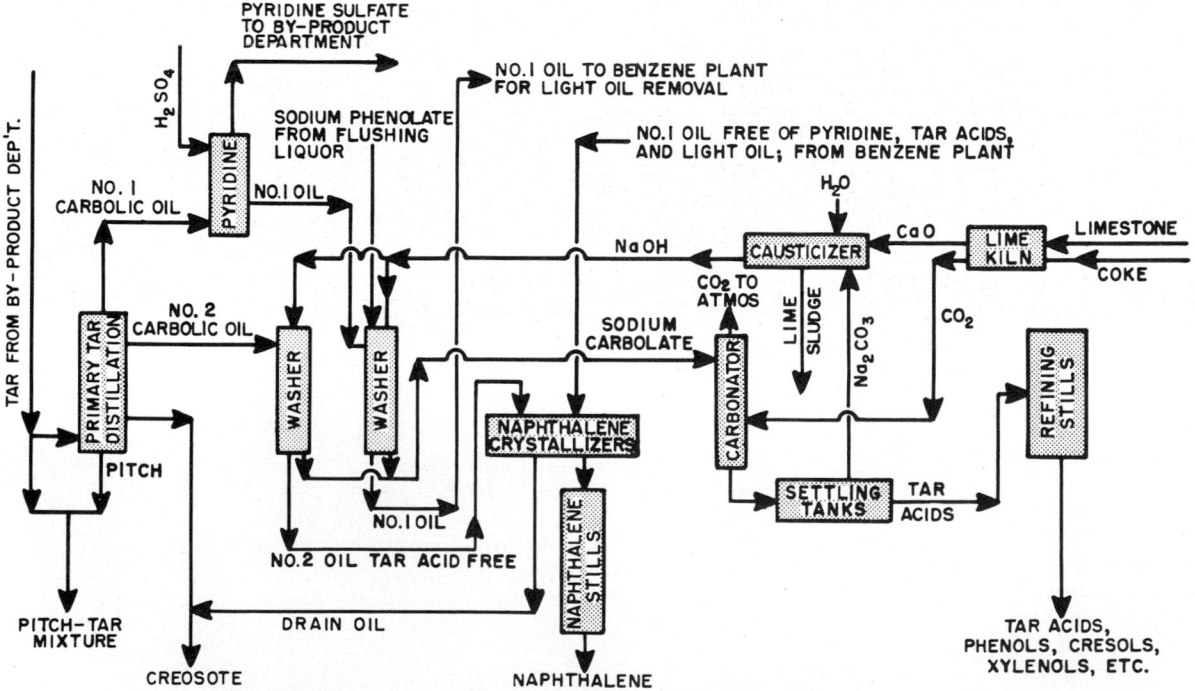

FIG. 4—38. Flow diagram of a tar plant. The part of the diagram showing primary tar distillation is symbolic of only a single still and not chain fractionation.

These coal tars consist essentially of aromatic hydrocarbons that are characterized by ring-type chemical structure and contain such compounds as benzene, naphthalene, anthracene and their related homologues; oxygenated compounds usually referred to as tar acids which include phenol, cresols, and xylenols; nitrogen compounds in which the nitrogen is included in the ring structure, such as pyridine, picolines, etc.; and only very small amounts of the paraffinic-type compounds (Table 4—II).

This type of tar, produced at high temperatures, is used for the recovery of tar acids, naphthalene, creosote oils, pyridine bases, and pitch (Figure 4—38). Their recovery requires the use of some combination of fractional distillation of the tar as the first operation; with subsequent use of fractional distillation procedures in some of the other operations, chemical extraction for the removal of acidic and basic compounds with subsequent purification and refining of the extracts and crystallizing operations for the recovery of such compounds as naphthalene, anthracene, carbazole and phenanthrene.

These operations may be conducted as batch or continuous operations depending principally upon the quantities of material to be processed. The trend, however, is now toward continuous stills on account of the larger volumes of tar that can be processed and the improvements in operating results attendant on the uniform flow and conditions.

Stills are "tailored" to the products they are designed to provide from a given tar. The nature of the tar, the required properties of the products, and the basic principles of distillation are all considered in their design and construction. Product specifications are steadily becoming more exacting, and closer fractions are required to meet the needs of the consumer. Another consideration is that the character of each tar, its chemical composition, and its volume is different, and demands alteration of process and equipment compared with previous installations.

Distillation of Tar—The following description of crude tar stills is restricted to a large multiple-column installation that is designed to separate from the feed tars a series of relatively close-boiling fractions, each of a quality suitable for meeting the latest requirements. A flow sheet of this chain fractionation facility is shown in Figure 4—39. Although this series of stills differs from single stills with sidestream takeoffs in use, it illustrates the objectives entering into the design of these pieces of equipment.

Crude coal tar is received into steam-heated feed tanks and then passed through preheaters prior to entry into a three-stage flashing phase, a preliminary process to the actual fractionation. The tar is flashed (or vaporized) to separate water and the lighter components from the pitch—the heavy residual constituent of the tar. In the first stage, the tar is dehydrated and any light oil which is entrained is recovered through continuous decantation of the condensate and returned to the dehydrating vessel as reflux.

The dehydrated tar then moves into the second stage where enough heat is added to flash off the lower-boiling components into the first fractionating column. In turn, the liquid material from the second

Table 4—II. Compounds Recovered from Coal Tar and Light Oil*

I. Neutral Compounds
(From Light Oil)

Name	Formula	Boiling Point, °C
Benzene	C_6H_6	80.1
Toluene	$C_6H_5CH_3$	110.6
Meta-Xylene	$C_6H_4(CH_3)_2$	139.3
Para-Xylene	$C_6H_4(CH_3)_2$	139.4
Ortho-Xylene	$C_6H_4(CH_3)_2$	144
Mesitylene	$C_6H_3(CH_3)_3$	164.6
Pseudocumene	$C_6H_3(CH_3)_3$	169.2
Coumarone	C_8H_6O	174
Indene	C_9H_8	182.4

(From Coal Tar)

Name	Formula	Boiling Point, °C
Naphthalene	$C_{10}H_8$	218
2—Methyl Naphthalene	$C_{10}H_7CH_3$	241
1—Methyl Naphthalene	$C_{10}H_7CH_3$	245
Dimethyl Naphthalene	$C_{10}H_6(CH_3)_2$	255-270
Acenaphthene	$C_{12}H_{10}$	281
Fluorene	$C_{13}H_{10}$	298
Phenanthrene	$C_{14}H_{10}$	340
Anthracene	$C_{14}H_{10}$	342
Fluoranthene	$C_{16}H_{10}$	382
Pyrene	$C_{16}H_{10}$	393
Chrysene	$C_{18}H_{12}$	448

II. Phenolic Compounds
(From Coal Tar)

Name	Formula	Boiling Point, °C
Phenol	C_6H_5OH	181
Ortho-Cresol	$C_6H_4(CH_3)OH$	191
Para-Cresol	$C_6H_4(CH_3)OH$	201
Meta-Cresol	$C_6H_4(CH_3)OH$	202
2, 4—Xylenol	$C_6H_3(CH_3)_2OH$	211.5
3, 5—Xylenol	$C_6H_3(CH_3)_2OH$	219.5
Alpha-Naphthol	$C_{10}H_7OH$	280
Beta Naphthol	$C_{10}H_7OH$	286

III. Nitrogen Compounds
(From Coal Tar)

Name	Formula	Boiling Point, °C
Pyridine	C_5H_5N	115
2—Methylpyridine (Alpha-Picoline)	C_6H_7N	129
3—Methylpyridine (Beta-Picoline)	C_6H_7N	144
2, 6—Dimethylpyridine (Alpha Alpha' Lutidine)	C_7H_9N	144.4
4—Methylpyridine (Gamma-Picoline)	C_6H_7N	144.6
2,4—Dimethylpyridine (Alpha Gamma Lutidine)	C_7H_9N	157.1
Quinoline	C_9H_7N	238
Isoquinoline	C_9H_7N	243
Quinaldine	$C_{10}H_9N$	247.6
2—Methyl Isoquinoline	$C_{10}H_9N$	252
4—Methyl Quinoline	$C_{10}H_9N$	264
Acridine	$C_{13}H_9N$	346
Carbazole	$C_{12}H_9N$	352

*This table does not list all of the compounds that have been identified. It does contain some compounds which are recovered commercially in very small amounts or not at all.

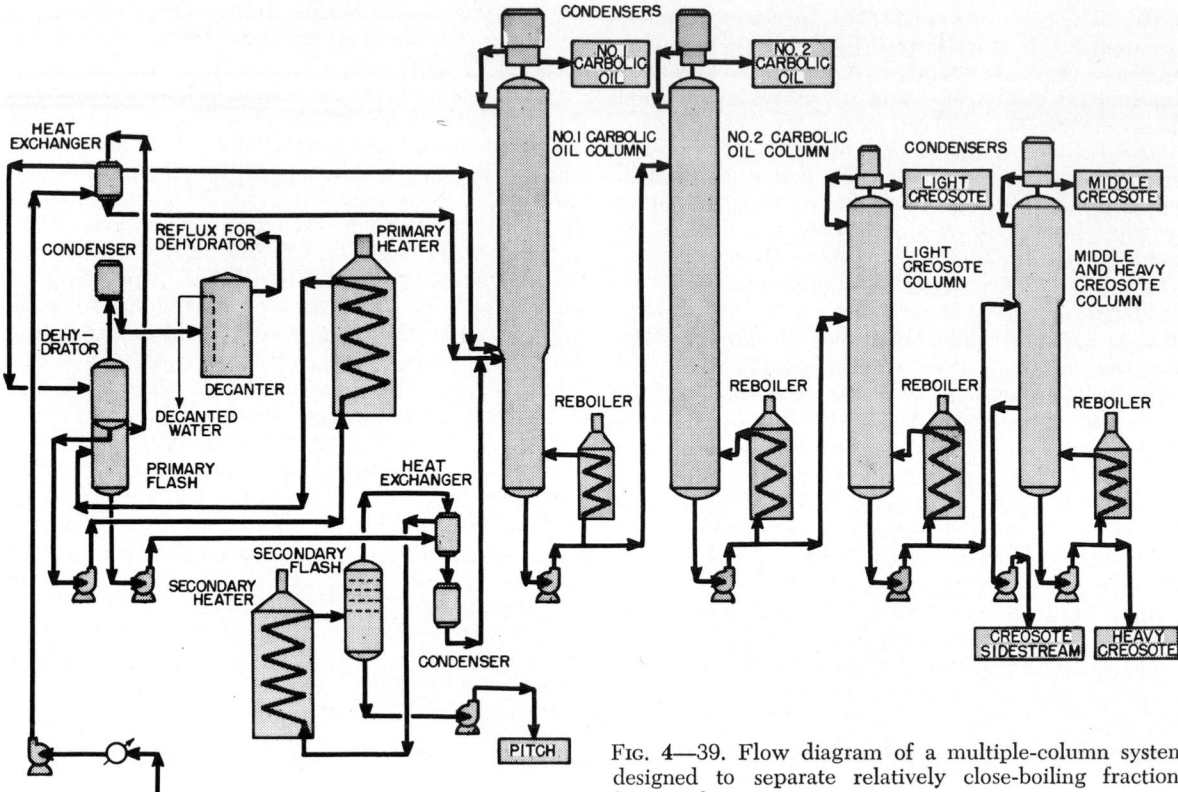

Fig. 4—39. Flow diagram of a multiple-column system designed to separate relatively close-boiling fractions from coal tar.

flashing stage is again heated to still a higher temperature in the third stage so that all components are vaporized except the pitch. The vapor is condensed and sent to the first column for further processing while the pitch is removed continuously from the bottom of the flash vessel for blending into specification products.

In the first column, a low-boiling fraction encompassing such tar acids as phenol, ortho-cresol, meta-para cresol and xylenols is separated from the material flowing through the process. The liquid bottoms from the first column continue to the second column where, in a similar manner, the naphthalene-bearing component of the tar is removed. Subsequently, various desired creosote products may be removed as overhead vapors from each of the last two columns with the high-boiling creosote bottoms from the last column likewise removed as a product.

The fractions for which this still has been designed are:

(1) No. 1 carbolic oil
(2) No. 2 carbolic oil
(3) Light creosote
(4) Middle creosote
(5) Heavy creosote
(6) Pitch

Much of the equipment is fabricated from stainless steel in order to reduce corrosion to a minimum. All of the fractionating plates are of a new design that gives a high degree of contact between the ascending vapors and descending liquids, but is less susceptible to accumulations of pitch and other materials than conventional bubble plates. By maintaining the cleanliness of the plates, better overall efficiencies of fractionation are secured.

No. 1 carbolic oil is processed for the recovery of pyridine bases and crude tar acids, after which the light oil is removed by distillation and the residual naphthalene is processed for the recovery of saleable naphthalene.

No. 2 carbolic oil is processed for the recovery of crude tar acids and then for naphthalene in the same process as noted above for the residual portion of the light-oil fraction.

The higher-boiling fractions are blended with the neutral oil from the naphthalene process for the production of various grades of creosote.

The residual pitch from the tar distillation is used for electrode-binder carbon pitch, fiber pitch and road tars. In some cases it is used as fuel in the open-hearth and heating furnaces in the various steel-producing facilities. For the latter purpose, it is necessary to blend it with an aromatic oil or virgin tar to lower the viscosity prior to burning it as a fuel.

A description of methods for the processing of the light-oil and intermediate-oil fraction will follow.

Pyridine Sulphate Recovery—Recovery of pyridine bases from tar oils is a comparatively simple process. Essentially, a solution of sulphuric acid is circulated through the oil, with solution of tar bases present to form pyridine sulphate, according to the following reaction:

$$C_5H_5N + H_2SO_4 \rightarrow (C_5H_5N)H_2SO_4$$

The solution of pyridine sulphate is separated from the lighter oil by gravity.

The first step in the process is dilution of the 60° Bé sulphuric acid with water in a lead-lined tank equipped with an agitator. A solution containing about 17 per cent of commercial acid has been found to give best results.

About 8,500 gallons of fresh oil is pumped into the washer, along with 1,500 to 1,700 gallons of the acid solution which has been partially saturated with bases by two previous washes. This effects a partial extraction of the pyridine, and completes the conversion of the sulphuric acid to pyridine sulphate. The crude pyridine sulphate solution is separated from the oil by decantation and is then ready to be rectified. The once-washed oil is washed a second time with acid solution that has been one-third spent in a single wash. The oil is finally stripped of remaining pyridine bases by the third wash, using the fresh sulphuric-acid solution.

Rectification of the pyridine sulphate is the next step. It consists simply of boiling the sulphate solution in a kettle with indirect steam, the undesirable oils, naphthalene, and tar acids being driven overhead. These vapors are condensed and processed for the recovery of tar acids.

The rectified sulphate is then ready for springing

with ammonia and distillation to recover refined pyridine, as described earlier under "Recovery and Refining of Pyridine Bases."

The pyridine-free oil which has been separated from the pyridine sulphate by gravity in the washer still possesses a small acid content which must be removed to make it suitable for further processing. A weak solution of soda ash in water (about 12 to 14 per cent) is used, giving the following reaction:

$$H_2SO_4 + Na_2CO_3 \rightarrow Na_2SO_4 + H_2O + CO_2$$

The reaction is carried out by continually pumping the oil through the neutralizer containing the soda-ash solution. The sodium-sulphate solution formed in the neutralizing reaction is a waste material and is disposed of in the waste water used for quenching coke.

Pyridine bases also are recovered from saturator liquors, as described earlier in this chapter.

Tar-Acid Recovery—Tar acids are usually recovered from the distillates by a caustic-washing process.

Washing removes tar acids in the form of phenol (C_6H_5OH) and phenol homologues from the carbolic oils by contact with caustic soda to form sodium phenolate, according to the equation:

$$C_6H_5OH + NaOH \rightarrow C_6H_5ONa + H_2O$$

The washer is a suitably proportioned cone-bottom

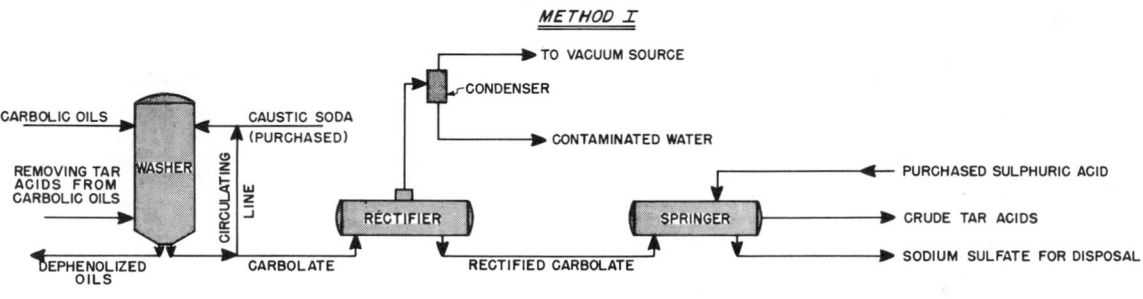

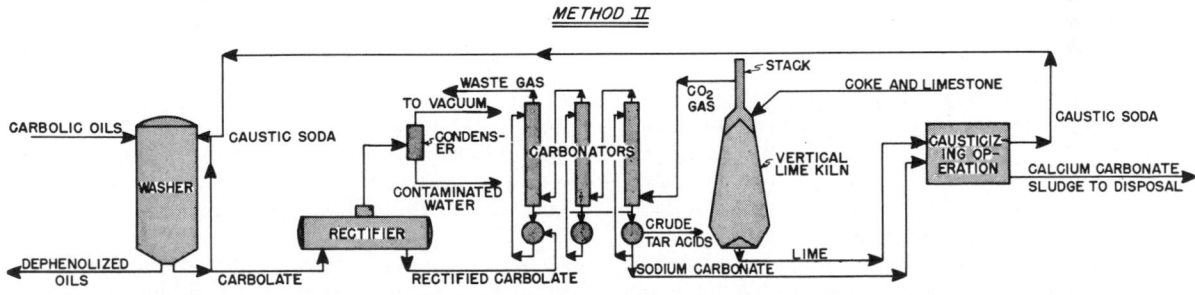

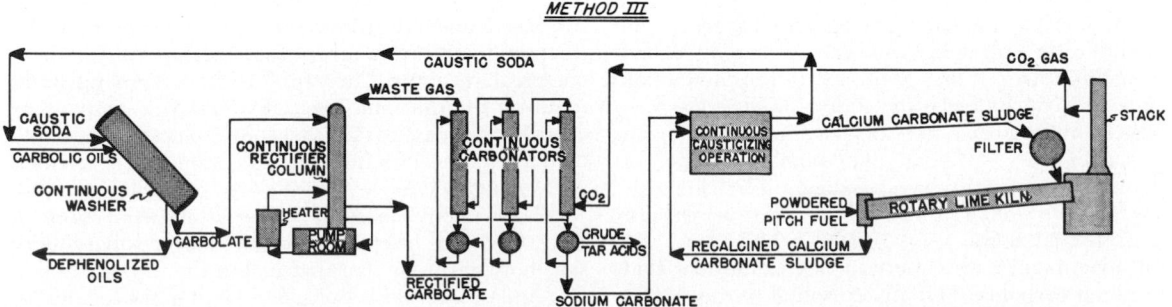

FIG. 4—40. Three methods for the recovery of crude tar acids.

tank with a spray or other flow-distributing mechanism at the top. Steam-heated coils are provided in the bottom of the washer to maintain fluidity of the oils and a desirable reaction temperature of about 167° F (75° C). A mixture comprising 50 per cent carbolic oil and 50 per cent caustic-soda solution (8.5 per cent NaOH) is added to the washer, and is circulated by pump from the bottom of the washer to the top, filtering down through the carbolic oil by gravity and removing tar acids from the oil by contact. This process is preferred because more violent methods, such as mechanically agitating the oil and caustic together, tend to form emulsions which, on occasion, are almost impossible to separate. Oil and carbolate are readily separated by gravity when no emulsion exists.

Rectifying is required to remove undesirable pyridine bases (if not previously removed), oils and naphthalene from the carbolate or sodium phenolate. The carbolate is boiled under vacuum to permit use of low-pressure steam and to reduce hydrolysis of carbolates to tar acids that would be carried over and lost with the vapors. This is a comparatively simple apparatus, the only design problem being provision of adequate heating and condensing capacities.

Springing (liberation of tar acids in sodium phenolate solution) can be accomplished by neutralizing the rectified carbolate with sulphuric acid or carbon dioxide gas, according to the following reactions:

$$2C_6H_5ONa + H_2SO_4 \rightarrow 2C_6H_5OH + Na_2SO_4$$
$$2C_6H_5ONa + H_2O + CO_2 \rightarrow 2C_6H_5OH + NA_2CO_3$$

If sulphuric acid is used, no special equipment is needed except a tank equipped for agitation. The acid is added to the carbolate during agitation, until the carbolate has been converted to tar acids and sodium sulphate. The tar acids and sulphate are separated by gravity.

If carbon dioxide gas is used, more complicated equipment is necessary in the form of a series of 3 to 6 towers packed with grids or baffles. Carbolate pumped to the tops of these towers trickles down through the grids, coming in contact with the CO_2 gas which is admitted to the bottom of the column and passes upward countercurrently to the flow of liquid.

Method I (Figure 4—40) shows the minimum plant for tar acid recovery with three items of processing equipment—washer, rectifier and springer. The chief advantage of this plant is the relatively small investment required. The crude tar acids it produces may contain small quantities of sulphur compounds causing corrosion of equipment in the subsequent distillation of the tar acids.

In **Method II,** the acid springer is replaced by the carbon-dioxide springing towers (commonly called carbonating towers), and facilities for the production of lime and caustic soda are added (Figure 4—40). A largely noncorrosive product is obtained at lower unit cost. Coke, limestone and small quantities of soda ash are required which produce the caustic soda for washing of oil and the carbon dioxide gas for springing of tar acids.

An advantage of this method lies in the fact that the sodium carbonate initially supplied to the system may be regenerated completely. The production of sodium hydroxide, the formation of sodium phenolate, the liberation of tar acids and the regeneration of the sodium carbonate are shown in the following series of formulas:

(a)　$Na_2CO_3 + CaO + H_2O \rightarrow 2NaOH + CaCO_3$
(b)　$C_6H_5OH + NaOH \rightarrow C_6H_5ONa + H_2O$
(c)　$2C_6H_5ONa + H_2O + CO_2 \rightarrow$
$$2C_6H_5OH + Na_2CO_3$$

Lime (CaO) and carbon dioxide gas (CO_2) are produced in the vertical lime kiln from limestone ($CaCO_3$) and coke fuel, according to the equation:

$$CaCO_3 + C + O_2 \rightarrow CaO + 2CO_2$$

Method III, as shown in Figure 4—40, is an all-continuous method in which the procedure and equipment are as illustrated.

Carbonating, or Springing System—Each tower (about 25 ft. high) contains steel hurdles or baffles. Carbolate, circulated by pump from the reservoir at the bottom to the top of the tower, trickles down through the hurdles to be contacted by the CO_2 gas moving countercurrently to the liquid. The CO_2 gas is delivered to the carbonators from the lime kiln by rotary positive blowers through the towers in series starting with No. 4 carbonator. The following description applies to a system employing four towers.

When the reaction has reached completion in the last carbonator (No. 4), the solution of free tar acids, carbonate and a low concentration of carbolate is pumped from the reservoir, and this reservoir recharged with the solution from the reservoir of No. 3 carbonator. The reaction in the solution in No. 3 carbonator has reached the stage of being three-fourths completed, having a higher concentration of carbolate and a lower concentration of free tar acids and carbonate than that in No. 4 carbonator. In turn No. 2 and No. 1 carbonator solutions are pumped to the carbonators ahead, No. 3 and No. 2 respectively, and No. 1 carbonator is recharged with fresh carbolate. In this way, the highest concentration of CO_2 gas is caused to react with the lowest concentration of carbolate in No. 4 carbonator, while the almost spent gas contacts the strongest concentration of carbolate in No. 1 carbonator. This system of circulation is designed to achieve maximum usage of the CO_2 gas.

The design problem is mainly one of capacity. If the contact time between liquid and gas is adequate, about 180 cu. ft. of 30 per cent carbon-dioxide gas will suffice to liberate each gallon of tar acid. Since salts have a tendency to build up on the hurdles in the towers, it is necessary to provide means for removing and cleaning the hurdles. Ordinary steel construction can be used throughout.

Lime Kiln—In order to reduce to a minimum the carry-over of undesirable salts into the subsequent chemical reactions, limestone of maximum purity is required for the lime kiln, as well as for most other chemical processes. The coke fuel must be carefully chosen as to size in order to be completely and efficiently consumed in the burning area of the kiln.

In operation, limestone and coke in proportions of 8 to 10 pounds of stone to one of coke are charged by skip hoist into the charging bell at the top of the kiln at regular intervals. Burned lime is removed either continuously or intermittently by rotation of the mound-shaped hearth at the bottom. Stack gases pass from the cast-iron acorn (situated at the center of the kiln near the top) to the atmosphere by way of the stack on one side of the acorn, or to the boosters for use in the system by way of the opposite side of the acorn. The reaction taking place in the kiln is chemically expressed by the equation:

$$CaCO_3 + C + O_2 \rightarrow CaO + 2CO_2$$

or, in other words, limestone plus coke (carbon) plus air (oxygen) produces lime and carbon dioxide gas when heat results from burning of the coke. The stack gases produced are first passed through a cyclone dust catcher of conventional design and a gas scrubber before use for springing. The scrubber is simply a limestone-packed tower into which water is sprayed at the top. The kiln gases, entering at the bottom and leaving at the top, are cooled and stripped of their water-soluble constituents.

Caustic soda (NaOH) is produced by bringing soda ash (Na_2CO_3) and lime (CaO) together in the proper proportions and at the right temperature in the presence of water according to the equation:

$$Na_2CO_3 + CaO + H_2O \rightarrow 2NaOH + CaCO_3$$

Batch Caustic System—A solution of soda ash in water of the desired concentration is added to the batch causticizers (or causticizing tanks), and heated to about 90° C. The necessary quantity of lime is then delivered to each causticizer and agitated by slowly rotating blades. Heat of reaction raises the temperature of the charge to about 98° C. After reaction is complete agitation is stopped and the batch allowed to settle, the calcium-carbonate sludge settling to the bottom. After settling, the clear caustic soda is skimmed off the top, and the calcium-carbonate sludge is filtered to recover all possible solution. The filter cake is disposed of to a dump to waste disposal.

It is impossible, with this kind of equipment, to prevent carry-over of small quantities of calcium-carbonate sludge with the caustic soda. This entrained sludge distributes itself all through the tanks and processing equipment used in the recovery of crude tar acids, necessitating periodic cleaning of facilities.

Continuous Causticizing System—By this method a predetermined concentration of soda ash in water, together with the proper proportion of crushed lime, is fed continuously into a slaker. A tubular steam heater automatically maintains the soda-ash solution at a temperature of 207° F (97° C) at the entrance to the slaker. The slaker is a rotating cylinder which serves the dual purpose of completely slaking the lime and eliminating large solids such as unburned coke and raw limestone cores. The mixture passes by gravity into a classifier which removes small solids, and is then pumped to three overhead cascaded mixers, or causticizers, equipped with agitators which serve the purpose of allowing necessary time for the chemical reaction to be completely finished before entering the thickener. The completely reacted mixture of caustic soda and calcium-carbonate sludge flows into the top center of the thickener, from which clear caustic soda is continuously drawn off the top outer rim while washed calcium-carbonate sludge is pumped off the bottom. The sludge, after filtering,

may be recalcined in a rotary kiln or sent to waste disposal.

Rotary Kiln—Calcium-carbonate sludge from the thickener is dried in the vacuum rotary filter shown above the charging end of the kiln in Figure 4—40. The filter cake is dropped to a worm conveyor which charges the cake into the rotating, brick-lined cylinder. Rotation of the slightly inclined kiln moves the sludge slowly toward the discharge end as the burning fuel converts the sludge to lime. A temperature of about 1650° F (900° C) is used for burning.

Tar-Acid Refining—Crude tar acids are refined by distillation, similar, in most respects, to benzene distillation. Crude tar acids are fractionated to produce the comparatively pure components, usually phenol, ortho cresol, meta-para cresol, and xylenols. Meta-para cresol is composed of two close boiling compounds, meta cresol and para cresol, differing in boiling point by about one degree Centigrade. Xylenols, composed of six isomers boiling between 410° F (210° C) and 437° F (225° C) and higher boiling tar acids, may be cut into such fractions as the market demands and the distilling facilities permit.

A still consists essentially of a pot still or heater, and a fractionating column. The number of trays in the column is dictated by the degree of purity desired in the finished product. Known installations vary from 40 to 80 trays or plates per column. The present trend is towards more trays to obtain products of higher purity. Distillation can be made at atmospheric pressure or under vacuum.

Horizontal Pot Still—The horizontal pot still consists of a horizontal tank resting upon a brick furnace with about one-third of its surface exposed to the heat. Gas is used as fuel. The arched brickwork of the combustion oven is studded with small flues or perforations which admit the heat to the bottom of the still without exposing the still bottom to direct flame. A disadvantage of this type of pot still is the comparatively small heating surface. Vapors from the boiling tar acids pass through the dome at the top of the still to the fractionating column. One of the problems of tar-acid distillation by this process is the necessity for frequent cleaning of salts and decomposition products from the inner surfaces of the pot.

Vertical Pot Still—This is a vertical tank resting upon a brick furnace with about two-thirds of the surface exposed to the heat. Residue removal from the pot is difficult, and the tail pipe (drain line) frequently is difficult to clean and maintain. Direct application of high heat not only causes a certain amount of decomposition of the tar acids with attendant loss of product but also causes burning, rapid deterioration, and corrosion of the pot itself. Maintenance is, therefore, high.

Steam-Heated Vacuum Batch Still—The kettle, or pot, is simply a horizontal tank which serves as a reservoir for the crude tar acids and a chamber for release of the vapors. The contents of the kettle are continuously circulated by a pump through a heater and back into the top of the kettle where vapors are released and pass into the column for fractionation. Since the whole system is maintained under high vacuum, steam at 150 pounds pressure is adequate

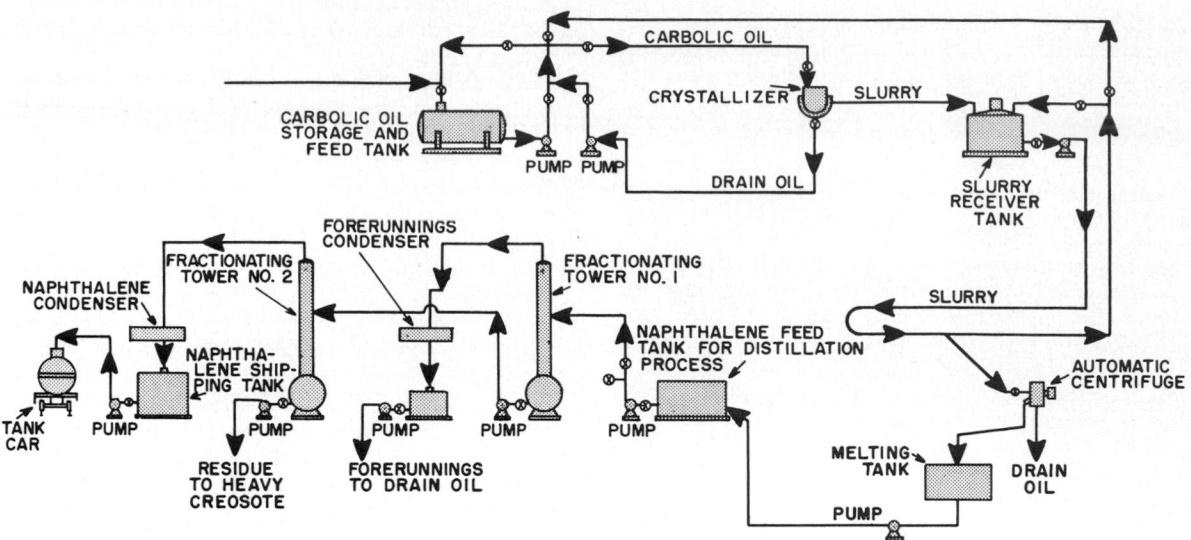

Fig. 4—41. Schematic representation of steps and equipment used in recovery of naphthalene.

as a source of heat. The heater consists of a bank of steam tubes around which the flow of tar acids is directed by a series of baffles.

This method of distilling tar acids reduces both decomposition of the material handled and corrosion of equipment. Standard materials of construction may be used throughout. Use of stainless steel in the vapor line, condenser and product line prolongs life and reduces contamination of products.

Naphthalene Recovery—Following the removal of tar acids by caustic washing, the remaining oils and naphthalene are pumped to equipment where the naphthalene is recovered by crystallization and/or distillation (Figure 4—41). The crystallization step is necessary when impurities are present that cannot be removed by distillation alone.

The crude separation of the naphthalene where crystallization is necessary is accomplished in a series of continuous crystallizer units, each water-jacketed for cooling purposes and equipped with a slow-speed spiral stirrer to keep the crystals in suspension in the oil. The crystallizer feed tanks are maintained at 170° F (77° C).

The crude naphthalene crystals obtained from these crystallizer units are centrifuged, melted, and then pumped to a refining still. To maintain a uniform feed for the centrifuges, the slurry from the crystallizers at a temperature of about 70° F is first passed into an agitated slurry tank. From this slurry tank, the slurry is pumped to automatically controlled centrifuges which separate the naphthalene crystals from the oils. Part of this oil is recycled to the crystallizers while the remainder is pumped to storage. The centrifuged naphthalene crystals are dropped into melting tanks to be melted by indirect steam and then pumped to a feed tank for distillation.

This still refines the melted naphthalene by separating it continuously into a light oil, refined naphthalene and a heavy oil. The first distillation column receives the melted naphthalene from the feed tank, which is maintained at 200° F. This column produces

an overhead fraction of light neutral oil which is condensed in a water-cooled condenser and passed to a surge tank; reflux from this tank is returned to the first column at a controlled rate. The residue is pumped to the second fractionating column at a controlled rate. An overhead of naphthalene is produced in the second column and condensed in a condenser using hot water. The liquid naphthalene is received in a shipping tank maintained at 250° F from which it can be pumped directly to tank cars or tank trucks for shipment. The residue from this second column is cooled to about 250° F and pumped to storage. The neutral oils after naphthalene recovery generally are blended with a higher-boiling fraction also separated from tar to produce specification grades of creosote oils for use as wood preservatives.

USES OF COKE, COKE-OVEN GAS AND COAL CHEMICALS

Metallurgical Coke—Coke is used for production of iron in blast furnaces and the coke breeze as a fuel for steam generation in boiler houses.

Fuel Gas—After the recovery of coal chemicals, the gas provides fuel for heating the coke ovens, and the excess gas goes to open hearths and reheating furnaces. When practicable, other gas of lower Btu value may profitably replace the coke-oven gas for firing coke ovens.

Ammonium Sulphate—The ammonium sulphate recovered from coke-oven gas is used for admixture with phosphate and potash constituents to provide balanced agricultural fertilizers for the various requirements, or it may be used for direct application where nitrogen is the only requirement at the time of use.

Phenol—Phenol (C_6H_5OH), sometimes called carbolic acid, is recovered from both coal tar and ammonia liquor. Its most important use is in the manufacture of resinous condensation products by reaction with formaldehyde, e.g., "Bakelite." As a chemical intermediate it is used in the preparation of synthetic tannins, dye intermediates, perfumes, plasticizers, picric acid, salicylic acid, and in the refining of lubricating oils.

Ortho Cresol—Ortho cresol ($CH_3C_6H_4OH$) is also used in the production of synthetic resins to control the plasticity of the resin. It is nitrated to produce insecticides and weed killers. It is used in various organic syntheses and in the production of artificial flavors and perfumes.

Meta-Para Cresol—Meta-para cresol ($CH_3C_6H_4OH$) is used chiefly in the production of synthetic resins and the plasticizer tricresyl phosphate. It is also used in organic synthesis and in the production of insecticides, dyestuffs, pharmaceuticals and photographic compounds.

Naphthalene—A large percentage of the naphthalene produced from coal is converted to phthalic anhydride. The principal use of the anhydride is in plasticizers, such as dioctyl phthalate and diisoctyl phthalate, for use in synthetic resins. Nearly as much phthalic anhydride is used, however, in the alkyd resins, the important outlet for which is in coatings. In addition, polyester resins, dyes, agricultural chemicals, pharmaceuticals, insect repellents, beta-naphthol, surface-active agents, tanning agents, and insecticides consume large volumes of phthalic anhydride.

Creosote—Creosote (from coal tar) constitutes a large part of the distillate from tar, and is a blend of different fractions to meet specifications established by the American Wood Preservers Association. Practically all of it goes into the pressure impregnation of wood, such as piling, poles and railroad ties.

Pyridine Bases—The pyridine bases produced from the lighter tar oils include pyridine (C_5H_5N), the picolines ($C_5H_4N \cdot CH_3$), lutidines ($C_5H_3N \cdot (CH_3)_2$), and some quinoline (C_9H_7N).

Pyridine is an excellent solvent and is used as such in the rubber, paint and plastic industries. It is a basic material for chemical organic synthesis of industrial and pharmaceutical compounds, such as piperidine. It is also used in the production of chemicals for waterproofing fabric and as a carrying agent for impregnation of the fabric with the waterproofing agents.

The picolines are also basic materials for organic chemical syntheses. Beta-picoline is used in particular for production of nicotinamide and niacinamide, both vitamin substances employed for augmenting the vitamin content of various foods and also as direct treatment for dietary deficiencies.

Pitch—Pitch is employed as a binder in making carbon electrodes, as roofing pitch, fiber pitch, road tars, and in pipe-line enamels. Pitch is also used as an open-hearth fuel when mixed with virgin tar to maintain fluidity.

Forerunnings—The forerunnings from light-oil refining contain cyclopentadiene. Polymerized products of cyclopentadiene are useful as plastics and resins for use in paints and protective coatings.

Benzene—Recovered from refining light oil, benzene is industrially the most important member of the aromatic family. The principal use is for the manufacture of styrene, which goes into polystyrene resins and important grades of synthetic rubber. Other important uses of benzene are for manufacture of phenol, nylon, synthetic detergents, aniline, and a host of other important organic chemicals, including DDT, maleic anhydride, benzene hexachloride, mono- and dichlorobenzene, and nitrobenzene. The uses for some of these benzene derivatives is evident, but others are intermediates, in turn, for additional chemicals, plastics, dyes, fungicides, and the like.

Toluene—The principal uses for toluene are in the manufacture of synthetic organic chemicals, detergents, resins, plasticizers, explosives, solvents, dye intermediates, pharmaceuticals, and for conversion to benzene.

Toluene is converted through synthesis to phenol, benzoic acid, benzoyl chloride, benzoates, para cresol, dye intermediates, toluene sulphonates, di-isocyanates and trinitrotoluene.

Considerable quantities of toluene are also used as a solvent in various types of coatings.

Xylene—The term xylene refers to a mixture of the three isomers ortho-, meta-, and para-xylene and, as such, is used primarily as a solvent. The isomers are separated by distillation and crystallization and, in their concentrated forms, are used for specific purposes.

Ortho-xylene is used for the production of phthalic anhydride and plasticizers.

Meta-xylene is used in the production of isophthalic acid which, in turn, is used in resins and plasticizers.

Para-xylene is used for the production of terephthalic acid that, in turn, is used for the production of synthetic fibers.

Crude Heavy Solvent—Crude heavy solvent is the source of coumarone-indene resins, which are thermoplastic resins used for rubber compounding, floor tile, printing inks, lacquers and chewing gum. It is used for ship-bottom paints, pipe coatings, shingle stains, wire enamel, brake linings, and bituminous and other dark-colored paints.

Refined Heavy Solvent—Refined heavy solvent is used in slow-drying solvents for manufacture of shoe polish, flat wall and interior paints, house paints, printing ink and enamels. It also is used in the linoleum industry.

CHAPTER 5

Iron Ores

SECTION 1

THE NATURE AND OCCURRENCE OF IRON ORES

Of the many natural raw materials that are required for the making of iron and steel, the most important as to tonnage and value is iron ore. In 1960, for each net ton of ingot steel produced by the American steel industry, slightly more than a net ton of iron ore (including agglomerates) was consumed.

The gross ton or long ton (2240 lb.) is the usual weight unit for iron ore and will be used throughout this chapter except where net tons or metric tons are expressly specified.

IRON-BEARING MINERALS

A large number of minerals contain iron; however, only a few are used commercially as sources of iron. Minerals containing important amounts of iron may

Table 5—1. Chief Iron-Bearing Minerals.

Class and Mineralogical Name	Chemical Composition of Pure Mineral	Common Designation
Oxide		
Magnetite	Fe_3O_4	Ferrous-ferric oxide
Hematite	Fe_2O_3	Ferric oxide
Ilmenite	$FeTiO_3$	Iron-titanium oxide
Limonite	$\begin{cases} HFeO_2* \\ FeO(OH)** \end{cases}$	Hydrous iron oxides
Carbonate		
Siderite	$FeCO_3$	Iron carbonate
Silicate		
Chamosite		
Stilpnomelane		
Greenalite	Various and sometimes complex	Iron silicates
Minnesotaite		
Grunerite		
Sulphide		
Pyrite (iron pyrites)	FeS_2	
Marcasite (white iron pyrites)	FeS_2	Iron sulphides
Pyrrhotite (magnetic iron pyrites)	FeS	

*Goethite
**Lepidocrocite

be grouped according to their chemical compositions into oxides, carbonates, sulphides and silicates. Table 5—I illustrates the various classes of iron minerals and indicates the mineral species commonly used as sources of iron. Oxide minerals are the most important sources of iron, followed by carbonates, sulphides and iron silicates. In the descriptions of the important iron-ore minerals or mineral groups that follow, the chemical compositions are for the pure minerals: the iron content of commercial ores or concentrates generally is lower, due to the presence of gangue and other impurities.

Magnetite—Chemical composition, Fe_3O_4, corresponding to 72.4 per cent of iron and 27.6 per cent of oxygen; color, dark gray to black; specific gravity, 5.16 to 5.18. It is strongly magnetic, sometimes possessing polarity so it will act as a natural magnet. The magnetic property of magnetite is important, for it permits exploration by magnetic methods and makes possible the magnetic separation of magnetite from gangue materials to produce a high-quality concentrate. Magnetite occurs in igneous, metamorphic, and sedimentary rocks. It is becoming increasingly important as a source of iron, as a consequence of the growing use of concentrated iron minerals. At times, magnetite contains titanium in small amounts as inclusions of ilmenite. When the titanium content reaches 2 to 15 or more per cent, the magnetite is termed **titaniferous magnetite**.

Hematite—Chemical composition, Fe_2O_3, corresponding to 69.94 per cent of iron and 39.06 per cent of oxygen; color, steel gray to dull red or bright red; earthy to compact or crystalline; specific gravity, 5.26. Common varieties are termed **crystalline, specular, martite** (pseudomorphic after magnetite), **maghemite** (magnetic ferric oxide), **earthy, ocherous,** and **compact.** Hematite is one of the most important iron minerals. It has a wide occurrence in many types of rocks and is of varying origins. It occurs associated with vein deposits; igneous, metamorphic, and sedimentary rocks; and as a product of the weathering of magnetite.

Hydrous Oxides—Limonite is the name commonly given to hydrous iron oxides that mineralogically are composed of various mixtures of the minerals **goethite** or **lepidocrocite.** The chemical formula for goethite is HFeO$_2$ and that for lepidocrocite is FeO(OH). Goethite contains 62.9 per cent of iron, 27 per cent of oxygen, and 10.1 per cent of water; specific gravity ranges from 3.6 to 4.0; color, commonly yellow or brown to nearly black; compact to earthy and ocherous. In non-technical parlance, the term "limonite" is used to denote unidentified oxides with a variable moisture content due to absorbed or capillary water. It is a secondary mineral, formed commonly by weathering, and occurs in association with other iron oxides and in sedimentary rocks. Limonites are important sources of iron throughout the world.

Ilmenite—Chemical composition, FeTiO$_3$, corresponding to 36.8 per cent of iron, 31.6 per cent of titanium, 31.6 per cent of oxygen. This is commonly considered an iron titanate. Ilmenite is often associated in small amounts with magnetite. Although generally mined as a source of titanium rather than as an ore of iron, iron may be recovered as a by-product.

Siderite—Chemical composition, FeCO$_3$, corresponding to 48.2 per cent of iron and 51.8 per cent of CO$_2$; specific gravity, 3.83 to 3.88; color, from white to greenish gray and brown. Siderite commonly contains variable amounts of calcium, magnesium or manganese. Siderite varies from dense, fine grained and compact to crystalline. The siderite ores are sometimes termed "**spathic iron ore**" or "**black-band ore.**" Carbonate ores are commonly calcined before they are charged into the blast furnace. They frequently contain enough lime and magnesite to be self-fluxing.

Silicate Group—There are a large number of silicate minerals containing small amounts of iron associated with other bases but there are comparatively few silicates with iron as the principal base. They often have a rather complex chemical formula, with specific gravities higher than 2.8, and occur in various shades of green or black. Important iron-silicate minerals are **chamosite, stilpnomelane, greenalite, minnesotaite,** and **grunerite.** The iron silicates, while not important in themselves as a source of iron ore, are of interest as a primary source of oxide iron ores which form through weathering or hydrothermal oxidation of the silicate minerals. They have a wide distribution in sedimentary rocks and metamorphic iron formations.

Sulphide Group—Iron occurs in a large number of sulphide minerals. The principal iron-sulphide minerals are: pyrite, pyrrhotite and marcasite. **Pyrite** (iron pyrites), chemical composition FeS$_2$, corresponding to 46.6 per cent of iron and 53.4 per cent of sulphur; specific gravity, 4.95-5.10; color, pale brass yellow; is the most widespread of the iron sulphides and occurs in sedimentary, metamorphic, and igneous rocks and in veins. **Pyrrhotite** (magnetic pyrite), a sulphide of iron that varies in chemical composition from FeS to FeS + S, typically contains 69.4 per cent of iron and 39.6 per cent of sulphur; its color is bronze yellow to copper red, frequently tarnished. Pyrrhotite is often considered to be an indicator of nickel deposits because of its common association with the nickel sulphide, pentlandite. When nickel occurs in pyrrhotite it is generally in the form of fine inclusions of pentlandite. **Marcasite** (white iron pyrites), chemical composition FeS$_2$, corresponding to an iron content of 46.6 per cent and a sulphur content of 53.4 per cent, is pale brass yellow in color and is commonly associated with limestones, clays, and lignite deposits. It differs from pyrite only in its crystal structure and greater chemical instability.

Iron sulphides are sometimes mined as a source of sulphur. More commonly they are mined because of their association with other valuable metallic elements such as copper, nickel, zinc, gold, silver, etc. Iron is sometimes recovered as a by-product after the removal of the more valuable metals and the sulphur. The sulphides are of growing importance as sources of by-product iron principally from pyrite and pyrrhotite. By-product iron or iron oxide is being produced from sulphide ores by International Nickel Company of Canada, Ltd.; Noranda Mines, Limited; Consolidated Smelting and Refining Company; Anaconda Corporation; and Tennessee Copper Division of the Tennessee Corporation.

GEOLOGY OF IRON-ORE DEPOSITS

Geologic Ages of Iron-Ore Deposits—Iron ores have a wide range of formation in geologic time as well as a wide geographic distribution. They are found in the oldest known rocks of the earth's crust, with an age in excess of 2.5 billion years, as well as in rock units formed in various subsequent ages; in fact, iron ores are forming today in areas where iron oxides are being precipitated in marshy areas, and where magnetite placers are being formed on certain beaches.

Many thousands of iron deposits are known throughout the world. The deposits range in size from a few tons to many hundreds of millions of tons. Many of the world's largest deposits of iron ore are located in the oldest geologic series—the Pre-Cambrian. Table 5—II illustrates the geologic age for selected iron deposits.

Genesis of Iron-Ore Deposits—Iron ores occur in a wide variety of geological environments in igneous, metamorphic or sedimentary rocks, or as weathering products of various primary iron-bearing materials. For convenience of study and comparison, iron ores may be grouped into types of similar geological occurrence, composition and structure. The following simplified classification based on genesis of the deposits and geological environment shows the chief modes of occurrence of iron ores and illustrates the varied geology of iron-ore deposits.

IGNEOUS ORES

Iron ores may be formed by crystallization from liquid rock materials, either as layered-type deposits that possibly are the result of crystals of heavy iron-bearing minerals settling as they crystallize to form iron-rich concentrations, or as bodies which show intrusive relationship with their wall rocks. These ore bodies may be tabular or irregular and are composed largely of magnetite with varying amounts of hematite. Igneous ores are usually high in iron content and are often high in phosphorus or titanium content. Deposits of this type include the ores at Kiruna, Gellivare and Grangesberg, Sweden; Iron Mountain and Pea Ridge, Missouri; titaniferous magnetite deposits

Table 5—II. Geologic Age of Selected Iron-Ore Deposits.

Geologic Age	Deposit	Location
CENOZOIC ERA		
QUATERNARY PERIOD		
Recent Epoch	Taza Hematite and Limonite	French Morocco
	St. Lawrence Magnetite placers	Quebec, New York
TERTIARY PERIOD		
Pliocene Epoch	*Kerch Oölitic Limonite	Crimea, Russia
	El Tofo Magnetite	Chile, South America
Miocene Epoch	Honshu and Hokkaido gravel placers	Japanese Archipelago
Oligocene Epoch	Cheikh-ab-Charg Hematite	Persia
Eocene Epoch	Upper Assam Clay Ironstones	India
MESOZOIC ERA		
CRETACEOUS PERIOD	*Salzgitter Limonite and Hematite	Germany
	Bilbao Hematite	Spain
	Algerian and Moroccan Magnetite and Hematite	North Africa
JURASSIC PERIOD	*Minette Limonite and Hematite	France, Germany and Luxemburg
	Iron Springs Magnetite	Utah
TRIASSIC PERIOD	Kashmir Calcareous Iron Ore (Hematite)	India
PALEOZOIC ERA		
PERMIAN PERIOD	Damuda Sandstone (Hematite)	India
CARBONIFEROUS PERIOD	*Black Band Ironstones	British Isles
	Ohio Siderite Ores	Ohio
DEVONIAN PERIOD	*Siegerland Siderite	Germany
	Oriskany Limonite and Hematite	Virginia
SILURIAN PERIOD	*Clinton Hematites	Alabama
ORDOVICIAN PERIOD	*Wabana Oölitic Hematites	Newfoundland
CAMBRIAN PERIOD	Residual Limonites of the Appalachians	Georgia, Virginia, Alabama, Tennessee
*PRE-CAMBRIAN ERA***	*Minas Gerais Hematite	Brazil
	*Krivoi Rog Hematites	Ukraine, Russia
	*Bihar, Orissa and Bastar Hematites	India
	*Labrador Hematite	Quebec and Labrador
	*Lake Superior Taconites and Jaspilites, Hematites and Magnetites	Michigan, Wisconsin, Minnesota, Ontario
	*Cerro Bolivar and El Pao Hematites	Venezuela
	*Kirunavaara Magnetite	Sweden

*Well-known, important deposits.
**Represents the time span of the combined Proterozoic and Archeozoic Eras. Sometimes divided, for convenience of reference, into Early, Middle, and Late Pre-Cambrian eras (see Table 5—VI).

at Lake Sanford, New York; Talberg, Sweden; and Bushveld, Transvaal, Union of South Africa.

CONTACT ORES

Iron-ore deposits formed at or near the contact between igneous rocks and sedimentary rocks, the latter usually limestones, are commonly composed of magnetite and hematite with associated carbonates and pyrite. The ore deposits are commonly in the sedimentary rocks as irregular or tabular replacement bodies. Deposits of this type include: Cornwall, Pennsylvania; Iron Springs, Utah; Mount Magnitnaya, Russia; Marcona, Peru; Dungun, Malaya; Larap, Philippine Islands; and Marmora, Canada.

HYDROTHERMAL ORES

Iron-ore deposits formed by hot solutions which transported iron and replaced rocks of favorable chemical composition with iron minerals to form irregular ore bodies, commonly in limestones, are termed hydrothermal deposits. The iron often occurs as siderite ($FeCO_3$) or sometimes as oxides. Examples of hydrothermal deposits include those at Bilbao, Spain; Cumberland, England; Kenifra, French Morocco; Ouenza, Algeria; Rudabanya, Hungary; hard ores of the Marquette Range, Michigan; and Iron Monarch ores of the Middleback Range, Australia.

SEDIMENTARY ORES

Bedded Ores—Sedimentary bedded iron ores, often composed of oölites of hematite, siderite, iron silicate or less commonly, limonite in a matrix of siderite, calcite or silicate, have a wide geographic distribution associated with other sedimentary rocks. The Clinton ores in Alabama also have fossil fragments coated or replaced with hematite, or sand grains and pebbles coated with hematite in a hematite and calcite matrix. These ores often have a fairly high phosphorus content and may be self-fluxing. Ores of this type include the Wabana ores, Newfoundland, Canada; Clinton ores, Alabama; Minette ores, France; Jurassic ironstones, England; and Kerch ores, Russia.

Siderite Ores—These ores consist of beds of siderite or siderite nodules associated with shales. They are common in the coal measures and are often termed **clay ironstones** or **black-band ironstones.** These ores commonly contain associated sulphides and often have a fairly high sulphur and phosphorus content. They were formerly of considerable importance in Great Britain and Germany.

Placer Ores—Iron oxides, when compact, are rather resistant to weathering and erosion and under favorable conditions may form placer deposits which, in a few instances, constitute iron ores. In general they are of rather minor importance as sources of iron. Magnetite sands are mined in Japan and are known in many areas. Deposits of iron-bearing rubble cemented with limonite and clay, that occur on hill slopes in tropical areas adjacent to pre-existing iron deposits, are termed **canga.** These are sometimes mined as ore. Placer iron-ore deposits include beach sands in Japan and New Zealand. Canga occurs in Brazil, India and Venezuela.

Bog Iron Ores—Bog ores occur in many swampy areas particularly in glaciated areas in Europe, Asia and North America. They occur commonly as dark-brown, cellular masses, or granular or fine particles of limonite. In years gone by, such deposits were mined rather widely to locally supply small iron furnaces. However, they have long ago ceased to be important commercially.

Metamorphic Ores—These ores include sedimentary iron-ore deposits which have been metamorphosed as well as ores associated with metamorphic rocks in which the origin of the ore is obscured by recrystallization. Essentially all of the Pre-Cambrian sedimentary iron formations are of this type: these include the magnetite taconites of Minnesota; jaspers of Michigan; itabirites of Brazil; magnetite gneiss of New York; quartz-banded ores of Norway and Sweden; concentrating ores of Quebec and Labrador; banded hematite-quartzites of Africa; hematite jaspers of India, and the banded iron formations of Manchuria, Korea and Australia.

Residual Ores—Residual ores are commonly products of the surficial weathering of rocks but may include ores formed by hydrothermal oxidation and leaching. Ores of this type were formed extensively in Pre-Cambrian iron formations by leaching of silica, which commonly constituted in excess of 50 per cent of the rock. Oxidation changes iron carbonate, silicate minerals, and magnetite to hematite or limonite. Examples of residual ores include: iron **laterites** formed by the weathering of basic igneous rocks as in Cuba, Conakry (Guinea, Africa), and Mindanao in the Philippine Islands; the **brown ores** of Alabama, Georgia and Missouri; **soft hematite** and **limonite** Pre-Cambrian ores such as occur in the Lake Superior District; Cerro Bolivar, Venezuela; Krivoi Rog, Russia; Minas Gerais, Brazil; Quebec-Labrador, Canada; Nimba, Liberia; Tonkolili, Sierra Leone; and India.

DEFINITION OF THE TERM "ORE"

The term "ore" is often used loosely—as it has been up to this point—in discussions of a general nature. However, a more restrictive definition must be used in discussions of ores used by the iron and steel industry and particularly in discussing iron-ore reserves.

Iron is one of the more abundant and widely distributed elements in the earth's crust, constituting not less than 4 per cent of the total. Its supply is essentially limitless in almost all regions of the world. However, most of this iron, because of its position in the earth's crust, is not available to us, and much of it is in a form that cannot be used in current iron-making practices. That part of the total iron in the earth's crust that is available to industry, both economically and spatially, may correctly be termed "ore." However, what constitutes "ore" varies widely from place to place and time to time. For example, the principal ores now being mined and used in France contain less than 25 per cent of iron. Such material would not be considered suitable furnace feed in most other sections of the world. However, in this particular case, the spatial proximity of this ore to sources of coking coal and to an important market area for steel, as well as its adaptability to the furnace practices developed in that area, give it a favorable price-quality relationship with respect to higher grade but more distant ores. Much the same situation exists in the Birmingham, Alabama, area, where ores containing only 37 per cent of iron are mined and used locally; although such low-grade, high-phosphorus ore would not be considered as commercial ore in other mining districts. Similarly, the basic Bessemer (Thomas) process of steelmaking, widely used in Europe, requires the use of high-phosphorus ores that would be quite unacceptable for general use in America. There are many factors which enter into determining what iron-bearing material can be classed as an "ore," but basically it is a question of economics, as discussed later in this chapter. Keeping this concept in mind, a logical definition of "iron ore" for commercial purposes as contrasted to discussion purposes is as follows:—"iron-bearing material that can be economically used at a particular place and time under then current cost and market-price conditions."

According to this definition, ferruginous quartzites would properly be classed as ore in the USSR because they are actually being so used. However, if located in India, they would not be classed as ore. Similarly, coarse-grained, non-magnetic taconites, such as those now being worked near Marquette, Michigan, would be classed as ore in the United States; but they would not be classed as ore in South Africa or Brazil because in those latter countries they are not now commercially usable. Under this definition, ferruginous by-products derived from the processing of materials for their content of sulphur, titanium, copper, or other metals would not be considered as iron ore in the strict sense of the term, nor would beach sands and laterites unless they were actually being utilized, as for example, beach sands in Japan and the laterite ores of the Conakry area in Guinea. Other iron-bearing material would also have to be denied classification as ore because of impurities, geographic inaccessibility, harsh climatic conditions, or, in some cases, simply because there is insufficent available information for a valid appraisal.

Table 5—III. World Iron-Ore Reserves and Resources. [1]
(Millions of Metric Tons)

| | Iron Ore | | | Iron-In-Ore | | | | |
| | Geologically Explored Reserves | | | Geologically Explored Reserves | | | | |
	Direct-Shipping Ore	Concentrating Ore	Potential Resources	Direct-Shipping Ore	Concentrating Ore	Total Explored	Potential Resources	Total
North America								
Canada	573	4,095	7,591	195.2	1,558.4	1,753.6	2,812.8	4,566.4
United States	671	7,124	19,983	269.9	2,284.3	2,554.2	6,042.2	8,596.4
Total	1,244	11,219	27,574	465.1	3,842.7	4,307.8	8,855.0	13,162.8
Central America								
Honduras			8				4.2	4.2
Mexico	105		146	60.0		60.0	89.7	149.7
Total	105		154	60.0		60.0	93.9	153.9
South America								
Argentina		106	80		47.5	47.5	36.5	84.0
Brazil	2,815	100	14,050	1,737.0	60.0	1,797.0	8,487.5	10,284.5
Chile	189		259	119.9		119.9	167.1	287.0
Colombia	50		50	24.0		24.0	24.0	48.0
Peru	42	500	52	25.7	275.0	300.7	31.4	332.1
Venezuela	1,039		565	622.7		622.7	316.5	939.2
Total	4,135	706	15,056	2,529.3	382.5	2,911.8	9,063.0	11,974.8
Europe								
Austria	110		230		37.2	37.2	78.1	115.3
Bulgaria	20	250		12.6	81.7	94.3		94.3
Czechoslovakia		70	160		24.3	24.3	54.3	78.6
Finland		250	220		87.5	87.5	64.0	151.5
France	6,020	540	5,120	1,924.0	257.8	2,181.8	1,880.0	4,061.8
Germany-East		35			11.5	11.5		11.5
Germany-West	65	1,457	3,830	19.8	425.9	445.7	1,021.6	1,467.3
Greece		82	85		38.6	38.6	41.4	80.0
Hungary		10	10		4.8	4.8	4.8	9.6
Italy	10	23	37	5.7	12.1	17.8	20.7	38.5
Luxemburg		200	70		60.0	60.0	21.0	81.0
Norway	10	222	1,246	5.4	73.9	79.3	424.8	504.1
Poland		315	300		91.1	91.1	92.5	183.6
Rumania	30		70	17.2		17.2	36.0	53.2
Spain	800		300	422.5		422.5	155.2	577.7
Sweden	1,830	370	890	1,164.8	228.5	1,393.3	507.9	1,901.2
Switzerland		36	34		10.0	10.0	9.5	19.5
United Kingdom	2,146		1,160	675.8		675.8	325.3	1,001.1
USSR	2,801	23,376	16,830	1,549.7	7,696.3	9,246.0	5,571.2	14,817.2
Yugoslavia	32	173	14	11.9	71.1	83.0	7.4	90.4
Total	13,874	27,409	30,606	5,809.4	9,212.3	15,021.7	10,315.7	25,337.4
Asia								
Burma		33			16.7	16.7		16.7
China	789	2,603	7,366	428.2	947.7	1,375.9	3,303.3	4,679.2
Hong Kong		9			3.6	3.6		3.6
India	5,240	84	10,215	3,360.0	33.6	3,393.6	6,555.0	9,948.6
Indochina	40		70	24.7		24.7	42.0	66.7
Indonesia	2		10	1.4		1.4	6.2	7.6
Iran			63				34.2	34.2
Israel		5	10		1.8	1.8	3.5	5.3
Japan	12	41		5.1	18.8	23.9		23.9
Korea		435	1,000		167.3	167.3	260.0	427.3
Malaya		50			28.8	28.8		28.8
Thailand			28				12.6	12.6
Turkey	39		19	24.6		24.6	11.7	36.3
Total	6,122	3,260	18,781	3,844.0	1,218.3	5,062.3	10,228.5	15,290.8

(Continued on next page)

Table 5—III. World Iron-Ore Reserves and Resources (Continued). [1]
(Millions of Metric Tons)

Australasia								
Australia	395	100	1,610	255.6	45.0	300.6	907.1	1,207.7
Philippines	8	26		4.7	14.4	19.1		19.1
Total	403	126	1,610	260.3	59.4	319.7	907.1	1,226.8
Africa								
Algeria	140			75.8		75.8		75.8
Angola	+148		148	98.4		98.4	98.4	196.8
Egypt	15		150	7.5		7.5	75.0	82.5
French Cameroons		100			40.0	40.0		40.0
Gabon		150			63.4	63.4	315.0	378.4
Guinea	500		2,100	260.0		260.0	1,170.0	1,430.0
Ivory Coast			200				130.0	130.0
Liberia	10	90	500	6.6	46.6	53.2	290.0	343.2
Mauritania	150			95.3		95.3		95.3
Morocco—French	10	30	90	4.6	12.9	17.5	37.8	55.3
Morocco—Spanish	15	15	30	9.2	9.2	18.4	18.4	36.8
Rhodesia & Nyasaland	+217			126.0		126.0		126.0
Sierra Leone		255			152.6	152.6		152.6
Union of South Africa	450	66	800	270.5	36.5	307.0	488.0	795.0
Swaziland	59		50	32.2		32.2	32.1	64.3
Tunisia	18	1	20	9.9	0.6	10.5	11.0	21.5
Total	1,732	707	4,588	996.0	361.8	1,357.8	2,665.7	4,023.5
World Total	27,615	43,427	98,369	13,964.1	15,077.0	29,041.1	42,128.9	71,170.0

[1] From "Iron-Ore Resources of the World," by R. W. Hyde, D. M. Lane, and W. W. Glaser (Arthur D. Little, Inc.). Eng. and Min. J. *163*, No. 12, Dec. 1962, pages 84–88.

IRON-ORE RESERVES

The potential iron "ore" known to exist is called iron-ore reserve. Such reserves can best be specified by using the definition of "ore" given in the preceding paragraph. Because the iron content of different ore bodies is sometimes widely different, it is often more realistic to compare them on the basis of the iron they contain rather than on the basis of the amount of ore. For this reason, reserves may be reported as "iron ore" or as "iron-in-ore," depending upon the use to be made of the information.

For convenience, reserves have been divided into two classes—"explored reserves" and "potential resources." The former comprise what geologists refer to as "proven" or "probable" ore or "measured" and "indicated" ore. These reserves have been explored by drilling, trenching, or tunneling, so that both the quality and quantity have been determined with a reasonable degree of certainty. "Potential resources," on the other hand, comprise what is sometimes referred to as "possible" or "inferred" ore. This includes those reserves which are believed to exist on the basis of geological evidence, but on which drilling is either lacking or so sparse as to leave uncertainty as to the quantity and grade of the ore.

On the basis of these definitions, staff members of Arthur D. Little, Inc. have estimated world reserves of iron ore, as shown in Table 5—III, in terms of both iron ore and iron-in-ore.

SECTION 2

MAJOR IRON-ORE DEPOSITS SUPPLYING FURNACES IN THE UNITED STATES

Following are brief descriptions of the major sources of iron ore available to the United States' iron and steel industry and the particular markets these sources serve. In this category are included iron-ore sources of North America (discussed in sub-sections A, B and C, following) as well as certain selected ore deposits in South America (see sub-section D) and West Africa (sub-section E) which, because of their location or ownership, supply ore to the United States' market. Information on other world iron-ore deposits can be obtained from the bibliography at the end of this chapter.

It should be borne in mind that the iron-ore industry is changing rapidly as new steel plants are built, as ironmaking technology advances, as transportation facilities improve, and as new ore sources of major importance are developed. The following comments refer to conditions as they existed in 1962.

The principal iron-ore deposits of North America are in the Lake Superior District, Quebec-Labrador Region, Newfoundland, and Alabama, with lesser deposits, which are locally very important iron-ore sources, in Pennsylvania, Missouri, Texas, Utah, Wyoming, California, British Columbia, Ontario, and

Mexico. Each iron-ore source has its market area which may be in part overlapping with other iron-ore sources. The Lake Superior ores and other Ontario ores serve the Great Lakes Region furnaces in the United States and Canada; Quebec-Labrador ores are shipped to the Eastern Great Lakes Region furnaces and Eastern seaboard plants, as well as being exported to Europe; Newfoundland ores have largely been placed in the European market; Alabama, Missouri, Texas, Pennsylvania and Mexican ores are used locally; the Utah, Wyoming and California ores serve western United States plants, with some exported to Japan; British Columbia ores (except the by-product material at Trail, B. C.) are exported to Japan.

The general ore reserves for North America total about 13 billion tons of iron-in-ore, as indicated in Table 5—III.

In addition to mined iron ore, by-product iron or iron oxide is currently available from several sources in both Canada and the United States.

A. DEPOSITS OF THE UNITED STATES

The principal iron ore deposits of the United States are shown in Figure 5—1. They can be conveniently grouped into five areas: Lake Superior; Northeastern; Missouri; Southeastern; and Western; the ore reserves of each being shown in Table 5—IV.

LAKE SUPERIOR DISTRICT

The iron-mining region known as the Lake Superior District is situated on the southwestern margin of a vast area of Pre-Cambrian rocks, covering much of

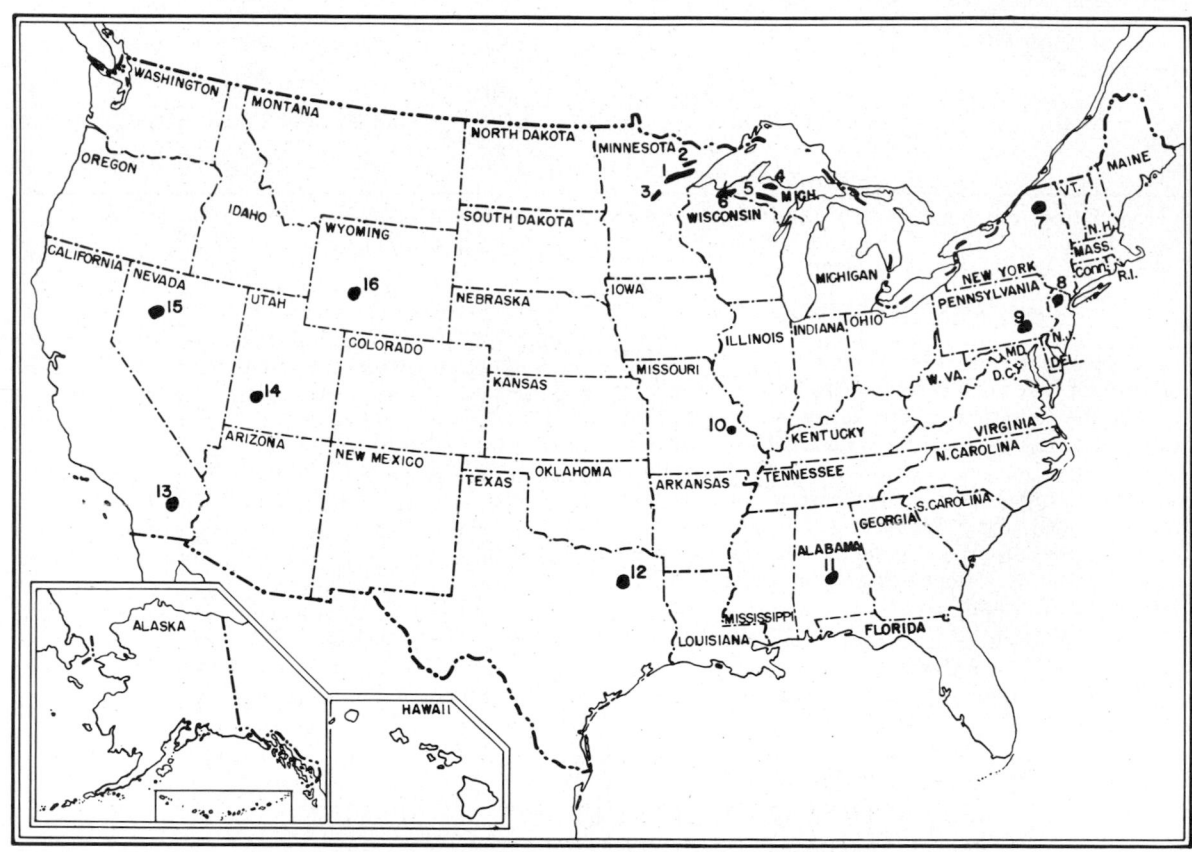

FIG. 5—1. Principal iron-ore deposits of the United States.

KEY

1. Mesabi Range
2. Vermilion Range
3. Cuyuna Range
4. Marquette Range
5. Menominee Range
6. Gogebic Range
7. Adirondacks (Benson Mines, Lyon Mt., Port Henry, Lake Sanford)
8. New Jersey (Scrub Oaks and Washington Mines)
9. Pennsylvania (Cornwall and Grace Mines)
10. Missouri (Iron Mountain and Pea Ridge Mines)
11. Birmingham District
12. Texas Brown Ore Fields
13. Eagle Mountain Mine
14. Iron Springs District
15. Mineral Basin
16. Atlantic City Mine

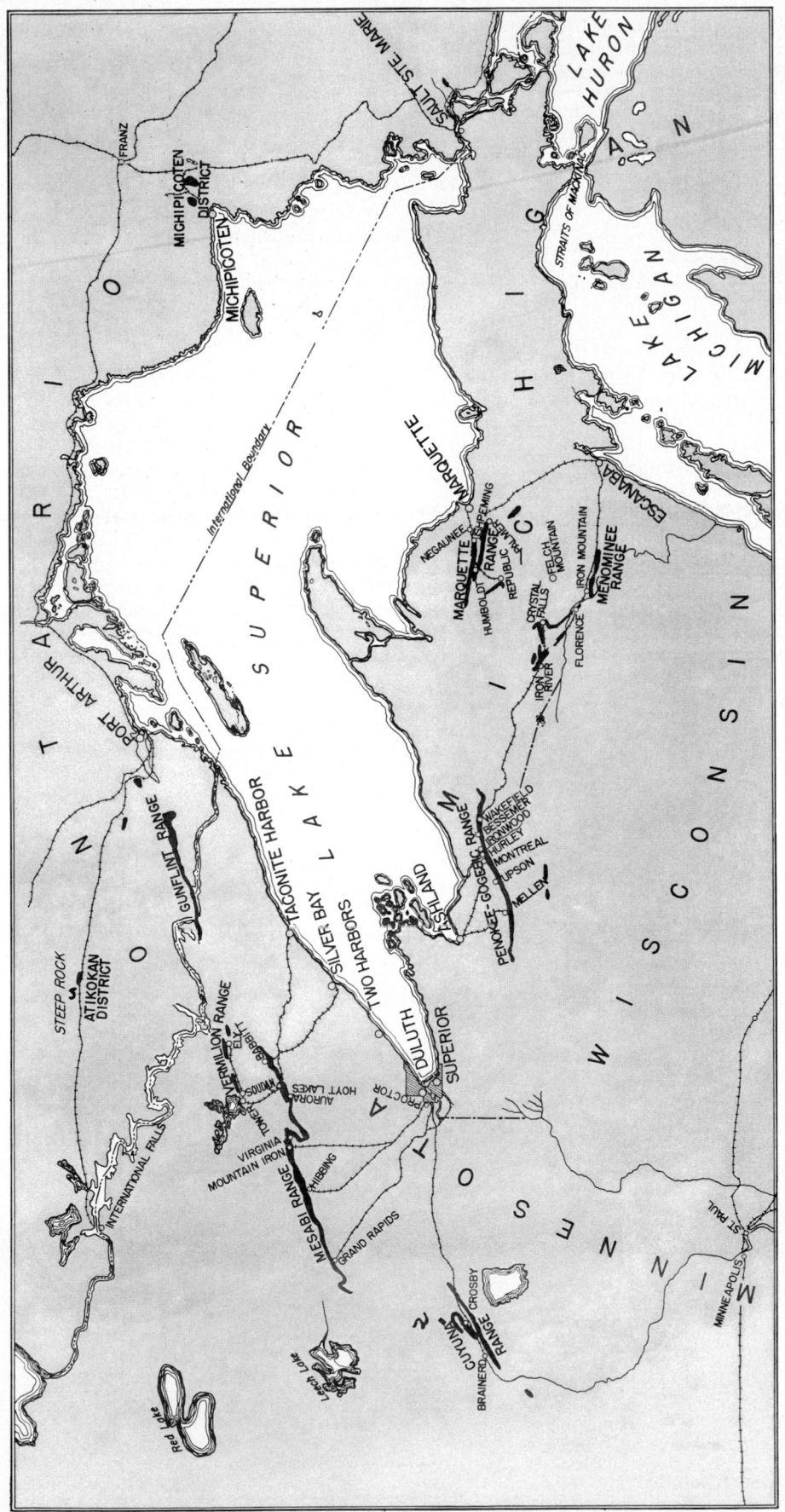

FIG. 5—2. Map of the Lake Superior District, showing location of individual iron-ore ranges in the United States and Canada, and the principal lake ports involved in the shipment of iron ore to lower lake ports.

Table 5—IV. Ore Reserves of the United States
(by Regions)
(Millions of long tons of ore)

	Ores Containing More than 45% Fe	Ores Containing Less than 45% Fe	Total
Lake Superior	740	22,990	23,730
Northeastern	50	1,085	1,135
Missouri	55	—	55
Southeastern	70	1,130	1,200
Western	942	716	1,658

Eastern Canada, geologically termed the Canadian shield. The district includes several separate mining centers, known locally as ranges, some of which lie within the United States and others in Canada (Figure 5—2). The ranges in the United States include the Cuyuna, Mesabi, and Vermilion ranges in northern Minnesota, the Penokee-Gogebic in northern Wisconsin and western Michigan, and the Menominee and Marquette ranges in northern Michigan. The Canadian ranges include the Atikokan, west of Lake Superior, the Michipicoten range east of Lake Superior, and the Moose Mountain, north of Lake Huron. In addition to these productive areas, the iron-bearing formations occur on the Gunflint Range near Port Arthur, north of Nakina, at Lake St. Joseph, the Onoman ranges and at Kaministikwia, etc., all in western Ontario. The Lake Superior District ores are accessible to the steel furnaces in the southern Great Lakes areas by water transportation after short rail hauls to lake ports.

The Lake Superior District is one of the greatest iron-mining regions in the world on a basis of either past production or future potential. Iron was first discovered in 1844 near the site of the City of Negaunee, Michigan by a government survey party in charge of William A. Burt. Some iron ore was mined in 1848 when an attempt was made to make iron in a local forge. This project was unsuccessful. Attempts were made to ship iron ore in the early 1850's, but regular shipments to the lower lakes did not start until 1856. Iron-ore explorations in the Lake Superior District were pressed with considerable vigor after the Civil War. Ore was discovered on the Vermilion Range, Minnesota in 1865; the Menominee Range in 1872; Crystal Falls, Florence and Iron River Districts in 1880; the Gogebic Range in 1882; the Mesabi Range in 1890; the Michipicoten District in 1898; and the Cuyuna Range in 1903. Iron-formation materials have been known in the Atikokan District since 1889 and at Steep Rock Lake since 1901; however, the important Steep Rock ore body was not discovered until 1938.

A summary of iron-ore production for the Lake Superior Range is given on Table 5—V. Shipments from the Lake Superior District through 1960 in the United States totaled 3,371,016,173 gross tons, and from the Canadian Ranges 48,773,000 gross tons; to give a grand total of 3,419,789,173 gross tons.

General Geology—The rocks of principal importance to the iron-mining industry in the Lake Superior region are of Pre-Cambrian age. For convenience of reference, these rocks are divided into early, middle and late Pre-Cambrian. These three periods are recognized by geological criteria and by radioactive dating. Each unit has a stratigraphic succession which is worked out in more or less detail for each of the range areas. Rocks of the early Pre-Cambrian are dated as older than 2.5 billion years, the middle Pre-Cambrian as between 1.7 and 2.5 billion years, and those of the late Pre-Cambrian as between 0.6 and 1.7 billion years. Rock formations in the Lake Superior District display a wide variety of lithologic types including metamorphic sedimentary rocks, quartzites, slates, dolomites and iron formations associated with volcanic extrusive and pyroclastic rocks, many of which are grouped under the general term of greenstones. Intrusive rocks in the region include granites and basic intrusives of various

Table 5—V. Iron-Ore Shipments, Lake Superior Ranges (Gross Tons)

Range	Total Shipments Through 1960	Maximum Shipment Year	Tons	1960 Shipments Merchantable	Beneficiated	Taconite or Jasper Conc.	Total
Mesabi	2,286,318,360	1953	75,953,215	18,139,828	22,283,732	11,368,147	51,791,707
Vermilion	98,199,115	1902	2,084,054	1,164,408	203,935	—	1,368,343
Cuyuna	95,541,212	1953	3,714,684	1,000,198	475,225	—	1,475,423
Penokee-Gogebic	313,342,274	1920	8,763,332	3,375,315	—	—	3,375,315
Marquette	307,559,193	1955	6,639,966	4,238,203	—	756,512	4,994,715
Menominee	270,056,019	1920	6,569,413	3,517,660	—	604,505	4,122,165
Total— U. S. A. Ranges	3,371,016,173	1953	96,317,141	31,435,612	22,962,892	12,729,164	67,127,668
Michipicoten	23,640,000	1959	1,935,000	—	1,438,000	—	1,438,000
Steep Rock	25,133,000	1956	3,317,000	2,350,000	112,000	—	2,462,000
Total— Canadian Ranges	48,773,000	1959	4,861,272	2,350,000	1,550,000	—	3,900,000
Total— Lake Superior Ranges	3,419,789,173						

Table 5—VI. Generalized Geochronology and Stratigraphic Succession of the Lake Superior Region

Era	Period-System	Orogeny	Major Sequence	Rock Types
Cenozoic	Quaternary (Pleistocene Epoch)		Wisconsin	Glacial drift, sand, gravel, etc.
Mesozoic	Cretaceous		Upper Cretaceous	Conglomerates, silt, clays and sand
Paleozoic	Ordovician		Middle Ordovician	Dolomite and limestone
	Cambrian		Upper Cambrian	Sandstone
		Grenville (1 b.y.)*		Gabbro, granophyre and granite
Late Pre-Cambrian (1–1.7 b.y.)*	Keweenawan		Upper Keweenawan	Sandstones, conglomerates, shales
			Middle Keweenawan	Basic flows, conglomerates
			Lower Keweenawan	Sandstones, conglomerates, shales and limestones
		Penokean (1.7 b.y.)*		Granite, basic intrusives
Middle Pre-Cambrian	Huronian		Upper Huronian	Slates, argillites, with some iron formation, quartzite, conglomerates and volcanics
			Middle Huronian	Quartzite, slate, major iron formation, with some basic flows
			Lower Huronian	Quartzite, slate, dolomite
		Algoman (+2.5 b.y.)*		Granite, gneiss
Early Pre-Cambrian (+2.5 b.y.)*	Timiskamian		Knife Lake	Slate, graywacke, conglomerate, flows, pyroclastics, iron formation in Canada
		Laurentian (? b.y.)*		Granite, gneiss
	Keewatin		Keewatin	Greenstones—flows and tuffs with iron formation, conglomerates, slates and graywackes

*b.y.—billion years

types. The general sequence of formations and the position of iron-bearing formations in the stratigraphic succession is shown on Table 5—VI.

Iron-ore deposits in the Lake Superior region are related to sedimentary banded iron formations of the early and middle Pre-Cambrian eras, in rocks of the Keewatin and the Huronian systems in the United States and in the Keewatin and Timiskamian systems in Canada. The term **iron formation** is applied to banded sedimentary rocks which are composed of layers rich in iron minerals and layers which are largely silica either in the form of chert or finely granular quartz. The iron formations are variously termed ferruginous cherts, ferruginous carbonates, carbonate-cherts, jaspers, ferruginous slates, taconite, depending upon mineralogy and texture. Mineralogically the iron formations consist of iron oxides as hematite, goethite or magnetite, iron carbonate (siderite), and the iron silicates—greenalite, Minnesotaite, stilpnomelane, grunerite, fayalite, and iron amphiboles and pyroxenes. The iron formation, as originally deposited, probably consisted of layers of iron oxides or iron carbonates and iron silicates interbedded with layers predominantly chert. Upon compaction and metamorphism the original sediments were transformed into materials which are termed magnetite taconites, ferruginous cherts, jaspers, carbonate-chert, etc. The magnetite taconites in Minnesota and the jaspers in Michigan are examples of metamorphosed iron formations which are currently important as sources of iron

ore. The term magnetite taconite is applied to iron formations in which the principal iron mineral is magnetite associated with varying but lesser amounts of iron carbonate and iron silicate. The silica bands are either chert or granular quartz. The term jasper is applied to the iron formation in Michigan where the principal iron mineral is a flaky, crystalline hematite, steel gray in color, associated with finely granular quartz. The jaspers in Michigan are either red-brown or gray-white in color. In some cases, the metamorphism of the iron formation resulted in the extensive development of iron-silicate minerals through the chemical combination of iron and silica, so that only a minor part of the total contained iron is in the form of magnetite. In these cases, the material is not of interest as an iron ore.

Iron ores occur within the iron formation either as soft, porous ores which formed by the oxidation and leaching of the iron formation in structurally favorable zones, or as hard ores formed by movement of iron minerals by hot solutions within the iron formation whereby iron oxides (hematite and magnetite) have replaced the silica in favorable areas to form ore bodies (see Figures 5—3, 5—4 and 5—5).

The Pre-Cambrian iron formations in Minnesota were exposed to erosion during the Cretaceous period which resulted in the local development of a conglomeratic ore along the Mesabi Range in which the pebbles were derived from the iron formation or ores and are cemented by secondary limonite.

Ores which may be of Cretaceous age occur in southeastern Minnesota in the Spring Valley District where a hard cellular limonite occurs in small deposits on the weathered surface of Paleozoic limestones associated with Cretaceous sands and gravels. These ore materials are believed to have originated in a manner similar to bog ores. The ore bodies are from a few thousand tons to a few hundred thousand tons in size with the average deposit about 40,000 tons. Ores are mined by open-pit methods, and crushed and washed to remove associated clay. They are unimportant commercially.

The Lake Superior region has been heavily glaciated and a mantle of glacial detritus covers essentially all of the area. The glacial deposits range in thickness from zero to in excess of 300 feet.

Types of Iron Ore—Iron ores of the Lake Superior region vary widely in mineralogy and chemical composition and physical characteristics. The ores include merchantable furnace ores and lump ores (commonly termed "soft ore" and "hard ore," respectively), beneficiating ores (material which can be beneficiated easily by gravity methods), magnetite-taconite, jaspers, and potentially concentratable oxidized iron formations (ferruginous chert and semi-taconite). The term "merchantable ore" is used to designate ore which is shipped as mined, without beneficiation. Until approximately 1950, iron ores of the Lake Superior region were restricted to the merchantable furnace ores, lump grade ores and beneficiating ores. Since 1956, magnetite-taconite concentrates have contributed substantially to the production of iron ores from Minnesota and, since 1954, jaspers have contributed important tonnages to the production of iron ore from Michigan.

The soft, porous hematitic and limonitic natural ores, including merchantable ores and beneficiating ores, are derived by the leaching of silica from the iron formation by solutions moving through the rock. In general, the ore deposits are related to channelways which would tend to localize the flow of downward moving ground waters, such as trough-shaped structures, either folds, dike and slate intersections or fault troughs, or fault and fracture zones. On the Mesabi Range, oxidation and leaching have extended to a maximum depth of about 800 feet although the ore bodies are commonly less than 500 feet in depth; on the Gogebic Range, iron-ore bodies have been found to depths in excess of 5000 feet; and on the Marquette Range to depths in excess of 3000 feet.

In the original iron formation, the iron content averages about 30 per cent with about 50 per cent of silica. Where the leaching of silica is sufficiently advanced so that the remaining silica is reduced to less than 10 per cent, merchantable ores result. Original iron-formation horizons which contained appreciable alumina commonly form "painty ore" or "paint rock" upon oxidation and leaching. These materials are comparatively high in alumina and moisture, low in natural iron, and have a poor structure which is fine-grained and sticky. The "paint rock" and "painty ores" are generally not marketable.

Beneficiating ores occur in areas where the leaching has been only partly complete resulting in a crude ore material that can be beneficiated by a combination of crushing, screening and gravity separation methods (such as by the use of jigs, spirals, cyclones and heavy-density media) to yield an iron ore.

Lake Superior hard ores are produced at the Pioneer Mine of United States Steel Corporation, located at Ely, Minnesota; the Cliffs Shaft of the Cleveland-Cliffs Iron Company, at Ishpeming, Michigan; and the Champion Mine of North Range Mining Company at Champion, Michigan on the Marquette Range. These ores are compact, fine grained, gray hematite with some magnetite at the Cliffs Shaft. The lump grade ores contain from 60.3 to 62.7 per cent of iron, 4.2 to 7.6 per cent of silica, and 0.079 to 0.20 per cent of phosphorus—all on a dry basis. The lump ores occur within the banded siliceous iron formation. They appear to be formed by the movement of iron by hot solutions to favorable areas where silica in the iron formation is replaced by iron oxides.

Magnetite taconite is the rock name applied to bedded sedimentary iron formations in which the principal iron mineral is magnetite. It is a hard, dense, compact, fine-grained rock, commonly containing from 40 to 55 per cent of silica and about 25 to 35 per cent total of iron or 15 to 35 per cent as iron in magnetite. Magnetite taconite ores are concentrated by magnetic methods after fine grinding. Plants concentrating this type of ore are located on the eastern Mesabi Range, Minnesota with plants operated at Mountain Iron by the United States Steel Corporation, at Hoyt Lakes by Erie Mining Company and at Silver Bay by the Reserve Mining Company. A plant is being constructed by the Empire Mining Company at Palmer, Michigan on the Marquette Range.

Jasper ore is the term applied to iron formations which are composed of steel-gray, crystalline or specular hematite, and finely granular quartz, with minor iron silicates. Jaspers are concentrated by froth flotation methods. Plants concentrating jasper ores are located at Humboldt (Humboldt Mining Company), Republic (Marquette Iron Mining Company) and Groveland (The Hanna Mining Company), Michigan.

Oxidized iron formations represent potential iron ores in the Lake Superior Region. They are commonly composed of fine grained to earthy hematite, goethite, and chert, and range from a rather friable material to a hard, compact rock. These materials are termed oxidized taconite, non-magnetic taconite or ferruginous cherts or, when they are somewhat friable, "semi-taconite."

Ore Grades—All ores shipped from the Lake Superior District are classed either as furnace ores (for use in the blast furnace) or open-hearth ores. The furnace ores are commonly blended products from more than one mine, and sometimes represent a blend of natural ores, coarse or fine, and beneficiated products. The natural ores are shipped as either standard unscreened ore, or in their coarse and fine screened fractions.

Furnace ores are commonly shipped as specific grades on a basis of chemical composition. Each ore producer establishes grades of guaranteed composition that are referred to by grade names, such as Tracy, Pearson, Beaver, and Oliver Coarse. Histor-

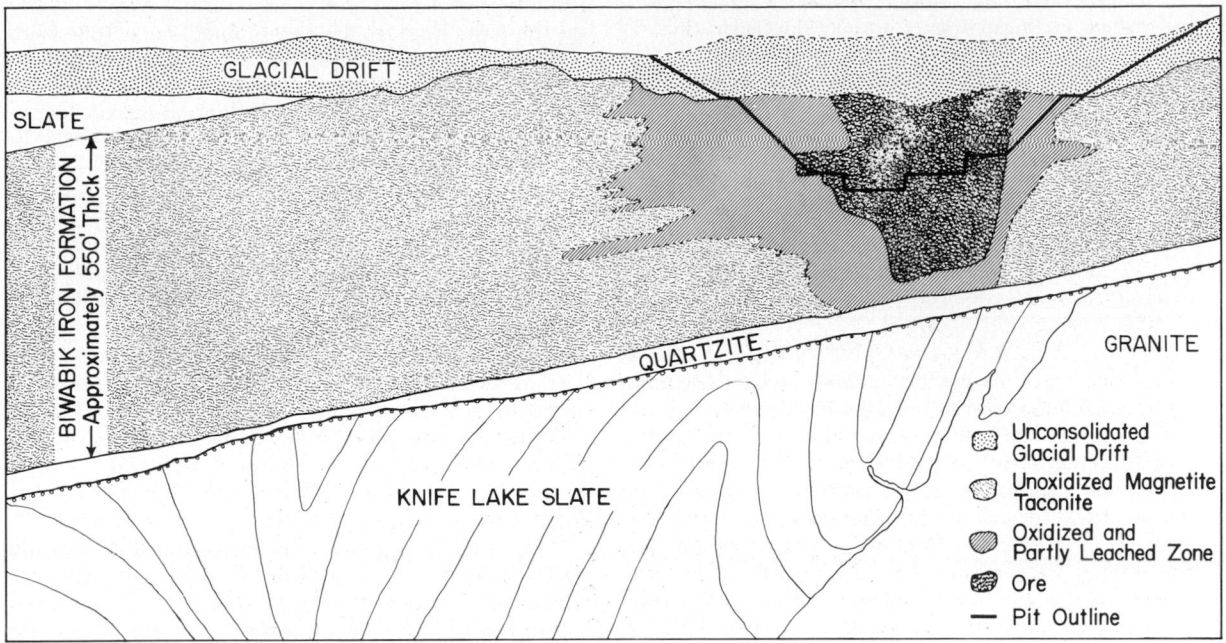

FIG. 5—3. Typical cross-section of an ore body on the Mesabi Range.

ically, the furnace ores have been classed as Bessemer (phosphorus not over 0.045 per cent), Low-Phosphorus Non-Bessemer (phosphorus over 0.045 per cent but less than 0.180 per cent), High-Phosphorus Non-Bessemer (phosphorus over 0.180 per cent), Manganiferous (manganese over 2 per cent) and Siliceous (silica 18 per cent or over). The distinction between Bessemer and Non-Bessemer grades is relatively unimportant today and is not made by some ore producers, as relatively little ore is sold for making iron (hot metal) for use in the Bessemer process.

Open-hearth ores include lump ores and agglomerates in the form of pellets and nodules with suitable chemical and physical characteristics.

The Mesabi Range—The Mesabi Range, located about 65 miles north of Duluth in Minnesota, consists of a belt of iron formation about 120 miles long with the town of Grand Rapids near the west end and Babbitt near the east end. Iron-bearing rocks of the iron formation have been known in this area since about 1866, but commercial iron ore was not discovered until 1890. The first shipment of ore was made in 1892. Total shipments of iron ore from the Mesabi Range through 1960 amounted to 2,286,318,-360 tons. The largest annual production was experienced in 1953 with the shipment of 75,953,215 tons. The shipments in 1960 totaled 51,791,707 tons.

The iron-ore deposits of the Mesabi Range occur in the Middle Huronian Biwabik iron formation which is overlain by a thick slate series and underlain by quartzite, as shown on the diagrammatic section, Figure 5—3. The iron formation ranges from 400 to 750 ft. in thickness and is commonly called "taconite." Where it is magnetic, it is termed "magnetite taconite," and where it has been weathered and the magnetite, iron carbonate and iron silicates are largely oxidized to limonite and hematite, it is commonly termed "oxidized iron formation" or "oxidized taco-

nite." The structure of the rocks on the Mesabi Range is comparatively simple. Rocks generally dip gently to the south, commonly at an angle of less than 10 degrees. In local areas the iron formation dips more steeply or is cut by faults.

The iron-ore materials of the Mesabi Range include: (1) merchantable furnace ores, (2) beneficiating ores, (3) magnetite taconites, and (4) as a potential ore, favorable portions of the oxidized iron formation. The Mesabi Range through 1960 had produced 1,772,-100,360 gross tons of merchantable iron ore and 514,218,000 gross tons of iron-ore concentrates. In 1960, approximately 60 per cent of the iron ores shipped from the Mesabi Range were concentrates and 40 per cent merchantable furnace ores. The trend is toward production of less merchantable ore and more iron-ore concentrates. The increase in concentrates is in part due to the production of iron-ore concentrates from magnetite taconites.

The merchantable, natural ores of the Mesabi Range are generally soft, porous, blue, red, yellow or brown containing various mixtures of hematite and limonites. These ores are largely produced from the portion of the Mesabi Range between Hibbing and Aurora. The natural ores are crushed and screened and graded to give a variety of structure and chemical compositions to meet customer requirements.

Magnetite taconites, which represent the primary ore (from which the merchantable and beneficiating ores of the Mesabi Range were formed by natural processes) themselves constitute an ore when they contain sufficient magnetite of a grain size which allows commercial concentration by magnetic methods following fine grinding. Following magnetic separation, the concentrate must be agglomerated to produce a suitable blast-furnace feed (see "Agglomeration Processes" in Section 5 of this chapter for a description of pelletizing, sintering and nodulizing).

Table 5—VII. Compositions of Sinter, Nodules and Pellets Produced from Concentrates Originating with Magnetite Taconites (1960)

	Fe	P	SiO₂	Mn	Al₂O₃	CaO	MgO	S
Oliver Sinter	66.47	0.013	5.52	0.16	0.25	0.92	0.38	0.005
Oliver Nodules	65.88	0.013	4.97	0.15	0.09	2.17	0.37	0.005
Reserve Pellets	63.10	0.027	8.16	0.24	0.41	0.48	0.54	0.003
Erie Pellets	62.79	0.018	8.99	0.22	0.30	0.68	0.44	0.003

Two types of magnetite taconite occur: (1) magnetite associated with minnesotaite, stilpnomelane and cherty quartz with minor greenalite and carbonates, and (2) magnetite associated with iron amphiboles (grunerite, cummingtonite, actinolite), pyroxenes, garnet, fayalite and finely granular quartz. The first type occurs westward from near Aurora, Minnesota; the second type from Aurora eastward, in an area where the iron formation has been metamorphosed by the intrusion, just to the south, of a large body of gabbro termed the Duluth Gabbro.

Magnetite taconites are concentrated in Minnesota by the Reserve Mining Company at Silver Bay, by Erie Mining Company at Hoyt Lakes, and in the Pilotac Plant of the United States Steel Corporation at Mountain Iron. In 1961, 14,352,157 gross tons of taconite pellets, sinter, and nodules were produced at these plants. Taconite concentrates produced at Silver Bay and Hoyt Lakes are pelletized, while the concentrates produced at Mountain Iron are agglomerated by sintering and nodulizing in an agglomeration plant at Virginia. The taconite pellets, sinter and nodules in 1960 had the compositions shown in Table 5—VII.

Research and pilot-plant work is in progress in an effort to develop a commercial process for the concentration of another type of low-grade ore, the somewhat coarser-grained portions of the oxidized Biwabik iron formation. This is termed "oxidized cherty iron formation" or "oxidized cherty taconite," or "semi-taconite" when it is somewhat friable and does not respond to gravity concentration. Work is being directed toward the conversion of hematite and limonite to magnetite, which can then be concentrated by the usual magnetic methods to yield a high-grade iron concentrate.

In 1960, reserves of iron ore on the Mesabi Range were estimated as follows: (a) Natural and beneficiating ores, 560,000,000 gross tons: (b) Magnetite taconite, 12,000,000,000 gross tons of material available to open-pit mining of which about 5,000,000,000 tons were explored reserves and 7,000,000,000 tons were potential. The magnetite taconite reserves should yield from 3,500,000,000 to 4,000,000,000 tons of shipping product: (c) Oxidized iron formation, 3,000,000,000 gross tons of potential reserves.

Vermilion Range—The Vermilion Range is situated in northeastern Minnesota about 75 miles north of Duluth and 55 miles from Lake Superior. The area generally referred to as the Vermilion Range is about 22 miles long with a productive area at each end, near the towns of Tower and Soudan on the west, and Ely on the east. Iron ore has been mined since 1884 with a total production of 98,199,115 gross tons through 1960. Ore reserves were estimated to be 9,500,000 tons in 1960. Mining is by underground methods. The Soudan (United States Steel) mine on the west end of the Range produced a hard, compact open-hearth lump ore, and the Pioneer (United States Steel) and Zenith (North Range Mining Company) mines near Ely produced both furnace ore and open-hearth lump ore. Only the Pioneer Mine was operative at the end of 1962.

Iron ore at Ely, Minnesota occurs in the basal part of a trough-like body of iron formation which is about 1¾ miles long and ¼ mile wide. The iron-bearing structure is about 500 feet wide and 5000 feet long at a depth of about 1500 feet. The bottom of the ore has been reached on both ends of the trough and has been mined. The depth of ore in the central part of the ore deposit is yet to be determined.

The iron-bearing materials are enclosed in volcanic rocks of Keewatin age and are intruded by basic and felsitic dikes. Rocks associated with the iron ores above the 1500 foot level, and more or less below, are strongly oxidized and leached. The volcanic rocks, dikes and slaty iron formation become a fine grained, soft, red-brown, clayey material termed "paint rock." The ore is composed of angular fragments of hard, steel-gray hematite which in the upper part of the deposit is in a soft, red, hematite and limonite matrix but, in depth, becomes secondary hard, gray hematite. Thus, in some areas, the ore is a hard, compact hematite. Locally, secondary pyrite occurs in the Ely deposit requiring care in mining to keep from obtaining objectionable amounts of sulphur. In fact, some ores are unminable because of the high pyrite content.

Iron ore at the Pioneer Mine is washed and screened to give three shipping products; lump ore, and coarse and fine blast-furnace ores. The lump ores contain about 62.7 per cent of iron with 4.25 to 5.7 per cent of silica, and the furnace ores contain from 59 to 60 per cent of iron and 5 to 7 per cent of silica, all on a dry basis.

The Cuyuna Range—This range is located in Minnesota, 100 miles southwest of Duluth, and has a maximum length of 68 miles. Mining activity has been largely confined to an area about 10 miles long and 3 miles wide near Crosby and Ironton. Iron ores are found in an iron formation which is overlain by slate and underlain by a series of quartzites and slates. The iron formation, which consists of interbedded iron-rich layers and cherty layers, ranges from 45 to 500 feet in thickness, and is probably the equivalent of the iron formation on the Mesabi Range to the north. The iron formation of the Cuyuna Range differs from that of other ranges in the Lake Superior District in its manganese content. The original unoxidized iron formation contains from 18 to 35 per cent of iron and from about 1 to 8 per cent of manganese. The Cuyuna iron ores and manganiferous iron ores were formed by the leaching of silica and the development of iron and manganese oxides as porous red-brown to red and black ore. The ores appear to be related to the present erosion surface and rarely are over 500 feet deep.

Merchantable and manganiferous iron ores are produced from the Cuyuna Range, with about one half of the material currently shipped requiring beneficiation by gravity concentration to meet grade requirements. Shipments in 1960 totaled 1,475,000 gross tons.

The ores produced from the Cuyuna Range contain from 37 to 51 per cent of iron, from 4½ to 13½ per cent of manganese, and from 11 to 16 per cent of silica on a dry basis. The Cuyuna ores are of interest because of their relatively high manganese content, but even so, these ores are of marginal character. Reserves in 1960 were estimated to be about 38,000,000 tons of which about one third is not manganiferous, has a high phosphorus content and is of doubtful commercial value.

Marquette Range—This range is located in the northern part of the Upper Peninsula of Michigan with its eastern end 10 miles west of the Lake Superior port of Marquette. It is about 30 miles long and six miles wide, strikes in an east-west direction and includes the towns of Negaunee, Ishpeming, Palmer, Humboldt, Republic and Michigamme (see Figure 5—2). Mining of natural ores is concentrated in the vicinity of Negaunee and Ishpeming; whereas the mining of concentrating materials is in the vicinity of Humboldt and Republic with a mine planned for the Palmer area. The first iron ore discovered in the Lake Superior District was found near Negaunee in 1844. Production from 1854 to 1960 totaled 307,-559,193 gross tons. The major portion of the ore has been mined by underground methods. The ores of the Marquette Range include both hard, lump, open-hearth ores and soft furnace ores.

Rocks of the Marquette Range comprise a large synclinal basin of Huronian rocks with iron formation in the middle and upper parts of the sequence. The Middle Huronian Negaunee iron formation is the main productive horizon both for natural ores and concentrating ores, although in the past some ore was produced from the Upper Huronian. The Huronian sequence is so well developed on the Marquette Range that it is considered a classic area for these rocks. The structure, although generally synclinal, is complex in detail as the rocks are cut by numerous faults and intruded by basic dikes and sills as illustrated in Figure 5—4.

The open-hearth lump ores are commonly mined from the upper part of the iron formation in areas where the silica of the iron formation has been replaced by iron possibly as a result of the action of hot solutions. The lump ores are commonly hard, blue hematite with some magnetite and range in composition from about 60 to 62.6 per cent of iron and 5.7 to 7.6 per cent of silica.

The soft, blast-furnace ores commonly occur in trough-like structures formed by folding and faulting. The complicated structure of the Range gives a variety of structural situations favorable for ore development. The soft ores are usually porous, from fine grained to lumpy, and are blue, red, brown or yellow in color. They range in composition from about 56 to 61 per cent of iron and from 6 to 11.7 per cent of silica on a dry basis, corresponding to about 50.5 to 54 per cent of iron on a natural-ore basis. Some siliceous iron ore is produced by open-pit mining. It contains about 40.4 per cent of iron and 40.5 per cent of silica on a dry basis.

In a few areas, the iron formation on the Marquette Range has been metamorphosed with the development of flaky, steel-gray hematite and granular quartz. This material is termed "jasper." The hematite can be concentrated by flotation after grinding the jasper to 65 to 100 mesh. The concentrating plant at Humboldt with an annual capacity of 700,000 gross tons and the plant at Republic with an annual capacity of 1,600,000 gross tons (to be expanded in 1962 to a capacity of 2,400,000) are both treating jasper ores. A plant near Palmer, Michigan is planned to treat a fine-grained magnetite-taconite, with a proposed annual capacity of 1,200,000 gross tons of pellets.

Reserves of merchantable ores on the Marquette Range were estimated in 1960 to be 55,500,000 gross tons. Reserve tonnages for jaspers and magnetite-taconite are not available, although the deposits under development or proposed for development are known to be adequate to support the existing and proposed plants for many years.

Menominee Range—The Menominee Range is located along the southern boundary of the Upper Peninsula of Michigan in the vicinity of Iron Mountain and in the adjacent part of northern Wisconsin. It includes three active iron-producing districts: Iron River, Crystal Falls and Felch Mountain; and three inactive areas: Menominee and Amasa in Michigan and Florence in Wisconsin. The Menominee Range

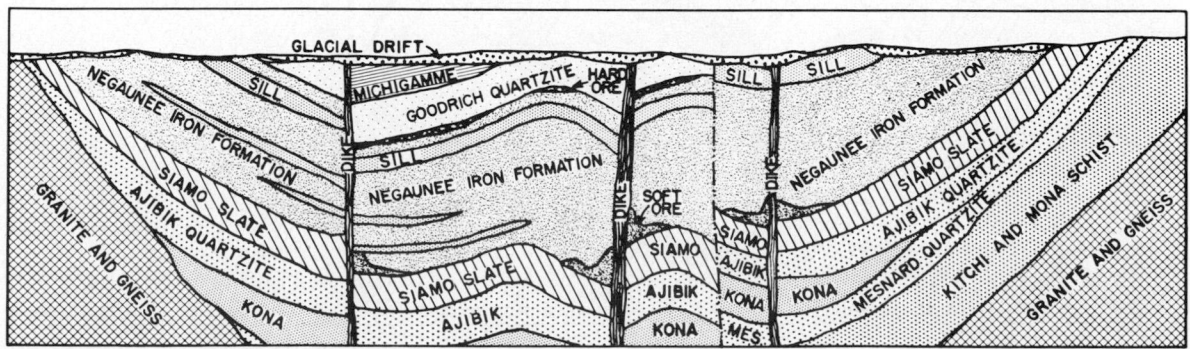

FIG. 5—4. Diagrammatic cross-section of the Ishpeming area of the Marquette Range in Michigan, looking west.

had produced 270,056,019 gross tons through 1960, the major production having been from underground mines.

Iron ores of the Iron River, Crystal Falls and Florence Districts, near towns of these same names, are in an Upper Huronian iron formation; whereas the ores of the Amasa area, near Amasa, Michigan, Felch Mountain, east of Randville, Michigan, and the Menominee area, extending from Iron Mountain to Waucedah, are in a Middle Huronian iron formation. Although no merchantable ores are currently produced from the Middle Huronian iron formations, important tonnages were produced in the past, particularly from the Menominee area, and concentrates are now being produced at the Groveland Mine in the Felch Mountain area.

Iron ores of the Upper Huronian iron formation occur largely in structural troughs developed by folding. They are composed of hematite and limonite, are bluish, red, brown or yellow in color with variable structure from soft and porous to lumpy. The ores commonly contain from 49 to 57 per cent of iron, 0.35 to 0.6 per cent of phosphorus, 4 to 9 per cent of silica, 0.1 to 5.5 per cent of manganese and 2.0 to 4.0 per cent of Al_2O_3, with 5 to 12 per cent of moisture.

Iron formation at the Groveland Mine consists of steel gray hematite in a granular quartz. The material is relatively coarse-grained so that liberation of the hematite is obtained by grinding to about a minus 65 mesh, which allows the coarser fraction to be concentrated in Humphrey spirals and the finer fraction by flotation. The current plant capacity is about 750,000 tons per year with plans to double the capacity in the near future. The Groveland concentrates contain about 60.7 per cent of iron, 8.0 per cent of silica, and 1.26 per cent of lime.

The Middle Huronian iron formation in the Menominee District, termed the Vulcan formation, includes a Trader's iron-formation member, a central Briar slate member, and an upper Curry iron-formation member. The iron formation is well banded with ferruginous layers and cherty layers. The iron-forma-

tion members commonly contain from 30 to 40 per cent of iron as fine, compact grains of hematite associated with finely granular quartz. Research is in progress by public and industrial research groups in an effort to develop a commercial process for the beneficiation of this material by means of a reduction roast to produce artificial magnetite which can be separated magnetically.

Reserves of mechantable ores on the Menominee Range in 1960 were 53,500,000 gross tons. An estimate of the reserves of the concentrating ores in the Felch Mountain area is not available but it can be assumed that they are adequate to support a million and one half ton plant for a considerable period of time.

Penokee-Gogebic Range—This range is located in northern Wisconsin and in the western end of the Upper Peninsula of Michigan. It is about 80 miles in length and strikes in an east-west direction with the towns of Mellen and Hurley, Wisconsin and Ironwood, Bessemer and Wakefield, Michigan situated along the Range. The district was discovered in 1882, with iron-ore production from 1884 to 1960 totaling 313,-342,274 gross tons.

The iron ore occurs in the Ironwood iron formation of Middle Huronian age. It consists of banded ferruginous cherts and carbonate cherts with some slaty iron formation. The iron formation dips to the north at angles of about 50 to 70 degrees. Iron mining has been confined to an area about 15 miles in length, extending from Montreal, Wisconsin to Wakefield, Michigan where the ores are, for the most part, soft and rather fine-grained red hematite with some limonite. Locally, there are some hard blue ores and in restricted areas manganiferous iron ore. The iron ores occur in trough-like structures formed by the intersection of basic dikes which cut the iron formation at high angles to the bedding (see Figure 5—5). The trough structures commonly pitch to the east with the ore extending for long distances along the pitch. Iron ore is known to occur to vertical depths of 5000 feet. The high cost of underground mining will, in all

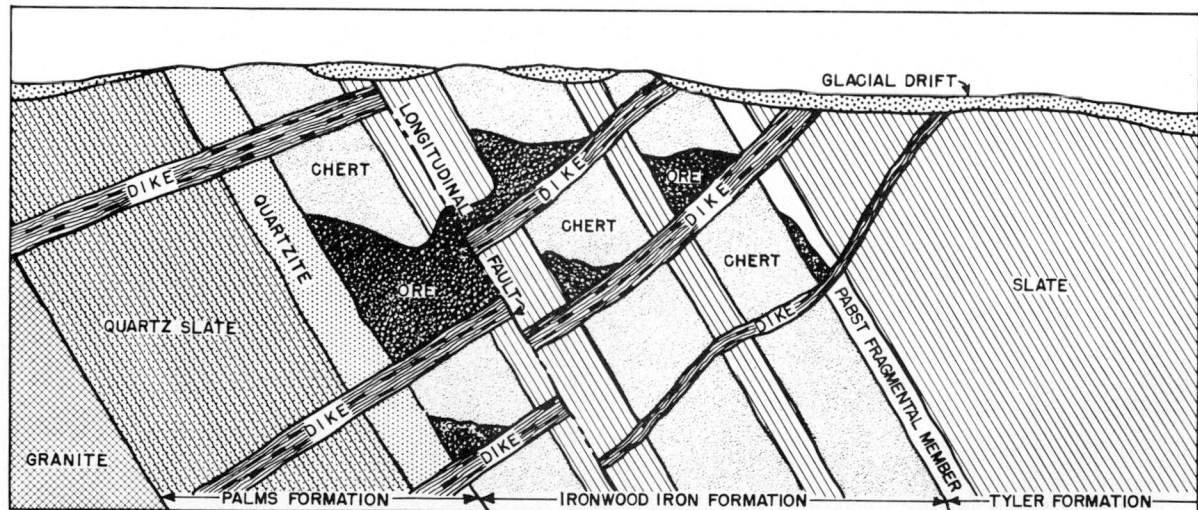

Fig. 5—5. Typical cross-section of the geologic structure of the Penokee-Gogebic Range, showing how ore deposits are located in trough-like structures formed by intersection of dikes with the iron formation.

probability, terminate operations before the deeper ore is exhausted.

West of the productive section of the range between Montreal and Upson, Wisconsin, although the iron formation is commonly oxidized, there are no significant deposits of merchantable ore. Between Upson and Bad River, near Mellen, Wisconsin, the iron formation largely consists of magnetite-taconite similar to that of the east central part of the Mesabi Range, with comparable concentrating characteristics. In this section, which has a length of about 14 miles, the iron formation commonly contains magnetite with minor iron silicates—minnesotaite and stilpnomelane —associated with fine-grained cherty quartz. West of Bad River the iron formation has been more strongly metamorphosed as evidenced by the occurrence of larger amounts of iron silicates as amphiboles and pyroxenes.

The underground mining of iron ore on the Penokee-Gogebic Range has progressed so that most mining is now at a depth of 3000 feet or more and is a marginal operation. The future possibilities of the Range appear to rest largely in the magnetite-taconites. The iron formation in the oxidized portion of the Range is very fine grained and does not respond well to concentration.

Reserves of natural ores in the Penokee-Gogebic Range were estimated in 1960 to be approximately 24,000,000 gross tons. The magnetite-taconite reserves in the Wisconsin section of this range are estimated to be 1,000,000,000 gross tons explored, 2,000,000,000 gross tons potential which should yield from 900 million to one billion tons of concentrates.

NORTHEASTERN UNITED STATES

In the northeastern United States, hundreds of iron deposits of diverse types have been worked at various times since the Colonial period. Operations have gradually been restricted to include only the larger and more important deposits. Mining is being conducted in New York State at the Benson Mines at Star Lake (Jones and Laughlin Steel Corporation), the Chateaugay Mine at Lyon Mountain and the Port Henry Mine at Minesville (Republic Steel Corporation) and the MacIntyre Mine at Tahawus, in the Lake Sanford area (Titanium Division of National Lead Company); in New Jersey at the Scrub Oaks Mine near Dover, and the Washington Mine near Oxford (Alan Wood Steel Company); and in Pennsylvania at the Cornwall and Grace Mines (Bethlehem Cornwall Corporation) at Cornwall and Morgantown, respectively. The Benson Mines deposit is operated as a large open-pit mine, whereas the other deposits are mined by underground methods. The Richards Mine and the Mt. Hope Mine near Dover in New Jersey were mined for a considerable length of time and have only recently closed.

These deposits can be grouped into three main classes: (1) magnetite deposits in Pre-Cambrian gneisses; (2) magnetite deposits in Paleozoic limestones near their contact with Triassic igneous rocks; and (3) titaniferous magnetite. The Pre-Cambrian deposits in the Star Lake and Lyon Mountain areas in New York and in part of the Scrub Oaks Mine in New Jersey, consist of magnetite and to a lesser extent hematite, disseminated in a granite gneiss. These ores are mined, crushed, ground and concentrated by magnetic and gravity methods to form a high-grade iron-ore concentrate. The deposits at Port Henry Mine in New York, the Washington Mine in New Jersey, and in part at the Scrub Oaks Mine in New Jersey, occur as medium to high-grade magnetite ores in Pre-Cambrian gneisses. These ores are higher in grade so that some of the ore can be shipped directly to the furnaces: the remainder requiring beneficiation.

Iron ores at the Cornwall and Grace Mines in Pennsylvania are contact replacement deposits in Paleozoic limestones where these are cut by Triassic diabase. The mineralization consists of magnetite with some pyrite and copper sulphides. Iron ores have been mined in the Cornwall area since 1740; whereas the Grace Mine, found as a result of an airborne-magnetometer survey, started operation in 1960. In these two mines, iron ores are mined underground, although in the past considerable tonnages at the Cornwall mine were mined by open-pit methods. The ores are ground to fine size, concentrated by magnetic methods, and pelletized (see Section 5).

Iron-ore concentrates are produced from the titaniferous-magnetite deposit at the MacIntyre Mine, at Tahawus, New York. This deposit contains ores associated with basic igneous rocks and consists of large irregular bodies of magnetite and ilmenite. The ilmenite occurs in relatively coarse grains so it can be concentrated by gravity and magnetic methods. This deposit is operated principally as a source of titania with magnetite concentrates obtained as a by-product.

Most of the iron ore shipped from the northeastern United States mines is in the form of concentrates, pellets, or sinter (see Section 5). In general, these materials contain over 62 per cent of iron. The average grade of materials from various sources in northeastern United States is shown on Table 5—VIII. The MacIntyre sinter contains about 10 to 11 per cent of titania.

Table 5—VIII. Average Grade of Northeastern Iron Ores (Dry Basis).

	Fe	P	SiO₂	Mn	Al₂O₃	CaO	MgO	S
Benson Sinter	64.9	0.022	4.9	0.25	2.64	0.24	0.27	0.03
Benson Non-Bessemer Sinter	62.4	0.223	4.5	0.17	2.46	0.59	0.28	0.03
Chateaugay Sinter	62.8	0.01	2.76	—	1.56	2.95	0.56	—
Port Henry Sinter	66.2	0.14	4.4	0.08	1.21	—	0.44	0.01
Scrub Oaks	66.6	0.022	5.4	0.03	0.67	0.06	0.18	0.016
Washington	56.41	0.320	9.49	0.14	2.63	1.67	0.77	2.10
Cornwall Pellets	63.0	0.005	5.10	0.05	—	—	—	0.02
Morgantown Pellets (Grace Mine)	65.6	0.005	3.09	0.07	0.76	0.46	1.98	0.03
MacIntyre Sinter	58.0	0.025	2.25	0.23	4.00	0.80	1.50	0.10

MISSOURI DEPOSITS

The iron-ore deposits of Missouri occur in the southeastern part of the state, near the towns of Bourbon and Iron Mountain, 50 to 75 miles southwest of St. Louis. Approximately 15,000,000 tons of iron ore and concentrates were produced from this area during the period 1815 through 1960. Most of the production in 1960 came from the Iron Mountain mine in St. Francois County. Annual production of 2,000,000 tons of high-grade pellets from the Pea Ridge deposit in Washington County was scheduled to

begin in 1963. Three types of iron deposits have been mined in Missouri; hematite-magnetite deposits in Pre-Cambrian rhyolite; hematite filled-sink deposits; and brown-ore deposits.

The Pre-Cambrian deposits have produced about 10,000,000 tons of concentrates. The greatest production to date has come from the Iron Mountain mine, where the ore consists of filled fissures and replacement veins in rhyolite. The chief ore mineral is hard blue specular hematite with up to 25 per cent of magnetite. The crude ore averages about 35 per cent

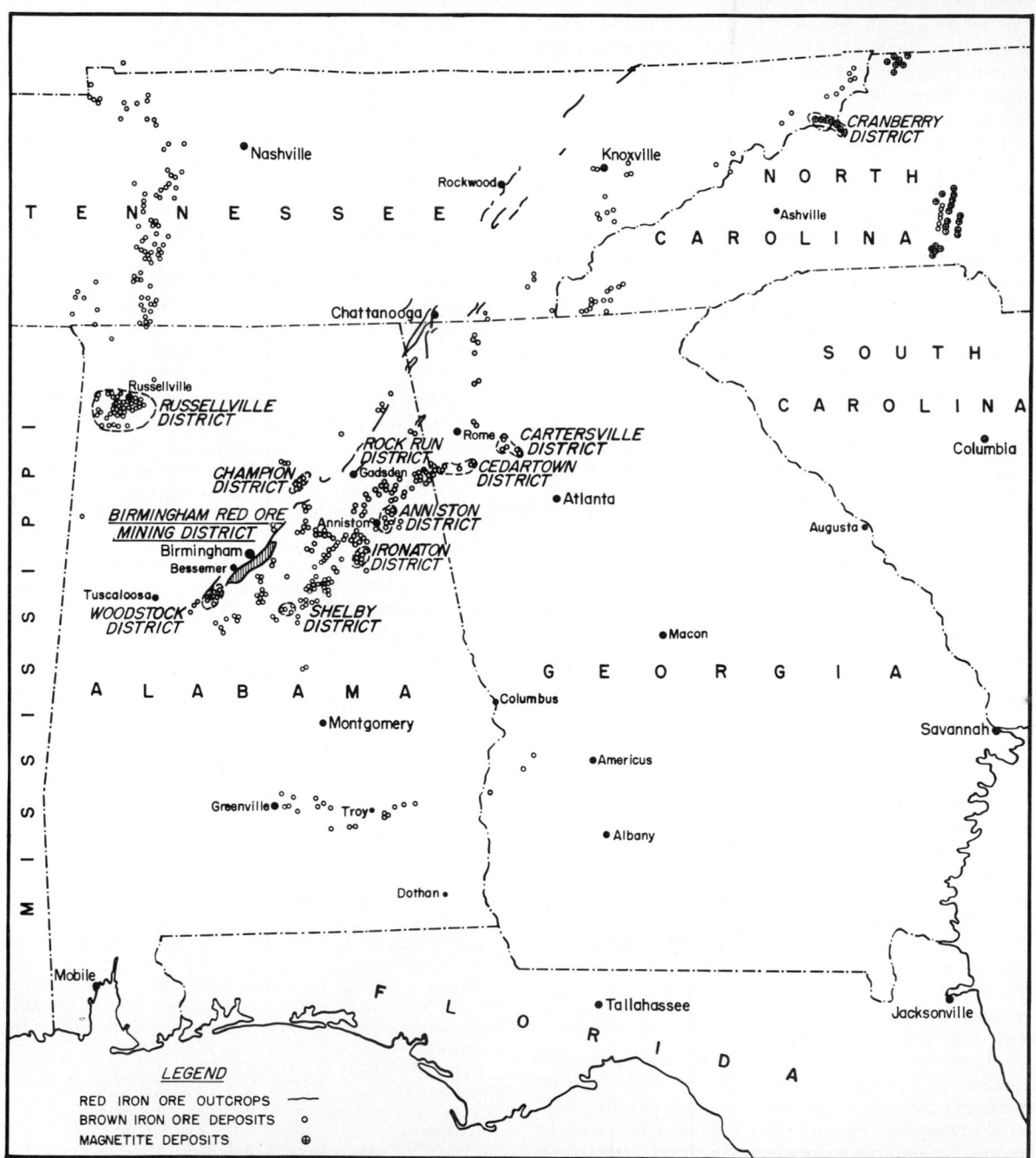

Fig. 5—6. Distribution of iron ores in the southeastern United States.

of iron. It is concentrated by jigs, tables and flotation after grinding to minus 8 mesh. Concentrates assay about 54 per cent of iron and 11.5 per cent of silica. Mining has been carried on by underground methods since 1954.

At Pea Ridge, the ore occurs as a one-mile-long lens-shaped body in a rhyolite porphyry, and geologically resembles the Kiruna deposit of Sweden. Magnetite is the chief ore mineral but some hematite is present. Much of the crude ore is reported to average about 55 per cent of iron with from 0.4 to 1.0 per cent of phosphorus. To reduce the phosphorus content, the crude ore will be concentrated magnetically after grinding from 70 to 80 per cent minus 325 mesh. The product will be a high-grade pellet. Mining will be by underground methods, beginning about 1700 feet below the surface.

The filled-sink deposits occur in limestones of early Ordovician age. Ore minerals include specular hematite and soft red hematite which may be alteration products of earlier pyrite deposits. Nearly 4,000,000 tons of ore had been produced from the filled-sink deposits up to 1945, but production since that date has amounted to only a few tons. The deposits are generally small, and not commercially important.

The brown iron ores are residual products from the weathering of Paleozoic limestones and dolomites and resemble the brown iron ores of the Russellville District of Alabama. Limonite is the chief ore mineral but hematite may also occur in the ore. The crude ore contains large amounts of clay and chert and is concentrated by washing, jigging and heavy-media separation to between 51 and 58 per cent of iron (dry basis). Few brown-ore deposits exceed 75,000 tons in size. Mining is by open-pit methods.

SOUTHEASTERN UNITED STATES

Hematite Ores—Red hematite ores of Alabama, along with smaller reserves of limonite or brown ores of the southeastern states, constitute the largest known potential source of domestic ore outside the Lake Superior district. Largest of the known red-ore deposits occur in the Birmingham district adjacent to abundant fluxstone deposits in proximity to the principal Alabama coal fields. This favorable grouping of major raw materials has been largely responsible for the development of Birmingham as a steel-manufacturing center.

The red hematite ores, termed "red ores" in Alabama, occur in bedded deposits of sedimentary origin within the Clinton formation of Silurian Age. This formation extends throughout the entire length of the Appalachian Valley from Alabama to Canada, but only in the vicinity of Birmingham do the ore beds attain the thickness and quality required for commercial exploitation (see Figure 5—6).

In the Birmingham district, Clinton beds occupy the upper half of the Red Mountain formation which consists of shale and sandstone beds about 250 feet thick. All units of the formation are ferruginous to some degree but iron in sufficient concentration to be actually or potentially attractive as a source of commercial ore or concentrate occurs only at four principal horizons; these being the Irondale Seam, Big

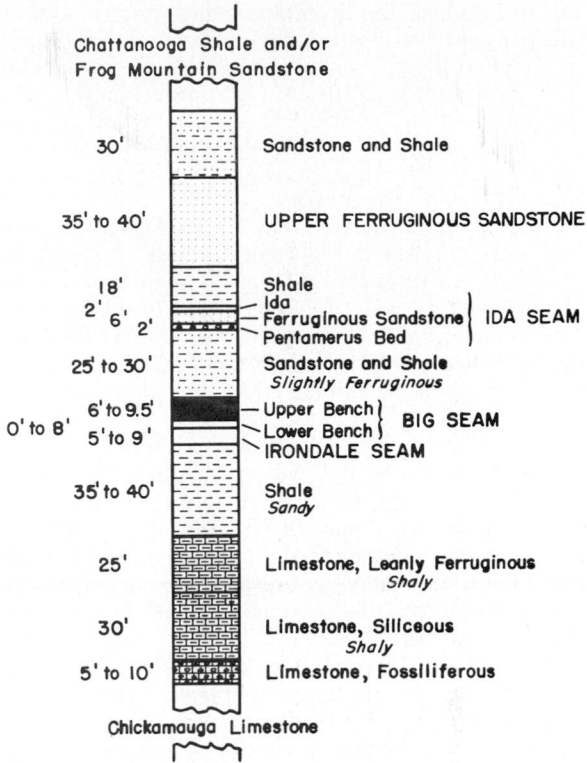

FIG. 5—7. Generalized columnar section of the Red Mountain Formation in the Birmingham District.

Seam, Ida Seam and Upper Ferruginous Sandstone. Distribution and thickness of these units are shown on Figure 5—7; average compositions in Table 5—IX.

In the vicinity of Birmingham, beds of commercial-grade ore vary in thickness between six feet and 9½ feet throughout a length of about 12 miles. The beds at surface dip 15 to 20 degrees toward the southeast, but flatten to low angles about a mile below the outcrop. Mining has extended nearly 3 miles down dip and is under about 1800 feet of cover.

Red ore has been mined at Birmingham almost continuously since about 1865. Between 1900 and the end of World War II, annual production averaged nearly 4 million tons. By selective mining of only the

Table 5—IX. Typical Compositions of Iron-Ore and and Ferruginous-Sandstone Beds of the Red Mountain Formation

	Composition			
Seam	Iron	Silica+ Alumina	Lime	Phosphorus
Upper Ferruginous Sandstone	23.2	54.9	4.3	0.08
Ida	31.0	43.7	4.1	0.16
Upper Bench Big Seam	36.7	18.1	14.9	0.32
Lower Bench Big Seam	30.6	29.8	13.4	0.26
Irondale	30.6	21.6	15.7	0.22

upper bench of Big Seam an average iron content of 37 per cent has been maintained. Despite the long production period, remaining reserves of commercial ore are adequate to sustain past production rates for an estimated 87 years. Untapped reserves of submarginal ores and ferruginous sandstones are approximately five times as large as the reserves of presently commercial ores.

Extending northeast from Birmingham, the red-ore beds outcrop intermittently across northeastern Alabama, northwestern Georgia, across eastern Tennessee and into western Virginia. The ores have been mined on a small scale in some localities, but the beds are usually too thin or the ore too low in iron content to permit profitable mining under prevailing economic conditions.

Brown Ores—The occurrence of brown ores, as shown in Figure 5—6, is widespread throughout most of the southeastern states. Historically, these ores have contributed about 14 per cent of the total ore consumed in southeastern furnaces and future reserves are estimated as adequate to maintain this proportion during the productive life of the Birmingham red-ore district.

Iron content of the brown ores varies between 40 per cent and 55 per cent; phosphorus between 0.27 per cent and 1 per cent; silica between 2 per cent and 28 per cent. The ore generally occurs as nodules, lumps and boulders in a residual clay matrix. Individual deposits are usually discontinuous and are invariably irregular and erratic in areal extent and thickness. Concentration of ore in the host material varies widely.

Brown-ore deposits are worked by small-scale open-pit or stripping operations. Clay and sand are separated from bank material in log washers, followed by hand picking or heavy-media concentration to upgrade the shipping product.

Since the end of World War II, the use of high-grade imported ores has become increasingly important in the southern iron and steel industry. These foreign ores contain about 60 per cent of iron, are of uniform quality, and lend themselves particularly to the production of quality steel.

This trend has resulted in reduced production from mines of the Birmingham district and consequently has stimulated interest in development of methods to upgrade the iron content of these local ores. However, conventional beneficiation methods have so far failed to produce a red-ore concentrate containing more than 56 per cent of iron. Although the red ores respond to direct-reduction methods, these methods have so far failed to produce an economic product.

The iron ores of the southeastern states are of substandard grade when judged by either foreign or domestic standards. Future demand for these ores, therefore, will probably be limited to local markets unless methods can be developed to economically upgrade them so that they can compete in quality with other available ores. Incentive for continued research in this field will be provided by the presence of substantial ore reserves in the Birmingham district together with proximity of these reserves to other raw materials essential for steelmaking.

WESTERN UNITED STATES

Iron ore deposits in the western states are numerous, widely scattered, and of diverse origin. Although important as a source of supply for the western iron and steel industry, they do not begin to compare in size with the iron ranges in the Lake Superior District or with the "red ore" deposits of the Birmingham District. Most of them require a certain amount of concentration to reduce the quantity of contaminants and gangue minerals sufficiently to produce a satisfactory blast-furnace feed.

Because of the geographical location of the iron-ore deposits of the western states and their dependence on comparatively costly rail transportation, western iron-ore production is limited, for the most part, to the requirements of the local steel plants. Only a few mines are in a position to market their ore outside of their own particular district, notably the Eagle Mountain Mine in Southern California and several small operations in Nevada, which ship to Japan.

Table 5—X lists the five western integrated steel

Table 5—X. Blast Furnaces of the Western United States and Their Principal Sources of Iron Ore Supply.

Plant	Location	Source of Iron Ore
Fontana	California	Eagle Mountain Mine, California; and Nevada
Pueblo	Colorado	Sunrise Mine, Wyoming; and Iron Springs District, Utah
Geneva-Ironton	Utah	Iron Springs District, Utah; and Atlantic City Mine, Wyoming.
Houston	Texas	Brown Ore from Northeastern Texas, Mexico, and Chile
Daingerfield	Texas	Brown Ore from Northeastern Texas

plants and their usual source of supply for iron ore. These plants have an aggregate capacity of somewhat less than six million net tons of iron. Because of this limited market, only a few of the many western iron-ore deposits are being actively exploited, the principal ones being as follows:

Eagle Mountain, California—The Eagle Mountain contact-metamorphic iron-ore deposits occur as replacements in limestone and dolomite horizons interbedded with quartzite. The sediments were domed and intruded by granitic and related rocks, resulting in a long east-west alignment with steep dips and considerable faulting. Contact metamorphism before introduction of iron mineralization resulted in the formation of serpentine, garnet, pyroxene, mica, pyrite, and other minerals in the lime rocks. The subsequent introduction of iron was accompanied by more pyrite, tremolite, mica and garnet. These minerals replaced the lime rocks but not the pre-existing skarn minerals so that the present occurrence of iron mineralization, originally magnetite, is very irregular and was restricted to the replacement of the irregularly distributed remnant carbonates. Numerous diabase dikes, intruded subsequent to mineralization, tend to further contaminate the orebodies. Subsequent surface weathering oxidized magnetite to hematite, and pyrite to limonite with locally varying amounts of gypsum. The oxidized zones extend downward from 3,000 feet above sea level to below sea level. The lower-lying orebodies are now buried beneath unconsolidated desert alluvium which ranges in thickness to more than 1,000 feet. Figure 5—8 shows diagramatically a cross-section of a part of the Eagle Mountain ore deposit.

Open-pit mining commenced in August 1948 on the well-oxidized ores of direct-shipping grade. Pit depths exceeded 200 feet. The ore ranged from 30 per cent up to 65 per cent of iron (dry basis) and averaged 52.5 per cent of iron (dry basis). As mining continued, ores of higher sulphur content were encountered, and had to be sintered.

Current operations comprise an open-pit, which will ultimately be about 8,000 feet long, and a concentrator that treats crushed ore of minus one-inch size. To produce uniformity in the feed for concentration, the ore is bedded and reclaimed, after which it is screened and the coarser sizes are concentrated magnetically. The magnetic concentrate is then ready for shipment. The non-magnetic portion of the coarse ore is concentrated by heavy-media methods. The fines and crushed middlings from the heavy-density plant are treated in jigs. The cut-off grade for mill feed has been lowered to 20 per cent of iron, and the shipping grade now averages about 58.5 per cent of iron (nat-

ural basis). This ore is shipped to the Fontana blast furnaces. Sintering is done at Fontana.

Mineral Basin, Nevada—Several small deposits are being mined as open pits in the Buena Vista area of Mineral Basin, about 20 miles southeast of Lovelock. The largest deposits are not now in operation. All of the deposits are of contact-metamorphic origin as replacements of meta volcanics. Unlike most contact-metamorphic deposits, which usually contain skarn minerals, the principal gangue minerals are scapolite and hornblende. Three types of mineralization are apparent: (1) Small, high-grade, non-Bessemer, direct-shipping orebodies, which are replacement deposits resembling veins in faulted or sheared zones, (2) Disseminated mineralization extending outward from and between iron-rich zones. This accounts for most of the tonnage potential, (3) Crackled or brecciated zones having narrow vein-like fracture filling. In these veins the magnetite is usually coarse-grained and is associated with apatite, often in large crystals.

Texas Brown Ores—These ores are found in many small deposits scattered over 22 counties of northeastern Texas, largely easterly and southwesterly from Daingerfield. The Sabine River divides the deposits into what is referred to as the North and South Basins.

These ores are of sedimentary origin and occur near the tops of flat-topped, sand-covered hills characteristic of much of the landscape of eastern Texas. The North Basin deposits occur in green-sand composed of a mixture of a granular iron-silicate mineral termed glauconite, in part altered to limonite and siderite and mixed with varying quantities of quartz,

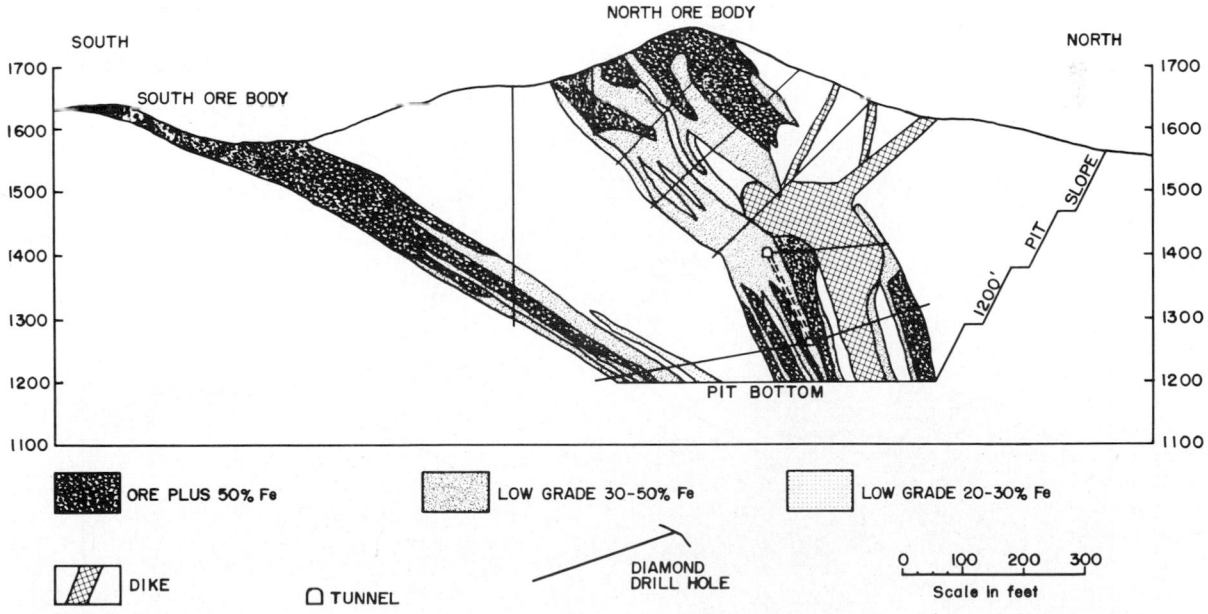

Fig. 5—8. Section through North and South orebodies of the Eagle Mountain iron mine, Riverside County, California. Two ore-bearing calcareous beds, 40 to 80 and 90 to 400 feet wide, are separated by 50 to 250 feet of quartzite. (Adapted from section and data originating with K. B. Powell, Superintendent of Raw Materials, Kaiser Steel Corporation, and published in Bulletin 176, "Mineral Commodities of California," by California Department of Mines, 1957.)

sand and clay. The glauconite sands range up to 100 feet in thickness and average about 25 feet, and include a weathered, limonite-rich zone averaging 9 feet thick. The sands of the South Basin contain abundant marine fossils with much glauconitic clay and much less quartz sand. These sands were deposited in deeper water than those of the North Basin and contain more limonite as laminated and massive ore. These shallow deposits in the aggregate are estimated to contain an indicated and potential reserve of 200 million tons.

The as-mined ores range from 12 per cent to 34 per cent of iron. They are concentrated to an average grade of about 42 per cent of iron before shipment. The ores from North Basin are used at a blast furnace at Daingerfield (Lone Star Steel Company). A blast furnace at Houston (Sheffield Division, Armco Steel Corporation) receives ore shipments from both Basins.

Iron Springs District—This district is located in southwestern Utah near Cedar City. The iron deposits are of contact metamorphic origin and, in large part, have replaced a limestone horizon intruded by three laccoliths, now partially eroded and termed "Iron Mountain," "Desert Mound," and "Three Peaks" (See Figure 5—9). These laccoliths, consisting of quartz monzonite, domed the overlying sediments, and, except for pre-intrusive folding and faulting, the quartz monzonite now forms the footwall of the limestone horizon with the regularity of a sill. In general, the limestone horizon now forms an eastward-dipping ring around the quartz monzonite cores of the laccoliths. The principal orebodies are replacement deposits in the limestone. In places the ore extends from

foot- to hanging wall and ranges in composition from 35 to 65 per cent of iron. An overlying siltstone where crackled or broken, often contains veinlets of magnetite. This lean ore averages about 22 per cent of iron. In addition, there is a series of small high-grade veins of magnetite with crystals of apatite in the quartz monzonite. Figure 5—10 gives an idealized cross-section of an Iron Springs ore body.

The gangue minerals in the Iron Springs District are unusual for a contact-metamorphic deposit. The "usual" skarn minerals, garnet, pyroxene and lime silicates, are scarce. The principal gangue minerals are mica, some apatite and locally pyrite with unreplaced limestone and impure limestone at its base and top.

The largest orebody including high- and low-grade ore contains about 100,000,000 tons of measured and inferred ore. Others, now partly mined, ranged up to more than 60,000,000 tons. The entire district is credited with a potential of 340 million tons, including high- and low-grade ore and some ore which may require underground-mining methods.

Some of the ore is now being concentrated to upgrade it and to lower the content of phosphorus. Reducing the mica content will also lower the percentage of sodium and potassium.

The ore now produced in the Iron Springs District is shipped to Pueblo, Colorado, and to Geneva-Ironton, Utah. Formerly, some ore was shipped to Fontana.

Shipping grades averaged 49 per cent to 55 per cent of iron, with concentrates better than 60 per cent of iron. The orebodies are of non-Bessemer grade.

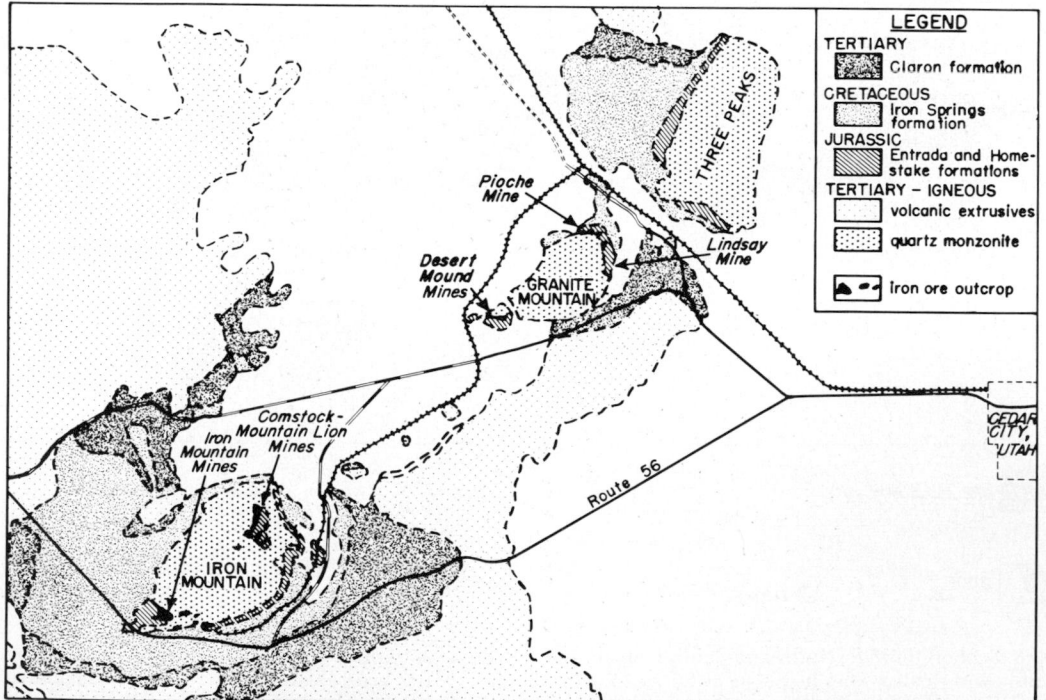

FIG. 5—9. Geologic map of the area of southwestern Utah in which the iron mines discussed in the text are located.

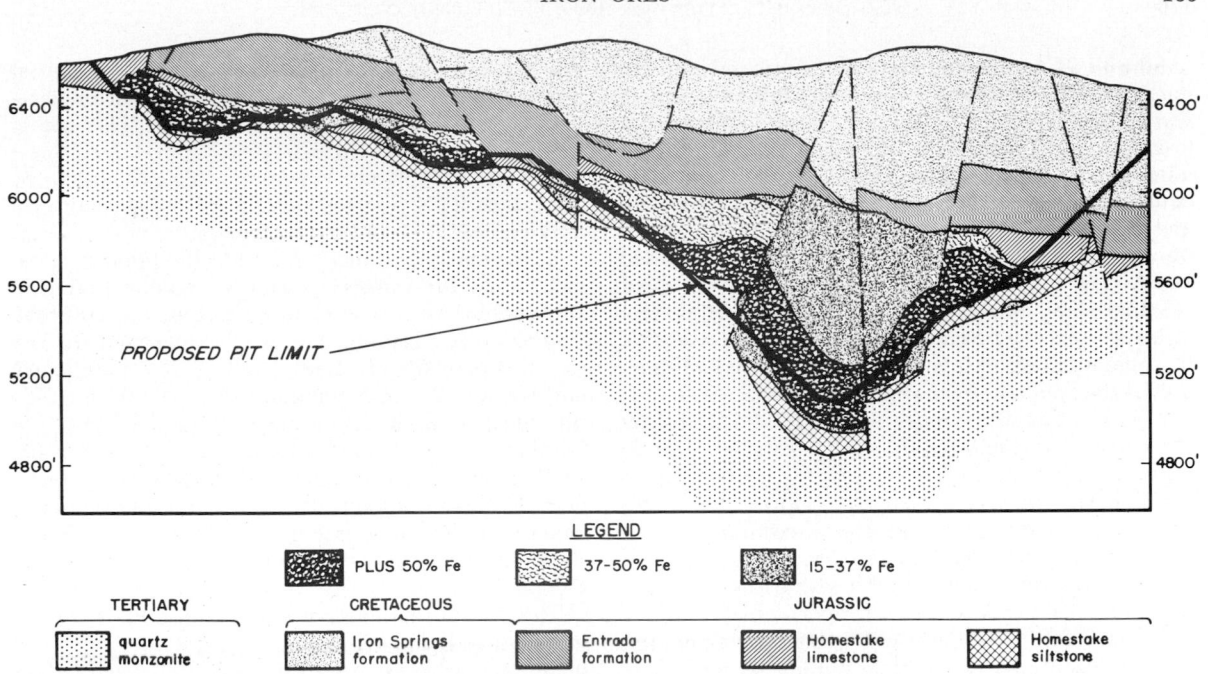

LEGEND

PLUS 50% Fe   37-50% Fe   15-37% Fe

TERTIARY   CRETACEOUS   JURASSIC

quartz monzonite   Iron Springs formation   Entrada formation   Homestake limestone   Homestake siltstone

FIG. 5—10. Idealized cross-section of an Iron Springs ore body.

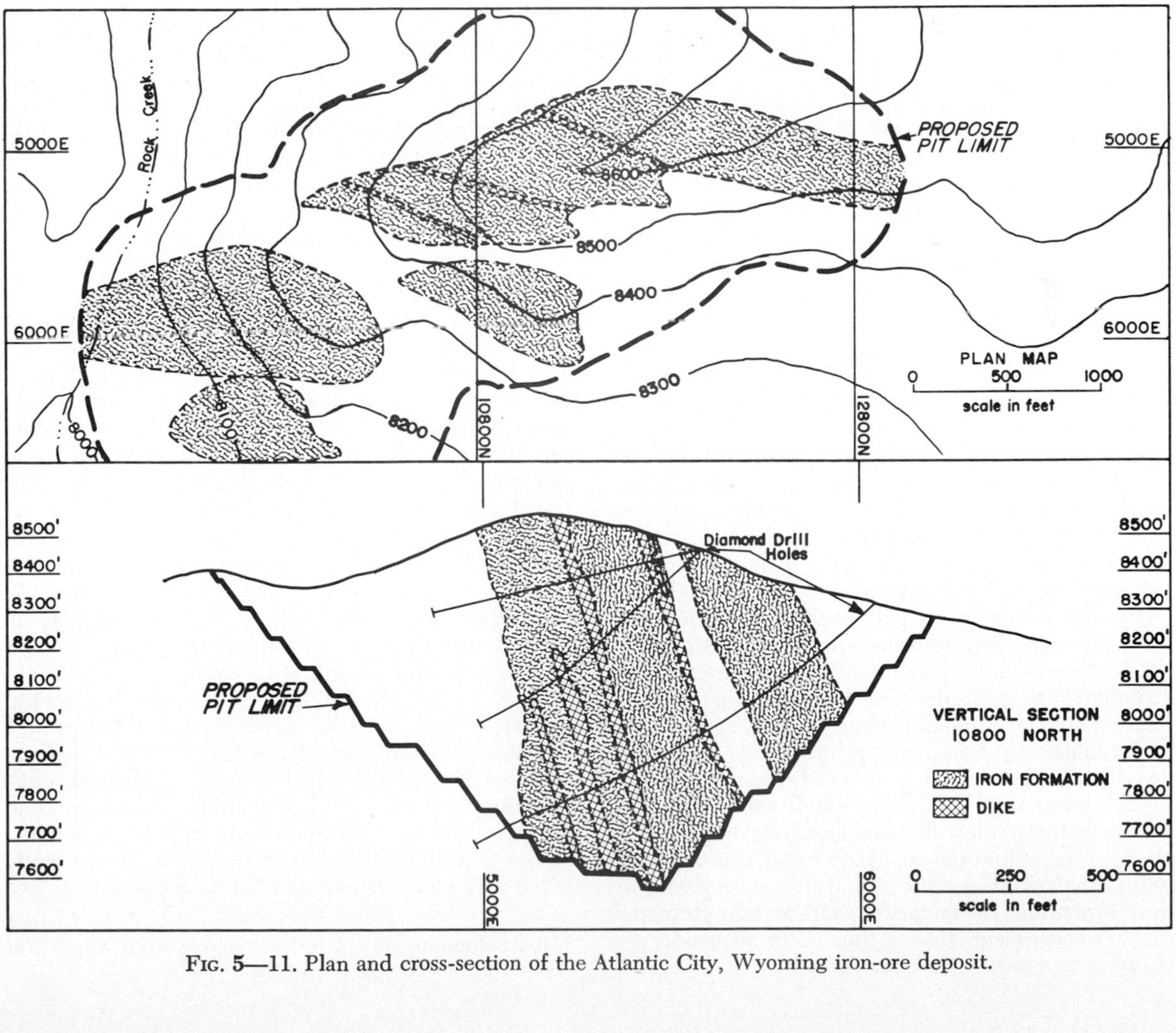

FIG. 5—11. Plan and cross-section of the Atlantic City, Wyoming iron-ore deposit.

Sunrise Mine, Wyoming—The Sunrise Mine is in the Hartville iron district of southeastern Wyoming, seven miles north of Guernsey. The orebodies occur in Pre-Cambrian iron formation associated with dolomite, quartzite and schist. The ore is soft and hard hematite which grades into lean banded siliceous ore and ferruginous chert, with carbonate pinite schist, pyritic graphitic schist, and dark-colored banded jasper. The orebodies vary from a few feet to about 100 feet wide, and some extend more than 1,000 feet in length. In many respects, these orebodies resemble the hematite-ore occurrences in Archean iron formation at the Soudan Mine, Minnesota.

The Pre-Cambrian rocks in the Hartville district are overlain unconformably by horizontal or gently dipping Mississippian limestone, which ranges up to 300 feet in thickness. Near the Sunrise Mine this limestone contains detrital masses of reworked hematite and secondary copper ore. Both hematite and copper ore outcropped at surface, and the first mining from 1880 to 1887 was for copper.

Subsequently, the iron was mined by open pit, followed by shafts to facilitate mining by glory-hole methods. With increased depth, sub-level-caving and block-caving methods were employed. At present, all mining is by the block-caving method. In mining by this method, there is some dilution of the better ore.

The grade of ore as shipped is about 51.0 per cent of iron, 14.00 per cent of silica, 0.07 per cent of phosphorus, and 0.05 per cent of sulphur. This ore is shipped to Pueblo.

Atlantic City Mine, Wyoming—The Atlantic City iron deposit is located about 26 miles south of Lander, near the Continental Divide.

This iron occurrence is a steeply dipping metamorphosed Pre-Cambrian iron formation ranging in stratigraphic thickness from 35 to possibly 200 feet. Complex drag folding has locally thickened the ore to more than 500 feet in width. It is exposed in a north-south direction for more than 10,000 feet. To the northward it is overlain, unconformably, by Cambrian quartzite and limestone. It lenses out to the southward and is interbedded with quartz, mica, hornblende and andalusite schists. Faulting is prominent with associated metagabbro dikes. Figure 5—11 shows the Atlantic City ore deposit in plan and cross-section.

This iron formation averages about 30 per cent of iron and is being mined by open-pit methods. The mined material is concentrated and pelletized before shipment to Geneva-Ironton. These pellets average about 61.6 per cent of iron (natural). The reserves of crude ore have been estimated at more than 100,000,-000 tons.

B. IRON-ORE DEPOSITS OF CANADA

Canada, which until recently imported most of its iron-ore requirements, is fast developing into a major source of iron ore for both domestic use and for export; in fact, in 1961 it ranked second only to Sweden in tonnage of ore sold in the international iron-ore market. The four principal sources of iron ore in Canada are: the Quebec-Labrador Region, the Northern Shore of the Great Lakes, the Coast of British Columbia, and by-product iron (see Figure 5—12).

QUEBEC-LABRADOR REGION

Much of the recent increase in production and the great bulk of the reserves are located in the Labrador Trough or Geosyncline, which comprises a broad belt of intensely folded and faulted Pre-Cambrian (Proterozoic) metasediments. This belt extends in an irregular arc from Lake Mistassini on the southwest to the northeast tip of Ungava Peninsula near Payne Bay, a distance of roughly 1,000 miles (see Figure 5—12).

Iron formation forms part of the regular sedimentary sequence, and is exposed in many places along the western boundary of the belt. In the eastern part sediments are generally less abundant and are interbanded with volcanic intrusives.

A typical sequence includes quartzites and quartz conglomerates succeeded upward by red to gray-black slates, iron formation, black slates and gray to greenish argillites; in some localities dolomite and chert occur below the quartzite or as thin members within the red-black slate and argillites overlying the iron formation. Secondary bands of iron formation may also occur from time to time in the sequence, presumably as a result of cyclic deposition.

The degree of metamorphism controls the mineralogical characteristics and grain size of the rocks and affects, correspondingly, the economic potentialities of the iron formation. Ordinarily, from the central part of the belt—characterized by the Knob Lake area and stretching north from Sawbill Lake to Finger Lake—the grade of metamorphism increases to north, south and southwest. Thus, characteristic ferruginous argillite, cherty magnetite-silicate-carbonate facies, jasper-magnetite-hematite facies and cherty iron silicate-carbonate beds in the Knob Lake area show gradual conversion to related coarse-grained silicate-carbonate-oxide facies to the south in the Wabush Lake-Mt. Reed-Mt. Wright region and as far west as Matonipi Lake. A similar metamorphic transition takes place northward from Finger Lake to Hopes Advance Bay and beyond in the isolated basins of Payne Bay and Armand Lake. The isolated basin in the Mistassini-Albanel Lake area bears iron formation and related rocks of similar metamorphic grade to those of the central part of the main trough, i.e., typical of the Knob Lake area.

It is within the low-grade metamorphic central portion of the belt that the typical direct-shipping* hematite-goethite ores of the Knob Lake type have developed as a result of silica leaching and the redistribution of iron. Within the highly metamorphosed northern and southwestern extensions large deposits of coarse-grained itabirite occur. These are presently being exploited or prepared for development. In the

---

*Direct-shipping ores are those that can be shipped as mined, without any beneficiation.

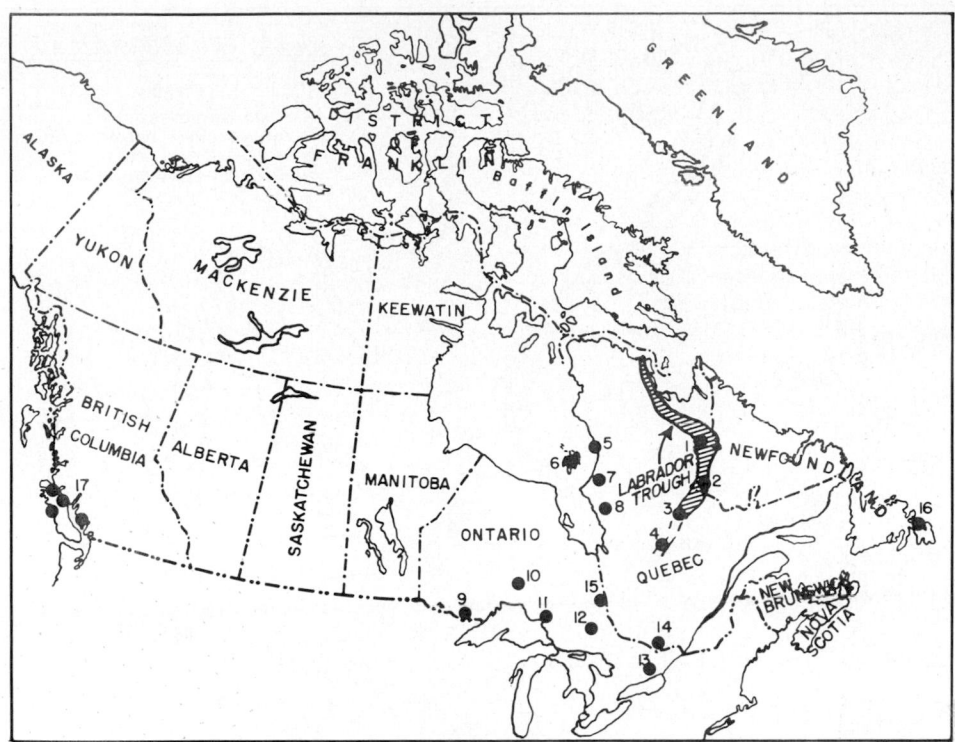

Fɪɢ. 5—12. Map showing location of the principal sources of iron ore in Canada.

LEGEND

1. Knob Lake
2. Wabush-Carol Lake-Mt. Wright
3. Gagnon
4. Mistassini-Albanel
5. Nastapoka Islands
6. Belcher Islands

7. Great Whale
8. Eastmain
9. Steep Rock Lake
10. Nakina
11. Michipicoten
12. Moose Mountain

13. Marmora
14. Hilton
15. Boston Township
16. Wabana
17. British Columbia

southern part of the belt the Carol Lake and Wabush Lake deposits are under development and the Lac Jeannine deposit is in production. In the north, near Hopes Advance Bay, studies are being made by several mining companies preparatory to development.

Within the Labrador Trough is a tremendous potential reserve of iron ore. Exploration has disclosed a number of important deposits, and many others will undoubtedly be discovered and developed in the future. The more important producing mines and those being actively developed for near-future production are described below.

Knob Lake Deposits—Within the low-grade iron formations of the central Quebec-Labrador Geosyncline, numerous commercial deposits of direct shipping hematite-goethite ore occur along a 12 by 90 mile belt in the Knob Lake region. Average grade of these deposits is 53 per cent of iron. It is generally accepted that these enriched deposits have developed through iron leaching and redistribution by groundwater action, localized by folding, faulting and brecciation in the steeply dipping iron-bearing members. The general ore area lies 360 rail-miles north of Seven Islands.

All told some 44 enriched iron-ore deposits ranging in size from one to 40 million tons have been located in the area, with total reserves of open-pit direct-ship-

ping ore approaching 800 million tons of crude ore.

Ore production began on July 31, 1954; since that date over 70 million long tons of this ore have been produced from six pits. Of this total, about 80 per cent is of non-Bessemer grade, with the balance about equally divided between Bessemer and manganiferous grades.

Mined ore is transported by rail to Seven Islands during the 200-day shipping season and thence by lake or ocean-going vessel. In recent years, these ores have been shipped mainly to ports of the United States and to European ports in the ratio of 3:1, respectively, with only a small amount going to Canadian consumers. Exports to Great Lakes and Atlantic ports of the United States have been approximately equivalent.

Recently, an ore-drying plant with a daily capacity of 300 long tons has been installed at Seven Islands, and consideration is being given to construction of a washplant at Schefferville.

Deposits in the Wabush Lake-Mt. Wright Area—This area lies some 40-50 miles west of Mile 230 on the North Shore and Labrador Railway. There are a number of important orebodies in this area now under development, including the Carol Lake Mine of Iron Ore Company of Canada and the Wabush Lake Mine of Wabush Iron Company.

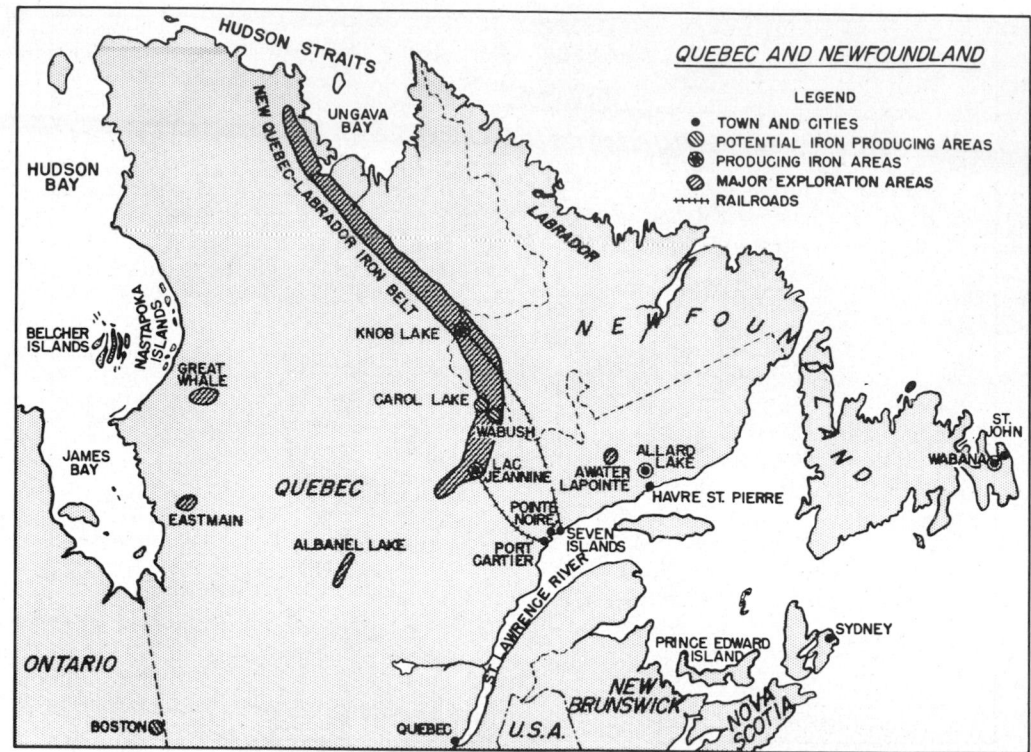

Fig. 5—13. Potential iron-producing areas, major exploration areas, and areas currently producing iron ore in Quebec and Newfoundland.

The orebodies of this area occur in intensely folded and faulted iron formation. The ore, in general, is a friable, granular, magnetite-hematite-quartz mixture that lends itself to autogenous grinding and gravity concentration. The iron content of the ore is typically 35 to 37 per cent. Reserves of open-pit ore are large— over 2 billion tons.

The Carol Lake project is designed to produce 7 million gross tons of concentrates grading about 66 per cent of iron, 4 per cent of silica, with phosphorus less than 0.1 per cent. A large part of this production will be pelletized.

The Wabush Lake Iron Company has announced plans for an annual production of some 5.5 million tons of concentrates commencing in 1965. Other important reserves are still in the exploration and planning stages.

Deposits in the Gagnon Area—Quebec Cartier Mining Company (a subsidiary of United States Steel Corporation) is operating a mine at Lac Jeannine with designed annual capacity for 8 million tons of concentrate. The orebody is located in the folded iron formation and is composed of a friable coarse-grained hematite-quartz itabirite containing about 30 per cent of iron. Prepared ore is processed in spirals to produce a concentrate containing 66 per cent of iron which is shipped 193 miles over the Cartier Railway to the all-year shipping port of Port Cartier.

Deposits in the Hudson Bay Area—Lake Superior-type iron formation occurs along the east coast of Hudson Bay, notably on the Belcher and Nastapoka Islands in the southwest part of Hudson Bay and in the Great Whale and Eastmain areas to the east. Pre-

liminary exploration drilling has evidenced considerable tonnages of siliceous hematite-magnetite ores containing 30 to 40 per cent of iron, susceptible of open-pit extraction and concentration to an acceptable blast-furnace feed. High transportation costs have deterred further development.

NORTH SHORE OF GREAT LAKES

A number of iron-ore deposits are being worked in this area. These may be divided roughly between those tributary to Lake Superior and those located in southeastern Ontario and adjacent parts of Quebec. Among the former are the Steep Rock Lake, Nakina, and Michipicoten ranges. In the latter category are included the Moose Mountain, Marmora, Hilton, and Boston Township areas. In addition are three sources of by-product iron, namely, International Nickel's operations at Sudbury, Noranda Mines, and Allard Lake.

Steep Rock Lake Area—The Steep Rock iron deposit is located three miles north of Atikokan, Ontario, and 140 miles west of Lake Superior at Port Arthur. Iron-bearing materials were reported in the area as early as 1889; but the Steep Rock ore body, situated under the waters of Steep Rock Lake, was not discovered until 1938. Production started in 1944 with 25,133,000 gross tons shipped through 1960. Shipments in 1960 totaled 2,462,000 gross tons. Iron mining in this area required the diversion of the Seine River, draining of Steep Rock Lake, which had a surface area of 7 square miles, and the removal of over 100 million cubic yards of silt and overburden. Mining is in progress in the Hogarth, Errington, and Roberts deposits by Steep Rock Iron Mines, Ltd., and in the Falls Bay ("C" orebody) area by the Caland Ore Company, a subsidiary of the Inland Steel Company. Major ore production is by open-pit mining with some underground production from the Errington mine.

Rocks of the Steep Rock area include an older granite upon which was deposited a thick Timiskamian series of conglomerate, dolomite, flows, tuffs, and agglomerates which are intruded by basic dikes and sills. The rocks are steeply dipping to the south and are cut by several faults. The iron ores occur in a zone between the dolomite and an overlying "ashrock." The ore zone is from 75 to 200 feet in width and has a maximum length of six miles, with mining developments along about four miles of the strike length.

The iron ore consists largely of goethite (limonite) with some hematite. Locally hematite is the principal mineral. The ore is porous and rather friable with bands and seams of dense, massive hematite and limonite with a variety of brecciated, fragmental, vuggy, and colloform structures. In general, five types of materials are found within the ore zone: (1) merchantable ore; (2) manganiferous ore; (3) painty ore; (4) siliceous ore; and (5) high-sulphur ore. Ores are shipped which include Caland lump and Raymond grade, shipped by Caland Ore Company, and Seine River, coarse or fines, or unscreened, shipped by Steep Rock Iron Mines, Ltd. These ores contain from 56 to 59 per cent of iron (dry basis), 6 to 10 per cent of silica, and less than 0.04 per cent of phosphorus, with 3 to 9 per cent of moisture.

Part of the iron ore at the Steep Rock Mine is treated in two beneficiation plants where the material is washed, screened, and separated by gravity methods including jigs, heavy media, and spirals. Research work is continuing on these ores with a study in progress of the technical feasibility of producing agglomerates. Reserves of Steep Rock deposits have been estimated to be in the order of 250 million gross tons of shipping-grade material to a depth of 1,000 feet with some ore shown by drilling to a depth of 2,000 feet.

Nakina Range—Anaconda Iron Ore, Ltd., has been testing an occurrence of low-grade iron ore lying about 140 miles north of Schreiber on Lake Superior. The ore occurs in an area of intricately folded Pre-Cambrian rocks. It is reported that there are over 350 million tons of open-pit ore grading 25 to 30 per cent of iron that can be processed to produce a high-grade concentrate. The possibility of transporting the concentrate by pipeline to Lake Superior is under study.

Michipicoten Range—This range is located about 12 miles east of Lake Superior at Michipicoten Harbor between the towns of Wawa and Hawk Junction, Ontario. It was discovered in 1898. Production from 1900 to 1918 was hematitic and limonitic ore from the Helen mine which bottomed in siderite. The mine was reopened in 1939 by the Algoma Ore Properties, Division of the Algoma Steel Corporation, Ltd., to mine the siderite ore. Since 1939, siderite has been produced from the Helen, Victoria, Alexander, Sir James, and MacLeod mines, with some hematite production from the Josephine mine. The Victoria, St. James, and MacLeod mines are currently active. Mining is by underground and open-pit methods. Production through 1960 totaled about 23,640,000 gross tons.

The iron-bearing rocks of the Michipicoten Range include siderite, pyrite, and banded-carbonate iron formation enclosed in steeply dipping Keewatin flows and pyroclastics. The area is cut by a number of northwest trending major faults which have broken the range into a series of major faulted segments that are from 1½ to 3 miles long. The important ore deposits occur as tabular bodies, from 40 to 350 feet in width and up to 6,000 feet in length, of fine-grained, dense, gray siderite with some disseminated pyrite.

The siderite ore commonly contains about 35 per cent of iron and 2.2 per cent of manganese. It is sintered to yield a product containing approximately 50.6 per cent of iron, 0.015 per cent of phosphorus, 11.0 per cent of silica, 2.8 per cent of manganese, 2.0 per cent of alumina, 4.3 per cent of lime, 7 per cent of magnesium, and 0.10 per cent of sulphur. Pyrite is used to some extent as a fuel in sintering. About 60 per cent of the product is shipped by rail to the Algoma Steel Plant at Sault Ste. Marie, Ontario, and the balance is shipped by boat to other consumers. The sinter facilities for calcining the siderite ore are located near Wawa. Production in 1961 totaled 1,600,000 gross tons of sinter. Reserves are estimated to be in excess of 100 million gross tons.

Moose Mountain District—This district is located 35 miles northwest of Sudbury, Ontario, and 80 miles north of Georgian Bay. Iron ore was discovered here in about 1900. During the period from 1908 to 1914, an unsuccessful endeavor was made to mine ore that could be shipped direct. Subsequently, in the period 1917-1920, attempts were made to produce briquettes from a finely ground magnetic concentrate. This was also unsuccessful. Finally, in 1959, property was again placed in production by Lowphos Ore Ltd., a subsidiary of Hanna Iron Ore Division of National Steel Corporation, after construction of a modern concentration plant designed to use magnetic-separation methods. The plant has an annual capacity of 500,000 gross tons.

The deposit consists of magnetite-taconite iron formation of Keewatin age which occurs as tabular lenses enclosed in greenstones. The iron formation is a hard, dense, fine-grained, thin-bedded rock composed of fine-grained magnetite and quartz with minor pyrite and iron silicates which commonly contains about 30 per cent of iron. The iron-formation lenses are from 30 to 250 feet in width and up to 7000 feet in length. The rocks strike generally northwesterly and dip at angles from 70 to 90 degrees. Rocks in this area are locally intruded by diabase dikes.

The Lowphos Ore Ltd. currently is shipping iron-ore concentrates which contained in 1961, on a dry basis, 66.3 per cent of iron, 0.017 per cent of phosphorus, 7.2 per cent of silica; or, on a natural basis, 59.6 per cent of iron with 10.1 per cent of moisture. The ore moves by rail 150 miles to Depot Harbor on Georgian Bay.

Production in 1961 amounted to 580,000 tons of concentrate.

Marmora Mine—Fine-grained, disseminated magnetite occurs with chlorite-epidote-garnet skarn and pyroxenite amphibolite rocks in steeply dipping metamorphosed impure limestones and quartzite of Pre-Cambrian age at the Marmora deposit in Hastings County, Ontario. The sediments near the deposit have been intruded by massive syenite-diorite and fine-grained diabase. The deposit, which was overlain by approximately 125 feet of undisturbed Ordovician sediments and Pleistocene glacial debris, was discovered by an aero-magnetic survey in 1950. The principal magnetic-bearing zone, averaging 37 per cent of iron, is a steeply dipping, lenticular body about 2,400 feet long by 400 feet thick.

The ore is mined by open-pit methods, crushed, cobbed, and concentrated magnetically and made into pellets. Production commenced in 1955, and in 1961 amounted to 440,000 tons of pellets containing 64 per cent of iron. Reserves are reported to be sufficient to maintain the present production rate for at least 20 years.

The mine is owned and operated by the Marmoraton Mining Company, Ltd., which is a wholly-owned subsidiary of the Bethlehem Steel Company. Most of the production is shipped to the Lackawanna Plant in Buffalo, either all rail or by vessel via Picton, Ontario.

Hilton Mines—Discontinuous lenses and veinlets of medium-grained, magnetite-bearing amphibolites occur in metamorphosed impure limey and quartzose sediments of Pre-Cambrian age in Bristol Township, Quebec, about 45 miles northwest of Ottawa. The magnetite occurs intermittently over a length of 2,500 feet and width of 500 feet. The strata dip gently 60 degrees to the northeast. Martite and red hematite occur with the magnetite, as does some fine-grained pyrite and chalcopyrite. Granite occurs north of the deposit. Metasediments in the area have been intruded by diorite-syenite and pegmatite dikes which sometimes cut and dilute the ore zone considerably.

The ore, containing 18 to 20 per cent of iron, is mined by open-pit methods, crushed, and magnetically cobbed and concentrated and made into pellets containing some 65 per cent of iron.

The deposit was known previously as the Bristol Mine and shipped small tonnages of ore from 1872 to 1894. The mine then remained inactive until 1956. At this time, Hilton Mines, Ltd., owned by the Steel Company of Canada and Bristol Quebec Mining Company, started the present operation. Annual capacity is 800,000 tons of pellets, all of which are shipped via rail to plants in Canada and the United States.

Boston Township Mine—The Jalore Mining Company, Ltd., a subsidiary of Jones & Laughlin Steel Corporation, is actively developing a source of iron ore in Boston Township, six miles southeast of Kirkland Lake, Ontario.

The iron formation in this area is thinly banded, with fine-grained chert and magnetite, and occurs as a number of lenticular zones in the volcanics. The crude ore contains about 25 per cent of iron and is minable by open-pit methods.

Jalore plans to produce about 1 million tons annually, commencing in 1964. The ore will be shipped all rail to affiliated plants in the United States.

NEWFOUNDLAND

Wabana—Oölitic hematite - siderite - chamosite (Clinton type) iron formation occurs in gently dipping Ordovician sandstones and shaly sediments at Wabana on Bell Island in Conception Bay, Newfoundland. These sediments, including the three minable iron horizons, dip approximately 8 degrees to the north under Conception Bay. The lowest seam varies from 5 feet to 35 feet thick; the middle and upper seams, which vary from 5 feet to 13 feet in minable thickness, are 230 feet and 290 feet respectively above the lower seam.

These mines, active since 1895, are operated by the Dominion Steel and Coal Corporation. The ore, containing 49 per cent of iron, is mined by underground methods, crushed, and conveyed to the surface. Secondary crushing and heavy-media treatment are performed in surface installations to produce a shipping product assaying 50 per cent of iron and 0.9 per cent of phosphorus. Production in 1961 totaled 2,500,000 tons, about 80 per cent of which was sold in Europe, principally in the United Kingdom and West Germany. The balance is consumed locally in the company's steel plant at Sydney, Nova Scotia.

BRITISH COLUMBIA

There are numerous small contact-metamorphic deposits of iron ore along the coast of British Columbia, principally on Vancouver and Queen Charlotte Islands. Several of these are being mined to supply ore to Japan.

Geologically, these are more or less similar, one to another, and consist of disseminated magnetite in altered limestone along the contact of andesitic intrusives. The crude ore generally contains from 35 to 45 per cent of iron. It is mined in small open pits, and concentrated magnetically producing a concentrate containing 55 to 60 per cent of iron.

Principal currently producing mines are operated by Texada Mines Ltd., Empire Development Company, Ltd., and Nimkish Iron Mines Ltd., with near-future production planned by Silver Standard Mines, Ltd., Zeballos Iron Mines, Ltd., and Noranda Exploration Company. Annual production rates run

Table 5—XI. Iron and Iron-Oxide By-Products Recovered by Canadian Non-Ferrous Metal Producers.

Company	Principal Product	By-Product	Iron Content (%)
International Nickel Company	Nickel	Iron-oxide pellets	68
Noranda Mines, Ltd.	Copper	Iron-oxide sinter	68
Consolidated Mining	Lead-zinc	Pig iron	—
Falconbridge Nickel	Nickel	Iron-oxide pellets	67–68
Quebec Iron and Titanium	Titanium	Pig iron	—

around 200,000 to 400,000 tons, and the ore reserves for any one mine are small, generally less than 5,000,-000 tons. However, in the aggregate, these mines can supply 1 to 2 million tons of concentrate annually to the Japanese steel industry.

CANADIAN BY-PRODUCT IRON

In recent years, several base-metal mines in Canada have undertaken to treat their sulphide tailings to recover iron or iron oxide. A list of these producers is given in Table 5—XI on Page 174.

C. IRON-ORE DEPOSITS OF MEXICO

Mexico possesses a number of iron-ore deposits that are being worked to provide ore for the local steel industry, with a small tonnage exported to the United States for consumption in Texas. The various deposits may be divided into two general classifications: (a) contact-metamorphic deposits along the Pacific Coast; and (b) hematite replacement bodies in limestones or acidic intrusives in the central and eastern part of the country.

Contact-metamorphic deposits are found scattered along the entire length of the Pacific Coast from Sonora to Chiapas. Geologically, they are much alike, being formed in limestone along the contacts of diorite intrusives. The ore is largely magnetite with varying amounts of pyrite, mixed with iron silicates. In general, the individual deposits are small and irregular. In the aggregate, they represent a significant source of iron ore. However, their remoteness from centers of consumption has discouraged their development. The only actual production from the western coastal area is coming from a group of mines in the

vicinity of Colima, which supply ore to the Hojalata y Lamina plant in Monterrey.

The bulk of the Mexican iron-ore production comes from the Cerro de Mercado deposit near the city of Durango and from a group of small mines in Coahuila and Nuevo Leon that supply ore to the Altos Hornos de Mexico plant at Monclova.

The Cerro de Mercado deposit is by far the most important iron-ore mine in Mexico, both as to past and present production, and as to reserves. The ore consists of massive hematite with scattered crystals of apatite. It occurs in several irregular bodies closely associated with and overlying Tertiary rhyolite. The ore is mined in open pits and contains 63 to 65 per cent of iron, with as much as 0.5 per cent of phosphorus. Reserves are estimated at 60,000,000 to 100,-000,000 tons. The production, amounting to about 500,000 tons annually, is consumed in the Monterrey plant of the Cia. Fundidora de Fierro y Acero de Monterrey, with a small tonnage of sorted ore—120,-000 tons in 1961—exported to steel mills in Texas.

D. IRON-ORE DEPOSITS OF SOUTH AMERICA

The treatment of iron ores in this volume is that of a raw material for the United States' steel industry. Most of the ore consumed in this country comes from domestic or at least continental sources. However, ores from overseas sources are being consumed in increasing quantities, especially in seaboard plants. Accordingly, it seems appropriate to give a very summarized description of some deposits that now provide, or are expected soon to provide, significant tonnages of ore to furnaces in the United States.

VENEZUELA

The Venezuelan iron-ore deposits are associated with the itabirite-type rocks in the Sierra de Imataca, a series of ridges lying along the south bank of the Rio Orinoco and extending westward from the British Guiana boundary to about the Rio Caura. There are two types of orebodies: partial replacement (El Pao) and residual (in situ) deposits (Cerro Bolivar). The replacement ores are primarily compact, consisting of dense crystalline hematite with minor magnetite. The residual ores consist of granular hematite with surficial limonite canga cappings.

The measured reserves, much of them held by the Venezuelan Government as a national reserve, are 1.5 billion tons averaging about 60 per cent of iron. Mining is by open-pit methods and the ore is moved by rail to deep-water ports on the Rio Orinoco where it is loaded into ocean-going vessels and transported 170 miles down the river, enroute to its destination.

Production for 1961 was 14.5 million tons which came principally from the Cerro Bolivar and El Pao districts. Of this total, 10.5 million tons were exported to the United States, with the balance going to West Germany, the United Kingdom, and Italy.

PERU

The iron deposits of Peru are located along the contact zones of the Andean intrusive grano-diorite with which they are believed to be genetically related. They occur either in tabular-shaped orebodies, as contact-metamorphic replacements of calcareous zones within the enclosing rocks, or as disseminated magnetite in siliceous meta-sediments. The iron-bearing minerals of these ore deposits are primarily magnetite and hematite with occasional pyrite and traces of copper. In the near-surface zones (upper 25 meters or about 80 feet), the ores have been oxidized to hematite (martite)-limonite, with a corresponding leaching of sulphur.

The estimated reserves of the known ore deposits are 550 million tons of about 60 per cent iron content, all of which are located within a short distance of the coastal waters of Peru and hence are easily accessible.

The principal mining operation is at Marcona, where the ore is extracted by open-pit methods and transported to the coast by truck and conveyor belt. In the past, production has all been shipped in the form of natural ore. However, an ore-processing and pelletizing plant is being built to improve the grade and the quality of the ore from the Marcona deposits.

The total export production for Peru during the year 1961 was 5.5 million tons of which the largest production was from the Marcona and Acari deposits. Principal shipments were made to Japan, West Germany, and the United States. A local steel plant consumes 100,000 tons of iron ore a year.

CHILE

The principal iron-ore deposits of Chile are located along the western slopes of the Andes mountains over a 600-mile stretch between the provinces of Coquimbo and Antofagasta. These orebodies, except the recently studied El Laco deposit, are situated relatively close to coastal waters. El Laco is 186 airline miles east of Antofagasta at an elevation of 14,000 feet.

The ore deposits occur as magmatic segregations and replacement bodies related to the intrusive Andean grano-diorites. The ore is composed of massive magnetite-hematite with the gangue minerals of amphiboles and apatite. The El Laco deposit is reported to be associated with recent volcanic activity.

Estimated reserves are 190 million tons of measured ore and 260 million tons of indicated-inferred ore with an iron content of 61 per cent.

Total iron production in 1961 was 6.9 million tons, coming principally from the open-pit mining operations at Carmen, El Romeral, Huanteme, Algarrobo, Cerro Iman, and Las Andrianitas. Principal exports were to the United States, Japan, West Germany, and

Argentina. Approximately 80,000 tons were used in domestic steel plants.

BRAZIL

The largest iron-ore reserves in South America are found in Brazil in the Quadrilatero Ferrifero district of Minas Gerais. The ore deposits were developed in place by the leaching and secondary enrichment of the metamorphosed Pre-Cambrian sedimentary iron formation called itabirite. Mineralogically, the fresh itabirite is composed of hematite and quartz with minor magnetite. The ore is both compact and powdery hematite. Near the surface the orebodies are frequently hydrated and converted to canga caps of variable thickness (from 3 to somewhat over 30 feet).

Reserves exceed 17 billion tons of ore containing 60 to 68 per cent of iron, of which about 800 million can be classed as high-grade lump ore.

Production for 1961 was approximately 9 million tons, of which 75 per cent was for export. Principal producing mines were in Itabira, Casa de Pedra, Andrade, Mutuca, and the Rio Paraopeba valley. Principal markets were the United States, West Germany, United Kingdom, and Czechoslovakia. Domestic consumption was about 2 million tons, principally at the national steel plant at Volta Redonda.

Mining is by open-pit methods and transport is either by rail to Vitoria (292 miles) or by rail and truck to Rio de Janeiro (302 to 380 miles).

E. WEST AFRICAN DEPOSITS

Historically, most of the iron ore produced in West Africa has been marketed in Europe. Geographically, however, certain West African deposits are no further removed from the Eastern Seaboard of the United States than are the iron-ore deposits of Brazil, Chile, and Peru. In 1961, the Bomi Hills Mine in Liberia shipped over 700,000 tons of iron ore to furnaces in the United States, and it seems probable that other West African mines will enter the American market in the future. The most probable sources of ore are:

LIBERIA

Bomi Hills—Bomi Hills, 38 miles north of Monrovia, contains a high grade magnetite-hematite lens conformable to a sequence of Pre-Cambrian metasediments composed of chlorite schists and itabirites. Reserves are estimated at 50 million tons of lump ore containing over 67 per cent of iron and 250 million tons of combined furnace ore, fines containing more than 65 per cent of iron, and concentrating ore with an iron content of over 42 per cent. Mining is by open-pit methods and the ore is rail-hauled 42 miles to the port at Monrovia. Production of lump and furnace ore began in 1951. In 1958 concentrates were first produced from the itabirites associated with the ore. Total ore production in 1961 was 3.1 million tons, of which about one half was in the form of lump ore and the balance largely in the form of concentrates. Principal sales outlets were the United States,

Germany, the United Kingdom, and the Netherlands.

Mano River—The Mano River district, 75 miles north of Monrovia, contains several hills which are capped or flanked with aluminous limonite-hematite, earthy iron deposits which are conservatively estimated to contain 50 million tons of ore. The ore is extracted by open-pit mining methods and after washing (to an iron content of 56 to 58 per cent) is rail-hauled 90 miles to the port at Monrovia. Production began in late 1961 with an initial shipment of 15,000 tons to Germany. Facilities have been installed to support an annual production rate of 2.5 million tons. Expected markets for the ore are Germany, the United Kingdom, Italy, France, Belgium and Luxemburg.

Mt. Nimba—The Mt. Nimba, Liberia, iron-ore district is located 180 miles northeast of Monrovia, adjacent to the Ivory Coast-Guinea frontier. Five individual orebodies contain a proven reserve of 200 million tons of fine-grained Lake Superior-type hematite-limonite ore containing more than 60 per cent iron (on a natural basis), developed in-situ from Pre-Cambrian itabirites. LAMCO, which holds a concession in the Mt. Nimba deposit, proposes to start production in 1963. The mine will be developed by open-pit methods, and the ore will be hauled 165 miles over a new railroad to a deep-water port constructed at Lower Buchanan, near the mouth of the St. John's River. Facilities are being installed to support an eventual production rate of 7 million tons per year; first shipments to be made in 1963.

Probable sales outlets will be the United States, Germany, France, Italy and Belgium.

MAURITANIA

Fort Gouraud—The iron-ore deposits of the Kedru d'Idjil range are located in the western Sahara in the vicinity of Fort Gouraud. There are estimated reserves of 150 million tons of ore averaging 63 per cent of iron. The ores, which are composed of both blocky and finely crystalline hematite, are residual enrichments of the Pre-Cambrian itabirites with which they are associated.

Mining (expected to commence in 1963) will be by open-pit methods, and the ore will be hauled 410 miles by rail to a new deep-water port at Port Etienne. Production is forecast at 4 million tons annually, with anticipated sales to France, the United Kingdom, and Italy.

SECTION 3

ECONOMICS AND THE MARKETING OF IRON ORES

From the discussion of iron-ore reserves in Section 1 of this chapter, it is apparent that ample supplies of iron ore exist to provide the foreseeable requirements of the world for over 150 years, despite the anticipated increase in requirements that are expected to more than double within the next 30 years. Furthermore, there exist almost unlimited amounts of iron-bearing material that will become available as new mining and steelmaking techniques are perfected and transportation and handling costs are reduced. In short, there is no foreseeable over-all shortage of iron ore, although it is possible that local shortages of short duration may develop as a result of special situations.

With such an abundance of iron ore available, what is it that influences a furnace operator to use iron ore from one source as opposed to another source? When a furnace operator "goes shopping" for iron ore, he is not looking for the lowest cost merchandise, nor the best quality merchandise. Rather, the search is for that particular ore which will give the most value per dollar in the furnaces—in other words, an ore that will give the best "price-quality relationship," and by price is meant the price the operator must pay for iron ore delivered to the furnace or, in other words, the cost to him. This rather elementary concept is the all-important factor in both domestic and international iron-ore trade.

If this "price-quality relationship" is analyzed, it is found that the principal items that determine "price" are: first, mine costs—that is, the cost of producing the ore at the mine, including wages, supplies, royalties and taxes; and second, transportation costs—that is, the cost involved in moving the product from the mine to the furnace. The relative importance of these cost factors varies widely from case to case; but transportation, over which the producer generally has no control, is often the larger of the two.

On the quality side of the "price-quality relationship" a number of factors are involved, the most important, as described above, being the iron content of the ore; the ratio of acid to basic gangue constituents; the presence or absence of deleterious substances; the size consist and physical structure of the ore particles; and the ease with which the ore can be reduced.

From this concept of the economics of iron ore, it follows that furnace operators in one area may prefer iron ore from certain sources, while furnace operators in another area will select materials from entirely different sources; and this applies equally well to different plants within the same area and even to different furnaces within the same plant. The iron and steel industry is very selective in its purchases of iron ore and is becoming even more so as competition within the industry and from other industries forces the iron-and steelmaker to operate plants at their highest possible economic efficiency. Gone are the days when operators could economically accept the high slag volumes that result from the use of leaner ores and could build more furnaces to increase pig-iron output rather than attempt to get the utmost "hot metal" from the facilities available.

When considering the future ore supply for the iron and steel industry of the United States, recognition must be given to the basic factors outlined above—the ample supply of iron ore, the price-quality concept, and the importance of transportation as a cost item.

Although the United States has an estimated ore reserve of about seven billion tons of iron-in-ore, sufficient to provide its anticipated requirements for generations, it has in recent years become a major importer of iron ore. This apparently anomalous situation is the result of two postwar developments.

The first of these is the dispersal of ironmaking plants to areas far removed geographically from the major source of domestic ore, the Lake Superior district. This district which contains 80 per cent of the nation's iron-ore reserve, is strategically located to supply ore to the Lower Lakes steelmaking areas, such as Chicago, Detroit, and Cleveland, which account for about 50 per cent of the nation's steelmaking capacity. However, Lake Superior district ores are less favorably situated with respect to plants in the Pittsburgh-Youngstown area and on the Eastern, Western, and Gulf coasts or the Western interior, where much of the post-war steelmaking expansion occurred. These plants, accounting for about 50 per cent of the nation's capacity, must obtain their iron from inadequate or not too satisfactory local sources or from more distant sources, either the Lake Superior district or foreign mines. As already noted, transportation is an important factor in the delivered cost of iron ore. The use of especially designed, very large ocean-going vessels and complementary deep-draft ports and efficient ore-handling facilities have greatly reduced ocean-freight costs. Thus, it may cost no more to transport ore 2,000 miles by sea under favorable conditions than to transport it 100 miles by domestic rail lines. Hence, imported ores can in many cases be delivered to seaboard plants at costs comparable to or lower than the cost of local ores and considerably lower than the cost of Lake Superior ores at such plants.

The second reason for the increasing use of foreign ores is that it has been found generally to be more economical to increase production from existing furnaces by using higher quality raw materials, even at higher prices, than to construct new blast furnaces. Many foreign ores in their natural state are of better quality than our natural domestic ores, and accordingly, are preferred by furnace operators. As a consequence, foreign ores have to some extent replaced local ores in Birmingham and Texas, and Lake Superior ores in Pittsburgh.

The demand for high-quality iron ore has, in turn, led to some important recent developments in the domestic iron-ore industry itself. The historical iron content of Lake Superior ores has varied from 50 to 55 per cent iron with 8 to 10 per cent silica. In the early days of the Lake Superior district, the entire ore production was in the form of natural ores shipped directly to the blast furnace without beneficiation. However, a trend began in 1910 towards improving the quality of the natural ores by removing unwanted silica. This upgrading or "beneficiation" of natural ores was accomplished at first by a simple washing. Subsequently, other processes such as jigging and heavy-media separation have been brought into play, using gravity to effect a separation of silica from crude ores not amenable to simple washing. In 1960, 45 per cent of all natural ore shipped from the Lake Superior district had received some beneficiation. However, while such beneficiation made it possible for Lake Superior mines to maintain an average shipping grade of 50 to 55 per cent natural iron, these methods are not adequate to supply the high-quality blast-furnace feed which operators are demanding.

After decades of research and experimentation, techniques have been developed whereby some of the taconites and jaspers can be commercially transformed into high-grade agglomerates (see Section 5) containing 62 to 67 per cent of iron and 5 to 9 per cent of silica which compare favorably with imported natural ores. Six commercial plants are now producing premium-quality furnace feed from low-grade ores of the Lake Superior district; and two pilot plants are carrying on further experimentation with the fine-grained, non-magnetic taconites and semi-taconites. It seems probable that, in the not too distant future, most of the Lake Superior production will come from taconites and jaspers of one type or another.

What has been happening in the Lake Superior area has been going on to a lesser extent elsewhere in the United States. However, the compulsion to make use of low-grade sources of ore in other parts of the country has been less, inasmuch as suitable foreign ores were more readily available to the consuming centers. This is particularly true along the eastern seaboard where, in the face of competition from foreign ores, mine production from New York has decreased during the last few years, and at Birmingham and in Texas, where technical difficulties in concentrating the local low-grade ores make it more attractive to utilize imported ores than to upgrade the local ores. On the other hand, the intermontane steel-making centers of Colorado and Utah, inaccessible to foreign ores, have followed much the same course as the Lake Superior area in making the most of the local ores. Here, more and more, the quality of the local ores is being improved by washing or other means of beneficiation, and there is even one "taconite" plant in operation in Wyoming.

At the same time that the North American iron-ore industry was attempting to make acceptable blast-furnace feed from the relatively low-grade domestic ores, they were also active in searching for and developing sources of iron ore in foreign countries that could be delivered economically to their seaboard plants. As a result of extensive explorations and investigations carried out during the post-war years, a number of important new iron-ore sources have been developed in Canada (Ontario and the Quebec-Labrador area); in Venezuela; in Peru; in Chile; and in various countries of West Africa, notably Liberia. Except for the Quebec-Labrador ores, which are in part of the taconite type, these new foreign developments consist largely of high-grade natural ores that can be shipped from the mines and utilized without beneficiation except possible agglomeration at the blast-furnace site.

In most instances, the ore from these new developments is sold in American markets, but some of the mines are so situated that they can advantageously ship ore to other markets as well. For example, ores shipped from the Seven Islands area of Quebec can move in three directions: west via the St. Lawrence Seaway to lower Great Lakes destinations, east to Europe, and south to the northern Atlantic seaboard. Ore from Venezuela moves to the Gulf Coast, the northern Atlantic seaboard, and to Europe. Ore from the west coast of South America can move to all seaboard areas in North America as well as to Japan, while ore from West Africa is about equidistant from American and European consuming centers. These new sources of ore are largely responsible for the recent growth in international iron-ore trade and the increase in United States' imports from an average of 9,300,000 tons in the 1949-53 period to a record 35,600,000 tons in 1959. It has been predicted that by 1975 the United States will be importing 40 per cent of its total iron-ore requirements. Whether or not this prediction is actually realized will depend largely upon the location of future steel-plant expansion, and the competitive position of foreign ores in the United States.

From the foregoing, it is evident that there need be no future shortage of iron ore for the steel industry of the United States even if, as has been forecast, the nation requires some 235,000,000 tons annually by 1980, which is almost double the record consumption of 1953. However, in order that this amount of ore becomes available in the form of high-quality material that will permit the maximum blast-furnace yields, very large investments will be required for new mining and beneficiating plants, both in the United States and in foreign countries. The potential sources of ore are abundant, and it is rather a question of which sources are developed rather than "Is there ore enough to meet the demands of the American steel industry?"

SECTION 4
DISCOVERY AND MINING OF IRON ORES

Introduction—The first part of this section will be confined principally to a brief discussion of modern geophysical methods for iron-ore exploration. The second part will discuss briefly the current methods used for mining iron ore.

DISCOVERY METHODS

Present geophysical techniques and instrumentation; sampling methods; drilling procedures; and some methods of geological investigation will be discussed here, but only as they apply to the search for iron ore.

The science of geophysics, as applied to iron-ore explorations, is primarily a reconnaissance tool that provides information that must subsequently be complemented by geological mapping, petrographic studies, drilling and the evaluation of ore analyses and treatment tests.

Some important iron-ore deposits outcropped at the surface. For example, iron ores in the Lake Superior region were first discovered in outcrops in the vicinity of Negaunee, Michigan and the recognition of iron ore and iron formation in outcrops first served to focus attention on the various iron ranges of the region. Non-outcropping or buried deposits have been located in the past by ground surveys to detect variations of the earth's magnetic field, using the simple **dip needle** or the Hotchkiss **"Super-dip,"** both of which were effective chiefly in detecting iron-bearing deposits that contained magnetite. The Cuyuna Range, where no outcrops occurred because the ore bodies were buried under glacial drift, is one example of an important series of deposits that were located solely by dip needle surveys.

The greater sensitivity and convenience of operation of modern **magnetometers** have all but retired the dip needle and Super-dip from practical employment in exploration for iron ore. Magnetometers for this purpose have passed through several successive stages of development, the principal forms being known, in the order of their conception, as balance-type, torsion-type and flux-gate magnetometers, followed in recent years by so-called "sophisticated" magnetometers that were conceived and developed in the field of atomic physics; these latter instruments include the rubidium-vapor and the proton-precession magnetometers.

All of the foregoing magnetometers are used to determine the strength of the earth's magnetic field or its vertical component at a given location. The earth's field is very weak, ranging from about 0.7 oersted at the magnetic poles to about 0.25 oersted at some points on the magnetic equator. In geomagnetic studies, field strength is measured in a much smaller unit than the oersted: the gamma, which is equal to 0.00001 or 10^{-5} oersted. The shape of the earth's magnetic field is not uniform, but shows large-scale regional irregularities due to variations in the shape and composition of the earth's crust and upper mantle. Variations on a smaller scale result from magnetic disturbances caused by concentrations of magnetic material near the surface and it is these local variations that are sought in searching for ore.

Magnetic Surveying—In one method of expediting the magnetic surveying of large areas, a magnetometer of the flux-gate type is mounted on an airplane that is flown back and forth at a fixed altitude along a series of predetermined flight lines. The magnetometer supplies records in the form of continuous profiles of magnetic intensity along the flight lines. Data from these records are plotted and displayed like a contour map, with lines connecting points of equal magnetic intensity on the map. The patterns formed by these lines indicate areas where magnetic anomalies (major local distortions of the earth's magnetic field) occur. The areas indicated by anomalies on the magnetic map may then be investigated in greater detail by gravity measurements, electromagnetic studies or other geophysical methods and by geological surveys.

The detailed magnetic study of anomalous areas may involve using a magnetometer in a helicopter, or ground surveys employing hand-held or other portable magnetometers. A new electromagnetic prospecting technique known as AFMAG (audio frequency magnetics) has been used, in areas where magnetic anomalies have been detected, to attempt to differentiate between buried deposits of volcanic glass or low-grade iron-bearing intrusives and deposits with high remanent magnetization that represent potential ore bodies. The rubidium-vapor magnetometer, likewise, may make possible the rejection of non-economic deposits by differentiating between magnetite deposits, high in magnetic susceptibility and electrical conductivity, and buried volcanic glass and low-grade non-conducting iron-bearing intrusives of low susceptibility which, however, are capable of producing attractive magnetic anomalies.

In the early period of iron-ore discovery, most of the exploration of potential ore bodies was done by test pits and shafts. In recent years, correlation and evaluation of the detailed data from magnetometer or other surveys is usually followed by a carefully worked-out drilling program to provide samples that, through geological and mineralogical studies, establish the kind, quality and extent of ore that may be present, and the nature and quantity of the overburden or rock formations associated with the ore.

Considerable attention is being given to the improvement of core-drilling methods to provide better samples. The most complete and undisturbed drill sample possible at a reasonable cost is the ultimate goal of these studies. Diamond drills are employed especially in hard formations. The use of drilling muds with diamond drills has been adopted where samples of the highest quality from alternately hard and soft banded material are desired. Rotary down-hole drills of several types can provide a rapid rate of penetration with satisfactory sample recovery in some sampling applications. Wire line drilling is employed in about half of the core-drilling operations in the United States.

Studies are continuing of the statistical evaluation of the results of exploration drilling to provide guides for planning drilling programs, especially with regard to the most economical spacing of holes and the most desirable degree of core recovery that would provide adequate sampling at the lowest cost.

MINING OF IRON ORES

Planning and Development—The general occurrence, size and shape of an iron-ore deposit is determined during the exploration phase, which is discussed above. Knowledge of the deposit is determined in more detail through development work. It is often necessary during the development of a mine to determine, in considerable detail, the position and nature of geological structures which affect ore distribution and availability. Currently, deposits are being exploited that contain ore with such a low iron content that they must be beneficiated or concentrated to produce an acceptable shipping product. In such ore deposits, the results of laboratory concentration tests of drill samples, supplemented by pilot-plant tests or by experience with commercial-plant results, are used to determine the economics of ore treatment.

After sufficient detailed information is obtained, various combinations of operating plans are studied using maps and sections prepared for this purpose. These show the size and shape of the ore body, crude-ore compositions and laboratory-test results. From these graphic representations, quantities of various classes of ores and waste materials are determined by the application of volume-weight factors. Computer systems are commonly applied in the preparation of tonnage estimates and in the preparation of detailed mining plans. Through the use of these systems, comparative evaluations of various mining methods and plans may be made to determine the most favorable plan for each particular deposit and to schedule the mining of the deposit.

Whether an ore body is to be mined by open-pit methods or underground methods depends upon its shape, attitude and its position with respect to the surface. Generally, iron-ore bodies occurring at a depth great enough to necessitate underground mining are developed only to a limited extent by drilling from the surface. In such case, provided surface drilling indicates favorable operating economics, shafts are sunk and the ore limits more precisely determined by drilling from underground drifts, or by the drifts themselves.

Open-Pit Mining—Inasmuch as open-pit mining provides the lowest-cost operation, it is employed wherever the ratio of overburden, either consolidated or unconsolidated, to ore does not exceed an economi-cal limit. Nearly all the large iron-ore mines in the world, Western Europe excepted, are worked by open-pit methods. Figures 5—14, 5—15 and 5—16 show examples of open-pit mining on the Mesabi Range.

The depth to which open-pit mining can be carried depends upon the nature of the overburden and the stripping ratio. The stripping ratio is the amount of overburden that has to be handled for each unit of ore mined. The economic stripping ratio varies widely from mine to mine and district to district, depending upon a number of factors. In the case of direct-shipping ores, it may be as high at 6 or 7 to 1; whereas, in the case of taconite, a stripping ratio of less than ½ to 1 may become necessary.

Overburden (stripping) may consist of unconsolidated material, rock, or lean ore material. In open-pit mining, removal of overburden may continue through a large part of the life of a mine as the pit walls are cut back to permit deepening of the mine to recover ore in the bottom. Unconsolidated materials are excavated by power shovels, draglines, power scrapers, hydraulicking or by hydraulic dredging, depending on local conditions. Other materials are generally excavated with power shovels.

Drilling and blasting is done to break consolidated materials into sizes capable of being handled by mining equipment and in beneficiation facilities, and is also done to loosen ore banks ahead of power shovels to increase the efficiency of loading.

Iron ore is loaded by power shovels equipped with buckets ranging in capacity from one cubic yard to ten cubic yards. The ore is transported out of the pit by railroad cars, trucks, truck-trailers, belt conveyors, skip-hoists, or combinations of these, to a loading dock for hauling to a crushing plant for size reduction, to a screening plant for sizing, or to a concentrating plant for treatment by washing (wet size classification and tailings rejection) or by gravity concentration.

The mining of taconite poses special problems because of its extreme hardness, which necessitates considerable additional drilling and blasting and more specialized and rugged equipment, as compared with the techniques and equipment used in mining most oxidized ores. Also, the relatively low iron content of taconite makes it necessary to handle two to four times as much mined material to obtain the same quantity of iron-in-ore as from higher grade ore deposits.

Water causes a variety of problems in iron-ore-mining operations. Except in rare instances, such as in hilltop mining or mining under desert conditions, water must be collected in sumps, wells or underground workings and pumped out of the mine. Such drainage water is often utilized directly to make up for water losses in concentration operations.

Underground Mining—When the stripping ratio is, or becomes, too high for economical open-pit mining, underground mining methods may be employed. In most cases, access to underground mines is obtained through vertical shafts sunk adjacent to the deposit but far enough away to avoid the effects of surface subsidence resulting from mining operations. Some inclined shafts are still in use and some ore is

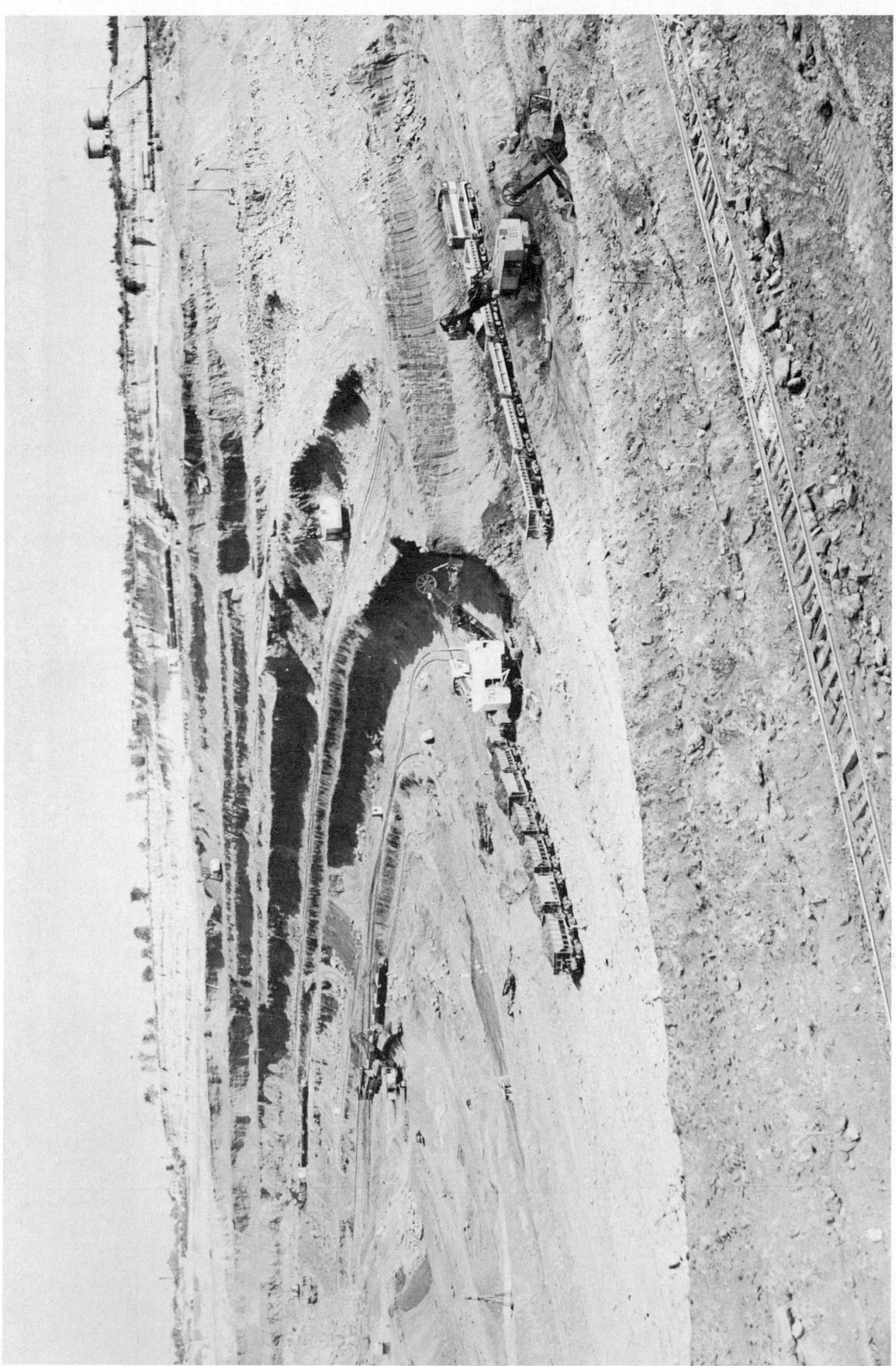

FIG. 5—14. Open-pit iron-ore mining.

Fig. 5—15. Electric power shovel on caterpillar tracks, making a "sinking cut" and loading ore into steel dump cars for haulage from an open-pit mine to a beneficiation plant. Diesel-electric locomotives handle the dump cars. Cable carries power to shovel.

FIG. 5—16. Electric power shovel loading crude concentrating ore in an open-pit mine. Trucks carry the ore to a screening pocket from which it is transported by belt conveyor to a surge bin and then to a washing plant for beneficiation prior to shipment. The discharge end of the conveyor belt, washing plant, loading pocket and waiting line-haul railroad cars can be seen in the extreme background.

removed through adits driven in from open-pit banks or hillsides.

Underground mining requires a larger capital investment per ton of annual capacity than open-pit mining because it depends upon costly shafts or tunnels, underground haulage and development workings, and elaborate pumping facilities. Moreover, the production of iron ore per man per day in an underground mine is only a fraction of that in open-pit operations, whereas the cost of supplies, maintenance, hoisting, and pumping, are all higher.

In underground mining, several methods of ore extraction may be used. Among the most common, in order of increasing cost, are: block caving, sub-level stoping, sub-level caving, top slicing, and modifications or combinations of these. All of these methods involve: drilling; blasting; transportation within the mine by rail tramming, trackless shuttle cars, scrapers, or conveyor belts; and hoisting or hauling to the surface. On the surface, the ore may be crushed, sized or concentrated prior to shipment.

In general, the higher costs of underground mining limit its use to ores simply requiring crushing or sizing, special ores such as open-hearth lump ore, or low-grade ores that are located so near a consuming market that transportation costs to the point of use are not significant.

Grading of Iron Ores—A wide variety of furnace practices, as described elsewhere in this volume, require the production or mixing of natural ores to meet the physical and chemical specifications required in iron- or steelmaking processes. In iron-ore-producing districts, the ores are "graded" by the producers and shippers to meet furnace demands for particular and uniform chemical composition and structure. Iron-ore merchant companies may satisfy grade requirements by purchase or exchange of ores, which are then mixed together in the correct proportions. Recognition of the importance of uniformity has led to the use of elaborate ore-blending facilities at some producing and consuming points, involving systematic layering in stockpiles and recovery for shipment or consumption by cross-cutting the layers (one method, known as "stacking and reclaiming," is discussed under "Blending" in Section 5 of this chapter).

Of particular significance in grading of ores, aside from the iron content, is the content of silica, phosphorus, manganese and alumina. A high lime content makes some ores self-fluxing. Sulphur, copper, nickel, titanium and other deleterious constituents may require close control in some producing areas. While ores are generally priced on the basis of natural iron content (that is, the amount of iron in the ore before the free moisture is removed), penalties or premiums may be applied for varying chemical and structural quality. Practices vary considerably in the various world iron-ore markets.

SECTION 5

BENEFICIATION OF IRON ORES

Introduction—The term "beneficiation" in regard to iron ores encompasses all of the methods used to process ore to improve its chemical or physical characteristics in ways that will make it a more desirable feed for the blast furnace. Such methods include crushing, screening, blending, grinding, concentrating, classifying and agglomerating. Because of the differences in structure and mineral content of ores from different deposits, beneficiation methods vary considerably. Consequently, the following brief and generalized descriptions are intended only to describe how some types of ore are beneficiated, and are not to be interpreted as suitable for all ores.

CRUSHING, SCREENING AND BLENDING

Crushing and Screening—Iron ore of merchantable grade from open-pit mines contains large chunks that, above certain sizes, may create handling problems by jamming hoppers and chutes and, more importantly, may limit heat transfer and be reduced so slowly in the blast furnace as to cause operating problems. For these principal reasons, merchantable ores are first screened over a scalping screen prior to shipment. With ores of high moisture content, the undersized material from the scalping screens may be dried before shipment or, in some cases, sintered at the mine both to remove moisture and to improve physical structure.

In the production of lump ore, the run-of-mine ore is screened one or more times to divide the ore into sized fractions: fines, if separated, may be shipped as such or agglomerated before shipment.

When beneficiating ores of the complex wash-ore type are treated, mined material passes over a scalping screen which removes coarse iron-poor rock that is discarded. The undersize material from the scalping screen is passed over a washing screen and the oversize from that screen is crushed to free siliceous material that is encrusted on pieces of the ore or held between bands of ore before passing to a second washing screen. The undersize from both washing screens is treated in a mechanical classifier from which the undersize or fine waste that consists chiefly of fine siliceous material is discarded. The combined oversize from the second washing screen and the mechanical classifier is the product that is shipped.

Blending—The mining program at individual mines is set up to produce a uniform product. When it is desirable to blend ores of different compositions or size consists (as when material from different sources are to be combined), mixing may be accomplished during the numerous handling operations involved in transportation of the ore to its point of use, or special blending facilities may be empolyed.

Iron ores of different characteristics and compositions can be blended to a more uniform composition by a method known as **stacking and reclaiming.** One mechanical method for stacking and reclaiming is exemplified by the Robbins-Messiter system. The ore, brought to the plant in railroad hopper cars, is piled by a machine called a **stacker.** Stacking results in "layering" of the ores (Figure 5—17). Each successive layer represents an ore that may differ in size consist or chemical composition from adjacent layers. The elongated pile is built up to a height limited by the stacking capability of the machine.

When the ore is to be reclaimed for use, an inclined rake is moved from side to side, horizontally, against the face of one end of the pile, in contact with the bedded ore. The projecting fingers of the rake loosen the ore, which rolls down the face of the pile to the scraper-type cross-conveyor located beneath the rake. This scraper-type conveyor carries the ore to a belt conveyor that carries the reclaimed ore to a screening station. The rake continues to move toward the pile at a controlled rate, thus making the reclaiming operation continuous.

As may be seen from Figure 5—17, this operation results in relatively small quantities of ore from each layer being intimately mixed with each other as the loosened material rolls down the face of the pile, is cross-conveyed, and dumped on the belt conveyor.

CONCENTRATING PROCESSES

The earliest methods for improving the quality of iron ores consisted chiefly of processes called by the general name of "washing," by which a large proportion of the sand, clay, and rock could be removed from the crushed and screened ore. The iron (oxide) content of the washed product was considerably higher than that of the crude ore. However, as ore-grade requirements became more stringent, other, more complex methods were tested and adopted to upgrade ores that are not amenable to simple washing operations. These additional methods include, among others: heavy-media separation, jigging, drying, flotation, and magnetic and electrostatic concentration.

The iron-ore industry is presently involved in the development of improved methods for utilizing low-grade ores such as magnetite taconite, jaspers and those oxidized iron formations that are termed oxidized taconite, non-magnetic taconite, or ferruginous cherts or, when somewhat friable, semi-taconite. Attention is being given to these sources because, in spite of their relatively low iron contents, they are susceptible to concentration into a high-quality blast-furnace feed by presently developed practices while the oxidized and leached ores, while containing more iron, cannot be upgraded much above 55 per cent of iron. Decades of research and experimentation have developed technologies whereby some low-grade materials can be economically concentrated. All require fine grinding to separate the grains of silica from the grains of iron oxide, the fineness of grinding required depending upon the grain size of the silica and iron oxides in the crude rock. This often necessitates grinding to 200-mesh or even finer.

In the instance of magnetite ores, including the magnetite taconites of Minnesota and Wyoming, the iron-oxide (magnetite) content of the finely ground crude ore can be successfully separated from the non-magnetic gangue material by magnetic means. Flotation has been found effective in the separation of non-magnetic specular hematite from silica in certain of the coarse-grained Michigan jaspers. Much of the

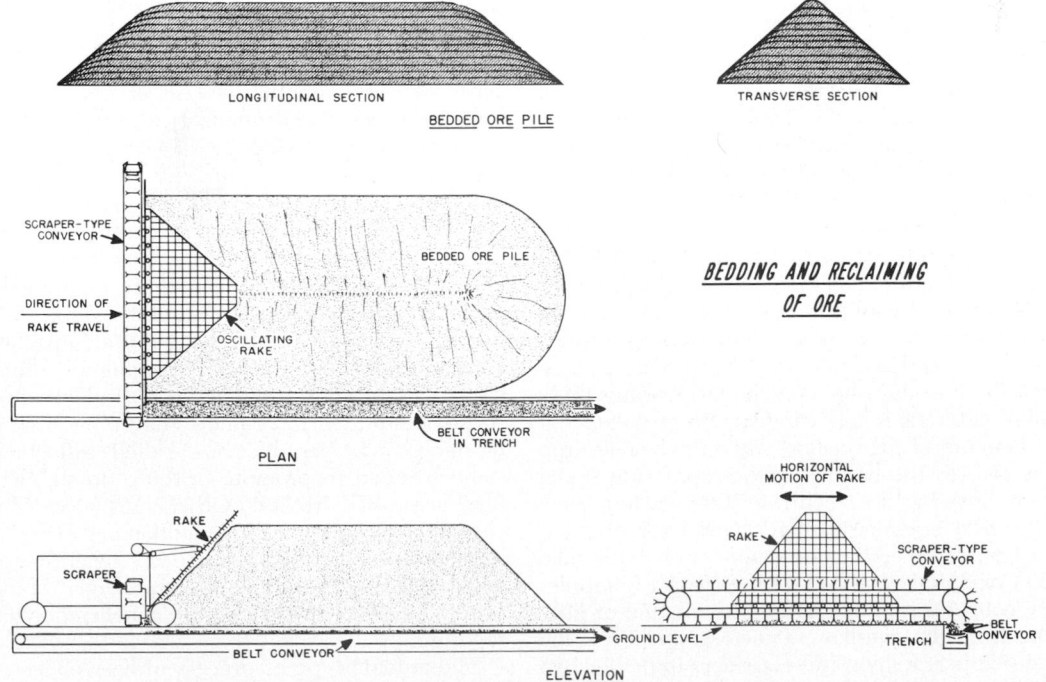

Fig. 5—17. Schematic representation of the principle of operation of a stacking and reclaiming system.

semi-taconite and other non-magnetic iron-formation materials respond favorably to roasting in a reducing atmosphere to convert hematite to magnetite. The converted material can then be ground and the magnetite separated from the siliceous gangue by magnetic methods to produce a high-grade concentrate. Concentrates obtained by the above methods contain 62 to 67 per cent of iron, with about 5 to 9 per cent of silica and, when agglomerated, make a desirable blast-furnace feed.

The investment required to produce concentrates from low-grade ore is high. Nonetheless, in the United States, three plants are now producing premium-quality blast-furnace feed from the magnetite taconites of the eastern Mesabi Range, four plants in Michigan are operating on relatively coarse-grained jasper, and other plants are carrying on further experimentation with the fine-grained magnetite taconite and non-magnetic taconites and semi-taconites of the western Mesabi Range and with Michigan iron formation.

The magnetite ores of New York and Pennsylvania all require magnetic concentration before shipment; concentrating and sintering plants have been operated in both states for many years.

At Birmingham, Alabama, technical difficulties in concentrating the low-grade local ores make it more attractive at present to utilize high-grade imported ores.

The intermountain steelmaking centers of the West in Colorado and Utah, relatively inaccessible to foreign ores, beneficiate local ores by washing or other means. The product of a concentration plant operating on magnetite taconite in Wyoming is shipped to blast furnaces in Utah.

It must not be inferred that the necessity for beneficiation applies only to North American ores, for the problem is world-wide and will become of increasing importance as high-grade deposits become depleted. However, space does not permit a review of the matter on a world-wide basis. Neither is it possible to discuss, except in a general way, the various processes and equipment employed in beneficiation of iron ores: further details on these and related matters will be found in the sources listed in the bibliography at the end of this chapter.

Washing—Washing is a form of concentration that utilizes the differences in specific gravity of valuable iron-bearing minerals and gangue to separate the two. Numerous types of washers are used in concentrating iron ores: they may be divided into **screening washers** and **classifying washers.** As applied to iron ores, washing removes fine clay and sand by suspending these unwanted materials in a flowing stream of water that carries them out of the washer, while the heavier iron minerals sink to the bottom of the separating vessel and are removed as a concentrate. **Log washers** have been the most common machines used for washing iron ores, often operating in conjunction with **rake classifiers** or **spiral classifiers** that perform a supplementary concentrating operation for removal of fine-sized ore from the overflow of the log washer. Some washing plants employ spiral classifiers in one or two stages without a log washer on ores containing a minimum amount of sticky clay gangue. **Hindered-settling**

classifiers of various types also have been used advantageously for washing iron ores of finer sizes than are normal feed for log washers and rake or spiral classifiers. **Vertical-current washers** and **turbo washers** have also been employed.

Jigging—Jigging is a more complex form of beneficiation than simple washing, and involves the stratification of ore particles and gangue by subjecting the crude ore to alternating upward and downward pulsations of water. The gangue overflows the jig, while the ore particles are removed as an underflow product, either periodically or continuously.

Heavy-Media Separation Processes—Heavy-media separation processes operate on the "sink-and-float" principle. When a mixture of particles of two minerals of different specific gravities is placed in a liquid having a specific gravity intermediate between the specific gravities of the two minerals, the lighter of the minerals will float and the heavier will sink. For example, quartz (sp. gr. = 2.65) will float in a medium having a specific gravity of 3.00, while hematite (sp. gr. = 5.00) will sink.

Heavy-media separation plants used in the concentration of iron ores all employ suspensions of magnetic material, the favored medium being ferrosilicon containing 15 per cent of silicon and 85 per cent of iron. Water suspensions of finely ground ferrosilicon (called "pulps") will give media with specific gravities ranging from 2.20 to 3.60 with the percentage of solids in the suspension ranging from 64 to 85 per cent, respectively. The vessels in which separation is effected are designed to provide for continuous removal of sunken iron-ore particles at one point and of floating waste minerals at another. The medium leaving the separator must be cleaned, its specific gravity adjusted, and the suspended particles redispersed before it is reintroduced to the separatory vessel: the use of magnetic media simplifies this operation because the recovery of media and separation of media from non-magnetic wastes can be effected in wet-type magnetic separators. Use of hydrocyclones as separatory vessels has greatly extended the utility of heavy-media processes for the beneficiation of iron ore.

Flotation Processes—Flotation processes operate on the principle that additions of certain substances to liquid suspensions of fine particles of iron minerals and gangue produced by grinding iron ore will cause one class of minerals or the other to exhibit an affinity for air. The minerals possessing this affinity therefore, cling to bubbles produced by passing air through the suspension, and are removed as a froth product. The substances added to promote the preferential affinity of minerals for bubbles are called **collectors:** substances added to promote frothing (to stabilize bubbles) are called **frothers.** Other substances added for control purposes are called **modifiers.**

Flotation processes are of two general types: (1) anionic, and (2) cationic. No commercial application of cationic processes to iron-ore beneficiation has been reported.

The anionic type of process utilizes collectors that ionize in solution to yield a collector ion that is negatively charged; some examples are fatty acids, resin acids, soaps, alkyl sulphates or sulfonates. Commercial plants concentrating specular hematite employ soap-type reagents in alkaline solutions for flotation.

Magnetic Separation—In principle this is one of the simplest of all beneficiation methods; however, a combination of technical and practical problems combine to add complexity to magnetic separation facilities. Fine particles of magnetite when exposed to a strong magnetic field tend to become tightly flocculated and when fine magnetite is being separated magnetically from fine waste particles, some waste inevitably becomes physically trapped in magnetite flocs. To eliminate this trapped waste, the magnetite must be demagnetized and the separation repeated. This practice is acceptable, however, because magnetic separation is an inexpensive process compared to the crushing and grinding operations that precede it. Furthermore, it is usually preferable to provide for elimination of waste particles after as little grinding as possible and so almost all plant flowsheets show both repeated separation and deflocculation steps at any particular fineness, and two or more of these separation stages separated by grinding and classifying operations.

Most contemporary plants employ magnetic separators to separate natural magnetite from a variety of less magnetic or nonmagnetic minerals and the separations are usually made in water suspensions. The equipment used may be broadly defined as low-intensity wet separators such as the drum device depicted in Figure 5—18. In this type of machine, magnetite particles are attracted to and held against the surface of the rotating drum until they are carried out of the magnetic field. The magnetite is then transferred from the drum surface to an appropriate concentrate receiver. Sometimes, two drums are employed in series in the same machine. In other devices essentially the same principles are applied but with different apparatus. For example, a rubber belt may be used in place of the drum, permanent magnets may replace electromagnets (and indeed are becoming

more popular as new and stronger magnets are developed), and different feed and discharge systems may be used.

Dry low-intensity separation systems have not been as widely applied as wet systems primarily because the presence of water is highly advantageous as an agent for flushing fine nonmagnetic particles out of the magnetic field. Recently, however, dry separators have been developed in which the magnetic particles are held in an alternating magnetic field. Under these conditions the individual magnetite particles rotate independently in response to the field alternation, and so fine nonmagnetic particles have a greatly increased opportunity to disengage and separate. As with wet separators, numerous dry separators are available, their differences being in large part in such features as the mechanisms used for transporting the magnetic particles, the magnet types and arrangements employed, and variations in the positions of the various separating stages employed. Machines of this type may find increased use in desert or subtemperate climates where water supply and freezing problems exist.

High-intensity magnetic separators have also been developed recently for separating hematite from minerals of even lower magnetic susceptibility. Both dry and wet devices have been developed but so far only the dry units have been applied commercially and these only to a limited extent. In these machines hematite is deflected from its free fall or imposed trajectory by an intense magnetic field created by electromagnets. These devices have numerous drawbacks, however, including high cost and low capacity compared to other methods for recovering hematite.

AGGLOMERATION PROCESSES

The blast furnace is a counter-current gas-solid reactor in which the solid charge materials are moving downward while the hot reducing gases are flowing upward. The best possible contact between the solids

Fig. 5—18. Sectional view of one cell of Jeffrey-Steffensen magnetic separator. (From U. S. Bureau of Mines Report of Investigation No. 4847.)

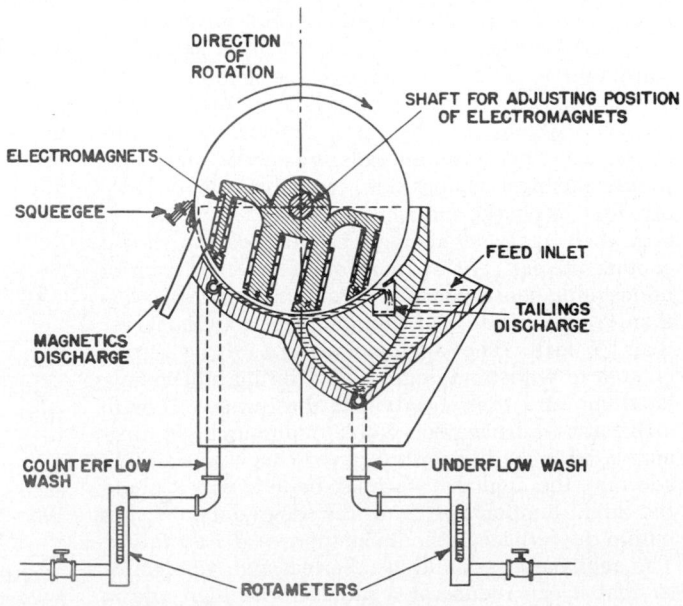

FIG. 5—19. Four types of iron-ore agglomerates.

and the reducing gas is obtained with a permeable burden which permits not only a high rate of gas flow but also a uniform gas flow with a minimum of channeling of the gas. The primary purpose of agglomeration is to improve burden permeability and gas-solid contact, and thereby reduce blast-furnace coke rates and increase the rate of reduction. A secondary consideration is the lessening of the amount of fine material blown out of the blast furnace into the gas-recovery system. Furthermore, in steelmaking furnaces, agglomerated materials, when they have the proper chemical composition, can substitute for lump ores used as charge and feed ores.

A good agglomerate for blast furnace use should contain 60 per cent or more of iron, a minimum of undesirable constituents, a minimum of material less than ¼-inch in size, and a minimum of material larger than ½-inch. The agglomerate should be strong enough to withstand degradation during stockpiling, handling, and transportation to the furnace so as to arrive at the furnace skip with a minimum of approximately 85 to 90 per cent of plus ¼-inch material. In addition, the agglomerate must be able to withstand the high temperature and the degradation forces within the furnace without slumping or decrepitating. The agglomerate should also be reasonably reducible so that it can reduce at a satisfactorily high rate in

the blast furnace. There is less definite knowledge about the following properties of agglomerates: preferred shape; most suitable size within the ¼-inch to 1-inch range; minimum strength required; and most desirable mineralogical structure.

Four principal types of agglomerating processes have been developed: sintering, pelletizing, briquetting, and nodulizing. Their individual products are known as: sinter, pellets, briquettes, and nodules (Figure 5—19). Because of the special features possessed by the first two processes, there appears to be a definite place for each. Comparative production data are listed in Table 5—XII.

Table 5—XII. Sinter and Pellet Production Capacity in the United States (Millions of Net Tons Per Year)

Year	Sinter	Pellets
1948	15	—
1950	25	Less than 1
1956	27	—
1957	42	—
1960	68	15
1962-3*	70	25
1970**	75	40

*Estimated
**Projected

Variations of the briquetting process have been operated from time to time without much success; however, recent work on hot-ore briquetting is promising enough that pilot plants have been operated and a small commercial plant was placed in operation in 1962. Thus, with several processes available for agglomerating ore fines, concentrates and other iron-bearing materials, careful evaluation should be made of processes, material to be agglomerated, and product desired before arriving at a final decision on a commercial installation.

Fine ores have also been agglomerated by extrusion and by direct-reduction methods in fluidized beds but neither these processes, nor nodulizing, have gained any substantial degree of commercial acceptance.

Sintering—Sintering has been referred to as the art of burning a fuel of extremely high ash content under controlled conditions. The flexibility of the process permits conversion of a variety of materials, including naturally fine ores and ore fines from screening operations, flue dust, ore concentrates, and other iron-bearing materials of extremely small particle size into a granular, relatively coarse form that is well-suited for use in the blast furnace.

The continuous sintering process, shown schematically in Figure 5—20, is carried out on a traveling grate that conveys a bed of ore fines or other finely divided iron-bearing material, intimately mixed with approximately 5 per cent of a finely divided fuel such as coke

breeze or anthracite. Near the head or feed end of the grate, the bed is ignited on the surface by gas burners (Figure 5—21) and, as the mixture moves along on the traveling grate, air is pulled down through the mixture to burn the fuel by downdraft combustion. As the grates (or pallets) move continuously over the wind boxes toward the discharge end of the strand, the combustion front in the bed moves progressively downward. This creates sufficient heat and temperature (about 2400 to 2700° F) to sinter the fine ore particles together into porous, coherent lumps. That location along the traveling grate where the combustion front touches the bottom of the bed is called the **burn-through point.** Thus, although the sinter bed is stationary with respect to the moving grates that support it, the bed travels continuously along the strand and the combustion front is, for all practical purposes, a standing wave that extends at a flat angle, as a more or less unbroken flame front, from the top of the bed at the ignition point near the feed end to the bottom of the bed at the burn-through point near the discharge end.

Although simple in principle, sintering plants require that a number of important factors in their design and operation be observed to attain optimum performance. Intimate mixing of the feed materials is one of the most important, and balling-drum or disc-pelletizer mixers (Figures 5—22 and 5—23) are employed to achieve this end. These mixers are operated to produce small rice-size balls that significantly im-

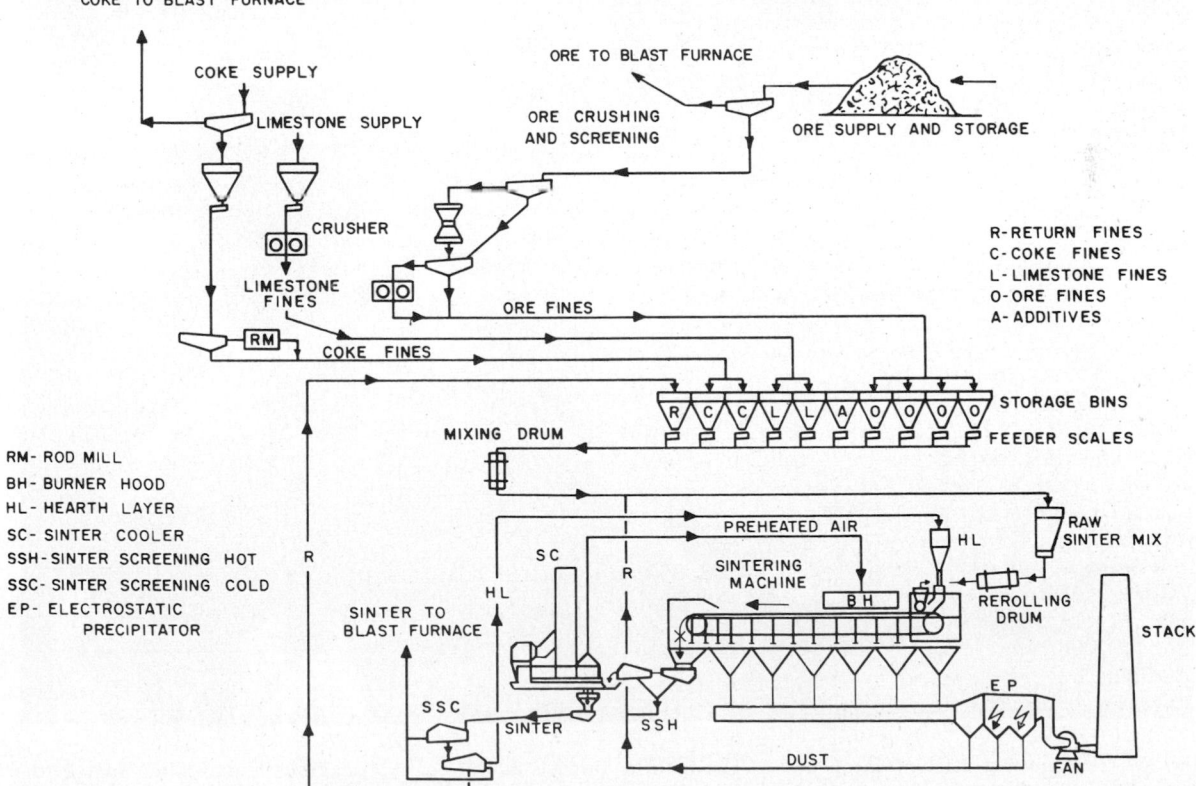

FIG. 5—20. Schematic flow diagram of continuous iron-ore sintering process (adapted from Metallgesellschaft A.G.).

prove the permeability of the sinter bed. Improved permeability, in turn, results in more rapid and uniform sintering. Desirable retention times vary from about one minute for sticky hematite ores to four minutes for more-difficult-to-ball ores.

In transferring the prepared mix from the balling

Fɪɢ. 5—21. Sintering machine in operation. The ignition furnace in the center background ignites the fuel in the surface layer of the sinter mix. As the bed of sinter progresses into the foreground, air is pulled down through the bed to cause the burning zone to move downward through the bed by igniting fuel in deeper and deeper zones in the mix. By the time the discharge end of the machine is reached, sintering will have taken place throughout the depth of the bed.

FIG. 5—22. Balling drum mixer.

mixer to the grate of the sintering machine, it is essential to feed the material carefully to provide a uniform, homogeneous bed and to prevent compacting of the bed. Chutes must be designed to avoid a direct drop of feed onto the grate, because such a drop does tend to compact the feed. Design of surge bins and feeders for distributing the prepared mix into these bins is equally important because, if the prepared mix is compacted or segregated during handling and loading onto the grate, all of the advantages gained through good feed preparation may be lost.

Proper ignition of the sinter bed is also important. Poor ignition results in spotty burning and may leave unsintered material over the surface of the bed. Conversely, too intense an ignition flame can result in slagging over of the bed and reduced sintering rates. The radiant hood ignition furnace (Figure 5—24) provides good ignition. Replacing part of the solid fuel with gaseous fuel results in sinter having a slightly improved strength and reducibility without affecting sinter-production rate. This practice is termed "mixed firing." Where a shortage of solid fuel exists, and gas is available, use of increased amounts of gaseous fuel should be desirable. Plants using increased ignition (extended firing) have approximately 25 per cent of the length of the sinter bed covered by a gas-fired ignition-type hood. The temperature in this hood ranges from about 2100° F in the first section where ignition begins to approximately 1500° F at the exit end of the hood. Depending upon the characteristics of the ore materials and the sintering conditions, daily average production rates of 2.3 to 4.4 tons per square foot of grate area are expected, and individual daily rates in excess of 5 tons per square foot have been attained.

Cooling of the sinter so that it can be handled is an important part of the operation. Present sinter coolers, such as the rotary-type shown in Figure 5—25, require up to 5 pounds of air for each pound of sinter cooled and the exhaust air is at too low a temperature to permit the economical recovery of heat from it. A shaft-type cooler, such as that shown schematically in Figure 5—26, is now under development. The shaft-type cooler could cut air requirements to as low as 1.5 pounds per ton of sinter produced, and permit recirculation of the hot exhaust air with consequent recovery of heat.

The use of sinter in the blast furnace has resulted in significant improvements in furnace performance, as discussed in Chapter 14. Additional improvements have also been obtained (1) by incorporating the blast-furnace flux into the sinter rather than charging it separately to the top of the furnace, as was formerly done, and (2) by use of sized sinter. The available data on the use of **flux sinter,** sometimes called **self-fluxing sinter,** indicate that for each net ton of limestone removed from the blast-furnace burden and charged into the sinter plant to make a flux sinter, approximately 400 pounds of metallurgical coke are saved. The coke saving results primarily from calcining the limestone on the sintering grate rather than in the blast furnace. Limestone in the form of "fluxing fines" for the production of sinter is made by crushing and screening methods that result in a product meeting exacting size specifications, as described in Chapter 6.

Use of sized sinter is desirable because iron-production rates in the blast furnace are further increased. Plant tests (Table 5—XIII) have demonstrated significant increases in iron-production rate as a result of screening out small-sized material in sinter before it is charged to the furnace.

Table 5—XIII. Effect of Sized Sinter on Iron Production

Percentage of $+\frac{3}{8}$-in. Sinter in Charge	Relative Iron Production
65	1.00*
75	1.15
85	1.25
95	1.32

*Base Period

Other tests have shown that sized sinter, which contains 85 to 90 per cent of 1-inch by ¼-inch material as compared to 60 per cent in standard sinter has a much higher permeability than standard sinter and performs as well as pellets of comparable size. It also appears that crushing to minus 1-inch size at the sinter plant yields a more stable sinter because the smaller size fractions are more resistant to degradation.

In conclusion, it should be noted that for economic reasons the size and capacity of single-strand sintering machines continues to increase. By 1961, the largest unit in the world, installed at Aliquippa, Pa., was equipped with a grate approximately 13 feet wide and about 184 feet long, and had a design capacity of 8500 net tons per day of self-fluxing sinter.

Pelletizing—Pelletizing, the newest of the agglom- erating processes, differs from sintering in that a "green," unbaked pellet or ball (sometimes referred to as a glomerule) is first formed and then hardened by heating (Figure 5—27). Experimental work, started

FIG. 5—23. Two disc-type pelletizing machines. Ore fines are fed to the discs by the belt conveyors (behind the operator). As the discs rotate, there is a "balling" action that causes the fines to agglomerate into pellet-like masses that are discharged from the discs over their lip at the bottom onto the belt conveyor shown at floor level that carries the pellets to the bins of the sinter machine.

FIG. 5—24. Radiant-hood ignition furnace.

FIG. 5—25. Induced-draft rotary or circular sinter coolers, shown in process of construction.

many years ago by E. W. Davis and his associates at the University of Minnesota on the concentration and agglomeration of low-grade iron ores, showed that it was possible to ball or pelletize fine magnetite concentrate in a balling drum and that if the balls were fired at sufficiently high temperature (usually below the

point of incipient fusion), a hard, indurated pellet (Figure 5—19), well adapted for use in the blast furnace, could be made. Consequently, despite the unquestioned benefits of sinter on blast-furnace performance, intense interest in the pelletizing process has developed in recent years because of the outstanding performance achieved by steel producers in extended operations with pellets as the principal iron-bearing material in the blast-furnace burden.

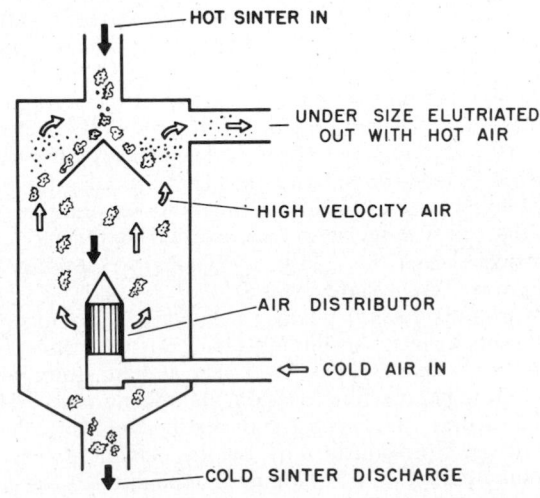

FIG. 5—26. Schematic diagram of shaft-type sinter cooler.

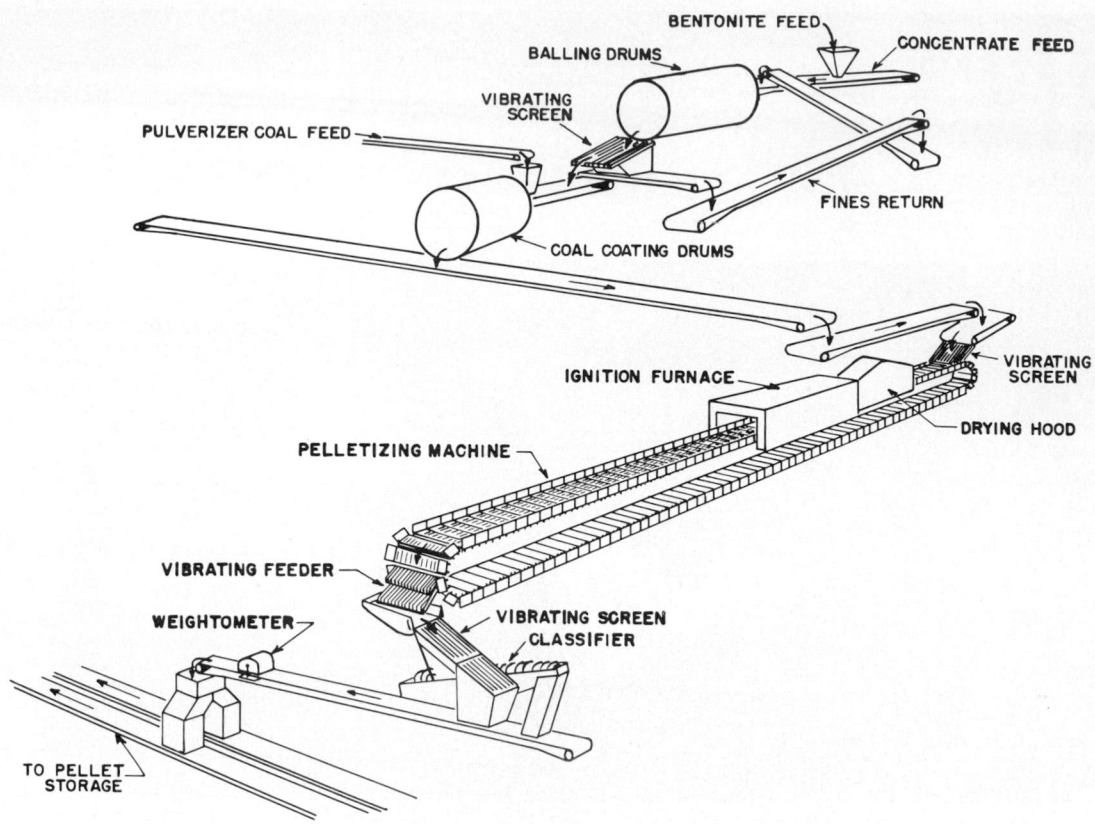

FIG. 5—27. Simplified flow diagram illustrating principle of the pelletizing process using the traveling grate method. All but one balling drum and one coal-coating drum have been eliminated from the original diagram. [Adapted by permission from an article in "Symposium on Agglomeration (edited by W. A. Knepper)" by K. M. Haley and W. E. Apuli entitled "Pelletizing on a Horizontal Grate Machine" copyrighted by the American Institute of Mining, Metallurgical and Petroleum Engineers (1962), page 933 and published by Interscience Publishers, a Division of John Wiley & Sons, Inc.]

In general, the pelletizing process is desirable for agglomeration of finely divided concentrates because they are normally of such fine size (or can be reground to the required size) that they will form into a green pellet with little difficulty. In contrast, minus ¼-inch ore fines, which can be readily agglomerated by the sintering process, must be ground to produce a suitable green pellet. Pelletizing is often distinguished from balling on the basis of the size of particles produced and the subsequent treatment: pelletizing is the preparation of relatively large particles (about ⅜ inch to 1 inch) for subsequent heat hardening by one of several systems prior to ultimate use; balling refers to the use of a device to increase slightly the average particle size of the charge so that its permeability is improved on the sinter strand.

Although several devices are available for use in forming pellets, the balling drum and the disc pelletizer are most widely used. The balling drum was the principal machine used for pelletizing until 1949 when Lurgi introduced the disc pelletizer which had been used previously only by the cement industry. Compared with the balling drum, the disc has the advantages of lighter weight and greater possibility for adjustment, including charge depth. Its inherent de-

sign averages out the effect of instantaneous fluctuations in the feed, whereas the drum cannot. Also, the classifying action of the disc promotes discharge of pellets of more uniform size, which simplifies screening of the product. However, the capacity of discs is low and discs generally require closer control than drums. Binders are generally used to raise the wet strength of green pellets to more acceptable levels for handling. Ballability and the strength of green pellets are influenced by the moisture content and particle size distribution of the concentrates and additives. Moisture content is extremely important, and it appears that balling characteristics are relatively independent of the chemical composition of a concentrate, but are strongly affected by its physical properties. For example, specular hematites are more difficult to ball than magnetite concentrates because of the "plate-like" structure of particles of the former. In any case, satisfactory pellet formation is usually achieved by regrinding to about 80 to 90 per cent minus 325 mesh.

Both the drop and compressive strengths of green pellets are important, but because dried pellets are not required to withstand much handling, their compressive strength is considered most important. The strength of fired pellets is important in minimizing degradation by breakage and abrasion during handling and shipping, and in the blast furnace. Strong bonding in pellets is believed to be due to grain growth from the accompanying oxidation of magnetite to hematite, or recrystallization of hematite. Although slag bonding may promote more rapid strengthening at slightly lower firing temperatures, pellet strength is normally decreased, especially resistance to thermal shock. Fired pellet strength is most commonly determined by compression and tumbler tests. Reported compressive strengths for individual pellets range from about 250 to nearly 5600 lbs., depending upon mineralogical composition and physical properties of the concentrate, additives used, the balling method, pellet size, firing technique and temperature and testing procedure. The minimum compressive strengths of commercially acceptable pellets are as low as 300 lbs. for ¼-inch pellets and from 800 to 1500 lbs. for 1-inch pellets. In the tumbler test 25 or 50 lbs. of plus 3-mesh (or ⅜-inch) pellets are tumbled for 200 revolutions at 25 rpm in a drum tumbler (ASTM D-294-50) and then screened. A satisfactory commercial pellet should contain not more than about 6 per cent of minus 28-mesh fines, and 85 per cent or more of plus ⅜-inch size, after tumbler testing. A minimum of broken pellets between ⅜-inch and 28-mesh in size is also desirable. Other important properties of fired pellets to be used for blast-furnace feed are believed to be reducibility, porosity, and bulk density. With some concentrates these can be varied within certain limits.

The flowsheet of the pelletizing process generally resembles that of the sintering process (Figure 5—20), and the features and material handling facilities are also similar to those of a sintering plant. Pelletizing rates per square foot of hearth (or equivalent) are lower than sintering rates. However, because of the critical nature of the green-pellet forming and heat hardening steps, there are important differences as brought out in the preceding discussion. Therefore, where practical, the associated mining, concentrating, and grinding installations are operated as a feed preparation section of the pellet plant.

In the pelletizing process a small amount of fine solid fuel may be added to the pellet mix or coated on the pellets to supply part of the heat (Figure 5—27). Oxidation of a pelletized magnetite concentrate to hematite during the firing step may also supply a significant proportion of the process heat requirement. Optimum moisture contents for good pellets depend upon the fineness of the concentrate and use

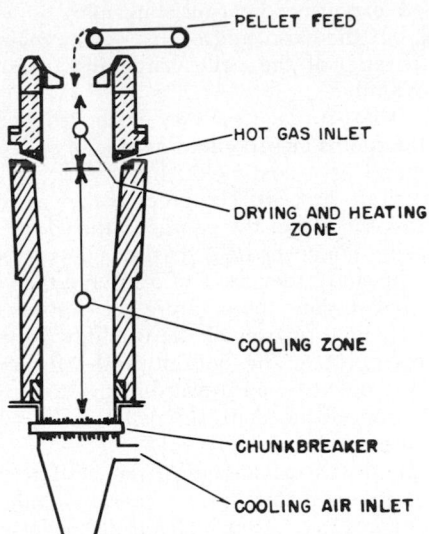

FIG. 5—29. Schematic diagram of the shaft-furnace system for producing pellets.

of additives, but are usually in the 9.5 to 12 per cent range. Bentonite is the principal additive in commercial operations, and approximately ½ to ¾ of one per cent is mixed with the concentrate. Other additives such as soda ash, limestone, or dolomite are sometimes used to improve pellet strength. Binders other than bentonite are being studied in the hope of futher reductions in the silica content of the final product. The production of self-fluxing and prereduced pellets is still in the experimental stage. Pelletizing processes are being improved constantly and further details on their technology and development may be found in the references listed for Section 5 at the end of the chapter.

The three most important pelletizing systems are the traveling-grate (updraft and/or downdraft) system, the shaft-furnace system, and the grate-kiln system.

The **traveling-grate** system for producing pellets from magnetite concentrates obtained from taconite, illustrated in Figure 5—27, is essentially a modification of the sintering process. In this method, "green" pellets coated in a balling drum with a thin layer of fuel are continuously fed to a traveling grate (Figure 5—28). The first few wind boxes are used to dry (updraft/downdraft) and preheat (downdraft) the moist pellets with recuperated hot air from the cooling zone; pellet damage from condensation of moisture in the bed resulted in this arrangement of hot air flows to overcome the problem. After ignition of the bed, a downdraft of air is continued until all the fuel is consumed and substantially all the magnetite is oxidized to hematite. An updraft of air is then applied to cool the pellets. Fuel requirements for the process have been reduced to as low as 600,000 B.t.u. per long ton of pellets, but total heat requirements of 1 million B.t.u. (700,000 from fuel and 300,000 from oxidation of magnetite) may be compared with about 2 million B.t.u. per ton for sintering. In the traveling-grate system, the necessity of constructing pellet

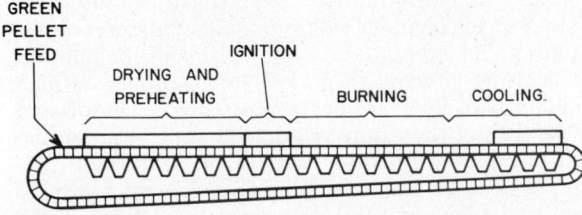

FIG. 5—28. Schematic diagram of the traveling-grate system for producing pellets.

frames of expensive heat-resisting alloy is a disadvantage, but the close control that can be maintained over each step of the pellet-hardening process is a great advantage.

In the **shaft-furnace** system, illustrated in Figure 5—29, the fuel is incorporated inside the pellet rather than applied as a coating on the outside, as in the traveling-grate process. The green pellets are distributed across the top of the charge in the shaft furnace by a moving conveyor belt. As the pellets pass down through the shaft, they are first dried and then heated to the pelletizing temperature of approximately 2400° F about a quarter of the way down the shaft. From this point to the bottom of the furnace, the pellets are cooled by an upward-rising stream of air. At the bottom of the shaft, the pellets are discharged through a chunkbreaker.

The greatest disadvantage of the shaft furnace is the difficulty in maintaining a uniform combustion zone: hot spots may occur which cause pellets to fuse together into large masses, producing discharge problems. Yet the shaft furnace has the advantages of simplicity of design and high degree of heat recuperation. Fuel requirements with a commercial-size furnace are said to be less than 500,000 B.t.u. per ton of pellets (with a magnetite concentrate), although figures up to 825,000 B.t.u. are on record. The shaft furnace has proved suitable for pelletizing magnetites, but to date it has not proved suitable for hematites, primarily because of the "hanging" and sticking that result from the additional heat input that must be supplied in the hardening of hematite pellets.

The **grate-kiln** system, illustrated in Figure 5—30, is relatively new and combines the advantages of the traveling grate with the rotary kiln. In this system, the pellets are dried and preheated on a traveling grate, with its advantages of close control of these steps, and then hardened by high-temperature heating in a rotary kiln. Hot gases discharged from the kiln are used in the downdraft drying and preheating sections of the grate. Commercial production of pellets

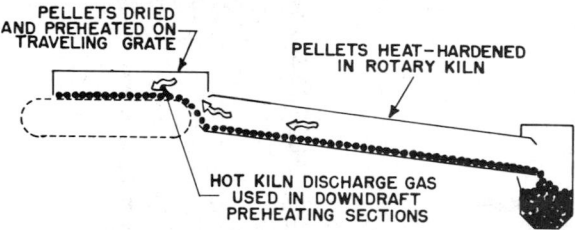

PELLETS DRIED
AND PREHEATED ON
TRAVELING GRATE

PELLETS HEAT—HARDENED
IN ROTARY KILN

HOT KILN DISCHARGE GAS
USED IN DOWNDRAFT
PREHEATING SECTIONS

Fig. 5—30. Schematic diagram of the grate-kiln system for producing pellets.

using this system began in 1960 in Upper Michigan. No solid fuel is added to the pellets, and fuel consumption, in the form of No. 6 fuel oil, amounts to about 1 million B.t.u. per ton of pellets.

Nodulizing—In this agglomerating process, fine iron-bearing materials moving through a rotary kiln are formed into nodules or lumps (Figure 5—19) by the rolling of the charge heated to incipient fusion temperatures. This process has been used at various places throughout the world to agglomerate fine iron-bearing materials. One of the first installations in the U. S. A. was at South Chicago where flue dust was nodulized in a 6 x 60 foot kiln about 1904. Magnetite concentrates from the Cornwall, Pennsylvania, mine were agglomerated by nodulizing in a bituminous coal-fired rotary kiln for 13 years in a plant that was shut down in 1920 because of the adoption of the cheaper sintering process. In World War II many nodulizing operations were initiated at existing cement plants to relieve the shortage of open-hearth charge ore; however, these plants had not necessarily been designed for efficient nodulizing of iron ores. Nodulizing has the advantage that feed moisture and particle size are not critical as they are in pelletizing. But, in addition to the disadvantage of high fuel consumption, which is reported to vary from about 2 to 4 million B.t.u. per ton of product, the formation of rings and large balls has been a serious problem at all installations at some time in their operation and seems to be the most frequent cause of shutdown. Although nodules appear satisfactory for open-hearth use, they are not acceptable as an agglomerate for good blast-furnace performance largely because of their nonuniform size and inferior reducibility. Further information on nodulizing may be found in the appropriate references under Section 5 at the end of the chapter.

Briquetting—Briquetting is an old art that has been used to agglomerate or form small or large lumps of regular shape from a wide variety of materials, including wood, coal, lignite, chars, cokes, ores, and flue dust. Various designs of punch and roll presses are or have been used. Between 30 and 50 years ago briquettes of fine ore, produced in punch, drop, or toggle presses and fired at high temperature before charging to the blast furnace, were believed to increase furnace capacity and lower coke rate. However, briquetting of cold or unheated material has not been successful as a means for producing satisfactory agglomerates for the blast furnace. "Cold" briquettes are usually formed with the use of a binder such as lime, cement, sulphite waste liquor, molasses, etc., so that they do not possess the cold and hot strength resulting from the high-temperature heating that is developed in pellets and sinter. Most "cold" briquettes that have been tried in the blast furnace have increased flue-dust losses and have not particularly improved furnace performance, probably because of decrepitation of the briquettes in the furnace.

In contrast, the hot-ore-briquetting (H-O-B) process, developed by United States Steel during the past several years, has shown promise experimentally as a means of producing a good substitute open-hearth charge ore and a suitable agglomerate for use as a blast-furnace charge (Figure 5—19). This process requires no added binder. In one version of the hot-ore-briquetting process (Figure 5—31), minus ¼-inch hematite-ore fines are heated to between 1600° and 1900° F and then briquetted while hot in a double-roll briquetting press at loads of 50 to 60 tons. Briquette strength and density increased as the temperature at which the ore was briquetted increased. In another version of this process, earthy and specular hematites, magnetites, and flue dusts are briquetted at somewhat lower temperatures by partial reduction of the material followed by briquetting at temperatures up to 1500° F at loads similar to those cited above. Briquette strength increased as the extent of partial reduction and the briquetting temperature and pressure were increased. Laboratory tests have shown that hot-ore briquettes have good cold strength and exhibit satisfactory hot strength under simulated blast-furnace conditions. In experimental blast-furnace tests, hot-ore briquettes exhibited the characteristics of an acceptable blast-furnace charge. Freezing and thawing tests indicate they should have excellent weathering resistance when stockpiled.

The H-O-B process requires only about half as much fuel per ton of product as sintering and about the same as that for pelletizing. The H-O-B process is less sensitive to changes in feed composition than the pelletizing process and requires little or no grinding of the ore to produce an acceptable product. Thus, it appears that hot-ore briquetting may well prove to be an important alternative to sintering and pelletizing as a means of agglomerating ore fines and concentrates for iron- and steelmaking operations. A commercial-size hot-ore-briquetting plant with a fluid-bed reactor for accomplishing the heating of the charge was installed in eastern Canada in 1962 on an ex-

perimental basis to briquette blast-furnace flue dust and is operating satisfactorily.

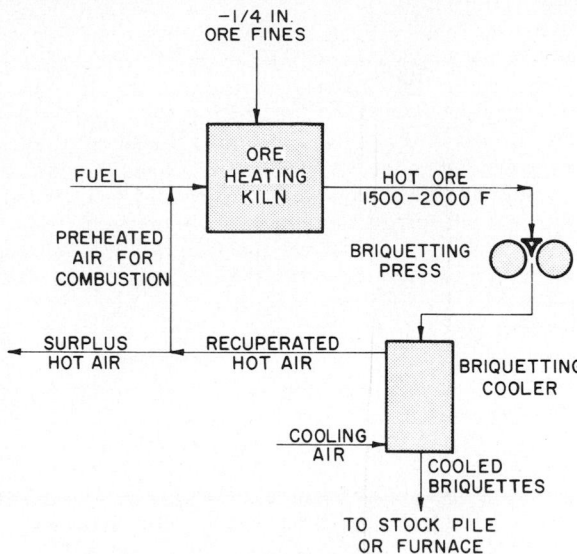

Fig. 5—31. Schematic diagram of hot-ore briquetting process.

SECTION 6

TRANSPORTATION OF IRON ORES

Historically, since the development of high capacity iron and steelmaking complexes, the avenues of iron ore commerce have been rail and water. The great Lake Superior Iron Ore District has occupied a very strategic location with respect to water routes along the Great Lakes to the steel centers on Lake Erie and Lake Michigan and in the Pittsburgh and Youngstown areas. As much as 96 million tons in one year have moved by rail to Great Lakes ports in Minnesota, Wisconsin, Michigan and Ontario, and thence by vessel to lower lake ports. Some is moved by rail again to inland points. There are now over 200 Great Lakes ore vessels in service or available for service, ranging in capacity per trip from 7,000 to 25,000 tons, and averaging 13,300 tons. Vessels of this type are shown in Figures 5—32, 5—34, and 5—37.

Discovery and development outside the United States of large deposits of high-grade ore close to deep-water ports but far removed from consuming centers has led to the utilization of ocean-going vessels specially designed for transporting iron ore. To realize the economies inherent in large-size vessels, modern ore carriers are being constructed with deadweight capacity of 60,000 tons and more. In order to accomodate these vessels, port and dock facilities have

to be engineered accordingly, in anticipation of a trend toward even larger vessels for economical intercontinental transportation of iron ores.

Transfer of iron ores from railroad cars to vessels is accomplished in the Great Lakes ports by unloading into dock pockets from which ore is discharged by gravity through chutes lowered into the holds of vessels (Figure 5—32). Elsewhere, and in more modern installations, ore is unloaded into shore bins or stockpiles from which it is recovered by shovels or ore-reclaim tunnels under the stock pile and transferred by conveyor belts for discharge into vessel holds (Figure 5—33). At receiving ports the ore is removed from the holds by Hulett electric unloaders (Figures 5—34 and 5—35) or unloading rigs (Figures 5—36 and 5—37) and transferred to stockpiles (Figure 5—37) or to railroad cars for shipment inland.

Under consideration for the future are pipelines for transportation of fine iron-ore concentrates from mine and concentrator to agglomerating facilities located at shipping ports. The possibility of year-round vessel movement on the Great Lakes is being given serious study, as likewise rail transport in modern integrated ore trains.

FIG. 5—32. Loading iron ore into the type of ore carrier commonly used on the Great Lakes.

FIG. 5—33. Loading dock at Puerto Crdaz, where ore mined at Cerro Bolivar is loaded into ocean-going vessels.

FIG. 5—34. Unloading ore from boats at a plant on the Great Lakes, showing Hulett unloaders in operation, with ore bridges in background.

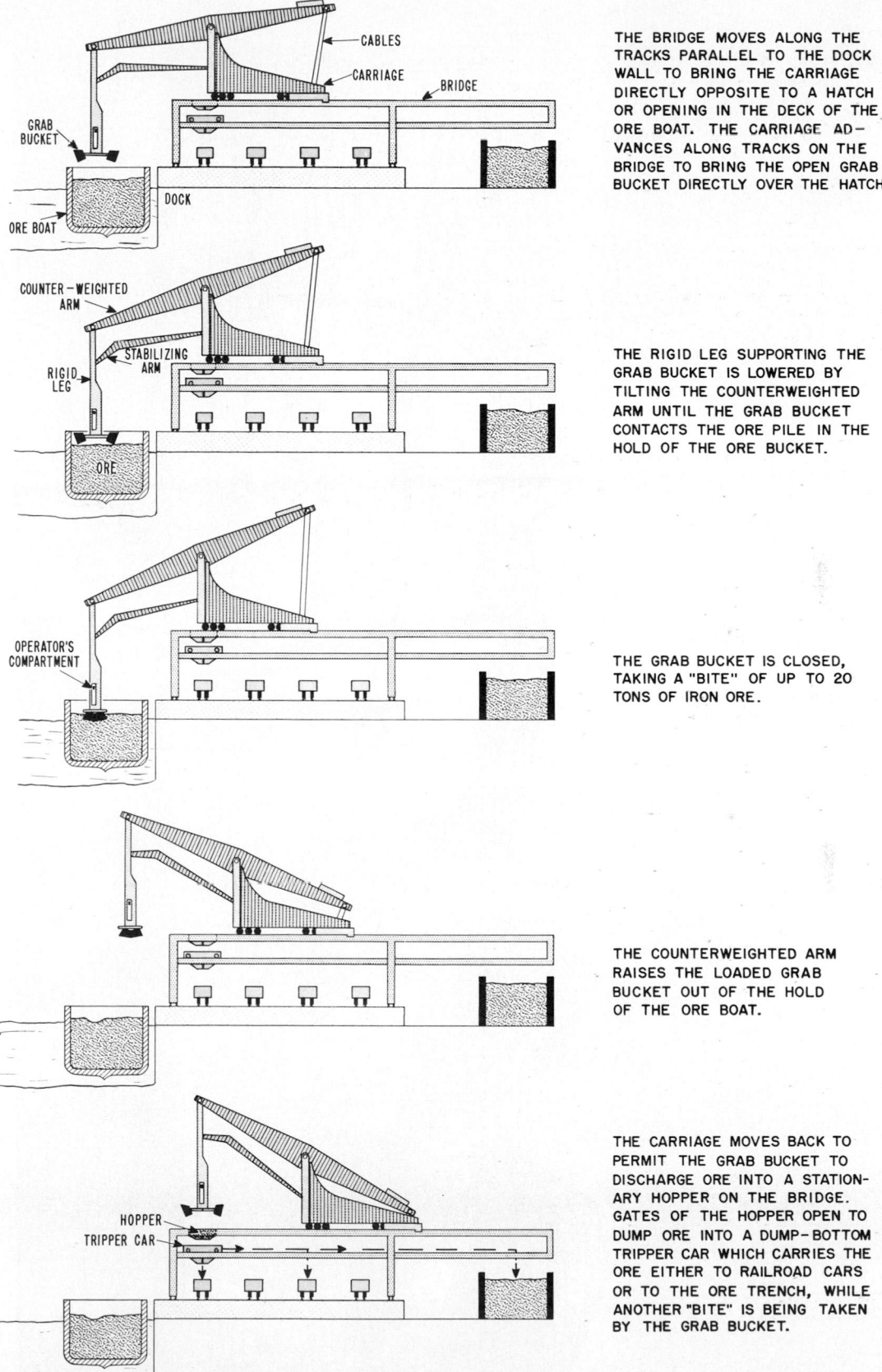

THE BRIDGE MOVES ALONG THE TRACKS PARALLEL TO THE DOCK WALL TO BRING THE CARRIAGE DIRECTLY OPPOSITE TO A HATCH OR OPENING IN THE DECK OF THE ORE BOAT. THE CARRIAGE ADVANCES ALONG TRACKS ON THE BRIDGE TO BRING THE OPEN GRAB BUCKET DIRECTLY OVER THE HATCH.

THE RIGID LEG SUPPORTING THE GRAB BUCKET IS LOWERED BY TILTING THE COUNTERWEIGHTED ARM UNTIL THE GRAB BUCKET CONTACTS THE ORE PILE IN THE HOLD OF THE ORE BUCKET.

THE GRAB BUCKET IS CLOSED, TAKING A "BITE" OF UP TO 20 TONS OF IRON ORE.

THE COUNTERWEIGHTED ARM RAISES THE LOADED GRAB BUCKET OUT OF THE HOLD OF THE ORE BOAT.

THE CARRIAGE MOVES BACK TO PERMIT THE GRAB BUCKET TO DISCHARGE ORE INTO A STATIONARY HOPPER ON THE BRIDGE. GATES OF THE HOPPER OPEN TO DUMP ORE INTO A DUMP-BOTTOM TRIPPER CAR WHICH CARRIES THE ORE EITHER TO RAILROAD CARS OR TO THE ORE TRENCH, WHILE ANOTHER "BITE" IS BEING TAKEN BY THE GRAB BUCKET.

FIG. 5—35. The sequence of operations of a Hulett unloader transferring iron ore from the hold of an ore boat to railroad cars or storage areas on the dock.

FIG. 5—36. Ocean-going vessel discharging cargo of iron ore. The bucket of the nearest unloading rig is rising from the hold of the vessel, carrying a "grab" of iron ore. Ore bridge of the blast-furnace stock yard is visible at the left.

FIG. 5—37. Aerial view of part of a raw-materials stock yard. The ore-unloading operation is shown in the foreground: some of the blast furnaces that utilize the raw materials are seen in the background.

SELECTED BIBLIOGRAPHY

Iron Ore Deposits of the United States

LAKE SUPERIOR DISTRICT

American Iron Ore Association. Iron Ore, 1961.

Dutton, C. E. Pre-Cambrian Geology of Parts of Dickinson and Iron Counties, Michigan. Michigan Basin Geological Society, 1958.

Goldich, S. S. et al. The Pre-Cambrian Geology and Geochronology of Minnesota. Minnesota Geological Survey Bulletin 41, 1961.

Gruner, J. W. Mineralogy and Geology of the Mesabi Range. Iron Range Resources and Rehabilitation Commission, 1946.

James, H. L. et al. Geology of Central Dickinson County. United States Geological Survey Professional Paper 310, 1961.

James, H. L. Sedimentary Phases of Iron Formation. Economic Geology, v. 49, 1954.

Lake Superior Iron Ore Association. Lake Superior Iron Ores, First and Second Editions.

Leith, C. K., Lund, R. J., and Leith, A. Pre-Cambrian Rocks of the Lake Superior Region. United States Geological Survey Professional Paper 184, 1935.

Schwartz, G. M., Goldich, S. S., and Marsden, R. W. Pre-Cambrian of Northeastern Minnesota. Geological Society of America Guidebook, 1956.

Tyler, S. A. Development of Lake Superior Soft Ores. Geological Society of America Bulletin, v. 60, 1949.

Van Hise, C. R. and Leith, C. K. Geology of the Lake Superior Region. United States Geological Survey Monograph 42, 1911.

Wade, H. H. and Alm, M. R. Mining Directory. University of Minnesota Bulletin, 1961.

White, D. A. Stratigraphy and Structure of the Mesabi Range. Minnesota Geological Survey Bulletin 38, 1954.

NORTHEASTERN DISTRICT

Bayley, William S. Iron Mines and Mining in New Jersey. Geological Survey of New Jersey, v. 7, 1910.

Gray, Carlyle and Lapham, Davis M. Guide to the Geology of Cornwall, Pennsylvania. Pennsylvania Topographic and Geologic Survey Bulletin G35, 1961.

Leonard, Benjamin F. Magnetite Deposits of the Saint Lawrence County District, New York. United States Geological Survey Open File Report, 1951.

Newland, D. H. and Kemp, J. F. Geology of the Adirondack Magnetic Iron Ores, With a Report on the Mineville-Port Henry Mine Group. New York State Museum Bulletin 119, 1908.

Postel, A. Williams. Geology of Clinton County Magnetite District, New York. United States Geological Survey Professional Paper 237, 1952.

Sims, P. K. Geology of the Dover Magnetite District, Morris County, New Jersey. United States Geological Survey Bulletin 982-G, pp. 245-305, 1953 (1954).

Spencer, A. C. Magnetite Deposits of the Cornwall Type in Pennsylvania, United States Geological Survey Bulletin 359, 1908.

Stephenson, R. C. Titaniferous Magnetite Deposits of the Lake Sanford Area, New York State Museum Bulletin 340, 1945.

MISSOURI DISTRICT

Ballinger, H. J. and Pesonen, P. E. Investigation of Southeast Missouri Secondary Limonite Deposits—Wayne, Butler, and Ripley Counties, Missouri. United States Bureau of Mines Report of Investigations 4314, 1948.

Brown, J. S. Iron Ores of Missouri. Presented at American Institute of Mining, Metallurgical, and Petroleum Engineers Meeting, St. Louis, 1958.

Christiansen, Carl R. Iron Ore Mining in Missouri. Skillings' Mining Review no. 5, v. 51, February 3, 1962.

Crane, G. W. The Iron Ores of Missouri. Missouri Bureau of Geology and Mines, v. X, second series, 1912.

Frommer, D. W. and Fine, M. M. Recovering Iron Concentrates from the Pea Ridge Deposit, Central Missouri. United States Bureau of Mines Report of Investigations 5550, 1960.

Hayes, W. C. Geology and Exploration of Missouri Iron Deposits. Missouri Division of Geological Survey and Water Resources Miscellaneous Publication, 1961.

Jones, E. A. Meramec Mining Company's Iron Mine at Pea Ridge, Missouri. Twenty-Third Annual Mining Symposium, University of Minnesota, and the Annual Meeting of Minnesota Section, American Institute of Mining, Metallurgical, and Petroleum Engineers, 1962.

Kline, H. D. Methods and Costs of Producing Brown Iron Ore at Two Small Southern Missouri Mines. United States Bureau of Mines Information Circular 7983, 1960.

New Mineral Developments in S.E. Missouri. St. Louis Commerce, December, 1960.

Pettit, R. F., Jr., Calhoun, W. A. and Reynolds, B. M. Mining and Milling Methods and Costs, Ozark Ore Company. Iron Mountain Iron-Ore Mine, St. Francois County, Missouri. United States Bureau of Mines Information Circular 7807, 1957.

SOUTHEASTERN DISTRICT

Brown, Andrew. North Alabama Brown Iron Ores. United States Bureau of Mines Report of Investigations 4229, 1948.

Chapman, H. H. The Iron and Steel Industries of the South. University of Alabama Press, 1953.

Pallister, H. D. Brown Iron Ore in South Alabama. Alabama Academy of Science Journal, v. 26, 1954.

Thoenen, J. R. and Clemmons, B. H. The Future of Birmingham Red Iron Ore. United States Bureau of Mines Report of Investigations 4988, 1953.

United States Bureau of Mines. Materials Survey—Iron Ore. 1956.

WESTERN DISTRICT
General

American Institute of Mining and Metallurgical Engineers. Ore Deposits of the Western United States. (Lindgren Volume) 1933.

Carr, M. S., and Dutton, C. E. Iron Ore Resources of the United States Including Alaska and Puerto Rico. United States Geological Survey Bulletin 1082-C, pp. 61-134, 1959.

Luttrell, G. W. Bibliography of Iron Ore Resources of the World (to January 1955). United States Geological Survey Bulletin 1019-D, pp. 187-371, 1957.

Open Pit Mine Production and Stripping Tonnages, 1958-1961; Underground Mine Production from Individual Mines, 1956-1961. Mining World, v. 24, no. 5, pp. 95, 97-98, 1962.

Singewald, J. T., Jr. The Titaniferous Iron Ores in the United States; Their Composition and Economic Value. United States Bureau of Mines Bulletin 64.

United States Bureau of Mines. Minerals Yearbooks.

United States Geological Survey. Geological Survey Estimates, United States Iron Ore Resources. Information Service Release 2905, 1957.

Arizona

Burchard, E. F. Iron Ore on Canyon Creek, Fort Apache Indian Reservation, Arizona. United States Geological Survey Bulletin 821-C, pp. 51-78, 1931.

Farnham, L. L., and Havens, R. Pikes Peak Iron Deposits, Maricopa County, Arizona. United States Bureau of Mines Report of Investigations 5319, 1957.

Joseph, P. E. Iron. Arizona University Bureau of Mines Bulletin 43, 1916.

Kerns, W. H., Kelly, F. J., and Mullen, D. H. The Mineral Industry of Arizona. United States Bureau of Mines Minerals Yearbook, 1960, v. 3, p. 107, 1961.

Stewart, L. A. Apache Iron Deposit, Navajo County, Arizona. United States Bureau of Mines Report of Investigations 4093, 1947.

California

California Division of Mines. Iron Resources of California. California Division of Mines Bulletin 129, 1948.

Carlisle, Donald, Davis, D. L., Kildale, M. B., and Stewart, R. M. Base Metal and Iron Deposits of South California. California Division of Mines Bulletin 170, chap. 8, pt. 5, pp. 41-50, 1954 (1955).

Harder, E. C. Iron Ore Deposits of the Eagle Mountains, California. United States Geological Survey Bulletin 503, 1912.

Hughes, M. J. Pit Operations at the Eagle Mountain Iron Ore Mine. Skillings' Mining Review, v. 49, no. 50, pp. 1, 4-7, 16, 1960.

Mining Methods at the Vulcan Iron Mine, San Bernardino County, California. United States Bureau of Mines Information Circular 7437, 1948.

Severy, C. L. Exploration of the Minarets Iron Deposit, Madera County, California. United States Bureau of Mines Report of Investigations 3985, 1946.

Shattuck, J. R. and Ricker, Spangler. Shasta and California Iron Ore Deposits, Shasta County, California. United States Bureau of Mines Report of Investigations 4272, 1948.

Trengove, R. R. Methods and Operations at the Kaiser Steel Corporation, Eagle Mountain Iron Mine, Riverside County, California. United States Bureau of Mines Information Circular 7735, 1956.

Wiebelt, F. J. and Ricker, Spangler. Iron Mountain Deposits, San Bernardino County, California. United States Bureau of Mines Report of Investigations 4236, 1948.

Montana

DeMunck, V. C. Iron Deposits in Montana. Montana Bureau of Mines and Geology Information Circular 13, 1956.

Holmes, W. T., II, Holbrook, W. F., and Banning, L. H. Beneficiating and Smelting Carter Creek, Montana, Iron Ore. United States Bureau of Mines Report of Investigations 5922, 1962.

Nevada

Geehan, R. W. Investigation of the Dayton Iron Deposit, Lyon and Storey Counties, Nevada. United States Bureau of Mines Report of Investigations 4561, 1949.

Kral, V. E. Modarelli Iron Deposit, Eureka County, Nevada. United States Bureau of Mines Report of Investigations 4005, 1947.

Mason Valley News, 1959-1962. Many articles on the Minnesota Mine, Yerington, Nevada.

Reeves, R. G., and Kral, V. E. Geology and Iron Ore Deposits of the Buena Vista Hills, Churchill and Pershing Counties, Nevada. Nevada Bureau of Mines Bulletin 53-A, pp. 1-32, 1955.

Reeves, R. G., Shawe, F. R., and Kral, V. E. Iron Ore Deposits of West-Central Nevada. Nevada Bureau of Mines Bulletin 53-B, pp. 33-78, 1958.

New Mexico

Kelley, V. C. Geology and Economics of New Mexico Iron Ore Deposits. New Mexico University Publications in Geology no. 2, 1949.

Kelley, V. C. Oölitic Iron Deposits of New Mexico. American Association of Petroleum Geologists Bulletin, v. 35, no. 10, pp. 2199-2228, 1951.

Paige, Sidney. The Hanover Iron Ore Deposits, New Mexico. United States Geological Survey Bulletin 380, pp. 199-214, 1909.

Sheridan, M. J. Lincoln County Iron Deposits, New Mexico. United States Bureau of Mines Report of Investigations 3988, 1947.

Soule, J. H. Capitan Iron Deposits, Lincoln County, New Mexico. United States Bureau of Mines Report of Investigations 4022, 1947.

Oregon and Washington

Reichert, W. H., compiler. Bibliography and Index of the Geology and Mineral Resources of Washington, 1937-1956. Washington Division of Mines and Geology Bulletin 46, 1960.

Steere, M. L., compiler. Bibliography of the Geology and Mineral Resources of Oregon, Second Supplement. Oregon Department of Geology and Mineral Industries Bulletin 44, 1953.

Twenhofel, W. H. Origin of the Black Sands of the Coast of Southwest Oregon. Oregon Department of Geology and Mineral Industries Bulletin 24, 1943.

Zapffe, Carl. A Review of Iron-Bearing Deposits in Washington, Oregon, and Idaho. Raw Materials Survey Resource Report 5, 1949.

Texas

Brown, W. F. Sampling East Texas Iron Ores. United States Bureau of Mines Report of Investigations 5488, 1959.

Eckel, E. B. The Brown Iron Ores of Eastern Texas. United States Geological Survey Bulletin 902, 1938.

Fine, M. M., Frommer, D. W., and Dressel, W. M. Preliminary Mineral-Dressing Investigation of East Texas Brown Iron Ores. United States Bureau of Mines Report of Investigations 5252, 1956.

Kenworthy, H., and Starliper, A. G. Electric Furnace Smelting of East Texas Iron Ores—A Progress Report. United States Bureau of Mines Report of Investigations 5427, 1958.

Utah

Allsman, P. T. Investigation of Iron Ore Reserves of Iron County, Utah. United States Bureau of Mines Report of Investigations 4388 (supplement to Report of Investigations 4076), 1948.

Cook, K. L. Magnetic Surveys in the Iron Springs District, Iron County, Utah. United States Bureau of Mines Report of Investigations 4586, 1950.

Leith, C. K., and Harder, E. C. The Iron Ores of the Iron Springs District, Southern Utah. United States Geological Survey Bulletin 338, 1908.

Mackin, J. H. Some Structural Features of the Intrusions in the Iron Springs District—Guidebook to the Iron Springs District, Utah. Published by the Utah Geological Society, in cooperation with the United States Geological Survey, 1947.

Young, W. E. Iron Deposits, Iron County, Utah. United States Bureau of Mines Report of Investigations 4076, 1947.

Wyoming

Ball, S. H. The Hartville Iron Ore Range, Wyoming. United States Geological Survey Bulletin 315, pp. 190-205, 1907.

Bayley, R. W. Iron Deposits Near Atlantic City and South Pass, Fremont County, Wyoming. United States Geological Survey Open File Report, 1958.

Diemer, R. A. Titaniferous Magnetite Deposits of the Laramie Range, Wyoming. Wyoming Geological Survey Bulletin 31, 1941.

Frey, Eugene. Hartville Iron District, Platte County,

Wyoming. United States Bureau of Mines Report of Investigations 4086, 1947.

King, R. H. Iron Deposit near Atlantic City, Wyoming. Wyoming Geological Survey Open File Report, 1949.

Lovering, T. S. The Rawlins, Shirley, and Seminoe Iron Ore Deposits, Carbon County, Wyoming. United States Geological Survey Bulletin 811-D, pp. 203-235, 1929.

Wideman, F. L. Block-Caving Methods at the Sunrise Mine, Platte County, Wyoming. United States Bureau of Mines Information Circular 7759, 1956.

Iron Ore Deposits of Canada

Elver, R. B. The Canadian Iron Ore Industry in 1960. Mineral Resources Division, Department of Mines and Technical Surveys, Ottawa, Canada, 1961.

Elver, R. B. Iron Ore. Canadian Mining Journal pt. 2, Mineral Reviews, pp. 88-94, February 1962.

Financial Post. Survey of Mines, 1961, pp. 279-284.

Goodwin, A. M. Structure, Stratigraphy and Origin of Iron Formations, Michipicoten Area, Algoma District, Ontario, Canada. Geological Society of America Bulletin, v. 73, no. 5, pp. 561-585, May 1962.

Gross, G. A. Classification of Iron Deposits in Canada. Geological Survey of Canada, Department of Mines and Technical Surveys, Ottawa, Canada, Reprint 5.

Gross, G. A. The Iron Ranges and Current Developments in New Quebec and Labrador, Canada. Geological Survey of Canada, Department of Mines and Technical Surveys, Ottawa, Canada, Reprint 10, 1960.

Gross, G. A. Metamorphism of Iron Formation and its Bearing on the Beneficiation. Geological Survey of Canada, Department of Mines and Technical Surveys, Ottawa, Canada, Reprint 23, 1961.

Guimond, R. Newfoundland—Labrador. Precambrian, September 1961.

Janes, T. A. and Wittur, G. A. The Primary Iron and Steel Industry in Canada. Mineral Resources Division, Department of Mines and Technical Surveys, Ottawa, Canada.

Jolliffe, A. W. Geology and Iron Ores of Steep Rock Lake. Economic Geology, v. 50, pp. 373-398, 1955.

Kindle, L. F. Moose Mountain—Wanapitei Area. Ontario Department of Mines, v. 41, pt. 4, p. 29, 1932.

Knowles, D. M., and Gastil, R. G. Metamorphosed Iron Formation in Southwestern Labrador. Canadian Institute of Mining and Metallurgy, Transactions, v. 62, pp. 265-272, 1959.

Lawton, K. D. Geology of Boston Township and Part of Pacand Township. Ontario Department of Mines, v. 66, pt. 5, 1957.

MacDonald, R. D. Iron Deposits of Wabush Lake, Labrador. Mining Engineering, pp. 1098-1102, October 1960.

Mining Industry of the Province of Quebec, pp. 18-19, 1960.

Iron Ore Deposits of South America and West Africa

SOUTH AMERICA

General

Blondel, F., and Marvier, L., eds. Symposium sur les Gisements de Fer du Monde. XIX International Geological Congress, 1952.

Reno, H. T., and Anderson, S. M. Iron Ore in South America. Twenty-First Annual Mining Symposium, University of Minnesota, pp. C1-13, 1960.

Venezuela

Iron Ore From Cerro Bolivar. Mining World, v. 16, 1954.

Lake, M. C. Cerro Bolivar—U. S. Steel's New Iron Ore Bonanza. Engineering and Mining Journal, v. 151, pp. 72-83, 1950.

Lippert, T. W. Cerro Bolivar—Saga of an Iron Ore Crisis Averted. Mining Engineering, v. 187, no. 2, pp. 178-192, 1950.

Rubio, E., and others. Geologia, Paragenesis y Reservas de los Yacimentor de Hierro de Imataca, Venezuela. Venezuela Direccion Tecnica de Geologia, Boletin de Geologia, v. 3, pp. 5-38, 1953.

Peru

Atchley, F. W. Geology of the Marcona Iron Ore Deposit, Peru. (abstract) Dissertation Abstracts, v. 17, pp. 2976-2977, 1957.

Herkenhoff, E. Marcona Iron Ore From Peru. Twenty-Third Annual Mining Symposium, University of Minnesota and the Annual Meeting of Minnesota Section, American Institute of Mining, Metallurgical and Petroleum Engineers, pp. 143-149, 1962.

Marcona—Four Months from Plan to Production. Engineering and Mining Journal, v. 155, pp. 84-88, 1954.

Peru Instituto Nacional de Investigacion y Fomento Mineros, Division de Geologia y Minas. El Fierro en el Peru. Lima, 1952.

Chile

Benitez, Fernando. The Iron Mines of Chile. Engineering and Mining Journal, v. 158, pp. 90-93, 1957.

El Algarrobo of Chile. Metal Bulletin, October 9, 1962.

Pena i Lillo, Oscar, Monografai Sobre el Mineral de Fierro del Tofo. Boletin Minero, Santiago, Ano 57, v. 53, 1941.

Brazil

Dorr, John Van Nostrand, II. The Iron Ore of Central Minas Gerais, Brazil. Engenharia, Mineracao e Metallurgia, Rio de Janeiro, v. 16, pp. 95-100, 1951.

Dorr, John Van Nostrand, II. O Problemas dos Minerios de Ferro Brasileiros Visto por um Geologo. Engenharia, Mineraco e Metallurgia, Rio de Janeiro, v. 124, pp. 365-372, 1956.

Dorr, John Van Nostrand, II. Reservas Estimadas de Mineracao de Ferro no Quadrilatero Ferrifero, Minas Gerais. Brasil Departmento Nacional da Producao Mineral, Rio de Janeiro, Anais 82, 1957.

Dorr, John Van Nostrand, II. Esboco Geologico do Quadrilatero Ferrifero de Minas Gerais. Brasil Departmento Nacional da Producao Mineral, Publication Especial no. 1, Rio de Janeiro, 1959.

Odman, Olaf. Iron and Manganese Ores of Brazil. Engenharia, Mineracao e Metallurgia, Rio de Janeiro, v. 23, pp. 219-221, 1956.

United Nations. Survey of World Iron Ore Reserves, pp. 211-213, 1955.

WEST AFRICA

Liberia

The Bomi Hills Development. Mining Engineering, v. 4, pp. 674-675, July 1952.

Fitzhugh, E. F., Jr. Bomi Hills—Liberia Mining Company's New High Grade Iron Ore Mine. Skillings' Mining Review, v. 41, no. 2, 1952.

LAMCO's Iron Ore Port Development at Buchanan, Liberia. Skillings' Mining Review, October 20, 1962.

LAMCO's Iron Ore Project in Liberia on Schedule. Skillings' Mining Review, June 9, 1962.

Newhouse, W. H., Thayer, T. P., and Butler, A. P., Jr. The Iron Ore Reserves at Bomi Hills, Liberia. United States Geological Survey Open File Report, 1945.

The Nimba Iron Ore Project in Liberia. Skillings' Mining Review, July 16, 1960.

Smith, Kenneth S. Liberian Co-op Mine is Yielding Ore. New York Times, December 3, 1961.

Mauritania

Blanchot, A. The Iron Ore Deposit of Fort Gouraud. Chronique Miner Coloniales, Paris, v. 19, p. 187, 1951.

Crowder, Michael. Iron Ore From Mauritania. Steel Review, July 1960.

La Fer d'Fort Gouraud. Europe France Outremer, nos. 382 and 384, September 1961 and February 1962.

Discovery and Mining of Iron Ores

Cummings, J. D. Diamond Drill Handbook. J. K. Smit & Sons, 1956.

McManus, C. E., and Stubbins, J. New Development in Open Pit Mining, Canadian Area. Twenty-Third Annual Mining Symposium, University of Minnesota, and the Annual Meeting of Minnesota Section, American Institute of Mining, Metallurgical, and Petroleum Engineers, pp. 115-120, 1962.

Moberg, N. A. New Developments in Exploration and Investigation of Iron Ore Properties. Twenty-Third Annual Mining Symposium, University of Minnesota, 1962.

Parks, R. D. Examination and Valuation of Mineral Property. Addison-Wesley Press, Inc., 1949.

Pearson, P. D. New Developments in Underground Mining Throughout the Lake Superior Iron Ranges. Twenty-Third Annual Mining Symposium, University of Minnesota, and the Annual Meeting of Minnesota Section, American Institute of Mining, Metallurgical, and Petroleum Engineers, pp. 101-107, 1962.

Peele, R., and Church, J. A. Mining Engineers' Handbook. John Wiley & Sons, Inc., 1941.

Woodle, M. G., and Bertie, R. New Developments in Open Pit Mining, Minnesota and Michigan Area. Twenty-Third Annual Mining Symposium, University of Minnesota, and the Annual Meeting of Minnesota Section, American Institute of Mining, Metallurgical, and Petroleum Engineers, pp. 109-114, 1962.

Young, G. J. Elements of Mining. McGraw-Hill Book Co., 1946.

Beneficiation of Iron Ores

Beneficiation

Berkolm, R. W. How Flotation Makes High-Grade Specular Hematite Concentrate at Humboldt. Mining World, pp. 30-33, November 1961.

Cohlmeyer, S. H., Henderson, A. S., and Morgan, R. C. The Story of Atlantic City. Twenty-Third Annual Mining Symposium, University of Minnesota, and the Annual Meeting of Minnesota Section, American Institute of Mining, Metallurgical, and Petroleum Engineers, pp. 133-138, 1962.

DeVaney, F. D. Iron Ore Beneficiation. Engineering and Mining Journal, pp. 141-143, February 1956.

McAneny, C. C., Special Report—Direct Reduction of Iron Ore. Engineering and Mining Journal, pp. 84-99, December 1960.

Ramsey, R. H. Teamwork on Taconite. Engineering and Mining Journal, pp. 82-93, March 1955.

Reserve's New Taconite Project. Engineering and Mining Journal, pp. 75-102, December 1956.

Reserve's Taconite Concentrator. Engineering and Mining Journal, pp. 228-229, June 1959.

Roe, L. A. Iron Ore Beneficiation. Minerals Publishing Co., 1957.

Scott, D. Beneficiation of Lake Superior Iron Ores, A Review and Appraisal of Recent Trends. Twenty-Third Annual Mining Symposium, University of Minnesota, and the Annual Meeting of Minnesota Section, American Institute of Mining, Metallurgical, and Petroleum Engineers, pp. 121-131, 1962.

Smith, R. R. Iron Ore Flotation in Michigan. Skillings' Mining Review, January 28, 1961.

Urich, D. M. Pelletizing Humboldt's Iron Concentrate by Grate-Kiln Process. Mining World, pp. 16-21, October 1961.

Wade, H. H. and Schulz, N. F. Magnetic Roasting of Iron Ores in a Traveling Grate Roaster. Mining Engineering, pp. 1161-1165, November, 1960.

World's Largest Taconite Plant. Engineering and Mining Journal, pp. 235-237, June 1959.

Barthelemy, R. E. How High Tension Electrostatic Separation Recovers Iron Ore. Engineering and Mining Journal, v. 159, pp. 87-91, December 1958.

Bernstrom, B. Grinding Iron Ore in a Wet Autogenous Mill. American Institute of Mining, Metallurgical, and Petroleum Engineers Transactions, v. 223, pp. 304-311, September 1962.

Bogdanov, O. S., Shapiro, R. B., and Danilova, E. V. New Trends in the Beneficiation of Ferrous and Nonferrous Metal Ores. Contemporary Problems of Metallurgy, A. M. Samarin, Editor, Consultants Bureau, pp. 29-42, 1960.

Everard, F. and Janes, R. Dry Autogenous Grinding and Dry Magnetic Separation of Iron Ores. American Institute of Mining, Metallurgical, and Petroleum Engineers Transactions, v. 223, pp. 88-96, March 1962.

Frommer, D. W. and Fine, M. M. Recovering Iron Concentrates from the Pea Ridge Deposit, Central Missouri. United States Bureau of Mines Report of Investigations 5550, 1960.

Gaudin, A. M. Principles of Mineral Dressing. McGraw-Hill Book Co., 1939.

Holliday, R. W. Iron. United States Bureau of Mines Bulletin 556, Mineral Facts and Problems, pp. 371-398, 1956.

International Mineral Dressing Congress Proceedings, 1960. Institute of Mining and Metallurgy, pp. 675-754.

Lee, Oscar. Taconite Beneficiation Comes of Age at Reserve's Babbitt Plant, Mining Engineering, v. 6, pp. 484-488, May 1954.

Linney, R. J. Economy Through Design. American Institute of Mining, Metallurgical, and Petroleum Engineers Transactions, v. 214, pp. 909-914, 1959.

Palasvirta, O. E., and Andreachi, J. R. High-Intensity Magnetic Separation of Iron Ores. Twenty-Third Annual Mining Symposium, University of Minnesota, pp. 37-41, 1962.

Reno, H. T. Iron. United States Bureau of Mines Bulletin 585, Mineral Facts and Problems, pp. 403-421, 1960.

Roe, L. A. Iron Ore Beneficiation. Minerals Publishing Company, 1957.

Scott, D. W., and Wesner, A. Properties of Nonmagnetic Taconites Affecting Concentration. American Institute of Mining, Metallurgical, and Petroleum Engineers Transactions, v. 199, pp. 635-641, 1954.

Shale, S. J. Cornwall Keeps Its Methods Up-to-Date. Mining Engineering, v. 7, pp. 670-675, July 1953.

Taggart, A. F. Handbook of Mineral Dressing. Section 2, Article 28, Iron Minerals. John Wiley and Sons, pp. 134-151, 1945.

Volin, M. E., Beebe, R. R., and Hockings, W. A. Problems of Beneficiating the Oxidized Iron Formations. The Mines Magazine, v. 51, pp. 16-20, October 1961.

Wade, H. H. Oxidized Taconite—Its Possible Utilization by Roasting and Magnetic Concentration. 23rd Annual Mining Symposium, University of Minnesota, pp. 67-72, 1962.

Watkins Cyclopedia of the Steel Industry. Steel Publications, pp. 61-72, 1963.

Webb, W. R. and Fleck, R. G. Beneficiation of Adirondack Magnetite. Blast Furnace, Coke Oven and Raw Materials Committee, American Institute of Mining, Metallurgical and Petroleum Engineers Proceedings, v. 9, pp. 220-230, 1950.

Sintering

Brandes, G. and Rausch, H. Mixing and Conditioning Sinter-Plant Feed. Blast Furnace, Coke Oven, and Raw Materials Committee, American Institute of Mining, Metallurgical, and Petroleum Engineers Proceedings, v. 18, pp. 232-249, 1959.

Davies, W. E. Some Practical Applications of Fundamental Sinter Research. Canadian Mining and Metallurgical Bulletin, v. 53, pp. 173-185, March 1960.

English, Alan. Iron Ore Agglomeration—Sintering and Pelletizing. Iron and Steel Engineer, v. 38, pp. 113-119, March 1961.

Knepper, W. A., Editor. Agglomeration; based on an International Symposium held in Philadelphia, Pa., April 12-14, 1961. Interscience Publishers, 1962.

Meredith, J. W. and Frankau, A. M. Control and Proportioning of Sinter Plant Raw Materials. Blast Furnace, Coke Oven, and Raw Materials Committee, American Institute of Mining, Metallurgical, and Petroleum Engineers Proceedings, v. 18, pp. 60-67, 1959.

Nyquist, Orvar. Studies of the Effect of Gangue in the Sintering of Rich Magnetite and Hematite Concentrates. Jernkontorets Annaler, v. 146, no. 2, pp. 81-145, 1962.

Porteus, J. H. A Review of Iron Ore Sintering. Iron and Steel Engineer, v. 38, pp. 144-155, May 1961.

Pritykin, D. P. Experience in Using Equipment at Sintering Plants. Metallurgist, no. 10, pp. 429-435, October 1960.

Robinson, A. W. Swedish Sintering Practice—The Holmberg System. Blast Furnace, Coke Oven and Raw Materials Committee, American Institute of Mining, Metallurgical, and Petroleum Engineers Proceedings, v. 9, pp. 246-258, 1950.

Rowen, H. E. Development of the Dwight-Lloyd Sintering Process. Journal of Metals, v. 8, pp. 828-831, July 1956.

Takahaski, Y., et al. New Sintering Process (Semi-Pellet) for Fine Iron Ores. American Institute of Mining, Metallurgical, and Petroleum Engineers Transactions, v. 220, pp. 499-505, 1961.

Walter, A. R. The Use of Anthracite Coal in Sintering Iron Ore at the Bethlehem Steel Company Concentrator Plant, Lebanon, Pa. Sixth Annual Anthracite Conference of Lehigh University, Bethlehem, Pa., May 6-7, 1948, Transactions, pp. 139-158.

Wendeborn, H. The Importance of the Sintering Process in the Production of Pig Iron. MetallGesellschaft, Review of the Activities, no. 1, pp. 2-12, 1959.

Pelletizing

Banks, G. N., Campbell, R. A., and Viens, G. E. Iron Ore Pelletizing—A Literature Survey. Department of Mines and Technical Surveys, Mines Branch, Extraction Metallurgy Division, Ottawa, Canada, Internal Report EMA 62-7, April 10, 1962. Presented before the Annual Meeting of the Canadian Institute of Mining and Metallurgy, Ottawa, April 1962.

Barrett, E. P. Shaft Furnace Reduction by the Glomerule Method. United States Bureau of Mines, Report of Investigations 3229, pp. 47-49, 1934.

Berkhahn, R. W. and Urich, D. M. Grate Kiln Pelletizing Process at Humboldt. Twenty-Third Annual Mining Symposium, University of Minnesota, pp. 25-32, 1962.

Bunge, F. H. and Wakeman, J. S. Pelletizing Butler, Groveland, and Carol Lake Concentrates. Twenty-Third Annual Mining Symposium, University of Minnesota, Minneapolis, pp. 49-59, 1962.

Davis, E. W. and Wade, H. H. Agglomeration of Iron Ore by the Pelletizing Process. University of Minnesota Mines Experiment Station Circular no. 6, 1951.

Firth, C. V. Agglomeration of Fine Iron Ore. American Institute of Mining, Metallurgical, and Petroleum Engineers Blast Furnace and Raw Materials Committee Proceedings, v. 4, pp. 46-65, 1944.

Haley, K. M. and Apuli, W. E. Pelletizing on a Horizontal Grate Machine. Agglomeration, edited by W. A. Knepper. Interscience Publishers, pp. 931-957, 1962.

Jewett, R. P., Wood, C. E., and Hansen, J. P. Effect of Particle Size Upon the Green Strength of Iron Oxide Pellets. United States Bureau of Mines Report of Investigations 5762, 1961.

Kolesanov, F. F. and Gavin, E. G. Production of fluxed pellets from sulfur-containing magnetite concentrates of Magnitogorsk and Sokolov-Sarbai ores. Stal in English, no. 4, pp. 247-250, April 1962.

Merklin, K. E. and DeVaney, F. D. The Coarse Specularite—Fine Magnetite Pelletizing Process. Agglomeration, edited by W. A. Knepper. Interscience Publishers, pp. 965-975, 1962.

Merklin, K. E. and DeVaney, F. D. Production of Self-

Fluxing Pellets in the Laboratory and Pilot Plant. American Institute of Mining, Metallurgical, and Petroleum Engineers Transactions, v. 217, pp. 46-51, 1960. Also United States Patents 2,816,016; 2,831,210; 2,990,268.

Rovenskii, I. I. and Berezhnoi, N. N. Travelling-Grate Machine for Firing Fluxed Iron-Ore Pellets. Stal in English, no. 3, pp. 174-177, March 1962.

Westwater, J. S. Pelletizing by the Grate-Kiln Method at Humboldt. Blast Furnace and Steel Plant, v. 49, pp. 513-518, 530, June 1961.

Briquetting

Byrns, H. A. Briquetting Fine Ores at Woodward, Alabama. Blast Furnace, Coke Oven, and Raw Materials Committee, American Institute of Mining, Metallurgical, and Petroleum Engineers Proceedings, v. 8, pp. 158-164; Discussion, pp. 165-170, 1949.

Fournier, E. Note on the Agglomeration of Fine Ore from the Iron Mines at Rouen. Revue de l'Industrie Minerals, no. 235, pp. 435-438, 1930.

Franke, G. Present State of the Briquetting and Agglomeration of Iron Ores in Germany. Revue de Metallurgie, v. 7, pp. 953-954, 1910.

Hansell, N. V. The Briquetting of Iron Ores. American Institute of Mining, Metallurgical, and Petroleum Engineers Transactions, v. 43, pp. 394-411, 1912.

Lueck, B. F., Olson H. S., and Wiley, A. J. Modified Spent Sulphite Liquor Products as Binders and Adhesives for Briquets and Other Products. International Briquetting Association, Proceedings of the Seventh Biennial Conference, Jackson, Wyoming, August 28-30, 1961, pp. 14-25.

Moore, J. E. and Marlin, D. H. Hot Briquetting of Partially Reduced Iron Oxide Ores and Dusts. Agglomeration, edited by W. A. Knepper, Interscience Publishers, pp. 743-781, 1962.

Onoprienko, V. P., Lebedev, A. E., and Furman, D. M. Production of Fluxed Briquettes for the Iron and Steel Industry. Stal in English, no. 2, pp. 77-80, February 1961.

Stillman, A. L. Flue Dust Briquetting by the Corrosion Process. Iron Age, v. 110, pp. 1571-1572, 1922.

Thompson, R. G., Franklin, R. L., Guseman, J. R., and Rohaus, D. E. United States Steel Hot Ore Briquetting Process. Blast Furnace, Coke Oven, and Raw Materials Committee, American Institute of Mining, Metallurgical, and Petroleum Engineers Proceedings, v. 20, pp. 316-323, 1961. See also United States patent 2,336,618.

Wolf, W. and Wysocki, H. Operating Data on the Briquetting of (Blast Furnace) Flue Dust. Stahl und Eisen, v. 81, no. 9, pp. 559-561, 1961. (Brutcher Translation No. 5158)

Nodulizing, Extrusion, and Fluid-bed

Bennett, R. L., Hagen, R. E., and Mielke, M. V. Nodulizing Iron Ores and Concentrates at Extaca. Mining Engineering, v. 6, pp. 32-38, January 1954.

Brownstead, E. F. Manufacture of Nodules at Ironton, Ohio, Using Mesabi Fines and Blast-Furnace Flue Dust. American Institute of Mining, Metallurgical, and Petroleum Engineers Proceedings, v. 8, pp. 139-142; Discussion, pp. 142-145, 1949.

Cavanagh, P. E. Pelletizing of Iron-bearing Fines by Extrusion. Blast Furnace, Coke Oven, and Raw Materials Committee, American Institute of Mining, Metallurgical, and Petroleum Engineers Proceedings, v. 9, pp. 54-72, 1950.

Langston, G. B. and Stephens, F. M., Jr. Direct Reduction of Fine Iron Concentrates in a Self-Agglomerating Fluidized Bed. Blast Furnace, Coke Oven, and Raw Materials Committee, American Institute of Mining, Metallurgical, and Petroleum Engineers Proceedings, v. 19, pp. 205-214, 1960.

Ludwig, Carl. Agglomerating Ores by Vacuum Extrusion. Presented before the Annual Meeting, American Institute of Mining, Metallurgical, and Petroleum Engineers, February 18-21, 1952.

Oesterle, A. A. Manufacture of Nodules from Fine Ore and Limestone at Buffalo, N. Y. Blast Furnace, Coke Oven, and Raw Materials Committee, American Institute of Mining, Metallurgical, and Petroleum Engineers Proceedings, v. 8, pp. 132-136; Discussion, pp. 136-138, 1949.

Transportation of Iron Ores

Benford, H., Thornton, K. C., and Williams, E. B. Current Trends in the Design of Iron-Ore Ships. Society of Naval Architects and Marine Engineers Transactions, v. 70, 1962.

Hussey, C. R. Transportation, Handling and Storage of Iron Ores from Mines to Docks in the Lake Superior Region. Twenty-Second Annual Mining Symposium, University of Minnesota, and the Annual Meeting of Minnesota Section, American Institute of Mining, Metallurgical, and Petroleum Engineers, pp. B38-41, 1961.

Meissner, J. F. World Development and Movement of Iron Ore. Society of Naval Architects and Marine Engineers Transactions, v. 70, 1962.

Power, R. E. Economic Factors in the Location of Agglomerating Facilities. Twenty-Second Annual Mining Symposium, University of Minnesota, and the Annual Meeting of Minnesota Section, American Institute of Mining, Metallurgical, and Petroleum Engineers, pp. B77-84, 1961.

Turner, J. R. From Dock to Steel Plants—Lower Lakes Ports. Twenty-Second Annual Mining Symposium, University of Minnesota and the Annual Meeting of Minnesota Section, American Institute of Mining, Metallurgical, and Petroleum Engineers, pp. B50-53, 1961.

Vines, F. D. Transportation, Handling and Storage of Iron Ores. Twenty-Second Annual Mining Symposium, University of Minnesota, and the Annual Meeting of Minnesota Section, American Institute of Mining, Metallurgical, and Petroleum Engineers, pp. B42-49, 1961.

Wilbur, J. S. Lower Lake Railroads and Iron Ore Industry. Twenty-Second Annual Mining Symposium, University of Minnesota, and the Annual Meeting of Minnesota Section, American Institute of Mining, Metallurgical, and Petroleum Engineers, pp. B54-66, 1961.

CHAPTER 6

Fluxes

Function of Fluxes—Any metallurgical operation in which metal is separated by fusion from the impurities with which it may be chemically combined or physically mixed (as in ores) is called **smelting**. Since in iron smelting both these conditions with respect to impurities are always present, the production of crude iron involves two processes: (1) the reduction of the metal from its compounds and (2) its separation from the mechanical mixture. Many of the impurities associated with iron ores are of a highly refractory nature, that is, they are difficult to melt. If they should remain unfused, they would retard the smelting operation and interfere with the separation of metal and gangue. *To render such substances more easily fusible is the primary function of a flux.* Some elements, being reduced almost simultaneously with the iron, dissolve in it, or even combine chemically with it. Some other compounds, already combined with the metal in the raw materials, cannot separate from it unless there be present a substance with which they can combine in preference to the metal under the prevailing conditions. *To furnish a substance with which these elements or compounds may combine in preference to the metal is the secondary function of a flux.*

Chemistry of Fluxes—Selection of the proper flux for a given process is chiefly a chemical problem requiring knowledge of the composition and properties of all materials entering the process. With this knowledge, selection will be governed by well-established physical and chemical laws which apply at smelting temperatures, as discussed in Chapter 12. These laws are not unlike those which govern chemical reactions at ordinary temperatures. Of most importance are the laws concerning the formation of salts from the interaction of acids and bases. Practically all of the slag-forming compounds that enter into a smelting or refining process may be classed as either "acids" or "bases" by virtue of the fact that they will react with each other to form compounds which are analogous to the salts formed in reactions taking place in water solutions. In like manner, stronger or more active "acids" and "bases" will replace weaker or less active ones in slag compounds. The substances which are conveniently considered to be the most active "bases" at the high temperatures encountered in smelting and refining are those which are compounds of the elements forming basic compounds in ordinary chemical reactions in water solutions, such as calcium, magnesium, sodium, etc.; while the most

active "acid" impurities are compounds of silicon and phosphorus. These latter elements normally form acids in water solutions. In addition to these are compounds which are analogous to the amphoteric compounds. These are capable of acting as acids or bases depending on the conditions imposed. Since one of the functions of a flux is to react chemically with unwanted impurities to form a fusible slag, it will naturally follow that to remove "basic" impurities, an "acid" flux will be required and to remove "acid" components, a "base" will be used as the flux. It is fortunate that, generally speaking, the slag compounds formed by reactions between acid and basic materials have lower melting points than the reacting compounds, so that the primary function of a flux, rendering impurities more fusible, is simultaneously fulfilled. However, in some instances, a "neutral" material may also be used to lower the slag melting temperature and to improve slag fluidity. In most ores the impurities will be both acid and basic, with the acid materials usually predominating. In certain Southern ores, however, the acids and bases are so well balanced, or can be made so by mixing, that no additional flux is required.

Acid Fluxes—Silica (SiO_2) is the only substance that is used as a strictly acid flux. For this purpose, it is available as sand, gravel and quartz in large quantities and in a sufficiently pure state. In acid-steelmaking processes, silica is seldom added as a flux, for the silica sand used on the banks to protect the lining of the furnace supplies what may be required. On occasion, silica may be used in basic processes where excess lime has been charged, or where the raw materials are too low in silicon to produce a sufficient quantity of slag. Acid-Bessemer slags may be charged in the blast furnace for their beneficial fluxing or scouring effect on accumulations of lime on the furnace wall, as well as to recover the iron and manganese they contain. Gravel is used frequently for the same purpose. Siliceous iron-bearing materials are charged in making blast-furnace grades of ferrosilicon, but the function of silica in this case is to provide a source of silicon rather than to act as a flux.

Basic Fluxes—The chief natural basic fluxes are limestone, composed principally of calcium carbonate ($CaCO_3$), and dolomite, composed principally of calcium-magnesium carbonate, $(Ca,Mg) CO_3$. Either dolomite or limestone may be used as a blast-furnace flux, the proportions of each depending on the other

Table 6—I. Representative Compositions of Limestone, Burnt Lime, Dolomite and Burnt Dolomite (Natural State Determinations).

Ingredient	Limestone	Burnt Lime	Washed Dolomite	Burnt Dolomite
$CaCO_3$............	95.06	....	54.74	....
$MgCO_3$............	0.54	0.76	39.61	....
Fe_2O_3 $\}$ Al_2O_3	0.70	0.93	0.43	1.57
SiO_2..............	1.73	2.55	0.74	1.53
Sulphur...........	0.049	0.07	0.026	0.037
Phosphorus........	0.020	0.03	0.006	0.009
H_2O..............	1.70	....	4.00	....
CaO..............	....	81.36	....	56.35
MgO..............	....	....	....	38.65
Loss on Ignition....	....	14.00	....	1.60

constituents of the slag and the amount of sulphur that the slag must remove. Where large amounts of sulphur are to be removed, limestone is preferred. The blast-furnace fluxes are either charged into the furnace top as raw stone or, if the iron-bearing materials are to be sintered, the fluxes may be crushed and added in proper proportions to the sinter mix in a form called **fluxing fines.** In the latter instance, the flux combines with some of the impurities before charging into the blast furnace, thereby lessening the amount of raw stone required in the process.

Availability and cost are important factors when choosing between limestone and dolomite for blast-furnace use. Among other factors affecting the choice is the fact that a slag high in magnesia content is not desirable as a raw material for cement manufacture, but for ballast or concrete aggregate it produces a much harder product which is less subject to degradation by abrasion. Representative compositions of limestone and dolomite are given in Table 6—I, together with typical compositions for calcined or "burnt" limestone and dolomite.

Lime is usually added as calcined or "burnt" lime in the basic open-hearth process where more than the amount supplied by the limestone charged is found to be needed at a later stage of the heat. When oxygen roof lances are used the limestone in pulverized form may be blown in with the oxygen: this method is also used in certain pneumatic processes (see Chapter 15). While in acid steelmaking processes iron and manganese oxides act as bases, they are not normally added for this purpose and cannot strictly be classed as fluxes. Dolomite is not used in the basic open-hearth process except as a refractory.

The effectiveness of a natural basic flux is reduced by the chemically-acid impurities it contains, since these also must be neutralized by some of the chemically-basic compounds in the flux. The effectiveness of a basic flux is expressed in terms of "available base," by which is meant the amount of basic substance that remains in the raw flux after its own acid contaminants have been satisfied.

Alumina—Although alumina is seldom employed as a flux, it deserves mention at this point because it is present in a large number of raw materials as an impurity and is therefore present in slag. In slags it may function as an acid or as a base, depending on the conditions imposed. For instance, in highly siliceous slags, it may form aluminum silicates; while in the presence of an excess of a strong base such as lime, it may form calcium aluminates.

Neutral Fluxes—For the purpose of making slags more fusible, neutral substances having low fusion points may be added. For this purpose, fluorspar is the most commonly used substance. A typical composition of fluorspar, in which calcium fluoride is the active ingredient, is given in Table 6—II.

Table 6—II. Typical Composition of Fluorspar (Dry Basis)

Ingredient	Per Cent
CaF_2	81.0
SiO_2	4.75
Al_2O_3, Fe_2O_3	1.00
S	1.00
$CaCO_3$	Remainder

Sources of Fluxing Materials—As mentioned earlier, sources of silica for fluxing purposes are sand, gravel, quartz, and, in some cases, such material as used brick from silica-brick lined vessels or ladles. Acid-Bessemer and acid open-hearth slags or siliceous ores may be used in special instances. Limestone of fluxing quality is distributed widely and underlies most of the area drained by the Mississippi and Ohio Rivers. The larger portion of the limestone for the Pittsburgh steelmaking district originates in Western Pennsylvania, while that for the Lakes district is obtained from the northeastern section of the lower peninsula of Michigan, from northern Ohio and from southern Illinois. Dolomite is quarried chiefly in eastern West Virginia for use in the Eastern district. Fluorspar for the steel industry comes primarily from western Kentucky and southern Illinois.

MINING AND QUARRYING LIMESTONE AND DOLOMITE

Limestone and dolomite are taken from the earth's surface by one of two methods: underground mining and open-pit quarrying. Underground mines are now being replaced by more efficient, less costly quarrying operations where the size of machinery is not limited to the space restrictions of most underground operations. Because of its wide occurrence, limestone is probably the least expensive of all raw materials used in industry. To economically process limestone, then, a successful quarry must meet three requirements: (1) it must produce a quality stone high in calcium content (high in calcium and magnesium in the case of dolomite) with few impurities; (2) it must contain a sufficient volume of this stone either on or near the surface of the earth to keep the costly stripping of overburden to a minimum; and (3) it must be near navigable waters, highways, or rail facilities for convenient transportation.

Exhaustive steps are constantly being taken by geologists to discover new limestone deposits that meet these requirements. Once operations begin at a new quarry, a continuing program of quality analysis is initiated on stone taken from test holes and from processed stone to establish conformity with the exacting requirements of the steel manufacturer. To gain the proper chemical balance to meet specifications, stone taken from several points in the quarry may be blended on the basis of results of analyses by the chemical laboratory. As stated earlier in this chapter, stone used in iron- and steelmaking processes must have a high calcium carbonate or a high calcium-magnesium carbonate content, and a low content of silica and sulphur. Continuous quality-control programs, then, are necessary from quarry to loading dock.

Quarrying operations for limestone and dolomite differ only in those areas where the greater hardness of dolomite requires modifications in standard excavating and processing methods. In open-pit quarrying, the stone is blasted loose from the deposit by charges of an ammonium-nitrate blasting agent or dynamite in a series of cuts made in the quarry face. In a typical blasting of stone by the ammonium-nitrate method, holes up to nine inches in diameter are drilled at predetermined distances and depths. A charge of dynamite of specified strength is first lowered to the bottom of the hole, attached to a detonating cord. Depending upon the force of the charge required, alternate amounts of ammonium nitrate and primers (blasting-cap or detonating-cord sensitive charges) are loaded into the hole until the required explosive charge is placed. The hole is then stemmed by filling the remaining space with drill cuttings, and the detonating-cord ends from each of the blasting holes are gathered and taken to a point a safe distance from the blast area. After the blast area is cleared of personnel and equipment, the holes are fired.

Secondary blasting is performed on those pieces of stone that are not shattered by primary blasting. Smaller holes machine-drilled in these pieces are generally charged with dynamite alone.

In most modern quarries, stone is dug from the shattered piles along the quarry face by electrically powered shovels of various capacities. The stone is shovel-loaded into large trucks or side-dumping railroad cars for the trip to the primary crusher. The recent trend toward substituting truck haulage for railroad haulage stems principally from the inherent economy and flexibility of truck haulage over short distances or within confined areas of irregular grades.

PREPARATION OF FLUXES FOR USE

The fluxes previously mentioned usually require only drying and sizing before use. Those materials that may be added to a slag after it has melted, such as fluorspar and burnt lime, are desired small in size so that they will rapidly react to produce the desired results. Limestone and dolomite for sintering or for use directly in the blast furnace and limestone for use in the basic open-hearth require careful sizing because the rate of calcination of these materials is controlled primarily by the surface exposed. The chemical reactions of calcination are:

A. For pure calcium carbonate:
$$CaCO_3 \rightleftarrows CaO + CO_2$$
B. For pure magnesium carbonate:
$$MgCO_3 \rightleftarrows MgO + CO_2$$

Both decomposition reactions are endothermic and are affected by temperature and pressure. Reaction A comes to equilibrium under a pressure of one atmosphere of carbon dioxide at a temperature of about 1625° F, and Reaction B does the same at about 750° F, so that calcination will begin at temperatures much below steelmaking temperatures. For a given limestone at a given calcining temperature the surface area (screen size and shape) determines the time for complete calcination. The times for complete calcination at 1780° F of different sizes of an ordinary grade of limestone are about as follows:

Screen Size of Stone (In.)	Calcining Time (Hr.)
1	1 to 1½
2	2 to 3
3	3 to 4½
4	4 to 6
5	5 to 7½
6	6 to 9

Thus, in a blast furnace, for example, it is possible through a sizing of the stone to have its decomposition take place at different elevations in the stack. In general, the preferred size of limestone for sintering is minus ⅛-inch, that for blast furnaces is 2 to 4 inches, and that for open-hearth use is 4 to 8 inches.

Burnt lime is produced by the calcination of limestone in large rotary kilns of the type described in Section 3 of Chapter 7; such kilns may be several hundred feet long. They are inclined at a slight angle and are fired from the lower end. The slow rotation moves the stone from the upper charge end and during its passage through the kiln it decomposes to calcium oxide or burnt lime and is discharged at the fired or lower end, the carbon dioxide passing out of the kiln with the waste gases from combustion of the fuel.

CRUSHING AND SCREENING OF LIMESTONE AND DOLOMITE

The first essential step to arrive at a marketable limestone product takes place in the **crusher house.** In the larger plants, the **primary crusher** is usually a gyratory crusher resembling a gigantic mortar and pestle. The mortar-like pit is lined with manganese steel, and the stone is crushed against the walls of the pit by the off-center gyrations of the pestle

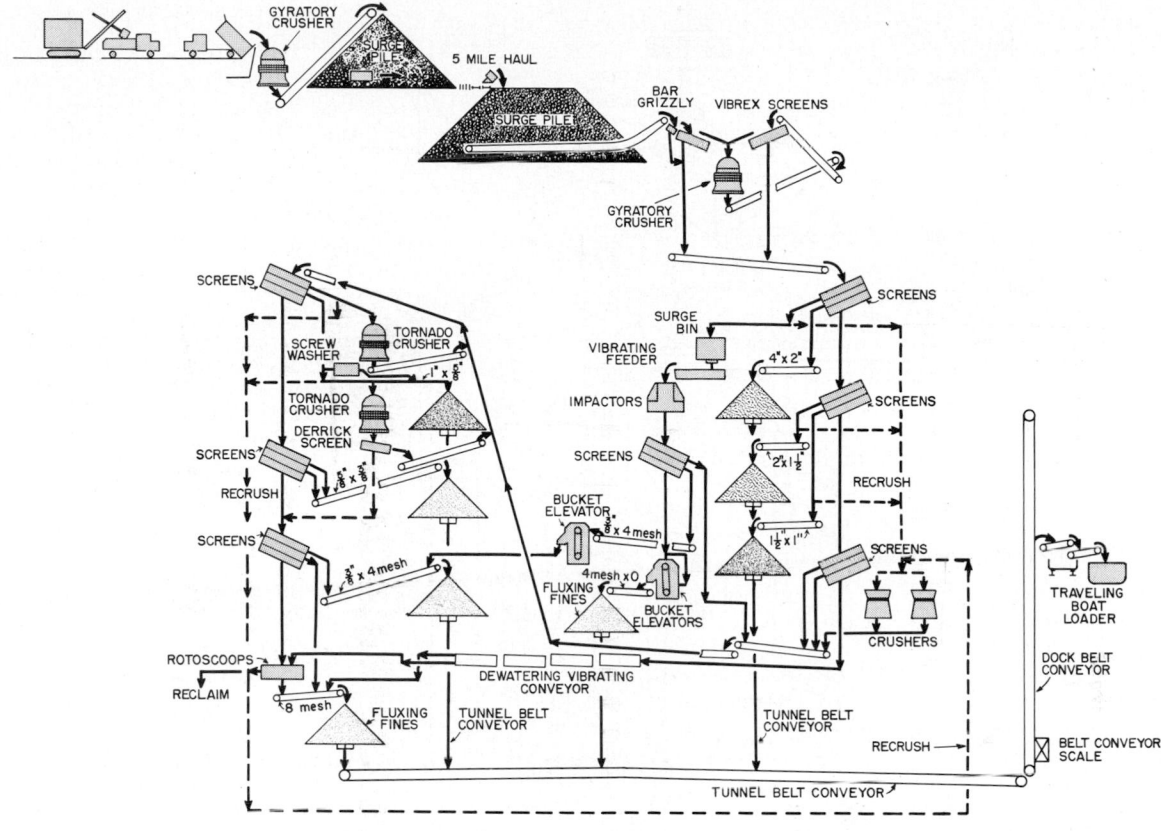

Fig. 6—1. Schematic flow diagram for the Cedarville Plant of United States Steel Corporation. Primary crushing is performed at the quarry site.

(mantle) that is usually made of chromium-molybdenum alloy steel. The large pieces of limestone or dolomitic limestone are reduced in size quickly by the action of the crusher and fall from a restricted opening at the base of the crusher onto a continuous belt conveyor. Throughput is rapid: a typical primary crusher can handle the crushing of over 1600 tons of stone per hour.

If the primary crusher is located within the quarry area (Figure 6—1), the crushed stone is generally lifted on the belt conveyor to a storage pile for shipment by truck or train to the **screen house.** Where the crusher is located at the plant site (Figure 6—2), the stone first travels over a scalping screen from a continuous belt conveyor. The **scalper** screens out all pieces of stone over a specified size, and the oversize stone is shunted to a **secondary crusher.** After it is re-crushed, this stone is returned to the conveyor carrying stone that passed through the scalping screen. All of the stone is then lifted to the top of the screen house or mill by belt conveyor to begin its descent through a series of crushers and screens equipped with water sprays to ensure cleanliness of the product. Stone intended for a particular product is subjected to a specific series of crushing and screening operations in the mill's system. As the stone reaches the predetermined size for the product group, it is transported by conveyor to storage piles on the shipping dock.

Thus, the ultimate size of the stone product required is determined by the amount of crushing and screening undertaken in the processing. Large openhearth flux stone is sized and separated out early in the process; however, fluxing fines, the finely ground stone of exacting size specifications used by the steel industry in the production of sinter, are produced by refinements in crushing and screening methods. Constant samplings of stone in process are taken and tested in the chemical laboratories to insure maintenance of the specified quality of the stone as it moves from quarry face to shipping dock.

TRANSPORTATION OF LIMESTONE

Limestone is transported from quarry to steel plant by rail, truck, or by lake carrier, depending upon the section of the country in which the consuming plant is located.

Major carriers of limestone from the large quarries located on the Great Lakes are self-unloader vessels, although some tonnage continues to be transported in the conventional bulk-cargo vessels. As the name implies, the self-unloader (Figures 6—3 and 6—4) is a self-contained carrier with its own unloading equipment, negating the necessity of unloading towers, crane bridges, or other unloading machinery at shore facilities. The self-unloader is a highly versatile cargo vessel that can accurately discharge from 10,000 to 25,000 tons of limestone at points as far as

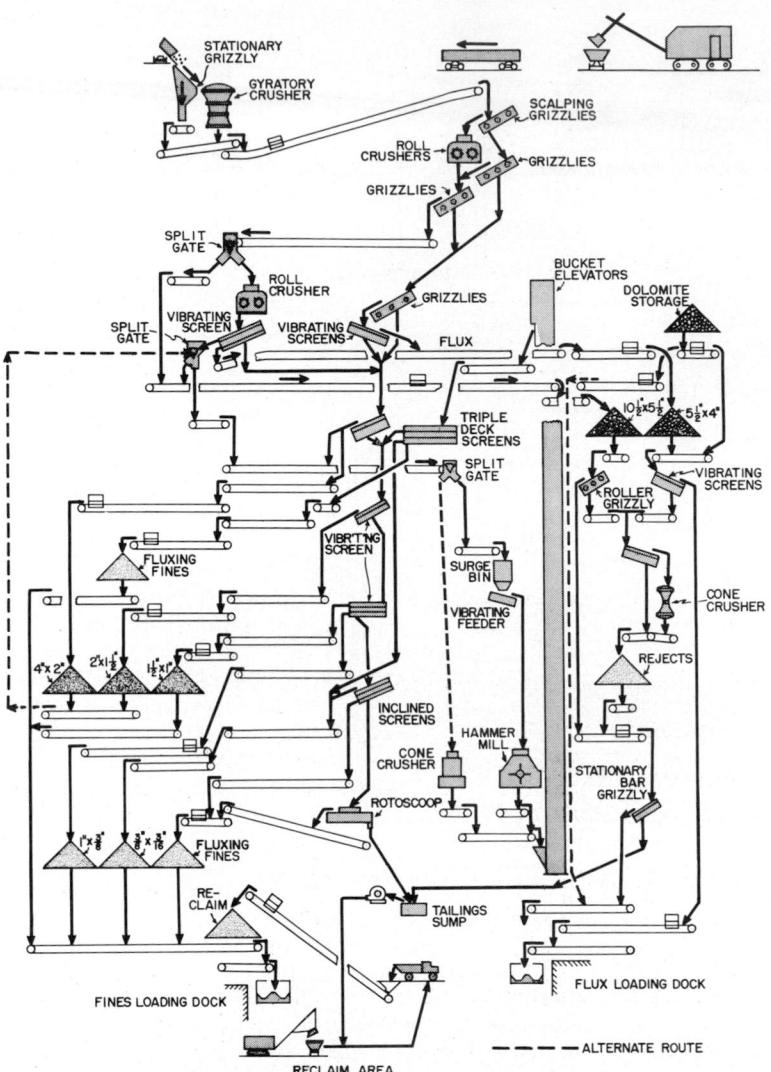

FIG. 6—2. Schematic flow diagram for the Calcite Plant of United States Steel. Raw stone is brought to the plant from the quarry by rail.

FIG. 6—3. A self-unloading limestone carrier with its boom swung overside, discharging its cargo onto storage piles at the receiving dock.

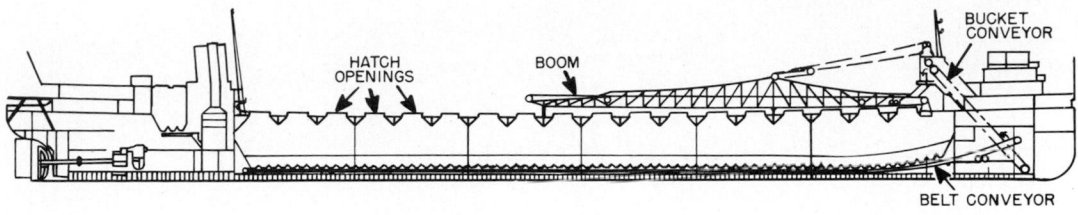

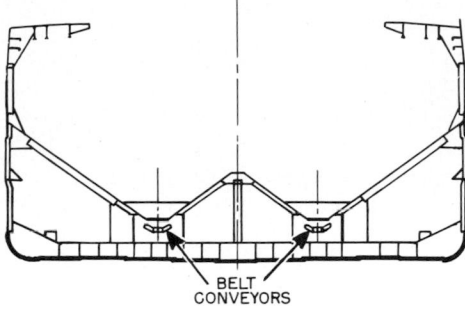

Fig. 6—4. Diagrammatic sections of a self-unloading limestone carrier. This particular vessel is slightly over 666 feet long, with a 72-foot beam. A geared turbine supplies 7000 shaft horsepower to propel the vessel at a service speed, loaded, of 16.75 miles per hour.

200 feet inland from the dock, depending upon the size of the vessel and the length of the vessel's mechanized boom.

Many of the limestone carriers now in service are bulk-cargo vessels that have been converted to self-unloaders by the installation of hopper bins, stone conveyors, bucket elevators and movable conveyor booms.

Below deck of the self-unloader is a series of hoppers. The hoppers are constructed in pairs, and each empties its cargo through a gate at the bottom of the hopper that is either mechanically or manually operated. Two belt conveyors run the length of the cargo hold, directly beneath the side-by-side hoppers. These parallel hold conveyors run from the stern of the cargo hold, carrying forward the limestone dropped from the various hopper gates and discharging the stone into chutes at the forward end of the vessel. The chutes, in turn, drop the stone into a large

bucket elevator that raises the limestone above deck to the boom conveyor. The stone then travels the length of the boom, to be discharged onto the dock.

The boom is designed not only to swing out a full 110 degrees from the longitudinal centerline of the vessel's deck to the dock area, but also to have its discharge end raised or lowered in any position.

Hopper gates are designed to give vessel personnel complete control over the flow of limestone. This control is particularly important in keeping the vessel on an even keel during the unloading operations.

A modern self-unloader can carry over 20,000 tons of limestone and unload its cargo at an average rate of 4,000 tons per hour.

When transported by rail, limestone and dolomite are carried either in gondola or hopper-bottom open cars, usually of 50-, 70-, or 90-ton capacity, according to the requirements of the plants where the stone is to be delivered.

CHAPTER 7

Slags

SECTION 1

METALLURGICAL CHARACTERISTICS OF SLAGS

Slag Defined—Slag is the name applied to the fused product formed by the action of a flux upon the gangue of an ore or fuel, or upon the oxidized impurities in a metal. As indicated in Chapter 6, they result from the neutralization of bases and acids, hence, correspond roughly to the salts formed in water solution during chemical reactions at ordinary temperatures. The subject of slags in general is a very large one, and the discussion in this section is intended merely to introduce certain of its more important aspects. A more detailed discussion of the chemical and physical properties of slags will be found in Chapter 12 on "Physical Chemistry of Iron- and Steelmaking."

Metallurgical Functions of Slags—On account of their fusibility, chemical activity, dissolving power, and low density, slags furnish the means by which impurities are separated from the metal and removed from the furnace in both iron- and steelmaking processes. Incidentally, as in the open-hearth process, for example, the slag performs other important functions. Lying upon the molten metal, it serves as a blanket to protect the metal from the action of hot gases. Because slag is a poor conductor of heat, it may sometimes prevent overheating of the metal and, at other times, conserve its heat. Since slags possess the power of dissolving oxides, the composition of the metal beneath the slag is controlled by changing the oxide content of the slag. In the metallurgy of ironmaking, the importance of slag cannot be overemphasized. In the blast furnace, the composition of the slag and the temperature of the metal and slag in the hearth furnish the means of control of the sulphur and silicon contents of the iron produced, as discussed in Chapter 12. In open-hearth steelmaking, particularly in the basic process, the slag is the only means by which the impurities in pig iron (excepting carbon) are removed. Slag is of equal metallurgical importance in other processes, such as the electric-furnace, pneumatic, and other steelmaking processes, including duplexing. To the metallurgist, a knowledge of the properties of slags, their chemical behavior, formation temperatures, fusibility and fluidity, and how to control these factors, is essential.

No attempt has been made in this brief statement to do more than call attention to the importance of slag in blast-furnace and steelmaking operations: the subject is covered in detail in Chapter 12, referred to above.

Secondary Metallurgical Uses of Slag—In addition to its metallurgical functions in different processes, slag, with its high iron and manganese contents, is used in the blast-furnace burden, as these elements are reduced and metallics recovered which otherwise would be wasted. The iron units in this slag are recovered in the pig iron, the lime present in the slag aids as a flux, and the manganese is reduced and increases the manganese content of the pig iron.

Special methods or treatments have been developed or are in the course of development for the recovery of valuable alloys from electric-furnace slag. The value of these processes, as in those mentioned above, is largely one of economics: that is to say, they are feasible only when the value of the material recovered amounts to more than the cost of its recovery.

SECTION 2

NON-METALLURGICAL USES OF SLAGS

After performing their useful functions in a particular process, the slags produced often are of value for other purposes.

Blast-furnace slag, depending upon its chemical composition and the physical form in which it is permitted to solidify, has many uses. Three general physical types are produced by different methods of cooling from the molten state; i.e., air-cooled, granulated, and expanded. **Air-cooled slag,** the "crushed slag" of commerce, is prepared by pouring the molten slag onto a slag bank or into a pit. After solidifying and cooling, the slag is excavated, crushed and screened. **Granulated slag** is prepared by three general methods: pit, jet, or dry granulation. Pit granulation consists of running the molten slag directly into a pit of water, producing a relatively coarse, friable product. In the jet process, a modification of the pit process, the stream of molten slag is broken up by a high-pressure water jet as it falls into the pit, and the granulated slag falls into the water in the pit to be quenched further. A product called dry granulated slag is made by a mechanical device using relatively small amounts of water. **Expanded** or **lightweight slag** is the foamed product produced when molten slag is expanded by applying a limited quantity of water or with a controlled quantity of water and air or steam. The amount of water used under controlled conditions is less than that required for granulation; consequently, a relatively dry, cellular lump product is formed in the process. Lightweight slag is made commercially in the United States in three general ways, which may be designated as the **machine process,** the **jet process** and the **bank process.** The objective of the machine process is the expansion of the molten slag in a revolving device with steam generated by contact of the slag with a controlled quantity of water. In the jet process, one or more high-pressure jets of water impinge on a stream of molten slag, and the product falls into a dry pit. The bank process is the application of water under pressure as the slag flows from the ladle down the face of the bank. The water is controlled or regulated by the pitman in order to expand the slag to a clinker properly and to prevent granulation. Expanded slag has a relatively high structural strength with good insulating and acoustical properties. Nearly 2,990,000 short tons were produced in 1958. The material is normally produced in two sizes, the coarse ranging from ½″ to No. 4 sieve and the fine from No. 4 sieve to dust. The cellular structure of the aggregate consisting of many nonconnecting cells surrounded by thin walls of slag is more pronounced than with the air-cooled slag.

Specific Uses of Blast-Furnace Slag—Blast-furnace slag has been very successfully put to many commercial uses, some of which are summarized in Table 7—I. The steps in processing the slag to convert it to useful forms are shown schematically in Figure 7—1.

Slag output in 1958, as reported by the Bureau of Mines, totaled 27,000,000 short tons. The value of the 1958 output was $45,208,000. In the processing of slag to produce screened slag products (Figure 7—1), slag that has passed through the primary crusher is passed over a magnetic pulley to separate particles of iron and iron-bearing materials from the crushed slag: the iron-bearing material, with the iron particles, are referred to as iron slag and the mixture contains an average of 60 per cent iron. The recovery of iron-slag by slag processors during 1958 totaled 364,000 short tons.

For concrete-making purposes, slag has many desirable features. The strengths, both compressive and flexural, developed in slag concrete are at least equal to those resulting from the use of other types of aggregate. Typical slag concrete weighs approximately ten pounds per cubic foot less than concrete made of other materials, this statement of course not applying to concrete made from special lightweight aggregate, of which lightweight slag is one.

Blast-furnace slag is especially adapted to macadam-road construction, for the particles, due to their

Table 7-I. Principal Uses of Blast-Furnace Slag

A. AIR-COOLED—Crushed and Screened Slag

> Ballast, Railroad
> Concrete, Portland Cement
> Concrete Units; Masonry, Hollow
> Binder Course, Sheet Asphalt Pavement
> Bituminous Concrete Base or Surface Course
> Bituminous Macadam Base or Surface Course
> Bituminous Surface Treatment
> Cushion Course for Brick or Block Pavement
> Sand for Sheet Asphalt or Bituminous Concrete
> Waterbound Base or Wearing Course
> Sewage Trickle-Filter Media
> Roofing Granules (Bituminous Built-up Roofing)
> Mineral Wool
> Sub-bases and Special Subgrade (Insulations)
> Traffic Bound Roads; Berms, Shoulders
> Stabilized Roads and Bases
> Porous Back-Fill and Underdrains
> Lightweight Aggregate (Expanded Slag)
> Embankments, Roadway Fills (Bank Slag)
> Glass Sand, Ceramic Ware

B. GRANULATED SLAG

> Slag Cements
> Soil Corrective, Agricultural Slag
> Roadway Insulation Courses
> Special Subgrade and Sub-bases
> Roadway Fills and Embankments
> Ceramic Ware, Glass Sand
> Concrete Units
> Building Blocks

C. EXPANDED SLAG

> Concrete Masonry Units
> Structural Concrete
> Fireproofing
> Floor Tile
> Precast Products
> Floor Joists and Slabs
> Building Blocks
> Brick
> Acoustical Tile
> Curtain Walls; Back-Up, Insulation, Fire Resistive

shape, interlock in such a way as to form a very good mechanical bond. The slag fines used to bind or fill the voids of larger macadam sizes are also very desirable because of the cementing value.

The characteristic rough, pitted surface of slag particles, together with the fact that they are hydrophobic in nature, makes them exceptionally suitable for bituminous construction of all types. These characteristics provide an excellent bond between the bitumen and aggregate, and also permit the application of a sufficiently heavy film of bitumen on the aggregate surface to assure durability and long life in the pavement. Slag sand is particularly valuable for use as fine

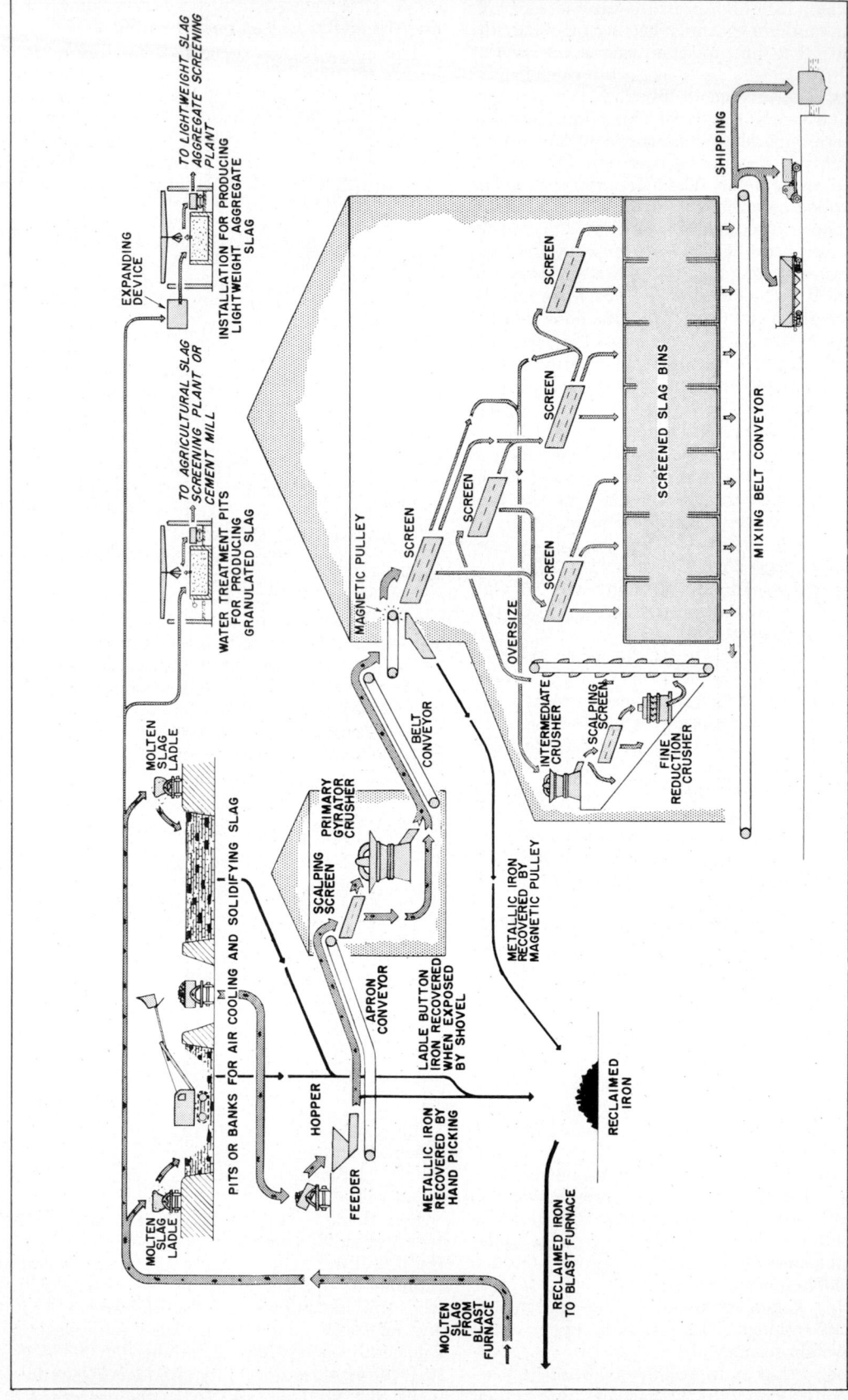

FIG. **7—1**. Schematic representation of the steps involved in processing blast-furnace slag to convert it to useful forms. The purpose of the multiple screens preceding the screened-slag bins is to sort the crushed slag into appropriate sizes.

aggregate in bituminous concrete of both the hot- and cold-mix types.

Slag has proved to be an excellent aggregate for airport runway construction of the macadam, bituminous or concrete types.

As railroad ballast, slag has been used successfully by the leading railroads in the United States for many years. Many of the most heavily-traveled tracks in the country are ballasted with slag. More than 2,900,000 tons were so used in 1958. Another use for crushed as well as granulated blast-furnace slag is for agricultural purposes, in which it serves three functions: (1) to reduce soil acidity; (2) to alter and improve physical characteristics of soils; and (3) to supply essential plant nutrients which many soils lack. In regard to (3), however, blast-furnace slag is considered as a soil conditioner rather than as a fertilizer. It contains many of the mineral elements necessary for plant growth, notably manganese, boron, sulphur and iron. Its action as a soil conditioner is similar to that of basic open-hearth slags used widely in the South for this purpose, as discussed later.

Slag also has proved of value as a trickle-filter medium for sewage disposal. This is especially true in the northern states where the filter medium is subjected to severe freezing and thawing as well as wetting and drying. Slag has withstood the extreme exposure in sewage-disposal filter beds to a remarkable degree with practically no breakdown, even after as much as thirty years of service.

Slag has been in great demand for many years for use as a covering for built-up bituminous roofs and as granules for covering asphalt shingles.

A demand for slag for use in the production of mineral wool in the past few years has materially increased. A large percentage of all mineral wool produced in the United States is made of slag. Slag is re-melted in a small cupola and the molten product, after reaching a desired temperature, is blown into wool by a jet of high-pressure steam or compressed air or spun into filaments by the action of a high-speed rotating disc.

Blast-furnace slag is used as an ingredient in the manufacture of transparent aluminum glass, black opaque glass, and amber glass, particularly for bottles. An important requirement of slag for glass-making is a low free-iron content.

One of the earliest uses for blast-furnace slag was in the manufacture of cement. Slag with a low magnesia content is required for cement-making. In granulated form, such slag has been used in large quantities in the manufacture of portland as well as other types of cement. For portland cement it is used as a part of the raw material that is burned in the usual way to form clinker, which, in turn, is ground into cement by methods described in Section 3 of this chapter. Over 1,270,-000 tons of blast-furnace slag were used for the making of cement in 1958.

Basic open-hearth slag has a more limited field of application as a by-product than has blast-furnace slag but, like the latter, it also has found an important use as a soil conditioner, especially in the southern states. In the northern states, with present steelmaking practices, the phosphorus content of basic open-hearth slag is low compared to that of the basic open-hearth slags produced in the southern states where ores of a much higher phosphorus content are used.

The largest single domestic source of basic open-hearth slag intended for use as a soil conditioner is the Ensley Works of United States Steel Corporation, located near Birmingham, Alabama, where steel is produced by the duplex process. The duplex process involves the use of acid converters and tilting basic open-hearth furnaces maintaining a dominant pool, as described in Chapter 16.

Both flush and tap slags from the conventional basic open-hearth process also may be used as soil conditioners.

Slags As Soil Conditioners—The chief food elements that plant life or vegetation obtains from the soil are potassium, phosphorus, and nitrogen, but other chemical elements such as iron, sulphur, and manganese are essential. For plants to thrive, soil conditions must be favorable, particularly with respect to humus content and basicity. Thus, if the soil is in clods, or if it is too acid or basic, unsatisfactory crop results are obtained, irrespective of the amount of fertilizer applied. An important function of slags is to correct such adverse conditions.

The chemical bases in slags consist mainly of lime, with some magnesia and small amounts of other basic compounds. The lime in slag, however, is in loose chemical combination with silica, iron, and manganese, so that it does not "burn" like ordinary agricultural lime nor revert to carbonate, but remains in a stable, almost neutral form, available as needed over long periods of time until exhausted.

While slags used for agricultural purposes cannot be called fertilizer, they do contain some fertilizing elements and, if of a suitable grade and properly prepared and applied to the soil, do promote conditions essential to profitable farming. Hence, they rightly are called soil conditioners.

The first basic slag used as soil conditioner was from the Thomas-Gilchrist or basic Bessemer process of steelmaking. The possibilities of this slag as a soil conditioner and stimulant to plant growth were investigated first in England in 1884. Its use was adopted in Scotland in 1890, and the practice spread rapidly throughout Europe in succeeding years.

As early as 1900, a German investigator reported on the use of blast-furnace slag as a fertilizer, with special reference to the beneficial effects of soluble silica in the material. Comparatively little comprehensive research work on the agricultural value of blast-furnace slag has been done in the United States, although coordinated test work has been undertaken in recent years and is still in progress.

In the South, the United States Steel Corporation has been preparing and marketing basic open-hearth slag from their duplexing process as a soil conditioner since 1915. The high-phosphorus content of the slag, previously referred to, justifies economically the cost of preparation and freight charges of the product for use in that area. Originally, it was the aim of the company to produce a slag for agricultural purposes in which the citric-acid-soluble phosphoric-acid content was high enough to meet fertilizer specifications. However, experiments established the fact that slags with a much lower phosphoric-acid content were so useful as soil conditioners that it appeared best to aim for greater tonnages containing between 8 and 12 per cent phosphoric acid, rather than a limited tonnage of product with an extremely high content of phosphoric acid. Steps in its preparation are as follows:

The high-phosphorus slag from the tilting open-hearth furnaces at Ensley Works, after cooling, is delivered to the soil-conditioner plant and mixed with flush slag containing less phosphorus that originates in the operation of conventional stationary basic open-hearth furnaces. The large slag cakes are first broken by a heavy steel ball, after which large pieces of steel are removed by the use of a conventional electromagnet. The slag is then transferred by a grab bucket to a roller crushing unit which breaks it down to 1½-inch maximum size. Elevating conveyors then deliver the slag over a magnetic roller and vibrating screens from which the larger pieces of slag are returned to be recrushed and shot-steel scrap is loaded for use in the blast furnaces. That portion of the slag which passes through the screen is then conveyed to a conventional tube mill for final grinding.

From the tube mill the slag is conveyed to storage bins and thence to a bagging unit where once again it is passed through screens to remove all tramp particles. Samples for chemical analysis and fineness testing are taken hourly from the product discharged from the tube mill. The product is packaged in paper bags, each containing 100 pounds net weight, and marketed under the trade name of "Ground Open Hearth Basic Slag." Phosphoric acid content ranges from 8 to 12 per cent; fineness 70 per cent through a 100-mesh screen. Facilities are available for the loading of this slag in bulk not only in railroad cars but spreader trucks as well.

Tap slags from conventional open-hearth furnaces at the Fairfield Works of United States Steel Corporation are also being used as soil conditioners. This product is used in areas that already are rich in P_2O_5. The slag is delivered in pots to the slag dump, where it is kept separate from flush slag. A heavy steel ball is dropped on the slag to break it into properly sized pieces. Steel scrap is then removed from the broken slag, after which the slag is run over a ½-inch screen. The oversize material is returned for further reduction in size under the drop ball. The minus ½-inch material is loaded into drop-bottom cars and shipped to Florida, where the slag is ground to a fineness of 100 per cent through a 20-mesh screen and 50 per cent through a 100-mesh screen. The ground material contains a minimum of 2.5 per cent P_2O_5, 35 per cent CaO, 6 per cent MgO, and 2 per cent MnO. Also present are minor amounts of elements such as iron, boron, zinc, molybdenum and copper, which are needed in Florida soils.

SECTION 3

MANUFACTURE OF PORTLAND CEMENT

Portland cement is a finely pulverized material consisting of certain definite compounds of lime (CaO), silica (SiO_2), alumina (Al_2O_3) and iron oxide (Fe_2O_3). Its most familiar use is in **concrete**. Concrete is a mixture in which a paste of portland cement and water binds fine and coarse materials (sand, pebbles, crushed stone, crushed blast-furnace slag, etc.) known as **aggregates** into a rock-like mass as the paste hardens due to the formation of new compounds through chemical action between the original compounds of the cement and the water. In simple terms, concrete is a mass of aggregates held together by a hardened paste of portland cement and water.

Raw Materials—Based on the 1958 "Minerals Yearbook" published by the Bureau of Mines, approximately 99,541,000 tons of raw materials (exclusive of fuels and explosives) entered into the manufacture of 306,609,000 barrels of portland cement in the United States in that year. This is an average of about 639 lb. of raw materials for each barrel of finished portland cement weighing 376 lb. Loss of weight is caused by the process of calcination in which moisture, carbon dioxide and other gases are driven off in the kilns. Materials are chiefly high-calcium limestone, clay or shale, argillaceous limestone, blast-furnace slag and marl (see Table 7—II).

Also from the "Minerals Yearbook," the following quantities of fuel were used by the portland cement industry in the United States and its territories in 1958

Table 7—II. Consumption of Raw Materials for the Manufacture of Portland Cement (1958).

Raw Material	Short Tons
Cement rock (argillaceous limestone) . . .	20,799,000
Limestone and oyster shells	62,306,000
Marl	1,487,000
Clay and shale	9,400,000
Blast-furnace slag	1,279,000
Gypsum	2,507,000
Sand and sandstone	1,121,000
Iron-bearing materials	535,000
Other materials such as:	
fluorspar, pumicite, pitch, red mud and rock, hydrated lime, tufa, calcium chloride, sludge, grinding aids, and air-entraining compounds	107,000
Total	99,541,000

(for all cement-mill fuel consumption including the process of burning in the kilns, independent power production and other uses):

Coal (tons)	8,427,000
Oil (gallons)	187,950,000
Gas (cubic feet)	164,994,967,000

Based on figures from this same source relating to cement production and fuel consumption in those plants that use only one fuel exclusively, the following

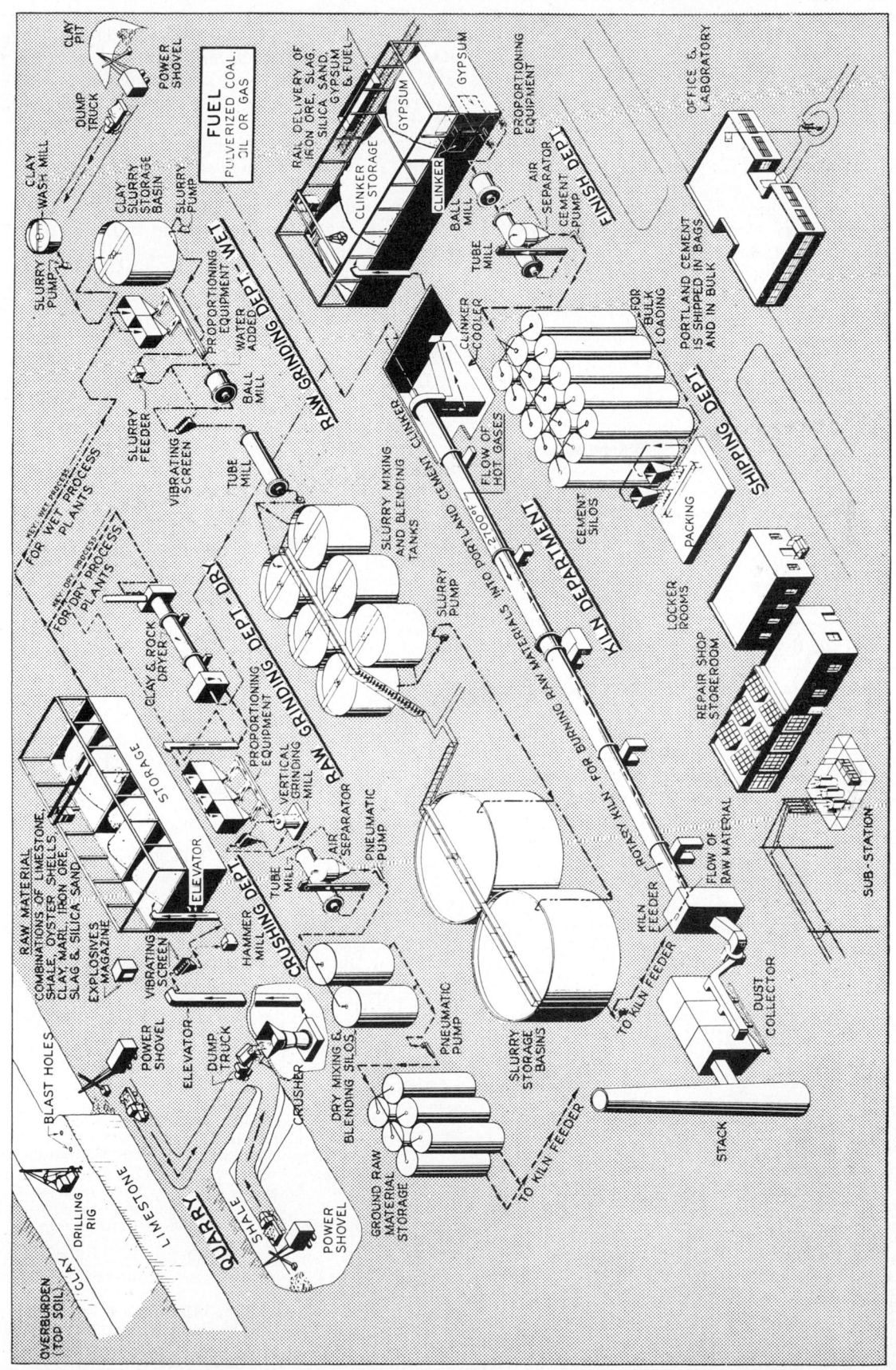

FIG. 7—2. Schematic representation of cement-plant layout and equipment for producing portland cement by the "dry" and the "wet" methods. (Courtesy Portland Cement Association.)

amounts of fuel were required to produce one barrel of cement.

Coal . . . .   105.8 lb.
Oil . . . .   7.80 gal.
Natural gas . . . .   1,223 cu. ft.

Dry and Wet Processes—There are two processes which may be used to make portland cement (Figure 7—2). These are called the "dry" and the "wet" methods. In the **dry process,** after the crushed raw materials are taken from storage, dried and blended in the proper proportions, the mixture is fed into huge rotating **ball mills** or impact mills of various types for preliminary grinding. The ball mills get their name from the hundreds of large steel balls inside them which are carried on ribs up one side of the rotating mill and cascaded down onto the material being ground.

The mixture then goes to a **tube mill,** which is similar to the ball mill except that the material is more finely ground by 40 to 50 tons of smaller steel balls. Some plants use combination ball-and-tube mills, called compartment mills. Motors up to 1,000 horsepower are required to operate them. Grinding is frequently done in circuit with air separators which remove the fine material from the mill discharge and return the coarse material for further grinding, effecting economies in grinding.

After the dry raw material is ground, it is carried to storage. Samples are analyzed for chemical content to insure uniform quality. Accurately proportioned amounts of the dry raw material are then ready to go to the kilns for burning.

The **wet process** is very much like the dry except that, at the ball mill, water is added and the material is ground wet to give it a thick, creamy, consistency. The cement makers call this **slurry.** Sometimes, this wet grinding is done in closed circuit with classifiers to remove finished fine material as fast as produced and return the coarse material for additional grinding. In this case, the finished slurry has a very high water content which is reduced in large thickeners before using the slurry as kiln feed.

The slurry is then pumped into tanks where it is tested and blended to the desired chemical composition. From the blending tanks, the slurry is pumped to large storage tanks to be held until needed for burning.

The Burning (Calcining) Operation—The prepared and blended mixture of raw materials is fed into **rotary kilns,** where the mixture is calcined or burned to what is known as **cement clinker.** Briefly described, a rotary kiln is a nearly horizontal steel cylinder, lined with suitable refractory brick and 6 to 12 feet in diameter and from 60 to 500 feet in length. Such kilns are continuous in operation. The raw material is fed continuously into the higher end of the long, inclined cylinder which rotates continuously at a rate of about one revolution per minute. By reason of the inclined position of the kiln and its rotary motion, the charge moves gradually and continuously toward the lower end of the kiln where it is discharged.

Heat for calcining the charge is supplied by combustion equipment that fires axially into the kiln at the discharge end. The direction of flame travel, therefore, is opposite to the direction of progress of the charge, and the charge is heated hotter and hotter as it travels toward the firing end. Pulverized coal, natural gas, or fuel oil is used as fuel. A temperature of 2800° F is attained in the hottest zone near the discharge end of the kiln. The heat serves two purposes: (1) to cause the desired chemical changes to take place in the raw mixture, and (2) to form clinker by fusing the transformed materials into small masses about the size of marbles.

The clinker resulting from the burning of the raw material in this way is then cooled and pulverized in equipment similar to that used for dry raw material grinding, together with a small amount of gypsum added to regulate the setting time, and becomes the portland cement of commerce.

The unit of measure for portland cement is a bag weighing 94 lb. net or a barrel weighing 376 lb. net. A bag of cement contains approximately one cubic foot. Cement has been shipped domestically in cloth sacks or paper bags, or in bulk; and for export, in wooden barrels or paper-lined cloth sacks. Today, nearly all cement is shipped by railroad or motor truck in bulk or in paper bags.

Bibliography

Am. Institute of Mining and Metallurgical Engineers, Iron and Steel Div., Committee on Physical Chemistry of Steelmaking, Basic open hearth steelmaking; 2nd ed. (Seeley W. Mudd series). N. Y., The Institute, 1951.

Bishop, H. L.; King, T. B.; and Grant, J. J. The Role of Slag Composition in Open Hearth Desulphurization and Oxidation. Yearbook of the Am. Iron and Steel Institute, 1955, 249–266.

Bowron, R. L., Basic open-hearth slag an important by-product at Ensley Works. Mining and Metallurgy 18, 198–199 (1937).

Furnas, C. C., Rate of calcination of limestone. Industrial and Engineering Chemistry 23, 534–538 (1931).

Hodges, P. C., Production and preparation of blast-furnace flux. Am. Institute of Mining and Metallurgical Engineers, Iron and Steel Div., Trans. 120, 121–133 (1936).

Lambing, L. A., Discussion: Influence of various limestones. Am. Institute of Mining and Metallurgical Engineers, Open Hearth Proc. 21, 84–85 (1938).

Lightner, M. W., Current concepts of open hearth slag control. Am. Institute of Mining and Metallurgical Engineers, Open Hearth Proc. 40, 304–314 (1957).

McCaffery, Richard S., A study of blast furnace slags. Yearbook of the Am. Iron and Steel Institute, 1938, 189–200.

Osborn, E. F.; De Vries, R. C.; Gee, K. H.; and Kramer, H. M., Optimum composition of blast furnace slag as deduced from liquidus data for the quaternary system $CaO-MgO-Al_2O_3-SiO_2$. Am. Institute of Mining and Metallurgical Engineers, Trans. 200, 33–45 (1954).

Portland Cement Association, Cement and concrete reference book. Chicago, Ill. The Association, 1957.

Turkdogan. E. T. and Pearson, J., Activities of constituents of iron and steelmaking slags. Part I—Iron Oxide, J. Iron and Steel Institute 173, 217–223 (1953); Part II—Manganous Oxide, J. Iron and Steel Institute 173, 393–398 (1953); Part III—Phosphorus Pentoxide, J. Iron and Steel Institute 173, 398–401 (1953).

Turkdogan, E. T. and Pearson, J., Reaction equilibria between metal and slag in acid and basic open hearth steelmaking. J. Iron and Steel Institute 176, 59–63 (1954).

U. S. Bureau of Mines, Iron blast-furnace slag: Production, processing, properties and uses, by G. W. Josephson, F. Sillers, Jr., and D. G. Runner (Bulletin 479). Wash., Govt. Printing Office, 1949.

CHAPTER 8

Scrap For Steelmaking

Scrap consists of the by-products of steel fabrication, and worn out, broken or discarded items containing iron or steel. It is one of the two principal sources of metal in steelmaking; the other principal source is iron from the blast furnaces, either molten as it comes from the blast furnace ("hot metal") or in solid pig form. Scrap is of great practical value. Every ton of scrap consumed in steelmaking is estimated to displace and conserve for future use 3½ to 4 tons of other natural resources including iron ore, coal and limestone. On the average, the steel industry consumes about equal quantities of scrap and blast-furnace iron. According to recently published figures of the American Iron and Steel Institute, the steel industry consumes an average of about 55,000,000 tons of iron and steel scrap in producing 100,000,000 net tons of ingots and steel for castings.

The various steelmaking processes differ widely in their abilities to consume scrap. The air-blown acid Bessemer process uses about 10 per cent while the same process, with oxygen-enriched blast, can use up to 25 per cent; the basic oxygen steelmaking process uses 25 to 30 per cent; and the Kaldo process about 40 per cent. The duplex open-hearth process consumes very little scrap; while the stationary open-hearth processes may utilize 35 to 60 per cent. The electric furnace usually is charged almost entirely with cold scrap. Table 8—I summarizes the consumption of scrap by several steelmaking processes and the blast furnace during 1962.

Table 8–I. Consumption of Scrap and Hot Metal and Pig Iron by Steelmaking Processes and Blast Furnaces During 1962*

| Process | Consumption (Net Tons) | |
	Scrap	Hot Metal and Pig Iron
Bessemer	52,306	877,351
Open Hearth	35,957,912	54,278,391
Basic Oxygen Steelmaking	1,527,094	4,877,536
Electric	8,381,184	166,450
Blast Furnace	3,550,918	—

* American Iron & Steel Institute.

Types and Sources of Scrap—Scrap iron and steel may be classified as originating from two sources: home scrap produced as unsalable products unavoidably resulting from steelmaking and finishing operations, and purchased scrap.

Home scrap (also called "revert scrap") includes such items as pit scrap; ingots too short to roll; rejected ingots; ingot crops; crop ends from blooms and billets; shear cuttings from trimming flat-rolled products to specified size; products irrecoverably damaged in handling or finishing; ends cut from bars, pipe or tubing to bring them to standard or exact ordered length; turnings from machining operations, and so on. Bloom crops constitute the largest single item of home scrap.

In general, according to the source referred to above, about 32,000,000 net tons of home scrap would result from the manufacture of 100,000,000 net tons of steel ingots (and steel for castings—a small percentage of the whole) and the processing of this steel into finished products.

Purchased scrap must be used to the extent of 23,000,000 net tons to supplement the 32,000,000 net tons of home scrap to provide the 55,000,000 net tons of iron and steel scrap needed to produce the 100,000,000 net tons of steel. Purchased scrap is divided into two general classifications: (1) dormant scrap and (2) prompt industrial scrap.

Dormant scrap comprises obsolete, worn out or broken products of consuming industries. Typical examples of dormant scrap are: discarded steel furniture, washing machines, stoves and other outdated consumer goods; beams, angles, channels, girders, railings, grilles, pipe, etc., arising from the demolition of buildings; useless farm machinery; obsolete, broken or damaged industrial machinery; old ships; railroad rails and rolling stock that have outlived their usefulness; wrecked automobiles, and so on. This type of scrap, because of its miscellaneous nature, requires careful sorting and classification to prevent the contamination of steel in the furnace with unwanted chemical elements that may be present in some of the scrap. It should also be of such physical size as to facilitate handling and loading into charging boxes. The need for proper classification and preparation of dormant scrap is emphasized by the existence of 75 different specifications covering various grades of scrap for use in blast furnaces, acid and basic open-hearth furnaces, electric furnaces, the basic oxygen steelmaking process, Bessemer converters, gray-iron foundries and elsewhere. In addition, the Association of American Railroads has forty-five specifications applying to scrap of railroad origin. These all have been prepared to facilitate proper classification of scrap for different uses.

Prompt industrial scrap is generated by steel consumers in making their products. It may consist of the unwanted portions of plate or sheet that has been cut or sheared to the desired final size and shape, trimmings resulting from stamping and pressing operations, machine turnings, rejected products scrapped during manufacture, short ends, flash from forgings, and other types of scrap. Prompt industrial scrap can usually be identified easily as to source and composition, provided that proper plans for segregation are in effect in the consumer's plant, the scrap dealer's yard, and in the steel plant.

According to the 1963 Annual Statistical Report of the American Iron and Steel Institute, the domestic steel industry in 1962 produced 34,088,478 net tons of scrap as a result of its own operations, and received 18,471,672 net tons from outside sources. In the same year, it consumed 51,156,295 tons of scrap in producing 98,327,785 total net tons of steel (ingots and steel for castings).

In its 1963 Yearbook, the Institute of Scrap Iron and Steel reported estimated total shipments of scrap in 1962 to have been 25.3 million gross tons. Of this amount, about 5.2 million gross tons were exported.

Although it is difficult to determine the sources of all of the scrap, the Institute estimated that most of it originated in 1959 from the sources indicated in Table 8—II.

Table 8–II. Estimated Amounts of Iron and Steel Scrap Obtained from Various Sources (1959).*

Source	Millions of Gross Tons
Prompt industrial scrap	10.2
Auto wreckers	2.5
Railroads	2.8
Detinning operations	0.7
Shipwrecking	0.8
Government agencies	0.3
Demolition projects	1.3
Farms	1.0
Public utilities	0.4
Interplant transfers**	1.9
Miscellaneous (mines, incinerators and other operations at dumps, general collection, housing repair and maintenance, oil fields and refineries, etc.)	10.0

* From 1960 Yearbook, Institute of Scrap Iron and Steel.
** Scrap shipped between plants of the same company, without passing through dealers' hands.

While a 1962 complete breakdown similar to Table 8—II is not available, the Institute has estimated that the 11.8 million gross tons of prompt industrial scrap in 1962 came from the sources given in Table 8—III that represent the same industry classifications employed by the American Iron and Steel Institute in reporting shipments of finished steel products.

Physical Preparation of Scrap—Scrap is classified according to its physical size and chemical composition. Pieces too large to be accommodated by charging-machine boxes must be cut into satisfactorily smaller sizes; shears, flame-cutting, impact devices

Table 8–III. Amounts of Prompt Industrial Scrap Originating in Various Industries (1962).*

Industry	Gross Tons
Construction, incl. maintenance	279,449
Contractors products	416,171
Automotive	4,706,167
Rail transportation	142,016
Shipbuilding and marine equipment	156,145
Aircraft	26,762
Oil and gas drilling	10,323
Mining, quarrying and lumbering	7,878
Agricultural	213,055
Machinery, industrial equipment and tools	1,090,178
Electrical machinery and equipment	560,909
Appliances, utensils and cutlery	319,032
Other commercial and household equipment	288,334
Containers	806,424
Ordnance and other military	59,779
Unassigned	1,994,338
Foundry products	690,000
Total	11,766,960

* 1963 Yearbook, Institute of Scrap Iron and Steel.

and other means may be used, depending upon the type of scrap being handled. Sometimes, very large pieces of scrap that cannot pass through the furnace doors may be charged into an open-hearth furnace by overhead crane when the furnace roof is off during rebuilding. Sheet shearings, punchings and similar types of relatively thin and usually small pieces of scrap may be compressed into block-like bundles in specially-designed hydraulic baling presses; since about half of the steel rolled in the United States at present is in the form of relatively thin flat-rolled products, large quantities of scrap require baling.

Assuming that scrap has been properly sorted with respect to its chemical composition, as discussed later, the primary purpose achieved by the proper preparation of scrap is to increase the amount of scrap that can be loaded at one time into a charging box for placing the scrap in the steel-producing furnace. The denser the load in the charging boxes, the fewer the number of boxes that need to be loaded, transported and their contents dumped into the furnace, and the less the time consumed in charging the furnace. Delays in charging can result in a corresponding loss of steel production.

The prime grade of purchased scrap for production of open-hearth steel must be at least ⅛-inch thick, no more than 18 inches wide, nor more than 5 feet long. Electric furnaces require purchased scrap of smaller dimensions ranging in size from 3 feet down to punchings; further details relating to scrap for electric-furnace melting are given in Chapter 17. Short lengths of turnings are the preferred form of scrap for blast-furnace use.

Chemical Composition of Scrap—Certain chemical elements are desirable constituents of scrap for steelmaking, especially when used in electric furnaces, as discussed in Chapter 17. In general, however, scrap for all of the steelmaking processes should be free from unknown and unwanted elements referred to as "tramp alloys." The increasing use of alloy steels of many compositions has aggravated the tramp alloy problem since more and more purchased scrap may be expected to include unidentified alloy steels.

The segregation of home scrap according to its chemical composition is relatively simple. Purchased scrap, especially dormant scrap, presents some problems since a large percentage of it is of unknown origin and composition. While it would be impractical to chemically analyze each individual piece of the huge amounts of dormant scrap consumed every year, the chemical analysis of selected samples of individual lots sometimes is employed by steel plants in the classification of scrap. Spectrographic analysis sometimes is employed instead of chemical analysis because it is more rapid; however, both are relatively time-consuming and expensive and both require careful selection and preparation of samples. Some less costly but less accurate tests are commonly used; these include magnetic tests, spark tests, spot tests and pellet tests as described briefly in Chapter 17.

When the chemical composition of scrap is known, the scrap can prove to be a valuable source of alloying elements needed in the production of alloy steels.

Full advantage is taken of this source in the production of alloy steels in the electric furnace. In the open-hearth furnace, however, the preponderance of production consists of carbon and low-alloy steels and, in general, alloying elements in scrap are a source of trouble.

Tin, copper, nickel and other elements present in scrap will alloy readily with steel and, in many instances, render it unfit for its intended use. Relatively small amounts of these metals can contaminate an entire heat of steel. Tin and copper in certain ranges of composition cause brittleness and bad surface conditions in steel. Nickel and tin not only contaminate heats into which they may be unintentionally introduced, but may deposit a residue in the furnace that is absorbed by successive heats with resultant contamination. Lead is extremely harmful to furnace bottoms and refractories and, if present in sufficient quantities, may cause furnaces to break out by penetrating joints or cracks in the bottom to form channels that may be followed by molten steel. The foregoing examples represent some of the difficulties caused by only a few of the chemical elements that may enter steel from poorly prepared or carelessly classified scrap.

CHAPTER 9

Addition Agents Used In Steelmaking

Definitions—Steelmaking involves the deliberate addition of various chemical elements to the molten metal to effect several desirable ends. These ends may include deoxidation of the molten metal to the desired degree, control of grain size, improvement of the mechanical and physical properties and corrosion resistance of the steel, increase of the response of the steel to subsequent heat treatment, or attainment of other specific effects that are discussed elsewhere in this book. Originally, the chemical element to be incorporated into the steel was added to the bath in the form of an alloy that consisted principally of iron but was rich in the desired element. Such alloys, because of their high iron content, became known as **ferroalloys,** and most of the available types were produced in the iron blast furnace. Eventually, the production of alloys for steelmaking purposes began to be carried out in electric-reduction and other types of furnaces as well, and a number of alloys now produced contain relatively little iron. For this reason, the term **addition agent** is preferred to describe any of the materials added to molten steel for altering its composition or properties; under this definition, the ferroalloys form a special class of addition agents.

The more common addition agents definitely in the ferroalloy class include alloys of iron with aluminum, boron, calcium, chromium, columbium, manganese, molybdenum, nitrogen, phosphorus, selenium, silicon, tantalum, titanium, tungsten, vanadium, and zirconium. Some of these chemical elements and others are available in addition agents that are not ferroalloys, as well as in almost pure form; these include relatively pure metals such as aluminum, calcium, cobalt, copper, manganese and nickel; oxides of molybdenum, nickel and tungsten; carbon, nitrogen and sulphur in various forms; and alloys consisting principally of combinations of two or more of the foregoing elements. The more important of the addition agents (including ferroalloys) will be discussed individually later in this chapter. Although work on the use of rare-earth alloys is in progress, the results reported thus far are still under investigation and the use of such alloys in steelmaking will not be discussed here.

Use of Addition Agents—Addition agents may be added with the charge in the steelmaking furnace, or in the molten bath near the end of the finishing period, or in the ladle or in the molds. Timing of the alloy additions is dependent on the effect of the addition on the temperature of the molten metal, ease with which specific addition agents go into solution, susceptibility of a particular addition agent to oxidation, and formation and elimination of reaction products.

Economy in manufacture of alloy steels requires consideration of the relative affinity of the alloying elements for oxygen as compared with the affinity of iron for oxygen. For example, copper, molybdenum, or nickel may be added with the charge or during the working of the heat and are wholly recovered. Chromium and manganese, because they are easily oxidized, should be added late in the heat and all or part of these two may be added in the ladle. In open-hearth practice, easily oxidized materials such as aluminum, boron, titanium, vanadium, and zirconium are normally added in the ladle in order to minimize oxidation losses.

It is often necessary to preheat the ferroalloy to avoid undue chilling of the bath. When large additions are made entirely to the bath, time must be allowed for the molten steel to be reheated to the desired temperature before tapping. The ferroalloy additions may be split between the furnace and the ladle, and in cases where excessive chilling of the metal in the ladle is to be avoided, the lower alloy recovery in the furnace must be accepted. To offset the chilling tendency of large additions and to minimize or eliminate the necessity for preheating, some addition agents such as ferromanganese and ferrochromium can be obtained mixed with chemical reagents to provide exothermic reactions that permit these agents to be added to the ladle without undue chilling of the steel.

The agents to be added to the bath should be lump size (say 5 inches) in order to penetrate the slag easily. For ladle additions, the alloy should have a maximum size of approximately 2 inches to assure rapid solution.

Storage Facilities for Addition Agents—From the standpoint of material handling and of conservation and identification, it is advisable to store addition agents in properly designed bins in which they are protected from the weather. The location and design of bins should make the contents quickly available and with a relatively low handling cost. All bins should provide identification of the contents since confusion may be costly due to failure to meet specified chemical composition of the finished steel. Certain addition agents are more easily broken on handling than others, and caution should always be exercised to avoid production of fines.

COMPOSITIONS OF COMMON
ADDITION AGENTS

Ferromanganese is the most important of the ferro-alloys used in steelmaking. **Standard ferromanganese** contains 74 to 82 per cent manganese, and contains not more than 1.25 per cent silicon, 0.35 per cent phosphorus, 7.50 per cent carbon, and 0.05 per cent sulphur. **Low-phosphorus ferromanganese** suitable for addition to acid open-hearth steel should not contain over 0.10 per cent phosphorus. **Low-carbon ferromanganese** is used when it is important to limit the amount of carbon entering the steel from the ferromanganese addition. This low-carbon product is available in several grades containing increasing amounts of carbon, e.g., 0.07 per cent, 0.10 per cent, 0.15 per cent, 0.30 per cent, 0.50 per cent, and 0.75 per cent (all maxima), and the lower the carbon content the higher the price per pound. All of the foregoing grades of low-carbon ferromanganese contain 80 to 85 per cent manganese. **Electrolytic manganese metal** is also being used as a source of low-carbon manganese. **Medium-carbon ferromanganese** contains a maximum of 1.5 per cent carbon and 80 to 85 per cent manganese. If low-carbon and medium-carbon ferromanganese are used as bath additions (to the furnace) such additions should be made after the bath has been deoxidized. Exothermic mixtures of ferromanganese with suitable chemical reagents permit sizable manganese additions to be made to the ladle without undue chilling effect on the molten steel.

Silicomanganese is used by some open-hearth furnace operators as a furnace addition to **block the heat** (retard the oxidizing reactions taking place in the furnace toward the end of the finishing period) because of the shorter holding time required from time of addition to tap, as compared with the use of ferrosilicon followed by ferromanganese. Silicomanganese contains 65 to 68 per cent manganese, 18 to 20 per cent silicon, and a usual maximum of 1.5 per cent carbon.

Spiegeleisen was formerly used in steelmaking to a much greater extent than at present. It is available in grades containing 16 to 28 per cent manganese, with the carbon content not over 6.5 per cent. The silicon content of spiegeleisen is from 1.0 to 4.5 per cent. A grade known as **silicospiegel** contains 25 to 30 per cent manganese, 2 to 3 per cent carbon, and 7 to 8 per cent silicon. Spiegeleisen (usually called spiegel) is still occasionally used as an addition to the bath in the open-hearth process.

Ferrosilicon—The low-silicon grades of ferrosilicon, which usually start at 10 per cent silicon and ordinarily do not exceed 17 per cent silicon, generally are blast-furnace products, and contain 1.50 per cent maximum carbon. **Electric-furnace ferrosilicon**, made by an electric-furnace process, is graded according to silicon content. The principal grades contain, respectively, 25 per cent, 50 per cent, 65 per cent, 75 per cent, 85 per cent, and 90 to 95 per cent silicon. The grades containing the most silicon can be obtained with special low aluminum content. The 50 per cent silicon grade is by far the most widely used, and is employed both as a blocking addition in the furnace and as a ladle addition. The 10 to 15 per cent and 25 per cent silicon grades are sometimes used in the open-hearth furnace for blocking the heat, and may also be used as deoxidizers added prior to addition of other more expensive alloys.

Ferrochromium, containing 65 to 72 per cent chromium and a maximum of 2 per cent silicon, is classified into grades by carbon content. The respective grades contain 0.06 per cent, 0.10 per cent, 0.15 per cent, 0.20 per cent, 0.50 per cent, 1.00 per cent, and 2.00 per cent carbon, along with the most commonly used and cheapest grade containing 65 to 69 per cent chromium and 4.50 to 8.50 per cent carbon. Ferrochromium containing the higher amounts of carbon is used as a furnace addition. As in the case of ferromanganese, the alloys of lower carbon content are the more expensive. Several silicon-bearing ferrochromium alloys containing from 58 to 65 per cent chromium, 5 to 12 per cent silicon, and 5 to 7 per cent carbon are occasionally used as blocking additions to the furnace in the open-hearth process. Similar ferrochrome-silicon alloys that contain only 0.05 to 2.5 per cent carbon are popular ladle additions. Briquettes of ferrochromium in which are incorporated chemical reagents to provide exothermic reactions permit chromium to be added to the ladle in this form without an undue chilling effect.

Ferrovanadium, containing 35 to 55 per cent vanadium, usually is added to killed steel in the ladle.

Ferromolybdenum, containing 55 to 75 per cent molybdenum, is used where the higher molybdenum contents are desired. For lower molybdenum contents, molybdenum oxide or calcium molybdate may be used. All are furnace additions.

Ferrotitanium available in the following grades generally is used as a ladle addition: regular grade containing 40 per cent titanium and a maximum of 0.10 per cent carbon; low-carbon grade containing 25 per cent titanium and a maximum of 0.10 per cent carbon; and a high-carbon grade containing 15 to 19 per cent titanium and 6 to 8 per cent carbon.

Zirconium is obtained from one alloy containing 12 to 15 per cent zirconium, 39 to 43 per cent silicon, and a maximum of 0.20 per cent carbon; or another containing 35 to 40 per cent zirconium, 37 to 52 per cent silicon, and a maximum of 0.50 per cent carbon. These zirconium alloys generally are added in the ladle.

Ferrophosphorus in two grades containing, respectively, 17 to 19 per cent and 23 to 26 per cent phosphorus, usually is added in the ladle.

Nickel, obtained in the forms of sheared electrolytic cathodes or as ingots produced from remelted cathodes, both containing a minimum of about 99 per cent nickel, is used as a furnace addition. Little or no nickel is lost through oxidation when it is added to the bath, so nickel steels can be made by charging nickel-steel scrap and adding metallic nickel after the charge has been melted completely. Nickel-oxide sinter and ferronickel (the latter containing 45 per cent nickel, balance iron) are also used as charge material. Nickel oxide is sometimes used in conjunction with reducing slags in the electric furnace as a source of metallic nickel.

Copper usually is added to the bath in the form of

virgin copper pigs or as scrap copper. It also can be recovered, with little or no loss, from copper-bearing steel scrap in the initial furnace charge. Some steel producers add copper pellets to individual molten ingots for alloying purposes when heat lots of copper steels are not required.

Lead is added to molten ingots in the form of lead shot by many steel producers to provide steel with free-machining properties.

Aluminum usually is added in the form of secondary aluminum having an aluminum content of from 85 per cent upward. It generally is used in the form of shot for addition to the ingot mold, or as shot or bars for addition to the ladle. In special cases, as when used for the deoxidation of small ingots, the metallic aluminum content of the addition may be as high as 97.5 per cent. Limitations are placed on the copper content of aluminum used in steelmaking operations: it generally is not to exceed 4.5 per cent.

Cobalt in metallic form (97 to 99 per cent pure) is usually added to the furnace in the form of shot or rondelles in the manufacture of high-speed steels, permanent-magnet steels and other special steels in the electric furnace.

Ferrocolumbium, containing 50 to 60 per cent of columbium and up to 8 per cent silicon with a maximum of 0.40 per cent carbon, is usually added through the reducing slag in electric furnaces in the production of austenitic stainless steels of the chromium-nickel type and alloys for use at high temperatures. Small amounts of columbium added to steel in the ladle or ingot mold are reported to promote a fine-grained structure in carbon and low-alloy steels, with some improvement in mechanical properties.

Ferroselenium, used for the addition of selenium to stainless steels to improve their machinability, is added to the ladle during the tapping of electric-furnace heats. It contains 50 to 60 per cent of selenium.

Tantalum for steelmaking purposes is available as ferrotantalum-columbium, which has a content of approximately 20 per cent tantalum, 40 per cent columbium and a maximum of 0.30 per cent carbon. It can be used as a replacement for ferrocolumbium in some cases.

Tungsten, used principally in the manufacture of high-speed tool steels in electric furnaces, is available from ferrotungsten, the standard grade of which contains 70 to 80 per cent of tungsten and a maximum of 0.60 per cent of carbon. Tungsten is also obtained from oxide forms such as scheelite and calcium tungstate.

Sulphur as required by specification is added to the ladle in the form of such addition agents as flowers of sulphur, stick sulphur, iron sulphide, or less often as manganese sulphide, sodium sulphide, etc.

Carbon—For raising the carbon content of the steel during tapping, additions may be made to the ladle in the form of coke, anthracite coal, graphite, or petroleum derivatives. It is desirable that such additions be low in sulphur and high in carbon. In some instances, a low hydrogen content is also desirable.

"Hardenability Intensifiers"—A number of ferroalloys are designed to increase the hardenability of steel when added in relatively small amounts. They usually contain boron together with one or more of the following elements: silicon, titanium, vanadium, zirconium, aluminum, manganese, calcium, or other deoxidizers or denitrifiers.

The foregoing brief descriptions of addition agents summarize only the principal sources of the various elements for the manufacture of steel, with some reference to the manner in which most of them are used. Specific reasons and the manner for the use of individual addition agents, or combinations of them, are discussed in other chapters describing the several steelmaking processes and the properties and heat treatment of AISI alloy steels, stainless and heat-resistant steels, and tool steels.

CHAPTER 10

Water Requirements For Steelmaking

SECTION 1

PROPERTIES AND GENERAL USES OF WATER

Water is such a common substance that its unusual properties and its importance to the iron and steel industry are seldom emphasized in the discussion of metallurgical processes. This is in spite of the fact that large amounts, variously reported as from 40,000 to 65,000 gallons, of water are used in the production of a ton of finished steel. Only a part of this water is actually consumed, as will be discussed later.

It has been estimated that the water required for daily living in the United States weighs more than 100 times as much as all other materials that are used; including food, fuel, metals, plastics, lumber, sand, gravel and stone.

Most water used by industry is self-supplied: that is, it is pumped by the user plants from the ground, streams, lakes, or reservoirs. Such natural water is treated as required to improve its clarity or purity, and then used in plant processes. In some cases, water picks up impurities during use and must be treated before the used water is discharged from a plant.

PROPERTIES OF WATER

Water and mercury are the only two common mineral substances that are liquids at ordinary temperatures. Water is denser as a liquid than as a solid. Its high specific heat and high latent heat of vaporization enable it to transfer heat energy very effectively. The high kinetic energy that can be imparted to water makes it useful in driving turbines for electric-power generation, in hydraulic placer mining, and in high-pressure jets for cleaning and descaling, to name only a few uses of this property of water.

The ability of water to dissolve, entrain and suspend many substances makes it a convenient means for transporting, mixing, grinding, separating and cleaning many materials used by industry. The fact that water dissolves or entrains many substances affects the purity of raw water from natural sources, and limits its use in many processes until it has been treated to remove or neutralize any undesirable impurities that may be present.

Suspended or undissolved contaminants (clay, sand, organic matter, etc.) can settle out and clog piping and passageways in cooling and control equipment, interfere with efficient heat transfer, and contribute to corrosion. Suspended solids are generally removed from water more easily than dissolved substances.

Raw natural waters may contain in solution considerable amounts of naturally occurring soluble substances, in addition to dissolved contaminants from non-natural sources. Some dissolved contaminants cause corrosion of equipment, some interfere with chemical reactions; others cause undesirable odors or taste or cause stains in products, and so on. Water containing more than about 1000 parts per million (ppm) of dissolved naturally occurring soluble substances is said to be slightly saline; between 3000 and 10,000 ppm it is moderately saline; with more than 10,000 ppm it is very saline; and with 35,000 ppm and over it is characterized as brine. Ocean water usually ranges between 33,000 and 35,000 ppm. Among the contaminants of raw water resulting from naturally occurring substances, sodium and chlorine ions predominate; however, significant quantities of calcium, magnesium, potassium, iron, manganese, silica, carbonic acid (HCO_3^-) and sulphate (SO_4^{--}) ions are also present. Waters containing appreciable quantities of calcium and magnesium are classed as **hard waters.**

Molecules of pure water contain, besides common atoms of hydrogen and oxygen, a type of hydrogen atom that is twice as heavy as the common variety. This isotope of hydrogen, named **deuterium,** has an atomic weight of 2, resembles hydrogen in many ways, and combines with oxygen to form the compound D_2O, or **heavy water.** A third isotope of hydrogen, **tritium,** also is found in water, along with three isotopes of oxygen (O^{16}, O^{17}, and O^{18}). Tritium and O^{18} are present in only minute traces, while deuterium and O^{17} average 200 and 1000 ppm, respectively. The six isotopes form 18 different substances that may be found in water.

CLASSIFICATION OF WATER USAGES

The uses of water are classified as **withdrawal** and **nonwithdrawal,** and **consumptive** and **nonconsumptive.**

Withdrawal and Nonwithdrawal Uses—Domestic, municipal, irrigation, water power, and industrial uses are classified as withdrawal uses, as water for these purposes must be pumped from the ground or diverted from a stream, lake, or reservoir. Navigation, recreation, and conservation of wildlife are examples of nonwithdrawal uses.

Consumptive and Nonconsumptive Uses—Water that is evaporated or incorporated into a product is said to be used consumptively. Most uses of water are consumptive to some extent. Excluding water for hydroelectric power generation, it has been estimated that one-fourth of all water withdrawn in a typical year is consumed. Irrigation is the greatest consumer of water because of evaporation or transpiration losses that may amount to as much as 60 per cent. Generally, not more than 10 per cent of municipal and industrial water is actually consumed, the remaining 90 per cent being returned ultimately to the ground or streams.

About two-thirds of the water for industry is used nonconsumptively for cooling in the condensers of steam turbines of electric-power generating stations. This use does not alter the chemical composition of the water, but only raises its temperature.

Water used to generate hydroelectric power amounts to four to six times that used for all other purposes; this use is entirely nonconsumptive.

Figure **10**—1 shows the estimated total average daily amount of water involved in all types of uses in the United States from 1900 to 1955, projected to 1975.

Treatment of Water—While raw natural water may serve for such purposes as hydroelectric power generation without any preparation, water for many other uses requires some treatment to meet the quality requirements of a specific use. For example, water for municipal purposes generally is settled and filtered

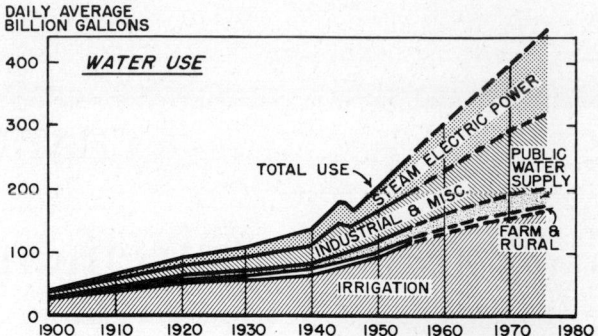

FIG. 10—1. Estimated total water use in the United States from 1900 to 1955, projected to 1975. (From: Mineral Facts and Problems, 1960 ed., Bulletin 585, U. S. Bureau of Mines.)

to remove suspended matter, chlorinated to kill residual microorganisms, and aerated for odor control. Water may also be treated to reduce its hardness by removing a large portion of the calcium and magnesium ions it may contain.

For certain industrial uses, water must possess a high degree of purity, attained by distillation or ion-exchange methods. Boiler water for steam generation must be of high purity, not only to minimize scale deposits on heat-transfer surfaces, but also to control corrosion in boilers, condensers, and associated piping. At the other extreme, simple clarification to remove most of the undissolved solids may be the only treatment required to prepare water for use.

SECTION 2
USES OF WATER IN THE IRON AND STEEL INDUSTRY

The water requirements of the main departments of a modern integrated steel plant are shown in Table **10**—I: these figures apply to a hypothetical plant, and are not necessarily to be regarded as typical. In the following paragraphs, some specific uses of water in the departmental areas referred to in the table and in other areas are listed.

Raw-Materials Preparation—The principal solid natural raw materials of the iron and steel industry are coal (most of which is converted to coke and coal chemicals), iron-bearing materials (iron ores and sinter), and fluxes (principally limestone and dolomite).

Considerable quantities of water are used in coal mining, principally for dust control at the working face, and in coal-cleaning (washing) plants where solid foreign matter is removed from the as-mined coal (see Chapter 3). Much of the water used in coal cleaning is collected in settling basins where it is clarified and returned to the cleaning cycle to minimize the amount of make-up water used in the process.

Large amounts of water are used in the beneficiation of iron ores; for cleaning (to remove clay and sand, for example) and in concentrating processes (see Chapter 5). In many operations, water of an inferior grade may be usable: some of the flotation processes, however, require water free from certain impurities and of generally higher quality. Lack of abundant wa-

Table 10—I. Water Requirements of the Main Departments of A Modern Integrated Steel Plant (Assuming A Balanced Production of Various Types of Finished Steel).*

Area of Use	Per Ton of Finished Steel	
	Volume of Water in Gallons	Per Cent of Total
Blast furnace (including blowers, furnace cooling, and gas washers)	10,000	25
Open hearth	5,000	12½
Coke plant	5,000	12½
Hot mills and related processes	10,000	25
Finishing mills and related processes	8,000	20
Sanitary, boiler make-up and miscellaneous	2,000	5
Total	40,000	100

* After Nebolsine.

ter at many mining and beneficiation sites makes it necessary to recycle as much water as possible after some form of treatment that will render effluent water suitable for repeated use. Clarification is the principal treatment given to water used in the mining industry.

Coke and Coal-Chemical Plants—The chief use of water in the manufacture of coke is to quench the hot coke after it is pushed from the ovens. Waste water from the coal-chemical plant, supplemented by whatever fresh water is required, can be used for quenching.

The various chemical processes employed in the recovery of coal chemicals require considerable amounts of water of suitable purity: for the generation of process steam for heating stills, etc.; for cooling purposes in heat exchangers and condensers; for washing certain crystalline products; and other uses mentioned in Chapter 4.

Sintering Plant—The principal uses of water in a sintering plant are as additions for controlling the moisture content of the mix, for dust control, and for cooling sinter.

Blast Furnace—The blast furnace requires very large amounts of water for its efficient operation, notably for cooling various parts of the furnace and its auxiliaries. For example, cooling water circulates constantly through the tuyeres, hearth staves, bosh and inwall cooling plates, cinder notch, and stove valves. Gas washing, to remove flue dust from the gases leaving the top of the furnace, requires considerable water, and additional quantities are used for slag granulation and other purposes.

Steelmaking Furnaces—The fuel burners of an open-hearth furnace are water-cooled, as are the valves that regulate the flow of air and waste gases into and out of the furnace system. In addition, the skewback channels and doors are cooled with circulating water. The roof lances used in some furnaces for injecting oxygen onto the bath are also water-cooled.

Electric-arc furnaces are equipped with water-cooled doors, and water cooling is applied also to the roof ring, the electrode rings, and electrode clamps (see Chapter 17).

Basic oxygen steelmaking requires the use of a water-cooled lance to inject oxygen into the bath. The gases emitted by the vessel are collected in a water-cooled hood and passed through water sprays for additional cooling prior to cleaning them by a dry process for the removal of entrained solids.

Rolling Mills—The reheating furnaces employed to heat steel for rolling employ water quite extensively for cooling furnace doors, skid pipes, skewbacks, and so on. Water also is used extensively as a coolant for rolling-mill rolls to maintain their contours, minimize fire checking, and lengthen their service life. On hot-rolling mills, water in the form of high-pressure jets is used to remove scale from the hot steel before rolling and to keep the surface clean between certain passes. Hot-strip mills also use cooling sprays over the runout table to cool the strip to the proper temperature for coiling.

The scale removed from hot steel by the high-pressure jets referred to above falls into a flume or sluice beneath the mill, where a running stream of water carries the scale to a collection point.

The roll-neck bearings of some mills are made of materials that permit the use of water as a lubricant.

Pickling—The removal of scale from the surface of hot-rolled steel generally is accomplished by immersing the steel in a water solution of sulphuric, hydrochloric, nitric, or other acid. The large scope of most pickling operations involves the use of large quantities of water, not only for making up the pickling solutions, but also for rinsing.

Electrolytic Tinning—Part of the sequence of operations in electrolytic tinning involves the electrolytic cleaning of the steel strip in an aqueous alkaline bath, followed by acid pickling, rinsing, and scrubbing—all prior to the actual plating of tin on the steel surface. After plating, the strip is rinsed to remove the drag-out of plating solution and dried. After this, a melting operation to "flow" the tin is followed by a quenching operation. The various baths for cleaning, pickling, rinsing and quenching require considerable amounts of high-quality water.

Steam Generation—Large amounts of water of controlled purity are required for boiler water for steam generation. The steam may be used to drive turbines for electric-power generation or to drive turbo-blowers, in both of which cases a great deal of water must be circulated through the condensers serving the turbines. Some steam is used as process steam for various heating, drying, and moisture-content-control operations, some of which consume large quantities of steam that add considerably to the water requirements of a plant.

Miscellaneous Uses—Hydraulic mechanisms that operate valves, open and close furnace doors, and actuate materials-handling devices, require considerable amounts of water; as do quenching tanks employed in heat-treating operations.

Ample supplies of potable water, along with water for sanitary purposes, fire protection, and landscape maintenance, must also be provided.

SECTION 3

WATER ECONOMY

Nearly every large steel plant practices, at least to some extent, the repeated use of the same water to limit the amount of new "make-up" water that must be supplied. It has been estimated that as little as 2 per cent of the circulated supply is actually consumed: the remainder is returned to the natural drainage basin in which it originated. Thus, it is obvious that, while a steel plant "uses" large amounts of water, by comparison it "consumes" relatively very little.

At the present time, the degree of water conservation practiced at any particular plant appears to be

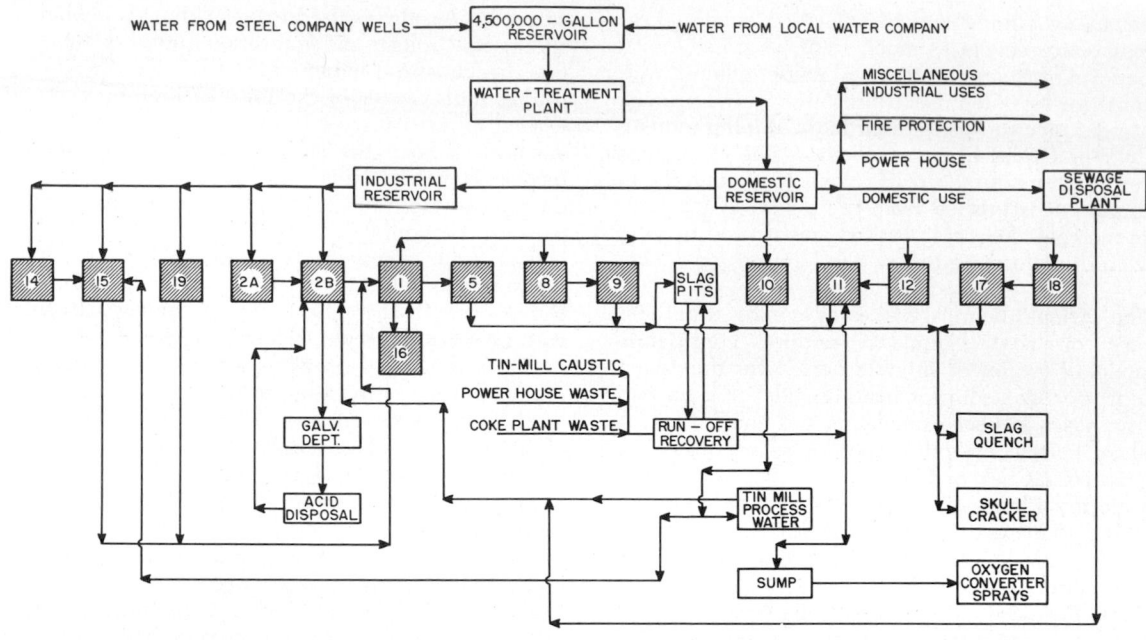

Fig. 10—2. Flow diagram of the water-supply system, at one stage in its development, at a Far Western steel plant where conservation practices limit consumption of water to as little as 1600 gallons per ton of finished steel. Shaded and numbered blocks each indicate a separate cooling-tower system. Figures 10—3A, B and C show components of individual tower systems. (After Riegel.)

governed mostly by the adequacy of local water supplies. Plants on the Great Lakes have a practically unlimited supply of good water, but even they recirculate some water. This may consist only of recirculating the discharge from turboblower and turbogenerator condensers as cooling water for blast

furnaces, following which some of the already twice-used water will be pumped to the gas washers.

At one Far Western steel plant, the principal source of water is from wells of limited capacity, supplemented by purchases from a local water company. Figures 10—2 and 10—3A, B and C show the

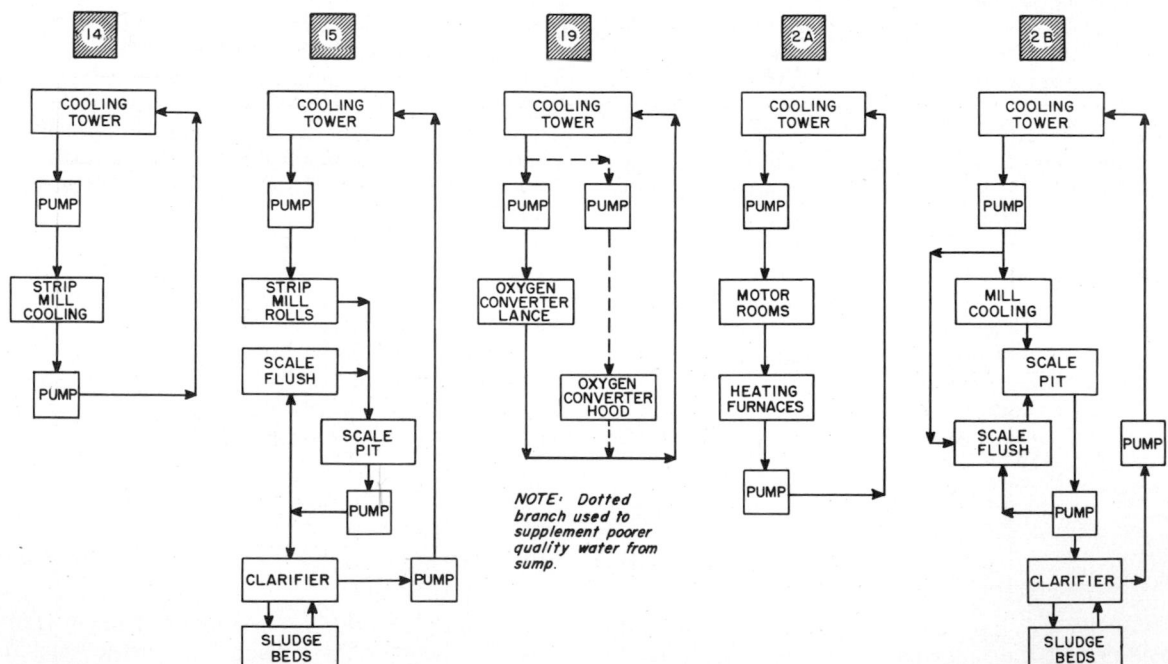

Fig. 10—3A. Details of individual cooling-tower systems in a Far Western steel plant that practices conservation to a marked degree. Numbers of systems correspond to numbers of shaded blocks in flow diagram in Figure 10—2. See also Figures 10—3B and 10—3C. (After Riegel.)

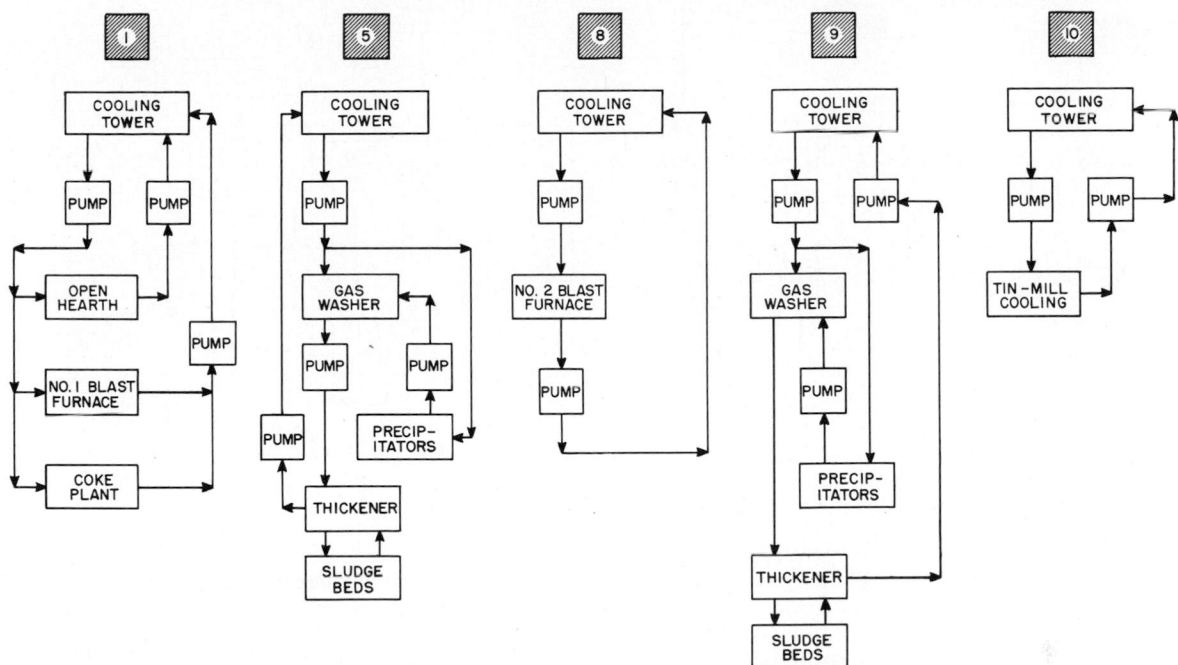

Fig. 10—3B. Details of individual cooling-tower systems in a Far Western steel plant that practices conservation to a marked degree. Numbers of systems correspond to numbers of shaded blocks in flow diagram in Figure 10—2. See also Figures 10—3A and 10—3C. (After Riegel.)

layout of the principal parts of the system at this plant. Water is stored in a 4.5-million gallon reservoir from which it is supplied to a water-treatment plant where the solids content of the water is reduced. The treated water then goes to an open industrial-water reservoir and a covered domestic-water reservoir. Water from the domestic reservoir is pumped to supply powerhouse and sanitary requirements, fire protection, lawn and shrubbery requirements, and some minor industrial uses. The industrial-water system

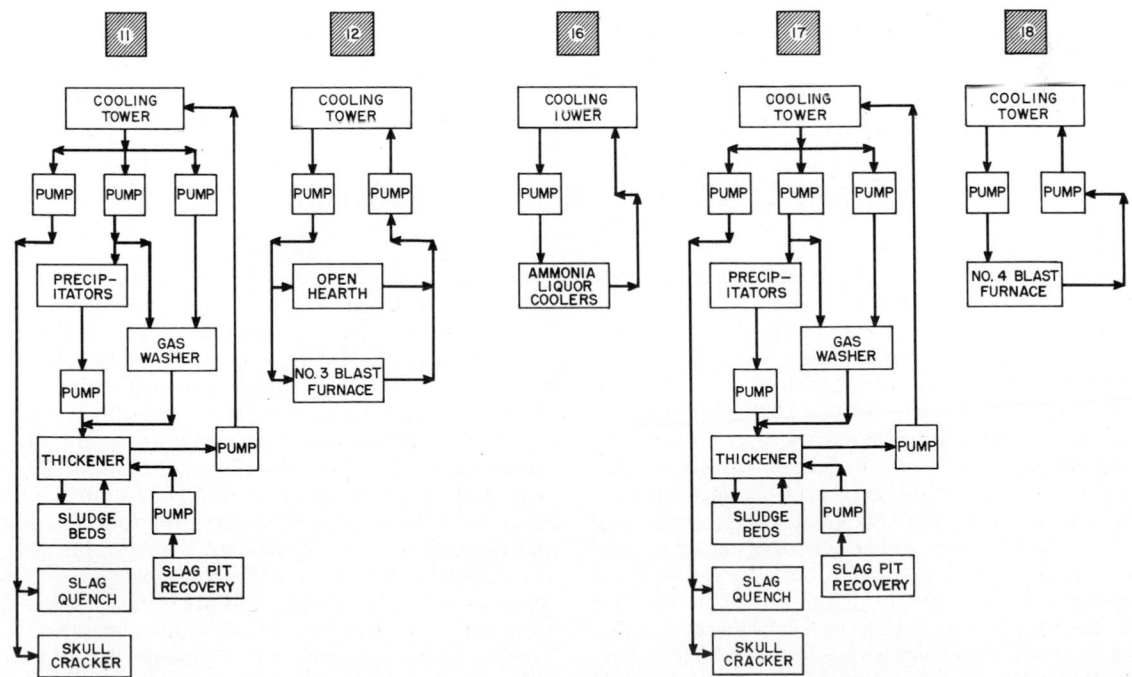

Fig. 10—3C. Details of individual cooling-tower systems in a Far Western steel plant that practices conservation to a marked degree. Numbers of systems correspond to numbers of shaded blocks in flow diagram in Figure 10—2. See also Figures 10—3A and 10—3B. (After Riegel.)

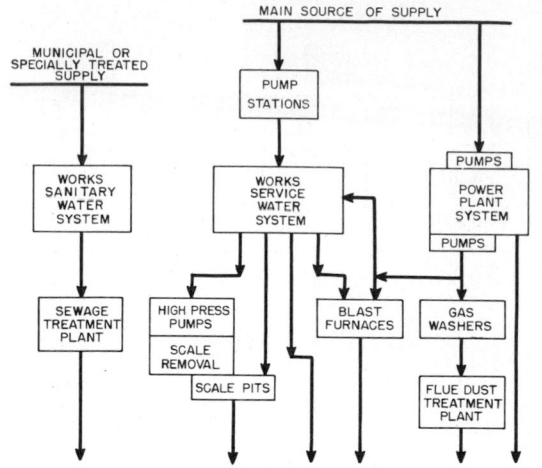

FIG. 10—4. Simplified flow diagram illustrating the use of water at an integrated steel plant with an abundant supply of high-quality water. (After Nebolsine.)

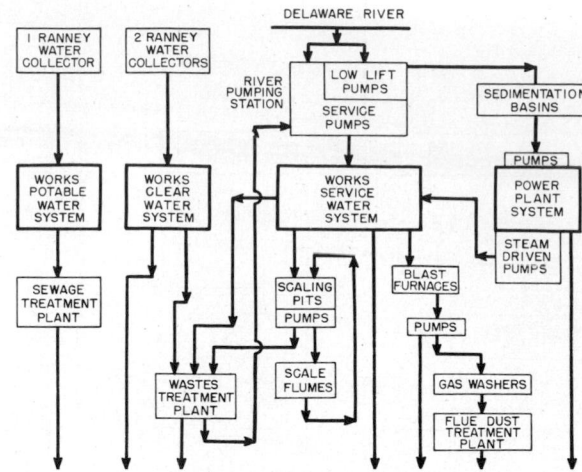

FIG. 10—5. Simplified flow diagram of the water-supply system at Fairless Works of United States Steel Corporation. (After Spitz.)

consists of a number of individual systems in series, with the water discharged from one system becoming the supply of the next succeeding system. Thus, the first system supplies water to meet the relatively highest quality requirements and the last system supplies water of relatively the poorest quality. Due to the high degree of re-use through recirculation, water consumption per ton of finished steel is less than 1600 gallons at this steel plant.

Figure 10—4 illustrates the relative simplicity of the water system of a plant located on the Great Lakes, where water of good quality is plentiful.

The water system that supplies Fairless Works of United States Steel Corporation is shown schematically in Figure 10—5. Designed for flexibility of operation, the system also provides for recirculation of

clarified waste effluents. The works requires about 230,000,000 gallons of water daily for all services. Of this daily total, 48,000,000 gallons are used in the manufacture of the various steel products; 38,000,000 gallons are used for cooling the condensers of the turboblowers that supply the air blast for the blast furnaces; and 72,000,000 gallons are used for the production of electric power (boiler water and condenser cooling water combined). Water is pumped from the Delaware River for general service and condenser-cooling requirements. Three horizontal-collector-type wells supply the potable-water system (one well) and the clear-water system (two wells). The clear-water system supplies water for processes in the sheet and tin mill that require water of better quality than general service water.

SECTION 4

TREATMENT OF EFFLUENT WATER

Because conditions vary from plant to plant as to the abundance and quality of water supply, as well as to the types of product manufactured, the present discussion will be limited to the treatment of waste water at Fairless Works.

Approximately one-third (over 75,000,000 gallons) of all the water taken into the works enters the waste-treatment system as individual wastes through more than forty separate outflows after collecting more than a dozen different chemical compositions and physical types of wastes. These wastes comprise solutions of acids, alkalies, and soluble oils; emulsions of insoluble oils; and suspensions of mill scale and flue dust. Sedimentation, flocculation, clarification, skimming, and neutralization processes are utilized as required to treat specific wastes. For convenience in processing, separate treatment plants handle the special wastes at the sheet and tin mill, and at the blast furnaces, as shown in Figure 10—6.

Sheet and Tin Mill Waste-Treatment Plant — In the waste-treatment plant of the sheet and tin mill (Figure 10—6), insoluble oil wastes consisting primarily of various oils in the effluent from the skimmer tanks of the five-stand mill, plus small quantities of oily waste water from the dirty-water sumps, flow to a primary receiver and oil-removal tank. Soluble-oil wastes discharged from the sumps or tanks of the roll shop, the electrostatic precipitators, the oil-skimmer tanks and rolling-solution tanks of the four-stand mill and the rolling-solution tanks of the Ferrolite reduction mill also flow to the primary receiver and oil-removal tank. The floating oils are removed by skimming and pumped to a 42,300-gallon storage tank. These oils are disposed of in an incinerator-type furnace or trucked away for disposal. The sludge is removed by a drag-out conveyor discharging into a container that is occasionally emptied on a refuse dump for disposal. The oily waste effluent, with the insoluble

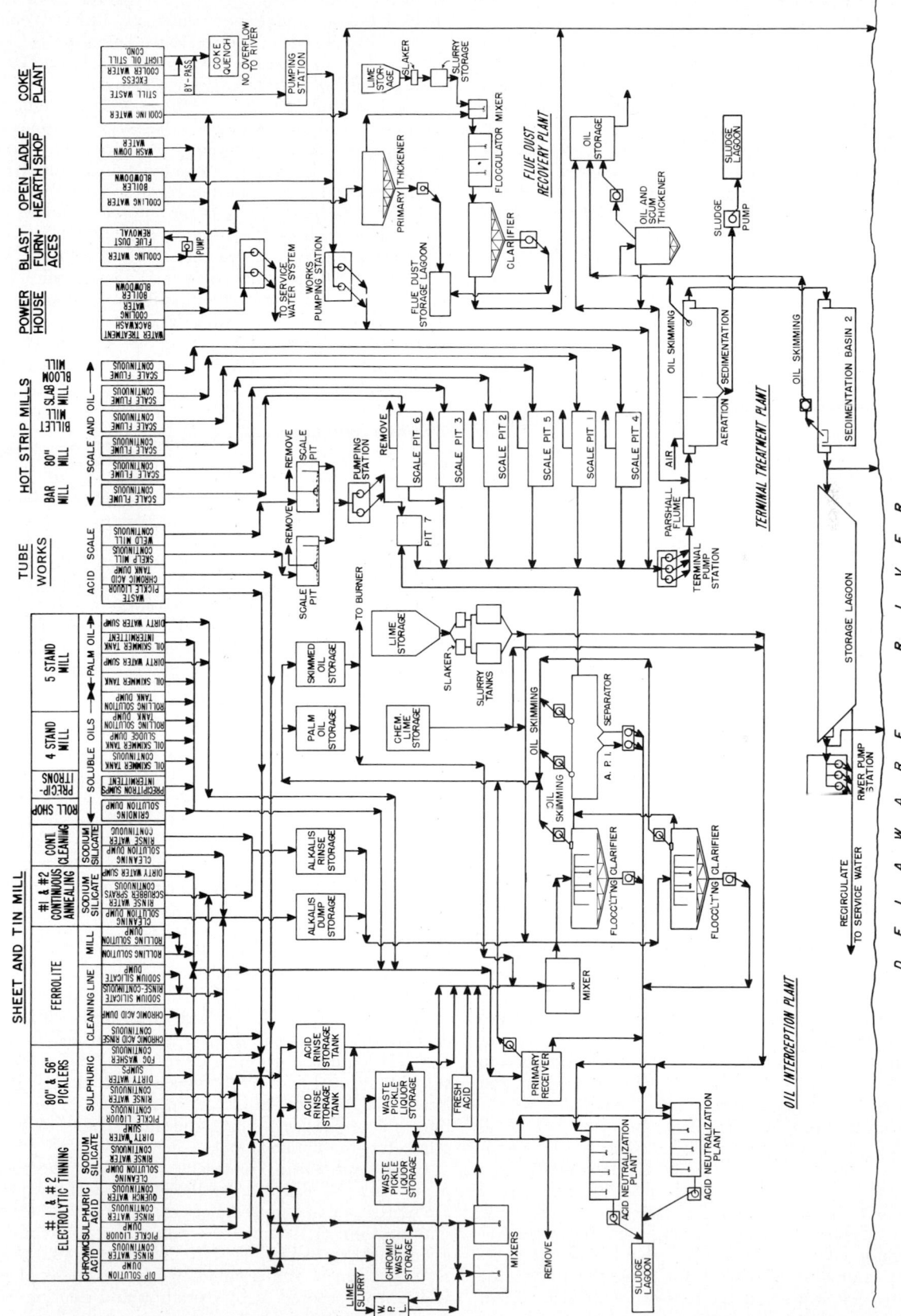

Fig. 10—6. Schematic arrangement of the water-treatment system at Fairless Works of United States Steel Corporation.

oils removed and the soluble oils remaining in solution, flows to a flash mixer.

Synthetic palm oil, sperm oil, various lubricating oils, hydraulic oils, rolling-solution oil, paraffin, greases, and soluble oils are present in the recovered oil. The bulk of the oil is received in the insoluble states. The recovered oils amount to about 55,000 gallons per month. Their water content varies from 5 to 10 per cent, and they contain from 15 to 60 per cent of solids consisting of iron oxides, dirt, and grit.

Oils from the five-stand mill usually arrive at the primary receiving tank in a heavy, viscous state having approximately the specific gravity of water and tend to "hang" in the water rather than float. When permitted to enter still water, some of the sludge-bearing oils will often settle to the bottom and form large masses that adhere to anything they contact. These masses soon choke any openings they pass through. The flow of these oils is semicontinuous, with periodic dumps of several hundred gallons. Of all the oils received, those from the five-stand mill are the most difficult to handle. The lubricating oils, hydraulic oils, and rolling-solution oil used on the four-stand mill remain in a fairly fluid state and will float to the surface, making their removal a problem of skimming.

Acid rinse water from the 56-inch and 80-inch continuous pickling lines, from the two electrolytic-tinning lines, and the Ferrolite cleaning line, is pumped to two storage tanks where it is stored and then pumped by controlled flow to the flash mixer. This water can also be pumped to the clarifiers or to the emergency acid-neutralization tanks. Acid wastes (waste-pickle liquor and chromic-acid wastes) from the tube-producing section also enter this system at the storage tanks.

Sufficient acid rinse water is fed to the flash mixer to mix with the effluent from the primary receiver to control the pH at about 3 and crack the soluble-oil emulsions. The balance of the acid rinse water is pumped to the acid-neutralization tanks, where it is neutralized with lime and the resulting sludge is pumped to a sludge lagoon.

The flash mixer discharges through controlling devices to two clarifiers, where alkaline wastes and lime slurry are added. Flocculation in the clarifiers, followed by detention in the sedimentation chambers with controlled flows, allows each clarifier to operate up to rated capacity for neutralization of large quantities of acid rinse water. Oil is skimmed from the clarifier surface and pumped to storage. Sludge is pumped to the sludge lagoon. The clarifier effluents combine and flow to an oil separator for further removal of oil.

From the foregoing, it can be seen that soluble-oil recovery is a two-stage process. First, the oil emulsions are broken by the addition of acidic wastes that lower the pH to a value of about 3: the addition of lime and alkaline wastes then raises the alkalinity to a pH of about 10. The resulting high pH of the oil-separator effluent could be lowered by further processing, but it is beneficial in raising the pH of the slightly acid wastes at the terminal wastes-treatment plant to which the effluent flows.

Waste pickle liquor from the two electrolytic-tinning lines, totaling about 100,000 gallons per day, is pumped to storage in two 200,000-gallon tanks located at the oil-interception plant site. Waste pickle liquor not required for the waste-treatment processes is trucked to an independent concern that produces paint pigments. Normally, the waste pickle liquor is removed continuously, leaving the tanks partly empty to provide temporary storage in the event of an interruption in trucking operations. Sufficient lime-handling and slaking facilities are provided to neutralize the entire pickle-liquor output in either one or both of two neutralization plants if for any reason neutralization becomes necessary. Approximately one pound of lime is added in slurry form for each gallon of solution treated. The lime, acid, and ferrous sulphate react to form two stable compounds—calcium sulphate and ferrous hydroxide. The resulting sludge and water are pumped to the sludge lagoon where solids settle out and the water percolates into the soil or evaporates.

Alkaline wastes, consisting primarily of cleaning solutions containing sodium orthosilicate, are effectively employed in the treatment process to raise the pH of the acid and soluble-oil wastes for sludging purposes. The contents of the cleaning-solution tanks of the tinning lines, the continuous-annealing lines and the continuous-cleaning line are pumped to storage and fed by controlled flow to the clarifiers. Slaked lime is added as slurry in sufficient quantities to raise the pH in the clarifiers to about 10 and precipitate the metals from solution. The flow formed in this process is of value in clarifying the effluent and removing some of the oils from the precipitated sludge.

Chromic-acid dump and rinse solutions from the tinning lines are mixed with the sulphuric-acid wastes from these lines and pumped to two 75,000-gallon acid rinse-water storage tanks at the oil-interception plant. Any pre-treatment with acid, therefore, takes place in the acid rinse-water storage tanks. The ferrous-sulphate content of the acid rinse waters is sufficient to reduce the sodium dichromate to trivalent chromium sulphate. Detention time in the storage tanks is more than sufficient to allow the reaction to go to completion. From the storage tanks, the chromic-acid wastes are pumped with the acid rinse waters to the flash mixer and pass into the clarifiers, where the addition of lime precipitates the chromium as chromic hydroxide. A 100 per cent removal of chromium is accomplished. The sodium acid phosphate is converted to ferrous phosphate and deposited in the clarifiers with the chromic hydroxide. The sodium sulphate formed by the reactions is not removed. The latter is highly soluble but harmless, and remains in the effluent in very dilute solution. The sludge is pumped to the sludge lagoon.

Coke-Plant-Waste Treatment—Wastes of the coke plant, with the exception of the ammonia-still waste, are segregated in a separate circulatory system, closed within itself. The ammonia-still waste, containing about 10 ppm of phenols, is pumped from the lime-settling basin to the terminal waste-treatment plant where it is disposed of by oxidation and dilution before entering the river. The other wastes are used for coke quenching and never enter the river.

Blast-Furnace Waste-Treatment Plant—Flue-dust-laden waters from the gas washers and electrostatic precipitators pass through a conventional primary thickener and then to a secondary clarification plant in the blast-furnace area where effluent from the primary thickener is mixed with lime slurry in a flash mixer and flows to a flocculator chamber. Sludge from the secondary clarifier is pumped, along with primary-thickener sludge, to a separate flue-dust storage lagoon. Clarifier effluent flows directly to the river through a measuring flume.

Scale-Flume Waste Disposal—The effluent from the scale flumes of the bar mill, the 80-inch hot-strip mill, the billet mill, the slab mill, and the blooming mill is led through scale pits, where solids settle out, from which the clarified water goes to the terminal treatment plant. Scale pits of the skelp mill and weld mill of the tube-producing section are tied into this system.

Miscellaneous Disposal Practices—Most of the cooling water used in the power house is pumped to the service water system. The remainder of this water joins power-house boiler blowdown and cooling water from the blast furnaces, open-hearth furnaces, and coke plant, and is discharged into the river. Backwash from the boiler-water treatment system, boiler blowdown from the open-hearth shop, and washdown water from the ladle shop go to the terminal treatment plant.

BIBLIOGRAPHY

Nebolsine, Ross, Water supply for steel plants. Iron and Steel Engineer **31,** April 1954, pages 78–88.

Riegel, Harry I., Vital importance of industrial water. Regional Technical Meetings of American Iron and Steel Institute, 1957, pages 463–484.

Spitz, H. S., Water processing at Fairless Works. Iron and Steel Engineer **32,** January 1955, pages 70–77.

U. S. Bureau of Mines, Bulletin 585, Mineral Facts and Problems, 1960 ed. Government Printing Office, Washington, D. C.

CHAPTER 11

Tonnage Oxygen For Iron- And Steelmaking

The iron and steel industry has become one of the largest industrial users of gaseous oxygen. In 1960, total consumption of oxygen in iron and steel plants increased to 486 cubic feet of gas for each ton of ingot steel produced. This figure is based on the consumption of oxygen for all iron- and steel-plant uses. As shown in Table 11—I, roughly 40 per cent of all the oxygen consumed by the industry is employed elsewhere than in the steelmaking furnaces. Thus, in 1960, the average amount of oxygen used directly in the production of ingot steel (by the open-hearth, electric-furnace, and basic oxygen steelmaking processes) was 294 cubic feet per ton.

Oxygen in the Blast Furnace—Increasing the oxygen content of the blast has proved beneficial to the operation of both iron and ferromanganese blast furnaces (see Chapter 14). For example, enrichment of the blast from the normal 21 per cent oxygen content of natural air to around 30 per cent has considerably increased production and moderately decreased coke consumption per ton of ferromanganese produced. However, air enriched to 25 per cent oxygen content did little or no good in one series of tests extending over a year on a ferromanganese-producing furnace.

Direct Steelmaking Uses of Oxygen—In the open-hearth furnace, gaseous oxygen can be introduced through the fuel burner when firing from either end of the furnace to intensify combustion and increase heat input to the furnace during the period when scrap and other solid raw materials are being charged

and melted. In the refining phase of an open-hearth heat, made in a furnace suitably equipped for the practice, hot metal is added to the furnace as soon as possible after scrap charging has been completed. Water-cooled lances extending into the furnace through the roof then are lowered to inject oxygen directly onto the metal. Such use of oxygen increases the rate of scrap melting, desiliconization and decarburization, and materially reduces heat time.

In the electric furnace, the use of auxiliary burners employing oxygen with a fuel gas increases the speed with which scrap can be melted, thereby reducing the amount of electric power consumed in this phase of the heat and minimizing breakage of electrodes. Lances inserted through the furnace charging door permit the injection of oxygen into the bath to assist in the rapid attainment of high bath temperatures and to speed up refining by rapidly oxidizing carbon and silicon from the metal.

The basic oxygen steelmaking process utilizes oxygen in the manner described in Chapter 15. Essentially, the process consists of charging proper proportions of scrap and hot metal into a furnace shaped like a Bessemer converter but with a solid bottom, and blowing high-purity oxygen downward onto the bath through a water-cooled lance inserted through the mouth of the vessel.

Purity of Oxygen for Steel-Plant Use—The oxygen used by the steel industry is usually produced in two degrees of purity: 99.5 per cent oxygen that is used in large quantities in open-hearth and electric steelmaking furnaces and in the oxygen steelmaking processes and, in much smaller volumes, for welding and cutting; and 95 per cent oxygen that is used to increase the oxygen content of air for the blast furnace.

Production of Oxygen—Gaseous oxygen of the desired purity is produced from atmospheric air by fractional distillation processes carried out at very low temperatures and elevated pressures; for instance, temperatures and pressures of the order of −300° F at 70 lb. per sq. in. gage pressure. The several commercially available processes are essentially the same, although many minor differences in arrangement are encountered, depending upon local conditions, special designs of the individual builders of process equipment, and the need for such additional products as liquid oxygen, nitrogen, or argon.

The processes start by compressing the air to an

Table 11—I. Consumption of Oxygen by the Iron and Steel Industry*
(Millions of Cubic Feet in Gaseous Form)

| Use | Year | | | |
---	1960	1959	1958	1957
Conditioning	9,755	8,139	6,051	**
Scrap preparation	1,540	1,256	1,065	**
Other burning and welding	1,309	1,270	1,983	**
Blast furnaces	4,362	4,484	5,876	**
Steelmaking	29,213	18,307	13,049	**
All other steelmaking	812	689		**
Maintenance and construction	1,272	308	810	**
Total	48,263	34,453	28,834	25,887

* From: Annual Statistical Report—1960, American Iron and Steel Institute.

** Only total consumption for all uses reported for 1957.

elevated pressure, followed by progressively cooling it to saturation temperature in steps in a series of highly efficient heat exchangers. Condensation and freezing out of moisture, carbon dioxide, and hydrocarbons take place as the temperature is lowered, after which hydrocarbons still remaining are removed in adsorbent traps. The cold, purified air is finally separated into its components in fractionating (distillation) columns. The requirements for heat removal by refrigeration at the low temperature level are met by expansion of a portion of the cold compressed air in an expansion turbine.

A typical flowsheet for one type of large plant for the production of low-pressure gaseous oxygen of 99.5 per cent purity, at about 10 lb. per sq. in. gage pressure, is shown in Figure 11—1. In this plant, the flow of filtered air from the compressors is split into three parts. One part goes to one of two reversing regenerators, and the other two parts to two reversing heat exchangers. In the regenerators, the incoming air is cooled against the outgoing waste products; and mois-

ture, carbon dioxide and most of the hydrocarbons are deposited as solids on the regenerator packing. The flow in the regenerators is reversed periodically between air and waste nitrogen to re-evaporate and flush out the accumulated moisture, carbon dioxide and deposited hydrocarbons. Those portions of the intake air that flow to the reversing heat exchangers are cooled against the outgoing oxygen and high-purity nitrogen products, respectively, plus outgoing waste nitrogen. For the sake of simplicity, some of the connections for waste nitrogen to the reversing heat exchangers, and the reversing mechanism, are not illustrated.

The streams of cooled, compressed air from the regenerators and reversing heat exchangers are recombined and run through a hydrocarbon-adsorbent trap to remove hydrocarbons not already deposited. The major portion (about 80 per cent) of the air, at saturation temperature and pressure ($-278°$ F, 72 lb. per sq. in. gage) then is delivered to the bottom of the lower fractionating column (Figure 11—2), where it

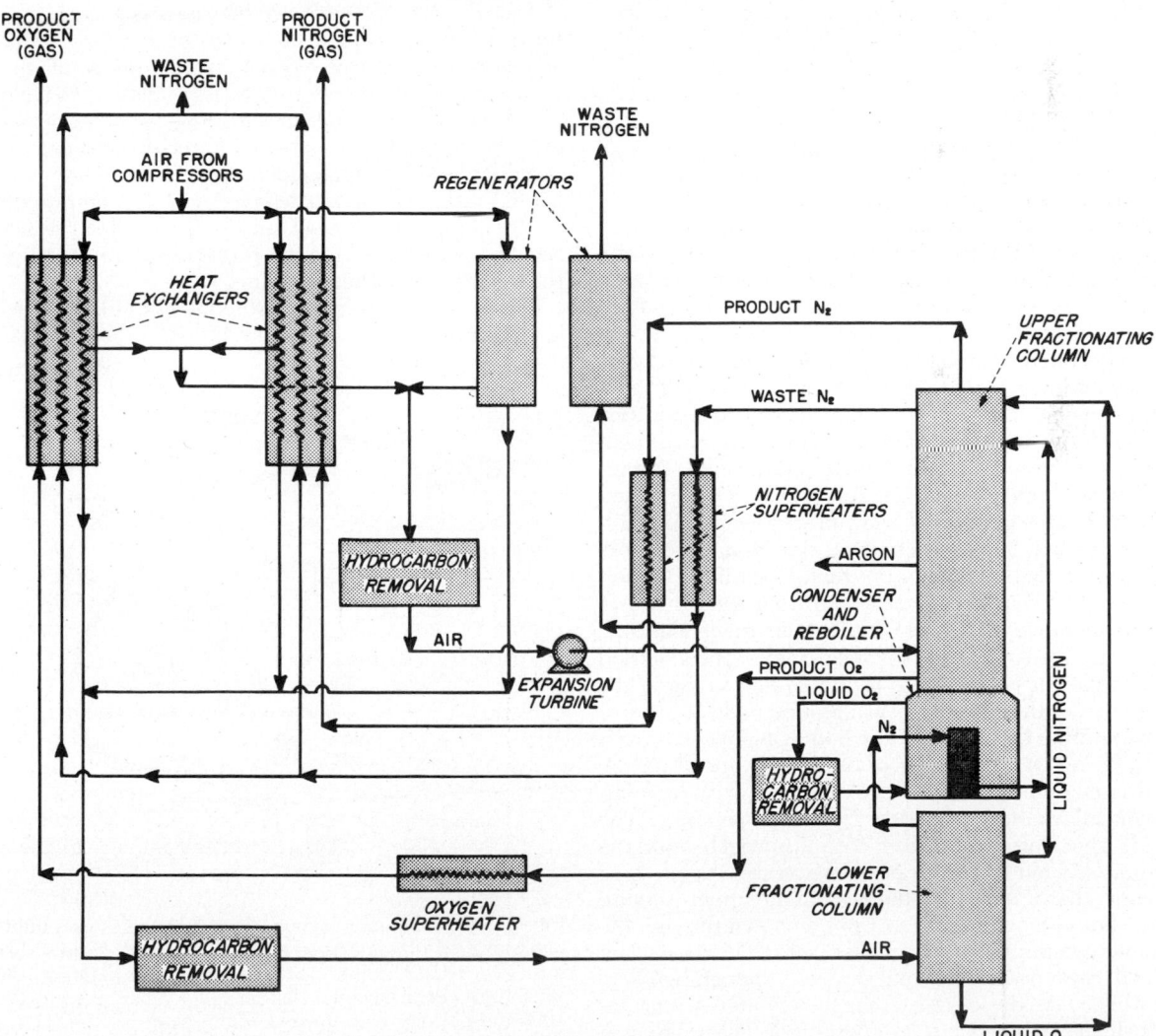

FIG. 11—1. Flowsheet of a plant for the production of low-pressure gaseous oxygen of high purity (see Figure 11—2 for details of operation of fractionating columns and condenser).

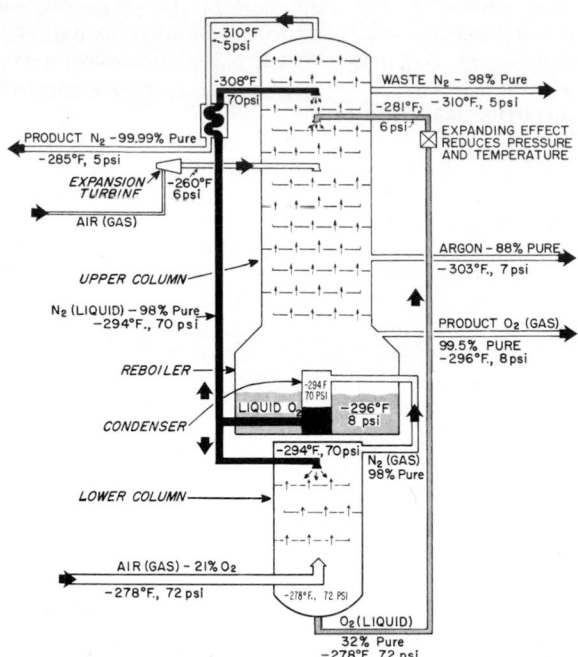

FIG. 11—2. Schematic diagram showing operation of fractionating (distillation) columns in a gaseous-oxygen generating plant. The hydrocarbon trap that removes the last traces of hydrocarbons from the liquid oxygen in the reboiler, shown in Figure 11—1, has been omitted from this diagram for the sake of simplification.

separates into a gas containing 17 per cent oxygen and a liquid containing 32 per cent oxygen. Side streams (totaling about 20 per cent of all the air) are taken from the regenerators and reversing heat exchangers and combined, then passed through a separate hydrocarbon-adsorbent trap, and next sent through the expansion turbine. In the expansion turbine, the air performs work and thereby removes heat from the low-temperature system to provide the refrigeration requirements of the cycle. The expanded air enters the middle of the upper fractionating column (Figure 11—2), together with liquid from the bottom of the lower column. Reflux liquid for the top of the upper column is provided from the condenser located above the lower column. In the condenser, gaseous nitrogen from the lower column is condensed by the lower temperature of the liquid oxygen in the reboiler. Although nitrogen normally boils at a lower temperature than oxygen, the boiling point of nitrogen can be raised above that of oxygen by operating the lower column at a higher pressure; this fixes the minimum allowable compressor discharge pressure. The heat given off by the condensing nitrogen boils the liquid oxygen (of 99.5 per cent purity) to produce vapors that rise through the trays of the upper column. The liquid flowing from tray to tray down through the upper column becomes progressively richer in oxygen (and the upward flowing gaseous product richer in nitrogen) as the oxygen from the countercurrent gas stream is stripped out by the liquid. The result is a high-purity, gaseous nitrogen product at the top of the upper column, and a high-purity gaseous oxygen product at the bottom of the upper column. These

two gaseous products are brought out through nonreversing passes of the reversing heat exchangers where they remove heat from the incoming air. A waste-nitrogen product also comes off the upper column and portions are led separately through the reversing heat exchangers and the regenerators, thus flushing out impurities deposited in the previous cycle when incoming air passed through these units. The liquid high-purity oxygen at the bottom of the upper column is passed through another hydrocarbon removal trap (Figure 11—1). This trap removes the last traces of acetylene and other hydrocarbons that possibly were not deposited in the regenerators or the reversing heat exchangers, or adsorbed by preceding traps.

Although not shown by Figures 11—1 or 11—2, a portion of the oxygen product can be withdrawn as a liquid directly from the bottom of the upper column, and a portion of the nitrogen product can be withdrawn as a liquid from the top of the lower column. This creates an additional refrigeration load, which must be provided for in the plant design.

Distribution Methods—When an oxygen-generating facility is installed adjacent to an iron or steel works to supply the oxygen requirements of that works, it is generally referred to as an "on-site" oxygen plant. The low-pressure gaseous oxygen from an on-site oxygen plant is compressed to the proper pressure and distributed through pipes to the consuming points. Liquid oxygen from on-site storage or delivered to the consuming plant from off-site storage is first gasified and then distributed, at the proper pressure, through the same system of plant piping.

Plants are built for the production of both high- and low-purity oxygen with capacities up to 500 to 1000

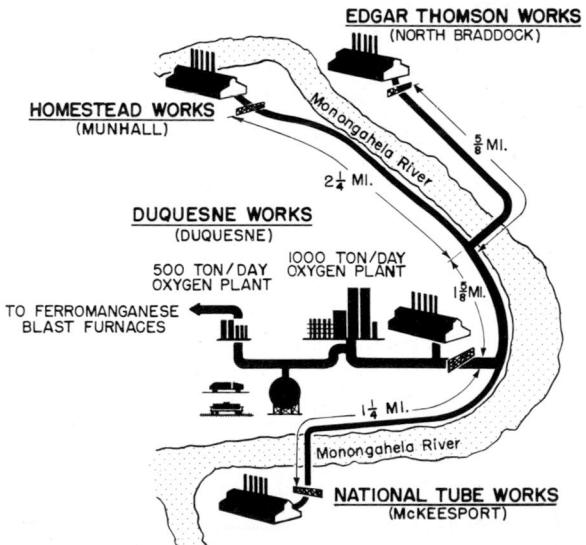

FIG. 11—3. Schematic layout of the first large-scale interplant oxygen-pipeline system in the United States that serves four United States Steel Corporation plants in the Pittsburgh, Pennsylvania, district. The pipeline from the 1000-ton per day high-purity oxygen plant is 20 inches in diameter, with 12-inch diameter branches to Homestead and Edgar Thomson Works and a 10-inch diameter branch to National Tube Works. Duquesne Works draws its supply of high-purity oxygen from the 20-inch line.

tons per day, and still larger plants have been projected.

A recent development is an extension of the "on-site" concept that involves the supplying of gaseous oxygen from a central generating plant to four steel plants (Figure 11—3). A 1000-ton per day oxygen generating plant has been erected at the Duquesne Works of United States Steel Corporation, and the high-purity oxygen gas is distributed through a 4.5-mile long pipeline to three additional mills in the Monongahela Valley. In addition to this large oxygen plant for producing high-purity oxygen, a 500-ton per day plant for producing low-purity oxygen is also located at Duquesne Works, to supply the requirements of a ferromanganese blast furnace at that steel works.

These oxygen plants are backed up by additional plants belonging to the oxygen-generating company, together with liquid-oxygen storage, at a number of locations. For adequate back-up of the oxygen plant at Duquesne Works, these additional sources of oxygen are required to be within a 15-hour delivery-time limit from the Monongahela Valley. Thus, in the case of Duquesne Works, six plants with a total capacity of 2730 tons of oxygen daily and liquid-oxygen storage capacity at 15 locations, totaling more than 19,000 tons, are within a 15-hour range for delivery by truck. Railroad tank cars are also available for delivery of liquid oxygen.

CHAPTER 12

The Physical Chemistry of Iron- and Steelmaking

PART I

Fundamentals of Thermodynamic Concepts

and Physical Chemistry

SECTION 1

INTRODUCTION

The subject matter of the physical chemistry of ferrous metallurgy covers an extensive field concerning the chemistry of ore beneficiation, preparation of other raw materials, smelting of iron ore, steelmaking, solidification, heat-treating, plating and other surface treatments, and corrosion. A chapter in a book is by no means adequate to discuss in sufficient detail the chemistry of all the processes from the preparation of the raw materials to the manufacture of finished steel products. In fact, several books are needed for complete coverage of this subject. The subject matter chosen for this chapter is limited to the discussion of those basic concepts of physical chemistry that are most directly applicable to an understanding of iron- and steelmaking processes.

In writing this chapter, an attempt has been made to limit the discussion to an average level suitable for the students of metallurgy pursuing graduate or post graduate education as well as for those, with some scientific background, engaged in the iron and steel industry. It is assumed that the reader has some basic knowledge of chemistry, physics and mathematics, so that the chapter can be devoted solely to the discussion of the chemistry of the processes.

This chapter consists of seven parts. The first part, which is one third of the chapter, describes briefly the fundamentals of thermodynamic concepts and physical chemistry. This is, of course, in a highly condensed form and confined to defining the basic concepts which are used frequently in describing the chemistry of metallurgical processes and in the study of problems associated with such processes. All the thermodynamic and kinetic equations which are used in this chapter are given in Part I with examples showing their application. For convenience, thermodynamic data on elements and compounds of interest in process metallurgy are compiled in tabular form in Part I.

To facilitate the application of physicochemical concepts to the study of problems on metallurgical processes, data are compiled in Parts II and III on the physicochemical properties of some iron alloys and slags, respectively; these include phase-equilibrium diagrams, activities, densities, surface tensions, and coefficients of diffusion and of viscosity. Although the data given have been reviewed critically, space does not permit the discussion of their derivation and the experimental techniques used in measuring these physicochemical properties.

In Parts IV to VII, inclusive, the following subjects are discussed: Part IV: reduction and oxidation reactions; Part V: silicon and manganese reactions; Part VI: phosphorus reaction; and Part VII: sulphur reaction. The reactions are discussed from the point of view of reaction equilibria and reaction kinetics based on laboratory investigations, and whenever possible, an attempt is made to analyze the state of chemical reactions in iron- and steelmaking processes on the basis of the knowledge gained from laboratory studies.

DEFINITION OF TERMS

As in any other subject, the concepts of physical chemistry and thermodynamics are described and defined or stated as "laws" or "rules" by using universally accepted terms.* Although the precise defi-

*C.g.s. (metric) units are used throughout this chapter. To convert c.g.s. units to ft.-lb.-sec. (British) units, refer to appendices at end of book.

nition of such terms may be difficult or cumbersome, the meaning attached to these terms should be well understood: definitions of a few of the most pertinent basic physicochemical terms follow:

System—Any constituent part of the universe can be considered to be a system. For example, if the reduction of hematite by hydrogen that produces iron and water vapor is being considered, the system under consideration consists of solid hematite, solid iron, and a gas containing hydrogen and water vapor.

Property—In physicochemical language, a system (on a macro scale) has two types of properties: **extensive properties** and **intensive properties**. The properties of a system which change proportionately with its mass are the extensive properties, such as weight, volume, energy. The ratio of two extensive properties gives an intensive property of the system. For example the density of a system is an intensive property as it is defined as mass per unit volume; some other examples of intensive properties are: refractive index, vapor pressure, temperature, viscosity, and surface tension. These thermodynamic properties do not include the micro properties, such as atomic properties or arrangements, and the systems are considered not to be under the influence of an external field as, for example, a gravitational, magnetic, electric, or other external field.

State—The state of a system is defined by all its properties; however, all the chemical and thermodynamic properties are inferred when only a few are given explicitly. For example, the statement: "one gram-molecule of oxygen (32.00 g. of O_2) at 0°C and 1 atm. pressure" defines the state of oxygen, since from this information one can find, experimentally or by reference to the literature, other properties of oxygen at this state. A relation between temperature, pressure and volume is known as the **equation of state**. Although it is reasonable to assume that all pure gases and liquids obey an equation of state, the same cannot be said for the state of solids. At a given temperature and pressure, a property of a given mass of a metal cannot be defined explicitly without stating the history of the metal. For example, the solubility of nitrogen or hydrogen in iron depends not only on temperature and pressure but also on the mechanical and heat treatments which were given to the metal.

Energy—The most comprehensive definition of energy is that given by Kelvin (1851): "The energy of a material system is the sum, expressed in mechanical units of work, of all the effects which are produced outside the system when the system is made to pass in any manner from the state in which it happens to be to a certain arbitrarily fixed initial (standard) state." Depending on the nature of the work performed by the system, its energy takes different forms, e.g. chemical energy, electrical energy, heat energy, kinetic energy (due to motion), potential energy (due to position), and so on. Since the energy of a system is determined by its properties, a change in the state of a system from state A to state B is accompanied by a change in the energy of the system, as expressed by the equation:

$$\Delta E = E_B - E_A$$

The total energy E of a system at any given state is not known, but any energy change ΔE accompanying a change of state, e.g. reaction, expansion, etc., can be evaluated and the study of the laws interrelating these energy changes constitutes the subject matter of thermodynamics. All forms of energy have the dimensions of: mass $\times$ (length)^2/(time)$^2 = ml^2/t^2$. Using c.g.s. units (length, l, in centimeters; mass, m, in grams, and time, t, in seconds) the unit of energy is the **erg** which is the work done when a force of 1 dyne acts through a distance of 1 cm. The unit of force, **dyne**, is defined as that force which, when acting on unit mass (one gram), gives it unit acceleration (1 cm./sec.^{2}). A larger unit of energy, the **joule**, is defined as 10^7 ergs and it is equal to one watt $\times$ sec. The **calorie** is defined as 4.1841 joules.

In this first part of Chapter 12, the following subjects are briefly discussed: basic gas laws; first, second and third laws of thermodynamics; solutions; reaction equilibria; phase rule; theory of diffusion; and kinetics of reactions. The scope of the subject matter is limited to the extent considered to be sufficient for the understanding of the physical chemistry of metallurgical reactions, with particular emphasis on the iron- and steelmaking processes.

SECTION 2

BASIC GAS LAWS

IDEAL GAS EQUATION

Boyle's law (1662) states that "at constant temperatures the volume of a definite mass of gas is inversely proportional to the pressure," thus

$$PV = \text{constant} \qquad (1)$$

where P and V are pressure and volume, respectively.

The variation of the volume of a gas with temperature, at constant pressure, was generalized by **Charles' law** (1787) and later by **Gay-Lussac's law** (1802). The law states that "at constant pressure, the volume of any gas expands by the same fraction of its volume at 0°C for every 1° rise of temperature." This is expressed mathematically as follows:

$$V - V_0 = \alpha t V_0 \qquad (2)$$

or

$$V = V_0(1 + \alpha t) \qquad (3)$$

where V_0 and V are volumes at 0° and t°C and α is the coefficient of cubical expansion.

These two laws, generalizing the effect of pressure and temperature on the volume of a gas, are not obeyed exactly by real gases. As a limiting case, a hypothetical gas which obeys the simple gas laws is called an **ideal gas** or a **perfect gas**. Generally speaking, deviations from these laws become noticeable with easily liquefiable gases and at low temperatures and high pressures. The behavior of gases becomes more ideal with decreasing pressure and increasing temperature. For ideal gases, the value of α is equal to $1/273.16$; equation (4) is derived by inserting this value in equation (3).

$$V_t = \frac{V_0}{273.16} (273.16 + t) \qquad (4)$$

If the ideal gas laws applied at very low temperatures, then the volume of an ideal gas at $t = -273.16°C$ becomes zero. This is known as the **absolute zero** of the ideal gas scale of temperature. The absolute temperature is defined as $T = 273.16 + t°C$ in degrees Kelvin, $°K$. Using this temperature scale, Charles' law may be restated, thus: "for a given mass of an ideal gas at constant pressure, the quantity V/T is constant"; therefore,

$$\frac{V}{T} = \frac{V_0}{T_0} \qquad (5)$$

Combination of two gas laws gives the following expression for a given mass of an ideal gas:

$$\frac{PV}{T} = \text{constant} \qquad (6)$$

Another basic gas law is that of **Avogadro** (1811): "Equal volumes of all gases under the same conditions of temperature and pressure contain equal numbers of molecules." That is, the volume occupied by one mole of an ideal gas, at a given temperature and pressure, is the same; therefore, for one mole of gas PV/T is a universal constant which is denoted by R; hence,

$$PV = RT \qquad (7)$$

or for an arbitrary number of moles (n),

$$PV = nRT \qquad (7a)$$

where R is known as the **molar gas constant.** Equation (7) is based on three gas laws applicable to an ideal gas and is called the **ideal gas equation.**

Based on Avogadro's law, one mole of an ideal gas (containing $N = 6.0247 \times 10^{23}$ molecules) occupies a volume of 22.414 liters at 1 atm. pressure and $273.16°K$ ($\equiv 0°C$). Using these units, $R = 0.08205$ liter-atm. per deg. per mole. If c.g.s. units are used, P is in dynes per cm.^{2} (1 atm. $\equiv 1.0132 \times 10^6$ dynes per cm.^{2}) and V in cm.^{3}, then $R = 8.3144 \times 10^7$ ergs per deg. per mole ($= 8.3144$ joules per deg. per mole). Since one calorie is equivalent to 4.1841×10^7 ergs, it follows that $R = 1.987$ cal. per deg. per mole.

MIXTURES OF GASES

Dalton's law (1801) states that "the total pressure of a mixture of gases is equal to the sum of the partial pressures of the constituent gases." Expressed as an equation, if the partial pressures of the individual gases are represented by p_1, p_2, p_3 . . . etc., and the total pressure by P, then:

$$P = p_1 + p_2 + p_3 + \ldots \qquad (8)$$

In a gas mixture containing n_1, n_2, and n_3 numbers of moles of gases 1, 2 and 3, occupying a volume of

V at a total pressure of P, the partial pressures of the constituent gases will be:

$$p_1 = P \frac{n_1}{n_1 + n_2 + n_3},$$

$$p_2 = P \frac{n_2}{n_1 + n_2 + n_3}, \text{ etc.} \qquad (9)$$

Using the ideal gas equation,

$$p_1 V = n_1 RT, \qquad p_2 V = n_2 RT, \text{ etc.} \qquad (10)$$

In real gas mixtures, particularly at low temperatures and high pressures, Dalton's law is not obeyed exactly. In order to account for this deviation from the law, which is applicable only to ideal gases, **Lewis** (1901) introduced the concept of **fugacity** which will be defined later when discussing the activities and activity coefficients of the components of solutions.

The real gases do not obey an equation of state derived for an ideal gas. The nonideality of gases, the extent of which depends on the nature of the gas, temperature and pressure, is attributed to two major causes: (i) chemical interaction between the different species of gas molecules or atoms and (ii) van der Waals' forces.

Nonideality Due to Chemical Interaction—Let us consider a gas mixture containing H_2 and CO_2. At ordinary temperatures these gases do not react, therefore, their partial pressures are readily computed from the composition using equation (9). Now, if the same gas mixture is heated to higher temperatures, these gases react producing some CO and H_2O, and when one of the gas laws is applied to this mixture, the original composition can no longer be used but due allowance must be made for the presence of the additional two new gas species. Examples of the calculation of partial pressures in gas mixtures at elevated temperatures are given later.

van der Waals' Equation of State and Critical Constants—The condition for the liquefaction of a gas was first discovered by **Andrews** (1869) based on a study of the pressure-volume-temperature relationship of carbon dioxide; this is shown in Figure 12–1, where pressure-volume isotherms are shown. At temperatures below the critical temperature, T_c, each isotherm consists of three distinct parts. For example, the isotherm $abcd$ represents the relation between pressure and volume for the vapor (ab), the co-existing vapor and liquid (bc) and the liquid (cd), respectively. Since liquid carbon dioxide is relatively incompressible, the cd part of the isotherm is nearly vertical. The volumes V_1 and V_2 are the specific volumes of the saturated vapor and the liquid under its own vapor pressure, respectively. With increasing temperature the difference between the specific volumes of the liquid and vapor becomes progressively smaller until at T_c the liquid and vapor can no longer be distinguished from one another. The temperature above which a vapor cannot be liquefied is called the **critical temperature**; the highest vapor pressure exerted by the liquid is the **critical pressure** and the **critical volume** is the volume of one mole of the liquid (or gas) at the critical temperature and

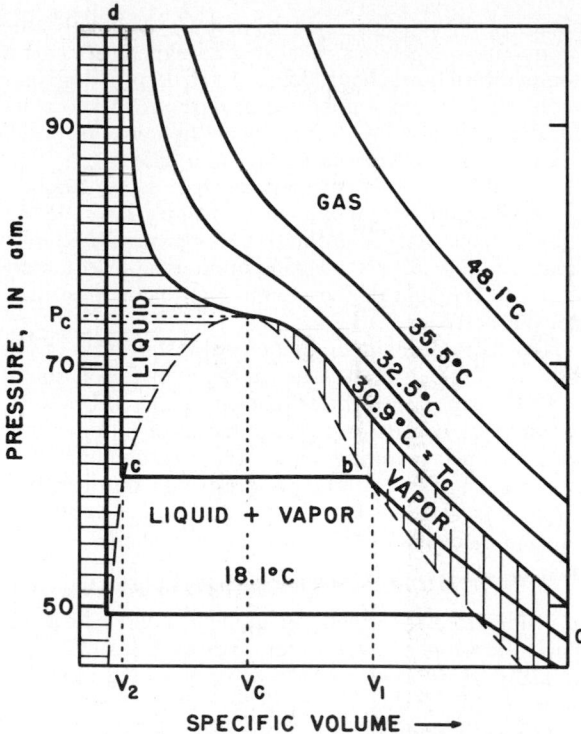

FIG. 12–1. Andrews' (1869) isotherms for carbon dioxide.

$$\left(P + \frac{a}{V^2}\right)(V\text{-}b) = RT \qquad (11)$$

where a and b are constants for a given gas. At the critical temperature the derivatives $(\partial P/\partial V)_T$ and $(\partial^2 P/\partial V^2)_T$ must be zero and, therefore, the following expressions may be derived from equation (11) for the critical isotherm:

$$P_c = \frac{a}{27b^2} \qquad (12a)$$

$$V_c = 3b \qquad (12b)$$

$$T_c = \frac{8a}{27Rb} \qquad (12c)$$

There are other equations of state for gases, but they will not be given here. The values of a and b can be found in reference books; the critical constants of some common gases are given in Table 12–I. It should be noted that the value of the **critical ratio** P_cV_c/RT_c, i.e. **compressibility factor** at the critical point, is about 0.29; this is often regarded as a universal constant for some simple gases and vapors (classified as spherical and nonpolar gases), and may be used to estimate one of the critical constants, if the other two are known.

Table 12–I. Critical Constants of Some Gases.

Gas	T_c (°K)	V_c (cm.³/mole)	P_c (atm.)	P_cV_c/RT_c
He	5.3	57.8	2.26	0.300
Ne	44.5	41.7	25.9	0.296
Ar	150.7	75.2	48.0	0.291
H_2	33.3	65.0	12.8	0.304
N_2	126.1	90.1	33.5	0.292
O_2	154.4	74.4	49.7	0.292
CO_2	304.3	95.6	73.0	0.279
CO	134.2	90.0	35.0	0.285
CH_4	190.7	99.0	45.8	0.290
H_2O	374.2	218.3	56.0	0.398

pressure. On the basis of the critical phenomena, Andrews defined vapor and gas as gaseous species below and above their critical temperatures, respectively; this is indicated by the vertically shaded area in Figure 12–1.

At temperatures just above the critical temperature, T_c, isotherms contain a kink, indicating the nonideal behavior of the gas. The pressure-volume-temperature relationship of one mole of gas and its transformation to the liquid state is most simply (though only approximately) formulated by the **van der Waals' equation of state** (1880), thus:

SECTION 3

THE FIRST LAW OF THERMODYNAMICS

This is the **law of conservation of energy** and may be stated as follows: "Energy may be converted from one form to another, but it cannot be destroyed or created." That is, the total energy of a system and its surroundings must remain constant although energy changes from one form to another. When a system undergoes a change from state A to state B, there is an exchange of energy between the system and its immediate surroundings such that the total energy of the system and its surroundings remains constant.

ENERGY, HEAT AND WORK

The energy of a system, E, (frequently called **internal** or **intrinsic energy**) includes all forms of energy other than the kinetic energy. Any exchange of energy between a system and its surroundings, resulting from a change of state, is manifested as heat and work.

Let us consider, for example, a system expanding against a constant external pressure, P, resulting in an increase of volume of ΔV; the work done by the system becomes $w = P\Delta V$. Since this is the work done by the system against the surroundings, the system absorbs a quantity of heat, q; the increase, ΔE, of the energy of the system in passing from state A to state B is,

$$\Delta E = E_B - E_A = q - w \qquad (13)$$

According to generally accepted convention, q is positive when heat is absorbed by the system and becomes negative when heat is lost from the system. The work, w, is positive when it is done by the system and negative when work is done on the system.

Although the total energy of a system cannot be evaluated, the change in energy, ΔE, can be determined by measuring q and w and, moreover, this change in E is independent of the path which the system takes in going from state A to state B. Although energy is a function of state, heat and work accompanying energy changes are not functions of state. If a system passes from the initial state A to any state B via a reaction path 1 then returns back to the initial state A via a different reaction path 2, the sum of the energy changes in the completion of one cycle is $\Delta E_{A1B} + \Delta E_{B2A} = 0$, as dictated by the first law. The heat absorbed and work performed depend on the path that the system takes in passing from one state to another; therefore, in a cyclic process from state A to B via path 1,

$$\Delta E_{A1B} = q_1 - w_1$$

from state B to A via path 2,

$$\Delta E_{B2A} = q_2 - w_2$$

and since the sum is zero,

$$q_1 + q_2 = w_1 + w_2$$

HEAT CAPACITY

The **heat capacity** of a substance is defined as the quantity of heat required to raise the temperature by one degree. The heat capacity of 1 g. of a substance is called the **specific heat** and that of one gram-molecule (abbreviated as mole) of a substance is called the **molar heat capacity.**

If q is the infinitesimally small amount of heat absorbed by the system when its temperature is raised by dT, then, by definition, the heat capacity C is expressed as:

$$C = \frac{q}{dT} \tag{14}$$

Heat Capacities of Gases—At a constant volume, heat absorbed is equivalent to the increase in the energy of the system, therefore, at constant volume:

$$C_v = \left(\frac{\partial E}{\partial T}\right)_v \tag{15}$$

When a system is heated at constant pressure, an infinitesimally small heat absorption is accordingly reflected in a volume change dV, and an energy change dE; these are related through the first law,

$$q = dE + PdV \tag{16}$$

for work against pressure only. Therefore, the heat capacity at constant pressure is formulated as

$$C_p = \left(\frac{\partial (E + PV)}{\partial T}\right)_p \tag{17}$$

From calculations based on equations (15) and (17) it can be shown that for an ideal gas the difference between the molar heat capacities, C_p and C_v, is given by

$$C_p - C_v = R \tag{18}$$

where $R = 1.987$ cal. per deg. per mole is the gas constant. At low temperatures and high pressures, this difference in molar heat capacities is somewhat higher than R.

Heat Capacities of Solids—The classical law derived by **Dulong and Petit** (1819) from experimental observations states that "all solid elements have the same heat capacity per g.-atom." Although the atomic heat capacities of most solid elements at room temperature are about 6.2 ± 0.4 cal. per deg. per mole, there are a number of exceptions to the rule: for example, at 25°C, atomic heat capacities of beryllium, boron, carbon (diamond) and silicon are 3.93, 2.65, 1.45 and 4.73 cal. per deg. per mole. Another generalization is that known as **Kopp's law** (1865) which states that "at ordinary temperatures the molar heat capacity of a solid compound is approximately equal to the sum of the atomic heat capacities of its constituents."

The first approximate theoretical justification of the law of Dulong-Petit was derived by **Boltzmann** (1871) on the hypothesis that an ideal solid may be assumed to consist of a space lattice of independent atomic units vibrating about their respective equilibrium positions without reacting with one another. From this classical theory, the atomic heat capacity of solid elements at constant volume becomes,

$$C_v = 3R = 5.96 \text{ cal. per deg. per mole} \tag{19}$$

Aside from the electronic contribution to heat capacity to be considered later, the first detailed theoretical derivation of heat capacity was made by **Einstein** (1907); this theoretical treatment was later modified by **Debye** (1912), who showed that the following expression represents the molar heat capacity of solids satisfactorily at very low temperatures, thus

$$C_v = \frac{12}{5} \pi^4 R \left(\frac{T}{\theta}\right)^3 \tag{20}$$

i.e.,

$$C_v = 464.5 \left(\frac{T}{\theta}\right)^3 \tag{21}$$

where θ is constant for a given substance, it has the dimensions of temperature and is called the **characteristic temperature** of the substance. Therefore, if C_v is plotted against T/θ, the same curve should apply to all solid elements. This generalization applies essentially to isotropic solids (cubic systems). It should be pointed out that in the derivation of the Debye equation, it was postulated that C_v for the solid was that contributed only by the vibrations of the atoms in a lattice assumed to be a continuous elastic medium. In this approximation, the electronic contribution to C_v and the effects of crystal structure and structural defects on C_v were not taken into consideration. From the free electron theory of metals, it is derived that the electronic contribution to heat capacity is directly proportional to the absolute temperature at low temperatures, therefore, for substances which exhibit no anomalies, e.g., Curie point, lattice defects, etc., C_v becomes,

$$C_v = C_v \text{ (lattice)} + C_v \text{ (electronic)}$$

For low temperatures,

$$C_v = 464.5 \left(\frac{T}{\theta}\right)^3 + \gamma T \tag{22}$$

where, depending on the substance, γ has a value within the range 1×10^{-4} to about 50×10^{-4} cal.

per deg.[2] per mole. With increasing temperature the electronic contribution to C_v becomes less pronounced. For temperatures at or above room temperature, the Debye equation reduces to $C_v \rightarrow 3R$, i.e. approaching to the value of Dulong and Petit.

Normally, the heat capacity is measured at constant pressure and in order to use equation (20), C_v is calculated from C_p by using the thermodynamic relation (derived from the second law),

$$C_p - C_v = \frac{a^2}{\beta} V T \qquad (23)$$

where α is the coefficient of thermal expansion and β is the coefficient of compressibility.

High-Temperature Heat Capacity—At temperatures much above 25°C, lattice and electronic contributions to heat capacity at constant pressure, C_p, are represented by an empirical equation,

$$C_p = a + bT - cT^{-2} \qquad (24)$$

where a, b and c are constants for a given substance and they are evaluated from the experimental data on C_p over a wide temperature range.

ENTHALPY (HEAT CONTENT)

Considering again the expansion of a system against constant pressure, P, the volume change, ΔV, may be written as $V_B - V_A$ and the first law equation (13) may be rearranged;

$$\Delta E = E_B - E_A = q - P\Delta V = q - P(V_B - V_A)$$

or

$$(E_B + PV_B) - (E_A + PV_A) = q \qquad (25)$$

The quantity $E + PV$ is called the **enthalpy** or the heat content of the system and denoted by H. When a reaction occurs at constant pressure, the change in enthalpy is given by

$$\Delta H = H_B - H_A = q \qquad (26)$$

That is, at constant pressure the enthalpy is a function of state only and independent of the reaction path followed. It follows from the first law that if a reaction occurs at a constant volume, no work is done by the system; in this case the increase in energy is equal to the heat absorbed; i.e. $\Delta E = \Delta H$ at constant volume.

The enthalpy is an extensive property of the system and, as in the case of energy, only the change in heat content can be measured. It is, therefore, essential that a standard reference state is chosen for each element so that any change in the heat content of the element may be referred to its standard state, and this change is denoted by $\Delta H°$. The natural state of elements is by convention taken to be the reference state; on this definition, the elements in their standard states have zero heat contents. The heat of formation of a compound is then the heat absorbed or evolved in the formation of one mole of compound from its constituent elements in their standard states.

When a reaction occurs isothermally at constant pressure, the system loses or gains heat to or from its surroundings, and in an adiabatic process, i.e., one in which no heat exchange occurs between the system and its surroundings, the temperature of the system decreases or increases as a result of the reaction. The difference between the enthalpies of the products and those of the reactants (both at the same temperature and constant pressure) is called the **heat of reaction**. Thus for the reaction at constant pressure

$$A + B = C + D$$

the heat of reaction, $\Delta H°$, is derived from the heats of formation of the reactants and products by the relation

$$\Delta H° = \Delta H_C^{°} + \Delta H_D^{°} - (\Delta H_A^{°} + \Delta H_B^{°}) \qquad (27)$$

The variation of enthalpy with temperature is derived from equation (17), thus

$$C_p = \left(\frac{\partial(E + PV)}{\partial T}\right)_p = \left(\frac{\partial H}{\partial T}\right)_p \qquad (28)$$

Rearranging and integrating

$$H_{T_2}^{°} - H_{T_1}^{°} = \int_{T_1}^{T_2} C_p dT \qquad (29)$$

Usually the relationship between C_p and T is formulated as in equation (24) for elevated temperatures, and equation (29) becomes

$$H_T^{°} - H_{298}^{°} = aT + \frac{b}{2} T^2 + cT^{-1} \qquad (30)$$

where the constants a, b and c are determined experimentally for each substance and most of these values are readily available in the technical literature.

It follows from the above considerations based on the first law of thermodynamics that the variation of the heat of reaction $\Delta H°$ with temperature is given by

$$\Delta H_{T_2}^{°} = \Delta H_{T_1}^{°} + \int_{T_1}^{T_2} (\Delta C_p)dT \qquad (31)$$

where ΔC_p is the difference between the heat capacities of reaction products and reactants. This relationship was first developed by **Kirchhoff** (1858). Although the heat content of a substance varies considerably with temperature, the influence of temperature on the heat of reaction is quite small, because ΔC_p is small for many reactions, especially if no gases are involved; this will be demonstrated later.

There are two fundamental thermochemical laws which express the first law specifically in terms of enthalpy. The first principle derived by **Lavoisier** and **Laplace** (1780) states that "the quantity of heat required to decompose a compound into its elements is equal to the heat evolved when that compound is formed from its elements," i.e., the heat of decomposition of a compound is numerically equal to its heat of formation, but of opposite sign. The second principle is that first discovered by **Hess** (1840); it states that "the heat of reaction depends only on the initial and final states, and not on the intermediate states through which the system may pass."

SECTION 4

THE SECOND LAW OF THERMODYNAMICS

The **law of dissipation of energy** or **degradation of available energy** constitutes the basis of the second law of thermodynamics. This law states that "all natural processes occurring without external interference are spontaneous (irreversible processes)." For example, diffusion of one gas into another, passage of electricity from a high to a low potential, conduction of heat from a hot to a cold part of the system are all irreversible processes. That is, the processes cannot be reversed without some change in the system brought about by external interference. For a process to be reversible, all sources of dissipation of energy must be eliminated. Let us consider an imaginary process carried out infinitesimally slowly, so that the system is always in equilibrium with its surroundings; if at any time the process is reversed by an infinitesimal change in the surroundings, the process is said to be reversible. This is, of course, an imaginary limiting case for the real processes.

THERMODYNAMIC EFFICIENCY

The thermodynamic efficiency was derived by **Carnot** (1824) by considering a reversible cyclic process occurring between temperatures T_1 and T_2 at four reversible steps, of which two are isothermal at T_1 and T_2 and two are adiabatic from T_1 to T_2 and from T_2 to T_1. When the cycle is completed, the system and surroundings return to the initial state. The application of the first law to such a reversible cyclic process gives

$$\frac{w}{q_2} = \frac{q_2 + q_1}{q_2} = \frac{T_2 - T_1}{T_2} \qquad (32)$$

which represents the efficiency of any reversible cyclic process operating between the temperatures T_2 and T_1. At the higher temperature T_2 the heat absorbed is q_2; $-q_1$ is the heat evolved at the lower temperature T_1. According to the first law, the difference between the heat absorbed and that evolved corresponds to the amount of cyclic work done, i.e. $w = q_2 + q_1$. Therefore, the efficiency of a reversible process is determined by the temperatures of source and sink; the maximum efficiency of unity can be obtained only when T_1 is at absolute zero.

ENTROPY

By rearranging equation (32), the following is obtained:

$$\frac{q_1}{T_1} + \frac{q_2}{T_2} = 0 \qquad (33)$$

Any reversible cycle may be regarded as being made up of a number of cycles (Carnot cycles) and equation (33) may be written in its general form as

$$\sum \frac{q}{T} = 0 \qquad (34)$$

That is, in a reversible cycle the sum of the change in q/T is zero. Since the ratio q/T is an exact differential for any thermodynamic system, the thermodynamic quantity **entropy**, S, as a function of state is defined so that the entropy change, dS, is identical with q/T, i.e.,

$$dS = \frac{q}{T} \qquad (35)$$

In a process occurring at constant pressure, $q = C_p dT$, therefore,

$$dS = \frac{C_p}{T} dT = C_p d\ln T \qquad (36)$$

where $\ln T$ is the natural logarithm of $T (\ln T = 2.303 \log T$, where log signifies a logarithm to the base 10).

When a phase change occurs, as in a transformation (t) from one crystalline state to another, in a fusion (f) or in a vaporization (v), the entropy increase is given by:

$$\Delta S_t = \frac{\Delta H_t}{T_t} \; ; \Delta S_f = \frac{\Delta H_f}{T_f} \; ; \Delta S_v = \frac{\Delta H_v}{T_v} \quad (37)$$

where ΔH_t, ΔH_f and ΔH_v are the latent heats of transformation, fusion and vaporization. It has been found that for many substances the ratio $\Delta H_v / T_v = 21$ cal. per deg. mole and $\Delta H_f / T_f = 2$ cal. per deg. mole; these are known as the **Trouton** and **Richards'** rule, respectively.

FREE ENERGY

A combined form of the first and second laws may be obtained from equations (16) and (35): thus, for a reversible process against pressure only,

$$dE = TdS - PdV \qquad (38)$$

In this differential equation, E is a function of the entropy S and of the volume V. However, experimentally, it is easier to control the pressure and temperature of the system and, therefore, a new function F was defined by **Gibbs**, thus

$$F = E + PV - TS \qquad (39)$$

and, since $E + PV = H$, for constant pressure

$$F = H - TS \qquad (40)$$

where F is known as the (Gibbs) free energy of the system. When a system changes isothermally from state A to state B, the change in the free energy is

$$F_B - F_A = \Delta F = \Delta H - T\Delta S \qquad (41)$$

where ΔF refers to the change in F accompanying the reaction.

During any process which proceeds spontaneously in such a manner that the pressure and temperature of the reactants and products are the same, the free energy of the system decreases. Another criterion is that the free energy change of a system undergoing a reversible process at constant temperature and pressure and doing work only against pressure is zero. Therefore, for any system at constant temperature, pressure and mass, which does no work other than against pressure,

$$\Delta F \leq 0$$

Although any process for a system of constant tem-

perature, pressure and mass for which $\Delta F < 0$ is thermodynamically possible, the reaction may not proceed at a perceptible rate if the activation energy required to overcome the resistance to reaction is too high. This is discussed later in the section on the kinetics of reactions. However, if $\Delta F > 0$ the reaction will not take place.

SECTION 5

THE THIRD LAW OF THERMODYNAMICS

Following the work of **Le Chatelier** (1888) and **Richards** (1902), **Nernst** (1906) put forward the following heat theorem which constitutes the third law of thermodynamics: In reactions with condensed phases, variations of ΔF and ΔH with temperature i.e. $d(\Delta F)/dT$ and $d(\Delta H)/dT$ approach zero tangentially at the absolute zero of temperature. Since $d(\Delta F)/dT = -\Delta S$ and $d(\Delta H)/dT = \Delta C$, the change in entropy and heat capacity is zero at zero absolute temperature.

CHANGE OF ENTROPY WITH TEMPERATURE

The change of entropy with temperature at a constant pressure was given in equation (36), thus

$$dS = \frac{C_p}{T}dT = C_p d\ln T$$

Therefore, the difference in entropy between a substance at $0°K$ and $T°K$ is obtained by integrating the above equation:

$$S_T - S_0 = \int_0^T \frac{C_p}{T}dT = \int_0^T C_p d\ln T \quad (42)$$

Integration may be carried out graphically from the plot of C_p/T against T or C_p against $\ln T$ ($=2.303$ $\log T$).

The entropy of any homogeneous substance which is in complete internal equilibrium is taken as zero at $0°K$. This third law of thermodynamics is true for chemical elements and compounds only when there is complete internal equilibrium. Although complete internal equilibrium is not reached at very low temperatures in actual practice and, consequently, the measured change $S_T - S_0$ is slightly smaller than the absolute value, by convention the value of entropy of crystalline elements and compounds is taken as zero at $0°K$ and the value of entropy at any other temperature is denoted by S.

SECTION 6

TABULATION AND USE OF THERMODYNAMIC DATA

As already stated, the free energy change accompanying a reaction is given by:

$$\Delta F° = \Delta H° - T\Delta S° \quad (43)$$

where the superscript (°) refers to the change in the thermodynamic property with respect to the standard state. Usually, the pure solid, liquid or gas in its stable form at atmospheric pressure and $298.16°K$ is chosen as the standard state.

It is customary to tabulate the heats of formation and entropies of substances for room temperature ($298.16°K$) and if the high-temperature heat capacities are known, the variation of the standard free energy change with temperature may be obtained by combining equations (31), (42) and (43), thus

$$\Delta F° = \Delta H°_{298} + \int_{298}^T \Delta C_p dT - T\Delta S°_{298}$$

$$- T\int_{298}^T \frac{\Delta C_p}{T}dT \quad (44)$$

In Table **12–II**, selected values of $\Delta H°_{298}$, $S°_{298}$ and high-temperature heat capacities are given for substances commonly encountered in the metallurgical processes.

The method of using these data is now demonstrated by evaluating the free energy change associated with the following reaction:

$$2Al\ (s) + 3CO_2\ (g) = Al_2O_3\ (s) + 3CO\ (g)$$

Data: The heat capacities, $\Delta H°_{298}$ and $S°_{298}$, are given below:

Heat Capacity in cal. per deg. per mole above 298°K

Al: $\quad C_p = 4.94 + (2.96 \times 10^{-3}T)$

CO$_2$: $\quad C_p = 10.57 + (2.10 \times 10^{-3}T)$
$\qquad - (2.06 \times 10^5 T^{-2})$

Al$_2$O$_3$: $C_p = 27.49 + (2.82 \times 10^{-3}T)$
$\qquad - (8.38 \times 10^5 T^{-2})$

CO: $\quad C_p = 6.79 + (0.98 \times 10^{-3}T)$
$\qquad - (0.11 \times 10^5 T^{-2})$

$\qquad \Delta C_p = C_p(Al_2O_3) + 3C_p(CO)$
$\qquad \quad - [2C_p(Al) + 3C_p(CO_2)]$

$\qquad \Delta C_p = 6.27 - (6.46 \times 10^{-3}T)$
$\qquad \quad - (2.53 \times 10^5 T^{-2})$ cal. per deg. $\quad$ (a)

Heats of formation at 298°K in cal. per mole

Al: $\quad \Delta H° = 0$

CO$_2$: $\quad \Delta H° = -94,050$

Al$_2$O$_3$: $\Delta H° = -399,600$

(Continued on Page 257)

Table 12–II. Thermodynamic Data[a] on Some Elements and Compounds Encountered in Ferrous Metallurgical Processes.

Units: ΔH°_{298} in cal. per mole; S°_{298} in cal. per deg. per mole; C_p in cal. per deg. per mole; transformation (t.p.) melting (m.p.) and boiling (b.p.) point temperatures in °C; heats of transformation and fusion in cal. per mole.

Notations: " " indicate nonstoichiometric compound; underlined m.p. indicates incongruent m.p.; values in ( ) are estimated. dec.=decomposes. Sub.=sublimes.

$C_p = a + bT - cT^{-2}$

Substance	$-\Delta H^\circ_{298}$	S°_{298}	a	$b \times 10^3$	$c \times 10^{-5}$	Temp. Range °C	t.p. °C	m.p. °C	b.p. °C	ΔH_t	ΔH_f	Remarks
Al	0	6.77	4.94	2.96	—	25–659	—	659	2467	—	2,570	
			7.00	—	—	659–2400						
Al_2O_3	399,600	12.2	27.49	2.82	8.38	25–1500	(1000)	2030	dec.	(20,600)	(26,000)	
Al_2S_3	172,900							1100 dec.	dec.			
AlN	76,470	5.0	5.47	7.80	—	25–600		dec.	dec.			
Al_4C_3	35,900	(31.3)	24.08	31.60	12.53	25–320						
Al_2SiO_5 (1)	39,900*	22.3	46.24	2.34	16.00	25–1300		1810				(1) Andalusite
(2)	40,000*	20.0	45.52	2.34	16.00	25–1400						(2) Kyanite
(3)	46,000*	23.0	40.09	5.86	10.13	25–1300						(3) Sillimanite — Heats of formation from oxides, Al_2O_3 + SiO_2.
$Al_6Si_2O_{13}$			59.65	67.00	—	25–300						Mullite.
B	0	1.40	4.13	1.66	1.76	25–2027		2027	3927	—	5,300	
			7.50	—	—	2027–2700						
B_2O_3*	305,300	12.87	8.73	25.40	1.31	25–450		450	(2300)	—	5,500	*Crystalline.
			30.50	—	—	450–1700						
B_2O_3*	301,000	18.58	2.28	42.10	—	25–450		450	(2300)	—	—	*Amorphous (glass).
			30.50	—	—	450–1700						
BN	60,700	3.67	1.82	3.62	—	25–900						
"B_4C"	12,200	6.47	22.99	5.40	10.72	25–1450						
Ba	0	15.50	5.36	3.16	—	25–370	370	710	1637	150	1,830	
			2.60	6.86	—	370–710						
			7.50	—	—	710–1600						
"BaO"	133,500	16.80	11.79	1.88	0.88	25–1700		1925	(2750)			
BaS	106,000	22.0						2200				
Ba_3N_2	87,000	36.4						dec.				
$BaSiO_3$	38,000*	26.8						1605			13,800	
Ba_2SiO_4	64,500*	43.5	29.03	2.04	4.58	25–1700		1760				
$BaTiO_3$			43.00	1.60	6.96	25–1700	5; 120	1705		16; 47		*from its oxides.
Ba_2TiO_4		47.0										*from its oxides.
Be	0	2.28	4.58	2.12	1.14	25–1283		1283	2477		2,800	
			7.50	—	—	1283–2400						
BeO	143,100	3.37	8.45	4.00	3.17	25–900		2530	4120		17,000	
BeS	55,900	8.4										
Be_3N_2	134,700		7.32	30.80		25–500						
Be_2SiO_4	12,000*	15.4	22.84			25		1560				*from its oxides.
C (1)	0	1.36	4.03	1.14	2.04	25–2200		Sub.	3727*		(33,000)*	(1) Graphite; *Sublimation point.
(2)	−454	0.58	2.27	3.06	1.54	25–900						(2) Diamond.

*See appropriate "Remarks."   (a) See note at end of table.

Table 12—II. Thermodynamic Data[a] on Some Elements and Compounds Encountered in Ferrous Metallurgical Processes—Continued.

Substance	$-\Delta H^\circ_{298}$	S°_{298}	a	$b \times 10^3$	$c \times 10^{-5}$	Temp. Range °C	t.p. °C	m.p. °C	b.p. °C	ΔH_t	ΔH_f	Remarks
CO	26,420	47.3	6.79	0.98	0.11	25–2200	−212	−205	−192	—	—	
CO_2	94,050	51.1	10.57	2.10	2.06	25–2200	—	Sub.	−79	—	—	
CS_2	−14,500	36.2	12.45	1.60	1.80	25–1500	—	−112	−46	—	1,050	
COS	33,900	55.3	11.33	2.18	1.83	25–1500	—	−139	−50	—	1,130	
CH_4	17,890	44.5	5.65	11.44	0.46	25–1200	−253	−183	−162	—	—	
Ca	0	9.95	5.25	3.44	—	25–440	440	850	1492	270	2,070	
			2.68	6.80	—	440–850						
			7.40	—	—	850–1500						
CaO	151,500	9.5	11.67	1.08	1.56	25–1700	—	2600	(3500)	—	19,000	
CaS	114,300	13.5	(10.20)	(3.80)	—	25–700	—					
Ca_3N_2	105,000	—	20.44	22.00	—	25–500	—	1195				
CaC_2	14,100	16.8	16.40	2.84	2.07	25–447	447	2300		1330		
			15.40	2.00	—	447–1200						
CaF_2	290,300	16.45	14.30	7.28	0.47	25–1151	1151	1418	2500	1140	7,100	
			25.81	2.50	—	1151–1418						
			23.90	—	—							
$Ca_3Al_2O_6$	1,600*	49.1	62.28	4.58	12.01	25–1500	—	—	—	—	—	*from its oxides.
$CaAl_2O_4$	3,700*	27.3	36.00	5.96	7.96	25–1500	—					*from its oxides.
$CaAl_4O_7$		42.5	66.09	5.48	17.80	25–1500	—					*from its oxides.
$Ca_3B_2O_6$	60,000*	43.9	56.44	10.42	13.02	25–1487	—	1487		—	35,490	*from its oxides.
			94.00	—	—	1487–1700						
$Ca_2B_2O_5$	45,800*	34.7	43.75	11.50	10.69	25–531	531	1312		1100	24,090	*from its oxides.
			52.29	2.40	—	531–1312						
			68.20	—	—	1312–1700						
CaB_2O_4	29,400*	25.1	31.02	9.76	8.07	25–1152	—	1152		—	17,670	*from its oxides.
			61.70	—	—	1152–1700						
CaB_4O_7	42,900*	32.2	51.34	19.16	17.16	25–987	—	987		—	27,060	*from its oxides.
			106.30	—	—	987–1700						
$CaCO_3$ (1)	288,400	21.2	20.13	10.24	3.34	25–300	50	dec.		45	—	(1) Aragonite.
$CaCO_3$ (2)		22.2	24.98	5.24	6.20	25–900	50	dec.		45	—	(2) Calcite.
$Ca_2Fe_2O_5$	7,400*	45.1	59.24	11.68	11.68	25–1435	—	1435		—	36,110	*from its oxides.
			74.20	—	—	1435–1700						
$CaFe_2O_4$		34.7	39.42	4.76	3.66	25–1237	—	1237		—	25,870	
			54.90	—	—	1237–1700						
$Ca_4P_2O_9$	172,910*	57.6	48.24	39.68	5.00	25–1100	1100			3700		*from its oxides.
			79.00	—	—	1100–1300						
$Ca_3P_2O_8$	162,680*											*from its oxides.
$Ca_2P_2O_7$		45.2	53.03	14.76	11.16	25–1140	1140	1353		1600	24,100	
			76.15	—	—	1140–1353						
			96.80	—	—	1353–1430						
$CaSO_4$	342,400	25.5	16.78	23.60	—	25–1100	1193	1465	dec.		(6,700)	

*See appropriate "Remarks."
(a) See note at end of table.

Table 12–II. Thermodynamic Data[a] on Some Elements and Compounds Encountered in Ferrous Metallurgical Processes—Continued.

Units: ΔH°_{298} in cal. per mole; S°_{298} in cal. per deg. per mole; C_p in cal. per deg. per mole; transformation (t.p.) melting (m.p.) and boiling (b.p.) point temperatures in °C; heats of transformation and fusion in cal. per mole.

Notations: " " indicate nonstoichiometric compound; underlined m.p. indicates incongruent m.p.; values in ( ) are estimated.   dec. = decomposes.   Sub. = sublimes.

Columns a, $b \times 10^3$, $c \times 10^{-5}$ are from $C_p = a + bT - cT^{-2}$.

Substance	$-\Delta H^\circ_{298}$	S°_{298}	a	$b \times 10^3$	$c \times 10^{-5}$	Temp. Range °C	t.p. °C	m.p. °C	b.p. °C	ΔH_t	ΔH_f	Remarks
Ca_3SiO_5	27,000*	40.3	49.85	8.62	10.15	25–1500		2130				*from its oxides.
Ca_2SiO_4	30,200*	30.5	34.87	9.74	6.26	25–697	697; 1437			440; 3390		*from its oxides.
			32.16	11.02	—	697–1437						
			49.00	—	—	1437–1700						
$CaSiO_3$	21,500*	19.6	26.64	3.60	6.52	25–1180	1190	1540		(1300)		
$CaTiO_3$		22.4	30.47	1.36	6.69	25–1257	1257			550	(13,400)	*from its oxides.
			32.03	—	—	1257–1700						
Ce	0	16.64	5.70	3.98	—	25–730	730	804	2927	300	2,200	
			8.20	—	—	730–804						
			8.00	—	—	804–2700						
CeO_2	245,000							>2600				
CeS	118,000	17.7	15.1	—	—	25–100						
Co	0	7.18	4.74	4.00	—	25–437	437; 1120	1495	2877	105; 0	4,100	
			2.16	7.02	—	437–1120						
			17.49	-4.92	—	1120–1495						
			9.00	—	—	1495–2900						
CoO	57,100	12.65	11.54	2.04	-0.40	25–1700	—	1805	dec.			
Co_3O_4	216,300	24.5	30.84	17.08	5.72	25–700	—	dec.	—			
Co_9S_8	197,000	(110.0)						835	dec.	—	—	
$CoS_{0.89}$	20,400	13.6						834	dec.			
Co_3S_4	75,000							625	dec.			
CoS_2	33,500							dec.	—	—	—	
Cr	0	5.68	4.16	3.62	-0.30	25–1903	1835	1903	2665	5,000		
			9.40	—	—	1903–2700						
"Cr_2O_3"	272,650	19.4	28.53	2.20	3.74	25–1500		(2400)	dec.			
CrO_2	139,400											
CrO_3	140,000	17.2	11.01	16.40	—	25–500		185	dec.			
"Cr_2N"	25,200	18.0	12.20	—	—	25–500						
CrN	28,100	8.0										
"$Cr_{23}C_6$"	98,300	151.8	169.16	42.66	29.83	25–1400		1520	—			
"Cr_7C_3"	44,100	48.0	56.96	14.54	10.12	25–1200		1780	—			
"Cr_3C_2"	23,200	20.4	30.03	5.58	7.40	25–1300		1890	—			
Cu	0	7.97	5.41	1.50	—	25–1084		1084	2547		3,120	
			7.50	—	—	1084–2500						
Cu_2O	40,400	22.45	14.90	5.70	—	25–900	(56)	1230	dec.		(13,400)	
CuO	37,600	10.2	9.27	4.80	—	25–980		(1110)	dec.			
Cu_2S	19,600	28.5	19.50	—	—	25–103	103; 350	1130	dec.	920; 200	2,600	
			23.25	—	—	103–350						
			20.32	—	—	350–1130						

*See appropriate "Remarks."   (a) See note at end of table.

Table 12–II. Thermodynamic Data[a] on Some Elements and Compounds Encountered in Ferrous Metallurgical Processes—Continued.

$C_p = a + bT - cT^{-2}$

Substance	$-\Delta H^\circ_{298}$	S°_{298}	a	$b \times 10^3$	$c \times 10^{-5}$	Temp. Range °C	t.p. °C	m.p. °C	b.p. °C	ΔH_t	ΔH_f	Remarks
CuS	12,100	15.9	(10.60)	(2.64)	—	25–1000	—	dec.	—	—	—	
Fe	0	6.49	3.04	7.58	−0.60	25–760	760*; 910; 1400	1537	3070	326; 215; 165	3,670	*Curie point.
			11.13	—	—	760–910						
			5.80	1.98	—	910–1400						
			6.74	1.60	—	1400–1537						
			9.77	0.40	—	1537–2700						
"FeO"*	63,800	14.05	11.66	2.00	0.67	25–1377	—	1377	dec.	—	7,490	$Fe_{0.947}O$, wüstite in equilibrium with iron.
			16.30	—	—	1377–1700						
Fe_3O_4	267,800	36.2	21.88	48.20	—	25–627	627	1597	dec.	0	33,000	
			48.00	—	—	627–1597						
Fe_2O_3	196,800	21.5	23.49	18.60	3.55	25–677	677; 777	dec.	dec.	160; 0		
			36.00	—	—	677–777						
			31.71	1.76	—	777–1500						
"FeS"	22,800	16.1	5.19	26.40	—	25–138	138; 325	1195	dec.	570; 120	7,730	
			17.40	2.38	—	138–325						
			12.20	—	—	325–1195						
			17.00	—	—	1195–1700						
"FeS_2"	42,400	12.7	17.88	1.32	3.05	25–700	—	—	—	—	—	
Fe_3N	2,700	37.4	(26.84)	(8.16)	—	25–700	—	—	—	—	—	
Fe_4N	1,100	—	(14.91)	(6.09)	—	25–700	—	—	—	—	—	
Fe_2N	900	—	19.64	20.00	—	25–190	—	—	—	—	—	
Fe_3C	−5,980	24.2	25.62	3.00	—	190–1200	190	—	—	180	—	
Fe_2SiO_4	−8,200*	34.7	36.51	9.36	6.70	25–1217	—	1217	dec.	—	22,030	*from its oxides.
			57.50	—	—	1217–1700						
$FeTiO_3$	—	25.3	27.87	4.36	4.79	25–1367	—	1367	dec.	—	21,670	
H_2	0	31.21	6.52	0.78	−0.12	25–2700	—	−259	−253	—	—	
H_2O (1)	68,320	16.75	18.04	—	—	25–100	—	0	100	—	1,436	(1) Liquid.
(2)	57,800	45.13	7.30	2.46	—	25–2500	—	—	—	—		(2) Gas.
H_2S	4,800	49.1	7.81	2.96	0.46	25–2000	−170; −147	−86	−60	370; 110	586	
Mg	0	7.77	4.97	3.04	−0.04	25–650	—	650	1105	—	2,140	
			7.80	—	—	650–1100						
MgO	143,700	6.55	10.18	1.74	1.48	25–1800	—	—	—	—	—	
MgS	83,000	10.2	8.82	0.08	0.61	25–1700	—	—	—	—	—	
MgC_2	−21,000	14.0					—	dec.	—	—		
$MgAl_2O_4$	—	19.25	36.80	6.40	9.78	25–1500	—	2135	—	—		
$MgCO_3$	262,000	15.7	18.62	13.80	4.16	25–500	—	dec.	—	—		
$Mg_3P_2O_8$	110,940*	—					—	—	—	—		*from its oxides.
Mg_2SiO_4	15,100*	22.75	35.81	6.54	8.52	25–1500	—	1890	—	—		*from its oxides.
$MgSiO_3$	8,700*	16.2	24.55	4.74	6.28	25–1300+	—	1560	—	—		*from its oxides; +dinoenstatite.
$MgTiO_4$	—	24.8	35.96	8.54	6.89	25–1500	—	1830	—	—		

*See appropriate "Remarks." (a) See note at end of table.

Table 12–II. Thermodynamic Data[a] on Some Elements and Compounds Encountered in Ferrous Metallurgical Processes—Continued.

Units: ΔH°_{298} in cal. per mole; S°_{298} in cal. per deg. per mole; C_p in cal. per deg. per mole; transformation (t.p.) melting (m.p.) and boiling (b.p.) point temperatures in °C; heats of transformation and fusion in cal. per mole.

Notations: " " indicate nonstoichiometric compound; underlined m.p. indicates incongruent m.p.; values in ( ) are estimated.　dec. = decomposes.　Sub. = sublimes.

Substance	$-\Delta H^\circ_{298}$	S°_{298}	a	$b \times 10^3$	$c \times 10^{-5}$	Temp. Range °C	t.p. °C	m.p. °C	b.p. °C	ΔH_t	ΔH_f	Remarks
MgTiO₃		17.8	28.29	3.28	6.53	25–1500		1840	—	—	3,500	
MgTi₂O₅		30.4	40.68	9.20	7.35	25–1700		—	—	—		
Mn	0	7.60	5.70	3.38	0.37	25–727	727; 1101; 1137	1244	2095	535; 545; 430	—	
			8.33	—	—	727–1101						
			10.70	—	—	1101–1137						
			11.30	—	—	1137–1244						
			11.00	0.66	—	1244–2000						
"MnO"	92,000	14.3	11.11	1.94	0.88	25–1500	−56	1785	dec.	—	—	
"Mn₃O₄"	331,400	35.5	34.64	10.82	2.20	25–1172	1172	1560	dec.	4,970		
			50.20	—	—	1172–1560						
"Mn₂O₃"	229,400	26.4	24.73	8.38	3.23	25–1100		dec.	—	—		
"MnO₂"	124,300	12.7	16.60	2.44	3.88	25–550	250	dec.	—	0	—	
MnS	49,000	18.7	11.40	1.80	—	25–1530		1530	—	—	6,240	
			16.00	—	—	1530–1700						
"Mn₄N"	31,200		21.15	30.50	—	25–500				—		
"Mn₅N₂"	55,200		30.55	38.40	—	25–500				—		
Mn₃P₂O₈	105,230*							1119				*from its oxides.
Mn₂SiO₄	11,800*	39.0						1340				*from its oxides.
MnSiO₃	5,900*	21.3	26.42	3.88	6.16	25–1200		1270	—	—		*from its oxides.
Mo	0	6.83	5.18	1.66	0.12	25–2617		2600	5550		6,650	
			10.00	—	—	2617–2700						
"MoO₂"	139,500	13.6	20.73	5.18	0.37	25–795		dec.	—	—		
"MoO₃"	178,200	18.6	32.00	—	—	795–1100		795	1100	—	12,500	
Mo₂S₃	102,000	28.0	11.19	13.80	4.18	25–500		2690				
"Mo₂N"	16,600	(21.0)										
"Mo₃C"	−4,200	(19.8)										
N₂	0	45.77	6.83	0.90	—	25–2700	−237.5	−210	−196	—	172	
NH₃	11,000	45.97	7.11	6.00	—	25–1500		−78	−33.5	—	1,352	
Na	0	12.3	4.02	9.04	—	25–98		98	905		622	
			6.83	1.08	—	98–905						
Na₂O	100,700	17.0	15.70	5.40	—	25–920		920	dec.	—		
Na₂S	92,400	23.5	19.81	1.64	—	25–700		950	dec.	—		
NaAlO₂	20,900*	16.9	19.18	7.14	3.36	25–467		—	—	310	(1,600)	*from its oxides.
			20.21	4.24	—	467–1400						
Na₂CO₃	271,600	32.5	27.13	15.62	4.78	25–851	359; 481	851	dec.	—	7,100	
			45.00	—	—	851–1200						

*See appropriate "Remarks."
(a) See note at end of table.

Table 12–II. Thermodynamic Data[a] on Some Elements and Compounds Encountered in Ferrous Metallurgical Processes—Continued.

Substance	$-\Delta H^\circ_{298}$	S°_{298}	$C_p = a+bT-cT^{-2}$			Temp. Range °C	t.p. °C	m.p. °C	b.p. °C	ΔH_t	ΔH_f	Remarks
			a	$b \times 10^3$	$c \times 10^{-5}$							
Na_2SiO_3	55,500*	27.2	31.14 42.80	9.60	6.47	25–1088 1088–1700	—	1088	—	—	12,470	*from its oxides.
$Na_2Si_2O_5$	60,500*	39.4	44.38 62.35	16.86	10.67	25–874 874–1700	678	874	—	1700	8,500	*from its oxides.
Ni	0	7.12	4.06 6.00 9.20	7.04 1.80	—	25–360 360–1452 1452–2900	360	1452	2910	0	4,210	
"NiO"	57,500	9.1	−4.99 13.88 11.18	37.58 — 2.02	−3.89	25–252 252–292 292–1700	252; 292	1960	dec.	0; 0		
"NiS"	22,200	16.1	9.25	6.40	—	25–300	396	>800	dec.	630		
O_2	0	49.02	7.16	1.00	0.40	25–2700	−250	−219	−183	224; 178	106	
P *	0	9.80	5.50 5.88	—	—	25–44 44–130	—	44	280	—	150	*white.
P *	4,400	5.46	4.74	3.90	—	25–500	—	Sub.	590	—		*red.
P_2 *	−33,600	52.1	8.31	0.46	0.72	25–1700	—	—	600	—	(5,800)	*gas.
P_2O_5	370,000	32.5	8.38	54.00	—	25–358	—	570	—	—		
S	0	7.62	3.58 6.20 8.73	6.24	—	25–95 95–119 419–444	95	119	444	85	335	
S_2	−31,000	54.4	8.72	0.16	0.90	25–2700	—	—	—	—		
SO	6,000	53.1	8.26	0.32	1.00	25–2700	—	—	—	—		
SO_2	70,950	59.25	11.04	1.88	1.84	25–1700	—	−76	−10	—	1,770	
Si	0	4.53	5.70 6.10	0.70	1.04	25–1412 1412–1700	—	1413	2600	—	12,100	
SiO	22,200	50.55	7.70	0.74	0.70	25–1700	—	(1610)	—	—		
SiO_2 *	218,500	10.0	11.22 14.41	8.20 1.94	2.70	25–575 575–1700	575	—	—	290		*alpha-quartz.
SiO_2	217,600	10.2	4.28 14.40	21.06 2.04	—	25–250 250–1713	250	1713	dec.	200	3,600	*beta-cristobalite.
Si_3N_4	179,000	23.0	16.83	23.60	—	25–600	—	dec.	—	—		
SiC	12,400	3.95	9.97	1.82	3.64	25–1700	—	>2700	—	—		
Th	0	12.76	5.17 11.00 11.00	4.56	—	25–1400 1400–1695 1695–2700	1400	1695	4227	670	4,500	
ThO_2	293,200	15.6	15.84	2.88	1.60	25–1700	—	(3000)	—	—		
Ti	0	7.33	5.25 7.50 8.00	2.52	—	25–882 882–1667 1667–2700	882	1667	3260	950	4,460	

*See appropriate "Remarks."

(a) See note at end of table.

Table 12–II. Thermodynamic Data[a] on Some Elements and Compounds Encountered in Ferrous Metallurgical Processes—Concluded.

Units: $-\Delta H^\circ_{298}$ in cal. per mole; S°_{298} in cal. per deg. per mole; C_p in cal. per deg. per mole; transformation (t.p.) melting (m.p.) and boiling (b.p.) point temperatures in °C; heats of transformation and fusion in cal. per mole.

Notations: " " indicate nonstoichiometric compound; underlined m.p. indicates incongruent m.p.; values in ( ) are estimated. dec. = decomposes. Sub. = sublimes.

Substance	$-\Delta H^\circ_{298}$	S°_{298}	a	$b \times 10^3$	$c \times 10^{-5}$	Temp. Range °C	t.p. °C	m.p. °C	b.p. °C	ΔH_t	ΔH_f	Remarks
"TiO"	123,900	8.3	10.57	3.60	1.86	25–991	991	1760		820		
			11.85	3.00	—	991–1760						
"TiO₂"	225,500	12.0	17.97	0.28	4.35	25–1500		1920	dec.			
"TiN"	80,400	7.24	11.91	0.94	2.96	25–1700		2950	dec.			
"TiC"	43,900	5.8	11.83	0.80	3.58	25–1700		3150				
V	0	7.0	4.90	2.58	−0.20	25–1917	—	1917	3350	—	5,050	
			9.50			1917–2700						
VO	102,000	9.3	11.32	3.22	1.26	25–1700		1700				
V₂O₃	294,000	23.5	29.35	4.76	5.42	25–1500		>2000				
VO₂	171,000	12.3	14.96	1.70	3.95	25–72	72	1545		1,025	13,600	
			17.85			72–1545						
			25.50			1545–2700						
V₂O₅	371,800	31.3	46.54	−3.90	13.22	25–670	—	670	dec.	—	15,560	
			45.60									
"VN"	60,000	8.9	10.94	2.10	2.21	25–1500		(2050)				
"VC"	(12,500)	6.77	9.18	3.30	1.95	25–1400		(2850)				
W	0	8.0	5.74	0.76	—	25–2700	—	3380	(5400)	—		
"WO₃"	200,000	19.9	(17.75)	(5.87)	—	25–1473	720	1473	(1850)	—		
WC	9,100	8.5	(7.98)	(2.17)	—	25–2700		dec.	—	—		
Zn	0	9.95	5.35	2.40	—	25–420	—	420	907	—		
			7.50			420–907						
ZnO	83,200	10.4	11.71	1.22	2.18	25–1700		1975				
ZnS	48,200	13.8	12.16	1.24	1.36	25–900	1020	dec.		(3,200)	1,765	
Zr	0	9.3	6.50	1.42	0.82	25–862	862	1857	(4750)	915	4,900	
			7.90			862–1857						
			8.00			1857–2700						
"ZrO₂"	259,500	12.1	16.64	1.80	3.36	25–1205	1205	2700	(4300)	1,420		
ZrN	87,300	9.3	11.10	1.68	1.72	25–1400	—	2950				
"ZrC"	44,100	8.5						3500				
ZrSiO₄		20.2	31.48	3.92	8.08	25–1500	—	2430				

References to the thermodynamic data:

ΔH°_{298} from O. Kubaschewski and E. Ll. Evans: "Metallurgical Thermochemistry," Pergamon Press, London, 1958 (with the exception of some recent data on a few compounds).

S°_{298} from K. K. Kelley: U. S. Bur. Mines Bull. No. 477, 1950.

C_p from K. K. Kelley: U. S. Bur. Mines Bull. No. 584, 1960.

CO: $\Delta H^\circ = -26,420$
$$\Delta H^\circ_{298} = \Delta H^\circ_{298}(Al_2O_3) + 3\Delta H^\circ_{298}(CO)$$
$$- 3\Delta H^\circ_{298}(CO_2)$$
$$= -196,710 \text{ cal.} \qquad (b)$$

Entropies at 298°K in cal. per deg. per mole

Al: $S^\circ = 6.77$
CO_2: $S^\circ = 51.1$
Al_2O_3: $S^\circ = 12.2$
CO: $S^\circ = 47.3$
$$\Delta S^\circ_{298} = S^\circ_{298}(Al_2O_3) + 3S^\circ_{298}(CO)$$
$$- [2S^\circ_{298}(Al) + 3S^\circ_{298}(CO_2)]$$
$$= -12.7 \text{ cal. per deg.} \qquad (c)$$

Now, the integrations $\int \Delta C_p dT$ and $\int \dfrac{\Delta C_p}{T} dT$

can be carried out using equations (a) and (b):

$$\int_{298}^{T} \Delta C_p dT = 6.27\,T - 3.23 \times 10^{-3}T^2 + 2.53$$
$$\times 10^5 T^{-1} - 2430 \qquad (d)$$

where the constant 2430 is the integration constant obtained from ΔC_p at 298°K.

$$\int_{298}^{T} \frac{\Delta C_p}{T} dT = 6.27\,\ln T - 6.46 \times 10^{-3}T + 1.27$$
$$\times 10^5 T^{-2} - 35.24$$

where 35.24 is the integration constant obtained from $\Delta C_p/T$ at 298°K. Since, $\ln T = 2.303 \log T$,

$$\int_{298}^{T} \frac{\Delta C_p}{T} dT = 14.44 \log T - 6.46 \times 10^{-3}T$$
$$+ 1.27 \times 10^5 T^{-2} - 35.24 \qquad (e)$$

Inserting the values from equations (b), (c), (d) and (e) in equation (44), gives the following:

$$\Delta F^\circ = -199,140 - 14.44\,T \log T + 3.23 \times$$
$$10^{-3}T^2 + 1.27 \times 10^5 T^{-1} + 54.21\,T \qquad (f)$$

for the temperature range 298–932°K (the latter is the melting point of aluminum).

In order to extend the calculations to temperatures above the melting point of aluminum, the free energy change resulting from the fusion of aluminum must be calculated. The data required are:

$$C_p(\text{liq. Al}) = 7.00 \text{ cal. per deg.}$$
$$\text{per mole}$$
$$\text{Heat of fusion } \Delta H_{932} = 2,570 \text{ cal. per mole}$$
$$\text{Entropy of fusion } \Delta S_{932} = 2.76 \text{ cal. per deg.}$$
$$\text{per mole}$$

Using these values together with C_p for solid Al, the free energy increase resulting from heating Al from 298°K to any temperature above its melting temperature is derived in a manner similar to those given above; thus for reaction

$$2Al(s) = 2Al(l)$$
$$\Delta F^\circ = 3,870 - 9.49\,T \log T + 2.96 \times 10^{-3}T^2$$
$$+ 21.21\,T \qquad (g)$$

Since at the melting temperature 932°K, solid and liquid aluminum are in equilibrium, $\Delta F^\circ = 0$ at 932°K.

For the reaction

$$2Al(l) + 3CO_2(g) = Al_2O_3(s) + 3CO(g)$$

the standard free energy change is obtained by subtracting equation (g) from equation (f), thus for temperatures above 932°K:

$$\Delta F^\circ = -203,010 - 4.95\,T \log T + 0.27 \times 10^{-3}T^2$$
$$+ 1.27 \times 10^5 T^{-1} + 33.00\,T \text{ cal.} \qquad (h)$$

Using equations (f) and (h), in Figure 12–2, ΔF° is plotted against temperature; although the above

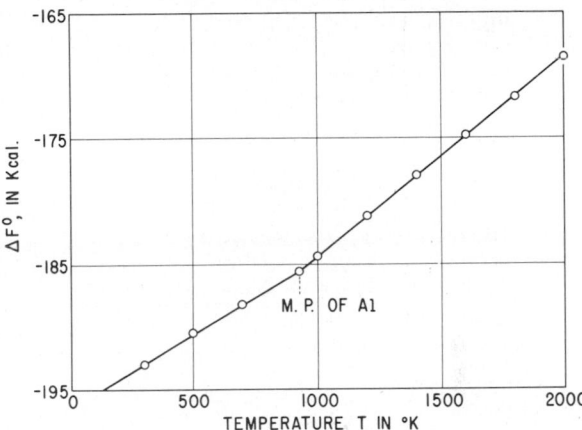

Fig. 12–2. Standard free energy change accompanying reaction $2\,Al + 3\,CO_2 = Al_2O_3 + 3\,CO$ calculated from the data on ΔH^0_{298}, S^0_{298} and high temperature C_p.

equations are complex, a linear temperature function of ΔF° can be obtained from the plot in Figure 12–2, thus, for the temperature range 298–932°K,

$$\Delta F^\circ = -196,600 + 11.80\,T \text{ cal.}$$

and for temperatures above 932°K

$$\Delta F^\circ = -200,550 + 16.15\,T \text{ cal.}$$

In Table 12–III, the standard free energy changes accompanying some metallurgical reactions are given as linear functions of temperature, thus:

$$\Delta F^\circ = A + BT \qquad (45)$$

If there are no high-temperature heat capacity data, equation (43) may be used, at least approximately, inserting $A = \Delta H^\circ_{298}$ and $B = -\Delta S^\circ_{298}$.

In order to simplify the calculations of free energy equations, the thermodynamic data are often tabulated in the form of $\dfrac{F^\circ_T - H^\circ_O}{T}$ and $H^\circ_T - H^\circ_O$ at even temperature intervals of 100°. By simple additions and subtractions, the free energy change in a reaction can readily be computed for any temperature. Using this simpler method, let us now calculate the change in the standard free energy for the following reaction at 1000°K.

$$H_2O + CO = CO_2 + H_2$$

The following are the data required (see Page 260):

Table 12–III. Standard Free Energies of Some Reactions Encountered in Ferrous Metallurgical Processes*

Notations: (g) gas, (l) liquid, (s) solid, " " nonstoichiometric compounds.

Reaction	$\Delta F_T^\circ = A + BT$ in cal.		$\pm$ Kcal.	Temp. Range °C
	$-A$	B		
$2Al\ (s) + 3/2\ O_2\ (g) = Al_2O_3\ (s)$	399,500	74.71	1	25–659
$2Al\ (l) + 3/2\ O_2\ (g) = Al_2O_3\ (s)$	402,300	77.83	1	659–1700
$Al\ (s) + 1/2\ N_2\ (g) = AlN\ (s)$	75,760	25.40	1	25–659
$Al\ (l) + 1/2\ N_2\ (g) = AlN\ (s)$	78,030	27.82	1	659–1700
$4Al\ (s) + 3\ C\ (s) = Al_4C_3\ (s)$	35,080	−2.60	4	25–659
$4Al\ (l) + 3\ C\ (s) = Al_4C_3\ (s)$	42,700	5.70	4	659–1700
$2B\ (s) + 3/2\ O_2\ (g) = B_2O_3\ (s)$	305,120	63.01	1	25–450
$2B\ (s) + 3/2\ O_2\ (g) = B_2O_3\ (l)$	295,630	50.41	1	450–1700
$B\ (s) + 1/2\ N_2\ (g) = BN\ (s)$	60,600	21.40	0.5	25–900
$4B\ (s) + C\ (s) = B_4C\ (s)$	13,580	1.69	1	25–900
$Ba\ (s) + 1/2\ O_2\ (g) = "BaO"\ (s)$	132,920	22.36	3.5	25–704
$Ba\ (l) + 1/2\ O_2\ (g) = "BaO"\ (s)$	133,400	22.87	3.5	704–1638
$3Ba\ (s) + N_2\ (g) = Ba_3N_2\ (s)$	87,000	57.4	9	25–704
$BaO\ (s) + SiO_2\ (s) = BaSiO_3\ (s)$	26,800	0.1	3	25–1300
$Be\ (s) + 1/2\ O_2\ (g) = BeO\ (s)$	142,900	23.13	0.5	25–1283
$Be\ (l) + 1/2\ O_2\ (g) = BeO\ (s)$	142,360	23.36	1.0	1283–1700
$3Be\ (s) + N_2\ (g) = Be_3N_2\ (s)$	134,700	40.6	12	25–700
$C\ (s) + 2H_2\ (g) = CH_4\ (g)$	21,550	26.16	1	25–2000
$C\ (s) + 1/2\ O_2\ (g) = CO\ (g)$	26,760	−20.98	1	25–2000
$C\ (s) + O_2\ (g) = CO_2\ (g)$	94,260	−0.27	1	25–2000
$C\ (s) + 1/2\ S_2\ (g) = CS\ (g)$	−59,000	−22.75	7	1600–1800
$C\ (s) + S_2\ (g) = CS_2\ (g)$	3,100	−1.73	1	25–1300
$CO\ (g) + 1/2\ S_2\ (g) = COS\ (g)$	22,860	18.7	3	25–1200
graphite = diamond	310	1.13	0.2	25–1200
$Ca\ (s) + 1/2\ O_2\ (g) = CaO\ (s)$	150,470	24.47	1	25–850
$Ca\ (l) + 1/2\ O_2\ (g) = CaO\ (s)$	152,020	25.80	1	850–1487
$Ca\ (g) + 1/2\ O_2\ (g) = CaO\ (s)$	187,980	46.21	2	1487–1700
$Ca\ (s) + 1/2\ S_2\ (g) = CaS\ (s)$	129,490	22.86	1	25–850
$Ca\ (l) + 1/2\ S_2\ (g) = CaS\ (s)$	131,780	24.94	1	850–1487
$Ca\ (g) + 1/2\ S_2\ (g) = CaS\ (s)$	168,360	45.72	2	1487–1700
$3Ca\ (s) + N_2\ (g) = Ca_3N_2\ (s)$	105,000	50.0	10	25–850
$Ca\ (s)\alpha + 2C\ (s) = CaC_2\ (s)$	13,600	−5.9	3	25–400
$Ca\ (s)\beta + 2C\ (s) = CaC_2\ (s)$	11,620	−8.64	3	400–850
$Ca\ (l) + 2C\ (s) = CaC_2\ (s)$	13,700	−6.80	3	850–1487
$Ca\ (g) + 2C\ (s) = CaC_2\ (s)$	51,210	12.3	5	1487–1900
$3CaO\ (s) + Al_2O_3\ (s) = Ca_3Al_2O_6\ (s)$	3,900	−6.3	2	25–1550
$12CaO\ (s) + 7Al_2O_3\ (s) = Ca_{12}Al_{14}O_{33}\ (s)$	17,460	−49.6	2	25–1500
$CaO\ (s) + Al_2O_3\ (s) = CaAl_2O_4\ (s)$	4,570	−4.1	2	25–1600
$CaO\ (s) + CO_2\ (g) = CaCO_3\ (s)$	40,250	34.4	1	25–880
$2CaO\ (s) + Fe_2O_3\ (s) = Ca_2Fe_2O_5\ (s)$	9,200	−2.33	1.5	600–1435
$2CaO\ (s) + Fe_2O_3\ (s) = Ca_2Fe_2O_5\ (l)$	−7,560	−12.13	1.5	1435–1600
$4CaO\ (s) + P_2\ (g) + 5/2\ O_2\ (g) = Ca_4P_2O_9\ (s)$	563,580	144.0	3.0	1300–1600
$3CaO\ (s) + P_2\ (g) + 5/2\ O_2\ (g) = Ca_3P_2O_8\ (s)$	553,350	144.0	3.0	1300–1600
$2CaO\ (s) + SiO_2\ (s) = Ca_2SiO_4\ (s)$	30,200	−1.2	2.5	25–1400
$CaO\ (s) + SiO_2\ (s) = CaSiO_3\ (s)\alpha$	21,300	0.12	1	25–1210
$CaO\ (s) + SiO_2\ (s) = CaSiO_3\ (s)\beta$	19,900	−0.82	2	1210–1543
$Co\ (s) + 1/2\ O_2\ (g) = CoO\ (s)$	57,380	18.65	2	25–1700
$3Co\ (s) + 2\ O_2\ (g) = Co_3O_4\ (s)$	206,590	82.86	3	25–1200
$9Co\ (s) + 4S_2\ (g) = Co_9S_8\ (s)$	316,960	159.24	2	25–778
$2Co\ (s) + C\ (s) = Co_2C\ (s)$	−3,950	−2.08	5	25–900
$2Cr\ (s) + 3/2\ O_2\ (g) = Cr_2O_3\ (s)\beta$	271,300	61.82	0.5	25–1898
$2Cr\ (l) + 3/2\ O_2\ (g) = Cr_2O_3\ (s)\beta$	287,900	70.00	1	1898–2500
$2Cr\ (s) + 1/2\ N_2\ (g) = Cr_2N\ (s)$	24,000	11.65	5	25–1898
$Cr\ (s) + 1/2\ N_2\ (g) = CrN\ (s)$	25,500	16.7	7.5	25–1898
$23Cr\ (s) + 6C\ (s) = Cr_{23}C_6\ (s)$	98,280	−9.24	10	25–1400
$7Cr\ (s) + 3C\ (s) = Cr_7C_3\ (s)$	41,800	−6.1	10	25–1200
$3Cr\ (s) + 2C\ (s) = Cr_3C_2\ (s)$	20,800	−4.0	10	25–1700
$Fe\ (s) + 1/2\ O_2\ (g) = "FeO"\ (s)$	63,200	15.47	0.5	25–1377
$Fe\ (l) + 1/2\ O_2\ (g) = "FeO"\ (l)$	57,070	11.60	1	1537–1700

*See note at end of table.   (Continued on next page)

Table 12–III. Standard Free Energies of Some Reactions Encountered in Ferrous Metallurgical Processes*, Continued

Notations: (g) gas, (l) liquid, (s) solid, " " nonstoichiometric compounds.

Reaction	$\Delta F_T^\circ = A + BT$ in cal.		$\pm$ Kcal.	Temp. Range °C
	$-A$	B		
$3Fe\ (s) + 2\ O_2\ (g) = Fe_3O_4\ (s)$	265,660	76.81	1.2	25–600
$3Fe\ (s) + 2\ O_2\ (g) = Fe_3O_4\ (s)$	261,200	71.36	1.2	600–1537
$3Fe\ (l) + 2\ O_2\ (g) = Fe_3O_4\ (s,l)$	248,240	64.42	2	1537–1700
$2Fe\ (s) + 3/2\ O_2\ (g) = Fe_2O_3\ (s)$	195,450	61.38	1.5	25–680
$2Fe\ (s) + 3/2\ O_2\ (g) = Fe_2O_3\ (s)$	192,800	58.30	1.5	680–1537
$Fe\ (s) + \frac{1}{2}\ S_2\ (g) = FeS\ (s)\alpha$	37,160	15.59	1	25–140
$Fe\ (s) + \frac{1}{2}\ S_2\ (g) = FeS\ (s)\beta$	35,910	12.56	1	140–906
$4Fe\ (s) + \frac{1}{2}\ N_2\ (g) = Fe_4N\ (s)$	1,130	9.7	1	25–600
$3Fe\ (s) + \frac{1}{2}\ P_2(g) = Fe_3P\ (s)$	51,000	11.3	8	25–1170
$3Fe\ (s) + C\ (s) = Fe_3C\ (s)$	−6,200	−5.53	1	25–190
$3Fe\ (s) + C\ (s) = Fe_3C\ (s)$	−6,380	−5.92	1	190–840
$3Fe\ (s) + C\ (s) = Fe_3C\ (s)$	−2,475	−2.43	1	840–1537
"FeO" $(s) + Al_2O_3\ (s) = FeAl_2O_4\ (s)$	11,800	5.43	4	25–1377
"FeO" $(s) + Cr_2O_3(s) = FeCr_2O_4\ (s)$	2,600	−3.37	2	25–1377
2"FeO" $(s) + SiO_2\ (s) = Fe_2SiO_4\ (s)$	7,950	3.65	2	25–1217
2"FeO" $(s) + SiO_2\ (s) = Fe_2SiO_4\ (l)$	−14,880	−11.49	2	1217–1377
2"FeO" $(l) + SiO_2\ (s) = Fe_2SiO_4\ (l)$	−3,450	−4.58	2	1377–1700
"FeO" $(s) + TiO_2\ (s) = FeTiO_3\ (s)$	1,410	−2.54	1	900–1377
$H_2\ (g) + \frac{1}{2}\ O_2\ (g) = H_2O\ (g)$	58,850	13.12	0.5	25–1700
$H_2\ (g) + \frac{1}{2}\ S_2\ (g) = H_2S\ (g)$	21,580	11.80	0.5	25–1500
$3/2\ H_2\ (g) + \frac{1}{2}\ N_2\ (g) = NH_3(g)$	12,050	26.7	2	25–700
$Mg\ (s) + \frac{1}{2}\ O_2\ (g) = MgO\ (s)$	143,000	25.91	1.5	25–650
$Mg\ (l) + \frac{1}{2}\ O_2\ (g) = MgO\ (s)$	145,830	28.10	1.5	650–1120
$Mg\ (g) + \frac{1}{2}\ O_2\ (g) = MgO\ (s)$	176,060	49.84	3	1120–1700
$Mg\ (s) + \frac{1}{2}\ S_2\ (g) = MgS\ (s)$	99,650	22.8	5	25–650
$Mg\ (l) + \frac{1}{2}\ S_2\ (g) = MgS\ (s)$	101,800	25.65	5	650–1120
$Mg\ (g) + \frac{1}{2}\ S_2\ (g) = MgS\ (s)$	134,350	48.75	5	1120–1700
$3Mg\ (s) + N_2\ (g) = Mg_3N_2\ (s)$	109,600	47.41	3	25–650
$3Mg\ (l) + N_2\ (g) = Mg_3N_2\ (s)$	115,810	54.20	3	650–1120
$MgO\ (s) + CO_2\ (g) = MgCO_3\ (s)$	28,100	40.6	3	25–700
$3MgO\ (s) + P_2(g) + 5/2\ O_2(g) = Mg_3P_2O_8\ (s)$	501,610	144.0	3	1000–1250
$2MgO\ (s) + SiO_2\ (s) = Mg_2SiO_4\ (s)$	15,120	0.0	2	25–1400
$MgO\ (s) + SiO_2\ (s) = MgSiO_3\ (s)$	8,900	1.1	1	25–1300
$Mn\ (s) + \frac{1}{2}\ O_2\ (g) = MnO\ (s)$	92,490	17.87	1.5	25–1244
$Mn\ (l) + \frac{1}{2}\ O_2\ (g) = MnO\ (s)$	97,360	21.12	1.5	1244–1700
$3Mn\ (s) + 2\ O_2\ (g) = Mn_3O_4\ (s)$	330,750	83.61	1.5	25–1244
$3Mn\ (l) + 2\ O_2\ (g) = Mn_3O_4\ (s)$	339,000	89.03	1.5	1244–1700
$Mn\ (s) + \frac{1}{2}\ S_2\ (g) = MnS\ (s)$	65,000	16.21	1.5	25–1244
$Mn\ (l) + \frac{1}{2}\ S_2\ (g) = MnS\ (s)$	69,010	18.86	2	1244–1530
$Mn\ (l) + \frac{1}{2}\ S_2\ (g) = MnS\ (l)$	62,770	15.40	2	1530–1700
$3Mn\ (s) + C\ (s) = Mn_3C\ (s)$	3,330	−0.26	3	25–740
$MnO\ (s) + SiO_2\ (s) = MnSiO_3\ (s)$	5,920	3.0	4	25–1300
$2Mo\ (s) + \frac{1}{2}\ N_2\ (g) = Mo_2N\ (s)$	15,250	13.25	3	25–1000
$2Mo\ (s) + C\ (s) = Mo_2C\ (s)$	6,700	0.0	8	25–1000
$Ni\ (s) + \frac{1}{2}\ O_2\ (g) = NiO\ (s)$	58,450	23.55	2	25–1452
$Ni\ (l) + \frac{1}{2}\ O_2\ (g) = NiO\ (s)$	62,650	25.98	3	1452–1900
$Ni\ (s) + \frac{1}{2}\ S_2\ (g) = NiS\ (s)$	39,980	17.20	3	400–580
$3Ni\ (s) + C\ (s) = Ni_3C\ (s)$	−8,110	−1.70	3	25–700
$2P\ (s,l) + 5/2\ O_2\ (g) = P_2O_5\ (s)$	361,300	113.6	10	25–280
$\frac{1}{2}\ S_2\ (g) + O_2\ (g) = SO_2\ (g)$	86,520	17.48	1	25–1700
$Si\ (s) + \frac{1}{2}\ O_2\ (g) = SiO\ (g)$	22,600	−19.71	3	25–1413
$Si\ (l) + \frac{1}{2}\ O_2\ (g) = SiO\ (g)$	36,150	−11.51	3	1413–1700
$Si(s) + O_2\ (g) = SiO_2\ (s)\ \alpha$ cristobalite	215,600	42.26	3	25–250
$Si\ (s) + O_2\ (g) = SiO_2\ (s)\ \beta$ cristobalite	214,400	40.32	3	250–1413
$Si\ (l) + O_2\ (g) = SiO_2\ (s)\ \beta$ cristobalite	226,500	47.50	3	1413–1700
$3Si\ (s) + 2N_2\ (g) = Si_3N_4\ (s)$	172,700	75.2	5	25–1413
$3Si\ (l) + 2N_2\ (g) = Si_3N_4\ (s)$	209,000	96.8	2	1413–1700
$Si\ (s) + C\ (s) = SiC\ (s)\ \beta$	13,000	0.73	2	25–1413
$Si\ (l) + C\ (s) = SiC\ (s)\ \beta$	25,100	7.91	2	1413–1700

*See note at end of table.　　　　　(Continued on next page)

Table 12—III. Standard Free Energies of Some Reactions Encountered in Ferrous Metallurgical Processes*, Concluded

Notations: (g) gas, (l) liquid, (s) solid, " " nonstoichiometric compounds.

Reaction	$\Delta F_T^\circ = A + BT$ in cal.		$\pm$Kcal.	Temp. Range °C
	$-A$	B		
Ti (s) + O$_2$ (g) = TiO$_2$ (s)	224,500	42.33	2	25–1700
Ti (s) + ½ N$_2$ (g) = "TiN" (s)	80,550	22.45	2	25–1300
Ti (s) + C (s) = "TiC" (s)	45,000	2.79	3	25–1700
2V (s) + 3/2 O$_2$ (g) = V$_2$O$_3$ (s)	291,350	56.49	6.5	25–1700
2V (s) + 5/2 O$_2$ (g) = V$_2$O$_5$ (s)	371,400	100.92	5.5	25–670
2V (s) + 5/2 O$_2$ (g) = V$_2$O$_5$ (l)	349,250	77.46	5.5	670–1700
V (s) + ½ N$_2$ (g) = "VN" (s)	41,650	19.35	10	25–1300
V (s) + C (s) = "VC" (s)	12,500	1.6	10	25–1700
W (s) + C (s) = WC (s)	9,100	0.4	3	25–1700
Zr (s) + O$_2$ (g) = ZrO$_2$ $(s)\alpha$	260,730	44.7	4	25–1205
Zr (s) + O$_2$ (g) = ZrO$_2$ $(s)\beta$	258,170	42.87	4	1205–1700
Zr (s) + ½ N$_2$ (g) = "ZrN" (s)	87,470	22.72	3	25–1300
Zr (s) + C (s) = "ZrC" (s)	44,100	2.2	3	25–1900

*The most of the data are taken from the following sources:
(1) J. P. Coughlin: U. S. Bureau of Mines Bull. No. 542, 1954.
(2) O. Kubaschewski and E. Ll. Evans: "Metallurgical Thermochemistry," Pergamon Press, London, 1958.
(3) J. F. Elliott and M. Gleiser: "Thermochemistry for Steelmaking," vol. I, Addison-Wesley Pub. Co. Inc., Mass., 1960.

Substance	$\dfrac{F^\circ_{1000} - H^\circ_0}{1000}$ cal./mole	$H^\circ_{298} - H^\circ_0$ cal./mole	ΔH°_{298} cal./mole
H$_2$	−32.738	2024	0
CO$_2$	−54.109	2238	−94,052
H$_2$O	−47.010	2368	−57,798
CO	−48.860	2073	−26,416

From these values the following are obtained for the above reaction:

$$\frac{\Delta(F^\circ_{1000} - H^\circ_O)}{1000} = (-32.738) + (-54.109)$$
$$- (-47.010) - (-48.860) =$$
$$9.023 \text{ cal.}$$

$$\Delta(H^\circ_{298} - H^\circ_O) = 2024 + 2238 - 2368 - 2073 = -173$$

$$\Delta H^\circ_{298} = (-94,052) - (-57,798) - (-26,416) = -9838 \text{ cal.}$$

and, therefore,

$$\Delta H^\circ_O = -9665 \text{ cal.}$$

Now, inserting this value of ΔH°_O in the free energy equation for 1000°K, the following is obtained

$$\frac{\Delta F^\circ_{1000} - (-9665)}{1000} = 9.023$$
$$\Delta F^\circ_{1000} = -642 \text{ cal.}$$

SECTION 7

SOLUTIONS

A solution is a homogeneous gas, liquid or solid, any portion of which has the same state properties. The composition of a gas solution is usually given in terms of partial pressures of species in equilibrium with one another under given conditions. In metallic liquid and solid solutions, the concentrations of the constituent elements, usually reported in weight per cent, are converted to atomic concentrations when considering the thermodynamic properties of the solutions. The atom fraction, N_i, is given by the ratio:

$$N_i = \frac{n_i}{\Sigma n}$$

where n_i is the number of gram-atoms of element i per unit mass of the substance and Σn is the total number of atoms. Since the composition is usually given in weight per cent, n_i per 100 g. of the substance is:

$$n_i = \frac{\%_i}{M_i}$$

where M_i is the atomic weight. For complex systems, e.g. solid and liquid solutions of oxides and liquid slags, the composition is often given in terms of concentrations of oxides; this is discussed in more detail in Part III of this chapter.

PARTIAL MOLAR QUANTITIES

Contribution made by each constituent of a solution to its extensive property, e.g. volume, free energy, enthalpy, entropy, is not additive. If a solution is made of n_1, n_2, n_3 . . . numbers of moles of constituents 1, 2, 3 . . . and G' is any total extensive property of the solution, the partial molar quantity is given by the partial derivative,

$$\overline{G}_l = \left(\frac{\partial G'}{\partial n_1}\right)_{P,T,n_2,n_3} \cdots \quad (46)$$

That is, if an infinitesimal amount, dn_1, of component *1* is added to a large amount of solution so that the composition of the solution does not change, at constant temperature and pressure the ratio $(\partial G'/\partial n_1)_{P,T,n_2,n_3}$ defines the partial molar quantity of component 1. Similar equations can be written for other components, and from the solution of the sum of these differential equations, the following basic equations are obtained.

$$G' = n_1\overline{G}_1 + n_2\overline{G}_2 + n_3\overline{G}_3 + \cdots \quad (47)$$

and since the molar quantity is

$$G = \frac{G'}{n_1 + n_2 + n_3 + \cdots}$$

the following is the relation for one mole of solution

$$G = N_1\overline{G}_1 + N_2\overline{G}_2 + N_3\overline{G}_3 + \cdots \quad (48)$$

where N is the atom fraction, i.e. $N_1 + N_2 + N_3 + \ldots = 1$.

Another basic equation is:

$$N_1 d\overline{G}_1 + N_2 d\overline{G}_2 + N_3 d\overline{G}_3 + \cdots = 0 \quad (49)$$

The special form of this equation for the partial molar free energies is known as the **Gibbs-Duhem equation,** and for binary solutions,

$$N_1 d\overline{F}_1 + N_2 d\overline{F}_2 = 0 \quad (50)$$

From equations (48) and (49) the following is derived for a binary system

$$\overline{G}_1 = G + (1 - N_1)\frac{dG}{dN_1} \quad (51)$$

and similarly,

$$\overline{G}_2 = G + (1 - N_2)\frac{dG}{dN_2} \quad (52)$$

These equations show the method of evaluating the partial molar quantities $\overline{G}_1$ and $\overline{G}_2$ graphically from the plot of the molar quantity G against composition. Figure 12–3 shows the variation of G with composition; to determine $\overline{G}_1$ and $\overline{G}_2$ at a composition indicated by point A, a line is drawn tangentially to the curve at A and the intercepts at $N_1=0$ and $N_1 = 1$ give the values of $\overline{G}_1$ and $\overline{G}_2$, respectively.

CHEMICAL POTENTIAL AND ACTIVITY

Another important derivation from the Gibbs free energy equation is that obtained by combining equation (38) with the derivative of equation (39), thus

$$dE = TdS - PdV$$
$$dF = dE + PdV + VdP - TdS - SdT$$
$$\overline{dF = VdP - SdT} \quad (53)$$

For constant temperature $dF=VdP$, and inserting $V=RT/P$ for one mole of an ideal gas, the following is obtained:

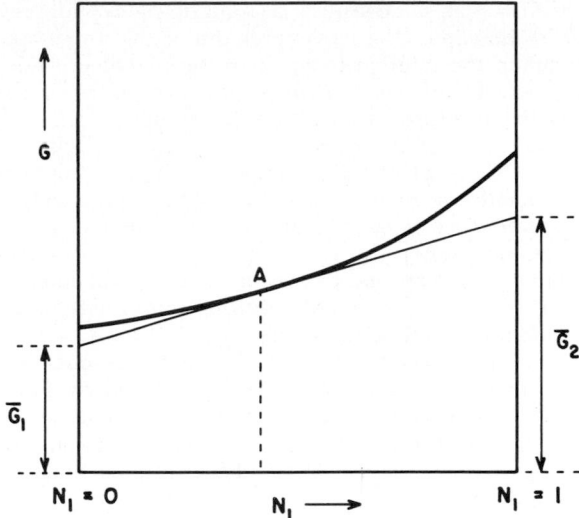

Fig. 12–3. Graphical method of evaluating the partial molar quantities from the molar quantity of a binary system.

$$dF = RT (dP/P)$$
$$= RT \, d \ln P \quad (54)$$

Similarly, for each component of the system, the partial molar free energy equation is:

$$d\overline{F}_1 = RT \, d \ln p_i$$

On integration

$$\overline{F}_i = F_i^\circ + RT \ln p_i \quad (55)$$

where p_i is the partial pressure of component i in an ideal solution and F_i° is the integration constant which is the free energy of the ith component at its standard state. The partial molar free energy $\overline{F}_i$ is also called the chemical potential of the ith component.

In real gases, particularly at low temperatures and high pressures, the ideal gas law $PV/T=R$ is not obeyed. In order to maintain the generality of equation (55) the concept of **fugacity** was introduced by **Lewis** (1901). The fugacity $\mathfrak{F}_i$ for a pure species i is defined in terms of chemical potential by the following isothermal relation,

$$RT \ln\mathfrak{F}_i = F_i + I \quad (56)$$

where I is the integration constant so chosen that the fugacity approaches the pressure as the pressure approaches zero. In an ideal gas mixture fugacities of gas species are numerically equal to their respective partial pressures. The effect of pressure on the deviation from the ideal gas law is illustrated from the following example. For CO_2 at 100°C at $P = 50$ atm. pressure, $\mathfrak{F} = 44.2$ atm. and at $P = 100$ atm., $\mathfrak{F} = 79$ atm. At atmospheric pressures and moderate to high temperatures, the fugacity and the partial pressure are almost equal and, therefore, in the subsequent considerations the partial pressures are used with the assumption that the ideal gas law is obeyed.

Now, let us consider a solution in equilibrium with its vapor; the vapor pressure of the ith component in the solution is equal to the partial pressure, p_i, of the ith component in the gas phase. If the partial pressure of the pure ith component is p_i°, then the ratio $p_i/p_i^\circ = a_i$ was defined by Lewis as the activity of the ith component in the solution. Although in many cases the pure component is chosen as the standard state, any other state can be a reference state; the choice of standard states and conversion from one to another is discussed later in this section. The activity of the component at its standard state is of course unity.

From the above definition of activity, the chemical potential derived for gases can be applied to liquid or solid solutions by using activity a_i instead of the partial pressure p_i (or fugacity $\mathfrak{F}_i$), thus at constant temperature and pressure and at complete internal equilibrium,

$$\bar{F}_i = F_i^\circ + RT \ln a_i \qquad (57)$$

or

$$\Delta \bar{F}_i = \bar{F}_i - F_i^\circ = RT \ln a_i \qquad (57a)$$

The value determined experimentally is the difference $\bar{F}_i - F_i^\circ = \Delta \bar{F}_i$, i.e. the difference between the free energy value for a given solution and that in a standard state. This difference $\Delta \bar{F}_i$ is called the **relative partial molar free energy**; similarly $\Delta \bar{H}_i$ and $\Delta \bar{S}_i$ are the relative partial molar heat and entropy of component i. For convenience, these terms are subsequently referred to as the free energy, heat and entropy of solution.

The ratio of activity to the mole fraction of the component is called the **activity coefficient**, γ, i.e.

$$\gamma_i = \frac{a_i}{N_i} \qquad (58)$$

The solutions are said to be ideal, if the activity is directly proportional to the mole (or atom) fraction, N. That is, the activity coefficient $\gamma_i = 1.0$ in ideal solution; this is known as **Raoult's law.**

DEVIATIONS FROM RAOULT'S AND HENRY'S LAWS

Depending on the nature of the elements constituting a solution, the activity vs composition relationship deviates from Raoult's law to varying degrees. Figures 12–4, 12–5 and 12–6 are examples showing the variation of activities with composition in iron-nickel, iron silicon and iron-copper melts at 1600°C. Raoult's law for the ideal solution is indicated by the dotted lines. When the activity coefficient is < 1.0, deviation from Raoult's law is said to be negative (Figs. 12–4 and 5) and for γ > 1.0, the deviation is positive (Fig. 12–6). The factors causing these deviations from the ideal solution will not be discussed here, except to point out that if the unlike atoms (as iron and silicon) tend to interact with one another more strongly than the like atoms (as iron and iron or silicon and silicon) the deviations from Raoult's law are negative. On the other hand, in iron-copper melts

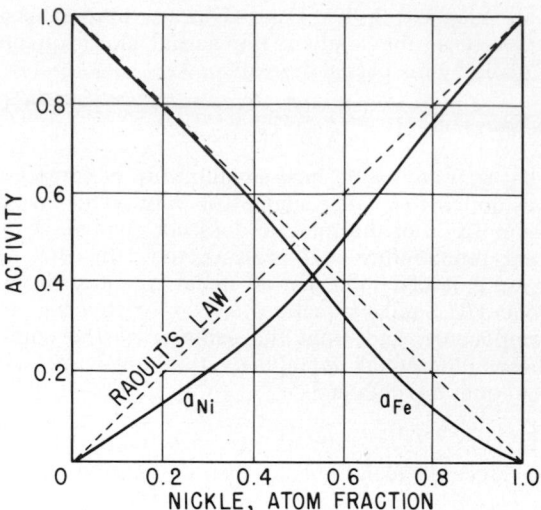

FIG. 12–4. Activities in iron-nickel binary melts at 1600°C. (From Zellars et al[1].)

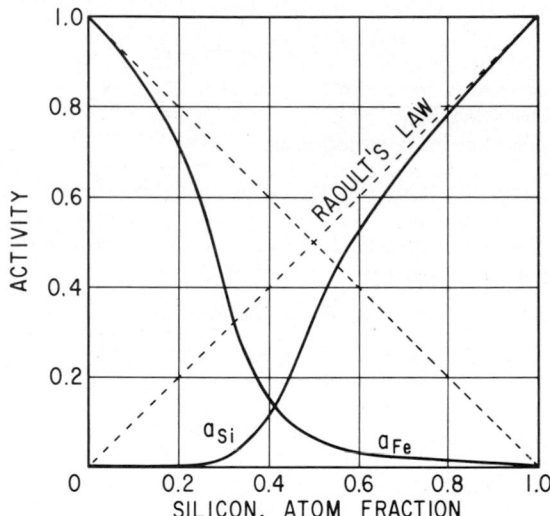

FIG. 12–5. Activities in iron-silicon binary melts at 1600°C. (From Chipman et al[2].)

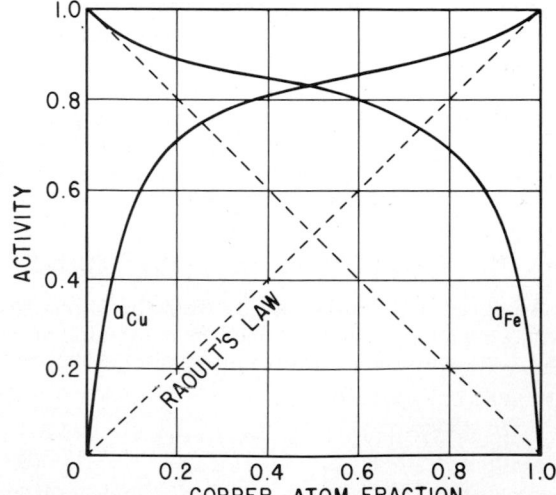

FIG. 12–6. Activities in iron-copper binary melts at 1550°C. (From Morris and Zellars[3].)

the unlike atoms repel one another, as if they were the same poles of a magnet, and the activity coefficients in this system are greater than unity.

If pure components are chosen as the standard states, i.e., $a_i = 1.0$ at $N_i = 1.0$, as N_i approaches 1.0, then $\gamma_i \rightarrow 1.0$; in dilute solutions, however, as $N_i \rightarrow 0$ the activity coefficient γ_i approaches a finite value; this is indicated by the superscript ($^{\circ}$), e.g. γ_i°. This is shown in Figure **12–7** where the activity of silicon (with reference to pure silicon as the standard state) is plotted against the concentration of silicon expressed as atom fraction in curve (a) and as weight per cent in curve (b). The variation of activity with composition in infinitely dilute solutions is generalized by **Henry's law** which states that at infinitely dilute solutions, i.e. $N_i \rightarrow 0$, the activity is directly proportional to concentration. The departure from Henry's law increases with increasing concentration of the solute. In general, a positive deviation from Raoult's law is accompanied by a negative deviation from Henry's law and vice versa. In many binary and complex systems, the deviation from Henry's law does not become noticeable until the concentration of the solute exceeds 1 or 2 wt. per cent.

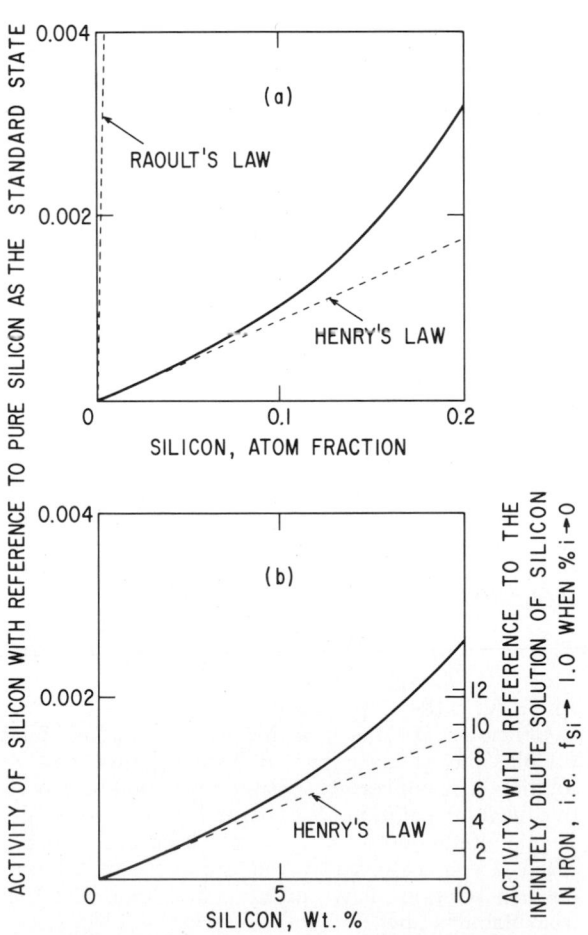

FIG. **12–7**. Activity of silicon in dilute solution in iron at 1600°C.

HYPOTHETICAL (1 PER CENT) SOLUTION AS THE STANDARD STATE

For evaluating activities any particular composition can be chosen as the standard state. Using equation (57) the chemical potential of a component i in a solution for two different standard states (1) and (2) is:

Standard state (1) $\bar{F}_i = F^{\circ (1)} + RT \ln (a_i)_1$

Standard state (2) $\bar{F}_i = F^{\circ (2)} + RT \ln (a_i)_2$

From the difference, the change of standard free energy is

$$\Delta F^{\circ} = F^{\circ (1)} - F^{\circ (2)} = RT \ln \frac{(a_i)_1}{(a_i)_2} \quad (59)$$

The atom fraction of the solute at 1 per cent concentration is

$$N_i = \frac{1/M_i}{1/M_i + 99/M_S}$$

where M_i and M_S are the atomic weights of the solute and the solvent. Since $1/M_i$ is much smaller than $99/M_S$, the former can be omitted, and assuming that iron is the solvent ($M_S = 55.85$)

$$N_i = \frac{0.5585}{M_i} \text{ at 1 per cent of solute } i \text{ in iron.}$$

If Henry's law is obeyed at concentrations up to 1 per cent, the activity coefficient γ_i° for the infinitely dilute solution can be used, i.e. for the standard state (1) $a_i = 0.5585 \gamma_i^{\circ}/M_i$ at 1 per cent. Inserting this value in equation (59), the standard free energy of solution of pure component i in iron, with reference to the hypothetical 1 per cent solution becomes:

$$\Delta F_i^{\circ} = RT \ln \frac{0.5585 \gamma^{\circ}}{M_i} \quad (60)$$

If ΔF_i° is in terms of cal. per mole, and converting (ln) to (log) scale,

$$\Delta F_i^{\circ} = 4.575 \, T \log \frac{0.5585 \gamma_i^{\circ}}{M_i} \quad (61)$$

Using this equation, let us now evaluate ΔF° for the solution of pure liquid silicon in liquid iron, 1 per cent being the standard state:

$$\text{Si (liquid)} = \underline{\text{Si}} \text{ (in Fe)} \quad (62)$$

According to the data in Figure **12–7**(a), $\gamma_{Si}^{\circ} = 0.0089$ at 1600°C, and inserting $M_i = 28.09$:

$$\Delta F_{Si}^{\circ} = 4.575 \times 1873 \log \frac{0.5585 \times 0.0089}{28.09}$$

$$= -32,160 \text{ cal. per mole Si at 1600°C}$$

In order to calculate the standard free energy of solution for other temperatures, the partial molar heat of solution of liquid silicon in liquid iron must be known. In terms of heat and entropy of solution $\Delta F^{\circ} = \Delta \bar{H} - T\Delta \bar{S}$; since $\Delta \bar{H} = -28,500$ cal. per mole Si, from the above value of

Table 12–IV. Standard Free Energies of Solution of Various Elements for 1 per cent Hypothetical Solution, γ_i° at Infinite Dilution and the Proportionality Factor a for $\log f_i = a\ [\%i]$*

Element	State	γ°_{1873}	ΔF° cal per g-atom	a
Aluminum	Liquid	0.063	$-10{,}300 - 7.71T$	0.048
Carbon	Graphite	–	$5{,}100 - 10.00T$	0.20
Chromium	Solid	1	$5{,}000 - 11.31T$	0
Cobalt	Liquid	1	$- 9.31T$	0
Copper	Liquid	8.5	$8{,}000 - 9.40T$	-0.021
Manganese	Liquid	1	$- 9.11T$	0
Nickel	Liquid	0.66	$-5{,}000 - 7.42T$	0
Nitrogen	Gas	–	$860 + 5.71T$	0
Oxygen	Gas	–	$-28{,}000 - 0.69T$	0
Phosphorus	Gas	–	$-29{,}200 - 4.6T$	0
Silicon	Liquid	0.0089	$-28{,}500 - 1.95T$	0.029
Sulphur	Gas	–	$-31{,}520 + 5.27T$	-0.028

*Data from those compiled by Chipman and Elliott[4].

$$\Delta F^\circ = -32{,}160 \text{ at } 1600°\text{C},$$

$\Delta \bar{S}$ can be evaluated, thus:

$$-32{,}160 = -28{,}500 - 1873 \times \Delta \bar{S}$$

$$\Delta \bar{S} = 1.95 \text{ cal. per deg. mole}$$

Since $\Delta \bar{H}$ and $\Delta \bar{S}$ can be assumed to be independent of temperature, the variation of ΔF°_{Si} with temperature is given by a linear equation:

$$\Delta F^\circ_{Si} = -28{,}500 - 1.95\ T \text{ cal. per mole} \quad (63)$$

The standard free energies of solution of several elements, gas, liquid or solid, in liquid iron are given in Table 12–IV; these values are taken from those compiled recently by Chipman and Elliott[4]. Since $\gamma = 1.0$ in solutions obeying Raoult's law, in ideal solutions $\Delta \bar{H} = 0$, as for example in Fe-Co and Fe-Mn melts.

INFINITELY DILUTE SOLUTION AS THE STANDARD STATE

For low concentrations of solutes, it is convenient to choose the infinitely dilute solution as the standard state such that the activity coefficient (to be denoted by f_i) $\rightarrow 1.0$ when $\%i \rightarrow 0$. The value of f_i is obtained from the ratio

$$f_i = \frac{\gamma_i}{\gamma_i^\circ} \quad (64)$$

where γ_i is the activity coefficient at any composition and γ_i° is that for the infinitely dilute solution, i.e. at $\%i = 0$.

Choosing the infinitely dilute solution as the standard state, equation (61) becomes

$$\Delta F_i^\circ = 4.575\ T\ \left(\log \frac{0.5585\ \gamma_i^\circ}{M_i} + \log f_i\right) \quad (65)$$

where $\gamma_i^\circ \rightarrow a$ finite value and $f_i \rightarrow 1.0$ when $\%i \rightarrow 0$. On the basis of this standard state the activity $a_i = f_i\ [\%i]$. Using the data in Figure 12–7(a), the values of f_{Si} are obtained and a_{Si} with reference to the infinitely dilute solution is given on the right hand ordinate of Figure 12–7(b).

In order to evaluate ΔF_i° using equation (65), the variation of $\log f_i$ with the concentration of i

must be known. In general, $\log f_i$ is directly proportional to wt.% i up to few percentages of the solute. The proportionality factor α for $\log f_i = \alpha[\%i]$ is given in Table 12–IV.

VARIATION OF ACTIVITY WITH TEMPERATURE

The effect of temperature on the activity can be computed from the relative partial molar free energy of the ith component in a solution,

$$\Delta \bar{F}_i = \Delta \bar{H}_i - T\Delta \bar{S}_i$$
$$= R\,T \ln a_i$$

Therefore,

$$\ln a_i = \frac{\Delta \bar{H}_i}{R\,T} - \frac{\Delta \bar{S}_i}{R}$$

and for $\Delta \bar{H}$ in calories and $\Delta \bar{S}$ in entropy units (e.u.)

$$\log a_i = \frac{\Delta \bar{H}_i}{4.575\,T} - \frac{\Delta \bar{S}_i}{4.575} \quad (66)$$

That is, for a given composition, $\log a_i$ is a linear function of the reciprocal of absolute temperature and the slope of the line multiplied by 4.575 gives the relative partial molar heat of solution of the ith component. In ideal solutions $\Delta \bar{H}_i = 0$, hence, a_i is independent of temperature. Similarly, activity coefficient can be related to temperature:

$$\log \gamma_i = \frac{\Delta \bar{H}_i}{4.575\,T\cdot} - \frac{\Delta \bar{S}_i}{4.575} + \log N_i \quad (67)$$

where N_i is the atom fraction.

Generally speaking, a negative deviation from Raoult's law is accompanied by a negative heat of solution and, conversely, positive deviation by a positive heat of solution. For example, because of the atomic interaction of iron and silicon, heat is evolved when silicon dissolves in iron and the activity/composition relation shows a strong negative deviation from Raoult's law.

Since $\Delta \bar{H}$ and $\Delta \bar{S}$ are relative partial molar quantities, they vary with composition as may be deduced from the schematic plot given in Figure 12–3.

RELATIONS BETWEEN ACTIVITIES OF SOLUTION COMPONENTS

If the activity of one component in a binary or a ternary system is known over a wide composition range, the activity of the other components of the solution can be computed by using the Gibbs-Duhem relation given in a general form in equation (49). Similarly, in dilute solutions of components 1 and 2 in a solvent M, the effect of component 1 on the activity coefficient of component 2 can be calculated from the knowledge of the effect of 2 on the activity coefficient 1. Because of the limitations imposed on

the scope of this chapter, these thermodynamic derivations and computations will not be discussed here; for detailed information reference should be made to the available text books[5, 6] and papers.[7, 8]

In a number of binary systems the ratio log $\gamma_1/(1-N_1)^2$ is either independent of composition or is a linear function of N_1; this ratio is sometimes referred to as the α-function. Several examples are given by Darken and Gurry[5] of the behavior of this function for binary metal systems.

The experimental data on the activities in iron-based alloys and oxide-melts relevant to ferrous metallurgy are compiled in Parts II and III of this chapter.

SECTION 8

REACTION EQUILIBRIA

EQUILIBRIUM CONSTANT AND MASS ACTION LAW

Let us consider the following equilibrium occurring at constant temperature and pressure

$$xX + yY \ldots = uU + vV + \ldots \quad (68)$$

where $x, y, u, v \ldots$ are the numbers of gram-atoms of $X, Y, U, V, \ldots$. In terms of the partial molar free energies, the change in the free energy accompanying reaction (68) is

$$\Delta F = (u\bar{F}_U + v\bar{F}_V \ldots) - \\ (x\bar{F}_X + y\bar{F}_Y + \ldots) \quad (69)$$

Similarly, when the reactants and products are in their standard states, the free energy change for the reference state is:

$$\Delta F^\circ = (uF_U^\circ + vF_V^\circ + \ldots) \\ - (xF_X^\circ + yF_Y^\circ + \ldots) \quad (70)$$

The difference $\Delta F^\circ - \Delta F$ becomes,

$$\Delta F^\circ - \Delta F = [u(F_U^\circ - \bar{F}_U) + v(F_V^\circ - \bar{F}_V) + \ldots] \\ - [x(F_X^\circ - \bar{F}_X) + y(F_Y^\circ - \bar{F}_Y) + \ldots]$$

According to equation (57), $F^\circ - \bar{F} = -RT \ln a$, therefore

$$\Delta F^\circ - \Delta F = -RT[(u \ln a_U + v \ln a_V + \ldots) \\ - (x \ln a_X + y \ln a_Y + \ldots)]$$

$$= -RT \ln \frac{(a_U)^u (a_V)^v \ldots}{(a_X)^x (a_Y)^y \ldots} \quad (71)$$

In terms of activities of reactants and products, the **equilibrium constant K** is defined by the ratio,

$$K = \frac{(a_U)^u (a_V)^v \ldots}{(a_X)^x (a_Y)^y \ldots} \quad (72)$$

When discussing the Gibbs free energy concept, equation (40), it was shown that $\Delta F = 0$ when the system is in a state of absolute rest, i.e., state of equilibrium. Therefore, inserting $\Delta F = 0$ in equation (71), the standard free energy change accompanying reaction (68) is related to the equilibrium constant by

$$\Delta F^\circ = -RT \ln K = -2.303 \, RT \log K \quad (73)$$

If ΔF° is in calories,

$$\Delta F^\circ = -4.575 \, T \log K \quad (74)$$

In terms of enthalpy and entropy changes,

$$\Delta F^\circ = \Delta H^\circ - T\Delta S^\circ;$$

substituting this in equation (74) and rearranging,

$$\log K = -\frac{\Delta H^\circ}{4.575 T} + \frac{\Delta S^\circ}{4.575} \quad (75)$$

where ΔH° and ΔS° are in calories and entropy units, respectively. As discussed in the early sections of this part, the enthalpy and entropy change accompanying a reaction is almost independent of temperature, hence the plot of log K against the reciprocal of absolute temperature gives a straight line. From the slope and intercept of this line ΔH° and ΔS° can be evaluated.

If Raoult's law is obeyed, the activity coefficient $\gamma_i = 1.0$, i.e. $a_i = N_i$ and, therefore, for ideal solutions K is represented in terms of concentrations:

$$K = \frac{(N_U)^u (N_V)^v \ldots}{(N_X)^x (N_Y)^y \ldots} \quad (76)$$

It is this form of the equilibrium constant which was first formulated by **Guldberg** and **Waage** (1864–67) based on the concept of **mass action law.**

It follows from the foregoing definition of the activity that in reactions involving gases and vapors, the equilibrium constant is given in terms of the partial pressures of the reacting gases.

It is self-evident from the relation in equation (75) that if the temperature of the system (at equilibrium) is increased, the reaction will proceed in the direction causing heat absorption. The pressure also has a similar effect on the direction of reaction. For example, consider the dissociation of carbon dioxide:

$$2CO_2 \rightleftarrows 2CO + O_2 \quad (77)$$

Since the dissociation is accompanied by volume expansion at constant temperature and pressure, increasing pressure will reverse the reaction from right to left, i.e., dissociation of carbon dioxide becomes less with increasing pressure.

These effects on the state of equilibrium are summarized by the **Le Chatelier principle** (1885) which may be stated as follows: "If a system in equilibrium is subjected to a constraint (addition of heat, increase of volume, pressure, etc.) which alters the equilibrium, the direction of the reaction taking place is such as to oppose the constraint, i.e., partially to nullify its effect."

HETEROGENEOUS REACTION EQUILIBRIA

A heterogeneous system consists of two or more homogeneous systems and any homogeneous part of a heterogeneous system is called a **phase.** For example, melting ice is a heterogeneous system consisting of two or three phases, ice and water, or ice, water and vapor, respectively. A system is made of **components** and the number of components of a system is the smallest number of independently variable constituents which are sufficient to define the composition of each phase at equilibrium in a heterogeneous system. For example, although water consists of two types of elements, it consists of one component, because of the identity of the composition of ice, water and water vapor (at moderate temperatures). Although structurally the atomic arrangements of H_2O are different in these phases, the composition does not change. Another example is the calcination of calcium carbonate:

$$CaCO_3(s) = CaO(s) + CO_2(g) \qquad (78)$$

This heterogeneous system consists of three phases, solid $CaCO_3$, solid CaO and gaseous CO_2, and two components. Taking CaO and CO_2 as the two components, the composition of the third phase can be determined from the stoichiometry of the above reaction.

The equilibrium constant of reaction (78) is,

$$K = \frac{a_{CaO} p_{CO_2}}{a_{CaCO_3}} \qquad (79)$$

At constant temperature and constant external pressure, the chemical potential ($ = F° + RT \ln a$) of a pure solid or a liquid phase is constant, i.e. its activity is constant. If the pure component is chosen as the reference state, the activity becomes unity. Therefore, the equilibrium constant for reaction (78) is equal to the partial pressure of carbon dioxide:

$$K = p_{CO_2} \qquad (80)$$

Although the metallurgical reactions, which are invariably heterogeneous reactions, may appear to be complex, they can often be simplified by considering the individual reactions. Let us take a gas-slag-metal system where all the phases are assumed to be at equilibrium. If the gas consists of CO and CO_2, the metal of Fe and Mn and the slag of FeO and MnO, the following basic reactions may be considered.

Gas reaction:

$$CO_2 = CO + \frac{1}{2}O_2 \qquad (a)$$

Solution of oxygen in Fe-Mn melt:

$$\frac{1}{2}O_2 = \underline{O} \qquad (b)$$

where the underscore indicates the element dissolved in iron.

Oxidation of $\underline{Mn}$:

$$\underline{Mn} + \underline{O} = MnO \qquad (c)$$

Oxidation of Fe:

$$Fe + \underline{O} = FeO \qquad (d)$$

Since the entire system is at equilibrium, all the possible combinations of the above reactions are permissible. For example, the oxidation of manganese may be represented by reaction

$$\underline{Mn} + FeO = MnO + Fe \qquad (e)$$

where there are only two phases to be considered: iron-manganese melt and iron oxide-manganese oxide melt. The equilibrium constant for this reaction is

$$K_1 = \frac{a_{MnO} a_{Fe}}{a_{FeO} a_{Mn}} \qquad (f)$$

If the manganese content is low, a_{Mn} can be replaced by %Mn and $a_{Fe} = 1.0$. It will be shown later in Part III that in pure FeO-MnO melts Raoult's law is obeyed. Therefore, their activities can be replaced by their mole fractions and the equilibrium constant takes the following form

$$K_2 = \frac{N_{MnO}}{N_{FeO}[\%Mn]} \qquad (g)$$

The following is another combination of some of the above reactions:

$$\underline{Mn} + CO_2 = MnO + CO \qquad (h)$$

$$K_3 = \frac{p_{CO} a_{MnO}}{p_{CO_2}[\%Mn]} \qquad (i)$$

Derivation of the equilibrium constant K_3 from the standard free energy data in Tables **12–III** and **12–IV** are given below:

Reaction	ΔF° cal.
$CO_2(g) = CO(g) + \frac{1}{2}O_2(g)$	$67,500 - 20.71T$
$\underline{Mn} = Mn(l)$	$+ 9.11T$
$Mn(l) + \frac{1}{2}O_2 = MnO(s)$	$- 97,360 + 21.12T$
$\underline{Mn} + CO_2(g) = MnO(s) + CO(g)$	$- 29,860 + 9.52T$

$$\log K_3 = \frac{6527}{T} - 2.081 \qquad (j)$$

The standard states are: infinitely dilute solution $\underline{Mn}$ in iron, pure solid MnO and 1 atm. pressure for the gases. The oxides of high melting temperatures have limited solubilities in liquid slags at iron- and steelmaking temperatures. When the activities of such oxides are considered, it is convenient to choose the solid oxide as the reference state so that at saturation the activity of the oxide is unity.

Complete equilibrium between all the phases present is never experienced in metallurgical processes. For example, in a steelmaking furnace there are essentially four phases, gas, slag, metal and refractory lining. Owing to the differences between the rates of various reactions between these phases, only a few of the reactions approach equilibrium. However, this complication does not invalidate the application of basic laws to the part of the system where equilibrium is established. The methods of studying these reactions from the point of view of local reaction equilibria are discussed in detail in the subsequent parts.

Another type of equilibrium is that known as the partial equilibrium which is demonstrated explicitly in Part VII of this chapter in connection with the counter-transfer of sulphur and oxygen through a molten slag-membrane.

For convenience, the equilibrium relation is often given in the form of mass action law, i.e. concentrations of reactants and products in the solid and liquid solutions are used instead of activities. If the slag or metal under consideration does not obey the ideal solution law, the equilibrium "constant" K', in the form of mass action law, is a function of composition. This equilibrium relation K' may be called the **equilibrium index.**

As a specific example, let us consider the equilibrium relations between iron-carbon melts and gas containing hydrogen and hydrogen sulphide. The reaction is:

$$H_2 + \underline{S} = H_2S \qquad (81)$$

where S is sulphur dissolved in iron. The equilibrium index for this reaction is

$$K' = \frac{p_{H_2S}}{p_{H_2}[\%S]} \qquad (82)$$

As seen from the data in Figure 12–8, the equilibrium index K' increases with increasing carbon content. Assuming that sulphur does not affect its own activity coefficient, as $\%C \to 0$ the activity coefficient of sulphur $f_S \to 1.0$, i.e. Henry's law is obeyed in dilute solution of sulphur in pure iron. Therefore, at $\%C = 0$, $K' = K$, the equilibrium constant, and the activity coefficient of sulphur for any carbon concentration is derived from the ratio $f_S = \dfrac{K'}{K}$. This technique is often used in determining the effect of alloying elements on the activity coefficients of sulphur, oxygen, carbon . . . etc., dissolved in iron or in other metals.

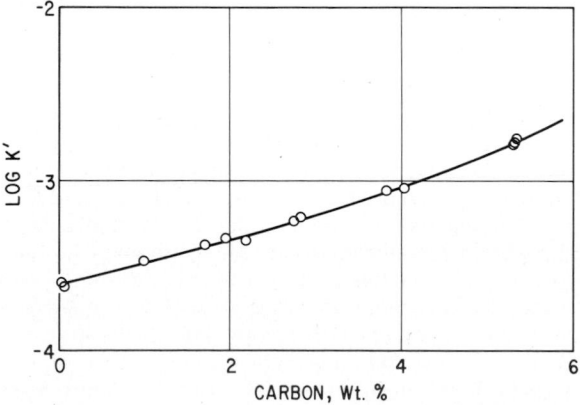

FIG. 12–8. Variation of the equilibrium index $K' = \dfrac{p_{H_2S}}{p_{H_2}[\%S]}$ with the carbon content of iron at 1600°C. (From Morris and Buehl[9].)

EQUILIBRIUM GAS PARTIAL PRESSURES IN MULTICOMPONENT SYSTEMS

When discussing the limitations of Dalton's law, reference was made to the gas reactions which control the partial pressures of the unlike gaseous species. This is now illustrated by considering a gas mixture initially containing CO_2, CO and SO_2. Let us assume that initially the gases in this mixture have the following partial pressures:

$$p_{SO_2} = 0.03 \text{ atm.}, \quad p_{CO_2} = 0.242 \text{ atm. and}$$
$$p_{CO} = 0.728 \text{ atm.}$$

and the total pressure is 1.0 atm. Now, this gas mixture is heated to 1550°C and the total pressure is maintained at 1.0 atm. In order to calculate the gas partial pressures for 1550°C, all possible gaseous species containing C, S and/or O must be taken into account; these reactions and the values of the equilibrium constants are listed below:

$$\tfrac{1}{2}S_2 = S, \quad K_1 = \frac{p_S}{(p_{S_2})^{\frac{1}{2}}} = 1.09 \times 10^{-2}$$

$$\tfrac{1}{2}S_2 + \tfrac{1}{2}O_2 = SO, \ K_2 = \frac{p_{SO}}{(p_{S_2})^{\frac{1}{2}}(p_{O_2})^{\frac{1}{2}}} = 1.29 \times 10^2$$

$$\tfrac{1}{2}S_2 + O_2 = SO_2, K_3 = \frac{p_{SO_2}}{(p_{S_2})^{\frac{1}{2}}p_{O_2}} = 4.01 \times 10^6$$

$$\tfrac{1}{2}S_2 + \tfrac{3}{2}O_2 = SO_3, K_4 = \frac{p_{SO_3}}{(p_{S_2})^{\frac{1}{2}}(p_{O_2})^{\frac{3}{2}}} = 4.39 \times 10^4$$

$$\tfrac{1}{2}S_2 + CO = COS, K_5 = \frac{p_{COS}}{(p_{S_2})^{\frac{1}{2}}p_{CO}} = 4.51 \times 10^{-2}$$

$$\tfrac{1}{2}O_2 + CO = CO_2, K_6 = \frac{p_{CO_2}}{(p_{O_2})^{\frac{1}{2}}p_{CO}} = 3.72 \times 10^3$$

In a given mixture of CO_2, CO, and SO_2 initially present in the gas, the total number of gram-atoms of carbon, ΣC, sulphur, ΣS, and oxygen, ΣO, are obtained from the sum of the gas species.

For the initial mixture:

$$\Sigma C = (n_{CO_2})_i + (n_{CO})_i \qquad (a)$$
$$\Sigma S = (n_{SO_2})_i \qquad (b)$$
$$\Sigma O = 2(n_{CO_2})_i + (n_{CO})_i + 2(n_{SO_2})_i \qquad (c)$$

where n is the number of moles of the gas indicated by the subscript.

When this gas mixture is heated to a temperature where all the gas reactions given above have reached equilibrium, the following equations give carbon, sulphur and oxygen balances.

For the equilibrated mixture:

$$\Sigma C = n_{CO_2} + n_{CO} + n_{COS} \qquad (d)$$
$$\Sigma S = n_S + 2n_{S_2} + n_{SO} + n_{SO_2} + n_{SO_3} + n_{COS} \ (e)$$
$$\Sigma O = n_{SO} + 2n_{SO_2} + 3n_{SO_3} + n_{COS} + 2n_{CO_2}$$
$$+ n_{CO} + n_O + 2n_{O_2} \qquad (f)$$

If the total number of moles of the gas species, CO_2, CO, COS, S, S_2 . . . etc., is denoted by Σn, the partial pressure of any species j is given by

$$p_j = P \frac{n_j}{\Sigma n} \qquad (g)$$

Similarly for the initial mixture

$$(p_j)_i = P \frac{(n_j)_i}{\Sigma n_i} \qquad \text{(h)}$$

where $P = 1.0$ atm. is the total pressure.

Since in the initial and final states the respective values of ΣC, ΣS and ΣO are the same, equations (a), (b), (c) and (d), (e), (f) can be combined. For example, in terms of the gas partial pressures in atmospheres and Σn and Σn_i, the carbon balance for the initial and final state are given by

$$\Sigma C = \Sigma n_i \left[(p_{CO_2})_i + (p_{CO})_i \right] = \Sigma n (p_{CO_2} + p_{CO} + p_{COS}) \qquad \text{(i)}$$

Similar equations can be written for ΣS and ΣO. The terms Σn_i and Σn are eliminated by taking the ratios $\Sigma C / \Sigma S$ and $\Sigma C / \Sigma O$, thus

$$\frac{\Sigma C}{\Sigma S} = \frac{1 - (p_{SO_2})_i}{(p_{SO_2})_i} = \frac{p_{CO_2} + p_{CO} + p_{COS}}{p_S + 2p_{S_2} + p_{SO} + p_{SO_2} + p_{SO_3} + p_{COS}} \qquad \text{(j)}$$

$$\frac{\Sigma C}{\Sigma O} = \frac{1 - (p_{SO_2})_i}{2 - (p_{CO})_i} = \frac{p_{CO_2} + p_{CO} + p_{COS}}{p_{SO} + 2p_{SO_2} + 3p_{SO_3} + p_{COS} + 2p_{CO_2} + p_{CO} + p_O + 2p_{O_2}} \qquad \text{(k)}$$

Since the total pressure is 1.0 atm.,

$$p_{CO_2} + p_{CO} + p_{COS} + p_S + p_{S_2} + p_{SO} + p_{SO_2} + p_{SO_3} + p_O + p_{O_2} = 1.0 \qquad \text{(1)}$$

By using the equilibrium constants for the gas reactions given above, equations (j), (k) and (1) can be expressed in terms of p_{S_2}, p_{O_2}, p_{CO} and the equilibrium constants K_1, K_2 . . . etc., and these partial pressures can be evaluated by solving the above three equations simultaneously for a given temperature and known initial composition of the gas mixture. Since the partial pressures p_{SO_3}, p_O and p_{O_2} are very low for the gas mixture under consideration, the terms involving these partial pressures can be omitted from the above equations. The results obtained for a particular mixture are given below:

In the initial gas mixture, partial pressures are:

$$(p_{CO_2})_i = 0.242 \text{ atm.,} \quad (p_{CO})_i = 0.728 \text{ atm. and} \quad (p_{SO_2})_i = 0.03 \text{ atm.}$$

and total pressure is 1.0 atm.

At 1550°C, the equilibrium gas partial pressures are:

p_S	$= 0.0012$	atm.
p_{S_2}	$= 0.0117$	atm.
p_{SO}	$= 0.0013$	atm.
p_{SO_2}	$= 0.0039$	atm.
p_{SO_3}	$= 0.0000$	atm.
p_{COS}	$= 0.0035$	atm.
p_{CO}	$= 0.718$	atm.
p_{CO_2}	$= 0.254$	atm.
p_{O_2}	$= 9.03 \times 10^{-9}$	atm.

SECTION 9

PHASE RULE AND PHASE EQUILIBRIUM DIAGRAMS

The number of variable factors which define the state of a system is called the **degrees of freedom.** From thermodynamic considerations **Gibbs** showed that provided the equilibrium between any number of phases is not influenced by external forces, e.g. gravity, electrical, magnetic, etc., but only by temperature, pressure and composition, the number of degrees of freedom (F) of a system at equilibrium is related to the number of components (C) and of phases (P) by equation

$$F = C - P + 2 \qquad \text{(83)}$$

This is known as the **phase rule.**

The application of the phase rule to heterogeneous equilibria is illustrated below by considering the solid-liquid-vapor equilibria for a system of one component. For a single phase such as water, $C = 1$ and $P = 1$ and, therefore, the number of degrees of freedom $F = 2$; this is a bivariant equilibrium where both temperature and pressure can be set or changed arbitrarily. For water-water vapor, water-ice or ice-water vapor equilibrium $C = 1$, $P = 2$ and $F = 1$, i.e. in this univariant equilibrium either temperature or pressure is the independent variable. When the three phases, ice, water and water vapor are in equilibrium, $F = 0$; this is an invariant system. Using the information obtained from the phase rule, a pressure/temperature phase diagram for a single

component system is drawn schematically in Figure 12–9. The curves separating two single-phase regions correspond to two-phase univariant equilibria. At the triple point O (invariant) three univariant curves intersect. As indicated in Figure 12–10, if the pressure for the invariant system is greater than 1 atm., the substance does not melt at atmospheric pressure, but rather sublimes. For example, at atmospheric pressure solid carbon dioxide sublimes at − 78.5°C; if pressure is increased to 5.11 atm., it melts at − 56.4°C.

Again, it follows from the phase rule that at constant pressure in a single component system the transformation of a substance from one crystalline formation to another, melting or boiling occur at particular temperatures characteristic of the substance, and during the process of transformation the temperature of the system remains constant. This is shown in a temperature/time cooling curve in Figure 12–11(a), where the horizontal line corresponds to the melting temperature of the single component system at a constant pressure. As indicated in Figures 12–9 and 12–10, increasing pressure increases the temperature of the phase transformation. However, this effect on solid-solid transformations and on the melting temperatures is small. Diffusion and nucleation play a dominant role in the processes of transformation; though this subject is not to be discussed here, under-

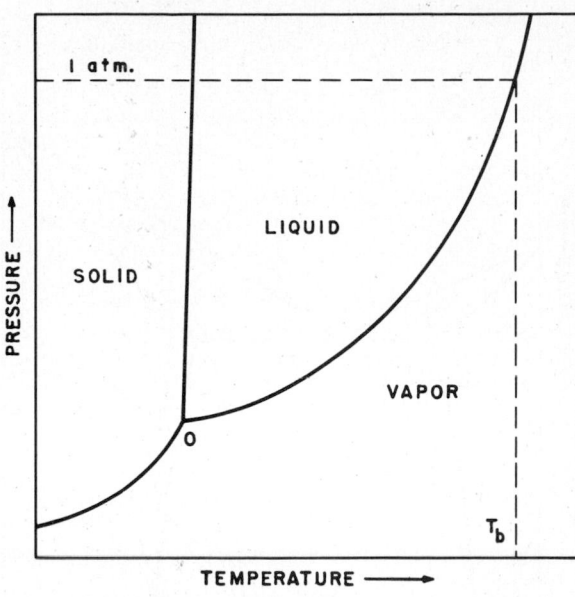

FIG. 12–9. Pressure/temperature phase equilibrium diagram for a single component system which has a normal boiling temperature.

cooling should be mentioned in connection with the cooling curve in Figure 12–11(a). In real systems, a certain amount of undercooling occurs before solidification sets in; that is, the melt is maintained in a metastable state at a temperature below its freezing point, and most of the cooling curves are as shown in Figure 12–11(b). The extent of undercooling in terms of temperature and time depend on several factors which will not be discussed here.

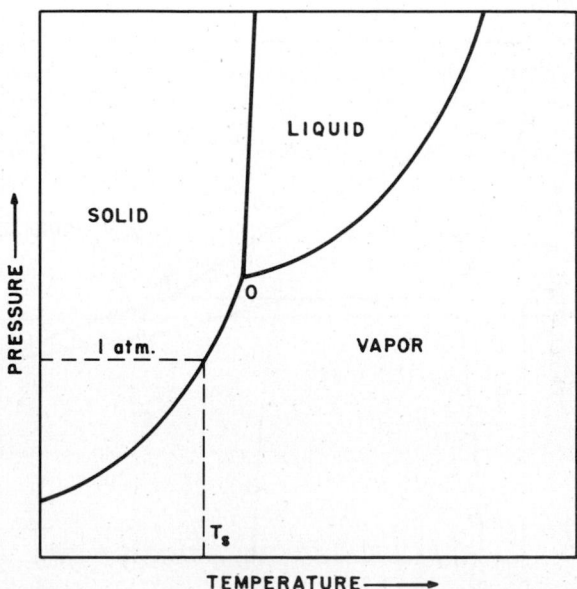

FIG. 12–10. Pressure/temperature phase equilibrium diagram for a single component system which sublimes at atmospheric pressure.

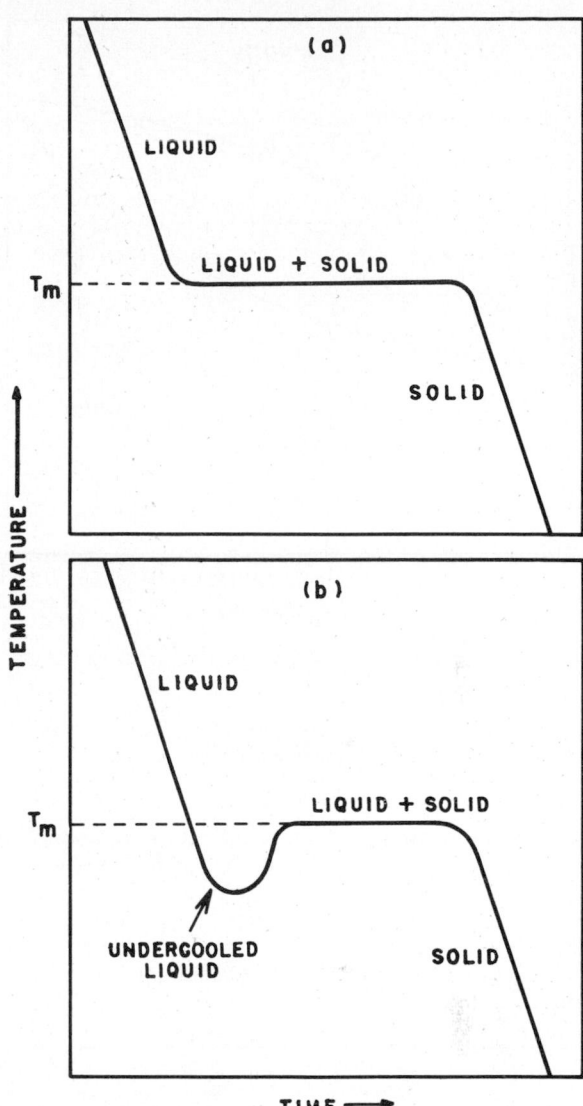

FIG. 12–11. Temperature-time plot for the solidification of a single component melt: (a) without undercooling; (b) with undercooling.

For the details of the theorem on the univariant curves intersecting at an invariant point in the pressure/temperature plots, references should be made to papers by Smits[10], Schreinemakers[11] and Morey and Williamson[12]. The application of these theorems on the construction of phase equilibrium diagrams for the Fe-Si-O and Fe-Ca-O systems are discussed by Darken[13] and Turkdogan[14].

PHASE EQUILIBRIUM COMPOSITION DIAGRAMS

Since metallurgical systems are essentially condensed systems (solid and liquid systems), the effect of external pressure on the phase equilibria is not perceptible, at least under normal atmospheric conditions. Since all the phase equilibrium diagrams are for a constant pressure of 1 atm., the only remaining independent variables of the system are temperature

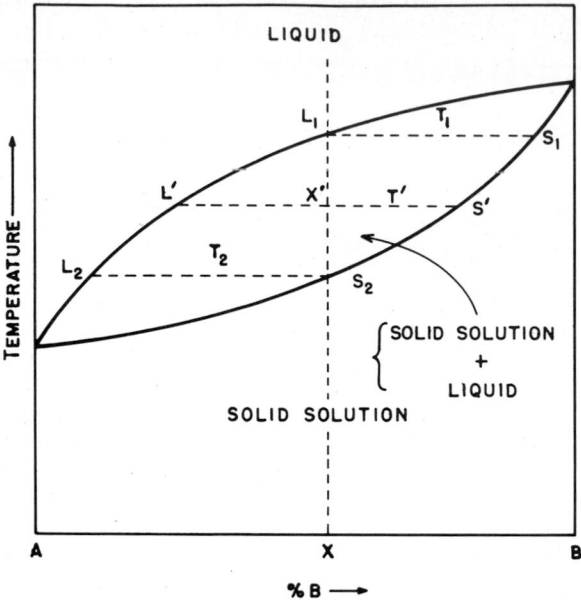

FIG. 12—12. Complete solid solution in a binary system.

and compositions, consequently the phase rule takes the following form for constant pressure:

$$F' = C - P + 1 \qquad (84)$$

The derivation of the temperature/composition phase equilibrium diagram from the free energy of the system will not be discussed here; adequate information on this subject is available in text books[5]. For the present purpose it is sufficient to give a few schematic examples on some typical binary and ternary phase equilibrium diagrams.

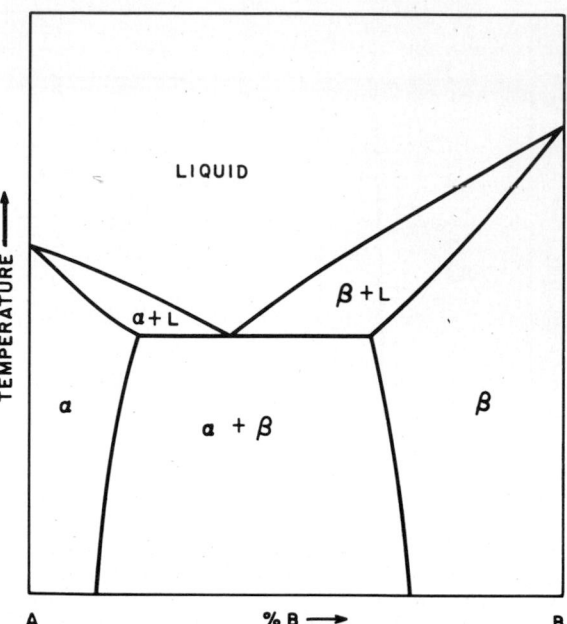

FIG. 12—14. Binary eutectic system with partial solid solubilities.

Binary systems—When the components A and B of a binary system are mutually soluble in the liquid and solid state, the simplest binary phase diagram is as shown in Figure 12—12. In this system, the solidification of a melt of composition X occurs within the temperature range T_1 and T_2, and the composition of the liquid and solid solutions in equilibrium with one another change along the L_1L_2 liquidus and S_1S_2 solidus curves, respectively. At an intermediate temperature T', solid solution S' is in equilibrium with liquid solution L' and the amounts solid/liquid = $L'X'/X'S'$.

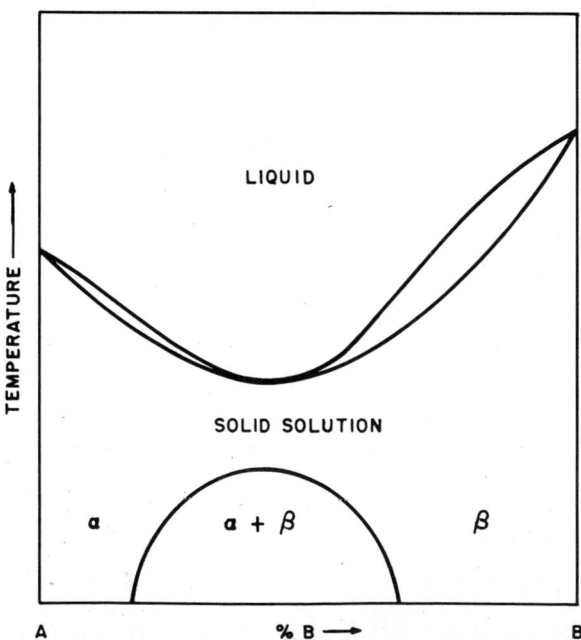

FIG. 12—13. Minimum on the liquidus and solidus curves and partial miscibility in the solid state.

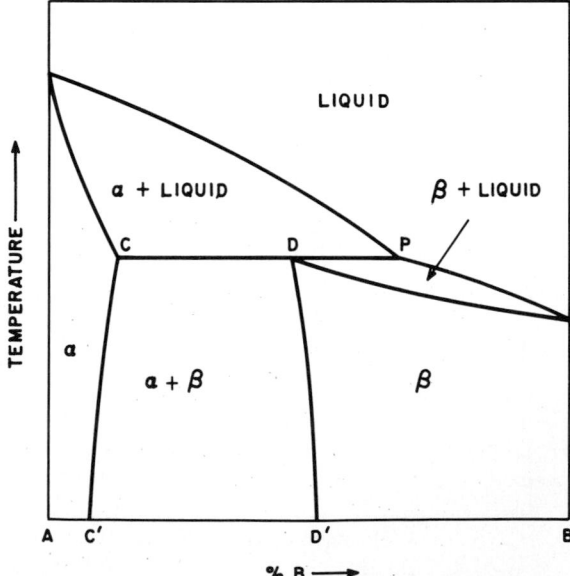

FIG. 12—15. Peritectic reaction in a binary system with partial solubilities.

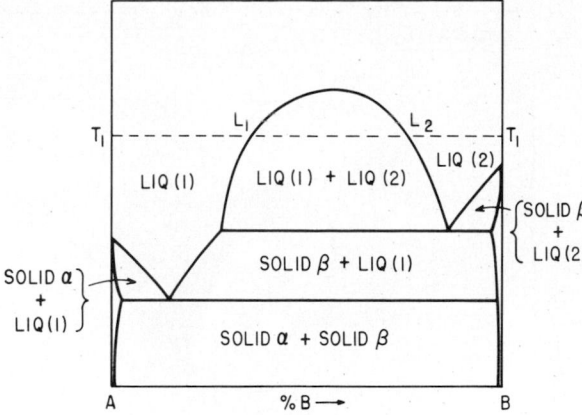

FIG. 12–16. Liquid miscibility gap in a binary system.

When there is a greater positive departure from ideality for solid solution than for liquid, the liquidus and solidus curves pass through a minimum and at a lower temperature the solid solution separates into two phases, as shown in Figure 12–13. With further increase in positive departure from ideality in the solid solution, a eutectic type of a diagram is obtained; this is shown in Figure 12–14 where, at the eutectic temperature, there are three phases shown, α, β and liquid. Hence, $F = 0$; this is an invariant system and, therefore, for a given system the eutectic composition and temperature is constant and the solidus line is drawn parallel to the composition abscissa.

Figure 12–15 is a typical example of a peritectic reaction with partial solid solutions. In this system, the peritectic reaction occurs at the peritectic temperature between the solid solution α of composition C and liquid P forming a solid solution β of com-

position D. Within the field CDC'D' there are two phases α and β, the compositions of which change with temperature along the solubility curves CC' and DD', respectively.

In a number of binary systems the components are not completely miscible in the liquid state; a typical example is given in Figure 12–16. With increasing temperature the mutual solubilities of liquid (1), rich in A, and liquid (2), rich in B, increase and above a particular critical temperature the two liquids are completely miscible. However, there are many systems where complete miscibility can never be reached at atmospheric pressures, e.g. Fe-Pb, Ag-S. The activity/composition relation for a system with miscibility gap is as shown in Figure 12–17. Since within the composition range L_1–L_2 the liquids L_1 and L_2 are in equilibrium, the activity of A (and B) in both phases are equal as indicated by the horizontal line L_1L_2 in Figure 12–17.

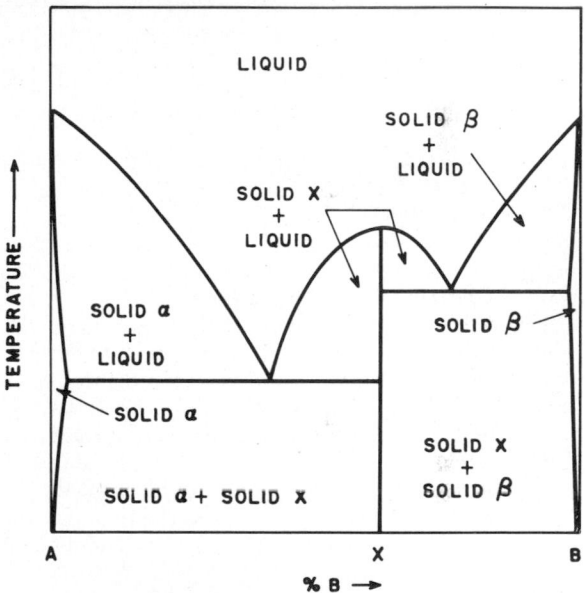

FIG. 12–18. Binary eutectic system with a compound.

Figure 12–18 shows the formation of a compound X in a binary system A-B. This can be visualized as two binary eutectic systems A-X and X-B with limited solid solubilities at the terminal ends of the system. When a chemical compound does not have a fixed composition, it is said to be a nonstoichiometric compound; this is shown in Figure 12–19 where the solid solution β phase is a nonstoichiometric compound.

Ternary Systems—There are three components in a ternary system; the composition of a ternary system is frequently plotted within a triangle as shown in Figure 12–20. Each side of the triangle is the composition abscissa for a binary system A-B, B-C and C-A; the composition of point M in Figure 12–20 is 50 per cent A, 20 per cent B and 30 per cent C.

The temperature/composition diagram for a ternary system takes the form of a prism with a triangle base for composition and height for temperature scale. Figure 12–21 is a photograph of a three

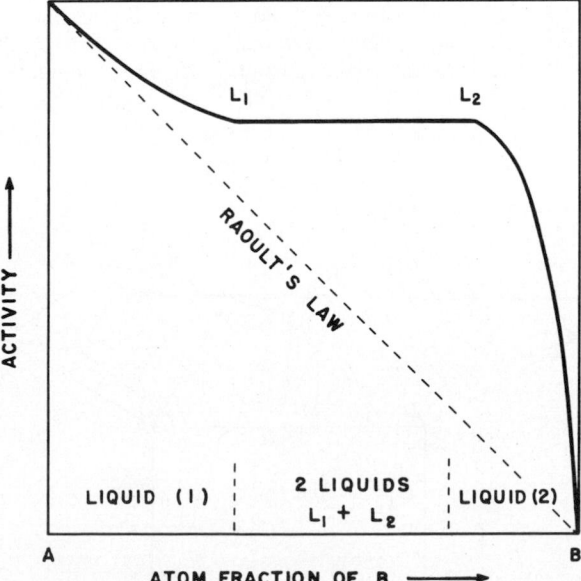

FIG. 12–17. Activity of component A at temperature T_1T_1 of the system given in Figure 12–16; pure liquid A is the standard state.

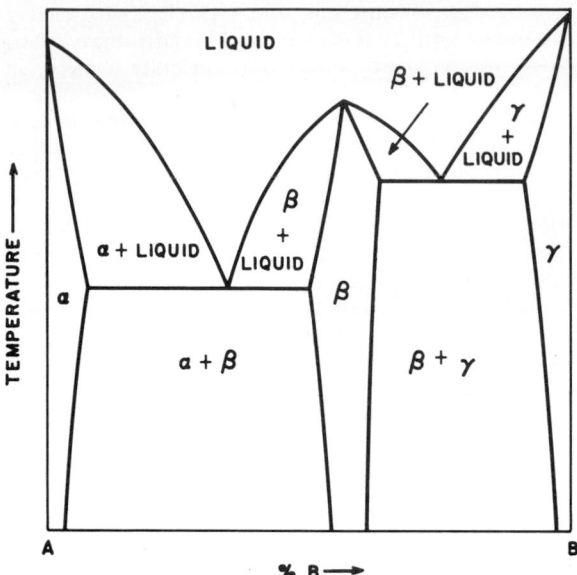

FIG. 12–19. Solid solution in a eutectic system with non-stoichiometric compound β phase.

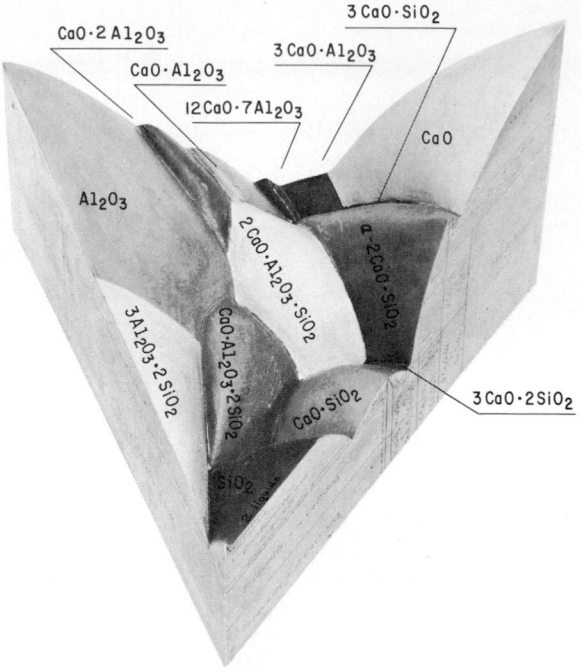

FIG. 12–21. Liquidus surfaces of CaO-Al₂O₃-SiO₂ ternary system.

dimensional solid, showing the liquidus surfaces of the CaO-Al₂O₃-SiO₂ ternary system. The position of a point on a liquidus surface is determined by two independent variables, e.g. either the concentrations of two of the components, or temperature and the concentration of one of the components.

Figure 12–22 is a polythermal projection of the primary liquidus surfaces of a ternary eutectic system, with limited solid solubilities near the compositions of the components A, B and C. The arrows on the gutters, where the primary liquidus surfaces intersect, indicate the direction of decreasing temperature. The convex curves on the liquidus surfaces are the isotherms which give the compositions of the melt in equilibrium with α, β or γ solid solution at a particular temperature.

The variation of phase distributions with temperature for the system in Figure 12–22 is shown by five isothermal sections in Figure 12–23. The points of intersection of tie-lines with the phase boundaries give the compositions of the phases in equilibrium with one another within the two-phase regions. Figure 12–24 shows the temperature/composition diagrams for two pseudo-binary sections M₁M₂ and N₁N₂. The diagrams in Figures 12–23 and 12–24 are self-explanatory, and require no further description.

In general, there are three types of liquid miscibility gaps in ternary systems; these are shown as isothermal sections in Figure 12–25. The conjugate

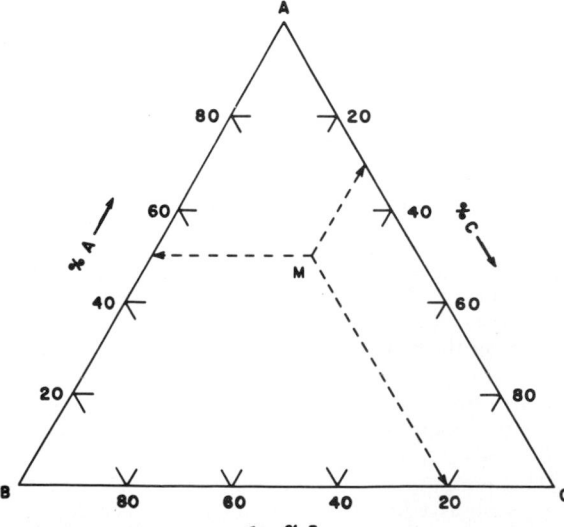

FIG. 12–20. Composition of a ternary system.

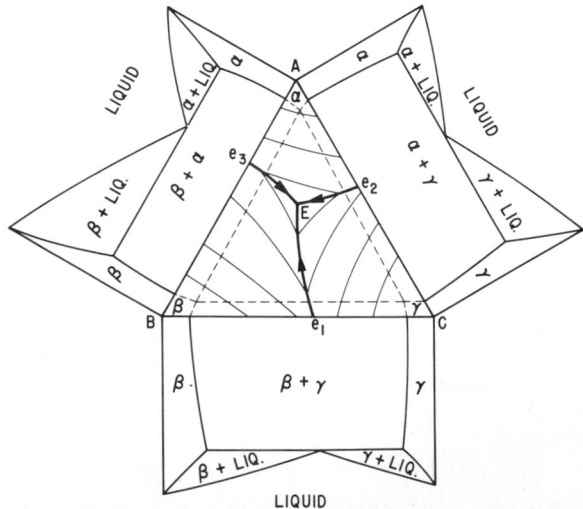

FIG. 12–22. Ternary eutectic system. Melting temperature of B > C > A and eutectic temperature of e₁ > e₂ > e₃ > E.

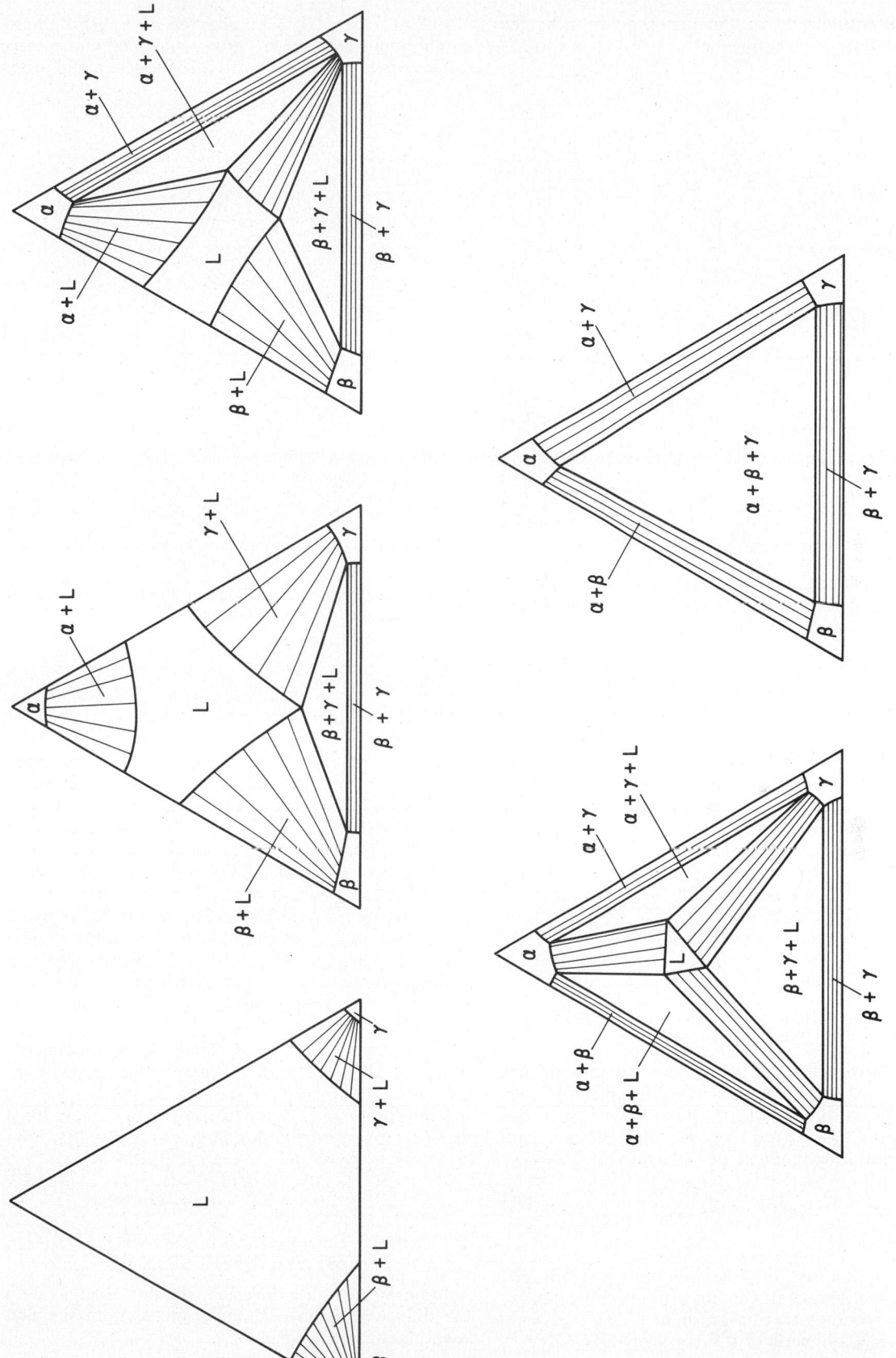

Fig. 12–23. Isothermal sections of the ternary system in Figure 12–22 (diagrams are not drawn to scale).

phases in equilibrium with one another are indicated by the tie-lines.

In Parts II and III of this chapter, a number of phase equilibrium diagrams are given for metal and metal-oxide systems used frequently in chemical metallurgy.

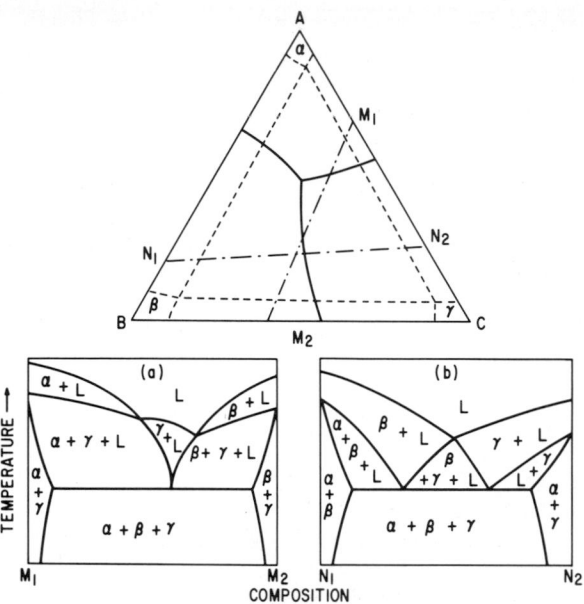

FIG. 12–24. Temperature/composition diagrams of pseudo-binary sections (a) M_1M_2 and (b) N_1N_2 of the above ternary eutectic system.

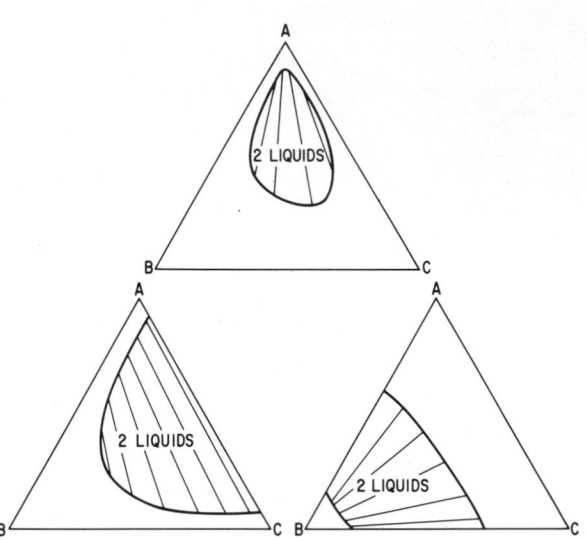

FIG. 12–25. Isothermal sections of three types of liquid miscibility gaps in ternary systems.

SECTION 10

THEORY OF DIFFUSION

Some knowledge of diffusion phenomena is prerequisite to the understanding of the kinetics of reactions, phase transformations, the rates of solidification, heat transfer, etc. In this chapter, only some of the basic principles of the diffusion theory are mentioned.

Diffusion is a process leading to equalization of chemical potentials. In discussing the basic diffusion theories, the concentration rather than chemical potential or activity of the diffusing component is used, on the assumption that the solution is ideal.

FICK'S FIRST LAW—STEADY STATE DIFFUSION

The diffusive flux J is defined as the amount of a diffusing species crossing a surface of unit area, perpendicular to the direction of flow, in unit time; this flux is equal to the product of the diffusivity, D, and the concentration gradient $\partial C/\partial x$, thus

$$J = -D \frac{\partial C}{\partial x} \qquad (85)$$

where

C = amount of substance per unit volume
x = distance in the direction of diffusion
$\partial C/\partial x$ = concentration gradient
D = coefficient of diffusion or diffusivity.

The diffusivity has the dimensions of (length)²/time; using c.g.s. units, D is given in cm.²/sec. The co-

efficient of diffusion is a function of state, i.e. varies with temperature, pressure and composition only.

Equation (85) states **Fick's first law,** and it is directly applicable for steady state diffusion with constant diffusivity. When a steady state is reached, flux J at any point along the diffusion path is constant and independent of time or distance. This is illustrated by an example in Figure 12–26, showing the diffusion of a gas through, for example, a metal diaphragm fixed inside a tube, the walls of which are impermeable to the gas. If the partial pressures p_1 and p_0 are kept constant on either side of the membrane, and that $p_1 > p_0$, i.e. in terms of gas concentrations $C_1 > C_0$, at steady state the concentration gradient through the diaphragm is constant, i.e. $\partial C / \partial x = \Delta C / \Delta x = (C_0 - C_1) / \Delta x$. Since the diffusivity is assumed to remain constant, for a given temperature the flux is given by the first law:

$$J = -D \frac{C_0 - C_1}{\Delta x} \qquad (86)$$

FICK'S SECOND LAW—NONSTEADY STATE DIFFUSION

In nonsteady state diffusion, the flux changes with the diffusion distance x, and time t; from the first law, this change $\partial J/\partial x$

$$\frac{\partial J}{\partial x} = -\frac{\partial}{\partial x}\left(D \frac{\partial C}{\partial x}\right)$$

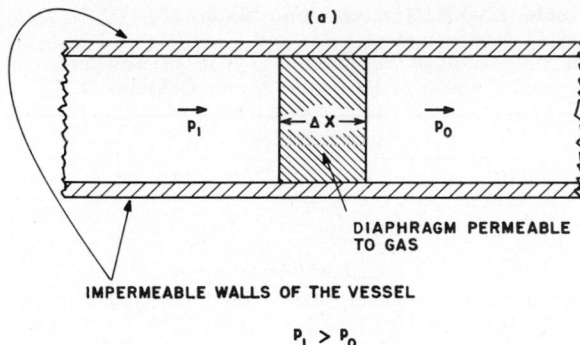

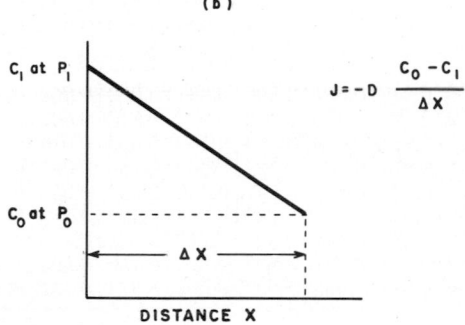

FIG. 12–26. Application of Fick's first law to a steady state diffusion through a diaphragm for constant diffusivity.

The difference in flux is equal to $-\partial C/\partial T$, negative rate of concentration change, therefore,

$$\frac{\partial C}{\partial t} = \frac{\partial}{\partial x} \left(D \frac{\partial C}{\partial x} \right) \qquad (87)$$

If the diffusivity D is independent of concentration (or substantially so under conditions of the experiment), **Fick's second law** may be written

$$\frac{\partial C}{\partial t} = D \frac{\partial^2 C}{\partial x^2} \qquad (88)$$

The solution of equation (88) depends on the geometry and on the boundary conditions of the medium into which a substance is diffusing. For details on the derivation of the diffusion equations for different boundary conditions reference should be made to the original papers[15-17] and text books[5, 18]. For the present purpose, considerations are limited to a few special cases which are most frequently encountered in the study of the kinetics of metallurgical reactions to be discussed in the subsequent parts of this chapter.

(1) Unidirectional diffusion in a semi-infinite medium—Figure 12–27(a) shows a cross section of a slab with impermeable side walls. If the length of the slab is large, compared with the distance over which change in composition has occurred due to diffusion, the medium is said to be semi-infinite. At the beginning of diffusion the concentration at the surface S is instantaneously brought to C_s and

maintained constant throughout the diffusion time. These boundary conditions are usually abbreviated as:

$$C = C_0 \text{ at } t = 0 \text{ and } 0 < x < \infty$$
$$C = C_s \text{ at } x = 0 \text{ and } 0 < t < \infty$$

where

C_0 = initial uniform concentration
C_s = constant surface concentration
x = distance from surface S
t = time of diffusion.

From the mathematical formula[15, 16] derived for these boundary conditions for constant D, the dimensionless variables have been computed and the values of $(C_x - C_0)/(C_s - C_0)$ for any value of $x/\sqrt{Dt}$ can be obtained from the appropriate tables, e.g. as given in Table 12–V. Since these variables are dimensionless, they can be used for any diffusion problem satisfying the boundary conditions given above. For example, if C_0, C_s and D are known, the concentration of the diffusate, C_x, at distance x can be calculated for any time of diffusion using the values in Table 12–V.

(2) Diffusion into a slab or cylinder—In this case, the unidirectional diffusion is considered to take place through the opposite sides of a plate of finite or infinite length or radial diffusion into a cylinder of finite or infinite length as shown in Figure 12–27(b). For objects of finite dimensions comparable with the diffusion distance, e.g. thickness of the plate or diameter of the cylinder, edges of the plate or the ends of the cylinder must be coated with an impermeable substance to insure unidirectional diffusion. For the boundary conditions, C_0 = initial uniform concentration, C_s = constant surface concentration and constant D, the solution of Fick's

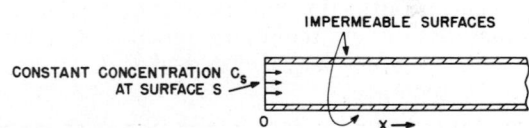

(a) UNIDIRECTIONAL DIFFUSION IN A SEMI-INFINITE MEDIUM.

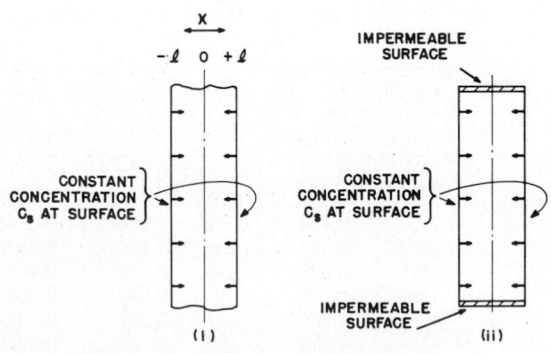

(b) UNIDIRECTIONAL DIFFUSION INTO PLATES (THICKNESS 2 *l*) OR INTO CYLINDERS (DIAMETER 2 *l*) OF (i) INFINITE LENGTH OR (ii) FINITE LENGTH.

FIG. 12–27. Some of the boundary conditions for unidirectional diffusion.

Table 12—V. Concentration Ratios $\dfrac{C_x - C_0}{C_s - C_0}$ **for Certain Values of** $x/\sqrt{Dt}$ **in Unidirectional Diffusion into a Semi-infinite Medium for Constant D. (*)**

$\dfrac{x}{\sqrt{Dt}}$	$\dfrac{C_x - C_0}{C_s - C_0}$	$\dfrac{x}{\sqrt{Dt}}$	$\dfrac{C_x - C_0}{C_s - C_0}$	$\dfrac{x}{\sqrt{Dt}}$	$\dfrac{C_x - C_0}{C_s - C_0}$
0	1.0000	0.9538	0.5000	2.8	0.0477
0.1	0.9436	1.0	0.4795	3.0	0.0399
0.2	0.8875	1.2	0.3961	3.2	0.0236
0.3	0.8320	1.4	0.3222	3.4	0.0162
0.4	0.7773	1.6	0.2579	3.6	0.0109
0.5	0.7237	1.8	0.2031	3.8	0.0072
0.6	0.6714	2.0	0.1573	4.0	0.0047
0.7	0.6206	2.2	0.1198	4.4	0.0019
0.8	0.5716	2.4	0.0897	4.8	0.0007
0.9	0.5245	2.6	0.0660	5.2	0.0002

*This table is taken from Darken and Gurry[5].
The boundary conditions are:

$$C = C_0 \text{ at } t = 0 \text{ and } 0 < x < \infty$$
$$C = C_s \text{ at } x = 0 \text{ and } 0 < t < \infty$$

C_x = concentration at distance x
C_0 = initial uniform composition
C_s = surface concentration maintained constant

---

second law[15, 16] are given in Table **12—VI**, in terms of dimensionless variables. If the diffusivity and the thickness of the plate or the diameter of the cylinder ($2l$) are known, the fractional saturation or desaturation of the diffusing substance can be calculated from the dimensionless variables in Table **12—VI**. The fractional saturation (or desaturation) is defined by

$$F = \frac{C_m - C_0}{C_s - C_0}$$

where C_m is the mean concentration of the diffusate. In Table **12—VII**, the values of $(C_x - C_0)/(C_s - C_0)$ are given for certain values of F and x/l. From these values the concentration at any distance x and time t can be calculated, if F, l, C_s, C_m and C_0 are known.

Table 12—VI. Fractional Saturation $F = \dfrac{C_m - C_0}{C_s - C_0}$ **for an Infinite Slab of Thickness** $2l$ **or an Infinite Cylinder of Diameter** $2l$ **for Certain Values of** Dt/l^2 **for Constant D. (*)**

$\dfrac{Dt}{l^2}$	$F = (C_m - C_0)/(C_s - C_0)$		$\dfrac{Dt}{l^2}$	$F = (C_m - C_0)/(C_s - C_0)$	
	Slab	Cylinder		Slab	Cylinder
0.02	0.161	0.302	0.40	0.702	0.9316
0.04	0.227	0.412	0.50	0.764	0.9616
0.06	0.275	0.488	0.60	0.816	0.9785
0.08	0.320	0.550	0.70	0.856	0.9879
0.10	0.357	0.606	0.80	0.887	0.9932
0.15	0.438	0.708	0.90	0.912	0.9960
0.20	0.503	0.781	1.00	0.931	0.9979
0.25	0.560	0.832	1.50	0.980	0.9999
0.30	0.612	0.878	2.00	0.994	

*This table is taken from Darken and Gurry[5].
C_m = mean concentration
C_0 = initial uniform concentration
C_s = constant surface concentration

Table 12—VII. Concentration Ratio $(C_x - C_0)/(C_s - C_0)$ **for Certain Values of** x/l **and** $F = (C_m - C_0)/(C_s - C_0)$ **in Unidirectional Diffusion into Slab of Thickness** $2l$ **and Cylinder of Diameter** $2l$, **for Constant D. (*)**

F	\multicolumn{8}{c}{Value of x/l}
	0.95	0.9	0.8	0.7	0.6	0.5	0.3	0.0
	\multicolumn{8}{c}{Values of $(C_x - C_0)/(C_s - C_0)$}
	\multicolumn{8}{c}{For Slab of Thickness $2l$}
0.1	0.703	0.435	0.100	0.020	0.004	0.000	0.000	0.000
0.2	0.842	0.688	0.420	0.223	0.105	0.045	0.007	0.000
0.3	0.890	0.787	0.590	0.420	0.282	0.180	0.063	0.015
0.4	0.918	0.842	0.690	0.550	0.422	0.320	0.177	0.090
0.5	0.935	0.874	0.754	0.640	0.536	0.443	0.305	0.223
0.6	0.950	0.902	0.807	0.718	0.633	0.558	0.447	0.376
0.7	0.963	0.928	0.856	0.788	0.724	0.667	0.582	0.530
0.8	0.976	0.951	0.905	0.860	0.817	0.780	0.720	0.687
0.9	0.987	0.975	0.951	0.929	0.908	0.890	0.861	0.843
	\multicolumn{8}{c}{For Cylinder of Diameter $2l$}
0.1	0.435	0.097	0.006	0.001	0.000	0.000	0.000	0.000
0.2	0.726	0.475	0.112	0.025	0.010	0.002	0.000	0.000
0.3	0.823	0.653	0.363	0.160	0.059	0.016	0.001	0.000
0.4	0.875	0.755	0.525	0.330	0.185	0.095	0.023	0.003
0.5	0.908	0.821	0.647	0.483	0.342	0.230	0.095	0.035
0.6	0.931	0.864	0.732	0.605	0.483	0.378	0.228	0.140
0.7	0.950	0.901	0.805	0.712	0.619	0.535	0.405	0.320
0.8	0.968	0.937	0.873	0.811	0.750	0.695	0.605	0.541
0.9	0.984	0.968	0.937	0.904	0.874	0.847	0.800	0.767

*This table is taken from Gurry[19].
C_x = concentration at distance x
C_0 = initial uniform concentration
C_s = constant surface concentration
x = distance from the center line of slab or cylinder

INTERDIFFUSIVITY AND INTRINSIC DIFFUSIVITY

If, in a binary system A-B the diffusing components A and B are identical in mass and size, the rates of transfer of A and B due to random motion across the welded junction SS in Figure **12—28**(a) are equal but of opposite sign. In general, however, differences of mass and size of A and B result in the transfer of A more or less than that of B. Consequently, a hydrostatic pressure tends to be built up in the region of the solution which contributes least to the volume rate transfer. This is equalized by a compensating mass flow of A and B together. The resulting concentration profile is as shown in Figure **12—28**(b). In order to evaluate the interdiffusion coefficient from this type of concentration profile, the distance x is measured from the reference plane MM; because of the mass-flow during diffusion, the reference plane MM does not coincide with the original welded junction SS. The amount of substance diffused on either side of the plane MM is equal but of opposite sign. The choice of this reference frame was first suggested by Matano[20] on an empirical basis, and this is referred to as the **Matano interface.**

If the concentrations C_A and C_B are kept constant on either end of the bar, the interdiffusivity is obtained from the concentration profiles on either side of MM using the dimensionless variables in Table **12—V**.

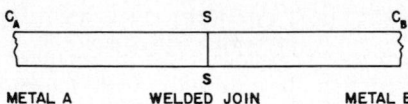

(a) DIFFUSION COUPLE. IF THE CONCENTRATIONS C_A AND C_B AT THE ENDS REMAIN UNCHANGED DURING THE DIFFUSION EXPERIMENT, THE COUPLE CAN BE ASSUMED TO CONSIST OF TWO SEMI-INFINITE MEDIUMS.

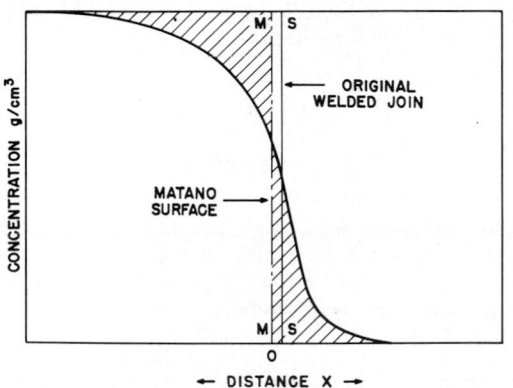

(b) CONCENTRATION PROFILE ALONG THE DIFFUSION PATH. AREAS ON EITHER SIDE OF THE MATANO SURFACE ARE EQUAL.

FIG. 12–28. Interdiffusion of A and B through welded join.

The mass-flow in metallic diffusion couples was demonstrated by Smigelskas and Kirkendall[21], by showing the movement of inert markers embedded in the metal, and this became known as the **Kirkendall effect.** Therefore, in measuring the diffusivities of individual components, the distance must be measured with respect to the position of the inert markers. On the assumption that during diffusion no volume change occurs, **Darken**[22] derived the following theoretical relation for a binary A-B solution.

$$D = N_A D_B + N_B D_A \qquad (89)$$

where

D = interdiffusivity with reference to the Matano surface

D_A, D_B = intrinsic diffusivities of components A and B with respect to the inert markers.

N_A, N_B = atom or mole fractions ($N_A + N_B = 1.0$)

The velocity v of the inert markers is related to the intrinsic diffusivities by

$$v = (D_B - D_A) \frac{\partial N_B}{\partial x} \qquad (90)$$

where x is the distance measured, for example, from the original welded join or from the ends of the specimen. Therefore, using inert markers, D_A and D_B can be evaluated from the concentration profile and

the simultaneous solution of equations (89) and (90) for known values of D and v.

If the solute B is in dilute solution in solvent A, equation (89) simplifies to $D = D_B$ and the velocity of mass-flow $v \to 0$.

DIFFUSION UNDER A CHEMICAL POTENTIAL GRADIENT

In the absence of an externally applied field, e.g. electrical, gravitational, etc., diffusion occurs when there is a chemical potential gradient in the solution. In solutions obeying Raoult's law, the chemical potential is directly related to the molar concentration, and the driving force under isothermal conditions is the concentration gradient. It is for these solutions that the above diffusion equations apply.

In nonideal solutions, the chemical potential or activity gradient determines the direction of diffusion, and not the concentration gradient. Using the Einstein[23] relation between diffusivity and mobility of the diffusing substance, the following relation was derived by Darken[22] for the interdiffusivity in terms of self-diffusivities and the activity coefficient for binary systems:

$$D = (N_A D_B{}^* + N_B D_A{}^*)\left(1 + \frac{d \log \gamma_B}{d \log N_B}\right) \quad (91)$$

where the asterisk indicates self-diffusivity. The self-diffusivity is the intrinsic diffusivity determined from the diffusion of the isotopes of A and B in a diffusion couple of equal chemical potential. In ideal systems obeying Raoult's law or Henry's law, the ratio $d \log \gamma_B / d \log N_B$ is zero and, therefore, intrinsic diffusivity D_i = self-diffusivity $D_i{}^*$ for the ith component.

Since the chemical potential is the driving force, diffusion against the concentration gradient can occur in ternary or multicomponent systems. This so-called "up-hill" diffusion was demonstrated by Darken[24], and Figure 12–29 is one of the examples of his findings. In this experiment two steel bars of different compositions were welded and kept at 1050°C for 10 days; it is seen from the concentration profile that carbon diffused from a low to a high concentration across the welded join. This is explained simply on the basis of the activity of carbon in the 3.8 per cent

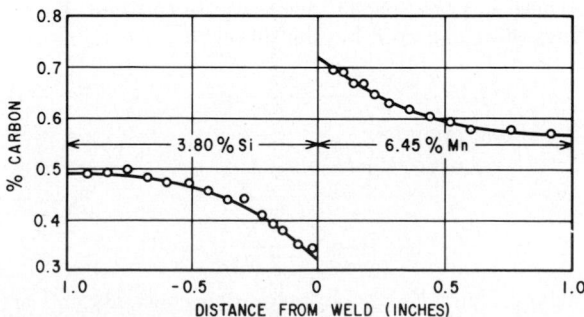

FIG. 12–29. Uphill diffusion of carbon from low concentration (but high activity) in Si-iron to high concentration (but low activity) in Mn-iron. Diffusion time, 10 days at 1050°C. (From Darken[24].)

Si alloy being greater than that in the 6.45 per cent Mn alloy.

VARIATION OF DIFFUSIVITY WITH COMPOSITION

Although in dilute solutions the diffusivity can be assumed to be constant, in many alloys diffusivity varies with composition. For example, the diffusivity of carbon in austenite[25] increases by a factor of about 4 with increasing carbon content within the composition range 0 to 1.5 per cent. Many examples are given by Rhines and Mehl[26] on the variation of the diffusivity with composition of nonferrous alloys.

VARIATION OF DIFFUSIVITY WITH TEMPERATURE

The variation of diffusivity with temperature is best understood after discussing the basic features of the **absolute reaction rate theory**. However, for the present it is sufficient to state that the logarithm of diffusivity (inter- or self-diffusivity) is a linear function of the reciprocal of absolute temperature, provided that the mechanism of diffusion is not altered within the temperature range considered.

For the data compiled on diffusivities in iron-based alloys and molten slags, reference should be made to Parts II and III of this chapter.

SECTION 11
KINETICS OF REACTIONS

The study of the rates of reaction, i.e. change of state, and the factors affecting these rates constitute the subject matter of reaction kinetics. Here, the discussion of this subject is limited to those basic principles to which references are made in the subsequent parts of this chapter on the kinetics of metallurgical reactions.

RATE AND ORDER OF HOMOGENEOUS REACTIONS

The rate of a reaction is defined as the time derivative of concentration dC/dt, i.e. change in concentration of the reacting species with time of reaction, and this is proportional to the product of the concentrations of the reactants. In systems obeying ideal solution laws, concentration in terms of grams or moles per unit volume is used and for nonideal solutions due correction is made by inserting the activity coefficients.

Let us consider the reaction

$$A + B \rightarrow product \qquad (92)$$

where the concentration of B is assumed to be very large compared to that of A and, consequently, the rate of decrease of the concentration A is proportional to the concentration, C_A, of A.

$$-\frac{dC_A}{dt} = kC_A \qquad (93)$$

where k is the **specific reaction rate constant**. On rearranging and omitting the subscript:

$$\frac{dC}{C} = -kdt$$

and integrating

$$\ln C = -kt + I \qquad (94)$$

or

$$\log C = -\frac{k}{2.303}t + I'$$

where I and I' are the integration constants and are readily evaluated from the concentration C_0 at zero time of reaction, so that $I' = \log C_0$, and

$$\log \frac{C}{C_0} = -\frac{k}{2.303}t \qquad (95)$$

where C is the concentration of A at time t and C_0 concentration at $t = 0$. Since the rate is directly proportional to the concentration of one reactant, equation (93) is said to be for a first order reaction and the rate constant is determined from the slope of the linear plot of $\log (C/C_0)$ against t.

In a second order reaction, the rate is directly proportional to the product of the concentrations of two reactants or to the square of the concentration of one reactant. For instance, for the reaction

$$2A + B \rightarrow product \qquad (96)$$

where the composition of B is assumed to remain constant during the reaction, the rate becomes

$$-\frac{dC}{dt} = kC^2 \qquad (97)$$

On rearranging and integrating

$$\frac{1}{C} - \frac{1}{C_0} = kt \qquad (98)$$

where C is concentration at time t and C_0 at $t = 0$.

In zero order reactions, the rate is independent of concentrations, i.e.

$$-\frac{dC}{dt} = k \qquad (99)$$

and, therefore,

$$C - C_0 = kt \qquad (100)$$

where C_0 is concentration at $t = 0$.

In derivation of the above rate equations it has been assumed that the system is far removed from the state of equilibrium and the reverse reaction is almost negligible. However, as equilibrium is approached, the velocities of both forward and reverse reactions must be considered together, thus, for a first-order reaction

$$A \underset{k_2}{\overset{k_1}{\rightleftarrows}} B$$

the reaction rate is

$$\frac{dC_A}{dt} = -k_1C_A + k_2C_B \qquad (101)$$

where k_1 and k_2 are the rate constants for the consumption and production of A by forward and reverse reactions, respectively.

When a state of equilibrium is reached, the velocities of these forward and reverse reactions are equal

$$k_1 C_A = k_2 C_B$$

and the ratio of k_1/k_2 is the equilibrium constant, and for an ideal solution the following is written:

$$K = \frac{k_1}{k_2} = \frac{C_B}{C_A} \qquad (102)$$

Substituting $k_2 = k_1/K$ in equation (101),

$$\frac{dC_A}{dt} = -k_1\left(C_A - \frac{C_B}{K}\right) \qquad (103)$$

For a given concentration C_B in the solution, there is a corresponding equilibrium concentration of A, denoted by $(C_A)_e$; substituting $C_B = K(C_A)_e$ in equation (103)

$$\frac{dC_A}{dt} = -k_1[C_A - (C_A)_e] \qquad (104)$$

After rearranging and integrating

$$\ln [C_A - (C_A)_e] = -k_1 t + I \qquad (105)$$

or

$$\log [C_A - (C_A)_e] = -\frac{k_1}{2.303}t + I' \qquad (106)$$

where I and I' are the integration constants and can be evaluated from the composition of the system at $t = 0$. In this expression C_A is the concentration of A at time t, and $(C_A)_e$ is that concentration which would be in equilibrium with the concentration C_B present in solution at time t.

Examples on the use of these rate equations are given in other parts of this chapter.

THEORY OF ABSOLUTE REACTION RATES

Unlike the laws of thermodynamics, the reaction rate theory is far from being rigorous. However, much progress has been made in the understanding of this subject during the past four decades, and many contributed to the development of this theory; the contributions made by Eyring[27] being the most outstanding.

The theory is based essentially on two principal concepts, (i) the formation of an activated complex in equilibrium with the reactants and (ii) universal specific rate constant for the decomposition of the activated complex.

When a system changes from a state A to a state B, its potential energy goes through a maximum during the process of this change. This is shown in Figure 12–30 where potential energy of the system is plotted against the reaction path (reaction coordinate). The difference between the final and initial free energies is the standard free energy change accompanying the reaction. The difference ΔF^* is the **standard free energy of activation** needed for the formation of an activated complex from the reactants, as a first stage of the change from A to B.

When reactants L and M gain sufficient free energy of activation, ΔF^*, activated complex is formed

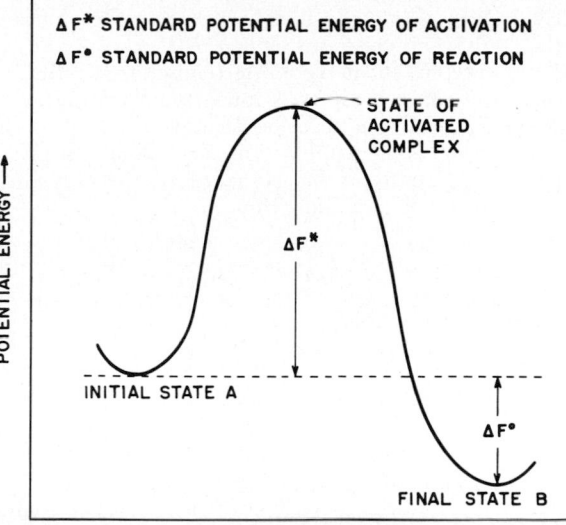

FIG. 12–30. Schematic potential energy diagram illustrating the energy barrier (activation free energy) that has to be surmounted as the system changes from state A to final state B.

$$\underbrace{L + M}_{\text{state A}} \rightleftharpoons \text{Activated complex} \qquad (107)$$

at the rate,

$$\text{Rate of reaction} = kC_L C_M \qquad (108)$$

The second concept of the theory of absolute reaction rates is that the specific rate constant for the decomposition of the activated complex into the products (state B)

$$\text{Activated complex} \rightleftharpoons \underbrace{P + Q}_{\text{state B}}$$

is given by a universal constant, RT/Nh, independent of the nature of reaction and the activated complex, i.e.

$$\text{Rate of reaction} = \frac{RT}{Nh}C^* \qquad (109)$$

where

R = gas constant
T = absolute temperature
N = Avogadro's number
h = Planck's constant
C^* = concentration of the activated complex

Equating equations (108) and (109), and rearranging

$$k = \frac{RT}{Nh} \frac{C^*}{C_L C_M} \qquad (110)$$

The equilibrium constant for reaction (107) is

$$K^* = \frac{C^*}{C_L C_M} \frac{\gamma_C^*}{\gamma_{C_L} \gamma_{C_M}} \qquad (111)$$

and combining it with equation (110)

$$k = \frac{RT}{Nh}K^* \frac{\gamma_{C_L} \gamma_{C_M}}{\gamma_C^*} \qquad (112)$$

The life of an activated complex can readily be

calculated for any temperature from the reciprocal of the universal rate constant by inserting the values of the universal constants in $Nh/RT = (4.77/T) \times 10^{-11}$ sec. Even at moderate temperatures, the life of an activated complex is much too short and, consequently, they can never be isolated.

Since K^* is an equilibrium constant, it can be expressed in terms of the standard free energy, heat and entropy of activation, thus

$$\ln K^* = -\frac{\Delta F^*}{RT} = -\frac{\Delta H^*}{RT} + \frac{\Delta S^*}{R} \quad (113)$$

or in exponential form

$$K^* = (e^{-\Delta H^*/RT})(e^{\Delta S^*/R})$$

Inserting this value of K^* in equation (112)

$$k = \frac{RT}{Nh} \frac{\gamma_{C_L}\gamma_{C_M}}{\gamma_c^*}(e^{\Delta S^*/R})(e^{-\Delta H^*/RT}) \quad (114)$$

Assuming that the activity coefficients do not change much within the composition range studied and since ΔH^* and ΔS^* can be assumed to be independent of temperature, the first term can be assumed to remain constant for a given system over a small temperature range

$$A = \frac{RT_m}{Nh} \frac{\gamma_{C_L}\gamma_{C_M}}{\gamma C^*}(e^{\Delta S^*/R})$$

where T_m is a mean temperature. The specific reaction rate constant can now be expressed more simply as

$$k = Ae^{-\Delta H^*/RT} \quad (115)$$

or

$$\log k = -\frac{\Delta H^*}{2.303RT} + \frac{A'}{2.303}$$

which is identical with that derived empirically by Arrhenius (1889). In simple reactions involving simple activated complexes, ΔS^* is small and the heat of activation essentially determines the value of the rate constant. As a general rule, high heat of activation means a low reaction rate constant. This is, of course, an oversimplification and reference should be made to text books[28] for further details.

For most purposes, equation (115) describes adequately the variation of the rate constant with temperature. However, this is true only if the mechanism of the reaction under consideration does not change with temperature. Depending on the nature of the rate process and the mechanism of the reaction, the heat of activation can have a value up to $+150$ or more kcal. per mole. Several examples are given in the subsequent parts of this chapter on the temperature and composition dependence of the rate constants.

KINETICS OF HETEROGENEOUS REACTIONS

Almost all the metallurgical reactions occur in heterogeneous systems involving two, three or more phases. Although in many authoritative text books the basic principles concerning the kinetics of heterogeneous reactions are clearly outlined, they are not often used to the best advantage when studying the kinetics of particularly the metallurgical reactions at elevated temperatures. The measurements of the rate of a reaction under given conditions is a means of studying the reaction kinetics. However, little significance can be attached to the actual rate measurements, unless the observed rate can be attributed to a specific reaction path, derived from sound theoretical reasoning, and if possible, from carefully designed experimental proofs.

Since heterogeneous reactions occur between two or more phases, they are essentially interfacial reactions, and the rate controlling processes can be divided into two major classes: (1) **transport processes** and (2) **chemical processes.** This broad classification is also subdivided into several specific rate controlling processes, depending on the nature of the reaction and nature of the system. Although the overall reaction between the two phases may be relatively simple, e.g. oxidation of carbon dissolved in iron by iron oxide in the slag $\underline{C} + FeO \rightarrow CO + Fe$, a large number of reaction steps could be involved. The reaction step that requires the highest free energy of activation is usually the rate controlling process; however, under certain conditions there may be more than one slow step controlling the observed rate of a reaction.

Transport processes—For the reaction to occur between two phases, the reactants and products must be transported to and from the interface. In many reduction and oxidation reactions between solid metal (or metal oxide) and gases, it is found that the rate of reaction, dx/dt, is inversely proportional to the thickness x of the reacted layer at the interface,

$$\frac{dx}{dt} = \frac{k}{x}$$

by rearranging and integrating

$$x^2 = 2kt \quad (116)$$

This is known as the parabolic law and can be derived from the solution of Fick's law for unidirectional diffusion. For example, for the boundary conditions, $C_s = $ constant surface concentration and $C_0 = $ initial uniform concentration, the total amount, n, of a reacting species transferred to a semi-infinite medium of unit area at time t is given by

$$n = 1.1284(C_s - C_0)\sqrt{Dt} \quad (117)$$

where D is the diffusivity assumed to be constant within the concentration range C_0 and C_s. Similar equations can be derived for diffusion-controlled reaction with a finite sized condensed phase. For example, in the case of a slab with thickness $2l$, the fractional saturation at short times is given by

$$F = \frac{1.1284}{l}\sqrt{Dt} \quad (118)$$

From the identity of equation (116) with (117) or (118), it follows that in reactions obeying the parabolic law the most probable rate-controlling process is the diffusion of the reactant or the product or the counterdiffusion of both. Examples on the rate processes of this kind are given in Parts IV and VII.

If reacting phases are gas-liquid, liquid-liquid, solid-liquid or gas-solid, forced or natural convection cur-

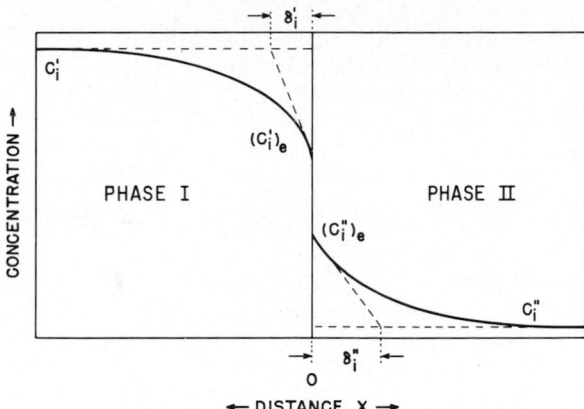

FIG. 12–31. Concentration profiles for solute i in liquid phases I and II resulting from stirring. C_i' and C_i'' are the uniform bulk concentrations and $(C_i')_e$ and $(C_i'')_e$ are equilibrium concentration at the interface, $x = 0$.

rents have a pronounced effect on the transport of the reactants and products to and from the interface. The following example underlines the principles of this particular transport process. When a fluid phase is in motion due to natural convection, gravitational force or stirring, a concentration profile exists near the interface boundary as shown in Figure 12–31 for two liquid phases. From the nature of the convection and the physical properties of the systems, these concentration profiles can be calculated[29, 30], but these will not be discussed here. In the following example, it is assumed that reaction at the interface is fast and the concentrations $(C_i')_e$ and $(C_i'')_e$ of the ith component are the equilibrium values between the phases I and II. In the bulk of the solution where turbulent flow prevails, the concentrations C_i' and C_i'' reach constant values, at a short distance away from the interface. According to the two-phase film theory developed by Whitman[31], the rate of transfer of solute i from phase I to phase II is given by:

$$J_i = h_i'[C_i' - (C_i')_e] = h_i''[C_i'' - (C_i'')_e] \quad (119)$$

where J_i is the rate of transfer of i from phase I to II per unit area per unit time; C_i', C_i'' are the bulk molar concentrations of solute per unit volume; h_i' and h_i'' are the film mass-transfer coefficients. The dimensions of h are cm./sec. and, in terms of diffusivities D_i' and D_i'', h is given as

$$h_i' = \frac{D_i'}{\delta_i'} \text{ and } h_i'' = \frac{D_i''}{\delta_i''}$$

where δ_i' and δ_i'' are the effective diffusion boundary layer thicknesses and can be determined from the tangent to the concentration profile at the interface, $x = 0$, as shown in Figure 12–31. The film mass-transfer coefficient, and consequently δ, is a complex function of temperature, composition, viscosity and density of the fluid medium and the hydrodynamic conditions in the system. With increased rate of stirring the film mass-transfer coefficient increases, and if the rate of the interfacial reaction is not very fast, transport as a rate controlling process can be eliminated by adequate stirring of the liquid.

Examples on the use of equation (119) are given later in the chapter. When this or similar equations on flux are used, the units of J and C are converted in the following manner to more practical units. Let us consider the first part of equation (119); if the interfacial area is A, the total amount in terms of moles per unit time is $n_i = J_iA$, i.e.

$$n_i = Ah_i'[C_i' - (C_i')_e]$$

If V' is the total volume of phase I, the rate of decrease in concentration C_i' is given by

$$-\frac{dC_i'}{dt} = \frac{n_i'}{V'}$$

inserting it in the above equation

$$-\frac{dC_i'}{dt} = \frac{A}{V'}h_i'[C_i' - (C_i')_e] \quad (120)$$

Since the same concentration term is present on both sides of this equation, any units may be used for C_i'. Furthermore, the ratio A/V' is the depth l' of the liquid I away from the interface; inserting $h_i' = D_i'/\delta_i'$ and omitting the superscript $(')$, the rate equation takes the general form

$$-\frac{d(\%i)}{dt} = \frac{D_i}{\delta_i l}[\%i - (\%i)_e] \quad (121)$$

If the amount of phase II is much larger than that of phase I, the equilibrium concentration at the interface $(\%i)_e$ can be assumed to remain constant. By rearranging and integrating equation (121)

$$\ln [\%i - (\%i)_e] = -\frac{D_i}{\delta_i l}t + I \quad (122)$$

or

$$\log [\%i - (\%i)_e] = -\frac{D_i}{2.303\delta_i l}t + I' \quad (123)$$

where I and I' are the integration constants, and can be evaluated from the initial composition of the liquid. It should be noted that this equation is identical with that for a first order reaction as given in equation (94). If the rate data for a heterogeneous reaction fits the equation for a first order reaction, the rate controlling process could be either the first order chemical reaction or the transport process under forced convection as discussed above. The only way to differentiate these two rate processes is to measure the rate of reaction with different rates of stirring. If the rate constant increases with increasing rate of stirring then it is conclusive that the rate-controlling step is a transport process. On careful analysis of the rate data one can also estimate whether it is the flux of reactants or products that is the rate-controlling process.

If the product of a reaction in the liquid is a gas, further complication arises, owing to the stirring effect of the gas bubbles evolved from the liquid. As the rate of gas evolution decreases, the rate of stirring decreases and, as a result, the effective boundary layer thickness, δ, increases. The net effect is that the order of the reaction appears (i) to change with time of reaction and/or (ii) to be higher than that expected from the stoichiometry of the reaction. As discussed in Part IV of this chapter, apparent high order of reaction between carbon-saturated iron and iron-oxide slag, forming carbon monoxide, can be explained on the basis of the above considerations.

Chemical processes—One of the reaction steps in gas-solid systems is the adsorption and desorption of gaseous reactants and products from the surface of the solid phase. In general, there are two types of adsorptions. When adsorption is brought about by forces of a physical nature, it is known as the van der Waals' adsorption which is accompanied by a small heat change of about 5 kcal. per mole or less and the heat of activation is very small. If the adsorbed gas interacts strongly with the solid substance, this is called chemisorption which is accompanied by heat evolution as if it were an exothermic chemical reaction and the heat of activation is of the order of 20 kcal. per mole, or more. Because of these differences in the heats of activation, usually van der Waals' adsorption occurs at lower temperatures but with increasing temperature chemisorption predominates.

The formation of a monolayer on the surface by sorption of reactant, for example, of A on active sites "S" can be treated as a chemical reaction, thus

$$A + \text{``}S\text{''} = \text{``}A{:}S\text{''}$$

where "S" represents an unoccupied site and "$A{:}S$" represents a site occupied by an A atom. In terms of fractional sites,

$$\text{fraction of occupied sites, } \theta = \frac{(\text{``}A{:}S\text{''})}{(\text{``}S\text{''}) + (\text{``}A{:}S\text{''})}$$

$$\text{fraction of vacant sites, } 1 - \theta = \frac{\text{``}S\text{''}}{(\text{``}S\text{''}) + (\text{``}A{:}S\text{''})}$$

the equilibrium constant becomes

$$K_A = \frac{\theta}{A(1 - \theta)}$$

On rearranging

$$\theta = \frac{K_A(A)}{1 + K_A(A)} \qquad (124)$$

This is known as the **Langmuir isotherm** which was originally derived by considering the rates of sorption and desorption at equilibrium.

If the reaction of gas A with a solid produces gas B, these two gas species compete for the active sites on the surface of the solid and, therefore, the following two reactions should be considered

$$A + \text{``}S\text{''} = \text{``}A{:}S\text{''}$$
$$B + \text{``}S\text{''} = \text{``}B{:}S\text{''}$$

Since the total number of sites is given by the sum ($\text{``}S\text{''}$) + ($\text{``}A{:}S\text{''}$) + ($\text{``}B{:}S\text{''}$), the following is obtained for the fraction of sites occupied by A molecules

$$\theta_A = \frac{K_A(A)}{1 + K_A(A) + K_B(B)} \qquad (125)$$

and, similarly, for the fraction of sites occupied by B molecules,

$$\theta_B = \frac{K_B(B)}{1 + K_A(A) + K_B(B)} \qquad (126)$$

where K_A and K_B are the equilibrium constants for adsorption of A and B, respectively.

In Part IV of this chapter, a few examples are given on gas-solid reactions where the reaction between chemisorbed species becomes the rate-controlling process.

Nucleation is another reaction step which may be classified as an interphase process, as it is associated with the surface energy. Although nucleation could be an important rate process in some metallurgical reactions, it will not be discussed here. One of the well known nucleation problems is that concerning the formation of gas bubbles in liquids. An example on this is given in Part IV of this chapter on the formation of carbon monoxide bubbles in liquid iron. In the kinetics of solid state reactions, e.g. phase transformations, crystal growth, precipitation of nitrides, carbides, etc., nucleation also plays an important role.

Molten oxides, silicates and slags in general are ionic solutions consisting of simple and complex ions. Therefore, all the gas-slag and slag-metal reactions are electrochemical reactions. If the species taking part in a reaction exist as simple ions in the slag, the rate of the chemical reaction is in general relatively fast, e.g. oxidation of manganese dissolved in iron by an iron-oxide slag,

$$\underline{Mn} \text{ (metal)} + Fe^{2+} \text{ (slag)}$$
$$= Mn^{2+} \text{ (slag)} + \underline{Fe} \text{ (metal)} \qquad (127)$$

On the other hand, silicon in the slag interacts strongly with the oxide ions forming a silicate network (more details on the ionic nature of slags are given in Part III of this chapter). For the present purpose this silicate network is symbolized by $(SiO_4)^{4-}$ with four negative charges. In the transfer of silicon from slag to metal the following overall reaction occurs.

$$(SiO_4)^{4-} \text{ (slag)} = \underline{Si} \text{ (metal)} + 2 \underline{O} \text{ (metal)}$$
$$+ 2 O^{2-} \text{ (slag)} \qquad (128)$$

As discussed in Part V of this chapter, this is an inherently slow reaction, owing to the high activation energy required to break the Si-O bonds in the silicate network, before silicon can be transferred to the metal. Since oxygen is transferred to the metal together with silicon, the rate of reaction (128) can be affected by adding suitable reducing elements, C, Mn, Cr, etc., in the metal.

In most slag-metal reactions there are two, three or more reactions occurring simultaneously and all these reactions are dependent on one another; utmost care must be taken in interpreting the rate data on such complex systems. An example on one of these complex reactions is given later in this chapter (Part VII) in connection with the kinetics of the sulphur reaction between slag and carbon-saturated iron.

Unless the rate-controlling process or processes of a reaction can be understood, laboratory rate data have little value in interpreting the rates of commercial processes, particularly for complex systems. As manifested by the examples given in the subsequent parts of this chapter, the experiments must be carried out under carefully controlled conditions so that the rate data obtained may be interpreted accurately on the basis of the theories of reaction kinetics.

The Physical Chemistry of Iron- and Steelmaking

PART II

Physico-Chemical Properties of

Some Iron Alloys

SECTION 1

INTRODUCTION

This part of Chapter 12 is devoted to the compilation of data on the frequently used physico-chemical properties of some iron alloys, comprising phase-equilibrium diagrams, activities and solubilities of some elements dissolved in iron, coefficients of inter-diffusion, viscosities and densities of iron alloys. Since

reference is often made to the valency, atomic number and periodicity of elements, it is considered desirable to mention some of the basic facts concerning the classification of elements and the atomic arrangements in crystal lattices: these fundamentals are presented in the following Section 2.

SECTION 2

CLASSIFICATION OF ELEMENTS

According to **Hume-Rothery's** classification[32], the elements, with the exception of hydrogen, nitrogen, oxygen, fluorine and inert gases, may be divided into three groups, thus **Class I, metals; Class II, intermediate elements; Class III, non-metals.** This classification is based essentially on the crystal structure of elements and the coordination number of atoms. The **coordination number** is defined as the number of nearest neighboring atoms to any particular atom in the space lattice.

Class I—As shown in Figure **12**—32, about two thirds of the elements of the periodic table have metallic properties. With the possible exception of manganese, all the elements in this class crystallize in one or more of the following structures: **body-centered cubic** (b.c.c.), **face-centered cubic** (f.c.c.) and **hexagonal close-packed** (h.c.p.). The atomic arrangements in these three crystal systems are shown in Figure **12**—33. The closest distance in the b.c.c. structure is that between the central atom and the corner atoms, i.e. closest distance $= \sqrt{3}\, a/2$, and therefore, there are eight nearest neighbors, i.e. the coordination number is 8. Since a corner atom is shared between eight cubes

and each cube has a central atom, it follows that in this crystal system there are two atoms per unit cell.

The following table gives some of the characteristics of these lattices:

Table 12—VIII. Some Characteristics of b.c.c., f.c.c. and h.c.p. Lattices

	b.c.c.	f.c.c.	h.c.p.
Unit cell volume	a^3	a^3	$3\sqrt{3}a^2c$
Number of atoms per unit cell	2	4	2
Coordination number	8	12	12

Class III—As seen from Figure **12**—32, the elements belonging to this class are those that fall in the B subgroups of the periodic table and obey the Hume-Rothery (8-N) rule. That is, if N is the group number in the periodic table, each atom of a crystalline element has (8-N) neighbors. For example, the elements in group IV B, carbon (diamond), silicon, germanium and gray tin posses the tetrahedral atomic arrangement as shown in Figure **12**—34 and therefore,

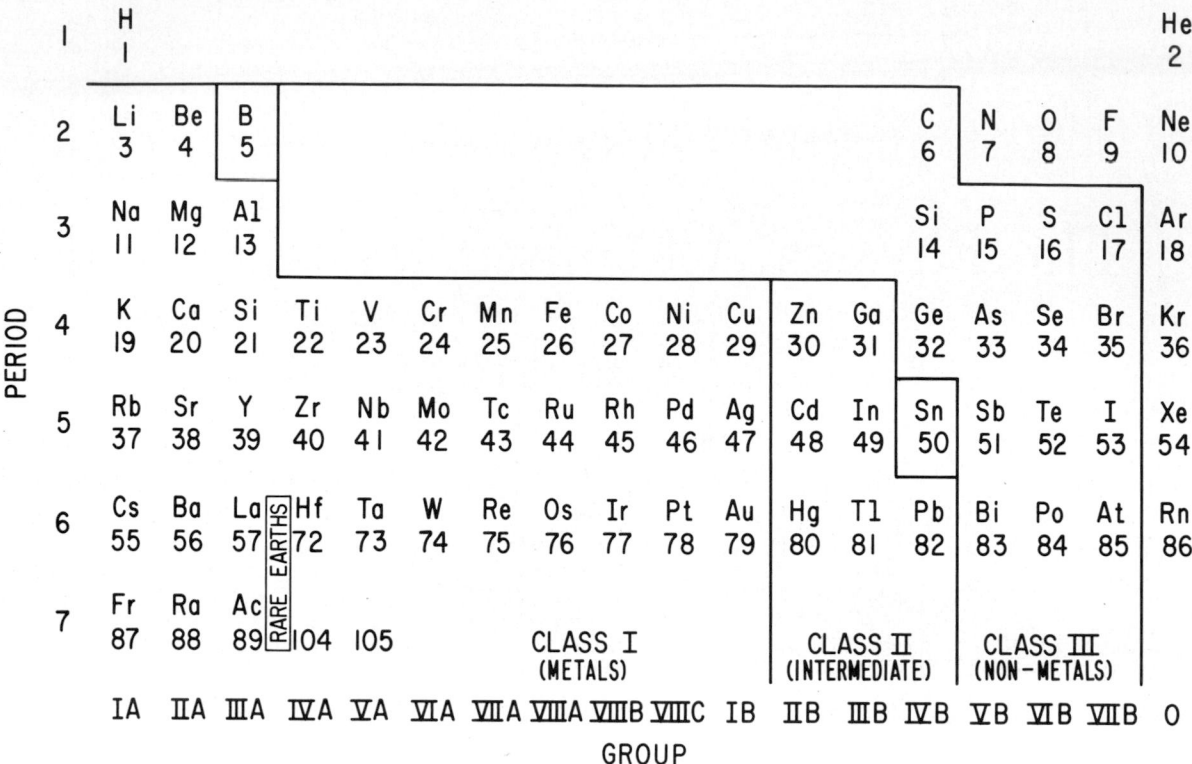

FIG. 12–32. Classification of the elements is shown in the periodic table.

the coordination number is 4. The structures obeying the (8-N) rule are summarized in Table 12–IX.

Table 12–IX. Structures Conforming to the (8-N) Rule

Group	Atomic Arrangement	Coordination Number = 8-N
IV B	Tetrahedral	4
V B	Rhombohedral	3
VI B	Spiral chains	2
VII B	Paired atoms	1

Class II—The elements falling into this class crystallize in forms similar partly to Class I and partly to Class III. For example, mercury crystallizes in a simple rhombohedral structure, i.e. a distorted simple cubic lattice, where the coordination number is 6, indicating that the (8-N) rule is obeyed. While gray tin, belonging to Class III, has a diamond structure, white tin has a tetragonal structure (distorted diamond) and the (8-N) rule is not obeyed; this form of tin belongs to Class II.

NATURE OF INTERATOMIC FORCES AND CRYSTAL-BONDS

The interatomic forces binding the atoms in elements and in the assembly of like and unlike atoms may be divided into four classes: (1) van der Waals forces, (2) covalent bonds, (3) ionic bonds and (4) metallic bonds.

(1) van der Waals forces—Although the trajectories of the electrons in their respective orbits cannot be pictured physically, it is certain that the electron clouds result from the motion of the various electrons. While an atom with a spherically symmetrical electron cloud will have no average electrical moment, i.e. **dipole** moment, at any instant when the electron is to one side of the nucleus, there will be excess negative electricity on this side of the atom and equivalent positive charge on the opposite side of the atom. If two atoms are approaching one another, each will affect the rapidly fluctuating dipole moment of the other atom, and a lower energy, i.e. attraction, will result if the movements of the electrons in these two atoms are synchronized. The attractive forces resulting from the harmonized electronic motion in two atoms are called van der Waals forces. In inert gases, van der Waals forces are the only attractive forces balancing the repulsive forces caused by the overlapping electron clouds of the atoms.

(2) Covalent bonds—It was postulated by Lewis[33] that in some elements and compounds the electrons in the outermost shells of the atoms are shared to build up stable shells containing a maximum of 2, 8, 18 and 32 electrons; designated, respectively, as the K, L, M, and N shells, each successively further from the nucleus. For example, each chlorine atom has seven electrons in the M-shell, and requires one more to complete a stable outer shell with an even number of electrons. When two free atoms are in close proximity, each supplies the other with one electron to establish the stable M-shell. That is, each atom in a molecule of chlorine, Cl_2, has six unshared and 2 shared electrons in the M-shell. In the case of diamond, the coordination number of

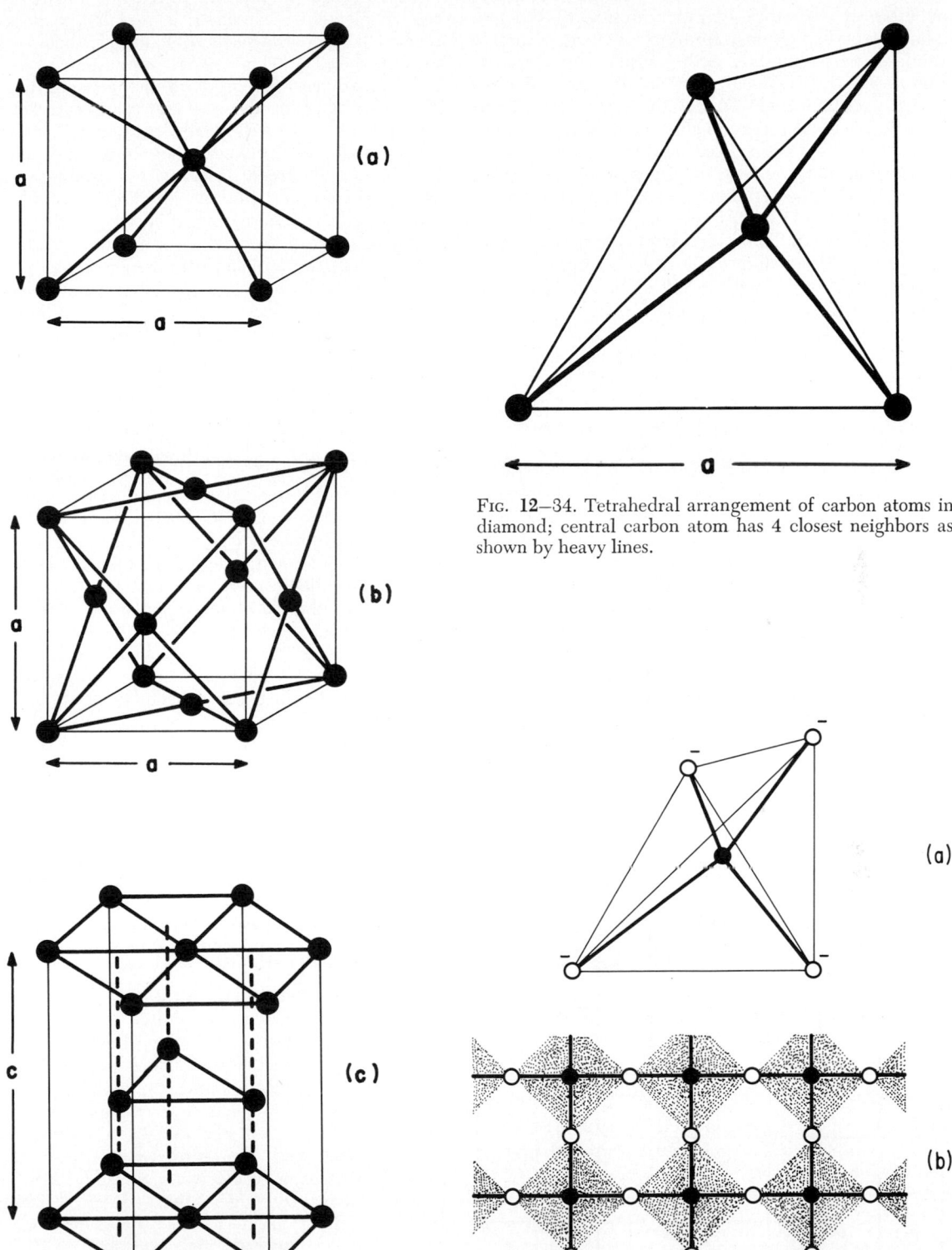

Fig. 12–34. Tetrahedral arrangement of carbon atoms in diamond; central carbon atom has 4 closest neighbors as shown by heavy lines.

Fig. 12–33. Atomic arrangement in: (a) b.c.c.; (b) f.c.c.; and (c) h.c.p. crystals (neighboring atoms are joined by heavy lines).

Fig. 12–35. Tetrahedral distribution of oxygen atoms around silicon atoms in silica. (a) Si-O tetrahedron with 4 negative charges; (b) in the continuous net-work of silica, Si-O tetrahedra share corners. Black circles represent silicon atoms: open circles, oxygen atoms.

carbon is 4 and each of the four valence electrons of an atom of carbon is shared with one of the four adjacent carbon atoms, forming covalent bonds. A similar type of bonding exists in silica; as shown in Figure 12–35(a), a silicon atom is surrounded by four oxygen atoms situated at the corners of a tetrahedron. Each oxygen atom shares one of its two electrons with the silicon atom and the resulting tetrahedron has four negative charges. However, in an assembly of these tetrahedra (shown in two dimensions in Figure 12–35b) the corners and not the edges are shared. That is, each silicon atom has four oxygen neighbors and each oxygen atom has two silicon neighbors and the resulting assembly of Si-O network in silica can be represented by the stoichiometric formula SiO_2.

(3) Ionic Bond—When the atoms in a crystalline solid are held together by coulombic forces, the nature of bonding is said to be ionic or polar. For example, when solid sodium chloride is formed, one valence electron of the sodium atom is given up to the chlorine atom so that the electronic configuration of the sodium atom becomes the same as that of neon with a positive charge and similarly the chlorine atom is the same as that of argon with a negative charge. These two inert gas-like atoms with positive and negative charges are held together by the coulombic forces. As shown in Figure 12–36, the space lattice of sodium chloride is f.c.c. where each ion is surrounded by six nearest neighbors of the opposite charge and twelve next nearest neighbors of the same charge. In this space lattice each unit cell contains 4(NaCl). The structure of sodium chloride may also be looked upon as a simple cube, the corners of which are occupied alternatively by Na^+ and Cl^- ions and the interionic distance is half the true lattice constant.

(4) Metallic bond—The physico-chemical properties of elements, classified as metallic, can be described best on the basis of **Pauling's** theory of the metallic bond[34]. This theory, supported by considerable evidence, is based on the concept that the chemical bond in the metallic state consists of a multiplicity of resonating covalent bonds. That is, the electrons shared between the atoms in a metallic lattice resonate freely from one electron-pair to another electron-pair. Since such resonance is accompanied by a decrease in the energy of the system, the strength and ductility of a metallic substance is greater than those of non-metals where there are no resonating bonds. Furthermore, because of this random resonance, electrons have high mobilities and, hence, metals are characterized by high electrical conductivity.

ATOMIC DIAMETER

The diameter of an atom is defined as the distance of closest approach, as if the atoms were solid spheres. For simple structures, the atomic diameters of solid elements may be calculated readily from the lattice constant of the unit cell. For example, the atomic diameter of an element crystallizing as b.c.c. is $\sqrt{3}\, a/2$, where a is the length of the unit cell.

Another scale of interatomic distance is that known as the Goldschmidt atomic diameter[35] which is the distance of closest approach of atoms assumed to have the coordination number of 12. When the coordination number changes from 12 to 8, 6 or 4, the atomic diameter becomes smaller by 3, 4 or 12 per cent respectively.

Figure 12–37 shows the variation of the interatomic distance with the atomic number of elements.

In ionic crystals, the equilibrium interionic distance for two ions is determined by the nature of the electron distributions for the ions, the structure of the crystal and the ratio of radii of cation and anion.

For further details on the interatomic distances and ionic radii reference should be made to the studies of Hume-Rothery[32] and Pauling[34].

NON-STOICHIOMETRIC COMPOUNDS

In the above examples on the structure of crystalline elements and some simple compounds the crystals are assumed to be perfect, that is, the atomic arrangement in the lattice sites is regular and the composition of the compound is such that the valency requirements are satisfied. For example, silicon has four valence electrons and oxygen has six electrons in the L-shell and, therefore, when silica, SiO_2, is formed by sharing of electrons, the outermost shells of both silicon and oxygen atoms contain 8 electrons. However, there are a number of compounds the composition of which do not correspond to those expected from the valency of the unlike atoms constituting the compound. For example, depending on the oxygen partial pressure, the composition of wüstite varies from $Fe_{0.95}O$ to $Fe_{0.87}O$ at 1373°C. Such compounds are said to be non-stoichiometric. Generally speaking, the non-stoichiometric compounds may be divided into three classes: (1) cation excess, (2) cation deficient and (3) interstitial compounds.

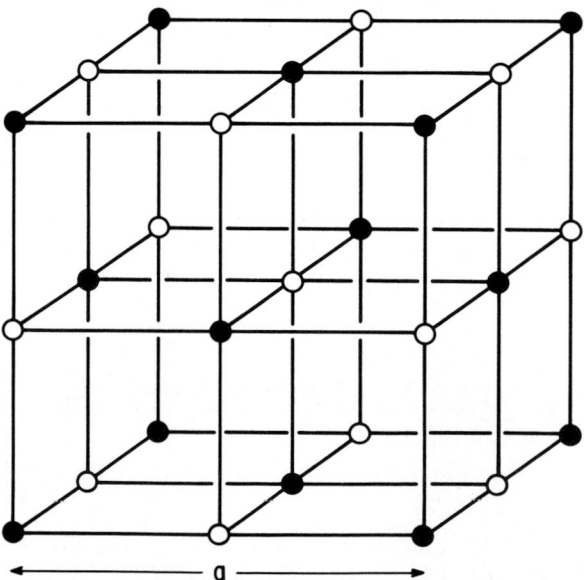

FIG. 12–36. Atomic arrangement in sodium chloride. Open circles represent chlorine anions; filled circles represent sodium cations.

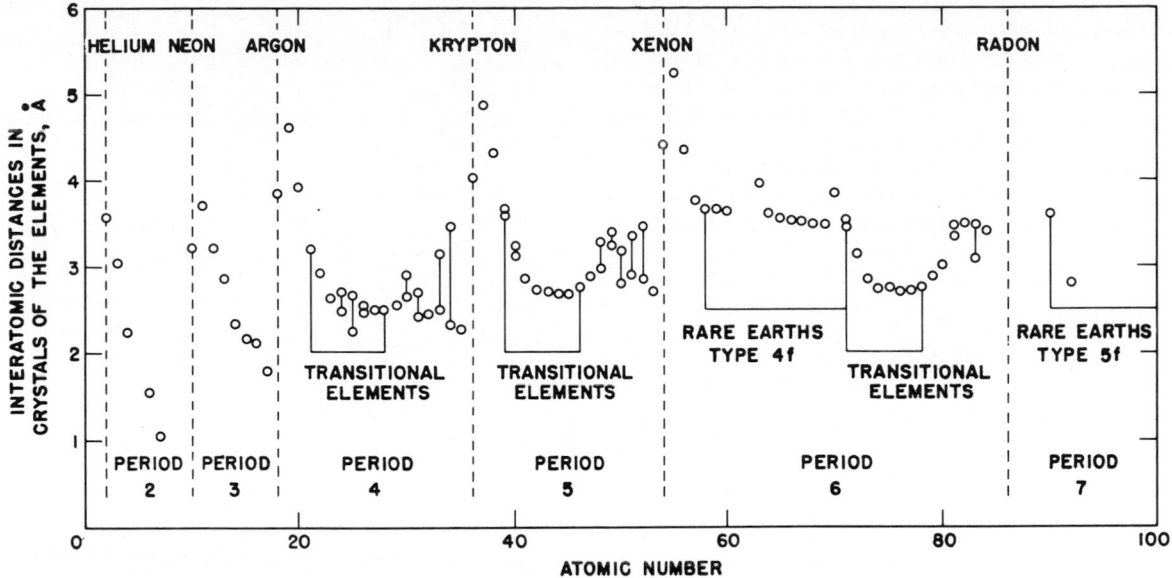

FIG. 12–37. Variation of interatomic distances of crystalline elements with the atomic number.

Some characteristic features of these non-stoichiometric compounds are given in the following examples:

(1) **Cation excess compounds**—When sodium chloride is heated in sodium vapor, some sodium dissolves in sodium chloride where the excess sodium cations occupy the regular sodium sites in the space lattice and the electrons accompanying the cations are situated at the anion vacancy sites.

(2) **Cation deficient compounds**—In these compounds the concentration of anions is greater than what would be expected from the valency considerations and the resulting vacant electron sites in the lattice are called "positive holes." These positive holes move through the lattice as positive electricity carriers (p-type electronic conduction). Wüstite, "FeO," is a classical example of this type of non-stoichiometric compound where the excess oxygen taken into solid solution raises the valency of some of the divalent iron cations to the trivalent state producing vacant cation sites. The extent of non-stoichiometry in wüstite depends on temperature and the oxygen partial pressure of the system; this is discussed in more detail later.

In some substances the non-stoichiometry extends over the range of cation excess to cation deficiency. For example, "titanium monoxide" has a composition range $Ti_{1.35}O$-$TiO_{0.60}$ and even in crystals corresponding to the stoichiometric composition TiO there are about 15 per cent unoccupied sites in both titanium and oxygen lattice, with cation vacancies (trapping of positive holes) and anion vacancies (trapping of electrons).

(3) **Interstitial compounds**—A large number of carbides and nitrides, where carbon or nitrogen is in the interstices of the metallic space lattice, form non-stoichiometric compounds. For example, at 400°C the nitrogen content of the γ' phase (nominally formulated as 'Fe₄N') is within the range 24 atom per cent–26.5 atom per cent, depending on the nitrogen pressure in equilibrium with the γ' phase.

GENERAL CONSIDERATIONS

As already discussed at some length, in crystalline phases the atoms (similar or dissimilar) are arranged in the space lattice in various ways depending on the basic properties of the elements constituting the phase. The chemical formula is nothing more than a simple way of representing the composition of a phase. When a substance undergoes a phase change brought about by changing the conditions of its environment, the atoms re-arrange themselves. For example, consider the oxidation of iron to magnetite,

$$3\ Fe\ (s) + 2O_2\ (g) = Fe_3O_4\ (s) \qquad (129)$$

where s and g indicate solid and gas states. When the partial pressure of oxygen of the system is higher than about 10^{-29} atm. at 500°C, a new phase is formed; in this the iron ions are situated in the interstices of the closely packed oxygen-ion lattice. At the stoichiometric composition Fe_3O_4, half the trivalent iron ions are situated in tetrahedral interstices between four oxygen ions and the other half, together with all the divalent iron ions, in octahedral interstices between six oxygen ions. At 500°C, this atomic arrangement will be stable until the oxygen partial pressure exceeds 10^{-18} atm., where further oxidation will occur to yield hematite,

$$4\ Fe_3O_4\ (s) + O_2\ (g) = 6\ Fe_2O_3\ (s) \qquad (130)$$

In the new phase produced, oxygen ions are arranged in close hexagonal packing with trivalent iron ions in two-thirds of the octahedral interstices.

Although the atomic arrangement in liquids is less rigid, there are considerable structural differences between different liquids. Generally speaking, the nature of the interatomic forces in liquids bears some resemblance to those in the crystalline state. For example, molten sodium chloride consists of sodium cations and chloride anions as in the solid state, except that the ions have greater mobilities. Similarly, in silicate melts silicon and oxygen atoms are held together by covalent bonds and cations are clustered around these oxy-acid anion complexes.

In chemical equations, reactants and products in the liquid phase are often indicated by definite chemical formulae, e.g.

$$CaO \text{ (in molten oxide)} + \frac{1}{2} S_2 \text{ } (g) =$$
$$CaS \text{ (in molten oxide)} + \frac{1}{2} O_2 \text{ } (g) \quad (131)$$

However, this does not mean that molecules CaO and CaS exist in molten oxides, as the chemical equation might suggest. Because of the ionic nature of oxide melts, reaction (131) may be written in terms of oxide and sulphide ions, thus

$$O^{2-} \text{ (in molten oxide)} + \frac{1}{2} S_2 \text{ } (g) =$$
$$S^{2-} \text{ (in molten oxide)} + \frac{1}{2} O_2 \text{ } (g) \quad (132)$$

This indicates that as sulphur dissolves in molten oxide, electrons are acquired from oxide ions and an equivalent amount of oxygen is liberated from the melt; this is true only when there are no other sources of electrons.

SECTION 3

IRON-BASED ALLOYS

IRON

On heating, iron undergoes two polymorphic phase transformations. Below 910°C, it crystallizes as b.c.c. (α), between 910°C and 1390°C as f.c.c. (γ) and between 1390° and the melting temperature, 1537°C, as b.c.c. (δ). As seen from the X-ray data in Figure 12–38, when f.c.c. structure (γ iron) is formed, the lattice constant increases. In metallurgical language, α — Fe is called the **ferrite phase** and γ — Fe, the **austenite phase.** The ferrite phase goes through a magnetic transformation at 768°C, above which iron is not magnetic; however, this is not a true polymorphic transformation. Since the lattice constant of austenite is larger than that of ferrite, the elements forming interstitial solid solutions in iron, i.e. within the iron space lattice, have larger solubilities in the austenite phase, e.g. H, B, C, N. In the substitutional solid solutions, solute atoms replace the solvent atoms in the space lattice of the latter. Depending on the nature of the alloying elements in iron, the transformation temperatures vary over a wide range. The elements with f.c.c. structure dissolved in iron favor the f.c.c. structure and, therefore, they extend the temperature stability range of the austenite phase, e.g. Ni, Co. Similarly, a solute element with b.c.c. struc-

ture extends the stability range of the ferrite phase, e.g. Si, Cr, V. The existence of these two crystalline forms of iron is largely responsible for the versatility of iron alloys in practical applications. The iron can be rendered malleable, ductile, tough or hard, by alloying with suitable elements and applying appropriate heat and mechanical treatments.

IRON–HYDROGEN

Solubility of Hydrogen in Iron—Initial studies on the solubility of gases in metals is attributed to Sieverts[37], who found experimentally that the amount dissolved in the metal is directly proportional to the square root of the partial pressure of the gas. This is known as the **Sieverts' law** and it states that when a di-atomic gas reacts with a metal, it dissolves in the atomic form. Thus, in the case of hydrogen:

$$\frac{1}{2} H_2 \text{ (gas)} = \underline{H} \text{ (dissol. in metal)} \quad (133)$$

whereby the hydrogen loses its gaseous character. Assuming ideal solutions, the equilibrium constant of reaction (133) is:

$$K = \frac{[H]}{(p_{H_2})^{\frac{1}{2}}} \quad (134)$$

The solubility of hydrogen in iron in equilibrium with $p_{H_2} = 1.0$ atm. is given in Figure 12–39 based on the data compiled by Geller and Sun[38]. Representing the concentration of hydrogen in iron in terms of cm.³ of H_2 at STP/(100 g. Fe $\times$ atm$^{\frac{1}{2}}$), the equilibrium constants and the free energies of solution of hydrogen in $\alpha(\delta)$, γ and liquid iron are given by the following equations

$$\log K_{a,\delta} = - \frac{1418}{T} + 1.677 \quad (135a)$$

$$\Delta F^\circ_{a,\delta} = 6490 - 7.672 T \text{ cal. per 0.5 mole } H_2 \quad (135b)$$

$$\log K_\gamma = - \frac{1182}{T} + 1.677 \quad (136a)$$

$$\Delta F^\circ_\gamma = 5408 - 7.672 \text{ cal. per 0.5 mole } H_2 \quad (136b)$$

$$\log K_l = - \frac{1637}{T} + 2.362 \quad (137a)$$

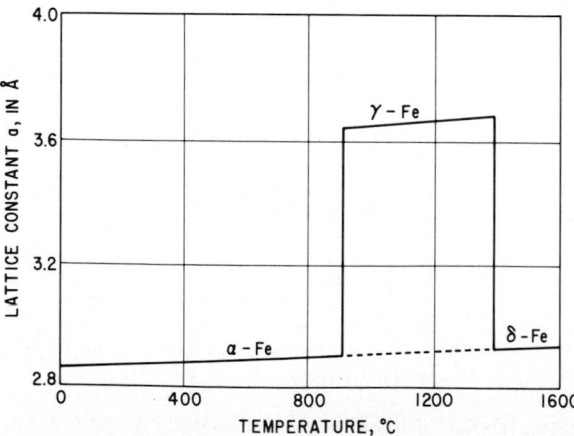

FIG. 12–38. Variation of lattice constant of pure iron with temperature. (From Basinski et al[36].)

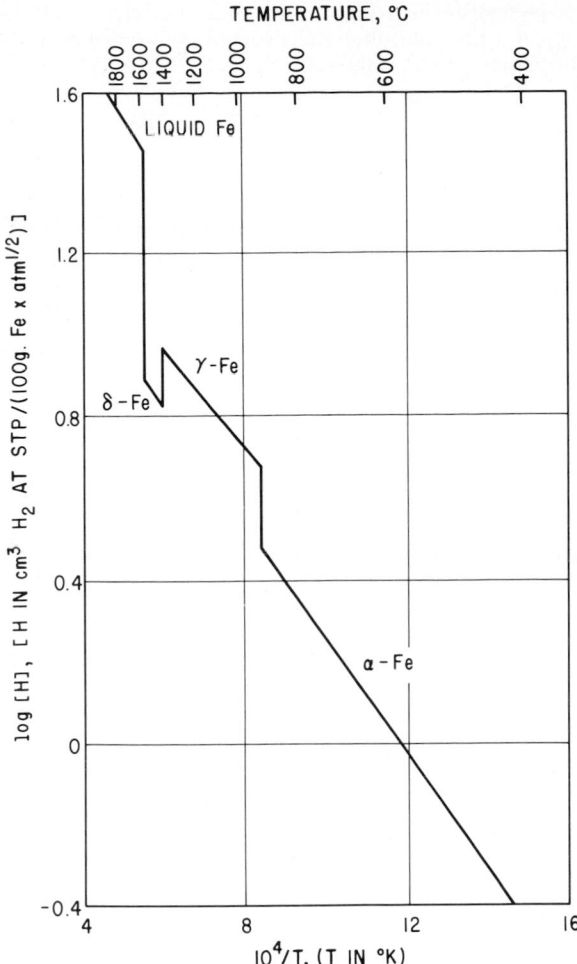

FIG. 12–39. Solubility of hydrogen in iron at $p_{H_2} = 1.0$ atm. (From Geller and Sun[38].)

$$\Delta F^\circ = 7490 - 10.806\ T \text{ cal. per 0.5 mole } H_2 \tag{137b}$$

If concentration of hydrogen in iron is required in terms of parts per million (ppm) by weight, the number 0.0494 should be subtracted from the values of log K obtained from the above equations.

Effect of Cold Work on Hydrogen Solubility— When determining the thermodynamic properties of solid systems, attempt is always made to insure that the solid substance is free of lattice defects brought about by lattice strains. If steel is subjected to some cold work it is found that the solubility of hydrogen and other gases increases. For example, Darken and Smith[39] observed that the solubility of hydrogen in plain carbon steel increased with increasing degree of cold work, e.g. hydrogen solubility at 35°C increased by a factor of about 15 when the steel was cold worked to the extent of 60 per cent reduction of area. Reference should also be made to a more recent publication by Hill and Johnson[40] on the effect of cold work on hydrogen solubility in steel. Detailed studies made by Podgurski[41] show that the anomalous hydrogen solubility in cold-worked plain carbon steels at temperatures above 200°C

could be attributed to the formation of methane through the reaction of hydrogen and cementite in the steel. For further details on this subject, reference should be made to the original papers cited.

Effect of Alloying Elements on Hydrogen Solubility—As seen from the data compiled in Figure

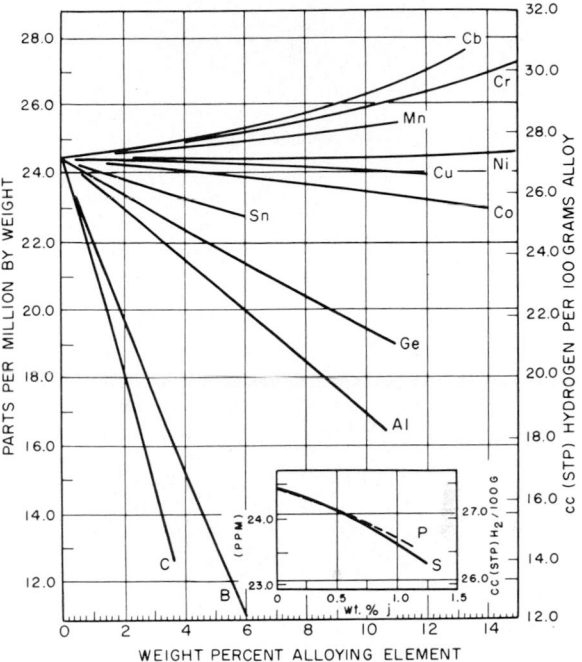

FIG. 12–40a. Solubility of hydrogen at 1 atm. pressure in binary iron alloys at 1592°C. (From Weinstein and Elliott[42].)

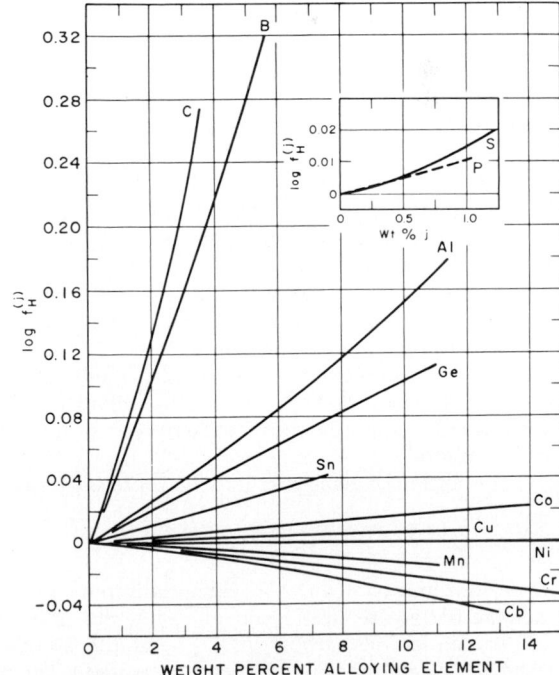

FIG. 12–40b. Effect of alloying elements on the activity coefficient of hydrogen in binary iron alloys at 1592°C. (From Weinstein and Elliott[42].)

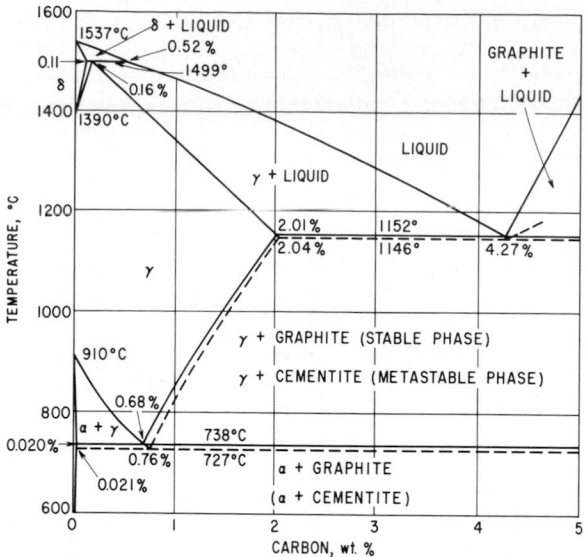

FIG. 12—41. Iron-carbon phase equilibrium diagram. Dashed line represents phase boundary for metastable equilibrium with cementite.

12–40a, on the solubility of hydrogen (at 1592°C and 1.0 atm. pressure) in molten iron alloys, the different elements dissolved in iron have different effects on this solubility. Denoting the solubilities in pure iron and iron alloys by $[H]°$ and $[H]$, respectively, the effect of the alloying element on the activity coefficient of dissolved hydrogen is given by the ratio $f = [H]°/[H]$ which can readily be evaluated from Figure 12–40a. The variation of $\log f_H^{(j)}$ with the concentration of the alloying element j is given in Figure 12–40b.

IRON-CARBON

Iron-Carbon Phase-Equilibrium Diagram—Since carbon is one of the most important ingredients of steel, the study of the iron-carbon phase-equilibrium diagram has received much attention during the past several decades. A comprehensive review of literature on this system is to be found in a book by Darken and Gurry[44] and in a recent paper by Benz and Elliott[45]. The phase diagram is given in Figure 12–41. There are three invariants in this system; peritectic at 1499°C, eutectic at 1152°C and eutectoid at 738°C. The phase boundaries shown by broken lines are for the metastable equilibrium of cementite, Fe_3C, with austenite. It was shown by Wells[46] that if sufficient time is allowed, iron-carbon alloys containing austenite and cementite decompose to austenite and graphite.

The solution of cementite may be represented as:

$$Fe_3C \text{ (cementite)} = 3 Fe (\alpha) + \underline{C} \text{ (in } \alpha\text{-Fe)} \tag{138}$$

Since iron and cementite are essentially pure phases, their activities are unity, and choosing the infinitely dilute solution of carbon in α-Fe as the standard state, i.e. $f_C \to 1.0$ when the carbon content (in per cent) approaches 0, the equilibrium constant of reaction (138) becomes equal to the concentration of carbon. Several investigators measured the solubility

of cementite in α-iron by the internal friction method, and the solubility data reviewed by Wert[47] may be represented by the equation:

$$\log [\%C] = -\frac{2120}{T} + 0.41 \tag{139}$$

However, Smith[48] showed from permeability measurements that the solubility calculated from the thermodynamic data on the iron-carbon system, expressed by the following equation, is more reliable:

$$\log [\%C] = -\frac{4330}{T} + 2.67 \tag{140}$$

The solubility of graphite in liquid iron is well established and the experimental data, reviewed by Neumann and Schenck[49], is summarized by the equation:

$$[\%C] = 1.30 + 2.57 \times 10^{-3} t \text{ (°C)} \tag{141}$$

If atom fraction (N_C) is used, the same set of data can be represented by the following equation in terms of $\log N_C$ and the reciprocal of the absolute temperature:

$$\log N_C = -\frac{560}{T} - 0.375 \tag{142}$$

Effect of Alloying Elements on the Solubility of Graphite in Liquid Iron—The effect of silicon, phosphorus, sulphur, manganese, cobalt and nickel on the solubility of graphite in molten iron was determined by Turkdogan et al[50, 51] and graphite solubility in iron-silicon and iron-manganese melts by Chipman et al[52, 53]. Similar measurements with iron-chromium melts were made by Griffing and co-work-

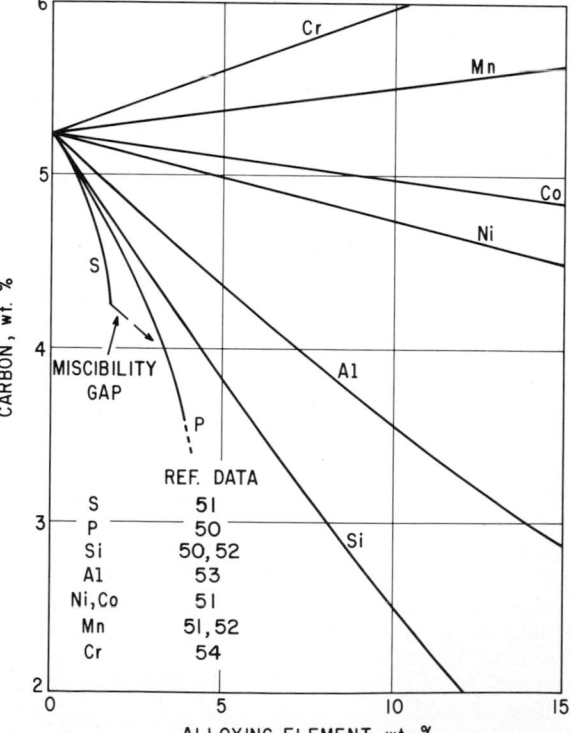

FIG. 12—42. Solubility of graphite in alloyed iron melts at 1500°C.

ers[54]. The experimental data are given graphically in Figure 12–42 for 1500°C; the solubility at other temperatures can be estimated from Figure 12–42, using the temperature coefficient given in equation (141) for pure iron. In the iron-sulphur-carbon system there is a large miscibility gap[51]. For example, at 1500°C the melt separates into two liquids containing: phase (I) 1.8 per cent S and 4.24 per cent C; phase (II) 0.90 per cent C and 26.5 per cent S.

Activity of Carbon in Iron—The activity of carbon in austenite was determined by Smith[55] by equilibrating pure iron-carbon alloys with CO-CO_2 and with H_2-CH_4 mixtures; his data are summarized in Figure 12–43, where carbon activity is given for two different standard states. When the standard state is so chosen that in infinitely dilute solutions $f_C \to 1.0$ when the carbon content (in per cent) approaches 0, the effect of temperature becomes almost negligible at least within the range 800°–1200°C.

The activities of carbon in the austenitic phase of Fe-Ni, Fe-Si and Fe-Mn alloys at 1000°C are given in Figures 12–44, 12–45 and 12–46, taken from the work of Smith[56, 57]. While manganese lowers the activity coefficient of carbon in austenite, nickel and silicon raise it. The minima observed on the isoactivity curves for the Fe-Ni-C alloys is in accord with similar observations on the solubility of graphite in nickel-rich iron melts (51).

The most reliable data so far available on the thermodynamics of iron-carbon binary melts (up to about 1 per cent C) are those presented by Richardson and

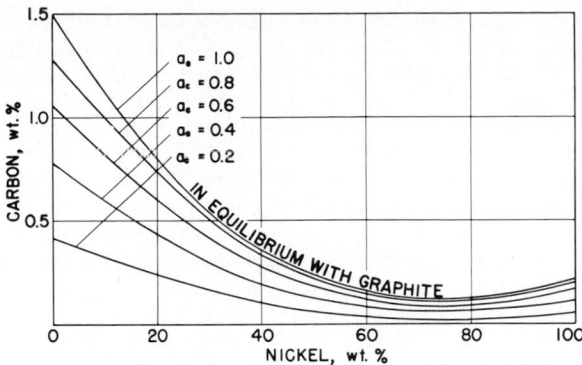

Fig. 12–44. Isoactivity curves for carbon in austenitic Fe-Ni-C alloys at 1000°C. (From Smith[56].)

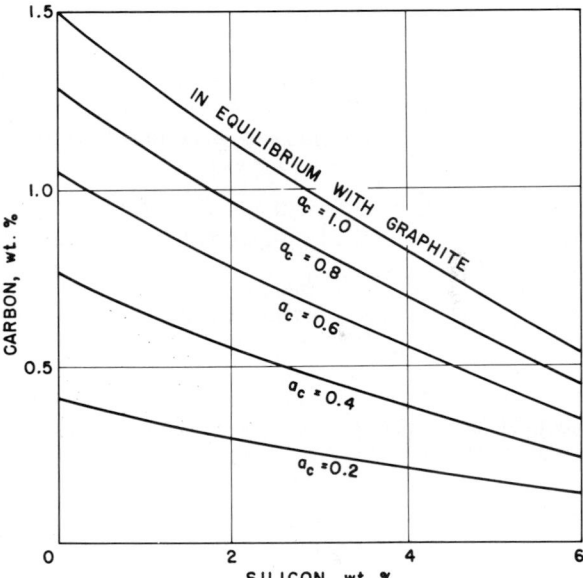

Fig. 12–45. Isoactivity curves for carbon in austenitic Fe-Si-C alloys at 1000°C. (From Smith[57].)

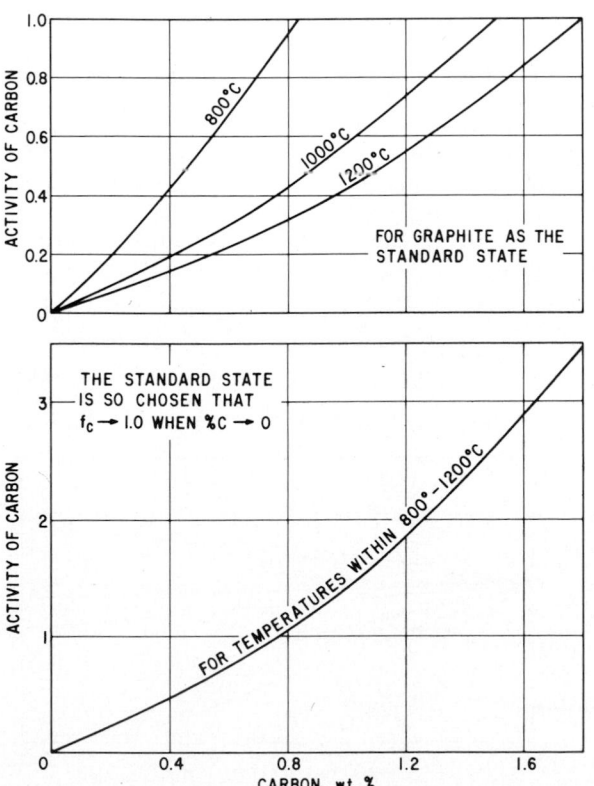

Fig. 12–43. Activity of carbon in austenite for two different standard states. (From Smith[55].)

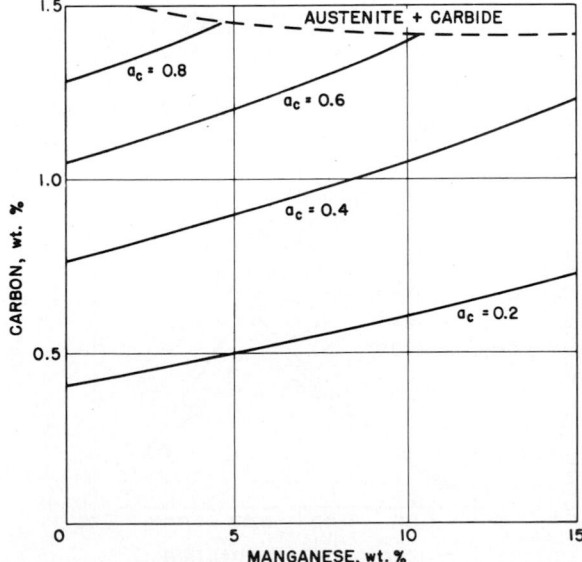

Fig. 12–46. Isoactivity curves for carbon in austenitic Fe-Mn-C alloys at 1000°C. (From Smith[57].)

Dennis[58]; their results on carbon activity are given in Figure 12–47. However, the activities measured by different investigators for high-carbon melts are at variance[59, 60, 61]. In the present considerations, the values obtained by Rist and Chipman[61] are used, and in Figure 12–48 the activity coefficient of carbon is given for which the standard state is that corresponding to $f_C \rightarrow 1.0$ when the carbon content (in per cent) $\rightarrow 0$.

The effects of various alloying elements on the activity coefficient of carbon in molten iron have recently been measured by Fuwa and Chipman[62]; these are shown in Figure 12–49. From thermodynamic considerations, Wagner[63] showed that the following expression applies for very dilute solutions:

$$f_i = f_i^i \times f_i^m \times f_i^n \times \ldots \qquad (143)$$

where f_i = activity coefficient of the ith component at low concentrations in a multicomponent system containing i, m, n, etc. solutes

f_i^i = activity coefficient of the ith component in a binary alloy with iron

$f_i^m, f_i^n \ldots$ = effects of the alloying elements m, n, .. etc. on the activity coefficient of the ith component.

In Figure 12–49, f_C^j represents the effect of any alloying element on the activity coefficient of carbon in liquid alloys at low carbon contents.

The standard free energy of solution of graphite in iron (1 per cent C hypothetical solution)

$$C \text{ (graphite)} = \underline{C}$$
$$\Delta F° = 5100 - 10.00\,T \text{ cal./g.-atom } \underline{C} \qquad (144)$$

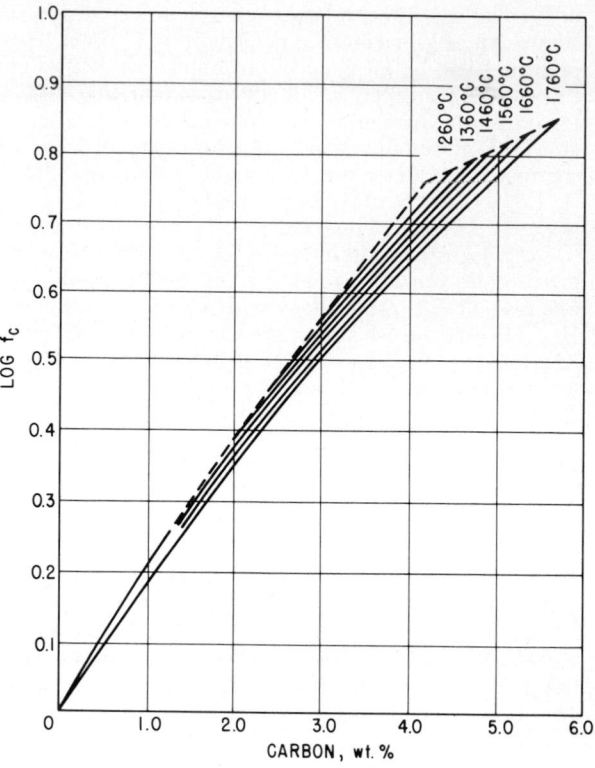

FIG. 12–48. Activity coefficient of carbon in liquid iron for the standard state $f_c \rightarrow 1.0$ when $\%C \rightarrow 0$. (From Rist and Chipman[61].)

IRON-NITROGEN

Solubility of Nitrogen in Iron—Since the initial work of Sieverts[37], several investigators have measured the solubility of nitrogen in α, γ, δ and liquid iron. Using the data considered to be most reliable, the solubility of nitrogen in iron at one atmosphere pressure is given in Figure 12–50, from which the following free energy equations are obtained; thus for the reaction:

$$\frac{1}{2}N_2(g) = \underline{N} \qquad (145a)$$

For α and δ iron:
$$\Delta F° = 7200 + 4.62\,T \qquad (145b)$$
$$\text{cal. per g.-atom } \underline{N}$$

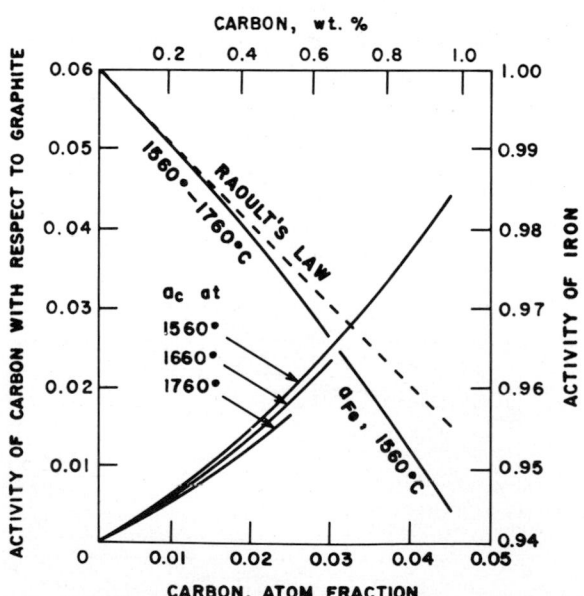

FIG. 12–47. Activity of carbon and iron in Fe-C melts. (From Richardson and Dennis[58].)

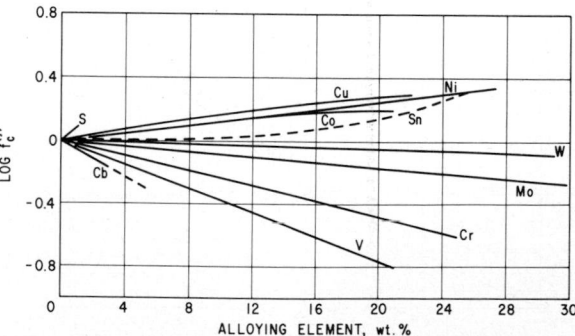

FIG. 12–49. Effect of alloying elements on activity coefficient of carbon for dilute solutions of carbon in iron at 1560°C. (From Fuwa and Chipman[62].)

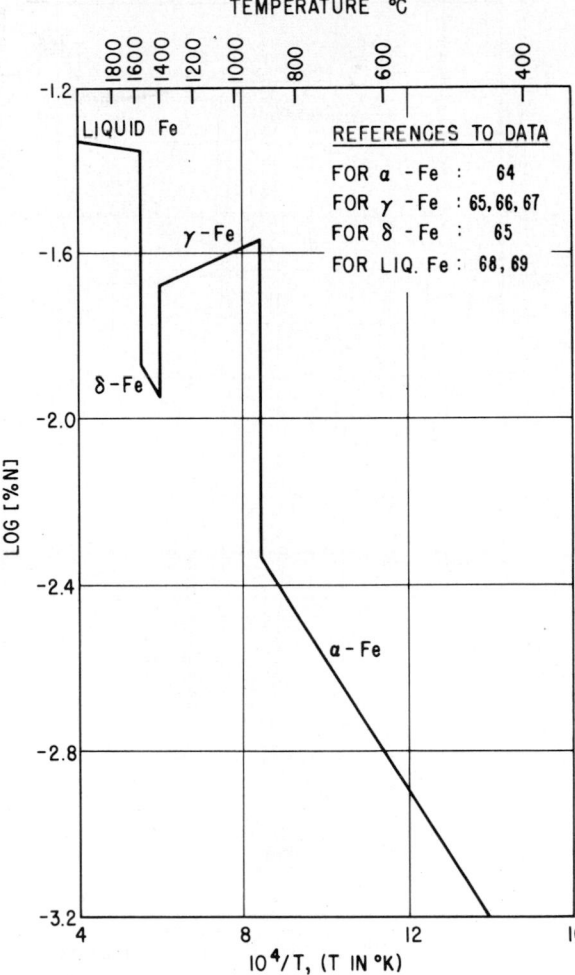

Fig. 12—50. Solubility of nitrogen in iron at $p_{N_2} = 1.0$ atm.

For γ iron:
$$\Delta F^\circ = -2060 + 8.94 \ T \qquad (145c)$$
$$\text{cal. per g.-atom } \underline{N}$$

For liquid iron:
$$\Delta F^\circ = 860 + 5.71 \ T \qquad (145d)$$
$$\text{cal. per g.-atom } \underline{N}$$

The standard state for N_2 is 1 atm. pressure and the standard state for $\underline{N}$ is such that $f_N \rightarrow 1.0$ when the nitrogen content (in per cent) $\rightarrow 0$.

As in the case of the iron-hydrogen system, the solubility of nitrogen in solid iron increases if the metal is subjected to some cold work; this effect is demonstrated well by Wriedt and Darken[70].

Effect of Alloying Elements on Nitrogen Solubility—The solubility of nitrogen in austenitic iron-silicon and iron-chromium alloys have been measured by Turkdogan and Ignatowicz[71, 72]; similar measurements have been made by Wriedt and Gonzalez[73] with iron-nickel alloys. The nitrogen solubilities in these alloys are given in Figure 12—51.

Figure 12—52 shows the effect of alloying elements on the activity coefficient of nitrogen dissolved in molten iron at 1600°C. Because of the similarity of the chemical characteristics of hydrogen, nitrogen and

carbon in the interstices of the iron lattice, the activity coefficients of these interstitial elements in solid or liquid iron are affected in a similar manner by the alloying elements, as manifested by the data in Figures 12—40b, 12—49 and 12—52.

Iron-Nitrogen Phase-Equilibrium Diagram—The phase-equilibrium diagram of the iron-nitrogen binary system is shown in Figure 12—53; for the details of work on this subject reference should be made to the papers reviewed by Hansen and Anderko[74]. It should be realized that this phase diagram is not for the iron-nitrogen system in equilibrium with one atm. pressure of nitrogen; the phases given are in equilibrium with very high nitrogen fugacities attainable by the dissociation, for example, of ammonia, thus

$$NH_3 = \underline{N} + 3/2 \ H_2 \qquad (146)$$

As seen from the results of Corney and Turkdogan[67] given in Figure 12—54, the nitrogen content of α-iron increases linearly with the gas ratio

$$P_{NH_3}/(p_{H_2})^{3/2}$$

as suggested by equation (146). The fugacity of nitrogen corresponding to the ammonia-hydrogen

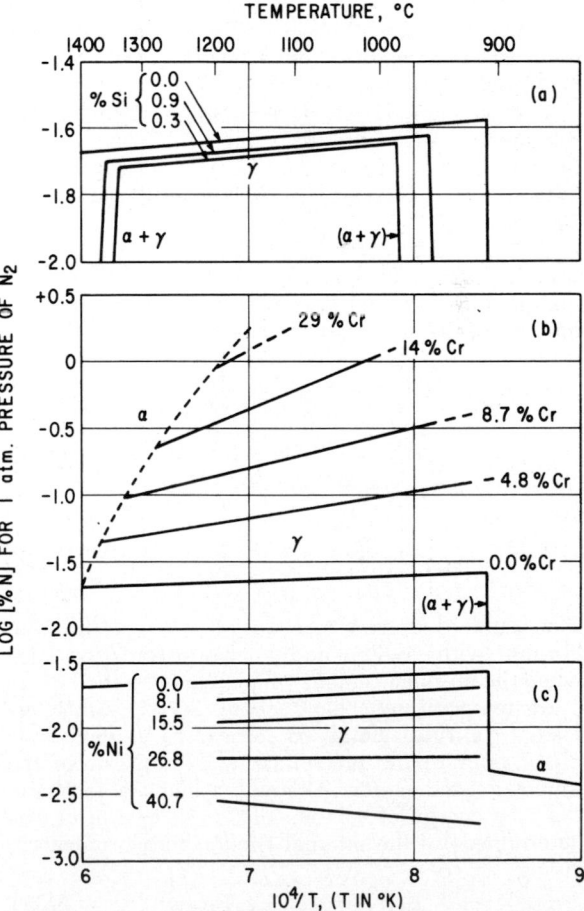

Fig. 12—51. Solubility of nitrogen in austenitic alloys at $p_{N_2} = 1.0$ atm. Diagrams (a) and (b) from Turkdogan and Ignatowicz[71, 72] diagram (c) from Wriedt and Gonzalez[73].

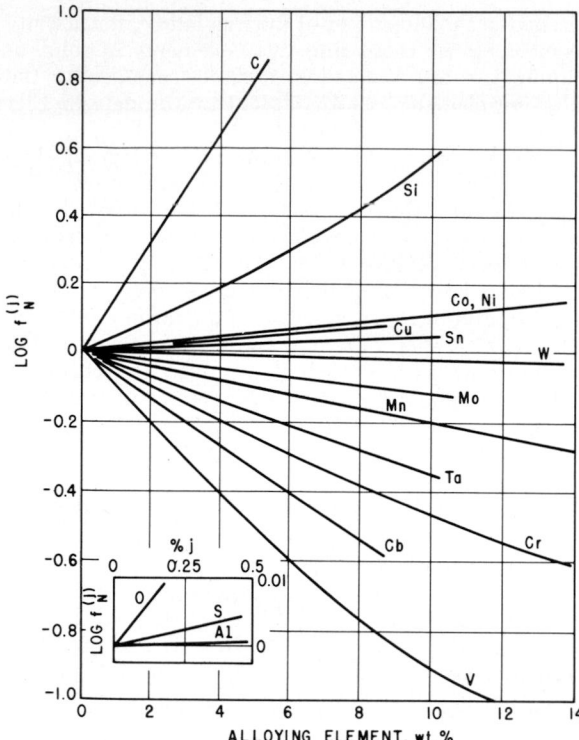

FIG. 12–52. Effect of alloying elements on the activity coefficient of nitrogen in iron at 1600°C. (From Schenck et al.[68] and Pehlke and Elliott[69].)

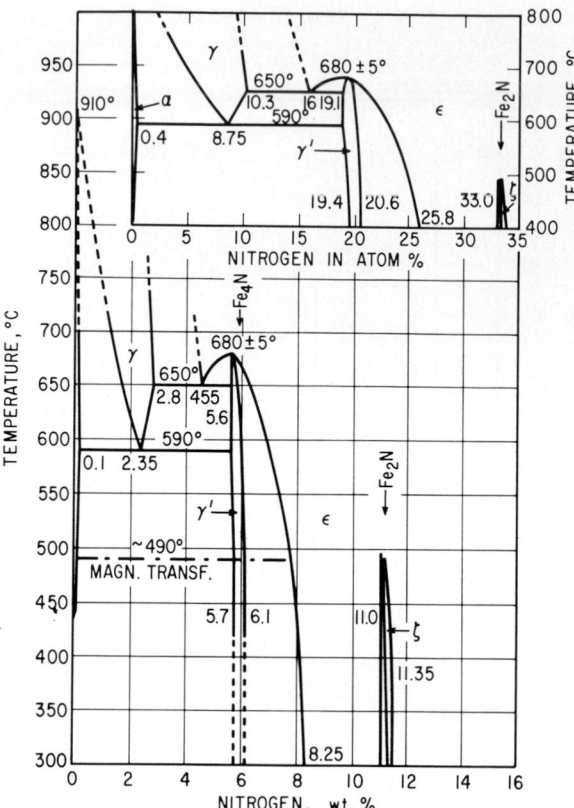

FIG. 12–53. Iron-nitrogen phase equilibrium diagram. (From Hansen and Anderko[74].)

mixtures are given for 502° and 605°C on the right hand ordinate of Figure 12–54. The horizontal lines indicate the univariant equilibria where α-iron and iron nitride, 'Fe$_4$N', co-exist.

The solubility of iron nitride, 'Fe$_4$N', in α-iron was determined by several workers; using the values obtained by Fast and Verrijp[64], from internal friction measurements, the following equation may be written for the free energy of solution of iron nitride in α-iron:

$$\text{'Fe}_4\text{N'} = \underline{\text{N}} + 4\,\text{Fe}\,(\alpha) \qquad (147a)$$

$$\Delta F^\circ = 8300 - 4.99\,T \qquad (147b)$$
$$\text{cal. per g.-atom }\underline{\text{N}}$$

and

$$\log[\%\text{N}] = -\frac{1814}{T} + 1.09 \qquad (147c)$$

The standard states are: pure α-Fe, 'Fe$_4$N' in equilibrium with α-Fe and for nitrogen $f_\text{N} \to 1.0$ when the nitrogen content (in per cent) $\to 0$.

At temperatures below about 300°C, an intermediate nitride, 'Fe$_8$N', is formed as a metastable phase prior to the precipitation of 'Fe$_4$N' from the supersaturated α-iron. Although a metastable phase, the free energy of solution of 'Fe$_8$N' in α-iron was determined by the internal friction measurements[64], giving

$$\text{'Fe}_8\text{N'} = \underline{\text{N}} + 8\,\text{Fe}\,(\alpha) \qquad (148a)$$

$$\Delta F^\circ = 9900 - 11.52\,T \qquad (148b)$$
$$\text{cal. per g.-atom }\underline{\text{N}}$$

IRON-OXYGEN

Iron-Oxygen Phase-Equilibrium Diagram—The thermodynamics of the iron-oxygen system was studied in detail by Darken and Gurry[75]. Figure

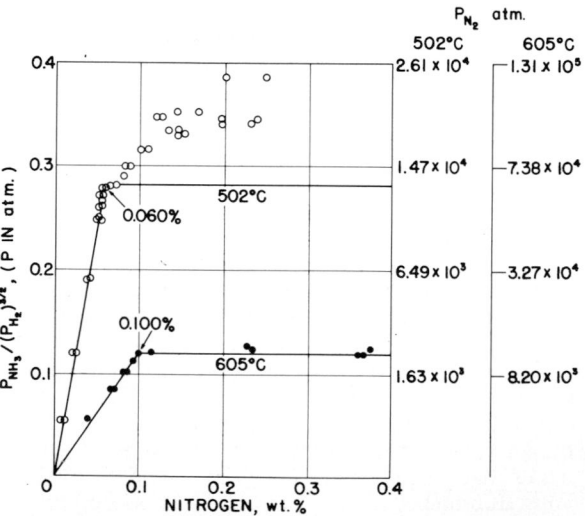

FIG. 12–54. The ratio $(p_{\text{NH}_3})/(p_{\text{H}_2})^{3/2}$ in equilibrium with the concentration of nitrogen dissolved in α–iron. Nitrogen pressures on the right hand ordinate are the nitrogen fugacities for the corresponding ratios $p_{\text{NH}_3}/(p_{\text{H}_2})^{3/2}$. (From Corney and Turkdogan[67].)

12–55 gives the temperature-composition phase diagram for a total pressure of one atmosphere. Temperatures, compositions and the equilibrium gas ratios p_{CO_2}/p_{CO} are also given in Figure 12–55 for certain fixed points in the iron-oxygen system. There are two characteristic features of this system. Oxygen is soluble in iron to a limited extent only; at the eutectic temperature 1524°C, the maximum solubility is 0.16 per cent O above which a liquid oxide phase, containing 22.6 per cent O, is formed. The second characteristic feature is the formation of wüstite, which has a variable composition and is not

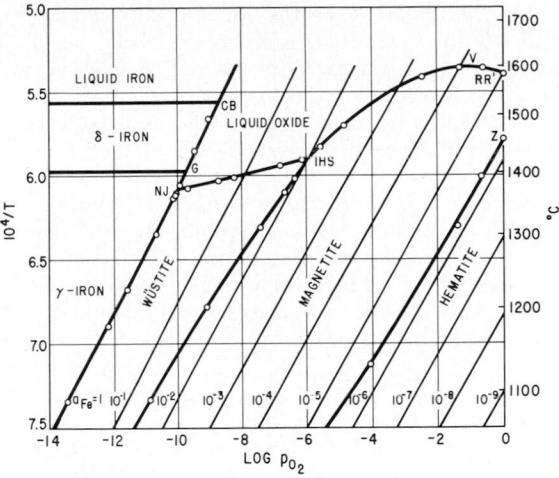

Fig. 12–56. Relation between $\log p_{O_2}$ and $1/T$ for the several three-phase equilibria, and the calculated isoactivity curves of iron in solid and liquid oxide throughout the range. (From Darken and Gurry[75].)

stable below 560°C. The stoichiometric ferrous oxide does not exist and the wüstite in equilibrium with iron has the composition corresponding to about $Fe_{0.95}O$ within the temperature range 800°–1371°C (melting temperature). That is, wüstite is deficient in iron cations and the electroneutrality is maintained by the presence of some trivalent iron cations together with the divalent iron cations in wüstite. Within the wüstite phase, the ratio Fe^{3+}/Fe^{2+} increases with increasing partial pressure of oxygen. Although magnetite in equilibrium with wüstite has the stoichiometric composition Fe_3O_4, in the presence of hematite the magnetite phase becomes deficient in iron with increasing temperature. The remainder of the diagram in Figure 12–55 is self-explanatory.

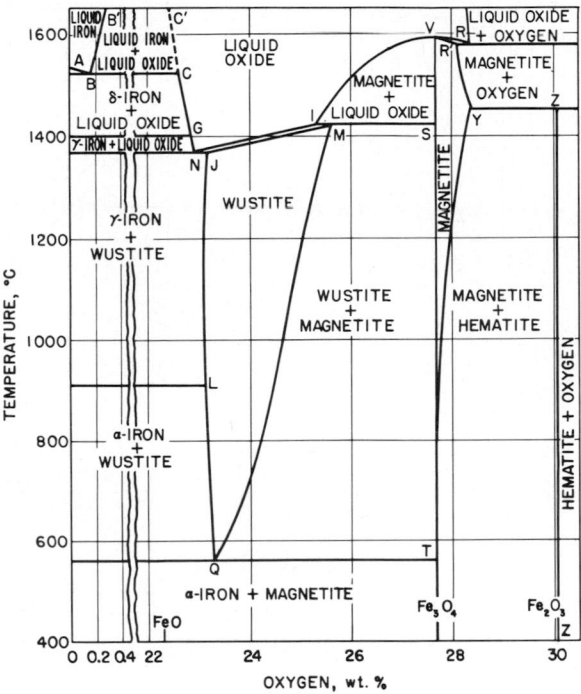

Fig. 12–55. The temperature-composition phase diagram of the iron-oxygen system at a total pressure of one atmosphere. Recommended values for certain fixed points are as follows:

IRON-OXYGEN SYSTEM AT
ONE ATMOSPHERE PRESSURE
(From Darken and Gurry[75].)

Point	°C	%O	p_{CO_2}/p_{CO}	p_{O_2}
A	1537			
B	1524	0.16	0.209	
C	1524	22.60	0.209	
G	1400*	22.84	0.263	
H	1424	25.60	16.2	
I	1424	25.31	16.2	
J	1371	23.16	0.282	
L	911*	23.10	0.447	
N	1371	22.91	0.282	
Q	560	23.26	1.05	
R	1583	28.30		1
R'	1583	28.07		1
S	1424	27.64	16.2	
V	1597	27.64		0.0575
Y	1457	28.36		1
Z	1457	30.04		1
Z'		30.06		

*Value for pure iron.

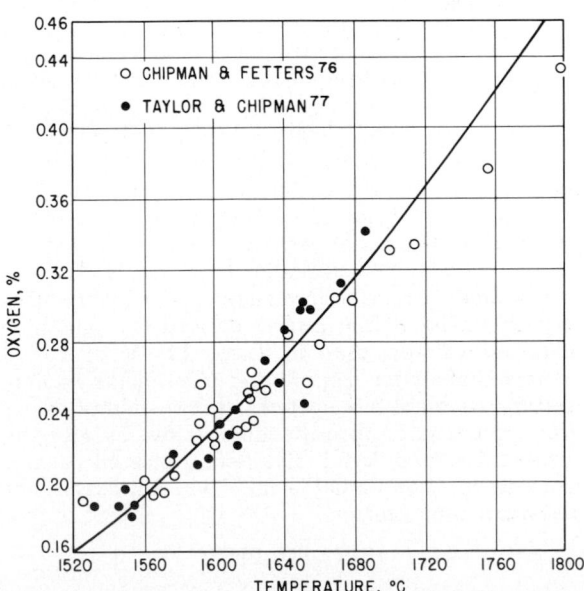

Fig. 12–57. Solubility of oxygen in liquid iron in equilibrium with almost pure molten iron oxide.

Figure 12–56 gives the relation between log p_{O_2} and $1/T$ for several three-phase equilibria, i.e. phase boundaries, and isoactivity curves of iron in solid and liquid oxides.

The thermodynamic data on the iron oxides were given in Tables 12–II and 12–III in Part I of this chapter.

Solubility of Oxygen in Iron—The solubility of oxygen in molten iron in equilibrium with almost pure iron oxide was determined by Chipman and co-workers[76, 77]; their results are given in Figure 12–57 and variation of solubility with temperature is represented by the equation:

$$\log (\%O) = -\frac{6320}{T} + 2.734 \qquad (149)$$

This also represents the equilibrium constant for the reaction

$$\text{'FeO'} = \underline{O} + \text{Fe} \qquad (150)$$

where the standard state for 'FeO' is pure iron oxide in equilibrium with liquid iron and for $\underline{O}$, $f_O \to 1.0$ when the oxygen content (in per cent) $\to$ zero.

The solution of oxygen in iron obeys Sieverts' law, and the following free energy of solution is derived from the work of Dastur and Chipman[78]:

$$\frac{1}{2} O_2 = \underline{O} \qquad (151a)$$

$$\Delta F° = -28,000 - 0.69\ T \qquad (151b)$$
$$\text{cal. per g.-atom } \underline{O}$$

for the standard states, p_{O_2} in atms. and $f_O \to 1.0$ when the oxygen content (in per cent) $\to$ zero.

The solubility[79, 80] of oxygen in pure α and γ-iron is exceedingly low; in fact, below the experimental uncertainty.

Effect of Alloying Elements on Oxygen Solubility—The solubility of oxygen in molten iron is affected by the alloying elements in two ways. First, the solubility is limited by the formation of an oxide phase, and secondly, the activity coefficient of oxygen is raised or lowered depending on the extent of interaction between oxygen and elements dissolved in iron. As seen from the data compiled in Figure 12–58, most of the elements lower the activity coefficient of oxygen. Generally speaking, the lower the oxygen potential of the oxide of an element j, the lower is the value of $f_O^{(j)}$. Using equation (143) one may estimate the activity coefficient of oxygen in iron containing several alloying elements.

The free energies of formation of oxides in equilibrium with liquid iron can be derived by combining equation (151b), $\Delta F°$ in Table 12–IV of Part I of this chapter for the solution of elements in iron, and the standard free energies of formation of oxides from elements in their standard states, as given in Table 12–III of Part I. The details of such calculations are given in Parts IV and V when discussing the deoxidation of steel.

IRON-SULPHUR

Iron-Sulphur Phase-Equilibrium Diagram—The iron-sulphur phase equilibrium diagram reviewed by Hansen and Anderko[74] is given in Figure 12–59.

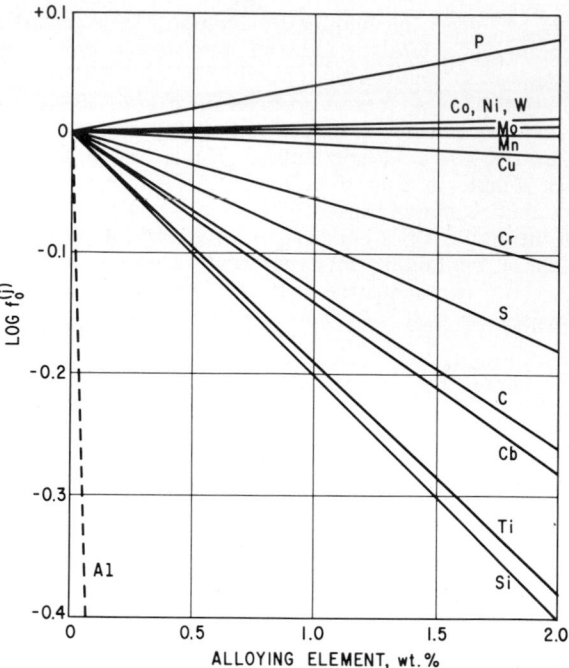

FIG. 12–58. Effect of alloying elements on activity coefficient of oxygen in iron at 1600°C. (From Chipman and Elliott[81].)

The composition of iron sulphide, FeS, in equilibrium with iron deviates from stoichiometry at temperatures above 1000°C; the iron sulphide forms a eutectic with

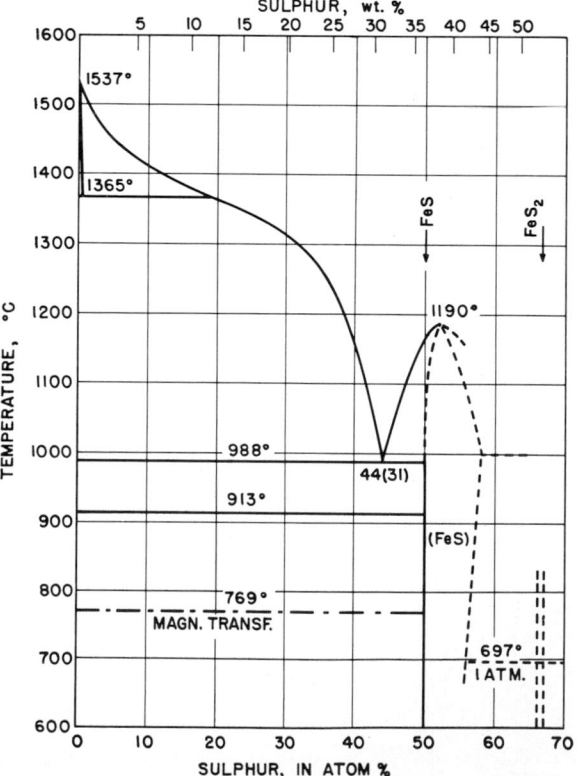

FIG. 12–59. Iron-sulphur phase-equilibrium diagram. (From Hansen and Anderko[78].)

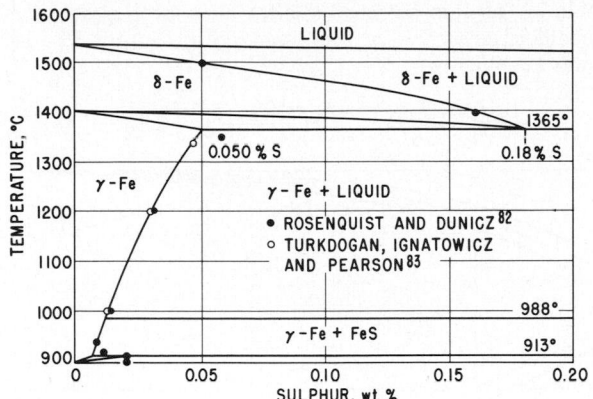

FIG. 12–60. Iron-rich corner of the iron-sulphur phase equilibrium diagram.

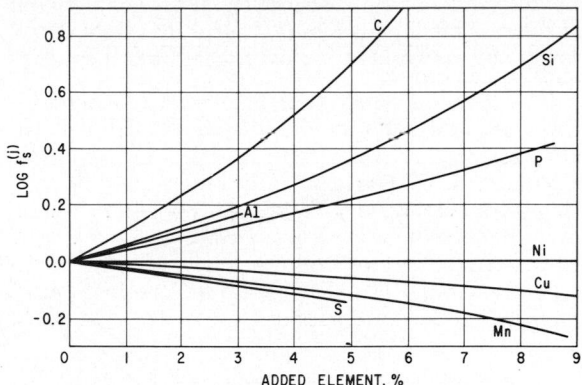

FIG. 12–62. Effect of alloying elements on the activity co-efficient of sulphur in iron at 1600°C. (From Sherman and Chipman[85].)

γ-iron at 988°C and 31% S. The solubility of sulphur in solid iron was determined by Rosenquist and Dunicz[82] and by Turkdogan, Ignatowicz and Pearson[83]; the iron-rich corner of this system is shown in Figure 12–60. The solubility in the γ-phase increases from 0.005 per cent S (at 913°C) to 0.050 per cent S (at 1365°C). The invariant at 1365°C is for the three-phase equilibrium between γ, δ-iron and iron-sulphur melt.

Activity Coefficient of Sulphur in Iron and Iron Alloys—Sherman, Elvander and Chipman[84] measured the solubility of sulphur in iron by equilibrating with hydrogen-hydrogen sulphide mixtures. As seen from Figure 12–61, there is a slight departure from Henry's law with increasing sulphur concentration. The results of this work lead to the following free energy of solution of sulphur in iron:

$$\frac{1}{2} S_2 = \underline{S} \qquad (152a)$$

$$\Delta F^\circ = -31,520 + 5.27\,T \qquad (152b)$$
$$\text{cal. per g.-atom } \underline{S}$$

Several workers studied the effect of alloying elements on the activity coefficient of sulphur in iron. The data compiled by Sherman and Chipman[85] are reproduced in Figure 12–62.

Similar to the effect of carbon, oxygen raises the activity coefficient of sulphur as manifested by the existence of a miscibility gap in the iron-oxygen-sulphur system; this is shown in Figure 12–63. The sulphur-oxygen equilibrium in this system was studied by Bog and Rosenquist[87], Dewing and Richardson[88] and Turkdogan and Darken[89]; reaction of iron oxide melts with sulphur and oxygen-bearing gases is discussed in Part III of this chapter.

IRON-SILICON

For the present purpose, consideration of this system is limited to the activity of silicon in molten iron-silicon and iron-silicon-carbon alloys.

Activity of Silicon—The activity of silicon in iron-silicon and iron-silicon-carbon melts was evaluated indirectly by Chipman and co-workers[90], from the

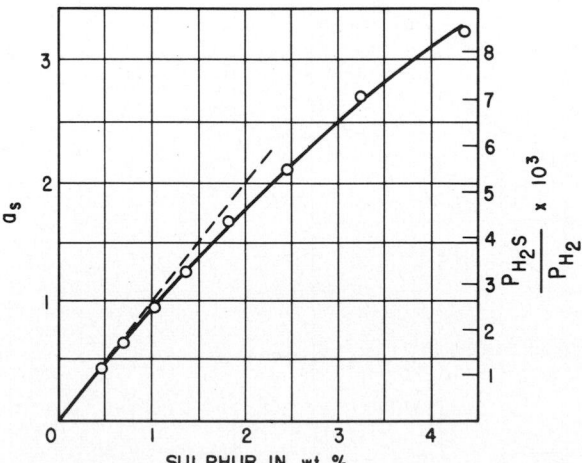

FIG. 12–61. Variation of sulphur content of iron at 1600°C. with p_{H_2S}/p_{H_2} (or activity). Standard state: $f_s \rightarrow 1.0$ when $\%S \rightarrow 0$. (From Sherman, Elvander and Chipman[84].)

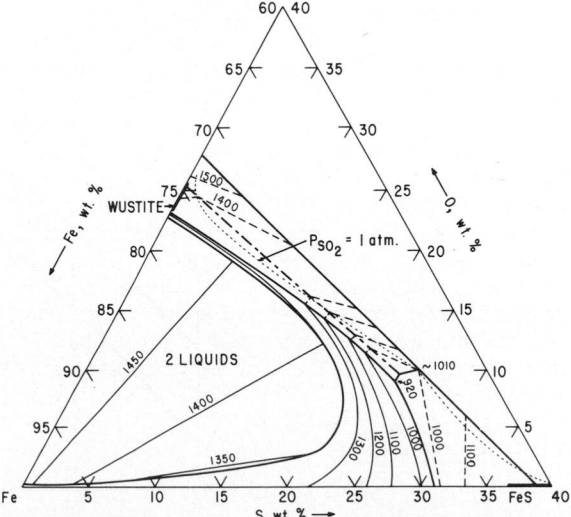

FIG. 12–63. Liquidus surfaces and miscibility gap in Fe-S-O ternary system. (From Hilty and Crafts[86] & Bog and Rosenquist[87].)

measurement of the distribution of silicon between the immiscible liquids iron and silver. Recently, Turkdogan and co-workers[91] reinvestigated the thermodynamics of this system. Their values of the activity coefficients γ_{Fe}, γ_{Si} are summarized in Figures 12–64 and 12–65.

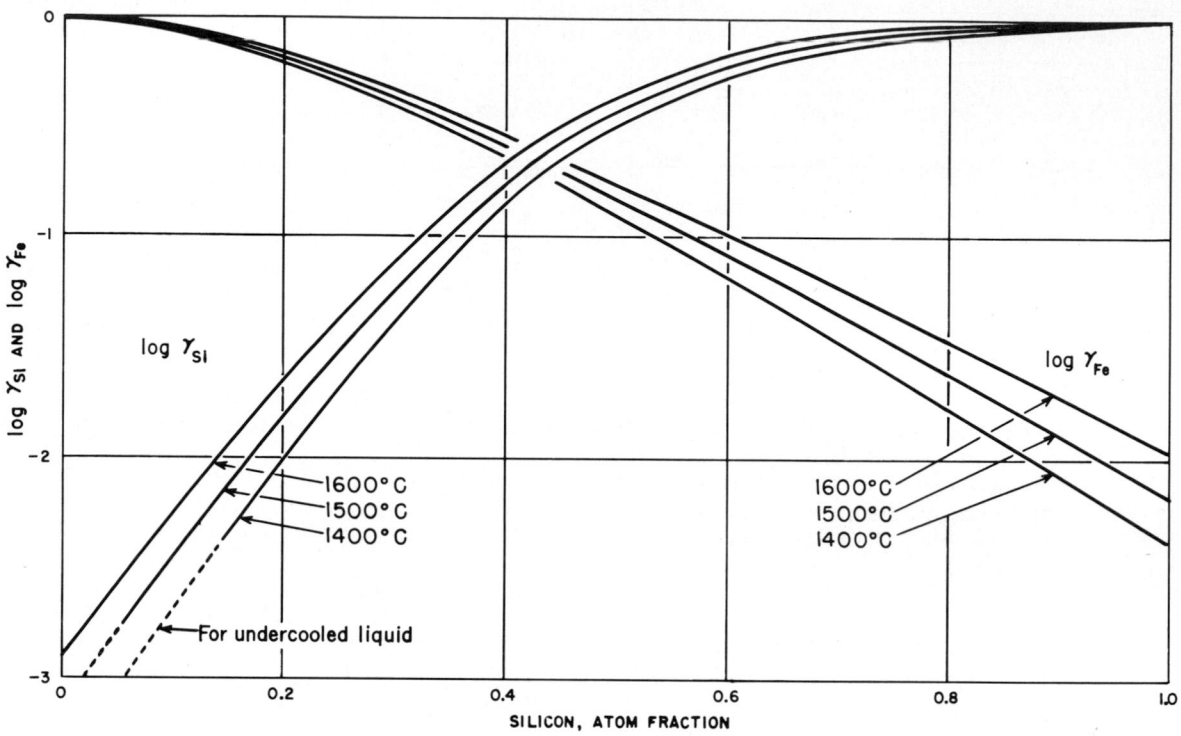

FIG. 12–64. Activity coefficient of silicon and iron in iron-silicon melts. (From Turkdogan et al.[91])

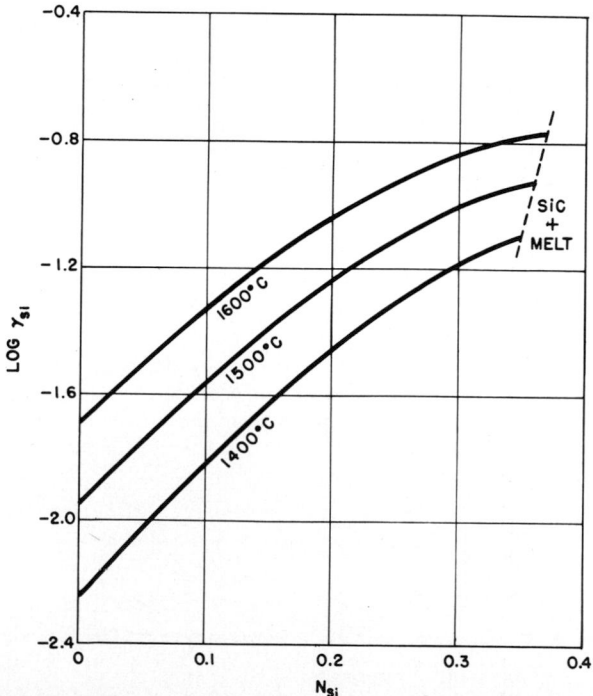

FIG. 12–65. Activity coefficients of silicon in graphite saturated iron-silicon melts. (From Turkdogan et al.[91])

SECTION 4

INTERDIFFUSIVITIES IN MOLTEN IRON ALLOYS

There is a lack of experimental data on the coefficients of diffusion in molten iron alloys, and the reliability of those measured is not certain. If the mechanism of diffusion is not affected by temperature, the variation of the coefficient of diffusion is represented by the following equation (**Arrhenius equation**) as derived from the absolute reaction rate theory (see Part I of this chapter).

$$D = D_0 \exp\left(-\frac{\Delta H^*}{RT}\right) \qquad (153)$$

where D_0 is constant and ΔH^* is the heat of activation for the diffusion process. However, equation (153) should be used only when the diffusivity data are reasonably accurate. In the case of diffusivity measurements in molten iron alloys, there are large discrepancies between the results of different workers and, therefore, little significance can be attached to the values of D_0 and ΔH^* derived from the experimental results obtained over a narrow temperature range.

Most of the measurements have been made with graphite-saturated ternary iron alloys. Using the available data, the interdiffusivities are calculated, by interpolation or extrapolation, for 1550°C and are given in Table 12–X; the uncertainty of each reported value is about $\pm$ 10 to 30 per cent. More serious, however, is the inconsistency of the results of different workers. For example, the results of Morgan and Kitchener[94] on the interdiffusivity in iron-carbon melts is not compatible with the value obtained by Grace and Derge[92]; the diffusivity of carbon is expected to be higher than that of the other elements dissolved substitutionally in the iron lattice. It should be realized that the coefficient of diffusion, as a property of state, varies with the composition of the system as well as with temperature and pressure. Therefore, the data compiled in Table

12–X should not be used for compositions much above the range for which the data were obtained experimentally.

Table 12–X. Interdiffusivities in Molten Iron Alloys at 1550°C*

Element	Concentration from 0.0 to wt. %	$D \times 10^5$ cm.^{2}/sec.	References to data
Dissolved in graphite-saturated iron			
Si	0.7	18	92
Si	3.0	2.5	93
Si	18	6.5	93
P	1.5	15	92
S	0.9	6	92
S	0.6	3.5	93
Ti	0.6	5.5	92
Mn	1.5	9	92
Mn	low	3.9	93
Ni	1.5	4	92
Dissolved in iron			
C	1.5	33	92
C	2.5	47	92
C	0.03	7.9	94
C	3.5	6	94
Si	low	3	93
Si	2	10	95
S	1	4.5	93
Mn	1	19	95
Co	low	4.6	94
Self-diffusivity of iron in iron-carbon melts			
Fe	2.5% C	14	96
Fe	4.6% C	14	96

*Derived by interpolation or extrapolation of the experimental data

SECTION 5

VISCOSITIES AND DENSITIES OF SOME MOLTEN METALS

Viscosity—Viscosity is a measure of the resistance of a fluid medium to flow. It is the property which opposes the relative motion of adjacent portions of the liquid (or gas). Let us consider two layers of a liquid (or a gas) moving parallel to one another at different velocities. Owing to the relative motions of the layers, there will be a transfer of some of the momentum from one layer to the other, resulting in a decrease of the rate at which one layer moves with respect to the other; in order to overcome this frictional effect, force must be applied to maintain the relative motions of the layers. The **coefficient of viscosity**, η, is therefore defined as the shearing force per unit area required to maintain a unit difference of velocity between the adjacent layers a unit dis-

tance apart. When c.g.s. units are used, the viscosity coefficient has the dimensions of dynes-sec. per cm^2 and this is called "poise" (**millipoise** = 10^{-3} poise and **centipoise** = 10^{-2} poise).

The reciprocal of the coefficient of viscosity is called the **fluidity**; this is a measure of the ease with which a liquid can flow.

The coefficients of viscosity of iron, cobalt, nickel and copper measured by Cavalier[97] are given in Figure 12–66. In these experiments, Cavalier was able to supercool metals 140°–170°C below their melting points and, as seen from the data in Figure 12–66, there are no discontinuities on the viscosity coefficient vs. temperature lines extending below the melting temperatures of the metals. Although the

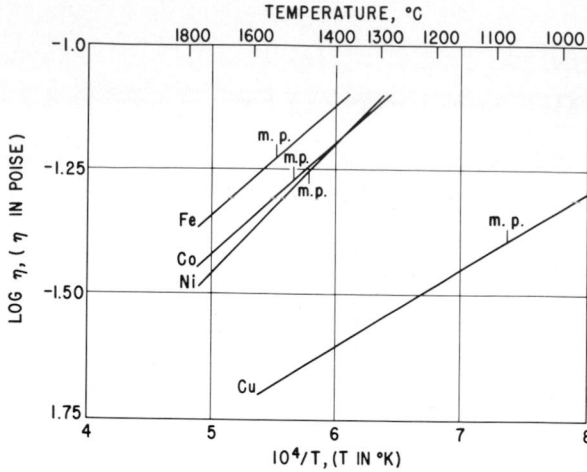

FIG. 12–66. Variation of viscosity of some metals with temperature. (From Cavalier[97].)

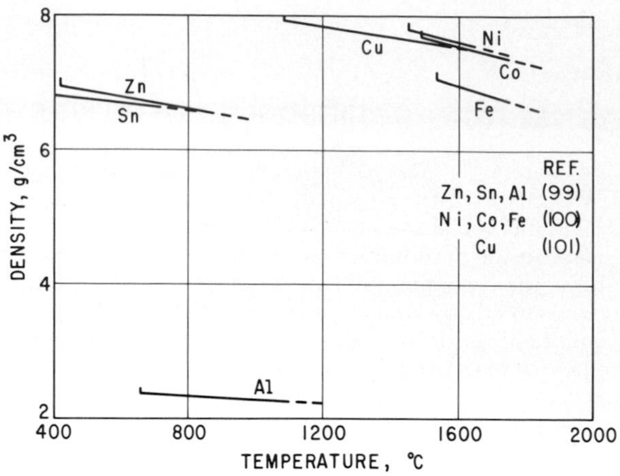

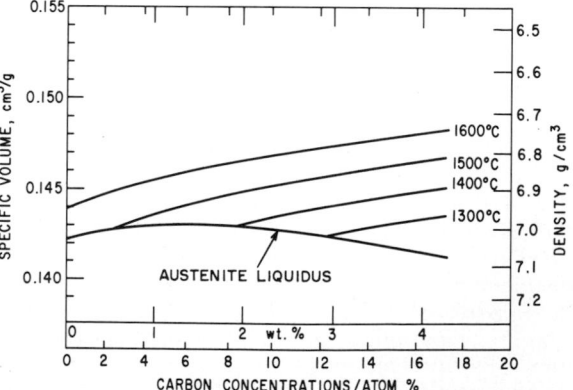

FIG. 12–68. Densities of some pure metals above their melting temperatures.

viscosity data on copper obtained by Barfield and Kitchener[98] are in complete agreement with those of Cavalier, the data on molten iron by the former authors are higher than Cavalier's values by about 1 centipoise.

The results of Barfield and Kitchener[98] given in Figure 12–67 show a small decrease in viscosity of iron with increase of carbon up to about 0.8 per cent. Within the composition range 0.8–2.5 per

cent C, the coefficient of viscosity does not change and above 2.5 per cent C, the viscosity decreases continuously with increasing carbon. Similar observations were made when measuring the flow of iron-carbon alloys into molds[99].

Density—Because of the experimental difficulties, the data on the density of molten metals and alloys are meager. In fact, at present the measurements on metals with high melting temperatures are confined to a few pure metals and those of some interest to ferrous metallurgy are given in Figure 12–68. Decrease in the density of iron with increasing carbon content and increasing temperature is shown in Figure 12–69; earlier work in this field reported by Widawski and Sauerwald[102]. Recently, Worth and St. Pierre[103] measured the densities of graphite-saturated iron-silicon melts; they found that the density of the alloys decreases smoothly with increasing silicon content from 6.8 g. per cm.³ at 1 per cent Si to 5.5 g. per cm.³ at 18 per cent Si.

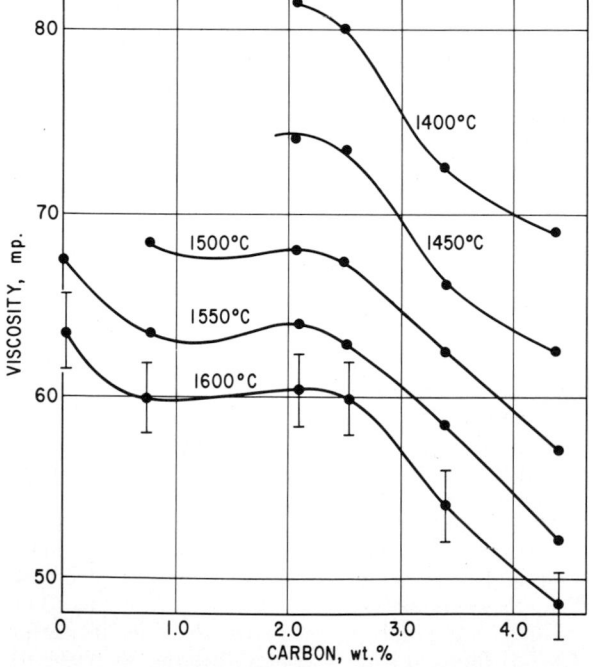

FIG. 12–67. Effect of carbon on the viscosity of iron. (From Barfield and Kitchener[98].)

FIG. 12–69. Specific volume and density of iron-carbon melts for the temperature range 1300°–1600°C. (From Lucas[104].)

CHAPTER 12 (Continued)

The Physical Chemistry of Iron- and Steelmaking

PART III

Physico-Chemical Properties of Some

Oxide Systems and Slags

SECTION 1
INTRODUCTION

Although slag is a by-product in the iron- and steelmaking processes, the understanding of the chemistry of these high-temperature processes and the study of the methods of control require some knowledge of the basic physico-chemical properties of slags and also of the oxide systems constituting the refractory materials used in the industry. With this in view, data are compiled in this part on the phase-equilibrium diagrams, activities, coefficients of diffusion of ions, viscosity, density and surface tension of some oxide systems of interest in chemical metallurgy.

The systems consisting of silicates, silico-phosphates, aluminates, borates, ferrites, etc., are generally called slags; their structure in the crystalline or molten state have some similar characteristics. Experiments on electrical conductivity and electrolysis carried out over 50 years ago indicated that natural silicates and slags consist of simple and complex ions. The theory of the structure of glasses in general was first studied by Zachariasen[105] and Warren[106] using data on X-ray diffraction measurements. The structural studies were later extended to molten slags, for example by Warren, et al[107]. Since the 1930's, many papers have been published on the structure of solid and molten glasses and slags. Although these investigations revealed several important facts about the structures of these systems, no fundamental changes were made to the original theory developed by Zachariasen and Warren, et al.

The basic concept is that, in glasses and molten silicates, the structure consists of tetrahedrally bonded Si-O networks or rings with cations randomly distributed in the interstices. In fused or vitreous

pure silica, each silicon atom is bonded to four oxygen atoms and each oxygen atom to two silicon atoms, and the network is continuous in three dimensions. Although in the crystalline state the tetrahedral arrangement of the silicon and oxygen atoms is symmetrical, in vitreous silica the lattice is distorted; in the molten state, there is a further decrease in the symmetry of the network, and in addition, there is a general weakening of the bond strength.

In representing the composition of systems consisting of oxides, sulphides, silicates, etc., it is not necessary to know anything about the composition of the complex ions. Depending on the circumstances, the composition may be given in terms of oxides, FeO, Fe_2O_3, CaO, SiO_2 . . . etc., in terms of atoms, Fe^{2+}, Fe^{3+}, Ca, Si . . . etc., or in terms of some assumed ions, SiO_4^{-4}, PO_4^{-3}, Ca^{2+} . . . etc. For convenience, the oxides are often used to represent the composition of the system. When considering the thermodynamics of the oxide system, the composition in terms of weight per cent of the oxides is converted to the mole fractions of the oxides, N, i.e.,

$$N_i = \frac{\text{wt. \% } i}{M_i \Sigma n} \qquad (154)$$

where M_i is the molecular weight of an oxide i and Σn is the total numbers of moles of oxides in 100 g. of the oxide mixture.

As already discussed in Parts I and II of this chapter, the reacting species may be given in terms of oxides, ions, etc., which ever is convenient, without any inference to the nature of the atomic or ionic configuration in the system.

The oxides, e.g., SiO_2, P_2O_5, Al_2O_3, etc., which form anion complexes in melts, e.g., silicate, phosphate, aluminate, etc. anions, are said to be acidic oxides. The oxides, e.g., CaO, MgO, MnO, FeO, etc., which break down the anion complexes in the melt are known as the net-work modifiers and are said to be basic oxides. The ratio of the concentrations of basic oxides to those of the acidic oxides is called the **basicity** of the slag. There are numerous ways of representing the basicity of the industrial slags. Since this is an arbitrary way of expressing the general chemical behavior of the slag, there is no particular rule dictating the manner in which the basicity should be represented.

In simple slags where lime and silica are the major constituent oxides, the basicity is usually defined by the concentration ratio $\%CaO/\%SiO_2$. However, the most of the industrial slags contain fair proportions of magnesia and phosphorus pentoxide; in the subsequent parts of this chapter the basicity of complex slags is defined as follows.

It is assumed that the concentrations of CaO and MgO are equivalent on molar basis; converting it to concentrations in weight per cent, CaO equivalence of MgO becomes $1.4 \times \%MgO = \%CaO$.

On molar basis $\frac{1}{2} P_2O_5$ is assumed to be equivalent to SiO_2, therefore, in terms of weight per cent SiO_2 equivalence of P_2O_5 is $0.84 \times \%P_2O_5 = \%SiO_2$.

The basicity is then given by the ratio $(\%CaO + 1.4 \times \%MgO)/(\%SiO_2 + 0.84 \times \%P_2O_5)$.

SECTION 2

PHASE-EQUILIBRIUM DIAGRAMS

Many investigators contributed to the present knowledge on the phase-equilibrium diagrams of the oxide systems. The detailed review of the subject is beyond the scope of this chapter and it is considered adequate for the present purpose to give the phase diagrams of interest in chemical metallurgy without discussing them at any length. Whenever possible, the references are made to those authors who made the major contributions to the construction of the phase diagrams, and for the sake of brevity, no reference will be made to those authors who made minor, though valuable, contributions to the present state of our knowledge on these phase diagrams. It should be mentioned that Levin, McMurdie and Hall[108] compiled the phase-equilibrium diagrams of binary and ternary oxide systems without discriminating between the correct and incorrect phase diagrams.

The phase diagrams given here are those believed to be the most reliable at present.

For convenience, the compounds are formulated in terms of the oxides of the constituent elements. Although, for example, di-calcium silicate is normally formulated as Ca_2SiO_4, in connection with oxide phase diagrams, this is usually written as $2CaO \cdot SiO_2$.

Binary Oxide Systems—The simplest oxide system is that between 'FeO' (wüstite) and MnO; under reducing conditions, the liquidus and solidus curves are as shown in Figure 12–70. In all the subsequent phase diagrams where wüstite is one of the oxide components, the system is for that in equilibrium with solid or liquid iron, unless stated otherwise. The complete solid solubility in this system was also demonstrated by Foster and Welch[110] by X-ray measurements.

In considering the silicate binary systems, mention should be made of the polymorphic forms of silica. The following are the major phase transformations of silica; melting temperature, 1713°C; cris-

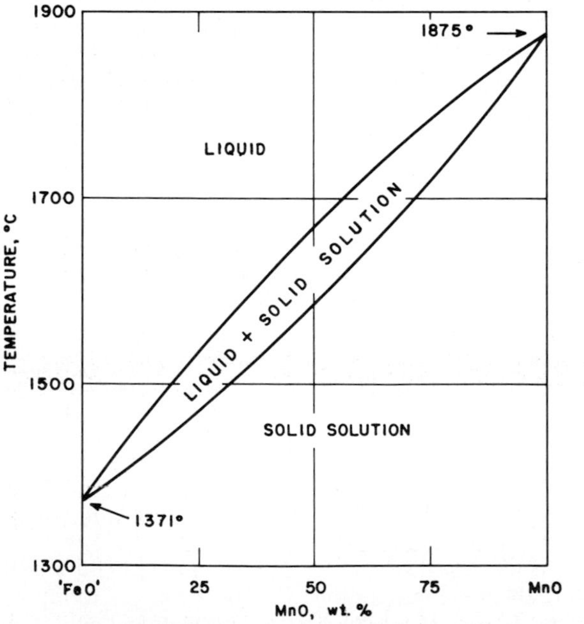

FIG. 12–70. Phase equilibrium diagram for 'FeO'-MnO system. (From Fischer and Fleischer[109].)

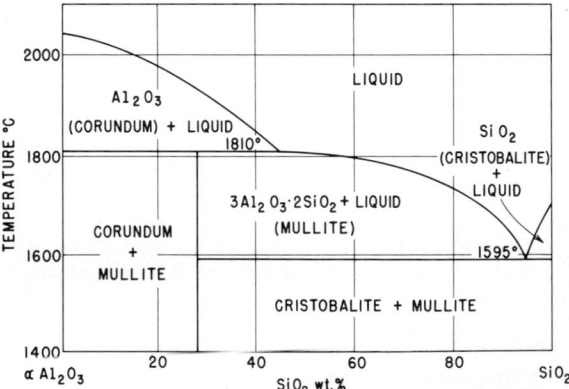

FIG. 12–71. Phase-equilibrium diagram for Al_2O_3-SiO_2 system. (From Bowen and Greig[114].) Aramaki and Roy[116] claim that mullite ($3Al_2O_3 \cdot 2SiO_2$) has a congruent melting temperature at 1850°C. and has a variable composition. Welsh[117] confirms the nonstoichiometry in mullite; but shows that mullite melts incongruently at 1880°C., decomposing to Al_2O_3 and melt.

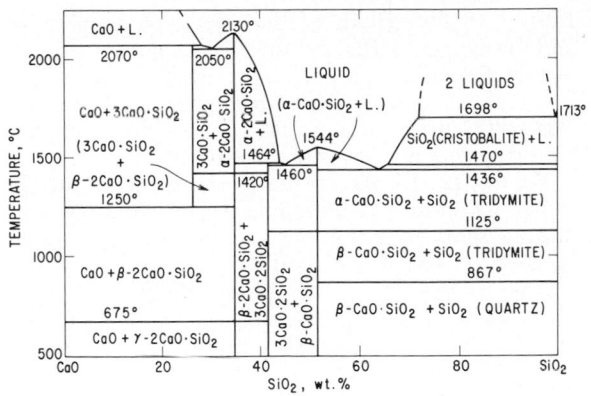

FIG. **12**–72. Phase-equilibrium diagram for CaO-SiO₂ system. (From Rankin and Wright[118] with certain modifications[119, 120, 121].)

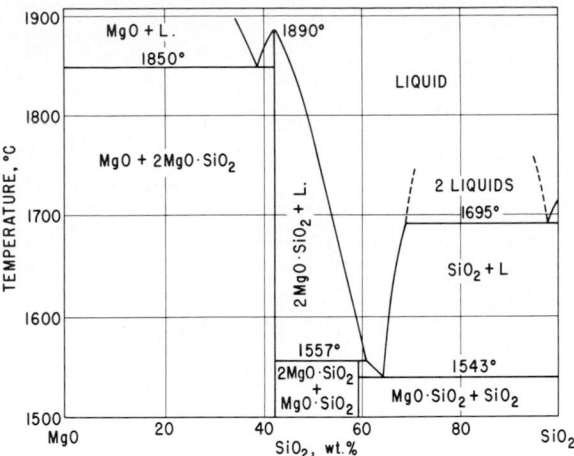

FIG. **12**–74. Phase-equilibrium diagram for MgO-SiO₂ system. (Originally by Bowen and Anderson[126], modified by Greig[127].)

tobalite → tridymite transformation, 1470°C; and tridymite → quartz transformation, 867°C. However, there is some doubt about tridymite being the true polymorphic form of pure silica. It has been suggested[111–113] that tridymite is formed within the temperature range 867°–1470°C only when some metal ions dissolve in solid silica. In most of the silicate systems, except those with alkali oxides and alumina, there is a liquid miscibility gap as seen from the phase diagrams in Figures **12**–72 to **12**–75. Another characteristic feature is that there is very little or negligible solid-solution formation in most of the silicate, phosphate, aluminate systems.

The diagram for the Al₂O₃ - SiO₂ system in Figure **12**–71 essentially is that given by Bowen and Greig[114] with a slight modification[115]. More recent studies[116, 117] indicate that mullite, 3 Al₂O₃·2 SiO₂, is a non-stoichiometric phase with a narrow solid solubility range, and at present there is a divergence of opinion[116, 117] on the question of dissociation of mullite at its melting temperature.

In the CaO-SiO₂ system there are two compounds with congruent melting points, $\alpha - CaO \cdot SiO_2$ and $\alpha - 2CaO \cdot SiO_2$, and two with incongruent melting points, $3CaO \cdot 2SiO_2$ and $3CaO \cdot SiO_2$, the latter being

stable only within the temperature range 1250°–2070°C as shown in Figure **12**–72. One characteristic feature of the di-calcium silicate is that on conversion from β to γ crystalline modification at 675°C, there is about 12 per cent volume expansion causing the solid mass to become powdery. In electric-furnace practice, the reducing slag used has a composition similar to that of di-calcium silicate, and because of the transformation from β to γ form, on cooling the slag becomes powdery; in industry this type of slag is often referred to as the "white falling slag." The formation of $\gamma - 2CaO \cdot SiO_2$ in blast-furnace slags is highly undesirable, if the slag is to be used as an aggregate for constructional purposes.

The phase diagram for the 'FeO'-SiO₂ system in Figure **12**–73 is that in equilibrium with solid or liquid iron; this is not a true binary system. The amount of ferric oxide in the melt along the liquidus curve, in equilibrium with iron, decreases from about 12 per cent at the 'FeO' corner to about 1 per cent at silica saturation. Reference should be made to the work of Schuhmann et al[123, 124] and Turkdogan and

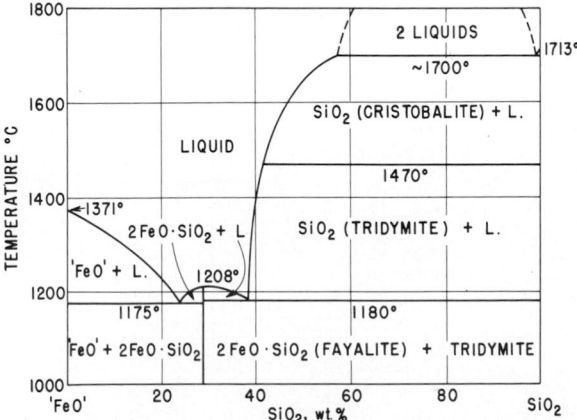

FIG. **12**–73. Phase-equilibrium diagram for 'FeO'-SiO₂ system. (Original diagram of Bowen and Shairer[122] was verified by Schuhmann and Ensio[123].)

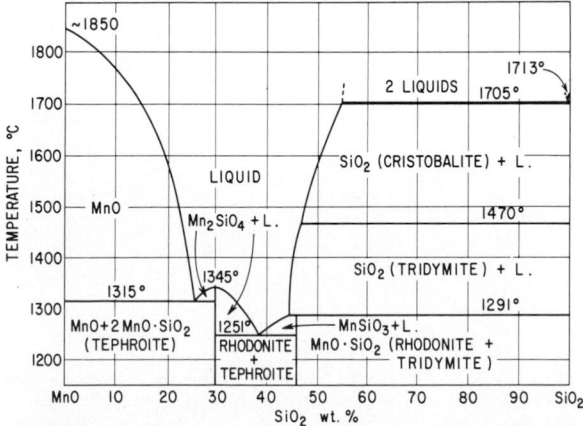

FIG. **12**–75. Phase-equilibrium diagram for MnO-SiO₂ system. (Original diagram by Herty[128] and White et al.[129]; the above modification by Glasser[130].)

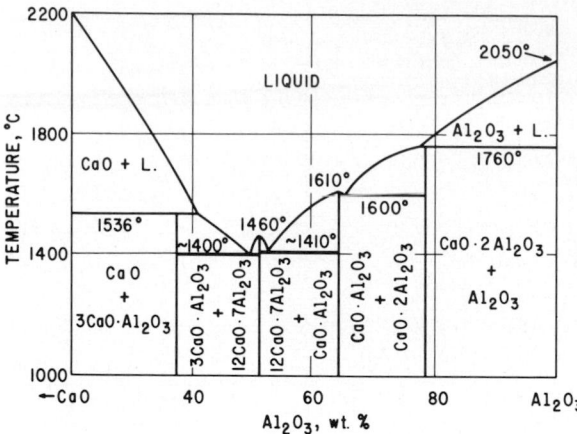

Fig. 12–76. Phase-equilibrium diagram for CaO-Al₂O₃ system. (Original diagram of Rankin and Wright[131] modified using later data[132–134a].)

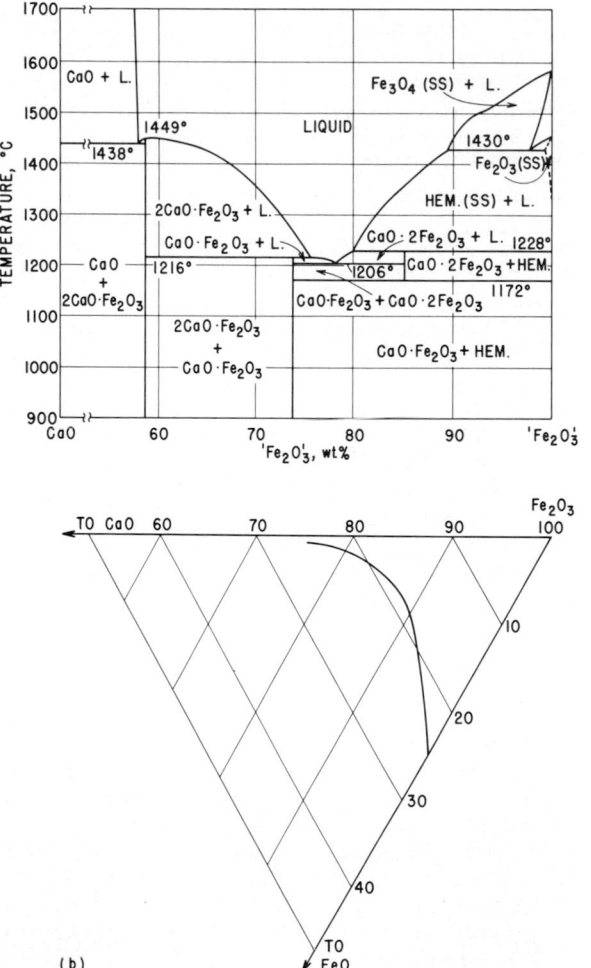

Fig. 12–77. (Above) Phase-equilibrium diagram for CaO-'Fe₂O₃' system at atm. pressure of oxygen. (Below) Variation of the composition of the melt along the hematite and magnetite liquidus curves. (Original diagram of Sosman and Merwin[135] modified by Edstrom[136], Swaze[137] and Phillips and Muan[138].)

Bills[125] on the details of the effects of temperature and the oxygen partial pressure of the gas on the state of oxidation of iron in iron silicate melts.

No further work has been reported on the MgO-SiO₂ diagram since 1927; the phase diagram on this system is given in Figure 12–74.

Figure 12–75 shows the phase diagram for the MnO-SiO₂ system re-examined recently by Glasser[130], making some modifications on the original diagram by Herty[128] and White, et al[129].

Figure 12–76 is the phase diagram for the CaO-Al₂O₃ system which, first obtained by Rankin and Wright[131], has been modified by incorporating the studies of Büssem and Eithel[132], Tavasci[133] and Goldsmith[134a].

Another compound CaO·6Al₂O₃ melting incongruently at 1850°C has been claimed to exist in this binary system by Filonenko and Lavrov[134b], however, this finding has not so far been confirmed by any other work and, therefore, it is not included in Figure 12–76.

The phase diagram in Figure 12–77 is for the CaO-'Fe₂O₃' system at 1 atm. pressure of oxygen; the curve in Figure 12–77 within a ternary diagram gives the composition of the liquid along the hematite and magnetite liquidus curves, given as a pseudo-binary section in Figure 12–77. For further details reference should be made to the papers cited[136–138].

The phase diagram for the CaO-P₂O₅ system determined by Tromel and co-workers[139, 140] is given in Figure 12–78.

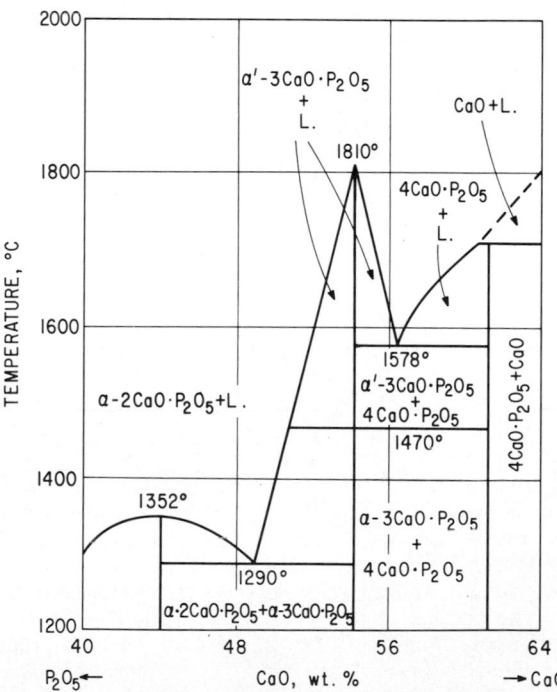

Fig. 12–78. Phase-equilibrium diagram for CaO-P₂O₅ system. (From Tromel et al.[139, 140].)

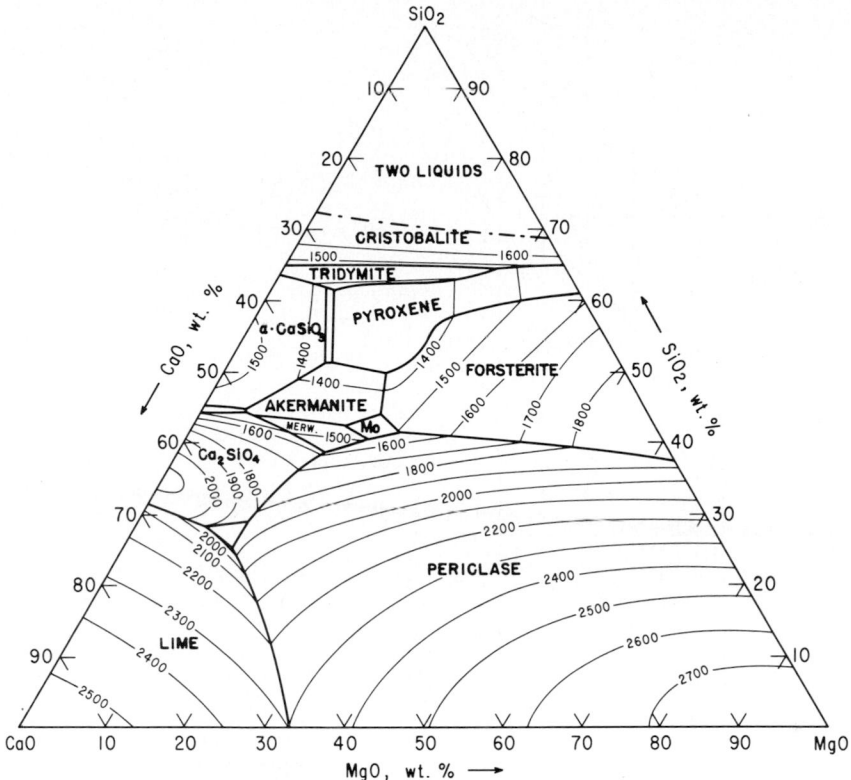

FIG. 12—79. Isotherms on the liquidus surfaces of the CaO-MgO-SiO₂ system. (From the compilation by Ricker and Osborn[144].)

COMPOUNDS

Name	Composition
Periclase	MgO
Cristobalite	
Tridymite	SiO₂
Lime	CaO
Diopside	CaO · MgO · 2SiO₂
Pyroxene	Solid solution along section MgO · SiO₂-diopside
Akermanite	2CaO · MgO · 2SiO₂
Monticellite (Mo)	CaO · MgO · SiO₂
Merwinite (Merw)	3CaO · MgO · 2SiO₂
Forsterite	2MgO · SiO₂

Ternary Oxide Systems—Since the 1920's a vast number of contributions have been made to the study of the phase relations in ternary oxide systems. The volume of this subject is far beyond the scope of this chapter and a brief outline here would hardly do justice to the extensive knowledge that has accumulated over four decades on complex oxide systems. Those interested in refractory oxides should refer to the available text books[141-143] and literature compilations[108] for information on this subject. However, the fact should be brought to the reader's attention that a large number of the phase-equilibrium diagrams on ternary systems are those based on early work, and on some of the systems, supposed to be well known, there is controversial experimental evidence on the existence or otherwise of ternary oxide phases. Therefore, the reader should refer to the original papers discussing a particular phase diagram instead of using non-critical literature surveys.

In order to demonstrate the complexity of the phase diagrams in ternary systems, a brief mention is made here of the CaO-MgO-SiO₂ system. The last revision of the data on this system was made in 1954 by Ricker and Osborn[144], from whose paper Figure 12—79 is reproduced, where isotherms are drawn on the primary liquidus surfaces. There are four ternary compounds:

Mineralogical name	Formula
Diopside	CaO·MgO·2SiO₂
Akermanite	2CaO·MgO·2SiO₂
Monticellite	CaO·MgO·SiO₂
Merwinite	3 CaO·MgO·2SiO₂

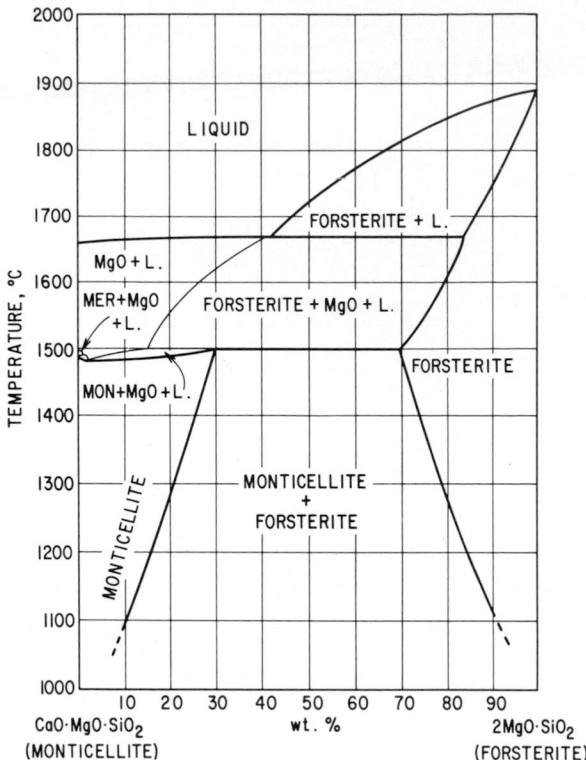

FIG. 12–80. Phase-equilibrium in the section monticellite-forsterite of the CaO-MgO-SiO₂ system. (From Ricker and Osborn[144].)

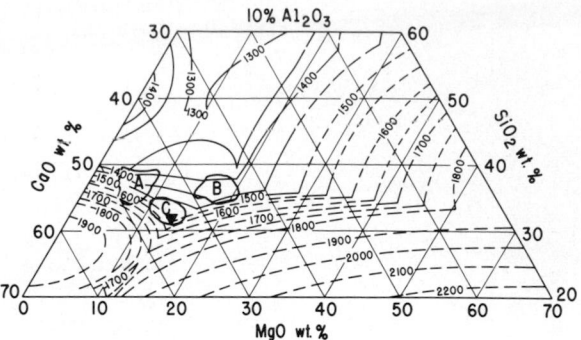

FIG. 12–81. Diagram of part of 10 per cent Al₂O₃ plane showing location of representative blast furnace slags recalculated to 100 per cent CaO + MgO + Al₂O₃ + SiO₂. Each area delimited by a heavy line (A, B, and C) includes daily average slag analyses from a particular furnace where Al₂O₃ was 10 ± 1 per cent. (From Osborn, et al[145].)

eleven ternary peritectic invariants and five ternary eutectic invariants. There are a number of solid solutions in certain parts of the system. At high temperatures there is a complete series of pyroxene solid solutions between the compounds MgO·SiO₂ and CaO·MgO·2SiO₂, a limited solid solution in α − CaO·SiO₂ and a series of solid solutions along the section 2MgO·SiO₂–CaO·MgO·SiO₂. One of these solid solution regions is shown in Figure 12–80 for the section between forsterite and monticellite.

Osborn and co-workers[145] measured the liquidus isotherms in parts of the quaternary system CaO-MgO-Al₂O₃-SiO₂. These isotherms are given in Figure 12–81 for part of the pseudo-ternary system containing 10 per cent Al₂O₃; the average compositions of the blast-furnace slags are those located within the areas A, B and C.

SECTION 3

OXIDE MELTS

It is only in recent years that the activities in molten oxide, silicate, aluminate, etc. melts have been measured with a reasonable degree of accuracy.

The activities in binary systems 'FeO'-CaO, 'FeO'-SiO₂, MnO-SiO₂, CaO-SiO₂ and CaO-Al₂O₃ are given in Figures 12–82 to 12–86. In all cases, pure oxides are chosen as the standard states, and when the melts are saturated with, for example, MnO, CaO, SiO₂, etc., the activity of the respective oxide in the melt becomes unity. The diagrams are self-explanatory and reference should be made to the original papers cited for details on the methods of evaluating these activities by experiments and thermodynamic calculations. The 'FeO'-MnO solution is ideal both in the solid and liquid state[151, 152], as would be expected from the phase equilibrium diagram given in Figure 12–70.

From the experimental data on the activity of oxygen, the activities of oxides in CaO-FeO-Fe₂O₃ and SiO₂-FeO-Fe₂O₃ ternary melts have been computed[146, 147] by the application of Gibbs-Duhem equation (see Part I), and the isoactivity curves thus obtained are plotted in the ternary systems in Figures 12–87 and 12–88.

The activity of silica (149) in CaO-Al₂O₃-SiO₂ melts at 1550°C are given in Figure 12–89.

Figure 12–90 shows the variation of the activity of manganous oxide[148] with composition of CaO-MnO-SiO₂ ternary system at 1500° and 1650°C. The activities of manganous oxide[148] in the quaternary system CaO-MnO-Al₂O₃-SiO₂ are given in Figure 12–91 for certain concentration ratios of CaO:SiO₂:Al₂O₃ at 1650°C.

The activity of ferrous oxide in CaO-MgO-FeO-SiO₂ melts were determined by Taylor and Chipman[153] by equilibrating the slags with pure iron and analyzing the latter for oxygen. The isoactivities of FeO as drawn by Taylor and Chipman is reproduced in Figure 12–92. In basic steelmaking practice the slags contain appreciable proportions of manganese and phosphorus oxides. Using all the available data on FeO activities in complex slags obtained from equilibrium measurements, the activity data were compiled in one diagram by Turkdogan and Pearson[154], and their diagram is reproduced in Figure 12–93. In order to do this simplification, the following approximation was made to reduce the system to that of a ternary: on molar basis (CaO + MgO +

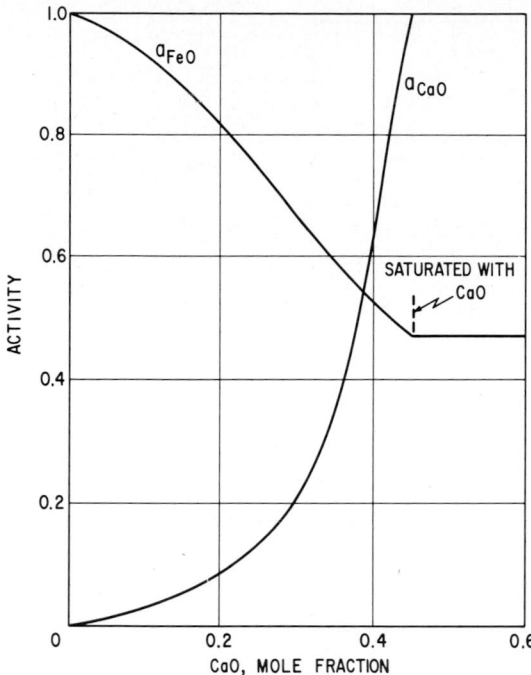

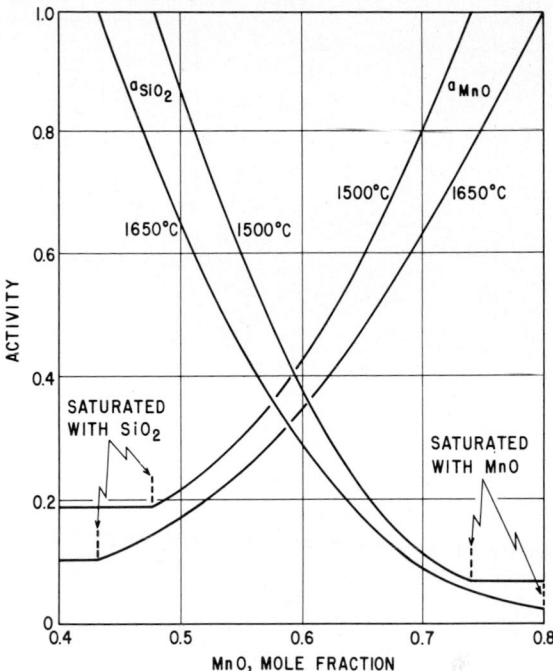

Fig. 12–82. Activities in 'FeO'-CaO melts in equilibrium with liquid iron at 1550°C. with respect to solid CaO and liquid 'FeO' as standard states. (From Turkdogan[146].)

Fig. 12–84. Activities in MnO-SiO₂ melts with reference to solid MnO and SiO₂ as standard states. (From Abraham, Davies and Richardson[148].)

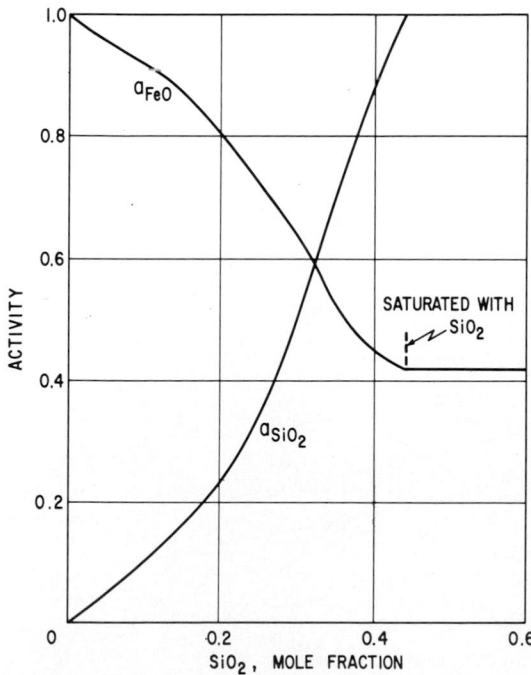

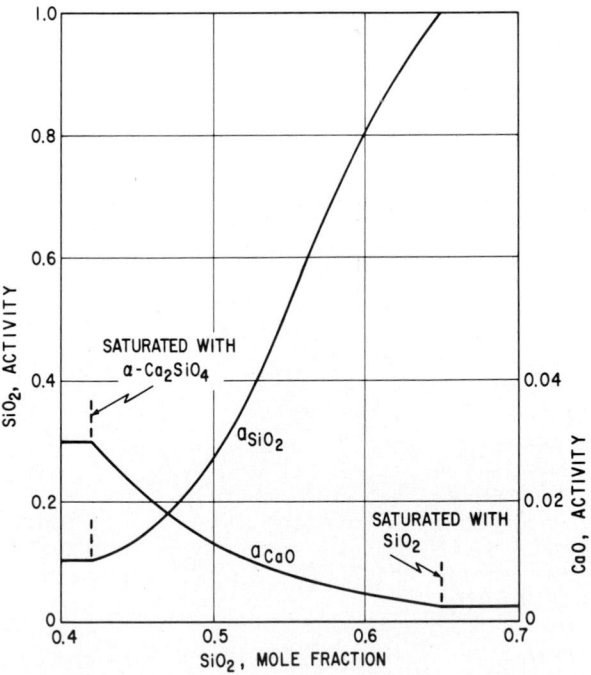

Fig. 12–83. Activities in 'FeO'-SiO₂ melts in equilibrium with liquid iron at 1550°C. with reference to wüstite and solid silica as standard states. (By extrapolating[147] the data of Schuhmann and Ensio[123].)

Fig. 12–85. Activities in CaO-SiO₂ melts at 1550°C. with respect to solid CaO and SiO₂ as standard states. (From Kay and Taylor[149].)

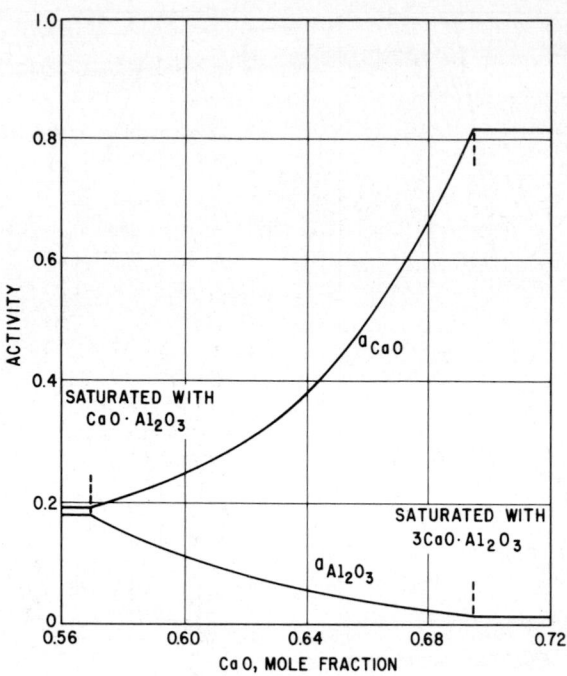

FIG. 12–86. Activities in CaO-Al₂O₃ melts at 1500°C., with respect to solid CaO and Al₂O₃ as standard states. (From Sharma and Richardson[150].)

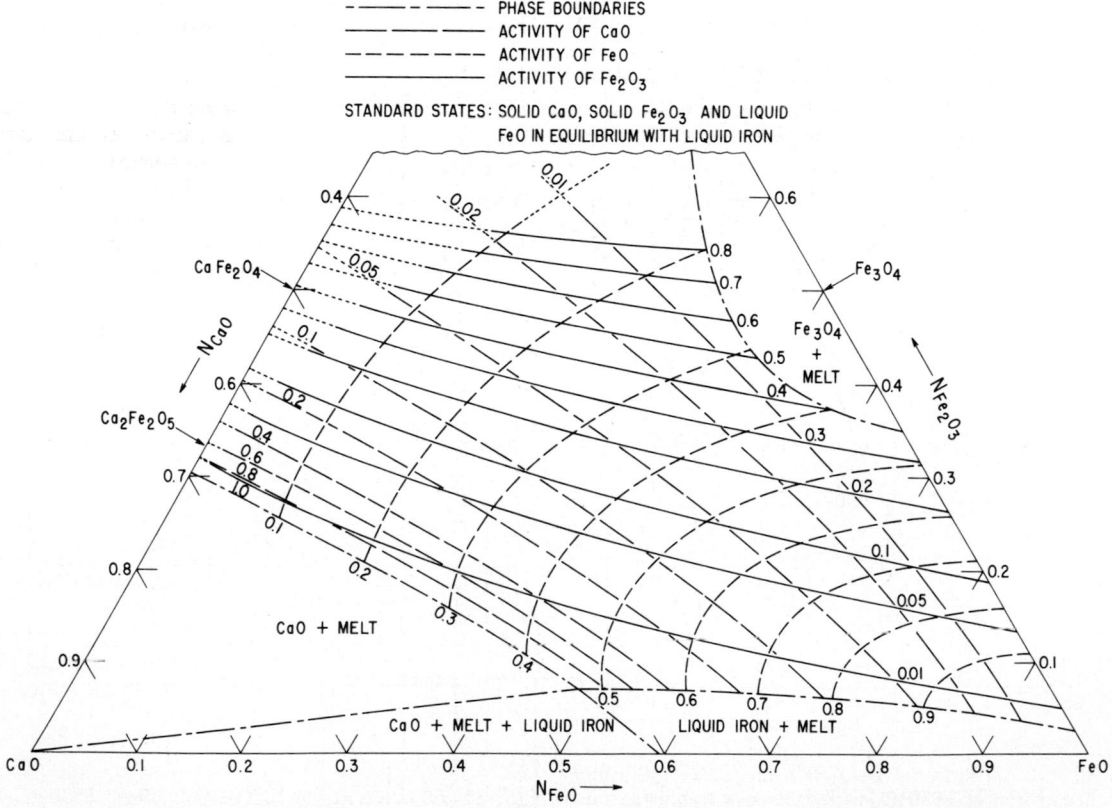

FIG. 12–87. Iso-activity curves in CaO-FeO-Fe₂O₃ melts at 1550°C. (From Turkdogan[146].)

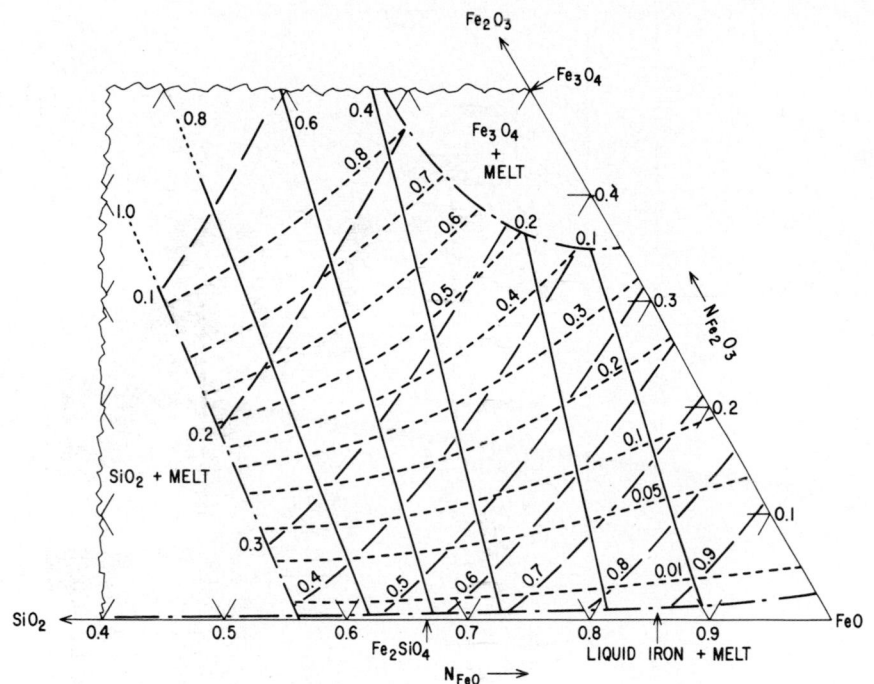

FIG. 12—88. Iso-activity curves in SiO₂-FeO-Fe₂O₃ melts at 1550°C. (From Turkdogan[147].)

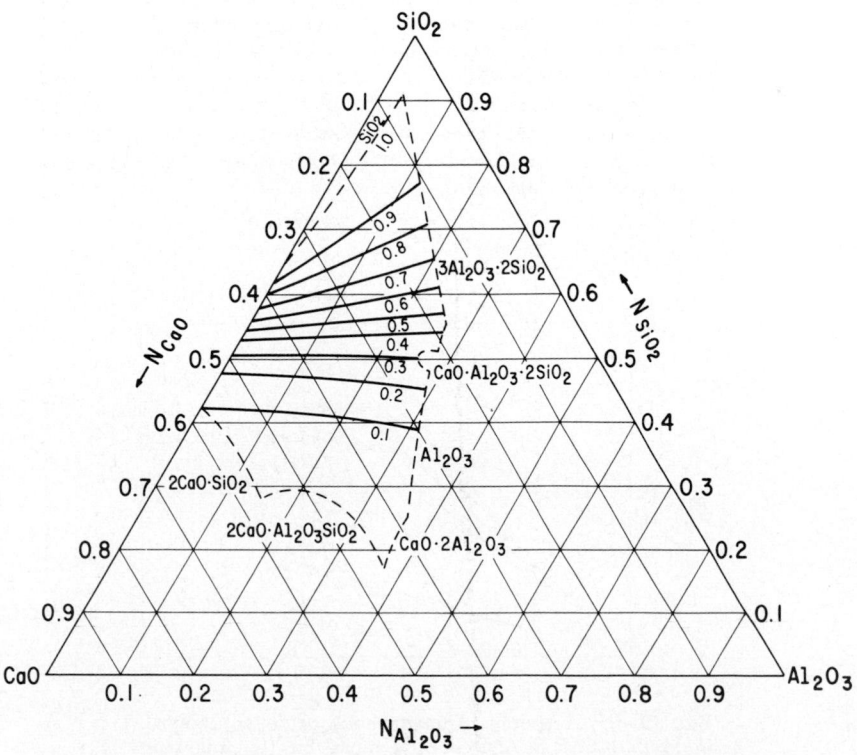

FIG. 12—89. Iso-activity curves for silica in CaO-Al₂O₃-SiO₂ melts at 1550°C., relative to solid SiO₂. Composition is in mole fraction and broken lines are the phase boundaries. (From Kay and Taylor[149].)

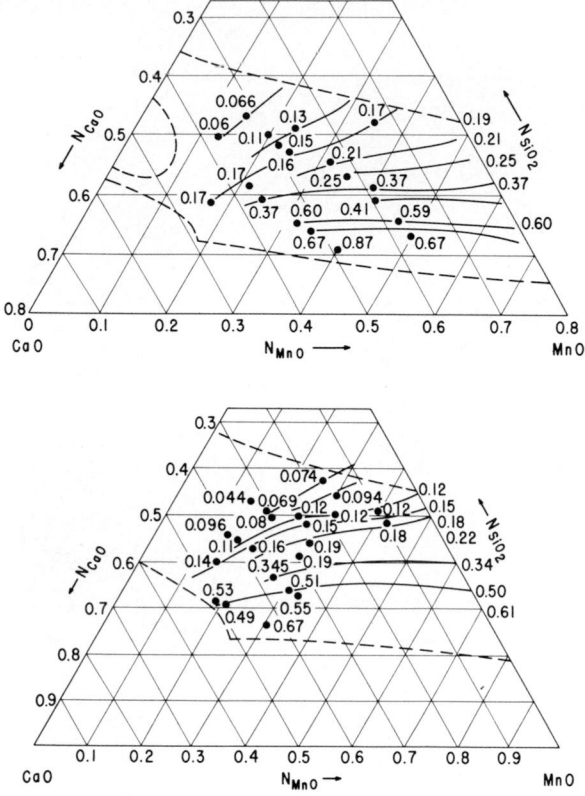

Fig. 12–90. Activities of manganous oxide in MnO-CaO-SiO₂ melts with respect to solid MnO as the standard state (above) for 1500°C. (below) for 1650°C. Broken lines indicate the probable phase boundaries. (From Abraham, Davies and Richardson[148].)

MnO)–(SiO₂ + P₂O₅)–(FeO + Fe₂O₃). It should be realized that the activity data in Figures 12–92 and 12–93 are useful only in the study of the slag-metal reactions in steelmaking furnaces; such data are not suitable for more precise thermodynamic computations.

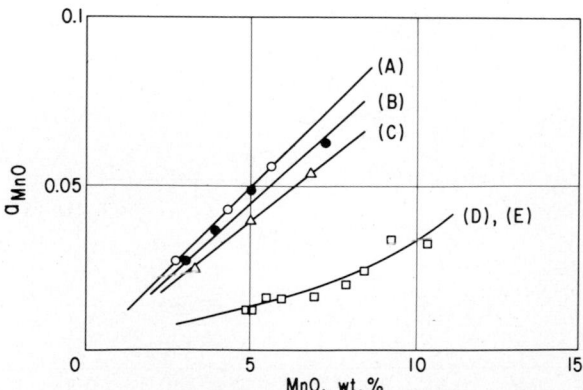

Fig. 12–91. Activities of manganous oxide at 1650°C. in MnO + CaO + Al₂O₃ + SiO₂ melts for the following weight ratios of CaO : SiO₂ : Al₂O₃ : (A) 52.0 : 37.2 : 10.8; (B) 47.2 : 38.2 : 14.6; (C) 36.7 : 33.3 : 30.0; (D) 30.0 : 63.3 : 6.7; (E) 16.7 : 66.7 : 16.6. (From Abraham, Davies and Richardson[148].)

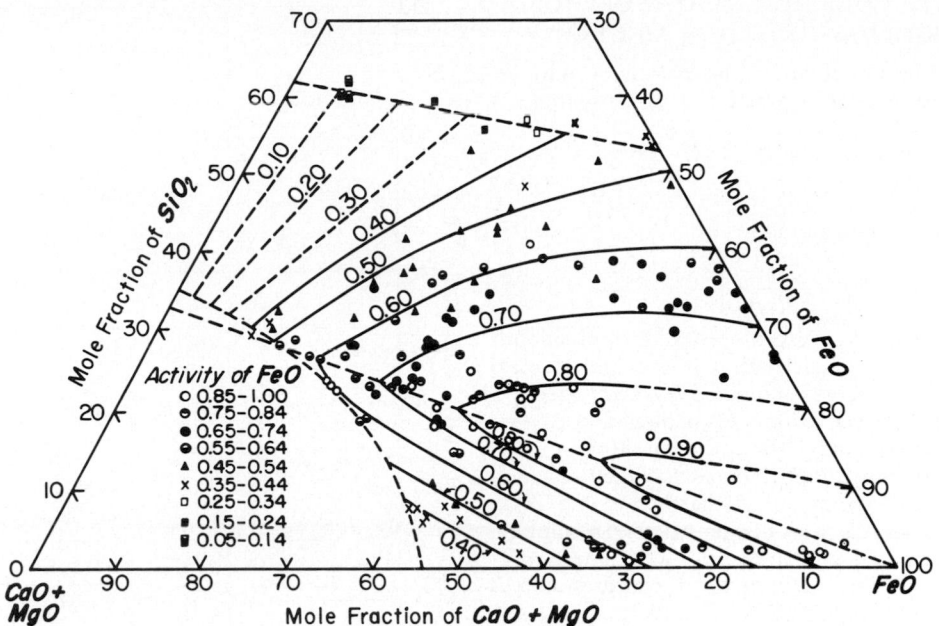

FIG. 12–92. Activity of ferrous oxide in complex slags at 1600°C. (From Taylor and Chipman[153].)

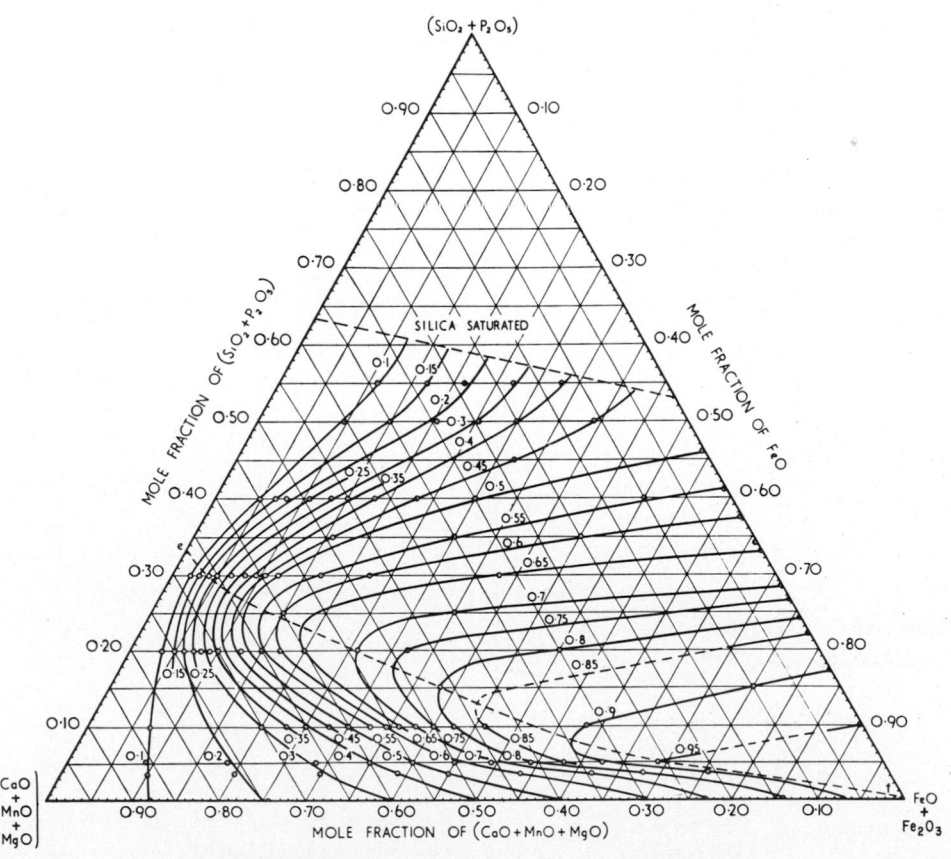

FIG. 12–93. Activity of ferrous oxide in complex slags.
(From Turkdogan and Pearson[154].)

ACTIVITY COEFFICIENT OF SULPHUR DISSOLVED IN OXIDE MELTS

The equilibrium of an oxide melt with sulphur-bearing gases may be expressed by the equation:

$$\tfrac{1}{2} S_2(gas) + O^{2-}(melt) = S^{2-}(melt) + \tfrac{1}{2} O_2(gas) \tag{155}$$

for which the equilibrium index is:

$$K' = \frac{N_S}{N_O} \left(\frac{p_{O_2}}{p_{S_2}}\right)^{\frac{1}{2}} \tag{156}$$

where N_S and N_O are atom fractions of sulphur and oxygen in the melt and p is the partial pressure of the gas species indicated by the subscript. Since the activity coefficients of sulphur and oxygen are omitted in equation (156), the equilibrium index K' varies with the composition of the melt. In fact, it was shown by Dewing and Richardson[155] and Turkdogan and Darken[156] that in iron oxide-iron sulphide melts, K' decreased with increasing concentration of trivalent iron. Whilst Dewing and Richardson equilibrated melts containing 20 to 50 mole per cent sulphur, in the work of Turkdogan and Darken sulphur in the iron oxide was below 4 mole per cent, but as seen from Figure 12–94, large change in the sulphur content has no effect on the value of K' for a given temperature. Therefore, it may be stated that the activity coefficient ratio γ_S/γ_O or $\gamma_{FeS}/\gamma_{FeO}$ is independent of the sulphur content of the melt.

For calcium-silicate, calcium-aluminate, calcium-ferrite, etc. melts, the sulphide and sulphate equilibrium may be expressed equally well by the equations

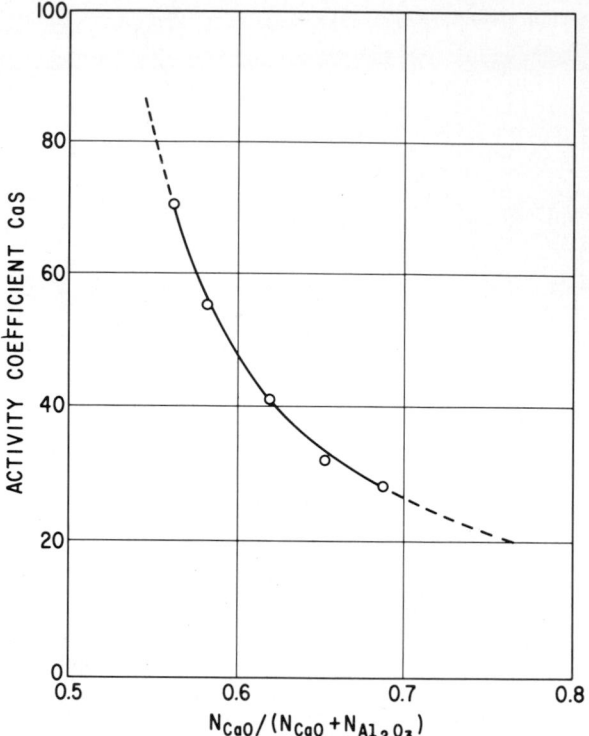

Fig. 12–95. Activity coefficient of CaS (with respect to solid CaS) in CaO-Al$_2$O$_3$ melts saturated with CaS at 1500°C. (N is in mole fraction.) (From Sharma and Richardson[150].)

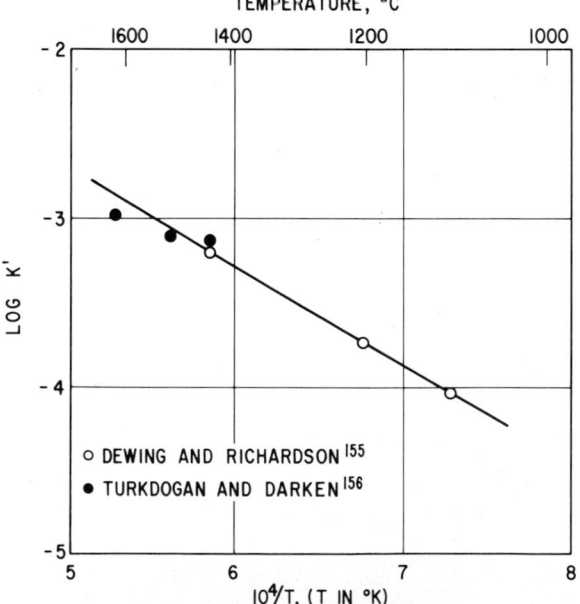
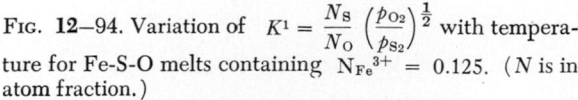

Fig. 12–94. Variation of $K^1 = \dfrac{N_S}{N_O} \left(\dfrac{p_{O_2}}{p_{S_2}}\right)^{\frac{1}{2}}$ with temperature for Fe-S-O melts containing $N_{Fe}^{3+} = 0.125$. (N is in atom fraction.)

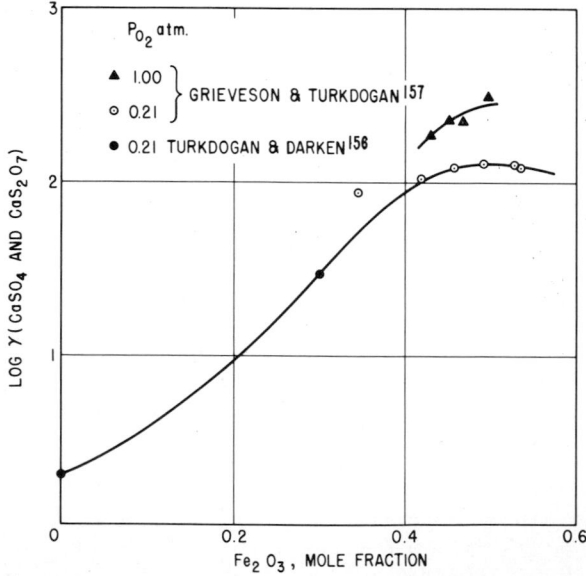

Fig. 12–96. Variation of Log γ (CaSO$_4$ and CaS$_2$O$_7$) with composition of CaO-FeO-Fe$_2$O$_3$ melts at 1500°C. and $P_{O_2} = 0.2$ and 1.0 atm. Standard states: liquid CaSO$_4$; liquid CaS$_2$O$_7$. (From Grieveson and Turkdogan[157].)

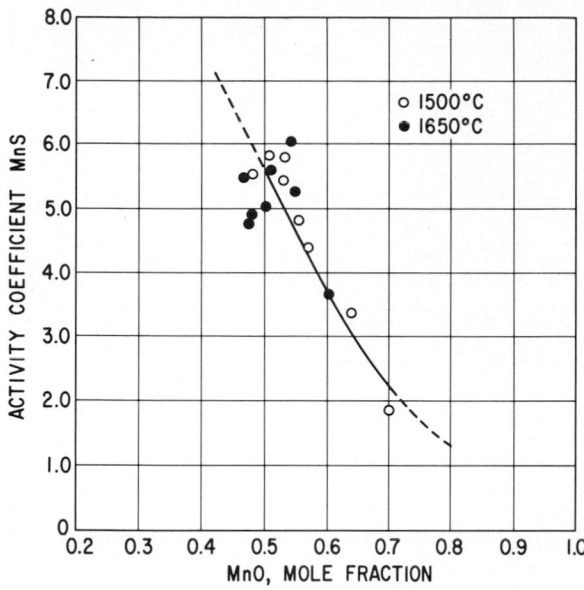

FIG. 12—97. Activity coefficient of MnS (relative to liquid MnS) in MnO-SiO₂ melts. (From Abraham, Davies and Richardson[158].)

$$\frac{1}{2}S_2(gas) + CaO\ (melt) = CaS\ (melt) + \frac{1}{2}O_2\ (gas) \tag{157}$$

and

$$\frac{1}{2}S_2(gas) + \frac{3}{2}O_2\ (gas) + CaO\ (melt) = CaSO_4\ (melt) \tag{158}$$

From the equilibrium measurements and known equilibrium constants the values of γ_{CaS} and γ_{CaSO_4} ($= \gamma_{Ca_{32}O_7}$) have been determined for some melts; the available data are summarized in Figures 12—95 and 12—96 for calcium aluminate[150] and ferrite

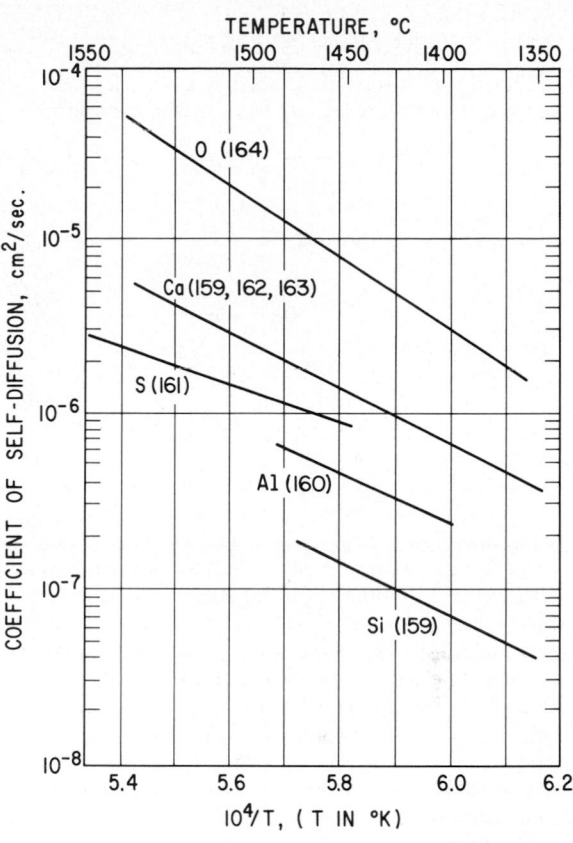

FIG. 12—98. Self-diffusivities in calcium alumino-silicate melts. (Numbers in parentheses are references to literature.)

melts[157], respectively. On similar considerations, the activity coefficient of MnS in MnO-SiO₂ melts have been evaluated[158] and the results obtained are given in Figure 12—97.

SECTION 4

DIFFUSION IN MOLTEN SLAGS

There is a growing need for accurate data on the coefficients of diffusion of ions in molten slags. Although some measurements have been made using the tracer techniques, present knowledge can hardly be regarded as adequate. However, the data available to date are summarized in Figure 12—98 where

log D (self-diffusivity in cm.²/sec.) is plotted against the reciprocal of absolute temperature for calcium alumino-silicate melts.

Further work must be carried out in detail before any suggestions can be made to explain the mechanism of diffusion of ions in slags.

SECTION 5

VISCOSITY, DENSITY AND SURFACE TENSION

Viscosity—Because of its industrial importance, the viscosity of alumino-silicates had been subjected to a detailed study for 40 to 50 years. For a literature survey on early work reference may be made to a paper by Rait[165]. However, more recent investigations showed that the accuracy of the results of the early workers is in considerable doubt. For example, the previous investigators claimed that in some binary

and ternary melts, the viscosity-composition relationships showed maxima at compositions where binary or ternary compounds form in the solid state. Such claims have since been proved to be wrong.

In the present considerations, the compilation of the data on the coefficients of viscosity is limited to slags which are similar to those used in iron and steelmaking. The coefficient of viscosity of lime-alumina-

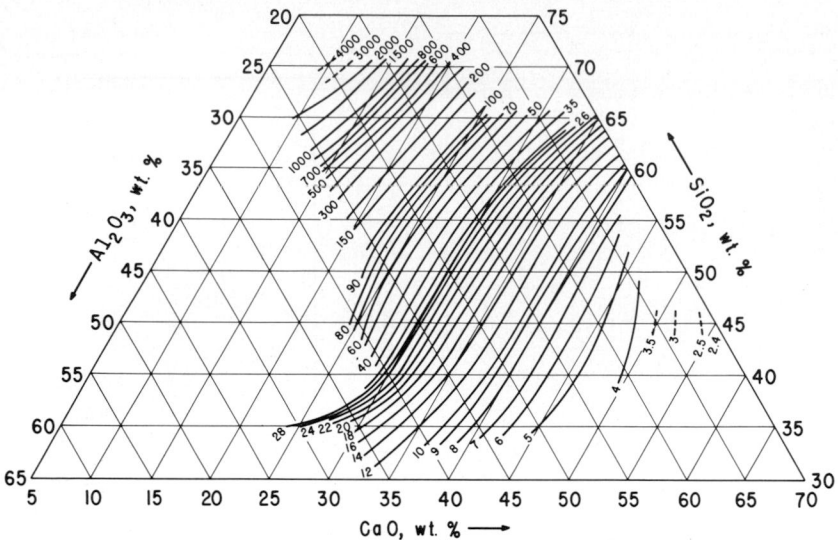

Fig. 12–99. Isoviscosity coefficients (isokoms) in poise of CaO-Al₂O₃-SiO₂ melts at 1500°C. (From Machin and Yee[166].)

silica melts have been measured by Machin and Yee[166] and Kozakevitch[167]. Figures 12–99 and 12–100 are examples showing the change of viscosity coefficient with composition and temperature. For a given alumina concentration, the viscosity of the melt increases with increasing silica content, and for a given composition, the melt becomes more viscous with decreasing temperature.

The viscosity measurements have been made by Machin and co-workers[168, 169] over wide temperature and composition ranges in the CaO-MgO-Al₂O₃-SiO₂ melts. The data relevant to blast furnace slags are given in Figures 12–101 and 12–102.

In a critical review of viscosity of CaO-MgO-Al₂O₃-SiO₂ melts by Turkdogan and Bills[170], it was shown that the replacement of lime by magnesia (on a molar basis) did not affect the viscosity of the melt. It

was also found that the silica equivalence of alumina (in terms of molar concentrations) was a function of the concentration ratio

$$N_{Al_2O_3}/N_{CaO}$$

(where N is the mole fraction of the oxide indicated by the subscript). This relationship is shown in Figure 12–103, where N_a is the silica equivalence of

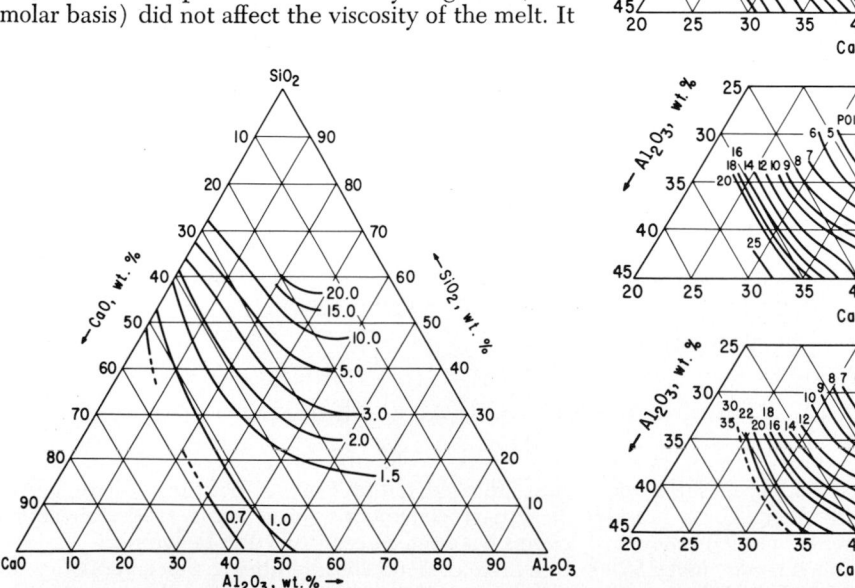

Fig. 12–100. Isoviscosity coefficients (isokoms) in poise of CaO-Al₂O₃-SiO₂ melts at 1800°C. (From Kozakevitch[167].)

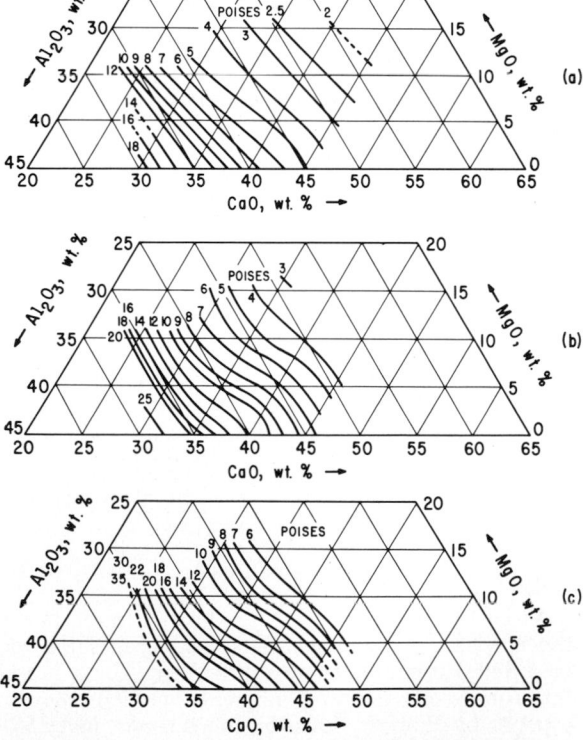

Fig. 12–101. Isokoms in CaO-MgO-Al₂O₃-35% SiO₂ melts at (a) 1500°C., (b) 1450°C., (c) 1400°C. (From Machin et al.[169].)

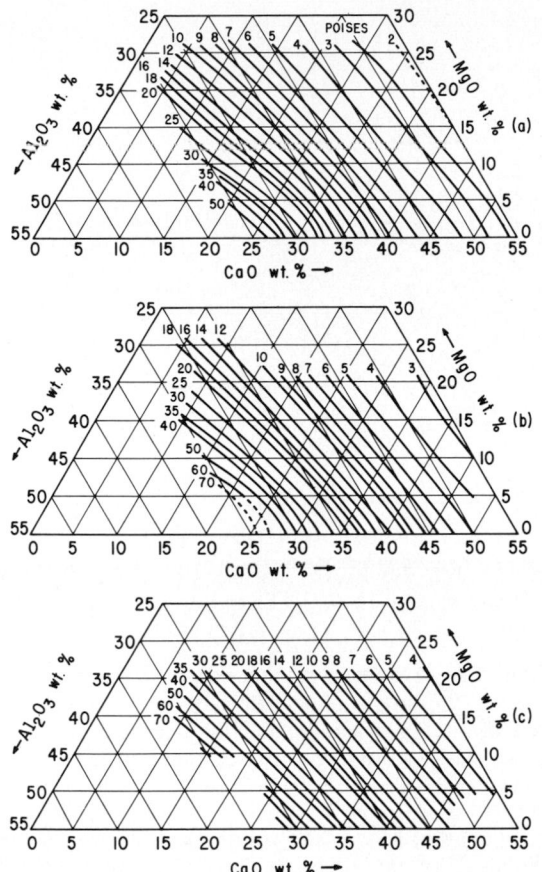

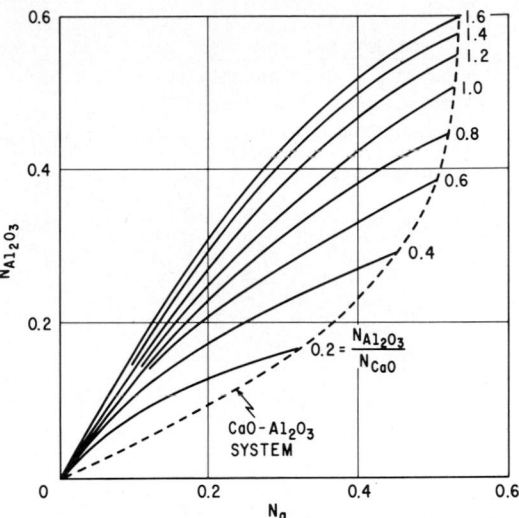

FIG. 12–103. Silica equivalence of alumina (N_a) related to molar alumina concentration and molar alumina/lime ratio in $CaO-Al_2O_3-SiO_2$ melts for the temperature range 1500°–1800°C. For melts containing MgO, the diagram may be used by taking MgO and CaO equivalent on molar basis, i.e. the molar ratio becomes $Al_2O_3/(CaO + MgO)$ for quaternary melts. (From Turkdogan and Bills[170].)

FIG. 12–102. Isokoms in $CaO-MgO-Al_2O_3-45\%$ SiO_2 melts at (a) 1500°C., (b) 1450°C., and (c) 1400°C. (From Machin et al.[169].)

alumina derived from the difference between the silica concentrations of the binary and ternary melts which have the same viscosities at the same temperature. That is, for a given temperature and viscosity

$$N_{Al_2O_3} = N_a = N_{SiO_2} \text{ binary} \\ - N_{SiO_2} \text{ ternary} \qquad (159)$$

As seen from the results in Figure 12–104, the variation of coefficient of viscosity, η, with composition of quaternary $CaO-MgO-Al_2O_3-SiO_2$ melts may be represented by a single curve by plotting η against $N_{SiO_2} + N_a$; the value of N_a being estimated from the data in Figure 12–103.

Although within a narrow temperature range log η varies linearly with the reciprocal of absolute temperature, as shown in Figure 12–105, there is a deviation from linearity over a wider temperature range. For a given value of $N_{SiO_2} + N_a$, the slope of the log η vs $1/T$ curve decreases, i.e. heat of activation for viscous flow decreases, with increasing temperature, indicating a gradual breakdown of the silicate network with increasing temperature.

Kozakevitch[172] found that the introduction of sulphur, up to at least 2 per cent, into the blast-furnace type of slags had no effect on viscosity. However, the addition of calcium fluoride was found to have a pronounced lowering effect on the viscosity

of calcium alumino-silicate melts as shown in Figure 12–106.

The viscosity measurements on steelmaking slags are less reliable than those discussed above in relation to blast-furnace type of slags. The results of Kozakevitch[173] are probably the best available on $CaO-FeO-SiO_2$ melts given in Figure 12–107. Below

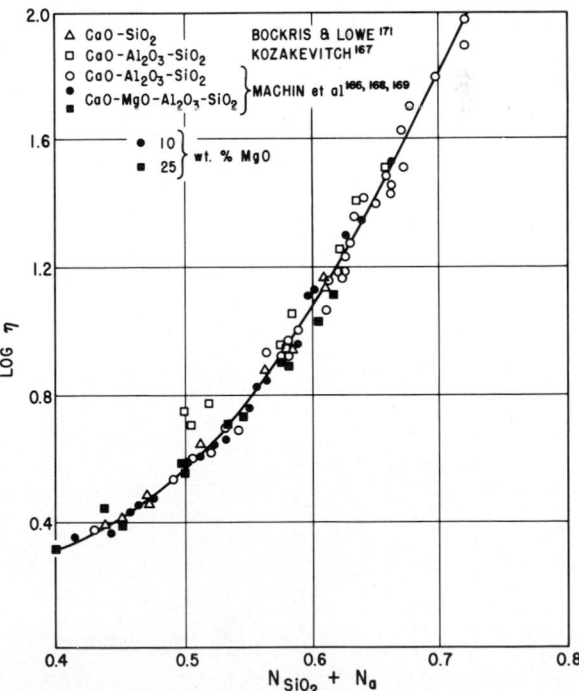

FIG. 12–104. Variation of coefficient of viscosity with composition of $CaO-MgO-Al_2O_3-SiO_2$ melts at 1500°C. The values of N_a are estimated using the data in Fig. 12–103. (From Turkdogan and Bills[170].)

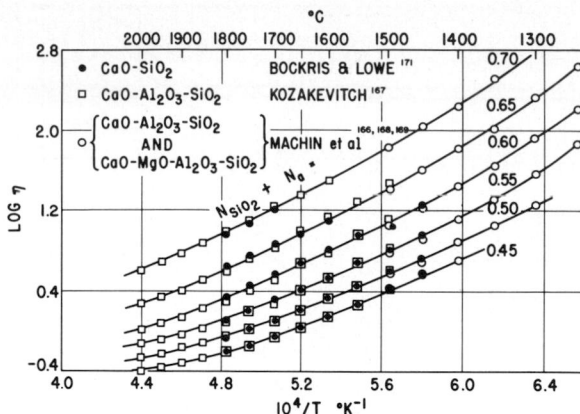

FIG. 12–105. Variation of the coefficient of viscosity with temperature and composition of silicate and alumino-silicate melts. (From Turkdogan and Bills[170].)

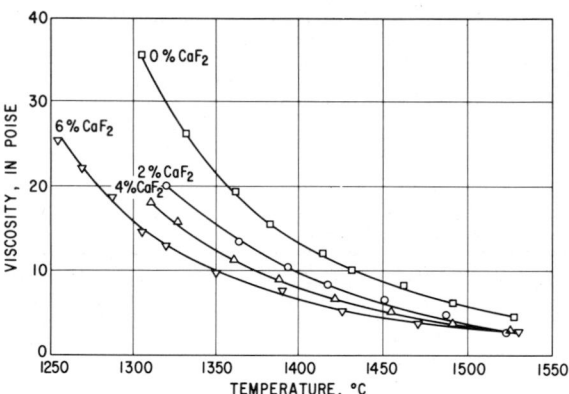

FIG. 12–106. Effect of calcium fluoride on the viscosity coefficient of alumino-silicate melts containing 44% SiO₂, 12% Al₂O₃, 41% CaO and 3.0% MgO. (From Kozakevitch[172].)

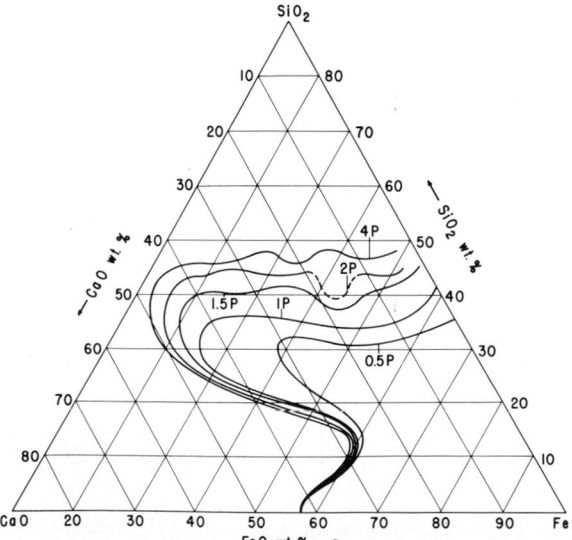

FIG. 12–107. Isoviscosity coefficients in poise of CaO-FeO-SiO₂ melts at 1400°C. (From Kozakevitch[173].)

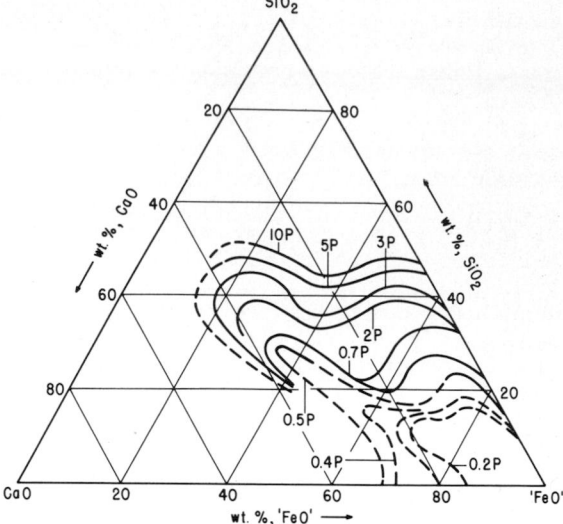

FIG. 12–108. Isoviscosity coefficients in poise of CaO-FeO-SiO₂ melts at 1300°C. (From Rontgen et al.[174].)

about 10 per cent SiO₂, the shape of the curves resembles the shape of the liquidus isotherms in this part of the diagram. Above 20 per cent SiO₂, the curves pass through maxima in the composition diagram at the ratio of %CaO/%SiO₂ ≅ 1:1; this could be due, at least partly, to the variation of the ferric oxide content of the slags with the ratio CaO/SiO₂. The viscosity data given in Figure 12–108 have been obtained recently by Rontgen and co-workers[174], their results are similar to those of Kozakevitch.

Density—Only a few density measurements have been made on molten-oxide mixtures at elevated temperatures. Bockris and co-workers[175, 176] measured the densities of alkali and alkaline-earth silicates; these binary melts are of little interest to present considerations, hence they are not discussed here. Barrett and Thomas[177] measured the densities of some calcium alumino-silicate melts over the temperature range 1350°–1650°C, these are given in Table 12–XI. Since the data are limited, no attempt is made to draw a series of isodensity curves within a ternary composition diagram. However, they may be useful in estimating, at least approximately, the densities of blast-furnace

Table 12–XI. Densities of CaO-Al₂O₃-SiO₂ Melts for the Temperature Range 1350–1650°C.
(From Barrett and Thomas[177])

Composition, Weight Per Cent			Density at t°C (g./cm.³)
CaO	Al₂O₃	SiO₂	
39	19	42	$3.771 - 6.5 \times 10^{-4} t$
35	10	55	$3.215 - 4.2 \times 10^{-4} t$
34	30	36	$3.535 - 5.0 \times 10^{-4} t$
30	25	45	$3.705 - 7.9 \times 10^{-4} t$
30	10	60	$3.165 - 4.8 \times 10^{-4} t$
29	40	31	$3.280 - 3.5 \times 10^{-4} t$
25	20	55	$2.955 - 3.1 \times 10^{-4} t$
25	10	65	$3.790 - 9.8 \times 10^{-5} t$
23	15	62	$3.332 - 6.6 \times 10^{-4} t$
15	20	65	$3.150 - 4.9 \times 10^{-4} t$

type of slags. Henderson and co-workers[178] measured the densities of iron silicates in equilibrium with solid iron crucible at 1400°C. The density of the melts decrease almost linearly from 4.56 g. per cm.³ at 0.0 per cent SiO_2 to 3.75 g. per cm.³ at 23 per cent SiO_2; with further increase in silica content the density decreases more gradually.

Surface Tension—The surface tension is an intensive property of the surface of a system where the surface defines the place of separation of two phases. At any point within a homogeneous phase, at internal equilibrium, the interatomic forces are the same in all directions. The atoms on the surface of the liquid separating the latter from the vapor phase are attracted to the liquid more than to the vapor phase. Because of this inward pull, the surface of a liquid tends to contract to the smallest possible area so that the resulting free surface energy has the minimum value attainable by the system. The work required to increase the surface area by 1 cm.² is called the **free surface energy** and has the dimensions of ergs per cm.². The surface tension, usually denoted by γ, is defined as the force in dynes acting at right angles to any line of 1 cm length in the surface. The quantities, free surface energy and surface tension, are thus identical.

The surface tension is that which refers to the surface separating the condensed phase from the gas phase (the latter being saturated with the vapor of the condensed phase). Since the adsorption of gases and vapors alter the surface properties, the nature of the atmosphere in any surface-tension measurements must be known. When two liquids, two solids or a liquid and a solid meet, the resulting surface is called the **interfacial surface** or simply **interface.** The interfacial tension (again in dynes per cm.) is evaluated from the surface tensions of the two media and the contact angle between the phases.

In the study of many metallurgical problems, some knowledge of the surface tensions of liquid metals, slags and refractory oxides are needed. In the present considerations, a few examples are given on the surface tensions of some liquid metals and some slags without discussing any of the problems where such data are used.

Figure 12—109 shows the variation of the surface tension of some binary silicate melts with composition, measured by King[179] at 1570°C. The results of Kozakevitch[180], given in Figure 12—110, show the varying effects of different oxide additions on the surface tension of molten iron oxide at 1400°C. Recently, Boni and Derge[181] measured the surface tensions of alkaline-earth alumino-silicates; some of their results are given in Figure 12—111. They also observed that increasing the sulphur content decreases appreciably the surface tension of the melts, as shown in Figure 12—112.

The variation of the surface tension of silicate melts with temperature depends on the nature of the cations present. For example, whilst in silicates of divalent elements[179] the temperature coefficient of surface tension, $\partial\gamma/\partial T$ is positive, in alkali silicates[182] $\partial\gamma/\partial T$ becomes negative. Figure 12—113 shows the variation of $\partial\gamma/\partial T$ with the composition of a number

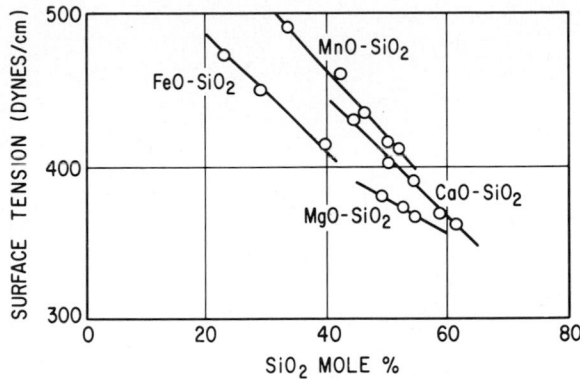

FIG. 12—109. Surface tension (in air) of binary silicates of some divalent elements at 1570°C. (From King[179].)

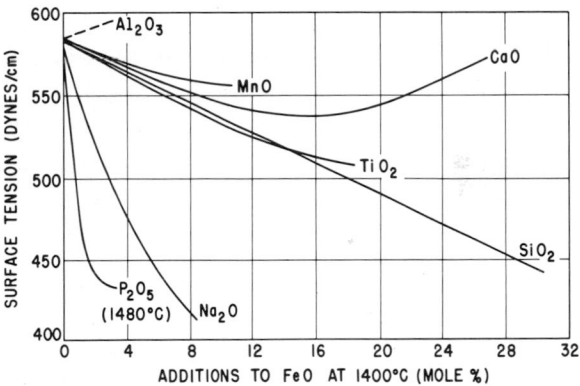

FIG. 12—110. Surface tension (in argon) of binary melts with iron oxide at 1400°C. (From Kozakevitch[180].)

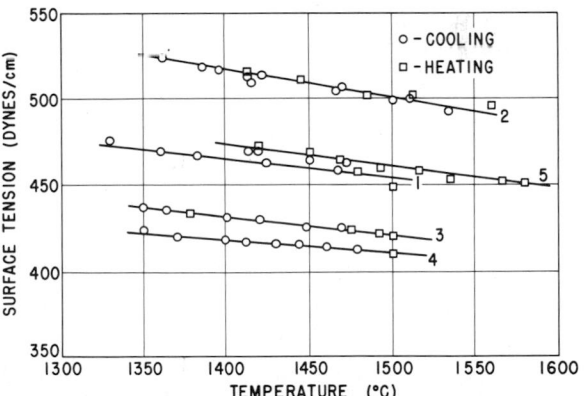

FIG. 12—111. Surface tension (in argon) plotted *vs.* temperature for SiO_2-Al_2O_3-alkaline-earth oxide slags. Numbers keyed to curves refer to slags of the following compositions:

SLAG COMPOSITION
(wt. %)

	MgO	CaO	BaO	SiO₂	Al₂O₃
1	—	31.3	—	52.4	16.3
2	—	44.8	—	40.3	14.9
3	—	—	54.0	36.2	9.8
4	—	—	69.2	22.4	8.4
5	23.6	—	—	60.0	16.4

(From Boni and Derge[181].)

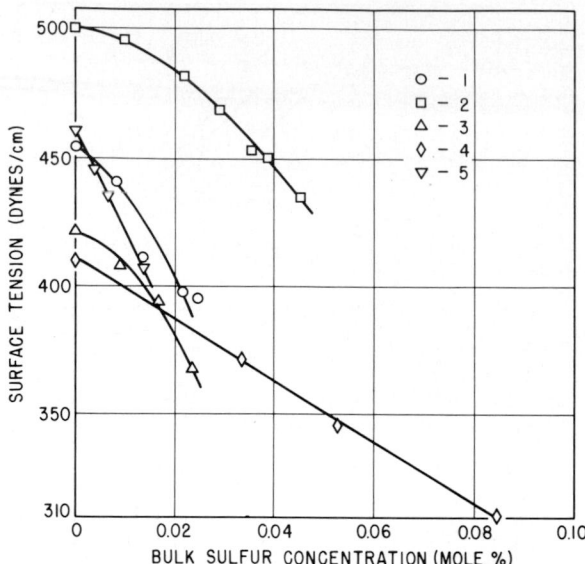

FIG. **12**—112. Surface tension (in argon) plotted *vs.* sulphur concentration for five slags at 1500°C. Numbers keyed to the curves refer to slags, the compositions of which are given in Fig. **12**—111. (From Boni and Derge[181].)

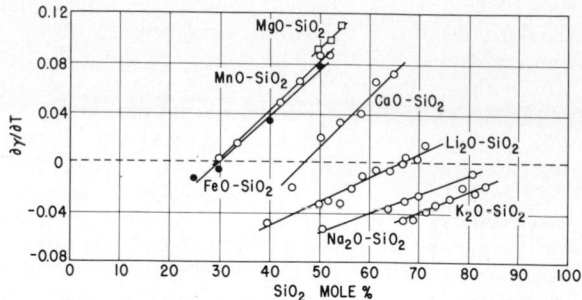

FIG. **12**—113. Variation of temperature coefficient of surface tension, $\partial\gamma/\partial T$, with composition of binary silicate melts. (From King[185].)

found that the addition of nitrogen, sulphur or oxygen lowers the surface tension of iron as shown in Figure **12**—114; carbon in solution does not seem to affect the surface tension of liquid iron.

of binary silicates, taken from a paper by King[185]. There are many speculative and semi-quantitative hypotheses which have been put forward in an attempt to explain some of these observations on the basis of the structures of liquids; however, more work is necessary to resolve the true pattern.

Since surface tension is brought about by the inward attraction of the surface atoms or ions, strong interatomic forces within a liquid results in a high surface tension. This is demonstrated by a few examples given in Table **12**—XII on liquids where the binding forces are classified metallic, ionic-covalent and molecular.

The impurities have large effects on the surface tension of molten metals. For example, Kingery[186]

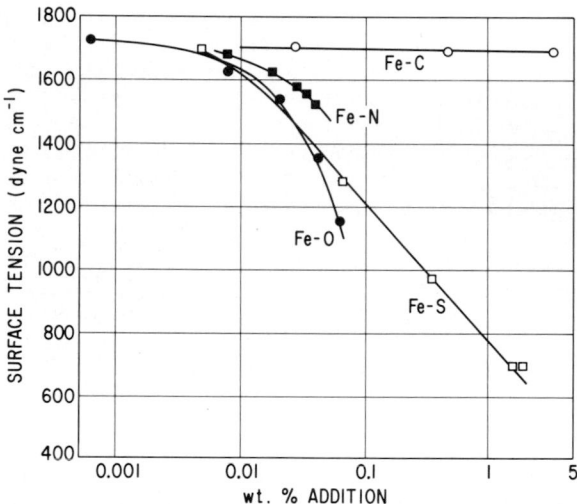

FIG. **12**—114. Effect of C, N, S, and O on the surface tension of liquid iron. (From Kingery[186].)

Table 12—XII. Surface Tensions of Metallic,
Ionic-Covalent and Molecular Liquids

Liquid	°C	γ dyne/cm	References to data
Metallic			
Ni	1550	1924 (in H_2)	Kozakevitch and Urbain 183
Co	1550	1936 (in H_2)	Kozakevitch and Urbain 183
Fe	1550	1835 (in H_2)	Kozakevitch and Urbain 183
Ionic-Covalent			
FeO	1440	584 (in Ar)	Kozakevitch 180
Cu_2S	1130	410 (in Ar)	Boni and Derge 181
CuCl	450	92 (in Ar)	Boni and Derge 181
Molecular			
H_2O	18	73 (in air)	Young and Harkins 184
CCl_4	20	27 (in its vapor)	Young and Harkins 184

The Physical Chemistry of Iron- and Steelmaking

PART IV

Reduction and Oxidation Reactions

INTRODUCTION

The reactions occurring in iron- and steelmaking processes are essentially reduction and oxidation reactions. In the blast furnace, iron oxides are reduced to metallic iron saturated with carbon. The metal produced also contains a number of other impurities, e.g., Si, S, P, Mn, which together with carbon are removed by oxidation during the steelmaking operation. The steel thus produced is invariably over-oxidized and, therefore, the final adjustments to the composition of the steel are made by adding suitable deoxidizers and alloying elements to satisfy the specifications requested by the steel users.

Much work has been done in the past to understand the chemistry of these high temperature reactions. In the light of present knowledge, an attempt will now be made to discuss the fundamentals of reaction equilibria and kinetics pertaining to reduction and oxidation in ferrous metallurgical processes.

REACTION EQUILIBRIA

FREE-ENERGY vs TEMPERATURE DIAGRAM FOR METAL OXIDES

In order to assess the feasibility of a reduction or an oxidation reaction to occur, consideration must first be given to the free-energy changes accompanying these reactions at various temperatures and pressures. The reactions to be considered may be written in a general form as:

$$\frac{2x}{y}\,\text{M} + \text{O}_2 = \frac{2}{y}\,\text{M}_x\text{O}_y \qquad (160)$$

where M and M_xO_y is metal and metal oxide, respectively. If M and M_xO_y are at unit activities, i.e. pure metal and pure metal oxide, the equilibrium constant for reaction (160) is inversely proportional to the equilibrium partial pressure of the system

$$K = \frac{1}{p_{\text{O}_2}} \qquad (161)$$

where p_{O_2} is in atmospheres and the standard state for oxygen is 1 atmosphere at the temperature under consideration. The standard free-energy change accompanying oxidation (reaction 160) is given by:

$$\Delta F^\circ = -RT \ln K = RT \ln p_{\text{O}_2} \qquad (162)$$
$$= 2.303\, RT \log p_{\text{O}_2}$$

where ΔF° = the standard free-energy change in calories per mole O_2

T = temperature in °K

R = the gas constant (1.987 cal. per mole per deg.)

In terms of standard heat and entropy changes, the standard free-energy change is expressed as:

$$\Delta F^\circ = \Delta H^\circ - T\, \Delta S^\circ \qquad (163)$$

where ΔH° = the standard change in heat content accompanying the reaction

ΔS° = the standard change in entropy accompanying the reaction

As discussed in Part I, ΔH° and ΔS° do not vary with temperature to a noticeable extent and, therefore, ΔF° varies linearly with temperature. However, at the melting and boiling points of the metal or the metal oxide, there is an abrupt change in the slopes of the free-energy lines.

The advantages of compiling the free-energy data in a graphical form were first demonstrated by Ellingham[187] and later in more detail by Richardson and Jeffes[188]. Using such a diagram for oxides, one can predict what oxides can be reduced by which elements from relative positions of the free-energy lines.

In Figure 12–115, the standard free-energies of formation of oxides per mole of oxygen are plotted against temperature in °C. Most of the data are those compiled by Coughlin[189]; where necessary, the data are brought up to date. Since the standard free-energy of formation of an oxide is directly related to its equilibrium oxygen partial pressure, Figure 12–115 is often referred to as the oxygen potential diagram.

It is to be noted that all the free-energy lines in Figure 12–115, except those for C-CO, C-CO₂ and Si-SiO have positive slopes; this is due to the decrease in the entropy of the system when an element in a condensed phase (solid or liquid) reacts with oxygen (gaseous) to produce a condensed phase (solid or liquid oxide). In the reaction C (solid) + O_2 (gas) $\rightarrow CO_2$ (gas) there is no volume change at a given temperature and pressure, therefore, $\Delta S°$ is almost zero. However, in reactions 2 C (solid) + O_2 (gas) $\rightarrow$ 2 CO (gas) and 2 Si (solid or liquid) + O_2 (gas) $\rightarrow$ 2 SiO (gas) there is an increase in volume for a given temperature and pressure, i.e. entropy change $\Delta S°$ is positive and, as a result, the free-energy line has a negative slope.

As discussed in Part III of this chapter, a number of elements form non-stoichiometric compounds, e.g. 'FeO', 'Fe₃O₄', 'TiO', 'VO' . . . etc. For the sake of clarity, these are not indicated in Figure 12–115. However, the free-energy lines drawn are for those oxides which are in equilibrium with the respective elements or other oxides. For example, in the system Fe-FeO, the latter has the composition $Fe_{0.95}O$ and in the system FeO-Fe₃O₄, the composition of ferrous oxide is $Fe_{0.87}O$, at 1373°C.

The tendency of an oxide to form or to decompose at a given temperature and pressure is predicted from the relative positions of the free-energy lines. For example, at an oxygen potential

$$\Delta F° = 2.303 \, RT \log p_{O_2} = -180 \text{ kcal. at } 1200 °C,$$

the elements Ti, Al, Mg, Ca, are oxidized, but the elements Si, V, Mn, etc. are not oxidized. Similarly, at $\Delta F° = -180$ kcal. and 1200°C, the oxides of Si, V, Mn, etc. will be reduced, but the oxides of Al, Mg, Ca, etc. will not be reduced. Above 700°C the free-energy line for Cu₂O is below that of Fe₂O₃, consequently, at temperatures above 700°C, Cu can reduce Fe₂O₃ to Fe₃O₄.

The value of carbon as a reducing agent is clearly revealed by the oxygen potential diagram. It is self evident that carbon can reduce most of the oxides. The oxides for which the free-energy lines are above that of CO can be reduced by carbon, and as the affinity of the metals for oxygen increases, i.e. $\Delta F°$ decreases, the temperature of reduction of the oxide by carbon increases. It will be observed in Figure 12–115 that although Mg has high affinity for oxygen, above the boiling point of Mg (1120°C) the slope of the $\Delta F°$ increases rapidly with increasing temperature and the Mg-MgO line cuts the

$\Delta F°$– line for CO at about 1780°C; therefore, above this temperature carbon should reduce MgO to yield Mg vapor.

For quick conversion of oxygen potentials to p_{O_2} or to ratios H₂/H₂O and CO/CO₂ appropriate scales are included in Figure 12–115.

Scale for p_{O_2} – It follows from equation (162) that, for a given partial pressure of oxygen, $\Delta F°$ varies directly with temperature; at its standard state $p_{O_2} = 1$ atm., $\Delta F°$ is zero at all temperatures and at the absolute zero $\Delta F° = 0$ for all oxygen pressures. Therefore, lines drawn from the point "O", on the ordinate for the absolute zero temperature, through the points marked on the right hand side of the diagram give the isobars. For example, at 1200°C, the oxygen potential corresponding to the equilibrium of γ-Fe with wüstite is −82 kcal.; by drawing the line passing through this point and the point "O", the oxygen partial pressure of about 7×10^{-13} atm. is read off the p_{O_2} scale.

Scale for H₂/H₂O Ratio–Since the free-energy of formation of water vapor from H₂ and O₂ is known, the oxygen potentials for the H₂-H₂O-O₂ equilibrium can be calculated for any ratio H₂/H₂O. The lines for iso gas ratios converge at point "H" on the ordinate at absolute zero temperature Referring to the above example on the equilibrium of γ-Fe and wüstite, the line drawn through $\Delta F° = -82$ at 1200°C and the point "H" intersects the H₂/H₂O scale at about 1.4/1 which is the gas ratio in equilibrium with Fe-FeO mixture.

Scale for CO/CO₂ Ratio–A grid for the iso-CO/CO₂ ratios is constructed in a similar way and these lines converge at point "C". By drawing a line through point "C" and a point on the free-energy line for an oxide, its equilibrium CO/CO₂ can be read off directly from the scale for the CO/CO₂ ratio.

The above graphical relations can readily be proved by considering, for example, the reaction:

$$2 \, H_2 + O_2 = 2 \, H_2O \qquad (164a)$$

for which the equilibrium oxygen partial pressure is given by:

$$p_{O_2} = \frac{1}{K} \left(\frac{p_{H_2O}}{p_{H_2}} \right)^2 \qquad (164b)$$

where K is the equilibrium constant. In terms of oxygen potential

$$2.303 \, RT \log p_{O_2} = \\ - 2.303 \, RT \left(\log K + 2 \log \frac{p_{H_2}}{p_{H_2O}} \right) \qquad (164c)$$

$$= \Delta F° - 4.606 \, RT \log \frac{p_{H_2}}{p_{H_2O}} \qquad (164d)$$

Assuming that $\Delta F°$, the standard free-energy change accompanying reaction (164a), is a linear function of temperature then for a given ratio H₂/H₂O, the oxygen potential varies linearly with temperature. Since $\Delta F° = \Delta H° - T \Delta S°$, the oxygen potential line for any ratio H₂/H₂O intersects the ordinate at point "H" at $T = 0°K$, corresponding to the value of $\Delta H°$ at zero absolute temperature. Errors involved

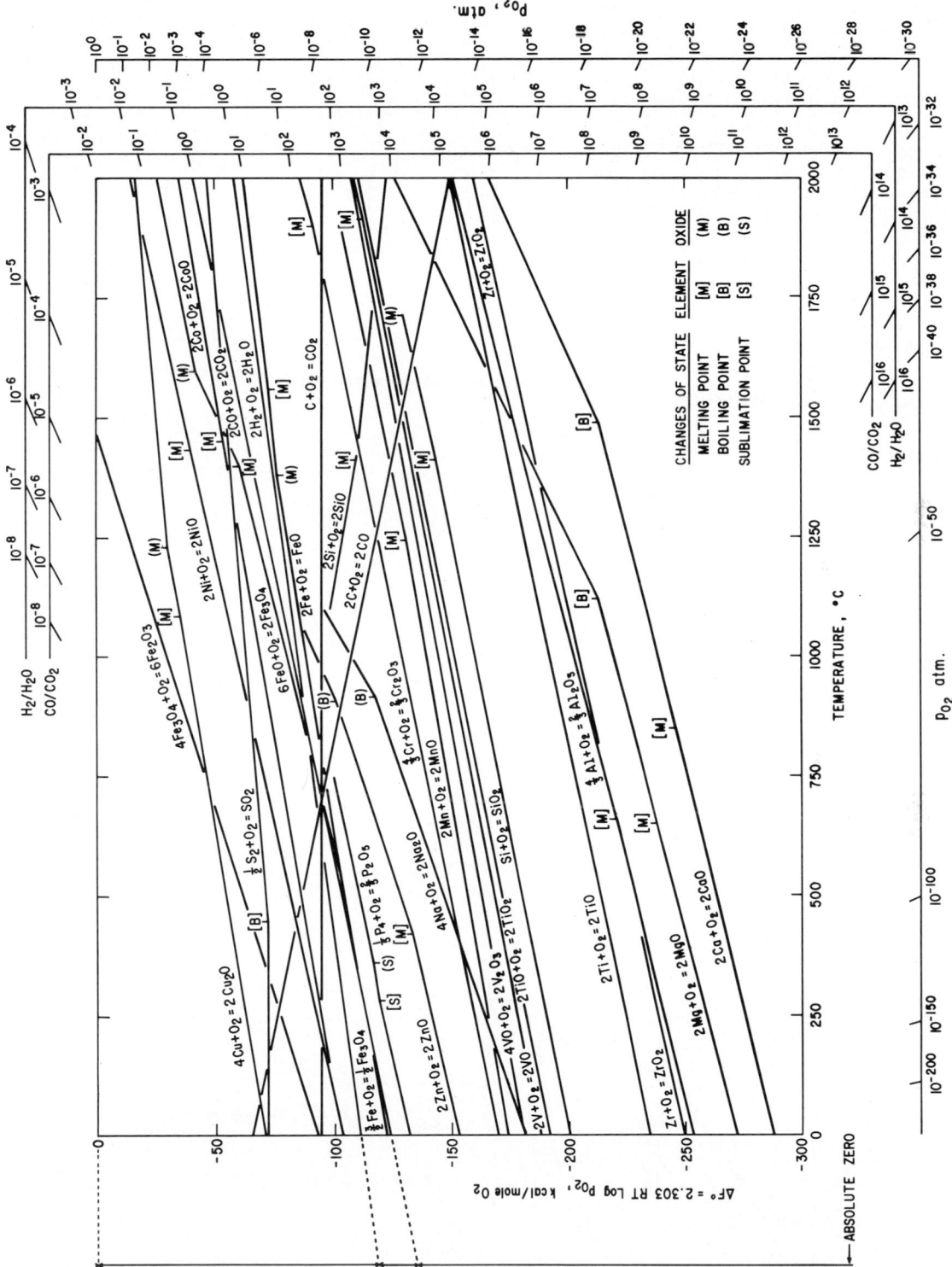

FIG. 12–115. The free energies of formation of oxides for the standard states: pure elements, pure oxides and gases at 1 atm.

in the assumption of the linearity of ΔF° vs T plot for reaction (164a), are much less than the uncertainty of the free-energy data on other oxides given in Figure 12–115.

By using the above grids, one can estimate quickly whether or not a metal will be oxidized at a given ratio of H_2/H_2O or CO/CO_2. However, for more accurate calculations, the free-energy equations should be used.

As already indicated, the data in Figure 12–115 are for pure elements and their oxides. For metals and oxides in solutions, due account must be taken of their activities in metallic and oxide solutions.

Using the oxygen potential diagram as the basic tool, it is possible to generalize some aspects of the reduction and oxidation reactions occurring in smelting and refining processes.

OXYGEN POTENTIALS IN THE BLAST FURNACE

Reduction by Carbon Monoxide—There are two basic reactions which occur in the shaft of the blast furnace: The reaction between coke and carbon dioxide produces carbon monoxide and the reaction between iron ore and carbon monoxide produces carbon dioxide. Many investigators have reported gas analyses and temperature measurements at various positions in the shaft of the blast furnace. Using the data given in Special Report 18 of the Iron and Steel Institute[190], Figure 12–116 shows gas ratios CO/CO_2 and temperatures plotted against the distance from the inwall at two cross-sections of the shaft. Across the radius of the shaft, temperature and gas composition vary in a systematic manner; that is, as temperature decreases the gas ratio CO/CO_2 decreases. The significance of this relationship is best illustrated by considering the following reaction:

$$2\,CO + O_2 = 2\,CO_2 \qquad (165)$$

From the data compiled in Table **12–III** of Part 1 of this chapter, the following is obtained for the standard free-energy change accompanying reaction (165):

$$\Delta F^0 = -135,000 + 41.42\,T \text{ cal. per mole } O_2 \quad (166)$$

and the corresponding relation for the equilibrium constant is

$$\log K = \frac{29,508}{T} - 9.054 \qquad (167)$$

where

$$K = \frac{(p_{CO_2})^2}{(p_{CO}{}^2)\,p_{O_2}} \qquad (168)$$

where p is in atmospheres. Equations (167) and (168) show that under equilibrium conditions, for a given oxygen partial pressure, a decrease in temperature is accompanied by a decrease in the ratio CO/CO_2.

Part of the oxygen potential diagram is reproduced in Figure 12–117; also included here is the oxygen potential of the gas, derived from the above-mentioned blast-furnace data. These indicate that near the top of the blast furnace, at about 400°–500°C, the oxygen potential of the gas is but slightly below that required to reduce magnetite to iron. The C-CO line is drawn for $p_{CO} = 0.5$ atm. as this is the average partial pressure of carbon monoxide in the blast-furnace shaft. The process of reduction and oxidation in the shaft of the blast furnace may be generalized by using the free-energy diagram as suggested by Goodeve[191, 192]. This is best illustrated by following the change in the oxygen potential of a volume of gas as it travels from the tuyere zone to the top of the furnace. The gas entering the tuyere is at about 700°–800°C and $p_{O_2} \simeq 0.3$ atm. and its position on the free-energy diagram is at A as shown in Figure 12–118. As a result of combustion of coke, the temperature rises and the oxygen potential of this volume of gas is reduced to about -140 kcal per

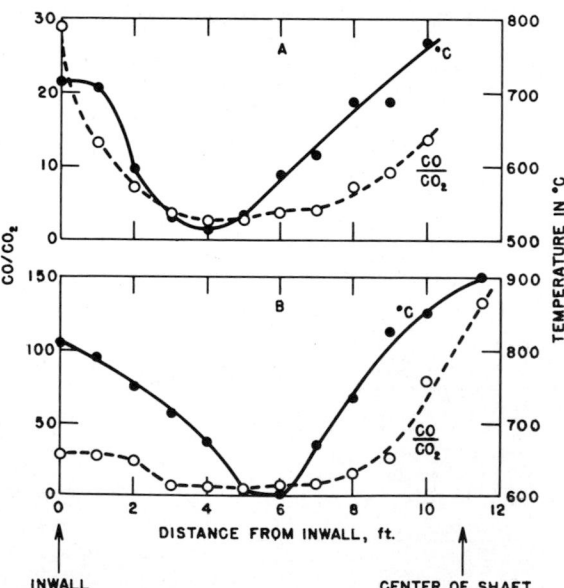

FIG. **12–116.** Variation of CO/CO_2 ratio and temperature with distance from the inwall of a blast furnace shaft at two planes: A, at 17 ft. 9 in. below the stock line, and B, at 26 ft. 6 in. below the stock line[190].

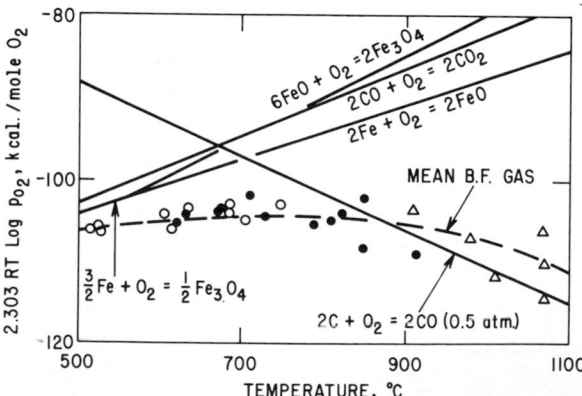

FIG. **12–117.** Oxygen potentials in the blast furnace shaft determined from gas analyses and temperature measurements. (Open circles, cross-section 17 ft. 9 in. below the stock line; filled circles, cross section 26 ft. 6 in. below the stock line; and triangles, cross section 44 ft. 0 in. below the stock line.)

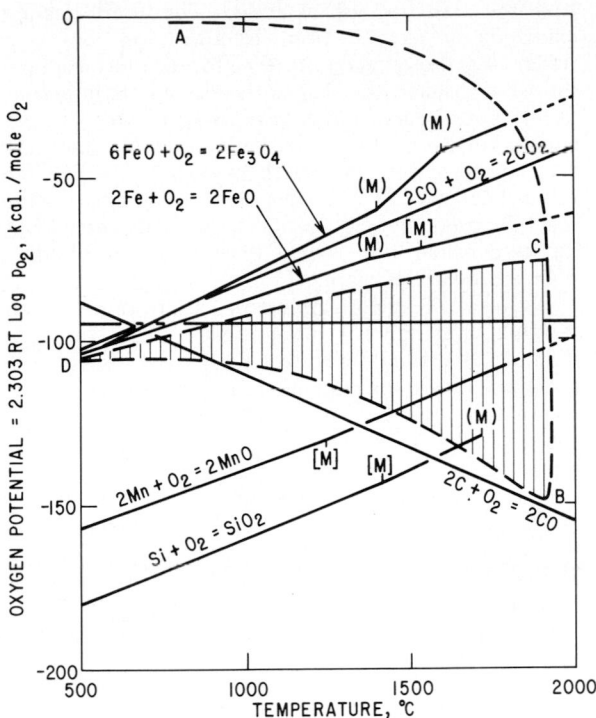

FIG. 12–118. Schematic diagram showing the oxygen potentials in the shaft of the blast furnace. (DC: at the gas-ore interface. DB: at the gas-coke interface.)

mole O_2 as shown by point B. As this gas ascends the furnace, its temperature is lowered and oxygen potential is raised as a result of the reaction with iron oxide, producing iron and carbon dioxide. The oxygen potentials at the ore-gas and coke-gas interfaces move along the curves CD and BD, respectively, as the gas ascends the shaft. At temperatures below 900°C, coke becomes less reactive and the oxygen potential of the gas is controlled essentially by the magnetite → wüstite and wüstite → iron reactions. The average oxygen potential of the blast-furnace gas lies within the shaded area shown in Figure 12–118.

Carbon Deposition—As shown in Figure 12–115, the oxygen potential lines for C-CO$_2$, C-CO and CO-CO$_2$ intersect at 704°C where the equilibrium CO/CO$_2$ ratio is 1:1. If a CO-CO$_2$ mixture in equilibrium with carbon is cooled unchanged from a high to a temperature below 700°C, the following reaction occurs:

$$2\,CO = C + CO_2 \qquad (169)$$

leading to carbon deposition. As the temperature decreases, more carbon is deposited, and the iron ore acts as a catalyst for this reaction to occur at a reasonable rate at temperatures of 400°–600°C.

Solution of Carbon in Iron during Smelting—As the ore is reduced to metallic iron, the latter absorbs carbon from the gas phase. If there is an appreciable solution of carbon in iron during the early stages of smelting, the partial melting of the iron takes place well below 1500°C, and the iron-carbon melt flows over the unreduced ore, which is reduced directly

by dissolved carbon. It is therefore unlikely that the melt is saturated with carbon before reaching the furnace hearth where very little or no iron oxides are present.

In addition to carbon, there are other impurities which dissolve in iron during smelting in the blast furnace, they will be discussed in detail later in this chapter.

OXYGEN POTENTIALS IN STEELMAKING FURNACES

The molten iron produced by the blast-furnace process is saturated with carbon and contains undesirable amounts of silicon, manganese, phosphorus and sulphur which have to be removed subsequently during the steelmaking operation. With the exception of sulphur, the removal of these impurities is accomplished by oxidation followed by solution of the oxides in the slag. For the present, the discussion is limited to the state of oxidation in the steelmaking processes with respect to the carbon-oxygen reaction and the influence of slag on the oxygen potential of the metal.

The Bessemer Process—In this process, the hot metal is refined by blowing air, oxygen-enriched air or steam-oxygen mixtures through the metal bath. The average total gas pressure in the melt is about 1.3 to 1.4 atm.; i.e., owing to the hydrostatic pressure of the metal and slag, pressure within gas bubbles in the metal are about 0.3 to 0.4 atm. in excess of the atmospheric pressure. If it is assumed that all the oxygen in air passing through the bath reacts with carbon to give carbon monoxide, its partial pressure will be about 0.5 atm., the remainder being nitrogen at about 0.8 atm. Since some of the oxygen is consumed by the oxidation of silicon, manganese and iron, the partial pressure of carbon monoxide given above is only approximate. If oxygen-enriched air or steam-oxygen mixtures are blown, the partial pressure of carbon monoxide in the melt will increase in accord with the increasing oxygen content of the blast.

Now, let us consider the change in the oxygen potential of the metal during the blow. The air blast entering the tuyeres at the bottom of the converter has an oxygen potential indicated by point A in Figure 12–119. The hot metal charged to the converter is at 1250°–1350°C and is saturated with carbon and, therefore, its oxygen potential at $p_{CO} = 0.5$ atm. is at B as shown in Figure 12–119. The oxygen potential of a volume of gas entering the bath is reduced to a value approaching that at point B, as a result of the following reaction:

$$2\,\underline{C} + O_2 = 2\,CO \qquad (170)$$

where $\underline{C}$ indicates carbon dissolved in iron. This volume of gas now contains essentially CO and N_2 and at the mouth of the vessel it burns to carbon dioxide. As discussed in Part II of this chapter, the ratios CO/CO$_2$ in equilibrium with Fe-C-O melts are very high even at low carbon concentrations. Likewise, CO$_2$ in the gas rising through the metal in the converter is negligibly small. The oxidation of carbon is also accompanied by the oxidation of silicon and

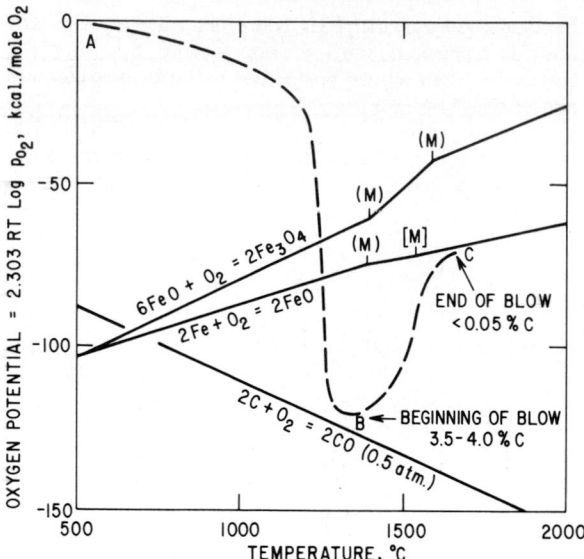

FIG. 12–119. Schematic diagram showing the change in the oxygen potential of the metal during blowing of the Bessemer converter.

manganese; these reactions will be discussed later. Since the oxidation of these impurities is exothermic, the temperature of the melt increases during the blow. It is to be deduced from the equilibrium constant for reaction (170), i.e.

$$K = \frac{(p_{CO})^2}{[a_c]^2 p_{O_2}} \qquad (171)$$

that for a given value of p_{CO}, the oxygen partial pressure of the system increases with decreasing carbon content of the melt. Therefore, during blowing, the oxygen potential of the melt increases along the curve BC in Figure 12–119. At carbon contents less than 0.1 per cent, the oxygen potential of the system becomes high enough to oxidize iron; this marks the end of the refining period which, in practice, is observed by the drop of the so-called "carbon flame."

At the end of the blow, carbon and oxygen contents of the metal are 0.02–0.05 per cent C and 0.10–0.06 per cent O, respectively. According to the equilibrium data on Fe-C-O melts given in Part II of this chapter, at 1650°C and $p_{CO} = 0.5$ atm. the product [%C] [%O] is about 1.2×10^{-3}. The oxygen content of the metal in equilibrium with 0.02–0.05 per cent C under the above conditions should be within the range 0.06–0.03 per cent O. This difference between the observed and the calculated (by assuming C-O equilibrium) oxygen contents indicates that, at low carbon concentrations, the carbon-oxygen reaction is not fast enough to maintain the equilibrium oxygen potential in the system and, therefore, some of the iron is oxidized near the end of the blow.

The Open-Hearth Process—In the conventional open-hearth process, the usual practice is to charge the furnace with scrap together with limestone and hematite ore and melt them using natural gas, coke-oven gas, tar-pitch mixture or oil as fuel. When the charge is almost molten, hot metal (molten iron

from the blast furnace) is added. The impurities are oxidized by oxygen from iron-ore additions and partly by the oxygen in the furnace atmosphere diffusing through the slag to the slag-metal interface. In the open-hearth furnace, the slag plays two roles simultaneously: (1) at the slag-metal interface the slag supplies the metal with oxygen to oxidize the impurities and (2) as a solvent, the slag absorbs the reaction products, e.g., MnO, SiO_2, P_2O_5, etc. First, let us consider the oxygen potentials prevailing in the open-hearth furnace.

Because of the inadvertent infiltration of air through openings (at the furnace doors, etc.) it is difficult to estimate the oxygen partial pressure in the atmosphere of the open-hearth furnace. However, above the slag layer in the middle portion of the bath, the oxygen partial pressure may be in the range of $10^{-2} - 10^{-3}$ atm. The oxygen partial pressure corresponding to the composition of steel normally manufactured in the open-hearth furnace is of the order of 10^{-10} atm. The oxygen partial pressure of the slag lies, of course, somewhere between these two limits.

At the gas-slag interface the following reaction takes place:

$$2 Fe^{2+}(slag) + \frac{1}{2} O_2(gas) = \qquad (172)$$
$$2 Fe^{3+}(slag) + O^{2-}(slag)$$

As a result of this reaction, the concentrations of the trivalent iron and the oxide ions at the gas-slag interface increase with respect to those at the slag-metal interface. Owing to the presence of forced convection in the slag bath, these ions diffuse rapidly to the slag-metal interface where the following reaction occurs:

$$2 Fe^{3+}(slag) + O^{2-}(slag) \qquad (173)$$
$$= 2 Fe^{2+}(slag) + \underline{O}\ (metal)$$

The oxygen thus transferred to the metal oxidizes carbon, manganese, phosphorus, iron, etc. In order to increase the flux of oxygen to the slag-metal interface, iron oxides are added to the slag or oxygen is lanced into the slag and metal. Whatever may be the practice, the oxygen potential of the slag can be estimated from its ferric-oxide content. As shown by Turkdogan and Bills[193a], there is an empirical but a simple relationship between the atomic fraction of Fe^{3+} and the equilibrium gas ratio CO_2/CO for a given sum of the atomic concentration of silicon and phosphorus and possibly aluminum in the slag, i.e. $3 N_{Al} + 4 N_{Si} + 5 N_p$. The part of this relationship applicable to open hearth slags is reproduced in Figure 12–120, where the atomic concentration of Fe^{3+} is plotted against log CO_2/CO for ranges of $3 N_{Al} + 4 N_{Si} + 5 N_p$ valid for temperatures of 1500°–1700°C.

In Tables 12–XIII and 12–XIV, two sets of data are compiled on the open-hearth steelmaking process where oxidation is carried out by iron-ore feed. The slags given in Table 12–XIII contain very little phosphorus, whilst those in Table 12–XIV are for refining high-phosphorus iron. The oxygen potential of the metal is calculated from its oxygen content as

Table 12—XIII. Data[a] on Basic Open-Hearth Steelmaking Process. (Oxidation by iron-ore feed.)

Heat No.	Metal Temp. °C	Metal Composition, wt. %					Slag Composition, wt. %[b]									Oxygen Potentials kcal/mole O_2	
		C	Mn	P	S	O	FeO	Fe₂O₃	CaO	MgO	MnO	SiO₂	P₂O₅	Al₂O₃	S	I, metal	II, slag
1680-13	1550	0.12	0.13	—	—	0.048	13.5	4.3	37.2	11.2	9.8	20.7	2.2	1.3	—	−80.5	−73.9
2095-25	1550	0.08	0.21	—	—	0.055	12.7	3.5	37.4	12.0	11.4	18.4	1.9	2.8	—	−79.5	−81.7
5393	1625	0.09	0.22	—	—	0.036	13.5	3.5	48.4	5.8	9.9	16.5	(1.5)	(2.0)	—	−83.7	−83.0
6190	1620	0.08	0.21	—	—	0.060	16.1	7.3	40.6	5.9	10.2	15.6	1.4	(2.0)	—	−79.8	−67.4
1288	1610	0.07	0.19	—	—	0.065	15.6	7.0	40.7	6.5	9.6	16.6	1.6	(2.0)	—	−79.1	−63.0
11060	1630	0.12	0.26	—	—	0.042	10.2	10.5	45.0	5.7	7.7	16.6	1.0	(2.0)	—	−82.6	−56.2
8122	1645	0.10	0.31	—	—	0.038	8.9	5.8	46.4	5.7	9.0	19.7	1.3	(2.0)	—	−83.6	−63.6
1144	1625	0.10	0.31	—	—	0.047	10.9	7.5	46.8	4.7	10.2	16.6	1.4	(2.0)	—	−81.7	−72.2
3149	1625	0.11	0.23	—	—	0.056	11.7	7.8	47.4	5.5	8.8	16.8	1.5	(2.0)	—	−80.3	−62.3
3134	1625	0.10	0.21	—	—	0.049	12.2	8.7	45.8	4.5	9.3	13.6	1.4	(2.0)	—	−81.3	−60.4
2127	1625	0.10	0.31	—	—	0.047	10.6	8.6	46.0	5.7	10.2	15.6	1.3	(2.0)	—	−81.7	−60.4
9397	1625	0.17	0.21	—	—	0.049	16.6	8.4	49.5	5.4	10.2	14.8	(1.5)	(2.0)	—	−81.3	−74.1
1405	1625	0.14	0.29	—	—	0.033	11.4	3.5	49.1	5.9	9.3	16.0	(1.5)	(2.0)	—	−84.3	−81.5

[a] The data obtained from USS Research Center.
[b] The values in ( ) are estimated.

follows: The free-energy change accompanying the solution of oxygen in iron is given by:

$$O_2(gas = 2 \underline{O} \text{ (metal)} \qquad (174)$$

$$\Delta F_I^\circ = -56,000 - 1.38\ T \text{ cal per mole } O_2\ (175)$$

and for a given temperature and oxygen content, the oxygen potential of the metal is derived from:

$$RT \ln p_{O_2} = 2\ RT \ln [\%O] + \Delta F_I^\circ \qquad (176)$$

and the values thus obtained are given in Tables **12—XIII** and **12—XIV**.

Similar calculation for the slag is more involved. First, the slag composition is recalculated in terms of atom fractions as described in Part III of this chapter, and using Figure 12–120, the equilibrium gas ratio CO_2/CO is found. This is then converted to the equilibrium oxygen partial pressure using the expression:

$$2\ CO\ (gas) + O_2\ (gas) = 2\ CO_2\ (gas)\ (177)$$

$$\Delta F_{II}^\circ = -135,000 + 41.42\ T \qquad (178)$$

For a given temperature and CO_2/CO ratio, the oxygen potential of the slag is obtained from:

$$RT \ln p_{O_2} = 2\ RT \ln \frac{p_{CO_2}}{p_{CO}} + \Delta F_{II}^\circ \quad (179)$$

where p is in atmospheres. It is a well known fact that in the open-hearth furnace the temperature of

Table 12—XIV. Data[a] on Basic Open-Hearth Steelmaking. (Oxidation by iron-ore feed.)

Heat No.[c]	Metal Temp. °C	Metal Composition, wt. %					Slag Composition, wt. %[b]									Oxygen Potentials kcal/mole O_2	
		C	Mn	P	S	O	FeO	Fe₂O₃	CaO	MgO	MnO	SiO₂	P₂O₅	Al₂O₃	S	I, metal	II, slag
2344 (1)	1580	0.24	0.23	0.092	0.073	0.022	7.6	3.3	41.9	8.8	8.6	16.2	11.3	(2.4)	0.09	−86.7	−67.7
(2)	1600	0.06	0.20	0.027	0.042	0.042	12.1	5.3	44.8	10.9	6.2	11.5	7.7	(1.4)	0.19	−82.2	−73.3
2650 (1)	1540	0.32	0.13	0.026	0.046	0.014	6.6	4.0	51.4	6.5	3.9	9.7	16.3	(1.4)	0.26	−89.3	−67.9
(2)	1615	0.07	0.11	0.017	0.025	0.029	14.2	5.8	48.0	9.4	3.3	7.6	10.4	(1.0)	0.30	−85.2	−72.9
2737 (1)	1580	0.20	0.11	0.030	0.059	0.015	8.7	3.4	50.2	8.8	2.1	6.9	16.9	(2.6)	0.44	−89.5	−73.4
(2)	1610	0.07	0.09	0.023	0.051	0.027	11.6	3.2	50.4	9.9	2.3	6.3	14.5	(1.4)	0.42	−85.6	−81.9
3010 (1)	1585	0.20	0.20	0.019	0.038	0.023	9.8	3.4	51.2	9.1	5.4	13.4	6.8	(0.6)	0.31	−86.4	—
(2)	1610	0.09	0.17	0.013	0.033	0.035	14.2	4.5	50.2	9.9	5.0	10.6	5.0	(0.3)	0.28	−83.7	−82.0
3045 (1)	1520	0.95	0.41	0.126	0.048	0.008	6.6	3.3	47.7	6.3	6.5	15.7	12.9	(0.9)	0.11	−90.9	−67.5
(2)	1575	0.19	0.26	0.038	0.039	0.021	8.3	3.7	48.9	7.6	7.0	12.2	11.2	(0.8)	0.27	−87.0	−69.5
(3)	1595	0.12	0.21	0.027	0.031	0.030	11.4	4.7	47.8	8.0	6.5	10.6	9.5	(0.7)	0.30	−84.6	−76.0
3242 (1)	1590	0.30	0.24	0.089	0.032	0.017	5.0	4.2	54.2	8.2	2.7	11.4	13.4	(0.6)	0.32	−88.8	−70.8
(2)	1610	0.08	0.14	0.024	0.028	0.032	12.3	4.9	48.0	9.2	4.0	9.1	10.9	(1.4)	0.23	−84.4	−72.5
3695 (1)	1520	0.40	0.29	0.089	0.050	0.014	5.8	3.5	48.4	7.3	5.2	11.2	16.3	(2.2)	0.19	−88.9	−67.5
(2)	1580	0.21	0.20	0.022	0.036	0.022	9.5	4.3	48.9	7.0	5.2	9.1	13.2	(2.5)	0.27	−86.7	−70.2
(3)	1595	0.11	0.18	0.020	0.030	0.029	11.1	5.7	48.2	7.3	4.8	8.6	12.0	(2.0)	0.25	−84.9	−66.1
3699 (1)	1540	0.44	0.30	0.139	0.049	0.012	6.8	3.9	48.3	5.9	5.1	11.1	16.5	(2.3)	0.14	−90.5	−63.3
(2)	1560	0.34	0.23	0.058	0.055	0.018	7.3	3.0	47.0	6.7	5.1	10.3	16.9	(3.5)	0.22	−87.9	−65.8
(3)	1600	0.11	0.17	0.026	0.036	0.027	10.8	3.3	47.5	8.4	4.8	8.8	14.0	(2.2)	0.23	−85.5	−78.1

[a] The data obtained from the British Iron and Steel Research Association.
[b] The values in ( ) are estimated.
[c] Numbers in ( ) refer to different samples taken during refining.

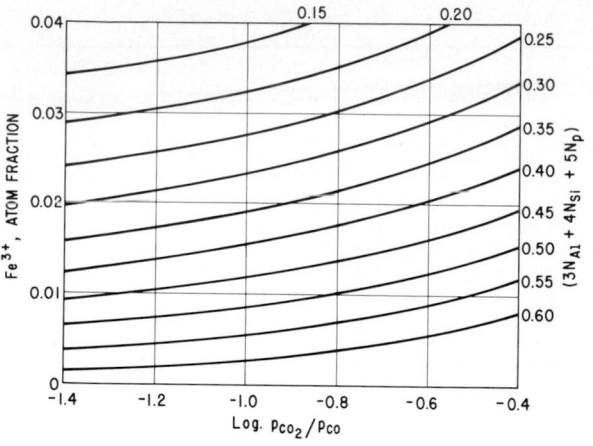

FIG. 12–120. Equilibrium p_{CO_2}/p_{CO} ratio for complex steelmaking slags for the temperature range 1500°–1700°C. Each curve is for a given sum of the atomic concentrations $3N_{Al} + 4N_{Si} + 5N_P$. (From Turkdogan and Bills[103a].)

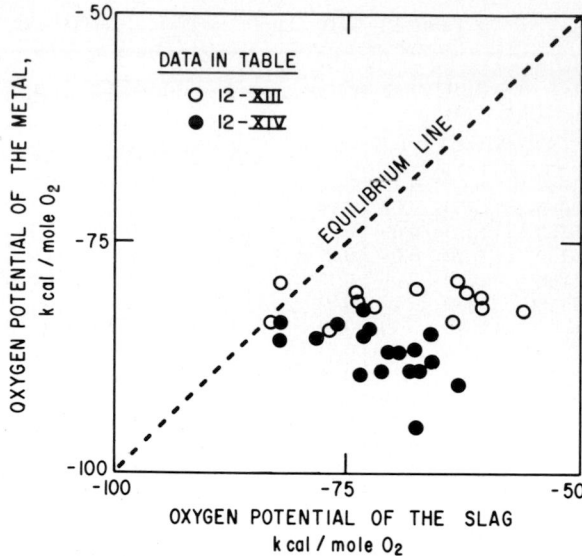

FIG. 12–121. Relationship showing the difference between the oxygen potentials of metal and slag in the open-hearth furnace.

the slag is noticeably higher than that of the metal. The temperatures recorded in the data are usually those of the metal; in the present computations it is assumed that the average slag-temperature is 100°C higher than the metal-temperature. The oxygen potentials thus obtained for the slags are given in the last columns of Tables 12–XIII and 12–XIV. It should be realized that small errors in the analyses of slags, particularly for Fe^{3+}, introduces noticeable uncertainties in the computed slag-oxygen potentials, i.e. uncertainty is estimated to be about 3 to 5 kcal.

As seen from the results plotted in Figure 12–121, the average oxygen potential of the metal is about -85 ± 5 kcal. per mole O_2, whilst for the slags the mean value is -70 ± 10 kcal. per mole O_2. The extent of this difference between the oxygen potentials of metal and slag will of course vary with the steelmaking practice. This is best illustrated by considering the use of oxygen in the open-hearth steelmaking.

In Table 12–XV are given some British data on the basic open-hearth steelmaking process where oxygen was blown through roof-lances into the slag during the entire refining period after the hot-metal charge. The main difference between the slag compositions in Table 12–XIV and those in Table 12–XV is that the ferric oxide concentration of the slag is higher by a factor of about 2 when oxygen is blown during refining. The average oxygen potentials of these slags as seen from Table 12–XV, is -60 ± 5 kcal. per mole O_2. This increase in the oxygen potential of the slag no doubt accounts, at least partially, for the increased rate of refining when oxygen is used as an oxidant rather than the ore feed.

The foregoing discussion may be summarized by Figure 12–122 which gives the average oxygen potential profile along the vertical section of an open-hearth furnace. At the gas-slag, slag-metal, metal-

Table 12–XV. Data[a] on Basic Open-Hearth Steelmaking Process. (Oxygen was lanced into the slag during refining.)

Heat No.	Metal Temp. °C	Metal Composition, wt. %					Slag Composition, wt. %									Oxygen Potentials kcal/mole O₂	
		C	Mn	P	S	O	FeO	Fe₂O₃	CaO	MgO	MnO	SiO₂	P₂O₅	Al₂O₃	S	I, metal	II, slag
G671	1600	0.040	0.15	0.020	0.028	—	18.3	12.2	42.8	4.7	4.3	9.0	4.4	2.8	0.21	—	−56.2
G965	1575	0.045	0.12	0.020	—	—	19.4	10.9	44.2	3.6	5.0	8.4	5.2	2.5	0.22	—	−59.6
H561	1590	0.040	0.13	0.020	0.029	—	9.0	8.0	46.0	5.2	7.4	13.7	6.3	2.8	0.23	—	−69.2
H570	1585	0.050	0.13	0.015	—	—	18.3	10.4	42.6	5.1	5.6	9.8	4.6	2.6	0.22	—	−62.0
H581	1600	0.040	0.12	0.015	0.030	—	21.6	12.3	41.2	3.8	4.3	9.1	4.4	2.6	0.19	—	−56.2
K499	1595	0.045	—	—	—	—	21.3	9.7	42.0	5.4	5.6	8.4	4.2	2.3	0.16	—	−62.5
L346	1595	0.050	0.17	—	—	—	18.8	9.9	44.0	3.3	6.9	7.4	4.7	2.9	0.24	—	−62.5
L350	1593	0.055	0.17	0.050	0.025	—	19.1	8.7	44.6	4.7	6.3	7.6	4.2	2.7	0.24	—	−64.3
L373	1600	0.035	0.18	0.025	0.025	—	15.5	9.2	41.4	5.6	7.9	10.6	5.7	2.4	0.18	—	−61.4
M112	1600	0.045	0.15	—	—	—	16.8	12.9	44.3	3.7	7.4	7.6	4.2	2.0	0.27	—	−56.9
M115	1585	0.050	0.10	—	0.024	—	17.8	10.3	46.8	4.1	5.0	8.5	4.7	2.1	0.20	—	−62.9
N100	1590	0.040	0.13	0.015	0.026	—	18.1	17.4	40.4	5.3	4.7	7.4	3.8	2.7	0.23	—	−53.7
O922	1583	0.045	0.09	—	0.026	—	22.7	9.6	45.9	4.3	3.0	8.8	2.9	2.5	0.23	—	−62.9
O924	1580	0.040	0.15	0.020	0.027	—	19.1	7.4	46.2	4.1	6.3	8.6	5.3	2.5	0.22	—	−64.7

[a] The data obtained from the British Iron and Steel Research Association.

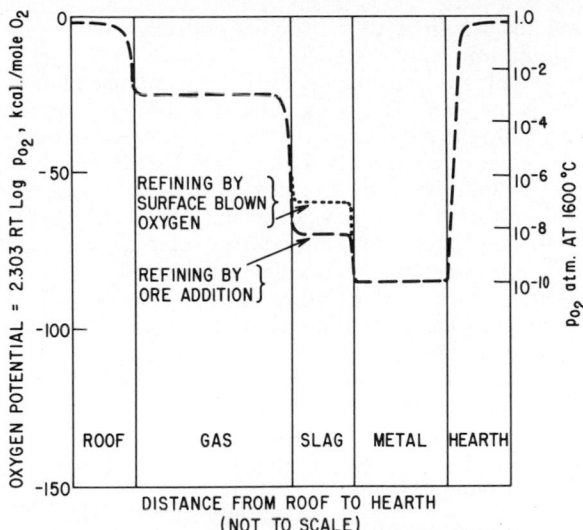

Fig. **12**–122. Average oxygen potential gradient along vertical section of an open-hearth furnace.

refractory interfaces there are boundary layers through which oxygen and other transported elements must diffuse and, therefore, the chemical potential profile across the interface is controlled by the hydrodynamic conditions in the gas and the melt; this has already been discussed in Part I of this chapter in connection with the transport-controlled reaction kinetics. The oxygen potentials across the roof bricks and the furnace hearth increase rapidly with increasing distance from the interfaces.

It is feasible to assume that at the slag-metal interface reaction (173) is at or near equilibrium. For a given rate of agitation at the interface, the flux of oxygen from slag to the metal under steady-state conditions is proportional to the oxygen concentration difference $[O]_e - [O] = \Delta[O]$ where $[O]_e$ is the oxygen content of the metal in equilibrium with the slag at the interface and $[O]$ is the oxygen content in the bulk of the metal. Assuming that the total iron content of the slag at the interface is the same as that of the bulk phase, the value of $[O]_e$ can be evaluated from the slag composition, using the ferrous-oxide activity data given in Part III of this chapter. This detailed analysis of the steelmaking data by Brower and Larsen[193b] showed that during the decarburization period the average value of $\Delta[O] \cong 0.04$ per cent.

DEOXIDATION

By the time the steel is refined to the required specification, it usually contains 0.05 to 0.10 per cent of dissolved oxygen. This is an appreciable amount of oxygen which interferes with the subsequent treatment of steel. For example, during the solidification of the ingots and steel castings, oxygen and carbon in solution react to give carbon monoxide, resulting in the formation of blow holes. Another deleterious effect of oxygen in steel is that on cooling oxygen comes out of solution as iron oxide, manganese oxide, etc., in the form of inclusions which may impair the hot and cold workability of the steel and its me-

chanical properties. Therefore, at the time of tapping, the oxygen content of over-oxidized steel must be reduced to the desired level to produce rimming, semikilled or killed (almost completely deoxidized) steel.

The carbon dissolved in iron plays an important role in maintaining the oxygen content of the steel at a reasonable level during refining. Had it not been for the presence of small amounts of carbon remaining in solution, at the end of refining the metal would have been heavily oxidized. The curve drawn in Figure **12**–123 shows the variation of the oxygen content with carbon concentration in equilibrium with carbon monoxide-carbon dioxide mixtures at one atmosphere pressure at 1600°C, reproduced from the data on Fe-C-O system discussed in Part II of this chapter. The curve obtained from the open-hearth data lies above the equilibrium value (as if at equilibrium with carbon monoxide at a pressure of 2 to 3 atmospheres). The supersaturation of the metal with carbon and oxygen with respect to $p_{CO} = 1.0$ atm. is a well-established fact and some aspects of this phenomenon are discussed later in this part of Chapter 12.

Since under steelmaking conditions carbon does not deoxidize steel to a low enough level, other deoxidizers having greater affinity for oxygen are added to the refined steel, partly prior to tapping and partly in the ladle. The deoxidation reaction may be expressed in a general form as:

$$x\underline{M} + y\underline{O} = M_xO_y \text{ (solid or liquid)} \quad (180)$$

where $\underline{M}$ is the deoxidizing element dissolved in iron. In most cases, the deoxidation product is pure

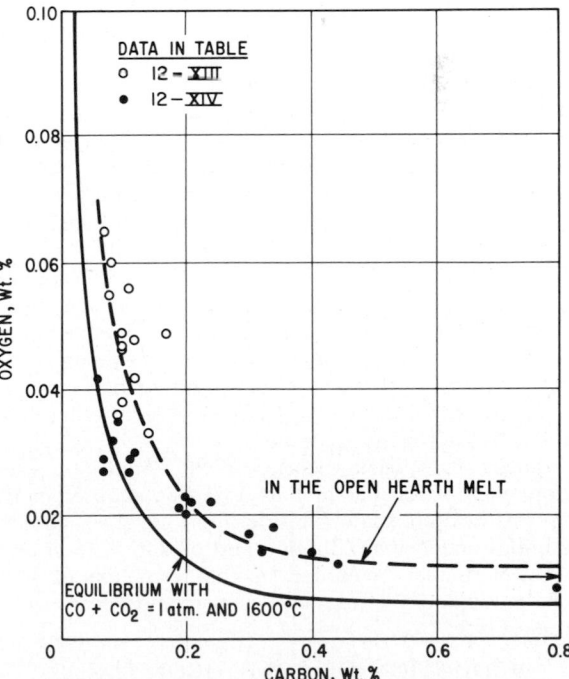

Fig. **12**–123. Carbon-oxygen relationship under equilibrium conditions ($p_{CO} + p_{CO_2} = 1.0$ atm. and 1600°C.) and in open-hearth melts.

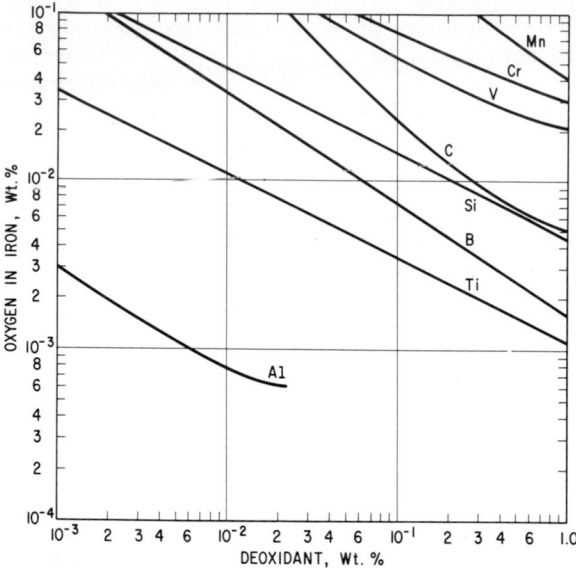

FIG. 12–124. Relationship between the concentrations of oxygen and deoxidants in solution in iron in equilibrium with their respective pure oxides at 1600°C. (Data are taken from those given in Part II of this chapter.)

solid oxide, e.g. SiO_2, TiO_2, Al_2O_3 and, therefore, under equilibrium conditions:

$$\frac{1}{K} = [a_M]^x [a_O]^y \qquad (181)$$

where K is the equilibrium constant and a_M and a_O

are the activities of deoxidants and oxygen in solution in iron.

Details on deoxidation by silicon and manganese are given later. However, for the present purpose it will suffice to summarize the relevant data graphically as shown in Figure 12–124, where the oxygen content in solution in molten steel is plotted against the concentration of the deoxidant dissolved in the metal.

In connection with the subject of oxidation and reduction reactions, reference should also be made to vacuum treatment of steel. When a ladle full of molten steel is poured in vacuum, oxygen is removed by the carbon-oxygen reaction occurring at much lower partial pressures of carbon monoxide. When operating at reduced pressures, some difficulties might be experienced with the refractory linings. For example, in the case of magnesia-lined containers the following reduction could occur:

$$MgO(s) = Mg\ (g) + \underline{O}\ (\text{in Fe})$$
$$K = p_{Mg}\ [\%O] = 4.43 \times 10^{-4}\ \text{at}\ 1600°C$$

where p_{Mg} is the partial pressure of magnesium vapor in mm Hg. If a neutral gas is bubbled through the steel bath or the steel is vacuum-treated so that the partial pressure of magnesium vapor is say 10^{-2} mm. Hg., then the iron in equilibrium with it will contain 0.044 per cent oxygen. Therefore, under these conditions there is some possibility of contaminating the steel with oxygen. With oxides of much lower oxygen potentials, e.g. BeO, Al_2O_3, ZrO_2 and ThO_2, the above problem will not arise.

SECTION 3

REACTION KINETICS

In discussing the chemistry of the iron and steel-making processes the foregoing thermodynamic considerations made it possible to draw some general conclusions on the reduction and oxidation reaction equilibria. However, the same cannot be said for the understanding of the kinetics of heterogeneous reactions, particularly those occurring at elevated temperatures. All the pyro-metallurgical reactions are heterogeneous reactions occurring between gas-solid or liquid oxides, gas-solid or liquid metal, oxide-metal and gas-oxide-metal systems. Although the mechanisms of these reactions tend to be complex, in many instances it has been possible to determine the rate-controlling processes.

Some of the basic theories on the kinetics of reactions were discussed in Part I of this chapter; now, in this section some consideration is given to the kinetics of specific reduction and oxidation reactions, with particular reference to the reduction of iron oxides, oxidation of iron and carbon, and decarburization of steel.

REDUCTION OF SOLID IRON OXIDES

Because of its industrial importance, much work has been done on the study of the kinetics of reduction of iron oxides. However, it is only in recent years

that some progress has been made in the understanding of these reactions.

Rate of Reduction of Iron Oxides by Hydrogen and hydrogen + Water Vapor Mixtures—Recently, McKewan[194-198] has measured the rate of reduction of dense iron oxide spheres in hydrogen and mixtures of hydrogen and water vapor; similar measurements were also made by Quets et al[199] using magnetite discs, showing that the thickness of the reduced layer increases linearly with reduction time. Although these studies are still in progress, some general conclusions may be drawn from the work so far completed. These studies indicate that the rate controlling process in the reduction of iron oxides is the chemical reaction occurring at the metal-oxide interface. Considering the reduction of iron oxide to iron by hydrogen, the following equation may be written in a general form:

$$\text{Iron oxides} + H_2 \rightarrow \text{Iron} + H_2O \qquad (182)$$

In this heterogeneous reaction, the activities of iron and iron oxides remain unchanged, and assuming that the transport of reacting species through iron and iron oxide layers is not the rate controlling process, the rate of decrease in the weight of oxide during reduction may be given by the following equation for a first order reaction:

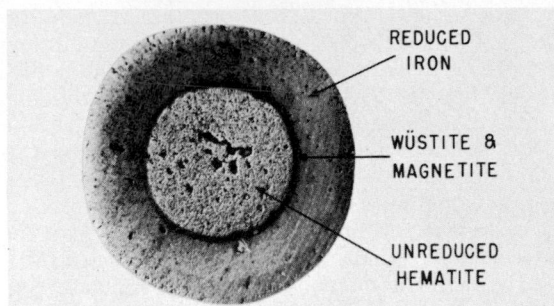

FIG. 12–125. Section of a partly reduced hematite sphere.

$$\frac{d\Delta W}{dt} = A\ (K_f p_{H_2} - K_r p_{H_2O}) \qquad (183)$$

where

ΔW = decrease in weight of oxide
t = time of reduction
A = metal-oxide interfacial area
K_f = rate constant of forward reaction
K_r = rate constant of reverse reaction
p_{H_2} = partial pressure of hydrogen
p_{H_2O} = partial pressure of water vapor

If the oxide has a cubic, spherical or a cylindrical, etc. shape, the metal-oxide interfacial area will decrease as the reduction front proceeds towards the center of the particle. The area of this receding reaction front is related to the thickness of the iron layer formed and the amount of oxygen lost from the oxide. For example, as shown by McKewan[195], for spherical oxide particles the rate of reduction per unit area can be obtained from the gross weight-loss measurements using the following expression:

$$R = \frac{d\Delta W/A}{dt} = \frac{0.3 r_o d_o \left[1 - (1 - W/W_o)^{\frac{1}{3}} \right]}{t}$$
$$= \frac{0.3 d_o (r_o - r)}{t} \qquad (184)$$

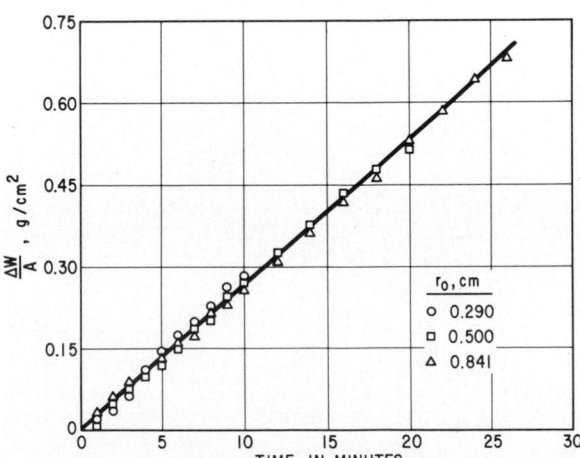

FIG. 12–126. Reduction of sintered spheres of Venezuelan ore at 811°C. in hydrogen at 0.97 atm. (From McKewan[195].)

where

R = rate of oxygen removal, g. per cm.² min.
r_o = initial radius of the oxide sphere, cm.
d_o = initial density of the oxide, g. per c.c.
W_o = initial amount of oxygen in the oxide
W = amount of oxygen in the oxide at time t
r = radius of the unreacted oxide at time t.

The only assumption made in the derivation of equation (184) is that the thicknesses of the intermediate phases wüstite and magnetite are small and do not change appreciably as the reduction proceeds. Figure 12–125 is a typical example of the cross section of a partly reduced hematite sphere.

It follows from equation (184) that loss of oxygen from the oxide per unit area of the reaction surface is directly proportional to the time of reduction, and the thickness of the iron layer grows linearly with the time of reduction. This conclusion derived from the theoretical considerations is supported by the experimental data, as shown in Figure 12–126, where $\Delta W/A$ is plotted against time for spheres of different sizes.

As discussed in Part I of this chapter, the rate constant K_r for the reverse reaction may be replaced by:

$$K_r = \frac{K_f}{K}$$

where, in this instance, K is the equilibrium constant for reaction (182). Using the above expressions, equation (183) becomes

$$R = K_f\ (p_{H_2} - p_{H_2O}/K) \qquad (185)$$

If the reduction is carried out in a stream of dry hydrogen, the water vapor formed will be swept away from the metal-oxide interface, and under these conditions the term $p_{H_2O}/K \to 0$ in equation (185). In fact, the experimental results of McKewan[195] and

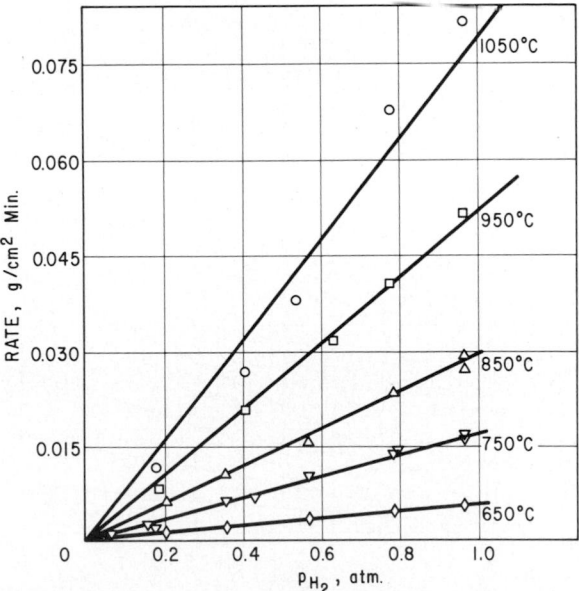

FIG. 12–127. Effect of partial pressure of hydrogen on the rate of reduction of hematite spheres. (From McKewan[195].)

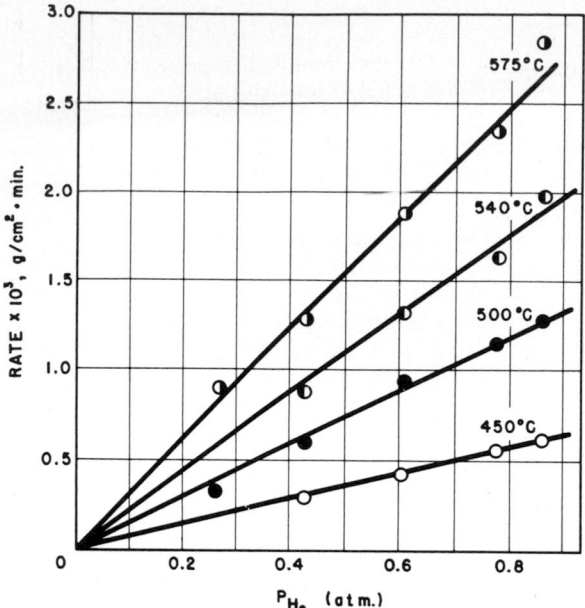

FIG. 12–128. Effect of partial pressure of hydrogen on the rate of reduction of magnetite discs. (From Quets, Wadsworth and Lewis[199].)

Quets et al[199], given in Figures 12–127 and 12–128, show that when hematite or magnetite is reduced in a stream of hydrogen + nitrogen mixtures, the rate of reduction per unit interfacial area increases linearly with the partial pressure of hydrogen, as would be deduced from equation (185) for $p_{H_2O} \rightarrow 0$.

As the water vapor content in the hydrogen stream increases, the rate of reduction of the oxide should decrease, as indicated by equation (185). In the Fe-O system (see Part II of this chapter) above 560°C the oxide in equilibrium with iron is the wüstite phase. Therefore, the equilibrium constant K in equation (185) is for the reaction:

$$\frac{1}{2} \text{FeO} + \text{H}_2 = \frac{1}{2} \text{Fe} + \text{H}_2\text{O} \qquad (186)$$

In fact, the results of McKewan show that at temperatures above 600°C the rate of reduction of

hematite to iron approaches zero when the water vapor content of hydrogen is that of the equilibrium amount for reaction (186). The experimental data given in Figure 12–129, where the rate of reduction is plotted against $p_{H_2} - p_{H_2O}/K$, proves that the kinetics of the reduction of hematite by hydrogen + water vapor mixtures can be described by the classical rate equation (185) for a first order reaction. The slopes of the lines in Figure 12–129 give the rate constant K_f, for the forward reaction (186). That is, in the reduction of hematite the rate controlling step is that due to the reaction occurring at the wüstite-iron interface. However, the foregoing generalization does not seem to apply to the reduction of magnetite by hydrogen + water vapor mixtures[196]; this apparent anomaly will not be discussed here.

As already shown in Part I of this chapter, the logarithm of the reaction rate constant varies linearly with the reciprocal of the absolute temperature, and from the slope of the line the heat of activation can be derived. From the results given in Figure 12–130, the heat of activation for the reduction of iron oxides by hydrogen is found to be $\Delta H^* = 14 \pm 1.5$ kcal. per mole H_2.

Rate Controlling Step in the Reduction of Magnetite by Hydrogen—The rate controlling steps in heterogeneous reactions may be divided into two major classes: (1) chemical reaction at the interface and (2) transport of reactants and product to and from the interface. It is conclusive from the experimental data discussed above that the rate of reduction of iron oxides is not controlled by the diffusion of iron and/or oxygen through the oxide phases. If this were the case, the rate of reduction should have obeyed the parabolic law, i.e. R should have been proportional to the square root of the time of reaction. The chemical reaction as a rate controlling step may be sub-divided into (a) adsorption and desorp-

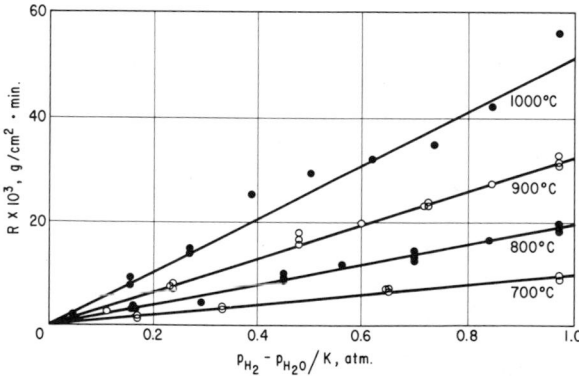

FIG. 12–129. Variation of the rate of reduction of hematite with the partial pressures of hydrogen and water vapor. (From McKewan[197].)

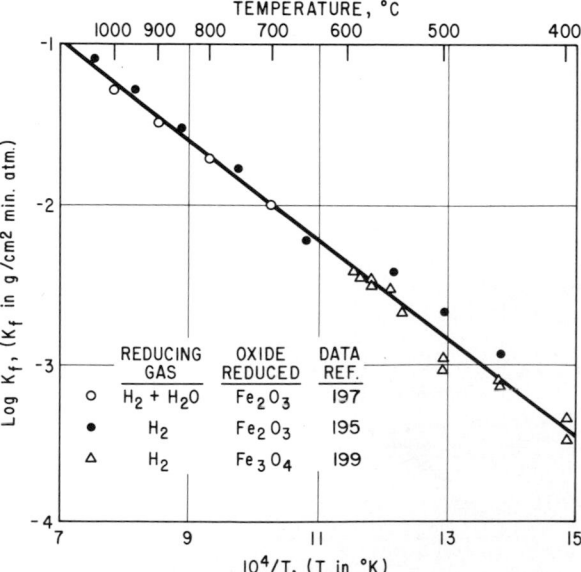

FIG. 12–130. Variation of reaction-rate constant K_f with temperature.

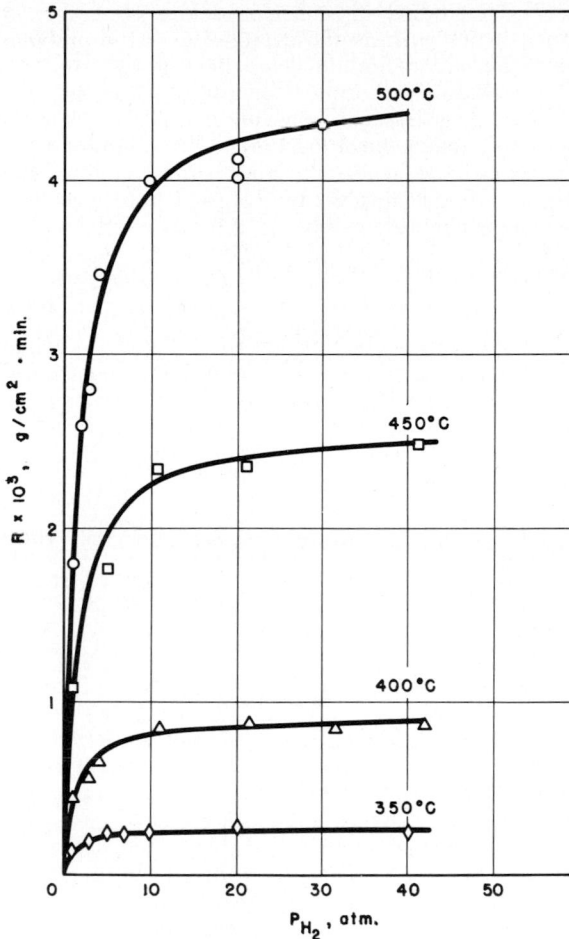

FIG. 12–131. Effect of hydrogen pressure on the rate of reduction of magnetite. (From McKewan[198].)

tion of reactants and products at the interface and (b) chemical reaction between the adsorbed gas molecules and the oxide. From his measurements of reduction of magnetite by flowing hydrogen at pressures up to 40 atm., McKewan[198] showed the reaction step (b) as being the rate controlling process.

The adsorption of hydrogen on the surface of the oxide may be considered as a reaction between hydrogen and reactive sites on the surface, thus

$$H_2 + \text{``S''} = \text{``H}_2\text{:S''} \tag{187}$$

where "S" is the number of vacant sites and "H_2:S" is the number of occupied sites. In terms of fractions,

$$\Theta = \frac{\text{``H}_2\text{:S''}}{\text{``S''} + \text{``H}_2\text{:S''}} = \text{fraction of occupied sites}$$

$$1 - \Theta = \text{fraction of vacant sites}$$

As discussed in Part I of this chapter, the state of equilibrium for adsorption (187) may be represented by the Langmuir isotherm. Thus,

$$\Theta = \frac{K_a p_{H_2}}{1 + K_a p_{H_2}} \tag{188}$$

where K_a is the equilibrium constant for adsorption (187) and p_{H_2} is the partial pressure of hydrogen.

The next stage now is to consider the reaction between the adsorbed hydrogen and the iron oxide.

$$\text{``H}_2\text{:S''} + \text{iron oxide} = \text{iron} + H_2O + \text{``S''} \tag{189}$$

If the reduction is carried out in flowing dry hydrogen, the rate of forward reaction is:

$$R = R_f \Theta \tag{190}$$

where R_f is the rate constant in g. per cm^2 min. Inserting the value of Θ in equation (190),

$$R = R_f \frac{K_a p_{H_2}}{1 + K_a p_{H_2}} \tag{191}$$

By rearranging:

$$\frac{R}{p_{H_2}} = R_f K_a - K_a R \tag{192}$$

That is, if the above theoretical argument applies to the reduction of magnetite, the plot of R/p_{H_2} against R should give a straight line. The effect of hydrogen pressure on the rate of reduction of magnetite is shown in Figure 12–131. Using these data of McKewan[198], in Figure 12–132, R/p_{H_2} is plotted against R; the relationship can be assumed to be linear. From the slopes and the intercepts of the lines, K_a and R_f are obtained for each temperature and in Figure 12–133, log K_a is plotted against $1/T$.

Since K_a is the equilibrium constant for reaction

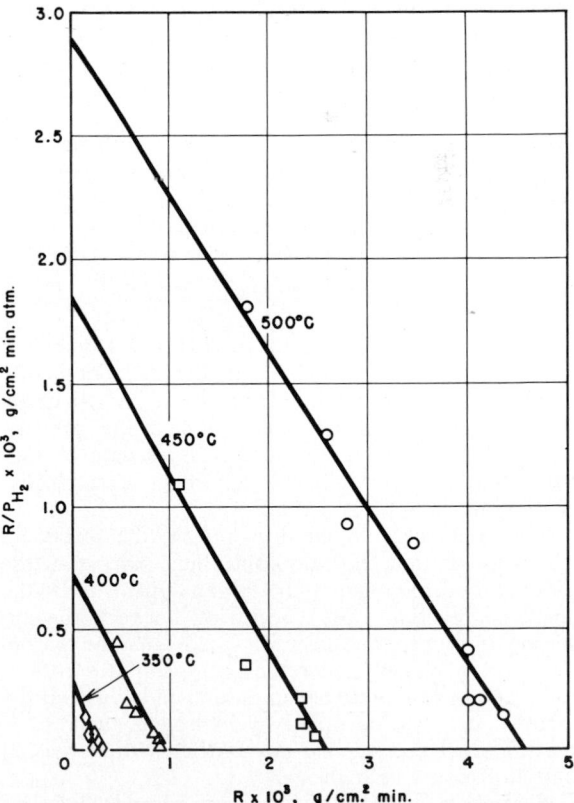

FIG. 12–132. Experimental verification of equation (192). (From McKewan[198].)

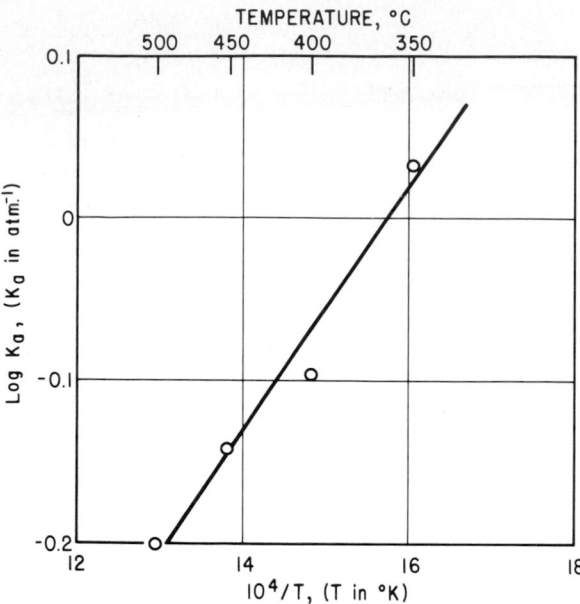

FIG. 12–133. Effect of temperature on the equilibrium constant for adsorption of hydrogen or magnetite.

(187), the free-energy change accompanying the adsorption of hydrogen is:

$$\Delta F_a = \Delta H_a - T\Delta S_a = -4.575\ T \log K_a \quad (193)$$

and from the slope and intercept of the line in Figure 12–133, the following heat and entropy values are obtained.

$$\Delta H_a = -3300 \text{ cal. per mole } H_2$$
$$\Delta S_a = -5.3 \text{ cal. per deg. per mole } H_2$$

It follows from equation (188) that with decreasing partial pressure of hydrogen the fraction of occupied sites, Θ, decreases and, as a limiting case, when the sites are sparsely occupied, equation (191) becomes:

$$R = R_f K_a p_{H_2} \quad (194)$$

which is the expression for a first order reaction. That is, the product $R_f K_a$ is the reduction rate constant K_f derived above from the reduction measurements at $p_{H_2} \leq 1.0$ atm. In fact, the product $R_f K_a$ obtained from the high-pressure data in Figure 12–132 agree well with K_f values given in Figure 12–130 for $p_{H_2} \leq 1.0$ atm.

The conclusion to be drawn from the foregoing discussion is that the rate controlling process in the reduction of iron oxide by hydrogen appears to be the chemical reaction (189) occurring between the adsorbed hydrogen and the iron oxide. As the partial pressure of hydrogen increases, the rise in the rate of reduction of the oxide becomes less, and when all the reactive sites are occupied by hydrogen, the rate of reaction does not increase any further with increasing partial pressure of hydrogen.

Reduction of Iron Oxide from Liquid Slags by Carbon-Saturated Iron—The kinetics of the reduction of oxides from liquid slags by liquid iron alloys have

not been studied in sufficient detail. However, in order to demonstrate the complexity of the problem some considerations are given here to the work of Philbrook and Kirkbride[200] on the reduction of iron oxide from a calcium alumino-silicate melt by graphite-saturated iron. Some of their results are summarized in Figure 12–134, where the iron oxide content of the slag is plotted against the time of reduction. This reaction may be represented by the following equation:

$$\underline{C} + Fe^{2+} (slag) + O^{2-} (slag) = \underline{Fe} + CO (gas) \quad (195)$$

where the underscore indicates the metal phase. If the rate controlling process is the interfacial chemical reaction, the following rate equation may be written for constant activities of carbon and carbon monoxide (for the details of its derivation reference should be made to Part I of this chapter):

$$-\frac{d(\% \text{ Fe})}{dt} = \frac{A}{V} k\ (\% \text{ Fe}) \quad (196)$$

where:

A = slag-metal interfacial area
V = volume of slag
k = specific rate constant

However, Philbrook and Kirkbride showed that their experimental data fit the rate equation for a second order reaction better than that for the first order reaction as given in equation (196).

In studying the kinetics of heterogeneous reactions, due considerations must be given to all the possible rate controlling processes, as discussed in Part I of this chapter. In the present case, if the diffusivity of iron ions in the slag is a slow process, the rate of evolution of carbon monoxide accompanying the reduction could be the rate controlling step. For a transport controlled reaction the rate equation takes the following form (for details see Part I of this chapter):

$$-\frac{d(\% \text{ Fe})}{dt} = \frac{A}{V}\frac{D}{\delta} [(\% \text{ Fe})^* - (\% \text{ Fe})] \quad (197)$$

where D is the diffusivity of divalent iron ions in the slag, δ is the effective diffusion boundary layer thick-

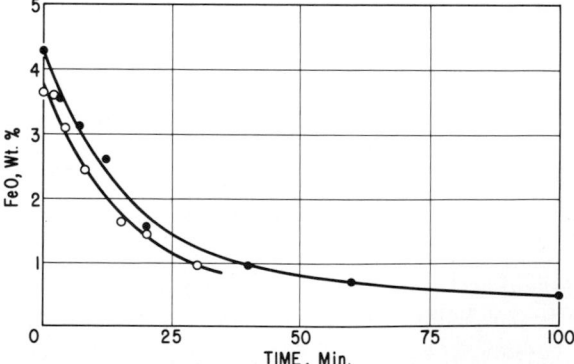

FIG. 12–134. Reduction of FeO from a CaO-Al₂O₃-SiO₂-FeO slag by carbon-saturated iron at 1430°C. (From Philbrook and Kirkbride[200].)

ness at the slag-metal interface. Since the concentration of iron at the slag-metal interface, $(\% \text{ Fe})^*$, is very small in the presence of graphite, equation (197) may be simplified to give:

$$\frac{d(\% \text{ Fe})}{dt} = \frac{A}{V} \frac{D}{\delta} (\% \text{ Fe}) \qquad (198)$$

The only time that the thickness of the diffusion boundary layer remains constant is when the hydrodynamic conditions in the melt are not altered. However, in the case of reaction (195), the reduction of iron oxide is accompanied by gas evolution at a rate decreasing with time of reaction. Consequently, the rate of stirring of the melt by gas bubbles decreases with reduction time, and this results in an increase in δ with reaction time. That is, δ is a function of $d(\% \text{ Fe})/dt$. There is no theoretical means of predicting what this function is; however, following Wagner's suggestion[201], an empirical equation as given below may be used

$$\delta = b \left(\frac{d(\% \text{ Fe})}{A\,dt} \right)^{-\beta} \qquad (199)$$

where b and β are constants. Substituting equation (199) in (198) the following is obtained:

$$\frac{d(\% \text{ Fe})}{dt} = A \left(\frac{D(\% \text{ Fe})}{Vb} \right)^{1/1-\beta} \qquad (200)$$

Since the results of Philbrook and Kirkbride fit an equation for a second order reaction reasonably well, it would follow that $\beta \simeq \frac{1}{2}$ and equation (200) becomes

$$\frac{d(\% \text{ Fe})}{dt} = k' (\% \text{ Fe})^2 \qquad (201)$$

where the rate constant $k' = A (D/Vb)^2$.

Although the foregoing discussion is a reasonable approach in an attempt to solve the rate equation for reaction (195), the approximate nature of equation (199) for δ should not be underestimated. Moreover, it has been assumed that the slag-metal interfacial area is not affected by the rate of gas evolution. This assumption is highly questionable; in fact it is well known that during gas evolution a fair amount of metal globules are thrown into the slag layer, increasing the total slag-metal interfacial area.

It follows from the above considerations that there is much to be learned about the kinetics of reaction (195). Furthermore, great care should be taken in conducting the experimental work so that the data can be interpreted on a sound theoretical basis.

Oxidation of Solid Iron and Iron Oxides—Although a detailed discussion of the kinetics of the oxidation of metals is outside the scope of this chapter, some reference should be made to the basic principles concerning the rate of oxidation of iron and iron oxides.

Davies, Simnad and Birchenall[202] measured the rate of oxidation of pure iron and iron oxides in pure oxygen at 1 atm. pressure at temperatures up to 1000°C. Some of their results are shown in Figures 12–135 and

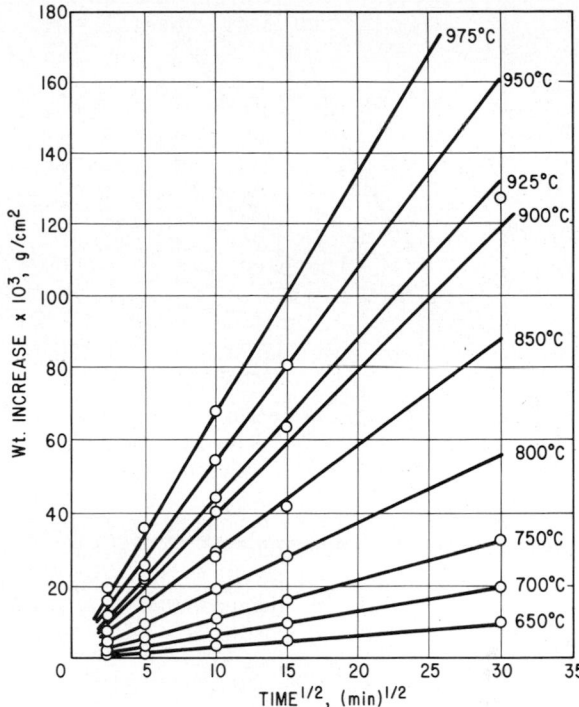

Fig. 12–135. Parabolic plot for the oxidation of iron in oxygen at 1.0 atm. For temperatures within the range 650°–975°C. (From Davies, Simnad and Birchenall[202].)

12–136. The experimental evidence indicates that the rates of reactions:

$$\text{Fe} + \frac{1}{2} \text{O}_2 = \text{FeO} \qquad (202a)$$

$$3 \text{ FeO} + \frac{1}{2} \text{O}_2 = \text{Fe}_3\text{O}_4 \qquad (202b)$$

are given by the parabolic expression

$$\frac{W}{A} = k \sqrt{t} \qquad (203)$$

where W/A is the weight increase per unit surface area, k is the rate constant and t is the time of oxidation.

As already discussed in Part I of this chapter, the

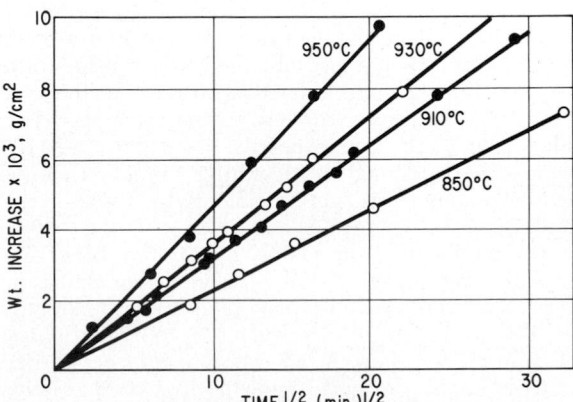

Fig. 12–136. Parabolic plot for the oxidation of "FeO" in oxygen. (From Davies, Simnad and Birchenall[202].)

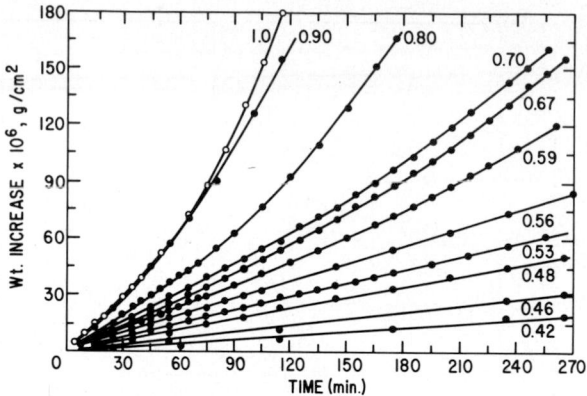

Fig. 12–137. Oxidation of iron in carbon dioxide-carbon monoxide atmospheres at 800°C. for p_{CO_2} within the range 0.42–1.0 atm. (From Smeltzer[205].)

rate controlling process in a reaction proceeding in accordance with the parabolic law is that due to the diffusion of reactants or products. By using silver markers, Davies et al[202] demonstrated that during the oxidation of iron to wüstite or wüstite to magnetite, iron diffused through wüstite or magnetite to the gas-oxide interface where the oxidation occurred. They observed that the oxidation of magnetite occurred at the magnetite-hematite interface, indicating that the oxide ions could be the diffusing species in hematite.

To verify the above conclusion, Himmel, Mehl and Birchenall[203] measured the self-diffusion coefficient of iron cations in iron oxides and by applying Wagner's theory on oxidation, they were able to prove that the rate controlling step was the diffusion of iron through wüstite and magnetite in the oxidation of iron and wüstite, respectively.

The results of some recent work carried out by Smeltzer[205] on the oxidation of iron by carbon-dioxide + carbon-monoxide mixtures are not concordant with the above conclusions. As seen from the results in Figures 12–137, for a given partial pressure of carbon dioxide, gain in weight of iron, due to oxidation, initially increases linearly with time then the rate of reaction becomes faster; this departure from linearity becomes appreciable with increasing partial pressure of carbon dioxide. The rates of oxidation of iron in CO_2-CO mixtures are found to be much lower than those obtained when using pure oxygen. Smeltzer attributes this slowness to the high activation energy for the dissocation of carbon dioxide. Departure from linearity in Figure 12–137 cannot be explained satisfactorily; the experimental evidence given is not sufficient to resolve this anomaly.

Oxidation of Iron Oxide in Molten Slags—Although slag plays a vital part in steelmaking, no serious attempts have been made to study the kinetics of the oxidation of divalent iron to the trivalent state in molten slags. A few experiments were carried out by Turkdogan and Goodwin[206] on the oxidation of iron oxide (contained in alumina crucibles) by oxygen at $p_{O_2} = 1.0$ atm. and 1550°C. As seen from the results in Figure 12–138, the initial rate of oxi-

dation of ferrous iron to the ferric state is fast. However, nothing further can be deduced from these results, because of the complications arising from the formation of $FeO \cdot Al_2O_3$ solid solution between the melt and the alumina crucible while the oxidation is taking place.

Oxidation of Carbon—Much work has been done on this subject and one of the general conclusions to be drawn on the kinetics of the oxidation of carbon, for example, by carbon dioxide or steam, is that the rate controlling process is the chemical reaction between the adsorbed species on the surface of carbon. Therefore, for the reactions:

$$C + CO_2 = 2\,CO \qquad (204a)$$
$$C + H_2O = CO + H_2 \qquad (204b)$$

the rate equations are those based on the Langmuir isotherm; thus rate of oxidation by $CO_2 + CO$ mixtures:

$$\text{Rate} = k\,\frac{K_a\,p_{CO_2}}{1 + K_a\,p_{CO_2} + K_b\,p_{CO}} \qquad (205a)$$

rate of oxidation by $H_2O + H_2$ mixtures

$$\text{Rate} = k\,\frac{K_a\,p_{H_2O}}{1 + K_a\,p_{H_2O} + K_b\,p_{H_2}} \qquad (205b)$$

where k is the reaction rate constant, K_a and K_b are the adsorption-desorption equilibrium constants for CO_2 and CO, respectively (or for H_2O and H_2, respectively). The mechanism of chemisorption in relation to the oxidation of carbon will not be discussed here; however, the general validity of the above rate equations may be illustrated by referring to the work of Gadsby et al[207] and Long and Sykes[208]. Figure 12–139a shows that, for a given temperature and $p_{CO} = 0$, the rate of oxidation of carbon increases with increasing p_{CO_2}; Figure 12–139b shows the retarding effect of carbon monoxide on the rate of oxidation of carbon by car-

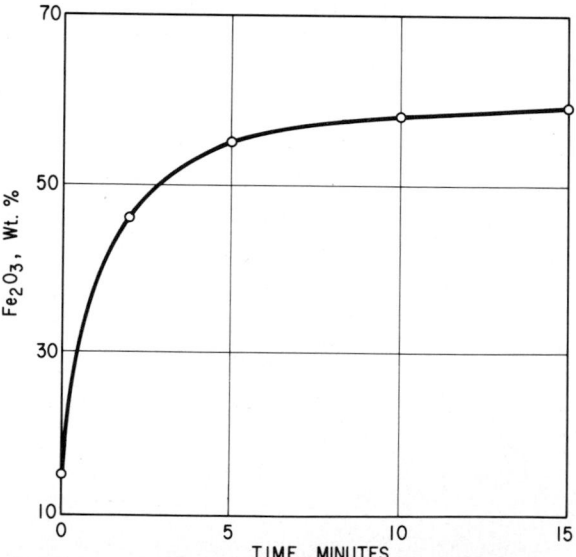

Fig. 12–138. Oxidation of liquid iron oxide containing ~ 20% Al_2O_3 by oxygen at 1550°C. (From Turkdogan and Goodwin[206].)

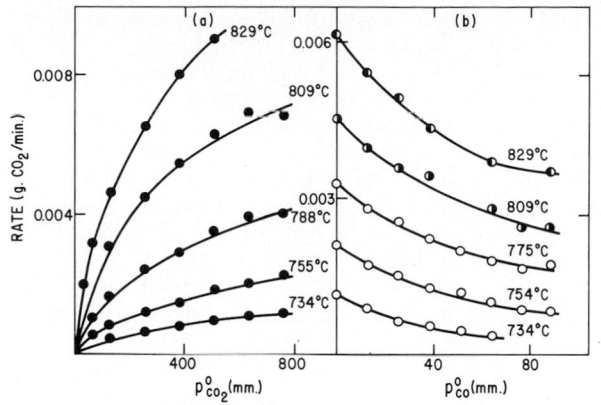

FIG. 12–139. Effect of partial pressures of CO_2 or CO on the rate of oxidation of charcoal. (a) Ingoing gas CO_2, (b) Ingoing gas CO_2 + CO + N_2. Initial p_{CO_2} (mm. Hg.): open circles, 633; circles with right half blacked, 253; circles with left half blacked, 127. (From Gadsby et al.[207])

bon dioxide. Similar relationships are shown in Figure 12–140 for the oxidation of carbon by H_2O and H_2 mixtures. From the data similar to those given above the values of K_a, K_b and k and their variation with temperature can be evaluated using equation (205a) or (205b).

In a heterogeneous reaction involving a porous solid and a gas, there may be three main rate controlling processes: (1) Mass transport of gaseous reactants and products through the stagnant gas film on the surface of the solid; (2) Mass transport of the reactants and products through the surface of the solid; (3) Adsorption and desorption of gaseous reactants and products. Although more than one of these rate controlling processes may operate simultaneously, many investigators[209-212] have found that at high temperatures the process (1) becomes the rate controlling step and at low temperatures, the rate of oxidation is controlled essentially by process (3), chemisorption; for intermediate temperatures mass transport through carbon becomes the main rate controlling process.

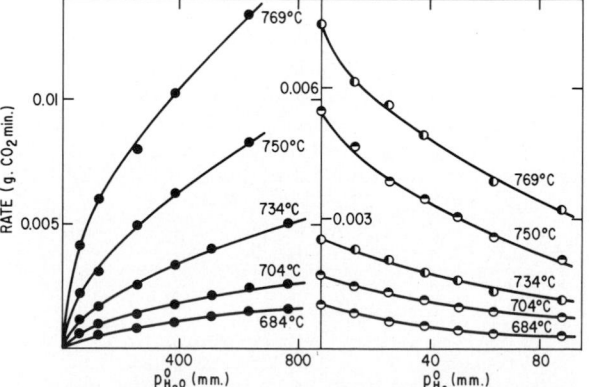

FIG. 12–140. Effect of partial pressures of H_2O or H_2 on the rate of oxidation of charcoal. (a) Ingoing gas H_2O, (b) Ingoing gas H_2O + H_2 + N_2. Initial p_{H_2O} (mm. Hg.): circles with top half blacked, 380; with left half blacked, 253. (From Long and Sykes[208].)

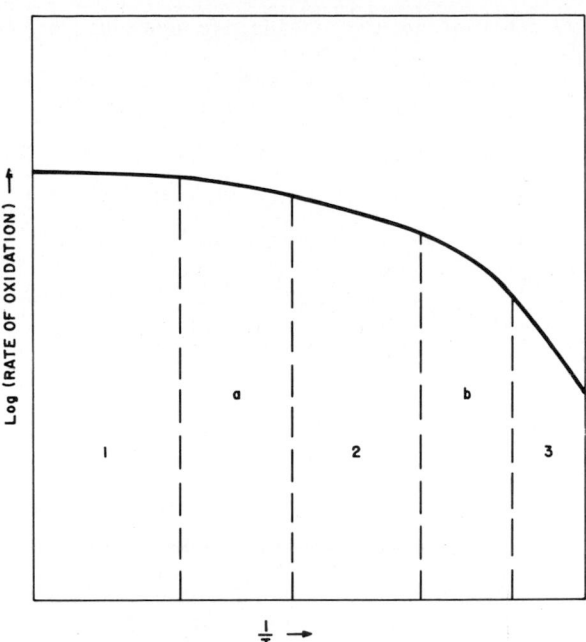

FIG. 12–141. General form of variation of the rate of oxidation of carbon with temperature. In temperature zones 1, 2 and 3 rate of oxidation is controlled mainly by: (1) mass transfer through the gas film at the solid-gas interface; (2) mass transfer through the solid; (3) chemisorption.

Therefore, the general form of the logarithm of rate of oxidation vs. 1/T plot has the shape shown in Figure 12–141. The rate controlling processes are indicated by zones 1, 2 and 3 with intermediate stages a and b.

When the oxidation of carbon is controlled by chemisorption, the crystal orientation on the surface has a pronounced effect on the rate of reaction. For example, Grisdale[213] and Smith and Polley[214] showed that the oxidation of graphite composed of carbon crystallites of mixed orientation was 10 to 20 times faster than that of graphite where the basal planes of crystallites were parallel to the surface.

Another factor to be considered is the effect of impurities on the rate of oxidation of carbon. For example, it was shown by Day[215] that the rate of oxidation of acetylene black was retarded by boron, titanium and tungsten, while iron, cobalt, nickel, copper and manganese increased the reactivity of carbon.

In the foregoing discussion only a brief mention is made of some of the most obvious factors which influence the rate of oxidation of carbon. For further details reference should be made to the papers published on this subject, and to a comprehensive literature survey by Walker and co-workers[216].

Oxidation of Carbon During Steelmaking—The mechanism of the oxidation of carbon in steel is a complex process, arising from the multiplicity of stages that the reactants and product have to pass through. In the reaction

$$\underline{C} + \underline{O} = CO \tag{206}$$

the following are the possible rate controlling processes:

(1) Transfer of oxygen from gas or slag to the metal at the interface, thus

$$\text{gas-metal:} \frac{1}{2} O_2 = \underline{O}$$

$$\text{slag-metal:} 2 Fe^{3+} + O^{2-} = \underline{O} + 2 Fe^{2+}$$

(2) Diffusion of oxygen through the boundary layer into the bulk of the metal.

(3) Diffusion of carbon from the bulk of the metal to the reaction site.

(4) Nucleation and growth of carbon monoxide bubbles.

In view of the complexity of the kinetics of this reaction, most of the laboratory experiments on the rate of decarburization of molten steel have been unsuccessful in resolving the mechanism.

As in any other liquids, the formation of gas bubbles in molten steel is not spontaneous. In the absence of nuclei for the formation of gas bubbles, the melts can be supersaturated with carbon monoxide. This was demonstrated by Korber and Oelsen[219] by supersaturating molten steel, held in glazed crucibles, with carbon monoxide to a value approaching 10 atm. However, when the melts were held in crucibles having rough surfaces, oxidation of carbon proceeded with very little or no supersaturation. Because of the surface tension effect, a gas bubble within the liquid is under an excess pressure given by the relation

$$p = \frac{2\gamma}{r} \qquad (207)$$

where γ is the surface tension of the liquid, r is the radius of the bubble and p is the excess pressure exerted by the liquid. In the absence of gas pockets, the formation of gas bubbles will be very difficult, if not impossible, because the pressure of the liquid exerted on a bubble is inversely proportional to its diameter. For example, taking $\gamma = 1500$ dynes per cm. for liquid steel, a bubble of 1-mm. diameter in molten steel is subject to an excess pressure of 0.06 atm., but a bubble of 0.001-mm. diameter is subject to an excess pressure of 61 atm. A simple calculation will show that a bubble containing a few molecules of carbon monoxide will be subject to pressures which can never be exceeded by the supersaturation of the molten iron with respect to carbon and oxygen, because both have limited solubilities.

In reality, the liquids are hardly ever free of particles on which the gas bubbles can nucleate. In the case of liquid steel, the crevices on the surface of the refractory container and on the solid inclusions in the bath provide sufficient sites for the formation of carbon monoxide bubbles without much supersaturation. For example, as seen from the data in Figure 12–123, the concentrations of carbon and oxygen in open-hearth-furnace melts are those corresponding to an apparent carbon monoxide pressure of about 2 or 3 atm.

In considering the rate of oxidation of carbon during the refining period, known as the "carbon boil," nucleation of gas bubbles can no longer be regarded as being the rate controlling process. As discussed in detail by Darken[217, 218], the rate of reaction (206) may be controlled by the flux of oxygen through the diffusion boundary layer on the metal side of the slag-metal interface. That is, the rate of carbon oxidation is proportional to the flux of oxygen as given by the expression (see Part I of this chapter for derivation of a similar equation):

$$-\frac{dC}{dt} = \frac{12}{16l} \frac{D}{\delta} ([O]_e - [O]) \qquad (208)$$

where D is the diffusivity of oxygen in molten steel, l is the depth of the metal bath, δ is the effective thickness of the diffusion-boundary layer at the metal-slag interface, $[O]_e$ is the oxygen content of the metal in equilibrium with the slag and $[O]$ is the oxygen content in the bulk of the metal bath. Taking an estimated value of

$$D = 10^{-4} \text{ cm.}^2 \text{ per sec., } \delta = 0.003 \text{ cm,}$$

an average depth of metal bath in an open-hearth furnace (estimated on the basis of a quiet bath), $l = 34$ cm. and an average value for $([O]_e - [O]) = 0.04$, the rate of carbon oxidation becomes:

$$-\frac{dC}{dt} = \frac{12 \times 10^{-4}}{16 \times 34 \times 3 \times 10^{-3}} 0.04 =$$

$$3 \times 10^{-5} \% C \text{ per sec. or } 0.11 \% C \text{ per hr,}$$

which agrees reasonably well with the observed rates of 0.12 to 0.18 per cent C per hour, obtained with ore-feed refining.

Although the above calculations are approximate, it appears feasible to suppose that the rate of oxidation of carbon during the carbon boil could well be controlled by the flux of oxygen to the metal. In fact, when this flux is increased, as in the case of the Bessemer process or the top-blown oxygen processes, the rate of carbon removal increases appreciably.

The Physical Chemistry of Iron- and Steelmaking

PART V

Silicon and Manganese Reactions

REACTION EQUILIBRIA

The distribution of silicon and manganese between metal and slag is determined by the following reactions:

$$\underline{Si} + O_2 = SiO_2 \qquad (209a)$$
$$2\,\underline{Mn} + O_2 = 2\,MnO \qquad (209b)$$

The free energy diagram in Figure 12–115 in Part IV of this chapter gives the oxygen potentials for these systems at unit activities of metals and metal oxides. In pyrometallurgical processes, iron contains small percentages of silicon and manganese; silica and manganous oxide contents of slags vary over a wide range, depending on the nature of the process. Therefore, in considering reactions (209a) and (209b) in any particular process, the activities in the metal and slag must be known. Furthermore, since these are oxidation-reduction reactions, the oxygen potential of the system is another factor which determines the distribution of these elements between metal and slag. This may be illustrated by considering the conditions prevailing in iron and steelmaking processes.

Iron Making—The iron ore invariably contains some silica and manganese oxides; another source of silica is, of course, coke. It was already pointed out in Part IV of this chapter that, since these oxides have low oxygen potentials, their reduction in the blast furnace does not begin until the temperature of the burden is in the range 1350°–1500°C. By the time the burden reaches the bosh of the furnace most of the iron ore is reduced and lime charged with the ore fluxes silica, alumina and other unreduced oxides, forming a slag. As the slag and metal flow over incandescent coke, reduction of silica and manganous oxide takes place and silicon and manganese formed dissolve in the iron, thus:

$$SiO_2 + 2\,C = \underline{Si} + 2\,CO \qquad (210a)$$
$$MnO + C = \underline{Mn} + CO \qquad (210b)$$

where the underscore indicates the elements dissolved in the iron. From the free-energy data given in Part I of this chapter, the temperature dependence of the equilibrium constants for these reactions may be obtained:

For Si-reaction (210a)

$$K_{Si} = \frac{[a_{Si}]}{(a_{SiO2})}$$

$$\log K_{Si} = -\frac{30{,}770}{T} + 15.43 \qquad (211a)$$

For Mn-reaction (210b)

$$K_{Mn} = \frac{[a_{Mn}]}{(a_{MnO})}$$

$$\log K_{Mn} = -\frac{15{,}430}{T} + 11.19 \qquad (211b)$$

For both systems it is assumed that the melts are saturated with carbon and $p_{CO} = 1.0$ atm. The standard state for the oxides is pure solid oxide; for the elements the standard state is so chosen that the activity approaches atom fraction at infinite dilution of all elements in iron.

Using the appropriate activity data and the values of K_{Si} and K_{Mn}, the equilibrium distributions of silicon and manganese can be estimated. Since the activities of these oxides vary appreciably with slag composition, the equilibrium distribution ratios in terms of weight percentages will also vary with slag composition. This relationship is shown in Figure 12–142 derived from the work of Fulton and Chipman[220] who equilibrated carbon-saturated iron-silicon melts with calcium alumino-silicates at various temperatures in carbon monoxide at one atm. pressure. It is seen from Figure 12–142 that for a given temperature and alumina content, Si/SiO₂ ratio de-

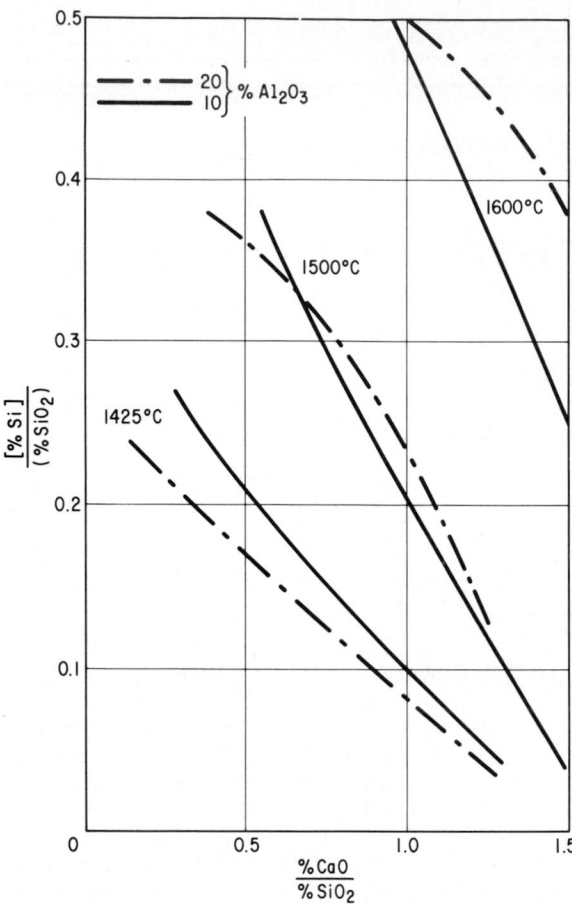

FIG. 12–142. Effects of temperature and slag composition on the equilibrium distribution of silicon between carbon-saturated iron and CaO-Al₂O₃-SiO₂ slags. (From Fulton and Chipman[220].)

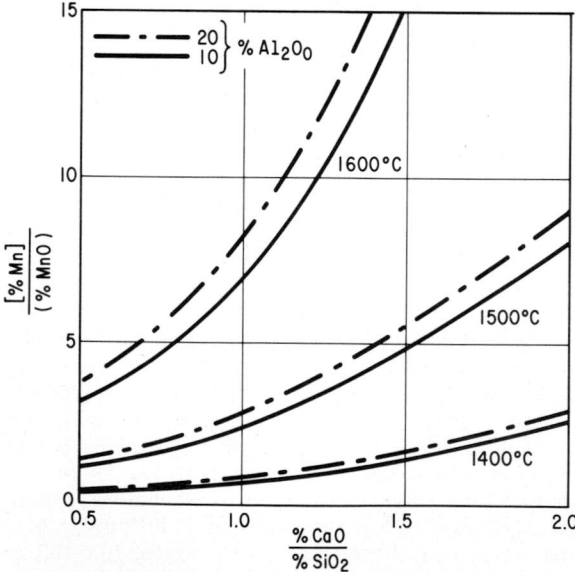

FIG. 12–143. Effects of temperature and slag composition on the equilibrium distribution of manganese between carbon-saturated iron and CaO-Al₂O₃-SiO₂-MnO (<5%) slags.

creases with increasing CaO/SiO₂ ratio; the effect of alumina is less pronounced. Since high temperatures are required for increased recovery of silicon, the ferrosilicon alloys saturated with carbon are normally produced in low-shaft (electric) blast furnaces.

The equilibrium measurements on the manganese reaction under iron making conditions are meager. However, the effects of temperature and slag composition on the manganese distribution ratio may be derived as follows. In terms of weight percentages and activity coefficients the equilibrium constant K_{Mn} may be written as

$$K_{Mn} = \frac{[a_{Mn}]}{(a_{MnO})} = \frac{[\gamma_{Mn}]}{[\gamma_{MnO}]} \frac{[\% Mn]}{n(\% MnO)} \quad (212)$$

where γ is the activity coefficient of the reactants indicated by the subscript and n is a factor to convert wt.%MnO to mole fraction. Although n varies with composition of the slag, for slags of blast-furnace type, a mean value n = 0.0114 may be taken. Since the manganese content of the iron is small, e.g. less than 2 per cent, $\gamma_{Mn} \simeq 1.0$. As shown in Part III of this chapter, for low concentrations of manganous oxide (MnO <5 per cent), γ_{MnO} increases with increasing CaO/SiO₂; using these activity coefficient data in Part III together with the known value of K_{Mn} for any temperature, the manganese distribution ratios can be calculated for calcium alumino-silicate melts. These calculated equilibrium data are given in Figure 12–143, showing that manganese recovery increases with increasing temperature and/or with increasing CaO/SiO₂ ratio; the alumina content of the slag has a small effect on the manganese distribution ratio.

By remelting a blast-furnace metal and slag in a graphite crucible at one atm. pressure of carbon monoxide, Filer and Darken[221] studied the extent to which the silicon and manganese reactions departed from the state of equilibrium. Some of their results are given in Figure 12–144 where the silicon and manganese distribution ratios are plotted against the time of reaction for 1400° and 1500°C. The points for zero reaction time are obtained from the composition of the metal and slag samples taken from a blast furnace. The major components of this slag are 34% SiO₂, 43% CaO, 7% MgO and 13% Al₂O₃. If it is assumed that on a molar basis the effects of lime and magnesia are equivalent, in terms of weight

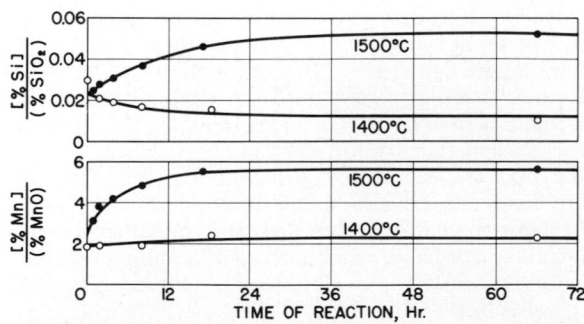

FIG. 12–144. Equilibration of blast-furnace metal and slag in graphite crucibles and at p_{CO} = 1.0 atm. (From Filer and Darken[221].)

per cent, CaO equivalence of MgO is $1.4 \times \%$ MgO. On this basis, $(\% \text{ CaO} + 1.4 \times \% \text{ MgO})/\% \text{ SiO}_2 = 1.55$ for which the equilibrium data given in Figures 12–142 and 12–143 for silicon and manganese ratios are in good agreement with those obtained by Filer and Darken.

According to the time experiments reported in Figure 12–144, the manganese reaction in the hearth of the blast furnace is close to a state of equilibrium for a temperature of about 1400°C. For the silicon reaction, the apparent equilibrium temperature is about 1430°C.

The silicon and manganese reactions between carbon-saturated manganese-based alloys and CaO-Al$_2$O$_3$-MnO-SiO$_2$ slags were studied by Turkdogan and Hancock[222]. Some of these equilibrium data relevant to the ferromanganese blast furnace are given in Figure 12–145. Similar to ironmaking conditions (Figure 12–144), silicon distribution ratio in the ferromanganese blast furnace is higher than the equilibrium values for 1400°C.

In practice, the temperature in the hearth is about 1500°C for iron making and about 1550°C or higher for ferromanganese making. Therefore, the ratio Si/SiO$_2$ obtained under practical conditions is expected to be higher than those indicated from the laboratory equilibrium data for 1400°C. The general indications are that the reduction of manganous oxide and silica are not far removed from the state of equilibrium, under practical conditions.

Acid Steelmaking—Oxidation of silicon and manganese at the slag-metal interface may be represented by the following equations:

$$\underline{\text{Si}} + 2\,\text{FeO} = \text{SiO}_2 + 2\,\text{Fe} \qquad (213a)$$
$$\underline{\text{Mn}} + \text{FeO} = \text{MnO} + \text{Fe} \qquad (213b)$$

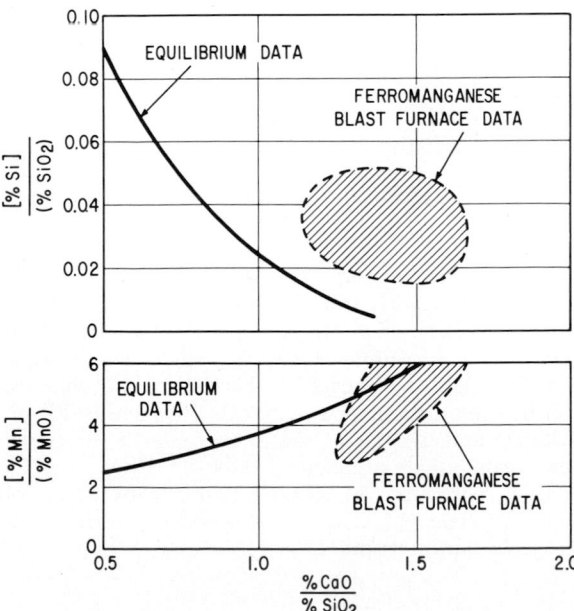

FIG. 12–145. Comparison of ferromanganese blast-furnace data with the laboratory data on carbon-saturated ferromanganese equilibrated with CaO-MnO-SiO$_2$-10% Al$_2$O$_3$ at 1400°C. and $p_{\text{CO}} = 1.0$ atm. (From Turkdogan and Hancock[222].)

The equilibrium conditions of these reactions were determined by Korber and Oelsen[223] for iron-manganese silicate melts saturated with silica. For dilute solutions of silicon and manganese in iron, their activity coefficients may be assumed to be unity and the equilibrium constants for the above reactions for unit silica activity take the following forms:

$$K_{\text{Si}} = \frac{1}{[\% \text{ Si}]\,(N_{\text{FeO}})^2}\,\frac{1}{(\gamma_{\text{FeO}})^2} \qquad (214a)$$

$$K_{\text{Mn}} = \frac{N_{\text{MnO}}}{[\% \text{ Mn}]\,N_{\text{FeO}}}\,\frac{\gamma_{\text{MnO}}}{\gamma_{\text{FeO}}} \qquad (214b)$$

Using the thermodynamic data compiled in Part I of this chapter, the following equations are obtained for K_{Si} and K_{Mn}:

$$\log K_{\text{Si}} = \frac{17{,}520}{T} - 5.774 \qquad (215a)$$

$$\log K_{\text{Mn}} = \frac{8810}{T} - 4.072 \qquad (215b)$$

These expressions are for the standard states: (i) infinitely dilute solutions of silicon or manganese in iron, (ii) liquid wüstite in equilibrium with liquid iron and (iii) solid manganous oxide and solid silica.

Equilibrium data of Korber and Oelsen[223] show that in silica-saturated melts, the replacement of MnO by FeO over a wide composition range does not alter to a measurable extent the activity coefficients γ_{FeO} and γ_{MnO}. This makes it possible to rewrite the equilibrium constants in much simpler forms, and using weight percentages instead of mole fractions, the equilibrium conditions may be represented by:

$$(K_{\text{Si}})_s = \frac{1}{[\% \text{ Si}]\,(\% \text{ FeO})^2} \qquad (216a)$$

$$(K_{\text{Mn}})_s = \frac{(\% \text{ MnO})}{[\% \text{ Mn}]\,(\% \text{ FeO})} \qquad (216b)$$

The subscript s indicates that the equilibrium constant is for a given type of slag and for convenience $(K_{\text{Si}})_s$ or $(K_{\text{Mn}})_s$ will be called the equilibrium index. The variation of these equilibrium indices with temperature were determined by Korber and Oelsen, thus for silica-saturated iron-manganese silicate melts:

$$\log (K_{\text{Si}})_s = \frac{19{,}057}{T} - 11.101 \qquad (217a)$$

and

$$\log (K_{\text{Mn}})_s = \frac{7940}{T} - 3.172 \qquad (217b)$$

Combining equations (216a), (217a) and (216b), (217b) and converting wt.% to mole fraction, the activity coefficients γ_{FeO} and γ_{MnO} can be calculated; thus for 1600°C $\gamma_{\text{FeO}} = 0.6$ and $\gamma_{\text{MnO}} = 0.2$. These values compare well with those given in Part III of this chapter for silica-saturated FeO-SiO$_2$ and MnO-SiO$_2$ melts, i.e. $\gamma_{\text{FeO}} = 0.7$ and $\gamma_{\text{MnO}} = 0.3$.

Using equations (216a), (216b), (217a) and (217b), the equilibrium silicon and manganese contents of steel can be estimated for known compositions of acid steelmaking slags.

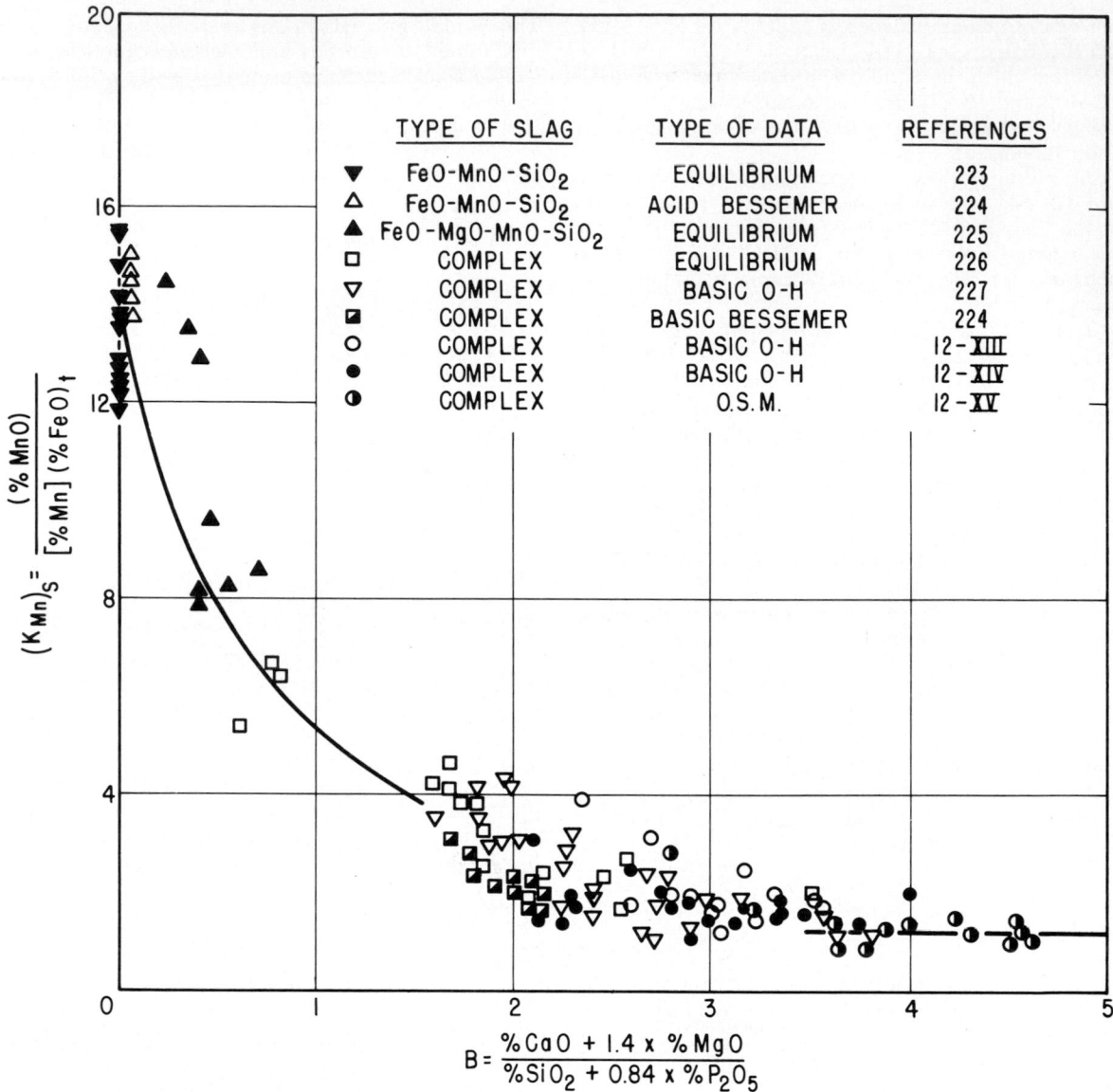

Fig. 12–146. Variation of the equilibrium index $(K_{Mn})_s$ with the basicity of simple and complex slags for temperatures 1550°–1650°C.

Basic Steelmaking—In basic steelmaking slags the activity of silica is very low and, consequently, the silicon content of the steel is reduced to very low values during the early stages of refining, e.g. less than 0.02 per cent Si. Therefore, except when silicon is added (as a block), there is very little to be said about the silicon reaction in the basic processes.

It will be noted from the activity data compiled in Part III of this chapter for simple oxide melts that the activity coefficients γ_{MnO} and γ_{FeO} increase with increasing ratio CaO/SiO$_2$. Although the equilibrium constant evaluated by equation (215b) is valid for any slag, its use to estimate the manganese distribution ratio is possible only when the ratio of activity coefficients, $\gamma_{MnO}/\gamma_{FeO}$, is known for any given slag. If the equilibrium index as given in equation (216b) is to be used, then the variation of this index $(K_{Mn})_s$ with slag composition must be known. Using some

of the available laboratory slag-metal equilibrium data together with some industrial data, in Figure 12–146 $(K_{Mn})_s$ is plotted against the basicity of the slag, $B = (\%\ CaO + 1.4 \times \%\ MgO)/(\%\ SiO_2 + 0.84\%\ P_2O_5)$. As discussed in Part III of this chapter, the lime equivalence of magnesia is taken as $1.4 \times \%MgO$, and similarly, silica equivalence of phosphorus pentoxide is taken as $0.84 \times \%P_2O_5$.

It is reasonable to assume that the oxidation of iron by ferric oxide at the slag-metal interface approaches equilibrium:

$$Fe_2O_3 + Fe = 3\ FeO \qquad (218)$$

and since this equilibrium ferric oxide concentration at the interface is small, the ferric oxide content in the slag sample is converted to the ferrous oxide equivalence, i.e. $1.35 \times \%Fe_2O_3 = \%FeO$ and in deriving $(K_{Mn})_s$, the total iron oxide concentration

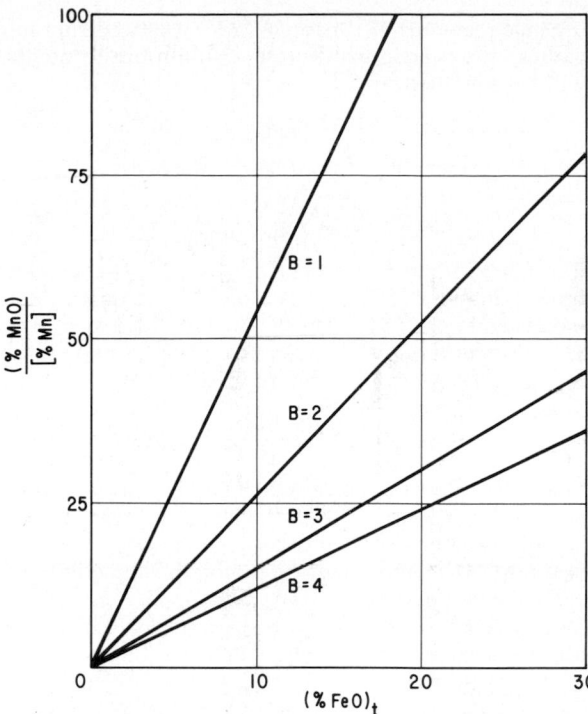

FIG. 12–147. Variation of MnO/Mn with total iron oxide content and basicity, **B,** of slags at about 1600°C.

$\%\text{FeO}_t = 1.35 \times \%\text{Fe}_2\text{O}_3 + \%\text{FeO}$ is used.

The points in Figure 12–146 for the basicity $B = 0$ are taken from the results of Korber and Oelsen for slags saturated with silica at 1600°C. The other points are for more complex slags and for temperatures within the range 1550°–1650°C. Close agreement between the laboratory results and the industrial data indicates that under steelmaking conditions the manganese reaction approaches close to equilibrium. When the basicity B is greater than about 3.5, $(K_{\text{Mn}})_s$ remains constant at about 1.2 ± 0.3, indicating that within this composition range $\gamma_{\text{MnO}}/\gamma_{\text{FeO}}$ does not change much with the slag composition.

Based on the relationship in Figure 12–146, the variation of the manganese distribution ratio with total iron as ferrous oxide is shown graphically in Figure 12–147 for basicities 1, 2, 3 and 4 for the average steelmaking temperature of 1600°C.

Deoxidation—General principles concerning deoxidation were discussed in Part IV of this chapter; more details will be given here on the deoxidation by manganese and silicon. Although in practice the deoxidizing reactions may not reach equilibrium, in order to understand the deoxidizing action of these elements, the following considerations will be based on equilibrium conditions. Whatever is the nature of the steelmaking process, at the end of refining the steel is invariably over-oxidized, and prior to casting, the metal must be deoxidized to a required specification.

Deoxidation by manganese—When steel is deoxidized by manganese, the reaction product is a liquid or a solid solution of FeO-MnO mixture. Therefore, the following two reactions have to be considered:

$$\underline{\text{Fe}} + \underline{\text{O}} = \text{FeO} \qquad (219a)$$
$$\underline{\text{Mn}} + \underline{\text{O}} = \text{MnO} \qquad (219b)$$

for which the equilibrium constants are:

$$K_{\text{Fe},\text{O}} = \frac{(a_{\text{FeO}})}{[\%\ \text{O}]} \qquad (220a)$$

$$K_{\text{Mn},\text{O}} = \frac{(a_{\text{MnO}})}{[\%\ \text{Mn}]\ [\%\ \text{O}]} \qquad (220b)$$

The temperature dependence of the equilibrium constant is derived from the thermodynamic data compiled in Part I of this chapter, thus:
(1) for liquid FeO-MnO deoxidation product:—

$$\log K_{\text{Fe},\text{O}} = \frac{6320}{T} - 2.734 \qquad (221a)$$

$$\log K_{\text{Mn},\text{O}} = \frac{12,970}{T} - 5.753 \qquad (221b)$$

(2) for solid FeO-MnO deoxidation product:—

$$\log K_{\text{Fe},\text{O}} = \frac{7955}{T} - 3.736 \qquad (222a)$$

$$\log K_{\text{Mn},\text{O}} = \frac{15,160}{T} - 6.758 \qquad (222b)$$

The standard states are: for case (1), pure liquid oxides and for case (2) pure solid oxides. For manganese and oxygen, the dilute solution in iron is chosen as the reference state.

As the manganese content of the steel increases, the deoxidation product becomes richer in manganous oxide. Assuming that the activities a_{FeO} and a_{MnO} are equal to their concentrations in liquid or solid FeO-MnO solutions, the manganese and oxygen contents of the steel in equilibrium with pure FeO-MnO deoxidation product can be calculated using equations (220a), (220b), (221a), (221b), (222a) and (222b). The results of such calculations are given in Figure 12–148 for three temperatures. Normally, the oxygen content of steel prior to deoxidation is below 0.1 per cent, therefore, the deoxidation product in practice will be the iron-manganese oxide solid solution.

Deoxidation by silicon—Many investigators determined the equilibrium conditions for silicon-oxygen reaction in liquid iron. For the reaction:

$$\underline{\text{Si}} + 2\underline{\text{O}} = \text{SiO}_2 \qquad (223)$$

in equilibrium with solid silica, the temperature dependence of the equilibrium index determined by Matoba, Gunji and Kuwana[228] will be used here.

$$K_{\text{Si},\text{O}} = \frac{1}{[\%\ \text{Si}]\ [\%\ \text{O}]^2} \qquad (224a)$$

$$\log K_{\text{Si},\text{O}} = \frac{30,410}{T} - 11.59 \qquad (224b)$$

As seen from the activity data compiled in Part II of this chapter, silicon dissolved in iron increases its own activity coefficient but decreases the activity coefficient of oxygen. The net result is that at concentrations up to 3 per cent Si, the product of the activity coefficients $(f_{\text{Si}} \times f_{\text{O}}^2)$ remains almost constant and, therefore, within this composition range $K_{\text{Si},\text{O}}$ does not vary noticeably with the silicon content of

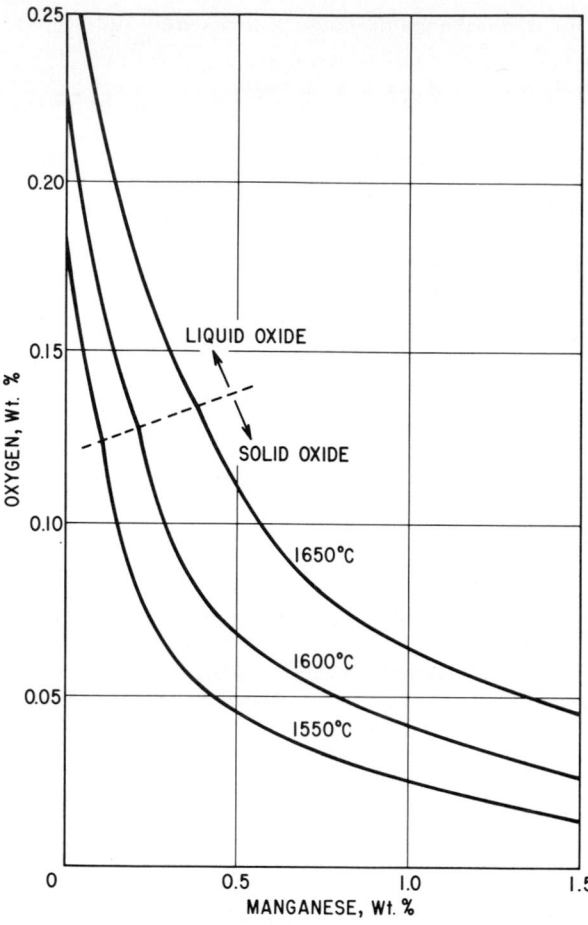

FIG. 12–148. Manganese and oxygen contents of iron in equilibrium with FeO-MnO liquid or solid solution.

the metal. Using equations (224a) and (224b), silicon and oxygen contents of iron in equilibrium with solid silica are calculated and the results are given in Figure 12–149. Because of the strong affinity of silicon for oxygen, liquid iron silicate as a deoxidation product occurs only at very low silicon and high oxygen contents. For example, at 1550°C liquid iron silicate saturated with silica forms when the metal contains about 0.001 per cent Si and 0.078 per cent O.

Deoxidation by manganese and silicon—Although deoxidation by silicon is much better than that by manganese, simultaneous deoxidation by these two elements gives much lower residual oxygen in solution. This fact was first demonstrated by Korber and Oelsen[223] in their study of the silicon and manganese reactions in liquid iron-slag systems. When silicon and manganese react simultaneously with oxygen in steel over a wide composition range the reaction product is mainly molten manganese silicate, where the activity of silica is less than unity and, consequently, for a given silicon content, the residual oxygen in solution is less than that obtained in the presence of solid silica. The effect of manganese on the deoxidation by silicon can be evaluated as follows from the known thermodynamic data on the system under consideration.

Since reactions (219b) and (223) are occurring together, the silicon-manganese equilibrium contents will be governed by the reaction:

$$\underline{Si} + 2\,MnO = 2\,\underline{Mn} + SiO_2 \qquad (225)$$

for which the equilibrium constant is:

$$K_{Si,Mn} = \frac{[\%\,Mn]^2}{[\%\,Si]}\,\frac{(a_{SiO_2})}{(a_{MnO})^2} \qquad (226)$$

For 1600°C the value of $K_{Si,Mn} = 76.21$, derived from equations (222b) and (224b). Assume that metal contains 0.8 per cent Mn and 0.25 per cent Si in solution; using equation (226) the ratio $(a_{SiO_2})/(a_{MnO})^2$ can be determined, thus:

$$\frac{(a_{SiO_2})}{(a_{MnO})^2} = 76.21\,\frac{0.25}{(0.8)^2} = 29.77$$

Since the deoxidation product is essentially pure manganese silicate with little iron oxide in it, the activity data on pure MnO-SiO$_2$ system may be used (see Part III of this chapter) to obtain the activity of silica corresponding to the ratio $(a_{SiO_2})/(a_{MnO})^2 = 29.77$; this is found to be $a_{SiO_2} = 0.84$. The equilibrium constant for reaction (223) is:

$$K_{Si,O} = \frac{(a_{SiO_2})}{[\%\,Si]\,[\%\,O]^2} = 4.42 \times 10^4 \text{ at } 1600°C$$

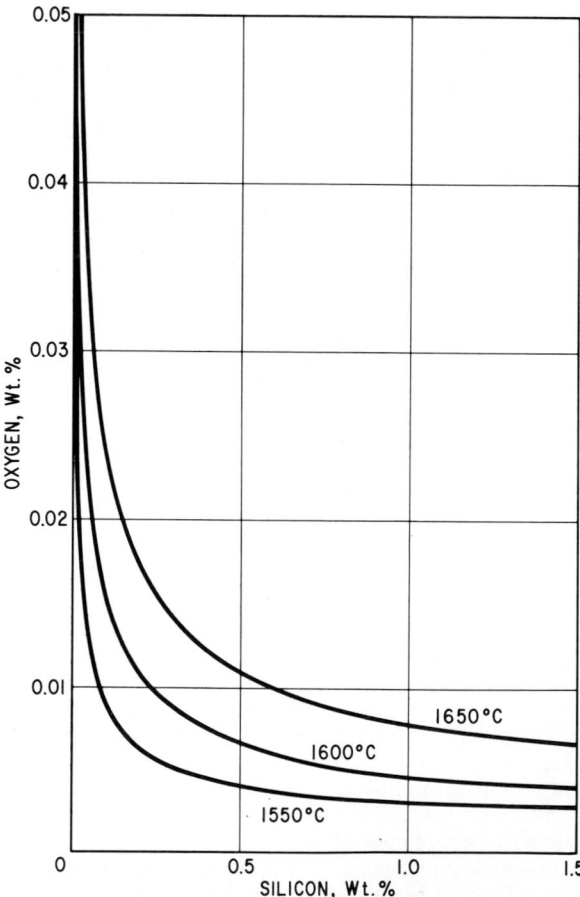

FIG. 12–149. Silicon and oxygen contents of iron in equilibrium with solid silica.

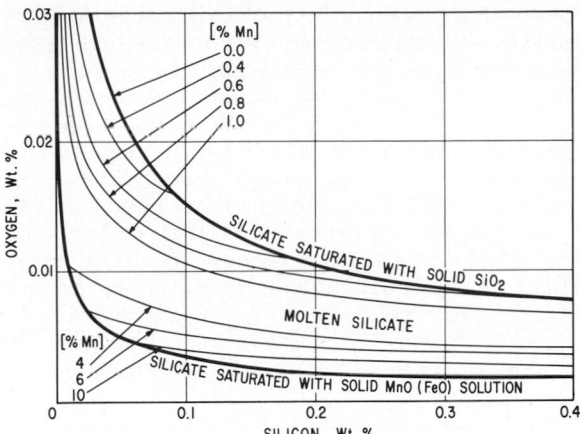

FIG. 12–150. Equilibrium data on simultaneous deoxidation of steel by silicon and manganese at 1600°C.

Now inserting % Si = 0.25 and a_{SiO_2} = 0.84,

$$[\% \text{ O}] = \sqrt{\frac{0.84}{0.25 \times 4.42 \times 10^4}} = 0.0087\%$$

The results of similar calculations over a composition range are given in Figure 12–150 where the oxygen content is plotted against the silicon concentration for a range of equilibrium manganese concentrations. As seen from Figure 12–150, the deoxidation product is molten over a wide range of silicon and manganese concentrations. The effectiveness of manganese in boosting the deoxidizing power of silicon decreases with increasing silicon content. For example, at 0.05 per cent Si in solution, the residual oxygen is lowered from 0.023 per cent to 0.016 per cent when the manganese content is increased from 0.0 to 0.8 per cent; whilst at 0.2 per cent Si, a similar increase in manganese lowers the residual oxygen from 0.0104 per cent to 0.0094 per cent.

The curves in Figure 12–150 derived from the thermodynamic data are in close agreement with those determined experimentally by Korber and Oelsen[223].

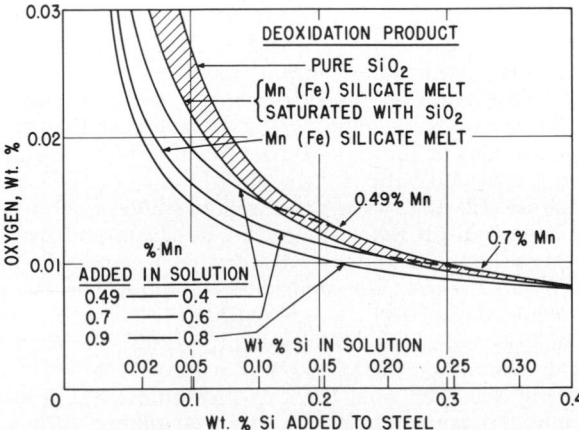

FIG. 12–151. Residual oxygen in iron at 1600°C. related to %Si and %Mn added to deoxidize steel containing initially 0.10% oxygen.

From the equilibrium data given graphically in Figure 12–150, it is possible to estimate the amount of silicon and manganese to be added to steel to deoxidize it to a certain oxygen level at a known temperature. As an example, let us assume that the steel contains 0.10 per cent oxygen and when deoxidized to 0.0122 per cent oxygen, the equilibrium manganese and silicon contents are 0.12 per cent Si and 0.6 per cent Mn; how much manganese and silicon should be added to achieve this particular end point at 1600°C?

The value of $K_{Mn,O}$ (with respect to solid MnO as the reference state) is 21.68 at 1600°C; therefore, the activity a_{MnO} is found by inserting the above values 0.0122 per cent O and 0.6 per cent Mn in equation (220b), thus:

$$a_{MnO} = 21.68 \times 0.0122 \times 0.6 = 0.159$$

From the activity data in Part III of this chapter on the MnO-SiO₂ system, the composition of the silicate melt corresponding to a_{MnO} = 0.159 is wt.% Si/ wt.% Mn = 0.562. Since the deoxidation product is a mixture of SiO₂ and MnO where %Si/%Mn = 0.562, the percentage of oxygen removed, e.g. 0.10 − 0.0122 = 0.0878 per cent O removed, is given by the following equation in terms of the silicon and manganese contents of the deoxidation product, thus:

$$0.0878\% \text{ O} = \frac{32}{28.09} \times \% \text{ Si} + \frac{16}{54.94} \times \% \text{ Mn}$$
$$= 1.139 \times \% \text{ Si} + 0.291 \times \% \text{ Mn}$$

From the above value of Si/Mn, substituting % Si = 0.562 × % Mn and solving for % Mn,

$$\% \text{ Mn} = \frac{0.0878}{1.139 \times 0.562 + 0.291} = 0.094$$

and therefore, % Si = 0.053.

These are the percentages of silicon and manganese consumed during deoxidation; since the deoxidized steel contains 0.12 per cent Si and 0.6 per cent Mn, the total added for the above deoxidation will be:

0.12 + 0.053 = 0.173 per cent Si added
0.60 + 0.094 = 0.694 per cent Mn added.

These computations are carried out over a range of silicon and manganese concentrations and the results are given graphically in Figures 12–151 and 12–152 for the initial oxygen content 0.10 per cent and 0.05 per cent, respectively. In the Bessemer process, the average oxygen content of the bath prior to deoxidation is about 0.1 per cent and in open-hearth practice this is about 0.05 per cent. For compositions within the shaded area, the deoxidation product is a heterogeneous mixture of a silicate melt and solid silica. As the per cent of silicon added is increased, more solid silica is formed at the expense of MnO until the deoxidation product is pure SiO₂. Under these conditions manganese does not take part in deoxidation. For example, as seen in Figure 12–151, at 0.7 per cent Mn addition, an increase in percentage of Si added decreases the residual oxygen

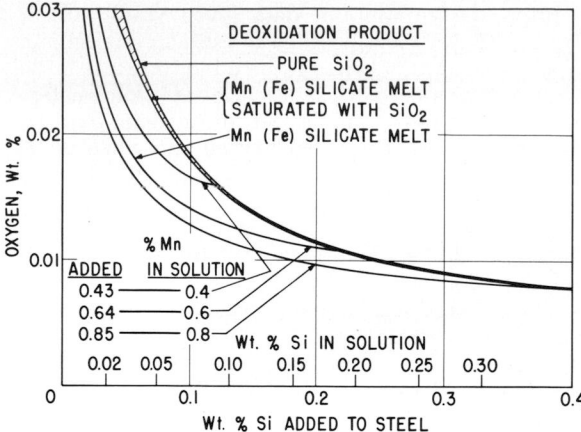

FIG. 12–152. Residual oxygen in iron at 1600°C. related to %Si and %Mn added to deoxidize steel containing initially 0.05% oxygen.

content until the first limiting value of [% O] = 0.0104 is reached at a percentage of Si added = 0.25, where the deoxidation product is saturated with silica. Further increase in silicon addition brings about a little more deoxidation and also the reduction of MnO, raising the manganese content of the bath from 0.6 per cent to 0.7 per cent.

The cleanliness of steel depends much on the nature of the deoxidation product formed. Since it is easier for liquid oxides to coagulate and separate from the melt, as compared with finely dispersed solid oxides, the additions of silicon and manganese as deoxidizers must be adjusted to give liquid deoxidation product.

Although the data in Figures 12–151 and 12–152 give the necessary information for 1600°C, the effect of temperature on the equilibrium conditions should also be known. This is shown in Figure 12–153

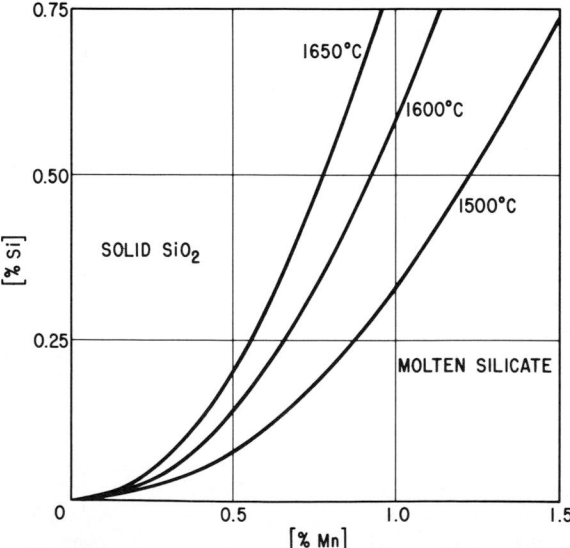

FIG. 12–153. Concentrations of silicon and manganese in iron in equilibrium with silica-saturated manganese-silicate melts.

where silicon content of steel is plotted against its manganese concentration in equilibrium with silica-saturated manganese silicate melts at temperatures 1500°, 1600° and 1650°C. If the steel contains, for example, 0.1 per cent Si and 0.4 per cent Mn, the deoxidation product at 1650°C will be liquid; however, for the same composition, the deoxidation product will be solid silica at temperatures below 1600°C.

Another phase of deoxidation is that occurring during solidification. This is brought about by an increase in the concentrations of silicon, manganese and oxygen in the melt as the primary solidification of relatively pure iron takes place. The curve in Figure 12–154 is that reproduced from Figure

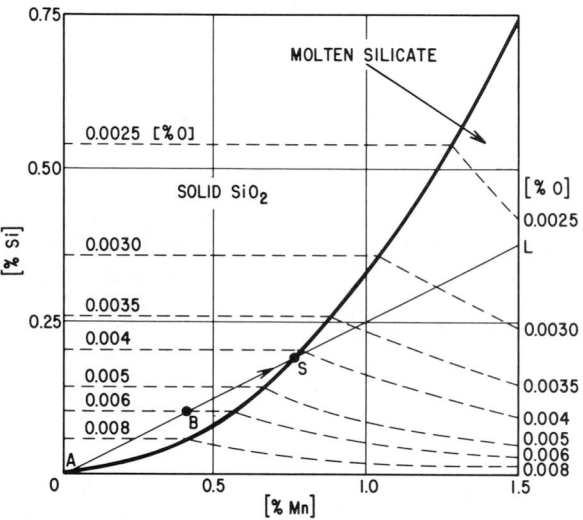

FIG. 12–154. Approximate relation showing the deoxidation of steel by silicon and manganese during solidification at 1500°C.

12–153 for melts at 1500°C in equilibrium with silica-saturated manganese silicate melts, assuming that the solidification takes place at 1500°C and that immediately before solidification starts the melt contains 0.1 per cent Si, 0.4 per cent Mn and 0.006 per cent O in equilibrium with solid silica, as indicated by point B in Figure 12–154. In order to demonstrate simply the method of calculating the extent of deoxidation during solidification, it is assumed that the solidified iron does not contain much silicon and manganese in solution, and that the concentrations of these deoxidizers in the melt increase at a constant ratio Si/Mn along the line ABSL in Figure 12–154. When the solidification progresses far enough for the melt to contain silicon and manganese more than the critical value S as shown in Figure 12–154, the deoxidation product becomes molten silicate and residual oxygen in solution in the melt decreases as solidification progresses. Because of the assumption made above concerning composition of the solidified iron, the data in Figure 12–154 are only approximate. Also, for steels containing carbon, such representation of progress of deoxidation during solidification becomes more complex, especially because of the carbon-oxygen reaction.

Since point B in Figure 12–154 corresponds to the start of solidification and point S to the beginning of the formation of a liquid deoxidation product, the extent of solidification when the composition of the melt reaches the critical point S can be estimated as follows:

$$\% \text{ of melt solidified} =$$

$$\left(1 - \frac{[\% \text{ Mn}] \text{ at B}}{[\% \text{ Mn}] \text{ at S}}\right) 100 = 47\%$$

From the results on equilibrium measurements and industrial trials on deoxidation, it may be concluded that with additions of manganese and silicon as deoxidizers at ratios within the range $\%\text{Mn}/\%\text{Si} = 8:1$ to $4:1$, the deoxidation product is essentially liquid manganese silicate with some solid silica formed only during the early stages of solidification. The adjustment of the addition of these deoxidizers within the above range promotes cleanliness of the finished steel.

SECTION 2

REACTION KINETICS

Very little is known about the kinetics and mechanism of silicon and manganese reactions in metallurgical systems. However, some work has been done recently by Turkdogan and co-workers[229] on the kinetics of the reduction of silica from silicate melts by graphite-saturated iron in the presence of carbon monoxide. The results of some of their rate data are given in Figure 12–155, for two silicate melts; these reaction rates are much higher than those observed by Fulton and Chipman[230].

The overall reaction, involving three phases, may be represented by the equation

$$\text{SiO}_2 \text{ (slag)} + 2\underline{\text{C}} \text{ (metal)} =$$
$$\underline{\text{Si}} \text{ (metal)} + 2\text{CO} \text{ (gas)} \qquad (227)$$

When considering the kinetics of a heterogeneous reaction, a three-phase reaction at an interface cannot be realized. Although nothing is known about the mechanism of individual reaction steps, the overall reaction (227) may be broken down to a few elementary steps. The most important of these reaction steps, in the system under consideration, is the desorption of silicate ions, adsorbed on the surface of the metal, as silicon and oxygen which in turn dissolve in the metal, thus

$$\boxed{\text{SiO}_2} = \underline{\text{Si}} + 2\underline{\text{O}} + \square \qquad (228a)$$

where $\boxed{\text{SiO}_2}$ and $\square$ represent occupied and vacant silicate sites on the metal surface.

Since the equilibrium oxygen potential of the metal is fixed for a given temperature and given activities of carbon and carbon monoxide, any increase in the oxygen content of the metal will lead to the reaction

$$\underline{\text{C}} + \underline{\text{O}} = \text{CO} \qquad (228b)$$

When a carbon monoxide bubble is present at the slag-metal interface, as achieved in the work of Turkdogan et al. by injecting carbon monoxide on the slag-metal interface, reaction (228b) is expected to keep pace with reaction (228a), because of the possibility of enhanced diffusion of oxygen along the interface from sites where reaction (228a) occurs, at a position where a carbon monoxide bubble is present.

On the basis of the above considerations, Turkdogan and co-workers derived the following rate equation for short reduction times and for the initial silicon content, $\%\text{Si} = 0$:

$$\%\text{Si} = A \frac{k_1 K_a (a_{\text{SiO}_2})}{1 + K_a (a_{\text{SiO}_2})} \qquad (229)$$

where A is a constant dependent of the geometry of the melt container, k_1 is the specific rate constant for forward reaction (228a) for constant carbon and oxygen potentials and K_a is the adsorption isotherm constant. That is, for a given temperature and silica activity of the slag, the mean silicon content of the metal should increase linearly with reaction time, if the postulated rate process is applicable to the system under consideration. This is in fact what is observed experimentally (Figure 12–155) at least up to about 5-10 hours reaction time. For longer reaction times the reverse of reaction (228a) should be taken into account in the derivation of the rate equation as discussed in detail by the above investigators.

In discussing the manganese reaction in iron- and steelmaking processes, it was shown that the distribution of manganese between slag and metal is in rea-

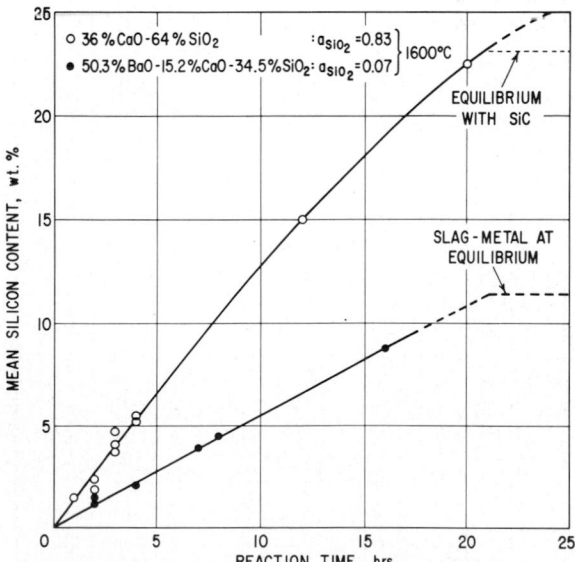

FIG. 12–155. Increase in mean silicon content of graphite-saturated iron melts with time, when reacting with silicate melts at 1600°C and CO at 1.0 atm. bubbled through slag at the slag-metal interface. (From Turkdogan, Grieveson and Beisler[229].)

sonable accord with the equilibrium data. That is, the reduction of manganous oxide from the slag or oxidation of manganese in the iron must be occurring at a high enough rate so that a partial equilibrium between slag and metal is maintained with respect to the manganese reaction in the reduction or oxidation processes. On the assumption that the rate of manganese reaction in the open-hearth furnace is controlled by the transport of manganese through the diffusion boundary layer, Darken[231] estimated that 30 to 40 minutes would be the time required to achieve or reachieve substantial equilibrium after an addition to the bath. This prediction is in good agreement with what is observed during steelmaking.

CHAPTER 12 (Continued)

The Physical Chemistry of Iron- and Steelmaking

PART VI

Phosphorus Reaction

SECTION 1

DEPHOSPHORIZATION IN OPEN-HEARTH AND ELECTRIC FURNACE STEELMAKING PRACTICE

Some iron ores contain appreciable amounts of calcium phosphate and apatite. During reduction of the ore in the blast furnace, substantially all the phosphates are reduced, and, via the gas phase, the phosphorus is transported to iron. Removal of phosphorus from iron can be achieved only by oxidation during steelmaking. The basic equation representing the phosphorus reaction is:

$$2\underline{P}\ (\text{metal}) + 5\underline{O}\ (\text{metal}) + 3O^{2-}\ (\text{slag})$$
$$= 2PO_4^{3-}\ (\text{slag}) \qquad (230)$$

or more simply,

$$2\underline{P} + 5\underline{O} = P_2O_5 \qquad (231)$$

for which the equilibrium constant is:

$$K = \frac{(a_{P_2O_5})}{[a_P]^2[a_O]^5} \qquad (232)$$

Since under steelmaking conditions the concentrations of impurities in the metal are low, the activities of phosphorus and oxygen in iron can be assumed to be proportional to their weight percentages and, therefore, the equilibrium constant becomes

$$K = \frac{(N_{P_2O_5})(\gamma_{P_2O_5})}{[\%P]^2[\%O]^5} \qquad (233)$$

where $N_{P_2O_5}$ and $\gamma_{P_2O_5}$ represent the mole fraction and the activity coefficient of phosphorus pentoxide in the slag. Turkdogan and Pearson[232] derived the following equation for the temperature dependence of the equilibrium constant:

$$\log K = \frac{36,850}{T} - 29.07 \qquad (234)$$

Because of the strong interaction of phosphate ions with basic oxides in the slag, $\gamma_{P_2O_5}$ decreases with increasing concentrations of basic oxides. That is, for a given state of oxidation in the furnace, the phosphorus distribution ratio between slag and metal increases with increasing basicity of the slag. The temperature has a noticeable effect on the phosphorus reaction and as seen from equation (234), for a given [% O], decreasing temperature increases the slag/metal phosphorus distribution ratio.

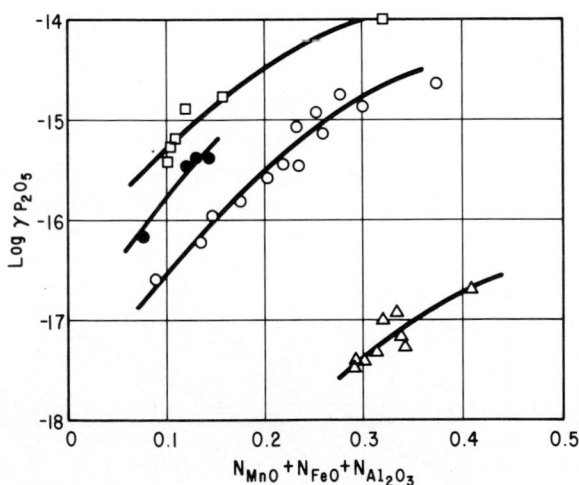

	N_{CaO}/N_{SiO_2}	N_{MgO}	$N_{P_2O_5}$
□	2.8 – 3.2	0.09 – 0.12	0.04 – 0.06
●	3.6 – 3.8	"	"
○	4.0 – 4.5	"	"
△	8.0 – 10.0	"	"

Fig. 12–156. Effect of slag composition on the activity coefficient of phosphorus pentoxide, at $1585 + 10°C$. (From Turkdogan and Pearson[232].)

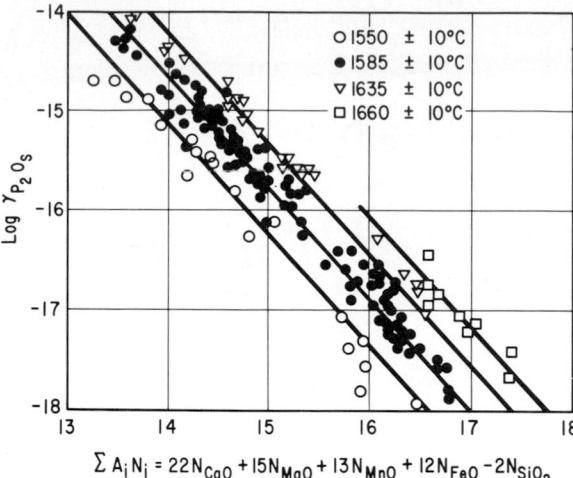

FIG. 12–157. Effect of slag composition and temperature on the activity coefficient of phosphorus pentoxide. (From Turkdogan and Pearson[232].)

A number of investigators (233-237) measured the equilibrium phosphorus distribution between molten iron and complex slags and different methods were used in representing the variation of the ratio $(P_2O_5)/[P]$ with slag composition. As already pointed out, for a given temperature and [%O], variation in $(P_2O_5)/[P]$ with slag composition is due to the variation in $\gamma_{P_2O_5}$. Using equations (233) and (234) and the available equilibrium data on slag-metal phosphorus reaction, Turkdogan and Pearson[232] computed the value of $\gamma_{P_2O_5}$ for complex slags. As a first approximation, the slags are considered to belong to a CaO-MgO-$(MnO + Al_2O_3)$-SiO_2-P_2O_5 system, and Figure 12–156 shows the variation of log $\gamma_{P_2O_5}$ with the sum of the mole fractions $N_{MnO} + N_{FeO} + N_{Al_2O_3}$ at fixed concentrations of MgO, P_2O_5 and CaO/SiO_2 ratios. Further simplification is made by plotting log $\gamma_{P_2O_5}$ against the sum of

$$(22N_{CaO} + 15N_{MgO} + 13N_{MnO} + 12N_{FeO} - 2N_{SiO_2})$$

as shown in Figure 12–157. The factors in this summation are derived by trial and error, but their relation to one another for basic oxides is that based on the free energies of formation of tri-calcium, tri-

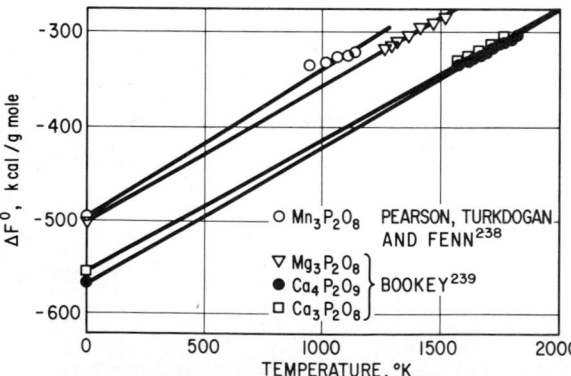

FIG. 12–158. Free energies of formation of various phosphates.

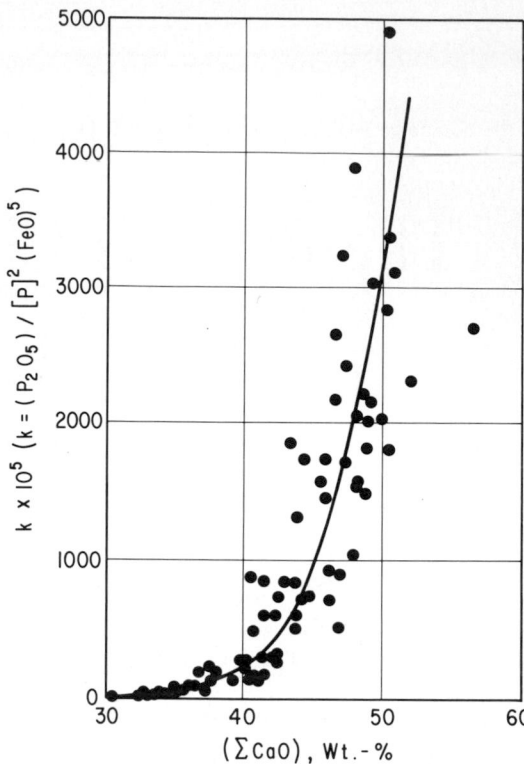

FIG. 12–159. Effect of lime upon k, using analytically determined (FeO). (From Balajiva, Quarrell and Vajragupta[234].)

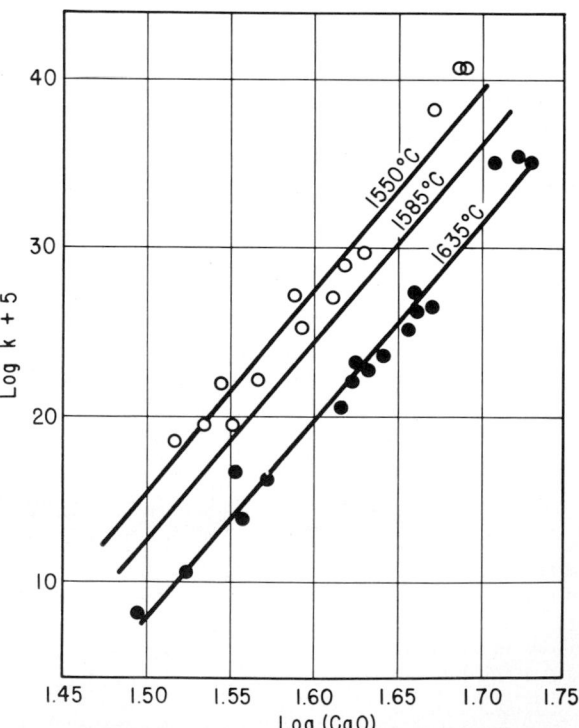

FIG. 12–160. Effect of temperature on the equilibrium constant k for the phosphorus reaction. (From Balajiva and Vajragupta[235].)

magnesium and tri-manganese phosphates. The free energies of formation of these phosphates are summarized in Figure 12–158.

Although the relationship in Figure 12–157 is somewhat empirical, the above considerations underline the basic principles concerning the phosphorus reaction equilibria in slag-metal systems. In basic steelmaking slags, variations in MgO and MnO contents are small, and the relationship pertaining to the phosphorous reaction may be simplified for easy application in the study of the industrial heats. This is shown in Figure 12–159 where the equilibrium index $k = (P_2O_5)/[P]^2(FeO)^5$ is plotted against the lime content of the slag, and the variation of log k with temperature is given in Figure 12–160. Although low temperature favors better dephosphorization, the slag temperature should be kept high enough to dissolve sufficient lime required for the removal of phosphorus. In practice some fluorspar is often added to increase the fluidity of the high lime-slags, enhancing rate of dephosphorization.

Apart from some practical details, the conditions for dephosphorization in open-hearth and electric-furnace practice are about the same. That is, the slag must be oxidizing, high in lime and low in silica contents. In most European steel works, high-phosphorus iron is used for steelmaking and, consequently, the tapping slags can be very high in phosphorus contents, e.g. 10 to 20 per cent P_2O_5, see for example Table 12–XIV in Part IV of this chapter. These high-phosphorus basic slags have commercial value as fertilizers, particularly the slags produced during refining of high-phosphorus iron in the Thomas process. If these phosphate slags are to be used as fertilizers, very little or no fluorspar should be added during refining. Otherwise the apatite, $CaF_2 \cdot 3Ca_3P_2O_8$, formed upon solidification, lowers the solubility of the phosphate in soil acids.

SECTION 2

DEPHOSPHORIZATION IN THE THOMAS PROCESS

In the Thomas process, which is often called the basic Bessemer process, dephosphorization takes place after the removal of carbon from the metal. This is explained simply in terms of the oxygen potential of the gas circulating the metal bath. From the thermodynamic data given in Part IV of this chapter on the reduction-oxidation reaction equilibria, it can be shown that the oxidation of phosphorus in iron occurs together with the oxidation of iron and for these reactions to take place, the oxygen potential of the gas blown through the melt must be high. In other words, dephosphorization in the bottom-blown process cannot start before all the carbon is removed. This dephosphorization period in practice is often called the "after blow" which lasts about 2 minutes.

Another reason for this delay in the phosphorus reaction is that the temperature of the bath is not high enough for the formation of a molten basic slag in the early stages of refining.

SECTION 3

DEPHOSPHORIZATION IN OXYGEN-STEELMAKING PROCESSES

The practical aspects of the use of oxygen in steelmaking are discussed in other chapters of this book and some chemical aspects of the oxygen steelmaking processes were discussed briefly in this chapter when considering the reduction-oxidation reactions. Here the discussion will be limited to the phosphorus reaction.

In steelmaking processes where oxygen is blown on the surface of the melt as in the case of the basic oxygen, L-D, Kaldo or Rotor processes[240, 241], a basic slag rich in iron oxide and lime is rapidly formed and since the oxygen potential of the system at the slag-metal interface is maintained high, dephosphorization occurs together with decarburization. In fact, by the time the metal is decarburized, the removal of phosphorus also has been achieved without the necessity of "after blow."

Sometimes oxygen blowing is utilized for pre-refining the hot metal-scrap charge for the electric-furnace steelmaking practice. The practical aspects of pre-refining have been discussed in detail by Davies[240]. He showed, for example, that a blast furnace iron containing 3.9 per cent C, 0.93 per cent Si, 0.72 per cent Mn, 0.06 per cent S and 0.40 per cent P is pre-refined by oxygen lancing to give 1.80 per cent C, 0.0 per cent Si, 0.12 per cent Mn, 0.048 per cent S and 0.08 per cent P. The important feature of the process is that the iron is dephosphorized appreciably in the presence of high percentages of carbon, owing to the conditions which favor faster rate of dephosphorization as compared with the rate of decarburization. In Figure 12–161 some examples are given on the relationship between the phosphorus content of the steel and the iron content of the slag obtained from data on the Kaldo process[241].

SECTION 4

REPHOSPHORIZATION OF STEEL IN THE LADLE

It follows from the foregoing discussions of phosphorus reaction equilibria that if the conditions in the slag change at the time of tapping, there could be reversion of phosphorus from slag to metal. In fact, experience has shown that after the metal is tapped into a ladle lined with fireclay bricks, there

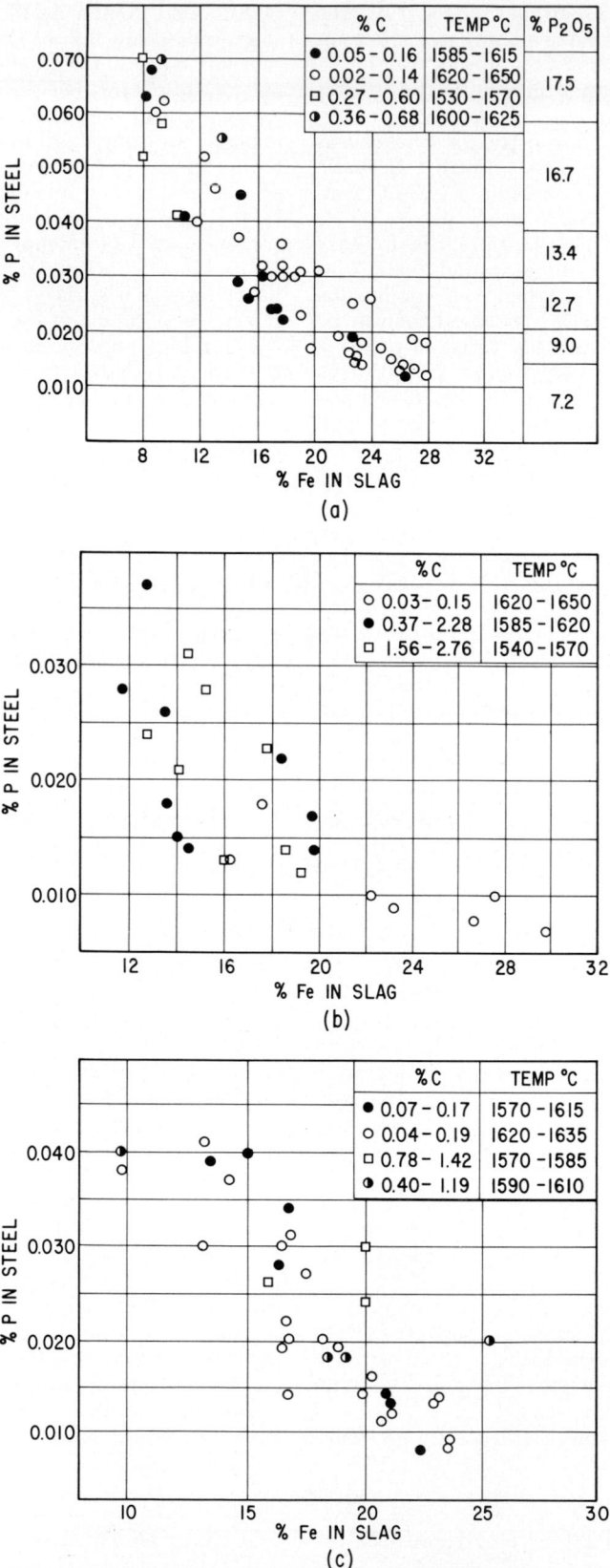

Fig. 12–161. Variation of phosphorus with the iron content of slag in the Kaldo process. Hot metal with: (a) 1.85% P (b) 0.20% P (c) 0.66% P. (From Kalling et al.[241].)

is a noticeable amount of reversion of phosphorus from the slag to the metal. There are three main factors responsible for this rephosphorization: (1) pick up of silica from the ladle bricks reduces the dephosphorizing capacity of the slag; (2) the small amount of slag covering the metal in the ladle is less oxidizing compared with the conditions prevailing in the furnace and (3) addition of deoxidizers without the complete removal of the slag. This problem was studied in detail by Zea[243] by analyzing data obtained from slag and metal samples taken from 10-ton teeming ladles.

SECTION 5

KINETICS OF PHOSPHORUS REACTION

Although adequate information is available on the phosphorus reaction equilibria, the same cannot be said for the reaction kinetics; in fact no laboratory experiments have been carried out to study the kinetics of this reaction. However, if the metal and slag baths were stirred well enough to eliminate the transport of the reactants and products, to and from the interface, to be the rate-controlling process, dephosphorization and rephosphorization reactions might occur at relatively fast rates.

The Physical Chemistry of Iron- and Steelmaking

PART VII
Sulphur Reactions

SECTION 1
REACTION EQUILIBRIA

General Considerations—Because of the industrial importance and theoretical interest, many investigators have studied the reactions between molten oxides, silicates and aluminates and gases containing oxygen and sulphur. The early work reviewed by Schenck[244] and studies made by Bardenheuer and Geller[245] indicated that solution of gaseous sulphur in an oxide melt resulted in the replacement of the oxide ions by the sulphide ions. Measurements made by Grant and Chipman[246] on the equilibrium partition of sulphur between molten iron and complex silicate melts also demonstrated that, for a given temperature and silicate composition, the distribution of sulphur between slag and metal increased with decreasing oxygen content of the metal.

In more recent studies of sulphur equilibria between gases and oxide-melts by Fincham and Richardson[247], St. Pierre and Chipman[248] and Turkdogan and Darken[249], it has been observed that at oxygen partial pressures below about 10^{-5} atm., sulphur dissolves in the melt as sulphide ions and at oxygen partial pressures higher than 10^{-3} atm., sulphur enters the melt as sulphate ions. This is shown in Figure 12-162 where log (%S) is plotted against log p_{O_2} (p_{O_2} in atm.) for a calcium ferrite and a calcium alumino-silicate melt. The theoretical slopes of the lines for sulphide and sulphate reactions are shown by broken lines AA and BB, respectively. Therefore, these two reactions are:

Sulphide reactions:

$$SO_2 \text{ (gas)} + O^{2-} \text{ (slag)} = \tfrac{3}{2}O_2 \text{ (gas)} + S^{2-} \text{ (slag)} \tag{235a}$$

Sulphate reactions:

$$SO_2 \text{ (gas)} + \tfrac{1}{2}O_2 \text{ (gas)} + O^{2-} \text{ (melt)} = SO_4^{2-} \text{ (slag)} \tag{235b}$$

It is shown by Turkdogan and Darken[249] that at temperatures below 1600°C pyrosulphate reaction also occurs, thus

Pyrosulphate reactions:

$$2SO_2 \text{ (gas)} + O_2 \text{ (gas)} + O^{2-} \text{ (slag)} = S_2O_7^{2-} \text{ (slag)} \tag{235c}$$

The oxygen partial pressures encountered under the conditions of iron and steelmaking are well below 10^{-4} atm., therefore, the subsequent considera-

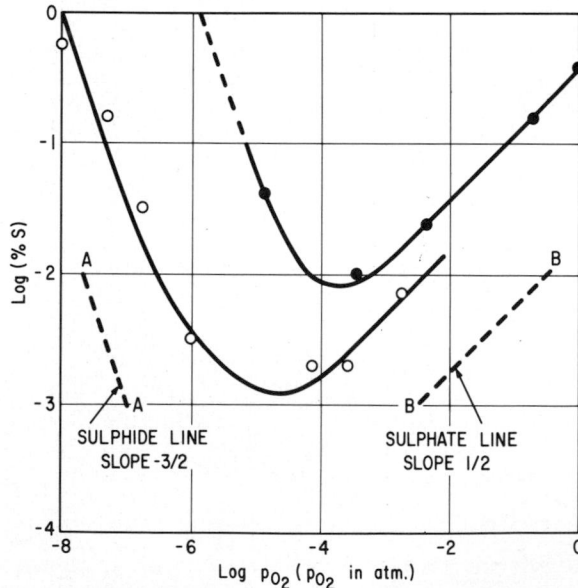

FIG. 12-162. Variation of sulphur content of oxide melts with partial pressure of oxygen. (Filled circles: from Turkdogan and Darken[249] for calcium ferrite melts at 1620°C. and P_{SO_2} 6 to 8%. Open circles: from Fincham and Richardson[247] for calcium-alumino-silicate melts at 1500°C. and $P_{SO_2} = 2\%$.)

tions on sulphur reaction are limited to the sulphide reaction.

In gases containing sulphur, oxygen, hydrogen . . . etc., the sulphur exists in several forms, e.g. S, S_2, SO, SO_2, H_2S . . . etc. Since all these species will have definite partial pressures in equilibrium with one another, any form of sulphur can be used in writing the gas-slag sulphur reaction. For simplicity, the partial pressure of diatomic sulphur may be used in representing the sulphide reaction, thus:

$$\tfrac{1}{2}S_2 \text{ (gas)} + O^{2-} \text{ (slag)} = \tfrac{1}{2}O_2 \text{ (gas)}$$
$$+ S^{2-} \text{ (slag)} \qquad (236)$$

for which the equilibrium constant is

$$K = \frac{(\gamma_S)}{(a_O)}(\%S)\left(\frac{p_{O_2}}{p_{S_2}}\right)^{\frac{1}{2}} \qquad (237)$$

where a_O is the oxide ion activity of the slag, γ_S is the activity coefficient of sulphur in the slag and p is the partial pressures of gases in atmospheres. The terms γ_S and a_O are functions of temperature and slag composition. Therefore, for a given temperature and slag composition, equation (237) may be rearranged to give the following equilibrium index for the sulphur reaction:

$$(K') = K\frac{a_O}{\gamma_S} = (\%S)\left(\frac{p_{O_2}}{p_{S_2}}\right)^{\frac{1}{2}} \qquad (238)$$

where the concentration of sulphur is in wt. %. The examples given in Figure 12–163 show the variation of (K') with the compositions of calcium ferrite, aluminate, silicate and phosphate and manganese silicate melts at 1650°C. With increasing concentration of the basic oxide, a_O increases and γ_S decreases and, consequently, the equilibrium index (K') increases considerably with increasing concentration of basic

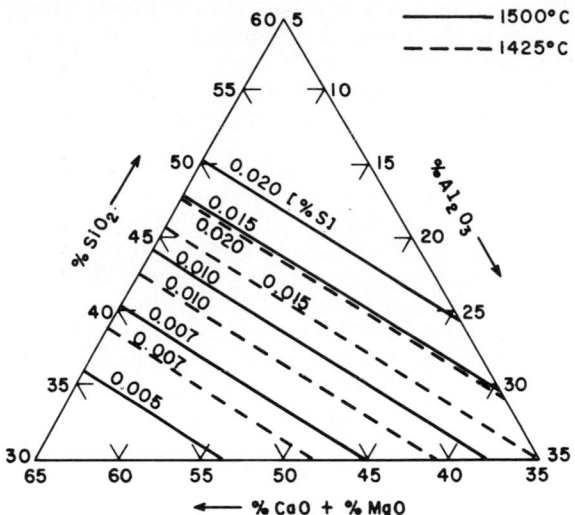

FIG. 12–164. Sulphur content of carbon-saturated iron in equilibrium with blast-furnace type of slags containing 1.5% sulphur. (From Hatch and Chipman[250].)

oxide. For a given melt composition a decrease in temperature decreases the value of K'.

In iron- and steelmaking processes, the sulphur reaction to be considered is that occurring between slag and metal for which the following may be written analogous to equation (236):

$$\underline{S} \text{ (metal)} + O^{2-} \text{ (slag)} = \underline{O} \text{ (metal)}$$
$$+ S^{2-} \text{ (slag)} \qquad (239)$$

and for a given temperature and slag composition, the equilibrium index is:

$$[K'] = (\%S)\frac{[a_O]}{[a_S]} \qquad (240)$$

where $[a_O]$ and $[a_S]$ are the activities of oxygen and sulphur in iron.

Using the basic equations (239) and (240), the equilibrium conditions for the sulphur reaction in slag-metal systems are discussed below in relation to iron- and steelmaking processes.

Iron Making—The equilibrium distributions of sulphur between graphite-saturated iron and blast-furnace type of slags were measured by Hatch and Chipman[250]. Their equilibrium data are summarized in Figure 12–164 where the iso-[%S] lines are plotted in the composition diagram for slags containing 1.5 per cent sulphur. Since the melts contain carbon, the following reaction occurs along with reaction (239):

$$\underline{C} + \underline{O} = CO \qquad (241)$$

From the sum of equations (239) and (241):

$$\underline{S} + \underline{C} + O^{2-} = S^{2-} + CO \qquad (242)$$

For melts saturated with carbon at 1 atm. pressure of carbon monoxide, the equilibrium index $[K']_C$ for a given temperature and slag composition becomes:

$$[K']_C = \frac{(\%S)}{[\%S]} \qquad (243)$$

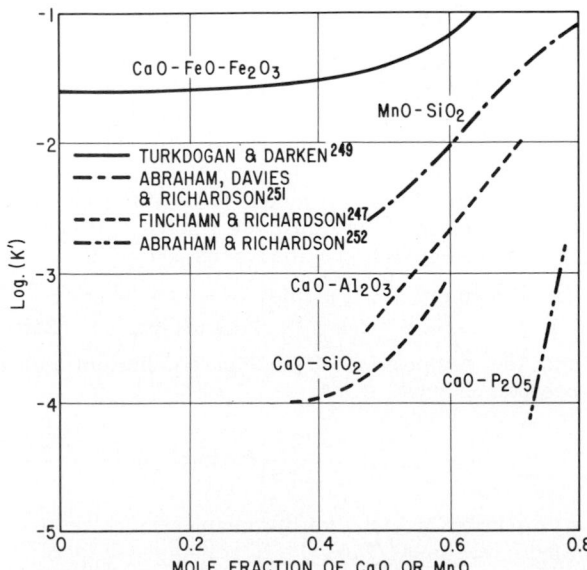

FIG. 12–163. Variation of sulphur equilibrium index (K') with composition of ferrite (at 1620°C.), aluminate, silicate and phosphate melts at 1650°C.

By means of this relation, the data in Figure 12–164 can be used for estimating equilibrium [%S] for slags containing sulphur other than 1.5 per cent. The temperature dependence of $[K']_C$ is similar to those of $[K']$ and (K'), i.e. they increase with increasing temperature.

Under industrial ironmaking conditions, the sulphur distribution ratio at tap varies within the range 20 to 80, depending on the slag composition and temperature. These ratios are lower than the equilibrium values by a factor of about 2 to 3. For example, Filer and Darken[253] showed that whilst the initial sulphur distribution ratio obtained from the analysis of blast-furnace slag and metal samples, was 54, on equilibration in a graphite crucible in an atmosphere of carbon monoxide, the sulphur distribution ratio increased to 89, 154 and 205 at temperatures 1400°, 1500° and 1600°C, respectively.

It should be borne in mind that in addition to carbon, iron in the blast-furnace hearth contains other reducing elements, in particular, silicon and manganese. Therefore, the following reactions should also be considered:

$$2\underline{S} + \underline{Si} + 2O^{2-} = 2S^{2-} + SiO_2 \quad (244)$$
$$\underline{S} + \underline{Mn} + O^{2-} = S^{2-} + MnO \quad (245)$$

and their equilibrium indices for a given temperature and slag composition are:

$$[K']_{Si} = \frac{(\%S)^2}{[\%S]^2}\frac{(\%SiO_2)}{[\%Si]} \quad (246)$$

$$[K']_{Mn} = \frac{(\%S)}{[\%S]}\frac{(\%MnO)}{[\%Mn]} \quad (247)$$

Since the variation of $(\%S)/[\%S]$ with slag composition can be obtained from Figure 12–164 and those of $(\%SiO_2)/[\%Si]$ and $(\%MnO)/[\%Mn]$ are given in Figures 12–142 and 12–143 of Part V of this chapter, respectively, the values of $[K']_{Si}$ and $[K']_{Mn}$ can readily be evaluated for any slag composition. Although the sulphur reaction does not reach equilibrium under industrial ironmaking conditions, it is a well known fact that high silicon and/or high manganese contents in iron are invariably accompanied with low sulphur contents, as would be expected from the equilibrium relations in equations (246) and (247).

If the raw materials charged to the blast furnace contain high percentages of sulphur, the iron produced can contain as much as 0.2 per cent sulphur. Under these circumstances, the metal can be desulphurized during tapping by adding sodium carbonate to the ladle; this is known as the soda-ash treatment, which is often used, particularly in the European ironmaking practices. It has been demonstrated by Hornak and Whittenberger[254] that hot metal can also be desulphurized effectively by injecting calcium carbonate, burnt lime, calcium cyanamide, and calcium carbide into the metal in the ladle.

Steelmaking—Many papers have been written on the subject of sulphur reaction under the conditions of steelmaking. The basic principles involved are essentially those already discussed for the gas-slag systems. The variation of the equilibrium index $[K']$

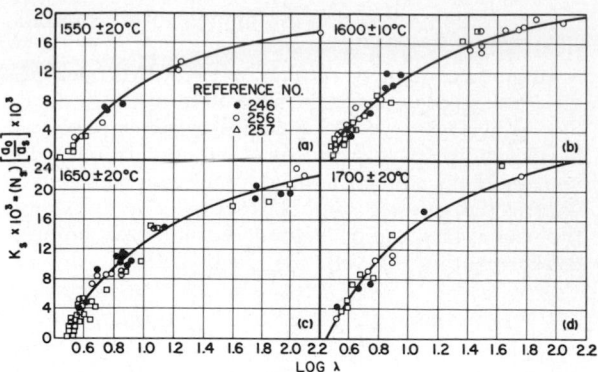

FIG. 12–165. Sulphur capacity related to slag composition for mean temperatures of (a) 1550 ± 20°C.; (b) 1600 ± 10°C.; (c) 1650 ± 20°C.; (d) 1700 ± 20°C. (From Turkdogan[255].)

in equation (240) with temperature and slag compositions is shown in Figure 12–165, reproduced from a paper by Turkdogan[255]. In this plot, the equilibrium index is given by:

$$K_s = (N_s)\frac{[a_O]}{[a_S]} \quad (248)$$

when N_s is the mole fraction of sulphur in the slag; a_O and a_S are the activities of oxygen and sulphur in the metal, i.e.

$$a_O = [\%O]f_O \quad (249a)$$
$$a_S = [\%S]f_S \quad (249b)$$

where f_O and f_S are the activity coefficients of oxygen and sulphur in iron; however, at low concentrations of alloying elements, f_O and $f_S \rightarrow 1$ (see Part II of this chapter for details). In plotting the data in Figure 12–165 the slag composition was represented in terms of mole fraction:

$$\gamma = \frac{1}{N_{SiO_2} + 1.5N_{P_2O_5} + 1.5N_{Al_2O_3}}$$

This is another arbitrary way of representing the slag basicity. Figure 12–165 shows that the sulphur equilibrium index increases with increasing basicity (increasing γ) or with increasing temperature; the effect of temperature is quite small.

In practice, it is convenient to use the iron-oxide content of the slag instead of [%O], and sulphur reaction can equally well be written as

$$\underline{S} \text{ (metal)} + \underline{Fe} \text{ (metal)} + O^{2-} \text{ (slag)}$$
$$= S^{2-} \text{ (slag)} + FeO \text{ (Slag)} \quad (250)$$

and the composition dependent equilibrium index becomes

$$[K']_F = \frac{(\%S)}{[\%S]}(\%FeO)_t \quad (251)$$

As discussed in Part V of this chapter on silicon-manganese reactions, $(\%FeO)_t$ in equation (251) is the total iron-oxide content of the slag ($= 1.35 \times \%Fe_2O_3 + \%FeO$). Using these practical units, in Figure 12–166 the equilibrium index $[K']_F$ is plotted against the basicity $B = (\%CaO + 1.4 \times \%MgO)/$

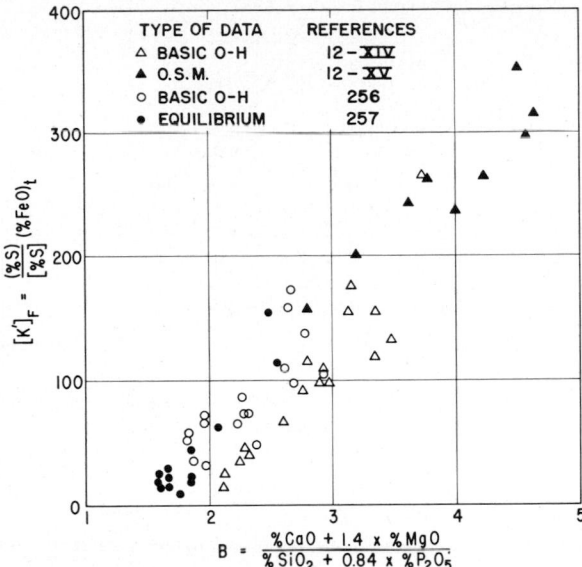

FIG. 12–166. Variation of sulphur equilibrium index $[K']_F$ with slag basicity.

($\%SiO_2 + 0.84 \times \%P_2O_5$); the data are the same as those in Tables 12–XIV and 12–XV in Part IV of this chapter. The scatter is as would be expected from the steelmaking data; however, the results indicate that under steelmaking conditions the sulphur-reaction approaches close to equilibrium. Using different analytical techniques the same conclusion was reached by other authors[255, 256].

One of the most important factors influencing the desulphurization is the state of oxidation of the bath. Desulphurization and deoxidation in a sense are equivalent, i.e. the sulphur distribution ratio (S)/[S] is inversely proportional to the iron-oxide content of the slag or the oxygen content of the metal. The oxidizing conditions prevailing in the open-hearth furnace do not favor appreciable removal of sulphur from the melt. For this reason care is taken in practice to keep the sulphur input into the furnace at a low level. The hot metal, scrap charge and fuel oil are the principal sources of sulphur. If unmelted scrap is exposed to the flame during the period of melt down, some sulphur is picked up from the furnace atmosphere. Transfer of sulphur to the bath is normally kept to a minimum by using heavy scrap and maintaining an oxidizing flame. The advantage of the oxidizing flame is obvious from equation (237); that is, by increasing the oxygen partial pressure of the flame impinging on the surface of the slag some sulphur should be removed from the slag, thus promoting subsequent transfer from metal to slag.

This was demonstrated by Larsen and Sordahl[258] who showed that by blowing oxygen gently over the slag surface in a gas-fired furnace containing 100 lb. metal, about ⅔ of the sulphur could be removed by the gas-slag reaction. This pumping action of oxygen on the sulphur removal is discussed more fully later under the section on reaction kinetics.

In basic electric-arc furnace practice there are

normally two stages of refining. In the first stage, the bath is kept oxidizing to remove carbon, phosphorus, etc. This oxidizing slag is then removed and the bath is reduced by charging calcium carbide, anthracite, lime and fluorspar. Under this slag, metal is desulphurized to concentrations below 0.01 per cent. In order to achieve much lower sulphur concentration in the metal, strong deoxidizers are injected directly into the metal bath. For example, Marples and Pears[259] observed that steel could be desulphurized rapidly under a reducing slag in the basic electric-arc furnace by injecting lime-magnesium powder mixtures and calcium-silico-magnesium alloys. Figure 12–167 is an example of the results obtained by these investigators.

The general conclusion to be drawn is that in the basic open-hearth and oxygen steelmaking processes, an oxidizing atmosphere assists desulphurization by removing some sulphur from the slag at the slag-gas interface. In the basic electric-arc furnace, however, injection of reducing agents into the metal under a reducing slag lowers the sulphur content of the metal.

Sulphide Inclusions in Steels—There is always some sulphur present in commercial steel, and it is often suggested that hot-shortness which, occurs during heat treatment and hot working of steel, be-

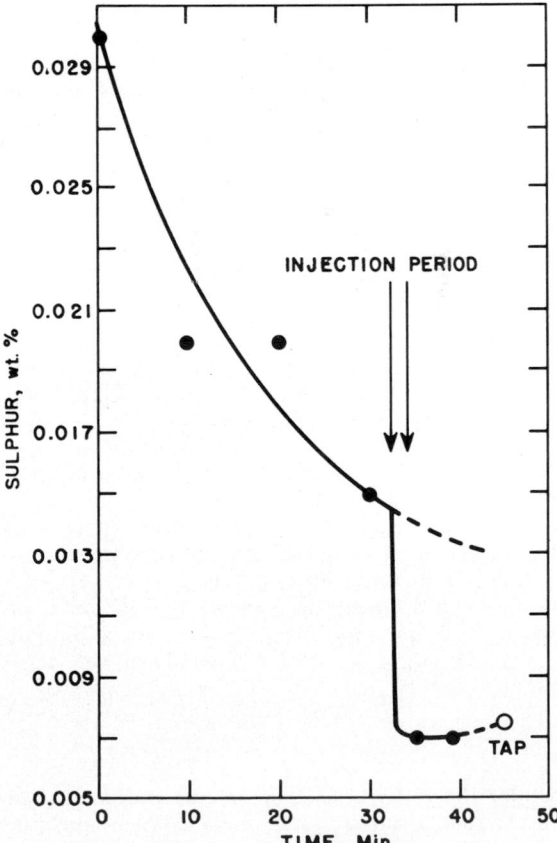

FIG. 12–167. Desulphurization under reducing slags in basic-electric process by injecting calcium-silico-magnesium alloy (20 lbs. injected per ton of iron). (From Marples and Pears[259].)

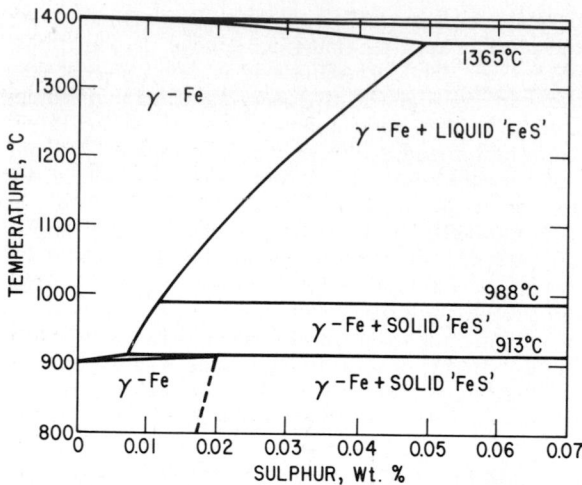

FIG. 12—168. Iron-rich corner of the iron-sulphur binary phase diagram. (For data see Part II of this chapter.)

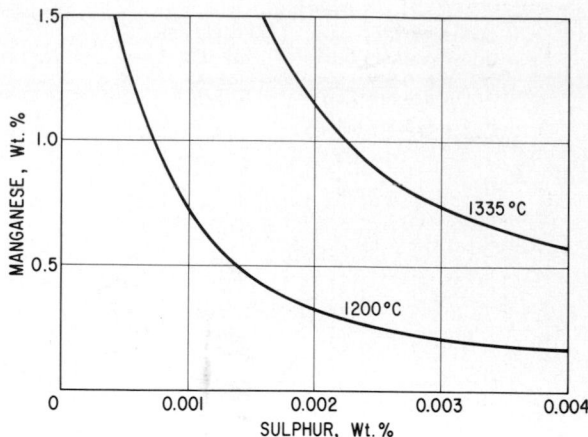

FIG. 12—169. Manganese and sulphur contents in solid solution in iron in equilibrium with MnS. (From Turkdogan and Ignatowicz[260].)

comes more serious when the sulphur content of the steel is high. This deleterious effect of sulphur may be explained by considering the iron-sulphur phase equilibrium diagram shown in Figure 12—168 (for further details on this system see Part II of this chapter).

From the solubility diagram it can be predicted that low-carbon and low-manganese steels containing less than 0.01 per cent S should not be subject to hot-shortness, because no liquid iron sulphide can form at the temperatures employed in heat treatment and hot-working. On the other hand, an iron containing 0.02 per cent S may produce a small quantity of a liquid phase within the temperature range 988°–1100°C. The presence of this liquid phase along the grain boundaries could weaken the metal.

In practice, it has been found that manganese reduces the risk of hot-shortness and similar phenomena encountered in hot-working. The effect of manganese on the solubility of sulphur in solid iron was determined by Turkdogan and Ignatowicz[260]; using their data, manganese and sulphur contents in solid solution in iron in equilibrium with MnS (+ little FeS in solution) are plotted in Figure 12—169 for 1200° and 1335°C. Whilst in the absence of manganese the solubility of FeS in iron at, for example, 1200°C is 0.031 per cent S (Figure 12—168), in the presence of 0.2 per cent Mn in solution the sulphur solubility is reduced to 0.0032 per cent S. Furthermore, when manganese sulphide is formed, the inclusions are in the solid state at hot-working temperatures and, therefore, hot-shortness does not occur.

SECTION 2

REACTION KINETICS

The reaction kinetics and the mechanism of transfer of sulphur between gas-slag-metal phases are reasonably well understood. The significant aspects of the kinetics of sulphur reaction are given below for particular gas-slag and slag-metal systems.

Sulphur Reaction in Gas-Slag Systems—It has already been discussed that when an ionic oxide-melt reacts with an atmosphere containing sulphur and oxygen-bearing gases, the following reaction occurs:

$$\frac{1}{2}S_2 \text{ (gas)} + O^{2-} \text{ (melt)} \qquad (252)$$

$$= S^{2-} \text{ (melt)} + \frac{1}{2}O_2 \text{ (gas)}$$

Under the restrictions that (i) electric conductance in the melt is purely ionic and (ii) each constituent element in the slag does not change valence, the solution of an atom of sulphur in the melt will result in the evolution of an atom of oxygen, so that the electric neutrality is maintained. For a given temperature and melt composition, the equilibrium concentration of sulphur in the melt is determined by the ratio p_{O_2}/p_{S_2} in the gas phase and not by the individual partial pressures of oxygen and sulphur. The reactions of this type are often called the coupled reactions. The validity of the above concept associated with coupled reactions has recently been demonstrated by Turkdogan and Grieveson[261] using the following experimental technique. A presintered mixture of Mn-MnS-MnO and prefused mixture of Fe-S-O, contained in iridium crucibles and separated by a thin layer of soda-glass (to act as an ionic membrane), were placed in an evacuated silica capsule as shown in Figure 12—170. This was then kept at 1127°C for a required time to allow reaction (252) to occur via the ionic membrane. The purpose of the condensed phases Mn-MnS-MnO (Mn-pellet) and Fe-S-O (Fe-melt) is to maintain the required sulphur and oxygen partial pressures on either side of the molten membrane. Since the phases of the Mn-pellets have fixed compositions at the temperature of reaction

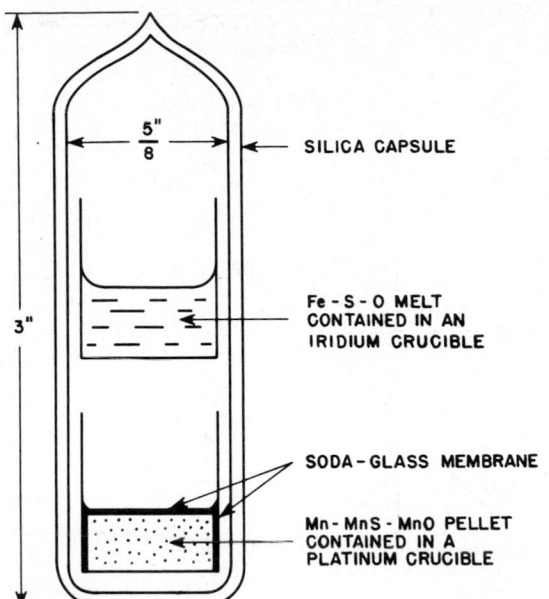

FIG. 12–170. Schematic diagram showing sealed silica capsule containing, in separate crucibles, Mn-MnS-MnO pellet glazed with soda-glass and Fe-S-O melt. (From Turkdogan and Grieveson[261].)

(i.e. solid Mn, MnS and MnO do not form solutions at 1127°C) the sulphur and oxygen potentials of this system, and hence the ratio p_{O_2}/p_{S_2}, remains constant at a given temperature. Therefore, the direction of the sulphur and oxygen transfer from one system to the other is determined by the composition of the Fe-melts.

Some of the results obtained are given in Figures 12–171 and 12–172 showing that when sulphur is transferred from the Mn-pellet to the Fe-melt through the ionic membrane, oxygen is transferred

in the opposite direction (Figure 12–171); Figure 12–172 shows the counter transfer in the reverse order. In both cases, the sum of the atomic concentrations of sulphur and oxygen in Mn-pellets and Fe-melts remains constant. The significant feature of these results is that although the sulphur and oxygen potentials of the system on the side of the Mn-pellet are much lower than those on the other side of the membrane, as a result of coupling, sulphur can be transferred from a low to a high chemical potential through an ionic membrane, when oxygen is transferred from a high to a low chemical potential and vice versa. The extent of this transfer depends entirely on the ratio p_{O_2}/p_{S_2} in the systems on either side of the membrane, but not on the individual partial pressures of oxygen and sulphur. When the ratios p_{O_2}/p_{S_2} for systems on either side of the membrane become equal, the sulphur and oxygen transfer ceases, i.e. partial equilibrium is established.

Assuming that the electrochemical processes of the sulphur-oxygen reaction at the gas-melt or gas-solid interfaces do not control the over-all counter transfer of sulphur and oxygen from one system to the other, then the rate controlling step may be that due to the interdiffusivity of sulphur and oxygen through the ionic membrane. Under the conditions of steady-state diffusion through thin liquid films, where stirring due to convection can be assumed to be negligibly small, Fick's first law may be used; thus,

$$\frac{dW_{S,O}}{dt} = -AD_{S,O}\frac{\Delta C_{S,O}}{l} \qquad (253)$$

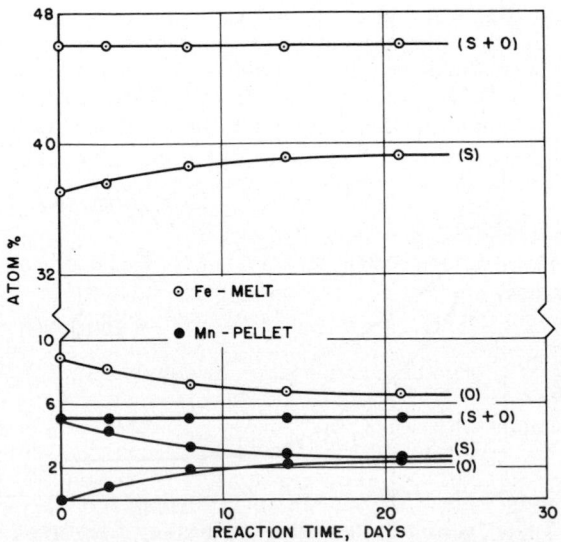

FIG. 12–171. Relationship showing the stoichiometric displacement of oxygen by sulphur and vice versa, in Fe-melt and Mn-pellet separated by an ionic membrane at 1127°C. (From Turkdogan and Grieveson[261].)

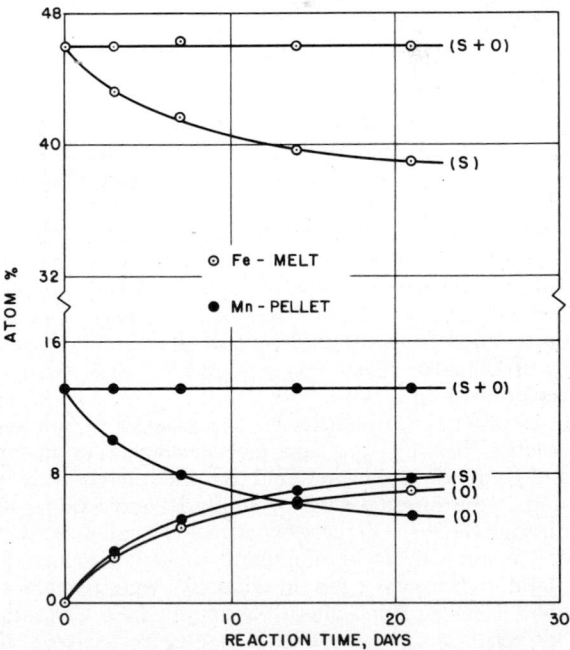

FIG. 12–172. Relationship showing the stoichiometric displacement of sulphur by oxygen, and vice versa, in Fe-melt and Mn-pellet separated by an ionic membrane at 1127°C. (From Turkdogan and Grieveson[261].)

where

$W_{S,O}$ = the total mass of sulphur or oxygen transferred through the membrane.

A = the surface area of the membrane

$D_{S,O}$ = the interdiffusivity of sulphide and oxide ions in the soda-glass membrane.

$\Delta C_{S,O}$ = the concentration difference of sulphur or oxygen across the membrane.

l = thickness of the membrane

Since the equivalent amounts of sulphur and oxygen transferred are the same, either W_S and ΔC_S or W_O and ΔC_O could be used. The concentration difference, ΔC_S, may be estimated from the ratios p_{O_2}/p_{S_2} on either side of the membrane, and the equilibrium constant k_S of reaction (252) for the soda-glass used as an ionic membrane, i.e.

$$k_S = (\%S)\left(\frac{p_{O_2}}{p_{S_2}}\right)^{\frac{1}{2}} = 6.457 \times 10^{-6} \quad (254)$$

For convenience the ratio $(p_{O_2}/p_{S_2})^{\frac{1}{2}}$ is denoted by r in subsequent equations (r_{Fe} and r_{Mn} referring to the iron and manganese sides respectively). The value of r for the Mn pellet is constant in all cases, and according to the thermodynamic data in Part 1 of this chapter, this may be taken as $r_{Mn} = 9.33 \times 10^{-5}$. The values of r_{Fe} for Fe melts are determined as discussed in Part III of this chapter. Therefore, the concentration difference ΔC_S, for any time of reaction can be estimated using the following equation

$$\Delta C_S = \frac{k_S}{(r_{Fe} - r_{Mn})} = \frac{k_S}{\Delta r} \quad (255)$$

Now, inserting the value of ΔC_S in equation (253) and writing it in logarithmic form, the following is obtained:

$$\log \frac{dW_S}{dt} = \log \frac{A k_S}{l} D_{S,O} - \log \Delta r \quad (256)$$

If the rate of the sulphur-oxygen reaction under consideration is controlled by the interdiffusion of sulphide and oxide ions in the membrane, then the plot of $\log dW_S/dt$ against $-\log \Delta r$ should give a straight line with a slope of one. In fact, this appears to be the case from the results plotted in Figure 12–173. Using the known values of $A = 1.29$ cm^2, $l = 0.07$ cm and $k_S = 6.457 \times 10^{-6}$, $D_{S,O}$ can be determined from the intercept of the line in Figure 12–163; this gives $D_{S,O} = (2.21 \pm 0.5) \times 10^{-7}$ cm^2/sec. at 1127°C.

In other recent studies on the kinetics of sulphur reaction between gas and molten slags, Turkdogan and Pearce[261] also have found that the rate controlling step is the interdiffusion of sulphide and oxide ions through the melt. In these experiments small quantities of calcium-silicate or aluminate melts, contained in platinum thimbles 1 cm. in diameter, were reacted at 1550°C in an atmosphere containing CO, CO$_2$ and 3% SO$_2$

$$(p_{CO}/p_{CO_2} = 3.0 \text{ and } p_{CO} + p_{CO_2} + p_{SO_2} = 1.0 \text{ atm.})$$

and the data on the rate of solution of sulphur in the melt were obtained until equilibrium was es-

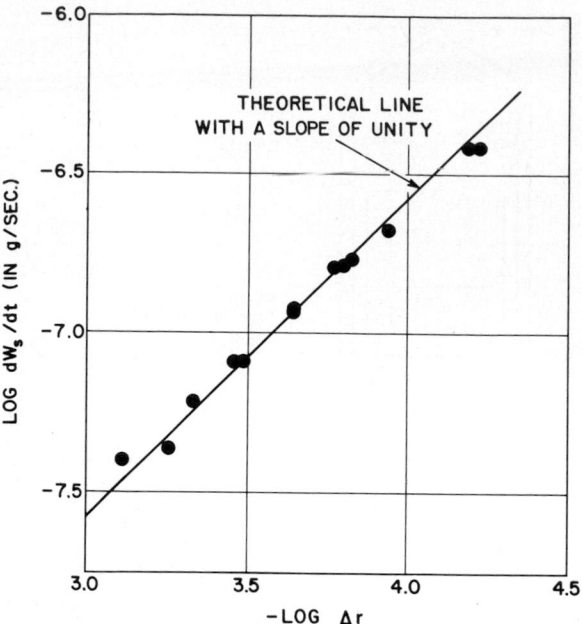

Fig. 12–173. Relationship between sulphur-oxygen counter-flux and driving force (see Equation 256). (From Turkdogan and Grieveson[261].)

tablished. In the initial experiments the slag samples were sectioned parallel to the gas-melt interface and sulphur concentration profiles were obtained. Some of the results obtained are given in Figure 12–174 for three reaction times. There is no doubt that the electrochemical process of reaction (252) is fast and, therefore, the melt at the interface quickly reaches equilibrium with sulphur and oxygen-bearing atmosphere, and so far as the bulk phase is concerned, the rate-controlling process is the diffusion of sulphur into the melt.

Since the melt in a platinum crucible is reacting with the atmosphere at one interface and, further-more, the sulphur content at the gas-melt interface is maintained constant (equilibrium value), the values of Dt/l^2 given in Table 12–VI of Part I of this chapter for fractional saturation of the melt can be

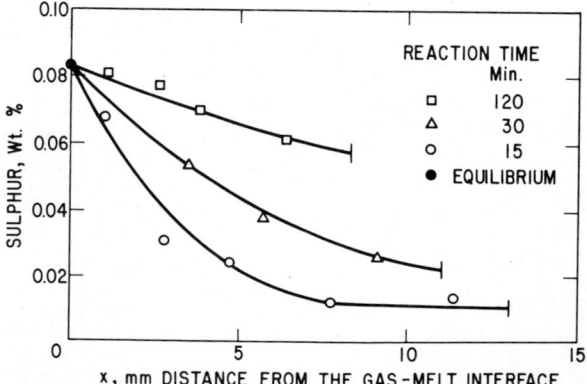

Fig. 12–174. Sulphur concentration profiles in calcium-silicate melts (46.7% CaO) reacted at 1550°C. with an atmosphere containing $p_{CO}/p_{CO_2} = 3.0$ and 3.0% SO$_2$ for 15, 30 and 120 mins. (From Turkdogan and Pearce[262].)

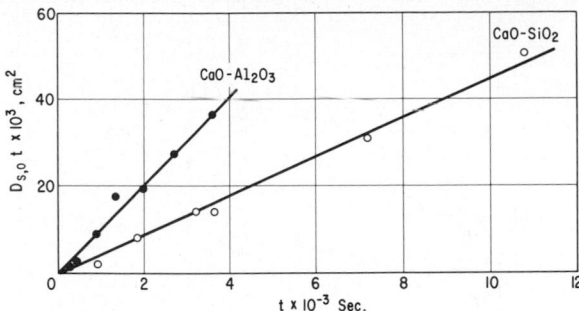

FIG. 12–175. Relation between $D_{S,0}t$ (obtained from fractional saturation of the melt with sulphur) and t, the time of reaction. (From Turkdogan and Pearce[262].)

used to evaluate the coefficient of interdiffusion. The values of Dt thus obtained for melts of known depth and fractional sulphur-saturation [= (mean % S – initial % S)/(surface % S – initial % S)], are plotted against the time of reaction in Figure 12–175. The slopes of the lines give the values of $D_{S,0}$ in silicate of aluminate melts, thus:

calcium silicate $D_{S,0} =$
    4.5×10^{-6} cm² per sec. at 1550°C
calcium aluminate $D_{S,0} =$
    1.0×10^{-5} cm² per sec. at 1550°C

When due allowance is made for the temperature difference, these values on interdiffusivities are comparable with that obtained from the previous work for 1127° C, using the ionic-membrane technique[261].

For further details on the kinetics of this reaction reference should be made to the papers cited above.

Sulphur Reaction in Metal-Slag Systems—Because of the ionic nature of molten slags and non-polar nature of metals, the transfer of an element from, for example, molten iron to a molten slag is accompanied by exchange of electrons between the reacting species. For instance, when sulphur is transferred from metal to slag electrons must be provided, thus

$$\underline{S}\,(\text{metal}) + 2\epsilon = S^{2-}\,(\text{slag}) \qquad (257)$$

Since electro-neutrality is maintained in the slag and metal, in the absence of an electric field across the slag-metal phases, the impurities in the metal become oxidized to provide the electrons required for reaction (257), thus

$$\underline{Fe}\,(\text{metal}) = Fe^{2+}\,(\text{slag}) + 2\epsilon \qquad (258a)$$
$$\underline{Mn}\,(\text{metal}) = Mn^{2+}\,(\text{slag}) + 2\epsilon \qquad (258b)$$
$$\underline{Al}\,(\text{metal}) = Al^{3+}\,(\text{slag}) + 3\epsilon \qquad (258c)$$
$$\underline{Si}\,(\text{metal}) = Si^{4+}\,(\text{slag}) + 4\epsilon \qquad (258d)$$
$$\underline{C}\,(\text{metal}) + O^{2-}\,(\text{slag}) = CO\,(\text{gas}) + 2\epsilon \qquad (258e)$$

It should of course be realized that although iron and manganese in the molten slag are present as cations, aluminum and silicon form anion complexes by interacting with oxide ions.

It follows from the above considerations that if sulphur is transferred from metal to slag at the rate n_S moles per sec., and this is accompanied only by the oxidation of silicon at the rate n_{Si} moles per sec., the two rates are related by $2n_S = 4n_{Si}$, to satisfy

the stoichiometric requirements. Since all the reactions in equations (258a, b, c, d and e) could accompany the sulphur reaction, the following general equation gives the rate of sulphur transfer in terms of rates of other elements from metal to slag:

$$2n_S = 2n_{Fe} + 2n_{Mn} + 3n_{Al} + 4n_{Si} + 2n_C \qquad (259)$$

In the above formulation, the sign of n is (+) for metal → slag transfer and (−) for slag → metal transfer.

The rates of these reactions were measured by Ramachandran, King and Grant[263] using carbon-saturated iron and calcium-alumino-silicate melts. The slag and metal was stirred, metal and slag samples were taken periodically and the amount of carbon monoxide evolved during the sulphur reaction was measured. As an example, the results of one of their experiments are given in Figure 12–176 where silicon and sulphur contents of iron, iron oxide and sulphur contents of slag and the amount of carbon monoxide evolved are plotted against the time of reaction. In the lower diagram, the change in iron, silicon contents, and carbon monoxide evolution are given in terms of sulphur equivalence and it is seen that the sulphur transferred from metal to slag calculated from n_{Fe}, n_{Si} and n_{CO} as in equation (259),

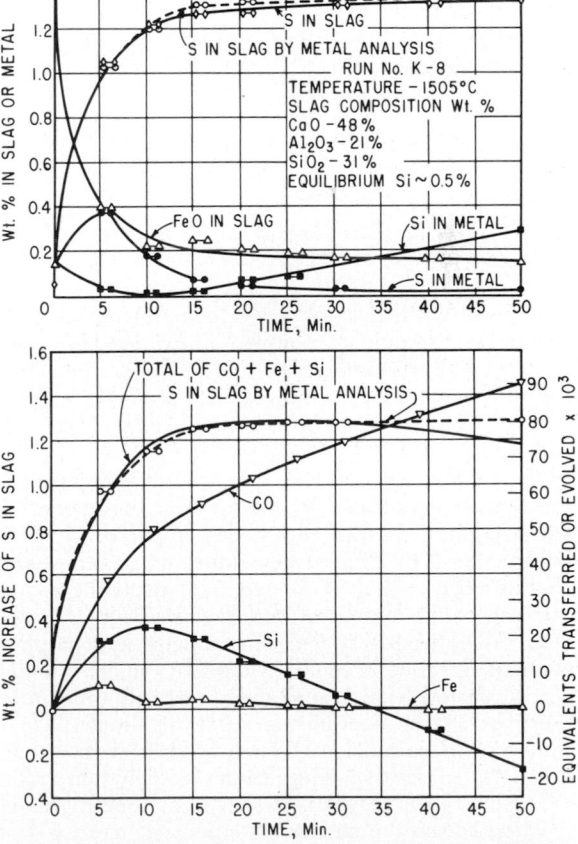

FIG. 12–176. Sulphur, iron and silicon transfer and CO evolution. (Above) compositions in weight per cent. (Below) chemical equivalents. (From Ramachandran, King and Grant[263].)

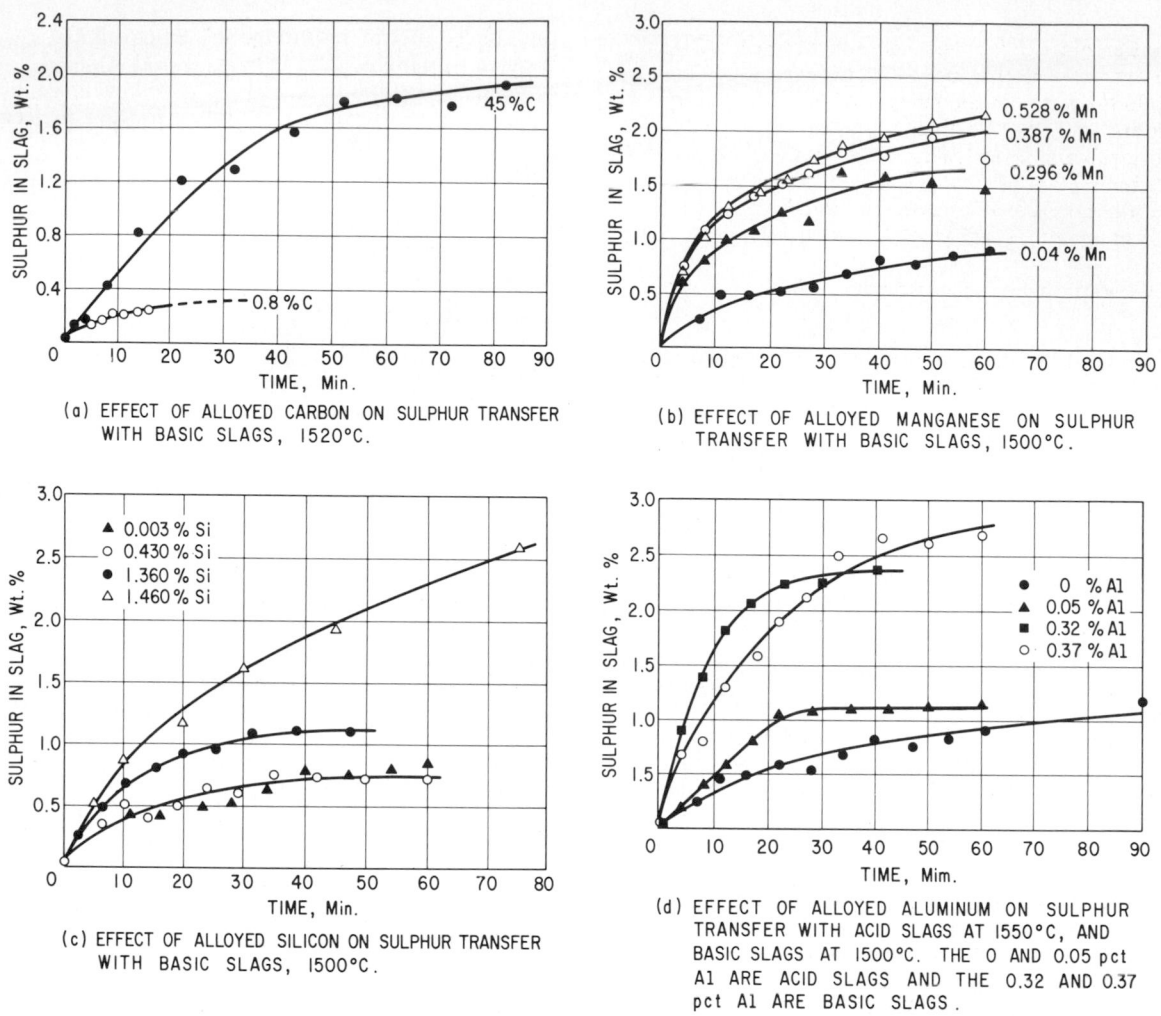

(a) EFFECT OF ALLOYED CARBON ON SULPHUR TRANSFER WITH BASIC SLAGS, 1520°C.

(b) EFFECT OF ALLOYED MANGANESE ON SULPHUR TRANSFER WITH BASIC SLAGS, 1500°C.

(c) EFFECT OF ALLOYED SILICON ON SULPHUR TRANSFER WITH BASIC SLAGS, 1500°C.

(d) EFFECT OF ALLOYED ALUMINUM ON SULPHUR TRANSFER WITH ACID SLAGS AT 1550°C, AND BASIC SLAGS AT 1500°C. THE 0 AND 0.05 pct Al ARE ACID SLAGS AND THE 0.32 AND 0.37 pct Al ARE BASIC SLAGS.

FIG. 12–177. Effect of alloying elements on the rate of desulphurization of iron. The data in Figures b, c and d are for carbon-saturated iron. (From Goldman, Derge and Philbrook[264].)

agree well with those observed experimentally. This is another example of coupled reactions. However, in view of the complexity of the system studied, this coupling cannot be formulated by a simple expression, except that given in equation (259) in a general form.

The complexity of the kinetics of simultaneous reactions is manifested by considering the maximum and minimum on iron and silicon upper diagram in Figure 12–176. The carbon-saturated iron initially contains 0.16 per cent Si and 1.39 per cent S and the iron oxide content of the slag is about 0.05 per cent FeO. In this system only silicon and sulphur contents are out of equilibrium, i.e. silicon should be transferred from slag to metal until its concentration reaches the equilibrium value of about 0.5 per cent Si and sulphur to be removed from metal to the slag until the equilibrium distribution ratio (S)/[S] $\simeq$ 70 is reached. However, as the slag-metal reaction starts, the sulphur reaction occurs at a fast rate and initially it is accompanied by the oxidation of iron and silicon, although the ultimate equilibrium conditions indicate that iron should not have taken part in the reaction and silicon should have been

reduced from the slag. This apparent anomaly is attributed to the higher rate of reaction (257) as compared with reaction (258c). That is, the rate of oxidation of carbon is not fast enough to maintain the electron requirements for the rapid sulphur reaction (257) and, therefore, oxidation of iron and silicon is forced to occur in the direction opposite to ultimate approach to equilibrium. After about 5 to 10 minutes of reaction time, the rate of sulphur transfer is lowered appreciably and the electrons provided by the carbon-reaction (258e) are sufficient for this reaction and, consequently, iron and silicon reaction are reversed in the direction of approach to equilibrium.

From the foregoing discussion it would follow that if the initial concentrations of manganese, silicon, aluminum, etc. of the metal are higher than the ultimate equilibrium values for a given metal and slag system, the rate of desulphurization of the metal should increase. In fact, this conclusion is borne out by the results of Goldman, Derge and Philbrook[264], some of which are given in Figure 12–177. Similarly, rapid desulphurization achieved by injecting suitable reducing agents into the metal under a reducing slag in the electric-furnace process (Figure 12–167) is in accord with the above conclusions.

In the study of the kinetics of reactions, serious considerations must be given to partial equilibria between certain species of the heterogeneous system where a number of reactions may occur simultaneously. The simultaneous oxidation and sulphurization of a ferrous silicate melt by a gaseous phase is shown in Figure

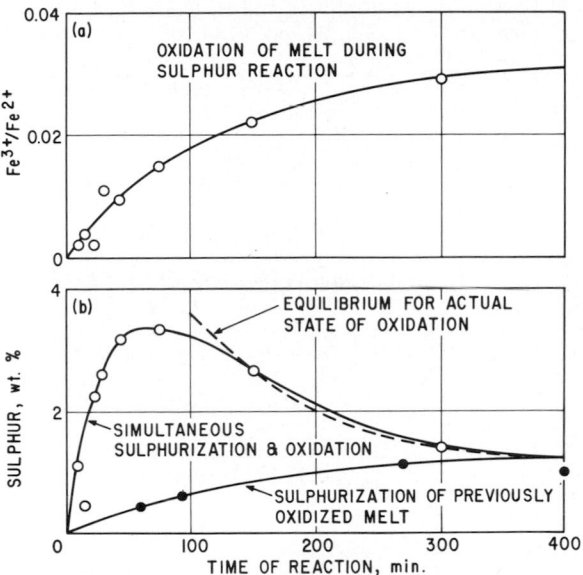

FIG. 12–178. (a) Oxidation and (b) sulphurization of iron-silicate melts (40% SiO_2) in a CO-CO_2-SO_2 atmosphere at 1550°C (ingoing gas composition p_{CO}/p_{CO_2} = 3.0 and p_{SO_2} = 0.028 atm.). (From Bills and Turkdogan[265].)

12–178 from data of Bills and Turkdogan[265]. Initially, sulphurization occurs rapidly whilst the oxidation of divalent iron to the trivalent state progresses more slowly, thus

Fast reaction: $\frac{1}{2} S_2 + CO + O^{2-} \rightarrow S^{2-} + CO_2$

$$(260)$$

Slow reaction: $2 Fe^{2+} + CO_2 \rightarrow 2 Fe^{3+} + O^{2-} + CO$ $\qquad (261)$

Since reaction (260) is faster than reaction (261), the ferrous silicate melt initially picks up sulphur from the gas very rapidly, to an extent in excess of the ultimate equilibrium value. As reactions (260) and (261) proceed at different rates, a state is eventually reached satisfying the following equilibrium

$$\frac{1}{2} S_2 + 2 Fe^{2+} = 2 Fe^{3+} + S^{2-} \qquad (262)$$

for which the equilibrium constant is

$$K_{Fe,S} = \frac{\% Fe^{3+}}{\% Fe^{2+}} \cdot \frac{(\% S)}{\sqrt{p_{S_2}}} \qquad (263)$$

However, since the system as a whole has not reached equilibrium, equations (262) and (263) are for partial equilibrium. As the oxidation of iron continues, the ratio Fe^{3+}/Fe^{2+} increases and since p_{S_2} is maintained constant, the sulphur content of the melt must decrease as dictated by the partial equilibrium. In fact the experimental results in Figure 12–178b follow the curve derived from equation (263). When the ferrous silicate melt is first equilibrated with the prevailing oxygen partial pressure of the atmosphere, the sulphurization proceeds in a normal manner as shown by the lower curve in Figure 12–178b.

REFERENCES

1. G. R. Zellars, S. L. Payne, J. P. Morris and R. L. Kipp: Trans. AIME, 1959, vol. 215, pp. 181-185.
2. J. Chipman, J. C. Fulton, N. Gokcen and G. R. Caskey: Acta Met. 1954, vol. 2, pp. 439-450.
3. J. P. Morris and G. R. Zellars: Trans. AIME, 1956, vol. 206, pp. 1086-1090.
4. J. Chipman and J. F. Elliott: "Electric Furnace Steelmaking," Chapter 16, (in press).
5. L. S. Darken and R. W. Gurry: "Physical Chemistry of Metals," McGraw-Hill, New York, 1953.
6. C. Wagner: "Thermodynamics of Alloys," Addison-Wesley Press, Mass., 1952.
7. L. S. Darken: J. Amer. Chem. Soc., 1950, vol. 72, pp. 2909-2914.
8. R. Schuhmann: Acta Met. 1955, vol. 3, 219-226.
9. J. P. Morris and R. C. Buehl: Trans. AIME, 1950, vol. 188, pp. 317-322.
10. A. Smits: Proc. Acad. Sci. Amsterdam, 1916, vol. 18, p. 793-807.
11. F. A. H. Schreinemakers: Proc. Acad. Sci. Amsterdam, 1916, vol. 18, pp. 116-126.
12. G. W. Morey and E. D. Williamson: J. Amer. Chem. Soc., 1918, vol. 40, pp. 59-84.
13. L. S. Darken: J. Am. Chem. Soc., 1948, vol. 70, pp. 2046-2053.
14. E. T. Turkdogan: Trans. AIME, 1961, vol. 221, pp. 546-553.
15. E. D. Williamson and L. H. Adams: Phys. Rev., 1919, vol. 14, Ser. II, pp. 99-114.

16. D. H. Andrews and J. Johnston: J. Am. Chem. Soc., 1924, vol. 46, pp. 640-650.
17. B. Serin and R. T. Ellickson: J. Chem. Phys. 1941, vol. 9, pp. 742-747.
18. W. Jost: "Diffusion in Solids, Liquids, Gases," Academic Press Inc., New York, 1960.
19. R. W. Gurry: Trans. AIME, 1942, vol. 150, pp. 172-182.
20. C. Matano: Japan. J. Physics, 1933, vol. 8, pp. 109-113.
21. A. D. Smigelskas and E. O. Kirkendall: Trans. AIME, 1947, vol. 171, pp. 130-134.
22. L. S. Darken: Trans. AIME, 1948, vol. 175, pp. 184-194
23. A. Einstein: Ann. Phys., 1905, (4), vol. 17, pp. 549-560.
24. L. S. Darken: Trans. AIME, 1949, vol. 180, pp. 430-438.
25. L. S. Darken: "Atom Movements," pp. 1-25, ASM, Cleveland, 1950.
26. F. N. Rhines and R. F. Mehl: Trans. AIME, 1938, vol. 128, pp. 185-221.
27. H. Eyring: J. Chem. Phys. 1935, vol. 3, pp. 107-115.
28. S. Glasstone, K. J. Laidler and H. Eyring: "The Theory of Rate Processes," McGraw Hill, N.Y., 1941.
29. E. R. G. Eckert and R. M. Drake: "Heat and Mass Transfer," McGraw-Hill, New York, 1959.
30. R. B. Bird, W. E. Stewart and E. N. Lightfoot: "Transport Phenomena," John Wiley, N.Y., 1960.

31. W. G. Whitman: Chemical and Metallurgical Engineering, 1923, vol. 29, pp. 146-148.

32. W. Hume-Rothery: "The Structure of Metals and Alloys," Institute of Metals, London (Monograph No. 1), 2nd edit., 1944.

33. G. N. Lewis: "Valence and the Structure of Atoms and Molecules," The Chemical Catalog Co., New York, 1923.

34. L. Pauling: "The Nature of the Chemical Bond and the Structure of Molecules and Crystals," Cornell University Press, 1939; J. Am. Chem. Soc., 1947, vol. 69, pp. 542-553; Proc. Roy. Soc., 1949, vol. A196, pp. 343-362.

35. V. M. Goldschmidt: Z. Physikal Chem., 1928, vol. 133, pp. 397-419.

36. Z. S. Basinski, W. Hume-Rothery and A. L. Sutton: Proc. Royal Soc., 1955, vol. A229, pp. 459-467.

37. A. Sieverts: Z. Physik Chem., 1911, vol. 77, pp. 591-613.

38. Von W. Geller and T. Sun: Arch. Eisenhutten., 1950, vol. 21, pp. 423-430.

39. L. S. Darken and R. P. Smith: Corrosion, 1949, vol. 5, pp. 1-16.

40. M. L. Hill and E. W. Johnson: Trans. AIME, 1959, vol. 215, pp. 717-725.

41. H. H. Podgruski: Trans. AIME, 1961, vol. 221, pp. 389-394.

42. M. Weinstein and J. F. Elliott: Trans. Met. Soc. AIME, 1963, vol. 227, pp. 382-393.

43. T. Busch and R. A. Dodd: Trans. AIME, 1960, vol. 218, pp. 488-490.

44. L. S. Darken and R. W. Gurry: "Physical Chemistry of Metals," McGraw-Hill, New York, 1953.

45. M. G. Benz and J. F. Elliott: Trans. AIME, 1961, vol. 221, pp. 323-331.

46. C. Wells: Trans. ASM, 1938, vol. 26, pp. 289-344; author's closure pp. 351-357.

47. C. A. Wert: Trans. AIME, 1950, vol. 188, pp. 1242-1244.

48. R. P. Smith: Trans. Met. Soc. AIME, 1962, vol. 224, pp. 105-111.

49. F. von Neumann and H. Schenck: Arch. Eisenhüttenw., 1959, vol. 30, pp. 477-483.

50. E. T. Turkdogan and L. E. Leake: J. Iron and Steel Inst., 1955, vol. 179, pp. 39-43.

51. E. T. Turkdogan, R. A. Hancock: J. Iron and Steel Inst., 1955, vol. 179, pp. 155-159; 1956, vol. 183, pp. 69-72.

52. J. Chipman, R. M. Alfred, L. W. Gott, R. B. Small, D. M. Wilson, C. N. Thomson, D. L. Guernsey and J. C. Fulton: Trans. ASM, 1952, vol. 44, pp. 1215-1230.

53. J. Chipman and T. P. Floridis: Acta Met., 1955, vol. 3, pp. 456-459.

54. N. R. Griffing, W. D. Forgeng and G. W. Healy: Trans. Met. Soc., AIME, 1962, vol. 224, pp. 148-159.

55. R. P. Smith: J. Am. Chem. Soc., 1946, vol. 68, pp. 1163-1175.

56. R. P. Smith: Trans. AIME, 1960, vol. 218, pp. 62-64.

57. R. P. Smith: J. Am. Chem. Soc., 1948, vol. 70, pp. 2724-2729.

58. R. D. Richardson and W. E. Dennis: Trans. Faraday Soc., 1953, vol. 49, pp. 171-180.

59. K. Sanbongi and M. Ohtani: Sci. Rept. Res. Inst. Tohuku Univ., Ser. A, 1953, vol. 5, pp. 263-270.

60. E. T. Turkdogan, L. E. Leake and C. R. Masson: Acta Met., 1956, vol. 4, pp. 396-406.

61. A. Rist and J. Chipman: Rev. Met., 1956, vol. 53, pp. 796-807.

62. T. Fuwa and J. Chipman: Trans. AIME, 1959, vol. 215, pp. 708-716.

63. C. Wagner: "Thermodynamics of Alloys," Addison-Wesley Press, Cambridge, Mass. 1952.

64. J. D. Fast atnd M. B. Verrijp: J. Iron and Steel Inst., 1955, vol. 180, pp. 337-343.

65. A. Sieverts, G. Zapf and H. Maritz: Z. phys. Chemie, 1938, vol. 183, pp. 19-37.

66. L. S. Darken, R. P. Smith and C. W. Filer: Trans. AIME, 1951, vol. 191, pp. 1174-1179.

67. N. S. Corney and E. T. Turkdogan: J. Iron and Steel Inst., 1955, vol. 180, pp. 344-348.

68. H. Schenck, M. Frohberg and H. Graf: Arch. Eisenhuttenw., 1958, vol. 29, pp. 673-676; 1959, vol. 30, p. 533-537.

69. R. D. Pehlke and J. F. Elliott: Trans. AIME, 1960, vol. 218, pp. 1088-1101.

70. H. A. Wriedt and L. S. Darken: to be published; some preliminary data presented by L. S. Darken in Proc. Nat. Phys. Lab. Symposium No. 9, June 1958, vol. 2, 4G.

71. E. T. Turkdogan and S. Ignatowicz: J. Iron and Steel Inst., 1957, vol. 185, pp. 200-206.

72. E. T. Turkdogan and S. Ignatowicz: J. Iron and Steel Inst., 1958, vol. 188, pp. 242-247; 1961, vol. 199, pp. 287-296.

73. H. A. Wriedt and O. D. Gonzalez: Trans. AIME, 1961, vol. 221, pp. 532-535.

74. M. Hansen and K. Anderko: "Constitution of Binary Alloys," 2nd ed., McGraw-Hill, New York, 1958.

75. L. S. Darken and R. W. Gurry: J. Am. Chem. Soc., 1945, vol. 67, pp. 1398-1412; 1946, vol. 68, pp. 798-816.

76. J. Chipman and K. L. Fetters: Trans. ASM, 1941, vol. 29, pp. 953-967.

77. C. R. Taylor and J. Chipman: Trans. AIME, 1943, vol. 154, pp. 228-245.

78. M. N. Dastur and J. Chipman: Trans. AIME, 1949, vol. 185, pp. 441-445.

79. J. A. Kitchener, J. O'M. Bockris, M. Gleiser, and J. W. Evans: Trans. Faraday Sov., 1952, vol. 48, pp. 995-997.

80. R. Sifferlen: Compt. Rend., 1955, vol. 240, pp. 2526-2528; 1957, vol. 244, pp. 1192-1193.

81. J. Chipman and J. F. Elliott: Chapter 16 of "Electric Furnace Steelmaking," vol. II, edited by C. E. Sims, Interscience Pub., New York, 1963.

82. T. Rosenquist and B. L. Dunicz: Trans. AIME, 1952, vol. 194, pp. 604-608; J. Iron and Steel Inst., 1954, vol. 176, pp. 37-57.

83. E. T. Turkdogan, S. Ignatowicz and J. Pearson: J. Iron and Steel Inst., 1955, vol. 180, pp. 349-354.

84. C. W. Sherman, H. I. Elvander and J. Chipman: Trans. AIME, 1950, vol. 188, pp. 334-340.

85. C. W. Sherman and J. Chipman: Trans. AIME, 1952, vol. 194, pp. 597-602.

86. D. C. Hilty and W. Crafts: Trans. AIME, 1952, vol. 194, pp. 1307-1312.

87. S. Bog and T. Rosenquist: Proc. Nat. Phys. Lab., Symposium No. 9, June 1958, vol. 2, 6B.

88. E. W. Dewing and F. D. Richardson: J. Iron and Steel Inst., 1960, vol. 194, pp. 446-450.

89. E. T. Turkdogan and L. S. Darken: Trans. AIME, 1961, vol. 221, pp. 464-474.

90. J. Chipman, J. C. Fulton, N. Gokcen and G. R. Caskey: Acta Met., 1954, vol. 2, pp. 439-450.

91. E. T. Turkdogan, P. Grieveson and J. F. Beisler: Trans. Met. Soc. AIME (to be published in 1963 or 1964).

92. R. E. Grace and G. Derge: Trans. AIME, 1957, vol. 212, pp. 331-337.

93. T. Saito, Y. Kawai, K. Maruya and M. Maki: in "Physical Chemistry of Process Metallurgy," ed. by

G. R. St. Pierre, Interscience Pub., New York, 1961, vol. 1, pp. 523-533. (AIME Metallurgical Soc. Conference, vol. 7).

94. D. W. Morgan and J. A. Kitchener: Trans. Faraday Soc., 1954, vol. 50, pp. 51-60.

95. M. Paschke and A. Hauttmann: Arch. Eisenhuttenw., 1935, vol. 9, pp. 305-309.

96. L. Yang, M. T. Simnad and G. Derge: Trans. AIME, 1956, vol. 206, pp. 1577-1580.

97. G. Cavalier: Proc. Nat. Phys. Lab., No. 9, June 1958, vol. 2, 4D.

98. R. N. Barfield and J. A. Kitchener: J. Iron and Steel Inst., 1955, vol. 180, pp. 324-329.

99. Third Report of the Steel Castings Research Committee: Iron and Steel Inst., Spec. Rept. 1938, No. 23, pp. 45-60.

100. "Liquid-Metals Handbook": edited by R. N. Lyon (2nd ed.) U. S. Atomic Energy Commission, Department Navy, Washington, D. C., 1952.

101. L.-D. Lucas: Compt. Rend. 1960, vol. 250, pp. 1850-1852.

102. E. Widawski and F. Sauerwald: Z. anorg. u. allg. Chem., 1930, vol. 192, pp. 145-160.

103. G. Worth and G. R. St. Pierre: to be published in Trans. AIME.

104. L.-D. Lucas: Compt. Rend., 1959, vol. 248, pp. 2336-2338.

105. W. H. Zachariasen: J. Am. Chem. Soc., 1932, vol. 54, pp. 3841-3851; Ind. Chem. Phys., 1935, vol. 1, pp. 162-163.

106. B. E. Warren: Z. Krist., 1933, vol. 86, pp. 349-358; Phys. Rev., 1934, vol. 45, pp. 657-661; J. Am. Ceram. Soc., 1934, vol. 17, pp. 249-254; ibid, 1935, vol. 18, pp. 269-276.

107a. B. E. Warren: J. Appl. Phys., 1937, vol. 8, pp. 645-655.
b. B. E. Warren and J. Biscoe: J. Am. Ceram. Soc., 1938, vol. 21, pp. 259-265 and 287-293.
c. B. E. Warren and A. G. Pincus: J. Am. Ceram. Soc., 1940, vol. 23, pp. 301-304.
d. J. Biscoe, A. G. Pincus and B. E. Warren: J. Am. Ceram. Soc., 1941, vol. 24, pp. 116-119.

108. E. M. Levin, H. F. McMurdie and F. P. hall: "Phase Diagrams for Ceramists", Am. Ceram. Soc., Part I, 1956 and Part II, 1959.

109. W. A. Fischer and J. Fleischer: Arch. Eisenhuttenw., 1961, vol. 32, pp. 1-10.

110. P. K. Foster and A. J. E. Welch: Trans. Faraday Soc., 1956, vol. 52, pp. 1626-1635.

111. O. W. Florke: Naturwissen., 1956, vol. 43, pp. 419-420.

112. M. L. Keith and O. F. Tuttle: Am. J. Sci., 1952, "Bowen Volume" Part 1, pp. 203-252.

113. S. B. Holmquist: J. Am. Ceram. Soc., 1961, vol. 44, pp. 82-86.

114. N. L. Bowen and J. W. Greig: J. Am. Ceram. Soc., 1924, vol. 7, pp. 238-254.

115. J. F. Schairer: J. Am. Ceram. Soc., 1942, vol. 25, pp. 241-274.

116. S. Aramaki and R. Roy: Nature, 1959, vol. 184, pp. 631-632.

117. J. H. Welch: Nature, 1960, vol. 186, pp. 545-546.

118. G. A. Rankin and F. E. Wright: Am. J. Sci., 1915, vol. 39, Ser. 4, pp. 1-79.

119. M. A. Bredig: J. Am. Ceram. Soc., 1950, vol. 33, pp. 188-192.

120. A. Muan and E. F. Osborn: Year Book of Am. Iron and Steel Inst., 1951, pp. 325-359.

121. J. H. Welch and W. Gutt: J. Am. Ceram. Soc., 1959, vol. 42, pp. 11-15.

122. N. L. Bowen and J. F. Schairer: Am. J. Sci., 1932, 5th Ser., vol. 24, pp. 177-213.

123. R. Schuhmann and P. J. Ensio: Trans. AIME, 1951, vol. 191, pp. 401-411.

124. E. J. Michal and R. Schuhmann: Trans. AIME, 1952, vol. 194, pp. 723-728.

125. E. T. Turkdogan and Patricia M. Bills: J. Iron and Steel Inst., 1957, vol. 186, pp. 329-339.

126. N. L. Bowen and O. Andersen Am. J. Sci., 1914, 4th Ser., vol. 37, pp. 487-500.

127. J. W. Greig: Am. J. Sci., 1927, 5th Ser., vol. 13, pp. 133-154.

128. C. H. Herty, Jr.: Metals and Alloys, 1930, vol. 1, pp. 883-889.

129. J. White, D. Howat and R. Hay: J. Royal Tech. Coll. (Glasgow), 1934, vol. 3, pp. 231-240.

130. F. P. Glasser: Am. J. Sci., 1958, 5th Ser., vol. 256, pp. 398-412.

131. G. A. Rankin and F. E. Wright: Am. J. Sci., 4th Ser., 1915, vol. 39, pp. 1-79.

132. W. Büssem and A. Eitel: Z. Krist., 1936, vol. 95, pp. 175-188.

133. B. Tavasci: Tonind. Ztg., 1937, vol. 61, pp. 717-719, 729-731.

134a. J. R. Goldsmith: J. Geol. 1948, vol. 56, pp. 80-81.
134b. N. E. Filonenko and I. V. Lavrov: J. Appl. Chem. (USSR), 1950, vol. 23, pp. 1040-1046.

135. R. B. Sosman and H. E. Merwin: J. Wash. Acad. Sci., 1916, vol. 6, pp. 532-537.

136. J. O. Edstrom: Jernkont. Ann., 1956, vol. 140, pp. 101-115.

137. M. A. Swayze: Am. J. Sci., 1946, 5th Ser., vol. 244, pp. 1-30.

138. B. Phillips and A. Muan: J. Am. Ceram. Soc., 1958, vol. 41, pp. 445-454.

139. Von G. Tromel, H. J. Harkort and W. Hotop: Z. anorg. allgem. Chem., 1948, vol. 256, pp. 253-272.

140. Von G. Tromel and W. Fix: Arch. Eisenhuttenw., 1961, vol. 32, pp. 209-212.

141. J. R. Rait: "Basic Refractories," Iliffe & Sons Ltd., London, 1950.

142. H. J. Chesters: "Steel Plant Refractories," United Steel Company, Ltd., Sheffield, 1957.

143. F. H. Norton: "Refractories," McGraw-Hill, New York, 1949.

144. R. W. Ricker and E. F. Osborn: J. Am. Ceram. Soc., 1954, vol. 37, pp. 133-139.

145. E. F. Osborn, R. C. De Vries, K. H. Gee and H. M. Kraner: Trans. AIME, 1954, vol. 200, pp. 33-45.

146. E. T. Turkdogan: Trans. AIME, 1961, vol. 221, pp. 1090-1095.

147. E. T. Turkdogan: Trans. Met. Soc., AIME, 1962, vol. 224, pp. 294-298.

148. K. P. Abraham, M. W. Davies and F. D. Richardson: J. Iron and Steel Inst., 1960, vol. 196, pp. 82-89.

149. D. A. R. Kay and J. Taylor: Trans. Faraday Soc., 1960, vol. 56, pp. 1372-1386.

150. R. A. Sharma and F. D. Richardson: J. Iron and Steel Inst., 1961, vol. 198, pp. 386-390.

151. P. K. Foster and A. J. E. Welch: Trans. Faraday Soc., 1956, vol. 52, pp. 1636-1642.

152. J. Chipman, J. B. Gero and T. B. Winkler: Trans. AIME, 1950, vol. 188, pp. 341-345.

153. C. R. Taylor and J. Chipman: Trans. AIME, 1943, vol. 154, pp. 228-247.

154. E. T. Turkdogan and J. Pearson: J. Iron and Steel Inst., 1953, vol. 173, pp. 217-223.

155. E. W. Dewing and F. D. Richardson: J. Iron and Steel Inst., 1960, vol. 194, pp. 446-450.

156. E. T. Turkdogan and L. S. Darken: Trans. AIME, 1961, vol. 221, pp. 464-474.

157. P. Grieveson and E. T. Turkdogan: Trans. Met. Soc., AIME, 1962, vol. 224, pp. 1086-1093.

158. K. P. Abraham, M. W. Davies and F. D. Richardson: J. Iron and Steel Inst., 1960, vol. 196, pp. 309-312.

159. H. Towers and J. Chipman: Trans. AIME, 1957, vol. 209, pp. 769-773.

160. J. Henderson, L. Yang and G. Derge: Trans. AIME, 1961, vol. 221, pp. 56-60.

161. T. Saito and Y. Kawai: Sci. Rept. Res. Inst. Tohuku University, 1953, vol. 45, pp. 460-468.

162. H. Towers, M. Paris and J. Chipman: Trans. AIME, 1953, vol. 197, pp. 1455-1458.

163. T. Saito and K. Maruya: Sci. Rept. Res. Inst., Tohuku Univ., Ser. A, 1958, vol. 10, pp. 306-314.

164. P. J. Koros and T. B. King: Trans. Met. Soc., AIME, 1962, vol. 224, pp. 299-306.

165. J. R. Rait: Trans. Brit. Ceram. Soc., 1941, vol. 40, pp. 157-169.

166. J. S. Machin and T. B. Yee: J. Am. Ceram. Soc., 1948, vol. 31, pp. 200-204.

167. P. Kozakevitch: "Physical Chemistry of Process Metallurgy," pp. 97-116, Interscience Pub., New York, 1961.

168. J. S. Machin and D. L. Hanna: J. Am. Ceram. Soc., 1945, vol. 28, pp. 310-316.

169. J. S. Machin, T. B. Yee and D. L. Hanna: J. Am. Ceram. Soc., 1952, vol. 35, pp. 322-325.

170. E. T. Turkdogan and Patricia M. Bills: Am. Ceram. Soc. Bull., 1960, vol. 39, pp. 682-687.

171. J. O'M. Bockris and D. C. Lowe: Proc. Royal Soc., 1954, vol. A226, pp. 423-435.

172. P. Kozakevitch: Rev. de Metallurgie, 1954, vol. 51, pp. 569-587.

173. P. Kozakevitch: Rev. de Metallurgie, 1950, vol. 47, pp. 201-210.

174. P. Rontgen, H. Winterhager and R. Kammel: Zeit. Erzberg u Metallhuttenw., 1960, vol. 13, pp. 363-373; Brit. Iron Steel Trans. Service, No. BISI 2475.

175. J. O'M. Bockris, J. W. Tonlinson and J. L. White: Trans. Faraday Soc., 1956, vol. 52, pp. 299-310.

176. J. W. Tomlinson, M. S. R. Heynes and J. O'M. Bockris: Trans. Faraday Soc., 1958, vol. 54, pp. 1822-1833.

177. L. R. Barrett and A. G. Thomas: Trans. Soc. Glass Tech., 1959, vol. 43, pp. 179-190.

178. J. Henderson, R. G. Hudson, R. G. Ward and G. Derge: Trans. AIME, 1961, vol. 221, pp. 807-811.

179. T. B. King: J. Soc. Glass Tech., 1951, vol. 35, pp. 241-259T.

180. P. Kozakevitch: Rev. de Metallurgie, 1949, vol. 46, pp. 505-516, 572-582.

181. R. E. Boni and G. Derge: Trans. AIME, 1956, vol. 206, pp. 59-64.

182. L. Shartsis and S. Spinner: J. Research, NBS, 1951, vol. 46, pp. 385-390.

183. P. Kozakevitch and G. Urbain: "Physical Chemistry of Steelmaking," pp. 27-33, Proc. of the Conference at Endicott House, Mass., U.S.A., May 1956.

184. T. F. Young and W. D. Harkins: "Handbook of Chemistry and Physics," 42nd Edition, 1960-1961, pp. 2175-2193, Chem. Rubber Pub. Co., Cleveland.

185. T. B. King: "Physical Chemistry of Melts," Institution of Mining and Metallurgy, London, 1953, pp. 35-41.

186. W. D. Kingery: "Physical Chemistry of Steelmaking," pp. 33-34, Proc. Conference at Endicott House, Mass., U.S.A., May, 1956.

187. H. J. T. Ellingham: J. Soc. Chem. Ind., 1944, vol. 63, pp. 125-133.

188. F. D. Richardson and J. H. E. Jeffes: J. Iron and Steel Inst., 1948, vol. 160, pp. 261-270.

189. J. P. Coughlin: Bureau of Mines, Bull. 542, U. S. Government Printing Office, Washington, 1954.

190. "Reports upon Blast Furnace Field Tests": Iron and Steel Institute, Special Report No. 18, 1937.

191. C. F. Goodeve: Discussions of the Faraday Soc., 1948, vol. 4, pp. 9-23.

192. F. D. Richardson and J. H. E. Jeffes: J. Iron and Steel Inst., 1949, vol. 163, pp. 397-420.

193a. E. T. Turkdogan and P. M. Bills: J. Iron and Steel Inst., 1958, vol. 188, pp. 143-153.

193b. T. E. Brower and B. M. Larsen: Trans. AIME, 1947, vol. 172, pp. 164-174.

194. W. M. McKewan: Trans. AIME, 1958, vol. 212, pp. 791-793.

195. W. M. McKewan: Trans. AIME, 1960, vol. 218, pp. 2-6.

196. W. M. McKewan: Trans. AIME, 1961, vol. 221, pp. 140-145.

197. W. M. McKewan: Trans. Met. Soc. AIME, 1962, vol. 224, pp. 2-5.

198. W. M. McKewan: Trans. Met. Soc. AIME, 1962, vol. 224, pp. 387-393.

199. J. M. Quets, M. E. Wadsworth and J. R. Lewis: Trans. AIME, 1960, vol. 218, pp. 545-550.

200. W. O. Philbrook and L. D. Kirkbride: Trans. AIME, 1956, vol. 206, pp. 351-356.

201. C. Wagner: "The Physical Chemistry of Steelmaking," M.I.T. Symposium, 1956, pp. 237-251.

202. M. H. Davies, M. T. Simnad and C. E. Birchenall: Trans. AIME, 1951, vol. 191, pp. 889-896.

203. L. Himmel, R. F. Mehl and C. E. Birchenall: Trans. AIME, 1953, vol. 197, pp. 827-843.

204. C. Wagner: "Atomic Movements," pp. 153-173, ASM, 1950; Z. phys. Chemie., 1933, vol. B21, pp. 25-41.

205. W. W. Smeltzer: Trans. AIME, 1960, vol. 218, pp. 674-681.

206. E. T. Turkdogan and D. J. Goodwin: J. Iron and Steel Inst., 1957, vol. 185, p. 104.

207. J. Gadsby, F. J. Long, P. Slightholm and K. W. Sykes: Proc. Royal Soc., 1948, vol. A193, pp. 357-376.

208. F. J. Long and K. W. Sykes: Proc. Royal Soc., 1948, vol. A193, pp. 377-399.

209. E. W. Thiele: Ind. Eng. Chem. 1939, vol. 31, pp. 916-920.

210. A. Wheeler: Advances in Catalysis, 1951; vol. 3, pp. 249-327; "Catalysis," vol. 2, pp. 105-165, Reinhold, New York, 1955.

211. P. B. Weisz and C. D. Prater: Advances in Catalysis, 1954, vol. 6, pp. 143-196.

212. D. A. Frank-Kamenetskii: "Diffusion and Heat Exchange in Chemical Kinetics," Princeton University Press, 1955.

213. R. O. Grisdale: J. Appl. Phys., 1953, vol. 24, pp. 1288-1296.

214. W. R. Smith and M. H. Polley: J. Phys. Chem., 1956, vol. 60, pp. 689-691.

215. J. E. Day: Ind. Eng. Chem., 1936, vol. 28, pp. 234-238.

216. P. L. Walker, F. Rusinko and L. G. Austin: Advances in Catalysis, 1959, vol. 11, pp. 134-221.

217. L. S. Darken: "The Physical Chemistry of Steelmaking," M.I.T. Symposium, 1956, pp. 101-108.

218. L. S. Darken: "Basic Open Hearth Steelmaking," AIME, New York, 1951, pp. 592-619.

219. F. Korber and W. Oelsen: Mitt. Kaiser-Wilhelm-Inst. Eisenforsch. 1935, vol. 17, pp. 39-61.

220. J. C. Fulton and J. Chipman: Trans. AIME, 1954, vol. 200, pp. 1136-1146.

221. E. W. Filer and L. S. Darken: Trans. AIME, 1952, vol. 194, pp. 253-257.

222. E. T. Turkdogan and R. A. Hancock: Trans. Inst. Mining and Metallurgy, 1957-58, vol. 67, pp. 573-600.

223. F. Korber and W. Oelsen: Mitt. Kaiser-Wilhelm-Inst. Eisenforsch., 1933, vol. 15, pp. 271-309.

224. H. Schenck: "Physical Chemistry of Steelmaking," p437, 453, BISRA, London, 1945.

225. H. B. Bell, A. B. Murad and P. T. Carter: Trans. AIME, 1952, vol. 194, pp. 718-722.

226. T. B. Winkler and J. Chipman: Trans. AIME, 1946, vol. 167, pp. 111-133.

227. L. S. Darken and B. M. Larsen: Trans. AIME, 1942, vol. 150, pp. 87-109.

228. S. Matoba, K. Gunji and T. Kuwana: Tetsu to Hagané, 1959, vol. 45, pp. 229-232; Stahl und Eisen, 1960, vol. 80, pp. 299-301.

229. E. T. Turkdogan, P. Grieveson and J. F. Beisler: Trans. Met. Soc. AIME, to be published in 1963 or 1964.

230. J. C. Fulton and J. Chipman: Trans. AIME, 1959, vol. 215, pp. 888-891.

231. L. S. Darken: "The Physical Chemistry of Steelmaking," pp. 101-106, John Wiley and Sons., Inc., New York, 1956.

232. E. T. Turkdogan and J. Pearson: J. Iron and Steel Inst., 1953, vol. 175, pp. 398-401.

233. T. B. Winkler and J. Chipman: Trans. AIME, 1946, vol. 167, pp. 111-133.

234. K. Balajiva, A. G. Quarrell and P. Vajragupta: J. Iron and Steel Inst., 1946, vol. 153, pp. 115-150.

235. K. Balajiva and P. Vajragupta: J. Iron and Steel Inst., 1947, vol. 155, pp. 562-567.

236. P. Vajragupta: J. Iron and Steel Inst., 1948, vol. 158, pp. 494-496.

237. W. A. Fischer and H. vom Ende: Stahl u Eisen, 1952, vol. 72, pp. 1398-1408.

238. J. Pearson, E. T. Turkdogan and E. M. Fenn: J. Iron and Steel Inst., 1954, vol. 176, pp. 441-444.

239. J. B. Bookey: J. Iron and Steel Inst., 1952, vol. 172, pp. 61-68.

240. New Continental Oxygen-Steelmaking Processes: Iron and Coal Trades Rev., 1958, Aug.-Nov.

241. Collection of papers on pneumatic processes: J. Metals, 1960, vol. 12, July.

242. M. Davies: J. Iron and Steel Inst., 1961, vol. 197, pp. 271-282.

243. Y. K. Zea: J. Iron and Steel Inst., 1945, vol. 151, No. 1, pp. 459-504.

244. H. Schenck: "Physical Chemistry of Steelmaking," BISRA, London, 1945.

245. P. Bardenheuer and W. Geller: Mitt Kais. Wilh. Inst. Eisenforsch., 1934, vol. 16, pp. 77-91.

246. N. J. Grant and J. Chipman: Trans. AIME, 1946, vol. 167, pp. 134-139.

247. C. J. B. Fincham and F. D. Richardson: Proc. Royal Soc., 1954, vol. A223, pp. 40-62.

248. G. R. St. Pierre and J. Chipman: Trans. AIME, 1956, vol. 206, pp. 1474-1483.

249. E. T. Turkdogan and L. S. Darken: Trans. AIME, 1961, vol. 221, pp. 464-474.

250. G. G. Hatch and J. Chipman: Trans. AIME, 1949, vol. 185, pp. 274-284.

251. K. P. Abraham, M. W. Davies and F. D. Richardson: J. Iron and Steel Inst., 1960, vol. 196, pp. 309-312.

252. K. P. Abraham and F. D. Richardson: J. Iron and Steel Inst., 1960, vol. 196, pp. 313-317.

253. E. W. Filer and L. S. Darken: Trans. AIME, 1952, vol. 194, pp. 253-257.

254. J. N. Hornak and E. J. Whittenberger: Proc. NOHSC, AIME, 1956, vol. 39, pp. 189-201.

255. E. T. Turkdogan: J. Iron and Steel, 1955, vol. 179, 147-154.

256. L. S. Darken and B. M. Larsen: Trans. AIME, 1942, vol. 150, pp. 87-109.

257. T. B. Windler and J. Chipman: Trans. AIME, 1946, vol. 167, pp. 111-133.

258. B. M. Larsen and L. O. Sordahl: "Physical Chemistry of Process Metallurgy," Part 2, Interscience Publisher, New York, 1959.

259. L. Marples and J. Pears: J. Iron and Steel Inst., 1960, vol. 195, pp. 195-201.

260. E. T. Turkdogan and S. Ignatowicz: J. Iron and Steel Inst., 1955, vol. 180, pp. 349-354.

261. E. T. Turkdogan and P. Grieveson: Trans. Met. Soc. AIME, 1962, vol. 224, pp. 316-323.

262. E. T. Turkdogan and M. L. Pearce: Trans. Met. Soc. AIME, 1963, vol. 227, pp. 940-949.

263. S. Ramachandran, T. B. King and N. J. Grant: Trans. AIME, 1956, vol. 206, pp. 1549-1558.

264. K. M. Goldman, G. Derge and W. O. Philbrook: Trans. AIME, 1954, vol. 200, pp. 534-540.

265. Patricia M. Bills and E. T. Turkdogan: Previously unpublished data given in a paper in reference 262.

CHAPTER 13

Direct-Reduction Processes

SECTION 1

HISTORICAL DEVELOPMENT OF DIRECT REDUCTION

Due to the desire (and in some countries the economic necessity) to employ the lower-grade ores and available fuels (non-coking bituminous coals, anthracite, lignite, etc., that are unsuitable for blast-furnace fuels), an intensive search has been underway in many quarters to develop a process or processes that would at least partially supplant the blast furnace as a source of iron for steelmaking. Such processes are referred to generically as **direct-reduction processes,** and their purposes are to either: (1) produce steel directly from iron ore; (2) make a product equivalent to blast-furnace pig iron for use in present steelmaking processes; or (3) produce low-carbon iron as a melting stock (sometimes referred to as **synthetic scrap**) for making steel by existing processes.

In spite of the intensity of effort, no commercially useful direct-reduction process has been developed to date that shows any immediate promise of supplanting the blast furnace as the chief source of iron units for steelmaking on a large scale.

Principles of Direct Reduction—Dry, pure iron oxides (Fe_2O_3 or Fe_3O_4) in the presence of an excess of reducing substance, form dark-gray, porous masses having the same size and shape as the original lumps or particles when reduced at temperatures below 1650° F (900° C). A temperature of 1740° to 1830° F (950° to 1000° C) is necessary to effect complete reduction in a reasonable length of time, unless the ore is of selected particle size. At 1830° F (1000° C) the product begins to sinter. At 2190° F (1200° C) a pasty, porous mass forms. At 2370° F (1300° C) the mass absorbs carbon rapidly, if the latter is present, and begins to fuse, though the upper melting (completely liquid) point of pure iron is 2785° F (1530° C).

It should be noted that direct-reduction processes, in one form or another, have been in use for many centuries for the production of sponge iron.

Sponge Iron—Sponge iron provided the main source of iron and steel for many centuries before the blast furnace was developed around 1300 A.D. As described in Chapter 1, sponge iron was produced in relatively shallow hearths or in shaft furnaces, both of which used charcoal in the double role of a fuel to supply heat and a chemical reducing agent to reduce the iron from the ore by combining carbon from the fuel with the oxygen from the ore. The product of all of these smelting processes was a spongy mass of coalesced granules of nearly pure iron intermixed with considerable slag. Usable articles of wrought iron were produced by first hammering the spongy mass while still hot from the smelting operation, to expel most of the slag and compact the mass. By repeated heating and hammering, the iron was further freed of slag and forged into the desired shape.

All of the methods whereby low-carbon wrought iron could be produced directly from the ore were called **direct processes.** After development of the blast furnace, which made large quantities of iron having a high carbon content available, low-carbon wrought iron was produced by refining this high-carbon material; because two or more steps were involved in the processes employed, they came to be known as **indirect processes.**

Direct methods are still in use among certain peoples, and, indeed, have never been wholly abandoned even by the most advanced nations. The ease with which iron ores are reduced makes the direct process appear enticingly simple and logical. The reduction takes place at low temperatures and absorbs little heat, some of the reactions actually being exothermic.

For the past hundred years, sponge iron itself has found increasing use in various industrial processes, other than in the manufacture of wrought iron. Since the iron produced in sponge form is of high purity, it is used extensively in the chemical industry as a strong reducing agent and is chemically much more active than steel or iron in the form of millings, borings, turnings, or wire, because of its porous or spongy nature. Sponge iron may be produced as a granular material or as a sintered mass, depending upon the methods of manufacture. In the granular form, in which it is commonly known as **powdered iron,** it is used in the manufacture of many useful articles by the techniques of **powder metallurgy,** in which the powders are first compacted by pressure alone into the approximate shape of the finished article; the compact is then "sintered" at a temperature ranging roughly between 1800° and 2000° F in furnaces provided with a protective atmosphere to prevent oxidation. The sintered articles are then pressed or otherwise processed to give them their final accurate shape.

It may be mentioned that iron powders are produced, not only by direct reduction of iron ores or oxides using solid carbonaceous reducing agents (coal, coke or charcoal), but also by electrolytic processes, by thermal decomposition of iron carbonyl which has the chemical formula $Fe(CO)_5$ and by the reduction of iron ore or pure oxides with various gaseous reducing agents such as carbon monoxide or hydrogen.

Direct-Reduction Processes for Making Iron and Steel—The production of sponge iron demonstrates that iron ore can be reduced directly with relative ease on a small scale.

While the process of producing low-carbon iron (or steel) directly from ore is theoretically very attractive and appears more logical than indirect processes (in which high-carbon pig iron is first produced and then purified to make iron and steel), direct processes have so far failed in competition with indirect methods. Apparently, the chief reasons are: (1) The ore must be very rich. (2) The ore must be finely divided and intimately mixed with or carefully placed over the reducing agent. (3) So far, no practical plan has been evolved whereby the ore and reducing agent may be mixed in proper proportions to leave no excess of either. If an excess of the former is permitted, the process is wasteful of ore, while in the presence of an excess of the latter, the iron is obtained at a low temperature in sponge or pasty form which is hard to handle. If produced at a higher temperature,

phosphorus in the ore will be reduced and the carbon absorbed from the fuel, giving a very impure metal, little better than pig iron. Sulphur, except when an excess of calcium oxide is present, is readily absorbed by the metal and cannot be removed except under highly reducing conditions such as prevail in the blast furnace or an electric furnace.

The attempts to develop a large-scale direct process for manufacturing iron and steel that could compete with the indirect processes now in use have embraced practically every known type of apparatus suitable for the purpose, including pot furnaces, reverberatory furnaces, regenerative furnaces, shaft furnaces, rotary and stationary kilns, retort furnaces, electric furnaces, various combination furnaces, and fluidized-bed reactors. Many different kinds of reducing agents have also been tried, such as coal, coke, graphite, char, distillation residues, fuel oil, tar, producer gas, coal gas, water gas and hydrogen.

In the remainder of this chapter, some of the direct-reduction processes that attained a degree of success in the past, and some that are now in commercial operation or still under development, will be briefly described (further details on these and other direct-reduction processes are given in the reference material listed at the end of this chapter). To facilitate classification, as shown in Table 13—I, the processes are divided into two broad categories: processes using

Table 13—I. Classification of Direct-Reduction Processes.*

1. PROCESSES USING SOLID REDUCTANTS.

    A. Kiln Processes
        Krupp-Renn
        R-N
        Bassett
        Sturzelberg
        Domnarfvet
        Hornsey-Wills

    B. Retort Processes
        Hoganas
        Chenot
        Larkins
        DuPuy
        Lang

    C. Electric-Furnace Smelting Processes
        Tysland-Hole
        Lubatti
        Elektrometall
        D.L.M. (Dwight-Lloyd-McWane)
        Strategic-Udy
        Edwin-Elektrokemisk

    D. Low-Shaft Blast-Furnace Processes
        Ougree-Liege
        Demag-Humboldt
        Weber

    E. Miscellaneous Solid-Reductant Processes
        Rudolph-Landin
        Leckie
        Gerhardt

2. PROCESSES USING GASEOUS REDUCTANTS.

    A. Kiln Processes
        Maier-Mococo
        Azincourt
        Scortecci

    B. Shaft-Furnace Processes
        Wiberg-Soderfors
        Norsk-Staal
        U. S. Bureau of Mines
        Skinner Multiple-Hearth
        Cape-Brassert
        United Verde
        Norwegian H-Iron
        Galluser

    C. Fluidized-Bed Processes
        Nu-Iron
        H-Iron
        A.D.L. (Esso Research-Little)
        Stalling
        Bubble-Hearth
        Novalfer-Onia

    D. Retort Processes
        Madaras-Mexican
        HyL

    E. Jet-Smelting Process
        O.R.F. (Ontario Research Foundation)

3. DIRECT-STEEL PROCESSES
        O.R.F. Direct-Steel (Cavanagh)
        Flame-Smelting (Cyclosteel)
        Twyman

*This table includes only those processes described in the text.

solid reducing agents, described in Section 2; and processes using gaseous reducing agents, described in Section 3. Certain direct-steel processes that are under development will be described in Section 4.

In considering the direct-reduction processes now in use, a proper perspective is obtained if it is remembered that the ferrous products presently made by direct reduction represent less than 2 per cent of the total iron and steel production of the world.

No effort will be made here to evaluate or compare the different processes from either the economic or technical standpoints. Those that were developed to meet purely local conditions with some degree of success might prove to be completely impractical under other conditions involving, for example, different fuels and different raw materials.

SECTION 2

PROCESSES USING SOLID REDUCING AGENTS

A. KILN PROCESSES

Krupp-Renn Process—The Krupp-Renn process (also known as the Johannsen process) is designed particularly to treat high-silica ore with a basicity ratio as low as 0.2 to 0.3, without the addition of limestone. In this process, a mixture of minus ¼-inch ore and a fine-grain carbonaceous reducing agent (e.g., coke breeze or bituminous-coal fines) is fed continuously into a rotary kiln (Figure 13—1). The kiln is heated by burning powdered coal at the discharge end with an excess of air. Carbon monoxide evolved from the charge during reduction is burned by the excess air to supply additional heat to the kiln. The maximum temperature in the kiln is about 2250° to 2300° F, which is sufficient to convert the gangue in the ore to a very viscous high-silica slag, but not high enough to melt the sponge iron obtained from reduction of the ore. The reduced iron welds into nodules called "luppen" which become embedded in the pasty slag. This product is discharged from the kiln. After cooling, it is crushed, and the luppen are magnetically separated from the slag. Recovery of iron in the luppen varies between 94 and 97.5 per cent.

In addition to high-silica ore, high-titania ore can be used in this process, and a separation of iron from titanium can be effected since the latter is not reduced. Almost any carbonaceous fuel can be used as a reducing agent.

Since a large part of the sulphur contained in the reducing agent goes into the luppen, the sulphur content of the metal is usually too high for economical conversion of the luppen into steel by any of the conventional steelmaking practices. In at least one instance, however, magnetite ores containing 55 to 60 per cent of iron are reduced to luppen that are successfully refined into steel. In some places, the process is used to concentrate low-grade iron ores containing up to 30 per cent silica, the luppen being fed into blast furnaces.

It has been stated that some 500,000 tons of iron are produced annually by the Krupp-Renn process.

R-N Process—The R-N process was developed originally in Norway, primarily to treat titanium-bearing ore for the production of paint pigments. However, further development showed that other iron-bearing ores could also be treated successfully to produce iron. Subsequently, a pilot plant capable of producing 50 to 75 tons of iron product per day was built in the United States. Pellets or crushed ore along with crushed coke and limestone are charged into the kiln (Figure 13—2). Operating temperature of the kiln is controlled within the range between 1830 and 1970° F to prevent fusion of these materials into clinkers. The solid product from the kiln is cooled in a quench tank. After cooling, unused coke is removed for recycling, and the reduced product is finely ground in ball mills and the iron is separated magnetically. Because of the fineness of the refined product, it must be briquetted before use. The process is able to make an iron product that contains only

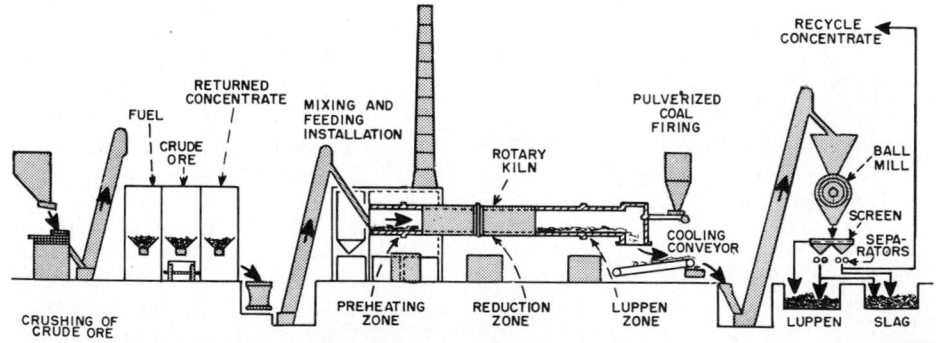

KRUPP—RENN PROCESS

Fig. 13—1. Schematic representation of the steps involved in carrying out the Krupp-Renn process.

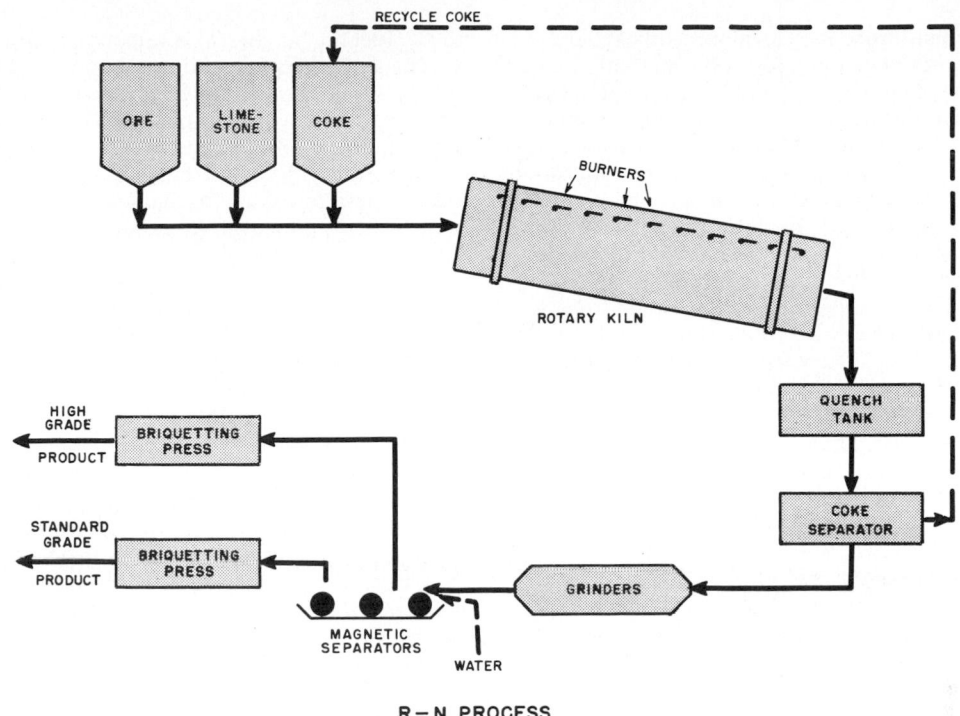

RECYCLE COKE

ORE

LIME-
STONE

COKE

BURNERS

ROTARY KILN

QUENCH
TANK

COKE
SEPARATOR

HIGH
GRADE
PRODUCT

BRIQUETTING
PRESS

STANDARD
GRADE
PRODUCT

BRIQUETTING
PRESS

MAGNETIC
SEPARATORS

WATER

GRINDERS

R — N PROCESS

Fig. 13—2. Simplified flow sheet of the R-N process.

0.02 to 0.05 per cent sulphur, which is a desirable level for conventional steelmaking practices.

Bassett Process—The Bassett process was developed commercially in Denmark and has been in operation there since 1939. The present output is 35,000 tons of pig iron per year from two kilns. This process differs from other rotary-kiln direct-reduction processes in that molten pig iron, instead of solid product, is discharged from the kiln.

The kiln is fired at the product-discharge end, using coal dust, oil, or gas as fuel. A mixture of minus ¼-inch ore, limestone, and fine-grain reducing agent (coal or coke in excess of the amount required to reduce the iron oxide) is fed continuously into the upper end of the kiln. The operating temperature range of the kiln is between 950° F at the charge end and 2300° F at the discharge end. Reduction of the ore is completed at an intermediate location in the kiln, where the temperature is about 2000° F. As the reduced iron travels toward the discharge end, its melting point is lowered by absorption of the excess carbon while its temperature gradually increases to 2300° F and it melts. During reduction of the iron oxides, sufficient carbon monoxide is evolved to maintain a reducing atmosphere above the reacting solids. Sufficient limestone is added with the charge to form a highly basic slag, with a lime-silica ratio of 2.8 to 3.0. The fusion point of the slag is high enough to prevent its melting in the kiln. This slag forms a protective layer above the molten iron and also absorbs sulphur. The slag is removed as required and the iron is tapped about every 90 minutes.

Because both reduction and melting take place in the kiln, the retention time is long, resulting in a low production rate. For example, the production of a 12-foot diameter by 225-foot long kiln, using a hematite ore with 60 per cent iron content, is about 70 tons of pig iron per day. Ores having high contents of alumina and silica decrease the production rate because a large amount of limestone is needed to maintain the required lime-silica ratio. Fuel consumption for this process has been reported to be about 1450 pounds of coke breeze and 775 pounds of fuel oil per ton of iron.

Sturzelberg Process—Although the Sturzelberg process was developed in Germany to utilize "purple" ore calcine from sulphuric-acid works, it has proved suitable for other ores also. Ore is reduced in a short, rotating furnace operated on a batch charging basis and heated by burning natural gas, fuel oil, or pulverized coal. The charge, consisting of fine ore, limestone, and coal or coke, is first dried by waste gases from the process, and then placed in the reducing furnace. The charge is reduced to molten iron, which is tapped by tilting the furnace. During the reduction period, the furnace is rotated about its long axis. Retention time is about 7 to 8 hours.

The rotating furnace is about 8 feet in internal diameter and 40 feet in length, and is capable of producing 40 tons of iron per day, using ore with a 60 per cent iron content. The estimated fuel consumption is between 1550 and 2200 pounds of coke breeze or between 1325 and 1500 pounds of pulverized coal per ton of iron. Because of the low silicon content of the iron product, about 0.015 per cent, it cannot be used satisfactorily in ordinary steel-refining processes, but must be converted to steel in a lance-blown converter by blowing with oxygen.

Domnarfvet Process—Development of the Domnarfvet process began in 1950. This method of reduction is similar to that of previously described kiln processes in that the ore and fuel are fed continuously into the kiln and heated by a burner firing at the discharge end of the kiln. However, heating of the charge in the Domnarfvet process is controlled by introducing heated air into the kiln through a central tube from which it is distributed to a series of jets directed onto the surface of the charge.

Powdered ore can be used in the Domnarfvet kiln; however, best results are obtained with lump ore, sinter, or pellets. The reducing agent used is coke breeze. A 90 to 95 per cent degree of reduction can be obtained with a 60 per cent iron content of the ore; however, sulphur in the reduced product is high (0.2 to 0.3 per cent). Attempts to control the sulphur content by adding limestone and dolomite in the kiln result in serious sticking problems. Consequently, desulphurization of the product must be carried out in a separate furnace.

If the kiln is very long, uneven distribution of the heated air through the central tube will result. This limits the length and diameter of the kiln to 30 feet and 6 feet, respectively. The production capacity of such a kiln is about 25 tons per day.

Hornsey-Wills Process—The Hornsey-Wills process was developed in England. It involved preheating iron ore, mixing it with ground coal as a reducing agent, heating the mixture to reducing temperature, cooling the product, magnetically separating the iron, and briquetting the iron for subsequent use. Equipment consisted of three rotary kilns connected in series by air-tight seals. The first of these three kilns was the preheater; the second, the reducing chamber; and the third, the cooling chamber. This process is not in current use.

B. RETORT PROCESSES

Hoganas Process—The E. Sieurin, or Hoganas, process was developed at Hoganas, Sweden in 1910 and is still in commercial use.

Alternate layers of high-grade ore (60 per cent Fe), dry coke breeze, and limestone are charged into cylindrical ceramic containers. The containers are then heated to a maximum temperature of 2300° F in a furnace of the type used for burning brick. The furnace is heated by burning producer gas and the carbon monoxide evolved by the reduction of the ore. The containers are cooled in the furnace, removed, and the reduced iron is separated and cleaned. Total retention time of a container in the furnace is 12 days. Most of the sponge iron produced is refined and sold as iron powder.

The largest Hoganas plant in operation has two tunnel kilns and is capable of producing 30,000 tons annually.

Chenot Process—The Chenot process is an old method for reducing iron from its ores, employing an externally heated vertical retort furnace.

High-grade ore mixed with a slight excess of charcoal (about 1.5 tons of calcined ore to 0.5 ton of charcoal) was charged into the top of a vertical retort of rectangular cross-section (1½ feet by 6 feet), 28 to 33 feet in height. The upper part of each retort was made of firebrick, and was surrounded and heated by a series of vertical flues, open at the top and connecting below with fireplaces. The bottom section was of sheet iron, water-jacketed, to receive the sponge iron and keep it out of contact with air until cold. Operation was continuous, and the reduction stage in the upper section of the retort required three days.

The reduction reaction absorbed so much heat that production was limited by the rate of heat flow into the charge. If the retort walls became too hot as a result of attempts to increase the flow of heat, the charge fused and stuck to the walls. The process proved to be very inefficient and only 50 to 60 per cent reduction was obtained, so that it was finally abandoned.

Larkins Process—In this long-abandoned process, magnetic concentrates were molded into bricks with carbonaceous matter and placed in D-shaped retorts that were externally heated with gas. Reduced iron powder was obtained after the retorts had been kept red hot for 24 hours.

DuPuy Process—In this method, which is no longer in use, charges of ground iron ore, mixed with carbonaceous matter and fluxes, were packed in cylindrical sheet-iron canisters. The reduced metal, still in the canister, could be converted to muck bar by hammering or squeezing followed by rolling, after which it was cut up to provide melting stock for the crucible process. Alternatively, the canisters could be charged hot into an open-hearth furnace, or melted down with pig or cast iron in the furnace in which reduction had been carried out.

Lang Process—No longer in use, this process consisted of mixing powdered ore and coal and packing the mixture in closed cylindrical steel shells. The loaded shells were heated in a reverberatory furnace and the ore was reduced. The product was dropped directly into an electric furnace, melted, and refined to steel.

C. ELECTRIC FURNACE SMELTING PROCESSES

Tysland-Hole Process—A low-shaft electric-arc furnace is used in this process to reduce iron ore and produce molten pig iron. The furnace, shown schematically in Figure 13—3, is similar to a steelmaking electric-arc furnace. It consists of a melting chamber with three or more electrodes extending downward through the roof, either in line or in a triangular arrangement. Openings are provided in the roof for charging the burden of agglomerated or lump ore, coke or coal, and limestone.

Reduction of the ore and melting of the resultant product take place continuously in the hearth. A 10,000-kilowatt furnace, the most common size presently in use, can produce 100 tons of pig iron daily, with a power consumption of 2500 kilowatt-hours per ton of pig iron. Coke consumption, with lump ore of 55 per cent iron content, is 850 pounds per ton of pig iron. This low coke consumption, together with the use of a basic slag, leads to a metal with a low sulphur content.

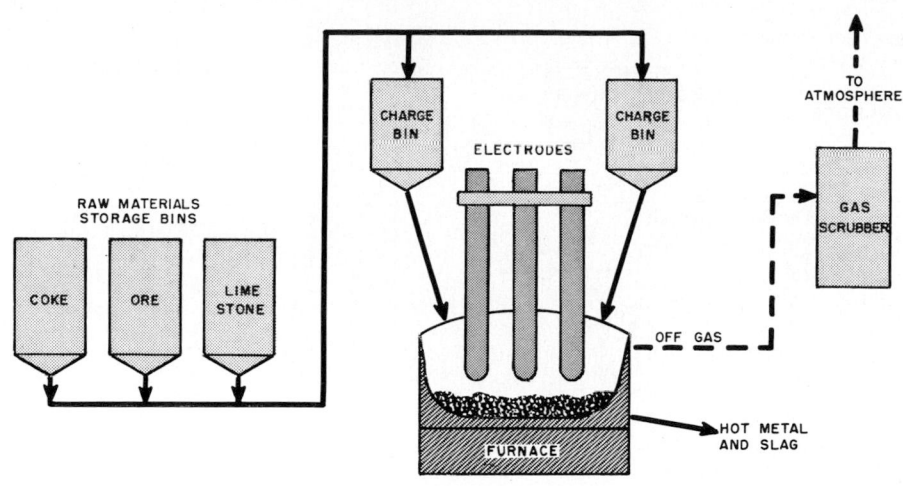

FIG. 13—3. Schematic representation of the Tysland-Hole process for producing molten pig iron.

The Tysland-Hole process is commercially practical in countries such as Norway, Sweden, Italy, Switzerland, Yugoslavia, India and Japan, where low-cost electric power is available and/or where metallurgical coals are scarce and expensive.

Lubatti Process—In Italy, ore-smelting experiments have been conducted on an electric furnace of a new design. The furnace consists of a shallow hearth with a hood over it. A thick molten-slag layer is maintained above the molten metal in the hearth, and a thin layer of fine-grain ore, coal, and limestone is charged on top of the slag. Electrodes are immersed in the slag layer so that heat is evolved in the slag without the formation of an arc. This provides heat for the reactions that reduce the ore floating on top of the slag. The reduced iron melts, passes through the slag, and collects in the hearth.

Elektrometall Furnace Process—The Elektrometall furnace, developed in Sweden, is a shaft-type furnace with an enlarged melting chamber at the bottom. Six or eight electrodes are inserted, in a slightly inclined

position, into the melting chamber at regular intervals around the shaft. Lump ore, or sinter, and charcoal are charged into the furnace at the top of the shaft. The ore is partially reduced in the shaft by carbon monoxide produced by the reduction of iron ore in the melting chamber. The molten iron is tapped in the same manner as in a blast furnace.

Elektrometall furnaces are built in small units with a production capacity of from 50 to 55 tons of pig iron per day. Average power consumption is 2000 kilowatt-hours per ton of metal. Since the introduction of the Tysland-Hole process, which permits the use of coke instead of charcoal in an electric reduction furnace, use of the Elektrometall furnace has been slowly abandoned and only a few remain, in Sweden.

D.L.M. Process—A direct-reduction process known as the D.L.M. (Dwight-Lloyd-McWane) process (Figure 13—4) utilizing a sintering strand and electric smelting furnace, has undergone considerable development. Green pellets of ore fines and coal fines are spread on an enclosed down-draft sintering strand and ignited. Burning is continued until approximately 60 per cent reduction has occurred, at which time the partially reduced pellets are discharged from the sintering strand into an electric smelting furnace. Coke and flux are added to the smelting furnace as needed to complete the reduction of the furnace charge to molten pig iron.

Strategic-Udy Process—Another combination of direct reduction and electric smelting is represented by the Strategic-Udy process which, it is claimed, can be controlled to produce molten iron containing from 0.2 per cent up to 3.5 per cent of carbon. A prototype plant (Figure 13—5) consisted of a rotary kiln, 80 feet in length and 6 feet in diameter, and three 1000-kva three-phase electric smelting furnaces, along with ore-drying, storage, and charging equipment.

Iron ore, flux, and a carbonaceous reductant (usually coal) are fed continuously into the kiln, where some pre-reduction of the ore takes place. The hot, pre-reduced ore is charged directly into the electric

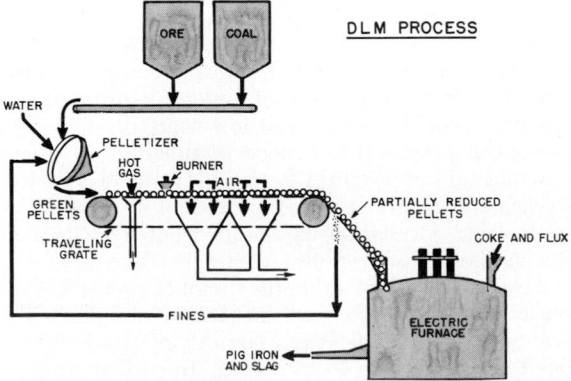

FIG. 13—4. Schematic representation of the relationship of the various units used in the D.L.M. process for making pig iron. (Adapted from "The Case for Direct Reduction," Steel, 141, 1957, Oct. 28.)

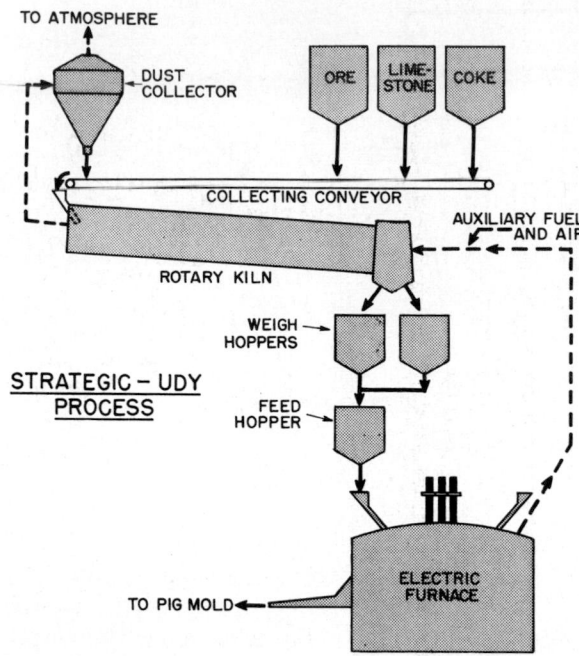

FIG. 13—5. Flow sheet for the Strategic-Udy process for producing molten pig iron, based on the layout of a prototype plant. (After Udy)

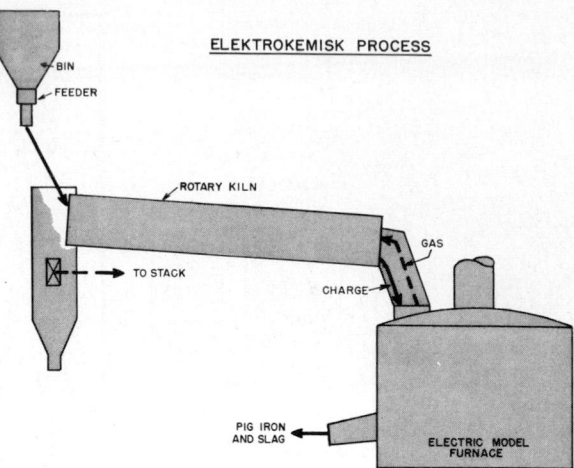

FIG. 13—6. Diagrammatic sketch of the principal operating units used in the Elektrokemisk process. (After Collin and Grytting)

furnaces where reduction is completed. The charge is fed so as to slide down the sides of the electric-furnace interior, so as to keep open the space above and adjacent to the area where the electrode tips are either in contact with or just above the molten slag in the furnace. This method of charging is referred to as a "floating charge" technique.

This process can be used to produce iron from ores contaminated with titanium, manganese, chromium or nickel that would not be suitable for direct use in the conventional blast-furnace process.

Using an ore containing 50 per cent iron, pre-reduced to an extent of 60 per cent in the kiln, it is estimated that about 1000 kwh of electric energy would be required to complete the reduction. The pre-reduction operation in the kiln under the above circumstances would require around 950 lb. of coal and about 675 lb. of limestone.

Edwin-Elektrokemisk Process—This process, developed in Norway, produces pig iron by partially reducing iron ore in a rotary kiln, with reduction being completed and melting of the reduced product effected in an adjacent closed-top electric furnace (Figure 13—6).

The kiln is fired from the discharge end by oil burners that raise the temperature of the kiln to about 1900° F at the firing end. Exhaust gases from the electric furnace, containing carbon monoxide, are burned in the kiln to supply additional heat. The kiln is charged with iron ore, coke breeze, and fluxes.

It has been reported that, where the kiln was used only to preheat a charge containing an ore of 53 per cent iron content to about 1470° F before it was charged hot into the electric furnace, power consumption was 2040 kwh per net ton of pig iron produced,

as compared to a requirement of 2420 kwh per ton for an untreated charge. Smelting of a self-fluxing sinter containing 63 per cent iron, preheated in the kiln with coke breeze to about 1800° F, required about 1730 kwh per ton of pig iron. By adding semi-coke to the charge for the kiln so that some pre-reduction of the self-fluxing sinter would be effected by the volatile matter from the semicoke, the energy consumption per ton of pig iron was lowered to 1400 kwh.

D. LOW-SHAFT BLAST-FURNACE PROCESSES

The concept of a low-shaft blast-furnace process originated with the finding that the temperature of blast-furnace top gases decreased with increasing oxygen content of the hot blast. This indicated that, with oxygen enrichment of the blast, the gases in the upper part of the shaft would not be hot enough to heat the burden and that this section would no longer serve a useful purpose. From this it was reasoned that, by using a high percentage of oxygen in the blast, the shaft of the furnace could be shortened and a low-strength coal could be used as fuel. It was also thought that ore fines could be used instead of lump or agglomerated ore required by the conventional blast furnace. Numerous experimental low-shaft blast furnaces are being operated, and the common objective of all is the utilization of low-grade ore and coal directly from the mine. The low-shaft blast furnace located at Ougreé near Liège in Belgium, is shown schematically in Figure 13—7. This furnace is used in studies sponsored by an international research committee, and is under the care of the Centre National de Recherches Métallurgiques (of Belgium).

Results have shown that the use of oxygen-enriched blast in a low-shaft blast furnace is practical. The optimum range for oxygen content of the blast appears to be 25 to 35 per cent, the exact amount depending upon the characteristics of the raw materials and the design of the furnace. However, the original premise that ore fines could be used without prior agglomeration has not been substantiated. Experimental results have indicated that close sizing of

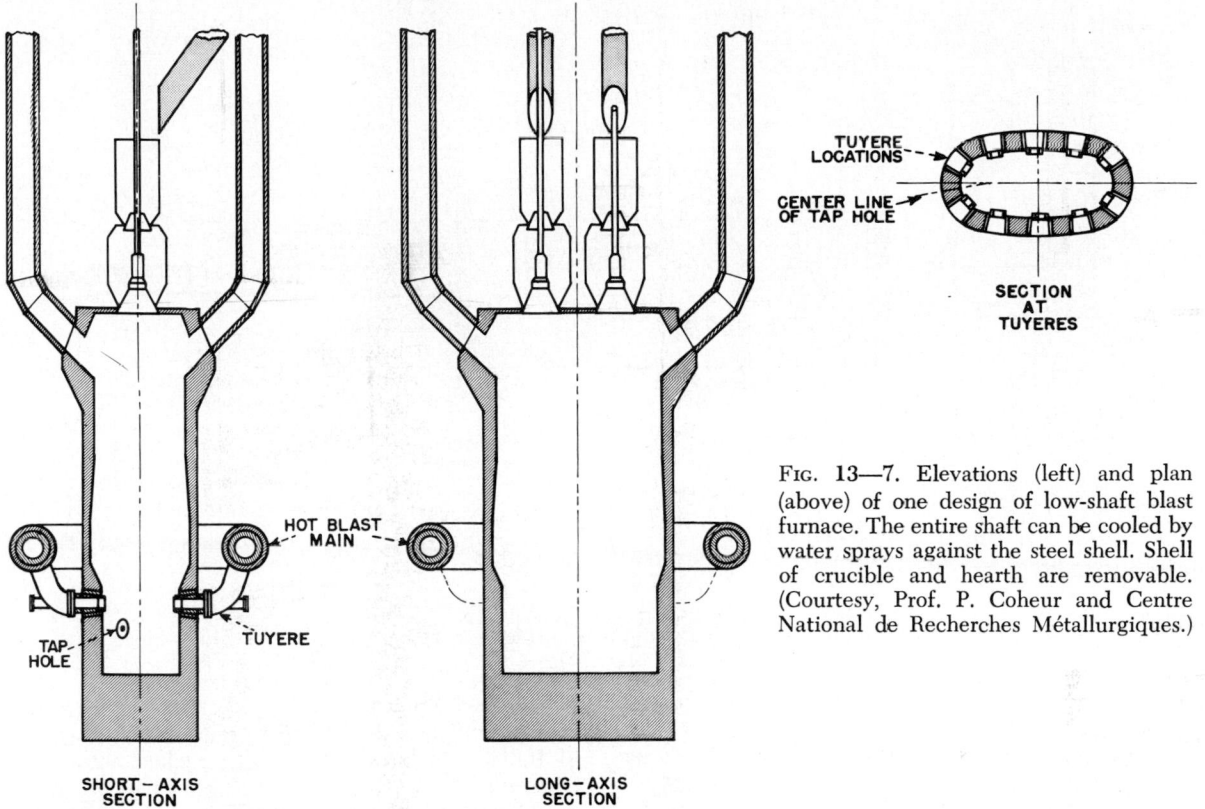

TUYERE LOCATIONS

CENTER LINE OF TAP HOLE

SECTION AT TUYERES

HOT BLAST MAIN

TAP HOLE

TUYERE

SHORT—AXIS SECTION

LONG—AXIS SECTION

FIG. 13—7. Elevations (left) and plan (above) of one design of low-shaft blast furnace. The entire shaft can be cooled by water sprays against the steel shell. Shell of crucible and hearth are removable. (Courtesy, Prof. P. Coheur and Centre National de Recherches Métallurgiques.)

the burden is very important for efficient operation. The optimum size range has been found to be minus ¾ inch plus ⅜ inch. The **Demag-Humboldt** low-shaft blast furnace has been operated on briquettes made by compressing a mixture of finely ground ore, coal, and flux, with a binder, in an attempt to obtain smooth furnace operation. In the **Weber process,** similar briquettes are carbonized in a retort before charging into a low-shaft blast furnace.

With respect to fuel, it has thus far been impossible to operate a low-shaft blast furnace efficiently with coal directly from the mine. The coke rate, calculated from coal to coke, on the most successful of the low-shaft furnaces is from 3500 to 4000 pounds of coke per ton of metal produced, when operating with an ore having an iron content of 55 per cent.

E. MISCELLANEOUS PROCESSES USING SOLID REDUCTANTS

(All obsolete)

Rudolph-Landin Process—Briquettes of fine ore, carbonaceous material, and fluxes, were reduced by passing them through a long furnace. The reduced briquettes were melted in a reverberatory furnace.

Leckie Process—Briquettes of ore and coal were heated and reduced in chambers connecting with an open-hearth furnace containing a bath of molten pig iron in which the reduced product was then melted.

Gerhardt Process—Briquettes made of a mixture of ore, flux, carbonaceous material, and tar, were heated in a puddling furnace to produce blooms of reduced iron.

SECTION 3

PROCESSES USING GASEOUS REDUCING AGENTS

A. ROTARY-KILN PROCESSES

A rotary-kiln type of operation for the reduction of iron ore by gaseous reagents has some inherent disadvantages. For example, operation with the reducing gases under pressure is highly impractical. Furthermore, because only a small portion of the total volume in a rotary kiln is occupied by reactant solids, the productive capacity per unit of reactor volume is relatively low. However, these disadvantages may be partly or wholly offset by the ability of a rotary kiln

to: (1) handle fine materials; (2) operate at high reducing temperatures (1800° to 2000° F) without sticking of reduced iron powder; and (3) operate in a true continuous countercurrent manner.

Maier-Mococo Process—This process was developed to recover a highly reduced iron product from the pyrite cinders and tailings from concentration processes resulting from the recovery of copper from its ores. A small rotary kiln (6 feet long, with 7-inch inside diameter) was used, with heated natural gas as the reducing agent. Supplemental heat was intro-

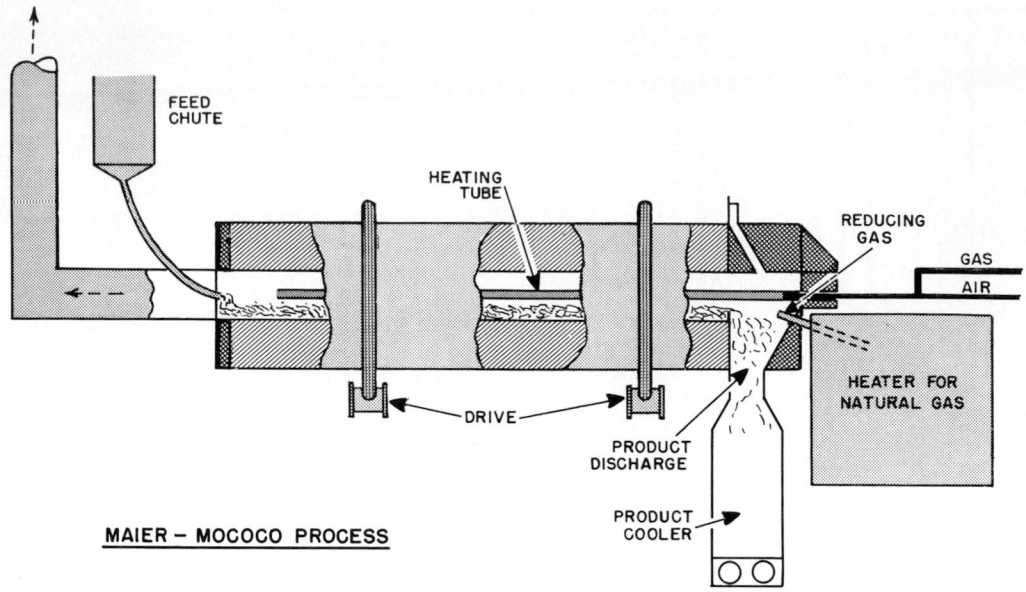

FIG. 13—8. Schematic representation of the rotary kiln and auxiliary equipment used in the Maier-Mococo process.

duced into the kiln by radiation from a central tube in which natural gas was burned with air (Figure 13—8). The reducing gas, introduced at about 1830° F, was a reformed mixture of air and natural gas consisting of about 43 per cent nitrogen, 20 per cent carbon monoxide, 36 per cent hydrogen, and less than 1 per cent each of methane, carbon dioxide, and water vapor. The production rate was 100 to 250 pounds per day of over 90 per cent reduced iron. Approximately 30,000 cu. ft. of natural gas were required to produce one ton of reduced iron.

Soft ores, in particular pyrite cinders, became sticky when reduced at 1560° to 1740° F, and ore finer than 60 mesh caused balling of the reduced particles; but it was claimed that the addition of lime prevented sticking of the charge in the kiln.

A larger (one ton capacity) kiln was used to reduce 65 tons per day of tailings (containing about 57 per cent iron) at an average kiln temperature of 1610° F. The average metallization was 84.2 to 91.2 per cent, and the fuel consumption was about 28,000 cu. ft. of natural gas per ton of metallic iron.

The Maier-Mococo process did not progress to the commercial stage, but it did demonstrate the feasibility of producing a highly reduced iron product in a rotary kiln with gaseous reducing agents.

Azincourt Process—This French process employs a rotary kiln about 95 feet in length. The kiln has a specially shaped combustion chamber where preheated iron ores (containing about 40 to 55 per cent iron) are reduced in a countercurrent flow of natural gas, coke-oven gas, or gases produced from other fuels. Reduction is carried out at temperatures between 2550° and 2750° F. The product is pig iron, containing between 1 and 3 per cent of carbon, 0 to 3 per cent of silicon, 0 to 0.7 per cent of manganese, and 0.15 to 0.7 per cent of sulphur. After some treatment, this product can be used as a liquid charge for steelmaking furnaces.

Scortecci Process—This process employs a rotary furnace and was developed to reduce various grades of Italian iron ores with a hot, cracked natural gas containing 85 per cent of hydrogen. The product is sponge iron that is used as a charge material for electric furnaces, with or without the addition of scrap.

B. SHAFT-FURNACE PROCESSES

Wiberg-Soderfors Process—The Wiberg-Soderfors process (Figure 13—9) is the most successful of all the shaft-furnace processes. The largest existing commercial installation has an annual capacity of 20,000 tons. This plant went into production in 1952 in Sweden, and several other plants have been constructed in that country.

The 20,000-ton-per-year Wiberg furnaces are 80-foot-tall structures of firebrick surrounded by insulation and enclosed in a steel-plate shell. The inside diameter of the bottom is 9 feet, 2 inches, the inside diameter of the top is 3 feet, 8 inches.

The reducing gases (about 20 to 30 per cent hydrogen and 70 to 80 per cent carbon monoxide) are produced at about 1900° F in an electrically heated coke or charcoal carburettor and passed through a bed of dolomite or limestone to remove sulphur before they enter the reduction zone (lower section) of the shaft. The hot gases, at approximately 1850° F, reduce the descending iron oxide (FeO). Approximately three-fourths of the partly spent gases are removed as they leave the FeO-to-Fe reduction zone and are recycled to the carburettor for regeneration. The remaining one-fourth of the gases enter the pre-reduction zone (the middle section of the shaft) where hematite or magnetite are reduced to FeO at about 1600° F. The off gases from the middle zone are burned in the preheating zone (the upper section of the shaft) and heat the ore charge to about 1850° F. The final waste gases are discharged at about 100° F.

The feed to the shaft furnace is lump ore, sinter, or

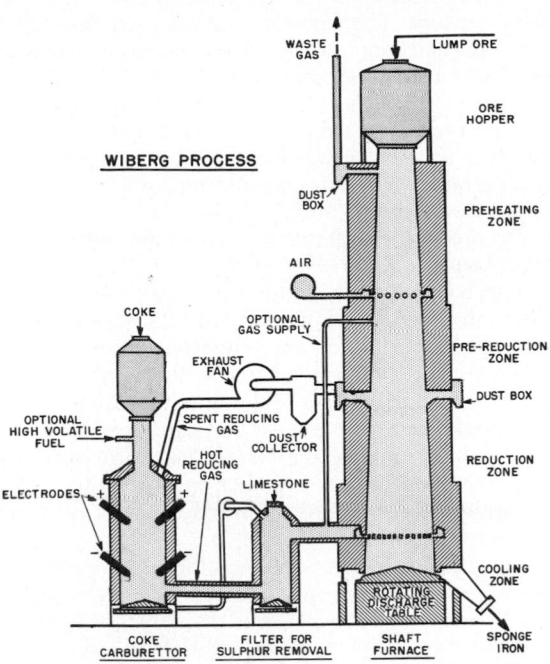

FIG. 13—9. Schematic cross-sectional diagram showing the principle of operation of the Wiberg-Soderfors process.

pellets, all preferably less than 2½ inches in diameter. The product (about 90 per cent reduced) is first cooled to between 200° and 300° F in a water-jacketed cooling chamber at the bottom of the shaft and is then discharged into steel cars of 4-ton capacity that transport it to the steelmaking furnaces.

The heat requirements for the process are low: only 7.5 to 9.0 million Btu per ton of metallic iron being required, as compared to 12 to 16 million Btu for most of the other processes. Several improvements in the process that are being considered are: (1) the direct charging of green pellets to eliminate the ore-agglomeration step; and (2) alternate methods of producing hot reducing gases to decrease or eliminate the need for electricity and high-grade coke or charcoal.

Norsk-Staal Process—The Norsk-Staal process was pioneered in Norway and was operated in Germany during the 1930's. It has since been abandoned because of mechanical complexity and operating difficulties. The operating difficulties arose because the briquettes (which were the principal charge, although lump ore and sinter also were used) sometimes disintegrated during reduction and plugged the shaft.

The reducing gas (55 per cent carbon monoxide, 40 per cent hydrogen, 5 per cent other gases) was made by passing a mixture of spent reducing gas and coke-oven gas or methane through an electric tube furnace, then through a coke-gas producer, and finally through a bed of lime for sulphur removal. The reducing gas (at 3000° F) then entered the top of a shaft furnace.

Shaft furnaces were formed by stacking hollow cylinders that had perforated fireclay bottoms and could contain about three tons of material. As shown schematically in Figure 13—10, three shafts were employed: one for preheating the ore, one for reduction, and one for cooling the product. The ore was preheated by burning gas with air and passing it into the bottom of the preheating shaft. Cold make-up gas was passed into the bottom of the cooling shaft and combined with the recycle gas after passing through the cooling stack. Every 1¼ hours, the gas flows were stopped, a fresh cylinder of ore was placed on top of the preheating shaft, and the heated bottom cylinder was transferred to the bottom of the reducing shaft, being replaced by the former top cylinder of the preheating shaft. The heated bottom cylinder from the

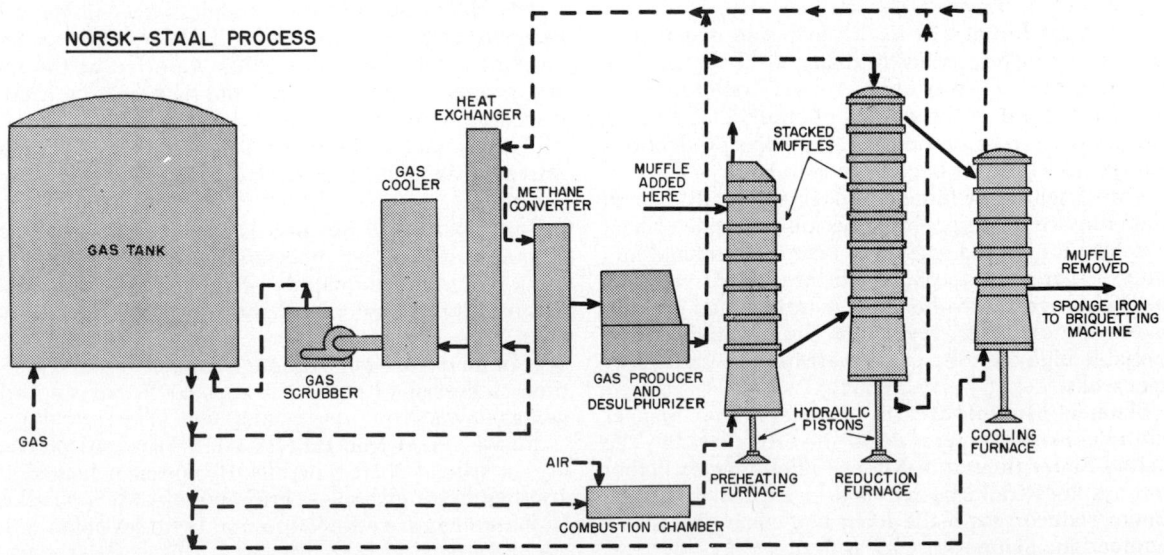

FIG. 13—10. Diagram showing relationship of the principal parts of a Norsk-Staal process plant for the direct reduction of iron ore by a gas composed chiefly of carbon monoxide and hydrogen. The large arrows indicate the movements of cylinders that are described in the text. (After Paige)

cooling stack. Every 1¼ hours, the gas flows were stopped, a fresh cylinder of ore was placed on top of the preheating shaft, the heated bottom cylinder from the preheating shaft was moved to the bottom of the reducing shaft and the cylinder of hot reduced product from the top of the reducing shaft was moved to the top of the cooling shaft. The cylinder at the bottom of the cooling shaft was removed and discharged. Shifting of the cylinders was accomplished by oil-operated pistons and swinging rails, the necessary movements being coordinated by interlocking controls and signals.

The best production rate achieved by the process at the German plant that served as the basis for the foregoing description was 38 tons per day of iron product from a single unit.

Bureau of Mines Shaft-Furnace Process—The United States Bureau of Mines conducted three interrelated investigations to develop a shaft-furnace process for the reduction of iron ores. In the first investigation, a refractory-lined shaft with 7-inch inside diameter and 14 feet tall was used. Glomerules of iron oxide (from waste pickle liquor), preheated to about 2000° F, were fed continuously into the top, and hydrogen at 1650° F was introduced into the bottom. Because the reactions involved in the reduction of iron oxide with hydrogen are endothermic, and because radiation losses of heat are high in small equipment, the required reaction temperatures of 1300° to 1750° F could not be maintained in the reduction zone, and only about 25 per cent reduction was achieved.

In the second investigation, an externally heated alloy-steel shaft furnace was used, having dimensions approximately the same as those of the furnace used in the first investigation. This shaft furnace was operated at 1300°, 1475°, and 1750° F. Both hydrogen and water gas were used as reductants. A highly reduced product was made, but the reduced glomerules tended to stick and weld together in the shaft.

The third investigation was similar to the second, except that a larger (one ton per day) externally heated shaft furnace (6 inches in inside diameter at the top, 12 inches in inside diameter at the bottom, and 10½ feet tall) was used. A highly reduced product (99 per cent reduced) was obtained, but sticking and melting of the product caused the product-discharge mechanism to become inoperable.

The design of a large-diameter externally heated shaft furnace is not practical because the rate of heat transfer through the walls of a reactor vessel and into the granular solids is poor, and the ratio of wall-surface area to reactor volume decreases with an increase in reactor diameter. A further disadvantage is the probable high cost of a large shaft furnace with alloy-steel walls.

Skinner Multiple-Hearth Process—The Skinner multiple-hearth process was investigated by the United States Bureau of Mines to determine whether iron-ore fines could be reduced in a Skinner furnace using producer gas made from non-coking coals and lignites. The Skinner furnace is designed for the treatment of finely divided solids with gases, and is similar to the Herreshoff furnace in construction. These furnaces have a series of horizontal circular hearths attached to a common vertical shaft that passes through their centers. The furnaces are charged through the top, charged material being moved downwards successively from one hearth to the next by plows or rabbles.

The furnace used in this investigation had ten hearths, four of which were muffle type to prevent mixing of heating gases with reducing gases. The furnace was 16½ feet high, with an inside diameter of 5 feet. During the tests, the hearth temperatures ranged from 1380° to 1560° F.

The best product made was 91 per cent reduced. Fuel efficiency was low, and only 23 per cent of the total gas was utilized for reduction. Sticking of the reduced iron, which interfered with the action of the rabbles, caused considerable operating difficulty.

Cape-Brassert Process—The Cape-Brassert process was probably one of the largest-scale attempts at direct reduction ever undertaken in the United States. It employed a standard 12-hearth Nichols-Herreshoff ore-roasting furnace.

The reducing gas used was desulphurized coke-oven gas, preheated in a heat exchanger by the hot gas leaving the furnace, and then further heated to about 1500° F by passage through a radiant-tube-fired gas heater. The heated reducing gas entered the furnace at various levels. The off-gas was passed through the heat exchanger to preheat the inlet gas, and was then purified and recycled.

The plant produced 85 per cent reduced iron, but at a much lower capacity than anticipated and the project was abandoned.

United Verde Shaft-Furnace Process — In the United Verde shaft-furnace process, iron oxide was reduced at 1830° to 1920° F, using hot reformed mixtures of air and natural gas (see the Maier-Mococo process). The iron oxide was ferrous-oxide slag (63.4 per cent FeO) obtained from a copper smelter, and was granulated into spherical pellets 1 to 5 mm (0.04 to 0.20 inches, approximately) in diameter.

The shaft furnace had a stainless-steel lining surrounded by thermal insulation. Hot reducing gas entered at the bottom. The solids were fed at the top and product was removed at the bottom by a rotary discharge table.

The product was about 95 per cent reduced, and was used as melting stock in an electric steelmaking furnace.

The mixtures of air and natural gas reformed according to the Maier process provided a gas containing a considerable quantity of carbon monoxide, and the reduction was only slightly endothermic. However, the reducing gas also contained 40 to 45 per cent of inert nitrogen. Although similar to the Wiberg process described earlier, it appears to have no advantage over it.

Norwegian H-Iron Process—This patented process uses a special shaft-type electric furnace, heated to 1650° F by ring-shaped perforated electrodes. Pelletized ore fines are reduced to iron by gases containing a high percentage of hydrogen.

Galluser Process—Sintered pellets of rich iron-ore concentrates are preheated in an induction-type electric shaft furnace and reduced to sponge iron by natural gas in this process. Cold gas, consisting of a mixture of carbon monoxide and hydrogen, enters the bottom of the induction furnace. During its ascent it cools the reduced pellets to keep them from becoming reoxidized, becoming heated itself in the process. Natural gas admitted to the reduction zone of the furnace cracks to form hydrogen, carbon monoxide, carbon dioxide, water vapor, and (unavoidably) up to 3 per cent carbon. Steam and carbon dioxide are removed from the exhaust gases, and the stripped gas is recirculated by entry into the bottom of the furnace.

C. FLUIDIZED-BED PROCESSES

Nu-Iron Process—The Nu-Iron process (Figure 13—11) is a continuous-reduction process developed by United States Steel Corporation. It uses the fluidized-bed technique for reducing minus 10-mesh ore by hydrogen in a two-stage reduction process. Hydrogen may be manufactured from natural gas, fuel oil, or powdered coal by several accepted methods.

In the process, a reducing gas at about 1550° F and 30 lb. per sq. in. gage pressure, containing about 85 per cent hydrogen, and solids as FeO at 1300° F, enter a second-stage reactor where FeO is reduced to Fe at 1200° to 1300° F.

The off-gas from the secondary stage, and ore preheated to about 1700° F, enter the upper or primary-stage reactor where Fe_2O_3 is reduced at 1300° F to FeO. The off-gas from the primary stage is purified after heat exchange, and a purge gas stream is removed to prevent the accumulation of nitrogen or other inert gas. The remaining gas is recycled with fresh make-up gas (96 to 98 per cent hydrogen). The

final product is briquetted while still hot (700° to 1100° F), and is then cooled in an inert atmosphere. The briquettes made in the process pilot plant have been successfully melted and refined to steel in an electric furnace.

H-Iron Process—The H-Iron process (Figure 13—12) is a fluidized-bed process that differs from the Nu-Iron process in that it operates on batch-reduction cycles at relatively low temperature and high pressure.

In the process, minus 20-mesh ore fines are preheated to about 900° F, transported pneumatically to a charge hopper, and then batch-charged into a reactor vessel equipped to maintain three fluidized beds in series. Preheated reducing gas at about 1000° F and 400 lb. per sq. in. gage pressure, containing about 85 per cent hydrogen, enters and reduces the fluidized beds of ore at 900° F. After a 5 to 8 hour reduction cycle, the material in the lower bed is about 95 per cent reduced, and the product is transferred to a dump hopper and briquetted. Because the briquettes are pyrophoric, they must be deactivated by heating to about 1600° F. The partially reduced material in the two upper beds is then dropped into the next lower beds, a fresh charge of preheated ore enters the uppermost bed, and a new reduction cycle is started. The off-gas from the reactor is heat-exchanged and purified. A purge gas stream is removed, and fresh make-up gas is added to the purified off-gas to form the reducing gas for the new cycle.

A.D.L. Process—The A.D.L. process, also known as the Esso Research-Little process, is a continuous fluidized-bed process that operates at essentially at-

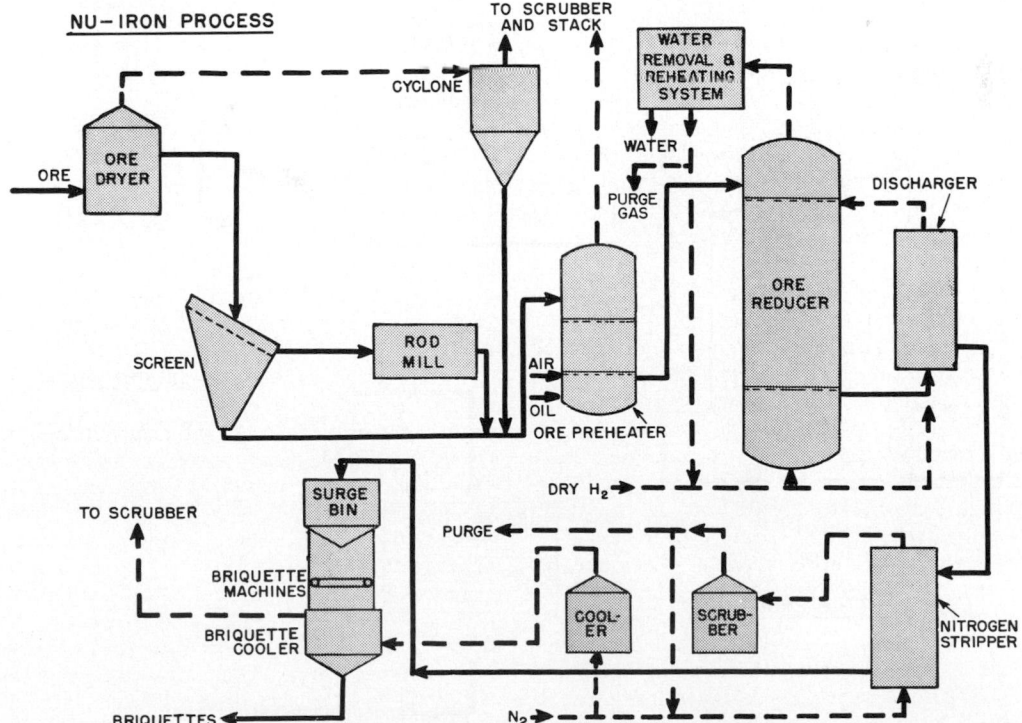

FIG. **13**—11. Flow sheet of the Nu-Iron continuous direct-reduction process employing a fluidized-bed technique.

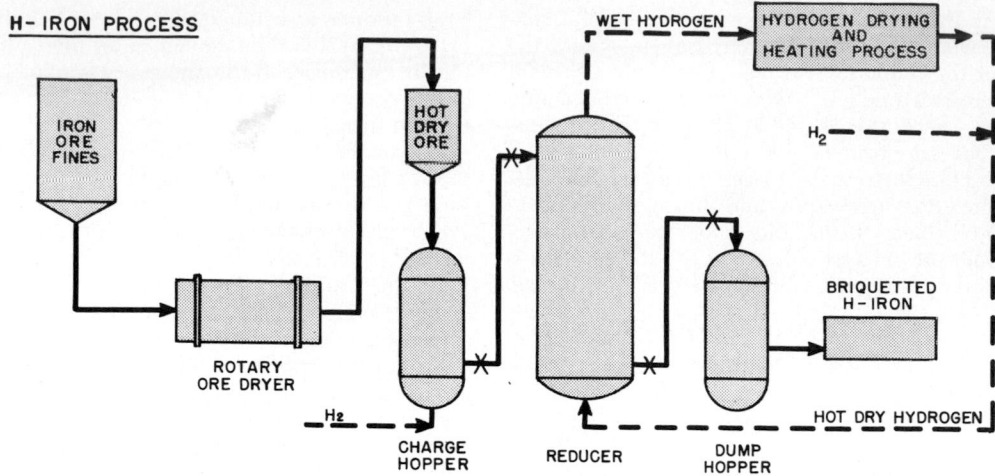

FIG. 13—12. Schematic representation of the steps involved in the H-Iron fluidized-bed direct-reduction process. (After Robiette)

mospheric pressure and at 1500° to 1600° F (Figure 13—13).

In the process, air preheated to 1500° to 1600° F, and natural gas preheated to 600° to 700° F, enter a fluidized-bed reactor where partial combustion occurs to provide heat for sustaining the endothermic reduction reactions and to generate the reducing gases. Partial combustion generates a reducing gas containing about 21 per cent carbon monoxide, 41 per cent hydrogen, and 38 per cent nitrogen. A portion of the off-gas is passed to an ore preheater and burned to

preheat the minus 10-mesh iron-ore fines to 1500° to 1600° F, and the preheated ore is reduced to iron during passage through two or three fluidized beds. The off-gas from the reducing beds has a calorific value of about 120 Btu per cu. ft. and, after cleaning, is used to preheat the inlet air and natural gas and to provide fuel for a power plant. The reduced-iron product may be agglomerated by briquetting.

Stelling Process—The Stelling process is a fluidized-bed process under pilot-plant development in Sweden. Except for using the techniques of fluidiza-

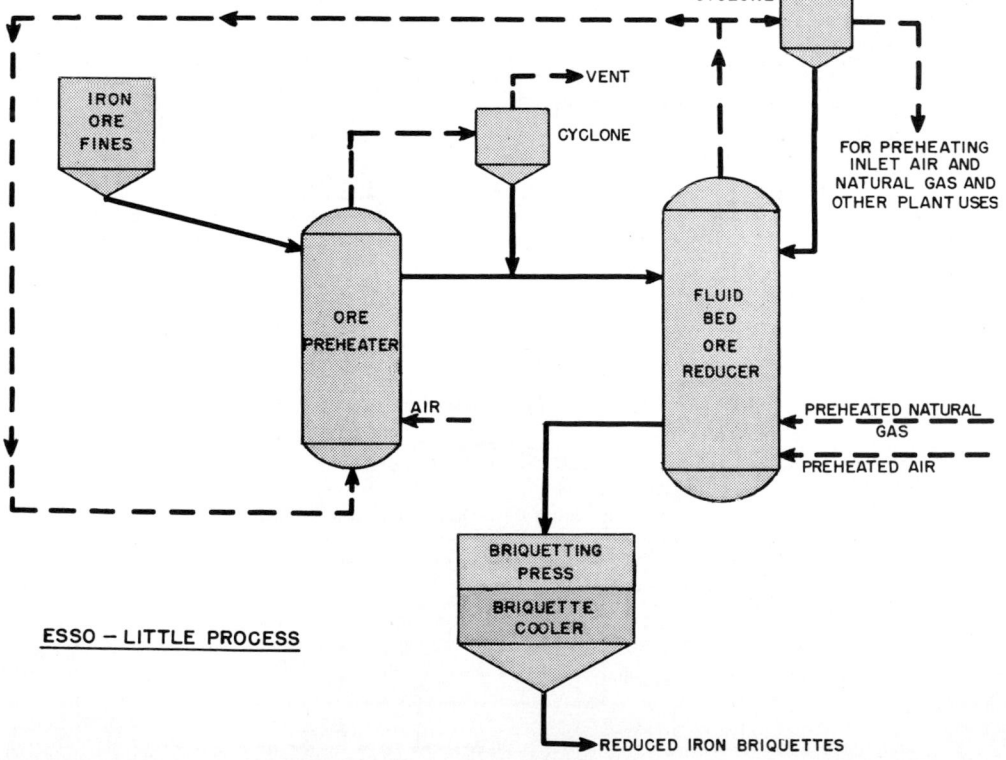

FIG. 13—13. Flow diagram representing the A.D.L. (Esso Research-Little) process for the continuous reduction of iron ore, utilizing the fluidized-bed principle.

tion, it differs radically from the fluidized-bed processes that have been described earlier.

It is a continuous process operating at atmospheric pressure in the 1100° to 1300° F temperature range, and the reducing gas is carbon monoxide. Hydrogen is considered an impurity that may cause difficulty if present in large amounts. Because of possible sticking and defluidization of a bed containing appreciable quantities of metallic iron, the desired product is not metallic iron but, instead, iron carbides. First, hematite or magnetite is reduced to FeO, which is then reduced to Fe_3C (cementite) or Fe_2C (Hägg carbide). The final product is mainly iron carbides, some FeO, and a few per cent metallic iron. It is claimed that by varying the holding time of the solids undergoing reaction in the bed, the process can yield nearly 100 per cent Fe_3C.

The following advantages are claimed: (1) sticking and defluidization of the beds are completely eliminated; (2) the iron carbide product is non-pyrophoric below 575° F; (3) carbon deposition from the decomposition of carbon monoxide does not occur; and (4) a heat economy comparable to that of the Wiberg process is attained.

Bubble-Hearth Process—The first fluidized-bed reduction process to be investigated on a pilot-plant scale was the bubble-hearth process. In this work, minus 60-mesh iron-ore fines were to be continuously reduced at 1100° F by hydrogen. The reactor vessel was externally heated (electrically) and had two hearths in series, each 3.7 sq. ft. in area and having 170 bubble caps for gas distribution. A fluidized-bed depth of 1 foot, about 600 pounds of material, was to be maintained on each hearth. Ore feed and product removal were to be continuous.

The operation of this pilot plant was not successful. The dust losses were excessive, the degree of reduction was poor, and the beds became defluidized because of sticking of the partially reduced solids. This work was important only in that it was the first pilot-plant scale investigation of reduction of iron ore in fluidized beds.

Novalfer-Onia Process—This is a French process based on the fluidized-bed principle, especially intended for the reduction of Algerian iron ores. The reducing gas is a mixture of carbon monoxide and hydrogen at a temperature between 1100° and 1300° F.

D. RETORT PROCESSES

Madaras-Mexican Process—The original Madaras process underwent extensive pilot-plant and semi-commercial development. It was designed to reduce preheated iron ore by hot hydrogen passed through the charge under pulsating pressure. The high-pressure portion of a pressure pulsation was to increase the quantity of gas in the retort, and it was postulated that this would promote diffusion of gas into the ore, minimize channeling of the gas, and increase the reduction rate. The low-pressure portion of the pulsation was to help remove the reaction products.

During the field trials, the pressure employed was 40 lb. per sq. in. gage, and the pulsation rate was 3 to 6 pulses per minute, but the charge moved as a piston, some crushing of the ore particles occurred, and some particles of the ore actually were forced out of the pressure seal. Poor reduction was obtained because of excessive heat losses from the reduction chambers. In addition, the iron product was sintered together and was difficult to discharge.

HyL Process—The HyL process involves the batch reduction of high-grade iron ore in retorts by reformed natural gas. It was developed by the Hojalata y Lamina Steel Company of Monterrey, Mexico. A 200-metric-ton-per-day plant in Monterrey, in production since late in 1957, had produced 100,000 tons of sponge iron by the end of 1960. A 500-metric-ton-per-day plant began operating about the latter date.

Figure 13—14 shows the flow diagram of a 200-metric-ton-per-day plant. Natural gas enters the plant and passes through preheating coils in the stacks of the reformer furnaces. It then flows through desulphurizing drums filled with activated charcoal and then a second time through preheating coils in the reformer stacks to further recuperate heat.

Steam is mixed with the preheated natural gas, and the mixture passes into hot, catalyst-filled tubes within the reformer furnaces. The reforming reaction takes place at about 1600° F according to the chemical equation:

$$CH_4 + H_2O = CO + 3H_2$$

and the gases emerge with a composition averaging (dry basis) about 73.1 per cent hydrogen, 16.3 per cent carbon monoxide, 6.6 per cent carbon dioxide, and 4.0 per cent unconverted methane.

The reformed gases are partially cooled (and heat is recuperated) by passing them through a water quench boiler, to generate steam. The gases then pass into a primary quench tower where direct contact with cold water removes the excess steam that was added as part of the gaseous feed to the reformer. The addition of excess steam to the reformer feed gases is generally necessary to prevent carbon deposition and plugging of the catalyst-filled tubes. The gases then pass into gas-preheating furnaces where they are heated to 1600-1800° F preparatory to flow through the reduction retorts. The presence of 6 to 7 per cent of carbon dioxide and the small amount of residual water vapor prevents carbon deposition in the gas-preheat furnaces.

The preheated primary-reducing gases enter the ore-filled retorts, which are in the primary cycle of ore reduction (final reduction). The gases pass downward through the fixed bed of ore and a portion of the hydrogen is converted to H_2O. At this point, the partially spent gases are called secondary reducing gases. In the 200-metric-ton-per-day plant being described, the secondary gases enter a quench tower, where water formed by reduction is removed from the gases by direct contact with cold water. The reducing gases, with water removed, are again heated in gas-preheat furnaces and passed through the retorts that are in the secondary ore-reduction cycle (initial ore prereduction stage). The exit gases from these retorts pass to a quench tower where water formed by reduction is removed. The gases leaving this quench tower are considered only as fuel gases, and are used

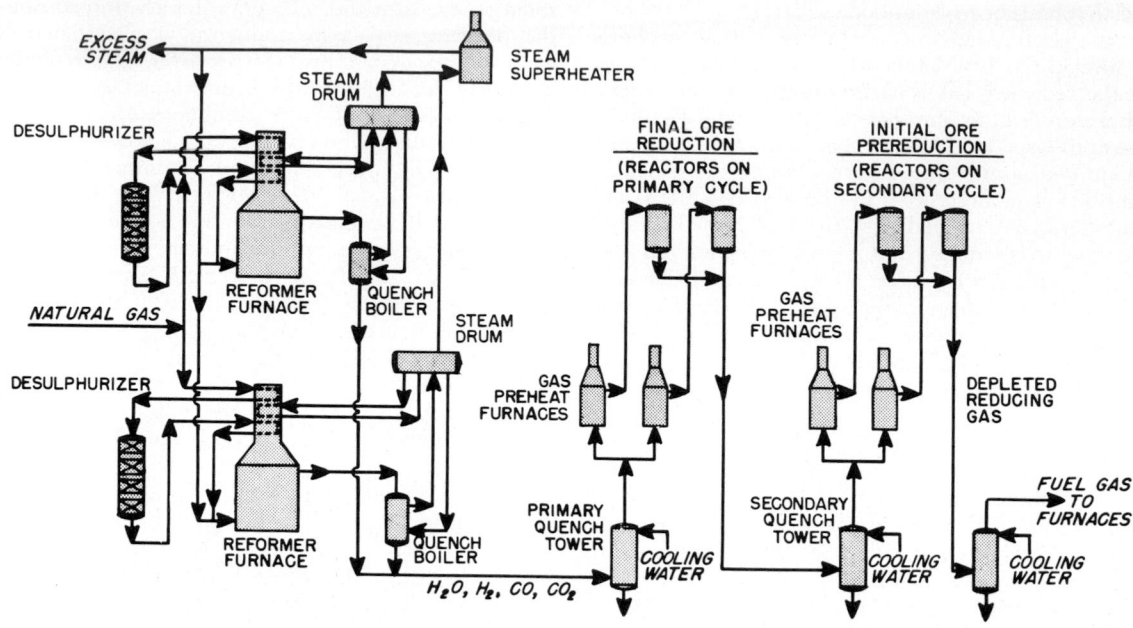

FIG. 13—14. Flow diagram of the HyL sponge-iron process as exemplified by a plant with a capacity of 200 metric tons per day. This diagram is applicable to plants of larger capacity, except that cooling and reheating of the reducing gases between the primary- and secondary-reduction retorts is eliminated.

for heating the reformer tubes, firing the gas-preheat furnaces, and generating and superheating steam. In the 500-metric-ton-per-day plant, the secondary gases are not quenched and reheated, but pass directly into the retorts in the secondary cycle of reduction.

Ores suitable for treatment by the HyL process must be either natural lump ores or agglomerate made from fine ores. The desired size range is plus ¼-inch, minus 1½ inches. Apparently, the operation can tolerate between 20 and 25 per cent of minus ¼-inch ore.

The ore cycle begins with one retort being emptied of reduced material and refilled with ore, which requires about one hour. The loaded retort then enters the secondary reduction cycle (initial or prereduction) for two hours (no ore preheating is done), after which it enters the primary reduction cycle (final reduction) for another two hours. Typically, the final degree of reduction, defined as the ratio of metallic iron to total iron, varies from 96 per cent at the top to 73 per cent at the bottom of the ore bed in the retort, and the average degree of reduction varies between 85 and 90 per cent.

A final operation not associated with iron-ore reduction is performed before a retort is discharged of sponge and recharged with ore. This operation is carburizing of the sponge iron preparatory to its use as a charge material for electric steelmaking furnaces. The hot sponge iron is carburized by passing natural gas through it for several minutes. Methane cracks and deposits carbon on the iron. Currently, about 0.3 per cent of carbon is deposited on the sponge: it is claimed that carbon contents up to 2.0 per cent can be attained.

Each reactor or retort is made up of two sections: a stationary, flanged top head with the inlet-gas connections permanently attached; and a lower flanged section that is free to move on wheels. The two sections are coupled together at the flanges by a series of hydraulically operated bolts. The exit pipe for gases leaving the lower section uses specially designed couplings for rapid disconnection. Each reactor is about 8 feet in diameter and holds about 15 tons of ore in a 5-foot-deep bed.

The entire sequence of operations for all reactors is automatic and is controlled from a central station. The reactors are uncoupled and rolled away from the fixed head into dumping position, and then are hydraulically tipped to discharge their contents into waiting hopper cars for transport to the steelmaking furnaces.

Among the advantages claimed for the process are: (1) The quantity of sulphur in the ore is diminished by about 85 per cent (however, no phosphorus is removed); (2) More than 50 per cent of the reducing gas (hydrogen) is utilized during a pass through the reduction cycles; and (3) Ore reduction can be carried almost to completion if desired, either by increasing the reduction-cycle time, or by increasing the flow of reducing gas relative to the quantity of ore processed.

E. JET SMELTING PROCESS

O.R.F. Jet-Smelter Process—The O.R.F. (Ontario Research Foundation) jet-smelter process is a direct-reduction process, in which fine magnetite concentrates are entrained in a high-temperature flame of oxygen and natural gas. The temperature of the ore particles is raised quickly to about 3500° F, partly by the oxidation of magnetite to hematite. The sudden temperature rise and the oxidation reaction cause the individual particles to decrepitate, and new surfaces are created. The hot-ore particles are then contacted by a large excess of natural gas, that cracks and decomposes to form a reducing gas composed largely of carbon monoxide and hydrogen. This gas then reduces the hematite ore particles to iron during a time interval of a fraction of a second. The flame and entrained particles are directed downward into a molten bath of metal and slag to minimize dust losses. The bath is maintained at a high carbon content to effect final reduction of any unreduced material.

SECTION 4

DIRECT-STEEL PROCESSES

O.R.F. Direct-Steel Process—In the O.R.F. (Ontario Research Foundation) direct-steel process, a bed of fine magnetite superconcentrate is laid down on a traveling grate, and hot flue gases are drawn through the bed to heat it to about 1800° F. Air is then drawn through the bed, causing the hot magnetite to burn to hematite, and the temperature rises to about 2200° F. At this temperature, the particles sinter lightly together into a highly permeable bed through which reducing gases can be passed without excessive dust losses. A reducing gas consisting of a 3:1 ratio of carbon monoxide to hydrogen is then passed through the bed, and complete reduction to iron is obtained in less than one hour. The final product is hot, porous, sintered iron, which is stripped from the grate and rolled into a steel sheet about 1/10 the thickness of the original bed.

The use of this process for the direct production of steel is limited to iron ores which can be concentrated to a purity of 0.5 per cent gangue, or less. The reduction step alone could use less-pure ores, but the final product would then have to be melted and refined by some steelmaking operation.

Cyclosteel Process—The Cyclosteel process is a new British method for making steel directly from iron ore, eliminating both sinter plants and coke ovens. In this method, powdered ore is first preheated in a fluidized bed. Powdered coal is then added to the preheated ore, and the mixture is blown tangentially into a reaction chamber. As the mixture spirals downward, it contacts hot gases produced by burning pulverized coal with oxygen in the bottom portion of the chamber. Because the reducing agent and the ore are finely divided particles at high temperature, reduction to carbonized iron takes place in a few seconds. Oxygen is added to burn off the carbon and phosphorus and to convert the iron to steel. A fine mist of molten slag and steel forms and proceeds, in a swirling motion, down to the bottom of the reactor where the droplets fall into a hearth, the steel settling to the bottom and the slag floating on the top of the molten bath.

Twyman Process—This is an abandoned method in which briquettes of iron ore and carbonaceous matter were thrown into the bath of metal in a basic open-hearth furnace to produce steel directly.

BIBLIOGRAPHY*

Ameen, E., Swedish sponge iron. Iron and Steel **17,** 1944, 608–612, 637–642. (18)

Ameen, E., Swedish sponge iron. Iron Age **153,** 1944, Jan. 20, 55–59, 150; Jan. 27, 56–65. (36)

Ameen, E., Production of sponge iron. Iron and Coal Trades Review **148,** 1944, Feb. 11, 211–213; Feb. 18, 249–251. (36)

Ballon, A., The electric reduction furnace. United Nations Department of Economic Affairs, A Study of the Iron and Steel Industry in Latin America, Bogota Meeting **2,** 1954, 172–175. (8)

Barrett, E. P., Sponge Iron and Direct-Iron Processes. U. S. Bureau of Mines Bul. 519, 1954, 10–11. (36)

Barrett, E. P., Gaseous reduction methods for the production of sponge iron. U. S. Bureau of Mines RI 4402, 1949. (36)

Barrett, E. P., et al., Investigation of bubble-hearth process for production of sponge iron. U. S. Bureau of Mines RI 4092, 1947. (30)

Barrett, E. P., Some important factors in sponge-iron production. U. S. Bureau of Mines RI 2955, 1929. (36)

Bhat, G. K., "Cyclosteel:" Steel direct from iron ore. Iron Age **179,** 1957, May 23, 129–130. (35)

Bourcoud, A. E., Method of and apparatus for reducing metallic oxides. U. S. Pat. No. 1,344,977; June 29, 1920. (15)

Bourcoud, A. E., Direct process for steel manufacture. Yearbook, American Iron and Steel Institute, 1921, 355–432. (15)

Brown, W. D., Production of sponge iron. U. S. Patent No. 1,979,729; Nov. 6, 1934. (15)

Brown, W. D., Sponge iron manufacture. U. S. Patent No. 1,984,727; Dec. 18, 1934. (15)

Brown, W. E., Sponge-iron experiments at Longview, Texas. U. S. Bureau of Mines RI 3925, 1946. (31)

Brown, W. E., An experiment in making sponge iron. Engineering and Mining Journal **145,** No. 11, Nov., 1944, 83–86. (31)

Buehl, R. C., et al., Use of sponge iron in steel production. U. S. Bureau of Mines RI 4096, 1947. (36)

Buehl, R. C., et al., Control of sulphur content of sponge iron produced in rotary kilns. U. S. Bureau of Mines RI 4057, 1947. (36)

Bull-Simonsen, I., Commercial production of sponge iron by the Norsk-Staal process. Stahl und Eisen **52,** 1932, 457–461. Henry Brutcher translation 105. (19)

Cavanagh, P. E., Manufacture of sponge iron in kilns. Journal of the Canadian Ceramic Society **17,** 1948, 77–87. (36)

* Numbers in parentheses following the listings correspond to numbers assigned to individual processes in list following bibliography. Processes are listed in same order that they appear in body of chapter, with exception of Chenot, Larkins, DuPuy, Lang, Rudolph-Landin, Leckie, Gerhardt and Twyman processes that have no modern significance (see Tiemann reference in bibliography).

(continued on next page)

Cavanagh, P. E., The tunnel kiln sponge iron process—III. Journal of the Canadian Ceramic Society **20**, 1951, 47–72. (7)

Cavanagh, P. E., Commercial production of sponge iron. Iron Age **163**, 1949, June 2, 67–71, 82. (36)

Cavanagh, P. E., Sponge iron. Metal Progress **63**, 1953, March, 67–69. (36)

Cavanagh, P. E., Manufacture of sponge iron in tunnel kilns—II. Journal of the Canadian Ceramic Society **19**, 1950, 62–67. (36)

Chemical Week **80**, 1957, January 26, 94–96. Cyclone reactor: In goes ore—out comes steel. (35)

Christiansen, B., Method of roasting and reducing ores. U. S. Patent No. 1,680,861; Aug. 14, 1928. (15)

Christiansen, B., Method of reducing ores. U. S. Patent No. 1,728,784; Sept. 17, 1929. (15)

Collin, F. C. and Grytting, O. A., A new approach in pig iron smelting. Journal of Metals **8**, Oct. 1956. (13)

Cope, S. G., The reduction of iron ores. The possibilities of an alternative to the blast furnace. Murex Ltd. Review **1**, 1957, No. 17, 465–497. (36)

Dean, R. S., et al., Progress reports—Metallurgical Division, 4. Studies in direct production of iron and steel from ore. U. S. Bureau of Mines RI 3229, 1934. (15)

Dean, R. S., Sponge iron. A progress report. U. S. Bureau of Mines RI 3790, 1945. (36)

Durrer, R., Verhütten von eisenerzen. Verlag Stahleisen m.b.h., 1954. 159 pages. (36)

Durrer, R., Fundamentals of iron production. Verlag Francke A. G., 1947. 210 pages. (7)

Durrer, R., Grundlagen der eisengewinnung. Verlag Francke A. G., 1947. (36)

Durrer, R., Electric smelting. Journal Iron and Steel Institute **156**, 1947, 257–260. (8)

Eketorp, S., Hoganas sponge iron process. Jernkontorets Annaler **129**, 1945, 703–721. Iron and Steel Institute (London) translation 275. (7)

Engineering **179**, 1955, 738–739. Pig iron and steel from low-grade ore and coke. (4)

Fastje, D., Reconstruction and initial operational results of the Krupp-Renn plant in Salzgitter-Watenstedt. Stahl and Eisen **78**, 1958, 784–792. (1)

Fornander, S., Iron and steel making processes used in Sweden. Journal Iron and Steel Institute **177**, 1954, 1–12. (18)

Galluser, H., The use of natural gases in reduction of iron ores. Blast Furnace and Steel Plant **46**, No. 12, Dec., 1958, 1301–2. (25)

Girardi, D. J., Production and use of sponge iron for steel in Sweden. AIME Electric Furnace Steel Conference Proceedings **9**, 1951, 25–34. (36)

Gottschalk, V. H., et al., Manufacture of sponge iron in tunnel kilns. U. S. Bureau of Mines RI 4271, 1948. (36)

Gustafsson, E. G. T., Process for producing metal sponge. U. S. Patent No. 1,848,710; March 8, 1932. (15)

Gustafsson, E. G. T., Method of producing metal sponge. U. S. Patent No. 1,864,593; June 28, 1932. (15)

Harman, E. S., Synthetic scrap by direct reduction. Iron and Steel Engineer **20**, Jan., 1943, 66–74. (3)

Hornsey, J. W., Reduction of metals from ores. U. S. Patent No. 1,690,820; Nov. 6, 1928. (6)

Hornsey, J. W., Reduction of metals from ores. U. S. Patent No. 1,786,999; Dec. 30, 1930. (6)

Jacobs, J. H., et al., First two years of operation of the Bureau of Mines electrolytic manganese pilot plant at Boulder City, Nevada. Metals Technology **11**, August 1944, AIME Technical Publication 1717. (21)

Jensen, K. E., The Bassett process for the production of pig iron in rotary kilns. United Nations Department of Economic Affairs, A study of the iron and steel industry in Latin America, Bogota meeting **2**, 1954, 210–216. (3)

Johannsen, F., The Krupp-Renn process. United Nations Department of Economic Affairs, A study of the iron and steel industry in Latin America, Bogota meeting **2**, 1954, 192–200. (1)

Johannsen, F., The preparation of high-silica iron ores by the Krupp-Renn process. Instituto del Hierro y del Acero **5**, 1952, 787–795. (1)

Johnston, T. L., Sponge iron in Japan. U. S. Bureau of Mines IC 7440, 1948. (36)

Johnston, T. L. and Mahan, W. M., Laramie sponge-iron pilot plant. U. S. Bureau of Mines RI 4376, 1948. (36)

Journal Iron and Steel Institute **156**, 1947, 293–298. Electric smelting plant at Choinez. (8)

Kalling, B., and Johannson, F., Reduction of iron ore without melting in a rotary furnace. Journal Iron and Steel Institute **177**, 1954, 76–85. (5)

Kalling, B., The rotary kiln process for sponge iron developed at the Avesta Iron and Steel Works and the Domnarfvet Iron and Steel Works, Sweden. United Nations Department of Economic Affairs, A study of the iron and steel industry in Latin America, Bogota meeting **2**, 1954, 216–219. (5)

Kalling, B. M. S. and Von Delwig, C., Method of reducing ore. U. S. Patent No. 1,964,402; June 26, 1934. (15)

Koyanagi, K., Simultaneous manufacture of cement and cast iron. Rock Products **52**, 1949, 60–62. (3)

Koyanagi, K. and Sudoh, T., Constitution of cement clinker obtained by Bassett process. Rock Products **53**, 1950, 129–132. (3)

Lameck, P., Manufacture of pig iron from ore fines and non-coking coal. Iron and Coal Trades Review **156**, 1948, 1173–1177. (14)

Lehmkuhler, H., Treatment of low-grade siliceous iron ores by the Krupp-Renn process of the industrial pilot plant of Fried. Krupp A. G. Stahl und Eisen **59**, 1939, 1281–1288. Henry Brutcher translation 1057. (1)

Lewis, W. K., Process for reducing oxidic iron ore. U. S. Patent No. 2,711,368; June 21, 1955. (28)

Madaras, J. D., Method of and apparatus for reducing ores and effecting other chemical reactions. U. S. Patent No. 2,243,110; May 27, 1941. (31)

Maier, C. G., Sponge-iron experiments at Mococo. U. S. Bureau of Mines Bul. 386, 1937. (15)

Malcor, H., The low-shaft blast furnace. Iron and Coal Trades Review **167**, 1953, 253–258. (14)

Mining Congress Journal, Direct reduction of iron ores in a rotary kiln. The Journal, Dec., 1958. (2)

Newkirk, D. L. and Ensign, E. E., Processing kiln. U. S. Patent No. 2,404,650; July 23, 1946. (15)

Olds, B. S., Processes for direct reduction of iron. American Iron and Steel Institute Regional Technical Meetings, 1957, 203–222. (28)

Paige, E. S., A review of direct-reduction ironmaking processes. Engineers' Digest **20**, 1959, 196–202. (36)

Pecorari, A., The Lubatti electric process for reduction of ores. Radex Rundschau, 1954, 152–162. Iron and Steel Institute (London) translation 1598. (9)

Ralston, O. C., et al., Recovering zinc from copper smelter products. Engineering and Mining Journal **136**, 1935, 167–169. (3)

Ramseyer, C. F., Sponge iron—its possibilities and limitations. Iron and Steel Engineer **21**, 1944, July, 35–44, 72. (30)

Reed, T. F., et al., Nu-Iron, a fluidized-bed reduction process. Journal of Metals **12**, 1960, 317–320. (26)

Reinfeld, H., The Sturzelberg pig-iron refining process. Giesserei **38**, 1951, 517–523. (4)

Reinfeld, H., Recent developments in the Sturzelberg iron reduction process. Radex Rundschau, 1951, 178–187. Iron and Steel Institute (London) translation 1597. (4)

(continued on next page)

Robiette, A. G., Alternative processes for making iron and steel. Iron and Coal Trades Review **177**, 1958, 209–216. (36)

Schmalfeldt, H., Process for the reduction of fine iron ores. U. S. Patent No. 2,107,549; Feb. 8, 1938. (15)

Schumacher, H., German work on the low-shaft blast furnace. Iron and Coal Review **166**, 1953, 1383–1386. (14)

Sem, M. O., Electric smelting of pig iron. United Nations Department of Economic Affairs, A study of the iron and steel industry in Latin America, Bogota meeting **2**, 1954, 175–178. (8)

Sieurin, E., Hoganas Jarnsvamp. Jernkontorets Annaler **n.s. 66**, 1911, 448–493. (7)

Smith, E. C., Experience to date on iron production methods other than coke blast furnaces; Direct reduction. Yearbook American Iron and Steel Institute, 1948, 302–342. (36)

Speight, G. E., Metallurgical meetings at Liege. Low-shaft furnace and converter processes. Iron and Steel **26**, 1953, 353–355. (14)

Squires, A. M. and Johnson, C. A., The H-iron process. AIME Blast Furnace, Coke Oven and Raw Material Conference Proceedings **16**, 1957, 32–42. (24)

Stalhane, O. and Stalhane, J. B., Rotary furnace for treating pulverized ore with gas. U. S. Patent No. 1,959,772; May 22, 1934. (15)

Stalhane, O. and Stalhane, J. B., Method of reducing oxide ores or the like by means of gas. U. S. Patent No. 1,964,680; June 26, 1934. (15)

Stalhed, J., Production of sponge iron according to the Wiberg-Soderfors method. United Nations Department of Economic Affairs, A study of the iron and steel industry in Latin America, Bogota meeting **2**, 1954, 204–209. (18)

Starratt, F. W., Low-shaft blast furnace holds new promise. Journal of Metals **9**, 1957, 1432–1434. (14)

Steel **141**, 1957, Oct. 28, 180, 182, 185, 188, 190, 192. The case for direct reduction. (11)

Stelling, O. and Pereswetoff-Morath, I., A process of direct reduction of iron ore concentrate by carbon monoxide without fusion. Jernkontorets Annaler **141**, 1957, 237–260. Henry Brutcher translation 4000. (29)

Stelling, P. O. and Pereswetoff-Morath, I. G. M., Process of treating pulverulent iron oxides. U. S. Patent No. 2,780,537; Feb. 5, 1957. (29)

Stewart, Alex and Work, H. K., R-N direct reduction process. Journal of Metals **10**, July 1958, 460–464. (2)

Thomas, S. B., Sponge iron kiln. U. S. Patent No. 1,990,-845; Feb. 12, 1935, (15) (31)

Tiemann, H. P., Iron and steel handbook. McGraw-Hill, New York, N. Y. 2nd ed., 1919. (36)

Torgeson, D. R., et al., Pilot-plant investigations. Production of sponge iron with producer gas. U. S. Bureau of Mines RI 3994, 1946. (21)

Udy, Dr. Marvin J. and Blackburn, Robert A., The Strategic-Udy direct iron reduction process. Yearly Proceedings, Association of Iron and Steel Engineers, 1959, 921–928. (12)

Udy, M. J. and Udy, M. C., A new direct-reduction method. Metal Progress, Dec. 1958. (12)

Wiberg, M., Relation of types of ore to smelting processes. United Nations Department of Economic and Social Affairs, Survey of World Iron Ore Resources; Occurrence, Appraisal and Use, 1955, 122–145. (3)

Wiberg, M., Reduction of iron ore by carbon monoxide, hydrogen and methane. Jernkontorets Annaler **124**, 1940, 179–212. Henry Brutcher translation 1417. (18)

Wiberg, F. M., Method of and furnace for reducing ores and oxygen compounds utilized as ores. U. S. Patent No. 1,401,222; Dec. 27, 1921. (18)

Wiberg, F. M., Method of treating solid materials with gases. U. S. Patent No. 1,849,561; March 15, 1932. (18)

Zuliani, G., A new electrothermal process for the manufacture of iron. The Lubatti process. Journal du Four Electrique et des Industries Electrochimiques **62**, 1953, 25–27. (9)

NUMERICAL IDENTIFICATION CODE
FOR LISTINGS IN BIBLIOGRAPHY

Ref. No.	Process	Ref. No.	Process
1	Krupp-Renn	20	Bureau of Mines Shaft Furnace
2	R-N	21	Skinner Multiple Hearth
3	Bassett	22	Cape-Brassert
4	Sturzelberg	23	United Verde Shaft Furnace
5	Domnarfvet	24	Norwegian H-Iron
6	Hornsey-Wills	25	Galluser
7	Hoganas	26	Nu-Iron
8	Tysland-Hole	27	H-Iron
9	Lubatti	28	A.D.L.
10	Elektrometall	29	Stelling
11	D.L.M.	30	Bubble-Hearth
12	Strategic-Udy	31	Madaras-Mexican
13	Edwin-Elektrokemisk	32	HyL
14	Low-Shaft Blast Furnace	33	O.R.F. Jet Smelter
15	Maier-Mococo	34	O.R.F. Direct Steel
16	Azincourt	35	Cyclosteel
17	Scortecci	36	General
18	Wiberg-Soderfors		
19	Norsk-Staal		

CHAPTER 14

The Manufacture of Pig Iron

SECTION 1

PRODUCTION AND KINDS OF PIG AND CAST IRON

As already mentioned in Chapter 1, the extraction of iron from its ores dates back to prehistoric times. However, it was not until the 14th century that furnaces were developed that could not only reduce iron but at the same time melt it so that the product could be cast from the furnace in a molten form. It is well to remember that the modern blast furnace (Figure 14—1) with its very high productivity and its excellent fuel efficiency is the result of the technical and engineering development of a process that was started over 500 years ago.

The Importance of Pig Iron—Pig iron is the intermediate form through which almost all iron must pass in the manufacture of steel. In addition to this, it is used in foundries for the manufacture of a wide variety of iron castings. The importance of pig iron is shown by Table 14—I, which summarizes the yearly production of pig iron and ferroalloys from blast furnaces in the United States for the years 1939 to 1962, inclusive.

Kinds and Grades of Pig Iron—Pig iron is the term applied generally to the metallic product of the blast

Table 14—I.   Yearly Blast-Furnace Production of Pig Iron and Ferroalloys (Net Tons)*

	Pig Iron							Ferroalloys and Silvery Pig Iron
Year	Basic	Bessemer	Low Phosphorus	Foundry	Malleable	All Other, Including Direct Castings	Total Pig Iron	
1962	58,806,123	2,822,674	174,733	1,428,614	2,153,957	254,723	65,640,824	650,181
1961	58,149,520	2,601,146	176,077	1,362,215	2,102,724	239,005	64,630,687	664,199
1960	58,261,108	3,403,599	387,260	1,467,358	2,672,875	288,448	66,480,648	839,481
1959	52,114,297	3,055,776	374,479	1,881,228	2,487,851	280,415	60,194,046	635,337
1958	49,114,646	3,599,873	320,278	1,606,028	2,304,904	211,978	57,157,707	606,393
1957	65,377,744	6,344,106	580,013	2,279,256	3,459,331	334,928	78,375,378	963,554
1956	61,638,748	6,664,957	504,189	2,398,346	3,467,117	395,132	75,068,489	891,071
1955	62,484,889	7,436,354	263,036	2,754,641	3,531,420	387,077	76,857,417	932,267
1954	47,023,175	5,625,503	211,893	2,273,032	2,629,662	202,283	57,965,548	721,336
1953	59,882,512	8,110,881	297,065	2,500,996	3,784,458	325,517	74,901,429	955,443
1952	47,511,189	7,445,715	307,478	2,670,210	3,120,168	258,178	61,312,938	837,988
1951	54,212,509	9,045,954	314,725	3,050,626	3,363,369	287,095	70,274,278	953,472
1950	49,880,440	8,090,608	335,418	2,807,247	3,181,043	293,151	64,586,907	852,862
1949	40,905,356	7,059,416	301,520	2,503,912	2,409,436	232,922	53,412,562	762,972
1948	46,315,064	7,731,530	384,425	2,769,510	2,590,656	264,031	60,055,216	988,590
1947	44,804,743	7,182,207	331,118	2,953,405	2,874,752	182,687	58,328,912	985,436
1946	33,727,655	5,932,414	167,013	2,545,936	2,190,285	215,493	44,778,796	769,111
1945	39,866,982	8,255,513	314,063	2,248,887	2,350,076	187,648	53,223,169	943,313
1944	45,886,008	9,756,836	474,686	2,190,681	2,494,659	204,569	61,007,439	1,065,244
1943	45,374,662	10,258,788	538,832	2,059,501	2,393,241	185,646	60,810,670	1,109,644
1942	43,532,865	9,865,220	562,672	2,546,530	2,399,520	169,137	59,075,944	1,039,443
1941	39,759,841	9,522,343	474,428	2,760,827	2,417,137	165,975	55,100,551	969,955
1940	33,987,734	7,386,320	448,956	2,292,175	1,832,401	124,080	46,071,666	907,425
1939	25,437,868	5,755,806	214,828	1,910,868	1,386,337	102,975	34,808,682	587,796

*From American Iron and Steel Institute Statistical Reports for corresponding years.

FIG. 14—1. General exterior view of a large, modern blast furnace.

Table 14—II.   Chief Metallic Products of the Blast Furnace[a]

Product	Composition Range				
	Silicon (%)	Sulphur (%)	Phosphorus (%)	Manganese (%)	Total Carbon[b] (%)
IRON FOR STEELMAKING					
Basic Pig— Northern	1.50 max.	0.05 max.	0.400 max.	1.01 to 2.00	3.5 to 4.40
In steps of	0.25	—	—	0.50	—
Basic Pig—Southern	1.50 max.	0.05 max.	0.700 to 0.900	0.40 to 0.75	3.5 to 4.40
In steps of	0.25	—	—	—	—
Acid Pig, Bessemer	1.00 to 2.25	0.045 max.	0.04 to 0.135	0.5 to 1.00	4.15 to 4.40
Acid Pig, Open-Hearth	0.70 to 1.50	0.045 max.	Under 0.05	0.5 to 2.50	4.15 to 4.40
Oxygen Steelmaking Pig	0.20 to 2.00	0.05 max.	0.400 max.[c]	0.4 to 2.50	3.5 to 4.40
MERCHANT IRON FOR FOUNDRIES					
Low Phosphorus	0.50 to 3.00	0.035 max.	0.035 max.	1.25 max.	3.0 to 4.50
Intermediate Low Phosphorus	1.00 to 3.00	0.050 max.	0.036 to 0.075	1.25 max.	3.0 to 4.50
Bessemer	1.00 to 3.00	0.050 max.	0.076 to 0.100	1.25 max.	3.0 to 4.50
Malleable	0.75 to 3.50	0.050 max.	0.101 to 0.300	0.50 to 1.25	3.0 to 4.50
Northern Foundry	3.50 max.	0.050 max.	0.301 to 0.700	0.50 to 1.25	3.0 to 4.50
Southern Foundry	3.50 max.	0.050 max.	0.700 to 0.900	0.40 to 0.75	3.0 to 4.50
All grades in steps of	0.25	—	—	0.25	—
FERROALLOYS					
Spiegel (3 grades)	1.0 to 4.5	0.05 max.	0.14 to 0.25	16 to 30	6.5 max.
Standard Ferromanganese (3 grades)	1.2 max.	0.05 max.	0.35 max.	74 to 82	7.5 max.
Ferrosilicon, Silvery Pig	5.00 to 17.00	0.06 max.	0.300 max.	1.00 to 2.00	1.5 max.
Ferrophosphorus	1.5 to 1.75	Under 0.05	15 to 24	0.07 to 0.50	1.10 to 2.0
FOREIGN PRACTICE					
Basic Bessemer (Gilchrist or Thomas)	0.3 to 1.00	0.20	1.9 to 2.5	0.7 to 2.5	3.50 to 4.0
Duplex Iron	1.2 to 1.75	Under 0.060	0.7 to 1.5	0.4 to 0.90	4.00 to 4.20

(a) Further information in: Steel Products Manual—Section 1—Pig Iron and Blast-Furnace Alloys, published by the American Iron and Steel Institute, 1951; and ASTM Standards 1961, Part I—Ferrous Metals (Specifications), published by the American Society for Testing and Materials.

(b) Carbon not specified.

(c) Up to 2.00 per cent phosphorus may be used by double slagging.

furnace when it contains over 90 per cent of iron. This term is used to distinguish it from blast-furnace products such as **ferromanganese** and **spiegeleisen** that are made from manganese ore or mixtures of manganese ore and iron ore, and still other blast-furnace products such as **ferrophosphorus** and **alloy iron.** Pig iron can be made in other ways than in a blast furnace. For example, it can be made in electric smelting furnaces or by melting steel scrap with an excess of carbon in a cupola. Only minor quantities are made, however, by these means. Most pig iron is transferred to the steelmaking shops and used in the liquid state: in this form it is referred to as **hot metal.** When it is required in solid form for convenient handling, it is generally cast into small molds where it solidifies to form what are called pigs. These molds are usually attached to a long inclined conveyor, to give the iron time to solidify before it is discharged

at the end of travel of the conveyor: this equipment is called a **pig machine.** The term **pig iron** arose from the old-fashioned method of casting iron into beds of molds formed in sand, so arranged that they could be fed from a common runner. Since the group of molds resembled a litter of suckling pigs, the individual pieces of iron were referred to as **pigs** and the runner as a **sow.**

Table **14—II** shows many of the different specifications for blast-furnace products. These fall into three general classifications: (1) iron for steelmaking, used in a variety of different processes; (2) iron for castings, the characteristics of which are discussed in Chapter 38; and (3) ferroalloys, which contain a high percentage of one or more metallic elements and are used to regulate the compositions of other ferrous metals.

SECTION 2

OUTLINE OF THE BLAST-FURNACE PROCESS

Furnace Input and Output—In the blast-furnace process, iron-bearing materials (iron ore, sinter, pellets, mill scale, open-hearth or Bessemer slag, iron or steel scrap, etc.), fuel (coke), and flux (limestone and/or dolomite) are charged into the top of the furnace.

Heated air (blast) and, in some instances, fuel (gas, oil or powdered coal) are blown in at the bottom. The blast air burns part of the fuel to produce heat for the chemical reactions involved and for melting the iron, while the balance of the fuel and part of the gas from the combustion remove the oxygen combined with the metal. The amount of each material used per ton of iron produced is about 1.7 tons of ore and other iron-bearing materials, 0.50 to 0.65 ton of coke or other fuel, and about 0.25 ton of limestone or dolomite, and 1.8 to 2.0 tons of air. The limestone or dolomite are often premixed with the iron-bearing material and sintered or pelletized to improve the efficiency of the process. From these materials are produced 1.0 ton of iron, 0.2 to 0.4 ton of slag, 0.05 ton or less of flue dust and 2.5 to 3.5 tons of blast-furnace gas. Figure 14—2 shows schematically the steps in assembling the raw materials and charging them into a modern blast furnace, along with the method for compressing and heating the blast, and the means for disposition of the products.

FUNCTIONS OF THE CHARGED MATERIALS

Iron-Bearing Materials—The function of the iron-bearing materials is to supply the element iron, which in turn represents about 93.5 per cent of the pig iron. The major iron-bearing materials are ore, sinter, and pellets. The ore usually is in the form of an oxide or hydrated oxide, either hematite (Fe_2O_3), limonite or goethite ($Fe_2O_3 \cdot XH_2O$), or magnetite (Fe_3O_4). Hematite represents the largest proportion of ores used. When chemically pure, hematite contains 70 per cent or iron, but most ores contain only about 50 to 65 per cent of iron, the balance (2 to 20 per cent) being gangue (which consists mostly of alumina and silica), and up to 6 per cent of chemically combined water and volatile matter. Sinter is an agglomerate made from small particles of iron-bearing materials that are fused or fritted together at a high temperature produced by combustion of carbon in the sintering-machine feed mix, as described in Chapter 5. It has recently become the practice to add flux of small particle size to the mixture being sintered to partially flux the gangue material before it is smelted in the blast furnace. Sinter generally contains from 52 to 65 per cent of iron.

Pellets are agglomerates made from very finely divided (minus 200-mesh) iron-ore concentrates to which have been added a small quantity of fuel and a binder. The mixture is then balled to form "green" pellets slightly larger than ¼-inch but smaller than ¾-inch in diameter. The fuel may be provided by "coating" the green pellets (made originally in a balling drum) with fine particles of a suitable carbonaceous material. In either case, the pellets are then hardened by firing in a shaft-type furnace or kiln or on a traveling grate. Pellets usually contain from 60 to 67 per cent of iron. Chapter 5 describes the methods used for pelletizing.

The minor iron-bearing materials are: roll scale, open-hearth-furnace or Bessemer-converter slag, and scrap.

Roll scale consists of oxides that form on the surface of steel during heating for rolling, and is usually a source of relatively pure iron oxide except from mills where it gets contaminated with hot-top brick or other refractories.

Basic open-hearth slag contains about 25 per cent of iron and an excess of bases over acids. Conse-

quently, it can replace a certain quantity of basic fluxes in the blast-furnace burden. Its use increases the total quantity of slag per ton of hot metal. Basic open-hearth slag also contains sufficient manganese to make it a useful source of this element. Its use is limited by the specification for the maximum phosphorus content of the iron produced. It is not used in blast furnaces producing "blowing iron" for the acid-Bessemer process, because the manganese it contains would adversely affect the properties of the slag in the converter.

Bessemer-converter slag does not contain as much excess bases or phosphorus as basic open-hearth slag. It is used as a source of iron and also manganese, especially when increased blast-furnace slag volume is desirable.

Scrap generated in casting the blast furnace is recharged for recovery of the iron units. Infrequently, scrap from external sources is used to increase production of hot metal.

Coke—The function of coke is to produce the heat required for smelting and also to supply the chemical reactants (primarily carbon monoxide) for reducing iron ore. In addition to this, it supplies the carbon that dissolves in the hot metal (about 70 to 80 pounds for every ton of pig iron).

Since all of the carbon monoxide cannot be used in the blast furnace (because of equilibrium limitations), the gas issuing from the top of the furnace contains enough combustible carbon monoxide to have a calorific value of between 85 and 100 B.t.u. per standard cubic foot. This gas is used to preheat the air blast and to generate power for running the blowers, thus returning as much of the energy back to

Table 14—III. Utilities Requirements of a Self-Contained Blast-Furnace Plant with Two Furnaces, Producing A Total of 4200 Net Tons of Hot Metal per Day.*

Utility	Quantity required daily
Recirculating Water	16,012,800 gal.
Make-Up Water	259,200 gal.
Other Service Water	3,326,400 gal.
Water to Utilities (Boiler House, Turbine Condensers, Etc.)	29,952,000 gal.
Potable Water	72,000 gal.
Coke-Oven Gas	1,008,000 cu. ft.
Natural Gas for Heat	172,000 cu. ft.
" " " " (3 mos.)	20,448,000 cu. ft.
Boiler-House Fuel	
Fuel Oil	172,800 gal.
Blast-Furnace Gas	446,400,000 cu. ft.
Compressed Air at 80 Lb. per Sq. In.	1,152,000 cu. ft.
Steam at 200 Lb. per Sq. In. and 100° F Superheat	9,600,000 lb.
AC Electricity—Purchased	151,200 kilowatt-hours
DC Electricity—(Own-Produced)	42,000 kilowatt-hours

*Volumes of gases refer to cubic feet at 60° F and 30 in. Hg, unless otherwise specified.

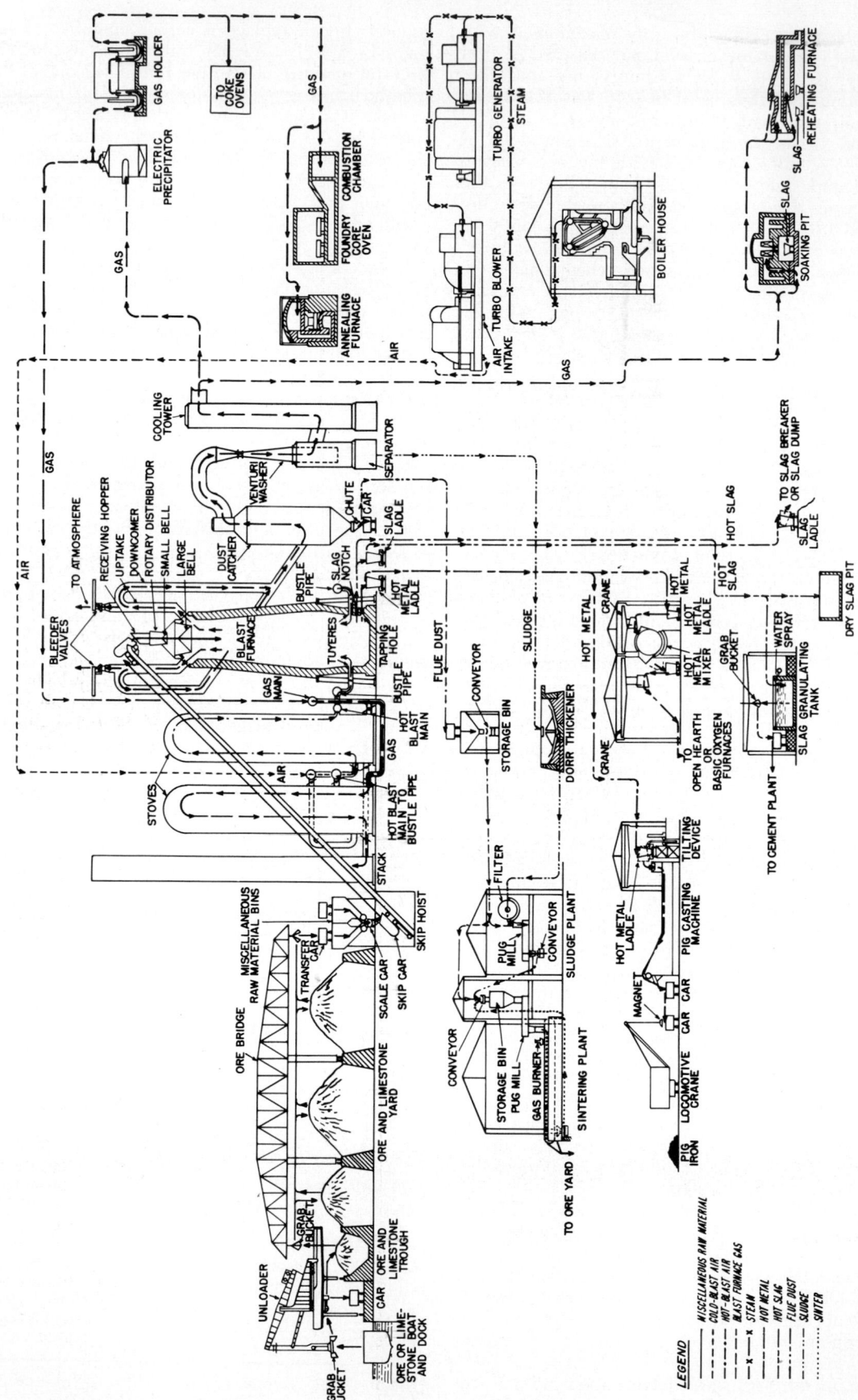

Fig. 14—2. Flow diagram depicting the principal units and auxiliaries in a modern blast-furnace plant, and showing the steps in the manufacture of pig iron from receipt of raw materials to disposal of pig iron and slag, as well as the methods for utilizing the furnace gases.

the process as possible. The gas in excess of that needed for the stoves and blowers is generally used for firing boilers to produce energy for other portions of the plant.

Function of Fluxes—The function of the limestone and/or dolomite is two-fold: (1) to form a fluid slag with the coke ash, ore gangue, and any other charged impurities, and (2) to form a slag of such chemical composition that it will provide a degree of control of the sulphur content of the iron.

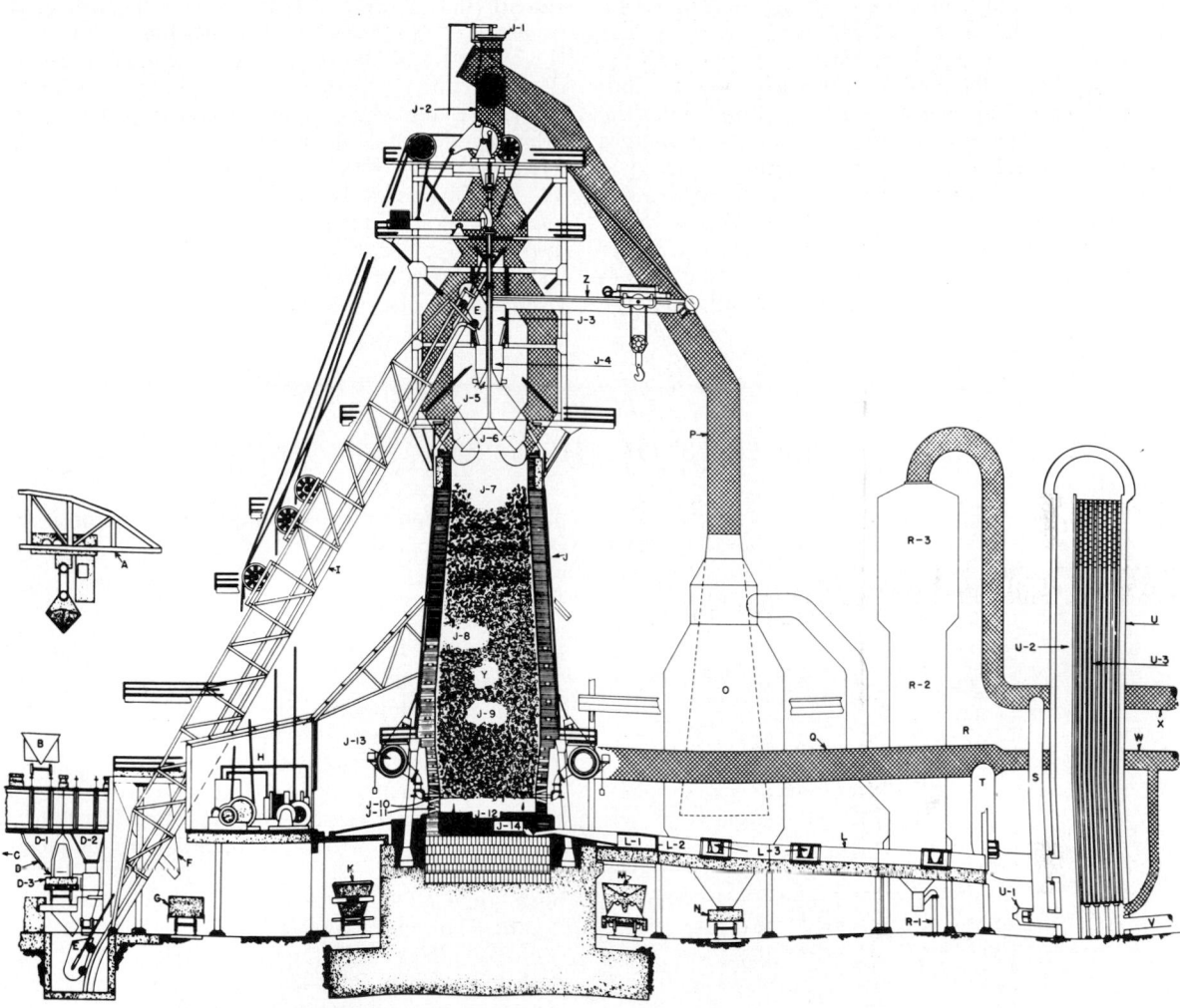

FIG. 14—3. Idealized cross-section of a typical modern blast-furnace plant. Details may vary from plant to plant: for example, Figure 14—2 shows a different arrangement for washing the gases leaving the dust catcher (O).

Legend

A. Ore bridge
B. Ore transfer car
C. Ore storage yard
D. Stockhouse
    D-1 Ore and limestone bins
    D-2 Coke bin
    D-3 Scale car
E. Skip
F. Coke dust recovery chute
G. Freight car
H. Skip and bell hoist
I. Skip bridge
J. Blast furnace
    J-1 Bleeder valve
    J-2 Gas uptake
    J-3 Receiving hopper
    J-4 Distributor

    J-5 Small bell
    J-6 Large bell
    J-7 Stock line
    J-8 Stack
    J-9 Bosh
    J-10 Tuyeres
    J-11 Slag notch
    J-12 Hearth
    J-13 Bustle pipe
    J-14 Iron notch
K. Slag ladle
L. Cast house
    L-1 Iron trough
    L-2 Slag skimmer
    L-3 Iron runner
M. Hot-metal ladle
N. Flue dust car
O. Dust catcher

P. Downcomer
Q. Hot blast line to furnace
R. Gas washer
    R-1 Sludge line to thickener
    R-2 Spray washer
    R-3 Electrical precipitator
S. Gas offtake to stove burner
T. Hot blast connection from stove
U. Stove
    U-1 Gas burner
    U-2 Combustion chamber
    U-3 Checker chamber
V. Exhaust gas line to stack
W. Cold blast line from blower
X. Surplus gas line
Y. Stock—Iron ore, coke, limestone
Z. Jib boom crane

PARTS OF A BLAST-FURNACE PLANT

Figure 14—3 is a schematic cross-section of a typical blast-furnace plant (see also Figure 14—2). The items shown as "A" through "I" are the equipment required for assembling the raw materials, for measuring out the right proportions and for hoisting them to the top of the furnace by means of a **skip car**. The principal parts of the furnace are marked with "J" showing the **receiving hopper**, the **revolving distributor** and the **bells** which dump the materials into the furnace and then close to seal the opening so that gas cannot escape. The upper portion of the furnace (J-8) where the burden is preheated and prereduced is called the **stack**, the inverted conical section where melting starts (J-9) is called the **bosh**, and the lower portion where the metal and slag collect (J-12) is called the **hearth**. The metal is removed from the iron notch into **transfer ladles** and the slag is drawn off either into **slag pots**, into a **dry pit** where it is allowed to solidify, or it is granulated with a stream of water and flushed into a **wet pit**. The gas leaves the top of the furnace through the **uptakes** (J-2), is conducted through a **dust catcher** (O), and a **cleaning system** (R-1, 2, and 3). Clean gas is burned in the **stoves** (U) to preheat the incoming blast air which is conducted by the **hot-blast line** (Q) to the **bustle pipe** (J-13) circling the furnace. The air enters the furnace through water-cooled opening called **tuyeres** (J-10) located at the top of the hearth.

In addition to the equipment shown in Figure 14—3, **blowers** or **blowing engines** are needed for compressing the blast, and other ancillary equipment is required to provide steam, electricity and water. Table 14—III on Page 387 shows the daily utility requirements of a typical two furnace plant.

SECTION 3

CONSTRUCTION OF THE FURNACE PROPER

Terminology—Before undertaking a discussion of blast-furnace construction, it is advisable to establish an understanding of the terminology applied to the component parts. Figure 14—4 identifies many of the principal dimensions and component parts of a blast furnace. Terminology deserving further clarification includes:

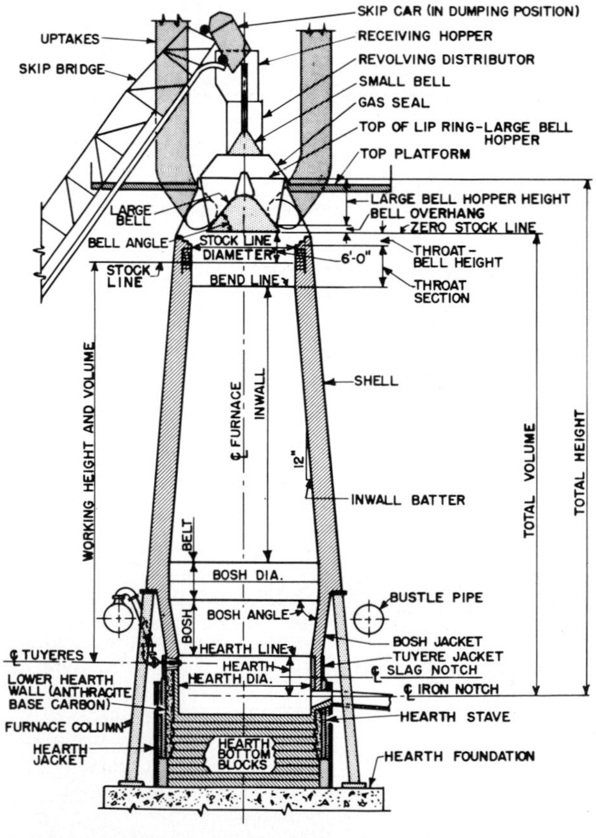

Hearth Diameter: Diameter of the circle determined by the tuyere-cooler noses.

Hearth Line: Horizontal line connecting points of intersection of the vertical line determined by the nose of the tuyere cooler and the sloping straight line of the bosh. The latter is determined by noses of bosh plates directly above tuyere cooler.

Height of Hearth: Vertical distance between hearth line and center line of tapping hole. The latter is determined by center of opening in the hearth jacket.

Bosh Angle: The acute angle formed by any horizontal line and the straight line connecting noses of bosh plates above the tuyere cooler.

Bosh Line: Horizontal line connecting points of intersection between sloping straight line formed by noses of bosh plates and vertical line of straight section of bosh (when present) or between inwall batter or lower continuation of inwall batter, irrespective of brickwork.

Bosh Diameter: Dimension of bosh line, irrespective of brickwork. (Represents also diameter of straight section above bosh.)

Height of Bosh: Vertical distance between hearth and bosh lines.

Inwall Batter: Length of base—in inches and/or fractions thereof—of a right triangle whose hypotenuse constitutes the inwall slope and whose altitude is 12 inches.

Bottom Inwall Line: Horizontal line connecting points of intersection between vertical line of straight section above bosh, determined by bosh diameter, and inwall batter or lower continuation of inwall batter. (In furnaces without straight section above bosh, the bottom inwall line coincides with the bosh line.)

Fig. 14—4. Identification of principal dimensions and components of a blast furnace.

Top Inwall Line: Horizontal line formed at upper termination of inwall batter.

Zero Stockline: Horizontal plane formed by bottom of big bell when closed. Accordingly, 6-foot stock level, for instance, is located six feet below closed bell.

Stockline Diameter: Diameter from face to face of brickwork, or armor where so used, at a plane six feet below zero stockline.

Venturi Batter: Length of base—in inches or fractions thereof—of a right triangle whose hypotenuse constitutes the venturi slope and whose altitude is 12 inches.

Height of Straight Section Above Bosh (or Belt): Vertical distance between horizontal planes containing bosh and bottom inwall lines.

Height of Inwall: Vertical distance between horizontal planes containing bottom and top inwall lines.

Heights of Individual Throat Sections: Vertical distance between planes containing top inwall line and upper termination of cylinder.

Throat-Bell Height: Vertical distance between horizontal planes containing upper termination of throat section and bottom of closed large bell.

Height Between Bottom of Large Bell and Top of Hopper: Vertical distance between horizontal planes formed by bottom of closed large bell and intersection of hopper, or hopper extension, with gas seal.

Bell Overhang: Vertical distance between horizontal planes formed by bottom of large bell when closed, and inner large-bell seat.

Height of Large-Bell Hopper: Vertical distance between horizontal planes formed by inner large-bell seat and intersection of hopper, or hopper extension, with gas seal.

Annular Space: The difference between the stockline radius and the large bell radius.

Total Height of Furnace: Vertical distance between horizontal planes containing center line of tapping hole, determined by the center of opening in the hearth jacket, and intersection of large-bell hopper, or hopper extension, with gas seal.

Working Height of Furnace: Vertical distance between horizontal planes containing center line of tuyeres and one 6 feet below closed large bell.

Volume below Tuyeres: Cubical content—in cubic feet—between horizontal planes formed by center lines of tapping hole and tuyeres.

Working Volume: Cubical content—in cubic feet—between horizontal planes containing center lines of tuyeres and 6 feet below closed large bell.

Volume above 6-Foot Stock Level: Cubical content—in cubic feet—between horizontal planes located 6 feet below, and bottom of, closed large bell.

Total Volume of Furnace: Cubical content—in cubic feet—between horizontal planes containing center line of tapping hole and bottom of closed large bell.

FOUNDATION

The foundation of a large modern furnace, as typified by Fairless No. 3 (Figure 14—5), has to support a structure of approximately 20,000,000 pounds, which rises over 200 feet above the point of molten-iron delivery (center line of the iron notch), has a side reaction from the weight of the skip incline and the downcomer pipes, and carries inside of the furnace a column of material about 85 feet high that will vary in temperature between 3200°F and 300°F (1760° and 190°C, respectively). H-beam piles are driven to bedrock or hardpan, with the tops of the piles about 10 feet below yard level. Upon the piles is placed a reinforced-concrete pad some 11 feet thick and 60 feet in diameter. The bases for the furnace columns rest on the top surface of the pad and are anchored to the concrete foundation, thereby providing a structure that will not move or slip. The columns are protected against a furnace breakout by a masonry sheath. A circular "Lumnite" (heat-resistant) concrete pad, approximately 2 inches to 3 inches in thickness, is laid over the concrete foundation to provide a level working support for the installation of the bottom course of hearth bricks.

COLUMNS AND BASE PLATES

The column bases are 4- to 6-inch thick steel slabs, about 5 feet square. The top of each column is covered by a steel cap that is about 2 to 4 inches thick and approximately 4 feet square. The mantle rests on these caps. The columns are provided at both top and bottom with thick gusset plates that are welded to the flange of the column and to the caps and bases. Each furnace column is generally a 14-inch H-beam piling section or 18-inch plate-and-angle section with 2-inch to 3-inch thick cover plates welded to the flanges to develop accurate stiffening and reinforcement. The distance between the bottom of the column base and the top of the column cap is about 40 feet. On a large furnace, such as that being described, there would be 8 to 10 columns.

MANTLE

The mantle is a heavy, horizontal steel ring, 2 to 4 inches thick, resting on the column caps. It supports the furnace shell and brickwork of the inwall or shaft so that, when necessary, the hearth and bosh brickwork may be removed without disturbing the inwall brickwork. It is built of heavy steel plates that are reinforced circumferentially by circular heavy welded-steel bands and by gusset plates.

SHELL

The **shell** of a blast furnace is in the form of a truncated cone with steep sides, topped by a flatter truncated cone called the **top cone**. The part from below the top cone to the mantle encloses the **shaft** of the furnace (Figure **14—4**). Formerly, the shell was constructed in "shingle" fashion; that is, the edges of adjacent plates were overlapped and riveted. However, on furnaces such as that being described, the shell is an all-welded structure, with the edges of adjacent plates matched and butt-welded. This design gives the shell a continuous, relatively smooth surface free from lapped and riveted joints; it uses less steel; and is stronger than the previous form of construction. The plates employed for the construction of the furnace shell are of various thicknesses from ¾-inch to 1⅛-inches, except for the first ring above the mantle which usually is 1⅛ inches to 1½ inches in thickness, and the top ring and top cone section that are 1 inch to 1¼ inches in thickness. The shell is welded at the bottom ring to the mantle. Openings at selected regular intervals in the shell allow for the insertion of stack-cooling plates into the refractory lining. The bottom of the top cone is welded to the top of the main shell structure. The top opening in the top-cone section receives the **lip-ring** or **top-ring** casting, a heavy steel casting either formed in a single piece or composed of bolted segments. The lip-ring or top-ring

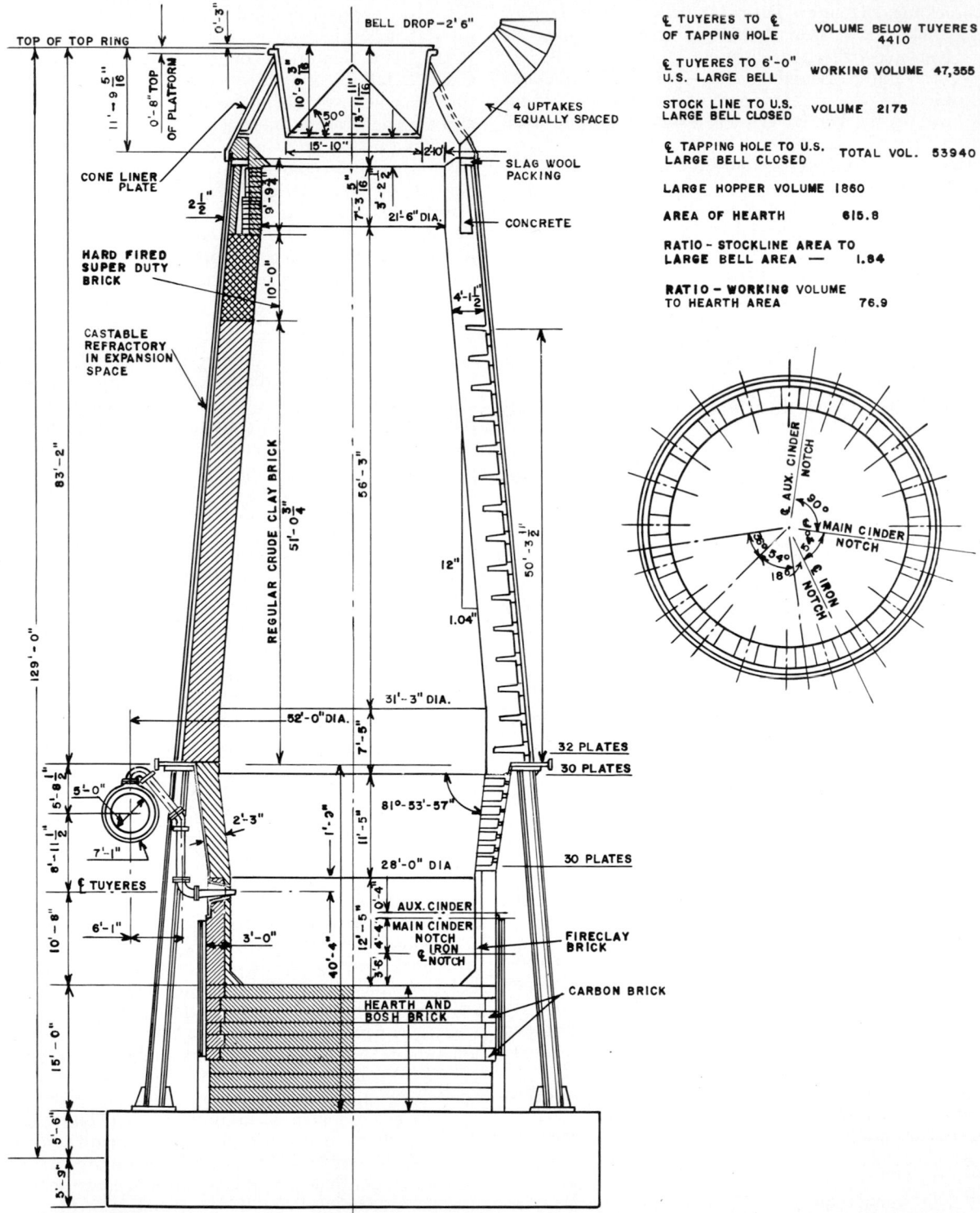

FIG. 14—5. Section through No. 3 blast furnace at the Fairless Works of United States Steel Corporation, showing principal dimensions.

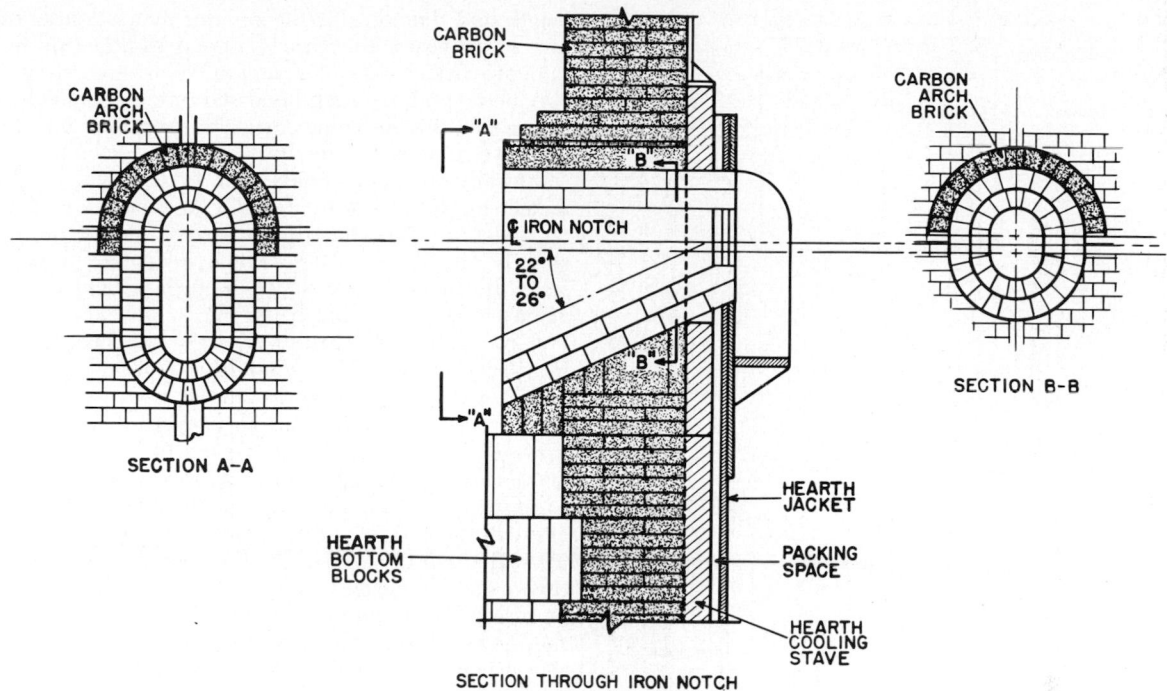

CARBON
ARCH
BRICK

CARBON
BRICK

"A"

"B"

IRON NOTCH

22°
TO
26°

"B"

"A"

SECTION A-A

HEARTH
BOTTOM
BLOCKS

CARBON
ARCH
BRICK

SECTION B-B

HEARTH
JACKET

PACKING
SPACE

HEARTH
COOLING
STAVE

SECTION THROUGH IRON NOTCH

Fig. 14—6. Schematic section through iron notch of a blast furnace. Refractories other than carbon arch brick are fireclay refractories. (The iron notch may also be constructed of all carbon brick or block.)

casting is usually bolted to the top-cone section, although it may be welded, after locating concentrically. It serves as a supporting ring for the large-bell hopper and, ultimately, the revolving and receiving hoppers, with the attachment to the gas-seal section that in turn is bolted to (and supported by) the top-ring casting. There are regularly spaced openings in the top-cone section to which the offtakes, usually four in number, are welded and which conduct the gas formed in the smelting process out of the furnace.

HEARTH

The initial or bottom course of 18-inch thick high-duty refractory hearth block is laid on the heat-resistant concrete pad mentioned in the description of the furnace foundation. The top and all remaining courses of hearth bottom block are 18-inch thick high-duty refractory brick, except for a protection zone of 3 or 4 courses of 18-inch thick super-duty refractory brick burned at Cone 23 (referred to as a "high burn") that are placed immediately below the top course of bottom block. A total of 7 to 11 courses of 18-inch bottom block are used. For a furnace similar to Fairless No. 3, having a hearth diameter of 28 feet, 10 to 11 courses of 18-inch thick bottom block are employed.

The hearth is composed of a series of bottom blocks, previously described, enclosed in a ring of either ceramic or carbon brick, varying in thickness from 22½ inches to 36 inches for the lower hearth wall and 27 to 36 inches for the upper hearth wall. The lower hearth wall and the upper hearth wall, at least to a height of the center line of the slag notch (preferably to the center line of the tuyeres) are sometimes con-

structed of anthracite-base carbon-brick shapes in preference to ceramic brick.

The lower hearth wall and a portion of the upper hearth wall to the height of the slag notch are externally cooled by the use of cast-iron segments with internal cooling coils, called **hearth staves.** A 1½-inch **hearth jacket** of steel plate surrounds the staves for approximately their full height to restrain the bursting forces from the inside of the furnace. The hearth staves at the iron and slag notches are designed with a removable section, about one-half the height of the ordinary stave, as a means for quick repair should a break-out or burn-through occur at either of these locations.

The iron produced in the smelting process is withdrawn at periodic intervals from the furnace, through the **iron notch** (Figure 14—6) constructed in the upper hearth wall at a distance of 3 feet to 3 feet 6 inches above the top course of hearth blocks. Since the slag formed in the smelting process (sometimes called "cinder") is lighter than iron, it floats on the top of the molten pool of iron on the hearth and its withdrawal is accomplished through a **slag notch,** usually called a **monkey,** that is located approximately 3 feet, 6 inches to 4 feet, 6 inches above the center line of the iron notch. The slag-notch assembly consists of three water-cooled, concentric, cast-copper frustums of cones; the largest, known as the **monkey cooler,** supporting on its inside a smaller frustum known as the **intermediate cooler** that in turn supports the monkey itself (Figure 14—7). The central opening in the monkey is closed by a **bott,** which is a tapered water-cooled plug at the end of a steel pipe. The bott on large furnaces is operated mechanically by a device

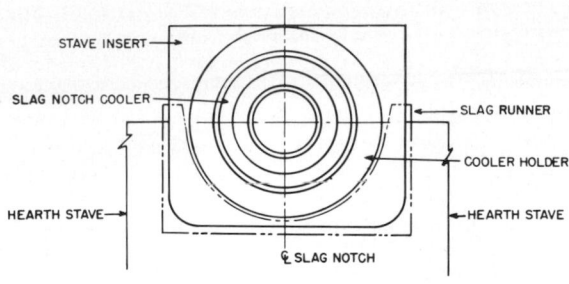

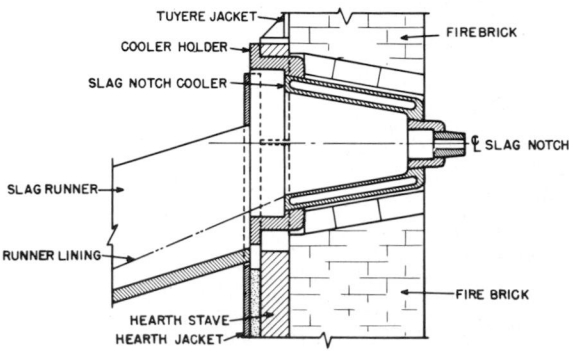

Fig. 14—7. (Below) Section through slag notch of a blast furnace. (Above) Developed view at slag notch.

known as the **slag-notch stopper.** In the construction of modern furnaces, two slag notches from 0 to 6 inches different in elevation, and at least one iron notch are employed.

In time, the bottom is eroded to various degrees and is replaced by a large mass of metal known as a **salamander** (or **bear**).

Above the tops of the hearth staves, the brickwork of the hearth wall is enclosed on the outside by a **tuyere jacket** or **breast plate,** made of welded 1½-inch thick steel plate. Reinforced openings are provided in this jacket for insertion of the **tuyere coolers,** slag notch, and **cooling plates,** all of which fit their respective openings closely. Some of these details may be observed in Figure 14—8, which shows a section of the bosh and the upper part of the hearth of a furnace such as that being described. The cooling plates are discussed in more detail later in the description of bosh construction. Usually, there are one or two rows of cooling plates below the tuyere-cooler level, and three rows between the tuyere-cooler openings. When carbon is used to line the bosh, the usual practice is to use external cooling rather than water-cooled copper castings inserted in the brick work. External cooling is described in more detail later in the description of bosh construction.

The heated blast enters the furnace through nozzle-like water-cooled copper castings known as **tuyeres,** usually about twenty in number in a large furnace, spaced equally around the hearth about a foot below the top of the hearth (Figure 14—5 and 14—8). The tuyere cooler supports the tuyere in the same manner as the slag-notch cooler supports the intermediate cooler. For different furnaces in the same plant, the

length and diameter of the tuyeres may be different but, in all cases, they are designed to fit inside the same size of tuyere-cooler casting.

A horizontal, ceramic-lined steel pipe about 5 feet long called the **blowpipe** carries the hot blast air from the tuyere stock to the furnace. The blowpipe has spherically machined ends that fit tightly into the machined end of the tuyere and the stock to give an air tight fit even though the tuyere and stock are slightly out of line. It is held in place by pressure from the **tuyere stock** which in turn is held tightly against one end of the blowpipe by a heavy spring and rod called the **bridle.** This is attached to the hearth jacket and allows limited motion as the stock and blowpipe expand and contract with changes in the hot-blast temperature. The tuyere stock curves upward on leaving the blowpipe to fasten to the **gooseneck,** and is lined with firebrick as a protection against the heat of the blast. In the outer part of the curve in the tuyere stock and on the center line of the blowpipe and tuyere is a small opening closed by the **tuyere cap** or **wicket** through which a small rod may be inserted to clean out the tuyere without removing the blowpipe. The tuyere cap must be of such form that it may be opened readily at any time and still be gas-tight when closed. This may be accomplished by a tapered plate inserted in guides, in which a small glass-covered opening called the **peep sight** is placed to permit the inspection of that portion of the interior of the furnace directly in front of the tuyeres. The upper part of the stock is connected by a swivel joint to the refractory-lined nozzle of the gooseneck to which it is clamped by lugs and keys that fit into seats of hanging bars. Each gooseneck in turn is connected by flanges and bolts to a neck extending radially from the inside diameter of the **bustle pipe.** The bustle pipe is a large, circular, refractory-lined and insulated pipe that encircles the furnace at about mantle level and distributes the heated blast from the hot-blast main to each tuyere connection (Figure 14—16).

When natural gas or oil are injected through the tuyeres, a header pipe or manifold circles the furnace

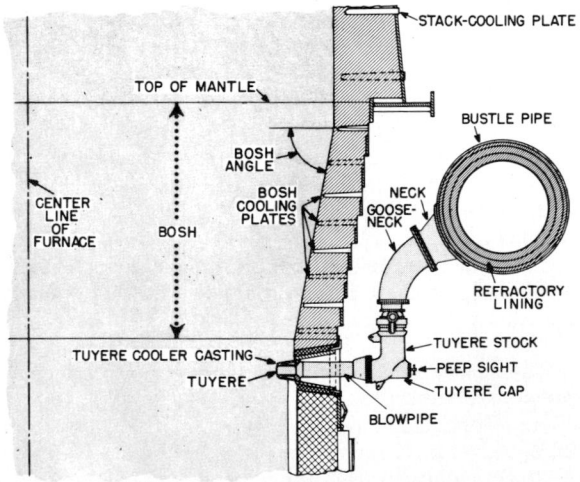

Fig. 14—8. Section through the bosh and upper part of the hearth wall of a large blast furnace showing details of connections between the tuyere and bustle pipe.

just above or just below the bustle pipe. From this header smaller pipes bring the gas or oil to the tuyere level. In the case of gas, a flexible connection is made to an opening through the tuyere; and in the case of oil, to a lance entering through the side of the blowpipe. When pulverized coal injection is used, the airborne coal is usually carried to the blowpipes from injection equipment set back an appreciable distance from the furnace proper.

BOSH

As previously mentioned, the bosh may be described more specifically as that portion of a furnace formed by an inverted frustum of a cone starting at the top of the vertical sidewalls of the hearth and extending upward to the level of maximum furnace diameter at the mantle. The bosh is lined either with ceramic brick, using a thickness of approximately 27 inches, or with carbon-brick shapes, 15 to 22½ inches thick.

When built with ceramic brick, the bosh is cooled by wedge-shaped, internally cooled copper plates that are inserted and fitted into the walls of the lining through the supporting steel bands and retained in position by cast-iron boxes or by fitting the plates directly in the brickwork openings. The spacing of these plates is customarily on 1-foot, 6-inch to 2-foot vertical centers, and from 3-foot, 3-inch to 4-foot horizontal centers, as measured from the periphery of each row. The bosh cooling plates are hollow copper castings with internal baffle ribs to direct the flow pattern of the cooling water and shaped with a flat bottom, arched top and tapered in length to form a wedge shape: each full-size plate weighs approximately 200 to 350 lb.

When the bosh is constructed with carbon shapes, the entire enclosure of the bosh lining is accomplished by a welded-steel frustum of a cone, and the external surface is water cooled by vertical structural-channel boxes welded to the shell in an almost continuous pattern at very close spacing, to cover the maximum area of exposed shell surface. While not employed in this country, external cooling of the bosh, and sometimes the external surface of the hearth, is accomplished by evaporative means by spraying cooling water over the shell.

INWALL

The inwall is the stack lining that comprises all that part of the furnace located above the bosh. The construction for all furnaces is fairly uniform in general features, but the brick thickness has varied from 9 inches to 60 inches. For example, as employed for the No. 3 blast furnace at Fairless Works, the refractory brick lining of the shaft is 54 inches thick at the mantle and in the belt zone, 49½ inches in the inwall, and approximately 48 inches in thickness at the stockline. In recent years, the "working lines" of worn inwalls have been restored for a period of time, without complete replacement of all of the refractory brickwork, by the hydraulic-gun placement (called "guniting") of a special, high-purity, low-iron, calcium-aluminate (castable) cement, applied directly to the cleaned surface of the remaining salvageable refractory lining. The refractory brick inwall lining is cooled in a manner similar to the cooling of a bosh constructed of ceramic brick by the placement, insertion and fitting of hollow, internally cooled copper plates into the lining. Customarily, these plates are placed on 2-foot, 6-inch to 3-foot, 6-inch vertical

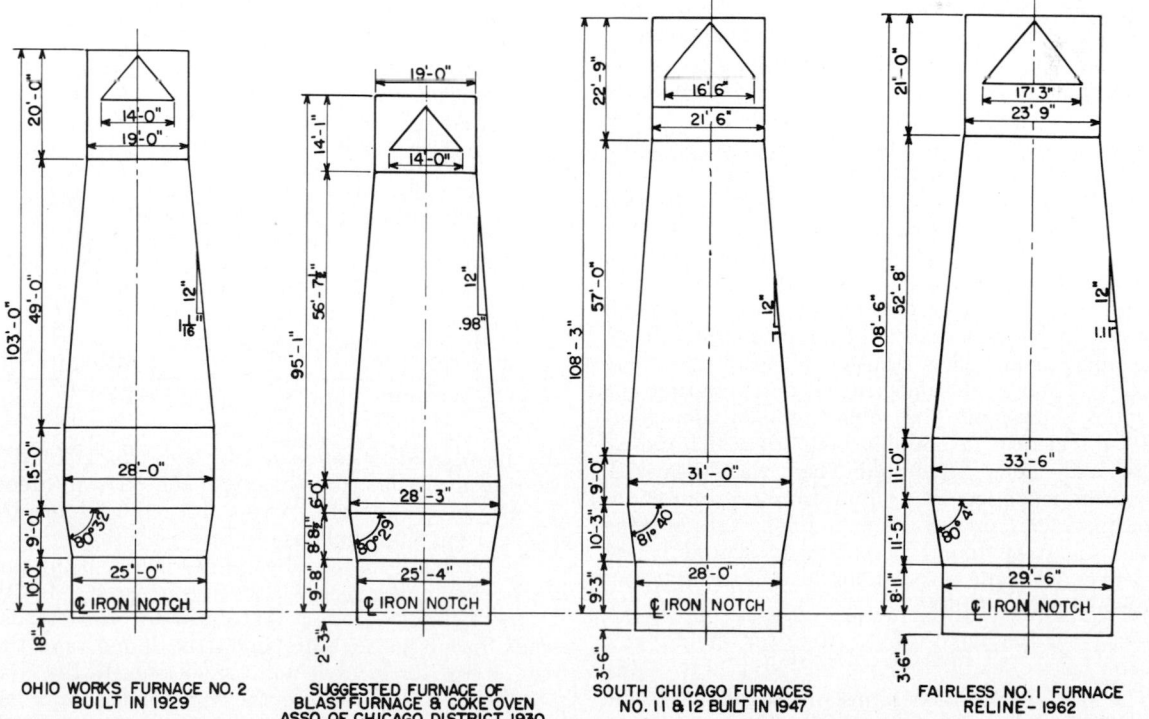

FIG. 14—9. Lines of typical modern American blast furnaces designed and built during the period 1929-1962.

Table 14—IV. Original Dimensions of Fairless No. 1 Blast Furnace for its Original Campaign Starting in 1953 and the Revised Dimensions for the Second Campaign Starting in 1962

	1953	1962
Diameter of hearth	28 ft.	29 ft.-6 in.
Diameter of bosh	31 ft.-3 in.	33 ft.-6 in.
Diameter of stockline	21 ft.-6 in.	23 ft.-8½ in.
Diameter of large bell	15 ft.-10 in.	17 ft.-3 in.
Bosh angle	80°-53′-57″	80°-03′-48″
Inwall batter	1.04 in. in 12″	1.11 in. in 12″
Working Volume	47,355 cu. ft.	56,494 cu. ft.
Ratio-Working volume: Hearth area	76.9	82.7
Number of tuyeres	20	20
Centerline iron notch to top of hearth	8 ft.-11 in.	8 ft.-11 in.
Centerline of iron notch to centerline of slag notch	4 ft.-0 in. & 4 ft.-6 in.	4 ft.-4 in. & 4 ft.-8 in.
Centerline of slag notch to centerline of tuyeres	3 ft.-2 in. & 2 ft.-8 in.	2 ft.-10 in. & 2 ft.-6 in.
Height of bosh	11 ft.-5 in.	11 ft.-5 in.
Height straight section lower inwall	7 ft.-5 in.	11 ft.-0 in.
Height sloping section inwall	56 ft.-3 in.	52 ft.-8 in.
Top sloping section to top of hopper	11 ft.-9–5/16 in.	11 ft.-9–5/16 in.
Rows of stack plates	15	22
Rows of bosh plates	8	8

centers, and extend from the top of the mantle at the belt zone to within 8 feet below the stockline wearing plates employed as protective armor.

RELATIONSHIP OF FURNACE DIMENSIONS

The relationship of the furnace dimensions, one with another, is most important. Practically all of these relationships are a result of a gradual evolutionary process which has been going on for many years. They do not lend themselves to theoretical calculations; however, they are dimensions and proportions derived from years of furnace campaign experience inspired by the continuous endeavor on the part of operators and engineers to improve furnace performance. Examples of good sound furnace design are shown in Figure 12—9 covering a period of more than thirty years. The increase in furnace size must not be confused with the changes in lines. The former is a direct result of increased demand for metal while the later represents a more subtle change.

No. 1 furnace at Fairless Works started its initial campaign in 1953. Hearth diameter was 28 ft. and the balance of the lines proportioned to this dimension; however, the overall physical proportions of the structure were designed to permit future enlargement. In 1962, following a successful campaign, the furnace was enlarged and lines adjusted to overcome where possible some slight deficiencies noted during the previous campaign. The following tabulation illustrates this clearly. It should be pointed out that radical changes are never attempted. There were many disappointing experiences resulting from over-ambitious departures from proven design in the past. Interesting reports may be found in papers presented before societies and trade associations in their transactions published prior to 1900.

FURNACE LININGS

The brickwork which forms the hearth, bosh and inwalls of a blast furnace is referred to as its lining. All the brick used in the construction of these parts are made of fireclay. The brick in the hearth and bosh are required to resist high temperatures and the action of flux and slag; brick in the inwall zone must be able to withstand abrasion at a moderately high temperature; and top brick, although always at a comparatively low temperature, must resist the impact and abrasive forces of the charges as they are dropped into the furnace.

The high temperatures attainable in the blast furnace are made possible and the furnace design dimensions are maintained by the use of the copper cooling plates and the hearth staves. A single modern blast furnace recently was constructed with the following water-cooled copper castings:

20 Tuyere Coolers @ 754 lb.	=	15,080 lb.
20 Tuyeres @ 172 lb.	=	3,440 lb.
2 Slag-Notch Coolers @ 754 lb.	=	1,508 lb.
2 Intermediate Coolers @ 103 lb.	=	206 lb.
2 Monkeys @ 35 lb.	=	70 lb.
380 Bosh Plates—280 @ 228 lb.	=	63,840 lb.
100 @ 289 lb.	=	28,900 lb.
480 Stack Plates—428 @ 288 lb.	=	97,584 lb.
22 @ 330 lb.	=	5,060 lb.
30 @ 369 lb.	=	11,070 lb.
10 Probe-Hole Castings @ 1055 lb.	=	10,550 lb.
916 Castings	=	237,308 lb.

The above coolers are cooled by approximately 195 water-feed circuits, together with the 65 water-feed circuits on the hearth, tuyere breast, and mantle staves, using 8,000 gallons of water per minute.

The brick are inspected carefully before being put in place in the furnace. Great care is exercised with respect to brick, because the life of the furnace depends in a large measure upon the lining, and the item of cost for brick is not a small one. In the construction of a large furnace, the equivalent of approximately 850,000 nine-inch brick is required. Firebrick are always laid in a thin slurry composed of refractory mortar. The slurry is applied by painting it on top of each course with a dipper, and is followed immediately with the next course of brick, which are hammered into place to squeeze out all of the slurry except that required to compensate for the inequalities of the brick.

WATER TROUGHS

Encircling the furnace bosh, at about the level of the bustle pipe, will be found one or more water troughs into which the water supplying the numerous cooling plates is discharged in visible streams, thus providing means of determining that water is circulating through the cooling member. The water, flowing from these troughs into a well, may be reused by pumping to the condensers or gas washers.

TOP

In olden times the tops of furnaces were left open, the escaping gases being allowed to burn in the air. The first attempt to heat the blast air by utilizing these gases was made in 1829, by circulating the air through tubes around the top of the furnace. It was not until 1845 that a plan was evolved by which the gases could be used in "stoves," which were separate structures designed for the sole purpose of preheating the air before blowing it into the furnace. To effect this purpose, changes in top construction were necessary. At first the gases were merely drawn off by the chimney draft of the stoves through openings below the stock line. The arrangement known as the **bell and hopper,** or **cup and cone,** was not put into use until 1850. It consisted of furnishing the top of the furnace with a large circular hopper, the bottom opening of which was closed by the cone-shaped bell that could

be lowered and raised at will. With the bell raised against the hopper, the materials were dumped into the hopper; then, when the bell was lowered, the charge dropped into the furnace. In principle, this method corresponds to that illustrated by the large bell and hopper in Figure 14—10, if there were no small bell.

Because large quantities of gas escaped with each lowering of the bell, this device was improved by the **double bell and hopper,** the operation of which is shown schematically in Figure 14—10, and which is of comparatively recent origin. Essentially, this improvement consisted in placing a second bell and hopper above the first, and providing a gas-tight space of large size between the two. The raw materials, upon being hoisted to the top, are first dropped or dumped into the upper hopper, whence they may fall into the large hopper when the small bell is lowered. The small bell being raised against the upper hopper, the large bell is lowered, and the charge falls into the furnace without the escape of gas. The bells are made of cast steel, in one piece, and of such a slope—50° to 55°—as to permit the charge to slide off readily. They usually are supported from their top centers by a rod and a sleeve, each attached to a counterbalance lever operated by a steam or air cylinder or an electric motor, controlled from the ground. The large bell is attached to the rod, and the small bell to the sleeve. The hoppers, of cast steel, generally are made in sections that are securely bolted together. The details of this construction differ somewhat from furnace to furnace to conform to the introduction of improvements, with the type of hoist, and with the preferences of the

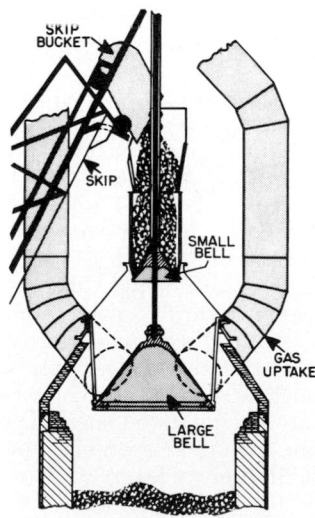 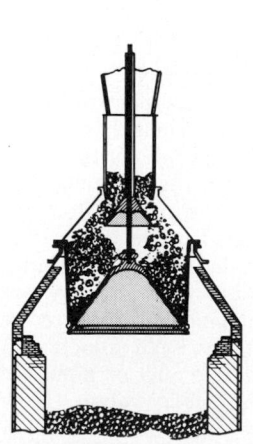 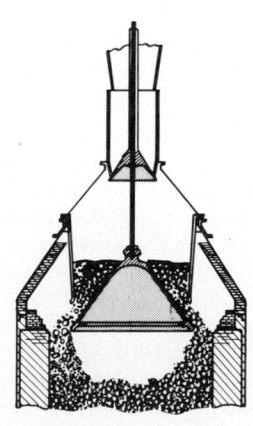 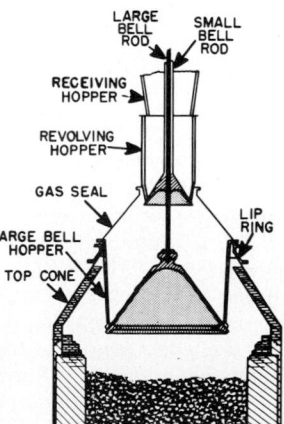

SMALL BELL AND LARGE BELL BOTH CLOSED, SKIP BUCKET TIPPED TO DUMP CHARGE IN HOPPER ABOVE SMALL BELL. GAS FLOWING FROM TOP OF FURNACE THROUGH UPTAKES LOCATED IN DOME (TOP CONE).	LARGE. BELL REMAINS CLOSED WHILE SMALL BELL OPENS TO ADMIT CHARGE TO LARGE BELL HOPPER.	SMALL BELL CLOSED TO PREVENT ESCAPE OF GAS TO ATMOSPHERE AND LARGE BELL OPEN TO ADMIT CHARGE TO THE FURNACE.	BOTH BELLS CLOSED, READY TO REPEAT CHARGING CYCLE. NOTE THAT ROD SUPPORTING LARGE BELL PASSES THROUGH HOLLOW ROD SUPPORTING SMALL BELL, PERMITTING INDEPENDENT OPERATION OF BELLS.

Fig. 14—10. Diagram of progressive steps by which the double bell and hopper permits charging raw materials into a blast furnace without escape of furnace gases.

different builders. Many of the bell and hopper surfaces are being hard-surfaced (up to ⅜-inch thick layers) by welding, using a high-alloy welding rod.

HOISTING APPLIANCES

The old-time method of charging by hand having been superseded by mechanical charging, there are now in use two types of these devices; namely, the **skip hoist,** and a few remaining **bucket hoists.** Although there are several installations in Europe where blast furnaces are being filled by conveyor-belt systems, there were none in North America at the time this chapter was written.

In all cases, there is an incline (a fabricated steel structure) extending from the top of the furnace to or below the bottom of the stock house (Figures **14—1, 14—2** and **14—3**), and over tracks on this incline the materials charged into the furnace must pass. In the skip hoist, the conveying vessel is a small open-ended steel car, called a skip, that automatically dumps the materials into the hopper above the small bell. Skip hoists generally are provided with double tracks and two skips, so that while a loaded skip is ascending the incline, an empty one is descending. The drive unit is a single drum driven by a pair of 250-hp, or larger, electric motors.

In the bucket hoist, the solid materials are raised in a bucket suspended from a truck or carriage that operates on rails supported by an incline. The bucket drops the charge directly into the space above the large bell. When in position for dropping its load, the bucket, being itself provided with a small bell at the bottom, takes the place of the little bell and hopper used with the skip hoist. While the bucket is being filled at the stock house, the opening left at the furnace top is closed by a special gas seal. The bucket hoist (known as the **Neeland top**) is being displaced by the skip hoist.

Figure **14—11** shows furnaces equipped with double skip hoists.

TOP APPLIANCES FOR DISTRIBUTING THE STOCK

It is apparent that, in a mechanically filled furnace, when the raw materials are dropped into the receiving hopper onto the small bell, and from the small bell onto the large bell, the larger lumps of ore and stone will have a tendency to roll and thus collect around the edges or, perhaps, at one side or the other, of the hoppers. This same segregation, if uncorrected, will also occur upon dropping the charge into the furnace. This tendency results in more or less open and continuous channels being formed through the materials and extending from the top toward the bottom of the stack. These channels offer less resistance than the remainder of the materials to the passage of gases through the furnace, with the result that a disproportionately large quantity of gas passes through them. This condition, called **channeling,** also results in excessively high temperatures along these passages. To overcome this defect, various plans and devices have been employed to introduce the materials into the furnace in such a way that this segregation of coarse and fine material will not occur.

Rotation of the position of the charge on the large bell by various means has been most effective in minimizing channeling. This can be accomplished in several ways, depending upon whether the furnace is bucket or skip charged. One of the most popular and effective devices is a rotating hopper above the small bell which can be rotated about its vertical axis through a prescribed arc before the small bell is lowered.

Some designers concentrate upon details of construction of the furnace top and of the large bell and hopper with good results. For example, it can be shown that as the diameter of the large bell approaches the internal diameter of the furnace top, the fines are concentrated next to the furnace wall, and as the bell diameter is decreased, a dimension is reached that throws some lumps against the wall and some toward the center, while a further decrease in diameter throws more and more lumps toward the wall until all the fines are concentrated at the center. Other factors, such as the angle of the bell, the angle of the hopper, the extension of the bell below the hopper, the distance below the hopper the bell can be dropped, and the speed with which the bell can be lowered, all may be adjusted to produce the best charge distribution.

TOP OPENINGS

The smallest opening in the top of a furnace is the **try hole.** In operating a furnace, it is necessary to be able to determine the position of the stock line. This is done by means of the **stock indicator,** which is a rod of steel passing through and fitting the try hole loosely so that one end rests upon the stock while the other is attached to a steel cable that leads to the stock house or the cast house below. Some stock indicators are automatic and self-recording. A majority of furnaces use two stock indicators, mounted 180° apart.

Gases resulting from the smelting operation are conducted from the top of the furnace by large vertical pipes called **uptakes,** normally four in number, each approximately 6 feet, 6 inches to 7 feet, 6 inches inside shell diameter and lined with 3 to 4 inches of monolithic castable cement lining applied over wire mesh that is anchored to the shell, or with 4½ to 6 inches of refractory brick. The tops of two adjacent uptakes are joined together to form two pairs, each pair being connected to a large descending duct or pipe called a **downcomer** (10 to 11 feet inside diameter) by a cross connection or duct called an **offtake.** Each joined pair of uptakes terminates as a single duct or pipe with an open-in or open-out type of bleeder valve at the top. Bleeder valves are counterweighted and/or operated by an air cylinder. These valves have a double purpose: first, they may be opened by mechanical means from ground level to permit surplus gas to escape from the furnace system; secondly, they may be adjusted, either by weights or mechanical means, to act as explosion valves and open at a predetermined pressure to relieve sudden increases in gas pressure occasioned by "slips" in the furnace, and thus prevent possible injury to the top. A third bleeder, on the offtakes, may rise above the

Fig. 14—11. Overall view of a blast-furnace plant, showing two furnaces and the stoves that operate in conjunction with them.

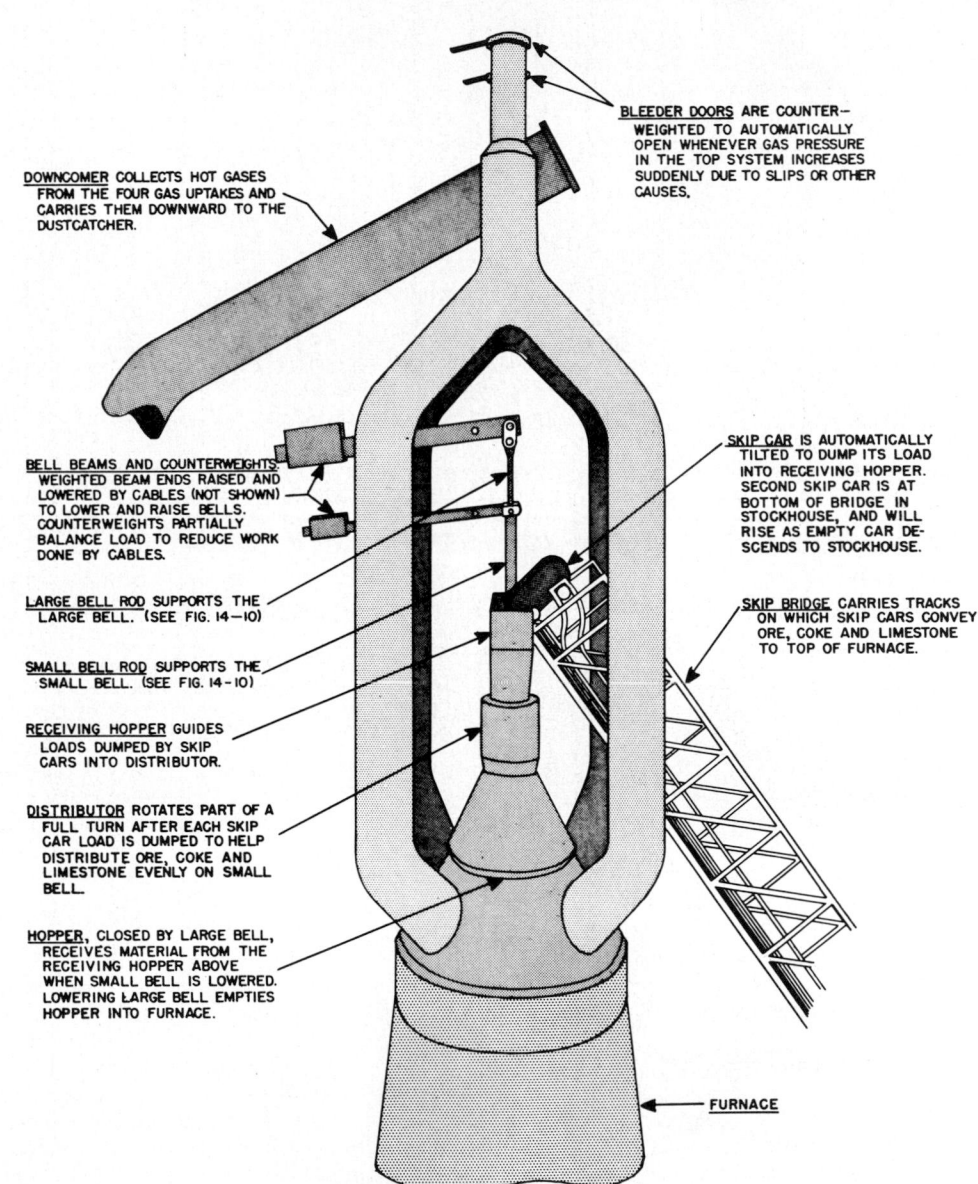

PRINCIPAL OPERATING PARTS OF A

BLAST FURNACE TOP *

BLEEDER DOORS ARE COUNTER-
WEIGHTED TO AUTOMATICALLY
OPEN WHENEVER GAS PRESSURE
IN THE TOP SYSTEM INCREASES
SUDDENLY DUE TO SLIPS OR OTHER
CAUSES.

DOWNCOMER COLLECTS HOT GASES
FROM THE FOUR GAS UPTAKES AND
CARRIES THEM DOWNWARD TO THE
DUSTCATCHER.

BELL BEAMS AND COUNTERWEIGHTS
WEIGHTED BEAM ENDS RAISED AND
LOWERED BY CABLES (NOT SHOWN)
TO LOWER AND RAISE BELLS.
COUNTERWEIGHTS PARTIALLY
BALANCE LOAD TO REDUCE WORK
DONE BY CABLES.

LARGE BELL ROD SUPPORTS THE
LARGE BELL. (SEE FIG. 14—10)

SMALL BELL ROD SUPPORTS THE
SMALL BELL. (SEE FIG. 14—10)

RECEIVING HOPPER GUIDES
LOADS DUMPED BY SKIP
CARS INTO DISTRIBUTOR.

DISTRIBUTOR ROTATES PART OF A
FULL TURN AFTER EACH SKIP
CAR LOAD IS DUMPED TO HELP
DISTRIBUTE ORE, COKE AND
LIMESTONE EVENLY ON SMALL
BELL.

HOPPER, CLOSED BY LARGE BELL,
RECEIVES MATERIAL FROM THE
RECEIVING HOPPER ABOVE
WHEN SMALL BELL IS LOWERED.
LOWERING LARGE BELL EMPTIES
HOPPER INTO FURNACE.

SKIP CAR IS AUTOMATICALLY
TILTED TO DUMP ITS LOAD
INTO RECEIVING HOPPER.
SECOND SKIP CAR IS AT
BOTTOM OF BRIDGE IN
STOCKHOUSE, AND WILL
RISE AS EMPTY CAR DE-
SCENDS TO STOCKHOUSE.

SKIP BRIDGE CARRIES TRACKS
ON WHICH SKIP CARS CONVEY
ORE, COKE AND LIMESTONE
TO TOP OF FURNACE.

FURNACE

*THE VARIOUS PLATFORMS AND STRUCTURES SUPPORTING THE TOP EQUIPMENT HAVE BEEN OMITTED FROM THIS DRAWING,
AS WELL AS THE CABLES AND SHEAVES THAT OPERATE THE SKIP AND THE BELLS. ALSO OMITTED ARE THE JIB
BOOM CRANES THAT ASSIST IN HOISTING REPAIR AND REPLACEMENT PARTS TO THE TOP OF THE FURNACE.

FIG. 14—12. Principal operating parts of a blast-furnace top.

junction of the uptakes. Some furnaces have a separate bleeder for each uptake. The bleeder valves are at the highest point of the furnace (Figures 14—11 and 14—12).

The downcomer usually is lined with 4½ to 6 inches of refractory brick, or 3 to 4½ inches of a monolithic castable cement applied over a wire mesh that is anchored to the shell.

GENERAL CONSIDERATIONS FOR TOP CONSTRUCTION

As previously pointed out, there are many types of tops, and the foregoing description is intended only to give a general idea of the essential parts and their uses. The chief endeavor in top construction is to perfect the distribution of the stock entering the furnace stack, and either eliminate or compensate for as many irregularities as possible, while a second aim is to hold to a minimum the amount of solids (coarse and fine dust from the raw materials) carried out with the gas. However, in attaining these ends, simplicity must be considered, as any great amount of mechanism on the top of a furnace is objectionable. It is important to prevent large material from being thrown out of the furnace in case of slips, and as little dust as possible at any time should be carried out by the gases. In locating the uptakes, care is taken to see that they do not enter the furnace directly over the tapping hole, slag notch, or the entrance of the blast main to the bustle pipe because, these being the most active points in the furnace, entering the uptakes over these points would tend to cause more uneven distribution of the gases through the stock.

SECTION 4

CONSTRUCTION OF FURNACE AUXILIARIES

Stoves—Blast-furnace stoves, usually three per furnace, are brick-lined regenerators enclosed in a circular steel shell with a flat bottom and a dome-shaped top. Their function is to preheat the blast before its admission into the furnace through the tuyeres. The result of preheating the blast is to intensify and speed up the burning of the coke at the tuyeres with a consequent reduction in the coke required for the smelting operation; this reduction in coke consumption is more than would correspond merely to the additional sensible heat carried in by the heated blast. Essentially, a stove consists of two parts; the first being the combustion chamber which is a vertical passageway (in which cleaned blast-furnace gas is burned) extending from a point near the bottom of the stove to the bottom of the dome, and through which the hot products of combustion pass upward to the dome. The second main part is the checkerwork, which contains a multiplicity of small passageways through which the products of combustion from the blast-furnace gas pass downwardly from the dome to a point near the bottom of the stove. This description applies to the **two-pass design** which is the most prevalent today but there still exist quite a number of stoves of the **three-pass design,** the difference being that an additional upward pass of checkerwork is added through which the products of combustion pass before their exit at the top of the stove. In a few rare cases, a **four-pass design** has been used which again simply adds a downward pass for the products of combustion over the three-pass design. In all designs, there is only a single combustion chamber. The two-pass design offers a larger percentage of the cross-sectional area for checkerwork than either the three- or four-pass designs because of the space taken up by the walls which separate the passes. With sufficient volume of the checkerwork installed, the two-pass design permits the spent gases to leave the stove at a temperature no higher than that from stoves with the more complicated and more costly three- and four-pass designs. The temperature of the exit gases is, of course, a measure of the efficiency of the stove. The design of stoves may be broken down further into either the side-combustion or the center-combustion types, which refers to the location of the combustion chamber inside the shell itself. The preference seems to be for the side-combustion type. Figure 14—13 shows vertical and horizontal sections for the side-combustion type.

Modern stoves for large furnaces are 26 to 28 feet in diameter and about 120 feet high from the bottom of a stove to the top of its dome. Depending upon the type of checkers used, the stoves contain between 250,000 and 275,000 square feet of heating surface. If the checkerwork walls are too thin, structural failures will result. It has been found that a ratio of weight of brick (in pounds) to square foot of heating surface of about 10 is the minimum. Below this ratio structural difficulties are encountered. Formerly the checkerwork was supported several feet above the bottom of the stove by brick piers but present construction uses cast-iron or steel columns to support steel grids which in turn carry the checkerwork. Insulation between the brick and the steel shell prevents the heat in the stove from distorting the steel plates. The blast-furnace gas used to heat the stoves is cleaned almost universally by wet washing, primarily in a tower-type washer and finally in a precipitator or disintegrator. Primary gas will contain about 0.2 grain per cubic foot of solids and should not be used in stoves with openings less than 4½ in. square. Final or secondary gas will contain less than 0.02 grains per cubic foot and can be used successfully in checkerwork with openings slightly less than 2 inches by 2 inches. An empirical factor of about 500 square feet of total heating surface per net ton of daily furnace production has been found to give adequate stove capacity. This excludes the area of any cross flues in the checkerwork.

The stoves for a furnace, when of the two-pass design, usually are provided with a common stack about

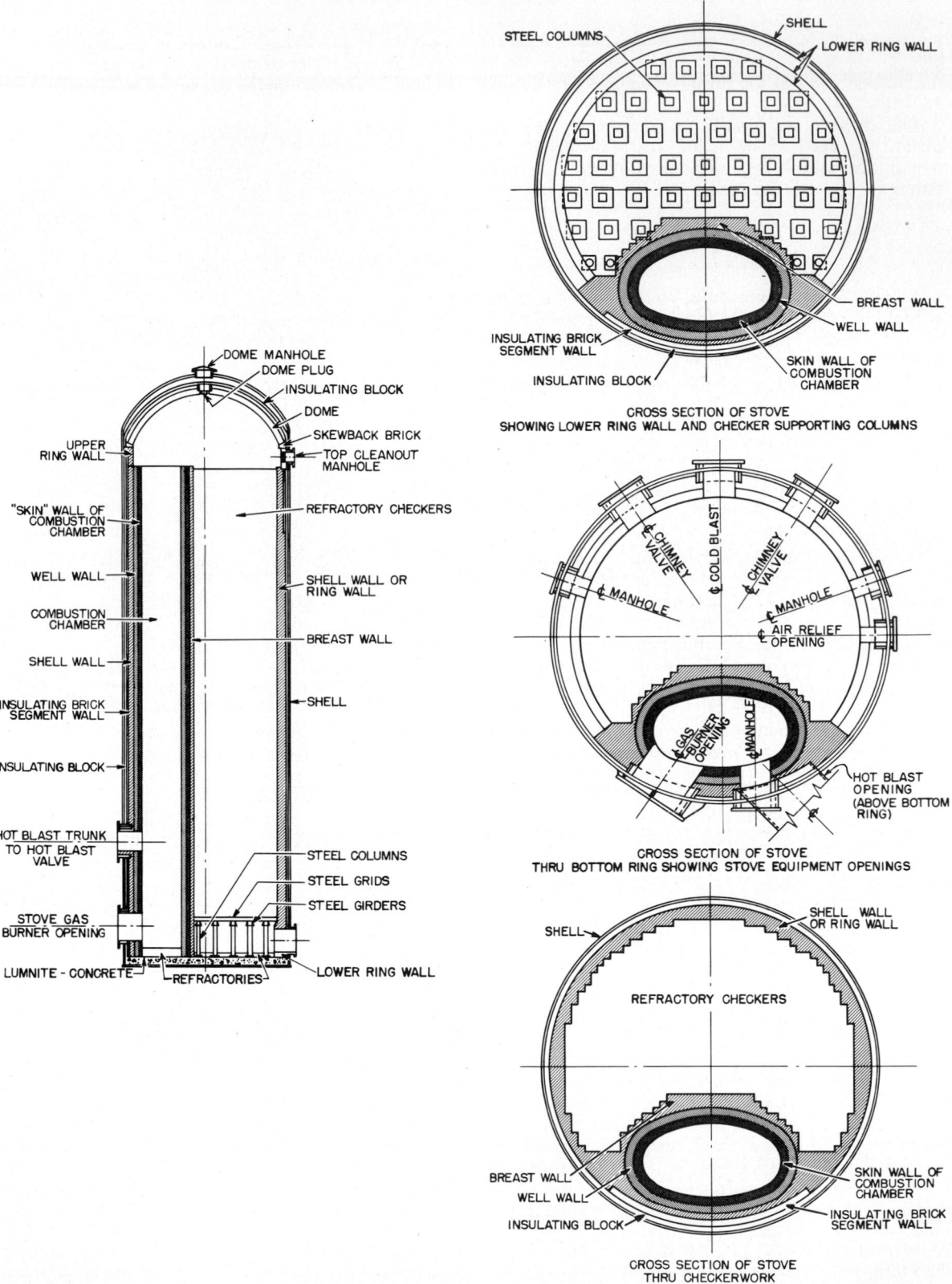

FIG. 14—13. Schematic diagrams (not to scale) showing principles of design and materials of construction for hot-blast stoves of the side-combustion type for blast furnaces. (Left) Vertical section through stove. (Right) Series of schematic sections at different elevations of stove. Top section shows lower ring wall and checker-supporting columns; middle section is through bottom ring, showing openings for stove equipment; bottom section is through the checkerwork (not shown). The spaces marked "refractory checkers" are filled with checkerwork of one of the designs shown in Figure 14—14, to provide continuous vertical flues extending from top to bottom of the checkers.

200 ft. high, while three-pass stoves have an individual stack for each stove mounted on top of the dome of the stove shell.

Air blast for the furnace passes through the heated stove in a manner counter-current to the passage of the gas. In a two-pass stove the gas passes upward through the combustion chamber, downward through the checkers, and out to the stack while the blast passes upward through the checkers, downward through the combustion chambers, and out into the hot-blast main. With three stoves to a furnace, one stove is "on blast" at a time while the other two stoves are "on gas" with the result that each stove is "on gas" twice as long as it is "on blast." In order to accomplish the changeover from gas to blast, and vice versa, certain valves are necessary.

The **hot-blast valve** is usually of the water-cooled mushroom type, closing on a water-cooled seat. Its function is to open the passageway for the heated blast from the combustion chamber to the hot-blast main. The **cold-blast valve** admits cold air from the blast line into the space directly below the checker-work and, not being subjected to high temperatures is usually of the gate type. The **chimney valves**, usually two in number, open and close the passageway for the products of combustion from the stove to the stack and are subjected to only moderately high temperatures. The **blow-off valve** releases the pressure in the stove when changing the stove from "on blast" to "on gas." Since the heated blast leaves the stove at a higher temperature after the stove has just been put "on blast" than after it has been cooled somewhat by the air undergoing heating that passes through it, and since it is desired to maintain, in most cases, the hot blast at a constant temperature, the **mixer valve** by-passes a certain amount of the cold blast into the heated blast and by its regulation maintains a constant hot-blast temperature. A pyrometer is installed in the hot-blast line beyond the point of entry of the mixer line; it can be set to the temperature desired and will operate a mixer valve automatically to maintain this temperature. The **burner valve** or door opens and closes the passageway from the stove gas burner into the combustion chamber. Most gas burners today are of the pressure type, in which the air for the combustion of the gas is blown by a fan into the burner in such quantities as to give theoretically perfect combustion. In the older type burners, the combustion air was aspirated into the combustion chamber with the gas with resultant mediocre combustion. The nose of the burner is movable so that it may be moved tightly against a flange on the burner door to prevent any infiltration of air or puffing out of the gas when the stove is "on gas." Inspection or cleanout doors are provided at the top and at the bottom of the stove. The **snort valve**, which derives its name from the noise made by blast escaping into the atmosphere, is located in the cold-blast line leading from the blowing room to the stove. Its function is to relieve the pressure of the blast entering the furnace when a "slip" occurs in the furnace, during casting, or when any emergency occurs. It consists of two interconnected butterfly valves, one closing the line against the blast, and the other opening a by-pass line to the atmosphere. Snort valves are

muffled to lessen the noise attendant upon their operation.

The brick lining of a stove, which includes all the brickwork enclosed by the shell, usually lasts from 15 to 20 years before it becomes necessary to replace it because of spalling, deformation, or clogging of the checkers. In addition, it may be necessary to replace the upper 10 to 20 feet of the checkerwork at the end of each furnace campaign, or from five to seven years. An insulating space of about 3 inches between the brickwork and the steel shell is filled with high-grade loose insulation or insulating strips. The bottom is insulated with insulating concrete, and the dome is covered by small insulating squares on top of which loose insulation is placed. The brick is first-grade fire-brick and should possess high thermal capacity and conductivity. The skin wall of the combustion chamber and the top 10 feet of checkerwork are constructed of a higher alumina brick than first-grade firebrick. Some designers prefer semi-silica brick, made from New Jersey clay, over the higher alumina brick. Formerly, checkers were built of the conventional rectangular formed brick and provided relatively large channels for passage of gases. With the advent of the use of secondary-cleaned gas in the stoves, the use of smaller openings has become feasible. Inserts were sometimes used in the passages of checkers built of rectangular brick, as shown in Figure 14—14. Special brick made in clusters with each cluster containing several openings are now more generally used; these facilitate laying and handling. Figure 14—14 shows several types of the more common clusters now in use. The thermal efficiency of a stove is about 85 per cent. The stoves use between 18 and 24 per cent of the gas produced by the furnace for heating the blast.

Dustcatcher and Gas Mains—The object of the dustcatcher is, as implied by its name, to remove as much as possible of the flue dust blown over from the furnace, with which the gas is heavily laden. If this dust is not removed, at least in part, it puts an unnecessary load upon the succeeding wet-cleaning units and, in addition, the dust is more easily and economically handled in the dry state as it comes from the dustcatcher. The dustcatcher is from 35 to 40 feet in diameter, usually lined with brick to prevent cooling and the attendant precipitation of water from the gas. It is a cylindrical structure fitted with a 60-degree inverted cone on the bottom and a cone-shaped top.

The single downcomer from the top of the furnace carries the gas to the top of the dustcatcher, where it enters a vertical pipe that is centrally located inside the dustcatcher and extends nearly to the bottom. This vertical pipe flares outward about 8 degrees and is thus larger in diameter at the bottom than at the top. As the gas passes downward through this pipe, its velocity (and therefore its ability to carry dust) is lowered, causing some of the dust to drop out of the gas stream and be deposited at the bottom of the dust-catcher. When the gas emerges from this pipe, it must change direction of flow suddenly and rise to the top of the dustcatcher, since the gas is removed from a convenient location at the top. The sudden change in flow direction causes more dust to be dropped from the gas stream. Efficiency of the dustcatcher is approx-

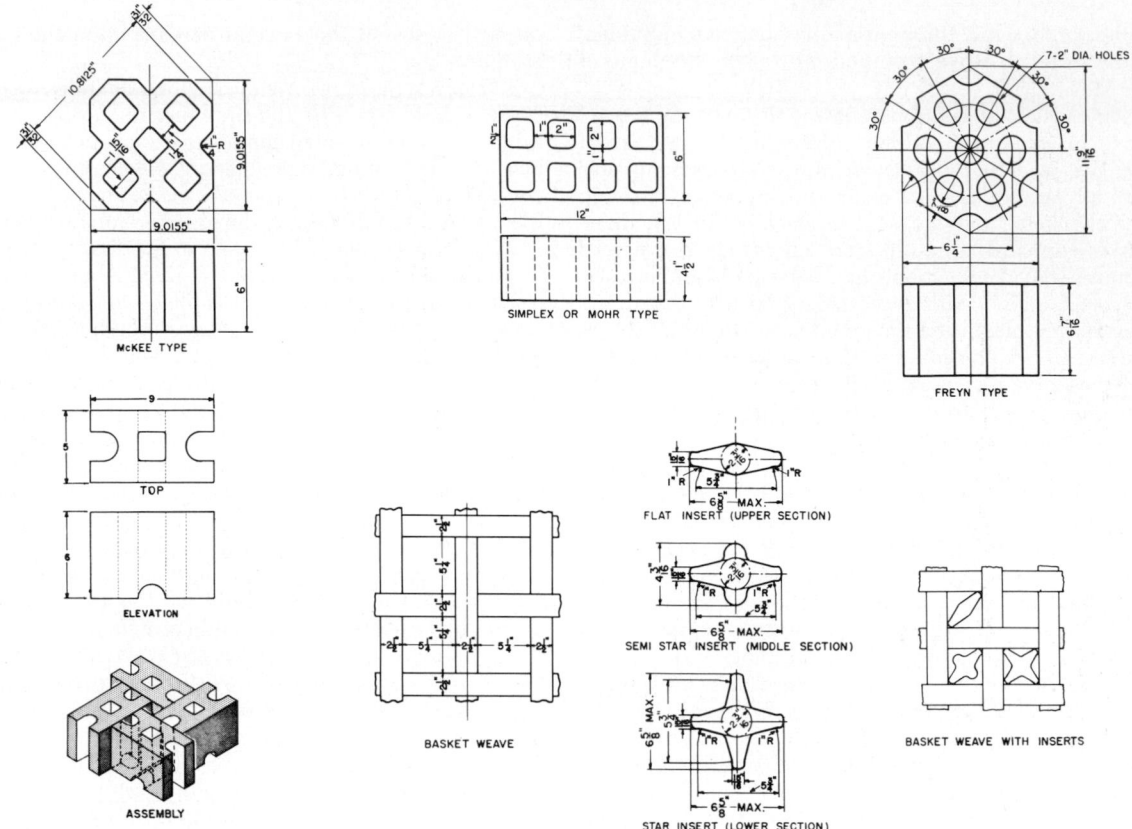

FIG. 14—14. Five different designs of checker-building shapes employed in the construction of modern blast-furnace stoves. The basket-weave design with inserts is no longer popular.

imately 60 to 75 per cent, depending upon the type of ores used and the blast volume. The accumulating dust usually is removed from the dustcatcher by a double-shaft pug mill which is rigidly fastened to the cone bottom. Water is added to the pug mill until the dust is slightly moistened, which prevents the dust from blowing around the vicinity as it drops into a railroad car. An auxiliary hand-operated gate also is provided which permits dust to be removed in case the pug mill is down for repairs. The exit gas passes from the dustcatcher into the bottom of the primary washer.

Gas-Cleaning Plants—Neglecting the larger lumps blown out occasionally when the furnace "slips," the dust particles in blast-furnace gas vary in size from ¼ inch to a few microns (1 micron = 0.00003937 inch) with practically all of the dust passing the dustcatcher being minus No. 20-mesh sieve size. The difficulty of cleaning increases as the particle size decreases, the removal of the very fine particles being comparable to the removal of smoke from air. On this account, plants generally are planned to clean the gas in two stages, a **primary stage** to remove the coarser particles, which form the larger proportion of the dust, and a **secondary** or **final stage** to remove as much of the remaining dust as possible. The approximate removal of incoming dust by the usual gas-cleaning system is 60 to 75 per cent in the dustcatcher, 90 to 95 per cent of the remainder in the primary cleaning unit, and 90 to 95 per cent of the dust still in the gas leaving the primary

unit is eliminated in the secondary cleaner. The gas entering the dustcatcher contains from 7 to 30 grains per cubic foot, an average dust content being about 16 grains per cubic foot. In some cases, a centrifugal cleaner is installed between the dustcatcher and the primary cleaning unit.

Either of two methods is used to clean the gas after it has passed through the dustcatcher, wet cleaning or dry cleaning. In **wet cleaning**, the aim is to wet the dust particles and wash them out of the gas with water. Incidentally, the gas is cooled to about the temperature of the wash water, and any moisture in excess of saturation at this temperature is precipitated. In **dry cleaning**, one of the aims is to remove the dust without cooling, thus conserving the sensible heat. In many cases, the temperature of the gas leaving the furnace is under 300° F (150° C) as contrasted with 500° F to 600° F (260 to 315° C) in former practice. The elimination of the water, which exists in the gas as superheated steam, and which is reduced to its dew point concentration at the cleaning-water temperature, more than balances the loss in sensible heat in wet cleaning. For these reasons, dry cleaning presently is not used to any great extent.

Primary wet cleaners include venturi washers, stationary-spray towers, revolving-spray towers, Feld washers as described later, baffle towers, spray fans and water separators. The venturi washer and the stationary-spray tower are most used, although many

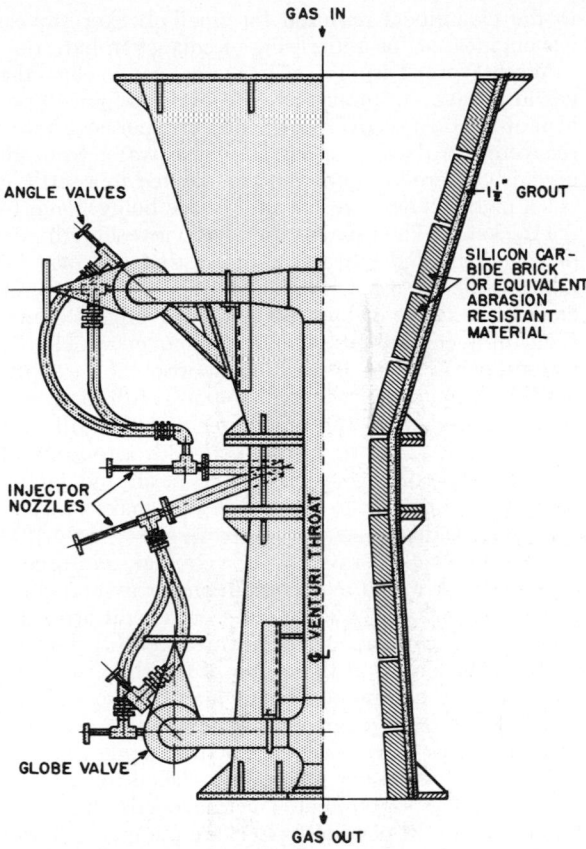

GAS IN

ANGLE VALVES

1½" GROUT

SILICON CAR-
BIDE BRICK
OR EQUIVALENT
ABRASION
RESISTANT
MATERIAL

INJECTOR
NOZZLES

VENTURI THROAT

GLOBE VALVE

GAS OUT

FIG. 14—15. Schematic arrangement of a venturi-type unit for washing blast-furnace gas, with right side cut away to show lining.

Feld washers remain in use, and sometimes a washer consists of a combination of one or two Feld washer revolving cones in the bottom, above which are several banks of stationary sprays. In almost all cases, a water separator is an integral part of the washer.

The **venturi washer** is a vertical-type unit that is installed adjacent to the dustcatcher (see Figure 14—2). Gas from the main enters the top of the unit and passes downward (see Figure 14—15). As the gas passes through the narrow "throat" of the unit, it is sprayed with water. There are two sets of water sprays, one operating at low pressure and entering the unit at right angles to the gas flow, and the other operating at high pressure and directed upward at an angle of 110° to the gas flow. The washer is lined with a suitable abrasion-resistant material to withstand the erosive effect of dust-laden gas. The venturi-type washer can clean gas to an average dust content of 0.05 grain per cu. ft.

The gas passes from the venturi washer into a water separator directly beneath it, and thence to a cooling tower where its temperature is lowered by passing through water sprays. The cooled gas then passes through a moisture eliminator before going to the secondary cleaning system.

The **stationary-spray tower** consists of a supported steel cylinder with conical bottom and conical top with the gas entering at a point near the bottom of the cylinder and leaving through a centrally located outlet on top of the top cone. Inside the cylinder are three or four banks of ceramic tile (with about 5-inch diameter round holes in them) which split up the rising gas and tend to prevent channeling. Above each bank are water sprays which uniformly cover the cross section of the washer with a falling "rain." A U-shaped seal pipe at the outlet of the bottom cone carries the dirty water away to a Dorr thickener or settling basin and prevents the gas from blowing to the atmosphere. A centrifugal-type water separator above the topmost bank eliminates any entrained water in the outgoing gas.

The **Feld washer** is a cylindrical shell with a flat bottom and a conical top in which there is a series of from 5 to 7 inverted frustums of cones which rotate on the same centrally-located vertical shaft, driven by a motor and reduction gear on top of the washer. The lower edge of each cone is immersed in a separate water tray. The centrifugal action of the rotating cones picks up water from each tray and throws it outward toward the shell as a spray through which the rising gas must pass. Baffles guide the water back into the trays for reuse, excess water spilling into the next tray below. A water separator similar to that on the stationary-spray tower is located above the topmost rotating cone.

Primary dry cleaners include various modifications of cyclone separators, centrifugal machines, metallic-wool-pad filters, and electrical or Cottrell precipitators. The dry-type Cottrell precipitator may also be classed as a secondary dry cleaner and will be discussed under that heading. The cyclone and centrifugal types present the problems of excessive wear and difficulty in handling the fine dust removed. The filters have a tendency to clog shortly after being placed in operation.

Secondary wet cleaners have consisted of wet-type Cottrell precipitators, high-speed disintegrators, and Theissen disintegrators. Formerly, Theissen disintegrators were used almost exclusively, but on later installations have been replaced by high-speed disintegrators or by the wet-type Cottrell precipitators, with preference being given to the latter type. The **Theissen disintegrator** is a type of fan that dashes water, introduced through small jets, into a spray which is forced to travel in one direction while the gas is forced through the same channels in an opposite direction.

The **high-speed** or **rotary disintegrator** is a smaller diameter machine than the Theissen but rotates faster (500 to 700 rpm) and consists of a casing in which is mounted a rotating "squirrel cage." This cage is made up of two heads fastened to the shaft with a series of bars parallel to the axis fastened to the heads. Vanes mounted on the heads reduce the pressure-drop through the machine and force the incoming gas through the rotating bars, upon which water is sprayed, to the center of the cage where it is taken off to the clean-gas main. These machines are built up to 40,000 cu. ft. per min. rated capacity, require from 400 to 500 horsepower to drive them, and will clean the gas to under 0.02 grains per cubic foot.

In the **Cottrell wet method** of cleaning, the primary-cleaned gas is forced to pass through narrow channels or ducts across which an electrostatic field is maintained. The dust particles are "precipitated" or separated from the gas through the action of electrostatic charges. The molecules of gas are ionized and, in turn, induce electrostatic charges upon the surfaces of the small dust particles. Under these conditions, the dust particles are attracted toward the electrode of opposite polarity. There is also an "electrical wind" or corona effect. Current is supplied from an alternating-current source, stepped up in voltage by a transformer, and made unidirectional by a mechanical rectifier or by vacuum tubes. In most precipitators cleaning cool gases, the unit collecting electrode is a vertical tube, 8 to 12 inches in diameter, or it may be of parallel steel plates through which the gas is forced upward, or sideways. In the former type the discharge electrode is a wire suspended coincident with the long axis of the tube and, in the latter, multiple wires midway between the plates. A thin film of water flows over the inside edge of each tube or plate which washes it free of dust that has been deposited thereon, the dirty water being conducted to a Dorr thickener or settling basin. The precipitator usually is divided into two units with valving so arranged that one unit may be shut down for inspection or repairs while the other unit is operating. In some installations, the precipitator is mounted directly above the primary washer. The rotary disintegrator has the advantage of lower first cost but has higher power cost than the wet-type Cottrell precipitator. The cleanliness of the gas may be slightly in favor of the precipitator.

Secondary dry cleaners have included bag filters and Cottrell precipitators. The bag-type filters, sometimes called the Halberger-Beth type, consist of a number of fabric "socks" made of cloth, glass threads, asbestos threads, or very fine Monel metal screen (or a combination), supported at the top and closed on the bottom, into which the gas passes from the outside forming a film of dust on the sock which acts as the filtering medium. When the film of dust becomes too thick, the exit end of the sock is closed thereby shutting off the gas flow and the sock is shaken or vibrated to drop the excess dust into a collecting hopper. The socks are stiffened both circumferentially and longitudinally to prevent their collapse. It has been difficult to find a fabric which does not break down under the temperature encountered with hot blast-furnace gas. Also, if the temperature of the gas should reach its dew point, moisture would deposit in the fabric thereby forming a deposit of dust on the sock which cannot be dislodged.

The dry-type Cottrell operates upon the same principle as the wet type but is constructed somewhat differently. The modification consists in using slabs of reinforced concrete as collecting electrodes to form channels for the passage of the gas, with the discharge wires suspended along the center lines of the channels. Periodically, each unit is taken out of circuit to permit the dust on the collecting electrode to fall into a hopper below. In this type, the dust is detached from the collecting electrode by suspended chains which are used as scrapers and which are operated by air cylinders. The dry-type precipitator has not cleaned the gas

to the cleanliness required for small-checker stoves, gas engines, or for underfiring of coke-oven batteries.

Wash-Water Disposal—The water used to clean the gas in the wet-cleaning system contains about 40 per cent of the dust recovered, the other 60 per cent being recovered in the dry state. The wash water from all units is gathered together and conducted to a settling basin or thickener, present preference being given to the thickener. The usual settling basin is rectangular in plan and divided into two units so that one may be filling while the other is being emptied by a tractor or locomotive crane or by a permanent overhead crane. Each unit consists of several weirs over which the water flows in series, depositing a portion of the solids in each compartment. When one unit is full the water is then switched to the other unit and the full unit emptied. The handling of the wet solids into railroad cars is a difficult task, both at the basin and in the vicinity, due largely to the inability to make railroad cars water tight.

A typical thickener consists of a circular, reinforced-concrete tank which may contain one or several compartments in each of which one or several arms revolve. The arms are driven from a central vertical shaft. Water enters at the center of the thickener and leaves over a continuous weir which follows the circumference of the compartment. Each arm carries a series of rakes or vanes set at such an angle that the solids which settle out are gently pushed toward the center of the compartment. The thickened solids, containing about 60 per cent water, are pumped out and delivered either pneumatically or by pump to a filter for further processing. The thickener may be built with either an open or closed top. Two types of filters are in general use, the cylindrical or drum type and the disc type. Both operate upon the underflow from the thickener, discharged into a basin into which an arc of the slowly rotating filter dips. The drum or disc consists of a framework over which canvas is stretched, and a partial vacuum is applied on the inside of that part which dips in the basin, thereby drawing the liquid through the canvas while the solids are retained by the canvas. When the drum or disc reaches another point in its rotation, a slight air pressure is applied on the inside of the canvas thereby bulging it and causing some of the filter cake to crack and drop off into a chute, the balance being scraped off by a scraper. The filtrate returns to the thickener and the filter cake, containing about 25 per cent moisture, is delivered by railroad car to the sintering plant or, if the sintering plant is located adjacent to the furnace, the filters are designed as an integral part of the sintering plant itself.

Sintering Plant—A sintering plant's primary function is to agglomerate the flue dust and filter cake produced in the operation of the blast furnace into a product more acceptable for recharging into the furnace, and its secondary function is to beneficiate some of the finely divided ore. The secondary function may transcend the primary function and for purposes of description it is assumed that part of the charge contains a portion of fine ore for beneficiation. Modern sintering methods and equipment already have been described in Chapter 5 on iron ores, along with other methods of agglomerating fines.

Cast House—Since the molten iron is heavier than the slag or cinder, it lies in the bottom of the hearth and is cast or removed from 4 to 10 times a day through the iron notch. This is an opening which is plugged with clay except when the furnace is casting. The usual method of casting is to drill into the clay with a pneumatic drill (Figure **14—16**) until the skull of iron is met, when an oxygen lance is used to burn through the iron skull. The iron flows into the main trough which has a skimmer located near its end. The skimmer separates any slag flowing with the iron and diverts it into the slag ladles, or to the dry slag pit or to the slag-granulating pit. The iron continues to flow down the main runner from which it is diverted at intervals into the iron ladles, the control of this operation being accomplished by gates or shutters located in the runners.

The closing of the hole at the finish of the cast is accomplished by means of the **clay gun** (Figure **14—16**). The gun is swung from an arm mounted on a pedestal in the cast house or on one of the furnace columns. It consists of a cylinder narrowed to a nozzle at the exit end and a capped opening on top into which soft clay is placed preliminary to casting time. The arm is normally parallel to the main trough but when placed in operation the arm is swung through 90° and the gun is tilted so that the nose enters the iron notch. The clay is forced from the gun by a plunger or screw; the plunger usually is operated by steam and the screw by an electric motor.

The slag is flushed usually from the furnace through the monkey between successive casts and it flows through runners, in much the same way as the iron, into slag ladles, into a granulating pit, into a dry pit or into a slag machine. The monkey is closed by pushing into the hole by hand, a steel, cone-shaped knob on the end of a long steel bar, called the **bott,** or this may be accomplished mechanically by arms attached to a framework which supports and guides a water-cooled bott (Figures **14—16** and **14—17**).

Iron Disposal—Iron ladles are of three types: the open-top ladle, the Kling-type ladle, and the mixer or

FIG. **14—16**. General view inside the cast house of a blast-furnace plant. The clay gun is shown in position for closing the tap hole. Suspended diagonally near the center of the illustration is the drill used to drill through the clay in the tap hole when the furnace is to be cast. The bott-operating mechanism for closing the slag notch is at the extreme left. The bustle pipe and connections to several of the tuyeres are also visible.

Pugh-type ladle, all of which are refractory-lined. The **open-top ladle**, as the name implies, is an inverted frustum of a cone with the top open to the atmosphere. The maximum capacity of this type is about 75 tons. The ladle is supported on the car or carriage by trunnion castings on the ladle, resting in corresponding castings on the car. In all types, the car usually is equipped with air brakes and automatic couplers. The **Kling type** is somewhat spherical in shape with an opening at the top through which the iron enters. Its advantage is less radiating surface with consequent less skull formation. It is built up to about 115 tons capacity and is supported on its car similarly to the open-top ladle. The **Pugh-type** ladle is cigar-shaped with an opening at the top. It is built up to 200 tons capacity and differs from the other two types in that it is not removed from the car, the ladle itself forming part of the car between trucks. To empty the Pugh ladle, it is rotated about its longitudinal axis and, due

to its large capacity in relation to the opening, offers the least radiating surface. In some cases, this type ladle functions as a metal mixer and the regular mixer is eliminated, with the iron going directly from the mixer ladle to the steel-making process. A ladle of the Pugh type is shown in Figure 14—18.

Normally, the iron ladles carry the molten iron to the metal mixer but there are times when it is necessary to dispose of the iron by casting it over the **pig machine**. Present pig machines differ only slightly from each other;—the chain in one type carrying rollers on each side that ride on a track; while, in the other type, the sides of the chain form a track which rides on stationary rollers. The endless chain, carrying a series of parallel cast-iron molds or troughs with overlapping edges, passes over a head and a tail sprocket wheel. The molten iron is poured into the molds near the tail sprocket, solidifies, and is cooled by water sprays as the chain rises to the head sprocket,

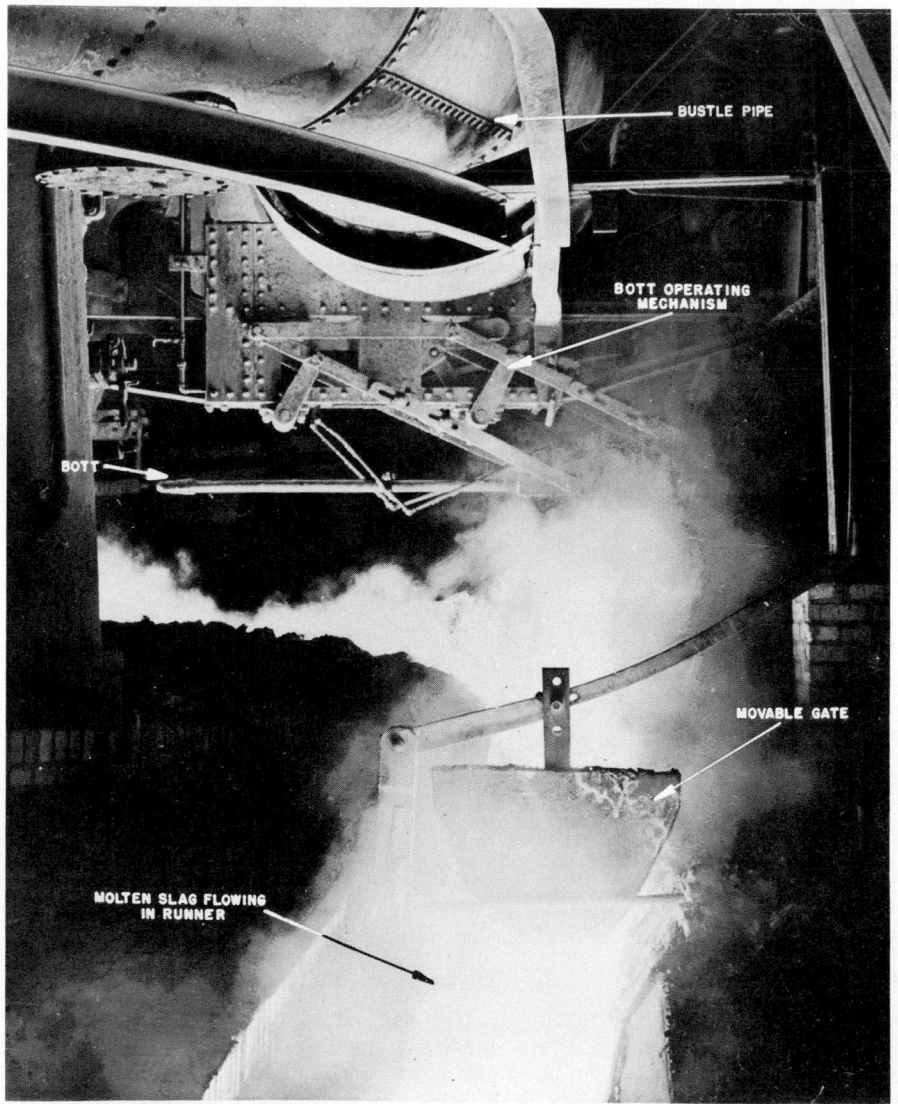

FIG. 14—17. Mechanical slag bott withdrawn from slag notch, with stream of molten slag running down slag trough.

FIG. 14—18. A Pugh-type hot-metal transfer car.

and falls from the molds into cars as the chain passes over the head sprocket. On the return travel of the chain, the molds are sprayed with a lime wash to prevent sticking of the iron to the molds but, in cases where the pigs do stick to the molds, a "pig sticker" at the head end loosens the pig from the mold. Most machines are of the double-strand type, that is, they are built with two parallel chains. In the operation of the machine, iron is poured from the ladle into a small basin, which reduces the splash and which then divides the stream of molten iron to serve the two branches, one for each chain. The speed of travel of the chains and rate of pour of metal from the ladle are controlled so that a full-sized pig is formed in each mold. Pigs for use in the steel mills weigh almost 100 pounds but, for some commercial uses, pigs weighing as little as 30 pounds are poured. Operation of a pig machine is illustrated in Figure 14—19.

Slag Disposal—The slag is handled in one of four ways: it flows directly into cinder ladles; it is granulated; it flows directly into cooling pits (Figure 14—20); or it is made into lightweight aggregate for concrete or insulation. The cinder ladles are unlined, tulip-shaped, cast-iron (sometimes steel) pots mounted

on cars or carriages on which they are moved from the furnace to the slag dump. The cars are equipped with air- or steam-operated cylinders which partially rotate the trunnion holding the ladle so that it can be dumped by the compressed air in the railroad train line (Figure 14—21).

Sometimes the molten slag, if of suitable composition is dumped in specially prepared dumps, from which it is removed by a power shovel (after weathering for a period of several weeks), screened, and sold as an aggregate for concrete or as ballast. In granulating slag, provisions are made for the molten slag to strike a stream of high-pressure water as it falls from the lip of the runner, forming a popcorn-like mass which later is loaded onto cars by grab bucket. In this form, it is used in the manufacture of cement. Some of the newer furnaces flush the slag directly in long, rectangular, concrete walled pits (Figure 14—20), open at one end, from which it is removed by a power shovel and loaded into railroad cars. The pits are usually two in number, one being filled while the other is being emptied, with from five to seven days being required to fill a pit. In this form the slag, after screening, is used as an aggregate for concrete. In a

FIG. 14—19. Pig-casting machine in operation, showing molten iron from transfer ladle being divided into two streams by the split runner to simultaneously fill molds in each of the two strands.

few cases, the slag as it flows from the runner is met by a small stream of water, steam, air, or a combination of these which *partially* granulates it, but with no excess water, so that the product formed consists of lumps which are filled with air cells. After screening out the fines, the product is used for insulation or, when cement is added, as a lightweight concrete. By adaptation of the method used, it is sometimes possible to make slag disposal a profitable operation.

Handling Ore from Vessel—The ore used in many furnace plants is mined at considerable distance from the plant and requires transportation either by rail or water, or a combination of both, before reaching the plant site. Coke and limestone, the other essential ingredients, are rarely stored in large quantities and are consumed as currently received. In the case of ore, weather conditions are often such as to prevent mining and transportation during the colder months so it is necessary to store during the warm months approximately half a year's supply adjacent to the furnaces. Since many of the furnaces in this country receive their ore from the Lake Superior District, as discussed at length in Chapter 5, the transportation of ore from there is described very briefly here as being typical of water transportation of ore. Ore, at the head of Lake Superior, is loaded by gravity, from long piers extending into the harbor and carrying overhead bins, into specially constructed ore boats. Upon reaching their destination, the ore is unloaded by Hulett unloaders or by special unloading rigs if the plant is large enough to justify this special equipment, or, if the plant is smaller, by an ore bridge which extends over the vessel and permits the ore-bridge bucket to unload the vessel.

The Hulett unloader (See Chapter 5) consists of a carriage mounted on wheels which permit it to move in and out in a direction at right angles to the dock, and which carries a counterweighted pivoted arm, on the harbor side of which is located the grab bucket. The operator rides in a compartment near the bucket and controls its movement from this location. The bucket itself can be rotated, and the entire unloader can be moved parallel to the dock. The bucket moves downward through the open hatch of the vessel, takes its "grab," and then moves upward and backward depositing its grab into a hopper. Under the hopper is a rotating feeder which places the ore into a small car that runs backward either to a hopper over railroad cars or to an ore trench in the ore yard. The ore bridge picks the ore from the ore trench and distributes it onto the ore pile.

The unloading rigs (See Chapter 5) perform the same function as the Huletts but differ somewhat in construction. Instead of the bucket being carried by a rigid arm, it is hung from a trolley resembling a crane trolley; consequently, it cannot be rotated and it cannot clean out the hold of the vessel as completely as the Hulett, and the additional use of a small bulldozer and hand labor is necessary to complete the job.

Car Dumper—For those plants located some distance from the point of vessel unloading, or where ore is received directly from the mines by railroad, a car dumper is the usual means used to unload ore. The ore, arriving at the plant in trainload lots, is switched to a siding ahead of the car dumper and the cars are unloaded one by one in rapid succession.

In one type of dumper, illustrated in Figure 14—22, a car, being pulled up an incline to the platform

FIG. 14—20. Slag-cooling pit adjacent to a blast furnace.

FIG. 14—21. Molten slag pouring from runner in cast house into slag ladle.

FIG. 14—22. Car dumper discharging iron ore from a railroad car into a transfer car.

of the dumper by a steel cable of a "mule" or "barney," is lifted bodily and turned over so as to empty its contents into a large transfer car which, in turn, discharges into an unloading trough opposite the location in the stock yard for that particular grade. The dumper then resumes its former position and the empty car is pushed off the platform, by the next car of ore, to an incline, down which the empty cars move to a siding. The transfer cars are usually designed to hold two railroad cars of ore. A nozzle carrying high-pressure water and mounted upon a rigid swivel can be turned on and directed by the operator to any crevice in the upturned car bottom where the ore has not been dislodged. The quantity of water used is so small that it is insignificant in the ore. The ore falling from the car passes over grids that hold back any large lumps and then drops into a bin. There are gates at the bottom of this bin which are operated by the transfer-car operator in filling the transfer car. Some dumpers have been built which are movable, in that they are able to move to any location and dump the ore directly into the ore trough. These dumpers, how-

ever, must be attended by a locomotive when operating (Figure 14—23); consequently, only one car can be spotted on the dumper at a time. Preference seems to be for the stationary dumper with transfer cars.

A third type of car dumper is the rotary dumper (Figure 14—24), in which a loaded car is inverted to dump its contents by rotating a structure with circular ends about its longitudinal axis.

Ore Yard and Ore Bridges—The ore yard (Figure 14—25) is a large space, sometimes with concrete bottom and sides, which parallels the furnace bin structure and serves as storage for approximately a half-year's consumption of ore. Its width is determined by the practical maximum span of the ore bridge, which for a bridge supported at each end amounts to about 350 feet. Other types of bridges are supported by two legs which run longitudinally through the ore yard (dividing the yard into three separate piles); such bridges have cantilevers on the outer sides of the two supporting legs. This type gives a longer trolley travel but does not necessarily store any more ore per running foot because of the space occupied by the supporting structures. A trolley running on the bridge proper carries a grab bucket of about 15 tons capacity which, when stocking, lifts the ore from the dumping trough and distributes it on the pile, or removes the

FIG. 14—23. Movable car dumper discharging ore from car into ore trough.

FIG. 14—24. Rotary car dumper with car in inverted position. Entire supporting structure rotates clockwise to right car, which is then unclamped and moved away to be replaced by the next loaded car.

ore from the pile and deposits it either directly into the bins or into a bin or transfer car (Figure 14—26) which in turn distributes the ore. Some bridges are provided with a bin hanging from the bridge into which the bucket dumps permitting the bridge to keep working while the bin car is dumping its load. In order to obtain the maximum benefit of mixing, the ore is stocked in horizontal layers and removed in vertical slices. For this reason, the use of ore direct from hopper cars unloaded from the trestle into the bins is undesirable. The details of the ore-handling system will vary considerably but the general scheme is essentially as stated.

Trestle and Stockhouse—If it were not for the fact that all parts of a blast-furnace plant are essential to its operation, the stockhouse might be considered as the most important unit of the plant, with the exception of the furnace itself, since its function is to deliver to the furnace the correct quantities of ore, fuel and flux without which the furnace cannot operate.

The constructional details of the **trestle** differ considerably but a trestle of modern design consists of a reinforced concrete wall on the stock yard side and steel columns on the furnace side, between which is a

crosswork of transverse and longitudinal girders. On top, these girders support three or four railroad tracks, and on the bottom, the bins proper. The track nearest the stock yard carries a side-dump bin car, the next track carries railroad cars containing materials such as limestone, dolomite, scale, scrap, etc., which are unloaded by manual operation of the hopper gates of the cars, and the next one or two tracks carry coke cars. When there are more than six furnaces in a line, it is desirable to have two coke tracks so that the coke cars, not fully unloaded, may be by-passed. Where the coke bins are filled by a belt conveyor (as described later), one coke track for emergency use is sufficient. This construction results in two lines of bins in the stockhouse, one line containing ore, flux and miscellaneous materials and the other containing coke.

A **scale car**, equipped with scales to weigh accurately each material drawn, runs underneath the first line of bins. The car may have a capacity of up to 40 tons and carries two pockets. The ore and miscellaneous material bins are equipped with gates on the bottom which may be operated either mechanically or by hand (Figure 14—27). The car delivers its load

FIG. 14—25. View of an ore yard serving the blast furnaces in the background.

by discharging into chutes leading to the skips. Underneath the second row of coke bins, a belt conveyor, fed by vibrating feeders at each coke bin, runs toward the skip pit while another conveyor on the other side of the skip pit performs the some function for the coke bins on that side. Each conveyor discharges upon a vibrating screen where the coke fines are screened out and the oversize discharged into a weigh hopper (Figure 14—28). Here the coke is weighed and at a

FIG. 14—26. Transfer or bin car of side-discharge type, in position to discharge load of ore into stockhouse bins. The ore must pass through the gratings shown, which effectively prevent oversize material from entering the bins.

predetermined weight an electrical contact stops the belt and vibrating coke feeders. Provision also is made usually to stop the belt and feeders in case a predetermined volume, rather than weight, is desired. From the weigh hoppers, the coke is discharged directly into the skips. Considerable time is saved by this method, as the operator can be drawing ore while the coke loading is being taken care of automatically. The undersized coke from the vibrating screen is removed by a small bucket hoist, or by conveyor belt, to a storage bin where it is rescreened into coarse and fine. The coarse may be recharged separately into the furnace or may be sold as domestic coke, while the fines are used under boilers, as fuel in the sintering processes, and to make up the bottom of soaking pits. In the **bucket hoist** the same scheme as that just described is used for the ore, flux and miscellaneous materials, but the bucket itself is placed, on descending, upon a revolving cone which keeps the bucket revolving during the time it is receiving the charge. A **charge**, or **round**, is that minimum combination of skip or bucket loads of materials which together provide the balanced complement necessary to produce hot metal of the desired specification. Normally, the entire charge is deposited on the large bell by successive skips or buckets and enters the furnace upon lowering of the bell. However, through preference or because of the limited capacity of the large bell hopper, the charge or round may be "split" and require two drops of the large bell.

Automatic Stockhouse Operation—As has already been described, the charging of coke has been made an automatic operation on many furnaces. Until re-

Fig. 14—27. Scale car in stockhouse, showing overhead ore bin gates from which car is filled, and chutes that carry coke from bins directly to skips.

Fig. 14—28. Coke being delivered by conveyor belt to weigh hopper at the skip pit. Chute at left permits charging coke into the hopper when belt is not operating.

cently, however, the weighing and assembly of iron-bearing and fluxing materials and their delivery to the skip pit were functions performed by the scale car—the operation of which was independently and manually controlled. Automatically controlled systems for assembling, weighing and transporting iron ore and fluxing material as well as coke have been designed to serve new furnaces or have been adapted to existing stockhouses, thereby eliminating the necessity for a scale car except for emergency operation. The system employs feeding conveyors equipped with weighing mechanisms beneath each stock bin. These conveyors deliver weighed amounts of materials to collecting belts that convey them to the skip pit (Figures 14—29 and 14—30).

With raw materials of known composition and the quantities of each that are to be charged in each round predetermined, and the order of the charges or rounds previously scheduled, these data can be programmed on punched cards or tape. The charging functions, integrated with skip-hoist operation, are then carried out automatically and uninterruptedly until a change is ordered. Alternatively, the programmed operation can be carried out by supplying the input data to the programmer through a panel of dials, set-up switches and pushbuttons.

Blowers, Boilers, Pump Houses, Etc.—These vital parts of the blast-furnace equipment present features of more interest to engineers than to metallurgists.

Fig. 14—29. View of the interior of a stockhouse converted to automatic operation, showing one of the collecting conveyors running beneath the row of stock bins at the left. Scale-car tracks parallel the rows of bins on either side.

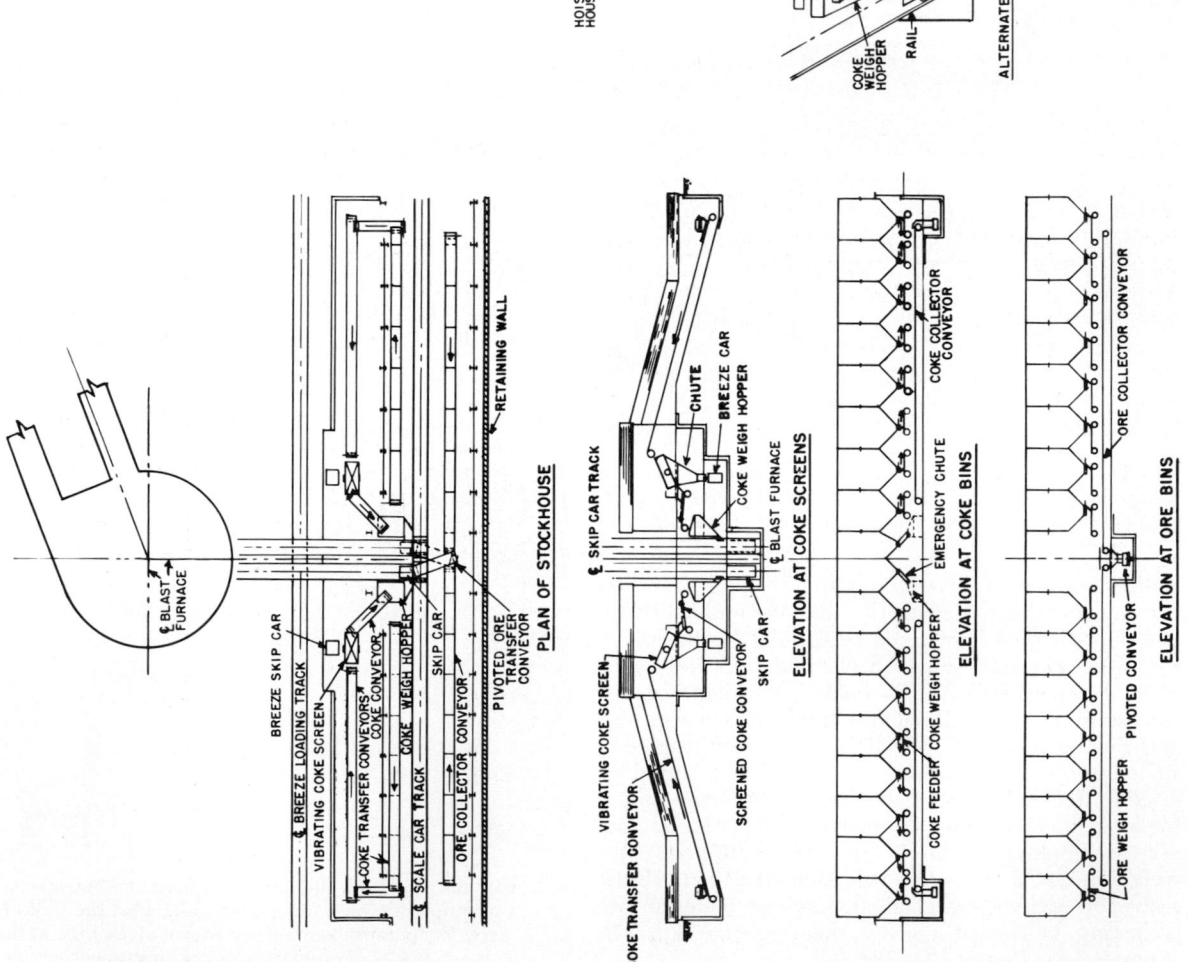

Fig. 14—30. Schematic arrangement showing mechanical handling for metallics and coke bins in plan and elevation.

The blowing of the furnace, on all later installations, is by turbo blower, this type of equipment having almost completely displaced internal-combustion gas engines and steam reciprocating engines. It is noted that many installations now receive steam at 700 pounds per square inch pressure with a total temperature of 750° F. There has been at least one installation abroad where a gas turbine has been used to blow a blast furnace. The boilers almost universally burn secondary clean gas, with unit coal pulverizers provided at each boiler for auxiliary firing. The water system is usually designed to deliver water at tuyere level at 30 pounds per square inch head. The water is treated with lime if it is of a corrosive nature, and may be chlorinated sufficiently to prevent algae growth.

Instrumentation and Control—The blast-furnace operator is aided and guided in establishing and maintaining the best possible balance between the many variable factors affecting furnace operation by numerous automatic devices which indicate or record conditions at various points in the furnace system and may operate control mechanisms that automatically regulate important variables.

Instruments considered essential to proper operation of a modern blast-furnace plant include:
Blast-pressure recorder and indicator.
Blast-temperature recorder and indicator.
Stockline recorder and visual indicator.
Top-temperature recorder.
Top-pressure recorder and indicator.
Blast-volume recorder and indicator.
Stove-stack temperature recorder.
Stove-dome temperature recorder.
Automatic hot-blast temperature controller.
Automatic combustion controls for stove burners with dome and stack temperature correctives.
Sequence recorder of large-bell movement and revolving distributor operation.
Annunciator for alarms warning of low gas pressure, high stove-dome temperature, high stack temperature, low blast pressure, and so on.

In addition, some plants employ multipoint inwall-temperature recorders, top-gas analyzers, and other instruments for measuring, detecting and/or recording conditions of interest to the operators of a particular plant or furnace.

SECTION 5
CHEMISTRY OF THE BLAST-FURNACE PROCESS

PRODUCTION OF HEAT AND REDUCTION OF IRON

When the burden materials and the coke are charged into the top of the blast furnace they come in contact with hot gases that are ascending from the hearth. The coke is preheated by these gases so that when it reaches the lower portion of the furnace and comes in contact with the air of the hot blast, adjacent to the tuyeres, it will burn with very great intensity. At the high temperatures that exist at this location (above 3000° F), carbon dioxide (CO_2) is not stable because of the large quantity of carbon (C) present as coke. For this reason if any CO_2 forms it reacts immediately with C to form carbon monoxide (CO). Consequently, the combustion of coke in the blast furnace can be expressed by the following chemical equation:

$$C + 1/2\ O_2 = CO \qquad \Delta H,\ -26{,}400\ \text{cal.} \qquad (1)^*$$

In modern blast-furnace operation between 600 and 900 pounds of carbon react in this manner for every ton of hot metal produced. This reaction is not only the main source of heat for the smelting operation, but it also produces a reducing gas (CO) that ascends into the furnace stack where it preheats and reduces most of the iron oxide in the burden as it descends through the furnace stack.

With the blast air there is always some moisture (H_2O) that also reacts with some of the carbon of the coke in the combustion zone. This reaction does not produce heat but rather consumes it. However, it produces more reducing gas for every unit of carbon

than that produced when carbon is burned with air. (When carbon burns in air it produces only one unit of CO, but when carbon reacts with water vapor it produces one unit of CO and one of hydrogen, H_2.) Consequently, in certain instances (particularly when a very high hot-blast temperature is available—between 1600° and 2100° F), it is advantageous to add moisture to the blast and keep it at a uniformly high level to provide the proper amount of hydrogen for the particular burden. This chemical reaction is expressed by the following equation:

$$C + H_2O = CO + H_2 \qquad \Delta H,\ 31{,}400\ \text{cal.} \qquad (2)$$

In the upper portion of the furnace where the temperature is below 1700° F, the ascending gases start to reduce the iron oxide of the burden. At these temperatures, the chemical equilibrium prevents all of the CO and H_2 from being used. Consequently, the amount of CO or H_2 must be more (approximately triple) than the amount shown by the following stoichiometric equations used to designate these reactions:

$$1/2\ Fe_2O_3 + 3/2\ CO = Fe + 3/2\ CO_2 \qquad \Delta H = -3{,}075\ \text{cal.} \qquad (3)$$

$$1/3\ Fe_3O_4 + 4/3\ CO = Fe + 4/3\ CO_2 \qquad \Delta H = -933\ \text{cal.} \qquad (4)$$

$$FeO + CO = Fe + CO_2 \qquad \Delta H = -3{,}850\ \text{cal.} \qquad (5)$$

$$1/2\ Fe_2O_3 + 3/2\ H_2 = Fe + 3/2\ H_2O \qquad \Delta H = 11{,}700\ \text{cal.} \qquad (6)$$

$$1/3\ Fe_3O_4 + 4/3\ H_2 = Fe + 4/3\ H_2O \qquad \Delta H = 12{,}199\ \text{cal.} \qquad (7)$$

$$FeO + H_2 = Fe + H_2O \qquad \Delta H = 6{,}000\ \text{cal.} \qquad (8)$$

---

* All heats of reaction are calculated from the heats of formation, ΔH_{298}, listed in Table 12-II of Chapter 12.

In the past this type of reduction was called "indirect reduction" in contrast to the type occurring at higher temperatures that was called "direct reduction." However, this nomenclature has become confusing because these same chemical reactions are called "direct reduction" in describing the Wiberg, the Nu-Iron, the H-Iron and similar processes (see Chapter 13). For this reason these terms are not used as generally as they were in the past.

The portion of iron oxide that is not reduced in the upper part of the furnace where the temperature is relatively low must be reduced in the lower part where the temperature is very high. Since CO_2 and H_2O are not stable at these temperatures in the presence of large quantities of coke, they react with C as rapidly as they form. Consequently, the over-all reduction reaction in this part of the furnace can be represented by equation (10) no matter whether H_2 or CO does the reduction. As can be seen, equation (10) is obtained by algebraically adding either equation (5) and (9) or equations (8) and (2).

$$FeO+CO=Fe+CO_2 \quad \Delta H = -3,850 \text{ cal.} \quad (5)$$
$$CO_2+C = 2CO \quad \Delta H = 41,250 \text{ cal.} \quad (9)$$
$$\overline{FeO+C = Fe+CO} \quad \Delta H = 37,400 \text{ cal.} \quad (10)$$
$$FeO+H_2 = Fe+H_2O \quad \Delta H = 6,000 \text{ cal.} \quad (8)$$
$$H_2O+C = CO+H_2 \quad \Delta H = 31,400 \text{ cal.} \quad (2)$$
$$\overline{FeO+C = Fe+CO} \quad \Delta H = 37,400 \text{ cal.} \quad (10)$$

Reaction (10) absorbs a large amount of heat; consequently, the larger the amount of reduction occurring in this way, the larger the quantity of heat that must be supplied to the furnace. Notice also that reaction (10) produces CO, which is the gas used in reactions (3), (4), and (5) in the blast-furnace stack. In most instances the most efficient operation is obtained when about one-third of the reduction is done according to equation (10) and the balance according to reactions (3) to (8).

The heat for the process is not produced entirely by the combustion of coke, since at most blast furnaces about 20 per cent is supplied by the sensible heat of the hot-blast air. In fact, when the temperature of the blast is sufficiently high (above 1600° F), a portion of the fuel can be economically injected through the tuyeres as natural gas, fuel oil or pulverized coal. In such instances the carbon in the fuel burns to CO but because of the large amount of coke present the hydrogen remains as H_2 and is not oxidized until it reduces iron oxide somewhere above the tuyeres.

REDUCTION OF MANGANESE, PHOSPHORUS AND SILICON

At the temperature in the upper part of the blast-furnace stack some of the higher oxides of manganese are reduced by CO according to the following chemical equations:

$$MnO_2+CO = MnO+CO_2 \quad \Delta H = -35,350 \text{ cal.} \quad (11)$$
$$Mn_3O_4+CO = 3MnO+CO_2 \quad \Delta H = -12,250 \text{ cal.} \quad (12)$$

However, the lower oxide of manganese (MnO)

cannot be further reduced by CO or hydrogen at any of the temperatures that are encountered in the stack. Consequently, the only chemical equation that can be used to express the final reduction of this element is as follows:

$$MnO+C=Mn+CO \quad \Delta H = 65,600 \text{ cal.} \quad (13)$$

This reaction takes place only at temperatures above 2700° F and absorbs large quantities of heat. At higher temperatures the percentage of Mn that can be reduced in a blast furnace increases, but in most basic practices this amounts to about 65 to 75 per cent of the manganese charged. The manganese that is reduced dissolves in the hot metal while the unreduced portion remains as part of the slag.

The reduction of SiO_2 takes place only at very high temperatures according to the following chemical equation:

$$SiO_2+2C=Si+2CO \quad \Delta H = 157,400 \text{ cal.} \quad (14)$$

The rate of this reaction is relatively slow but accelerates with an increase in temperature. For any particular burden and slag composition the silicon content of the hot metal is proportional to the hot-metal temperature. The percentage of silicon in the hot metal can also be varied by increasing the silicon content of the charge and the coke input.

The reduction of phosphorus is most conveniently expressed by the equation:

$$P_2O_5+5C=2P+5CO \quad \Delta H = 238,000 \quad (15)$$

The final reduction of phosphorus also takes place only at very high temperatures; however, unlike Mn and Si the phosphorus is almost completely reduced. For this reason, almost all of the phosphorus in the charge will dissolve in the hot metal. The only means of controlling the phosphorus content of the hot metal is by limiting the amount in the charge.

ELIMINATION OF SULPHUR

Sulphur enters the blast furnace mainly in the coke and is released into the blast furnace gas stream, as H_2S or a gaseous compound of carbon monoxide and sulphur (COS), when the coke is burned. As the gas ascends through the stack some of the sulphur combines with lime of the flux and some combines with the iron. The exact mechanism of the reaction by which sulphur combines with iron is not known; however, it is generally believed to be as follows:

$$FeO+COS = FeS+CO_2 \quad \Delta H = -19,150 \text{ cal.} \quad (16)$$

The sulphur that combines with the iron must be removed at the very high temperatures that exist in the hearth. This is done by reduction of the iron sulphide in the presence of a basic flux such as lime (CaO). The chemical reaction for this reaction is often written as follows:

$$FeS+CaO+C = CaS+Fe+CO \quad \Delta H = 43,600 \text{ cal.} \quad (17)$$

The extent of sulphur removal depends on the temperature in the hearth, the ratio of basic oxides lime

(CaO) and magnesia (MgO) to acid oxides silica (SiO_2) and alumina (Al_2O_3) in the slag. For a more complete explanation of the effect of slag composition on fluidity and melting temperature, please refer to Chapter 12 on "Physical Chemistry of Iron- and Steelmaking."

REACTION OF LESS ABUNDANT ELEMENTS

Titanium, potassium, sodium, zinc, arsenic, barium, beryllium, boron, copper, chromium, nickel, selenium, tellurium, tin, zirconium, and vanadium are some other elements which are present in very small, but varying, amounts in the raw materials going to the blast furnace.

Titanium enters the furnace as titania, TiO_2, combined with some base, or as ilmenite ($FeTiO_3$ or $FeO \cdot TiO_2$). When titania comprises less than about two per cent of the ore burden, 50 to 60 per cent of the titania will appear in the slag as TiO_2, and the balance will be reduced and appear in the iron. When TiO_2 in the slag exceeds about 1.5 per cent, slags may be very viscous and result in irregular furnace operation. Also, the character of the hot metal may be adversely affected, resulting in excessive skulling of hot-metal ladles. Under the conditions prevailing in the furnace, titanium exhibits a slight tendency to combine with carbon and nitrogen to form titanium cyanonitride. This substance is sometimes found in the salamander on the hearths of furnaces being repaired. Here, it occurs in the form of small cubes that have the appearance of copper.

Beryllium and **zirconium** are similar to titanium, but much more difficult to reduce, so that they probably pass through unchanged.

The **alkalies,** soda and potash, are found in nearly all blast-furnace slags; when they are present in the raw materials to a considerable extent, they may, however, flux the furnace lining, and in part be volatilized to escape with the gases from which they later may condense to form troublesome accretions (scaffolds) on the furnace lining. They may play a part in the furnace reactions, for it is known that Na_2CO_3 and K_2CO_3 accelerate somewhat the reduction of Fe_3O_4 at 1650° F (900° C).

Zinc is a very troublesome element when present in blast-furnace material. Its compounds may be reduced in the lower regions of the stack; and, if so, the zinc is volatilized, driven upward and oxidizes to zinc oxide, which condenses on the walls of the colder part of the flues and in time closes up small passages to such an extent that the flow of the gases is restricted seriously. Zinc oxide also tends to combine with the alumina in the firebrick lining of the furnace, causing the brick to expand with damaging results.

Arsenic acts very much like phosphorus. Its compounds are reduced, and the resultant elementary arsenic then combines with iron to form iron arsenide, which dissolves in the metal.

Barium is similar to calcium, acting as a nonreducible basic flux; in an ore, it may be present as the carbonate, silicate, or sulphate. BaO is a base similar to CaO, but of higher molecular weight, hence does not increase basicity on a percentage basis, nor the desulphurizing power, as rapidly as CaO by almost one-third. On a molar basis its effect is similar to CaO.

The compounds of **boron** presumably behave as a flux.

Copper compounds are readily reduced yielding metallic copper, which alloys with the iron.

Chromium is reduced from its oxides with difficulty in the blast furnace, an exceedingly high temperature and an acid slag being most favorable for the reduction of its oxides. Small amounts appear to be more nearly completely reduced than large amounts.

Compounds of **nickel** and **vanadium** are almost completely reduced, the resulting nickel and vanadium alloying with the iron.

Tin is rare in raw materials of the United States; if introduced, its compounds are reduced and the tin alloys with the iron.

Selenium and **tellurium,** though somewhat rare, may be present in some raw materials; in their reactions, they are somewhat similar to sulphur but with an even greater tendency to remain with the metal.

BLAST-FURNACE ENERGY AND MATERIAL BALANCE

The over-all blast-furnace process can be appreciated more fully by referring to the energy balance in Table 14—V and the material balance in Figure 14—31. Both of these balances are for a 28-foot-hearth diameter blast furnace for a period of operation using a wind rate of 86,000 standard cu. ft. per min. and a hot-blast temperature of 1896° F. The coke rate was 1028 lb. per ton of hot metal and in addition, natural gas was injected in the tuyeres at a rate of 962 standard cu. ft. per ton of hot metal. The production rate for this period was 2737 net tons per day.

Table 14—V.   Energy Balance for a 28-ft. Hearth Diameter Blast Furnace

	Millions of Btu per Ton of Hot Metal
Energy Input	
Calorific value coke........	12.80
Sensible heat of hot air blast..	1.68
Calorific value of tuyere-injected fuel.............	0.96
Total	15.44
Energy Output	
Calorific value of recoverable top gas................	6.37
Energy Consumed	
Heat for chemical reactions, heat lost and sensible heat of hot metal and slag.....	9.07

The results of energy balance show that although 15.44 million Btu are actually put into the furnace for each ton of metal, 6.37 million Btu are recovered as usable gaseous fuel, so that in effect only 9.07 million Btu are consumed.

BLAST FURNACE MATERIAL BALANCE

ALL QUANTITIES IN AMOUNT PER TON OF HOT METAL

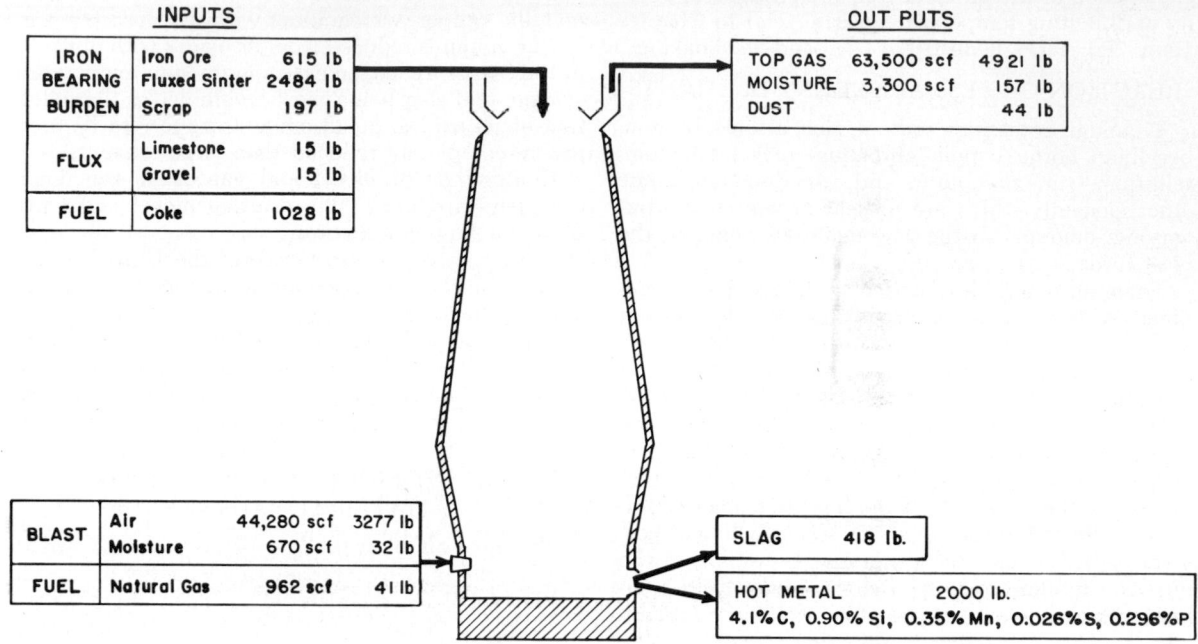

INPUTS			
IRON BEARING BURDEN	Iron Ore	615 lb	
	Fluxed Sinter	2484 lb	
	Scrap	197 lb	
FLUX	Limestone	15 lb	
	Gravel	15 lb	
FUEL	Coke	1028 lb	

OUT PUTS			
TOP GAS	63,500 scf	4921 lb	
MOISTURE	3,300 scf	157 lb	
DUST		44 lb	

BLAST	Air	44,280 scf	3277 lb
	Moisture	670 scf	32 lb
FUEL	Natural Gas	962 scf	41 lb

SLAG	418 lb.

HOT METAL	2000 lb.
4.1% C, 0.90% Si, 0.35% Mn, 0.026% S, 0.296% P	

FIG. 14—31. Blast-furnace material balance.

SECTION 6
OPERATION OF THE FURNACE

BLOWING IN

In blast-furnace parlance, the process of starting a furnace is called "blowing in." It is carried out in four steps, viz., drying, filling, lighting, and operating until routine production is established. The act of lighting in modern days is relatively insignificant but must be mentioned since it marks the start of operation and certain other preparations of extreme importance are best mentioned at this point. Some years ago, filling and lighting was assessed with more form and procedure than was necessary to effectively accomplish the task. Probably, the fourth step could be considered in two parts and called heating the bottom and operating until quality hot metal is obtained. The latter generally requires several days, as it is imprudent to lower hearth temperatures until a thermal balance has been established.

Drying—Newly constructed furnaces and stoves are carefully dried before they are put into service. The reason is; to avoid as much as possible extreme thermal shock to the structure and to drive off the vast amount of water absorbed by the brick during construction and contained in the slurry used in bricklaying. Water from these sources, if not evaporated before blowing in, could literally drown a furnace in the early blow-in stages, since it would condense in the upper cool area of the stack filled with cool burden material and drip down into the bottom in quantities

sufficient to chill and freeze the slag starting to build up in the hearth.

Any one of several methods can be used to dry a furnace and stoves. The usual method for stoves, where natural gas is available, is to place a gas pipe in the lower combustion chamber and start with a small flame and increase gas input for several days until a small quantity of blast-furnace gas can be used, keeping the natural gas as a pilot light. It is desirable to slowly increase the heat for at least 10 days to 2 weeks in a new stove before starting to bring the unit up to operating temperatures. Stoves which have had previous service have been warmed up in from 36 to 72 hours without apparent difficulty. Another method of drying or heating where natural gas is not available, is a wood fire built in the bottom of the combustion chamber. The wood fire requires consistent attention until wall temperatures are sufficient to insure proper combustion of blast-furnace gas.

The best method for drying a blast furnace is the use of hot blast. It is simple and drying is under control at all times. In applying this method, the conventional hot-blast system is used similar to an operating furnace except that initial blast temperature is held to about 400° F and wind volume at slow blast level. Temperature is slowly increased for a couple of days to 800° F and maintained for a few additional days. The entire operation can be accomplished in a week. Some operators install elbows and pipes inside a few

of the tuyeres to direct heated air down to the hearth. It is desirable during the latter part of the period to turn low-pressure steam into the hearth-cooling staves and bosh plates to assist drying. The large bell is closed while drying and furnace bleeders are adjusted to retain as much heat as possible. No pressure reading should be observable at the blast-pressure gage while drying.

In single-furnace plants, the above method cannot be entirely ruled out because of unavailable blast-furnace gas. Auxiliary fuel can be used to heat the stoves sufficiently for the low level of heat required.

Other less desirable methods of drying out are:

(1) **Dutch ovens**—Two, three, or more furnaces or ovens are constructed outside the blast furnace and the products of combustion from the ovens plus excess heated air are directed through pipes into the tapping hole and into some tuyere openings. Other tuyere and cooler openings are blocked off and draft regulated by adjusting furnace bleeders. As in hot-blast drying, the large bell remains closed. The Dutch ovens are fired with coke, coal, or wood, and require a crew to maintain the fires, haul fuel, and clean out ashes. Temperature control is more difficult in this case, but some regulation is maintained by the intensity of the oven fires and adjustment of furnace bleeders.

(2) **Gas**—The least desirable method is an open gas flame inside the furnace. The practice was to install a gas pipe through the tapping hole and ignite the gas by a small wood fire maintained at all times. Tuyere openings equipped with shutters to regulate air input and the top of the furnace regulated as in the two previous methods completed the control. Obvious hazard of this method precludes further discussion and it may be regarded as obsolete.

(3) Another method for lack of a better name will be called herein, the **hearth-fire** method. It simply consists of a wood, coke, or coal fire built in the hearth of the furnace and controlled similarly to the other methods with tuyere shutter and bleeders. Fine temperature regulation is difficult and frequent replenishment of fuel interrupts the process. If used for drying only this method is as simple as stated, but it could be applied as the start of a controlled or slow blow-in process. Some operators claim that improved "warm-up" is achieved through this technique. After drying, as noted above, a very heavy coke blank is charged followed by a regular blow-in burden. A low blast is then maintained and hearth and inwall temperature slowly raised before wind rates are increased to conventional blow-in rates. Several days may elapse before actual blow-in takes place. In theory, the scheme has merit in that there is less chance of damage to brick from thermal shock with reduced tendency for the brick to spall: however, the process is time consuming and more expensive. Superior campaign life has been obtained through the use of conventional methods and no evidence to date has been observed to indicate superior results from slow blow-in techniques.

Filling—At the conclusion of the drying operation, furnace bells and bleeders are opened, blow pipes taken down, some tuyeres and coolers removed, if desirable, and paraphernalia around the cast house used in the drying process is cleared away. In a rela-

tively short time the interior of the furnace will have cooled sufficiently to permit personnel to enter the hearth to prepare for filling. In the event a hearth fire was used for drying, all ashes and refuse are cleaned out.

An inspection of the furnace-cooling system will now be made and water turned on. It is usual practice to maintain a constant watch on all cooling members starting at this time. In cases where the furnace lining is not new and the furnace is empty, the above inspection affords an excellent opportunity to replace cooling members when necessary. Any plates considered suspicious or showing a sign of moisture must be replaced before filling is started. Many hours of grueling and frustrating work may be avoided through attention to these details. In fact, this checkout detail applies to all mechanical, electrical and physical equipment before filling is started. Usually, a check list is prepared and each item checked off as reports are received that the item is satisfactory. In the mass of detail to attend to before starting, it might be anticipated that oil or grease could be forgotten in a bearing or a limit switch might be out of adjustment or a water valve might be closed. These little things, if neglected, can result in annoying delays later.

Some mention should be made of earlier filling and blow-in techniques because of general interest, but modern practice is far removed from some of these methods; however, close teamwork between all members of operating, maintenance and management remains vital to smooth efficient operation and never is more essential than when operation begins.

Other preparations have preceded and some are going ahead at this point coincident to the start of the filling operation. For example, iron ladles are being heated, stockhouse bins filled according to prearranged plan, cinder ladles, if used, are being prepared for service, furnace gas lines inspected and vents opened or closed as directed, steam purging lines checked to make sure steam will be available when needed and the cast-house iron and slag runners prepared. Activity in the power house and blowing-engine house is going on with equal intensity. Perhaps turbines were opened for inspection and numerous preventative maintenance chores performed. Boilers are being warmed up, turbo-blowers warmed and turned over and over, speed trip mechanism checked out, water turned into condensers, pumps inspected and placed in operation, wind schedules posted and reconfirmed with blast-furnace personnel, boiler-water treating plant started and switch house and sub-station activated.

The final activity at the furnace before filling is begun is the making up of the tapping hole, packing the last cooler or two which were removed to obtain access to the hearth and to install the cinder notch. In preparing the tapping hole, men working inside and outside of the furnace pack clay around a tubular form, probably a length of 6-inch pipe or wooden form carefully lined up to insure the hole is properly centered. Clay is also packed up against the inside of the hearth around the tapping hole and covered with a few wheelbarrow loads of coke breeze. After this is completed the form is removed. The clay

lining is then placed in the iron trough, skimmer and dam are prepared and the mud gun aligned and adjusted to insure proper centering in the tapping hole. Some operators provide a coke-breeze or light clay protection around the cinder notch, but the benefit is questionable since the slag formed early in the blow-in freezes over the cool surface providing all the protection it ever has during operation.

One practice which has been used for years is slipping into disuse. The advantage is doubtful, but it is mentioned since its use is still current in some locations. This is the use of a blow-in pipe. As above, the tapping hole is made up around a 6-inch or 8-inch pipe, but at the inner end of the tapping hole a coupling is placed with the threads removed to permit an easy sliding fit. The pipe extends several feet into the trough and a couple of holes are cut or burned near the end for hooks to be inserted to enable the pipe to be quickly withdrawn as the blow-in progresses. Usually lagging strips of thin wood are placed around the pipe inside the tapping hole which burn away and permit easy withdrawal through the clay. Inside the furnace a long extension to the pipe is slipped into the coupling and set up on bricks to provide alignment. Numerous small openings are burned in the extension to allow gas to enter along the full length. Often worn-out coke screens or in earlier days, cord wood was laid tent fashion over the pipe to make a little house for the gas to find entrance to the pipe.

The above is the final chore before filling is started. Coke is then charged up to the level of the coolers by the regular filling equipment—skips, small and large bell. Tuyeres, and sometimes blow pipes may be installed at this time, but probably the blow stock caps will not be closed until time for the wind to be put on and the furnace lighted.

The initial filling today is as simple as stated above, but the occasion was not always so.

One practice was the use of cord wood. Four-foot lengths were very carefully arranged in the bottom, log-cabin style, each layer 90 degrees from the next, or layers were set up on end or combinations of the two were used until the hearth and bosh were filled to the mantle. Care was exercised to provide soft kindling wood around the tuyeres or frequently charcoal, oil-soaked waste or shavings were preferred to start the fire. Sometimes coke for the hearth layer was brought into the cast house and forked into the hearth through cooler openings. Another scheme was based on the belief that the furnace required a sudden jolt to start stock movement. A heavy scaffold was built in the hearth to hold the cord wood, coke and burden. When the scaffold burned out and collapsed, stock movement was assured, at least for the moment.

But, in returning to current practice, with the initial coke at tuyere level a second coke blank, without flux (limestone), is charged in quantity to fill the bosh to about mantle level. Following this heavy charge of coke, about an equal amount is charged with limestone and siliceous material such as Bessemer slag, possibly some blast-furnace slag or gravel to provide a slag volume roughly 2,500 to 3,000 lb. per ton of iron based upon iron entering the furnace in the coke ash, slag, etc.

Theoretical slag composition is calculated assuming the initial iron composition will be 4.00 to 4.50 per cent silicon. Effort is made to adjust the composition of the blow-in burden to insure a gray (limey), fluid, free-flowing slag.

Following the two coke blanks, a light burden is started with a ratio of iron (Fe) by weight in the burden divided by the coke weight of about 0.5 or 0.6. Burden weight (iron ore) is increased every 8 to 10 charges in increments of approximately 0.03 or 0.05 ratio of iron to coke. The theoretical burden composition is altered for each increase in ratio of iron to coke, reducing slag volume and accounting for decreasing silicon in the hot metal.

The furnace will be filled before the ratio of iron to coke in the blow-in charges has exceeded about 0.75.

Reference to an actual furnace burden practice has been avoided because of the many variations in burden materials, furnace sizes and favorite tested and proved methods. In general, the blow-in burden consists of a heavy coke blank to heat the hearth and bosh; a minimum amount of slag is produced at first to keep the hearth open and allow hot gases to warm it sufficiently to insure slag remains fluid. Rather early in the blow-in burden, large slag volume at very high temperature is desirable to prepare the hearth for increasing volumes of iron. Recognition is also given to the fact that high temperatures reduce silica to silicon which dissolves in the iron and thus is not available as a slag-forming constituent. Further, as temperatures decrease when heavier ore charges arrive the flux (limestone) must be increased to compensate for additional silica available for slag. Sulphur control is not a problem in a blow-in since temperatures are high, slag volume is high and the slag composition is conducive to absorbing sulphur at a high ratio.

Lighting—any one of several methods may be used to light a blast furnace: however, hot-blast lighting is the best, and probably used more than any other. It merely consists of blowing hot blast into the furnace. Low blast volume at approximately 1000° to 1200° F is applied and within a matter of minutes all tuyeres are bright. Blast-furnace coke is easily ignited and blast temperature at probably 700° F would accomplish the task effectively.

The process naturally requires heated stoves which may present a problem in a single-furnace plant or in starting up cold in a multi-furnace installation. Frequently auxiliary fuel is used to preheat the stoves where conventional blast-furnace gas is non-existent. The best practice demands that some consideration should be given to having at least a token blast temperature available since the blow-in may be needlessly prolonged waiting for stoves to be brought up to operating temperatures: however, maximum operating blast temperatures are not commonly used for several days after blow-in. It is highly desirable to have a reserve of heat in the event some unforeseen difficulty should develop as it is about the only remedy to minimize what might be a very exhausting experience.

Other methods to light a furnace are identical in

principle, in that flames, torches, oxygen lances or red-hot bars are applied to some easily combustible material placed in front of the tuyeres. Natural draft will provide ample air for initial combustion and within 10 to 15 minutes a light blast may be used.

Activity in connection with lighting is not confined to the cast house alone. Of prime importance is preparation to handle blast-furnace gas which begins to be produced the instant ignition of the fuel in the furnace takes place. For simplicity, details will be described in a general way confining the discussion to an imaginary gas system from the furnace to a valve or plate connecting the individual furnace gas line to a common plant line.

Before lighting, the gas system is isolated, or divided into two sections by filling the furnace water seal or closing the goggle valve normally used to isolate the furnace during routine pauses in operation for tuyere changes, etc. In conventional arrangement of facilities, this valve is located after the dust-catcher and before primary wet-gas-cleaning equipment. It is also possible that the closure may be after the venturi-type gas cleaner. Thus, the system is divided into two sections, furnace to water seal or goggle valve and a second section to the common or plant gas line.

Before lighting, both blast-furnace bells and bleeders will be opened, dust-catcher dump valve (and bleeder if so equipped) will be closed and a full head of steam will be admitted to the dust catcher through the purge lines. The vent line on the furnace side of the seal will be closed and a head of steam turned on to drive air from this part of the line back through the dust catcher and out through the furnace bleeders. Operators will make sure a good plume of steam is emerging from the bleeders before lighting. Within 15 or 20 minutes all air should be forced from this section of the gas system.

Later when operators are satisfied all tuyeres are bright and air has been driven from the furnace shaft, furnace bells will be closed, forcing all gas out through the bleeders. Steam will be kept in the dust catcher. In the meantime, steam will have been turned into the primary gas-cleaning equipment and vents opened and observed for indications of a good head of steam emerging at the end against the goggle valve to the common gas system. There are two ways of bringing gas through this particular section. If gas is available in the common plant line, then the goggle valve may be opened and cold gas forced back through the line and out of the vents at the washer and against the furnace seal or valve. In case the plant line is empty, then at the moment operators are satisfied gas generation in the furnace is adequate, the furnace seal will be dumped or valve opened and gas forced out to the far valve. As soon as a flow of gas is observed vents will be closed and purging steam turned off. Furnace gas pressure at this point is ample to keep gas in the lines even though furnace bleeders are open, however, it may be the decision of the operators to partially close furnace bleeders at this point.

Not all plants are provided with mechanical valves which simplify gas handling as above. Plate valves are frequently the only means of closing lines beyond the furnace and procedures for handling gas and turning valves of this sort are more complex. Detailed description of this phase cannot be explained in general terms as the procedures apply to specific plants, no two of which are exactly alike.

Operating until Routine Production is Established —The moment wind is turned into the tuyeres and the furnace is lighted, official operation is underway. With the exception of the first four or five days when higher than normal temperatures are maintained, things begin to settle down to routine. It may well be assumed that except for an infrequent shutdown for a few minutes to replace copper cooling members and possibly one major repair outage lasting 4 or 5 days to replace the bells, continuous operation may be expected for the next 5 to 7 years.

In recent years several large modern furnaces have exceeded four million tons production during campaign life.

The instant wind is blown into the furnace and coke ignited, part of the gas generated will emerge from the open tapping hole or blow-in pipe (if used). Either a good-sized wood fire will have been prepared in the furnace trough or a substantial gas jet made ready to ignite this gas as soon as operators determine air has been displaced from the hearth. Ignition of the escaping gas which is forced out in increasing velocity as wind volume is increased is extremely important. The high carbon-monoxide content and volume would, in a very few minutes, create a lethal condition in the area. Fortunately, the heavy gas flame blowing from the tapping hole also performs a service. In the twelve to sixteen hours before the hole is closed the trough, skimmer and dam are thoroughly dried and heated, requiring no further attention before the first cast.

Generally, rapid increase in wind volume is essential to obtain blast penetration to prevent channeling of the gas along the furnace stack wall. Likewise, it insures that heat will be driven down into the hearth. Frequently operators will blank off every other tuyere and progressively open them as wind volume is increased. Others prefer to install bushings inside the tuyeres to effectively reduce diameter and increase wind velocity. These methods are time saving and have generally superseded starting with smaller diameter tuyeres and unnecessarily wasting time a couple of days later to install large tuyeres. Operators usually plan to have anywhere from 75 to 85 per cent of the standard wind volume on the furnace at the end of the fourth operating day and will probably have all of it on at the end of the first week.

After the initial coke blank is consumed slag will begin to accumulate in the hot hearth as the second blank with slag-making materials descends. By this time, the furnace will have started to move and charging according to schedule has started. Gas blasting from the blow-in pipe or tapping hole is intensely hot by this time and no longer requires a pilot fire to keep it burning.

Furnace men are vigilant in their observation of the tapping hole, watching for signs of slag. The first indication is a sudden decrease in gas volume, a puffing or pulsation. At this instant, an immediate slacking of wind is made and the blow-in pipe is pulled and the hole plugged, or where a pipe is not used, the mud gun is swung around and the hole is stopped. It was noted earlier the mud gun should be in perfect alignment and filled ready for use, as a delay in the stopping operation could allow a substantial volume of slag to flow resulting in needless delay at this stage of the blow-in.

Six or more hours may elapse before sufficient slag has accumulated to warrant flushing. Several tries at ¾ to 1 hour intervals will be made with only a gas blow for the effort, but operators are anxious to see the first slag since this will be the first visual indication to determine how the blow-in is progressing. However, it is most unusual to find anything out of the ordinary. Usually the timing for these flushes is estimated in two ways: (1) by experience and visual observation by operators and (2) from arithmetical calculations based on amount of coke burned, number of charges placed in the furnace and wind blown which affords a reliable figure on the volume of slag produced and iron accumulation for any given time interval.

Within approximately 24 to 28 hours after the wind was turned on the furnace and after several flushes, the first cast will be made. In all respects, a normal cast is expected, naturally less tonnage than under normal operation due to the lighter burden and high temperature (silicon). Upon completion of the first cast, a casting schedule is established and rigidly adhered to.

Very close attention is given to operation for the next four or five days to watch for any indication of variation from the calculated blow-in plan for slowly decreasing silicon content of the iron, slag temperature and composition. Changes in plan are an anticipated event and alternates are prepared in advance and ready for instant execution. Examples of what may occur to alter procedures are as follows: sustained high silicon content in the iron, a rapid decrease in silicon content of the iron, slag-temperature drop, or unaccounted for change in slag composition. In these latter cases, temperature drop can be very rapid because little reserve heat has been built up in the hearth. Ability to raise blast temperature to maximum obtainable at this point is highly desirable and could prevent a very trying experience. It must be remembered that 8 to 10 hours are required for extra coke to descend through the furnace and about 12 hours to become effective, so prompt recognition of prospective trouble is essential. On the other hand, when blowing in cold (without heated stoves), blow-in procedure is slow in order to keep hearth temperature on the hot, safe side at all times.

As a general rule, however, blow-in of a new furnace is a routine affair and on the fifth or sixth day iron is produced to the desired specifications. Blowing in of a banked furnace will be described after the discussions of "Banking" and "Blowing Out" that follow the present review of techniques for blowing in of a new or rebuilt furnace.

BANKING

Plans for an extended shut down or interruption to furnace operation either for a breakdown, scheduled repair or because business conditions indicate a pause in production is desirable, may influence management to bank a blast furnace. The word banking is applied because of similarity to the operation of banking a fire. The origin is lost in antiquity, however generally it means covering a fire either with ashes or fresh fuel to restrict air, reduce the combustion rate, and to preserve for future use.

Also, banking is resorted to as an emergency measure when some unforeseen event requires a furnace shut down. In this case, the blast is taken off, the blowpipes are dropped and the tuyere openings are plugged with clay to prevent air from drafting through. Thus, hearth heat is preserved and the furnace can be returned to operation with a minimum effort. If the down time exceeds four or five days duration, some difficulty can be expected in resuming operation although instances are on record that no trouble was experienced after a seven-day bank.

More common is the furnace bank carried out as a planned event. Preparation made depends upon the length of time anticipated. If only for a few days, an extra blank or two of coke may be charged without flux and the furnace taken off when the coke descends to the bosh zone. If for a slightly longer time, the ore and stone burden may be reduced 5 to 10 per cent following the coke blank possibly for ten or fifteen charges before normal charge weight is resumed.

A banking burden for a shut down for an undetermined length of time is very similar to a blow-in burden. Prior to the start of a banking burden, miscellaneous iron-bearing materials are removed from the charge and a large reduction in the amount of limestone charged is made. Extra coke also may be charged ahead of the banking burden. The purpose is to develop a hot, siliceous slag which has a tendency to clean off the lime accumulation on the bosh walls and prevent an excessively limey slag during blow-in. Limey slag is more viscous and is apt to cause some operating problems early in the blow-in period. Often during the initial warm-up period, temperatures may be very high in the bosh which will increase reduction of silica to silicon with the result that slag contains a higher proportion of lime. For this reason, effort is made to have a hot siliceous slag at the time the furnace is banked and a like condition upon the resumption of operation.

Following initial preparatory charges noted above, a heavy coke blank is charged and subsequent charging parallels a characteristic blow-in burden. Charging continues until the coke blank reaches the upper bosh area of the furnace. At this time the final cast is made. Effort is made to drain the hearth until a dry blow at the tapping hole is observed to insure a clean hearth for the future start up and eliminate as much as possible the need for melting cold slag early in the blow-in period. Prior to the last cast the furnace dust catcher is emptied. Accumulated dust has a tendency to consolidate into a rock-like mass if undisturbed for a time and could present a difficult problem after operation begins again.

About the end of the cast, before the furnace is taken off, a heavy blanket of ore may be dumped in the furnace to cover the upper burden surface, thus reducing the natural drafting tendency of the furnace.

At the conclusion of the cast, the tapping hole is plugged, wind is taken off the furnace, bleeders opened, steam is turned into the dust catcher, the furnace is isolated from the common gas system and stove valves manipulated to draft gas back through the bustle pipe, hot-blast main and out through the stove chimney. Furnace men quickly drop the blow pipes and plug the tuyeres with clay. Many operators prefer to remove the tuyeres to avoid any chance of a stray water leak permitting water to accumulate in the furnace and also to provide an opportunity to observe the coolers for possible leaks. Clay is solidly packed into the tuyere openings and backed up with sand to eliminate any chance of air filtering in. Often this is followed by bricking up the openings as further insurance against air infiltration.

As soon as blow pipes are down after the final cast, blowing engines are stopped, and stove burner valves, chimney and hot-blast valves are closed to preserve heat as long as possible. As a precaution, blow-off valves are opened slightly to prevent a pressure build-up from developing in the stoves resulting from an undetected water leak or from some unsuspected source.

Within a day or two the furnace bells are opened and steam is shut off in the dust catcher. Daily inspection of the stock level is important. A slow stock movement is an indication that air is infiltrating and coke is being consumed. A movement of a few feet can be expected but a continual drop is undesirable and may force operators to spray the bosh with a sealing material. A thin mixture of water, clay and waterglass is sometimes used since the material is cheap and does an effective job: however, a "mothballing" material can be and is used by some operators who report good results from the practice.

If the furnace is banked for an extended period, after a lapse of a month to six weeks, water flow will be reduced on the cooling members and finally after 2 to 3 months, turned off entirely except for the hearth staves.

Very often after a bank of six or more weeks, when tuyeres are opened, all signs of fire in the tuyere area will disappear. Furnace operators are pleased when this condition is discovered since full benefit of the coke blank will be available to supply heat when operation begins.

BLOWING OUT

If business conditions deteriorate to the extent production is no longer required, the decision may be made to blow out a furnace. Starting the furnace again under conditions approaching those of starting a new furnace is generally accomplished faster and with less effort than starting from a bank: however, the cost in connection with blowing out, raking out and cleaning preparatory to starting is likely to exceed the cost of banking.

When a furnace has reached the end of its campaign (lining worn out), it is usually blown out except under most unusual circumstances.

Blowing out is accomplished in two general ways. (1) Charging is stopped and the stock allowed to descend until a minimum remains and (2) Iron-bearing components are removed from the burden and silica gravel or coke is substituted until all iron is reduced. The latter method is preferred since the blow out can be accomplished faster, and the longer time required to rake out is partly compensated for by the longer blow-out time required in the former method.

Method No. 1—In the first method, 12 to 16 hours before the last cast is to be made, operation is stopped for a short time to permit installation of water sprays in the top of the furnace, or around the large bell, test rods are removed, and a special test weight (attached to a long cable leading to a winch on the ground) is substituted to enable operators to ascertain the stock level for the full height of the stack. Thermocouples are installed in the uptakes and connected to recording instruments in the pyrometer house or to supplementary instruments installed for the blow out.

If water sprays on the large bell are used to control top temperature, the large bell must be blocked open. Usually, heavy chains are hung around the bell rod and draped over the seat to effectively insure the large bell will remain open regardless of irregular internal pressures or possible operating error which might occur. When the large bell is pulled up, the annular opening of 2 to 3 inches forms an ideal means of distributing water completely around the furnace. In both methods of supplying water to the furnace top, a positive supply of high-pressure water controlled from ground level must be provided. Use of hose connections are avoided if possible, pressure gages and valves are arranged at ground level and means of determining the volume of water flowing into the furnace are made available.

Prior to the stop to install blow-out equipment, burden changes are made to alter slag composition drastically. A highly siliceous slag is developed to remove as much lime as possible from the hearth and bosh walls. The purpose is the same as in banking; namely, to drain out as much slag as possible during the last cast and to avoid the formation of quantities of calcium hydroxide when the lime is contacted with water later in the cooling-off period.

After the changes to alter slag composition, a rather heavy coke blank may be charged. While not essential, it permits all the iron-bearing burden to be reduced and eases the job of raking out the furnace. The larger portion of the coke used for this purpose is not consumed and is salvaged for use in other operating furnaces.

When the wind is put on following the installation of the special blow-out equipment, charging is stopped and the stock allowed to descend. Water sprays will be turned on immediately and water volume increased as required. Effort is made to keep top gas temperature below 500° F, maximum. Wind volume is decreased as blast pressure eases during the blow-out or if temperature becomes difficult to control. Frequent measurement of the stock level is made. The furnace is usually isolated from the plant gas system about the middle of the blow-out, as determined by the stock level.

Preparation is made to start the final cast when the stock line is a few feet above the mantle. Blast volume will have been reduced to about ¼ of the normal volume and the pressure will have dropped to approximately 6 or 8 pounds.

The last cast is slow because of the low furnace pressures, but is carried on as long as possible to thoroughly empty the furnace. Operators may close down the bleeders a bit to raise furnace pressure to speed up the flow of iron and slag from the furnace.

At the conclusion, bleeders are opened wide, steam turned into the dust catcher (which has been emptied earlier), water turned off the top, wind taken off the furnace, and the gas pulled back through the stoves. The tapping hole is not closed, which allows some additional drainage from the hearth.

Furnace crews quickly remove blow pipes and plug the tuyere openings with clay to prevent the inflow of air due to the natural drafting characteristic of the furnace. Blowing engine or turboblower engineers are notified to shut down the blowing equipment.

Furnace crews then place barriers around the cast house and warn all people to stay out as the watering down or quenching is started. Water is started slowly through the top sprays and as the furnace settles down, increasing volumes are turned on.

Water soon appears in the bosh area and begins to run out of the tuyere openings. Within 24 hours the furnace is usually cooled off sufficiently to allow furnace crews to start raking out the remaining coke and burden materials.

Method No. 2—The second or preferred method of blowing out as mentioned earlier is faster and is considered safer in that the furnace stack is kept almost full, less water is used while the blast is on, and the chance of developing high top temperature is virtually eliminated.

Preparation is similar in some respects to the first method discussed in that the burden is altered, water sprays are installed in the furnace top and a special stock-line indicator may be used: however, large-bell sprays or chains on the large bell are not used.

After installation of the blow-out equipment, the blast is put on and charging is continued. If a gravel blow-out is the method chosen, a heavy coke blank will be charged first. The volume will be equivalent to approximately the volume of the bosh. Following the coke blank, washed and screened silica gravel, about minus 2 inch + 1 inch size, is charged. The furnace is kept full early in the blow out and then the stock line is permitted to drift down 20 to 30 feet towards the end (when all iron-bearing burden has been reduced). During blow out, water is judiciously used to control top temperature: however, the additional charges of gravel are very effective in keeping top temperature low. A reduction in wind will be required towards the end but the reduction does not approach the wind cuts needed in the first method described above, consequently the time required for blowing out by this second method may be as low as 6 to 8 hours.

A coke blow-out is the same as above except that coke is used instead of gravel. Sometimes plus ¾-inch minus 1-inch coke screenings is used. This size is commonly called domestic coke.

Following the last cast, the stock is watered down as described above. When cooling has progressed far enough, sluice ways frequently are built from a couple of cooler openings to an open-top railroad car and the contents of the furnace washed out with high-pressure-water jets.

DRAINING THE SALAMANDER

Subsequent to blowing out and when the furnace is to be completely relined, the salamander may be drained. The operation saves days and even weeks in relining time which might be otherwise lost in blasting out the heavy chunk of solid iron that would be formed if the metal that accumulated in the hearth as bottom block eroded over the campaign was permitted to solidify. Initial preparation is made before blowing out by drilling a pre-determined distance into the furnace bottom below the hearth staves and installing a trough or runner for the iron. If the furnace layout is amenable, pig beds will be constructed and made ready for use immediately after the last cast is completed. In case an outside area is not available for a pig bed, then, after the last cast, ladle tracks will be removed and the pig beds arranged under the cast house. The 8- to 12-hour delay in this case is negligible since residual heat in the hearth will keep the salamander molten for several days.

When all is ready, a long oxygen lance is inserted in the drilled hole and the remaining brick work is burned through into the pool of iron. Usually the flow of iron is slow and several hours are required to empty out an accumulation of from four hundred to six hundred tons.

BLOWING IN FROM BANK

Blowing in a banked furnace has been developed to the point where operators accept the process as a routine event. Present knowledge of the art has grown immensely in the past twenty years. In the years preceding, blowing in a banked furnace was a task approached with misgiving and the performance was usually a disappointing experience.

About the only obstacle which otherwise upsets a smooth routine operation is infrequently encountered when blowing in older furnaces, where an undetected water leak may cause extended delays and set-backs in returning to operation. Accompanying this difficulty and often resulting from the water leaks noted above are other delays from break-outs around cooling plates and coolers. In these older furnaces there may be only a little brick work remaining in the slag-line area and the natural carbon and lime buildup is dissolved from the action of the siliceous slag intentionally developed. This situation is conducive to opening up of interstices between the bricks and is aided by temperature changes as bosh heat is increased during blow-in.

Skill, experience, and good judgment on the part of operators is of inestimable value and is never more important to the success of any undertaking than in bringing in a furnace from bank.

A discussion of methods of blowing in a furnace from an extended emergency bank where no preliminary preparation has been made is omitted because of the numerous circumstances which effect the actions taken by operators. The job, at best, is a lengthy laborious undertaking.

Blowing in from bank, when adequate preparation was made, follows somewhat the pattern of blowing in a new or empty furnace. The exception which alters the technique is that the hearth level is higher and cold slag laying in the hearth must be heated and liquefied to prevent chilling of the new slag which begins to form when wind is put on the furnace. Under these circumstances operators must be sure "communication" is established between tapping hole and the areas in the hearth where liquid is being formed in order to get it out of the furnace as fast as it is made. Working with this goal in mind, heat is brought down into the hearth as the new slag forms, which transfers some heat to the bottom and is removed before it has a chance to chill.

Several methods are used in starting: all of them have proven successful and the operators are apt to choose any one of them which he feels may fit his particular problem. But, in all cases, when wind is first put on, only a few tuyeres will be opened. These are directly above and on each side of the tapping hole or cinder notch. As the blow-in progresses, following each cast, a tuyere next to an open tuyere will be opened and wind volume increased. If the following cast is not up to expectation, that is, the volume or temperature of slag is lower than it is thought that it should be, then opening of the next tuyere will be postponed until hearth heat is built up again.

In general, earlier preparations are similar to blowing in an empty furnace. Coolers are opened up and coke ash and refuse cleaned away. Operators make sure good clean coke is in front of the coolers before installing tuyeres. Then all but the few mentioned above are securely packed with clay or clay and brickbats to prevent any blast air from entering until the plug is removed.

The tapping hole is dug and burned back to where coke is visible and then made up similar to the method used in a new furnace. Some operators lightly plug the hole; others blow through the hole until slag appears to insure that the hot gas warms the hearth in the tapping-hole area. Another method has produced good results and is quite unique. The hole is made up and a blow-in pipe installed to blow air or an air-oxygen mixture into the hole. Tuyeres are closed during this 4 to 8 hour operation. Then the pipe is pulled, the hole plugged and air is blown in a few tuyeres as above. Still others prefer to remove the cinder notch and build a tapping hole in its place and construct a runner to carry slag and iron produced until hearth heat is built up to permit normal casting.

In any method, casts are made at 2 to 3 hour intervals until operators are certain the hearth is heated sufficiently to keep the contents fluid. The tapping hole is drilled straight in early in the blow-in and the angle slowly increased as temperatures increase and the entire body of the hearth begins to return to normal operating temperature.

Burden regulation follows blow-in practice with regular increases in iron-bearing materials as the blow-in progresses.

Approximately six or seven days are required to bring in a furnace and attain a reasonable operation approaching normal practice.

MAINTENANCE OF RUNNERS

After the tapping hole has been closed, the troughs are emptied, and preparations for the next cast are begun. The runners are cleaned carefully of both metal and slag, and their inside surfaces are carefully brushed with a thick clay or loam slurry which, when dry, protects the trough and prevents iron from sticking to the runner, or the runner may be lined with sand to afford the same protection. More recently, preference has been shown for lining the main trough with carbon brick due to the lesser amount of scrap produced, since iron does not stick to the carbon brick. Such main runners consist of a steel-plate trough lined with firebrick with a carbon-brick facing laid over the firebrick. The carbon-brick surface is plastered with clay before cast time to keep the carbon from oxidizing during the cast. Water can be turned directly on the hot carbon after a cast without damage.

SAMPLING THE IRON

Sampling of the pig iron is a very important part of every tapping (cast). As the iron is graded by chemical composition, care must be taken to obtain a sample that will be representative of the whole cast. This sample, therefore, is generally made up of a number of equal portions taken from the main runner beyond the skimmer and at periods representing the first, middle, and last thirds of the cast: samples may be taken more frequently in the case of large-tonnage casts. These samples consist of small castings made by pouring the metal into a mold. Chill tests of all slags are also taken and a daily composite of individual flush and/or cast samples is analyzed for each furnace.

OPERATION OF CHANGING THE STOVES

The temperature of a furnace at the hearth is a matter of great importance, as this is one of the two main factors that control the quality (temperature and chemical composition) of the iron produced: the other main factor is the composition of the slag. One of the means of regulating hearth temperature is by control of the hot-blast temperature. This may be raised or lowered by use of the mixer valve, and can be kept high by proper manipulation of the stoves. As a routine part of blast-furnace operation, the tending of stoves is of importance. They must be changed regularly and at not too long intervals. In changing stoves, the hot stove must be put on blast before the cold one is taken off. To put a stove on hot blast, the burner gas shut-off valve is closed, the burner air supply is shut off, and chimney valve(s) are closed. Then, in succession, the cold-blast valve is opened in such a way that the blast pressure will not be reduced excessively until the stove pressure equals the blast pressure, when the mixer valve is opened slightly (attempting to maintain a constant hot-blast temperature) and the hot-blast valve is opened to permit the blast to flow through the hot stove. The cold stove is then taken "off blast" and put "on gas" by the following procedure: (a) close cold-blast valve, (b) close hot-blast valve, (c) open blow-off valve until stove is depressurized, (d) open chimney valve(s), (e) close blow-off valve, (f) open burner gas shut-off valve slightly, (g) turn on burner air supply, (h) open burner gas shut-off valve to obtain desired flow of blast-furnace gas.

The process of changing stoves may be carried out manually or the valves may be mechanized and operated by motors or cylinders. The entire operation may be controlled electronically, resulting in semi-automatic or automatic operation. In semi-automatic operation, the operator must actuate the stove-changing cycle by pushing a button. In automatic operation, the sequence may be controlled on a time basis, or the cycle may be actuated whenever hot-blast or stove-dome temperature reaches a preset lower limit. The control panel for an automatic stove-changing system is shown in Figure 14—32. A stove may be changed automatically in less than 3 minutes, compared to the 15 to 25 minutes usually taken when changing manually. This results in more efficient utilization of the stove and higher available hot-blast temperatures. Hot-blast temperatures in the range of 1800° to 2000° F may be obtained through the use of automatic stove changing on furnaces where, before installation of automatic equipment, difficulty was met in attaining hot-blast temperatures in the range of 1400° to 1500° F.

CHARGING THE FURNACE

The charging of the blast furnace is part of the routine that must be done with great care and should not be interrupted as long as the furnace is on full blast. Should charging be interrupted, the furnace would tend to empty itself rapidly, and constant vigilance is necessary to keep the stack full for uniform operation. The proportions of the materials used are predetermined quantities; therefore, all the materials are weighed before charging into the furnace. The charging is usually done in **rounds** (or **charges**).

The basis of charging is the weight of fuel in each charge. For a given furnace and operation, the fuel usually is kept at a fixed quantity, and any variations in the charge are effected by changing the quantities of ore and flux (this is by far the most prevalent method; however, with automatic coke charging, some operators may vary the coke charge). The coke in the charge is usually weighed; infrequently, the coke may be charged by volume (for example, when the coke moisture content is varying over a wide range) to give a known dry weight. The weight of this coke unit varies among furnaces and is affected by: the size of the furnace; volumes of skip, receiving hopper and large bell hopper; and filling sequence

FIG. 14—32. That part of the panel board to the right of the outline of the blast-furnace contains the controls related to the automatic changing of stoves on a large modern furnace. The sequence of operations involved in automatic stove changing is described in the text.

(number of skips of coke in the round). Top-gas distribution and temperature are influenced by and can be altered by changes in filling practice. The weight of the coke unit used on large furnaces is usually from 20,000 to 40,000 lb. The relative weights of ore, flux, and coke vary according to the composition of the ore; some ores and sinter requiring very little, if any, flux.

The manner of charging the materials also is subject to much variation. Sometimes all the ore will be charged and followed by all the coke: in some cases, the coke may precede the ore. An example of filling is one where part of the ore is charged, followed by part of the coke, and this sequence is repeated. Such a filling would be: ore—coke—stone—ore—coke—coke. This filling is normally written OCSOCC/, in abbreviated form. Each letter designates a skip of material that is delivered to the small bell and dumped on the large bell before receipt of the next skip load (see Figure 14—10). The letters signify the kind of material being delivered to the skip, with O for ore or agglomerate, C for coke, S for stone, M for miscellaneous. If two kinds of material were charged in the same skip, it would be designated S + M. The symbol, /, designates dumping the large bell. The large bell may be dumped more than once during a charge, this procedure being known as **split filling**. A split-filling sequence that has achieved considerable success on large furnaces that are charging a high percentage of sinter is COOCC/COOC/. Changes of charging sequence can correct irregularities in blast-furnace operation but, in order to provide some logical basis for making changes, gas-sampling devices should be available to indicate the effect of changes on what is happening in the furnace.

When a charging sequence is selected that has an even number of skips, the stone and other materials will always be deposited by the same skip on the same side of the furnace. Besides causing uneven wear of the skip, receiving hopper, and other parts of the materials-handling equipment, such a charging sequence may result in uneven distribution of stock in the furnace. Uneven distribution can be prevented by the use of a rotating distributor, and should not be a factor under such circumstances, but some operators prefer to use charges made up of an odd number of skips (even with a distributor) to increase the probability of obtaining a good distribution of the stock in the furnace. Examples of typical charges employing an odd number of skips are OCSOC/ or OCCOSCC/.

The flexibility of charging is limited by the weight of coke that can be handled in one skip, and by the time available to put up a charge. In designing new installations or rebuilding old ones to larger capacity, care must be taken that a bottleneck does not exist in the facilities for filling the furnace.

FANNING

Occasionally, during the campaign of a blast furnace, situations arise when the full productive capacity of the furnace is not required for a period of time. When this occurs, the problem can be solved by shutting the furnace down or curtailing the operation of the furnace by reducing the quantity of wind being blown. When the wind volume is less than 20 to 25 per cent of normal, the technique is known as **fanning**. Fanning has the advantages of keeping the gas system pressurized and furnishing a small quantity of blast-furnace gas for use as fuel, and enables a resumption of near full operation on short notice. This technique is used for emergency situations or short periods only. Prolonged use, such as 8 hours out of every 24, or on week-ends, results in a hearth build-up and frequently promotes inwall scab formation. A careful economic study is necessary before adoption of this method.

FURNACE IRREGULARITIES

The blast furnace, even in its highest development, is by no means the even-going, easily regulated monster that the casual observer may take it to be. Although furnace operations are under better control now than ever before, furnaces are still capable of acting in unpredictable ways. Hence, a full discussion of this subject would be almost endless. There are few industrial operations wherein promptness of action, forethought and good judgment, based upon skill and experience, are more needed than about a blast furnace in trouble. It is to be remembered that the operator must think six to ten hours "ahead" of the furnace because any burden change will require that time to travel through the furnace and reach the hearth where its effect will be manifest. A few of these troubles are here enumerated.

Slips—Slips are due to an initial wedging or bridging of the stock in the furnace. When this occurs, the material underneath continues to move downward and a void is created. The void tends to increase in size until the "bridge" collapses, causing a sudden downward movement of the stock above. In severe cases, this causes a sudden increase in gas pressure and an effect like an explosion. In rare cases, considerable damage may be done to the top gear.

There is reason to believe that hanging may be due to at least five separate causes. In one case, previously fused slag may resolidify, causing a large impervious mass that interrupts the smooth movement of the stock. Secondly, where the coke contains considerable fines, these may be wedged between the larger lumps by the flow of gases and cause both arching of the solid material and resistance to flow of the gases. Thirdly, fine carbon deposited by the reaction $2CO \rightarrow CO_2 + C$ may fill the voids between large particles of ore and thus impede countercurrent flow of gases and materials. Fourth, alkali vapors may condense in the upper part of the stack and cement the solid material into large impervious masses. Fifth, too much wind may be being blown for the character of the materials being used.

Scaffolding—Scaffolding may occur near the top of the bosh. This condition is often due to irregularities in the working of the furnace, the following explanation often being suggested.

If the zone of fusion is suddenly lowered, the pasty mass at its top tends to adhere to the encircling wall, with the result that an incrustation is formed that projects toward the center of the furnace. This mass offers obstruction to both the gases and the descent of the stock. If this condition is not soon remedied, the blast gases will channel, perhaps on one side, in which case serious damage to the lining would result. A measure to combat this condition, in stubborn cases, is to charge extra coke. Reducing the quantity of blast tends to reduce the buoyant effect of the blast, with the result that the weight of the material above usually will break off the incrustation.

A furnace is said to be **hanging** when the uniform descent of the stock is interrupted either by wedging or bridging of the stock or by scaffolding.

Distribution—The proper distribution of the solid materials charged in the top, and of the blast introduced in the bottom, is essential for efficient furnace operation. The ore, coke and flux that have been deposited on the big bell slide off as the bell is opened, striking the stockline protecting plates, with the finer materials remaining close to the wall and the coarser materials rolling toward the center of the furnace. If a unit volume sample is taken of those materials near the wall, it will contain a larger percentage of ore and finer pieces of sinter and coke, and a lower overall percentage of coke than one taken near the center of the furnace. The blast entering through the tuyeres contacts incandescent carbon and its oxygen is completely combined to form carbon monoxide within three and one-half feet from the nose of the tuyere. The ascending gas contacts the descending charge, and the more efficiently this contact is made, the more efficiently the furnace will operate. The distribution of solids and gases, when viewed on a vertical section taken in any direction through the center of the furnace, should be identical with any similar section.

If the distribution is bad, the activity will be much greater in one section of the furnace than in the remainder of the furnace. This section of activity may be adjacent to the brick lining of the furnace, with the result that the lining in this section wears out excessively fast: in fact, it may wear so badly that the steel shell will be entirely unprotected. The heat may be so intense that the steel shell locally assumes a red heat at what is known as a **hot spot**. Hot spots also may arise from lining failures not necessarily associated with bad distribution but due to other causes; for example, chemical attack. A furnace with a hot spot may often be held in blast for a while by the liberal use of water on the shell at the location of the hot spot. A short stop may be taken on the furnace and temporary stack-cooling plates inserted at the location, resulting in cooling the stock at this point and

the formation of a scab that protects the lining to some degree. Of course, the cause of the bad distribution should be determined and corrected. Attempts to control the air distribution to furnaces so that all tuyeres are receiving an equal amount of air (say, plus or minus five per cent versus as much as one hundred per cent variation encountered frequently) has shown beneficial results.

The distribution of gases in the stack can also be aided by skillful adjustments to the filling sequence. When coke is placed first on the large bell, the velocity of gases increases toward the inwall; and when ore is placed first on the large bell, the gas velocity increases toward the center of the furnace. Generally, the gas temperature increases when gas velocity increases. Temperature and distribution of the top gas also can be changed by varying the level to which the furnace is filled. These statements in this paragraph comprehend furnace design such as discussed in Section 3.

Breakouts—Breakouts are caused by failure of the walls of the hearth, with the result that liquid iron or slag or both may flow uncontrolled out of the furnace and cause considerable damage to the furnace and surrounding auxiliaries. Slag breakouts are usually not as serious as iron breakouts, since there is not so much danger from explosions as is the case when molten iron and water come into contact. With either type of breakout, it is essential, if possible, to cast the furnace, thereby draining off as much liquid material as possible, and to take the blast off the furnace.

A slag breakout may be chilled by streams of water, and the hole closed by laying brick, pumping fireclay grout, or ramming a plastic cement or asbestos rope into it.

However, there is practically no control over an iron breakout, and the iron runs out of the hole until the furnace is dry. After the accumulated iron has been cleared away, brick, ganister, and fireclay, either used separately or in combination, may be used to close the hole. It may be necessary to renew one or several of the hearth-cooling staves or the breakout may be so severe that the operator will take the furnace out of blast for a complete hearth repair. The use of carbon brick in the hearth sidewall has given indications of providing a construction that is not as susceptible to this trouble as ordinary firebrick construction.

SECTION 7

THE BLAST-FURNACE BURDEN

The regulation of the proportions of ore, agglomerates, flux, coke, and other miscellaneous materials charged to the blast furnace is called **burdening** the furnace. It has two objects: namely, the most efficient operation of the furnace, and the production of metal of the desired composition.

A term often used in relation to blast furnace burdening is the **burden ratio**. It may be defined as the ratio of the weight of iron-bearing burden materials

per charge to the total weight of coke per charge.

Another, and possibly more meaningful, term often used is the **Fe/coke ratio**. This is defined as the ratio of the total iron in all iron-bearing burden materials to the total weight of coke.

A typical burden calculation is shown in Table 14—VI. The amount of each material is shown in the first column, and the per cent of each of the components (on a natural basis) silica, alumina, lime, magnesia,

Furnace No._____ Date_____, 19

Table 14—VI. Burden Calculation for a Blast Furnace.

Material	Weight Per Charge %	Weight Per Charge Lbs.	Silica %	Silica Lbs.	Alumina %	Alumina Lbs.	Lime %	Lime Lbs.	Magnesia %	Magnesia Lbs.	Phosphorus %	Phosphorus Lbs.	Manganese %	Manganese Lbs.	Iron %	Iron Lbs.	Sulphur %	Sulphur Lbs.
Sinter	90	103500	5.50	5693	1.0	1035	5.13	5310	0.94	973	0.041	42	0.07	72	62.1	64274		
Ore	10	11500	0.85	98	1.10	127	0.09	10	0.03	9	0.120	14	0.03	3	60.1	6911	0.01	1
TOTAL ORE		115000																
Slag		5000	14.10	705	3.72	186	31.70	1585	7.24	362	0.59	30	4.38	219	27.21	1361		
Scrap		2000	7.44	149	2.50	50	8.17	163	3.83	77	—	—	2.22	44	61.37	1227		
Coke		41600	2.80	1165	1.98	824	0.22	91	0.06	25	—	—	—	—	0.10	42	0.63	262
Stone																		
Dolomite																		
Total Charge				7810		2222		7159		1446		86		338		73815		263

PIG IRON PRODUCED

	Theoretical Pounds	Theoretical %	Actual %
Fe	73815	94.25	
Si	783	1.00	
P	86	0.11	
Mn (x70%)	237	0.30	
S	23	0.03	
Total	74944		

Total Tons Charged 73815/0.9425 = 78318 = 39.1 ton

Less SiO_2 for 1% Si in Pig, 78318×0.01×2.14 = 1676

SLAG PRODUCED

	Theoretical Pounds	Theoretical %	Actual %
SiO_2	6134	35.3	
Al_2O_3	2222	12.8	
CaO	7159	41.2	
MgO	1446	8.3	
MnO	—	—	
FeO	—	—	
S	240	1.4	
Total	17201	99.0	

Other Oxides in S.ag = (17201/0.99) − 17201 = 17374 − 17201 = 173 lb.

PRODUCT RATIOS

Slag Per Ton	444 Lbs.
Slag Ratio $\left(\dfrac{CaO - MgO}{SiO_2 - Al_2O_3}\right)$ = 1.03	
Coke Per Ton, 1064 lb.	
Mix to Coke	
Stone to Mix %	
Lbs. Stone Per Ton	

phosphorus, manganese, iron, and sulphur are shown in the appropriate columns. With this information a determination is made to show the total amount of pig iron that will be produced and the total amount of silica and manganese oxide that will be reduced into the metal. This shows the amount of material that will remain as slag and provide a means of determining the amounts and types of flux to be added to produce slag of the desired composition. If the total quantity of slag is too small to contain the sulphur that must be absorbed, additional silica in the form of gravel and additional flux is added. Although calculations of this type have been made manually, many plants now use high-speed computing equipment to make these calculations.

In the example presented, one complete charge is the basis for the calculation of the burden. The makeup of the charge and the size of the charge are dependent upon such factors as available raw materials, size of the furnace skip, and size of the furnace itself. The operator must choose a coke rate or, in this case, a certain amount of coke per charge. A step-by-step explanation of the procedure follows:

Step 1—The weights of raw materials per charge and the chemical composition of each are entered in the appropriate space in the burden sheet.

Step 2—Based on the weight and composition of each material, the weight of each of the compounds or elements present is calculated and entered in the appropriate space.

Step 3—The individual compounds and elements are totaled.

Step 4—Under "Pig Iron Produced" is entered the total pounds of Fe charged; the pounds of Si as determined by dividing the Fe charged by 0.9425 (the percentage of Fe normally present in hot metal) or $73815/0.9425 = 78318$ lb. of hot metal containing, for example, 1% Si which equals $1\% \times 78318 = 783$ lb. of Si in hot metal; the total pounds of P charged; 70 per cent of the Mn charged; and the pounds of sulphur, as determined by multiplying the weight of hot metal 78318 by, for example, 0.030 per cent which equals 23 lb. Total of these elements is 74944 lb. The difference between the 74944 and 78318 is practically all carbon with very minor

amounts of such alloying elements as may be present in the raw materials.

Step 5—Under "Slag Produced" is entered the weight of silica charged to the furnace minus the weight of silica needed to supply the 1 per cent silicon in the hot metal which equals $78318 \times 0.01 \times 2.14$ or 1676 lb. of silica, which subtracted from the 7810 pounds of silica charged gives 6134 lb. of silica in slag; the total pounds of alumina charged to the furnace; the total pounds of lime charged; the total pounds of magnesia charged; and the pounds of sulphur not reporting to the hot metal $(263 - 23 = 240)$. Total of these compounds is 17201 lb. Other oxides (Mn, etc.) amount to approximately 1 per cent of the slag produced: therefore, $17201/0.99 = 17374$ lb., which equals the total weight of slag produced per charge.

Step 6—Based on a total weight of 17374 lb., the percentage of each of the slag constituents is calculated and shown in the percentage column.

Step 7—The slag volume, or the weight of slag produced per ton of hot metal made is calculated by dividing the total weight of slag produced by the total tons of hot metal made in one charge: $17374/39.1 = 444$ lb. of slag per ton of hot metal.

Step 8—The slag basicity ratio is calculated by dividing the total bases (% CaO plus % MgO) in the slag, by the total acids (% SiO_2 plus % Al_2O_3) in the slag: or, $(41.2 + 8.3) \div (35.3 + 12.8) = 1.03$.

Step 9—The coke rate, or the weight of coke used per ton of hot metal, is calculated by dividing the weight of coke per charge by the total tons of hot metal made in one charge, or: $41600 \div 39.1 = 1064$ lb. of coke per ton of hot metal.

A proper slag composition or coke rate may not be developed the first time. It then is necessary to make additions or adjustments in the amount of sinter, flux, gravel, or any other burden constituents until an acceptable slag composition and volume, and coke rate, is arrived at. During the operation of the furnace, further adjustments to the burden may be made based on actual compositions of hot metal and slag being produced.

SECTION 8

MODERN TECHNIQUES FOR INCREASING BLAST-FURNACE PRODUCTIVITY

Blast-Humidity Control—Prior to 1950, the temperature of the hot blast was usually below 1200° F, and the moisture content of the blast air was not controlled. Under these conditions, small changes in the atmospheric humidity had a pronounced effect on the furnace operation because of the heat absorbing (endothermic) reaction taking place when steam comes in contact with hot coke. A moisture change of only

3 grains per standard cu. ft., for example, would change the amount of water vapor by about 40 pounds per ton of iron. Such a change would affect the thermal balance to such an extent that it would cause wide swings in the chemical composition of the product. A good example of the effect of moisture could be seen in the effect of seasonal variation on the blast-furnace operation. In summer when the humidity was

high, the coke rates were always higher than in the winter when the air was relatively dry. Because of this, some plants went to the expense of installing units to refrigerate the blast air to obtain a uniformly low moisture content.

In later years as better hot-blast stove procedures were developed and higher hot-blast temperatures were used, it was observed that very high hot-blast temperatures caused the furnace to hang and operate irregularly. This poor operation was attributed to the fact that with the higher hot-blast temperature the flame temperature in the hearth was higher than necessary. From this conclusion it was realized that by adding moisture to the blast in the form of steam the moisture content could be held at a uniformly high level to control the flame temperature and thus a smoother furnace operation could be obtained. The higher the hot-blast temperature, the higher the moisture content of the blast had to be to give a suitable flame temperature. With the very high hot-blast temperatures (1400°–2000° F) that have been used for the last ten years, the optimum moisture content is well above atmospheric; consequently, controls are now used at most furnaces to measure the moisture content of the blast air and automatically adjust the opening of a steam valve to keep the blast moisture content at a fixed level. These instruments are equipped with selectors so that the operator can set the moisture content to the most desirable level for any particular hot-blast temperature or can raise or lower the moisture as desired when some unpredicted change in furnace operation changes the thermal requirement in the hearth. The use of very high hot-blast temperatures together with addition of the proper amount of moisture in the blast has made it possible to increase blast-furnace production rates substantially during the last decade. As explained in the section about the chemistry of the process, moisture produces more reducing gas per unit of volume than dry air does. Consequently, when very high blast temperatures are used, it is absolutely essential to use moisture (or a hydrocarbon fuel) in addition to air to speed up the chemical reactions so that they can keep pace with the higher rates of heat input.

Fuel Injection—With the development of means for obtaining higher hot-blast temperatures and the need for controlling the flame temperature, it became apparent that cold hydrocarbon fuels could be injected into the blast-furnace tuyeres to control the flame temperature and at the same time replace some of the coke. This is possible because in the presence of large quantities of coke the hydrocarbon fuels can burn only to carbon monoxide and hydrogen; consequently, they produce less heat than that produced by the hot coke they replace. As long as a blast furnace has the stove capacity for obtaining higher hot-blast temperatures, or as long as moisture must be added to the blast to lower the flame temperature, hydrocarbon fuels can be used to advantage, because their endothermic effect provides a means of controlling the temperature in the hearth. Generally when tuyere-injected fuels are used, the moisture content of the blast must be decreased. Natural gas, coke-oven gas, fuel oil, pulverized coal, tar and slurries of

oil and coal have been used in this manner. The selection of a suitable fuel for any plant depends on the relative cost of coke and the auxiliary fuel, and on the cost of the equipment required for injecting it. The equipment for injecting gas is the least expensive and that for coal is the most.

When natural gas is used it is generally fed, at a pressure well above that of the air blast, to a pipe encircling the furnace. From this "circle pipe" individual lines carry the gas to each tuyere. A small opening through the side of the tuyere permits the gas to enter the air stream about 4 to 6 inches back from the nose. In this way, combustion of the gas takes place in the zone just inside the furnace. The rate of injection is controlled by the rate of gas flow into the circle pipe. Check valves prevent air from backing up into the gas lines and automatic shut-off valves between the circle pipe and the tuyeres close when the blast-air pressure exceeds or drops below a predetermined range.

When oil or coal are used, they are usually introduced into the air blast by a lance entering the air stream through the sides of the blowpipes. Since the combustion rate for oil and coal are lower than that for gas, this provides a longer period of time for combustion. It is most desirable to have the injected fuel completely gasified and combusted before it leaves the raceway just inside the furnace. When oil is used it is fed to a circle pipe and then to each tuyere in much the same manner as gas. Coal however must be pulverized and then conveyed to the tuyere in high-pressure air, by dense phase transport.

Oxygen Enrichment of the Blast—Although enrichment of the blast air with oxygen has been used experimentally on blast furnaces producing basic pig iron, it has had little commercial interest because of the high cost of oxygen. If the blast air is enriched, the flame temperature increases so that with oxygen contents above 22 per cent, moisture or hydrocarbon fuels must be added to control the flame temperature. For every per cent of enrichment, a production rate increase of about 3 to 4 per cent can be obtained. The higher the hot-blast temperature the smaller the improvement in production rate for each per cent of increase in oxygen content. With enrichments above 25 per cent oxygen, the total fuel rate increases and the increase in production rate for each per cent increase in oxygen content begins to decrease. Unless the cost of oxygen is lowered substantially, oxygen enrichment will not appear commercially attractive for basic iron production.

In the manufacture of ferromanganese where the high-temperature heat requirements are much greater than those for basic pig iron, oxygen enrichments as high as 30 per cent are now used commercially.

High-Pressure Operation—One of the limiting factors in attempting to increase the production rate of a blast furnace is the lifting effect that is caused by the large volume of gases blowing upward through the burden. This lifting effect prevents the burden from descending normally and causes a loss rather than an increase in production. To increase production rates above normal, many furnaces are equipped with septum valves in the top-gas system to increase the exit-gas pressure. This increase in pressure compresses the gases throughout the entire system and permits a larger amount of air to be blown. With this increase in the quantity of air blown per minute there is a corresponding increase in production rate.

When the pressure of the top gas is thus increased, the pressure of the inlet air blast is increased proportionately. At many furnaces, if the top pressure were increased, it would be necessary to use a larger blower capable of delivering the increased blast volume at the higher pressure.

The furnace shell, stove shells, dust catcher, primary washer, and gas mains must be structurally strong enough to withstand the increased pressure. For obvious reasons, the throttling valve that is used to increase top pressure is located beyond the primary gas washer where the sand-blasting effect of the gas has been reduced by removal of a large portion of the dust carried by the gas from the furnace. The exit water line from the primary washer must be equipped with a regulator so that the gas pressure within the washer will not blow the water seal. Clean gas is piped into the space between the large and small bells to equalize the pressure in the furnace with the pressure in this space. A compressor may be used to increase pressure of the gas for this purpose. The equalization of pressure in this location permits the large bell to be opened and reduces erosion that is caused by top gas leaking past the seat of the large bell. The pressure between the bells is reduced to atmospheric by a by-pass valve to permit opening of the small bell. With the use of high top pressure, many maintenance problems have been encountered with the bells, hoppers, bleeders, and so on. Experiments are still being conducted with abrasion-resistant materials of construction and such new designs as a 3-bell top to improve high-pressure operations.

Beneficiated Burden Materials—During the last decade, the productivity of the blast furnace has been increased to a great extent by both chemical and physical beneficiation of the raw materials.

As already described in Chapter 3, one means of improving coke quality is by washing the coal to remove both ash and sulphur. The coke strength can be improved by using suitable mixtures of different coals and by pulverizing the coals to obtain better blending. The fine portion of the coke, minus ¾-inch, is removed by screening before the coke is used and recently it has been shown that better furnace performance can be obtained by crushing the coke to a top size of only 2 or 2½ inches.

The fine portions of the ores are screened out and agglomerated by sintering or pelletizing. Tests have demonstrated that proper sizing of these materials is required to obtain the maximum production rate. It is generally believed that the most suitable particle size for blast-furnace burden materials is between ⅜ and 1 inch. Material finer than that interferes with the permeability so that the maximum wind rates cannot be obtained and material much coarser than that requires too long a time to heat and reduce properly. Actual demonstrations made with all of the burden materials crushed and screened so that they were within this ideal range have indicated how great the improvement in production will be when all of these means for increasing the production rate are used simultaneously.

Bibliography

Am. Iron and Steel Institute, Annual statistical report, N. Y., The Institute, 1961.

Austin, J. B., Efficiency of the blast-furnace process. Am. Institute of Mining and Metallurgical Engineers, Iron and Steel Div. Trans, **131**, 74–98; discussion, 98–101 (1938)

Brewster, W. E., Carbon in pig iron. Am. Institute of Mining and Metallurgical Engineers, Iron and Steel Div. Trans. **120**, 134–146; discussion, 146–154 (1936)

Byrns, H. A., Experience with conditioned blast at the Woodward Iron Co. Am. Institute of Mining and Metallurgical Engineers, Blast Furnace, Coke Oven and Raw Materials Committee Proc, **11**, 41–44; discussion, 45–49 (1952)

Dobscha, H. F., Effect of sized and sintered Mesabi iron ores on blast furnace performance. Am. Institute of Mining and Metallurgical Engineers, Blast Furnace, Coke Oven and Raw Materials Committee Proc. **7**, 49–57; discussion, 57–67 (1948)

Droege, J. W., P. G. Hershall, A. W. Lemmon, Jr. and R. B. Filbert, Jr., Determination of viscosity of low-silica, high-alumina blast-furnace slags. Unpublished data compiled for U. S. Steel Corp. at Battelle Memorial Institute.

Elliot, G. D., J. A. Bond and T. E. Mitchell, Ironmaking from high-sinter burdens. Iron and Steel Institute Journal **175**, 241–247 (1953)

Ergun, S., Pressure drop in blast furnace and in cupola. Industrial and Engineering Chemistry **45**, No. 2, 477–485 (1953)

Flint, R. V., Effect of burden materials and practices on blast furnace coke rate. Regional Technical Meetings, Am. Institute of Mining, Metallurgical and Petroleum Engineers (1961).

Greiner, E. S., J. S. Marsh and B. Stoughton, The alloys of iron and silicon. N. Y., McGraw-Hill, 1933.

Gumz, W., Cas producers and blast furnaces. N. Y., Wiley, 1950.

Hazard, P., Fuel oil injection in a blast furnace. Iron and Steel Institute Journal **199**, Part I, 127–133 (1961)

Hazel, J. J., Carbon refractories for blast furnaces. Am. Iron and Steel Institute Yearbook, 1952, 309–352.

Hoffman, C. F., Manufacture of low-silicon pig iron using high blast temperatures. Am. Institute of Mining and Metallurgical Engineers, Open Hearth Conference Proc. **23**, 146–150 (1940)

Hogberg, C. G., Technical aspects of northern and southern blast furnace practice. Iron and Steel Engineer **27**, 37–47; discussion, 47–54 (Oct. 1950)

Holbrook, W. F. and T. L. Joseph, Relative desulfurizing powers of blast-furnace slags. Am. Institute of Mining and Metallurgical Engineers, Iron and Steel Div. Trans. **120**, 99–117; discussion, 117–120 (1936)

Holbrook, W. F., C. C. Furnas and T. L. Joseph, Diffusion of sulphur, manganese, phosphorus, silicon, and carbon through molten iron. Industrial and Engineering Chemistry **24**, 993–998 (1932)

Howe, H. M., The metallography of steel and cast iron. N. Y., McGraw-Hill, 1916.

Johnson, H. W., Correlations of some coke properties with blast-furnace operation. Am. Institute of Mining and Metallurgical Engineers, Blast Furnace and Raw Materials Committee Proc. **1**, 12–45; discussion, 46–48 (1941)

Johnson, J. E., Jr., Blast furnace construction in America. N. Y., McGraw-Hill, 1917.

Johnson J. E., Jr., Principles, operation and products of the blast furnace. N. Y., McGraw-Hill, 1918.

Joseph, T. L., Oxides in basic pig iron and in basic open-hearth steel. Am. Institute of Mining and Metallurgical Engineers, Iron and Steel Div. Trans. **125**, 204–245 (1937)

Joseph, T. L., Porosity, reducibility and size preparation of iron ores. Am. Institute of Mining and Metallurgical Engineers, Iron and Steel Div. Trans. **120**, 72–90; discussion, 90–98 (1936)

Kerr, W. R., Practical application of ore sizing. Am. Institute of Mining and Metallurgical Engineers, Blast Furnace, Coke Oven and Raw Materials Committee Proc. **11**, 229–237; discussion, 237–241 (1952)

King, C. D., Seventy-five years of progress in iron and steel. N. Y., Am. Institute of Mining and Metallurgical Engineers, 1948.

King, C. D., Washing of Pittsburgh coking coals and results obtained on blast furnaces. Am. Institute of Mining and Metallurgical Engineers, Blast Furnace and Raw Materials Committee Proc. **3**, 3–22; discussion, 22–31 (1943)

Kraner, H. M., Refractories service conditions in the blast furnace. Am. Ceramic Society Journal **25**, 311–320 (1942)

Macdonald, N. D., Effect of screened sinter on furnace productivity. Am. Institute of Mining, Metallurgical and Petroleum Engineers; Blast Furnace, Coke Oven and Raw Materials Proceedings **20**, 2–10; discussion, 10–15 (1961)

Marshall, W. E., Taconite pellets in the blast furnace. Journal of Metals **13**, 308–313 (1961)

Martin, P. V., Effect of the solution-loss reactions on blast-furnace efficiency. Am. Institute of Mining and Metallurgical Engineers, Iron and Steel Div. Trans. **140**, 31–58; discussion, 59–64 (1940)

Mashin, J. S., T. B. Yee and D. L. Hanna, Viscosity studies of the system $CaO-MgO-Al_2O_3-SiO_2$, III, 35, 45, 50% SiO_2. Jour Am. Ceramic Society **35**, 322–325 (1952)

Meissner, John F., The automatic stockhouse. Iron and Steel Engineer **88**, 99–104; discussion 104–106 (Jan. 1961)

Negomir, J. M., and J. W. Carlson, Oxygen teams up with fuel to hike iron output. Iron Age **188**, Oct. 5, 1961, 69–71.

Osborn, E. F., R. C. De Vries, K. H. Gee and H. M. Kraner, Optimum composition of blast furnace slag as deduced from liquidus data for the quaternary system $CaO-MgO-Al_2O_3-SiO_2$. Am. Institute of Mining and Metallurgical Engineers, Blast Furnace, Coke Oven and Raw Materials Committee Proc. **12**, 281–315; discussion, 315–317 (1953)

Prince, A. T., Phase equilibrium relations in a portion of the $CaO-MgO-Al_2O_3-SiO_2$ system. Jour. Am. Ceramic Society **34**, 44–51 (1951)

Rice, O. R., Blast furnace gas conditioning. Iron and Steel Engineer **19**, 66–89 (Dec. 1942).

Sayer, C. E., The gas-turbo-driven blower for blast furnace service. Iron and Steel Institute Journal **179**, 359–371 (1955)

Schwartz, H. A., American malleable cast iron. Cleveland, Penton, 1922.

Slater, J. H., Operation of the iron blast furnace at high pressure. Am. Iron and Steel Institute Yearbook, 1947, 125–200.

Snow, R. B., Melting temperature charts for the system $CaO-MgO-Al_2O_3-SiO_2$ as related to the MgO and Al_2O_3 content of blast furnace slags. Am. Institute of Mining, Metallurgical and Petroleum Engineers; Blast Furnace, Coke Oven and Raw Materials Proceedings **21**, 125–138 (1962)

Stapleton, J. M., Results obtained from surveys of gas at furnace tops. Am. Institute of Mining and Metallurgical Engineers, Blast Furnace and Raw Materials Committee Proc. **2**, 89–118 (1942)

Stephenson, R. L., Improved productivity and fuel economy through analysis of the blast furnace process: Iron and Steel Engineer **39**, No. 8, 91–98, 1962.

Symposium on blast furnace blowing-in practice. Am. Institute of Mining and Metallurgical Engineers, Blast Furnace, Coke Oven and Raw Materials Committee Proc. **12**, 216–245 (1953)

Symposium on blast furnace hearth construction. Am. Institute of Mining and Metallurgical Engineers, Blast Furnace, Coke Oven and Raw Materials Committee Proc. **7**, 127–171 (1948)

Thompson, R. G., R. L. Franklin, J. R. Guseman and D. E. Rohaus, United States Steel hot-ore briquetting process. Am. Institute of Mining, Metallurgical and Petroleum Engineers; Blast Furnace, Coke Oven and Raw Materials Proceedings **20**, 316–323; discussion, 323–328 (1961)

Turner, T., The metallurgy of iron; 3rd ed. London, Griffin, 1908.

U. S. Bureau of Mines:
   Blast-furnace stock column, by S. P. Kinney (TP 442) 1929.
   Composition of materials from various elevations in an iron blast furnace, by S. P. Kinney (TP 397) 1926.
   Effect of sized ore on blast-furnace operation, by S. P. Kinney (TP 459) 1930.
   Flow of gases through beds of broken solids, by C. C. Furnas (Bull 307) 1929.
   Heat transfer from a gas stream to a bed of broken solids, by C. C. Furnas (Bull 361) 1932.
   Iron blast furnace, by T. L. Joseph (IC 6779) 1934.
   Iron blast-furnace reactions, by S. P. Kinney, P. H. Royster, and T. L. Joseph (TP 391) 1927.
   Oxides in pig iron; their origin and action in the steel-making process, by C. H. Herty, Jr. and J. M. Gaines, Jr. (Bull 308) 1929.
   Solubility of carbon in iron-manganese-silicon alloys, by C. H. Herty, Jr. and M. B. Royer (RI 3230) 1934.

Wagstaff, J. B., Further studies of the tuyere zone of the blast furnace. Am. Institute of Mining and Metallurgical Engineers, Metals Branch Trans. **197**, 895–902 (1953)

White, R. H., Recent advances in iron production techniques. Presented before Minnesota Section, American Institute of Mining, Metallurgical and Petroleum Engineers, Duluth, Minn., January, 1962.

Zherebin, B. N., V. P. Dembovetskii, V. M. Minkin and I. D. Nikulinskii, Coke oven gas in blast furnaces. Stal in English **8**, 549–554 (1961)

CHAPTER 15

The Pneumatic Steelmaking Processes

SECTION 1

INTRODUCTORY

General Principles of Steelmaking—The physico-chemical principles governing the chemical reactions involved in steelmaking were given in some detail in Chapter 12: a much simplified discussion will be undertaken here.

Pig iron consists of the element iron combined with numerous other chemical elements, the most common of which are carbon, manganese, phosphorus, sulphur, and silicon. Depending upon the composition of the raw materials used in the blast furnace—principally iron ore (beneficiated or otherwise), coke and limestone—and the manner in which the furnace is operated, pig iron may contain 3.0 to 4.5 per cent of carbon, 0.15 to 2.5 per cent or more of manganese, as much as 0.2 per cent of sulphur, 0.025 to 2.5 per cent of phosphorus, and 0.5 to 4.0 per cent of silicon. In refining pig iron to convert it into steel, all five of these elements must either be removed almost entirely or at least reduced drastically in amount.

Modern steelmaking processes, including the pneumatic processes, are divided into two general classes from the chemical standpoint: **acid processes** and **basic processes**. Carbon, manganese, and silicon can be removed with relative ease by any of the processes, either acid or basic. The removal of phosphorus and sulphur requires special conditions that can be met only by the basic processes wherein lime is added to the chemical system to form a basic slag that is capable of forming compounds with phosphorus and sulphur during refining operations, thereby removing them from the metal. Because of the chemical nature of the slags, each of the processes must be carried out in equipment lined with refractories of the proper chemical composition. Otherwise, the slags would react with and be neutralized by the lining material and thereby destroy the lining rapidly.

The chemical principle of oxidation is employed to convert pig iron into steel. Each steelmaking process has been devised primarily to provide some means whereby controlled amounts of oxygen can be supplied to the molten metal undergoing refining. The oxygen combines with the unwanted elements (with the exception of sulphur) and, unavoidably, with some of the iron, to form oxides, which either leave the bath as gases or enter the slag. The mechanism by which sulphur is removed does not involve direct reaction with oxygen but depends instead on whether the slag is sufficiently basic and high enough temperatures are attained. As the purification of the pig iron proceeds, the melting point of the bath is raised, and sufficient heat must be supplied from some source to keep the bath molten.

In general, steels that have similar chemical compositions have similar mechanical and physical properties. Steels made by pneumatic steelmaking processes that have the same composition as those made in the basic open-hearth furnace, particularly with regard to phosphorus, sulphur, nitrogen and other contents, will have properties quite similar to the basic open-hearth steels and may be used in the same general applications. There are some applications where pneumatic steels, particularly those produced by the acid Bessemer process or variations of it, are superior to steel produced by any other method because of the desirable mechanical and physical properties resulting from the chemical composition of the pneumatic steels.

Principles and Types of Pneumatic Processes—The historical development of pneumatic steelmaking was discussed in Chapter 1. In common with other steelmaking methods, there are two chemical types of pneumatic process—acid and basic. In both types, air, high-purity oxygen or combinations of these and other oxidizing gases are blown under pressure, through, onto, or over the surface of, molten pig iron to produce steel. If air alone is used for blowing, its nitrogen content serves no useful purpose and actually removes heat from the system. In some cases, nitrogen absorbed during blowing is considered as an undesirable impurity in the finished steel. The problems with nitrogen do not arise when oxygen alone is used as the blowing agent.

There are various ways in which the oxidizing gas can be supplied to a pneumatic process: the five methods presently used in commercial processes are shown schematically in Figure 15—1. The **bottom-blown converter** has been the principal type used in both the acid and basic air-blown pneumatic processes for the production of steel ingots (see Sections 2 and 3), the blast traveling the full length of the bath, thus representing the extreme of submerged blowing practices. The **side-blown converter** can be arranged for either submerged or surface blowing,

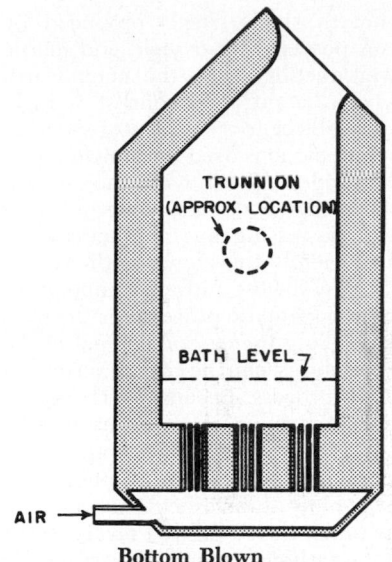

Bottom Blown

The Blast Enters the Wind Box Beneath the Vessel Through the Pipe Indicated by the Arrow and Passes into the Vessel Through Holes in Tuyeres Set in the Bottom of the Converter.

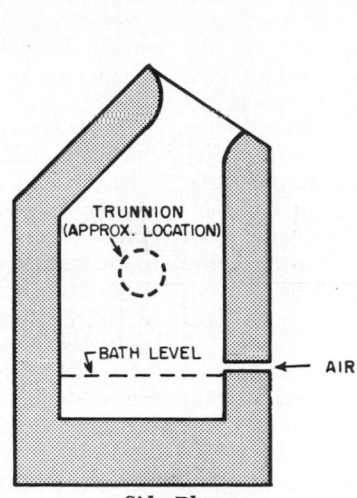

Side Blown

The Blast Enters the Vessel Through Tuyeres in Its Side, Indicated by Arrow. Angle at Which Centerline of Tuyeres Intersects Horizontal Surface of Bath Can Be Varied by Tilting Vessel.

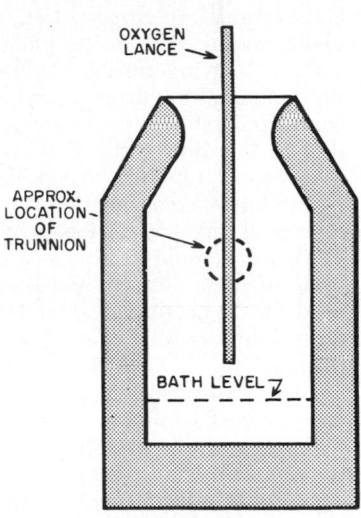

Top Blown

Oxygen of Commercial Purity, at High Pressure and Velocity, Is Blown Downward Vertically onto Surface of Bath Through a Single Water-Cooled Pipe or Lance, Indicated by Arrow.

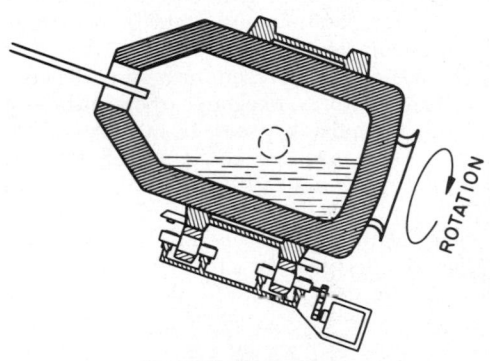

Stora Kaldo Process

Oxygen (95 Per Cent Purity) Is Blown at Relatively low Pressure and at A Small Angle to the Bath Surface Without Impinging upon the Molten Metal in the Bath Contained in An Inclined Rotating Vessel.

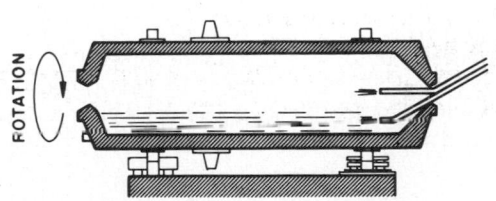

Rotor Process

High-Purity Oxygen is Injected below the Molten Steel Surface and Low-Purity Oxygen into the Space above the Bath, by Separate Lances. The Vessel Rotates about Its Longitudinal Axis at Slow Speed during Refining.

FIG. 15—1. Entirely schematic representation, not to scale, of five presently used principal ways in which air, oxygen, or mixtures of oxidizing gases can be supplied to pneumatic processes. Horizontal dotted lines represent approximate level of the bath. Dotted circles indicate approximate location of trunnions that permit vessels to be tilted for charging, pouring, etc. Rotor vessel is mounted on a horizontal turntable for moving to various operating positions, and vessel can be tilted for charging and pouring.

and significantly different performance characteristics obtain for the two arrangements. The submerged-side-blown converter presents a number of difficult maintenance problems and the design has not been popular, although a few Thomas converters have been modified to introduce the blast through the side of the vessel: a discussion of the aims and results of this modification will be found in Section 3. At present, the only side-blown converters in extensive commercial use are acid-lined vessels arranged for surface blowing, and these are used chiefly in foundries to produce steel for castings (see Section 4). While basic-lined versions of these foundry converters have never been successful, considerable experimentation has been underway for some time in the United States and several foreign countries to develop a commercially useful side-blown pneumatic process, using surface blowing in a basic-lined converter, for the production of ingots: none of these has as yet attained commercial status, so they will not be discussed further in this book. The last variety of surface-blown converter can be termed **top-blown,** the oxidizing gas being introduced by a pipe or lance through the mouth of the vessel. Bessemer and other early investigators employed this or a similar arrangement in some of their designs, and these practices are being used at the present time, chiefly by surface blowing with a high-velocity jet of high-purity oxygen (see Section 5).

In the **Stora Kaldo** process, oxygen is introduced at a low angle to the surface of the bath in a rotating inclined cylindrical furnace, without impinging on the molten metal (see Section 6).

In the **Rotor** process, high-purity oxygen is injected into a slowly rotating cylindrical furnace, below the surface of the bath, while oxygen of lower purity is introduced into the space above the molten bath (see Section 7).

Characteristics of Pneumatic Steels—While the pneumatic steelmaking processes possess the advantages of speed and simplicity, with some of the earlier-developed processes there were certain inherent chemical disadvantages (most of which have been overcome in the modern pneumatic methods).

For example, bottom-blown acid Bessemer steels blown with air alone are generally higher in phosphorus, sulphur and nitrogen contents than basic open-hearth steels. Steels produced by the bottom-blown basic pneumatic processes may approach basic open-hearth steels with respect to phosphorus and sulphur contents, but it is more difficult to produce steel of low nitrogen content by this process, if air alone is used for blowing. When their phosphorus, sulphur and nitrogen contents are high in comparison

with basic open-hearth steels, steels produced by pneumatic processes possess higher yield and tensile strengths and lower ductility than the open-hearth steels. Further, when the nitrogen content is high, pneumatic steels are subject to some loss of ductility due to aging. When air alone is used for blowing, bottom-blown vessels produce steel with the highest nitrogen content: side-blown vessels blown with air alone produce steel possessing an intermediate nitrogen content, and vessels top-blown with oxygen produce steel with the lowest nitrogen content. A disadvantage of some pneumatic processes is the relative difficulty of controlling the carbon content of the finished steels as closely as can be accomplished in the basic open-hearth process. Because of the speed of some of the air-blown pneumatic processes, it is more difficult than in the open-hearth process to closely control the final carbon content of pneumatic steels by stopping the blow at the exact time when the carbon content has fallen to the desired level, except at very low levels of carbon content. This generally limits the variety of steels made to those containing 0.30 per cent and less of carbon (although commercial steels containing up to 0.50 per cent of carbon are produced). The high-carbon steels may be made by blowing the metal to a consistently low carbon content and then adding the required amount of carbon in the form of recarburizers. In addition to the control of carbon, some difficulty is experienced in controlling the final temperature and state of oxidation of air-blown pneumatic steels.

The use of pure oxygen, oxygen-enriched air, oxygen-steam mixtures, oxygen–carbon-dioxide mixtures, and other oxidizing gases or mixtures of gases for blowing—in vessels of conventional design or built to entirely new concepts—have made it possible in recent years to develop pneumatic processes that obviate many of the chemical limitations of the earlier, simpler processes that employed air alone for blowing.

SECTION 2

THE BOTTOM-BLOWN ACID PROCESS

The bottom-blown acid process now known generally as the acid Bessemer process was the original pneumatic steelmaking process. Many millions of tons of steel have been produced by this method. From 1870 to 1910, the acid Bessemer process produced the majority of the world's supply of steel.

The success of acid Bessemer steelmaking is dependent upon the quality of pig iron available which, in turn, demands reliable supplies of iron ore of relatively high purity and metallurgical coke. At the time of the invention of the process, large quantities of suitable ores were available, both abroad and in the United States. With the gradual depletion of high-quality ores abroad (particularly low-phosphorus ores) and the rapid expansion of the use of the bottom-blown basic pneumatic, basic open-hearth and basic oxygen steelmaking processes over the years, acid

Bessemer steel production has declined to a very low level percentagewise in the United Kingdom and on the Continent of Europe.

In the United States, the Mesabi Range has provided a source of relatively high grade ore for making iron for the acid Bessemer process for many years. In spite of this, the acid Bessemer process has still declined from a major to a minor steelmaking method in the United States. The reasons are partly metallurgical and partly economic.

The early use of acid Bessemer steel in this country involved production of a considerable quantity of rail steel, and for many years this process was the principal steelmaking process as shown in Table 15—I. At the present time, the acid Bessemer process is used principally in the production of steel for buttwelded pipe, seamless pipe, free-machining bars, flat-rolled

Table 15—I. Annual Production of Steel for Ingots and Castings in the United States (Net Tons) (a)

Year	Bessemer	Open Hearth		Electric Furnace	Basic Oxygen Steelmaking	Crucible	Steel for Castings	Total
		Acid	Basic					
1870	42,000		1,500	None		(b)	(b)	77,000
1880	1,203,173		112,953	None		(b)	(b)	1,397,015
1890	4,131,536		574,820	None		79,716	(b)	4,790,320
1900	7,486,942		3,805,911	(b)		112,629	(b)	11,410,928
1910	10,542,305	876,742	16,641,355	56,919		136,979	(b)	29,226,309
1911	8,901,596	681,131	16,149,623	29,494		109,371	(b)	26,517,238
1920	9,949,057	1,451,712	35,140,810	566,370		80,937	(b)	47,188,886
1921	4,497,851	325,640	16,648,360	190,897		8,527	(b)	22,157,853
1929	7,977,210	1,254,926	52,900,309	1,065,603		7,442	(b)	63,205,490
1930	5,639,714	874,559	38,380,514	676,111		2,523	(b)	45,583,421
1931	3,386,259	424,668	24,785,046	460,255		1,733	(b)	29,058,961
1932	1,715,925	184,406	13,151,804	270,044		722	(b)	15,322,901
1933	2,720,246	363,469	22,464,004	471,747		763	(b)	26,020,229
1934‡	2,421,840	307,651	26,047,187	404,651		595	119,331	29,181,924
1935	3,175,235	396,695	34,004,585	606,471		719	170,407	38,183,705
1936	3,873,472	471,858	48,288,605	865,150		914	285,653	53,499,999
1937	3,863,918	559,768	51,265,211	947,002		1,046	280,616	56,636,945
1938	2,106,340	305,017	28,774,999	565,627		7	155,848	31,751,990
1939	3,358,916	581,100	47,828,700	1,029,067		931	261,275	52,798,714
1940	3,708,573	690,243	60,882,840	1,700,006		1,024	332,822	66,982,686
1941	5,578,071	1,076,768	73,312,851	2,869,256		2,313	404,892	82,839,259
1942	5,553,424	1,318,892	75,183,065	3,974,540		2,010	485,755	86,031,931
1943	5,625,492	1,413,934	77,207,870	4,589,070		146	451,510	88,836,512
1944	5,039,923	1,195,659	79,168,294	4,237,699		25	399,585	89,641,600
1945	4,305,318	869,726	71,069,876	3,456,704		24	310,831	79,701,648
1946	3,327,737	599,663	60,112,300	2,563,024		(c)	267,624	66,602,724
1947	4,232,543	664,525	76,209,268	3,787,735		(c)	298,133	84,894,071
1948	4,243,172	625,305	78,714,852	5,057,141		(c)	286,595	88,640,470
1949	3,946,656	506,693	69,742,110	3,782,717		(c)	248,135	77,978,176
1950	4,534,558	600,858	85,661,651	6,039,008		(c)	296,461	96,836,075
1951	4,890,946	779,071	92,387,447	7,142,384		(c)	346,187	105,199,848
1952	3,523,677	703,039	82,143,400	6,797,923		(c)	323,756	93,168,039
1953	3,855,705	646,094	99,827,729	7,280,191		(c)	283,555	111,609,719
1954	2,548,104	307,866	80,019,628	5,436,054		(c)	191,099	88,311,652
1955	3,319,517	554,847	104,804,570	8,049,872	307,279	(c)	247,372	117,036,085
1956	3,227,997	672,596	102,167,989	8,641,229	506,338	(c)	277,723	115,216,149
1957	2,475,138	630,051	101,027,725	7,970,574	611,508	(c)	294,472	112,714,996
1958	1,395,985	377,605	75,501,789	6,656,145	1,323,361	(c)	180,786	85,254,885
1959	1,380,283	443,984	81,225,013	8,532,514	1,864,338	(c)	179,303	93,446,132
1960	1,189,196	403,569	85,963,937	8,378,743	3,346,156	(c)	217,382	99,281,601
1961	881,060	393,774	84,108,297	8,664,203	3,967,158	(c)	186,011	98,014,492

(a) From Annual Statistical Reports, American Iron and Steel Institute.
(b) Figures not available.
(c) Included with electric steel.
‡ The figures for 1934 and subsequent years include only that portion of the steel casting production which was produced in foundries operated by companies producing steel ingots.

products, wire, steel castings, and blown metal for the duplex process. Most of the steel in this country is manufactured by the basic open-hearth process and, since 1949 when the United States Steel Corporation completed a new acid Bessemer plant at Lorain, Ohio, no new acid converters have been installed in the United States for the manufacture of Bessemer-steel ingots.

Fully-killed acid Bessemer steel was used for the first time commercially by United States Steel Corporation in the production of seamless pipe. In addition, dephosphorized acid Bessemer steel has been used extensively in the production of welded pipe and galvanized sheets.

The more recent shops for using the acid Bessemer process usually were built to take advantage of the so-called "duplex" process (see Chapter 16). Since the production of duplex steels is covered in a later chapter, the present discussion is confined to that part of the Bessemer converter tonnage manufactured as acid Bessemer steel in ingot form.

PRINCIPAL FACILITIES

Plant Layout—Newer installations usually consist of three bottom-blown **converters**, also called **vessels**, of from 25 to 30 tons capacity, one of which is maintained as a spare. The shop is on three levels with the **pouring floor** at ground level. Two sets of standard-gage track service the vessels. The first set runs along the back of the shop with spurs running under each vessel. On these spurs are placed the **slag pots** and, when it is necessary to change bottoms, the **bottom-hoist car**. The other tracks run in front of the vessels and are used to position the **ladles**. A **teeming floor**, with the necessary cranes for handling the ladles from the cars, is located close to the converter shop.

On the second level are located the vessels, **vessel-repair car** and the **iron-transfer ladle car** to carry the molten metal from the mixer to the vessels (Figure 15—2). To the side of the shop are located the **mixers** and the **bins** for ferromanganese and other ladle additions. On the same level, but located across the shop from the vessels, is the **control pulpit**. On the third level are the tracks for **ladle cars** used to fill the mixers, the mixer controls and **scales** for the iron-transfer ladle.

The Air Blast—Adjacent to the converter building is located the **blowing room**, wherein the air blast is

FIG. 15—2. General view of an installation of Bessemer converters, showing one of the three vessels blowing. Slag pots and the bottom-hoist car operate on standard-gage tracks on the level beneath the vessels.

generated by turboblowers, although in older shops, steam-driven, vertical, reciprocating-type blowing engines are still in use. The blast is carried into the converter building through large mains which lead to the hollow trunnion of each vessel. Each line is fitted with control valves which are regulated from the pulpit by the blower. Also connected to each air-blast line is a steam line fitted with valves for injection of steam into the blast for temperature-control purposes. These valves also are regulated from the blower's pulpit. The pressure in the main is regulated by an automatic blow-off valve, which functions when the vessel is off blast during charging or pouring. Blast pressures normally range from twenty to twenty-five pounds per square inch. Pressures up to thirty-five pounds per square inch are used on larger vessels. Although pressures as low as eighteen pounds per square inch are sufficient to prevent the molten iron from entering and blocking the tuyere holes, the use of this low pressure would prolong the blowing time unnecessarily.

Pressures over the indicated maximums are not used because of the large amount of metal which would be ejected from the converter during blowing.

Bottom House—The bottom of the converter is the part subject to the most wear and requires frequent replacement. Adequate facilities must be provided to insure a constant supply of rebuilt bottoms. These facilities include adequate storage bins or hoppers for the refractories used, equipment such as pug mills for the grinding and mixing of the refractories, pneumatic tools for ramming the bottom material in place, a storage area for tuyeres, and ovens for drying the completed bottoms. These ovens may be either of the in-and-out batch type or tunnel ovens of the continuous type.

THE CONVERTER OR VESSEL

The cylindrically shaped **vessel** consists of a steel shell of riveted or welded construction, supported on two horizontal **trunnions** upon which it can be made to rotate in a vertical plane (Figures 15—3 and

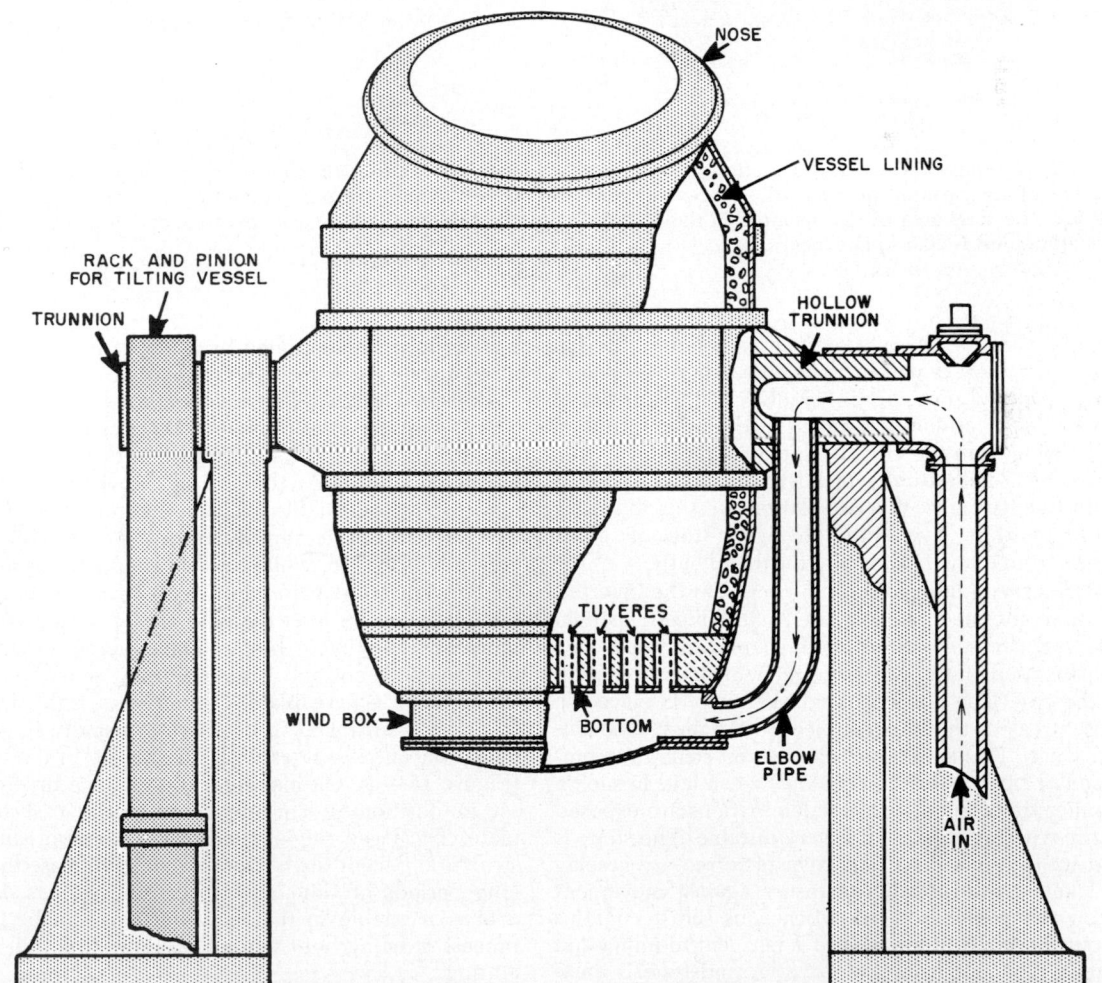

FIG. 15—3. Diagram illustrating the details of construction that permit air to enter the converter through a hollow trunnion, so that the vessel can be turned down without interrupting the flow of air. This schematic diagram is not intended to show actual details of vessel construction, many of which are visible in Figure 15—5 that shows an actual converter in operation. (See also Figure 15—4.)

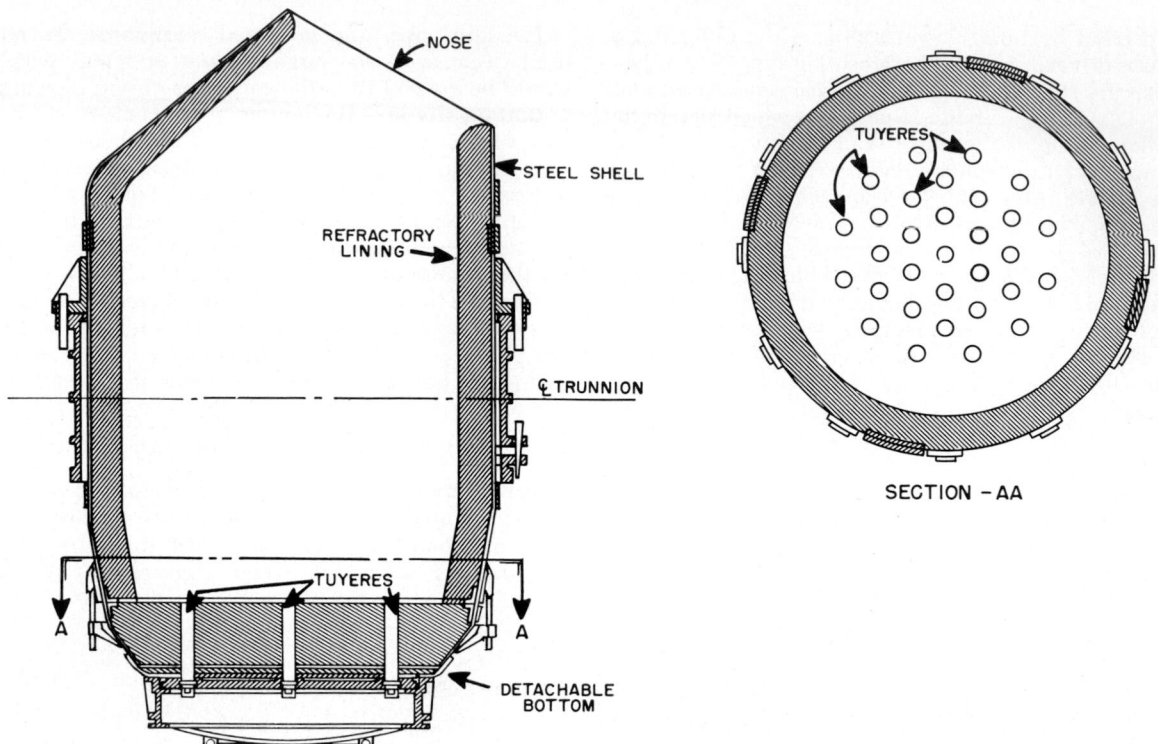

NOSE

STEEL SHELL

REFRACTORY
LINING

℄ TRUNNION

TUYERES

A   A

DETACHABLE
BOTTOM

TUYERES

SECTION - AA

FIG. 15—4. Plan of bottom and section through a 25-ton eccentric Bessemer converter, so-called because of the location of the opening in the nose. Concentric converters have the nose opening parallel to and concentric with the bottom. The total area of the openings in the 31 tuyeres of the bottom shown (each tuyere containing seven ⅝-inch diameter holes) is 66.6 square inches.

15—5). One of these trunnions is hollow, through which the blast is passed by a pipe called the **gooseneck** or **elbow pipe,** to the **windbox** at the bottom of the vessel. A **pinion** is fastened to the other trunnion and engages an electrically operated **rack** to tip the converter. The **bottom,** which is detachable, is pierced with twenty-eight **tuyeres**—larger vessels have as many as thirty-five—through which the air blast passes from the wind-box into the metal bath.

Refractory Lining—With the vessel in the inverted position, the steel shell is lined with siliceous stone. Cut and dressed sandstone (firestone) or micaceous schist is used, most operators preferring a combination of the two. The micaceous schist usually is placed in those areas of the lining subject to the most mechanical wear. This stone has a laminated structure composed of tiny plates of mica, and, when laid in such a manner that the edges of the laminations are exposed as the wearing surface, it is very durable. The stone is laid up tightly with a thin layer of refractory fireclay and keyed into position to insure against movement when the vessel is tilted. Micaceous schist contains about 90 per cent silica, 3 to 7 per cent alumina and 2 to 4 per cent iron oxide; while sandstone is composed of approximately 93 per cent silica and about 4 per cent alumina, the remaining 2 to 3 per cent being iron oxide, lime and magnesia. Linings of this type have a life of approximately 25,000 tons of steel ingots. The linings are dried before using by a flame

inside the vessel, supplied by a "lance" burning gas or oil that is inserted through the mouth of the converter.

Bottom Design—The tuyeres which admit the air blast from the wind-box into the vessel proper are cylindrical in shape, ranging in length from 26 to 36 inches depending on the size of the vessel. They are made of a good-quality fireclay, medium burned. Soft tuyeres deteriorate rapidly during blowing and decrease bottom life, while hard-burned tuyeres are too friable. The most commonly used tuyere is one containing seven ⅝-inch diameter holes which run the length of the tuyere block. The tuyeres are slightly mushroomed on one end, so that, when inserted through the **tuyere plate,** they form a tight fit. The tuyeres are arranged in the bottom usually in two or more concentric circles with one tuyere in the center (Figure **15**—4). On making a bottom, the tuyeres are set in position protruding through the cast tuyere plate. The large ring-shaped castings comprising the structural part of the bottom are used repeatedly over long periods of time. Extra bottom castings are, of course, available so that new bottoms can be in the process of being built while the converting mill is operating.

After positioning the tuyeres, long rectangular tile brick are positioned vertically throughout the bottom. The number used may vary anywhere from as few as six to as many as forty per bottom. It is felt that these tile brick act as stiffeners and prolong the bottom life.

Fig. 15—5. Close-up view of a Bessemer converter during the progress of a "blow."

The number used must be balanced against the expected increase in bottom life, since their use increases the cost of the bottom.

The spaces between tuyeres and tiles are then filled with a refractory material suitably ground and moistened in a pug mill. The bottom material, consisting of siliceous stone such as ganister, brickbats and clay together with reclaimed material from spent bottoms, all thoroughly ground and mixed together, is shoveled into place and rammed solidly, particularly around the tuyeres, to form a compact mass. This constitutes the so-called **dry bottom,** which is then thoroughly dried and baked in the ovens for a minimum of forty-eight hours at temperatures ranging from 300 to 400° F to insure complete drying. Some operators prefer a **wet bottom,** in which materials are moistened to the consistency of a concrete and poured much in the same manner. Longer drying cycles and higher temperatures are required for this type of bottom.

Life of Bottoms—The bottom of the converter, as already stated, is subject to severe wear. On the average, bottom life will range only from twenty-five to thirty-five "blows" for a plant whose total output is mixed steel ingots and duplex metal. The vesselman examines the bottom periodically while the vessel is inverted. If he notices that a particular tuyere is wearing more rapidly than the other tuyeres, which is referred to as **boring,** and thus endangering the life of the bottom, he will direct the removal of the plate from the bottom of the wind-box. The bad tuyere will then be plugged with a blanking plate or clay to prevent the blast from passing through it. As many as ten or twelve tuyeres may be so blanked before the bottom is replaced.

The bottom is changed when the tuyeres are worn down to a length of about eight inches. The change requires approximately thirty minutes. The bottom plate of the wind-box is removed. A small car is set in position under the vessel, and the vessel is turned to the vertical position. A hydraulic jack raises the car until it contacts the bottom. The keys holding the bottom in place are knocked out, the connecting links

disengaged, and the bottom allowed to settle on the car. The car is then lowered to ground level and pulled out of position by a standard-gage locomotive. The new bottom, mounted on a similar car, is placed in position, and the operation reversed.

Cupolas and Hot-Metal Mixers—Many early acid-Bessemer plants were small, isolated units often located some distance from the source of pig iron. To supply the liquid-iron charge required by the process, solid pigs of iron were melted in reverberatory furnaces, superseded in a short time by cupolas. Spiegel, a high-manganese pig iron, containing about 5 per cent carbon, formerly was melted in a similar manner and was used to recarburize the blown metal.

The use of the cupola had certain inherent disadvantages which from the standpoint of production and quality control were most undesirable. Much of the sulphur and phosphorus in the coke was absorbed by the iron. These elements being undesirable above certain limits in the steel, and the acid process being incapable of removing them, it was necessary to use the best type of coke available. For this reason, as well as for economy, the amount of coke charged was held to a minimum. These factors, combined with fluctuations in iron composition, caused erratic swings in iron temperatures, resulting in difficulties in controlling the blowing of the converters. The desirability of using molten iron from blast furnaces became apparent at an early date, but the intermittent casting of the blast furnace, coupled with the large amount of molten metal taken from the furnace at one time, made such practice impracticable until the hot-metal mixer was invented. The advantages of the hot-metal mixer described in Chapter 16 were quickly recognized in the industry and, at those plants where sufficient blast-furnace facilities were available, it replaced quickly those cupolas used for melting iron for blowing in the converters.

OPERATION OF THE PLANT

Sequence of Operations—After completion of the previous blow, the vessel is turned on its trunnions un-

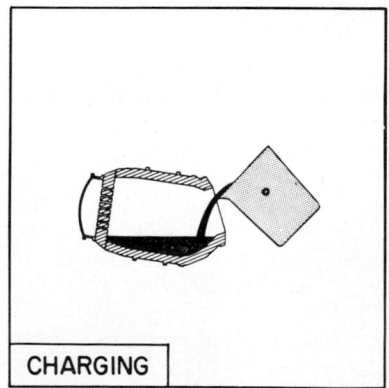 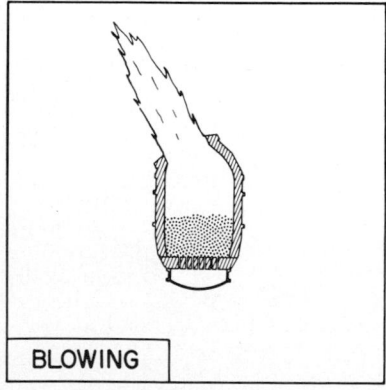 

CHARGING   BLOWING   POURING

FIG. 15—6. Cross-sections showing positions assumed by the Bessemer converter when [left] pouring molten pig iron into the vessel, [center] blowing compressed air through the molten metal, and [right] pouring the refined metal [steel] into the ladle whence it is poured into ingot molds. The left sketch shows how tilting the vessel raises the tuyeres above the level of the molten pig iron charged into the converter. The center illustration is drawn to indicate the highly turbulent condition of the molten metal due to the passage of gases during the blow. Note that some slag, not indicated on the drawings, accompanies the molten metal.

til it assumes an almost horizontal position and scrap, scale, or ore is dumped into the vessel as desired. The molten pig iron is then poured in from the transfer ladle, as shown schematically in Figure 15—6. In this horizontal position the metal is contained in the belly of the converter and does not come in contact with the tuyeres. The blast is started and the vessel is turned to a vertical position and remains in this position throughout the balance of the blowing period, unless "side blowing" is resorted to for increasing temperature, as discussed below.

The Bessemer blow is usually thought of as being divided into three parts, the first period, the second period and the after blow.

The first period, or the **silicon blow,** as it is commonly called, begins as the blast is turned on and the vessel turned up. During this period of the blow, a short, transparent flame extends from the mouth of the vessel. As the blowing continues the flame starts to lengthen after about four minutes and the second period or **carbon blow** begins.

The long, brilliant flame which is characteristic of the carbon blow continues until the elimination of carbon approaches completion, whereupon there is a definite change in the appearance of the flame. The flame gradually shortens in length and seems to fan out. As viewed through the blower's colored glasses, streaks of red appear in the flame at the mouth of the converter, and then almost instantaneously the whole flame changes from the usual golden yellow to a reddish-appearing flame. This change, which always occurs at almost the same carbon content from blow to blow, has been designated as the **end point.** As such it has been established as a control reference point by the blower. On some grades of steel the blow will be terminated promptly on reaching the end point. These blows are then said to be **young blown** heats. In other cases, it is necessary to prolong the blowing beyond this point as long as fifteen or twenty seconds. The time interval from end point to turn down is referred to as the **after blow,** and heats handled in this manner are said to be **full blown.**

It is during the second period that the flame attains its full brilliance and length, extending as much as thirty feet beyond the mouth of the converter. This flame results from the evolved carbon monoxide burning to carbon dioxide as it comes in contact with the air at the mouth of the converter. It is at this time that the blower carefully studies the flame to determine if his judgment regarding temperature control, and in estimating the amount of scrap needed, initially was correct. If the flame shows brilliant white patches and is extremely feathery around the edges, the temperature in all probability is too high. By introducing steam into the blast line the temperature can be lowered because of the heat absorbed through the dissociation of water vapor. A dull flame streaked with dark patches is indicative of low temperature. The temperature can be increased by resorting to **side blowing.** This involves tipping the converter over on its back, thereby exposing several of the tuyeres above the metal bath. By so doing, oxidation of carbon monoxide to carbon dioxide is promoted within the vessel

Table 15—II. Effect of Coolants in Bessemer Blowing

Addition of 100 lbs.	Cooling Effect Produced
Pig iron	55,000 Btu
Steel scrap	59,000 Btu
Dry ore	128,000 Btu
Steam or water vapor	141,500 Btu

itself, thereby increasing the temperature of the bath by the radiation of heat.

The comparative effect of various coolants used in the process to control temperatures are shown in Table 15—II.

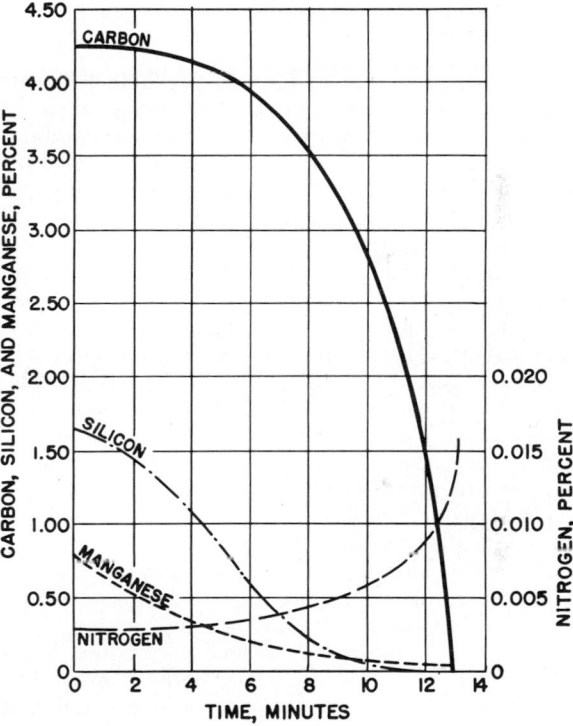

FIG. **15**—7. Changes in chemical composition of the metal in the bath of a 25-ton acid Bessemer converter during the progress of a blow.

Changes in chemical composition of the bath during progress of a 25-ton blow are shown diagrammatically in Figure 15—7.

There is a definite relationship between the carbon and oxygen in the metal, as discussed in Chapter 12. Uniformity of product is influenced by control of oxygen content. After the carbon content has been lowered to 0.05 per cent, any further lowering of the carbon is accompanied by a substantial increase in oxygen content. It is, therefore, apparent how important the determination of the end point becomes in insuring uniformity of product from blow to blow.

Iron of the correct chemical composition and temperature is required. For the best blowing, both from the standpoint of production and of quality, iron within the following ranges in composition is desired:

Element	Per Cent
Silicon	1.10 to 1.50
Manganese	0.40 to 0.70
Phosphorus	0.090 max.
Sulphur	0.030 max.

It is believed that for best blowing conditions a ratio of silicon to manganese of two or two and one-half to one should be maintained. The carbon content of the iron will range from 4.00 to 4.50 per cent, but chemical determination of this element in the iron generally is not made.

A typical charge for a 25-ton acid Bessemer converter is as follows:

Hot Metal (Bessemer)	55,000 lbs.
Scrap	7,000 lbs.

With the above charge the blowing time will vary from eleven to fifteen minutes, depending upon the chemical composition of the iron and the condition of the bottom in respect to the number of blanked tuyeres. For the smaller, 10-ton converters, the time is shorter, averaging nine to eleven minutes.

Roll-scale additions are sometimes made in order to decrease blowing time. The roll scale, which is largely iron oxide, begins immediately to react with the silicon and manganese in the iron, and thus hastens their elimination. The scrap is added as a coolant. The amount required is estimated by the blower from his observations as to whether or not a satisfactory final temperature was obtained on the previous blow. The amount necessary to use will vary with the actual or physical temperature of the iron, as well as the potential chemical heat available in the iron, which in turn depends on its composition.

After the blower has made the decision that the blow should be terminated, the vessel is turned down and the blast turned off. Molten iron is added to the vessel at this time if it is desired to produce killed Bessemer steel, as described later under "Carbon Deoxidation." The ladle is positioned under the mouth of the converter to permit the blown metal to be poured into it. This operation is done slowly and carefully in order to retain as much slag in the vessel as practical. While the metal is pouring into the ladle, the recarburizers and deoxidizers are added. When the vessel has been drained, the ladle is withdrawn and the vessel turned further from the vertical to permit the remaining slag to drop out into a slag pot mounted on a car below. The ladle is carried to the teeming platform, and the steel is teemed into the ingot molds.

The ladles, ingot molds, and the stripping machines for removing ingots from the molds are generally similar to those described and illustrated in Chapter 16 in connection with the manufacture of steel by the open-hearth process.

Phosphorus and Sulphur Control—In the acid process, the phosphorus and sulphur suffer no oxidation from the action of iron oxide. Assuming that the loss in weight in the bath from elimination of the metalloids, mechanical ejection by the blast and oxi-

dation of iron and retention as iron oxide in the slag was 10 per cent, if an iron contained 0.030 per cent sulphur and 0.075 per cent phosphorus, the metal at the termination of the blow would contain approximately 0.033 per cent sulphur and 0.083 per cent phosphorus.

Iron ores with a low phosphorus content (less than 0.045 per cent) are required in the production of blast-furnace iron that can be converted into low-phosphorus steel by the acid Bessemer process without employing a separate dephosphorizing process.

Dephosphorization in the ladle has been used successfully for a number of years in the production of acid Bessemer steel with less than 0.050 per cent phosphorus. This is accomplished by adding a mixture of lime, iron oxides and flux, all in the solid state, to the blown metal as it flows into the ladle. Another method for phosphorus removal consists of the well-known duplex practice in which a tilting basic open-hearth furnace is employed.

Sulphur in coke is also an important factor in Bessemer steel production as this element is not removed in the acid Bessemer process. If higher sulphur coke is used in Bessemer iron production, it is necessary either to remove sufficient sulphur in the blast furnace or resort to other treatments. In the blast furnace, limestone in the charge is adjusted with the burden for sulphur removal. Ladle treatments have been developed in which fused sodium carbonate or sodium hydroxide has been used successfully, particularly with cupola iron. In the duplex process, sulphur may be removed to some extent in the basic open-hearth furnace. A certain amount of sulphur also may be removed in the basic Bessemer process.

PROCESS AND QUALITY CONTROL

End Point Evaluation—Although visual characteristics continue to be the most widely used means of controlling the Bessemer blow and determining the end-point characteristics, several instruments have been investigated in an attempt to obtain better control. The spectroscope, one of the first instruments investigated, has been used with reasonable success. The amount of natural light and other conditions in the Bessemer plant may interfere with and limit its applications. It is necessary, depending on the grade of steel being produced, to select a time interval after changes in the spectrum are observed in order to turn down the vessel at the proper carbon content.

Automatic recording of the radiation characteristics of the flame as measured by a photocell also has been used to aid in control of the Bessemer blow. As the flame drops at the end of a blow, the curve drawn by the recorder indicates an arrest which is taken as the end point. Each type of steel requires a specific afterblow, measured in seconds, which is determined by statistical studies of variations in yield and quality with time of afterblow, beyond this end point.

One of the most important features of end-point control is the elimination of overblowing which results in the absorption of excessive amounts of oxygen and nitrogen. This not only affects the efficiency of deoxidation, but also influences behavior of the product during processing in the rolling mills.

Temperature Control—The production of steel by the converter process requires careful temperature control in order to insure satisfactory practice. If the finished steel is too low in temperature, ladle skulling and pouring nozzle difficulties will be encountered which are undesirable from the viewpoint of steel quality. Steel with a high temperature contains excessive quantities of nitrogen and oxygen. The Bessemer blower is, therefore, confronted with the problem of producing steel at a satisfactory temperature which can be determined conveniently at the present time only with an optical pyrometer as the blown metal is poured into the ladle or during teeming. Many attempts have been made to develop a satisfactory device to measure temperature of the molten charge during the Bessemer blow, but a satisfactory technique has not been developed. The blower still must continue to depend upon the characteristics of the flame.

A photronic cell located in the wind-box has been investigated and the possibilities of making accurate temperature determinations by this method are promising, but additional experimental work will be required to develop a satisfactory technique.

Chemical composition of the iron is a fundamental consideration with respect to temperature control, particularly with regard to silicon. The oxidation of silicon is an exothermic chemical reaction and data showing the actual silicon content in the iron should be available to the blower. If the silicon content is high, cold metal (scrap) or pig iron may be added to the vessel to eliminate the necessity for steaming. If the silicon content is too low, it may be necessary to side blow in order to increase the temperature of the metal. During the blow, if the temperature is excessive, all of the silicon may not be removed before carbon oxidation predominates.

A cold ladle or vessel and the amount of ferroalloy addition at the end of the blow are among the factors which must be considered by the blower in producing steel with a satisfactory temperature. The blower, therefore, must take into consideration the many variables which affect temperature and, by judging character of the flame, produce a satisfactory quality steel. The accurate determination of temperature during the blow with a radiation instrument, consequently, would be of considerable assistance in the production of Bessemer steel.

Oxygen-Enriched Blast—Extensive investigations of the use of an oxygen-enriched blast in the acid-Bessemer converter have been carried out with the following results:

(1) Shorter blowing time resulted.
(2) Greater utilization of cold iron and scrap was achieved.
(3) With a blast containing about 30 per cent oxygen, the bottom and vessel linings were not abnormally worn in a limited number of heats.
(4) Steel quality was similar to regular Bessemer heats.
(5) Flame characteristics were readily distinguishable by blowers and satisfactory teeming temperatures were obtained.

Blowing Time and Quality—One of the important factors in the production of Bessemer steel is that a blow usually lasts for a period of only 10 to 15 minutes, and the problem of controlling quality of the product, therefore, differs somewhat from open-hearth practice. Speed of the operation is so rapid that the necessity for certain control measures differs from those required by the open-hearth melter. The Bessemer process, to a marked degree, is automatic in its operation.

The composition of the steel cannot be regulated satisfactorily by stopping the blow at an intermediate point due to the speed of reactions and other conditions. It is possible to blow a Bessemer heat to any selected carbon level, but a product more uniform in chemical composition is obtained by blowing to the drop of the flame and adding carbon and manganese as required. High-carbon blown metal is sometimes produced in the duplex process as further refining and adjustment in chemical composition are made in the open-hearth furnace. At the first indication of a drop of the flame and other changes in appearance of the flame, the converter may be turned down "young," and the carbon content will be approximately 0.10 per cent. However, most of the acid Bessemer steel is blown "full" to insure uniform composition. The vessel is turned down as height of the flame continues to decrease and certain changes in appearance are observed. Full-blown heats contain approximately 0.04 per cent carbon. If the manganese content of the metal at the beginning of the blow is too high, a fluid slag which contributes to "slopping" is produced. Therefore, the ratio of silicon to manganese must be controlled. Silicon already has been described as a source of heat and therefore an important factor in temperature control during the blow.

Metal Losses—Metallic yield in the acid Bessemer process is comparable with stationary open-hearth practices and is influenced by metalloid losses, oxidation of iron, slopping and other operation characteristics. Depending upon facilities and operating conditions, the performance of acid Bessemer plants in terms of metal yield has been similar to that of open-hearth plants.

DEOXIDATION OF ACID BESSEMER STEEL

General—In the Bessemer process, characteristics of the flame at the end of the blow and the deoxidation practice employed are fundamental factors which control quality of the product. The additions required to produce various grades of acid Bessemer steel are incorporated in the deoxidation practice and may be added to the vessel, ladle, or mold.

In the deoxidation of acid Bessemer steel, the oxygen content of the blown metal is one of the significant factors involved. The iron oxide content is also related to the nitrogen content in that both are increased by higher temperatures and overblowing. In the production of killed acid Bessemer steels, the deoxidation practice also must take into consideration the fixation of nitrogen. Therefore, for proper deoxidation, it is essential to control carefully the temperature and end point of the Bessemer blow.

Rimmed and capped acid Bessemer steels usually

Table 15—III. Approximate Compositions of Some Deoxizers (Per Cent)

Deoxidizer	Fe	C	Mn	P	Si	Ash
Ferromanganese	12.0	6.50	75.0-80.0	0.15	1.00	—
Ferrosilicon (50%)	48.0	0.15	0.30	0.035	50.0	—
Ferrosilicon (85%)	15.0	—	—	—	85.0	—
Pig or Molten Iron	93.0	4.25	0.6	0.08	1.30	—
Anthracite	—	85.50	—	—	—	4.50

	Fe	Al	Cu	Si
Aluminum	2.0	90.0	4.0	3.0

are blown fully and finished with a low carbon content. These steels are not completely deoxidized so that a strong evolution of gas occurs during solidification in the mold. Sufficient deoxidizer may be added, either in the ladle or mold, to control action in the mold (Table 15—III). In capped steels, the period of gas evolution in the mold is further controlled by using a steel cap which chills and solidifies the top of the ingot. Steel of this type usually contains about 0.07 per cent carbon, 0.45 per cent manganese, 0.08 per cent phosphorus, 0.025 per cent sulphur and 0.005 per cent silicon. In the manufacture of killed acid Bessemer steel, strong deoxidizers, including carbon, ferrosilicon and aluminum are added to the molten steel at the end of the blow. Ingots with a dense, homogeneous structure, relatively free from porosity or blowholes, are produced from killed steel. Steel of this type may contain 0.10 per cent or more carbon, 0.35–1.25 per cent manganese, 0.10–0.30 per cent silicon, 0.08 per cent phosphorus and 0.025 per cent sulphur. Alloys also may be added if desired. The factors responsible for the superior quality of deoxidized as compared with rimmed or capped acid Bessemer steel do not depend entirely on the fact that a killed steel is involved but, more precisely, are related to the method of killing the steel.

Carbon Deoxidation—The oxygen content of rimmed or capped acid Bessemer steels is high and must, to a certain degree, be evaluated by behavior of metal in the mold. These steels are generally low in carbon, and carbon deoxidation is not an important factor in the production of "open" steels.

The carbon content of killed acid Bessemer steel varies from 0.10 per cent to any higher level desired, depending upon the grade of steel. A sufficient amount of deoxidizer is added to produce a steel which has no action in the mold. In order to meet carbon requirements and properly deoxidize the steel, molten blast-furnace iron containing about 4 per cent carbon is added to the vessel at the end of the blow. After the addition of hot metal, a reaction takes place for several minutes in the vessel which results in the formation of carbon monoxide gas. The carbon monoxide burns at the mouth of the converter. Removal of oxygen as a gas not only deoxidizes the steel but removes oxygen immediately instead of forming a solid metallic inclusion which must rise to the surface of the steel. Steel made by this process is distinctly different from regular acid Bessemer steel. The steel contains fewer non-metallic inclusions than if silicon or aluminum had been added before the carbon reaction.

In the use of hot metal for deoxidation of acid Bessemer steel, provisions must be made for accurate weighing of the addition. Other means may be used for carbon deoxidation in which solid materials are added, but the simplest method is the use of hot metal.

Manganese and Silicon Additions—In the manufacture of killed acid Bessemer steels manganese and silicon may be added after carbon deoxidation either to the vessel or ladle in sufficient quantity to provide the amount desired in the finished steel. Additions to the vessel are preferred. Usually, 75 per cent ferromanganese and 50 per cent ferrosilicon are employed. Special types of deoxidizers containing silicon and/or manganese with aluminum have been used successfully. In the manufacture of rimmed or capped acid Bessemer steels, silicon is seldom used, and manganese is added to the ladle to improve rolling characteristics. The efficiencies of the various additions are similar to open-hearth practice at the same carbon level.

Although aluminum is added to steel primarily for deoxidation purposes, it also is used for nitrogen fixation in killed acid Bessemer steels. The fixation of nitrogen with aluminum or other elements imparts superior toughness and improved resistance to notch sensitivity. The proper use of aluminum or its equivalent is essential in the production of a satisfactory killed acid Bessemer steel.

SECTION 3

THE BASIC BESSEMER OR THOMAS PROCESS

Historical—The bottom-blown basic pneumatic process known by the several names of the **Thomas, Thomas-Gilchrist** or **basic Bessemer process,** was patented in 1879 by Sidney G. Thomas in England. The process (never adopted in the United States) developed much more rapidly on the Continent than in Great Britain and, in 1890, Continental production was over 2 million tons as compared with 400,000 tons made in Great Britain.

The simultaneous development of the basic open-hearth process resulted in a decline of production of steel by the bottom-blown basic pneumatic process in Europe and, by 1904, production of basic open-hearth steel there exceeded that of basic pneumatic steel. From 1910 on, the bottom-blown basic pneumatic process has declined continuously except for a short-lived revival during the great demand for steel occasioned by World War II.

Composition of Pig Iron for Basic Process—The bottom-blown basic pneumatic process requires the use of a basic lining in the converter, and the use of lime or limestone as a slag-making material. The basic slag makes the process capable of removing phosphorus and sulphur from the blast-furnace iron. Thus, iron can be produced from iron ores of lower grade, using lower-grade coke as fuel, than would be permissible in production of iron for the acid Bessemer process which cannot remove phosphorus or sulphur and requires irons with a low content of these two elements.

A typical blast-furnace iron for the bottom-blown basic pneumatic process contains from 1.4 to 2.0 per cent of phosphorus and approximately 0.5 per cent of silicon. Iron ore and other raw materials of the type required to produce iron of this composition in the blast furnace, or to give a molten product of this composition when pig iron is melted in the cupola, have been and still are available abroad in rather large quantities.

Since most of the phosphorus and some of the sulphur are removed in the bottom-blown basic pneumatic process, the chemical composition and properties of steels produced by this method more closely approach the composition and properties of basic open-hearth steels of similar grade than do comparable steels made by the acid Bessemer process. However, the nitrogen content of the bottom-blown basic pneumatic steels is definitely higher than that of basic open-hearth steel. For this reason, the properties of air-blown steels made by the basic Bessemer (Thomas) process, while more similar to basic open-hearth steels than are acid Bessemer steels, are still inadequate for certain applications because of their higher strength, lower ductility and susceptibility to strain aging. As described later in this section, various modifications of the basic Bessemer process have removed some of the chemical limitations of the method.

PRINCIPAL FACILITIES

The equipment for the bottom-blown basic pneumatic process is very similar to that described for the acid Bessemer process in Section 2. Consequently, the following description will mention largely differences between the types of equipment used for the two processes.

Mixer—Hot-metal mixers for the Thomas plants are of the same general size and type as those already described in connection with acid Bessemer steel plants. Some so-called "active" mixers with regenerators are used to keep the iron hotter, and through the addition of lime some refining also is carried out prior to charging the metal in the converters. Many mixers are lined with magnesite brick rather than with siliceous refractories.

Blowing Equipment—There are no marked differences in blowing equipment for the bottom-blown basic pneumatic process from that already described for the acid Bessemer process. The normal air-blast pressure in the basic process is 35 pounds per square inch, which is somewhat higher than that employed for the acid Bessemer process in the United States, because the depth of the bath in the basic process is greater and the total area of the tuyere openings is less.

THE CONVERTER OR VESSEL

The size of bottom-blown basic converters varies from 25 tons to 60 tons capacity. The design of vessels is similar to that of the acid Bessemer converters used in America. A large number of basic vessels are concentric rather than eccentric, in relation to the position of the opening in the nose. To conserve heat, the nose opening in some basic vessels is quite small. Further, the bottom design and the lining, of course, are different. Almost all of the bottom-blown basic pneumatic converters are lined at present with a mixture of tar and burned dolomite rammed into place in the vessel.

Bottom Design—The bottom of the basic converters used in most plants contains about 200 holes, each ½ inch in diameter representing a tuyere-opening area of about 39 square inches, total. Separate tuyere brick are not used in these bottoms; instead the holes are formed by ramming the refractory bottom material around copper tubes. The bottom is then heated in an intermittent-type oven for a period of six days, after which the tubes are removed. Bottoms with tangentially inclined holes have been tried over a long period but have not been proven to have any appreciable effect in improving operations.

Lining and Bottom Life—The lower part of the lining of a bottom-blown basic converter requires replacement after about 200 blows, on the average. The remainder of the lining, with the exception of the bottom, withstands about 400 blows. Bottom life averages about 40 blows. Dolomite consumption has been reported as about 22 pounds per ton of steel produced.

SEQUENCE OF OPERATIONS

The steps in making a heat of steel in a bottom-blown basic converter vary largely because of recent innovations and changes introduced in an effort to consistently produce steels of low nitrogen content. The general sequence in one British plant is as follows: the blast-furnace iron is partially desulphurized between the blast furnace and the mixer or between the mixer and the converter by additions of soda ash. Slag produced by the desulphurization operation is carefully skimmed off before charging the iron into the converter. With the vessel in the horizontal position, the necessary burnt lime (averaging 300 pounds per ton of iron) is added by an overhead chute. The vessel is then turned down past the horizontal position and a weighed molten iron charge is added. Blowing is started with a blast pressure of 30 pounds per square inch. The time of addition of scrap, required to control the temperature of the blow, varies with the type of scrap available. With bloom-end scrap the addition is made two or three minutes before the drop of the flame but, with heavy ingot scrap, the addition is made early in the blow to allow for the complete melting of the scrap.

The total duration of the blow depends upon time of additions and other operating factors. The end point is determined by visual inspection of the flame, confirmed by the blower's judgment of a fractured sample of steel taken from the vessel. After blowing is completed, most of the slag is removed by tilting the vessel, following which the necessary amount of ferromanganese is added to the steel in hot lump form. The residual slag is retained in the vessel by the formation of a lime dam in the mouth of the vessel while the steel is poured into the ladle held underneath the vessel by the casting car. For a 40-ton converter, the total duration of blow is 15 to 16 minutes, including an after blow of 3 to 5 minutes. It should be noted that the after blow in the basic process is relatively long as compared with the acid Bessemer process; this is necessary to accomplish removal of phosphorus from the bath. The end point of a basic Bessemer blow is very similar to that of the acid Bessemer process, and occurs at the same carbon content of the metal in both processes. Because of the lower silicon content of the iron used in the basic process, which results in a shorter silicon blow, the total elapsed time between start of blowing and drop of the flame is somewhat shorter than in the acid process for the same blowing rate. About 12,000 cubic feet of air are blown per ton of steel produced.

CHEMISTRY OF THE THOMAS PROCESS

Oxidation Reactions—The major chemical differences between the bottom-blown acid and basic pneumatic processes lies in the chemical reactions involving removal of phosphorus and, to some extent, sulphur from the iron. The effective removal of these elements depends on slag-metal reactions which are absent in the acid Bessemer process. Oxidation of carbon, manganese and silicon occurs in essentially the same manner as was described for the acid Bessemer process. These reactions are discussed in some detail in Chapter 12.

The removal of both phosphorus and sulphur in the basic pneumatic process depends upon the concentration of lime in the slag; however, removal of phosphorus is favored by a high content of iron oxide in the slag and oxygen in the metal, while sulphur removal is favored by the reverse conditions. Thus, only a small amount of sulphur is removed in the basic pneumatic process unless slags with a high lime content are formed. Further, because of the nature of the

dephosphorization reaction, it occurs largely after the removal of the majority of the carbon, in the after-blow period. Figure 15—8 illustrates the course of the oxidizing reactions during a typical Thomas blow. As in most basic steelmaking processes, an undesired reversion of phosphorus from slag to metal is more probable if high finishing temperatures are attained.

Thermal Requirements—In the bottom-blown basic pneumatic process, lime is added with the hot metal. This added cold material, as well as the greater slag volume produced, requires additional heat as compared with the acid process. In the basic pneumatic process, iron of higher silicon content cannot be used to obtain this additional heat, since the more silicon the iron contains, the more lime will be required to flux the oxidized silicon (silica, SiO_2) both to prevent the silica from attacking the lining and to keep the slag basic enough for effective phosphorus and sulphur removal. The higher the silicon content of the iron, the greater will be the slag volume produced. Fortunately, in the bottom-blown basic converter, a portion of the additional heat required is obtained from the oxidation of phosphorus in the iron. For this reason, a proper thermal balance in the bottom-blown basic converter makes the relative percentages of silicon and phosphorus in the iron critical. A typical blast-furnace iron for use in the Thomas process contains 0.2 to 0.4 per cent silicon, 0.6 to 1.0 per cent manganese, 1.5 to 2.0 per cent phosphorus and 0.03 to 0.05 per cent sulphur. The phosphoric acid anhydride (P_2O_5) content of the final slag produced in bottom-blowing iron of the above composition in a basic converter, using 300 pounds of lime per ton of steel, is about 16 to 18 per cent, with a slag volume of about 20 to 22 per cent. Slags of this composition make desirable fertilizers and they are processed and sold for this purpose, thus aiding the economics of the process.

Temperature Control—During a bottom-blown basic converter blow, the temperature normally rises during the oxidation of silicon, remains fairly constant during the carbon blow, and rises rapidly during the after blow. In some respects control of temperature in the bottom-blown basic converter is more important than in the acid Bessemer vessel because of the need for effective control of phosphorus content of the finished steel. The methods used for temperature control during a blow are very similar for both the basic and acid processes. The most important factors relating to temperatures in the vessel are the as-charged temperature and composition of the iron being blown and the blowing time. Common methods for controlling temperature during blowing are the use of side blowing to increase temperature and the use of steam and scrap to decrease temperature. The photocell and immersion thermocouples have been used with some success in quite a few plants for controlling the end point and for accurately indicating the final bath temperature. The main reason for this closer control of temperature is the concern over residual nitrogen and the desire to produce low-nitrogen steels. Residual nitrogen contents are markedly affected by the bath temperature.

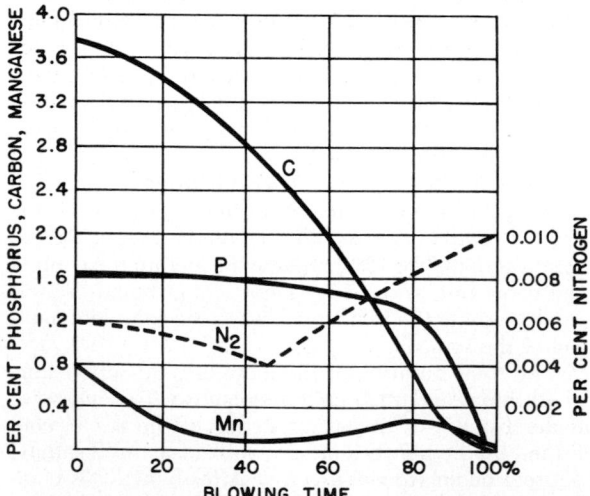

Fig. 15—8. Changes in chemical composition of the metal in the bath of a bottom-blown basic-lined pneumatic converter during a typical Thomas blow (after Carney).

Deoxidation Reactions—There are no major differences in the deoxidation reactions between the bottom-blown acid and basic pneumatic processes. A fair number of heats produced in the bottom-blown basic converter in Europe are fully killed. In the United States considerable tonnages of killed acid Bessemer steel are produced. Deoxidation with aluminum is practiced more generally abroad than in the United States. Much of the deoxidation with aluminum in Europe is accomplished by ladle additions compared with mold additions in this country.

Nitrogen Control—Since bottom-blown basic pneumatic steels have sulphur and phosphorus contents similar to or slightly higher than those of basic open-hearth steels, many attempts have been made to develop practices that would make it possible to reduce the nitrogen content of these steels to levels approaching that normally attained in basic open-hearth steels (0.003 to 0.005 per cent nitrogen). Some of the factors which influence the nitrogen content of the pneumatic steels were covered in Section 2 where the acid Bessemer process was discussed. The following items are some that have been found to be important in the commercial production of low-nitrogen bottom-blown pneumatic steels:

(a) The blow must be worked at a low temperature.

(b) A shallow metal bath is desirable to limit time of contact between gases and metal.

(c) High nitrogen content of the blowing gases, especially during the latter part of the blow, should be lowered when possible by use of oxygen-enriched air, mixtures of oxygen and steam (the OV or oxygen-vapor process), mixtures of oxygen and CO_2, or other means.

The most frequently used methods for producing low-nitrogen steels in the basic bottom-blown converter have been based upon shortening the after blow and also upon cooling the bath at this point. In one method, this is accomplished by adding ore or roll scale (up to 2.5 per cent) a little before the carbon flame drops to effect oxidation without the introduction of nitrogen while simultaneously cooling the bath. This method may contribute to difficulties arising from low finishing temperatures that cause ladle-skull formation and pouring difficulties due to cold steel.

A second method obviates some of the pouring difficulties while speeding up the process. Best suited to

50 to 60-ton converters, this method consists of double-blowing the metal. Half of the total iron and all of the lime is charged first and blown down to about 0.1 per cent of phosphorus. The shallow bath permits high-pressure blowing without excessive spitting. The balance of the charge is then added and blowing continued, again at high pressures made possible by the diluting effect of the first-blown metal. The total blowing time can be reduced from 16 to 17 minutes to 11 to 12 minutes by this method which is said to increase average size of charge, increase yield and still produce steel lower in phosphorus and nitrogen content than steels produced by ordinary blowing.

A third means for reducing the nitrogen content of Thomas steel involves a modification of the converter so that the blast is introduced through the side of the vessel at a point intermediate between the bottom of the vessel and the level of the bath. The aim of this modification is to reduce the length of travel of the blast through the bath and thus minimize the time for absorption of nitrogen without sacrificing the other characteristics of bottom blowing. It has been observed that nitrogen absorption in acid surface blowing practices is quite low. Consequently, it has been hypothesized that the degree of nitrogen absorption, other things being equal, would be related to the length of travel or time of contact of the air blast with the metal. Modification of the Thomas converter in this manner does not influence the remaining operations and the typical course of the refining remains the same as that shown in Figure 15—8, with the exception that lower nitrogen values are achieved.

Considerable quantities of low-nitrogen steel have been produced by the basic bottom-blown pneumatic process for wire, ship plates, deep-drawing steels, high-carbon high-tensile steels, and killed steels for various purposes. These products have properties quite similar to basic open-hearth steels of comparable grades.

Control of End Point—The discussion of the control of end point in Section 2 dealing with the acid Bessemer process applies equally well to the basic bottom-blown process. The spectroscope is used very little in Europe, the most common methods of control being visual observation of the flame by the blower, the use of fractured samples, and the use of the photocell.

SECTION 4

THE SURFACE-SIDE-BLOWN ACID PROCESS

The side-blown acid pneumatic converter is sometimes referred to as a surface-blown converter. One form was known as the Tropenas converter. The chemical reactions which occur in the side-blown acid converter are similar to those occurring in the bottom-blown acid converter; the major difference is the mechanism by which these reactions take place. There have been numerous variations of design of converters employing the side-blowing technique, but all are characterized by having all of the tuyeres above the

liquid level of the bath and entering through the side of the vessel.

In bottom-blown converters, the exposure of some of the tuyeres above the liquid level by tilting the converter while blowing increases the temperature inside the vessel, as discussed in Section 2. With all of its tuyeres above liquid level in normal operating position of the vessel, the side-blown acid converter can produce much hotter steel from a similar iron charge than can the bottom-blown acid converter.

Temperatures in excess of 3200° F (1760° C) can be attained if desired, blowing cupola-melted iron in lots as small as 1000 pounds. Its ability to process small heats at high temperatures and at frequent intervals that can keep up with pouring-floor schedules makes the side-blown acid converter useful to foundries making steel castings.

The quality of ore, coke and other raw materials required to produce iron for the side-blown acid process is similar to that required for the bottom-blown acid process; however, because additional heat is obtained from the oxidation of carbon to carbon dioxide inside the vessel, the silicon content of the iron can be somewhat lower.

The Converter and Its Auxiliaries—Since most side-blown vessels are used in foundries at present, hot-metal mixers are seldom available to provide a source of liquid iron for side-blown acid converters. Mixers, when used, are quite small. Generally, the cupola is employed to melt solid pigs of iron of the proper composition; the cupola can be tapped frequently to supply the side-blown converter with liquid iron as needed. Side blowing requires lower blast pressures than bottom blowing; blast pressures between 4 and 10 pounds per square inch are common.

The majority of side-blown acid converters are of one-half to two-ton capacity, although a few larger vessels have been built. Figure **15—9** is a sectional drawing of a typical side-blown acid converter. The refractories used for lining are similar to those used in bottom-blown converters.

Sequence of Operations—While the chemical reactions of the side-blown acid process proceed at a slightly different rate and in a different manner than those of the bottom-blown process, the physical steps in making heats by both processes are quite similar. The end point is observed from the drop of the flame. The length of the flame is shorter than that for the bottom-blown vessel. In the acid processes, the addi-

tion of controlled amounts of ferrosilicon to the vessel during blowing to make available more potential heat units is practiced much more frequently in side blowing than in bottom blowing.

Oxidation Reactions—While the chemical reactions which occur in the side-blown acid pneumatic process are similar to those in the other pneumatic processes, the mechanisms by which these reactions take place are somewhat different. The elimination of carbon, manganese and silicon in the side-blown acid process may be considered as taking place in three stages:

(1) The blast of air impinges on the surface of the bath of molten iron and immediately forms a slag of iron, silicon and manganese oxides.

(2) From the time when the metal is completely covered with slag, the oxidation of manganese and silicon is accelerated; the reactions are considered to be between the slag and the metal and not between air and metal as in the bottom-blown converter. During this period, there is a rapid rise in temperature of the bath because of the exothermic reactions involved. Ferrosilicon can be, and is, added before and during the blow, these additions being governed by vessel temperature, metal composition, and metal temperature. Larger additions of ferrosilicon are made when low-carbon metal (2 to 3 per cent carbon) is being blown. The higher silicon content of the bath provided by ferrosilicon additions functions as a kindling agent, and during the oxidation of silicon the temperature of the bath increases to about 2640° F; at this temperature the silicon content of the bath is about 0.6 to 0.7 per cent.

(3) After the silicon content has been lowered to the above figure, the oxidation of carbon increases to a very rapid rate and the temperature of the bath increases considerably. The oxidation of carbon in the metal by oxygen in the slag produces carbon monoxide, which may burn to carbon dioxide in the presence of excess air within the vessel. This represents an essential difference between the side-blown and bottom-blown processes, insofar as considerably more heat per unit of carbon in the bath is generated in side-blown practice.

Toward the end of the carbon-oxidation stage, when the bath is attaining its final temperature of 3000 to 3100° F, other reactions take place which result in the reduction of SiO_2 and MnO by carbon. It has been established that, under the above conditions of slag and metal, the silicon content of the final metal after the additions of deoxidizing agents and alloys is always greater than can be accounted for by the silicon content of the additions, thus indicating some reduction of silica in the slag to silicon which enters the metal.

Temperature Control—The methods of temperature control used in side blowing are quite similar to those already discussed for bottom blowing. Ferrosilicon is frequently added to the cupola iron during blowing to raise the temperature. Accurate temperature control is vital to the production of quality steel, but apparently is not so critical in regard to the final nitrogen content of the steel as it is with bottom blowing. Little trouble with excess nitrogen absorption in

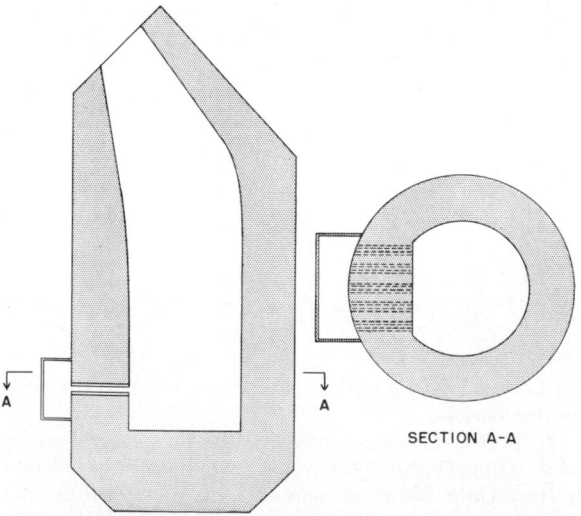

SECTION A-A

Fig. **15—9**. Sectional drawing of a typical side-blown acid converter. While the cross-section of the interior of the type shown is D shaped, many side-blown acid converters are circular in interior cross-section.

the side-blowing process has been reported, even with steel temperatures up to 3100° F.

Deoxidation Reactions—Deoxidation reactions of side-blown acid pneumatic steels are similar to those in finishing bottom-blown acid heats. However, since the majority of the side-blown steel is used for castings, these steels are fully killed, using as much as four pounds of aluminum per ton of steel.

Nitrogen Control—A major part of the side-blown acid steels are produced with a relatively low nitrogen content (0.003 to 0.008 per cent). Because of the short time of contact of gases and metal, nitrogen control is not as difficult in side blowing as it is in bottom blowing. The use of low finishing temperatures or ore additions is not practiced to any great extent. However, some work has been done on the use of oxygen and oxygen-enriched air for blowing to reduce the nitrogen content to even lower levels (0.002 to 0.003 per cent). These latter practices are not common at present.

Control of the End Point—End-point control in the side-blown acid pneumatic process is very similar to the control exercised in the bottom-blown processes, even though the size of the flame is quite different. The end point is usually determined visually by the drop of the flame.

Oxygen and Oxygen-Enriched Air for Blast—Experiments using oxygen-enriched air and 98 to 100 per cent oxygen for blowing in the side-blown acid process have shown that blowing time was shortened and the final bath temperature was increased. Blowing losses increased after the proportion of oxygen in the blast exceeded 30 to 35 per cent.

SECTION 5
THE OXYGEN-BLOWN STEELMAKING PROCESSES

Variations of the pneumatic steelmaking processes that employ oxygen of high purity (99.5 per cent oxygen) or of commercial purity (95 per cent oxygen), blown onto or into the bath in a suitable vessel or furnace appear destined to become of increasing importance.

The advantages of oxygen over air as the blowing agent in pneumatic steelmaking operations already have been discussed. Although the superiority of oxygen was recognized by Bessemer and others early in the development of pneumatic practices, air has, until recently, afforded the most economical blowing agent. Improvements in commercial methods and apparatus for the production of oxygen, however, have made pure oxygen available in quantity and at low cost. This, together with other changes affecting the economy of steelmaking operations has made the substitution of oxygen for air a practical matter and several **basic oxygen steelmaking** practices are now in commercial use.

At the present time, no commercial production of steel by oxygen blowing in an acid vessel is being conducted, although the principle has been employed for desiliconizing pig iron to be used in the basic open-hearth process.

The extensive use of oxygen in the basic open-hearth process here and abroad is an entirely separate subject that will be referred to in Chapter 16.

THE BASIC OXYGEN PROCESS

In the basic oxygen process, substantially pure oxygen is introduced from above the surface of the bath in a basic-lined vessel. Several arrangements of equipment have been devised to accomplish this; at present the most common comprises a vertical pipe or lance inserted through the mouth of a Bessemer-like vessel.

Blowing with oxygen was investigated by R. Durrer and C. V. Schwarz in Germany and by Durrer and H. Hellbrügge in Switzerland. Bottom-blown vessels proved unsuitable because the high temperature attained caused rapid deterioration of the refractory tuyere bottom; blowing pressurized oxygen downwardly against the top surface of the molten metal bath, however, was found to convert the charge to steel with a high degree of thermal and chemical efficiency.

Plants utilizing top blowing with oxygen have been in operation since 1952-53 at Linz and Donawitz in Austria. These operations, sometimes referred to as the Linz-Donawitz or L-D process, were designed to employ pig iron produced from local ores that are high in manganese and low in phosphorus; such iron is not suitable for either the acid or basic bottom blown pneumatic processes. The basic oxygen process, however, is readily adapted to the processing of blast-furnace metal of medium- and high-phosphorus contents and is particularly attractive where it is desirable to employ a steelmaking process requiring large percentages of hot metal as the principal source of metallics.

Presently, there are 35 basic oxygen steelmaking plants in operation throughout the world; six of them in the United States and two in Canada. A total of 17 furnaces was installed in the six plants in the United States with an estimated ability to produce 7,500,000 net tons of steel annually. The five furnaces in the two Canadian plants were capable of producing 1,600,000 net tons annually. The output per furnace per heat ranged from 60 to 200 net tons.

Equipment Design—The most common arrangement for oxygen steelmaking used in America today is a cylindrical basic-lined furnace which may be either eccentric or concentric in design (Figure 15—10). The furnace, which is rotatable about a fixed horizontal axis, is held upright while the oxygen is injected. A permanent lining next to the furnace shell plates consists of a single course of burned magnesite brick. Next may come a layer of basic ramming mix, which is removed each time the furnace is relined. The inner, or working, lining is of unfired tar-bonded dolomite, dolomite-magnesite, or magnesite bricks. A taphole usually is provided to facilitate separation of slag and metal during pouring.

The dished solid bottom of the furnace, which may be either integral or detachable, is built up much like a basic open-hearth furnace bottom. A single course of clay brick may be used against the shell, then single or multiple courses of magnesite brick, and, finally, a course of tar-bonded dolomite-magnesite brick to form the working surface.

The oxygen-jet equipment consists of a tubular, water-cooled, copper-tipped retractable lance kept in a vertical position above the center of the bath. At the top of the lance, armored rubber hoses are connected to a pressure-regulated oxygen source and to a supply of recirculated cooling water.

Method of Operation—After the furnace is charged with controlled amounts of scrap and molten iron, it is rotated to an upright position and the oxygen lance is lowered to a predetermined position above the surface of the bath. Pure oxygen gas issues from the jet nozzle at high velocity under a pressure that is normally held between 140 and 180 lb. per sq. in. The action of the oxygen jet is partly chemical and partly physical. Striking the surface of the liquid bath, the oxygen immediately starts reactions leading to the formation of iron oxide, part of which disperses rapidly throughout the bath. Carbon monoxide is evolved, which gives rise to a vigorous boiling action and accelerates the refining metallurgical reactions.

Slag-forming fluxes—chiefly burned lime, fluorspar, and mill scale—are added in controlled amounts from an overhead storage system immediately after the oxygen jet begins. These materials, which serve to produce a slag of the desired basicity and fluidity, are added through an inclined chute built into the side of a water-cooled smoke hood that covers the furnace. No flame is visible outside the mill buildings, although a dense cloud of reddish-brown fumes is emitted from the furnace. An efficient system for collecting and cleaning the dust-laden effluent gas is therefore essential.

A major advantage of the basic oxygen process is its flexibility in handling raw materials of many types and compositions. The scrap used can be either heavy or light, and the oxide charge, if used, may be dry ore, sinter, pellets, or mill scale. The process can be operated on any kind of hot metal that can be used in the basic open-hearth furnace. Oxygen steelmaking plants around the world operate on blast-furnace metal that contains from 0.2 to 2.0 per cent of silicon, from 0.4

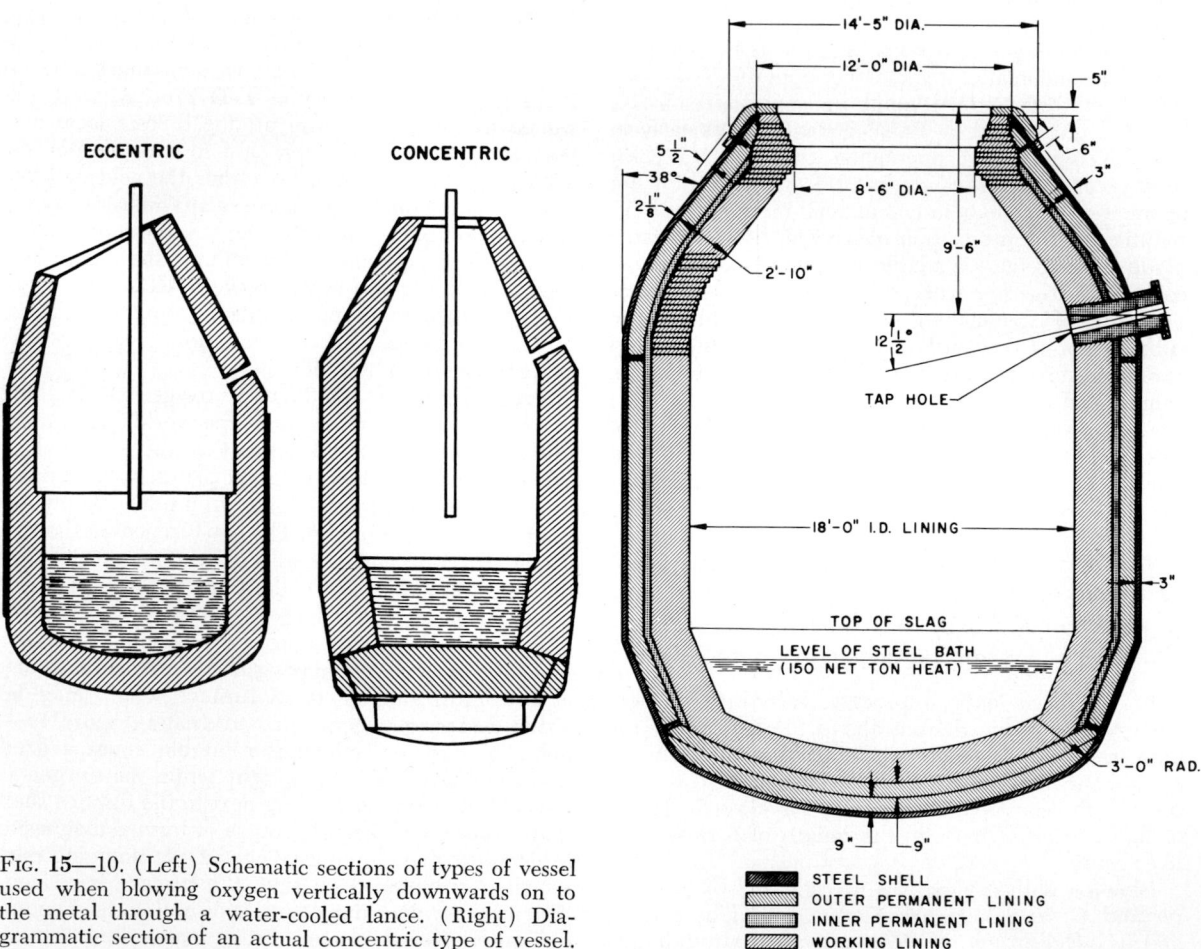

FIG. 15—10. (Left) Schematic sections of types of vessel used when blowing oxygen vertically downwards on to the metal through a water-cooled lance. (Right) Diagrammatic section of an actual concentric type of vessel.

to 2.5 per cent of manganese, and up to 0.3 or 0.4 per cent of phosphorus with a single slag. With double slagging, it is possible to adapt the basic oxygen process to accommodate blast-furnace iron containing up to 2 per cent of phosphorus. One such technique injects powdered lime through the lance with the oxygen-gas stream, as described later under "Variations of the Basic Oxygen Process."

Chemistry of the Process—The basic oxygen process is characterized by: (1) use of gaseous oxygen as the sole refining agent, thereby assuring that the refining reactions generate the maximum possible amount of heat; (2) a metallic charge composed largely of blast-furnace iron in a molten condition, thus greatly reducing the thermal requirements of the process; and (3) chemical reactions that proceed quite rapidly in a bath of comparatively low surface-to-volume ratio, thus minimizing external heat losses. This combination results in an extremely versatile autogenous process that requires no external fuel yet provides a capability for melting an appreciable quantity of scrap (12 to 30 per cent). The use of pure oxygen for refining, however, in no way alters the fundamental chemical reactions and equilibria involved in steelmaking. The reactions of greatest importance are those pertaining to the elements carbon, silicon, manganese, phosphorus, sulphur, nitrogen, and oxygen. Changes in bath content of the five first-named elements during the blowing of a basic oxygen heat are shown schematically in Figure 15—11.

Carbon—The mechanics of carbon elimination are identical in both the basic oxygen and the open-hearth processes and involve oxidation of carbon for removal as carbon monoxide and carbon dioxide. The chemical reactions and end results are the same in both cases.

Silicon—The general reaction in basic open-hearth practice, whereby silicon is oxidized to silica and transferred to the slag, applies also to the basic oxygen process. Silicon oxidation is important mainly due to its thermal effects. Only a trace of silicon remains in the steel at the end of the refining period.

Manganese—Residual manganese content of the metal before ladle additions generally is higher than in open-hearth practice. Under certain circumstances, the level of residual manganese is sufficient to elim-

inate the necessity of adding ferromanganese in the ladle. Residual manganese is closely related to the manganese level of the molten iron used in the charge.

Phosphorus—A high degree of slag fluidity and excellent slag-metal contact provide efficient removal of phosphorus in the slag.

Sulphur—Efficiency of sulphur elimination is as good as or better than in the open-hearth. Factors in favor of better sulphur removal in oxygen steelmaking are: more vigorous bath action, higher operating temperatures, and elimination of the fuel as one source of sulphur. Published data show an approximate average residual-sulphur content of 0.020 per cent.

Nitrogen—Because the basic oxygen process uses a refining agent containing practically no nitrogen, the steel produced is distinguished by its exceptionally low nitrogen content—generally lower than 0.004 per cent.

Oxygen—Residual oxygen levels in basic oxygen steels are slightly lower than those obtained in normal open-hearth practice, in which oxygen content will range from approximately 0.04 per cent at 0.10 per cent of carbon to about 0.09 per cent at 0.04 per cent of carbon. Evidence of low oxygen content is the somewhat lower aluminum addition required for deoxidation of basic oxygen heats.

Residual alloy elements such as copper, nickel or tin are usually considered undesirable in low-carbon steels because they adversely affect ductility. The main source of these unwanted elements is purchased scrap. The generally low production of scrap used in the basic oxygen process therefore results in a low residual alloy content. Moreover, in the basic oxygen process, iron ore may be substituted for part or all of the scrap if desired.

Temperature Control—A major problem in the top-blown basic process is one of decreasing rather than increasing the temperature. This is associated with the use of oxygen rather than air for blowing. The principal method used for temperature control is regulation of the quantity of scrap additions. Steam has not been used to any extent for cooling of the bath.

End-Point Control—The end point is observed visually by the drop of the flame at the mouth of the vessel at the end of the carbon blow.

Product Characteristics—In a wide variety of applications—including welded and seamless tubular products, wire products, tin plate, hot- and cold-rolled sheets, plates, structurals, and bar products—basic oxygen steel has shown itself to be at least equivalent to basic open-hearth steel of similar carbon content. This is especially true in applications where desired quality characteristics are directly related to chemical composition—particularly minimum sulphur, nitrogen, or residual alloy content.

VARIATIONS OF THE BASIC OXYGEN PROCESS

As stated earlier, basic oxygen steelmaking plants around the world operate on blast-furnace metal which ranges from 0.2 to 2.0 per cent of silicon, from 0.4 to 2.5 per cent of manganese, and up to 0.3 or 0.4 per cent of phosphorus with a single slag; with the use of double or multiple slags, it has been possible to utilize blast-furnace metal containing up to 2.0 per

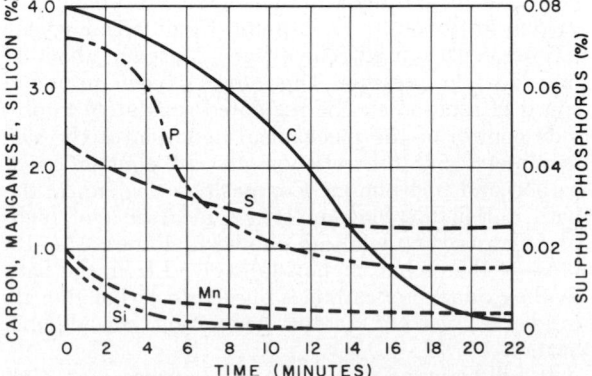

FIG. 15—11. Schematic representation of progress of refining in a top-blown basic-lined vessel.

cent of phosphorus. Multiple-slag techniques make use of powdered lime that is injected through the lance with the oxygen-gas stream. This principle is employed in the basic oxygen steelmaking operations in Luxembourg, Belgium and France when refining the high-phosphorus (Thomas) irons commonly encountered in these countries.

The first slag in double-slag processes is decanted by tilting the vessel backward. Rich in phosphorus, this slag can be finely crushed and used as agricultural fertilizer. When employing a multiple-slag technique, a taphole is provided to allow the finished steel to be poured from the vessel while retaining the second slag for use in the next heat.

Another method for refining high-phosphorus blast-furnace metal is called the **buffer-slag process.** This is also a double-slag process but, instead of having powdered lime injected into the system through the lance, employs a mode of operation in which the oxygen jet and oxygen pressure are controlled to merely flood the space above the slag with oxygen instead of penetrating the slag: the slag forms a buffer between the oxygen and the metal and all reactions are necessarily slag-metal ones. Lump lime is employed for slagmaking in this process.

At Phoenix Rheinrohr in Duisburg, high-phosphorus iron is bottom-blown in a Thomas-type converter until the carbon content reaches 0.1 to 0.4 per cent. The vessel is then turned on its side for top blowing with oxygen to eliminate phosphorus with little further oxidation of carbon, following which the vessel is righted and the process completed by a short bottom blow to give a low-carbon, low-nitrogen product.

Numerous other variations of the basic oxygen steelmaking process have been described in the literature but, with the exception of the Stora-Kaldo and the Rotor processes, none are of sufficient commercial importance, at the present time, to warrant discussion.

THE STORA-KALDO PROCESS

The **Stora-Kaldo process,** which will be referred to hereafter as the Kaldo process for brevity, was developed at Stora Kopparbergs Bergslags A/B in Domnarvet, Sweden. In this process, oxygen is introduced at an angle with respect to the surface of the bath contained in a tilted, rotating vessel. The method is sometimes referred to as the Kaldo rotary oxygen steelmaking process. The first plant in the United States to employ the Kaldo process began operating in 1962, with two Kaldo vessels of 150 tons heat size each. In addition to the Swedish installation, Kaldo steelmaking facilities were in operation in England and France at the time this chapter was written.

The vessel employed in the Kaldo process is similar in shape to the familiar Bessemer converter, but has a solid bottom that, in the larger vessels, is removable. In addition to being capable of being tilted backwards and forwards on trunnions for charging and discharging, the Kaldo furnace can be rotated rapidly about its longitudinal axis. The working lining is of tar-dolomite brick: the underlying permanent lining is of magnesite brick.

In contrast to bottom-blown Bessemer vessels and top-blown oxygen vessels, the Kaldo furnace is tilted at about 15 to 20 degrees from the horizontal while operating and, in this position, can be rotated about its longitudinal axis at speeds up to 30 rev. per. min. A single opening in the Kaldo vessel serves for charging of liquid metal and other elements of the charge, for making additions, for slag removal, for introducing the oxygen required for refining, for discharging the refined metal, and as an outlet for the exhaust of waste gases.

Sequence of Operations—The sequence of operations in the Kaldo process are as follows: (1) the vessel is tilted backward (Figure **15**—12) until the mouth of the vessel is beneath the charging chute and the necessary additions of lime and iron ore are made; (2) the vessel is turned down to approximately its operating position and hot metal is poured into it; (3) the water-cooled waste-gas hood and oxygen lance are swung into position with the lance extending into the vessel; and (4) oxygen blowing and rotation of the vessel are begun and continued until the refining is carried to the desired end-point. Commercial oxygen (95 per cent) is used. The oxygen is used at about 45 lb. per sq. in. pressure. The rate of oxygen input and speed of rotation can be regulated separately to provide control of the mechanical agitation of the slag and metal and the relative rates of elimination of carbon and phosphorus. Composition changes in the bath during the blowing of a typical heat of high-phosphorus hot metal are shown in Figure **15**—13. Most of the carbon monoxide evolved from the bath by the oxidation of carbon is burned to carbon dioxide inside the vessel, thereby generating considerable heat.

It will be noted that in the Kaldo process, as in all top-blown pneumatic processes, phosphorus is eliminated simultaneously with carbon, whereas phos-

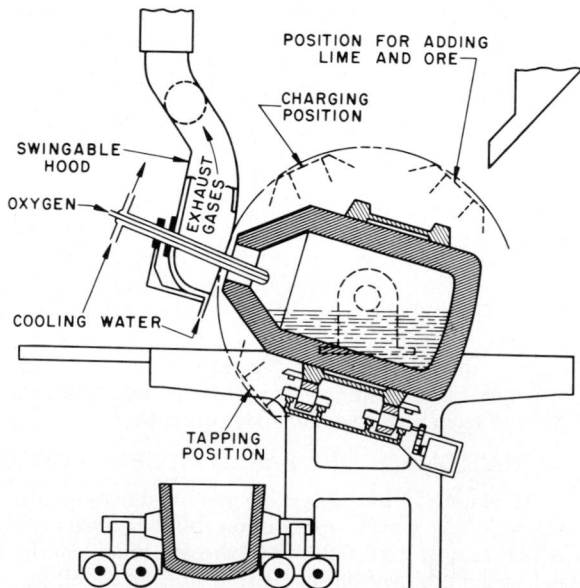

FIG. **15**—12. Kaldo vessel in the blowing position. (After Hacking)

POSITION FOR ADDING
LIME AND ORE

CHARGING
POSITION

SWINGABLE
HOOD

OXYGEN

EXHAUST
GASES

COOLING WATER

TAPPING
POSITION

phorus elimination in the basic Bessemer process does not occur until practically all of the carbon has been eliminated (Figure **15**—8). When blowing hot metal of medium- or high-phosphorus type, multiple slags are employed to effect the desired degree of removal of phosphorus.

Iron ore or scrap can be used as a coolant; over 30 per cent scrap can be regularly consumed in the Kaldo process; scrap consumption as high as 40 per cent has been reported as feasible when refining medium-phosphorus hot metal typified by the "basic iron" used in the United States in the basic open-hearth process.

THE ROTOR PROCESS

Another basic oxygen-steelmaking process, called the **Rotor process,** was developed in Oberhausen, Germany. The Rotor furnace, sometimes referred to as the Oberhausen rotary furnace, employs the same rotary principle as the Kaldo furnace, except that the speed of the rotation is much slower, being only about ½ to 2 rev. per min. Also, the Rotor furnace (Figure **15**—14) has the appearance of a rotary kiln rather than the Bessemer-converter-like shape of the Kaldo furnace. The furnace can be used for the direct production of steel, or to pre-refine high-phosphorus hot metal for use in other steelmaking processes. Rotor units are in operation in Germany, South Africa, and Great Britain.

A 66-ton-capacity Rotor furnace is 12 ft. in outside diameter, 9 ft. in inside diameter, and 48 feet in length. It is mounted in a "cradle" so that it can be tipped (about 3 ft.) toward either end. The cradle also carries the supporting rollers and drive mechanism that permit the furnace to rotate about its longitudinal axis.

The Rotor furnace is charged and tapped at opposite ends. The taphole is located in the periphery of

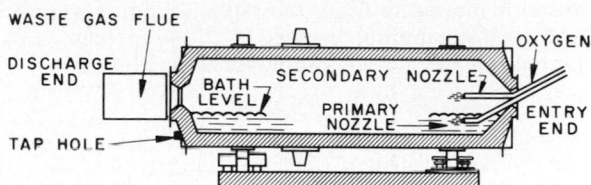

FIG. **15**—14. Schematic diagram of the Rotor vessel. (After Hacking)

the discharge end. The working lining is built of tardolomite brick, backed with magnesite brick.

A distinct feature of the Rotor process is the use of two oxygen lances, one of which injects high-purity oxygen into the metal bath in which it is immersed, while the other lance blows low-purity (as low as 45 per cent) oxygen into the space above the bath to burn carbon monoxide evolved by the bath reactions to carbon dioxide. The lances are installed on a movable cart to facilitate their handling.

Sequence of Operations—The furnace is tipped toward the entry end to receive the molten charge of hot metal and the solid iron ore, burned lime, or other charge materials. The vessel is then returned to the horizontal position and the lances are inserted through the opening at the entry end. One lance is positioned to inject high-purity oxygen directly into the molten bath, while the other discharges oxygen of lower purity into the open space in the vessel above the bath. The process can use up to 15 per cent of the total charged materials as iron ore for cooling purposes; this is equivalent to around 40 per cent of scrap utilization for cooling.

Figure **15**—15 shows the changes in composition of the bath during a typical heat. It will be seen that phosphorus removal is effected prior to complete removal of carbon. When high-phosphorus hot metal is employed, a double-slag technique is necessary. Upon completion of refining, the furnace is tilted toward the discharge end, the taphole is opened, and the

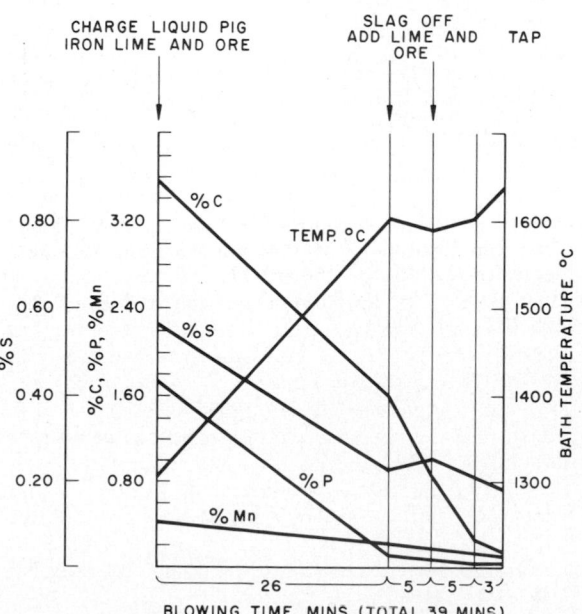

FIG. **15**—13. Typical composition changes during a Kaldo heat. (After Hacking)

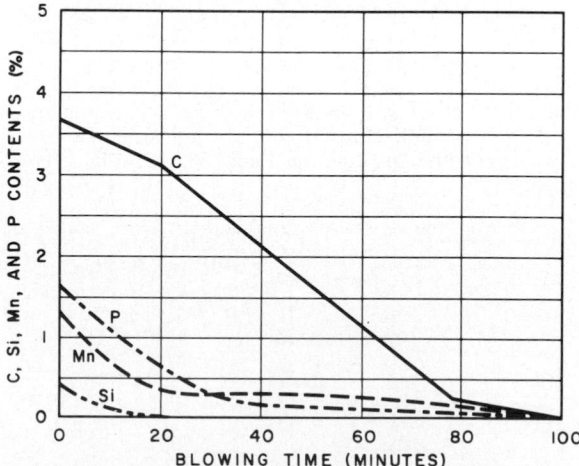

FIG. **15**—15. Course of changes in composition of the molten bath during the refining operation on high-phosphorus hot metal in a Rotor furnace. (After Graef)

vessel is rotated to bring the taphole into the proper position for tapping the heat. Tap-to-tap time on a 66-ton capacity vessel is approximately 2 hours.

Bibliography

American Iron and Steel Institute, The basic oxygen process. (Contributions to the metallurgy of steel) N. Y., The Institute, 1960.

Bading, W., Stand und entwicklung der windfrischver-fahren. Stahl und Eisen 71, 373-386; discussion, 386-388 (1951)

Burgess, G. K., Temperature measurements in Bessemer and open-hearth practice. American Institute of Mining and Metallurgical Engineers, Trans. 56, 432-447 (1917)

Carnegie, D., Liquid steel; its manufacture and cost. London, Longmans, Green, 1913.

Carney, D. J., Pneumatic steelmaking processes. Blast Furnace and Steel Plant 43, 635-640 (June); 753-760 (July); 1006-1010 (Sept.); 1139-1141 (Oct. 1955)

Coheur, P., On the pneumatic processes of converting high-phosphorus iron. Iron and Coal Trades Review 181, 1049-1054 (Nov. 11, 1960)

Cope, S. G., The Bessemer's progress. Murex Review 2, no. 21 (1960)

Creswell, S. J., Increasing importance of the Bessemer process. American Iron and Steel Institute Yearbook, 162-182 (1943)

Fetters, K. L. (and others), Effect of raw materials on steelmaking. American Iron and Steel Institute, Technical Committee Activities 47-56 (1948)

Graef, Rudolf., Principles and results of making steel in a rotary kiln. Stahl und Eisen 77, 3-10 (1957)

Graef, R., and L. von Bogdandy, The Rotor steelmaking process. Iron and Coal Trades Review 177, 1151-1155 (Nov. 14, 1958)

Graham, H. W., Acid Bessemer process of 1940. American Institute of Mining and Metallurgical Engineers, Trans. 145, 113-131 (1945)

Graham, H. W., Production of Bessemer steel. Steel 124, 102-114 (April 25, 1949)

Hacking, R. A., The practical chemistry of oxygen steel-making processes. Iron and Coal Trades Review, 181, 1107-1114 (Nov. 18, 1960)

Hall, J. H., Converter process in steel foundries. Foundry 74, 82-83, 221-224 (March 1946); 107, 160, 162, 164 (April 1946); 174, 316-319 (May 1946)

Harrison, J. L., W. C. Newell, and A. Hartley, Application of oxygen enrichment to side-blown-converter practice. Iron and Steel Institute Journal 159, 281-290 (1948)

Iron and Steel Institute, Report on the Bessemer process. (Special report No. 42) London, The Institute, 1949.

Johansson, Folke, and Bo Kalling, Fuel and energy required for manufacture of steel by the Kaldo process. Journal of the Institute of Fuel, 34, 172-176 (May, 1961)

Kalling, B., F. Johansson, and L. Lindskog, Use of oxygen/carbon dioxide instead of air in the final stage of the basic Bessemer process. Iron and Steel Institute Journal 168, 337-343 (1951)

Kalling, Bo, and Folke Johansson, The Kaldo steelmaking process. Iron and Coal Trades Review 177, 1277-1285 (Nov. 28, 1958)

King, C. D., Seventy-five years of progress in iron and steel, p. 108. N. Y., American Institute of Mining and Metallurgical Engineers, 1948.

Kurzinski, E. F., Oxygen and steelmaking processes—A comparison of open-hearth, LD, Kaldo and Rotor processes. Iron and Steel Engineer 37, no. 2, 65-75 (Feb. 1960)

McDonough, W. G., Oxygen as a means of increasing Bessemer production. American Iron and Steel Institute Yearbook, 164-184 (1951)

McGinley, E. E. and L. D. Woodworth, A study of modern Bessemer steels. American Institute of Mining and Metallurgical Engineers, Trans. 145, 151-159 (1941)

Merk, R. N., and D. R. Berg, Sharon Steel's Kaldo furnace first in U.S. Journal of Metals 13 no. 9, 635-637 (Sept. 1961)

Metz, P., New researches on the conversion of iron using pure oxygen—Development of the OCP process. Iron and Coal Trades Review 177, 931-936 (Oct. 17, 1958)

Naeser, G., Oxide film theory as a basis for the production of high quality basic Bessemer steel. Stahl und Eisen 68, 375-378 (1948)

Pearson, J., The theoretical basis of oxygen steelmaking. Iron and Coal Trades Review 181, 1407-1413 (Dec. 30, 1960)

Price, E. G., Acid Bessemer process in the manufacture of pipe. American Iron and Steel Institute, Technical Committee Activities, 111-125 (1948)

Rogers, W. T. and L. T. Sanchez, Use of oxygen in the Bessemer converter. American Institute of Mining and Metallurgical Engineers, Trans. 194, 933-938 (1952)

Sebardt, Carl, On Sweden's second Kaldo plant. Journal of Metals 13, no. 9, 638-640 (Sept. 1961)

Strassburger, J. H., Tonnage oxygen for increased iron and steel production. American Iron and Steel Institute Yearbook, 214-249; discussion, 250-259 (1948)

Trentini, B., and M. Allard, Refining pig iron with oxygen and lime powder—IRSID's oxygene-lance-poudre (OLP) process. Iron and Coal Trades Review, 177, 871-874 (Oct. 10, 1958)

Wilder, A. B., The Bessemer converter process. Journal of Metals (Technical Section) 1, 22-27 (Nov. 1949); 20-28 (Dec. 1949)

Work, H. K., Photocell control for Bessemer steelmaking. American Institute of Mining and Metallurgical Engineers, Trans. 145, 132-150 (1941)

Young, P. A., The Kaldo process. Iron and Steel, 34, 455-462 (Oct. 1961)

CHAPTER 16

Open Hearth and Duplex Processes

SECTION 1

INTRODUCTION

In 1962, approximately 84.0 per cent of the steel produced in the United States was made by the basic open-hearth process, 0.4 per cent by the acid open-hearth process, 0.8 per cent by the acid Bessemer process, 9.2 per cent by electric-furnace processes (acid and basic combined), and 5.6 per cent by the basic oxygen steelmaking process.

On a tonnage basis, steel production during 1962 in the United States was divided between the various processes as shown in Table 16—I.

The preponderance in favor of the basic open-hearth process for the production of steel for ingots has been based on the ability of this process to remove phosphorus and some sulphur, as well as carbon, silicon and manganese; while the acid open-hearth process is limited to removal of carbon, silicon, and manganese and must use carefully selected raw materials that contain less than specified amounts of phosphorus and sulphur.

Table **15**—I in Chapter 15 on "The Pneumatic Steelmaking Processes" shows the production of steel ingots by the various processes over an extended period.

Table 16—I. Steel Production in the United States by Various Processes (1962).

Process	Production (Net Tons)
Basic open hearth	82,578,234
Acid open hearth	379,084
Total open-hearth steel production	82,957,318
Basic oxygen steelmaking	5,552,697
Electric furnace	9,012,806
Acid Bessemer	804,964
Grand total	98,327,785

SECTION 2

BASIC OPEN-HEARTH PLANT LAYOUT

Because of their greater extent and complexity as compared with acid open-hearth steelmaking plants and plants employing duplex processes, only the arrangement of large, modern basic open-hearth plants employing stationary furnaces of over 200 tons individual capacity and engaged in the production of steel ingots from hot-metal and scrap charges will be considered in this section. Duplex processes and the tilting basic open-hearth furnaces usually employed therein will be described in the final sections of this chapter (Sections 11 and 12).

LAYOUT OF THE MAIN FURNACE BUILDING

Open-hearth furnaces are housed in large steel buildings, generally over 300 feet long, designed and arranged to facilitate the charging of the furnaces, the making of the heats, and handling of the finished molten steel.

The furnaces are arranged lengthwise approximately between the columns and along the centerline of the building, with the same distance between the ends of adjacent furnaces (Figure 16—1). Space may be left at either end of the line of furnaces for storage or other purposes. It is preferred by most designers that not over 12 furnaces be placed in one row. Between each pair of furnaces is a vertical, composite steel column which performs two functions (Figure 16—2). The tall central section of each column rises to a height sufficient to support the main roof truss above it. On opposite sides of this section are two shorter, heavy steel sections that each support one of the tracks of the two electric overhead traveling crane runways that extend the length of the building. The other track of each of the two runways is supported by columns at the two sides of the building. The distance between these columns may be from 75 to 117 feet, depending upon the length of the furnaces. The longitudinal centerline of the furnaces is parallel to the line of the columns between them, but several feet in front, so that the bridge of the charging-floor crane extends over most of the top of each furnace when positioned over it. This permits the crane hoist to be operated directly over the furnace when occasion demands.

Fig. **16**—1. General view of the charging side of a group of modern furnaces, showing charging machine in left background.

That part of the floor area in front of the row of furnaces is called the **charging floor** and, in modern shops, it is elevated about 22 feet above the general yard level of the plant as shown in Figure **16**—3. The part of the furnace building above the charging floor is 75 to 85 feet wide. Shops with this arrangement are designated as **two-level shops,** to distinguish them from plants of older design in which the charging floor was at general yard level.

The remainder of the floor space of the building, located on the tapping side of the furnace, is called the **pouring floor** or pit side, and is at general yard level.

CHARGING SIDE

On the charging side of the furnaces and close to them is laid a broad-gage track on which operate the locomotives (usually Diesel in modern plants) that move the buggies which carry the **charging boxes** loaded with the scrap and other solid materials to be charged into the furnaces. Parallel to this track on the charging floor is a special track of very wide gage on which operate the **charging machines,** illustrated in Figure **16**—4. These electrically operated machines are equipped to pick up the charging boxes (which have a capacity up to 50 cubic feet) one at a time, from the buggies in position before the doors of a furnace, thrust the boxes through an open door into the furnace and turn them to dump their contents on the hearth; following this, the boxes are withdrawn from the furnace and replaced on the buggies (Figures **16**—5 and **16**—6). The empty boxes then are hauled away and refilled in preparation for the next charge.

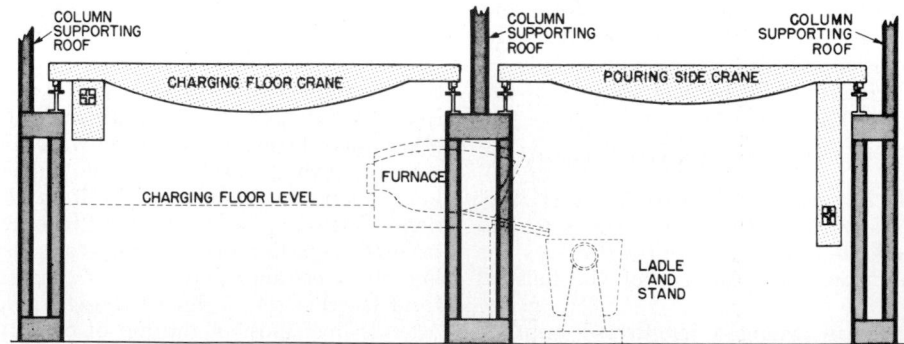

Fig. **16**—2. Arrangement of the columns supporting the roof trusses and crane runways of a modern open-hearth furnace building.

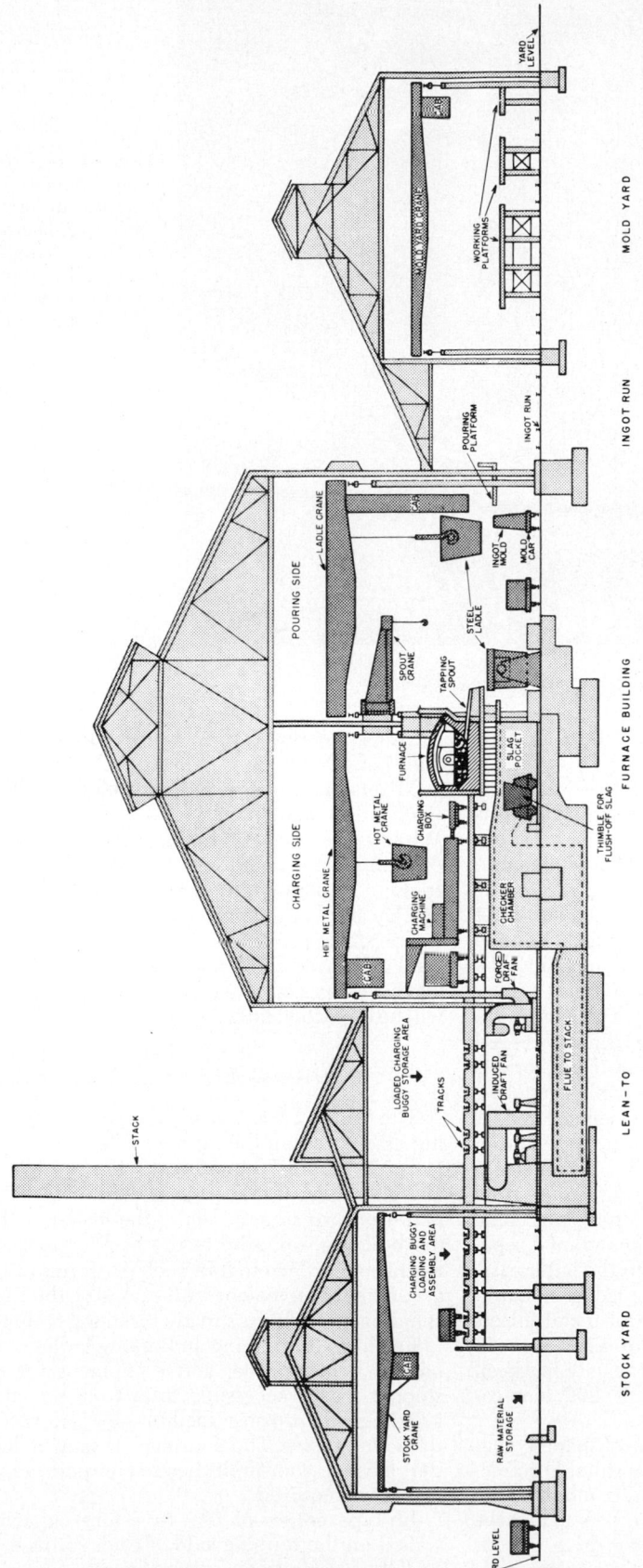

FIG. 16—3. Diagrammatic cross-section of a modern open-hearth plant, showing the relative locations and sizes of the various buildings, and the disposition of the chief operating units required for charging and operation of the furnace and disposition of the finished steel.

FIG. 16—4. Typical charging machine in position before an open door of an open-hearth furnace, with a charging box engaged by the peel and ready to be moved into the furnace and dumped.

Two to four charging machines of 10 to 15 tons capacity may be provided.

Electric overhead traveling cranes operating on the crane runway over the charging floor are known as **charging floor cranes.** They have a main hoist designed with capacity for handling ladles of molten iron from the mixer to be charged by pouring into the open-hearth furnaces, and also have an auxiliary hoist for miscellaneous work on the charging side. The main hoist capacity ranges from 100 to 150 tons and the auxiliary hoist capacity may approach 40 tons.

A mixer serves the dual purpose of (1) having a supply of molten pig iron available whenever needed for charging, and (2) mixing successive "casts" or lots of iron from blast furnaces, so that possible irregularities in the iron are smoothed out or compensated. A hot-metal building or **mixer building** usually is located at one end of the charging floor. This arrangement permits the transfer of molten pig iron (in ladles) from the metal mixer by electric overhead traveling crane or, better, by an electric ladle car running on a separate track laid on the charging floor. In the latter case, the cranes are employed to dump the ladles in charging the molten iron into a furnace. Hot metal mixers have been built with capacities up to 1500 tons. In plants of recent design, the holding capacity has been divided between two mixers, each of 800 tons capacity.

Hot-metal mixers generally are barrel-shaped, constructed of steel plate and lined with suitable refractories. The steel shell of the mixer is mounted on rocker-shaped castings which rest on rollers so that the mixer can be tilted by an electric-motor drive to pour off the desired amount of metal into a transfer ladle for transport to the open hearth furnaces (see Figure 16—7).

Mixers have been lined with natural siliceous rock (high silica content) or dense fireclay refractories. While these types of linings still predominate, more difficult service conditions have led in recent years to trials of superior refractories such as the super-duty fireclay and high-alumina types.

The **stockyard** where scrap and other solid materials are loaded and the **lean-to aisle** where loaded charging boxes on cars are stored while awaiting charging will be described later.

POURING FLOOR OR PIT SIDE

The pouring floor, or pit side, of the furnace building extends along the tapping side of the furnaces. It is usually about 70 to 80 feet wide and as long as the charging floor, but at general yard level. The **pouring platforms** are situated along the inside of the wall of the building, opposite to the back or tapping side of the furnaces. Two to four such platforms are installed, at a height convenient to the tops of the ingot molds standing on mold cars ready for filling (Figure 16—8).

Facilities for relining and drying ladles are installed on the pouring side, and equipment for preparing stopper rods is accessible to or from this area, as are grinding and mixing facilities for preparing plastic refractory mixes. The pouring side may be longer than the charging floor if pits needed for pouring very large ingots are required.

Jib-type cranes of 5½ to 7 tons capacity are installed on the tapping side of each furnace to handle such items as furnace tapping spouts.

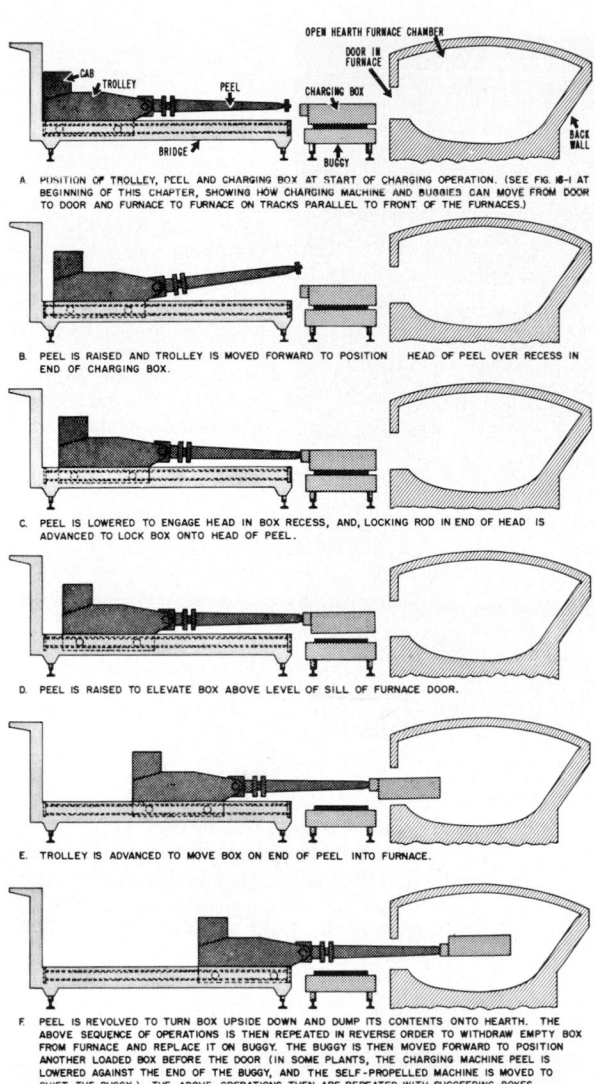

A. POSITION OF TROLLEY, PEEL AND CHARGING BOX AT START OF CHARGING OPERATION. (SEE FIG. 16—1 AT BEGINNING OF THIS CHAPTER, SHOWING HOW CHARGING MACHINE AND BUGGIES CAN MOVE FROM DOOR TO DOOR AND FURNACE TO FURNACE ON TRACKS PARALLEL TO FRONT OF THE FURNACES.)

B. PEEL IS RAISED AND TROLLEY IS MOVED FORWARD TO POSITION HEAD OF PEEL OVER RECESS IN END OF CHARGING BOX.

C. PEEL IS LOWERED TO ENGAGE HEAD IN BOX RECESS, AND, LOCKING ROD IN END OF HEAD IS ADVANCED TO LOCK BOX ONTO HEAD OF PEEL.

D. PEEL IS RAISED TO ELEVATE BOX ABOVE LEVEL OF SILL OF FURNACE DOOR.

E. TROLLEY IS ADVANCED TO MOVE BOX ON END OF PEEL INTO FURNACE.

F. PEEL IS REVOLVED TO TURN BOX UPSIDE DOWN AND DUMP ITS CONTENTS ONTO HEARTH. THE ABOVE SEQUENCE OF OPERATIONS IS THEN REPEATED IN REVERSE ORDER TO WITHDRAW EMPTY BOX FROM FURNACE AND REPLACE IT ON BUGGY. THE BUGGY IS THEN MOVED FORWARD TO POSITION ANOTHER LOADED BOX BEFORE THE DOOR (IN SOME PLANTS, THE CHARGING MACHINE PEEL IS LOWERED AGAINST THE END OF THE BUGGY, AND THE SELF-PROPELLED MACHINE IS MOVED TO SHIFT THE BUGGY.) THE ABOVE OPERATIONS THEN ARE REPEATED WITH SUCCEEDING BOXES.

FIG. 16—5. Sequence of operations of a charging machine.

STOCK YARD

The stock yard where scrap and other solid materials are received and loaded should be located as conveniently with respect to the charging floor as possible. Stock yards in most modern plants are located parallel to the charging floor, and on that side of the furnaces beyond the furnace stacks. The stock yards are 70 to 100 feet wide, almost as long as the main or furnace building, and preferably are roofed in. Three or four electric overhead traveling cranes of 10 to 15 tons capacity and equipped with lifting magnets usually are required to handle the raw materials. It is preferable to have two levels under the crane runway. The upper, at charging floor level, may have two or three standard-gage tracks on which charging buggies are loaded; the lower or general yard level may have one standard-gage track where melting stock and furnace materials are received and where some scrap may be stocked (Figure 16—3).

LEAN-TO

Between the stock yard and the charging floor is the **lean-to** (Figure 16—3). This may be as much as 60 feet wide, and usually is not equipped with cranes. The main floor of the lean-to is at charging floor level, and carries tracks on which the charging cars or buggies carrying loaded charging boxes from the stock yard are stored until needed at the furnaces. The furnace stacks usually pass upward through the lean-to. In the spaces between columns at the sides of the main floor of the lean-to, enclosures may be built to house furnace control equipment, laboratories, locker rooms, weighing equipment, bins for various ferro-alloys, and so on.

Beneath the main floor of the lean-to and at general yard level (Figure 16—3) are installed the **waste-heat boilers** and the **fans** that regulate the flow of combustion air to the furnaces. This area usually is equipped with standard-gage tracks.

TRACKAGE

There should be sufficient trackage, interlinked with cross-overs, from the stock yard to the charging floor

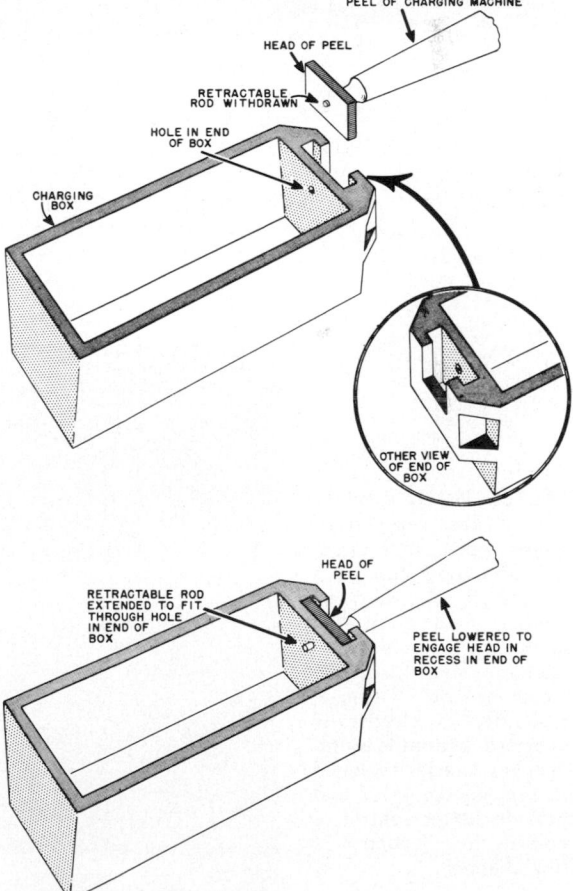

FIG. 16—6. Sketch showing one method by which the head of a charging machine peel is temporarily locked onto the end of a charging box to permit the box to be turned upside down for dumping its contents onto the bottom of an open-hearth furnace.

FIG. 16—7. Two identical hot-metal mixers, each of 800 tons capacity, installed in a separate mixer building at one end of the charging floor of an open-hearth furnace building. The mixers rotate counter-clockwise to pour molten pig iron into the transfer ladle shown.

to prevent interference in the movement of charging boxes on cars and their placement before the proper furnace at whatever time they are needed. It is preferable to use standard-gage track throughout this portion of the plant. This permits the use of a charging car of greater width that can accommodate larger charging boxes than when using narrow-gage track, and this facilitates the charging of scrap and other solid materials. Another advantage is that direct loading in and out of standard-gage railroad cars in all parts of the plant is feasible when standard-gage tracks are available.

FIG. 16—8. By manipulating the lever, the pourer opens and closes the nozzle of the ladle to control the flow of molten steel from the ladle to the molds. The operation shown is called "teeming" or "pouring." Recently, an electrically operated hydraulic cylinder has been developed to replace the lever and provide better control of pouring (see Section 5 of this chapter).

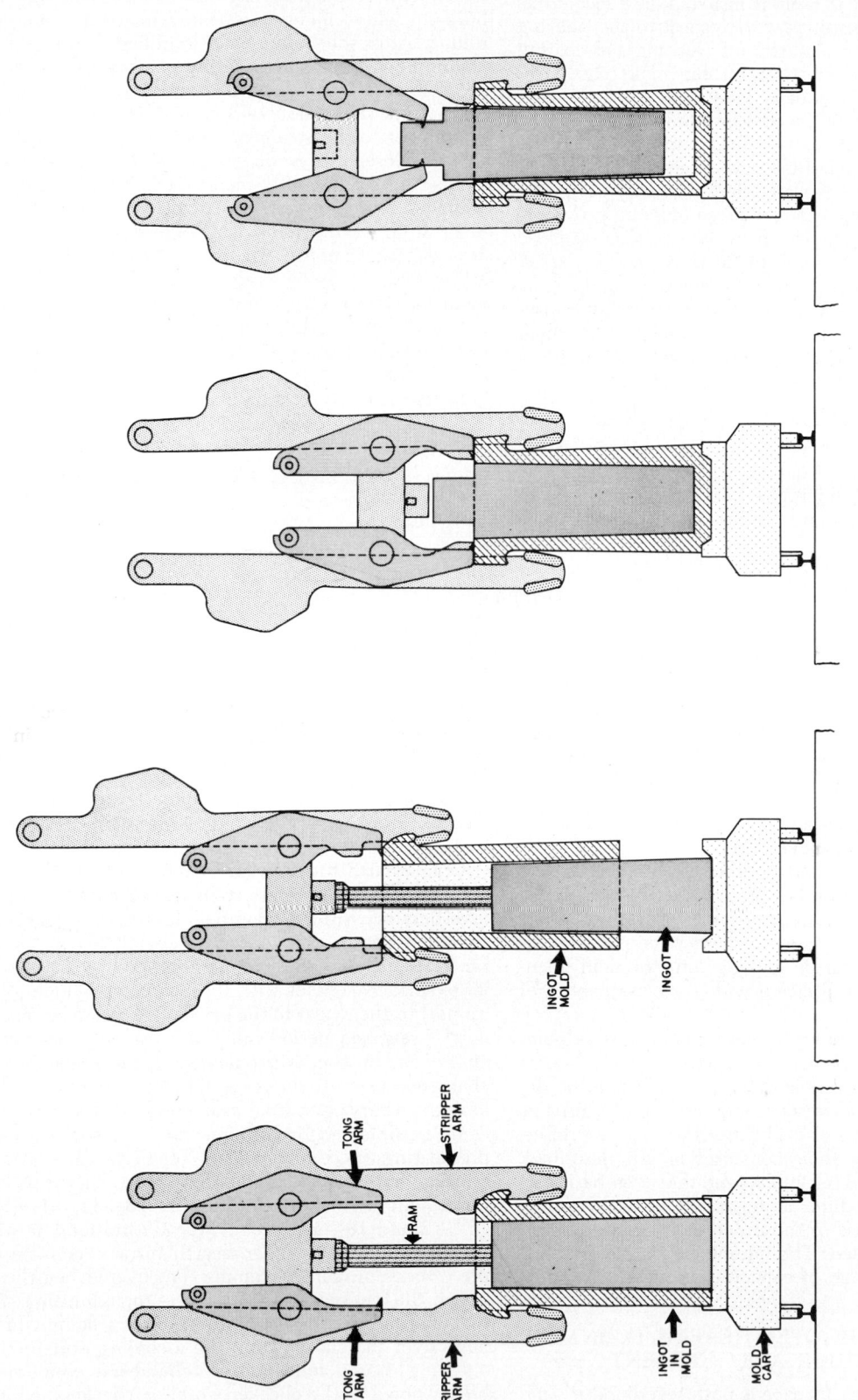

FIG. 16—9. Schematic representation of the action of an ingot stripper in removing the molds from (left) big-end-down ingots and (right) big-end-up ingots.

MOLD YARD

The mold yard is housed in a building located as conveniently as possible with respect to the pouring platforms. In it are facilities for cleaning and coating molds and replacing them on the mold cars. For modern plants, it is 70 to 100 feet wide and somewhat shorter than the main furnace building. The mold cars are handled in sets called **drags,** and for these the tracks are usually paralleled by a platform from which the molds may be inspected and cleaned and the hot tops adjusted. Mold-storage space must be provided, and all facilities are served by two or three electric overhead traveling cranes of 25 to 60 tons capacity. Where the mold yard parallels the main building, a lean-to from the mold yard to the main building provides a desirable cover over the tracks over which mold cars are transported or on which they are stored ready for placement at the pouring platforms.

MISCELLANEOUS FACILITIES

Other buildings making up the complete open-hearth plant are the **slag yard** where slag is broken to proper size and steel scrap recovered from it, the **scrap drop** where steel scrap is broken or burned with cut-ting torches into desired sizes, and a **stripper building** which, in best practice, may be located adjacent to the building where ingots are heated in soaking pits for rolling. After the ingots have solidified in the molds, having been held at the pouring platforms for periods determined by metallurgical experience, the drag of molds with their contained ingots are drawn by motive power to the **strippers** which usually are special electric overhead traveling cranes. With big-end-down molds, the stripper lifts the mold from the ingot car while a plunger forces the ingot down against the ingot stool on the mold car (Figure 16—9). Molds after lifting from the ingots are transferred by the stripper to a parallel drag of cars. With big-end-up molds, it is necessary to pull or push the ingot up and out of the mold while the latter is held against the stool and car (Figure 16—9). Modern stripper cranes, rated at 200 to 250 tons capacity, usually are designed to handle either type of molds.

As discussed in Chapter 11, the facilities for gaseous oxygen will depend upon the quantity of gas required for normal and peak operations, whether or not the plant is isolated or part of a steelmaking complex, and so on.

SECTION 3

OPEN-HEARTH FURNACE CONSTRUCTION

Description—In order to avoid repetition, the following description of the open-hearth furnace is made to serve for both basic and acid furnaces. They are similar with respect to form and arrangement of their parts, the chief difference being in the kind of materials used in constructing their hearths or bottoms in which the metal is refined. The extensive use of basic materials has introduced basic brick into certain sections of the basic open-hearth furnace structure which may not be permissible in furnaces operating on the acid open-hearth process, because basic material introduced by erosion or spalling into the acid open-hearth slag would interfere with the close control of the acid process.

Since, in this country at least, from the standpoint of the number of furnaces and annual production of steel, the basic process is the more important, the description which follows is based on the basic furnace, and only such parts of acid furnaces as require different materials for their construction are described. However, it should be emphasized that even basic furnaces at present differ as to details of construction, principally because of the different fuels and operating procedures used. The number of the various furnaces and the range of capacities are given in Table 16—II.

PARTS OF THE OPEN-HEARTH FURNACE AND THEIR ARRANGEMENT

The open-hearth furnace is both reverberatory and regenerative. It is reverberatory in that the charge is melted on a refractory hearth, which is shallow in relationship to the length of the hearth, by a flame pass-ing over the charge so that both the charge and the relatively low (above the hearth) roof, built of refractory brick, are heated by the flame, with a part of the heating effect on the charge accomplished by radiation from the heated roof. Radiation from the flame is an effect the intensity of which varies with the kind of fuel used and the method by which it is burned.

Open-hearth furnaces are regenerative in that the hot gases (from the combustion of fuel) pass out of the reverberatory furnace chamber through passages into chambers known as **regenerative chambers** containing fire brick. These brick are so arranged as to give a large surface contact with the hot gases, which give up part of their heat to the brick. The direction of gas flow is reversed periodically, and the cold incoming air for combustion is pre-heated in the regenerative chambers so as to increase the temperature of the flame by a very considerable amount above that which could be obtained by burning the same fuel without pre-heating the combustion air (see Figure 16—10).

The parts of the open-hearth furnace and their arrangement are shown in Figures **16—11, 16—12, 16—13** and **16—14.** From these illustrations, it will be observed that an open-hearth furnace consists of the furnace proper, containing the covered **hearth** on which the charge is placed; **ports** for admitting the fuel and air for combustion to produce a flame which flows over the charge from the incoming port to the outgoing port; **regenerative chambers** containing brick known as the **checker-work,** or **checkers,** which store up heat transferred to them from the products of combustion, and subsequently impart a large part of this stored-up heat to the fuel and to the air for com-

Table 16—II. Open-Hearth Furnaces in the United States
(As of January 1, 1960)

Rated Capacity Per Heat (Net Tons)	Basic Stationary	Basic Tilting	Total Basic Furnaces	Acid Stationary	Acid Tilting	Total Acid Furnaces	Total Both Groups
11–30	4	3	7	4	2	6	13
31–50	9	..	9	13	..	13	22
51–70	11	..	11	7	4	11	22
71–90	16	..	16	2	..	2	18
91–110	37	..	37	1	..	1	38
111–130	66	..	66	1	..	1	67
131–150	147	12	159	..	..	..	159
151–170	129	9	138	..	..	..	138
171–190	72	..	72	..	..	..	72
191–210	80	6	86	..	..	..	86
211–230	95	..	95	..	..	..	95
231–280	72	..	72	..	..	..	72
281–330	50	..	50	..	..	..	50
331–380	27	..	27	..	..	..	27
381–400	2	..	2	..	..	..	2
401–450	5	..	5	..	..	..	5
451–500	12	..	12	..	..	..	12
501–550	7	..	7	..	..	..	7
551–600	1	..	1	..	..	..	1
Total	842	30	872	28	6	34	906

bustion; **fantail flues** and **uptakes** connecting the regenerative or checker chambers with the furnace proper; **slag pockets** which are located at the base of the uptakes; **flues** leading from the air supply to the regenerative chambers, with connections to the **stack** and to the **waste-heat boiler** (when the latter is installed); **valves or dampers** (Figure **16**—14) for regulating flow of air and waste gases; and the stack itself.

The furnace proper is located with respect to the level of the charging floor so that it can be charged easily. It rests on steel bed beams which are supported, in modern practice, on steel columns which

are bricked in for protection from the heated atmosphere and from molten slag or metal.

The slag pockets, regenerator chambers, flues and valves are located on a lower level in an area known as the **cellar**, the general ground level of which is, in modern plants, twenty-two feet below the charging-floor level. The base of the stack is set on an approximate level with the bottom of the regenerator chambers.

The Furnace Proper—This is a rectangular brick structure, supported on the sides and ends by steel **buckstays** in the form of steel beams, channels, or (for

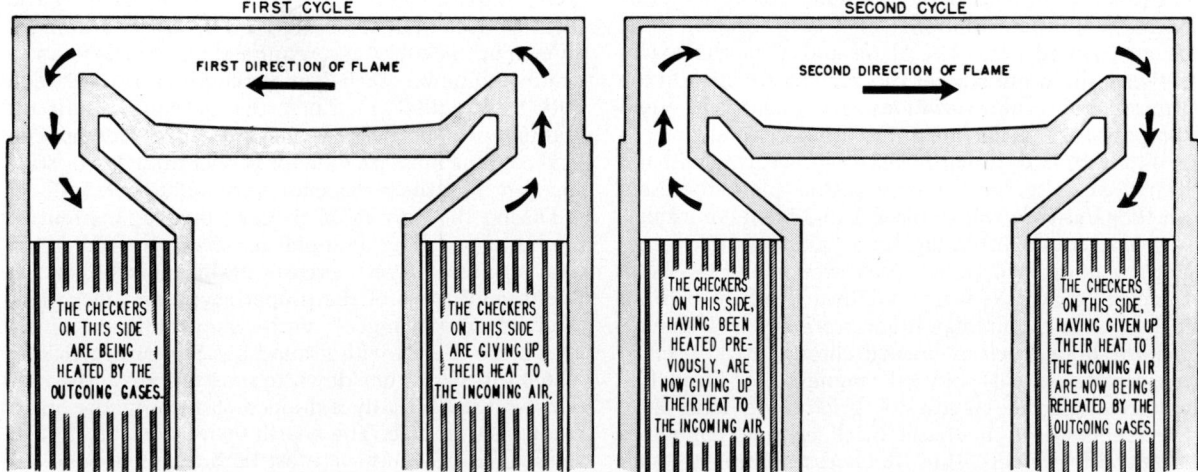

FIG. **16**—10. These diagrams show the function of the checkers in preheating air for combustion in regenerative furnaces. Fuel is admitted to the furnace through end burners at the same end as the preheated air for each cycle.

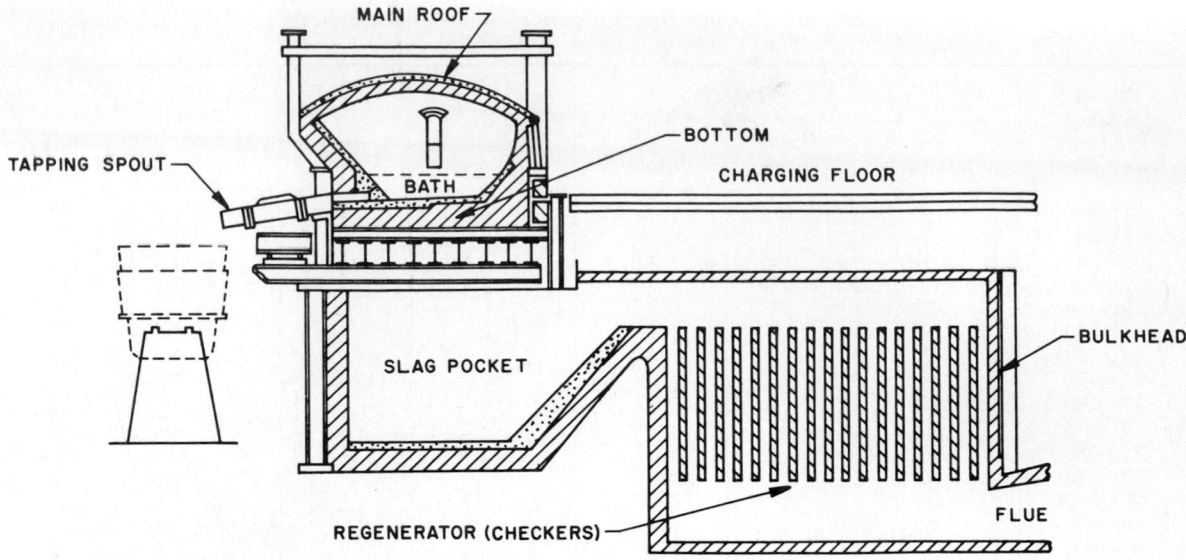

FIG. 16—11. Vertical section across the width of an open-hearth furnace, not to scale, indicating names and relative locations of principal parts. Upper section is through taphole of furnace: bottom section is through slag pocket and regenerator (see also Figures 16—10 and 16—12).

the walls on the front and back of the hearth) slabs, bound together at their tops, both longitudinally and crosswise above the furnace chamber and ports, by **steel struts** and **tie rods.** The buckstays rise vertically from their place of attachment to the steel bed under the furnace hearth, except those supporting the back wall. The back wall buckstays rise vertically from the steel bed to approximately the level of the furnace door sill level, then follow the sloping back-wall contour to approximately the top of the back wall, when they again become vertical.

THE BASIC HEARTH

The **hearth** (Figure 16—15) covers that part of the furnace below the charging door sill level, including the **bottom** and the **banks.** Older furnaces have "solid" bottoms resting on concrete foundations. Modern furnaces have "pan" bottoms of closely spaced steel beams covered with steel plates and, thus, the spaces between the beams under the bottom are open to the atmosphere. Wide variations are found in bottom composition and thickness, the latter varying from 15 to 44 inches in different furnaces and varying with the hearth capacity. On the steel bottom plate, the usual practice formerly was to place 1 to 3 inches of insulating concrete or insulating brick, although this sometimes was omitted in the area around the tap hole. Fireclay brick next were laid to a depth of 5 to 12 inches. Over the fireclay brick, from 4½ to 18 inches of basic brick, such as burned chrome brick (used to the greatest extent), burned magnesite, or burned or unburned chrome-magnesite brick were laid. Both the fireclay and the basic brick courses sometimes were laid in increasing thicknesses from the flat centerline section to the banks and hearth ends.

While this type of hearth construction still may be employed in some furnaces, large furnaces of more recent design do not have insulated bottoms and the

basic subhearth brick are 90 per cent magnesite rather than chrome-magnesite or chrome brick. Details of the newer construction are summarized in Chapter 2 on "Refractories."

From the contour established by the hearth brick construction, completion of the bottom may proceed according to any of the following general methods:

1. Burned-In Grain Magnesite Bottoms. This is the earliest type of open-hearth furnace basic bottom used after magnesite became available in this country, and was the most commonly used until recent years. After raising the temperature of the furnace chamber to 2900° to 3000° F and maintaining this temperature for 16 to 24 hours, dead-burned grain magnesite, intimately mixed with 8 to 20 per cent of ground basic open-hearth slag, is burned in, or sintered, layer by layer, starting with the upper surface of the basic brick courses mentioned above. The layers are about an inch in thickness, and require about 2 to 3 hours of heating to sinter each one at temperatures between 2900° and 3000° F. Thus, the bottom is built up gradually to the desired thickness and contour. The final contour must provide for proper drainage of steel and slag from the furnace through the tap hole.

During the burning-in process, the slag content of the bottom-making material may be decreased as the total burned-in layer increases in thickness. When the hearth contour is of the proper shape and elevation, the bottom is "slagged"; in this step the banks of the hearth are dusted with ground basic open-hearth slag which fuses and runs down to form a pool on the bottom. This pool shortly is drained off through the opening at the tap hole. The hearth then usually is chilled, after which the furnace must be brought back to operating temperature. Any cracks which appear in the burned-in bottom then are filled with fine magnesite, after which the furnace is charged.

2. Rammed Magnesite or Plastic Chromite Sub-

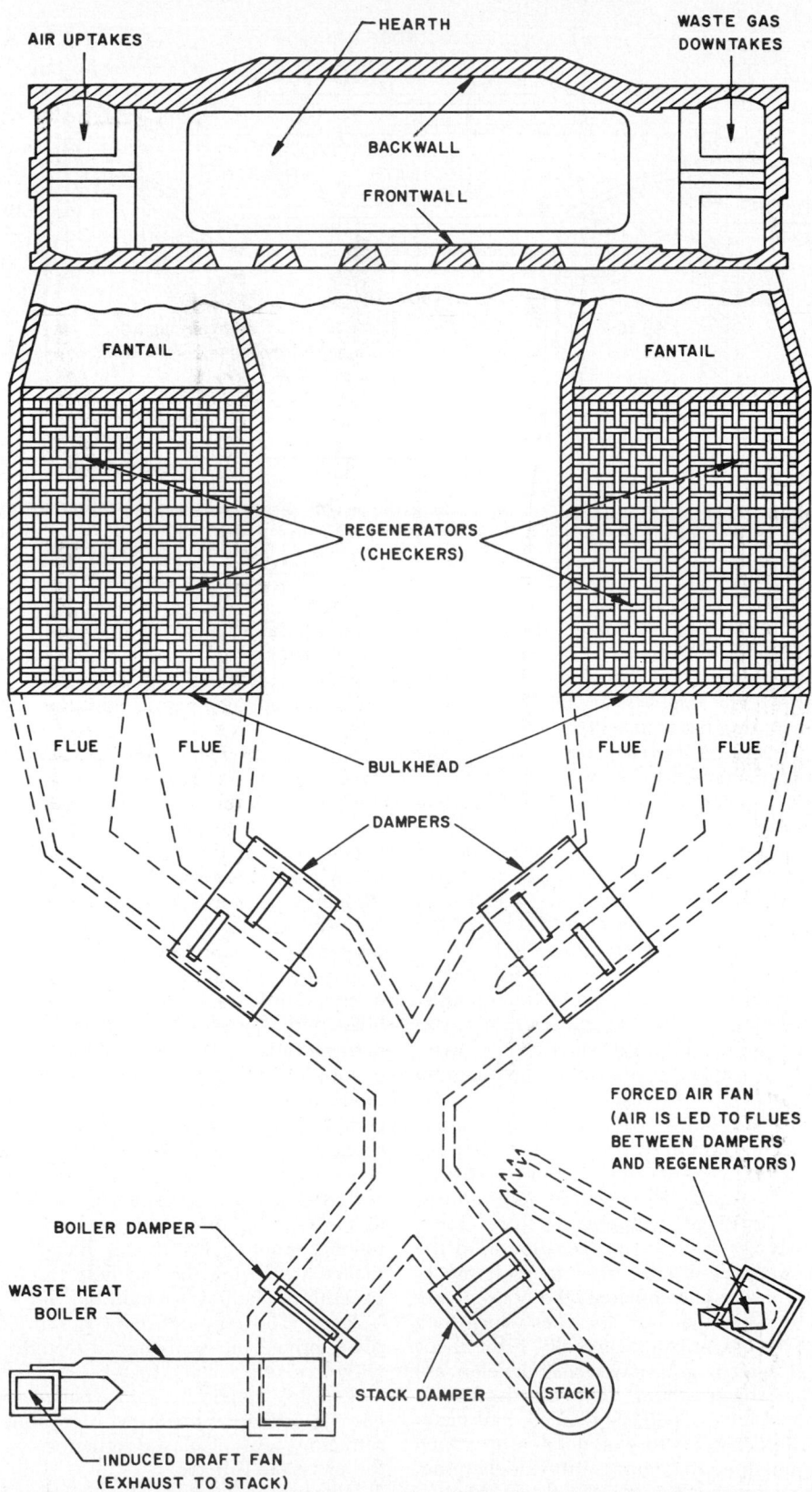

Fig. 16—12. Sectioned schematic plan (not to scale) of the arrangement of a liquid-fuel fired open-hearth furnace, showing location and names of principal parts. Note that air from forced-air fan enters flues between dampers and regenerators, controlled by a suitable duct and valve arrangement.

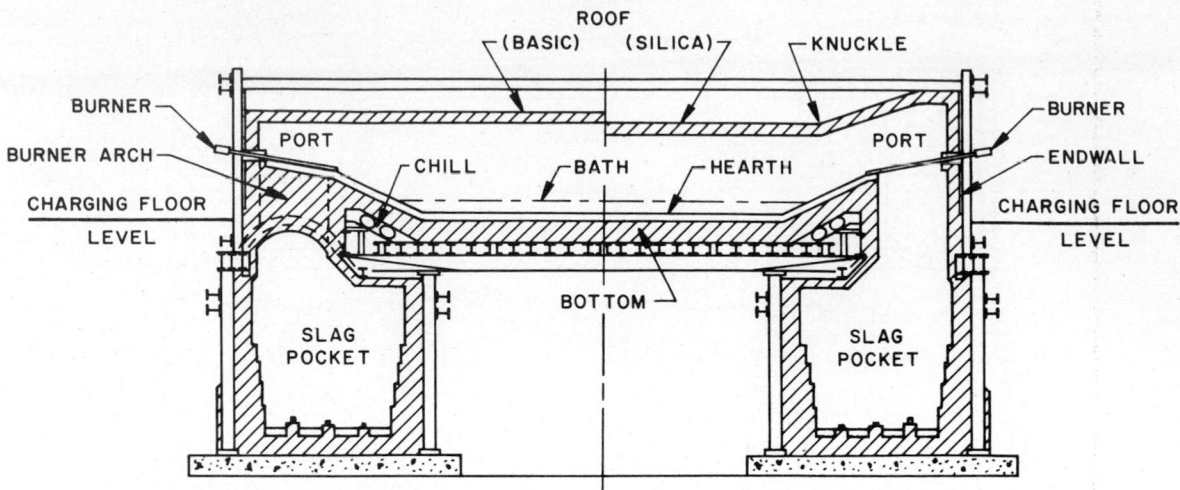

FIG. 16—13. Diagrammatic section (not to scale) along the length of a liquid-fuel fired open-hearth furnace, giving nomenclature of major parts. Left half of roof simulates basic construction; right half, silica construction. Burner arch has been omitted from design at right.

Hearths with Burned-In Working Hearth. The rammed or plastic type of bottom is being employed to a considerable extent, the rammed subhearth replacing an equivalent thickness of burned-in magnesite, thus permitting faster installation which makes it possible to charge the furnace sooner than in the case of a completely burned-in hearth.

The special, prepared, grain-sized, cold-setting magnesite or dolomite-magnesite materials, containing 5 to 6 per cent moisture, generally are rammed to a depth of 6 to 10 inches with pneumatic rammers, while the plastic chromite mixtures are installed in thicknesses ranging from 3 to 6 inches. On top of the rammed-in bottom material, after raising the temperature in the furnace chamber to from 2900° to 3000° F and maintaining this for 16 to 24 hours, the top layer of the final bottom, from 3 to 10 inches in total thickness, is burned in with grain magnesite, layer on layer, as described in the previous section on burned-in grain magnesite bottoms.

3. All-Rammed Bottoms. Most of the basic bottoms installed in large furnaces in recent years have been of this type, as they require a shorter time for installation than other types, and provide more accurate contours. The specially grain-sized magnesite mixtures mentioned previously are rammed in over the top of the brick courses, using forms and careful tamping procedure. When ramming is completed, the bottoms are dried with flames from gas burners, after which they finally are heated to approximately 3000° F for about 48 hours, after which any cracks that develop are filled with ramming material. The hearth then is "slagged" as described previously, chilled, and again dressed with the fine refractory material, after which it is brought up to operating temperature for charging.

The foregoing procedures describe the installation of a new hearth. Such a new hearth will last for possibly five years or more. Its life thus covers the making of possibly 3,000 to 6,000 heats, and is called a "campaign." After each heat is tapped from a furnace during a campaign, it usually is necessary to make at least minor repairs to the banks and bottom. The techniques employed for making these repairs to maintain the furnace in good operating condition are described in a later section.

Basic Hearth Tap Hole—The **tap hole**, located midway between the ends of the hearth and at a point in the back bank toward which the hearth slopes, should have a continuous fall (about 1 inch per foot) from the lowest level of the bottom. It is about 6 inches in diameter and is formed by first placing a steel pipe through a circular hole in the hearth brickwork which is lined with basic brick. The opening between the pipe and the basic brick is rammed with magnesite, magnesite and chrome ore, or basic bottom ramming material. Before the furnace is charged, the tap hole is filled with burned dolomite, being faced with this same material on the inside of the furnace. In the rear, or tapping-spout end, a mixture of burned and raw dolomite is tamped into the hole. A plug of clay loam completes the sealing of the rear end. Tap hole and spout locations are shown diagrammatically in Figures 16—14 and 16—15 mentioned previously.

A casting on the ladle-pit side of the furnace, known as the **tapping-hole casting,** provides a seat for the **tapping spout** against the tap hole, so that the flow of molten steel from the tap hole through the tapping spout to the ladle is smooth and free from undue turbulence. The tapping spout is formed from a steel plate formed into a U-shaped trough, which is lined with fireclay brick and may be surfaced with fireclay, magnesite, magnesite and cement, magnesite and chrome ore, occasionally with graphite in the mix. A refractory joint of plastic refractory is made between the spout and furnace.

When the percentage of molten iron in the charge is high enough to require a slag run-off or flush-off in the period following the addition of the molten metal, provision is made in the back bank and through the back wall, between the tap hole and the end of the furnace,

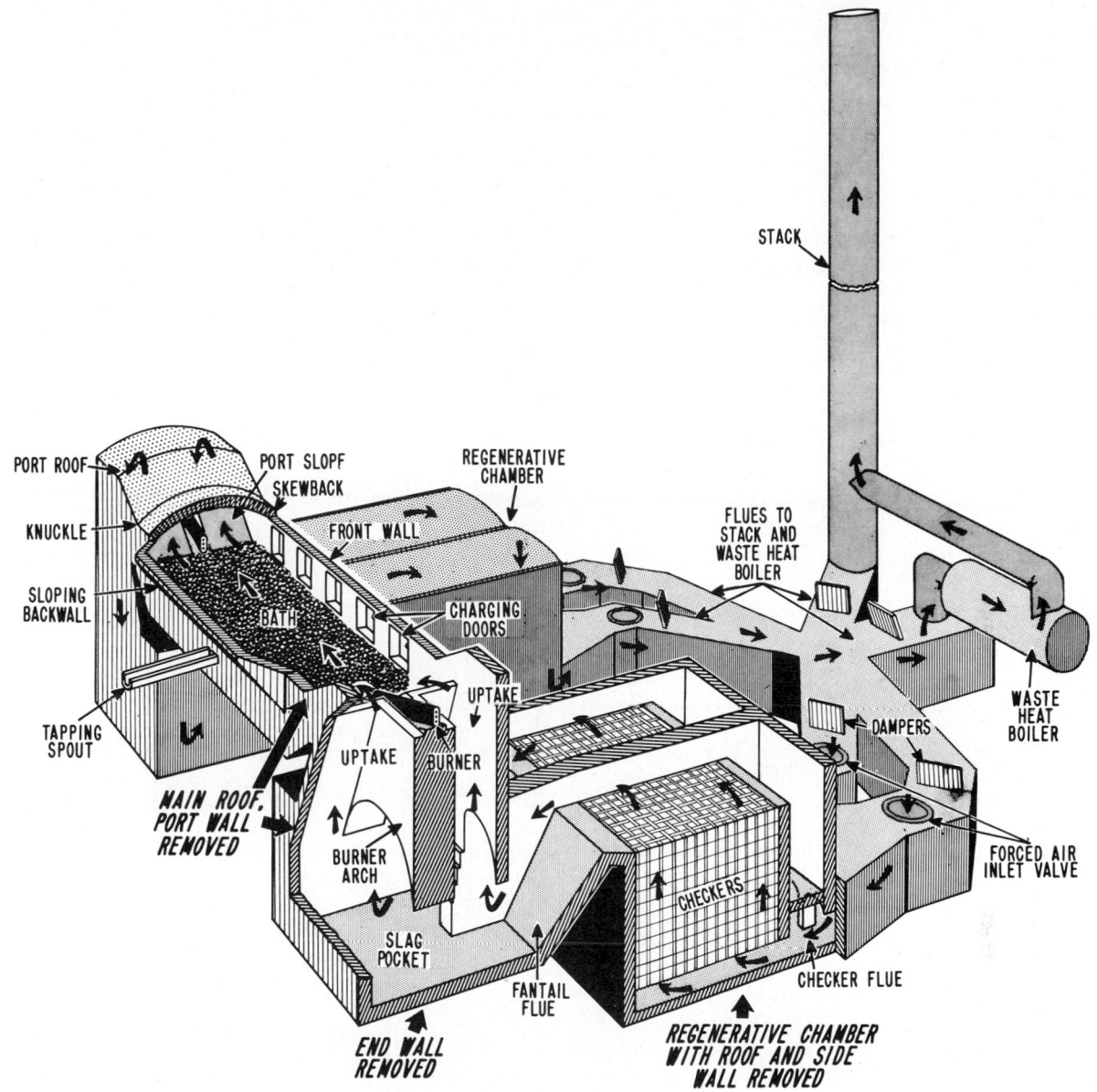

FIG. 16—14. This diagram illustrates the principal parts of an open-hearth furnace (with silica roof) sectioned to show as much as possible of the interior. The heavy curved arrows indicate the direction of the flow of preheated air, flame, and waste gases when a liquid fuel is fired through a burner in the trench at the right end of the furnace. The five doors shown are in the front wall of the furnace, and the checker chambers extend under the charging floor, which is not shown. When reversal of firing takes place, the function of the uptake is reversed, and it becomes the downtake. (See also Figures 16—11, 16—12, 16—13 and 16—15 for some additional details of construction.)

for a **run-off notch.** This is to provide an opening through the back wall through which the early slag may be run off through a spout and into a slag pot. In modern installations, the sill plate of the middle furnace door is designed to permit the drainage of slag from the furnace so that it may be removed from both the back and front of the hearth although the present trend is to use only the front flush.

THE ACID HEARTH

The Acid Hearth—The hearth of an acid open-hearth furnace is similar in contour to that of a basic open-hearth furnace, the difference in construction being that acid brick instead of basic brick are used in the hearth structure and only acid material is used above the hearth brickwork

The average capacity of acid furnaces in the United States is approximately 60 tons, and the largest acid furnaces are of 125 tons capacity. A modern acid open-hearth furnace would have the same steel bottom pan as used in the latest designs for basic furnaces.

One and one-half inches of insulating concrete may be used next to the steel bottom plate. Fireclay brick

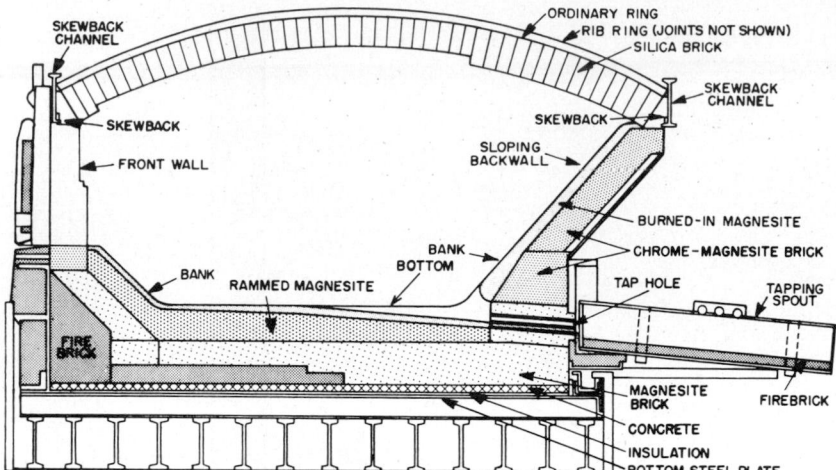

Fig. 16—15. Vertical cross-section through the tap-hole of a modern basic open-hearth furnace (with silica-brick roof) indicating materials of construction of the various parts. Buckstays and other binding elements are not shown. (See Figure 16—18 and 16—19 for design of one type of basic roof.)

next are laid to a depth of 5 to 11 inches. Over the fireclay brick are laid silica brick to a thickness of 11 to 12 inches. On top of the silica brick, the upper part of the hearth, which receives the charge, is built up with fritted or sintered silica sand to a minimum thickness of 9 inches at the tap hole, and to an increasing thickness progressing towards the ends of the hearth. The drying and heating of the acid furnace preliminary to making the bottom of silica sand are conducted in the same manner as for the basic furnace. Before the furnace is heated to too high a temperature, the tapping hole must be put in shape.

Acid Hearth Tap Hole—In most furnaces, the opening left in the brickwork for a tapping hole is square in section, except at the top, which is arched. This opening, measuring about sixteen inches across, must be lined with some acid refractory material that will set hard and resist the eroding effect of the liquid metal and slag. To form this lining, a tapered plug of iron or wood, from four to ten inches in diameter at the large end, varying in accordance with the size of the furnace, is inserted centrally into this hole in the brickwork, and the space between the plug and brick is rammed full of ground ganister (silica sand) containing a little plastic clay as a binder. When this mixture has set, the plug is removed, and the round opening is filled with anthracite coal, which is covered immediately on the inside of the furnace with a little sand, so the coal will not be burned out during the heating of the furnace. Outside, the coal is held in place with a plug of fire clay. Some shops prefer to use a graphite plug, such as might be made from a used electric furnace electrode. In this case, the plug is surrounded by silica sand and is left in place while the bottom is being made. The tap hole is approximately 6 to 8 inches in diameter. Some melters prefer to tamp the hole full of ganister containing 5 to 7 per cent moisture, and then dig out with a sharp curved spoon some of this filling to form a small cylindrical-shaped hole, which is left open until after the bottom and banks have been fritted in. This hole is then stopped as described above.

Making the Acid Bottom—After the tapping hole has been made ready, the heating of the furnace is

carried on as described under the basic process. In the meantime, preparations are made for fritting or glazing the sand bottom and banks. As a first step, enough sandstone of granite chippings, if such chippings are procurable, are scattered over the bottom and banks to cover the surface. Then, as soon as the furnace has come to a red heat, more fuel is admitted and the valves are reversed at about twenty-minute intervals until these chippings begin to fuse. This procedure permits the bricks and bottom to absorb more heat than if sand is spread directly upon them, and the partly fused chippings form a better bond between the almost infusible silica brick and the sand fritting. By means of shovels, rabbles, and long-handled spoons, silica sand is now spread evenly over the surface of the bottom and banks to a depth of about one-fourth inch, and the heating is continued until this sand begins to fuse, thus forming a glaze over the entire surface. Another layer of sand is then spread and glazed on as before, and these operations are repeated until the bottom and banks have been built up to the desired thickness, which varies according to the size of the furnace, from nine to twenty inches. The bottom may now be compared to a big oval dish, the semi-vitrified layers of sand forming practically a solid one-piece wall about the sides and bottom.

After the bottom and banks have been fritted properly, or glazed in, the tapping hole is punched through from the outside and again made up as before, using a mixture of anthracite coal or coke and sand, and securing this in place with a plug of fire clay rammed in from the outside, at some shops. The hearth then is filled nearly half full of acid open-hearth slag. If the slag is not at hand, red brickbats or other easily fused siliceous material is subsituted, and some light scrap, such as sheet trimmings, is scattered on top. Other shops prefer to add only as much slag as the bottom and banks will absorb. When this charge has melted, rabbles are inserted through the doors and the liquid slag is splashed up against the banks to wash them down. Then the bottom itself is raked over carefully to smooth it, after which the tapping hole is opened and the slag is drained out of the furnace. This treatment tends to consolidate the bottom and banks, and make them much more resistant to the buoyant action of the liquid metal of subsequent charges. According to some practices, the next two or three charges will be small, not over two-thirds the capacity of the furnace, and will consist mainly of cold pig iron. Then, if it is apparent that the bottom is holding well, the size of the charge and the proportion of scrap used may be increased gradually until the furnace is working on its normal charges. Some melters prefer to test each layer of the bottom as it is fritted in by scraping it with sharp rods. When each layer has shown a hard glazed surface, and examination of the material removed in shaping up the tap hole indicates a firm vitrified bottom, the first charge may be of normal size.

The quality of the sand used for this purpose is of very great importance. If the sand is very pure, that is, composed almost entirely of silica, great difficulty is experienced in fritting it on the bottom, while if it contains too high a percentage of impurities, it will be fritted easily but also will be worn away rapidly after the furnace is put into operation. The silica content of the sands, or sand mixtures, that gives the best results is usually between 94 and 97 per cent. No definite figures can be given for the composition of a good sand, because the adaptability of the sand for this purpose depends not only upon the kind and relative amounts of impurities present, but also upon the physical make-up of the sand itself. Certain natural sands, including some beach sands and a few deposits in Ohio and other midwestern states, give the best results. In Western Pennsylvania some of the most desirable material occurs as hard sedimentary rock, which has to be crushed to render it suitable for this purpose. In fineness, this stone is crushed so that all will pass a one-fourth inch screen. Frequently a relatively coarse and pure sand mixed intimately with a certain proportion of a fine and less pure sand will give good service as bottom material, even when either sand alone has proved unsatisfactory. Table 16—III has been found helpful in the selection of suitable sands for this purpose.

FRONT WALL AND DOORS

The walls of all open-hearth furnaces begin on the top course of the brick which form the upper rim of the hearth. The **front wall** extends from the door sill line to the bottom of the **skewback channel** that

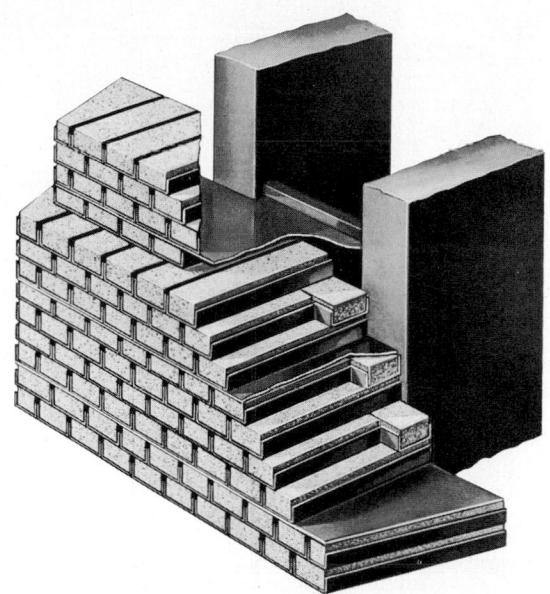

FIG. **16**—16. Sketch showing how steel plates are inserted between every fourth course of metal-encased basic brick and then welded to bars welded to the solid buckstays to make a more stable front-wall construction for an open-hearth furnace. Note increased thickness of wall near the bottom. (Courtesy, Harbison-Walker Refractories Co.)

supports the skewback brick on which the roof is supported. The walls, in the larger modern furnaces, are generally at least 13½ to 18 inches thick, being thickest at the base of the wall. Basic brick for basic furnace walls usually are laid up to 12 to 15 inches above the sill line. The courses of brick above these are usually of silica brick where brick arches above the doors are employed and of basic brick when archless door frames are used. With silica walls, it is preferred that the underlying basic brick be chrome-magnesite, their composition being predominantly chrome ore, to limit fluxing of the silica brick. Front walls built entirely of basic brick often employ steel-encased magnesite-chrome brick in which magnesite is the predominating ingredient of the composition. These are "tied" to the furnace buckstays with steel plates laid horizontally between selected courses, usually by spot-welding them to the buckstays, to provide greater stability and resistance to mechanical abuse (see

Table 16—III. Chemical Compositions of Different Sands Used for Acid Open-Hearth Bottoms and Banks

GRADE	Good	Bad	Fair	Fair	Good	Mix*	Mix*
Composition	(%)	(%)	(%)	(%)	(%)	(%)	(%)
Silica, SiO_2	95.83	88.46	97.38	95.01	96.34	98.45	92.36
Iron Oxide, FeO	0.40	0.96	0.45	0.51	1.05	0.13	2.90
Alumina, Al_2O_3	2.76	8.27	1.48	3.44	1.60	0.85	2.85
Lime, CaO	Trace	Trace	Trace	0.10	0.21	Trace	Trace
Magnesia, MgO	0.13	0.23	0.08	Trace	0.21	Trace	Trace
Alkalies, $K_2O + Na_2O$	None	None	Trace	Trace	None	Trace	Trace
Ignition Loss	0.88	2.08	0.64	1.05	0.62	0.52	1.57

*These sands may be mixed in about equal proportions.

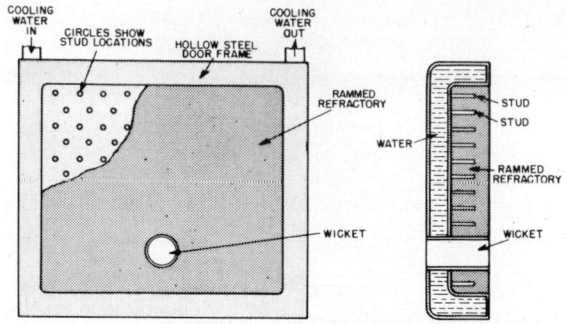

Fig. **16—17.** A hollow steel casting, through which cooling water is circulated, has a studded recess which is rammed with a plastic refractory to make one type of an open-hearth furnace door.

Figure **16—16**). Silica brick front walls sometimes are insulated by applying plastic clay-bonded exfoliated vermiculite by a spray gun or trowel to a thickness of 1 to 2 inches.

When the walls are built of basic brick, it is not usual to insulate them, but rather to seal them against air infiltration by using a thin coating of the materials ordinarily used for insulation.

Modern stationary furnaces generally are equipped with five doors. Recently, some of the larger new furnaces and some enlarged older furnaces have had the number of doors increased to seven. Practically all doors in use on open-hearth furnaces are water-cooled, and generally are lined with used or new fire-clay brick, although increasing use is being made of plastic chrome ore, rammed on steel studs set in the steel door plate (Figure **16—17**).

A peep hole, called the **wicket,** is provided on each door to provide for inspection of the interior of the melting chamber, and to provide access to the furnace for dipping out molten samples, for stirring, for poling, and for taking temperature measurements.

The doors slide on water-cooled welded-steel frames which are placed between the front-wall buckstays and against the front wall. The doors are raised and lowered by electric door hoists in modern installations.

The front and back walls of acid open-hearth furnaces are built entirely of silica brick, 13½ inches thick.

BACK WALL

The back wall may be vertical, or so-called full sloping (40 to 50 degrees with the vertical), or a compromise between the two. Modern practice dictates a slope which will provide easy maintenance through the doors of the furnace (Figure **16—15**). In this case, the back wall slopes in such manner as to be essentially a continuation of the sloping back area of the furnace banks. Underlying the hot face of the sloping back wall are about 13 inches of basic brick, or of basic brick over firebrick. Vertical back walls, like the front walls, may be all basic or silica in the upper sections. Magnesite-chrome steel-encased brick are used quite widely. Back walls, particularly of the

vertical type, may be insulated the same as front walls if the brick are silica, restricting the coating to a sealing coat if basic brick are used (see the description of front walls, above).

MAIN ROOF

The main roof of an open-hearth furnace may be designed in one of two ways, depending upon whether it is built of silica or basic refractory brick.

Open-hearth furnace roofs are generally arched from the front wall to the back wall. Although silica-brick roofs are still in use, they are steadily being replaced by basic-brick roofs. There are many designs of silica roof but, generally, they consist of two port roofs (one above each burner) that slope downward to meet the main roof at the **knuckles,** as illustrated in Figure **16—13**.

Basic roofs are built in a continuous straight line (without knuckles), as shown in Figure **16—13**: this type of construction is referred to as a **box-car roof.** Other types of construction are discussed below.

Some details of construction of silica-brick and basic-brick roofs are given in the following paragraphs.

Silica-Brick Roofs—Formerly, silica brick were used almost universally to construct open-hearth furnace roofs, and some roofs of this type are still used (on about 20 per cent of existing furnaces).

Both **bonded** and **ring** silica brick roofs have been used in different thicknesses or combinations of thicknesses, although 12, 13½, 15 and 18 inch roofs have been most common.

In the bonded roof, the brick are overlapped to "break" the joints, while in the ring roof, the joints are not broken. Ring roofs may be plain or ribbed. It has been common practice to employ the ribbed construction for greater stability. The ribs run from front to back of the furnace. The ribs may be 3 to 6 inches thicker than the rest of the roof and extend above the regular roof brick at every third, fourth or sixth ring. The location of the rings depends on the width of the roof span.

In some shops, basic brick are used in the roof adjacent to the front and back skewbacks, generally in alternate rings with silica brick.

The **rise** of the silica-brick roof arch is generally 1½ to 2 inches per foot of span. **Skewback brick** (Figure **16—15**) which take the thrust of the arch at each of its ends, should be designed very carefully so as to have the angle best suited for distributing bearing pressure, and there should be the minimum number of shapes in one skewback line. In some plants, sloping channels are used to replace the shaped skewback brick.

Roof design and thickness require careful consideration in each plant with respect to maximum economical life as related to the fuels commonly used and normal operating practices. All other parts of the furnace should be designed so as to be "balanced" with roof life and thus require replacement in intervals that are even multiples or fractions of roof life. This desirable condition can be promoted through careful selection of refractories and their proper applications. Different types of water-cooled skewback channels are employed frequently, particularly at the front-wall side of the roof.

Silica roof brick are bonded with silica cement or may be laid dry with a surface grouting of silica cement. In the relatively small number of cases when insulation is applied to furnace roofs, exfoliated vermiculite is employed either as a loose blanket or in plaster form, although an intervening layer of sand or crushed silica brickbats containing a small amount of lime may be used. The total thickness seldom exceeds 3 inches.

Acid open-hearth furnaces have roofs built of silica brick, 12 to 15 inches thick.

Basic-Brick Roofs—With the advent of the use of the oxygen lance to accelerate rate of production of steel in the basic open-hearth furnace, basic refractories have become widely used for construction of the roof. The development of a satisfactory basic roof entailed considerably more than the simple substitution of basic brick for silica brick.

Numerous designs involving both suspended-arch and sprung-arch construction have been developed, some of which have proven to be successful only in given furnaces and shops under a particular set of operating conditions involving type of charge, types of steel made, available fuels, variations in practices in the use of oxygen, and so on. Descriptions of many of these designs and the results obtained from them have been published elsewhere (see bibliography at end of chapter for some sources of information on this subject). The only design that will be discussed here is

that which was developed at Fairless Works of United States Steel and has proven quite successful in many other plants. The principles of design of this particular roof are shown in Figures **16—18** and **16—19**.

Some of the design features incorporated in roofs of the type shown in Figures **16—18** and **16—19** include the use of a rise of 2¼ to 3 inches per foot of span, as compared to the conventional 1½-inch rise employed in the design of silica-brick roofs; the use of steel tie plates; and control of the contour of the arch by the use of longitudinal hold-down beams of sufficient rigidity to prevent buckling of any portion of the roof.

PORT ENDS

Port Ends—The port ends (Figure **16—13**) include the **port side** and **end walls, fuel ports, port roof, port slope,** and **uptakes** from slag pockets to the port roof. Some furnaces have **wing walls** (also called monkey walls) built entirely of chrome-magnesite brick, or faced with these brick and backed up with fireclay brick; they form part of the throats where the gases from the ports enter or leave the hearth chamber and may be water-cooled to maintain their contour, with the consequent effect of maintaining control of the flame.

The end walls may be built completely of silica brick, 13½ to 27 inches thick, or of basic brick from slightly below charging floor level to the port roof, in which case the walls are 9 to 13½ inches thick. The basic brick may be burned or unburned magnesite-chrome and preferably steel-encased, or at least, laid

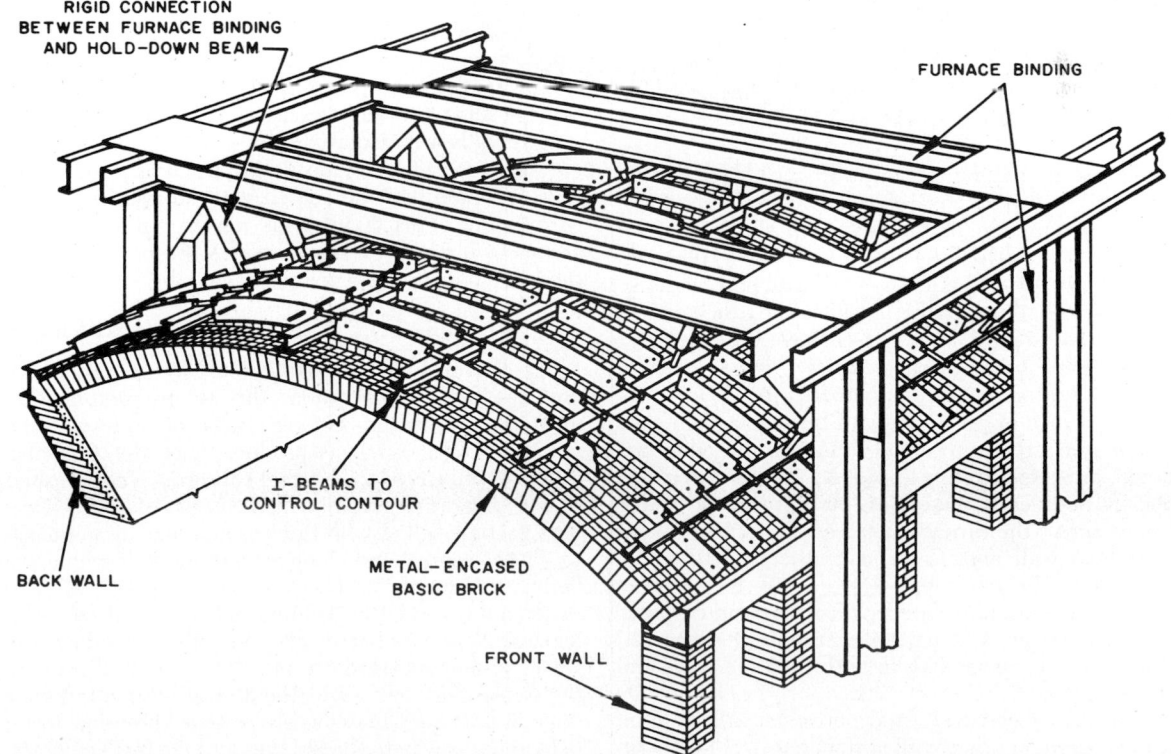

FIG. **16—18.** Simplified diagram of the method of installing a basic roof on an open-hearth furnace.

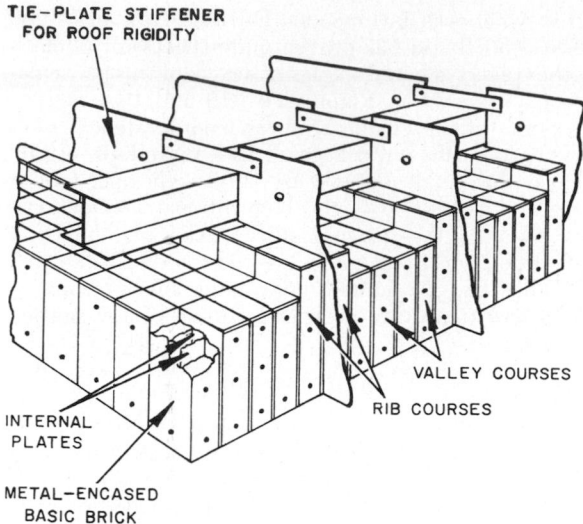

TIE-PLATE STIFFENER
FOR ROOF RIGIDITY

INTERNAL
PLATES

METAL-ENCASED
BASIC BRICK

VALLEY COURSES

RIB COURSES

Fig. 16—19. Enlarged sectional detail of basic roof construction, showing rib and valley courses.

with steel plates which are tied to the port-end buckstays every few courses.

Fuel ports on furnaces fired with fuels other than producer gas consist of water-cooled burners which are usually, but not always, covered by a **doghouse** of basic brick or silica brick covered with chrome ore, the whole generally supported on a solid, silica-brick arch dividing the uptake on each end of the furnace in the direction of the longitudinal axis of the furnace. Fuel gas may be introduced through the same water-cooled burner as liquid fuel, or may be introduced through shaped brick at the sides of the ports near the uptakes.

Where gaseous oxygen or compressed air are used to intensify combustion of the fuel, they also are introduced through separate lines in the water-cooled burner.

The port roof usually is built of silica brick, with a minimum roof thickness of 9 inches except at the knuckle or junction of the port roof slope with the main roof, where the thickness is the same as the main roof (Figures 16—13 and 16—14). The port slopes or floors from edge of uptake to end of hearth are built similarly to sloping back walls with fireclay brick covered with basic brick, followed by a layer of magnesite bottom mixture or chrome ore.

Maintenance of port ends and furnace hearth ends is facilitated greatly by good design in the **wind box** or **chill**, indicated in Figure 16—13. This is a steel box open at both ends, extending at both ends of the furnace across the furnace between the hearth side of the uptake wall and the end of the hearth, which portion of the hearth it supports.

Success has been attained with a port end built entirely of basic brick. Magnesite-chrome steel-encased brick are used, suspended, in both port-end roofs and vertical walls.

Insulation of end walls and port side walls is more common than on other wall surfaces above the charging-floor level and, in general, consists of a sprayed

or troweled coat of plastic vermiculite, 1 to 2 inches thick in the case of silica brick and a sealing coat in the case of basic brick.

Modern acid furnaces have port ends (roof, side walls, ends) built of silica brick, the walls 13½ inches to 9 inches thick and the port roof 12 inches thick.

SLAG POCKETS

The slag pockets extend downward from the bottom of the uptakes (see "Port Ends") to a level which provides sufficient volume for the accumulation of oxides. These oxides are in the form of fine dust carried by the hot exit gases that have passed over the charge. The oxides are mainly iron oxide, but may carry other dust; for example, lime after an addition of burned lime to the furnace. The oxides are deposited from the gases descending from the outgoing port without blocking the entrance of these gases to the fantail flues and regenerator chambers. The walls of the slag pocket are built of silica or fireclay brick or, often, of silica brick backed by fireclay brick walls, usually insulated. False walls of loosely laid used brick generally are used inside the silica brick walls to facilitate slag removal. Slag pocket floors are covered with a layer of sand over hard-burned, low-duty fireclay brick. Location of the slag pockets is shown in Figures 16—11, 16—13 and 16—14.

In a number of cases, the bottoms of the slag pockets are built so as to incorporate some mechanical means of loosening and breaking up the oxide deposit, including means for inserting explosives, so as to shorten the time of cleaning out the pockets at the time of furnace rebuilding.

In the case of acid open-hearth furnaces, the silica brick extends on down from the port ends and uptakes to meet fireclay walls extending from the bottom of the slag pockets half way to the charging-floor level.

The fantail flues (Figures 16—12 and 16—14) are built of silica or of fireclay brick. The slag pockets and fantail walls are insulated with 3 to 4½ inches of diatomaceous or fireclay insulating brick or vermiculite blocks, which may be coated with an inch of plastic vermiculite. This is used, as a rule, on the fantail arches to a depth of 2 to 3 inches. From the fantail, the gases flow to the regenerator chambers.

REGENERATOR (CHECKER) CHAMBERS

To obtain sufficient flame temperature and economical fuel consumption, the air for combustion must be preheated (where fuels of low calorific value are used, such as producer gas, the fuel also must be preheated). The preheating is accomplished by a regenerative system which consists of brick chambers partially filled with brick which take up about 60 to 75 per cent of the chamber volume and which are known commonly as **checker work** or **checkers.** The brick comprising this volume are arranged so as to leave a great number of passages through which the waste gases from the furnace pass on their way to the stack and, later on, as the flow is reversed, the air for combustion passes in the reverse direction to be heated on its way to the uptakes and the furnace ports. With natural gas, coke-oven gas or liquid fuel, only the air is preheated. The checkerwork and the chamber, flue, uptake, and port walls abstract a large part of the sensible heat from the outgoing waste gases and return it later to the incoming air which is being preheated. Since a number of furnaces now in operation were built originally to use producer gas, they were constructed with two regenerator chambers at each end of the furnace, the smaller chamber preheating the gas and the larger the air. Such chambers find use even when employing fuels of higher calorific value, such as natural gas, because all of the chambers are then used to preheat air. Furnaces converted from producer gas to liquid fuel continued to use all chambers for preheat and the air for combustion passed through all of them. With later designs not intended for fuels requiring preheat, modifications have been made to arrange the chambers to obtain the best preheat of the air.

The principal parts of the regenerator system are:
(1) The chambers enclosing the checkerwork.
(2) The checkerwork.
(3) The rider wall system which supports the checkerwork and forms the passages conducting the cooled gases from the checkerwork passages to the exit end of the chamber, or, in reverse, conducting the air from the air-inlet valves and flues to the checkerwork.

The entire system of regenerator chambers, including the roof, checkerwork, side walls and flues, generally is built of high-heat-duty fireclay brick, although silica brick may be used in the top courses of the checkerwork and lower quality clay brick in the flues from chamber to stack. There are a large number of checkerwork designs involving the method of laying the brick, the brick size and shape, and the method of allowing horizontal and vertical openings. Simple brick shapes that can be reused are most in favor (Figure 16—20). The brick of the checkerwork usually are laid with fairly large openings, generally 6 inches (or more) square on a horizontal plane, which permits easy cleaning during furnace operation, thus retaining a high regenerative efficiency during a furnace campaign. The regenerator chamber roof is generally a sprung arch although, recently, suspended

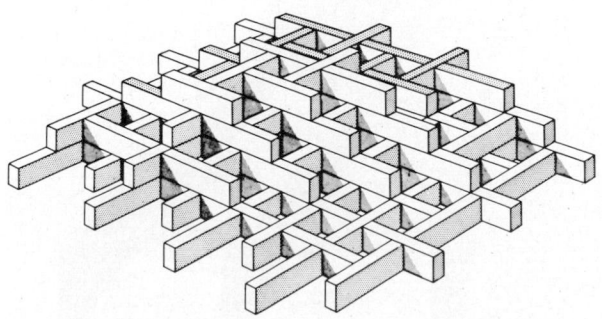

Fig. 16—20. One type of checkerwork construction, showing how simple, rectangular refractory shapes are laid in an interlocking manner to provide a series of smooth, vertical flues.

arches have been used successfully. The latter construction permits a greater checkerwork volume because of greater permissible height of checkerwork and the opportunity to eliminate the division wall for furnaces not using preheated fuels. For maximum efficiency of regeneration and, consequently, of furnace performance, air infiltration through the walls of regenerator chambers, slag pockets and furnace ends must be kept to a minimum. All of these walls should be well sealed. The regenerator chamber walls usually are insulated with 3½ to 4 inches of block insulation of vermiculite, magnesia, or asbestos composition. The outside of the chamber walls, including the block insulation, often are encased with light steel plates. When steel is not employed, the insulating blocks are coated with asbestos or vermiculite cement for sealing. These plastic coatings, or insulating blocks plus coatings, are used to a depth of 3 to 4 inches on the chamber roofs. Vermiculite or diatomaceous concrete may be used on the floors of the chambers. Insulating bricks or blocks of vermiculite or asbestos may be used on the flue walls and arches.

FORCED-DRAFT FANS

A forced-draft fan (Figure 16—12) is the most important auxiliary of relatively recent adoption for modern furnaces. When operating on natural draft, the only force causing air flow into the furnace ports from the regenerative system is the heat head or stack effect of the checker chambers and uptakes. Thus, not only the temperature of the air varies from one end of the air cycle to the other, but also the quantity of air. In addition, since the checkers are under a pressure less than atmospheric because of natural draft, air infiltration is induced.

It should be noted that the actual positive and negative pressures within the furnace referred to in discussing forced draft and natural draft are only slight, amounting to only a few hundredths of an inch of water pressure.

The benefits of forced draft are threefold:
(1) The volume of air entering the furnace through the regenerators is maintained constant at a given setting, being influenced only by changes in motor and fan speed or valve settings.
(2) The delivery of air under slight positive pressure to the furnace system by a fan lessens air infiltration through flues, checker chambers, fantails and slag pockets during the cycle when air is passing through on its way to the inlet port.
(3) Delivery of air under pressure to the furnace constitutes an automatic warning system in the sense that it will cause a decided outflow of heat into the furnace cellar in case of leaks in the auxiliary system. This factor promotes prompt attention by maintenance crews to any leaks that may develop and keeps furnace efficiency at a constant high level.

FLUES

The type of flue generally used for modern open-hearth furnaces between the regenerative system and the stack or waste-heat boiler is one which has a relatively flat arched top and is supported by a hori-

zontal concrete pad under the flue with concrete retaining walls on the sides. They generally are built
with 13½ inch walls and arches of second-quality
fireclay brick. On the top of the arch and between the
side walls and the concrete retaining walls is used a
layer of insulating concrete or similar material having
an insulating and sealing effect. The floor of the flue
is paved with second-quality fireclay brick, and between this and the concrete pad underneath is a 6-inch
layer of insulating concrete.

VALVES

Figure 16—21 shows a flue and valve system for an
open-hearth furnace with two checker chambers at
each end. With the slides of the two double-deck
reversing valves at the right in lowered position, air
from the forced-air fan passes through the upper
opening in each valve to enter the flues leading to the
checkers at one end of the furnace. The raised slides
on the two reversing valves at the left permit waste
gases from the other end of the furnace to pass to the
stack if the stack valve is open and the waste-heat-
boiler valve is closed, or through the waste-heat
boiler and thence to the stack if the stack valve is
closed and that of the waste-heat boiler is opened.

Figure 16—22 shows a simplified installation of one
type of double-deck slide valve for a furnace of the
smaller type using non-preheated fuel, to illustrate
how the positions of the slide influence the path of
travel of the gases.

The sliding dampers or slide valves are fabricated
from steel plates and are water-cooled. The seats on
which they slide are made of cast iron, and also are
water-cooled. The seats and dampers are machined to
provide gas-tight closure.

WASTE-HEAT BOILERS

Up to 33 per cent of the fuel input to an open-
hearth furnace (gross heating value of the fuel) can
be recovered in the form of steam by the use of a
proper waste-heat boiler with an economizer. The 33
per cent figure is based upon the equivalent fuel
energy represented by actual steam. Taking boiler efficiency into account (say, 80 per cent) the actual heat
recovered equals 33 divided by 80 or 41 per cent
equivalent fuel. The waste-heat boiler imposes additional resistance to the flow of waste gases and involves the use of an induced-draft fan (Figure
16—12). This fan, however, actually provides an
improvement to the furnace system proper, because

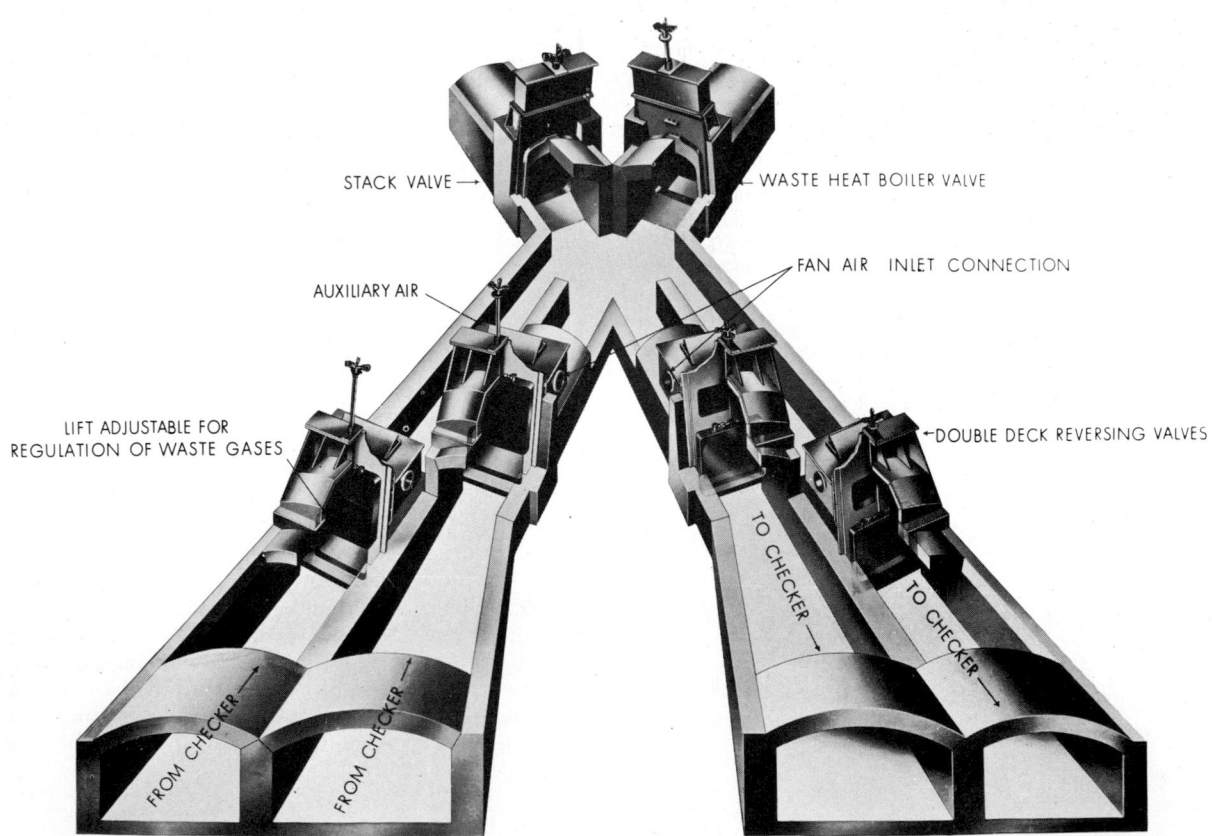

FIG. 16—21. Flue arrangement and valve system for modern regenerative furnace with two checker chambers at each
end. (Courtesy, Blaw-Knox Company.)

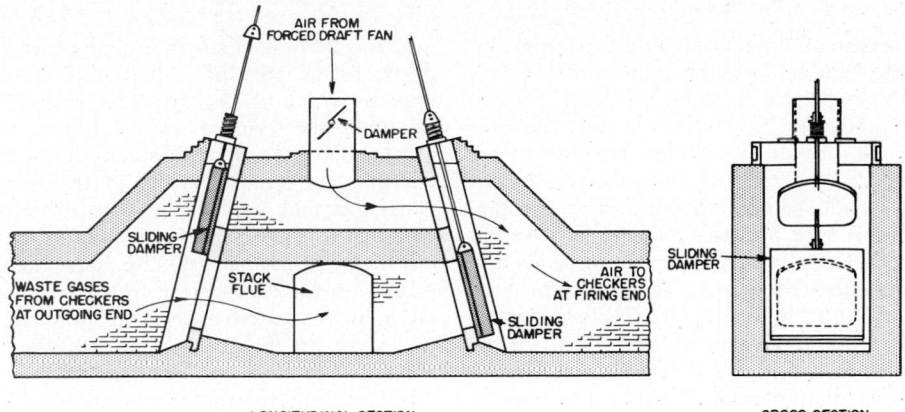

FIG. 16—22. Arrangement of one type of slide valve controlling flow of combustion air to, and waste gases from, an open-hearth furnace fired with non-preheated fuel. The two sliding dampers are operated simultaneously by the same winch, so that as one slides upward the other slides downward to reverse the directions of flow of air and waste gases through the system.

of the following reasons: (1) the induced-draft fan assures ample draft to remove waste gases from the furnace system almost regardless of the condition of the checkerwork. (2) Since the induced-draft fan is independent of temperature and temperature variation, and has the power to accelerate the movement of the column of waste gases, it permits more accurate control of furnace pressure.

While conventional water-tube boilers were used formerly in waste-heat recovery, the use of such boilers has been abandoned almost entirely in favor of the horizontal fire-tube type.

Waste-heat boilers, in the modern plants whose general layout was described previously, are located on the ground-level floor of the lean-to building, but, in any case, they must be located close to the stack.

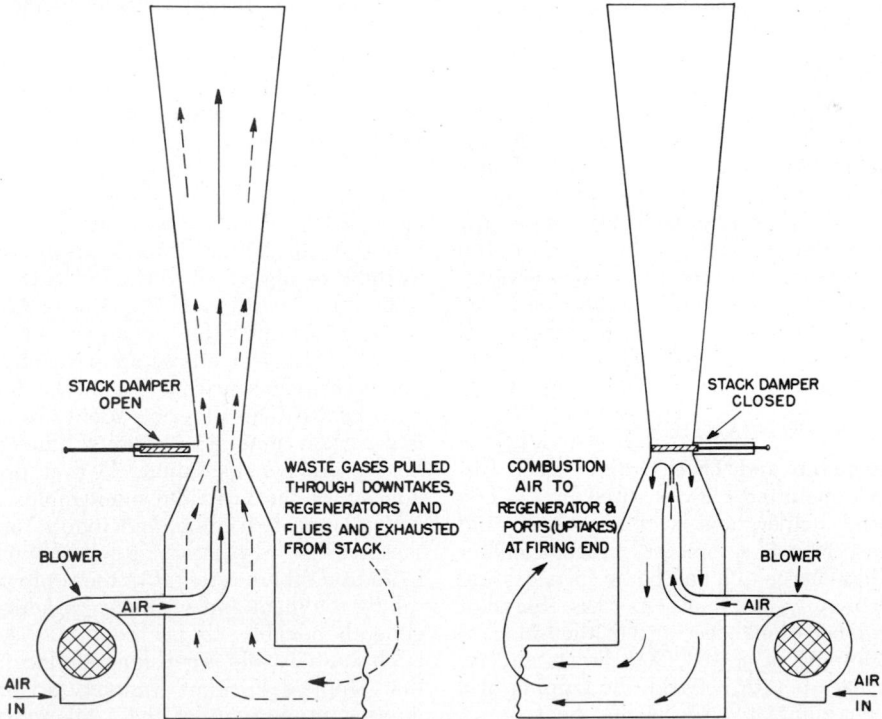

FIG. 16—23. Schematic arrangement of a special type of stack utilizing the venturi principle for controlling gas flow through an open-hearth furnace. There is a stack for each end of the furnace. Height of these stacks is considerably less than conventional open-hearth stacks that depend largely on natural draft for their operation.

STACKS

While in the case of a modern open-hearth installation with waste-heat boilers, the induced-draft fans produce the larger part of the total draft effect in exhausting the furnace gases, stacks still must be provided. They must provide enough natural draft to enable the process to be carried on when the waste-heat boilers are on repair, or enough draft when the furnaces are being rebuilt and the regenerative system is being cleaned. This draft during cleaning is needed so that the regenerative system will be kept cool enough to permit entry by the repair crew for cleaning out dust under the checker work. Stacks are brick-lined steel shells, from 150 to 225 feet high above the base, with inside diameters of 7 feet in the case of modern furnaces.

A special type of stack, utilizing forced and induced draft, forms part of a patented system (the Isley system) which utilizes two forced-draft fans and two relatively short venturi stacks (Figure 16—23). Alternately, one fan with the stack valve open is used to energize an ejector nozzle in the one stack at the waste-gas end while, with the other stack damper closed, the second fan, prevented from blowing air out of the stack because the stack damper is closed, pushes air for combustion to the furnace through the regenerative system at its corresponding end. In order to reverse the flow of air and furnace gases, it is only necessary to close the one stack valve and open the other one, and to regulate the amount of air blown by the fans to supply draft effect and air for combustion.

SECTION 4

OPERATION OF A BASIC OPEN-HEARTH

It was stated in preceding Section 3 that, so far as *construction* is concerned, the only important difference between acid and basic furnaces is the fact that basic materials are required in the bottom and banks of the basic furnace, while the acid process requires a bottom and banks lined with silica brick and sand. There is, however, a great difference in their *operation* and in the raw materials used for each, the difference being so great as to make a separate treatment of the two processes from this point necessary. Since the basic open-hearth process is the leading steelmaking process in this country, it will be described first. The acid open-hearth process will be described in Sections 9 and 10.

The basic process will be discussed under two headings: "Ore Practice," and "Oxygen Roof Lance Practice." The reason for this is, that while similar chemical reactions occur in both practices, in the older ore practice the progress of a heat is in several rather well-defined stages occurring at slower rates than in the newer oxygen practice. Consequently, an understanding of ore practice will simplify the description of how the adoption of oxygen practice has benefitted the process.

ORE PRACTICE

Furnace Attendants and Their Duties—Each furnace requires an operating crew of three men: a first helper, a second helper, and a third helper, and supervising these men is a foreman, called a melter foreman, who has charge of a number of furnaces and their crews. Ordinarily, the first helper has charge of the furnace (with occasional checkups by the foreman) except at the tapping of a heat, and directs any repairs to the furnace hearth between the tapping of a heat and the charging of a succeeding heat or repairs during the heat.

Charging—When a basic open-hearth furnace is ready to receive its charge for the first heat after it is built (or, subsequently, when a furnace bottom or hearth has been replaced by a new one) it is usually considered necessary to use a special charge in which limestone, scrap and cold pig iron are charged in the order given. The amounts of scrap and cold pig iron are proportioned so that when the charge is all melted and the lime resulting from the calcination of the limestone has risen through the melted charge, the carbon content of the bath and its temperature will permit the finishing of the heat to make a product acceptable in the current practice of the steel works. The next three or four heats are made using a molten pig iron charge (if molten iron is available) that is less in amount than the normal molten pig iron charge currently used in the furnaces of the shop, and a correspondingly higher amount of scrap. Following these heats, the normal charge is used. In normal practice, a predetermined quantity of iron ore is charged to provide low-cost iron units, and oxygen for controlling the carbon content of the bath when the charge is all melted. The range in composition permissible in pig iron to be used in the production of basic open-hearth steel is given in Chapter 14.

After the first few charges, proportioning the amount of pig iron and scrap in the charge is usually a matter in which neither the melter foreman nor the open-hearth shop superintendent has a choice. There is a certain amount of scrap produced in the open-hearth process, including (1) that produced in the pouring of the heat into ingot molds, i.e., pit scrap, and (2) rejected ingots and ingots too short to roll, these two items comprising possibly 4 or 5 per cent; in addition there is item (3), the scrap produced when rolling the ingot and secondary products, which is, in general, possibly 25 per cent of the ingot weight. Such scrap usually is consumed in local melting rather than shipped to other company shops or sold. The limiting proportions of the total scrap and pig iron charge, and the proportionate parts of the pig iron in molten and cold forms, are governed and restricted by economic considerations. These economic considerations change with the location of the shop, with respect to the proximity of an adequate supply of raw materials, the amount of molten pig iron available, and the scrap available from integrated units.

In order to consider the matter of the charge for basic open-hearth furnaces in the United States, it is necessary to make a preliminary classification of charges as follows:

Type 1—**All Liquid Iron (generally called "hot metal")**, where the blast-furnace capacity associated with a given shop is in excess of demand. This type of charge is very seldom used because it has been found more economical, when such a proportion of molten pig iron is available, to oxidize part of the supply of molten pig iron in a Bessemer converter and to charge the incompletely decarburized metal in a special type of open-hearth furnace (see duplex process, Section 11), or to speed up the melting rate of the usual open-hearth furnaces by making such blown metal a part of their charge.

Type 2—**Liquid Iron and Liquid Steel.** This method grew out of the attempt to develop a practical and economical method of using 100 per cent liquid pig iron, as shown in Type 1 (see duplex process). Ordinarily, the charge is molten pig iron and blown metal from a Bessemer converter (where molten iron was charged and was blown with air). The greater proportion of the charge to the open-hearth furnace is blown metal in the case of tilting furnaces employed in the duplex process. Blown metal is used at present in stationary open-hearth furnaces for producing only a small proportion of the steel made in such furnaces.

Type 3—**Solid Steel (Steel Scrap) and Liquid Iron (with some cold pig iron).** A quite common situation calls for the use of solid scrap and molten pig iron. Thus a mill which rolls its own steel ingots and has its own blast furnaces would use this method. Where the supply of scrap is restricted, liquid iron may also be used to make up such deficiency of local scrap. The amount of iron ore charged is proportioned to control the carbon content of the bath when it is completely melted.

Type 4—**Solid Steel (Steel Scrap) and Solid Iron.** Where molten pig iron is not available locally, and where cheapness of available scrap prevents justification for building blast furnaces, the pig iron may be used in solid (cold) form.

Type 5—**All Solid Steel (Steel Scrap).** Where no pig iron is available or the cost makes its use prohibitive, the charge may consist of all steel scrap. The carbon content at which the bath is completely melted is controlled by the weight of coke or other carbonaceous material charged with the scrap. The charging and working of heats of this type require considerable skill and the method is a specialized one not representing common practice.

There are some few cases in which the charge is proportioned between scrap, cold pig iron and molten iron in order to secure special features in the quality of the product but, in general, cold pig iron, scrap iron castings, and broken scrap molds are charged in varying amounts depending upon availability of molten iron. However, high quality steel may be produced from almost any of the common types of charge.

The solid parts of the charge are placed in the furnace and heated for a sufficient time before charging molten pig iron. The limestone is charged first and scrap is charged directly over the limestone except where ore is charged, in which case the latter is spread over the limestone. Sometimes several charging box loads of scrap are spread on the furnace bottom and the limestone is placed above this. In many shops there is a quantity of cold pig iron which must be used and, in practically all cases, there are pit scrap, ingots too short to roll, scrapped ingots, and broken ingot molds to be consumed.

It is very desirable in most cases to charge the solid materials as fast as the volume of this material permits. Steel scrap may vary from steel turnings and sheet shearings which are graded as "light scrap" to bloom shearings and ingot butts which are in the "heavy scrap" grade. The time required to get the solid charge into the furnace has a marked influence on the time required to make the heat of steel (taken from the beginning of charging to the tapping of the heat from the furnace). Since the scrap comprises the greater part of the solid charge and the weight per unit volume varies over a considerable range, its value as an item of the charge should be based in part on the space it occupies per unit of weight as charged in the furnace. Taking into consideration the space occupied in charging box or furnace and the desire that the total charge will become liquid at a required carbon content, it follows that light scrap requires more pig iron or less ore to be charged than does a heavy grade of scrap. In charging a group of furnaces, it is necessary to consider very carefully the proper proportioning of the amounts of light, heavy and medium scrap. Light scrap requires more charging boxes, which take up much track space and increase the time required for charging. Scrap that is relatively too heavy gives the minimum time in charging, but slower melting.

The charging practice for limestone and scrap is usually the same whether cold pig iron or molten pig iron is used. The quantity of limestone for the greater part of American practice ranges from 5 to 8 per cent of the total metallic charge; burned lime for equivalent fluxing effect being 3 to 4 per cent. The pounds of lime (CaO) required (to be added by these fluxes) must be proportioned on the basis of pounds of silicon, phosphorus and sulphur in the total charge, and silica in the limestone and ore, with additional consideration for the sulphur in the fuel and a knowledge of the quantity of lime and silica provided for slag reactions from the dolomite used as a refractory.

Before considering the amount of ore required to be charged, it is necessary to review the sources from which oxygen is available for the process. These sources are:

Scale formed during heating of the charge, rust (oxides, carbonates) on solid scrap.

Oxidizing oxides in slags at different stages. (Oxidizing oxides are reducible oxides FeO, MnO, etc., but not stable oxides CaO, MgO, Al$_2$O$_3$, etc.)

Carbon dioxide (CO$_2$) resulting from calcination of limestone.

Oxygen from combustion air causing direct oxidation of metal.

Iron ore, roll scale (including heating furnace cinder), sintered ore, nodulized ore, ore briquettes; as charged with initial charge or fed after bath is melted.

The quantity of ore to be charged must be proportioned so that, with the other sources of oxygen available up to the time the bath is melted completely, the net effect will lead to the desired content of carbon in the completely melted bath with the lime all up from the furnace bottom. In most cases, the amount of ore is dictated by experience, and spot decisions may have to be made by the first helper or melter depending on the actual charge materials at the furnace: e.g., he may omit charging of one or two boxes of ore if the quantity of light scrap is more than expected.

The ore charged is usually spread on the limestone. The quantity varies from 0 to 25 per cent; the high limit being required with unusually large proportions of molten pig iron. The ore charged is usually fine so that it is classified as "soft," but part or all of this natural ore may be replaced with sintered, nodulized or briquetted ore, or imported ore, some of which is harder and contains less fines than domestic ores.

When the per cent of molten pig iron in the total charge is greater than 45 per cent, the resulting higher carbon content makes it necessary to add a considerable quantity of ore after the charge is completely melted, or even to charge ore with the initial charge. With charges of above 45 to 50 per cent of molten pig iron, general practice is to charge ore with the initial charge, and then to feed ore to the completely melted charge if needed.

Solid pig iron is added immediately after the scrap charge or even after the scrap is melted down partially. Molten pig iron, on the other hand, must be added at a carefully judged moment, for the melting and oxidation of the scrap must progress to a stage which insures that the oxides start to work in oxidation of the metalloids of the molten pig iron as soon as it is charged. If the molten metal is added too soon, it will be chilled by the scrap. If the charging is delayed too long and the scrap is too highly oxidized, the carbon content of the bath, when the charge is completely melted, may be too low, and the progress in completing the process delayed. Molten pig iron is poured from the metal mixer or from large mixer type ladles into a transfer ladle. This may be carried on an electric overhead crane all the way to the furnace or it may be placed on an electric transfer buggy and transported to a point near the front of the furnace to be charged, lifted off by an electric overhead crane and its contents poured through a runner or spout inserted through one of the furnace doors by the charging machine (Figure 16—24).

Two of the more common types of charge, which should be listed under Type 3 above, are outlined below.

"Fifty-Fifty" Practice—This term refers to a charge which consists of roughly 50 per cent pig iron and 50 per cent scrap. Such an amount of molten pig iron is large enough to require the use of ore in the initial charge and, depending on the local procedures and efficiency of the furnaces in heat transfer to the charge, a run-off or flush practice is used. Limits of molten pig iron are usually 45 to 55 per cent and the charge may include a relatively small amount of solid pig iron, cast iron scrap or broken ingot molds. With this charge, equipment usually is provided for a run-off or flush practice (see "Melting Down After Molten Pig Iron Addition"). Limestone is normally used since burned lime is more expensive. Fine ore, sintered ore, nodulized ore, or ore briquettes may be used interchangeably. The amount of ore required in the charge is not sufficient to cause serious trouble from violent evolution of combined moisture (water of crystallization), unless an excess of combined moisture is present; i.e., ignition loss is over 5 per cent.

High Molten Pig Iron Practice—This includes those cases in which the percentage of molten pig iron is about 55 to 80 per cent of the total charge and leads to the use of a run-off or flush-off slag for economical operation.

A considerable amount of metallic iron is recovered from the ore which is necessarily charged, and this displaces scrap in the charge to the extent that necessary purchase of scrap is lessened. Because of the relatively large amount of ore used, the physical characteristics and chemical composition of the ore are critical in attaining the desired production rate and quality of product. Excessive fineness and higher silica and combined moisture contents are objectionable characteristics. The degree of fineness and combined moisture of many ores may be corrected partially by sintering, nodulizing and briquetting. The charged ore in this practice is placed on the limestone so that the latter is well covered. Since the proportion of scrap is low, it is important to heat and oxidize the scrap well before charging the molten iron so that a good flush ensues after the hot metal is added to promote elimination of oxidizable metalloids (especially silicon).

Melting Down the Charge—The melting period really begins when the first scrap has been charged. It is important to melt the scrap and other solid metallic elements of the charge quickly, and to oxidize them by sufficient excess oxygen in the flame so as to have them at such a temperature and degree of oxidation that, on the one hand, the molten pig iron charged will not be chilled by the scrap and, on the other hand, the oxidation of the metalloids of the pig iron will not be delayed by insufficient oxygen supply from the oxidized scrap. Therefore, a high rate of fuel input is desirable with a flame which transfers the maximum

FIG. 16—24. Making the hot metal (molten pig iron) addition to an open-hearth furnace. Rate of flow of the hot metal is controlled by the rate at which the crane hook attached to the rear of the ladle near the bottom is raised.

number of heat units to the charge over the largest possible area of the charge. This must be subject to the restriction that the roof refractories must not be fused nor the flame extend to the outgoing end of the furnace. When the solid charge is relatively cool in relation to flame temperature, the best condition for heat transfer to the charge exists and the roof will remain relatively cool. Recent developments in burning fuel over the charge have permitted an increase in rate of fuel input and transfer of heat units to the charge, thus considerably decreasing the time from the start of charging to tapping. These developments include the use of oxygen or compressed air introduced in proper relationship to the fuel stream and the preheated primary air coming in from the "incoming" furnace port. In the case of liquid fuels, the use of more than one burner at each end of the furnace has increased the rate at which heat can be transferred to the solid charge.

Later in the melting down period, after charging molten pig iron, and still later when lime comes up, proportionately more heat units are absorbed by the roof and walls than in the earlier stages of melting when the charge was relatively cold. The fuel input must therefore be controlled carefully.

With proper attention to the techniques of fast charging, e.g., mixing light and heavy scrap, and to maintaining high fuel rate and a flame favoring efficient heat transfer, it is possible, with the aid of an experienced and skilled first helper, to have the temperature and oxidation of the charge advanced to the point which permits charging of the molten pig iron two hours after the start of charging. At this time, part of the solid metallic charge has melted and, mixed with a slag of oxidized metalloids, has trickled down over and through the charge.

Melting Down After Molten Pig Iron Addition—In the period following the addition of hot metal, important reactions take place, dictated by the chemical conditions of the process and the proportioning and timing of the charge. The chemical reactions have to do with removing carbon, manganese, phosphorus, sulphur and silicon from the metallic bath. First to be removed are silicon and manganese. These are oxidized to SiO_2 and MnO, and become part of the slag. When these have been largely removed from the bath, the oxidation of carbon has already begun and now becomes vigorous. The carbon is oxidized to CO gas which, in escaping, causes agitation of the bath. Eventually phosphorus is oxidized to P_2O_5 and this becomes part of the slag. Sulphur is transferred to the slag and held there as CaS.

When using a high percentage of molten pig iron, the evolving CO gas causes foaming of the slag, which can begin to run from the furnace through openings provided for the purpose. The method of open-hearth operation that involves slag removal in this manner is referred to as **flush practice.** In addition to a notch or hole through the back wall that is common to all furnaces using flush practice, most modern furnaces have in addition facilities for flushing slag from the front of the furnace also. To permit **front flushing,** a notch or trough is cut in the dolomite of the front bank at the center door. Slag running from the flushing hole at the back or pit side of the furnace may be carried by a spout to a slag pot set beneath the spout, or the slag may be allowed to run onto the floor of the pit to be removed when solidified. Slag leaving the furnace over the bank at the front or charging side of the furnace passes through the opening in a hollow casting set in the charging floor and runs into a slag pot set on a car running on tracks at cellar level (see Figure 16—5). This car can be handled readily by locomotives. The openings for slag removal are maintained carefully at the best level to obtain a prompt and adequate slag run-off containing as little metal as possible. The openings in the banks originally are dammed with crushed dolomite, which is raked out to provide an adequate channel for the molten slag. The run-off period may last for an hour in good operating practice. From study of the composition of run-off slags, it is evident that considerable phosphorus and silicon (as oxides) and also sulphur (as sulphides) are removed by the run-off from the furnace. The oxidation of the liquid portion and the melting of the solid portion of the charge continues until the ore in the charge has completed its reaction with the liquid metal.

When carbon monoxide is generated by oxidation of carbon, the turbulence it causes is different in appearance from that caused by release of CO_2 in calcination of the limestone. The CO gas evolution or agitation is more even and gentle, and is commonly called the **ore boil,** and the more violent turbulence caused by CO_2 is called the **lime boil.** It is, of course, true that the oxidation of carbon and resulting gas evolution in the first case results from reaction of carbon with all the reducible oxides in contact with molten metal, not alone the ore, so that it could be more correctly designated as the **iron oxide boil.** This stage of the heat is suppressed in degree of oxidation when scrap is a high percentage of the total charge. Usually it is not until the slag run-off is completed that sufficient heat has been transferred downward through the charge to start the calcination of the limestone and begin the lime boil.

The melting of scrap and solid pig iron charges exhibit the same reactions as those in the practice using molten pig iron. Melting is slower because the total charge is cold at the start, and the vigorous nature of the hot metal reaction is missing. The lime boil occurs later.

One difficulty occurring with high molten pig iron practice when a poor flush is obtained is the tendency toward formation of foamy slags which, containing entrained gas bubbles, are relatively poor heat conductors. This condition results in a cold bath with sluggish action, and a lack of stirring action which further decreases heat transfer from the flame. This presents a difficult problem—how to transfer heat from flame to bath while absorption of heat by the bath is limited by foamy slags. Under these conditions, the liquid fuels (and even the gaseous fuels of higher specific gravity) have distinct advantages over a light fuel gas such as coke-oven gas, since liquid fuel gives more jet action and suppresses the foaming.

As the carbon content of the bath decreases and its temperature rises, the ore boil subsides or changes character, the calcination of limestone becomes more rapid and the lime boil predominates. As it progresses, solid lime rises up through the liquid bath, which is bubbling violently, largely because of the CO_2 given off by calcining limestone; the CO_2 oxidizes some carbon to CO on its upward travel. Lime, by rising to the top of the bath, is now available to replace iron and manganese oxides in the phosphates, sulphates and silicates present and thus become part of the slag, with any excess of lime being taken up to make the slag more basic. The basic property of the slag makes it more capable of retaining both the phosphoric and silicic oxides in the same slag, and renders the phosphate less liable to be reduced with resultant return of phosphorus to the metal. Since the CO_2 released in calcination of the limestone has an oxidizing effect, limestone is equivalent in net effect to a certain amount of ore charged and, theoretically, this oxidizing power is equal to that of 60 per cent by weight of charged ore of the average quality. The lime boil has another function which helps to promote the process. It definitely helps to equalize the temperature and chemical composition of the bath as between levels from top to bottom. The ore boil also has this function but with less effect because in its phase the bath has not advanced as far towards complete fluidity and mobility.

The lime rises to the surface of the bath mostly in lumps that are appreciably smaller than those charged. In the case where burned lime is charged, it finally rises without a preliminary boil. The solid risen lime gradually dissolves in the slag formed from the earlier oxidation of Mn, Si, P and Fe, into which has been introduced some CaO and MgO contributed by erosion of the basic hearth during the early stages of the heat. Special fluxing agents are used in many cases to facilitate the solution of lime lumps in the slag, fluorspar being the one most used.

After the ore boil and the lime boil have subsided, the **working period** or **refining period** begins. The end of the melting period generally is taken as approximately the time when all the lime has risen from the bottom through a substantially melted charge. The usual indication of an approach to the condition known as "lime up" is the cessation of the lime boil.

As removal of carbon from the all liquid bath proceeds, the melting temperature of the steel rises. This requires an increase in fuel rate to provide an increased transfer of heat to the bath to maintain proper fluidity. Efficiency of combustion of the fuel in this case is aided by a high level of preheat of the air for combustion, and this preheat level can be raised by utilizing the heat in the checkers, by reversing the flow of fuel and air more frequently.

The aims of the working period are: (1) to lower the phosphorus and sulphur contents to levels safely below the maximum level specified, (2) to eliminate carbon as rapidly as possible and still allow time for proper conditioning of slag and attainment of proper process temperature, and (3) to bring the heat to a condition ready for final deoxidation in the furnace or

for tapping, with the slag having the proper viscosity and chemical composition and with the desired carbon and oxygen levels in the bath and the proper final bath temperature for the composition and grade of the steel being produced. The slag must contain large quantities of oxidizing agents during the working period, but must be strongly basic at the end of that period. The conditions under which these aims are advanced to a conclusion depend on the grade of steel being made, whether it is to be finished as of fully killed, semi-killed or rimmed quality, and also on the carbon range specified.

The carbon content of the bath when melted is extremely important. The open-hearth process is used to produce steel with carbon contents as poured which vary from over 1.00 per cent carbon to less than 0.02 per cent. Usually, the procedure is to oxidize the carbon in the bath to a point slightly lower than the final content desired in order to allow for the inevitable increase in carbon content due to the carbon contained in the final ferroalloy additions. Modifications of this method have been used frequently in past practice but in up-to-date practices are used in a relatively small proportion of the heats of steel produced. These modifications involve oxidizing the carbon in the bath to a much lower level than is desired in the finished steel and then "re-carburizing" the metal by addition of molten pig iron into the furnace just before tapping or by adding carbonaceous material, such as coke or coal, to the steel as it runs into the ladle. In all cases, it is necessary to have the heat melt at a higher carbon content than the percentage desired when the heat is ready to tap. The general procedure is to balance the charge in the beginning of the process so that the heat will melt 0.30 to 0.50 per cent carbon above the carbon content at which the heat is to be tapped. This is based on the principle that, during the time required to oxidize this amount of carbon from the bath, ample time for controlling slag and bath composition and temperature will be available.

It was stated above that, in the melting period preceding the working period, a certain proportion of the carbon, manganese, phosphorus and silicon was eliminated from the bath by oxidation. During the working period also the final controlled elimination of these elements is accomplished by oxidation, the sources of oxygen being oxygen from the furnace gases, iron oxides such as **feed ore** added to the bath, and the blowing of gaseous oxygen by a lance inserted under the metal surface. With respect to the oxidizing influence of the flame, a given open-hearth furnace, burning a selected fuel, has a characteristic range in oxidizing effect which changes to some extent with the life of the furnace. The limit of this oxidizing rate also is affected by the requirement that the maximum heat output must be obtained from the fuel. The oxygen from the iron oxide fed to the bath provides the predominating oxidizing effect so that it, rather than oxidation by the flame, is used to provide the major control element for regulating rate of oxidation. The iron oxide fed also hastens the solution of undissolved lime floating in the slag and generates a boiling action of the bath which assists in removing gases and controlling the temperature.

Lump ore, fine ore, ore briquettes and, to a minor degree, roll scale, are the forms in which iron oxide is added to the bath. Lump ore or briquettes float, so as to project through the slag into the liquid metal and, therefore, give relatively more contact with the metal bath than does fine ore or roll scale. As a result, oxidation occurs much more rapidly when the relatively bulky oxides are used than with the finer, lighter material. Lump ore has been found preferable but at present an adequate supply of "hard" lump ore is becoming more difficult to obtain and the procedure of compacting fine ores into sintered or briquetted masses equivalent to lump ore is receiving increasing attention. The silica content of these iron oxides is important because of the lowering of basicity of the slag by silica. The iron oxide addition causes a decrease in bath temperature, compensated for, to some extent, by the effect of the vigorous action of oxidation in providing a more efficient heat transfer from flame to slag and metal. When the bath receives the oxidizing agents it must be sufficiently hot to prevent freezing by the additions and must also be at a temperature sufficient to promote the endothermic reaction by which oxygen leaves the iron oxide and combines with carbon, silicon and phosphorus (see Section 8).

On the lower carbon grades of steel, it is customary in many plants to add pure oxygen in gaseous form. This is accomplished by inserting a steel lance below the metal surface through one of the furnace doors. The pure oxygen reacts rapidly and raises bath temperature; furthermore, no impurities are added. For each furnace and for each practice in making a desired product there is a rate of adding iron oxide which appears best for the combined objectives of high production rate and adequate quality level. The quantity of iron oxide added and the time between additions is governed by the rate at which heat can be introduced into the bath. If too much ore is added at one time or the additions are too close together, the bath will be chilled and its temperature will approach too closely its melting point. Such a heat would be too cold to tap and pour successfully and, because of its sluggishness, would be very difficult to heat back to proper temperature. After each addition of iron oxide has been allowed time to react, a test is taken in order to make an approximation of the carbon content of the steel by examining the fracture of a broken, cold sample, or to obtain a more accurate carbon determination by chemical analysis, or by an instrument such as the Carbometer. In the last half hour or hour of the process, no iron oxide will be added. To obtain the agitation necessary to final oxidation of carbon to the level desired before adding deoxidizers to the furnace or tapping, stirring with steel rods, or the turbulence caused by inserting green-wood poles into the bath, may be employed.

On the steel samples taken soon after the heat is melted, determinations of phosphorus and sulphur are often made by rapid laboratory methods in order to determine what additions and slag-control procedures must follow in order to obtain less than the maximum content specified for these elements. Sulphur removal is relatively slow and difficult to predict and its introduction through the scrap, pig iron, fluxes, fuel and additions should be kept to a minimum. The basicity and viscosity of the slag must be controlled because certain chemical compositions and physical conditions of the slag are favorable for various stages of the heat and finally for various types of heats. Higher basicity levels are necessary to prevent subsequent phosphorus reversion at higher carbon levels. Its chemical composition may be adjusted by additions of burned lime, limestone, iron oxide or silica sand; its basicity is increased through lime additions, and it may be made more fluid by additions of fluorspar and roll scale. CaO is usually provided by burned lime, but sometimes by raw limestone. Fluorspar should be used sparingly. Slag samples may be taken by a spoon either for the purpose of obtaining samples for chemical (or spectrographic) analysis or for the purpose of observing the physical appearance of slag pancakes made by pouring molten slag on a steel plate or in a mold. From experience with slags of many compositions, this latter method of judging the basicity and the iron content of the slag has become dependable. This procedure is discussed further in Section 8 of this chapter.

The appearance of the slag and metal in the furnace, and that of the metal as poured from the sample spoon into a sample mold, are used by furnace operators to check other methods for determination of temperature and composition. Each slag or steel sample must be considered as revealing only part of a history of events so that a number of samples are necessary for proper interpretation of conditions and appraisal of future developments.

Actually the first step in slag control is the control of composition of the open-hearth furnace charge since this, with the other factor of the amount of silica and phosphorus removed in the run-off slag, determines the amount of limestone to be charged. Most of the elements oxidized, which combine with lime from limestone or from eroded refractories to form slag, come from the molten or solid pig iron charged. This leads to the conclusion that slag control begins with the control of blast furnace operations. In this connection, it may be pointed out that some sulphur may be eliminated from the molten pig iron on the way from the blast furnace to the open hearth by combining with manganese in the iron, if the sulphur and manganese are above certain limits, and the time of transportation from the blast furnace to the open hearth is long enough, including time in the mixer, to permit the reaction to take place under the proper cooling conditions. Thus, there may be some removal of sulphur before the chemical reactions in the basic open-hearth process take place.

The aims of slag control may be stated as follows:

1. To remove phosphorus and sulphur originally in the bath to below the desired levels in the finished steel.

2. To produce the required degree of oxidation of the bath at the end of the refining period.

3. To arrive at the proper level of oxidation of the

bath in the minimum of time consistent with the steel quality desired.

4. To use the minimum quantities of lime and deoxidizers.

5. To produce the required product with the minimum quantity of iron lost in the slag.

The second aim of slag control given above, to produce the required degree of oxidation of the bath at the end of the refining period, will vary within a wide range, depending on the type of steel being produced.

There are three general types of steel, classified according to their behavior in the molds and the resulting ingot structure: rimming steels, semi-killed steels and killed steels. The production of a particular type of steel involves control of the degree of oxidation of the bath at the end of the refining period. How the oxygen content of steel affects the manner in which steel solidifies in the ingot molds is discussed in detail in Chapter 18.

Duration of Various Periods in Production of Basic Open-Hearth Steel—Based upon employing ore practice, a modern, large, basic open-hearth furnace of 200 to 225 tons capacity, fired with a liquid fuel such as tar or oil, the amount of time consumed during various stages of a heat are as follows:

Melt Down (simultaneous with charging) ..	2.5 hr.
Hot Metal Addition	0.5 hr.
Ore Boil	3.0 hr.
Lime Boil	1.5 hr.
Working Period	2.5 hr.
Total Heat Time	10.0 hr.

The use of oxygen may shorten both the melt-down and working periods by about 0.5 hr. each, as discussed later.

OXYGEN ROOF-LANCE PRACTICE

Because of the numerous variations in the methods employed for using oxygen in the basic open-hearth furnace, this discussion will be based largely upon the practices ordinarily employed in plants of the United States Steel Corporation. As previously stated, the two principal factors that have made possible the present extensive use of oxygen were: (1) the increased availability of low-cost tonnage oxygen, and (2) the development of improved basic refractories and a practical design of basic roof that permitted the use of oxygen in optimum quantities.

The use of gaseous oxygen in the open hearth increases flame temperature and the rate of heat transfer to the charge, and thereby speeds melting of high-scrap charges. It also compensates for deficiencies in air supply and regenerator capacity, and has been practiced for some time, wherever it was considered economical. Some steelmaking plants have experimented with the use of mixtures of natural gas and oxygen to provide intense sources of supplemental heat to still further hasten the melting of solid components of the charge.

Oxygen was first applied in the open hearth to obtain low carbon contents and was later applied to increase the rate of carbon removal. The oxygen flowed through bare steel pipes inserted into the metal bath through the wicket holes in the furnace doors. This practice is still used in some plants to produce steels with tapping carbon contents of less than 0.04 per cent. However, the lance or pipe burns off rapidly at the slag-metal interface and has to be replaced, even when protected by wrappings or refractory coatings. The use of a lance inserted through a wicket hole has the disadvantage that the connecting hoses and protruding pipe interfere with operations and with movements of buggies in front of the furnaces.

In experiments to increase production rates, water-cooled oxygen lances have been inserted at various positions (the backwall, the endwalls, and the roof). The end of the lance has been held at different levels above the metal surface, oxygen has been injected at various velocities (even supersonic), and single-hole and multiple-hole lances have been tried. Although oxygen-lancing practice remains quite varied, the general trend is toward the use of two six-hole roof lances, a basic roof construction, and oxygen injection starting immediately after the hot-metal addition. One successful design of oxygen lance is shown in Figure 16—25.

In the open-hearth process, the production rate depends upon the rate at which heat can be absorbed for melting the metallics, reducing the iron ore, and forming the slag. In regular practice, the overall efficiency of heat transfer is generally between 20 and 30 per cent of the heat input. This range reflects the conditions during the melting down of scrap when the rate of heat transfer is high, as well as after the bath is molten and covered with slag and the efficiency of heat transfer is low. When conventional fuels are burned over a bath of liquid metal and slag, the efficiency of utilization of the heat generated is relatively low—about 15 per cent of the heat from the fuel and preheated air. This efficiency depends on the fourth power temperature difference between the flame and the bath. Of course, some of this heat in the waste gases is recovered in regenerators and waste-heat boilers. When oxygen is injected into the bath, the heat generated by the chemical reactions of the oxygen in the bath is absorbed very rapidly and the efficiency of heat transfer is probably close to 100 per cent.

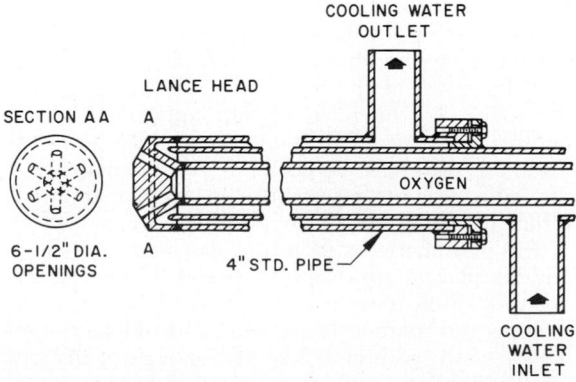

FIG. 16—25. Diagrammatic construction of oxygen roof lance.

In modern oxygen roof-lance practice, the flow of oxygen to the furnace is begun immediately after the addition of hot metal, and is continued throughout most of the refining period.

According to data from over 600 open-hearth heats made under comparable conditions in three United States Steel plants, there is a saving in heat time of 10 to 25 per cent, and a decrease in fuel consumption of 18 to 35 per cent when roof lances, supplying 300 to 600 cu. ft. of oxygen per ton, are used. The causes of the disproportionately large fuel saving are: (1) the fuel input can be decreased; (2) the accompanying reduction in combustion air results in less heat-absorbing nitrogen passing through the system; and (3) the faster elimination of carbon from the bath (0.75-0.90 per cent per hour compared to 0.20-0.45 per cent per hour in ore practice) provides more turbulence and, therefore, improved heat transfer.

The faster and more active flush obtained when oxygen is used may result from the higher iron-oxide content of the flush slag than occurs in ore practice with high hot-metal charges. In both practices, the iron-oxide contents of the tapping slags are similar.

Because of the increased rates of reaction and the higher production obtained with oxygen, the temperature and carbon content of the bath must be more frequently observed, so that proper control measures can be taken.

Since the flow of oxygen is commenced as soon as hot metal has been added, the ore boil, lime boil and working period tend to merge into one. The increased rates of reaction due to the increased availability of oxygen and higher temperatures attainable with oxygen practice have reduced the overall heat time to about 8 hours charge-to-tap, compared with the 10-hour heat time for an ore-practice heat stated previously, for a similar furnace with a comparable charge making a similar grade of steel.

SECTION 5

TAPPING AND POURING

Tapping—The finishing temperature of a basic open-hearth steel heat will be in the neighborhood of 2900° F, varying according to the composition and grade of the steel.

When the heat of steel is ready to be tapped, the second helper, working from the tapping side, digs out the clay-loam plug and most of the dolomite with which the tapping hole had been closed before the furnace was charged. The hole either is burned out with oxygen from the tapping side or opened by a **jet tapper** which consists of a hollow explosive charge that concentrates its energy when discharged against the obstruction in the taphole, quickly opening the hole. Sometimes, opening of the hole must be completed by driving out dolomite remaining in it by the use of a long steel tapping rod inserted through the wicket hole of the middle door on the opposite or charging side of the furnace. When the hole is completely opened, the furnace is emptied of its molten contents, which are directed into the steel ladle through the tapping spout (Figure 16—26A). Since the tapping hole is located with its highest level at the lowest part of the hearth and slopes downward to meet the tapping spout, the greater portion of the steel flows out of the furnace before slag appears in the spout and this relatively late appearance of slag permits additions of alloying, recarburizing and deoxidizing materials to the spout and, principally, to the ladle. It is not permissible practice for these materials to come into contact with the slag, since some of the phosphoric oxide in the slag may be reduced and the phosphorus re-enter the steel. Further, a coating of slag on these materials may slow down their melting and solution in the steel and reduce the efficiency of the additions. The vertical axis of the ladle usually is placed with respect to the direction of the tapping spout so as to give a swirling motion to the metal in the ladle which tends to mix and make it more homogeneous. As soon as the liquid stream from the furnace no longer contains steel, and a depth of slag regulated by good practice remains as a covering for the steel in the ladle, the tapping spout is removed by a spout hoist and the ladle lifted from its supporting ladle stands by one of the pouring cranes and conveyed to a position over the ingot molds at the pouring platform. In some plants, excess slag overflows the ladle through a slag spout on the ladle and is received in a slag pot. In a later practice, the excess slag is permitted to accumulate on the ground adjacent to the ladle stands and, when solidified, is loaded by a remotely controlled high-lift into trucks for removal (Figures 16—26A and 16—26B). The front flush slag after leaving the furnace runs through a hole in the charging floor into the cellar from which it also is removed by the remotely controlled high-lift.

Ladles—A vertical section through a typical ladle used in basic open-hearth steelmaking is shown in Figure 16—27. The ladle shell itself is fabricated from steel plate by riveting or welding. The horizontal section usually is circular, but a greater capacity often is obtained for a given distance between the trunnions by use of an oval section. The diameter of the ladle increases toward the top to facilitate removal of the shell of metal that occasionally solidifies on the sides and bottom of the interior of the ladle and which commonly is called a **skull**.

The refractory lining of a ladle varies to some extent with the size of the ladle, the thinnest being 3½ inches thick. Thicker linings than this are the rule, and lower portions of the side wall usually are installed with an extra thickness of brick in that location to compensate for the additional time that this part of the lining is in contact with the molten metal. Extra thickness also may be provided in that portion of the side wall opposite the furnace spout which receives

FIG. 16—26A. A steel ladle, supported on stands, in position beneath the tapping spout of an open-hearth furnace near the end of a tap. Excess slag has been allowed to overflow the ladle into the pit, from which it will be removed when solid (see Figure 16—26B).

the impact of the stream of metal flowing from the furnace.

The type of brick in most common use is fireclay brick which softens at a temperature as low as 2350° F; the brick bloats and swells to one and one-quarter times its original size. In service, only a fraction of an inch of the brick beneath the surface exposed to the molten metal actually reaches a temperature above 2300° F, but this is an important consideration since it is this portion which expands (bloats) enough to seal the joints between the individual brick of the lining. This characteristic of ladle brick provides a smooth, tight, almost monolithic working surface that increases ladle life by preventing the penetration of metal into the joints with subsequent premature loss of the lining during removal of a skull. Therefore, though it may have a somewhat lower resistance to erosion by molten steel and slag than a more highly refractory material, the fireclay type of brick usually is the most acceptable for this service. Ladle linings

may be installed with a fireclay mortar but, because of the effectiveness of the bloating action in sealing joints, such linings frequently are installed without mortar except as a means for leveling up courses. All ladle linings must be dried carefully by gas, oil, or solid fuel fires prior to use.

The working lining (that next the molten steel) lasts from 10 to 25 heats, and the life varies with the depth, basicity and fluidity of the slag, the composition and temperature of the steel, and the length of time both steel and slag remain in the ladle.

Practically all basic open-hearth steel is cast from the bottom-pour type of ladle shown in the illustration. With this method of pouring, the stopper assembly acts as a valve to control the flow of metal through the nozzle at the bottom of the ladle (Figure 16—28).

Ladle Nozzles—The external size of the nozzle is controlled largely by the capacity of the ladle and the thickness of the lining, but the length must be sufficient to produce a smooth, solid stream of metal

FIG. 16—26B. Remotely
controlled high-lift used
to load slag from pit side
of furnace into trucks for
removal. High-lift opera-
tor is standing some dis-
tance behind the left rear
of the machine.

through the central orifice, as free from turbulence and spraying as possible. The diameter of the orifice is determined by considerations such as the grade of steel or size of ingot, and may vary from 1¼ to 3 inches in diameter. A typical nozzle for a 100-ton capacity ladle would be approximately 6 inches in outside diameter and 12 to 15 inches long, with an orifice 1¾ inches in diameter. General purpose nozzles most frequently are made from low heat-duty fireclay and possess properties very similar to those of the ladle brick previously described. They normally are very dense to reduce orifice erosion and, because of their low refractoriness, the surface of the nozzle seat softens to a depth of about ¼ inch when in contact with molten steel. This condition provides a soft, yielding seat for the harder stopper head. A new nozzle usually is inserted into the **nozzle retaining plate** after each heat. Above the nozzle seat, a shallow well usually is formed with plastic clay or loam for the purpose of guiding the stopper head into the nozzle seat. A **pocket block** or **well block** made of low or intermediate-duty fireclay burned to brick sometimes is used to form the well. Both nozzle and the well must be dried thoroughly prior to use.

Stopper Rod Assembly—A typical stopper-rod assembly, as shown in Figure 16—28, consists of the steel **stopper rod**, refractory **stopper rod sleeves**, refractory **stopper head,** and steel **stopper head pin** by which the stopper head is keyed to the stopper rod. While other methods for securing the stopper head to the rod are used, the pin and key arrangement is employed by the majority of operators.

The stopper head and nozzle constitute a valve and best results are obtained when one member is harder than the other at steel-pouring temperatures. Since

the surface of the nozzle seat is normally quite soft under steel-pouring conditions, the industry now almost universally employs the relatively hard clay-graphite stopper head composed of 15 to 25 per cent graphite blended with various highly refractory clays.

Prior to tapping the heat into the ladle, the stopper is keyed rigidly into the nozzle seat and the entire nozzle and head area are preheated to insure dryness.

The sleeves used to protect the steel stopper rod are manufactured in 9 and 18-inch lengths from fireclay which, when burned, has a similar or somewhat greater refractoriness than ladle brick. Their essential properties are resistance to thermal shock, resistance to slag and metal attack, low thermal conductivity, and snugly fitting male and female parts. A plastic fireclay or air-setting refractory mortar is placed between the joints and the entire series of sleeves is drawn together by the nut on top of the rod. The metal flange at the lower end of the stopper rod takes the thrust of the sleeves during the tightening opera-

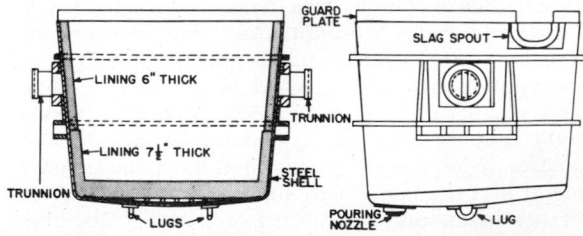

FIG. 16—27. (Left) Vertical section of a steel ladle through the trunnions, showing increased thickness of lining in its lower portions. (Right) Side view of same ladle.

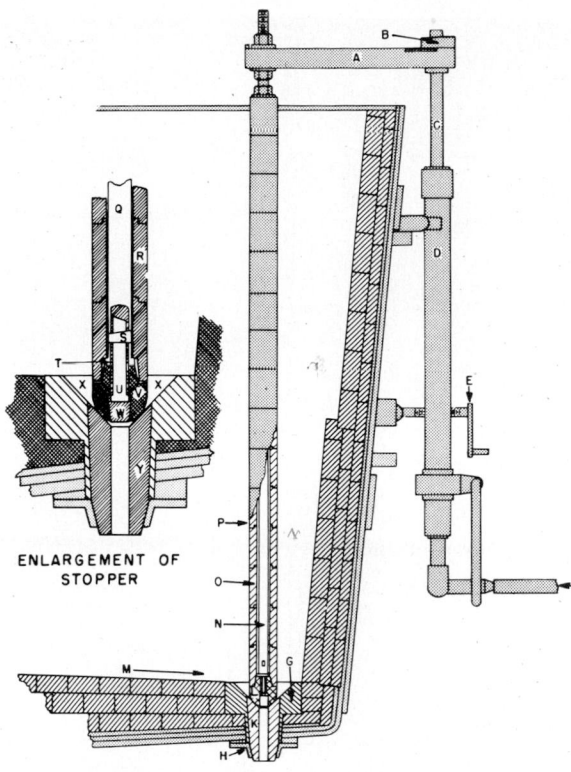

ENLARGEMENT OF STOPPER

FIG. 16—28. Stopper rod, well, and nozzle assembly for a modern steel ladle, indicating materials of construction and method of installation.

LEGEND

A —Gooseneck
B —Key
C —Slide
D —Barrel
E —Adjustment
F —Control lever
G —Rammed well
H —Nozzle plate
K —Nozzle
L —Head
M —Slope to drain
N —Rod

O —Sleeve
P —Stopper
Q —Low-carbon steel rod
R —Sleeve (fireclay brick)
S —Steel key
T —Flange on rod end
U —Low-carbon steel bolt
V —Head (graphite and clay)
W —Undercut fill
X —Ladle well profile
Y —Fireclay nozzle

tion, preventing breakage of the head. After the completed stopper rod has been dried thoroughly and installed in the ladle, the sleeve nut is backed off about ⅛ inch per foot of stopper rod to provide for the thermal expansion of the sleeves.

As shown in Figure 16—28, the **ladle rigging** required for raising and lowering the stopper rod consists essentially of a **barrel** within which a square or cylindrical **slide** is operated by an appropriate lever arrangement placed at the lower end. In recent times, a hydraulic cylinder mounted on the ladle rigging (Figure 16—29) has been substituted for the manually operated lever in many installations. Actuated by an electric-hydraulic power unit mounted on the ladle crane, to which it is connected by flexible hoses, the cylinder can exert considerably more force to raise or

lower the stopper than can be applied manually by the lever. Known as the "Autopour," this device is push-button operated from some distance away from the ladle and provides better control of the pouring operation.

The stopper rod is bolted, at its upper end, to a rigid **stopper carrier,** which in turn is keyed or bolted securely to the upper end of the slide. The entire rigging is attached to the side of the ladle shell in a manner that permits a certain amount of lateral movement of the stopper with respect to the nozzle and the well, through proper adjustment of the **adjusting wheel and screw** placed within reach of the steel pourer. This adjustment can be made while setting the stopper or during the pouring of the heat.

Proper manipulation of the pouring assembly to start or stop the flow of molten steel to the mold requires a thorough knowledge of the manner in which pouring affects the surface quality of steel ingots as well as an understanding of the refractories and equipment.

Pouring—The pouring operation (Figure 16—8) is critical, first in controlling molten steel so that it does not endanger personnel or damage equipment, second because poor practice in the assembly, adjustment or manipulation of pouring equipment may seriously and adversely affect the surface quality of the product.

One of the most important factors affecting the surface of the ingot and subsequent product is the rate of flow of the pouring stream and the resultant rate of rise of molten steel in the mold. This **rate of rise** is determined primarily by nozzle size, mold size, temperature and fluidity of the steel and height of metal in the ladle.

The optimum **pouring rate** is determined primarily by the grade of steel, but is also dependent upon such factors as mold design, type of mold coating, and temperature of steel.

Caution should be exercised to prevent dirt or refractory material from falling into the molds and becoming entrapped in the ingot.

Tundish or Basket Pouring—As an alternative to casting steel directly from the ladle to the molds, an intermediate pouring vessel may be used. Such vessels are termed **pouring baskets, pouring boxes,** or **tundishes.** They may be suspended from the main ladle, attached to the pouring platform or carried on an auxiliary carriage, or supported directly by the mold. The method usually involves pouring from the tapping ladle through a large nozzle into the pouring vessel. Steel may be poured into the molds from one or two smaller nozzles in the pouring vessel, one nozzle to a mold.

Use of this practice is more costly than conventional pouring, but offers the following advantages: (1) greater opportunity for non-metallic inclusions to become separated from the metal, (2) less splashing in the mold, (3) the possibility of better control of pouring rates, and (4) a reduction in pouring temperature.

Bottom Pouring—Some of the disadvantages of top pouring may be eliminated through the use of a bottom-pour assembly in which the steel is cast into a funnel lined with refractories, passes down through hollow refractory runner brick, and finally emerges to

FIG. 16—29. Hydraulic cylinder mounted on barrel of ladle rigging raises and lowers stopper rod to control flow of molten steel from ladle to ingot mold. (Courtesy, Blaw Knox Company.)

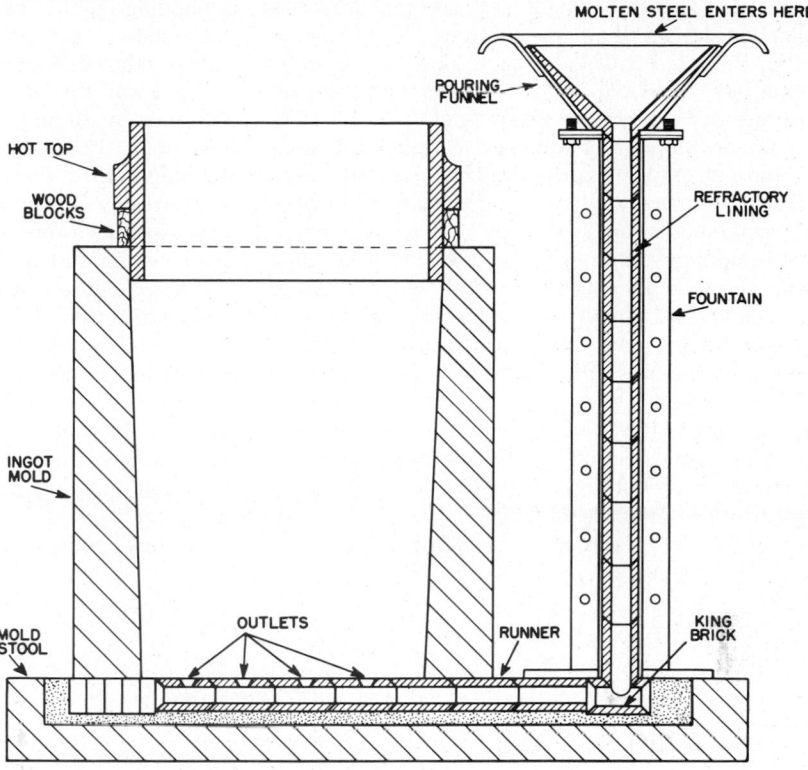

FIG. 16—30. Schematic arrangement and nomenclature of parts of a mold assembly for bottom pouring.

(Figure labels: MOLTEN STEEL ENTERS HERE; POURING FUNNEL; HOT TOP; WOOD BLOCKS; REFRACTORY LINING; FOUNTAIN; INGOT MOLD; MOLD STOOL; OUTLETS; RUNNER; KING BRICK)

enter the bottom of various molds through outlet brick (Figure 16—30). The assembly of funnel and vertical runner which receives the molten steel from the ladle is sometimes called a **fountain.** The metal rises steadily in the molds with very little agitation since the main falling force of the stream from the nozzle is absorbed in the runner. One or more molds may be cast from the same fountain, so that the rate of rise can be varied also by the size and number of molds used. The cost of this operation involves more expense than for top pouring. However, it usually provides better surface quality for certain grades of steel. On the other hand, erosion of fountain and runner brick provides an additional source of non-metallic inclusions which may be a disadvantage in some steels.

Sampling the Steel—During the pouring of the heat, samples of the molten-steel stream from the nozzle (with the flow momentarily slackened) are taken in a steel spoon, containing a required small amount of aluminum wire to "kill" the sample. From the spoon, steel is poured into suitable diminutive cast-iron molds, depending on the method of analysis, to form test specimens for the chemical laboratory where they are analyzed by various methods for the elements which are significant. These are called the **ladle analyses** and are supplemented on some grades by additional **check analyses** on samples taken from blooms, billets or the finished products.

After the pouring of the heat of steel into molds is complete, the slag remaining in the ladle is dumped into slag ladles or pots which are subsequently con-veyed to the slag yard on special cars. The mold cars with the filled molds thereon are held at the pouring platform for various intervals of time, depending on the grade of steel made and are then transferred to the stripper cranes where the molds are removed from the ingots or the ingots withdrawn from the molds. The removal of mold from ingot is called "stripping" (Figure 16—9).

Ingot Molds are of many types, shapes and sizes. In shape they vary from round, square or oblong molds to those occasional ones that roughly take the form of the section into which the steel is to be rolled. An example of the latter is the mold used to cast an ingot which is roughly of a beam shape which is finally finished as a large, wide-flanged beam. Generally, ingots to be rolled are of square or oblong cross section, corrugated or fluted in some cases to minimize the cracking of the ingot surface as it solidifies and continues to cool. Ingots to be rolled into blooms or billets are usually of square cross section and those to be rolled into slabs and then into flat-rolled product are usually of oblong cross section. Ingots for forging are generally of a round or many sided cross section, corrugated or fluted.

Ingot cross sections and weights must be established according to the final cross section in rolling and forging, and the weight per piece of final product, with due consideration to the rolling or forging equipment of the individual plants which process the material to the final product.

Molds usually are tapered from one end to the other so that the top of the ingot cast in them is either smaller or larger than the bottom, according to whether the mold is of the big-end-down or big-end-up type (see also Chapter 18). Taper is necessary in both types to facilitate the stripping of the ingot from the mold. In the case of the big-end-up molds, taper also helps to emphasize the freezing from the sides and bottom in such a manner that the last part of the ingot remaining liquid is directly under the hot top, thus promoting soundness. The hot top itself may contain 10 to 15 per cent of the total ingot weight.

Originally hot tops were refractory hollow-tile shapes, or metal casings lined with refractory material, placed upon the tops of the mold which usually were good for one pouring. At present, the larger proportion of hot tops are refractory-lined steel or iron castings with suitable coatings applied between pourings. The linings may last for twenty-five heats or more. Practically all hot tops, whether of the lined-metal-casing or hollow-tile type, are now inserted into the top of the mold and are supported at various heights depending on the length and required weight of the main body of the ingot. Chapter 18 describes and illustrates the effect of a hot top.

Mold wall thickness ranges from about 4 inches for a 20-inch by 20-inch ingot to about 6 inches for a 32-inch ingot. For molds used to cast large ingots for slabbing mills, the wall thickness may be made somewhat greater for optimum mold life. The life of ingot molds has been found to be a function of the ratio of mold weight to ingot weight.

Ingot Height—There are limits to ingot height, determined by such factors as desirable ingot structure, desirable rimming action in pouring, and design of the pit furnaces in which ingots are heated.

Usually ingot molds are made of blast furnace or cupola iron, a relatively small proportion of cast steel. Big-end-down, big-end-up, open-top and bottle-top, open-bottom, plug bottom, and solid-bottom molds, along with mold coatings, are discussed at some length in Chapter 18.

SECTION 6
KEEPING THE BASIC OPEN-HEARTH FURNACE IN REPAIR

Preparation of the Furnace for the Next Charge— After the runner or tapping spout is lifted and thus detached from the furnace, the slag and any steel that remains in the furnace flow out of the tapping hole into the cinder pit. The second helper must keep the tapping hole open until everything that can flow from the furnace has done so. Fluorspar usually is thrown in on the slag left so that it becomes sufficiently fluid to flow out and its building up on the bottom of the furnace prevented. Often the effective draining of the bottom is prevented by a ridge of lime adhering to the bottom, forming a dam which holds back the slag and steel. Usually at the start, lime ridges hold back only a small portion of the steel. This may seem insignificant, but if allowed to remain, these small pools will develop into larger pools of oxidized steel. Eventually this will result in a **bottom boil** that will allow the intrusion of steel below the surface by bringing up the basic material forming the bottom of the pools. Liquid slag and liquid steel held back by lime ridges or remaining in the bottom depressions can be disposed of most effectively by blowing with either compressed air or steam. This is done by reducing the fuel input to the furnace and inserting a long steel pipe through the wicket hole of the furnace door and applying air or steam under pressure. The use of paddles or rabbles on the end of the charging-machine peel is also practiced in some shops to break up the lime ridges and allow the steel and slag to drain. After all the steel and slag are removed, the smaller holes may be filled with prepared dolomite; however, the practice of repairing larger ones may differ in that magnesite may be used instead of dolomite, and the work of repairing the bottom may progress by sintering layer on layer of the refractory material in the holes.

To reduce the time required for bottom repairs, prepared mixes high in magnesia content are now frequently used. These require a minimum of time for sintering since the composition is regulated to make them "quick-setting" when properly mixed with specified quantities of water at time of use.

Another method of draining holes is to rabble the metal toward the taphole by means of rabble plates attached to bars. When dry (drained of slag and steel), the bottom is repaired in the same manner as when using air or steam for draining.

The described methods are most advisable from the standpoint of bottom upkeep and economy of time.

While the bottom is being repaired with the fuel on, the entire hearth is examined and simultaneously reconditioned. The fuel is considerably increased as soon as repairs to the bottom have been completed, to burn in the bottom as much as possible before charging the next heat.

Proceeding to the next step, the second helper and third helper remove the steel that has chilled in the taphole, rake out and free the hole of slag and steel, and close it up with dolomite. A plug of clay is used to seal up the outside of the hole and hold the dolomite in place. The banks are repaired by fettling either manually or with a dolomite machine and the furnace is ready for charging again. Use of the dolomite ma-

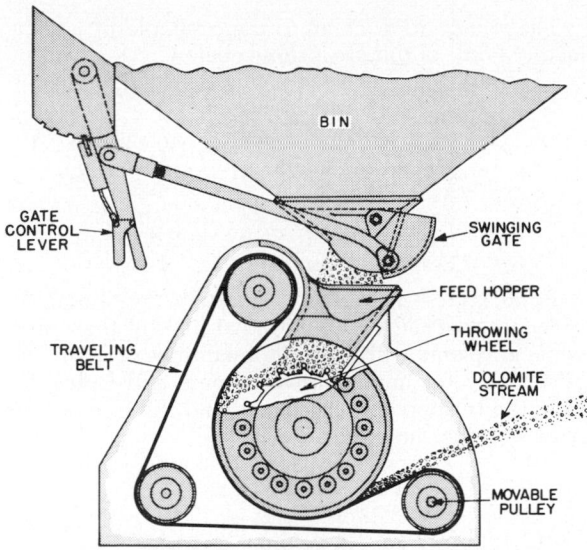

GATE
CONTROL
LEVER

BIN

SWINGING
GATE

FEED HOPPER

THROWING
WHEEL

TRAVELING
BELT

DOLOMITE
STREAM

MOVABLE
PULLEY

FIG. 16—31. Schematic diagram of the main working parts and principle of operation of a dolomite-throwing machine. Raising or lowering of the moveable pulley (lower right) changes the trajectory of the stream.

chine, in which a hopper-fed belt throws dolomite to the required position within the furnace chamber, has become almost standard practice, especially in maintaining the hearths and banks of the larger furnaces. Operation of one of these machines is illustrated in Figure 16—31.

Generally normal bottom maintenance should be adequate to preserve bottom contour so that all of the steel and slag flows out of the taphole and assures a reasonable amount of time for repairing the bottom. However, during the years of bottom life it is possible that, either due to the method of bottom maintenance or to the prevailing steelmaking practices, the nature and extent of bottom erosion may require general resurfacing. The bottom is then given a thorough cleaning as described above and built up again with 5 to 8 inches of either magnesite or double burned dolomite applied as for a new bottom.

The thick layer of newly sintered bottom effectively reduces bottom delays for approximately 300 to 400 subsequent heats.

Furnace Troubles—In the operation of a furnace, troubles of a very serious nature may occur at any time, unless the furnace is watched closely and carefully handled. Thus, the taphole may break out prematurely if it is not properly tamped and capped, or it may become hopelessly clogged with frozen steel if it is not properly cleaned after each heat. Sometimes, sections of the bottom become detached, and these will rise at once due to the buoyant force of the metal; when this occurs the heat must be tapped at once, and no more heats may be charged until the damaged bottom is repaired. The walls and roof often wear out long before the rest of the furnace needs repairing. Silica roofs usually last for about 200 heats, while basic roofs will go over 400 heats. The roof can be

repaired in a few hours, and a cave-in of the roof is of a serious nature only when it falls when a heat is nearly finished. The most disastrous mishap that can occur to a furnace is a breakout. Breakouts may be caused by several things. A hole near a bank may not have been noticed or may have been insufficiently repaired, in which case the steel works down into it and gradually makes it deeper until, finally, the metal finds its way through the wall and out of the furnace. Sometimes, owing to a thin spot on the banks or to slag having worked down through the banks from above, the slag gradually cuts its way out through the walls, in which case it is usually followed by steel. Breakouts are always serious matters. Once a breakout occurs, the tapping hole should be opened immediately, and as much of the steel as possible tapped into the ladle or cinder pit. The spread of cinder and metal upon the floor where the breakout has occurred can be contained usually by throwing dolomite around it.

After several hundred heats, the checkerwork has become so badly clogged and the furnace brickwork is so eaten away that it becomes necessary to close down the furnace for general repairs, during which the greater part of the brickwork may be torn out and replaced.

Repair Materials—It is evident that, in making up the bottom and for doing the repair work about a furnace, much depends upon the materials employed. Great care always must be exercised to see that they are of the right chemical composition, and physically suited for the work in hand, as otherwise the best of workmanship in making the repairs will go for naught. The few remarks here are supplemented in the chapter on refractories.

Dolomite is found in deposits similar to those of limestone. Like the latter it varies in composition through quite wide ranges, but generally it may be stated that to be suitable for open-hearth work, it should not have over 1 per cent SiO_2. Three types of dolomite are used for repairing the furnace:

(1) Raw dolomite for normal fettling and banking the doors.

(2) Single burned dolomite prepared locally by burning dolomite in shaft kilns at a temperature of 2200 to 2300° F, for normal fettling and minor bottom repairs.

(3) Synthetically prepared clinker dolomite in which lime and magnesia are transformed into a crystalline state by burning at a high temperature in a rotary kiln at which time some iron oxide is introduced as a flux. Generally this material is used to supplement raw dolomite and single burned dolomite, and for bottom repairs of a more serious nature.

Magnesite—Prior to the first World War, practically the entire supply of magnesite was imported from Austria. However, since that time, the demands of the American steel industry have been supplied predominantly by domestic sources, principal of which is Chewelah magnesite in the State of Washington. There are several brands of magnesite available, both of foreign and domestic origin. Magnesites from sea-water magnesia have been introduced in competition with natural magnesite.

Chrome Ore—Chrome ore has always been imported, as the limited deposits so far discovered in the United States and Canada are of an inferior grade for open-hearth use. It is received in the form of small lumps. It is ground and mixed, in a wet pan, often with some magnesite or suitable bonding material, and is used in repair work where a chemically neutral substance (neither acid nor basic in characteristics) is required, such as in patching flues, tapping holes, ports, and so on.

The composition of an average sample of a satisfactory grade of this ore is shown below.

Ingredient	Per Cent
SiO_2	4-9
FeO	10-14
MnO	Less than 1
Al_2O_3	10-30
CaO	Less than 2
Cr_2O_3	32-42
Loss on Ignition	1-3

Besides these materials, a quartzite containing 98 to 99 per cent silica is employed at some of the works, while all plants will use large quantities of loam and of fire clay for lining furnace spouts and ladles, for making up stopper-sleeve joints, and for other repair work of minor importance.

SECTION 7

FACTORS AFFECTING ECONOMY OF FURNACE OPERATION

Fuel Consumption—Beside the fuel required for carrying on the metallurgical process of steelmaking from the beginning of charging to tapping the finished heat, it is necessary to burn fuel for heating the furnace to a temperature which permits the operators to begin the "burning-in" of the hearth, and for maintaining the proper temperature during the installation of the furnace hearth. In the periods between tapping of one heat and charging of the next, fuel is required for drying and preheating ladles, drying ladle-stopper rods, maintaining metal mixers at the proper temperature level, heating tapping spouts, drying hot tops, preheating ferroalloys, and sometimes thawing materials. Fuels used for other than actual furnace requirements may be of lower calorific value and consequently cheaper than those needed in the open hearth.

The approach to an economical use of fuel in quantities per ton of steel produced is subject to a number of conditions, such as the kind of fuel used, continuity and rate of production, the design of the furnace (in which hearth area per ton of heat tapped and bath depth are important factors), the proper maintenance of the furnace, its walls, passages, the insulation and sealing against air leakage (on the parts of the furnace system where insulation and sealing are necessary), the degree of control of melting chamber pressure (so as to prevent infiltration of relatively cold air which lowers flame and bath temperature), the proportioning of air supply to fuel burning rate, the control of flame shape, its direction and coverage of the charge and bath, and the promotion of high radiating effects from flame to solid charge and to slag and molten bath, the proportion of molten pig iron used, the elimination of delays in introducing the charge into the furnace, the grade and type of steel to be made, and the care and intelligence with which the furnace is operated. Included in the last item are the very important matters of regulating fuel consumption rate in proportion to metallurgical requirements and of timing the reversals of the regenerator system and the fuel flow so that the transfer of heat from waste gases to

preheat the air for combustion is made at the maximum level of efficiency. This timing is determined and carried out in modern practice by the assistance of automatic devices which are actuated by pyrometers installed in the regenerator system. Modern control and indicating equipment give the furnace operator a good visual indication of fuel rate and help to select a rate of fuel supply for combustion according to predetermined proportion of air weight to fuel weight for each stage of the heat, such as: (1) high fuel rate for melt down; (2) low fuel rate after hot metal addition and during vigorous ore and lime boil; and (3) increasing fuel rate after melt depending on temperature readings.

A list of the controls and instruments related to fuel burning, with which a large number of modern open-hearth furnaces are equipped, follows:

(1) Control and recording gage for atomizing-steam pressure.
(2) Control and recording flowmeter for coke-oven or natural gas.
(3) Control and recording flowmeter for liquid fuel.
(4) Automatic furnace-pressure control and recording pressure gage.
(5) Recording draft gage.
(6) Recording pyrometers for checker temperatures, waste-heat boiler, and stack temperatures.
(7) Fuel-air ratio indicator.
(8) Forced-air control, including predetermined automatic fuel-air ratio control.
(9) Roof-temperature indicator, with automatic roof-temperature control of part of fuel rate.

The calorific value of fuel usually is expressed by its gross heating value in British thermal units per unit of volume, weight or liquid measure. These concepts were discussed in Chapter 3 on fuels.

Fuel consumption in terms of total calorific value of the fuel used per ton of steel produced usually is expressed in total net heating value of the fuel (millions of Btu) per ton of ingots produced. In the steel industry, the range of fuel consumption by open-hearth

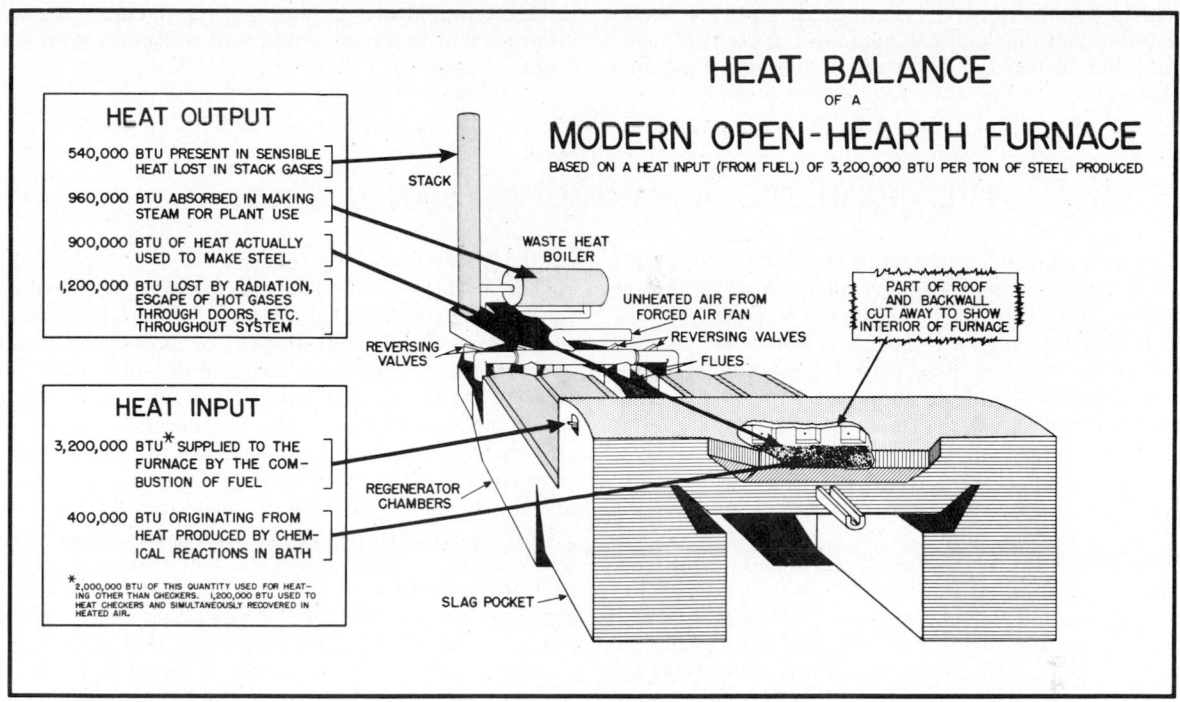

HEAT BALANCE
OF A
MODERN OPEN-HEARTH FURNACE
BASED ON A HEAT INPUT (FROM FUEL) OF 3,200,000 BTU PER TON OF STEEL PRODUCED

HEAT OUTPUT

540,000 BTU PRESENT IN SENSIBLE HEAT LOST IN STACK GASES

960,000 BTU ABSORBED IN MAKING STEAM FOR PLANT USE

900,000 BTU OF HEAT ACTUALLY USED TO MAKE STEEL

1,200,000 BTU LOST BY RADIATION, ESCAPE OF HOT GASES THROUGH DOORS, ETC. THROUGHOUT SYSTEM

HEAT INPUT

3,200,000 BTU* SUPPLIED TO THE FURNACE BY THE COMBUSTION OF FUEL

400,000 BTU ORIGINATING FROM HEAT PRODUCED BY CHEMICAL REACTIONS IN BATH

*2,000,000 BTU OF THIS QUANTITY USED FOR HEATING OTHER THAN CHECKERS. 1,200,000 BTU USED TO HEAT CHECKERS AND SIMULTANEOUSLY RECOVERED IN HEATED AIR.

STACK
WASTE HEAT BOILER
UNHEATED AIR FROM FORCED AIR FAN
REVERSING VALVES
PART OF ROOF AND BACKWALL CUT AWAY TO SHOW INTERIOR OF FURNACE
REVERSING VALVES
FLUES
REGENERATOR CHAMBERS
SLAG POCKET

Fig. 16—32. Heat balance of a modern basic open-hearth furnace, using ore practice. The more rapid rates of reaction with oxygen roof-lance practice considerably reduces fuel requirements and would, accordingly, require adjustment of the figures given in the diagram for heat input from fuel; stack and other heat losses; and heat recovered by regeneration.

furnaces is from 3,000,000 to 4,000,000 Btu per net ton for furnaces in which molten pig iron is used to 4,200,000 to 5,300,000 Btu when the charge is all cold. The consumption decreases considerably when using oxygen roof-lance practice, as stated earlier. The heat balance of a modern basic open-hearth furnace is shown schematically in Figure 16—32.

Rate of Steel Production—Practically all of the conditions given above for an economical use of fuel are approximately though not necessarily precisely those which provide maximum rate of steel production for a given quality requirement in the product. Thus, with ore practice, it may be possible to operate a furnace on the low fuel rate of 3,000,000 Btu per net ton of ingots, but it may be necessary to increase this fuel rate by at least ten per cent above this in order to increase the tonnage rate to that desired. The conditions which improve production rate with ore practice (in addition to those which were discussed in the section dealing with fuel consumption) include the following: relatively large hearth area per ton and relatively small bath depth (these can be considered as matters related to furnace design), size of heat in tons, ability to burn fuel at a high rate in melting down the solid part of the charge, iron ores for the charge which are relatively superior in physical and chemical properties (for example, more massive, low in fines, low in silica and water of crystallization), silicon in the molten and cold pig iron held within a specified maximum, bundling and pressing of light scrap to promote rapid charging, rapid preliminary

analyses of bath samples, careful planning and carrying out of the process procedure for each grade and quality of product.

The use of oxygen or compressed air with the fuel stream and of oxygen in eliminating carbon from the bath increase the rate of production. Oxygen or compressed air are of particular value as combustion aids during the melting down of the solid part of the metallic charge (scrap, cold pig iron) and will show the greatest effect in speeding up production rate in furnaces as the ratio of the cold to molten parts of the charge increases, the effect being much less when large proportions of hot metal are used. The oxygen usually is introduced through the regular liquid-fuel burner, with the oxygen jet entering just below the fuel jet.

With ore practice, twenty-four tons per 1000 square feet of hearth area per operating hour where the area of the bath is taken on the brick work at the door sill level before rammed or burned-in sections of the furnace hearth are installed may be considered a satisfactory operating rate for a larger furnace (200 tons and up). As discussed in Section 4 under "Oxygen Roof-Lance Practice," the use of oxygen can considerably increase production rate.

When waste heat boilers are used, the exhaust fans in the system assist in maintaining high production rates by maintaining uniform drafts to give the desired removal of waste gaseous products.

The kind of refractories used is important in preventing relatively early failure of the furnace hearth chamber and port ends, in maintaining the contour of the inner surfaces of the areas of the above exposed to high temperature and hot gases and, consequently, an important factor in promoting continuity of operation.

SECTION 8
THE CHEMISTRY OF BASIC OPEN-HEARTH MELTING

In melting down, the item of greatest interest is the action of flame and furnace atmosphere upon the charge. The charge at the beginning consists generally of steel scrap, but may consist of both cold pig iron and scrap; the pig iron with a low melting range around 2100° F, and the scrap with a melting range of 2500 to 2700° F. At the start, the temperature is low due to the large heat absorption from the flame by the relatively cold charge. If the fuel contains sulphur, the metal may absorb some of this element as the temperature rises, although the amount may be small if conditions are maintained to give rapid and complete combustion of the fuel with a proper excess of oxygen as noted elsewhere. During the melting, which begins with the metal at the top of the charge and progresses gradually downward, iron may be oxidized by the gases oxygen, carbon dioxide, or water vapor. For a given furnace atmosphere, the amount of iron oxidized will depend on the "bulk density" of the charge, oxidation being the least in pig iron, and the greatest in the lightest steel scrap because of the much greater surface area exposed by the latter to the gases. The degree of oxidation of the scrap is an important factor as the oxides formed are equivalent in action to any ore which might have been charged to furnish oxygen for the elimination process.

The other elements which may be oxidized during melting either by the atmosphere or by oxides of iron from the oxidation of the scrap are carbon, manganese, phosphorus and silicon, all of which are always present, and chromium, vanadium, aluminum, titanium, tungsten, columbium, zinc, etc., all of which may or may not be present. The oxides of some of these elements may be reduced later, in the working period, depending on the amounts present and the composition of the slag formed. In the case of all the oxidizable impurities (except carbon, where the oxidation product is a gas), there will result eventually a condition approaching equilibrium where they distribute themselves between slag and metal as determined by the natural laws governing heterogeneous systems for the chemical reactions involved. Other elements which may be present, such as copper, nickel, molybdenum, cobalt, tin, arsenic, etc., are held in the iron because the iron would have to be completely oxidized before these elements could be removed by oxidation. Proof of these statements may be had by analysis of the first slags formed, which collect with the molten metal in certain parts of the furnace before all the scrap is melted. Results of analyses of two of these slags are shown in Table 16—IV.

CHEMISTRY OF THE ORE (IRON OXIDE) BOIL

The reactions following the melting period depend on the make-up of the charge. With a high scrap charge, no ore may be charged, because oxidation of the scrap during melting (or use of the oxygen lance) can furnish the desired amount of oxygen. With no charged ore, or a smaller charge of ore, the limestone charged also may be reduced by the amount that would have been required to flux the silica in the ore, and the silica from silicon in extra pig iron. Likewise, the oxidizing effect of the CO_2 from calcination of the stone will not be as necessary because of greater oxidation of a larger amount of scrap. The following description is for the usual scrap and pig iron charge, with the pig iron added in the molten condition after a part of the scrap has been melted and the temperature of the hearth and contents is high enough to prevent solidification of the molten metal. As soon as this hot metal is added, reactions begin between the silicon, manganese, phosphorus, and carbon of the pig iron, first with the oxygen supplied by oxidation of the scrap and later with the oxygen supplied by the charged ore, or by the oxygen lances as melting progresses. These reactions are exothermic and help to keep the iron molten, as well as contributing to the general supply of heat to the furnace. In general, these elements are oxidized out of the metal in the order silicon, manganese, phosphorus, and carbon. The reactions representing the oxidation of these elements, may be represented by the following equations:

1. Si (in Fe) $+ 2O$ (in Fe) $= SiO_2$ (solid)
2. Mn (in Fe) $+ O$ (in Fe) $= MnO$ (solid)
3. $2P$ (in Fe) $+ 5O$ (in Fe) $+$
$$4\,CaO \text{ (solid)} = 4\,CaO{\cdot}P_2O_5 \text{ (liquid)}$$
4. $2C$ (in Fe) $+ 3O$ (in Fe) $= CO$ (gas) $+ CO_2$ (gas)

The above reactions express equilibria; that is, they

Table 16—IV. Compositions of First Slag Formed in Basic Open-Hearth Heats

Constituent	Slag from Furnace A (Per Cent)	Slag from Furnace B (Per Cent)
SiO_2	8.54	1.00
FeO*	61.05	78.24
Fe_2O_3**	11.10	15.31
MnO	2.31	0.81
P_2O_5	0.26	0.14
Al_2O_3	1.98	2.70
CaO	9.13	2.70
MgO	5.48	1.12
S***	0.16	0.25

*As calculated from analysis for ferrous iron.
**As calculated from analysis for ferric iron.
***Nature of sulphur-bearing slag constituents unknown.

may proceed from left to right or right to left, depending on the relative activities of the substances involved. Reaction (1) results in the formation of the acidic oxide SiO_2, which is insoluble in iron, and in the liberation of heat. Reaction (2) likewise furnishes heat, but results in the formation of the basic oxide MnO, which is only slightly soluble in iron. It will be noted that reaction (3) includes the slag-forming compound CaO. The reason for this is that the high vapor pressure of P_2O_5 precludes the possibility of its existence in the free state, yet analysis of slags always shows phosphorus present as the phosphate, indicating that P_2O_5 is formed in the oxidation. It is probable, therefore, that the oxide of phosphorus combines with lime to form $4CaO \cdot P_2O_5$. This is borne out further by the fact that the reaction will be reversed quickly provided sufficient oxygen is not available or the amount of lime over that required to balance the other acidic oxides is insufficient, allowing the phosphorus to return to the metal. Reaction (4) produces the gases CO and CO_2 in proportions depending on the carbon content of the bath. Usually over 90 per cent of the gas is CO, which burns to CO_2, as it bubbles off the bath. The elimination of carbon, therefore, produces no oxide which requires a flux for its removal from the iron. There should be supplied to the furnace atmosphere sufficient air to oxidize the CO to CO_2 in order that oxidizing conditions will obtain, as well as to provide extra heat near the bath surface.

In order that the transfer of silicon and manganese from the metal to the slag may be visualized clearly, the reactions above must be supplemented by others involving neutralization as well as oxidation. In the case of phosphorus, this neutralization already has been indicated.

Oxidation and Neutralization of Silicon and Manganese—Since silica is strongly acidic and iron oxide and manganese oxide are basic, all or a large part will be neutralized to form fusible silicates of iron and manganese. These will be a major constituent of the first slag, which is formed before the lime boil. As soon as lime begins to rise from the bottom of the furnace, these silicates will be broken down with the formation of calcium silicates as explained later. In flush practice, a considerable amount of these undesirable silicates will have been removed, of course.

Behavior of Sulphur during Melting and the Ore Boil—Compared with the elimination of the other impurities, the removal of sulphur from the steel in the open hearth is relatively inefficient. As a consequence, an attempt is made to keep the amount of sulphur in all the raw materials at a low value. Fuels other than natural gas contain varying amounts of sulphur, and during the melting period it is not uncommon that the scrap may absorb sulphur from the furnace gases. This may be minimized by maintaining more oxidizing conditions in the furnace so that the sulphur is converted quickly to SO_2, in which form it is absorbed less readily, and by melting rapidly so that the scrap is exposed for the shortest possible time.

It is probable that sulphur in liquid iron exists as iron and manganese sulphides, and it is possible that it exists in the slag either as calcium sulphide or as calcium sulphite or sulphate. Since it is impossible to analyze slag and metal for individual sulphides, no exact chemical mechanism for sulphur removal has been established. It is usual, consequently, to express the reaction as a simple ratio of "sulphur in slag" to "sulphur in metal." Neither iron sulphide nor manganese sulphide can be oxidized in the open hearth, so that the ratio is not affected by the state of oxidation of the metal, but only by slag composition. Higher ratios are found for the more basic slags, containing free lime. As the slag becomes more basic later in the heat, the ratio becomes more favorable for sulphur removal, but in spite of this fact, rarely more than 50 per cent of the sulphur in the metal can be removed without using excessive slag volumes.

CHEMISTRY OF THE LIME BOIL

Before the refining reactions described above are completed, the limestone will have reached its calcining temperature and begun to give off CO_2 in accordance with the following reaction:

$$CaCO_3 \text{ (solid)} = CaO \text{ (solid)} + CO_2 \text{ (gas)}$$

This reaction starts at about 1475° F, but progresses only slowly even at higher temperatures, because it is endothermic and because the limestone is charged in large lumps exposing relatively little surface. The CO_2 formed by the calcination reacts with the iron or one of the metalloids to form oxides, and thereby contributes a considerable proportion of the oxygen required by the process when ore practice is employed. One end product of this oxidation is CO, which bubbles through the bath and produces a desirable agitation which promotes the absorption of heat from the flame by the bath.

The CaO which is a product of the calcination, floats to the slag and replaces iron and manganese oxides as previously stated, forming calcium silicates and aiding in the removal of phosphorus. As more lime becomes available, the basicity of the slag increases, favoring the removal of sulphur by increasing the sulphur-holding power of the slag.

The slag now represents a liquid mixture of some complexity, consisting of calcium silicates, or double silicates of calcium and other bases, sulphates or sulphides, calcium phosphates or double phosphates, iron oxide, manganese oxide, with oxides of the other oxidizable impurities in the charge, plus such compounds as alumina, magnesia, chromic oxide, etc., gathered from ore, limestone, and refractories. The nature of open-hearth slags is very complex and not completely understood, since it is very difficult to study the slag while in the liquid state.

Preliminary Adjustments in the Slag; Objects of the Run-Off—It is evident from the preceding discussion that a certain excess of calcium oxide over that required to neutralize the silica is necessary to assure lowering the phosphorus content to the small proportion desired in nearly all basic steel. Also, it has been established that for practical phosphorus elimination, the ratio of lime to silica should be at least 2:1, corresponding to the formula $2CaO \cdot SiO_2$. Provided the total silicon content in the charge is known and all the slag formed is held in the furnace until the steel is

Table 16—V. Typical Composition of Hot Metal, Run-Off Slag, and Finishing Slag for 55% and 70% Hot Metal Charge (Ore Practice)

Heat No.	Composition of Hot Metal (%)		Composition of Slag (%)	
			Run-Off	Finish
			55% Hot Metal Charge	
1	C —4.26	SiO$_2$	26.4	18.4
	Mn—2.36	CaO	14.1	45.0
	P —0.271	FeO	22.3	12.2
	S —0.029	Fe$_2$O$_3$	3.0	3.4
	Si —1.33	MnO	21.6	8.6
		Al$_2$O$_3$	2.9	2.5
		MgO	6.5	5.9
		P$_2$O$_5$	2.4	3.4
		S	0.08	....
2	C —4.35	SiO$_2$	22.2	18.1
	Mn—2.23	CaO	14.6	43.2
	P —0.273	FeO	29.3	11.6
	S —0.028	Fe$_2$O$_3$	3.6	3.3
	Si —1.43	MnO	18.4	7.7
		Al$_2$O$_3$	2.3	2.8
		MgO	4.9	7.8
		P$_2$O$_5$	3.0	2.6
		S	0.08	0.09
			70% Hot Metal Charge	
1	C —4.32	SiO$_2$	19.2	17.7
	Mn—2.20	CaO	7.5	45.9
	P —0.255	FeO	42.8	11.1
	S —0.030	Fe$_2$O$_3$	4.6	4.3
	Si —1.34	MnO	15.8	6.3
		Al$_2$O$_3$	2.5	4.0
		MgO	3.7	6.2
		P$_2$O$_5$	2.5	2.6
		S	0.09	0.06
2	C —4.32	SiO$_2$	17.8	19.2
	Mn—2.13	CaO	9.7	43.4
	P —0.273	FeO	37.9	9.4
	S —0.023	Fe$_2$O$_3$	7.4	2.5
	Si —1.18	MnO	14.5	7.2
		Al$_2$O$_3$	2.5	3.7
		MgO	5.2	7.3
		P$_2$O$_5$	2.7	2.9
		S	0.07	0.06

tapped, this relation makes it easy to calculate the total limestone required.

With a high iron charge and, therefore, a high silicon content in the charge, keeping all the slag in the furnace may make it difficult to control the temperature of the bath because of the thickness of the slag layer. The fuel input needed to drive heat through a thick insulating slag layer may also lead to overheating the furnace roof. Furthermore, the silicon content of the charge may not be known at the time the limestone is charged. These difficulties may be overcome by the **run-off**. If the furnace has been charged to hold the limestone on the bottom and the run-off

is timed to begin shortly after addition of molten pig iron and before the lime boil begins, a large portion of the silica and phosphorus are carried out of the furnace, as shown in Table 16—V that relates to ore practice: with oxygen practice, iron-oxide contents of run-off (flush) slags is usually somewhat higher than in ore practice. The run-off slag, of course, carries with it the iron and manganese oxides in this early slag which may make necessary further additions of ore to obtain rapid elimination of carbon. If the charging of the furnace, the timing of the addition of hot metal, and the run-off are managed skillfully, the silicon remaining to be neutralized with lime can be reduced to a small and almost constant amount, making possible a relatively small limestone charge. Since lime can be of service only in the slag and the calcination of the limestone absorbs heat, holding the limestone charge to a minimum not only decreases slag volume and cost of flux, but gives increased production with a decrease in fuel consumption.

Finally, attention should be given to the timing of the run-off to see that the temperature and fluidity of the run-off slag are sufficiently high and that the state of agitation of the bath is such that mixing of run-off slag and metal is not occurring extensively during the outward flow of slag. If conditions are not thus maintained, a disproportionate loss of metallic iron from the bath will result from metallic particles carried out with the run-off slag.

CHEMISTRY OF THE WORKING PERIOD

The chief aims during this period are to oxidize the remaining phosphorus out of the metal and neutralize it in the slag, to eliminate the carbon to the percentage desired for the start of the finishing period, and to raise the temperature of the bath to a point suitable for finishing and tapping the steel. To eliminate carbon, oxygen dissolved in the bath is necessary, and to oxidize and neutralize phosphorus both oxygen in the metal and calcium oxide in the slag are required, as indicated by the reactions in the discussion above. The rate of oxidation of the carbon must be kept in step with the rise in temperature, since the melting point of the metal bath rises as the carbon decreases. Although it has been pointed out that the reaction between carbon and oxygen dissolved in the bath is exothermic, it is not sufficiently so to furnish enough heat to supply that required for the decomposition and solution of the ore, so that the net over-all reaction requires the addition of heat. In addition, the oxidizing power and basicity of the slag must be controlled to give the best finishing conditions for the different grades of steel. Since it is through the slag that the refining reactions in the metal are accomplished, this control involves control of the temperature and the physical and chemical properties of the slag. The agents for controlling slag composition and properties are numerous, including ores, lime, limestone, sand, fluorspar, etc., but for economy the skilled melter will depend on iron ore, or other iron oxides, and calcium oxide. Any control system must be based upon chemical composition of the raw materials, and upon tests systematically made during the heat. The system may be based chiefly on slag tests, chiefly on metal tests, or both. Whatever the system, it must meet the requirement that it will give the melter a true picture as to the exact changes the metal is undergoing, both in temperature and composition. Much study has been given to all phases of this subject by many investigators and research workers, but practices still vary to such an extent that no one example can be selected as truly illustrative of the many practices in this part of the process.

Limitations of the Various Systems of Control—All three items for control; namely, temperature, slag composition, and metal composition, as well as the three systems of control, are limited by the ability of the chemist, physicist, and metallurgist to provide reasonably accurate methods for the determination of the temperature and the various components of the slag and metal that are sufficiently rapid to be of value as instruments of control. The following determinations have been developed to a stage that can be considered satisfactory for this work:

1. *Temperature*—While most melters used to adhere to the empirical methods of "cutting a rod," visual observation, or pouring metal from a spoon to estimate temperatures, these methods have been supplemented. By radiation pyrometers sighted on the roof of the furnace, the heat input to the bath can be controlled at the maximum allowable by the roof refractories. Similar pyrometers installed so as to sight on the checkers are used for automatic reversal of the burners, and the valves in the flues, thereby giving most efficient operation of the regenerative system. The temperature of the metal bath may be measured by "quick immersion" thermocouples or by photronic or radiation pyrometers sighting on the bottom of a tube inserted into the bath. The readings of these instruments are sufficiently reproducible to provide control. Optical pyrometers were previously used to measure temperatures on tapping and pouring, but most shops now rely completely on the bath temperatures determined by immersion thermocouples just before tap.

2. *Slag Control*—Rapid chemical methods exist for determining contents of total iron, ferrous iron, ferric iron and manganese. The results usually are expressed as the oxides FeO, Fe_2O_3, and MnO. Chemical methods for determining lime, silica, phosphorus, etc., are too slow for control purposes. Spectrographic methods now exist which will determine the lime-silica ratio in about 5 minutes. Other control tests are primarily physical. Slag pancakes may be used to estimate both basicity and iron oxide content, and serve well when used by experienced melters. Another control method is measurement of fluidity or viscosity by a flow test. The flowing properties of a slag depend on temperature as well as composition.

3. *Metal Control*—The carbon content of the bath can be determined in 2 to 15 minutes, depending on the equipment used. Modern combustion carbon analyzers utilizing thermal conductivity principles for direct readout of the carbon content, produce accurate results in less than 2 minutes. Gravimetric tests for carbon require 3 to 15 minutes. Physical tests for carbon, such as fracture, Carbometer, or Carbanalyzer tests require 2 to 3 minutes but the results are generally less accurate than those obtained by combustion methods. Manganese can be determined chemically in 10 to 15 minutes, and spectrographically in less time. Accurate results for sulphur can be obtained in 4 to 5 minutes by combustion methods. The chemical determination for phosphorus requires 15 to 20 minutes: this element can be determined on a vacuum direct-reading spectrometer and some air path spectrometers in 2 to 3 minutes. Chemical analysis for silicon requires 30 to 40 minutes for accurate results, although this element may be determined spectrographically in 2 to 3 minutes with accuracy comparable to chemical methods. Chemical or spectrographic analysis is frequently made for the "residual elements," such as copper, nickel, molybdenum, chromium, tin, etc., which enter with scrap. In the production of alloy steels, X-ray fluorescence techniques are being successfully used for determining the major alloying constituents of the bath.

Laws of Chemical Action—The general laws of chemical action which relate to reactions within and between slag and metal are discussed in Chapter 12.

The question of whether or not the open-hearth process is an "equilibrium" process has been debated often. According to a strict definition of equilibrium, concerned with all phases of the process, obviously the system is not in a state of equilibrium because the conditions are being changed constantly by such things as additions to slag and metal or variation of temperature. At the temperature involved in steelmaking, it is probable that reactions progress at an extremely rapid rate and consequently follow the changed conditions closely. Therefore, it may be said that with respect to the reacting species, or individual reactions, equilibrium is approached closely; while the whole aim of the operator of the furnace is to shift these equilibria, by the means under his control, towards the conditions desired when the heat is to be tapped. There can be no doubt that the natural laws apply to the steelmaking reactions, so that while the thermodynamic relationships between substances reacting in an open-hearth furnace have not been thoroughly determined, the natural laws can at least be used to make intelligent predictions as to the effect of a condition change.

Composition of Slags—A normal basic open-hearth slag, such as the melter has to deal with at the end of the lime boil, may be considered as a fused mixture of the oxides formed by the oxidation of the manganese and metalloids in the charge, together with the calcium oxide formed by the calcination of the limestone, and iron oxides from the charged ore and from the oxidation of scrap. Other oxides which may be present are magnesia and alumina, derived from the ore charged and from the hearth refractories, and oxides of other oxidizable elements which may have been present in the charge in small amounts; for instance, chromium, vanadium, and titanium. Sulphur is also present in the slag, in a form at present unknown. These many compounds are capable of forming numerous chemical and physical combinations so that the properties of individual components may be no indication of the properties of the mixture as a whole.

A large amount of experimental work has been performed, chiefly by thermal analysis and by the petrographic microscope, to determine the molecular species which may be present in a slag at different stages of a heat. Since both of these methods are subject to limitations, the definite existence of specific species in liquid slag has not been proved, but there is sufficient evidence to lead to the belief that the complex compounds most likely to exist, perhaps partly ionized, at various stages of a heat, include:

$$\left.\begin{array}{l} 2FeO \cdot SiO_2 \\ 2MnO \cdot SiO_2 \end{array}\right\} \text{or } 2(FeO,MnO) \cdot SiO_2 \left\{\begin{array}{l} \text{Iron-manganese} \\ \text{silicate} \end{array}\right.$$

$2CaO \cdot SiO_2$ or $4CaO \cdot 2SiO_2$ . . . . . Di-calcium silicate

$3CaO \cdot SiO_2$ . . . . Tri-calcium silicate

$4CaO \cdot P_2O_5$ . . . . Calcium phosphate

$FeO \cdot P_2O_5$ . . . . Ferrous phosphate

$$\left.\begin{array}{l} FeS \\ MnS \end{array}\right\} \text{or } (Fe,Mn)S \ldots \ldots \text{Iron-manganese sulphide}$$

FeO . . . . Ferrous oxide

Fe_2O_3 . . . . Ferric oxide

CaO (free) . . . . Calcium oxide

$CaO \cdot Fe_2O_3$ . . . . Mono-calcium ferrite

$2CaO \cdot Fe_2O_3$ . . . . Di-calcium ferrite

Phase diagrams for numerous slag systems have been developed which are useful in interpreting slag behavior. Examples of two- and three-component diagrams are given in Chapter 12.

Slag Composition in Relation to Refining Reactions —Since the basic open-hearth process is both chemically "basic" and oxidizing in nature, the melter must concern himself with the effects of changes in slag composition on these two factors.

Basicity of a slag may be defined as the ratio of the "basic" components of the slag to the "acid" ones. The most important "base" is CaO, while the most important "acid" is SiO_2; therefore, the simplest basicity ratio is CaO/SiO_2. Numerous refinements of this ratio have been suggested in an effort to arrive at a more exact measure of basicity, but for usual control purposes the simple lime-silica ratio is satisfactory.

The elimination of phosphorus requires that the slag be both highly oxidized and basic. In the early stages of the heat before the lime boil, a variable portion of the phosphorus may be held in the slag and eliminated in the run-off. The importance of iron oxide in the slag is observed in the furnace where phosphorus may revert to the steel if the iron oxide content of the slag is reduced to too low a value by virtue of a furnace block or the addition of a deoxidizer.

The distribution of sulphur between slag and metal likewise is affected by slag composition. In general, the removal of sulphur from the metal is favored by a large slag volume, a high basicity, and low iron oxide content. However, the latter two items are usually incompatible in basic open-hearth slags, as high basicity (low silica) is usually associated with high iron oxide.

CHEMISTRY OF THE FINISHING PERIOD

The finishing period of a heat is that period in which final adjustments for temperature are made in the furnace and adjustments of composition are made in furnace, ladle, or molds. Since many grades of steels, ranging from nearly pure iron to complex alloy steels, are made by the basic open-hearth process, it is obvious that the practices used during the finishing period will vary widely. At the beginning of this period, the elimination of manganese and the metalloids, with the exception of carbon, should be essentially completed, and the sulphur and phosphorus should be stabilized in a slag of the proper composition to prevent their reversion to the metal. The last of the ore additions will have been made and the carbon content will be falling at a slow, controllable rate to the desired value. The temperature is controlled by the rate at which fuel is burned, and additions to adjust the composition of the steel are made on the basis of chemical analyses made during this period.

Relation of Carbon to Oxygen in the Metal—The carbon and oxygen contents in the metal are closely related and the elimination of carbon is accelerated by a high proportion of active iron oxide in the slag. The mechanism by which carbon is removed is by diffusion of oxygen from the slag to the steel, where it reacts with the carbon to form predominantly CO and CO_2. The rate of diffusion of oxygen is relatively slow compared to reaction rates at the temperature involved, so that it is probable that the carbon-oxygen reaction closely approaches a state of dynamic equilibrium; that is to say, an equilibrium where the carbon content is dropping slowly but at no time is there a great excess of oxygen over that required for the chemical balance. The relation of carbon to oxygen in the metal is discussed in Chapter 12.

Frequently it is necessary to stop the progress of a heat because the carbon content may be dropping too rapidly for accurate control by chemical analysis or because the drop in carbon content must be stopped until other control analyses may be completed. Holding the carbon content at a given level, or "blocking the heat," is accomplished by adding to the metal bath sufficient deoxidizing agent to lower its oxygen content below the amount required for reaction with carbon. These deoxidizers may be special-quality pig iron or one of numerous ferroalloys which contain elements having a high affinity for oxygen. Blocking the heat is only a temporary measure, and the effect of the blocking agent is often cancelled by diffusion of oxygen from the slag before the heat is tapped. In this case, the oxygen content may again be estimated from the carbon analysis, provided the carbon-oxygen reaction has begun again to some degree.

Chemistry of Steel in the Ladle and Molds—The chemistry of ladle additions is a subject of great importance, as indicated by the objects to be accomplished.

(1) Final deoxidation to the point desired.
(2) Final adjustment to the composition desired.
(3) Final additions to develop special properties in the product, such as resistance to corrosion or aging, or machinability.

Every addition made is subject to reaction with the metal itself or some other element or compound in the metal that may be added to it. For this reason, ladle additions must be correlated with the treatments the heat has received in the furnace in order to produce the many types and grades of steel. In general, elements which are not oxidizable, such as copper or nickel, may be added to the furnace before tapping. Large amounts of deoxidizers, or easily oxidizable elements, are not commonly added to the furnace because of excessive losses due to the highly oxidized condition of the slag, and because of the danger of phosphorus reversion.

The degree of deoxidation obtained through ladle additions will depend on the kind and amount of deoxidizer used, as discussed in Chapter 12.

The additions which are made to *molds* are primarily for the purpose of obtaining the type of solidification desired. Small amounts of aluminum, usually a few ounces per ton of steel, may be used to control the rimming action in making rimming steel, while either ferrosilicon or aluminum are employed for control of the solidification of semikilled steels. In the manufacture of some killed steels the deoxidation may be completed with aluminum during the filling of the mold. On some grades of steel which may be difficult to rim, "rimming agents," of which sodium fluoride is the chief example, are used to promote gas evolution. In general, mold additions are kept quite small because the opportunity for good mixing is not great and the pouring temperature is too low to insure the melting of large amounts of cold material.

NONMETALLIC INCLUSIONS

The nonmetallic inclusions which are normally found in steel may be traced to one of the following sources:

Refractory Material—Since the liquid metal is in contact with refractories until it is teemed into the molds, there is a possibility that small fragments of refractory material may be broken away or removed by erosion or reaction and enter the metal. Usually the particles are large and, unless trapped, will rise rapidly to the surface of the metal in the ladle or mold. As a result, nonmetallic inclusions from this source are found only infrequently.

Oxygen and Sulphur—These elements are responsible for most of the nonmetallic inclusions, and only by their complete elimination from the process would it be possible to produce steels without inclusions.

While the steel composition is a factor, it is generally true that sulphur is quite soluble in steel at all temperatures above the melting point so that if sulphur is present, sulphide inclusions will not form until the steel solidifies, and thereby will be trapped in the ingot.

This is likewise true of oxygen in the case of steels which are not deoxidized. When strong deoxidizers, such as silicon or aluminum, are added to the ladle, their oxides are formed with the dissolved oxygen in the steel. It is probable that the majority of these oxides will float to the top of the ladle and be eliminated. However, the deoxidizing power of most deoxidizers increases as the temperature falls so that oxides are continually forming as the temperature drops to the solidification point of the steel. This effect is discussed in Chapter 12.

The rate at which spherical particles will rise from liquid steel is indicated by **Stokes' law:**

$$V = K \cdot \frac{2}{9\eta} \cdot r^2 \, g(d' - d)$$

where

V = Rising velocity
K = a constant
r = Radius of the particle
g = Acceleration due to gravity
d' and d = Density of liquid steel and inclusion, respectively
η = viscosity of liquid steel

The most important variable in this expression is "r," the radius of the particle which should be large for rapid rates of rise. The most desirable deoxidizer would consequently be one which produces a liquid oxide, since liquids possess the ability to coalesce and form larger particles. Nevertheless, it will be evident from the above discussion that inclusions are inherently a part of steel as made by commercial processes, and it is their location and distribution throughout the ingot which will determine whether or not they are harmful.

SECTION 9

OPERATION OF AN ACID OPEN-HEARTH FURNACE

Materials for the Charge—In acid open-hearth practice, the initial charge consists normally of cold pig iron, or cold pig iron and scrap. No ore can be added with the charge as in the basic process, for the iron oxide, being a base, would combine with the acid lining and rapidly destroy the bottom and banks. For the same reason the melting of scrap alone would be bad practice for its oxidation products would have a similar detrimental effect. Hence, the use of hot metal (molten pig iron) to supply the whole of the pig iron part of the charge is impracticable, for it would necessarily have to be added after the scrap was hot and had been considerably oxidized.

The proportion of scrap to pig iron may vary over wide limits. As previously pointed out, Siemens originally used no scrap, and as ore was added to the pig iron after melting to hasten oxidation, his process was called the pig and ore process. Later, the Martin brothers used scrap with only enough pig iron to make the melt have the carbon content desired in the finished steel. As they used no ore, their method of working was called the pig and scrap process. The modern method, in which a charge of pig and scrap is melted, then "ored down" or "pigged up" as required, may be looked upon as a combination of these two methods. In it, the relative amounts of pig iron and scrap in the charge are controlled largely by plant and market conditions; that is, the supply and relative cost of these materials. If both are available, then the only thing considered in proportioning the charge is the carbon content it is desired the charge should have when melted. In times of extreme shortages of pig iron, substitutes such as Mexican graphite, silicon carbide, or silicon-steel scrap may be used with an increased scrap charge. Coke cannot be used because of its high sulphur content.

Grade of Scrap and Iron for the Charge—Only a trace of the phosphorus and none of the sulphur are eliminated in the acid open-hearth process. Indeed, the finished steel may contain a slightly higher percentage of both of these elements than the average of the charge. This increase is due to the fact that, while the weights of the sulphur and phosphorus remain practically constant, the weight of the metallic bath may be decreased appreciably, owing to losses through oxidation of iron and metalloids. In addition, the bath is likely to absorb some sulphur from the flame. Consequently, great care must be exercised to see that the average sulphur and phosphorus content of the charge is somewhat below that required in the finished steel. Silicon, manganese, and carbon are oxidized very readily in this process; consequently, require less consideration in the selection of materials. The specifications for acid open-hearth pig iron usually call for a silicon content under 2.00 per cent, manganese 1.00 to 2.00 per cent, and phosphorus and sulphur under 0.03 per cent. In steel for some grades of sheets, the phosphorus content may be somewhat higher, under 0.06 per cent being satisfactory. It is an easy matter, either at the blast furnaces or at the steel works, to secure a representative sample of any lot of pig iron, and its selection offers little difficulty. But it is almost impossible to secure a representative sample of the scrap for analysis; hence, the scrap must be selected by inspection and with much care and judgment. For example, in order to produce a steel with a phosphorus and a sulphur content each under 0.05 per cent, such scrap as tubes, pipe, Bessemer rails, and castings from unknown sources must be avoided. The size of the scrap is also of some importance. Unless the proportion of pig iron is large, light scrap makes it difficult to get a full charge into the furnace. Besides, light scrap is excessively oxidized in melting, unless extraordinary precautions are taken in charging. This oxidation of the iron not only decreases the yield, but the resulting iron oxide also combines with the siliceous lining and rapidly fluxes out the bottom and banks of the furnace.

Manner of Charging—A few small and isolated furnaces still may be charged by hand, but in the main all the larger furnaces will be charged by machine. As to the order in which the pig iron and scrap are charged, it is unimportant which is charged first if the scrap is heavy or makes up less than half of the total charge. But if the scrap is light, many prefer to charge it ahead of the pig iron which, being spread out on the top, tends to shield the scrap from direct contact with the flame and to prevent its being oxidized excessively. Others make a practice of charging part of the pig iron on the bottom and part on top of the scrap. The pig iron on top melts first and, trickling down over the scrap beneath, the silicon and carbon it contains react with iron and manganese oxides as soon as formed, thus insuring that the latter do not come in contact with the bottom or banks. The added protection afforded by a little pig iron on the bottom is obvious, and is a great advantage. It not only will increase the yield but also will save much repairing of the bottom. As soon as the liquid basic oxides of iron and manganese come in contact with the acid oxides of silicon in the lining, silicates of these oxides are formed and become slag. Then, not only are the banks rapidly eroded away, but also the iron and manganese oxides are neutralized and lose their power of oxidizing and neutralizing the metalloids in the pig iron.

Melting—As soon as the furnace has been charged, the fuel, which is usually partly or wholly turned off during the charging, is turned on full, and the flame is reversed every twenty to thirty minutes in order to raise the temperature and melt down the charge as quickly as possible. The heat usually requires little attention during the first part of this period, so the time generally is occupied in preparations for tapping. The steel ladle requires a new nozzle and a new stopper, and the ladle and cinder pits must be cleaned out—duties performed by men on the pouring floor. On the charging floor the second helper cleans and repairs the steel runner, sets it in place, and sees that it is thoroughly dried; procures, or has brought to the furnace, the ferromanganese, ferrosilicon, anthracite coal, and other deoxidizers and recarburizers required. From four to five hours are required to melt the charge. Toward the end of this period, the first helper, or melter, will keep a close watch upon the action of the heat. If the charge contained a larger proportion (over half) of pig iron, especially if the iron carries a high silicon and low manganese content, the slag formed will be very thick or viscous and, in order to hasten the process and increase the yield, it is necessary to add a little ore or lime. Great care must be used in adding lime, to prevent the banks from being destroyed. On the other hand, if the charge was composed chiefly of scrap, or the pig contained a low percentage of silicon, it may be advisable, in order to save the banks and bottom from excessive scorification, to add some sand, old bricks or other siliceous material.

Adjusting Conditions After Melting—After the charge has melted completely, the heat, if handled properly, should and usually does contain about 20 to 40 points (hundredths of a per cent) more carbon than is required in the finished steel. Some melters prefer to have the heat melt with a carbon content of more than one per cent in all cases, but for soft steels this practice will not improve the steel and may cause additional labor.

If the charge was made up largely of a low-silicon pig iron and the heat was given proper attention during the melting period, practically all of the silicon and manganese will have been oxidized and neutralized, forming the slag. This slag, at first black in color, is normally made up of about 50 per cent of bases, principally iron and manganese oxides, and about 50 per cent of acids, principally silica. Such a slag tends to be self adjusting in that the slag will tend to retard the elimination of silicon and carbon from the metal, if the silica content of the slag is increased, whereas if the iron and manganese contents be increased, silica will be absorbed from the furnace banks. Where the melting has been such that considerable oxidation may have occurred, the first slag may be sufficiently oxidizing to complete the elimination of carbon without the necessity of ore additions. This first slag tends to adjust itself as follows: As the temperature rises, the carbon in the bath reduces iron oxide in the slag, causing the slag to grow lighter in color. Also, the slag gains more manganese oxide so that the color changes are black to brown to greenish yellow to a light green color, tinted according to the manganese it contains. These color changes are still sometimes used to follow the course of the heat. However, more recently there have been developed slag fluidity measurements which, in conjunction with temperature measurements, give a more accurate picture of the condition of the slag. The measurement is based on the fact that the silica content of the slag greatly affects its fluidity and this fact can be used to determine the need for additions to the slag to cause it to be more or less oxidizing to the bath. The changes, which the slag tests indicate are necessary, may be made by lime or ore for more oxidizing conditions or by carbon and the regulation of fuel input when the oxidizing power of the slag is too great.

Working the Heat—The problem now before the melter is to reduce the carbon content as rapidly but controllably as possible, and at the same time get the metal heated up to a temperature that will permit the heat to be tapped and teemed satisfactorily. In order to determine the carbon content of the bath, a fracture test of the metal may be taken, but more often an instrument such as the "Carbometer," or "Carbanalyzer" or chemical analysis is used.

If the metal appears to be too cold, attempts are made to raise its temperature by burning more fuel and reversing the flame frequently, before any necessary ore is added. If the carbon is relatively high and the bath is quiet and sufficiently hot, a few lumps of ore are added to start a boil. After this ore has had time to react with carbon, more ore may be added, but this is not done so rapidly that a large excess of iron oxide is created in the slag, as this would result in erosion of the banks of the furnace and cause excessive slag volume.

If, by virtue of a large ore addition, the carbon content becomes lower than desired, it may be restored by adding pig iron to hold the carbon at the desired level until the tapping temperature is reached. Thus, by frequent sampling of the bath and treating it as required, the carbon content and the temperature will be so adjusted that the heat may be tapped. Low carbon heats, under 0.30 per cent carbon, may be normally worked down to a carbon content of 0.10 per cent to 0.12 per cent and recarburized to the desired composition by ladle additions, and some melters prefer to do this. However, especially in the case of higher carbon heats, it is customary to "block"

the heat with ferrosilicon at the required carbon content. Since no phosphorus is removed in this process, the addition of large amounts of pig iron or spiegel for recarburizing is inadvisable, unless low-phosphorus pig iron is available, lest the phosphorus content be increased beyond the limit allowed. Therefore, medium- and high-carbon heats are usually "caught on the way down."

Finishing Acid Open-Hearth Steel—During the last hour the heat is in the furnace, little ore is added so that the carbon content may drop slowly and under control to the desired value for tapping. However, the slag must not become too depleted in iron oxide, for if the temperature is high, as in the case of low-carbon heats, some silica may be reduced and the silicon content of the steel will be increased. This condition will be indicated to the melter by a cessation of boiling and by an increase in the viscosity of the slag. It may be prevented by the addition of a small amount of limestone, which will decrease the viscosity of the slag and make available iron oxide by combining with the silica of the iron silicates. In Table 16—VI are shown the compositions of three finishing slags illustrative of the widest variations to be expected under normal conditions. Only the significant components are given.

When the temperature has been raised to the proper level and the slag is in the proper condition for tapping, the heat may be blocked or allowed to work slowly down to the required carbon content. At this time, additions to adjust the amount of alloying elements may be made. If the charge for the heat has been selected with care, the preliminary analysis, taken when the charge was completely melted, will have shown that the phosphorus and sulphur specifications will be met. However, if error or lack of satisfactory control of raw materials causes either the phosphorus or sulphur content, or both, to be too high, the heat must be rejected in the case of most steel foundries, or applied to an order with higher specifications for these elements, for there are no corrective measures that can be applied to reduce their contents.

Tapping—When ready, the heat is tapped by methods described for basic furnaces.

Additions to the Heat—In the acid open-hearth process, additions to the heat are made both in the furnace and in the ladle. In making high-carbon heats in which the carbon is caught on the way down, most

Table 16—VI. Composition of Acid Open-Hearth Slags (Per Cent)

Constituent	Heat Number		
	1	2	3
SiO$_2$...........	54.25	52.06	55.60
FeO...........	25.87	20.38	28.90
MnO...........	11.27	20.52	10.23
P$_2$O$_5$...........	0.045	0.035	0.022
Al$_2$O$_3$...........	3.28	3.07	4.16
CaO...........	5.37	4.35	0.70
MgO...........	0.12	Trace	0.12

of the additions, including ferromanganese and ferro-chromium, are added in the furnace, as well as un-oxidizable additions such as copper, nickel, and molybdenum compounds. In making medium and low-carbon steels, adjustments in carbon content are made in the ladle, preferably with anthracite coal of about pea size. To facilitate the addition, the coal usually is contained in paper bags, each holding a known weight. Ferromanganese also may be added in the ladle, for which purpose it usually is crushed to pass a 2-inch screen. Additions made to the steel in the ladle also include such materials as ferrovanadium, ferrosilicon, ferrotitanium, and aluminum. All ladle additions should be completed before much slag begins to flow from the furnace. Additions to the heat during the pouring of ingots usually are confined to aluminum.

Teeming—The proper manufacture of an acid open-hearth steel heat leads to tapping temperatures of the order of 3000° F. For the manufacture of small and intricate castings where many molds must be poured, such a temperature may be necessary at the start of the pour in order that the last molds may be filled. In pouring large castings, however, a temperature of this magnitude may be too high for what has been established as good practice. Pouring temperatures and rates will depend on mold sizes and the use for which the castings are intended. Small molds are usually filled by "hand shanking" whereby sufficient metal for one mold is taken from the large ladle in a small hand ladle for pouring. Larger molds are filled by the conventional ladle with stopper and nozzle.

The temperature and rate conditions mentioned above also apply in the pouring of ingots whose sizes may vary from 500 pounds for small forgings to as much as 400,000 pounds for very large forgings. The types of pouring employed are top pouring, bottom pouring, and basket or tundish pouring, which already have been discussed in Section 5.

Preparation of the Furnace for the Next Charge—Efficient operation of the furnace requires that the next heat be charged with little delay after tapping. This is possible only if the furnace is kept in good condition from day to day and heat to heat; consequently, as soon as the heat is out of the furnace, the melter inspects the interior carefully. Steel remaining in low places on the hearth is removed by rabbling and holes are filled with bottom sand. All steel and slag are cleaned from the tapping hole, which then is closed in the same manner as described previously. While the taphole is being made up, the banks are repaired by shoveling sand on them and fritting it into place. This work requires about an hour if the banks can be rebuilt with one layer of sand. If the banks have been eroded badly, the sand must be applied in two coats and about forty-five minutes are required for each coat. As soon as this repair work is completed, charging of the furnace may begin.

SECTION 10

CHEMISTRY OF THE ACID OPEN-HEARTH PROCESS

Chemistry of Melting—The elimination of silicon, manganese, and carbon is effected in two stages corresponding to the melting and boiling of the heat. Analyses show that during melting nearly all of the silicon and manganese and a part of the carbon are oxidized. Since no ore is charged in the acid process, the only source of oxygen for oxidation during this stage is the furnace gases, which consist of the products of combustion of the fuel and any excess air which may have leaked into the furnace. Carbon dioxide, water vapor, and oxygen in the furnace atmosphere will oxidize iron rapidly above a red heat. The extent to which the oxidation will proceed will depend on the proportions of these gases and the gaseous products of the oxidation in the atmosphere, and the temperature. This action is confined to the surface until the fusion point is reached. When the melting point of the iron oxides is reached, they begin to flow off, thus leaving the metal beneath exposed to further oxidation. This action applies to the scrap only, because the melting point of the pig iron is about the same or lower than that of the oxide.

Purifying Reactions—The fact that the melting point of the pig iron is lower than that of the scale is a fortunate circumstance, for otherwise the liquid scale would trickle to the bottom of the furnace and there react with the silica hearth to form a slag. With the pig iron in a molten state on the bottom of the furnace, these oxides of iron react with the metalloids, removing them from the bath and giving up some of the iron contained in the iron oxides.

After the greater portion of the silicon and manganese has been oxidized, a small part of the phosphorus may be oxidized; but later, when the slag becomes higher in silica, the phosphorus compounds will be reduced, returning the phosphorus to the metal. Therefore, seldom more than traces of phosphorus can be removed from the charge; in fact, the phosphorus content may increase slightly by virtue of the removal of the other metalloids.

Elimination of Carbon During the Melting Period—If the melting could be effected instantaneously, very little carbon would be oxidized until after the silicon and manganese were eliminated. But since melting takes place gradually, a part of the pig iron coming in contact with the highly oxidizing basic slag, both being in the liquid state, loses its metalloids, including carbon, quickly; consequently the percentage of carbon in the bath, immediately after melting is complete, will be considerably lower than the average of the charge. While the amount of carbon thus oxidized cannot be predicted accurately, melters are quite successful in properly proportioning pig iron and scrap to the condition of the furnace and method of charging, to have the heat melt near the carbon content desired for proper finishing.

Chemistry of the Boil—By the time the charge has melted completely, a substantial portion of the silicon and manganese will have been oxidized to form a slag. If the melting has been rapid, there may not have been enough oxidation of the scrap to start a boil, so ore must be added. On the other hand, if the melting has been slow, enough oxidation may have occurred for the boil to be completed without the use of ores. If the carbon content is low, the melter will first attempt to increase the temperature of the bath by increasing the fuel rate and reversing the flame more often, but if the carbon content is high, for example fifty points over the content desired, the feeding of ore may begin as soon as the temperature is sufficiently high. If the temperature is too low when ore is added, its action is delayed and is too violent when it occurs. The mechanism of metalloid elimination involves the same chemical reactions as those discussed under basic practice. The ore additions are made gradually to keep the boil under control and to protect the banks of the furnace.

SECTION 11
DUPLEX PROCESSES

Definition—The term *duplex process* may be applied to any combination of two processes for manufacturing steel but, in the United States at least, custom has restricted the unmodified term to mean only a combination of the acid Bessemer converter and the basic open-hearth processes, in which the latter plays the part of a finishing process. Briefly, the duplex process consists of blowing molten pig iron in the Bessemer converter until the silicon, manganese and most of the carbon have been oxidized, and then transferring this semi-finished metal to a basic open-hearth furnace where, through the agencies of iron oxide and lime, the phosphorus and the remainder of the carbon are oxidized and lowered to desired limits. The steel is then finished, recarburized and deoxidized as in the usual open-hearth practice.

Tilting Open-Hearth Furnaces—Open-hearth furnaces of the tilting type are especially adapted to the duplex process and the major portion of the tonnage of duplex-process steels is made in such furnaces. This type of open-hearth furnace was originally designed for purposes other than duplexing. The first tilting open-hearth furnace was placed in operation in 1889 at the Steelton Plant of the former Pennsylvania Steel Company by H. H. Campbell. This antedated the introduction of the duplex process by more than ten years.

The **Campbell tilting furnace** was introduced as a means of readily using high percentages of pig iron and avoiding some of the operating difficulties then inherent in stationary furnaces. The furnace proper rested on rollers arranged in a circular path, providing rotation on its longitudinal axis. With this arrangement, fuel could be fired even when the furnace was in tipped positions. The advantages claimed by Campbell for the tilting feature were the ease of removal of

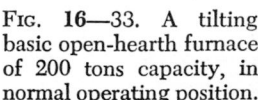

FIG. **16**—33. A tilting basic open-hearth furnace of 200 tons capacity, in normal operating position.

Fig. 16—34. This illustration shows the 200-ton tilting basic open-hearth furnace of Figure 16—33 in tapping position.

large slag volumes when high-pig-iron charges were used; the elimination of delays and difficulties in maintaining tapholes, the taphole being located above the level of the bath; the greater ease in repairing bottoms or hearths because the furnace could be drained by tilting; and finally, the greater ease of maintaining the backwalls.

The Campbell furnace was shortly followed by the **Wellman tilting furnace,** in which the furnace proper rolled forward on a horizontal track, necessitating fuel and air shut-off when the furnace was in tipped position.

Figure 16—33 shows a typical modern tilting open-hearth furnace of the Campbell type in normal operating position; Figure 16—34 shows the same furnace in tilted position during tapping. Schematic longitudinal and transverse sections of another tilting furnace are shown in Figure 16—35.

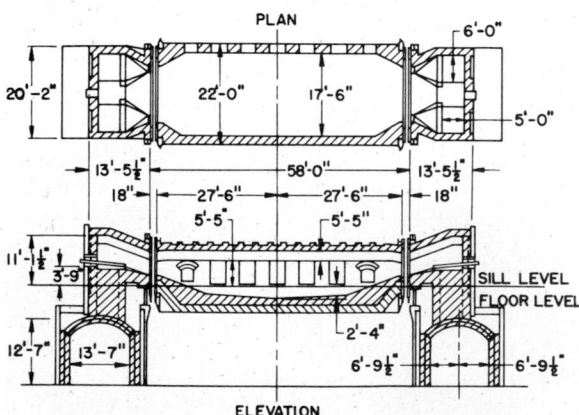

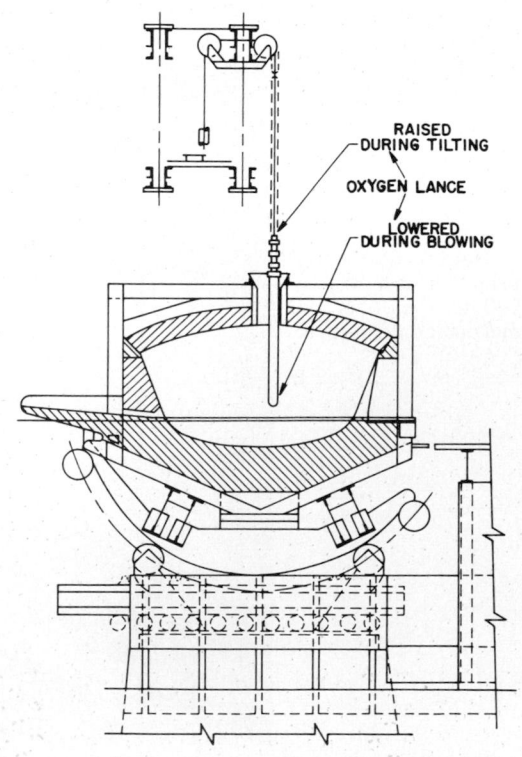

Fig. 16—35. (Above) Longitudinal section of a 190-ton tilting basic open-hearth furnace. (Right) Transverse section of the furnace, showing location of rollers on which furnace tilts, and method of installing oxygen lance for rapid decarburization of the bath.

DUPLEX PLANT LAYOUT AND EQUIPMENT

Description of Duplex Plant—In a plant to make steel only by the duplex process, Bessemer capacity should balance tilting-furnace capacity, and the converters should be in close proximity to the tilting furnaces to facilitate transfer of metal from one to the other. An exact balance is difficult to plan in advance, for the time the steel is held in the open-hearth furnace varies with the grade of steel being made. For this reason, it is better to arrange for the production of some Bessemer steel along with the duplex production in order to utilize the equipment more fully. Also, the relative number of furnaces necessary to maintain a workable balance depends somewhat upon the tonnage to be produced. For example, one 20-ton converter serving a 200-ton tilting furnace would be an unsatisfactory combination, as interruptions in the operation of either would delay the other. But a combination in which three 25-ton converters serve three 200-ton tilting furnaces gives a well-balanced operating unit for the continuous production of steel.

In addition to the required number of furnaces and converters for the steel production desired, it is generally considered necessary to have at least two hot-metal mixers. Adequate facilities for transfer of iron to the converter and of blown metal from the converters to the open-hearth floor must be provided in order to prevent delays in furnace charging.

In general, all other facilities provided for a scrap-melting shop, including facilities for ladle repair, mold preparation and slag disposal, must be provided. The requirements for charging machines, boxes and buggies are not so heavy as in a scrap shop. On the pit side, pouring facilities must be particularly well organized in order to tap, pour and move the heats on the rapid schedules attained in duplex operation.

In addition to the auxiliary equipment necessary for an open-hearth shop, much of the apparatus necessary for a Bessemer shop must also be provided. In this connection blowing equipment, vessel-tilting machinery, vessel and vessel-bottom repair equipment are the most important.

The application of the principles of the duplex process to the making of steel has resulted in various modifications. The most recent has been adoption of the use of oxygen roof lances to shorten heat time, and increase production. Some of the most common examples will be described in the following sections, using figures based on practices in typical plants (without the use of oxygen).

A. CONTINUOUS PROCESS MAINTAINING
A DOMINANT POOL

This description will cover a process developed in the South for the manufacture of steel in basic-lined tilting open-hearth furnaces, using hot metal produced in blast furnaces charged with a blended iron ore of relatively high phosphorus content. Typical contents of various constituents of the fractions of such a blended ore may be as follows:

| | Percentage Content | | |
	Coarse Fraction	Medium Fraction	Sinter Fraction
Constituent			
Moisture	3.40	5.23	1.50
Iron (Fe)	43.23	49.10	58.33
Silica (SiO_2)	11.00	6.92	6.57
Alumina (Al_2O_3)	2.61	2.23	2.58
Lime (CaO)	9.50	5.72	4.98
Manganese (Mn)	0.13	0.09	0.09
Phosphorus (P)	0.25	0.19	0.19

Hot metal produced from ore of this composition by the blast furnaces may be expected to have a composition falling within the following specification ranges:

Element	Per Cent
Silicon	0.70–1.00
Sulphur	0.075 maximum
Phosphorus	0.40–0.60
Manganese	0.13–0.30

The basic tilting open-hearth practice developed to use high-phosphorus hot metal of this composition for steelmaking requires the following essential steps: the maintenance of a **dominant pool** of metal in a tilting basic open-hearth furnace, adding approximately 80 per cent of the next succeeding heat in the form of blown metal from the acid-Bessemer converters, impregnating the basic finishing slag of the previous heat with the phosphorus contained by this blown metal, and then flushing the phosphorus-laden slag from the furnace.

One open-hearth plant employing this process consists of two shops with five and four tilting furnaces, respectively. Between these two shops is a converting department with one 1250-ton and one 650-ton mixer, together with three 20-ton acid-Bessemer converters. The location of the converting department lends itself to an operation with a minimum of delay in delivering blown metal to the open-hearth furnaces. In case of a delay in one shop, the blown metal generally can be delivered to one of the furnaces in the other. Blown metal is poured out of the converters on the open-hearth charging-floor level and is transported in 25-ton ladles mounted in trunnions on ladle cars. Metal is poured into an open-hearth furnace by tilting the ladle in its trunnions on the car.

The tilting open-hearth furnaces are of the Campbell type in which the furnace is mounted on rocker arms and rollers and can be tilted forward and backward about a horizontal axis. The axis of rotation of each of these furnaces is coincident with the centerline of the ports and rotation of a furnace does not interfere with firing. The framework is of much stronger construction than that for ordinary open-hearth furnaces in order to resist twisting stresses and vibration which would be very harmful to the brickwork.

Only that section of a furnace comprising the hearth, sidewalls, and roof is made tilting; all the ports and flues are stationary, and, together with the checkerwork, are of the same construction as in stationary furnaces. The clearance between the movable and stationary parts of the ports is kept very small by the use of water-cooled joints, in order to keep air and gas leakage to a minimum. On the pouring side, these furnaces have but one opening, a tapping hole located above the slag line and provided with a lip or spout for directing the stream of molten metal into the steel ladle. As in the case of stationary furnaces, doors for introducing the materials into the furnace are located on the front side. Slag notches are also located in the middle doors on the front side.

Preparing the Furnace for Charging—The process may be said to be continuous. When it is necessary to make repairs, the tilting furnace is thoroughly drained, the bottom and slag lines are made up, the ports are cleaned and repaired, and everything is made ready for the resumption of standard production. Of course, during operation the front and backwall must be attended to and such minor repairs made as are found necessary. Before any iron is blown in the converters, the preparation of a slag is begun by charging and melting down lime and oxides. Considerable care is given by the melter to the preparation of a good slag, for, as in all open-hearth work, the success of the process depends upon the slag.

Except for the first heats, there are from 25 to 35 tons of each 175-ton heat of steel retained in the furnace at each tapping; this forms what is referred to as the "dominant pool."

Cycle of Operations—When a ladle is filled with finished steel tapped from one heat, the steel in the ladle is covered with a blanket of slag which flows out of the taphole as the furnace is rolling back to an upright position. Most of the slag is retained in the furnace. When a furnace is completely upright, the slag level is below the taphole. As soon as tapping is completed, approximately 80 per cent of the next succeeding heat is immediately added to the furnace in the form of full-blown metal which usually consists of five "pots" or ladles full of blown metal totaling approximately 100 tons. The blown metal, being washed through the highly-basic finishing slag of the previous heat, is rapidly dephosphorized. This slag is then immediately poured off the washed metal over the foreplate into slag pots on cars on narrow-gauge tracks at basement level. The slag-making constituents, for refining the washed metal that is the starting point for the new heat, is then charged; these usually consist of burnt lime and oxides as required. From 1 to 1½ hours are required for the charged burnt lime and oxides to melt and form a suitable slag. When the slag is in proper condition, two pots or ladles of partially-blown high-carbon metal are added to supply the carbon necessary for working the heat. The refining period from time of the addition of the last partially-blown or high-carbon pot requires from one hour and thirty minutes to two hours and thirty minutes, depending upon the type of steel being produced.

In the blowing operation silicon, carbon and manganese are all practically removed when blowing a full-blown, low carbon or "soft" pot. The phosphorus content, due to the loss of carbon, silicon, manganese and some iron during blowing, is increased from an average of 0.50 per cent in the iron to around 0.55 per cent in the blown metal. The greater part of the silicon, along with some of the carbon and manganese are removed in blowing a high-carbon pot. A definite range of ferrous-oxide content of the slag is necessary for effective dephosphorization of the blown metal, and this is maintained by suitable additions to the bath of burnt lime, mill scale, ore and ferromanganese or ferrosilicon.

With this operation it is possible to produce steel ranging from low-metalloid grades to carbon tool steels.

Advantages of the Process—Considerable benefit is derived from the use of full-blown metal charges, eliminating contamination of the bath by undesirable alloys normally present in scrap. This is especially true when producing a low-metalloid heat.

One of the benefits derived from this process is a minimizing of reaction between slag and steel during tapping; more of this reaction occurs at tap in conventional stationary open-hearth practice. This advantage is made possible by plugging the taphole of the tilting furnace with bagging which holds until the slag rises above the hole while the furnace is being tilted. The only slag removed is that amount coming out after the ladle is filled, and the furnace is being rolled back to an upright position. This provides a relatively thin blanket to prevent the steel in the ladle from freezing.

The process provides uniformity from heat to heat through the duplication of desired heat cycles. During all periods the fuel is not checked and little loss in temperature occurs. This is advantageous as regards the useful life of the roof and other brickwork of the furnace.

This process can be flexible in its use of charged materials. When, due to shortages of hot metal, increased percentages of scrap are required, the additional scrap may be charged in small amounts into several furnaces or may be confined to one furnace, although increasing the percentage of scrap charged does lengthen the heat cycle. The tilting furnace facilitates bottom repair in that the furnace may be tilted forward or backward to drain a hole which would have to be rabbled out in the stationary type of furnace.

Slag Composition—Composition of a typical refining slag and composition of the slag after the addition of the full-blown "soft" pots is as follows:

Constituent	Refining Slag (%)	Before Slagging Over Foreplate (%)
Ferrous oxide (FeO)	14.00	4.50
Ferric oxide (Fe_2O_3)	8.60	5.50
Silica (SiO_2)	9.75	12.50
Lime (CaO)	48.00	49.00
Magnesia (MgO)	4.00	4.00
Manganous oxide (MnO)	2.50	1.50
Phosphoric acid (P_2O_5)	8.00–13.00	10.00–20.00

The high-phosphorus slag obtained after the addition of the full-blown "soft" pots is diluted to some extent by the "kick-off" or flush slag resulting from the reaction at the time of addition of the partially-blown high-carbon pots of metal.

Deficiencies of the Dominant Pool Method—The most valid criticisms of the dominant pool method are that, (1) the tapping slag which remains in the furnace after a heat contains a high phosphorus content, (2) the pool of metal remaining in the furnace is likely to become too highly oxidized before the furnace is filled up again, (3) the fluxing materials for the next heat are charged on top of and float on the remaining pool, failing to give the beneficial effects that can be derived from a prolonged boil from lime charged on the bottom, (4) frequent examination of the furnace bottom is impossible with resulting long "bottom delays."

B. THE DRY BOTTOM OR SINGLE HEAT DUPLEX PROCESS

This duplex method is commonly used in northern United States at present, except where special conditions dictate continuation of the dominant pool method. It is a continuous operation with no week-end bottom-repair period. Several different practices of preparing the charge are used and local conditions are the factors that determine which practice shall be employed. The method is so flexible that all of the practices in use produce steel of satisfactory quality and quantity; consequently, only one dry-bottom practice is described.

The Charge—After the previous heat has been tapped, the furnace is turned into its normal operating position. The melter foreman examines the bottom and, if no repairs are necessary, orders the next charge from the Bessemer steel blower. The amount of limestone charged is determined by the grade of steel to be made. If a heat of rimmed steel is to be produced, 16,800 pounds of raw limestone will be charged for a 145 ton heat. If the heat is to be semikilled or killed, this amount is reduced to 11,200 pounds. As soon as the melter foreman has ordered the charge, approximately one-half of the limestone is charged on the furnace bottom and the furnace crew proceed with the slag line repairs to the front, back, and ends.

To produce an open-hearth heat of 145 tons, approximately 335,000 pounds of liquid pig iron are ordered for the converters. Two heats (blows) of 45,000 and 50,000 pounds each are blown simultaneously in the Bessemer converters and when they reach a point in the blow where the carbon content is between 0.10 and 0.20 per cent they are turned down and poured into one ladle. This ladle of metal is carried by an overhead crane and poured through a spout into the open-hearth furnace. After the first ladle of metal has been poured into the furnace, the remainder of the limestone is charged. The balance of the blown metal follows, there being three ladles in all.

After the last heat has been blown in the converters, liquid basic iron in amounts ranging from 35,000 to 47,000 pounds is brought from the mixers and charged into the open-hearth furnace. The unblown basic hot metal is used because its manganese content is higher than blown Bessemer hot metal, thus assuring a residual manganese in the charge comparable to that encountered in any regular open-hearth heat. Varying amounts of this metal are used to provide the initial carbon content of the bath necessary for different grades of steel. The amounts of blown metal, therefore, must obviously be adjusted so that the complete charge will total approximately 310,000 pounds.

There are three reasons for stopping the blow when the carbon content reaches 0.10 and 0.20 per cent; first, this eliminates the possibility of over-oxidation of the metal; second, the nitrogen content of the steel will be lower than in full blown metal; and third, it assists in producing a slag in the acid converter that is sufficiently thick (viscous) to minimize its carry-over to the basic open-hearth furnace.

A summary of the charge is as follows:

	Rimmed Steel (Pounds)	Semi-killed or Killed Steel (Pounds)
Limestone	8,400	7,000
Blown Metal	90,000	90,000
Limestone	8,400	4,200
Blown Metal	90,000	90,000
Blown Metal	90,000	90,000
Basic Hot Metal	40,000	40,000
Total Limestone	16,800	11,200
Total Blown Metal	270,000	270,000
Total Hot Metal	40,000	40,000

The difference between the 335,000 pounds of metal ordered from the mixers and the 310,000 pounds in the open-hearth charge is, of course, that portion lost during the blowing process.

Working the Heat—Approximately thirty minutes after the furnace has been completely charged, a test is taken and analyzed for carbon and manganese. This analysis indicates to the furnace crew the amounts of lump ore necessary to reduce the carbon to the desired point. All heats are charged to provide an initial carbon content about 40 "points" (0.40 per cent) above the tapping carbon, with the exception of certain grades for extra-deep-drawing applications. On these latter grades a much higher initial carbon is desired and provided because the increased ore additions necessary for the carbon reduction promote an active boil of the bath for a longer period of time and thus reduce the nitrogen content of the steel. The normal nitrogen content of steels made by the liquid-charge method is 0.006 to 0.008 per cent, while in standard basic open-hearth steels the range is 0.004 to 0.006 per cent. The additional bath activity described above, however, reduces the nitrogen content to the 0.004 to 0.006 per cent range, and it is this slight reduction in nitrogen content that permits steel made by the liquid-metal process to compete favorably on applications demanding a high degree of ductility and relative insensitivity to strain aging.

During the early working period of the heat, the lime boil takes place until the limestone charged on the bottom is thoroughly calcined and rises to the surface to form the slag.

When the bath has reached the necessary temperature, additions of lump ore are begun and proceed periodically throughout the working period as demanded. During this period chemical analyses are made for phosphorus and sulphur, and carbometer tests are taken to indicate to the furnace crew the extent of carbon elimination.

Pancake slag tests are also taken and additional burnt limestone or mill roll scale is added for the purpose of providing the proper slag consistency.

The heat is "worked down" in the same manner as any basic open-hearth heat, and when the desired carbon content is reached, a ladle is set on the tapping side of the furnace. The furnace is then tilted to permit the slag to rise above the tap hole and the metal to flow into the ladle.

Recarburizing material is usually kept to a minimum, the carbon being "caught on the way down." Deoxidizing materials, such as ferromanganese, silicon, aluminum, titanium, etc., are added to the ladle the same as in any other open-hearth heat.

The Slag—The slag volume for steel made by this duplex process is less than on regular open-hearth steel, running approximately 6.5 per cent of the weight of the finished heat. The limestone charged is normally 90 to 95 pounds per ton of steel; this is possible because of the very low silicon content of the charge. No difficulty is experienced in the removal of phosphorus, except when a considerable amount of Bessemer slag is allowed to enter the furnace with the charge.

The average composition in per cent of tapping slag of a steel tapped at 0.09 per cent carbon and 0.17 per cent residual manganese follows:

SiO_2	11.58%	MnO	8.86
Al_2O_3	1.16	CaO	41.50
TiO_2	0.29	MgO	6.23
FeO	18.55	P_2O_5	3.16
Fe_2O_3	5.57	S	0.17

Heat time averages approximately four hours tap to tap.

C. COMBINATION SCRAP AND BLOWN METAL METHOD

This type of operation may be used in tilting-furnace shops, but is particularly adapted for use in plants that have stationary furnaces, yet desire to take advantage of the faster-melting duplex practice. Although many variations of the method are possible, depending upon local operating and economic conditions, the system described is one that has been very successful from a production standpoint in one of the eastern plants.

The practice employed is to charge the limestone, ore, scrap and hot metal as for a regular high-iron charge. After the slag flush is finished, the full-blown Bessemer metal is added in amounts of about 16 or 32 per cent of the total charge, and a second quantity of slag is flushed off. Satisfactory slag flushes are obtained when the blown metal is either 16 or 32 per cent of the total charge. The amount of ore charged is regulated to specific conditions, such as type of scrap, age of furnace, and carbon desired at melt down. The limestone requirements for the blown-metal heats are regulated by the amount of silica in the charge in the same manner as for regular high-iron charges. The fuel requirements for 16 and 32 per cent blown-metal heats are about 10 and 20 per cent, respectively, below those of high-iron-charge heats made in the same shop. The melting times for these two types of heats are approximately 10 and 25 per cent less than the corresponding high-iron-charge heats, but approximately 100 per cent longer than liquid-metal heats made by dry-bottom practice.

As soon as the melt-down is complete, the working of the heat and slag adjustments take place just as in dry-bottom duplex or scrap and hot-metal heats. When the analysis shows that the heat is ready to tap, additions are made as in other heats produced in a stationary furnace, the furnace is tapped out clean and the steel is deoxidized in the usual manner.

Table 16—VII indicates the time-saving and corresponding increased production possible with this type of operation.

The quality of the steel made with this type of charge corresponds favorably to that of regular basic open-hearth steel.

ADVANTAGES AND DISADVANTAGES OF THE DUPLEX PROCESSES

In the northern district of the United States, the chief advantages of the duplex process are the increased tonnage which it produces in a given time, and its freedom from dependence on purchased scrap. In the southern district, the duplex process also provides a method of manufacturing high quality steel from high phosphorus pig iron, and, in addition, produces a highly basic slag containing a high percentage

Table 16—VII. Comparison of Heat Times and Production Rates for High-Iron, 16% Blown-Metal, and 32% Blown-Metal Charges.

Type of Charge	No. of Heats in Avg.	Time of Heats				Improvement in Chg.–Tap Time			Avg. Tons per 24 Hrs.
		Chg.–Tap		Tap–Tap					
		hrs.	min.	hrs.	min.	hrs.	min.	percent	
High Iron	726	10	53	12	22	...	...	...	326.4
16% Blown	291	9	41	11	18	1	12	11.0	356.0
32% Blown	79	8	12	9	48	2	41	24.7	417.0

Type of Charge	Percentage Increase In Production per 24 Hours
High Iron	......
16% Blown	9.05%
32% Blown	27.70%

of citric-acid-soluble P_2O_5 which is valuable as a soil conditioner. Thus, while the product is similar in quality and of the same grades as basic open-hearth steel, the time of the open-hearth operation is shortened by more than half. Whereas one open-hearth furnace will turn out an average of about fifteen heats in a week of melting scrap and hot metal or scrap and ore heats, the same furnace operated as a duplexing unit will produce about forty heats in the same period. This shortening of the time of heats saves fuel, and this factor, together with the elimination of the silicon in the converter slag, tends to prolong the life of the open-hearth furnace. The process does not require the use of scrap, an advantage when scrap is scarce and high in price.

The duplex process is capable of making any type of heat which can be made in a basic open-hearth furnace, but because of the ability of a scrap shop to recover alloys from scrap, most alloy steels are made in shops charging scrap rather than in duplex shops. On the other hand, where heats of low residual-alloy content are desired, a duplex shop is at a distinct advantage as compared with a scrap and hot-metal shop. In respect to flexibility, a duplex plant is in a far better position than one equipped only for scrap and hot metal because of the possibility of charging either scrap or blown metal, whichever is cheaper at the time. Naturally, a shop designed for duplex operation which changed over to scrap melting in order to take advantage of cheap scrap, would fail to melt the tonnage attainable on duplex operation.

In recent years, steel produced by the duplex process, according to the improved practices discussed earlier, has been applied to an ever-increasing number of uses for which basic open-hearth steel formerly was thought to be better suited. As knowledge increased as to the effects of relatively small amounts of various constituents of steel on its properties, it was established that the relatively higher nitrogen content of duplex steel (as compared with basic open-hearth steel) was the principal factor influencing its properties and resulting in certain disadvantages of that earlier duplex steel. The chief effect of the higher nitrogen content of the earlier duplex steel was to in-

crease its susceptibility to strain aging. When these facts were ascertained, duplex steelmaking practices were altered and improved in a way which would consistently produce steel having a controlled nitrogen content but little greater than that of basic open-hearth steel, as indicated by the following ranges of nitrogen content common to present-day Bessemer, duplex, and basic open-hearth steels:

Type of Steel	Average Nitrogen Content
Bessemer	0.012 to 0.020%
Duplex	0.005 to 0.008
Basic open-hearth	0.004 to 0.006

Because the chemical composition of duplex steel made by the improved practices approaches that of basic open-hearth steel, and can be controlled closely, it is understandable that the new duplex steel now can be applied to many purposes for which it once was considered less suitable than open-hearth steel.

The duplex process is now employed to produce many high-quality grades of steel for such applications as forged automotive crankshafts, seamless tubes, rolled sections for automotive-wheel rims, and other products ranging from high-grade thin flat-rolled materials to railroad rails. It may be noted that the slightly higher nitrogen content of duplex steels makes them somewhat harder than open-hearth steels of otherwise similar composition; this may be an actual advantage in a few cases, for example, in the manufacture of low-phosphorus steel for tin plate that must meet high-temper specifications.

The principal disadvantages of the duplex process are the initial cost of providing a plant with both open-hearth and Bessemer facilities, and lower ingot yield brought about through the combined Bessemer and open-hearth conversion losses. The double conversion cost of producing steel by this method would also appear to place it in an unfavorable competitive position and, with the advent of the basic oxygen steelmaking process (see Chapter 15), the duplex process will undoubtedly see only limited use. Based on its higher rate of production, however, the seriousness of the initial cost is offset to a great extent.

SECTION 12

TRIPLEX PROCESSES

The term "triplexing" refers to a combination steelmaking practice in which the same steel is processed successively in Bessemer, open-hearth and electric furnace with the usual aim being to produce a steel of electric-furnace quality.

Just as there are theoretically many possible duplexing combinations, as outlined earlier, so there are even more possible combinations of both acid and basic furnaces for the manufacture of triplex steel. However, only a limited number of these combined processes has been used for any length of time. The excessive maintenance cost of three furnaces, high cost of handling molten metal, and the excessive heat losses in handling have prevented the use of the proc-

ess except under highly specialized conditions. Also, electric-furnace steels have been produced by charging blown metal direct from an acid converter into a basic electric furnace to produce electric-furnace steel of good quality at a high rate. The knowledge that this is possible serves to illustrate the wastefulness of triplexing when, as in most cases, the same end can be accomplished by a duplex process.

Bibliography*
Am. Institute of Mining and Metallurgical Engineers, Iron and Steel Div., Committee on Physical Chemistry of

* See also bibliography appended to Chapter 12 on "The Physical Chemistry of Iron- and Steelmaking."

Steelmaking, Basic open hearth steelmaking, 2nd ed. (Seeley W. Mudd series) N. Y., The Institute, 1951.

Am. Institute of Mining and Metallurgical Engineers, National Open Hearth Committee Proc. **27**, 1944-date (published annually).

Bartels, K. D., Installing a sprung basic open hearth roof. Iron and Steel Engineer **48**, No. 6, June 1961, 120–123; discussion, 123.

Brandt, W. E., Oxygen lance installation and practice. Iron and Steel Engineer **48**, No. 6, June 1961, 116–119; discussion, 119–120.

Emerick, H. B. and S. Feigenbaum, Duplex process for the manufacture of basic open hearth steel. Am. Institute of Mining and Metallurgical Engineers, Open Hearth Conf. Proc. **25**, 9–23 (1942).

Ess, T. J., The modern open hearth. Iron and Steel Engineer **25**, O–19—O–66 (July 1948).

Fetters, K. L. and J. Chipman, Slag-metal relationships in the basic open hearth furnace. Am. Institute of Mining and Metallurgical Engineers, Iron and Steel Div., Trans. **140**, 170–198; discussion, 199–204 (1940).

Furst, J. K., Duplex process for making steel. Iron Age **94**, 882–886 (Oct. 15, 1914).

Furst, J. K., Steel production by the duplex process (2 parts) Blast Furnace and Steel Plant **5**, 393–397, 458–461 (1917).

Gold, J. D. and S. M. Newbrander, Use of blown metal at Weirton for making basic open hearth steel. Am. Institute of Mining and Metallurgical Engineers, Open Hearth Conf. Proc. **25**, 134–138 (1942).

Heuer, R. P. and M. A. Fay, The all-basic open hearth furnace. Iron and Steel Engineer **44**, No. 2, Feb. 1957, 95–117; discussion, 117–118.

King, C. D., Metallic charge in basic open hearth operations—some factors affecting operating economies. Am. Iron and Steel Institute Yearbook, 1931, 387–451.

Kirkpatrick, J. W., Oxygen in open hearth steelmaking. American Iron and Steel Institute Yearbook, 1961, 199–232; discussion, 232–234.

McCaffery, R. S., Metallurgical considerations of duplexing (2 parts), Blast Furnace and Steel Plant **7**, 209–212, 287–288, 297 (1919).

Open hearth molten metal processes. Iron Age **76**, 609–612 (Sept. 7, 1905).

Parker, H. A. and Philip Schane, Jr., Use of oxygen lances and basic brick in open hearth furnace roofs. Am. Iron and Steel Institute Yearbook, 1960, 125–152; discussion, 153–157.

Parker, H. A., et al, Furnace roof and method of making the same. U. S. Pat. No. 3,013,510; Dec. 19, 1961.

Pearson, Oscar, The use of oxygen in duplex and stationary open hearth practice. Blast Furnace and Steel Plant **47**, No. 9, Sept. 1959; 947–954, 961; No. 10, Oct. 1959; 1063–1070.

Schane, P., Jr., et al, Open hearth steelmaking process. U. S. Pat. No. 2,878,115; Mar. 17, 1959.

A steel plant unique in flexibility. Iron Age **94**, 614–619 (Sept. 10, 1914).

Waterhouse, G. B., Duplex process of Lackawanna Steel Company. Iron Age **98**, 999–1001, 1035–1037 (Nov. 2, 1916).

Wortman, Stephen, New trends and ideas in operation and design of open hearth furnaces. Blast Furnace and Steel Plant **49**, No. 9, Sept. 1961; 878–882, 893.

Wright, E. C., Potential for oxygen in steelmaking. Metal Progress **76**, Sept. 1959, 101–107.

CHAPTER 17

Electric-Furnace Steelmaking

SECTION 1

PRESENT STATUS OF ELECTRIC MELTING FURNACES

Numerous types of furnaces utilizing electric current as the source of heat have been developed by a large number of investigators, but relatively few types have survived as practical tools for steelmaking.

Methods of Electric Heating—Electric current can be used for heating in only two ways: (1) by utilizing the heat generated in electrical conductors by their inherent **resistance** to the flow of current; and (2) by utilizing the heat radiated by the **electric arc.**

Two general methods of heating by resistance are possible: (a) the **indirect method** in which the charge is heated by radiation and conduction from separate resistors through which the current is passed, and (b) the **direct method** in which the current is passed through the metal charge or bath itself. The indirect method of resistance heating for steel-melting operations is not practicable, for many reasons. The direct method in which high-voltage, low-amperage current is transformed to low-voltage, high-amperage current that passes through the bath or charge is successfully employed. The bath in this latter method acts as the secondary circuit for the current which is generated from a primary circuit by induction; the method being known, therefore, as **induction heating.**

Likewise, arc heating may be applied in two general ways: (1) The arcs may be made between electrodes supported above the metal in the furnace, which thus is heated solely by radiation from the arc. This method is known as **indirect-arc heating.** (2) The arcs may be made between the electrodes and the metal. In this second method, known as **direct-arc heating,** the current must flow through the bath, so that the heat developed by the electrical resistance of the metal, though relatively small in amount, is added to that radiated from the arcs. This plan makes it possible to use two types of furnaces, namely, those with a **non-conducting bottom,** and those with a **conducting bottom.** The latter type has not been successful for practical steelmaking use.

In furnaces with a non-conducting bottom, the path of the current is through one electrode and thence through the arc between the foot of the electrode and the bath, then through the bath and up through an arc between the bath and an adjacent electrode, completing the circuit through this second electrode. Path of the current through furnaces with conducting bottoms would be from the electrode or electrodes above

the bath, through the arc into the bath and thence out of the furnace through an electrode forming part of the bottom in contact with the bath.

Table **17**—I presents a listing of basic principles of electric heating which also will serve as a basis for classifying electric furnaces as to type. From among the many types listed therein, only two appear to have been able to stand against practical tests and competition as suitable for melting steel; these are the direct-arc furnace (series arc) originally developed by Heroult (Figure **17**—1) and the high-frequency coreless induction furnace, which are discussed in Sections 2 and 5, respectively, of this chapter.

Field of Application of Electric-Arc Furnaces—In Chapter 1, it was pointed out that the electric-arc furnace for steelmaking first was introduced into the United States in 1906. The real expansion of this phase of the industry, however, was more recent with respect to both basic-lined and acid-lined electric-arc furnaces. The first development was due to the wide use of the SAE low-alloy steels. Then came the development and expanding use of higher alloy and stainless steels, which have been largely responsible for the more recent increasing use of basic-lined electric-arc furnaces in the steel industry.

The steel-casting industry found originally that acid-lined electric-arc furnaces were well qualified to meet their needs in regard to control of operations and quality of product. This was the important factor in the use of this type of furnace in foundries.

Both the acid and basic processes for making steel in electric furnaces were used extensively during World War II. Since then, technical and economic obstacles to the use of select scrap and the increasing utilization of alloy steels have greatly decreased the use of acid-lined furnaces. Almost all furnaces used for ingot-steel production and a large percentage of the foundry furnaces are now basic-lined: this is because of the ability of basic-lined furnaces to use combinations of high-alloy steel scrap, lower grades of alloy scrap, and plain-carbon steel scrap to produce steels that will meet rigid chemical, mechanical-property and cleanliness requirements.

The basic electric-arc furnace utilizes a bottom consisting of a burned-magnesite brick subhearth with a working surface, 6 to 12 inches thick, of rammed granular magnesite (Figure **17**—2) The use of dolo-

Table 17—I. Classification of Electric Furnaces for Making Steel According to Principles of Heating Employed.

Resistance Furnaces	**Indirect**—The current is passed through a special resistor to generate heat, which is used to heat the charge by radiation, convection and conduction. Such furnaces are used for heat treating but not for melting steel.			
	Direct—The current passes through the material to be heated.	Using current from low voltage transformers. Not successful for melting steel.		
		Induction	**Low frequency**—Using a core transformer with the bath forming the secondary circuit.	
			High- and Medium-Frequency Coreless Induction. Current of high or medium frequency is passed through a coil surrounding a crucible containing the charge.	
Arc Furnaces	**Indirect or Independent Arc**—The bath is heated by an arc or arcs above it.	**Direct Current Arc**—Used for consumable-electrode furnaces.		
		Alternating Current	Single phase { Rolling furnace with horizontal electrodes. Furnaces for special purposes.	
			Two phase { Straight arcs. Deflected arc. } not used.	
			Three phase { Straight arcs. Repel-arc. } not used.	
		Furnaces may be stationary, oscillating, or rolling.		
	Direct Arc—The current arcs from electrode to bath.	**Series Arc.** Current arcs from one electrode to the bath, passes through the bath, and arcs to another electrode. (Three-phase units used almost exclusively.)	Single phase Two phase Three phase	
	Combination Arc and Resistance—Use the arc and resistance of refractory bottom material for heating charge.	Two phase Three phase	**Single Arc.** Current arcs from one electrode to the bath, passes through the bath, and out through an electrode in the bottom of the furnace.	Single phase Two phase Three phase

mite is generally confined to bottom fettling and door banking: materials of higher magnesia content generally are used for bank and slag-line repair, being applied with refractory "guns." Sidewalls are lined with chemically bonded steel-reinforced magnesite or magnesite-chrome brick, except the bottom 6 to 12 inches of the wall subject to slag contact, where burned-magnesite brick are used. Fused-cast brick are used in the sidewall "hot spots" in some large high-powered furnaces to provide more even sidewall wear and, consequently, longer overall refractory life. Little, if any, silica brick are used in the sidewalls of basic furnaces. Some recent investigations of the use of tar-bonded dolomite brick for sidewalls have been made, following the successful use of such material in the linings of basic oxygen steelmaking furnaces.

Basic electric-arc furnace roofs are generally constructed with high-alumina brick, with high-alumina rammed or castable materials for the center section around the electrodes. Some experimentation has been made in the use of magnesite brick for roof linings, but economic considerations appear to limit the use of such refractories to "hot spot" areas only, particularly in large, high-powered furnaces. The use of such "composite" roof construction has not as yet received any general acceptance. The use of silica brick for roof linings has, to a large extent, been discontinued, particularly in top-charged furnaces, because of the inferior spalling and chemical characteristics of this type of refractory in this particular service.

Basic electric-arc furnaces of the type just described are used to produce practically all of the electric-furnace steel made in ingot form and, as stated earlier, are finding increasing use in foundries for making steel castings. Furnaces of this type usually are found in integrated steel works having installations for making steel by other processes also, where facilities already are available for stripping the ingots, heating them, and rolling or forging them to the desired size and shape. Such integrated plants make possible the use of the **cold-melt process** or one of the **hot-metal methods** such as duplexing, triplexing, or the refinement of molten open-hearth steel by special slags that can be prepared and removed more conveniently in the electric furnace than in the open hearth.

The replacement of cold-charged open-hearth furnaces in non-integrated plants with basic-lined electric-arc furnaces for ingot production has accounted for an appreciable part of the increase in electric-furnace steelmaking capacity over the past ten years and is expected to account for a larger portion of the increase in the future. This is due to several factors, among which are: improvement of the economic position of electric-furnace steelmaking resulting from changes in the cost relationship between scrap and cold pig iron and increases in the operating costs for open-hearth furnaces; the increasing demand for alloy steels for new applications and applications previously using carbon steels; and the ability of the electric furnace to operate on an intermittent basis. Because of its

FIG. 17—1. A large, modern, three-phase Heroult electric-arc furnace.

flexibility with respect to charge materials and its suitability for intermittent operation, the electric furnace has also found a place in large integrated mills for producing steel to supplement the output of other steelmaking processes to meet short-term demand peaks, where the startup of large hot-metal units to meet the temporary need for additional steel would be uneconomical.

The acid electric furnace, with an acid bottom of ground ganister and silica-brick sidewalls and roof (Figure 17—2), seldom is used outside of steel foundries and forging shops. Straight-carbon, low-alloy and some high-alloy steels can be made by the acid process.

The importance of electric furnaces as steelmaking units in ingot-producing plants in the United States is indicated by the annual tonnages shown in Table 17—II, which also shows the increasing trend in production of electric-furnace steels during the twenty-six-year period from 1935 through 1961. It should be noted that these figures do not include steel made in electric furnaces by foundries that do not produce ingots.

Although the production of electric-furnace steels during normal times represents only about nine per cent of the total tonnage of ingot steel produced in this country, the electric-furnace products represent practically all of the stainless, constructional alloy, tool, and special alloy steels used in the chemical, automotive, aviation, machine-tool, transportation, food processing and many other important industries. While at the present time the electric-arc furnace cannot always compete with the larger open-hearth furnace as to cost in the production of the commoner grades of steel, yet the electric furnace, if operated in a favorable scrap-producing area with favorable power rates, in many cases can produce ordinary carbon steels at costs comparable to, and sometimes less than, open-hearth costs.

General Comparison of Basic and Acid Electric-Arc-Furnace Processes—In this comparison, the acid process involving complete oxidation of the bath, using a single, oxidizing slag, is compared with the basic process.

1. Slags in the acid process are more siliceous than those in the basic process. Since acid slags do not react with the steel bath to remove phosphorus from the steel, the use of more expensive, carefully selected scrap and other raw materials of low phosphorus content are imperative. Conversely, basic slags do react

Table 17—II.   Annual Production of
Electric-Furnace Steels[1]
(Steel Ingots and Steel for Castings—Net Tons)[2]

Year	Electric-Furnace Steel	Total All Processes, Including Electric	Percentage Represented by Electric-Furnace Steel
1961	8,664,203	98,014,492	8.8
1960	8,378,743	99,281,601	8.4
1959	8,532,514	93,446,132	9.1
1958	6,656,145	85,254,885	7.8
1957	7,970,574	112,714,996	7.1
1956	8,641,229	115,216,149	7.5
1955	8,049,872	117,036,085	6.9
1954	5,436,054	88,311,652	6.2
1953	7,280,191	111,609,719	6.5
1952	6,797,923	93,168,039	7.3
1951	7,142,384	105,199,848	6.8
1950	6,039,008	96,836,075	6.2
1949	3,782,717	72,978,176	4.9
1948	5,057,141	88,640,470	5.7
1947	3,787,735	84,894,071	4.5
1946	2,563,024	66,602,724	3.8
1945	3,456,704	79,701,648	4.4
1944	4,237,699	89,641,600	4.7
1943	4,589,070	88,836,512	5.2
1942	3,974,540	86,031,931	4.6
1941	2,869,256	82,839,259	3.5
1940	1,700,006	66,982,686	2.5
1939	1,029,067	52,798,714	1.9
1938	565,627	31,751,990	1.8
1937	947,002	56,636,945	1.7
1936	865,150	53,499,999	1.1
1935	606,471	38,183,705	1.6

[1] From Annual Reports of American Iron and Steel Institute.

[2] The figures include only that portion of the capacity and production of steel for castings used by foundries which were operated by companies also producing steel ingots.

with and retain phosphorus, and practically all types of scrap and raw materials can be used in the basic electric furnace. It may be mentioned here that sulphur cannot be removed in the acid process, but can be in the basic process, as will be discussed later.

2. Oxidizing action takes place in a shorter time in the acid process and the time required for "working the heat" also is shorter than in the basic process, mainly because of the selected scrap used in the acid furnace as compared with the wide variety of scrap used in the basic process.

3. In the acid process, because of the selected materials making up the charge, a one-slag process predominates, while a multiple-slag practice is used more widely with the basic process.

4. Iron loss is lower with the single-slag acid process than with the multiple-slag basic process because the oxidizing period is shorter, less metal is trapped in the much smaller volume of slag, and, since there is no slagging-off in the single-slag acid process, there is no loss of metal from this source.

The metallurgical differences in the two processes indicate that none of the advantages of one process over the other is sufficient to justify the selection of one or the other process without full consideration of all

factors, many of which have already been discussed and which explain the present preference for the basic process in the majority of applications.

Cold Scrap vs. Hot Metal—When the first electric melting furnaces were installed in the steel industry, electric power was not available in large amounts. Since the melting operation requires about three times the power that is required by the refining period, it was thought then that the cost of this extra electric power was too high to permit economical melting of cold charges. For this reason, the early installations at Halcomb and Illinois Steel, referred to in Chapter 1, were provided with a separate source of hot metal to provide a molten charge. The former had a tilting 30-ton basic open-hearth furnace and the latter a Bessemer converter department. Later, as more electric power became available, it was recognized that cold melting was feasible. At the present time, there is no appreciable tonnage of steel being produced in electric furnaces using hot-metal charges. With the advent of new pneumatic processes (Chapter 15), it is possible that these processes may be used to prepare molten charges for finishing in electric furnaces to produce steel.

Advantages of the Electric-Arc Furnace—The increasing number of basic electric-arc furnace installations is evidence that, as steelmaking units, these furnaces provide certain advantages. Among the more important considerations for selecting this method over other steel production methods are the following:

Practically all of the known grades of steel can be produced in the basic electric-arc furnace. The products made include the plain carbon steels of rimmed, capped, semi-killed and killed types, low-alloy SAE-AISI constructional steels, high-manganese steels (up to 14 per cent), high-silicon steels (up to 5 per cent), aluminum steels (up to 4½ per cent), the entire range of stainless steels, super-alloy steels for high-temperature applications, and high-speed and other alloy tool steels.

The basic electric-arc furnace may be selected as the more economical steel producing method when: (1) carbon and low-alloy steel production requirements are insufficient to justify use of the blast furnace—open hearth combination to produce steel, (2) facilities are installed in industrial areas of high steel-scrap availability but at a distance from natural sources of coke, limestone and high-grade iron ores, (3) the nature of subsequent processing is such that steel-production requirements are intermittent or molten metal must be supplied within controlled time limits.

The electric-arc furnace process is capable of producing killed-steel grades with very low residual phosphorus because: (1) the initial charge contains less phosphorus than the charges of steelmaking processes containing blast-furnace iron, and (2) the phosphorus-bearing oxidizing slags of the electric furnace heat may be removed prior to furnace deoxidation and thus avoid phosphorus reversion to the metal.

The greater desulphurizing power of basic electric-arc furnace reducing slags facilitates the production of steels with lower sulphur residuals.

The absence of an oxidizing heat source permits

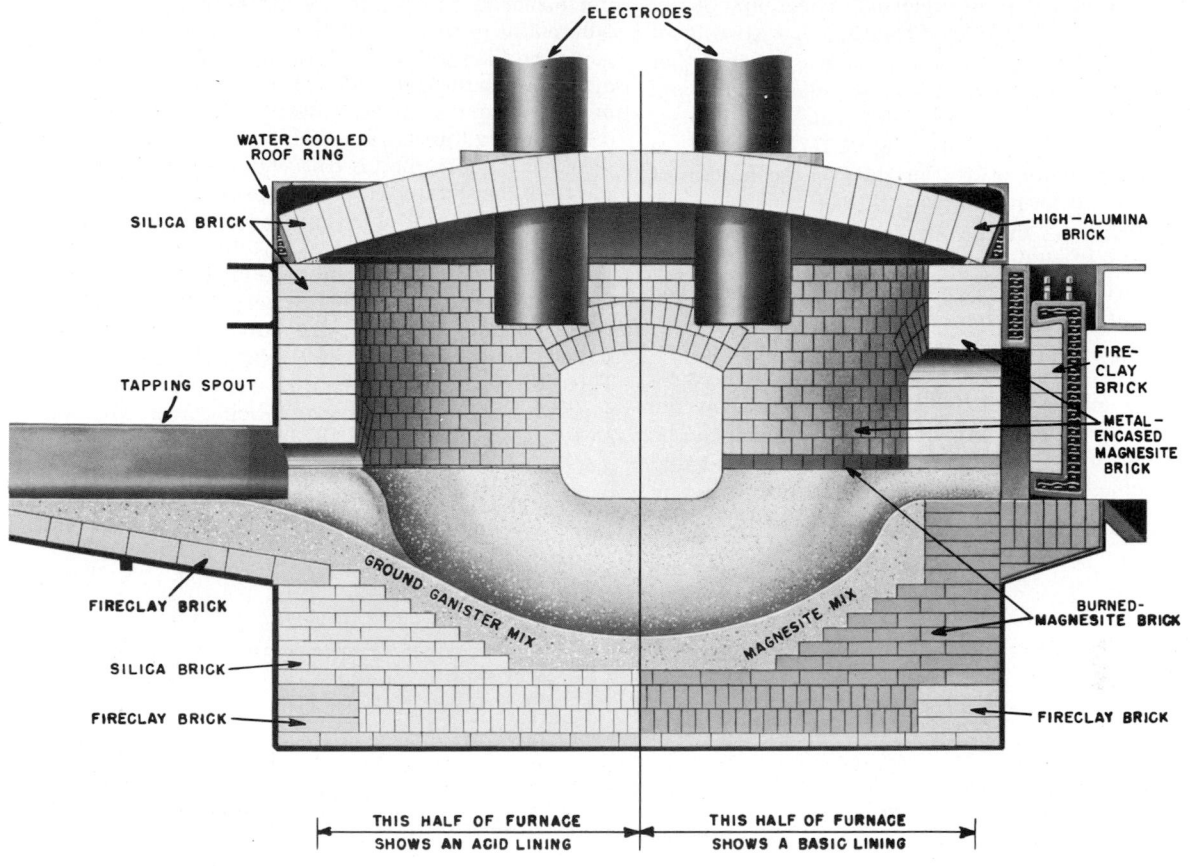

FIG. 17—2. Schematic cross-section of a Heroult electric-arc furnace with a flat-bottomed shell and stadium-type subhearth construction, indicating typical refractories employed in (left) an acid lining and (right) a basic lining. Although only two electrodes are shown in this section, furnaces of this type (which operate on three-phase current) have three electrodes. (See Figure 17—3 for stadium-type and inverted-arch-type subhearth construction applied to furnaces with shells having dished bottoms.) (Courtesy, Harbison-Walker Refractories Company.)

heats that have been deoxidized in the furnace to be held without becoming rapidly reoxidized; this feature, coupled with the ability to use reducing slags, makes it possible to produce steels containing fewer nonmetallic inclusions.

The production of steels alloyed with high percentages of oxidizable metallic elements can be produced more efficiently in the basic electric-arc furnace as such alloying elements or ferroalloys can be added in the furnace under reducing conditions at a high efficiency of recovery and in any amount required. Moreover, with proper slag manipulation, a relatively-high efficiency of recovery of oxidizable elements, such as chromium, manganese, etc., can also be obtained from alloy-steel scrap.

Because it can be tilted to pour off slag, the electric-arc furnace can be operated with slag volumes controlled to a minimum (2 to 4 per cent of the bath weight) and therefore the slag composition can be adjusted and controlled quickly by relatively small additions of slag-making, oxidizing or deoxidizing materials. Therefore, the steel may be treated under oxidizing, reducing or neutral slags, or any succession of such slags.

Under oxidizing slags, the electric furnace with a definite regulation of heat input provides good control of carbon content at melt-down and later while working the heat. Also, the removal of this oxidizing slag, with its comparatively high phosphorus content, limits the amount of phosphorus reversion that can occur by taking a large proportion of this element out of the field of action.

A reducing slag in the basic electric furnace, following the slagging off of an oxidizing slag, makes possible a high degree of refinement of the bath and minimizes loss of alloys by oxidation. Objectionable elements, such as sulphur, can be removed to a high degree after the oxidizing slag has been replaced by a reducing slag. The reducing slag also decreases the oxygen content of the bath to a low value; consequently, relatively few deoxidation products are formed when the final deoxidizers are added because less of the latter are needed. The deoxidation products that are formed have a better opportunity to rise through the steel bath and enter into the slag than would similar substances formed if large amounts of deoxidizers had to be added in the ladle. As a result, relatively few sulphide and oxide inclusions are present in electric-furnace steel, remembering, however, that limited circulation of the bath under this reducing slag necessitates a long refining time.

It should be noted, as discussed in Section 3 of this chapter under "Induction Stirring," that stirring of the bath in electric furnaces is quite feasible by either mechanical means or magnetic-induction stirrer and that agitation of the bath by either means minimizes refining-time requirements. Figure 17—4 shows a magnetic-induction stirrer installed on the bottom of an electric-arc furnace.

Disadvantages of the Electric-Arc Furnace—The disadvantages common to the operation of electric-arc furnaces are largely a matter of economics. The costs of auxiliary equipment, operating labor, power, electrodes, and refractories usually are higher than similar costs in the open-hearth and other processes. The costs exclusive of net metallic charge show the electric furnace to be at a disadvantage which can be overcome only partially by faster time of heat and greater efficiency. Individual open-hearth furnaces, in general, are of considerably larger capacity than elec-

tric furnaces; the possibility of overcoming the size differential in furnaces of the two types is limited by power problems. Peak loads during melt-down periods may increase the difficulties of the power plants which must maintain sufficient power for regular requirements during this same period.

While the foregoing is true with respect to *physical size* from the standpoint of the size of individual heats, the *production rate* of a standard 20-foot shell diameter electric furnace in terms of tons of finished steel produced per hour will compare favorably with 150-ton or larger open-hearth furnaces. Also, in 24-foot, 6-inch diameter electric-arc furnaces recently installed, heats of nearly 200 tons have been made. Thus, the former advantage of the open-hearth furnace with regard to heat size is being overcome, and other factors (some of them economic and some metallurgical) now are the criteria for comparing the two methods of steelmaking.

For example, changes in relative cost of fuels and

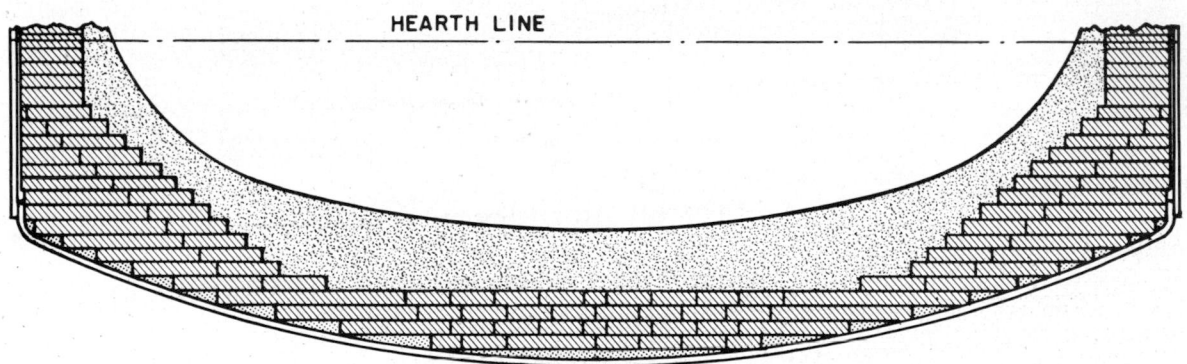

STADIUM-TYPE SUBHEARTH CONSTRUCTION

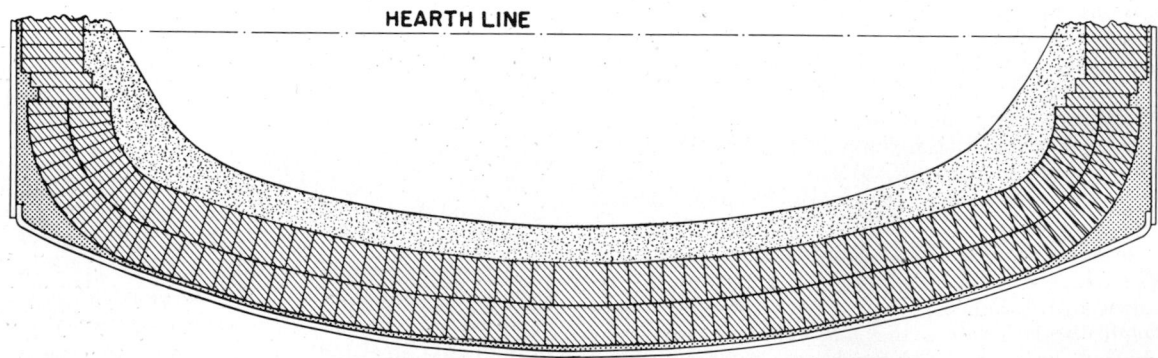

INVERTED-ARCH TYPE SUBHEARTH CONSTRUCTION

FIG. 17—3. Schematic representation of vertical cross-sections of the two types of subhearth construction employed in the lining of dished-bottom electric-arc steelmaking furnaces.

Fig. 17—4. Electric-arc steelmaking furnace in backward-tilted position, showing magnetic-induction stirrer mounted on bottom of furnace shell (between rockers), and toothed rockers and rails on which the furnace rests and on which it can be tilted.

of scrap and hot metal or pig iron have lessened the economic advantage of the hot-charged open-hearth furnace over the electric-arc furnace. However, the recent advent of the basic oxygen steelmaking process has introduced a new economic factor that accentuates the disadvantage of the electric-arc furnace for the production of plain-carbon and low-alloy grades of steel.

SECTION 2

DIRECT-ARC ELECTRIC FURNACES AND AUXILIARIES

Mechanical Parts—All furnaces of the Heroult type are designed to tilt in two directions, the one for pouring and the other for slagging. Heroult furnaces are mounted on toothed rockers which rest on and inter-mesh with toothed rails (Figure 17—4). They are tilted by a motor-driven rack-and-pinion mechanism, usually placed underneath the furnace. On large furnaces where a slag-off operation is required, the tilting mechanism is designed to permit movement of a car-mounted slag pot through the foundations to the tapping pit (Figure 17—4).

Capacity of Furnaces—The inside diameter of the shell determines the capacity of the electric furnace. Many standard sizes have been developed to provide for the different practices and types of scrap used in various shops. Heroult furnaces now are being built by American Bridge Division of United States Steel Corporation in sizes of 7-foot shell diameter and up (Table 17—III). They are usually equipped with roof-moving mechanisms (described later) to permit top charging. Door-charge furnaces and furnaces of special design, including units equipped with austenitic-steel bottoms to permit induction stirring (see Section 3), are also built.

The Furnace Shell and Lining—The shell of the modern electric-arc furnace is cylindrical in shape with a dished bottom (Figure 17—3). Welded and bolted construction is used throughout; no riveted construction is employed. The shell is braced with structural-steel sections.

As the development of the electric-steelmaking process required the design of larger, more complex, higher-powered furnaces, problems arose which affected design, operation and maintenance. The shell became a source of increasing trouble due to warping,

burning and rupturing, because it was an integral part of the furnace structure. Damage to the shell might weaken the structure and cause misalignment of operating parts mounted on it.

There are two methods that have been developed for overcoming this difficulty on large, modern furnaces:

(1) The shell is built as a unit structurally separate from the rest of the furnace structure; that is, to require the shell only to retain the refractories and charge while the operating parts of the furnace are supported on an independent structure unaffected by shell distortion.

(2) Rigid connections are eliminated between the steel plates of the shell and the supporting yokes and buck-stays, at least above the hearth line, to allow these parts to expand and contract independently of each other.

The shell of a cylindrical furnace has a flat or dished bottom which can be laid first with a layer of clay, magnesite, or silica brick as required (Figures 17—2 and 17—3). When the stadium type of construction is used for the subhearth, successive courses of brick are set back to provide ledges for the granular material that will, after sintering in place, form the working bottom or hearth as shown in Figure 17—3. With the inverted-arch type of subhearth construction (Figure 17—3), the subhearth is constructed of shaped brick that follow the contour of the bottom. Modern practice utilizes a much smaller amount of granular material than formerly was employed, and, with this design, it is possible to recover a large proportion of the bottom refractories when relining becomes necessary. The brick is placed easily around the door jambs, arches and in the door lining, as both jambs and doors have flat surfaces. The roof is a simple flat dome, and the water-cooled skewback type of roof ring eliminates the necessity for special skewshaped brick.

CHARGING METHODS

Charging methods for electric-arc furnaces fall into two classes—**top charging** and **door charging**. Most modern furnaces are top charged.

Top-Charged Furnaces—There are two types of top-charged furnaces, based upon the method used for handling the roof for opening the top of the furnace for charging: the **swing type** and the **gantry lift.**

In the swing type (Figure 17—5), the roof and the supporting structure for the electrode masts are lifted and swung to one side by motor-driven or hydraulic equipment.

The gantry-lift type has the electrode masts and the roof-raising mechanism built into a gantry crane that travels on rails along the charging floor. When the furnace is to be charged, the electrodes are raised to clear the shell, the roof is lifted and moved by the crane to one side of the furnace.

Table 17—III. Heroult Furnace Sizes, Capacities, and Transformer Ratings.

Inside Shell Diameter	Nominal Steel Capacity (Pounds)	Usual Transformer Capacity (kva)
7'0"	8,300	1500/2500
8'0"	13,000	2000/3000
9'0"	20,000	3000/4000
10'0"	28,000	4000/5000
11'0"	38,000	5000/6000
12'0"	50,000	6000/7500
13'6"	61,000	7500/10,000
15'0"	77,000	10,000/12,500
16'0"	98,000	12,500/15,000
17'0"	126,000	15,000/17,500
18'0"	154,000	17,500/18,750
19'0"	183,000	18,750/20,000
20'0"	221,000	20,000/25,000
22'0"	301,000	25,000/30,000
25'0"	420,000	30,000/35,000

FIG. 17—5. A very large, modern Heroult electric-arc steelmaking furnace, with swing-type roof moved aside to permit top charging of the furnace by bucket.

All modern furnaces are of the swing-roof top-charged design, although many gantry-lift type furnaces are still in operation.

Top charging has the advantage of speed, as the entire charge can be placed in the furnace by drop-bottom buckets in a short time (Figure 17—5). In addition, very large pieces of scrap can be charged without being cut into charging-box sizes as would be necessary if the charge were placed through a door. However, scrap dropping from a considerable height results in a shock to the furnace bottom. It is desirable, therefore, to load the bucket with a layer of light scrap on the bottom to provide some cushioning of the fall of the larger pieces of scrap. Scrap charges of as much as 100 tons are being charged into large furnaces with one bucket. Extremely large pieces of scrap, such as large ingot butts, broken roll sections, and so on, are preferably charged by magnet onto the bottom of the furnace prior to bucket charging. In modern electric-furnace melt shops, no use is made of open-hearth type charging machines for charging scrap. Small trackless mobile machines are generally used in the larger shops for charging additions and for stirring the bath. Utilizing the top-charging principle, furnaces may be filled completely with light scrap very quickly, and the charge can be melted rapidly by the use of transformers that supply power at high rates to the furnace.

Door-Charged Furnaces—Since the availability of heavy scrap has decreased, and considerable quantities of light scrap have become available, the advantages of top charging of light scrap have caused most of the new large furnaces to be top-charge units and many of the older furnaces, designed to be charged by machine through the door, to be converted to top charging.

Hand charging through the door is utilized for very small furnaces, and, on somewhat larger units, charging with a chute is the method used. If very large furnaces are to be charged through the front door, a charging machine of the type used in open-hearth plants is required: this practice is feasible only where heavy scrap is available in quantity.

Auxiliary Equipment—If the plant is designed for the use of hot metal, or uses the practice of refurnacing employed by many shops that produce stainless steels, a 75- to 100-ton, four-girder, two-trolley crane is required for handling the ladles in the charging aisle. This can also serve as the utility crane for the charging floor.

If top-charged furnaces are utilized, cranes in the charging bay should have ample capacity for handling loaded charging buckets of whatever size is necessary. Since top-charging buckets normally are sized to have approximately 80 per cent of the volumetric capacity of the furnace, with scrap having an average density of about 50 lb. per cu. ft. approximately one-half of the nominal capacity heat weight of the furnace can be accommodated in one bucket and crane capacities must be chosen accordingly.

In plants with door-charged furnaces that do not use hot metal, one or two 25-ton cranes with an auxiliary 10-ton hoist will be needed in the charging bay.

Another item requiring space on the charging floor is equipment for drying any additions to the charge. This is necessary to prevent explosions in the furnace, with resultant blowing out of slag and damage to the furnace. It is also important that the moisture, both free and combined, be eliminated in order to reduce the possibility of absorption of hydrogen by the steel. The degree of dryness varies considerably in different shops due to the methods used. Some shops run a gas pipe into a pile of material and hope to obtain results with a gas flame. Other shops use large, flat pans set on blooms and heated by gas jets under the pans. A better method is to have one or two ovens heated with gas to about 1000° F, and place the material in charging boxes in these ovens. This method, however, has two disadvantages:

1. It is difficult to obtain uniform drying with the bulk load in the box, and

2. It requires a considerable amount of space on the charging floor.

The best method for drying is a small rotary kiln which does give uniform drying and does not require a large floor space.

Fume Control—Almost without exception, the design of every proposed new electric-arc furnace installation includes consideration of an acceptable fume-control system.

Two primary problems have been encountered in the development of fume-control systems for electric-arc furnaces:

(1) Efficient collection of furnace fumes by means that would not require excessive maintenance, that would not interfere appreciably with normal furnace maintenance and repair, and that would not detrimentally affect metallurgical conditions within the furnace.

(2) Efficient cleaning of the collected furnace gases by low-cost, low-maintenance means that would be applicable to small non-integrated plants and foundries as well as large integrated plants.

Of the two problems, the one dealing with collection is the more difficult. Various means have been used, including hoods mounted directly on the furnace, hoods mounted separately over top of the furnace, offtakes that apply suction to the furnace directly through an opening in the roof or sidewall and, most recently, a variation of the direct offtake called a **snorkle** that collects fumes by stack effect through an opening in the furnace roof. The hood on top of the furnace appears to offer the best functional advantage from the standpoints of efficiency of collection and minimal effects on metallurgical conditions but, from the standpoint of maintenance, appears to be the least desirable.

For the cleaning of gases emitted by the electric-arc furnace, various devices have been used, including wet centrifugal, dynamic, orifice and venturi types; dry electrostatic precipitators; and dry centrifugal and cloth filter types. Electric-furnace gases have the characteristic of being very dry and, consequently, possess very high electrical resistivity. Such gases carry a widely varying dust loading of submicron mean particle size and the cloth-type filter appears to be the most efficient and economical means of cleaning them. The status of the cloth filter for this application has been particularly enhanced by the development of synthetic- and glass-fiber cloths for filter media.

Disposal of collected dust presents a third problem in fume control. Attempts to recharge the dust into the electric furnace and to sinter the dust for charging into the blast furnace have been unsuccessful. Collected dust currently is being dumped, with some attempts to agglomerate it in pug mills to prevent objectionable dusting from the dumps. The value of the alloy contents in dust from alloy-steelmaking operations, however, indicates the desirability of developing an economical recovery process.

Pouring Facilities—The foregoing remarks have concerned the charging side of the furnace building. The pouring side has similar problems in track layout, cranes, and drying.

Since a large portion of the product will be alloy steel and, occasionally, some other killed steels that are teemed into hot-topped molds, provision must be made for preparing the molds. If it is to be done in the furnace building, track and floor space must be provided for preparing the molds for at least two heats. Since this requires considerable space, it is better for the work to be done in an adjacent building as, in addition to the floor space required, preparing the molds may interfere with crane service needed for other operations. If mold preparation is done on the pouring floor in a shop with a 200,000-ton annual capacity for steel making, a 25-ton crane is required in addition to a ladle crane.

Cranes are rated in net tons of 2000 pounds and it should be noted that the capacities are based on the load on the hooks in accordance with the Association of Iron & Steel Engineers standard specifications, which make the load on the hooks the capacity rating. Previous to this time the weight carried by the drums was often used; and the weight of the cables, load beam, and hooks had to be subtracted to get the useful lifting capacity. It is the total ladle weight lifted and not the weight of hot metal that determines lifting capacity. The ladle, with its refractory lining, may be 40 per cent of the total weight, so that for 60 tons of liquid steel, a 100-ton crane is required.

After the heat has been poured into the molds, time must be allowed for the outer portions of the ingot to solidify and form a shell of adequate thickness or, in some cases, for the ingot to become completely solid before the mold can be removed by the stripping crane. On hot-topped molds, some plants provide a stationary stripper, located in the pouring aisle, to loosen the ingots. This device is installed on the floor with a base for holding one mold plus the ingot.

Ladle Drying and Preheating—Another requirement for the pouring floor is drying and preheating facilities for ladles, stoppers, and hot tops. When ladles are relined, the entire lining must be thoroughly dried and preheated, and after each heat the nozzle and replaced brick must be dried. This is necessary for three reasons:

(a) To prevent explosions due to generation of steam.

(b) To reduce thermal shock to the brick.

(c) To reduce the chilling effect of the brick on the hot metal.

The usual method for drying ladles is to place a gas line with a crude burner in the ladle; this is fairly satisfactory for drying around a new nozzle.

Another method is to lay the ladle on its side, placing the open top against a brick wall and introducing the gas burner through a hole in the wall. This gives more uniform drying results.

Stopper Drying—The latest installations for drying the stopper-rod-assembly consist of a traveling-chain conveyor passing through a gas-heated oven. The stopper rods are suspended vertically on this chain and pass slowly through the oven. The cycle is about 24 hours and when removed at the exit end, the stoppers and rods have been thoroughly and uniformly dried.

Hot-Top Drying—In most shops, hot tops are dried with heat from an open gas torch before they are placed on the molds. This is particularly true of the refractory-lined metal-encased type which are placed on metal stands for both preparation and drying between uses. Some plants have completely mechanized the cleaning, coating, and drying of these tops through use of a conveyor line and suitable auxiliary equipment, which results in more uniform preparation and fully-dried tops. Refractory hot tops also may be dried separately in ovens where thorough drying at a uniform rate can be secured.

Electrodes—Sir Humphrey Davy, in his experimental work around 1800, used the current from a storage battery for the arc, and made his electrodes from wood, charcoal, and syrup of tar, molded under 100 pounds pressure.

In 1907, Dr. Heroult imported electrodes from Sweden for use in this country, because the largest electrode made in the United States at that time was only 12 inches in diameter. Importation was both slow and expensive, so he built a plant to produce carbon electrodes up to 24 inches in diameter. This plant supplied the electrodes for the large Heroult electric-arc steelmaking furnaces installed in what is now the South Works of the United States Steel Corporation, in Chicago, Illinois.

To the steel maker, there are two kinds of electrodes. Graphite electrodes (made from petroleum coke at high heat to form artificial crystalline carbon) are required in large electric steel furnaces, particularly for the manufacture of high-alloy steels. Carbon (amorphous) electrodes are widely used in small steel furnaces and in submerged-arc furnaces for the manufacture of ferroalloys, aluminum, calcium carbide,

phosphorus, et cetera. Both carbon and graphite electrodes are used in electric furnaces because of their infusibility, insolubility, chemical inertness, electrical conductivity, mechanical strength and resistance to thermal shock.

Carbon electrodes in turn can be divided into two types; one, made of calcined petroleum coke, is used in aluminum reduction; the other, based upon calcined low-ash anthracite coal, is suitable for the other uses listed. Carbon and graphite electrodes are chemically essentially the same, but differ widely in their purity and electrical and physical properties.

In manufacture, both carbon and graphite electrodes start with mixtures of raw materials properly proportioned with a suitable bonding material, such as hot pitch or tar, and extruded or molded while still hot onto "green" shapes. These are cooled, packed in powdered petroleum coke in furnaces, and baked at the desired temperatures. Carbon products are usually gas-fired in kilns to approximately 2000° F. Graphite products undergo this same gas-firing, followed by repack in Acheson electric-resistance furnaces, where they are heated to temperatures above 4000° F. This second treatment in the electric-resistance furnace results in the formation of graphite (crystalline carbon) and, through volatilization, removes most of the impurities. Electrodes of both types, after the foregoing processes, are cleaned, then bored and tapped—usually on both ends.

Carbon and graphite electrodes vary widely in physical shape, dimensions and properties. These must be selected carefully, depending upon intended usage. A general comparison of the two types is shown in Table 17—IV. Where a single value is given it may be taken as average for a variety of sizes and shapes.

Table 17—IV. Comparison of Carbon (Amorphous) and Graphite Eelectrodes

Properties	Graphite Electrodes	Large Carbon Electrodes
Specific resistance (ohm–inches)	0.0004	0.0017
Specific resistance (ohm-cm.) ...	0.0010	0.0043
Weight (lb. per cu. ft.)	96	99
Apparent density (grams per c.c.)	1.52	1.57
Tensile strength (lb. per sq. in.):		
Lengthwise	500	200
Crosswise	350	150
"Practical" oxidation point	900°F	700°F
Ash	0.50%	7.0%
Size ranges:		
Diameter (inches)	¼–30	8–40
Length (inches)	24–84	60–110
Weight (pounds)	1.6–2,960	160–7,100

Carbon electrodes cost less than one-half as much per pound as graphite electrodes. However, the field of application for the carbon electrodes is limited by their capacity for carrying electric current, one of 20-inch diameter being rated at 17,000 amperes, while the 20-inch graphite electrode is rated at 34,600 amperes. For this reason, carbon electrodes seldom are used in furnaces with transformer capacities above 3000 kva.

Because of their greater current-carrying capacity, graphite electrodes are used almost exclusively in electric steelmaking furnaces. Figures 17—6 and 17—7 indicate the nominal current-carrying ranges for graphite electrodes of various diameters in open-arc applications.

As an electrode is consumed in operation, a threaded nipple is inserted in the top and a new electrode is screwed down tightly on the exposed end of the nipple. When carbon nipples are used, a carbon paste is used to improve electrical contact. Presently, graphite nipples are generally used for joining both carbon and graphite electrodes. Tapered nipples and sockets are used to join graphite electrodes. The tapered design facilitates the joining of two sections, which is particularly important when this work must be done on top of the furnace.

Pitch reservoir nipples, i.e., graphite nipples having a small amount of pitch placed in a small hole drilled into the threaded body of the nipple, were developed to assure the maintenance of tight joints. When the joint becomes hot, the pitch melts and flows into the threads where it bakes in place, securing the joint. The disadvantage of the use of such nipples is ap-

parent if and when it becomes necessary to loosen a joint, for example, to remove a broken or split stub.

The securing and maintenance of tight electrode joints is very important to successful furnace operation. Loose joints cause overheating of the electrode due to increased electrical resistance which, together with the reduced mechanical strength of the electrode column, causes a large percentage of the electrode breakage that is experienced. Since electrode consumption constitutes one of the largest items of cost in electric-furnace operation, the importance of tight joints is obvious. Much work has been done on this problem, and special wrenches have been devised to attempt to assure proper tightening torque. The tightening torque recommended for 20-inch diameter electrodes, for example, is approximately 2000 foot-pounds. Because of the obvious difficulty in consistently obtaining these high tightening torques when adding electrode sections on top of a hot furnace, most new electric-furnace plants have been designed with off-furnace electrode make-up facilities wherein the whole electrode string is removed from the furnace with the overhead service crane and set into a stand, and a new string of proper length is placed in the electrode holder on the furnace. A new section can then be added to the removed string, taking the time and care necessary to assure a proper joint: this string

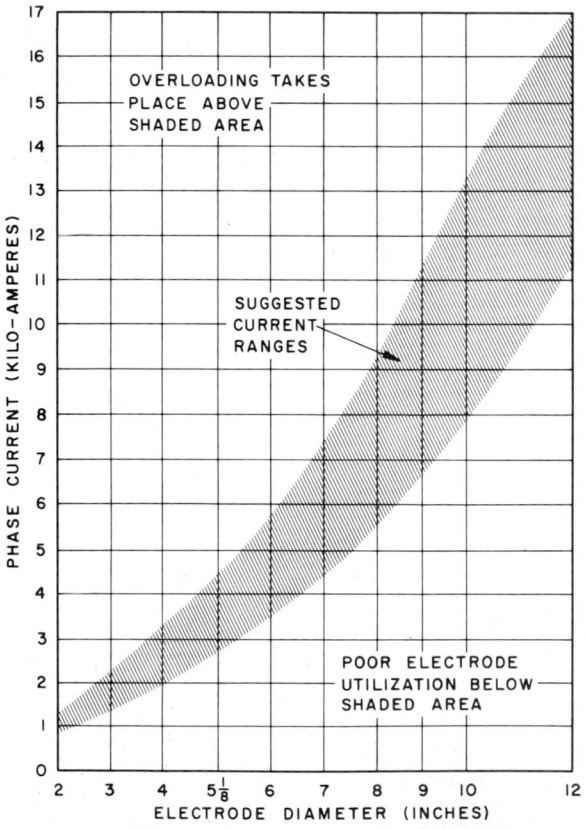

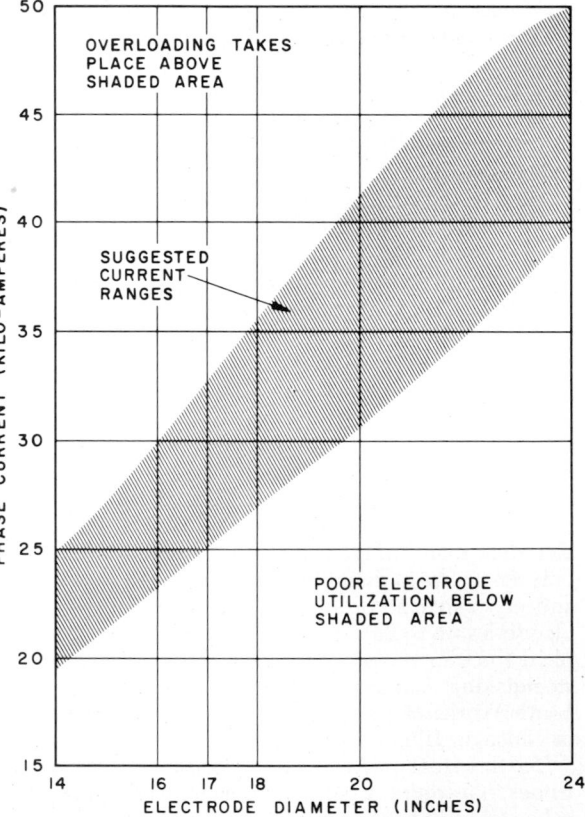

Fig. 17—6. Nominal current-carrying ranges of graphite electrodes in open-arc applications for electrode diameters ranging from 2 to 12 in. See Figure 17—7 for similar data on larger electrodes. (Courtesy, National Carbon Company.)

Fig. 17—7. Nominal current-carrying ranges of graphite electrodes in open-arc applications for electrode diameters ranging from 14 to 24 in. See Figure 17—6 for similar data on smaller electrodes. (Courtesy, National Carbon Company.)

is then used to replace another string on the furnace when an electrode addition is required.

Electrode strings and sections are handled with a special steel lifting nipple that screws into the top electrode socket. The nipple has a threaded pin connecting it to the hook ring. The thread of the pin has the same pitch as the electrode socket thread. Thus, as an electrode section is turned to screw it into connection with the string, the lifting nipple lowers at the same rate, eliminating the necessity for lowering the section with the crane hoist and the consequent possibility of broken socket threads. The lifting nipples are removed when the electrode strings are in place on the furnace since the difference in thermal-expansion characteristics of the steel nipple and graphite electrode may cause splitting of the electrode at the socket.

When installed on the furnace, the electrodes pass through circular openings in the roof, spaced at the corners of an equilateral triangle (see Figure 17—8). Water-cooled rings are placed over these openings and around the electrodes to act as a seal. The electrodes are supported by water-cooled **clamps** at the ends of the horizontal arms that extend over the furnace from vertical standards or **masts**. These clamps form the electrical connection between the power supply and the electrodes, and their design is a very important detail of furnace construction. Electrode holders of the wedge type have been used for some time but have been supplanted on all new furnaces by remotely controlled electrode holders, usually of the spring-clamp air-release type which can be operated from furnace-platform level to adjust the electrodes (Figure 17—8).

On a typical arc furnace, the secondary leads extend in the form of bars through the transformer case. From this point, the shortest possible delta connection is made with heavy copper terminals placed generally in the transformer vault wall. The necessary secondary cables are utilized and placed in the form of a hollow rectangle to minimize the reduction in current-carrying capacity due to skin effect. These cables connect to terminals on water-cooled bus tubes mounted on non-magnetic castings, remote from steel parts so as to minimize hysteresis and eddy current losses. The electrode arms, with horizontal section insulated at the rear, carry the bus tubes and electrode holders. The arms are usually in the form of an inverted-L cantilever mast. Each mast is capable of being raised or lowered independently to provide separate movement of any electrode.

The raising and lowering of the electrodes is accomplished through wire cables with motor-driven gears and winch units. It is the control of the motors driving these units that governs the successful operation of the furnace during the melting period.

Soderberg Electrodes—This is a continuous type of electrode made of a special paste that is baked by the heat of the furnace. A thin-steel cylindrical casing supported by two pieces of strip steel welded to the casing, one on either side, is filled with this paste. As the casing is lowered into the furnace, a new section of casing is welded to the top of the last section. As the bottom of the electrode is consumed in the furnace, the supporting strips are lowered and the electrodes slipped through the clamps. The heat of the conducting current plus the heat of the furnace bakes the paste on its downward travel.

This type of electrode has been built in sizes up to 27 inches by 66 inches, with a conducting capacity of 80,000 amperes. It is used on reduction furnaces where rapid movements of the electrodes are not required. Its application to arc furnaces, however, is doubtful because of the complicated design of the supporting structure plus the mechanism for quickly raising or lowering the electrodes for control of power during the melting operation.

The Power Transformer—Transformers for electric arc furnaces are similar in design to large power transformers, except that they are designed so that the primary winding can be connected in either delta ($\triangle$) or wye (Y). The primary winding is also constructed with several taps to provide various secondary voltages for melting and refining. Because of widely fluctuating load, which at times approaches short-circuit conditions, special bracing of the windings and extra insulation between turns is required. This latter is needed to withstand the high-voltage **surges** set up by switching operations. In normal **practice, there** may be 125 switching operations per 24 hours, and the resulting surges often equal five times normal voltage. These transformers are designed to suit the furnace, and their specifications usually are written by the furnace manufacturer.

All transformers are rated in *kva capacity*. The characteristics of an alternating-current circuit may result in the voltage and current being out of phase. This results in a loss of power, and the ratio of the useful power in the circuit to the apparent power supplied to it is called the power factor. The unit "kva," an abbreviation of "kilovolt-amperes," represents the product of the impressed voltage and the current in the circuit, and is a measure of the apparent power.

$$kva = kilovolts \times amperes$$

The useful power in the circuit is measured in kilowatts.

$$kilowatts = kilovolts \times amperes \times power\ factor$$

Kilowatts are equal to kva in the unusual case when the power factor is 1.0. The power factor is usually less than 1.0, so that the useful power (kilowatts) is usually less than the apparent power (kva).

Transformer Cooling—All arc-furnace transformers, except perhaps very small ones, are oil-insulated. This oil, which is a highly refined petroleum product having a high dielectric characteristic, helps to electrically insulate the various parts of the transformer windings from one another and from the iron core and case and, at the same time, serves as a cooling medium to carry away the heat generated in the windings and the core by resistance loss and eddy-current and hysteresis losses. Special non-flammable synthetic fluids can be employed in place of the flammable petroleum oil, but the minimal fire hazard in a properly installed furnace transformer seldom warrants the appreciable added cost of the non-flammable fluid.

The transformer oil must in turn be cooled by some

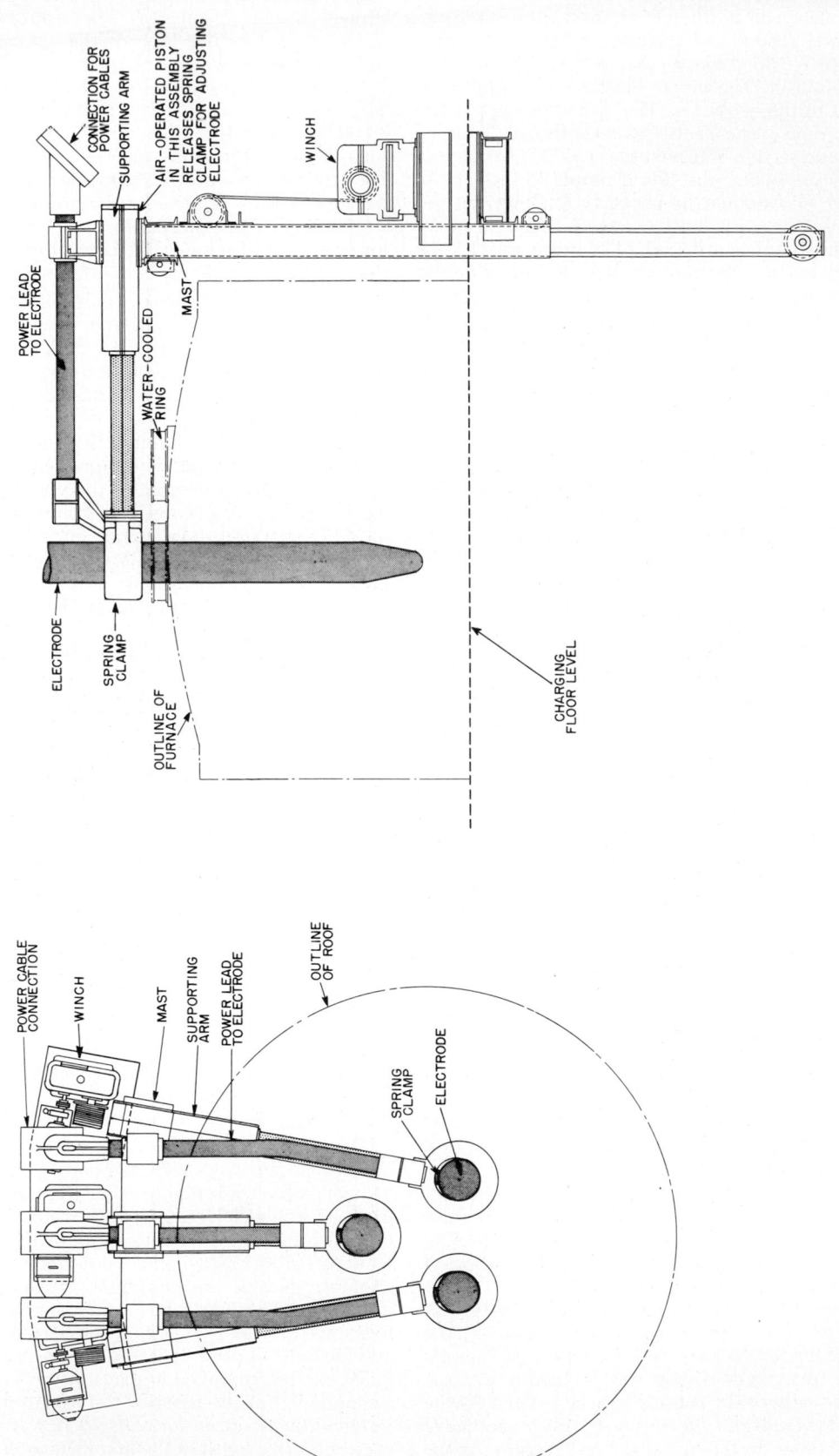

FIG. 17—8. Schematic arrangement of the electrodes, their supporting masts, and the electrical power leads for an electric-arc steelmaking furnace.

external means to maintain the temperature of the windings at a level commensurate with the thermal capabilities of the materials used to insulate the winding conductors and the leads. Furnace transformers customarily are designed to a 55 deg. C maximum top oil temperature rise above 25 deg. C maximum temperature of the external cooling medium in accordance with accepted ASA (American Standards Association) standards for power transformers. Recent developments in insulating materials, however, permit an allowable increase in maximum top oil temperature of 10 deg. C, which can be utilized either as effective overload capacity or as a higher allowable cooling-medium temperature.

Small oil-insulated furnace transformers rated below 750 kva may be convection-oil to convection-air cooled (Type OA), wherein the insulating oil flows by thermal convection through banks of external pipes and is cooled by the flow of air by thermal convection past these pipes. Because, however, furnace transformers are always installed indoors, economics and technical feasibility generally dictate that furnace transformers above these small sizes be water- or forced-air cooled, water being used for cooling in most cases.

All modern water-cooled furnace transformers utilize externally mounted straight-tube oil-to-water heat exchangers. The water tubes are made of corrosion-resistant metal and great care is exercised in the design and construction of the heat exchangers to minimize water-to-oil leaks. Cooling water preferably is drained to atmosphere, and water pressure in the heat exchanger maintained at a minimum commensurate with the required flow for proper cooling. The heads of the heat-exchanger casings are removable for cleaning of the water tubes. This type of construction, as compared to past practice of locating cooling coils inside the main transformer tank, makes visual inspection possible and facilitates cleaning of the tubes to maintain heat-exchanger efficiency.

For economic reasons, transformers up to and including 7500-kva capacity are generally convection oil-to-water cooled, wherein the heat exchangers are mounted high on the tank and oil flows through the heat exchangers by thermal convection (Type OW), while transformers above 7500-kva capacity are generally forced oil-to-water cooled, wherein the oil is pumped through the heat exchangers by sealed electric-motor-driven pumps (Type FOW).

Furnace transformers of all capacities can be built with forced oil-to-air cooling, wherein the oil is pumped through radiator-type heat exchangers through which cooling air is blown by fans (Type FOA). It is necessary, however, in the installation of such transformers either to duct outside air to the transformer or to locate the radiators outside. In the latter case, long oil-line runs are required. FOA units are generally employed only where suitable cooling water is unavailable or where climatic conditions make the use of water less preferable.

Furnace transformers are provided with temperature-measuring devices to which alarms or interlocks can be applied.

Tap Changers—The primary winding of the transformer generally is provided with six taps, giving the operator a selection of six high melting voltages when the primary is connected in delta, and six lower refining voltages when the primary is connected in wye. The primary-winding taps and end leads are connected to a motor-driven tap changer and delta-wye switch, located in a separate oil-filled compartment mounted externally on the main transformer tank. The ratio of secondary voltages obtained with the primary connected in wye to those obtained with the primary connected in delta is $1:\sqrt{3}$ ($1:1.732$ or $0.576:1$). Usually, the transformers are designed with winding and tap-changer current capacities such that only the top three delta voltage taps are rated at full transformer kva capacity, and the kva capacity of the lower delta voltage taps and the wye voltage taps decreases with decreasing voltage. Rated secondary current at the lowest full-capacity tap is maximum rated secondary current of the transformer and is the current value on which the current-capacity requirements of the secondary circuit and electrodes is based.

Off-load tap changers, which are not designed to change taps with the transformer excited and require that the primary circuit breaker be opened before the tap changer is operated, have been used customarily in the United States for arc-furnace applications, whereas the more costly on-load tap changers that permit the changing of taps with the transformer excited have been used customarily in Europe, primarily because the smaller European power systems could not readily accommodate the large frequent changes in system loading imposed by off-load tap changing. On-load tap changing does present some advantages to the furnace operator in convenience and demand-limit control and in reduced circuit-breaker maintenance, but these advantages are not generally believed to justify the additional cost.

Reactors—As explained later in this chapter, it is necessary for maintaining a stable arc to have a certain minimum amount of reactance in the circuit through which power is furnished to the arc. For the smaller-sized furnaces with physically shorter secondary-circuit components, the inherent reactance of the total circuit including the primary circuit and the transformer usually is not high enough to effect arc stability—particularly on the higher-voltage higher-current melting taps where the inherent transformer reactance is at a minimum. Accordingly, it is necessary to provide supplementary circuit reactance for these smaller-sized furnaces: preferably, this supplementary circuit reactance should be variable so that, on the lower-voltage lower-current refining taps where the total reactance requirements are less and the inherent transformer reactance is higher, the value of the supplementary reactance can be reduced to maintain maximum power factor. This supplementary reactance is generally provided in the form of a three-phase iron-core reactor with a tapped winding, mounted inside the main transformer tank and wired into the primary circuit in series with the primary windings. A terminal board usually is incorporated into the interconnection circuit, providing a selection of several supplementary-reactance values for each voltage tap. On some recently built transformers, however, a second tap changer has been provided for the reactor to give the operator an easier, wider, and more flexible selection of supplementary-reactance values for each voltage tap. The reactor windings are usually tapped to provide incremental changes in supplementary-reactance value of 5 per cent (per unit).

Supplementary reactors generally are provided for furnaces operating on 60-cycle power-supply systems and utilizing transformers of 7500-kva capacity and below. For lower-frequency power systems, the use of supplementary reactors must be extended to larger furnaces, the limit for 25-cycle furnaces, for example, being about 15,000 kva.

For larger furnaces the problem is reversed, in that the physically longer secondary-circuit components tend to result in a total circuit reactance considerably higher than that required for arc stability, with the consequent lower power factor that means less useful power in the furnace. An important consideration in the design of large furnaces is, therefore, the minimization of secondary-circuit resistance.

Another problem that has become particularly evident on large furnaces as transformer capacities have been increased is the unequal distribution among the three electrodes of the power input to the furnace, resulting in "hot spots" in the furnace sidewall adjacent to the electrodes carrying the most power, with consequent uneven wear of the sidewall refractories and higher refractory costs. This unequal distribution of power is a result of unequal impedances in the three electrical phases, due primarily to the necessarily asymmetrical arrangement of the secondary-circuit components and the resultant differences in mutual inductance between the phases. Attempts have been made with some success to correct this unbalance by the addition of iron reactor cores to the hot phases to increase the self impedance of these phases and thus counter-balance the inequalities in mutual impedances; and by special arrangements of the secondary flexible power cables to effect a balance of both mutual and self impedances of the whole circuit. Practical application of the cable-arrangement method of correction has required the use of water-cooled cables that are less bulky than air-cooled cables and are individually insulated electrically. Water-cooled cables have not been generally acceptable in the past because of high maintenance costs, but recent developments in the design and construction of such cables appear to have overcome some of the past objections.

Size of Transformers—The size of furnace transformer required is governed by several factors.

(1) Whether hot metal or a 100 per cent cold charge is to be used.
(2) Restrictions that may be imposed by the power supply.
(3) The capability of the electrodes to carry the heating current and the ability of the charge to absorb it.

The rate at which a given charge will absorb heat is measured by the temperature gradient within the mass. This rate declines continuously as the average temperature of the charge rises and reaches zero at temperature equilibrium in the furnace chamber.

On arc furnaces up to and including 3000-kva capacity, voltage taps generally range from 250 volts, phase to phase, with transformer primary connected delta, down to approximately 90 volts with transformer primary connected wye. On larger furnaces with transformers of 20,000 kva and greater, secondary voltage taps may range from 550 volts with primary connected delta, down to 150 volts with primary connected wye.

The Secondary Circuit—An electric arc converts large quantities of electric power into heat in a space of small volume. This concentration of heat developed at a high temperature—about 6300° F (3500° C) for the carbon arc—is the initial consideration in the design of the furnace chamber. A peculiar electrical feature of the arc is that its voltage drop decreases with an increasing current as shown in Curve A (Figure 17—9). Hence, the arc is inherently unstable.

The condition for stability of an electric circuit is a positive volt-ampere characteristic, that is, an increase in voltage drop in the circuit simultaneous with an increase in current. Curve B (Figure 17—9) shows the

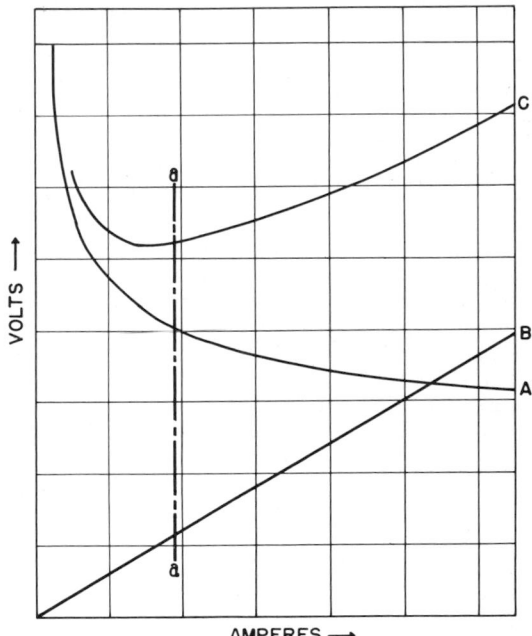

FIG. 17—9. Diagram depicting the volt-ampere characteristics of an arc with respect to its stabilizing element.

curve for this part of the secondary circuit, and since this reactance is in series with the arc circuit, the two curves combine and form the total curve C. The dotted line a-a shows the lower limit of stability, and stable arc conditions are obtained by adjusting the length of the arc for some amount of current higher than the critical value indicated by the line a-a. In general, the circuit is stable with about 50 per cent reactance-volts drop in the arc circuit. This does not cause an energy loss, but does lower the power factor to about 87 per cent.

The arc-furnace circuit, when operated at a constant given voltage, supplies a constant power factor load during the phase of operations when that selected voltage is used. However, the reactance of the secondary circuit is what determines the value of the power factor.

The secondary circuit thus consists of a fixed reactance of supply lines, cable, transformers, bus and furnace leads, and a variable resistance consisting of the fixed resistance of these same circuit elements plus the variable resistance of the arc itself. The voltage applied to the circuit may be varied by adjustment of the transformer taps. The power at any given voltage is varied by changing the resistance of the arc. This may be done by raising or lowering the electrodes; this is accomplished by an automatic control that seeks, by positioning the electrodes, to find and maintain constantly the current value that has been selected by the furnace operator.

If the kilowatt and the kilovolt-ampere inputs are plotted for any given voltage with variations in the current input, the curves will be similar to those shown on Figure 17—10. As the current increases, the kilovolt-amperes input increases in a straight line, since it is the product of kilovolts and amperes. The kilowatt input, however, increases only until a current is reached that will produce a power factor of 0.707

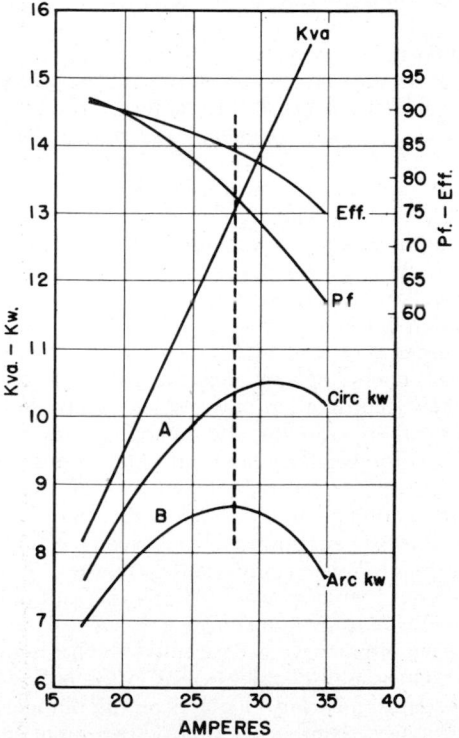

Fig. 17—10. Curves illustrating electrical characteristics of the electric arc-furnace circuit.

in the circuit. Further increases in current beyond this point causes a decrease in kilowatt input with increased kilovolt-ampere input and lower power factor.

Since a part of the energy input is dissipated in I^2R (heat) losses in the transformer bus and leads, the ac-

tual kilowatt input to the furnace itself will be less than that shown on curve A (Figure 17—10) and will follow curve B, reaching a maximum at some circuit power factor higher than 0.707, depending upon the resistance of the other circuit elements. Since the losses to these other elements of the circuit vary as the square of the current, the result is a falling efficiency curve as shown (Figure 17—10).

It is perhaps unfortunate that current provides the most convenient factor for automatic control of the circuit. Furnace operators may thus be misled into associating heat input with amperes rather than kilowatts, and in their attempts to get high heat input into a furnace, use current settings beyond those that give the optimum kilowatt input, as defined above. Such practice results not only in high kilovolt-ampere demand and lower power factor, but also in the actual loss of steel production and increased incidental costs.

It is the custom in modern shops to determine this maximum current for each voltage setting and give this information to the melter. The following table has been worked out for a three-phase, 10,000-kva furnace transformer:

Volts	200	250	300
Optimum current (amperes)	12,910	16,130	19,300
Maximum power (kw.)	3000	4700	6765
Approximate power factor (per cent)	74	74	74

The Primary Power Supply and Switchgear—The large power requirements of electric-arc furnaces and the undesirable voltage fluctuations (flicker) created in power systems by the rapid and widely varying current fluctuations imposed by arc-furnace operation generally require that furnace installations be serviced directly from high-capacity primary power-system circuits. The characteristics of primary power services generally used for arc-furnace installations range from 11,000 to 34,500 volts, with short-circuit capacities from 250 mva to 1,500 mva.

The problem of "flicker" on power systems serving arc-furnace installations has become increasingly important as the connected load on these power systems has increased, often out of proportion with the increase in capacity of the systems. Consequently, power companies have become more strict in the application of furnaces to their systems and have in several recent furnace installations required the use of corrective equipment, generally in the form of synchronous condensers, to help minimize the voltage fluctuations caused by furnace operations. Because of the necessary high reactance of arc-furnace circuits to maintain stability, large fluctuations of current caused by shorting out of the arc are at low lagging power factor, drawing large amounts of reactive kva. The purpose of the corrective equipment is to draw similar amounts of reactive kva at leading power factor, thus cancelling out the lagging component of the furnace surge or, in effect, supplying the lagging reactive component of the furnace surge, thus minimizing the portion to be supplied by the power system. Since furnace surges are never consistently of the same magnitude, it is necessary for effective correction to provide equipment that can be adjusted rapidly to the varying reactive load requirements. The synchronous condenser, which is basically an unloaded synchronous motor with over-excitation of the field, is with its sensitive field-excitation control system the most suitable corrective equipment for this application. The capital cost of such equipment is, however, quite high and the requirement of such equipment certainly affects the favorable capital-investment position of the electric-arc furnace. Some return on the investment in such equipment is realized in the form of decreased power-factor penalties in the power costs.

The on-off control of arc furnaces generally is accomplished by a circuit breaker in the primary power-supply circuit to the furnace transformer. The customary use of off-load tap changers on furnace transformers requires that the primary circuit be opened every time the furnace operating voltage is changed, resulting in as many as 125 breaker operations per day on a furnace in continuous operation. If this circuit breaker also is to be used for protection against faults in the transformer and in the primary circuit between the transformer and circuit breaker, it must have a high interrupting capacity and be capable of maintaining this capacity under the condition of frequent operation with reasonable maintenance. An oil-type circuit breaker which, due to oil carbonization, generally loses some interrupting capacity with each operation and, accordingly, requires frequent replacement of oil to maintain rated capacity, generally is not suitable for furnace-switching duty unless a second "back-up" breaker is provided for primary fault interruption duty and the furnace breaker is limited to switching and secondary fault and overload protection. Because of the inherent impedance in the transformer and secondary circuit, secondary fault currents rarely exceed four to five times full load current. Consequently, air-type circuit breakers, especially designed for frequent operation, generally are used for arc-furnace duty.

Two types of air circuit breakers generally are used for furnace duty: the air-magnetic type wherein electromagnets excited by the current to be interrupted are used to create a magnetic field in the path of the arc drawn between breaker contacts as these contacts open, and aids in extinguishing the arc by deionization and by forcing the arc to "blow out" into an arc chute; and the compressed-air type wherein dry air is blown at high pressure into the arc stream, helping to extinguish the arc by cooling and "blow out." Breakers of the air-magnetic type are available for furnace duty up to 15,000 volts and 500 mva interrupting capacity, and are generally of the steel-enclosed draw-out type, obviating the need for a separate disconnect switch ahead of the breakers. For primary service voltages above 15,000 volts, compressed-air-type circuit breakers normally are used, and breakers of this type also generally are limited to 500-mva interrupting capacity. Thus, for primary power service having a short-circuit capacity in excess of 500 mva, a "back-up" breaker normally is provided for primary fault protection. Recent use has been made of a foreign-designed compressed-air-type breaker that is reportedly suitable for furnace duty up to 1000-mva

interrupting capacity. At least one installation has also been made using a vacuum-type breaker, wherein the contacts operate in an evacuated chamber, minimizing arcing because of the absence of ionizable gas, thus making possible high interrupting capacities and low maintenance.

Compressed-air-type and vacuum-type circuit breakers normally are of the open type and, therefore, each of these types requires a disconnect switch installed ahead of the breaker. Such switches generally are of the manual gang-operated type. Key-operated mechanical interlocks are provided on the switch and on the circuit breaker to assure that the switch cannot be operated unless the breaker is in the open position.

A special compressed-air supply unit usually is furnished with compressed-air-type breakers to assure a suitable source of dry air at proper pressure. Plant air supplies can be used for emergency standby service in these installations, but their use as normal supplies for these breakers is not recommended because of the entrained moisture usually encountered and variations in pressure.

Tripping power is obtained preferably from a wet-cell type of battery, which provides the most reliable source of power for this important function. Automatic chargers are used to maintain the proper battery charge.

Standard inverse time-over-current relays are used most commonly for fault and overload detection. Where a back-up breaker is required, the relays for the furnace breaker are energized from current transformers in the secondary circuit and the back-up breaker from current transformers in the primary circuit. A system of relaying that provides a measure of differential protection for the primary circuit and transformer has been developed and used in numerous installations, particularly where relay-system coordination presents a problem. Because normal furnace surges may be as high as two to three times rated current, depending upon furnace size and other factors, relay coordination may present a problem, particularly where more than two relaying stations are involved. To prevent trip-out on normal surges, furnace relays in some cases must be set as high as 150 per cent of rated capacity for the longest time delay and 300 to 400 per cent for the instantaneous setting.

Control of Power Supply to the Charge—The early arc-furnace regulator was a simple current-operated device. The current transformers in each phase of the secondary circuits were connected to the regulating coils, and the pull of this current in the coil was balanced against a spring. Contacts on the plunger made connections with either the up or down set of contacts when the electrode current was higher or lower than the current setting. These contacts were relayed to the control of the electrode motors and caused them to operate in the proper direction as the current varied from some pre-determined value.

This control was unsatisfactory because the restraining force of the spring was constant. The variations of current during melt down are rapid, and the mechanical movement of the electrodes comparatively slow, so that this control responded to the av-

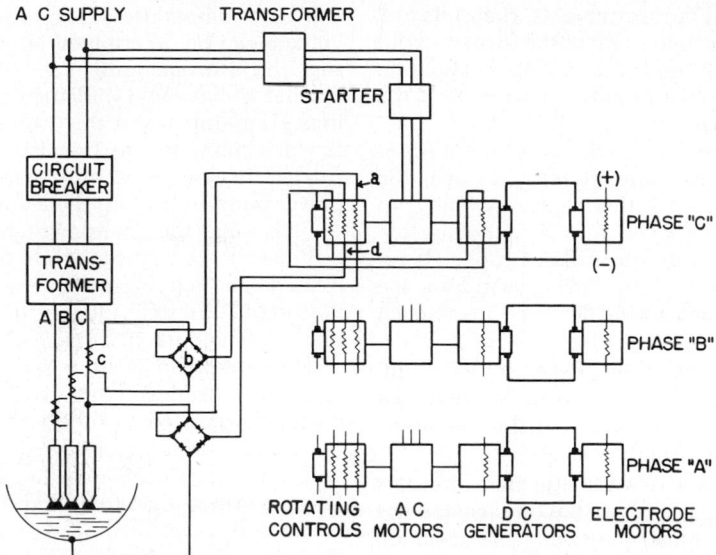

FIG. **17**—11. Schematic elementary diagram of one type of regulating system for electric-arc furnaces. (Courtesy, Westinghouse Electric Corporation.)

erage value of current variation. Furthermore, a three-phase system of currents in an electric furnace is very complex and the values of the currents in the regulator are interdependent, the value in any phase at a given time being determined by conditions in the other two phases, as well as by the length of the arc in that particular phase.

It is well known that the voltage drop across the arc will increase as the current decreases, and vice versa (Figure **17**—9). Hence, if the varying pull of a coil or other regulating device, which is proportional to the current in the electrode, is matched against a restraining force that is proportional to the voltage drop across the arc, the utmost sensitivity to changes in arc length can be obtained in the regulator.

The above is the principle used for the constant-potential, magnetic control systems used on most arc furnaces and, when combined with dynamic braking on the electrode-motor circuit, has been the standard method of control. This is known as the **balanced-beam control.**

Quite independently of the arc-furnace industry, new methods of regulation using rotating equipment with variable-voltage control were developed. When applied to electrode control, the several systems based on this principle balance currents in the electrode circuits against the voltage across the arcs and combines these with variable-voltage controls on the electrode motors.

The advantages claimed for these methods are as follows:

1. Variable-voltage control of the electrode motors results in motor torques directly proportional to the average unbalance between the current in the electrode and voltage across the arc, and gives an increased speed of response to these motors, resulting in smooth acceleration and deceleration.

2. When maximum unbalance occurs, the maxi-

mum permissible voltage can be applied to the motors causing high-speed withdrawal of the electrodes.

Figure **17**—11 shows an elementary wiring diagram of one of these systems. The current-control field of the regulating element (a) is energized by a dry-type rectifier (b) which in turn is connected to a current transformer (c) in the electrode circuit. The potential-control field (d) is energized in a similar manner from the voltage drop between the electrode and the shell of the furnace.

When the breaker is closed, voltage is applied to the potential control field which causes the generator voltage to build up in the direction to lower the electrodes. When the first electrode strikes the metal charge, the voltage drops to zero causing the electrode motor to stop. When a second electrode strikes the metal, a current will flow causing the current-control field to become energized, which acts to raise the electrode and establish an arc. As the arc is lengthened, its voltage increases and the current decreases until a balance is established between the potential and current-control fields.

Provision is made for manually controlling the electrodes individually, or automatically in a group. The operator sets the voltage tap on the furnace transformer and adjusts current input by a rheostat to the value desired.

3. Installations with this type of control, having smaller load fluctuations because of the increased speed of response, decrease electrode breakage and result in a decrease of kwh.-consumption per ton of ingots.

Operator's Control Panel—With each electric-arc furnace, it is customary to mount a control panel, usually in the wall of the transformer vault, with the instrument side of the panel flush with the outside wall.

This panel contains all the instruments, rheostats and control switches for the operation of the furnace, with the exception of the control for the tilting mechanism. This master control station usually is located near the charging side of the furnace.

One of the control switches, with a red and a green indicating lamp on either side, closes and opens the main circuit breaker. Another operates the tap changer, but is so interlocked that it cannot be operated unless the main circuit breaker is open. If rotating-type control is used, the starting switch for the set, plus three switches to manually control each electrode motor, are needed.

There are three ammeters, one for each phase, and above each a rheostat. The value of the current that is to be maintained in each phase by the automatic control is set by the individual rheostats.

Above the ammeters is a wattmeter that indicates the useful power being taken into the furnace and the power factor. There is some question of the accuracy of the power-factor reading, because of the complexity of the varying currents in all three phases, but it is a guide point and is required on all boards.

An integrating watthour meter, which adds up the kilowatt hours on the furnace, completes the normal complement of meters. Some operators install a recording watthour meter to provide a record of the power changes and consumption at various times during the heat.

Power Requirements—Power requirements for actual melting are variable and depend upon the definition of when the charge is melted. Generally, it is assumed that the charge is melted when no further scrap remains and the metal has reached a temperature of 2850° F. Depending upon thickness of the lining and other variables that affect furnace efficiency, the kilowatt-hours required for actual melting vary from between 400 and 425 per ton.

The problem of determining the amount of power to be used during the meltdown period has to be based on several factors incident to the furnace installation and type of charge, but the maximum useful power that can be used is determined by the characteristics of the secondary circuit.

The arc itself is virtually a resistance drop, which is in series with a large reactance drop caused by the leads and transformer winding. The resistance drop is in phase with the secondary current, while the reactance drop is 90 degrees out of phase. The resultant relation is the vector sum of these two drops, and the cosine of the angle between the resultant current and the voltage is called the power factor. The useful power or kilowatts used to melt equals the product of the voltage drop times the resulting current times the power factor. When the ampere loading reaches a point where the power factor of the secondary circuit is 0.707, maximum power is going into the secondary circuit. Since the current and potential transformers that operate the power-factor meter are installed on the primary circuit of the power transformer, there is an additional reactive drop in these windings; so that maximum power input to the furnace occurs at from 0.75 to 0.80 power factor as read on the meter.

The maximum useful amperes for a given secondary voltage can be determined approximately by increasing the current until the kilowatt-meter reading reaches a maximum and then gives decreasing readings. The amperes at this value are somewhat above the maximum to use (see Figure 17—10), and any further increase not only will reduce the melting power but also heat up the leads and the transformer.

Following the meltdown period, the power requirements are reduced while the heat is worked and refined. The refining procedure depends on the composition of the steel, quality of scrap, furnace condition, and shop practice.

The rapidity of melting is a function of the amount of energy introduced in a given time. However, if the energy introduced to the furnace is not absorbed by the charge, high localized temperatures occur which will cause deterioration of the side walls and the roof. It is important, therefore, that the rate of power input be carefully controlled. It is always advisable to utilize the minimum secondary voltage necessary to introduce the required amount of power at the proper power factor. On this basis, the arc length is at a minimum and damage to refractories is lessened.

Some melters start a meltdown with a lower voltage and amperage than they use after the melt has started. In a published record of a 50-ton furnace having the following transformer taps: 282, 242, 220, 199, 165 and 115 volts, good furnace results were obtained with these values:

	Volts	Amperes	Minutes
Start	199	25,000	15
	282	32,000	130
	242	25,000	15

In a shop using a 90,000-pound charge of alloy steel, the average kwh. per heat was 24,600 or 547 kwh. per ton for 200 heats. If 450 kwh. per ton were required for melting, then 97 were required for refining. The average time from tap to tap was 6 hours, 8 minutes, of which 37 minutes were required for charging. The average input during the meltdown period was 12,300 kva.

In connection with power input, the maximum input to the furnace is measured by two factors:

1. The rate at which a given charge will absorb the heat declines continuously as the average temperature of the charge rises. The rate of heat absorption by the charge is largely dependent upon the area exposed to the radiation; hence, with large pieces of heavy scrap, the rate of heat absorption is considerably less than that which is afforded by the use of very light scrap with large area.

2. On small furnaces, the electrical circuit, including the reactor, is adjusted so as to give an average primary power factor during meltdown of approximately 87 per cent at full load. There are cases, however, where the companies supplying power object to the maximum swings in demand and insist on additional reactance in the primary circuit to reduce the magnitude of these swings. The additional reactance might at full load reduce the power factor to 80 per cent or 82 per cent.

SECTION 3

THE BASIC ELECTRIC-ARC FURNACE PROCESS

Before the location for an electric-furnace plant for the production of ingots by the basic process can be selected, its capacity and probable growth must be known, as an ample electric-power supply must be available. If it is assumed that the plant will have an initial annual capacity of 200,000 tons of ingots per year and a future capacity of 400,000 tons per year, a power supply of 50,000 to 60,000 kilowatts must be available.

This amount of power is not available in the generating stations of the steel plant and due to the highly fluctuating loads, poor power factor and load factor, it is not desirable on some utility systems. For these reasons, a source of power must be found before deciding on a plant location.

Installations have been made as additions to existing open-hearth shops. These involved low investment charges, as the electric furnace was installed either on the location of a dismantled open hearth or in an addition to the building. Hence, existing cranes, stock facilties, utilities, etc., could be used for the new installation.

Some of the objections to this type of layout are:

(1) The chance of carbon pick up from the hot metal mixer (from flakes of graphite or kish floating in the air).
(2) Difficulties in scrap segregation.
(3) Congestion on the pouring floor.

Several plants were installed as complete steelmaking units which required a full complement of buildings, cranes and tracks. This arrangement is more costly but allows for segregation of materials, setting up a working force who are concerned only with making electric-furnace steels, and supervision is concentrated on the products.

Stocking and Charging Facilities—A most modern design for a basic-process electric-furnace plant calls for a lower level stockhouse located as an extension to the end of the furnace building or adjacent and parallel to the furnace building. At either of these two locations, drop-bottom charging buckets, ranging in capacity from 100 to 3300 cubic feet as required by furnace size, are loaded at ground level and subsequently moved by an overhead crane in the first instance or by transfer car and overhead crane in the second instance to the furnace floor, from which point they may be charged into the furnaces. Some older plants originally equipped with door-charged electric furnaces have two-level stockhouses, the higher level being for the charging cars which can be loaded on the furnace level and the lower level used for storage bins.

In electric-furnace practice, the different lots of alloy scrap are kept in separate bins and, during normal times, between twenty and forty bins are required. When the use of virgin alloys is restricted, scrap must be segregated further and perhaps 65 or more kinds of scrap must be used, depending upon the grade of

steel being made, as discussed later under "Utilization of Steel Scrap." Few stockhouses are designed for this practice and this may result in stocking out of doors.

Since the charge should be dry before it is placed in the furnace, a covered stockyard is advantageous. For a 200,000-ton plant, at least two 10-ton cranes equipped with lifting magnets are required in the stock yard. In those plants where the boxes are loaded on the lower level, they are placed on platens which are raised to the charging cars on the furnace floor. A 30-ton crane is required for this service. This layout calls for the loaded boxes to be carried to the scales and weighed before placing on the platen, which holds three or four boxes. This system has the advantage of easy, accurate weighing and conserves space in the stockyard. With this system of stocking, a study of crane movements with timing cycles is required as the operation can be bottlenecked by the cranes.

Tracks for both the incoming supplies and the charging cars are important factors in the plant layout. The daily supply of scrap for a 200,000-ton annual capacity shop will require a minimum of 11 railroad cars, in addition to those required for limestone, ore, brick, etc. In addition, storage tracks, located nearby, are required for these materials to provide for possible irregularity of railroad movements.

UTILIZATION OF STEEL SCRAP

Scrap Segregation—The necessity for conserving the valuable alloy content of steel scrap, to economize in the use of virgin alloys and to insure that only the elements desired are introduced in making the steel, makes it absolutely necessary to segregate or separate the available scrap into stock piles of identified grades. When the "product mix" (grades of steel produced) varies a great deal, the scrap classification by alloy content must be much more extensive than for a specialty plant producing the same grade continuously. One plant, making various grades of steel by the basic process, including alloy and stainless steels, has found it necessary to segregate their scrap stock into 65 classifications.

The scrap stock may be revert or home scrap from the rolling mills and forge shops of the same plant where the electric furnace operates; it may be obtained from scrap dealers, from customers, from other steel producers, or from sister plants. To produce economically the wide range of steels common to modern practice requires careful selection of the scrap, and a scrap segregation and control plan is essential.

The term "segregation" as used here may be defined as the separation of a mass of mixed scrap into piles of individual compositions. Close adherence to a definite scrap-segregation program is essential if the greatest benefits are to be obtained with respect to alloy conservation and melting close to the desired composition. Consistent melting practice is an aid in maintaining mill schedules for the production and delivery of steel, and helps to obtain optimum tonnage from a given unit as well as to maintain steel quality at the high standards demanded by industry. Any even temporary disregard of the scrap-segregation program will lead to loss of alloys, and non-oxidizable elements such as nickel and copper may enter and remain in the bath and cause the heat to be scrapped or, at best, diverted to another order which originally did not require the use of so many valuable elements. For example, chromium can be oxidized from a heat ordered as nickel-molybdenum steel but it is a costly and wasteful process. On the other hand, nickel cannot be oxidized from a chromium-molybdenum heat; therefore, if it is present and the order restricts the nickel content to no nickel or very low limits, the heat must be diverted or scrapped.

Methods for Insuring Proper Segregation of Scrap —The segregation of home scrap is comparatively easy but the introduction of outside or foreign scrap imposes a problem. Several methods are available for testing the scrap to determine if it is what it is supposed to be. These include chemical analyses of selected samples, spectrographic analysis, and less costly and less accurate methods such as magnetic tests, to separate magnetic from non-magnetic scrap, and the "spark" test. The latter is made by holding a piece of scrap against a grinding wheel and observing the shower of sparks; it is possible for a trained observer to differentiate between the various kinds of steel scrap by noting the color of the spark, the length of the spark lines, and the characteristics of the ends of these lines. In addition, a couple of rough tests may be mentioned; for example, "spot tests" which permit rough estimates to be made of the amount of nickel or one of several other elements present by the use of a chemical solution or solutions applied to a clean surface of the sample to be tested. Another rough test is the "pellet" test by which a few elements may be detected by viewing oxidized particles from "spark" tests under a magnifying glass.

Physical Requirements of Scrap—The size of the scrap or its bulk density is of importance. The size may vary from ingots of various sizes to turnings from machine shops. Heavy scrap (ingots, ingot butts, crop ends) has considerable weight per unit volume, while the weight per unit volume for light scrap is low. Therefore, if there is too much light scrap in the charge for a given heat, the total volume of heavy and light scrap will exceed the volume of the furnace and part of the scrap cannot be charged until a portion of the charge is melted down. A charge made up entirely of heavy scrap is also objectionable, because it does not permit the shielding of roof and walls during the melt-down period to the same extent as a mixed charge of greater volume, and results in decrease of refractory life. Another physical requirement, especially with heavy scrap, is that the pieces are not too long, so that the charge in the furnace may be kept relatively dense and not opened up by longer pieces which, as a rule, do not lie in a horizontal plane. If the scrap charge is made up of approximately 40 per cent heavy, 40 per cent medium, and 20 per cent light scrap, a density usually is obtained which reduces the number of "back charges" (the charging of additional

scrap after the original scrap charge has melted down).

Selection of the Scrap Charge—With an efficient scrap-segregation plan in effect and with scrap available that has the proper physical characteristics, the charge should be made up as follows:

1. Grades of scrap must be selected which together contain the elements necessary to make the heat ordered. The charge may contain all or part of the specified elements, with care being taken to see that no scrap is included that contains elements which are not a part of the specification. This is imperative if the scrap contains an element which cannot be oxidized by regular practice.

2. For economical operation, each element contained in the scrap selected should approach by weight, as closely as possible, the number of pounds of that element required to meet the lower range of the chemical specifications (for that element) in the ordered heat.

3. Knowing the amount of the various elements contained in the combination of scrap selected for a heat, the total amount of virgin alloys necessary to make the heat are calculated. This calculation is based on the weight of the heat to be made (furnace capacity and amount specified by an order) and the specification. In making these calculations, allowance must be made for adjustments during the making of the heat; for example, losses in melting some alloys and the possible absorption of certain alloying elements from the bottom and banks of the furnace. In regular practice, a heat made to a low alloy specification occasionally finishes outside of the specified composition ranges when the heat is made immediately following a high alloy specification, such as a stainless grade, or high-manganese steel, etc. The usual practice to overcome this difficulty is to make a so-called **wash heat;** i.e., a heat of medium alloy specifications, but containing the same elements, made following the high-alloy grades. The purpose of the "wash heats" is to have any absorption of elements from the furnace bottom and banks take place in a heat in which the increase in certain elements is not harmful and thus prevent high residuals in the low-alloy heats which will follow.

4. Efficient operation makes it necessary that the scrap selected for a given charge is not only satisfactory for that charge but that it be selected on the basis of the scrap available for efficient operation over a period of time. If only heavy or medium scrap were used for a few heats, it is probable that these particular heats would be speeded up. If, however, at the same time a large inventory of light scrap (turnings, punchings, etc.) were accumulating, excessive amounts of this light scrap would have to be charged in later heats, probably with back-charging, and the delays and damage to refractories would far off-set any gains in the few heats made with heavy and medium scrap.

5. It is probable that no part of the routine of charging the furnace is of more importance than the loading and weighing procedures. Unless the proper type of scrap is selected and correctly weighed, the final product probably will be of the wrong composi-

tion, because all adjustments are based on what is assumed to be the correct weight of the scrap charged originally.

CHARGING, MELTING AND FINISHING

Charging the Furnace—The various types of charging equipment have been described earlier in this chapter. Regardless of the type of furnace, whether door or top-charged by hand, chute, bucket, or charging machine, an effort should be made to place the charge as accurately as possible.

The power is turned off and the roof and electrodes are moved out of the way in the case of top-charged furnaces. With door-charged furnaces, the electrodes are raised as high as possible to prevent breakage during charging, and the charging started. Light or medium scrap is charged in a thin layer on the bottom or hearth, because this type of scrap melts faster than large pieces when the metal directly under the electrodes melts and drips down through the charge and collects on the bottom of the furnace. Heavy scrap is charged in the area within or adjacent to the triangle or "delta" formed by the electrodes and must be charged in such a way that it will not shift during melting down and cause possible breakage of electrodes by falling against them. After this, light or medium scrap is usually piled high around the sides of the furnace to protect the roof and side walls from the arc during the melt-down at high power input.

Alloying materials that are not easily oxidized, can be and usually are charged in the furnace prior to melting down.

It is desirable to melt down with excess carbon in the bath in order that some carbon may be worked out by ore additions or oxygen injection. If the metallic charge is too low in carbon, a recarburizer in the form of coke or scrap electrodes is charged with the scrap to allow for a carbon content of the bath at melt-down that will be 0.15 to 0.25 per cent higher than the carbon content of the finished steel.

Although ore or mill scale is still used to lower the carbon content, the use of gaseous oxygen injected into the bath is becoming more common. Various operators may charge the ore with the scrap, or when the charge is partially melted, or when the charge is completely melted.

Any general description of making steel in the basic electric-arc furnace must be broad enough to include double- and single-slag methods with other variations.

The double-slag, cold charge practice can be divided into: (1) the meltdown and/or oxidizing period, (2) the slag-off period, (3) the reducing period, and (4) the tapping period.

Melt-Down and/or Oxidizing Period—When charging has been completed, the bank in front of the charging door is built up with refractory material (dolomite) to form a breast or dam to keep the molten metal from slopping out the door (furnaces may have more than one door if the size warrants). The door (or doors) is closed and the electrodes are lowered to about an inch above the scrap. The main circuit breaker is closed, an intermediate voltage is selected with proper current setting on the rheostats, and the arcs are struck under automatic control. After approximately 15 minutes (to allow the electrodes to bore into the scrap), maximum voltage and current should be applied for the fastest possible melting of the scrap. The initial slow start is to shield the lining and roof from the heat of the arc, which lengthens as the voltage is increased.

The melting period in the basic electric furnace is the most expensive period in its operation because power and electrode consumption are at the highest rate during this period.

The electrodes melt the portion of the charge directly underneath them, and continue to bore through the metallic charge, forming a pool of molten metal on the hearth. From the time the electrodes bore through the scrap and form the pool of molten metal on the hearth, the charge is melted from the bottom up by radiation from the pool, by heat from the arc, and by the resistance offered to the current by the scrap. This continues until the charge is entirely melted.

From the time molten metal begins to form until the entire charge is in solution, oxidation occurs in varying degrees. During this period phosphorus, silicon, manganese, carbon, etc., are oxidized.

Oxygen for these, as well as other oxidizing reactions, is obtained from (1) oxygen gas injected into the bath, (2) oxygen in the furnace atmosphere, (3) calcination of limestone (if used), (4) oxides of alloying elements added in the furnace, and (5) ore, cinder and scale (if charged or added later). The direct use of oxygen gas (Item 1) is extremely important in modern practice from the standpoint of removing carbon from the bath rapidly.

Oxidation practice must be varied with different grades of steel. For example, low-carbon steels require a relatively high degree of oxidation. As the oxidation progresses, the temperature of the bath is raised to promote carbon removal and to increase the fluidity of the bath so that inclusions may rise through the molten metal to its surface and into the slag. The reaction of oxygen with carbon forms CO gas, and this gas generated in the bath gives rise to the **boil**. Maximum cleanliness of the steel demands a hot, active bath. Oxygen blown into the bath is of great assistance in attaining these ends.

The reactions taking place in the bath of the basic electric-arc furnace during the oxidation period are similar to those in the basic open-hearth, except that the electric-furnace bath can be made hotter (hence, there is more chance of phosphorus reversion unless the slag is strongly basic). Also, there is no continuous supply of oxygen to the bath as from the open-hearth flame.

The lime-silica ratios (the so-called "V" ratios) are used generally in calculating the basicity of slag.

Electric-furnace steel is sometimes made by a single slag process in which the slag is first oxidized as described and then made reducing by adding the proper materials during the refining period. The usual practice with the cold-melt process is to use a double-slag method, an oxidizing slag followed by a reducing slag.

Refining—In the double-slag method the original slag, with its oxidation products, is slagged off or largely removed from the surface of the bath by cutting off the electric power to the electrodes, raising the electrodes, back-tilting the furnace slightly, and then raking the slag out through the charging door with wooden or steel rabbles. The original slag should be removed thoroughly to prevent delay in making up the second slag and reversion of any elements from slag to metal.

The materials used in making up the second or reducing slag are burnt lime, fluorspar, and silica sand, with powdered coke to supply carbon for forming calcium carbide. Typical proportions are 5 to 8 parts of lime, ½ to 2 parts of fluorspar, 1 to 2 parts of coke, and ½ to 1 part of silica sand. The above amounts are premixed in proportions determined by experience. Sufficient sand and fluorspar should be used to flux the lime quickly. Coke usually is added after the slag becomes fluid. Very often, small amounts of crushed ferrosilicon also are added. In producing low-carbon grades of steel, under 0.12 per cent carbon, a lime-silica, a lime-alumina, or a modified carbidic slag containing less coke, is used.

The object is to form as quickly as possible a reducing slag containing calcium carbide, and maintain it through the refining period. The presence of carbide may be detected readily by the odor associated with the acetylene generated when a slag sample is made wet with water. A carbide slag acts to return reducible oxides such as those of manganese, chromium, vanadium, tungsten, iron, etc., from the slag to the metal; consequently, such oxides may be added for direct reduction as soon as the carbide slag is formed. The slag also serves to reduce the oxides in the bath and facilitates the removal of sulphur as calcium sulphide.

Desulphurization is aided by a high manganese content, by the addition of lime and fluorspar, by agitation of the bath, and by high temperature. If very low sulphur is required, sometimes two carbidic slags may be necessary. The carbidic slag should be completely shaped up 20 to 40 minutes after the first slag has been removed. The carbide content of the slag is kept to a relatively low figure for the lower carbon heats, and, for very low carbon heats, silicon can be substituted for coke in the slag to prevent carbon pick-up by the metal.

Lime-alumina slags are made from lime and aluminum in the form of shot and/or granules. Calcium aluminate is formed, which both desulphurizes and deoxidizes the bath. However, as the lime-alumina slag absorbs metallic oxides from the bath, metallic aluminum must be added periodically to the slag to keep the content of these oxides in the slag at a low level and thus continue its reducing role throughout the refining period.

The steel should not be held under the second slag any longer than is absolutely necessary. As soon as results of the last preliminary analyses are reported, the necessary additions are made to the bath for adjustment of the carbon and alloying element content. The additions of alloying elements must be made in quantities sufficiently small to prevent chilling of the bath. When all of the additions are in solution, the slag is again shaped up and ferrosilicon is added. Final additions of aluminum for grain-size control usually are made just before tapping. The aluminum is put into the furnace, tied on the end of long bars to insure getting it through the slag into the bath. About one-half of the aluminum usually is added to the stream of metal in the spout as the heat is being tapped into the ladle. The furnace is tapped usually from 10 to 15 minutes after the final shaping of the slag and additions of ferrosilicon and aluminum have been made.

Induction Stirring—In recent years, there has been considerable interest in stirring of the steel bath by electric induction. The original development occurred in Sweden, and some large furnaces in the United States are equipped with the Swedish type of inductor stirrer. Some other furnaces are equipped with a rotating-type stirrer developed in the United States.

In the Swedish design, an inductor constructed of steel laminations, in which is imbedded a two-phase winding, is installed under the bottom of the furnace. In order to permit penetration of the magnetic flux and to minimize bottom heating, the carbon-steel bottom plates ordinarily used are replaced by austenitic stainless-steel plates, which are treated theoretically as an air gap. A special generator and exciter is provided to produce two-phase current at a frequency of approximately ½ cycle per second. During operation, a magnetic flux is produced in the form of a moving field. This moving magnetic field, reacting with a field induced in the bath, causes the bath to flow at a low rate of speed across the bottom of the hearth. Thus, a stirring action is obtained.

With the type of stirrer developed in the United States, a two-pole electromagnetic rotor is revolved underneath the furnace by a motor-and-gear mechanism. The rotor is excited by current from either the shop supply or a special generator. This causes a movement of flux across the bottom of the furnace, the bottom plates of which are made of austenitic stainless steel. In turn, this induces a movement in the molten steel bath similar to that previously described.

It has been proved that with induction stirring the stratification of the alloying elements is greatly minimized, thus giving more accurate chemical sampling leading to better control of final composition. The temperature of the bath is much more uniform. It has also been demonstrated that, due to the movement of the steel, the interface contact between the slag and the steel is greatly improved, with less time required to obtain the necessary metallurgical reactions.

Tapping—In tapping a heat, the electrodes are raised to the maximum height after the power is shut off, the tap hole is opened and the furnace is tilted by a control mechanism so that the steel is drained from the furnace into a ladle set on the pit side of the furnace. The slag comes after the steel and serves as an insulating blanket during tapping. A clean, round taphole and a clean, smooth tapping spout reduce the possibility of having a ragged, easily oxidized stream when tapping into the ladle.

LADLE, MOLD AND POURING PRACTICES

Ladle Practices—After all the molten steel in the furnace has been drained into the ladle, the ladle crane moves the ladle to the pouring platform where the steel is poured into molds. Both the ladle and pouring practices are practically identical with open-hearth practice, except both the inner and outer linings of the ladles are constructed of first-quality fire brick and special precautions are taken in setting the nozzles and stoppers because of the higher tapping temperatures employed in electric-furnace practice and the closer control desired for most electric-furnace products. The steel may be reladled (i.e., poured from one ladle into another) before teeming to insure the proper mixing of the alloys and reduce pouring temperatures.

Mold Practice—When the steel is ready to be poured, it is teemed into carefully prepared molds. Molds of the big-end-up type are used generally for the killed electric-furnace steels, while rimmed steels are poured into the conventional big-end-down molds. Shapes and sizes of molds vary considerably, depending on the steel being produced and the size and shape of the product. Round, square, and rectangular molds with smooth or fluted inside surfaces may be used.

The molds are scraped carefully, cleaned, coated with mold coating, preheated (if necessary), and all dirt is siphoned out after the hot tops have been set—about 30 minutes to 45 minutes before the heat taps. Each shop usually has several different mold coatings and mold practices that have been developed for the particular grades of steel being produced. For instance, steel has been poured into clean uncoated molds, as well as molds coated with tar, salt brine, lime slurry, resin smudge, acetylene smudge, molasses, lamp black, oil, graphite, aluminum paint, and various other coatings.

Pouring Practice—Either of two pouring practices may be employed, the direct or the indirect. The former practice is accomplished by raising the stopper rod and allowing the steel to run directly into the mold from the ladle. In the indirect method, the steel is allowed to run through a refractory funnel and runner (as in bottom pouring). Basket pouring, a modification of indirect pouring, utilizes a small intermediate ladle which is filled from the large ladle. When the small ladle is filled, the nozzle in its bottom is opened, allowing the steel to run into the mold or molds through one or more openings or nozzles in the bottom of the basket. The purpose of indirect pouring is to reduce the splash in the bottom of the mold with the view of reducing scabs and other defects on the ingot surface. The theory justifying basket pouring is based on the premise that nonmetallic inclusions in the steel rise rapidly through relatively short distances at higher temperatures; thus, in conjunction with tapping the heat hot, inclusions rise out of the steel in the lower area of the ladle before that steel issues from the bottom to fill the basket, and also rise in the basket while the molds are being filled.

The molds are usually filled slowly at first until the pool of steel on the bottom of the molds is about 6 inches deep, and then a full stream is permitted. When a conventional brick hot-top is used, a full stream is maintained until the steel rises to the bottom of the hot-top, at which moment the stopper is lowered to shut off the stream to permit the steel to freeze

at the junction between the mold and hot-top, after which more steel is poured to fill the hot-top. When using a hot-top which seals the junction, the stream is permitted to flow full until the hot-top has been filled.

If the junction does not seal, steel will leak out and run over the top of the mold. The blocks supporting the hot-top are knocked out immediately after the junction seals to prevent "hanger cracks" in the ingot. Burnt lime, straw, brick dust, or manufactured hot-top covering materials are used on top of the molten metal in the hot-top to hold the metal in a molten condition long enough to fill up the shrinkage cavity in the ingot.

The ingots usually remain at the pouring platform for 1 to 2 hours, depending on the size of the ingot, to permit solidification of the greater part of the ingot. They are then sent to the stripper, enroute to the rolling mills or forge department.

Special pouring techniques have been developed for the removal of hydrogen and oxygen from the liquid steel. In these techniques, the liquid steel passes into another ladle or an ingot mold within an evacuated chamber. The high vacuum causes the gases H_2 and CO to leave the liquid steel, as discussed in Chapter 18.

Repairs to Furnace Bottom and Banks—After the furnace is tapped, it is tilted back to its stationary operating position, the doors opened to permit smoke and fumes to clear out, and the furnace is inspected for damaged areas on the banks, bottom, roof and around the tap hole, or any other location where repairs may be needed; also for furnace skulls. The reducing slag cuts the basic lining and it usually is necessary to make up the "cinder line" where it has been eroded by the slag. If the refractory lining requires repairs, the patching is done immediately to allow the material to be sintered into place by the heat of the furnace.

Electrode Adjustments—If the electrodes are not sufficiently long to finish the next heat, there will be a delay during the making of the heat while the necessary adjustments are being made to the electrodes. The usual practice, therefore, after making repairs to the furnace, is to run the electrodes down until they are a short distance from the bottom to enable the operator to decide how much longer the electrodes will last. Adjustments are made either by adding new sections to the tops of the present electrodes or by allowing the electrodes to slip down through the holder to the desired position as the holder is raised, provided there is sufficient electrode extending above the holder to permit this to be done.

SLAG CONTROL IN THE BASIC PROCESS

The preceding discussions on slags indicate that slag control is a very important factor in electric-furnace steel production. The electric-arc furnace permits the slags to be controlled to meet almost any desired characteristic, a fact that is the real basis of the flexibility of the arc furnace.

As pointed out, the function of the melt-down slag is to oxidize carbon and phosphorus out of the steel and to remove some sulphur and nonmetallic substances. The lime-silica ratio should be between 2.2 and 3.0. The iron-oxide content of the slag varies with the carbon in the steel at the end of the boil, and may range from 13.0 to 20.0 per cent for medium-carbon steels. A typical composition of a melt-down slag is as follows:

Constituent	Per Cent
Lime, CaO	40.9
Silica, SiO$_2$	13.4
Iron Oxide, FeO	14.8
Alumina, Al$_2$O$_3$	3.5
Magnesia, MgO	8.2
Manganous Oxide, MnO	12.7
Phosphorus Pentoxide, P$_2$O$_5$	0.6
Sulphur, S	0.1

Lime-silica ratio and iron oxide content can be estimated from the appearance of slag "pancakes," and a skilled operator can judge these values very closely. A "pancake" is a slag sample prepared by pouring molten slag into a small, flat iron dish possibly 4 inches in diameter and ½ inch deep. In solidifying, the "pancake" acquires visible markings characteristic of its composition.

The refining slag removes dissolved oxides from the bath, protects alloy additions from oxidation, and removes sulphur. This slag is black to light gray in color, according to the amount of carbide present, and disintegrates or slakes to powder upon cooling. A typical composition of such a chemically reducing carbidic refining slag is as follows:

Constituent	Per Cent
Lime, CaO	67.8
Silica, SiO$_2$	22.4
Iron Oxide, FeO	0.5
Alumina, Al$_2$O$_3$	0.5
Magnesia, MgO	6.9
Manganous Oxide, MnO	0.2
Sulphur, S	0.3
Calcium Carbide, CaC$_2$	1.5
Chromium Oxide, Cr$_2$O$_3$	0.4

It is essential that furnace doors and openings be closed tightly if a good reducing slag is to be maintained. If a heat is too hot, the carbidic property of a slag will be lost very quickly. The carbon pick-up from such slags is fairly high and close checking must be maintained.

With low-carbon steels (0.15 per cent carbon or less), the carbide slag is modified by using a higher lime and lower coke ratio. In making low-carbon heats of 0.08 per cent carbon or less, crushed ferrosilicon or aluminum is substituted for carbon in the slag, forming calcium silicate or calcium aluminate.

Following is a typical composition of a lime-silica slag with no carbon added:

Constituent	Per Cent
Lime, CaO	57.9
Silica, SiO$_2$	27.5
Alumina, Al$_2$O$_3$	3.7
Iron and Manganous Oxide, FeO and MnO	1.0
Magnesia, MgO	7.7
Chromium Oxide, Cr$_2$O$_3$	0.3

The above slag is white and, when cooled, will disintegrate to a powder. For 0.12 per cent carbon and lower stainless-steel heats, lime-silica and lime-alumina slags are used because they are carbon-free and easy to manage.

SECTION 4

THE ACID ELECTRIC-ARC FURNACE PROCESS

The acid electric-furnace process is, as previously mentioned, employed chiefly for the production of steel for castings by the foundry industry. Four major variations of the acid process are used: (1) partial oxidation, (2) complete oxidation (with a single slag), (3) complete oxidation with silicon reduction, and (4) double-slag practice.

Partial oxidation practice is used chiefly to produce low-priced steel castings that do not require any acceptance tests other than superficial surface inspection, because it is the cheapest method of making steel for such castings. The double-slag process is employed where it is desirable to have positive control to keep the FeO content of the finishing slag to a low value (about 10 per cent). Silicon in the slag can be reduced to enter the metal in acid-electric practice, and this procedure is employed in European practice but is not generally followed in this country.

The great majority of all American steel foundries employ the complete-oxidation process, and this method will be taken as the basis for the ensuing discussion.

With the exception of selection of scrap (which must have a low phosphorus and sulphur content), the melting down of the charge in the acid electric furnace is similar to that of the basic electric furnace. As with the basic electric furnace, the electrodes melt the scrap and bore their way through to the hearth of the furnace. If the pool of molten metal formed on the bottom does not cover sufficient area to extend beyond the area covered by the electrodes, the arc will act on the sand in the hearth of the furnace. The conductivity of a nonmetal increases with temperature; consequently, the furnace hearth is a fairly good conductor of electricity if it is hot. This working on the hearth or boring a hole into the hearth by the electrodes is called "pulling bottom" and generally is indicated by the appearance of white smoke accompanied by bright yellow flames around the electrode ports. When this occurs, the electrodes should be raised out of the charge and enough clean scrap added and melted to form a pool extending out from under the electrodes. If enough heavy scrap is used and is packed compactly enough on the bottom of the furnace, there is very little danger of pulling bottom.

Working the Heat—As soon as the charge is melted or nearly all melted, it is time to start working the heat. A little iron ore and silica sand should be spread over the bath at this time. If, as is often the case, a high percentage of returned foundry scrap is charged, very little silica sand need be added, because the oxidation of silicon and manganese in the scrap will form almost enough slag. Some iron also will be oxidized in melting down, forming FeO which will contribute to the slag. Enough slag-making material should be added to each heat to form a layer covering the metal at least ⅛ of an inch thick.

Although such a thin layer of slag may cause some difficulties, it is never advisable to have more slag on the metal than necessary at any time, because this will slow down the deoxidation of the steel. If "slag" (the term often used for silica sand in acid furnace practice) is not added, the bath will take silica from the hearth.

Slag samples taken from the furnace at melt-down should have a glassy, black color, indicating a high iron-oxide (FeO) content, which is necessary if a boil is to be expected later. A sample of the metal should be taken from the furnace at the same time and the carbon content determined. The carbon content after melt-down, as in the basic process, should be higher than the carbon desired in the finished steel after it has been killed by additions of silicon and manganese near the end of the heat. The excess carbon will be removed by the boil.

If the slag test taken from the furnace has a brown or greenish color instead of black, it is an indication that there is insufficient FeO present. Ore is then added shovel by shovel-full until a black slag results. If the charge is made up of a large percentage of returned scrap, the ore should be added before all of the scrap is melted. The FeO added in this way will be taken up by the bath and the oxygen will react with silicon and manganese in the melting metal to form silicon dioxide (SiO_2) and manganous oxide (MnO), respectively. Because these oxides are of lower specific gravity than the molten metal, they will rise to the top of the bath, and because of their chemical affinity for each other—one being an "acid" and the other a "base"—they will unite to form slag.

After the bath is covered with a black or oxidizing slag and the carbon content is high enough, the temperature should be increased until the steel is hot enough to boil. The "boil" is the reaction between the carbon and oxygen dissolved in the steel, and is necessary in the manufacture of clean, high-quality steel.

Enough ore and carbon should have been in the bath, either naturally or by additions, to maintain the boil for at least ten minutes. A sample of the metal is taken from the bath and the carbon determined by a fracture test or by some rapid analytical test. Silicon and manganese should then be added as ferroalloys for deoxidation and the heat tapped soon after they are melted completely and diffused through the bath.

The temperature at which the steel is tapped from the furnace depends largely on the size of the castings to be poured and the equipment for handling the molten metal. If poured into many small castings the steel must be hot, while it may be about 100° F colder when tapped from the furnace if the steel is poured directly from a large ladle into a mold for a large casting.

The preceding discussion refers specifically to production of plain or carbon steel for casting. Alloy cast steels are coming more and more into use, and present a new problem. Fortunately, three of the alloys commonly used in steel-foundry practice, copper, nickel and molybdenum, can be added at any time without loss due to oxidation and subsequent absorption by the slag during the steelmaking process. If these alloys are not added with the cold charge, they should be added from 15 to 30 minutes before the heat is tapped to give ample time for their solution and uniform distribution throughout the bath of molten metal.

When the steel ordered calls for manganese in excess of 1.25 per cent, it is very difficult to maintain this manganese content in the metal under an acid slag. It is, therefore, advisable at times to add lime to the slag before tapping, thus decreasing its acidity and ability to absorb manganese.

Chromium presents a problem, as it is easily oxidized. It usually is added as ferrochromium to the bath after the steel has been deoxidized (just after the final silicon addition).

Alloys such as aluminum, titanium, zirconium, vanadium and boron are added in the ladle. The common practice is to add these alloys in paper sacks, thrown into the ladle as the steel is being tapped so that the sack hits the metal stream.

SECTION 5

INDUCTION ELECTRIC-FURNACE PROCESSES

In most steel plants using induction furnaces, the melting procedure is essentially a crucible or "dead-melt" process. The charge is selected carefully to produce the composition desired in the finished steel with a minimum of further additions except, possibly, small amounts of ferroalloys as final deoxidizers.

The charge may consist of a single lump of metal, a number of small pieces of selected steel scrap, or even turnings or other light scrap with which is mixed a moderate amount of larger pieces to provide initial conditions which are favorable to the generation of heat. The charge is collected in pans placed on the working platform and either is dropped into the furnace through the top opening by tipping the pan, or by raking the pieces out of the pan and into the furnace. If the charge consists of pieces of scrap of varying size, the larger pieces are charged first, and the smaller pieces are packed about them as closely as possible. Even with the closest packing it is sometimes necessary to add some of the charge as the melting progresses. As a rule, no refining is attempted in acid-lined furnaces, and it is seldom tried in a basic-lined furnace. If the furnace is equipped with a tight cover over the crucible, very little oxidation occurs during melting. Such a cover also serves to prevent cooling by radiation of heat from the surface of the molten metal. Hence, from the standpoint of heat loss, the use of a slag covering to protect the metal is unnecessary. Slags are being used successfully both during melt-down and refining, in special cases.

Melting the Charge—As soon as the furnace is charged, the switches admitting the primary high-frequency current to the coil of the furnace are closed. Immediately, the rapidly changing magnetic field at high flux density generates heavy secondary currents in the charge which are converted into heat by the electrical resistance of the charge itself. This heat is developed mainly in the outer rim of the metal in the charge, but is carried quickly to the center by conduction. Soon a pool of molten metal forms in the bottom, causing the charge to sink and at this point, any of the charge remaining is added. The current exerts a strong **motor effect** upon the liquid metal, which accelerates the melting by washing the still-solid part of the charge with molten metal, thoroughly mixing the metal as it is melted. This motion of the metal continues after all the charge is melted, in eddies giving the bath a convex surface, and varies in intensity with the power input. As the convex surface is not a favorable condition for slag treatment, the power input always is decreased to flatten the convexity and reduce the circulation rate when refining under either an oxidizing or a reducing slag. The flow of the liquid metal, even though less vigorous, then becomes a favorable condition, accelerating the purification reactions by constantly bringing new metal into close contact with the slag. When no purifying is attempted, the chief metallurgical advantages of the process are attributable to the stirring action, which promotes the uniformity of the product, the control over the super-heat or temperature above that of the melting point, and the opportunity afforded by the conditions of the melt to control deoxidation through proper additions. As soon as the charge has "melted clear," and refining actions have ceased, any objectionable slag is skimmed off, and the deoxidizers or other necessary alloying elements are added. When these additions have melted and become diffused in the bath, the power input may be increased to bring the temperature of the metal up to the point most desirable for pouring. The current then is turned off and the furnace is tilted for pouring, either directly into ingot molds or into a ladle, the ladle being used with the larger furnaces. As soon as pouring has ceased, any slag adhering to the wall of the crucible is scraped out and the furnace is righted for charging again.

Advantages of Induction Melting—Induction furnaces (Figure **17**—12) are relatively low in cost, as compared to other types of melting units and, as a result, several furnaces for operation from a single frequency changer can be installed at little extra expense, and furnaces of various capacities can be

FIG. **17**—12. Dual installation of coreless electric induction melting furnaces, with control panel in background. (Courtesy, Allis-Chalmers Mfg. Co.)

used as required or individual furnaces can be retained for making melts of special alloys without danger of contamination or the necessity of making "wash heats." Among other advantages, there is very little heat radiated from the furnaces as they are water cooled, and there is practically no noise attending their operation.

This type of furnace requires about 650 kwh. of input power per ton of molten metal and heats are melted in about an hour to an hour and fifteen minutes.

For the melting of high-alloy chromium steels, there is quite an advantage in using the induction type of furnace because the highest temperature to which the scrap is subjected is that of the bath. In the arc furnace the temperature of the arc is above 7200° F (4000° C) and vaporizes the chromium in exposed scrap, causing a loss of up to 15 per cent of this element. Since the capacities of induction furnaces have been limited to about three tons, the popular range being from 200 to 2000 pounds, this type of furnace is used only for small heats.

In remelting alloy-steel scrap in these furnaces, it is possible to make melts in less time than with other methods of melting and this minimizes loss of valuable alloying elements by oxidation. Heat is induced in the metal by eddy-currents due to circulating electrical currents of high magnitude. Where heat must be absorbed from radiant energy, as in other types of furnaces, there is a limit to the rate at which the metal charge can absorb heat.

Molten metal in an induction furnace is caused to circulate automatically by electromagnetic action. When alloy additions are made to a molten charge, the stirring action results in creating a homogeneous product in a minimum of time. Due to the turbulent action in the bath and the skim slag, it is possible to get accurate temperature readings with a radiation pyrometer and, by electronic control, hold the bath temperature within ±5° F. This is an advantage when pouring small castings, when thirty minutes or more are required to empty the furnace.

Up to a few years ago, the standard equipment used to supply power to these induction furnaces was a rotary motor-generator set, which supplied a frequency in the neighborhood of 1,000 cycles. Lately, mercury-arc frequency changers have been used which have several advantages; the efficiency is higher than that of motor-generator sets and the static device presents no problems in vibration or air ventilation, and the cost is kept to a minimum. Another feature of this type of melting is that the frequency output is determined by the output circuit. If the frequency characteristic of the circuit changes during operation, the mercury-arc inverter automatically will supply the frequency required by the melting circuit.

Special alloys can be produced by melting in a vacuum, or under pressure in an inert-gas atmosphere, by enclosing the entire coreless induction furnace and mold in an airtight container which can be evacuated or put under pressure. When melting is complete, the molten contents of the furnace are poured into the mold; this is accomplished entirely by control elements outside the container that make it possible to tilt the container for pouring the furnace without opening the container. After the metal solidifies, the container can be opened for emptying the mold and recharging the furnace. Section 6 of this chapter gives further details on vacuum and atmosphere melting.

SECTION 6

VACUUM, ATMOSPHERE AND CONSUMABLE-ELECTRODE MELTING

Methods have been developed for commercial melting of metals and alloys of certain types in vacuum or under controlled atmospheres. Vacuum-melting techniques are employed in the case of some steels to obtain improved physical and mechanical properties unobtainable in any other way. Some other metals, notably titanium, cannot be melted successfully at all except under such conditions. Vacuum furnaces have been heated by electrical induction, by the electric-arc principle, by electrical resistance, and by gas: however, only the two first-named have been used on any sizeable scale for melting steels and this discussion will be confined to processes employing one or the other of these two principles.

Vacuum and Atmosphere Melting in Induction Furnaces—This method employs a high-frequency coreless induction unit (see Section 5), enclosed in a container or tank which can be either evacuated or filled with an atmosphere of any desired composition and pressure. Provision is made by suitable electrical and mechanical mechanisms and controls for making additions to the melt and for tilting the furnace after melting to pour its molten contents into the ingot mold which also is enclosed in the tank or container (Figure 17—13). Most of the vacuum furnaces in operation in the United States are of one-quarter and one-half ton capacity, but larger units melting up to five tons have been proved practicable.

The electrical frequency employed by the coreless induction furnaces for vacuum and atmosphere melting depends upon the capacity of the melting unit, as it does in the case of such furnaces used in ordinary melting processes. Most of the crucibles for vacuum melting have basic linings.

While vacuum melting often has been employed simply as a remelting operation for very pure materials or as the first stage in duplex refining operations involving remelting of the product from the vacuum induction furnace in a vacuum consumable-electrode furnace, it is more generally useful in those applications where some refining also is accomplished. Oxygen, nitrogen and hydrogen can be removed from

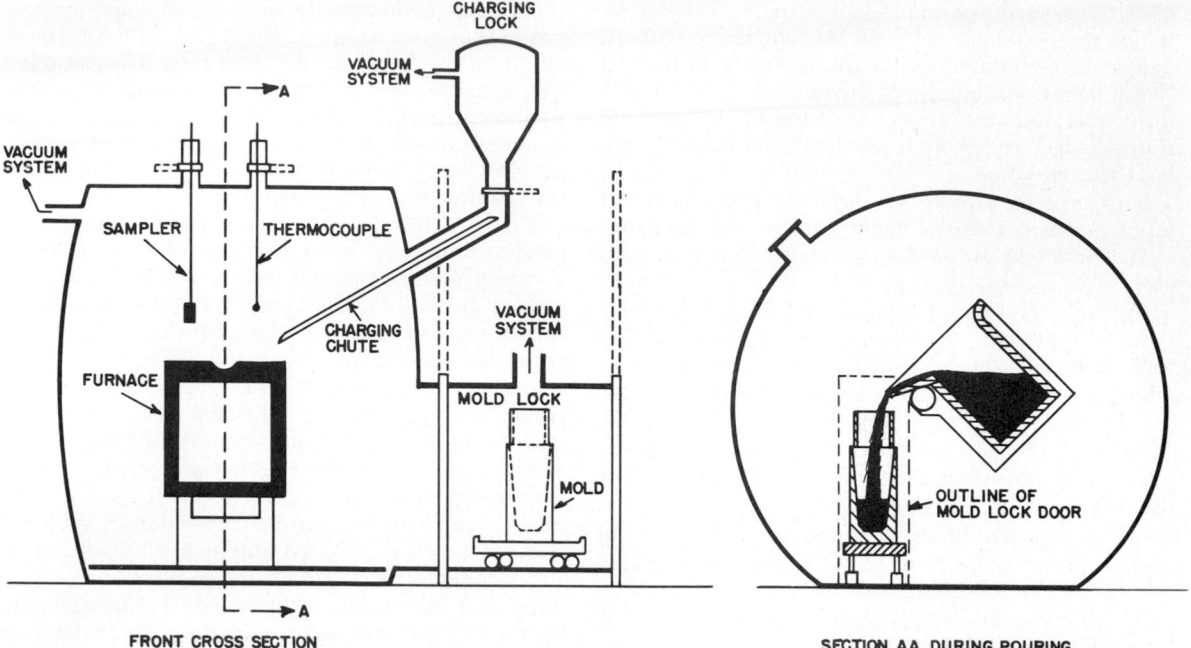

FRONT CROSS SECTION   SECTION AA DURING POURING

Fig. 17—13. Schematic arrangement of furnace in vacuum chamber equipped with charging and mold locks, for vacuum induction melting.

the molten metal in vacuum melting as well as carbon when alloys having very low carbon content are being produced (i.e., some of the stainless steels).

The control of pressure and composition of the gas over a melt makes it possible to deoxidize the melt with carbon or hydrogen, both of which produce gaseous deoxidation products, thus preventing the formation of solid non-metallic inclusions in the finished steel. Also, when melting in a vacuum, the absence of nitrogen from the atmosphere over the melt prevents formation of nitrides and carbonitrides that appear in many steels and high-temperature alloys melted under ordinary atmospheric conditions. The exclusion of oxygen by vacuum melting prevents oxidation losses and permits very close control of the composition of alloys containing easily-oxidized components.

The volatility of certain alloying elements such as chromium, aluminum and manganese may result in high losses of these elements if they are added to steel under a high vacuum. These losses may be minimized by replacing the vacuum with an inert gas as the atmosphere over the melt during the period when such additions are being made.

Consumable-Electrode Melting (in Vacuum)— While the consumable-electrode melting process has other applications, only its use in the production of special steels will be considered here. This is a refining process used to produce special-quality alloy and stainless steels (originally produced by any suitable conventional steelmaking process) by casting or forging them into an electrode that is remelted in a vacuum. Some of the special steels include bearing steels, heat-resistant alloys, ultra-high-strength missile and aircraft steels, and rotor steels.

Figures 17—14 and 17—15 show a consumable-electrode furnace and the principle of its operation, respectively. The furnace in Figure 17—14 is capable of producing 32-inch diameter round ingots weighing up to 20,500 lb.: larger furnaces are in operation that produce ingots as large as 50 inches in diameter and weighing as much as 40,000 lb.

As shown in Figure 17—15, a consumable-electrode furnace consists of two sections: a water-cooled tank above ground level that encloses the electrode, and a water-cooled copper mold in the lower section below ground level in which melting and solidification of the ingot takes place. Direct current is employed for melting. The electrode usually is connected to the negative and the copper mold to the positive terminals of the electrical circuit.

Steam-ejector vacuum pumps first evacuate the furnace to an absolute pressure of about 5 microns of mercury. Power is then turned on, and an arc is struck between the electrode and a starting block that is placed in the mold before the operation begins. Heat from the arc progressively melts the end of the electrode. Melted metal is transferred across the arc and deposited in a shallow pool of molten metal on the top surface of the ingot being built up in the mold. Solidification of the melted metal takes place almost immediately. The rate of descent of the electrode is automatically controlled to maintain the proper distance to maintain the arc between the end of the electrode and the top of the ingot as the end of the electrode is "consumed" or melts away.

The following benefits accrue to steel that has been remelted by this process:

(1) Contents of gases (hydrogen, oxygen, and nitrogen) are much reduced.

FIG. **17—14.** Worker checking alignment of the electrode in a consumable-electrode vacuum melting furnace in a United States Steel Corporation plant, prior to start of remelting operation.

(2) Cleanliness of steel is improved (fewer non-metallic inclusions).

(3) Center porosity and segregation in the ingot resulting from the process are practically eliminated.

(4) Hot workability of the metal is improved.

(5) Mechanical properties of the remelted steel (ductility, impact strength, fatigue strength, creep and rupture strength) at both room temperature and at elevated temperature are improved.

Status of Vacuum and Atmosphere Melting—The entire subject of vacuum melting of steels is still in the relatively early stages of development. As work continues with this technique, it will be possible to compare the characteristics of metals and alloys melted under reduced pressure or controlled atmosphere with those of materials melted in air by ordinary methods. Vacuum and atmosphere melting of steels and other ferrous alloys will grow in proportion to the need for metals possessing whatever special properties may be developed by these techniques.

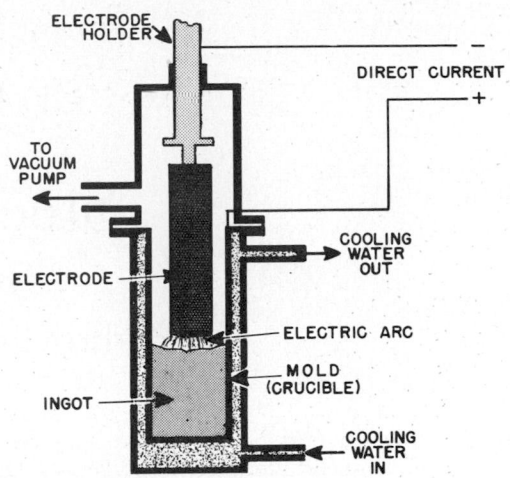

FIG. **17—15.** Schematic representation of the principles of design and operation of a consumable-electrode furnace for the remelting of steels in a vacuum.

Bibliography

Am. Institute of Mining, Metallurgical and Petroleum Engineers, Electric Furnace Steel Conference Proc. **1,** 1943-date (published annually).

Blakeslee, R. N. and G. V. Luerssen, The induction furnace process of steel melting. Am. Society for Metals, Metals handbook, 1948 ed., pp. 332-334. Cleveland, The Society, 1948.

Campbell, D. F., High-frequency steel furnaces. Iron and Steel Institute Journal **122,** 85-94; discussion, correspondence, and author's reply, 95-109 (1930).

Durand, S. R., Mercury arc frequency changing equipment for induction heating. Iron and Steel Engineer **24,** 102-110 (April 1947).

Ess, T. J., The modern arc furnace. Iron and Steel Engineer **21,** 7AF-58AF (Feb. 1944).

Geiselman, R. A., C. C. Levy, and W. R. Harris, Rotating regulator for arc furnaces. Electrical Engineering **62,** 671-674 (1943).

Montgomery, T. B., Control method for electric arc furnaces. Steel **111,** 145, 148, 150, 174 (Sept. 14, 1942).

Orehoski, M. A., and J. N. Hornak, Effect of Vacuum stream degassing on properties of forging steels. Electric Furnace Steel Conference Proc. 1958, 68-83; published by Am. Institute of Mining, Metallurgical and Petroleum Engineers, New York.

Shaad, G. E., Amplidynes for arc-furnace control. Blast Furnace and Steel Plant **31,** 879-882 (1943).

Sims, C. E., editor, Electric furnace steelmaking. Vols. I and II, Interscience Publishers, New York, 1962.

Wissmann, C. C., Acid electric furnace steelmaking practice. Cleveland, Am. Society for Metals, 1947.

CHAPTER 18

Steel Ingots

SECTION 1

INGOT CHARACTERISTICS

Ingots—After a heat of steel is properly refined either in an open-hearth furnace, an oxygen-steelmaking furnace, a Bessemer converter, or an electric furnace, the liquid steel is tapped into a refractory-lined open-topped vessel called a **steel ladle.** Alloying materials and deoxidizers may be added during the tapping of a heat. The steel ladle has an off-center opening in its bottom equipped with a nozzle, a stopper rod assembly, and a mechanism for raising and lowering the stopper-rod assembly to open and close the opening. The ladle is moved by an overhead crane to a pouring platform where the steel is then poured or teemed into a series of molds of the desired dimensions. The steel solidifies in each of the molds to form a casting called an **ingot.** During the course of solidification and cooling, the surface of an ingot is colder than its interior. In fact, for some types of steel, the centers of ingots are still molten during the subsequent stripping operation, in which the ingots are removed from the molds.

The stripped ingots are placed in a tightly covered soaking pit that is equipped with fuel burners to supply heat to the pit when necessary. There, the ingots are heated to the desired temperature for rolling and held a suitable time at that temperature ("soaked") so as to equalize the temperature throughout the cross-section of the ingots. The rolling of ingots with liquid centers would be undesirable since this would produce internal discontinuities. Modern soaking pits are, in reality, special heating furnaces, as described in Chapter 21. However, in early steel-processing practices, the soaking pits functioned differently. It was the custom at that time to strip the ingots from the molds as soon as possible after pouring and to place them in tightly covered holes or pits in the ground, where the heat from the interior (sometimes molten) of the ingot was conveyed to the relatively colder surface. This procedure not only equalized temperature throughout the ingots, but also supplied heat to the pits so that, with careful manipulation, ingots could be heated and maintained at the proper rolling temperature. This early process was

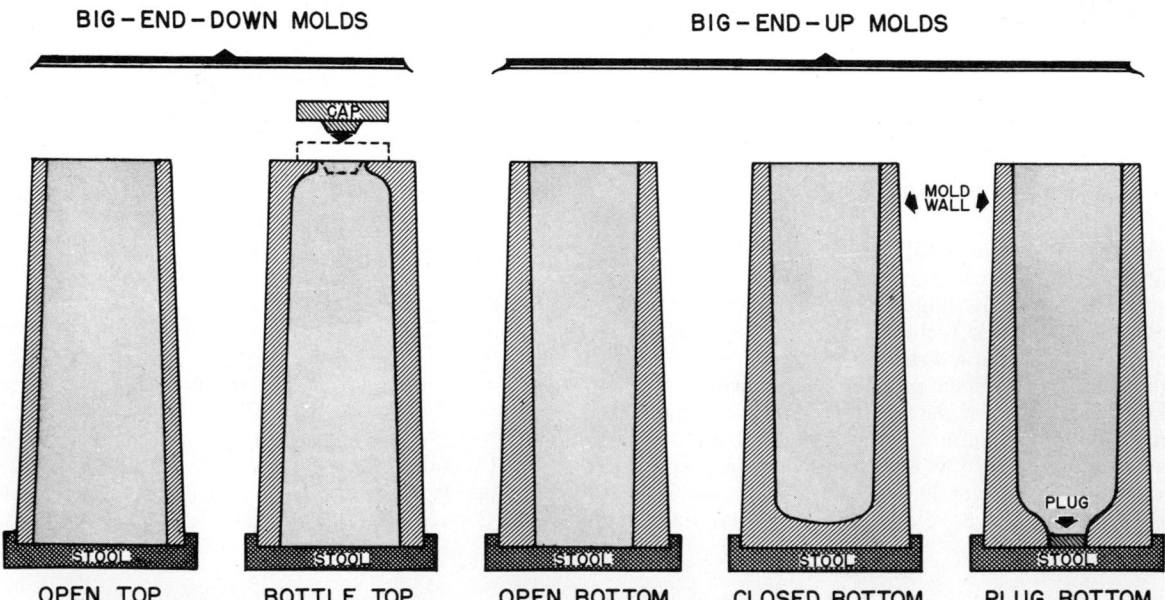

FIG. 18—1. Cross-sections (not to scale) of the five principal types of ingot molds. Molds usually are cast from molten pig iron directly from the blast furnace.

called **soaking**; hence the designation soaking pits.

Ingot Characteristics—An ideal ingot would be one that was homogeneous both physically and chemically. It would have a fine, equiaxed crystal structure, and would be free of chemical segregation, nonmetallic inclusions, and cavities. Unfortunately, the natural laws that govern the solidification of liquid metal operate against attainment of the ideal condition and, instead, ingots develop within their interiors the well-known phenomena of pipe, blowholes, chemical segregation, nonmetallic segregation, columnar crystal structure, and internal fissures. Added to these manifestations of internal non-uniformity are detrimental surface occurrences such as ingot cracks, seams, and scabs. For a proper understanding of such phenomena, a brief description of the mechanism of ingot solidification is warranted.

Type of Ingot Molds—Ingot molds that are in common use are tall box-like containers made of cast iron and weigh from about 1 to 1.5 times as much as the ingots that are cast in them. The mold cavity for receiving the molten steel is usually tapered from the top to the bottom of the mold, primarily to facilitate stripping of the ingot. As shown in Figure 18—1, the taper gives rise to the two principal types of molds: **big-end-down** and **big-end-up**. The big-end-down molds are further classified as **open-top** and **bottle-top**; the big-end-up molds as **open-bottom**, **closed-bottom**, and **plug-bottom**. The mold **stool** serves as the bottom closure for the mold cavity in all big-end-down molds and in the open-bottom big-end-up molds. The mold itself provides the bottom closure in the closed-bottom big-end-up mold. In the plug-bottom big-end-up mold, the interior is constricted at the bottom to a small, circular opening that is closed with a refractory or metal plug prior to casting (see Figure 18—1). Although erosion from impingement of the pouring stream is expected to be confined to the plug in the plug-bottom mold, some erosion of the mold occurs because the plug is too small in diameter to completely protect the bottom. Also, while the small opening in the bottom originally was intended to facilitate the use of a plunger to loosen ingots that might stick in the molds, most plants do not use a bottom plunger: however, the plug-hole facilitates cleaning and such molds are preferred over closed-bottom molds for this reason.

The inner walls of molds may be **plain sided, corrugated**, or **fluted**.

Types of Steel—As the mold is being filled with molten steel, the metal next to the mold walls and mold stool is chilled by contact with the cold surfaces and solidifies in these regions to form an ingot **shell** or ingot **skin**. Early during solidification, the ingot skin contracts as it cools and forms an **air gap** between itself and the mold wall: this gap reduces the rate at which heat can be transferred from the steel to the mold and thence to the atmosphere. Also, as solidification proceeds, the thermal gradients become less steep. The thickness of the ingot skin (frozen zone) increases rapidly at first but slows down greatly as solidification proceeds.

The solubility of gases in molten steel decreases with decreasing temperatures, especially when the steel changes from the liquid phase to the solid phase. During the solidification of ingots, the gases are liberated in amounts dependent upon the amount of gases originally present in the molten steel. Oxygen is the chief gas that is involved. In the form of FeO, it reacts with carbon in the steel and produces carbon monoxide that is evolved from the steel. The addition of deoxidizing agents to the liquid steel decreases the amount of dissolved oxygen, and the degree of deoxidation establishes four types of steel—killed, semikilled, capped, and rimmed—to be discussed later.

Time for Solidification of Ingots—The rate at which heat is extracted from an ingot and, hence, the rate of solidification, is affected by many factors, some of which are the thickness, shape, and temperature of the mold; the amount of superheat of the liquid steel; the cross-section of the ingot; the type of steel; and the chemical composition of the steel. Figure 18—2 shows the idealized solidification pattern of a 32-inch by 32-inch killed-steel ingot. The lines marked

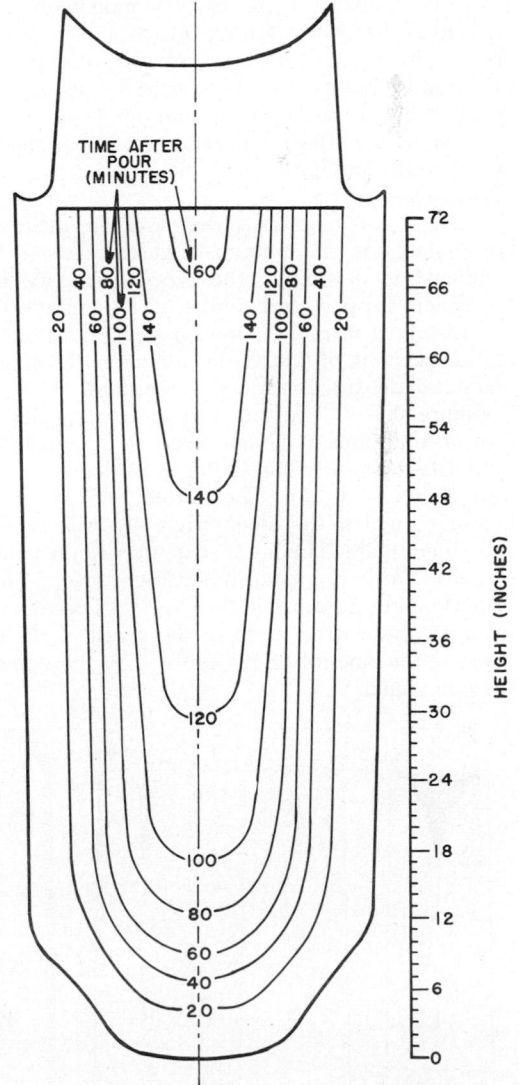

Fɪɢ. **18**—2. Solidification pattern of 32-inch by 32-inch hot-topped big-end-up ingot of killed steel.

20, 40, 60, etc., indicate the progress of ingot solidification for the corresponding number of minutes that had elapsed after pouring. The location of these lines was established on the basis of data obtained by casting a series of identical ingots and then dumping each ingot after progessive predetermined intervals to pour out the remaining liquid steel. The solidified shells were then removed from the molds and split vertically for examination and study. The ingots used in the experiment had the following chemical composition:

Element	Per Cent
C	0.83
Mn	0.77
P	0.014
S	0.024
Si	0.18
Ni	2.08
Cr	0.15

The relationships for determining the comparative rates of ingot solidification for various sizes and shapes are complex and outside the scope of this book.

SECTION 2

TYPES OF INGOT STRUCTURES

When molten steel cools to the temperature range in which it begins to solidify, the solubility of gases dissolved in the steel decreases and the excess gases are expelled from the metal. Of greater importance, the chemical equilibrium between carbon and oxygen changes with decreasing temperatures, so that the two elements react to form carbon monoxide that is evolved as the system attempts to attain a new equilibrium. Molten steel does not solidify at one definite temperature but over a temperature range, so that the gases evolved from still-liquid portions may be trapped at solid-liquid interfaces of the remaining liquid with previously solidified metal to produce **blowholes.**

The amount of gases, chiefly oxygen, dissolved in liquid steel and the amount of gases released during solidification determine the types of ingots: **killed, semikilled, capped,** and **rimmed.** The amount of oxygen dissolved in molten steel is dependent upon the carbon content of the steel and upon the type and amount of deoxidizers added to the steel.

Figure **18**—3 illustrates diagrammatically eight typical conditions of commercial ingots, cast in identical bottle-top molds, in relation to the degree of supression of gas evolution. The dotted line indicates the height to which the steel originally was poured in each ingot mold. The ingot structures range from that of a fully killed or dead-killed ingot (No. 1) to that of a violently rimming ingot (No. 8). The differences between these structures are the result of the differences in the amount of gas evolved by these ingots as they solidified.

The fully killed ingot (No. 1) evolved no gas, its top was slightly concave, and directly below the top was an intermittently bridged shrinkage cavity that is commonly called **pipe.** While fully killed steels are almost always poured in big-end-up molds that have refractory-type hot tops so as to confine the pipe cavity entirely to the hot-top portion that is later discarded, ingot No. 1 has been included here for comparative purposes.

A typical semikilled ingot is shown as ingot No. 2. In this ingot, only a slight amount of gas was evolved; however, the resulting blowholes were sufficient in volume to compensate fully for the shrinkage encountered during solidification. Ferrostatic pressure (hydraulic pressure exerted by liquid steel due to gravity) prevented the formation of blowholes in the lower half of the ingot. The pressure caused by the trapped gases in the blowholes was sufficient to bulge the surface of the ingot to produce a domed top.

Ingot No. 3 evolved more gas than ingot No. 2 during solidification. The resulting blowholes had a greater volume than that required to compensate for the shrinkage resulting from solidification. Some of the blowholes formed very close to the side surface in the top half of the ingot. Blowholes are undesirable so close to the ingot surface since they may result in surface defects upon subsequent heating and rolling, as discussed later under "Blowholes." Also, the gas pressure ruptured the initially frozen top surface of the ingot and forced liquid steel up through the rupture where it froze: this phenomenon is called **bleeding.**

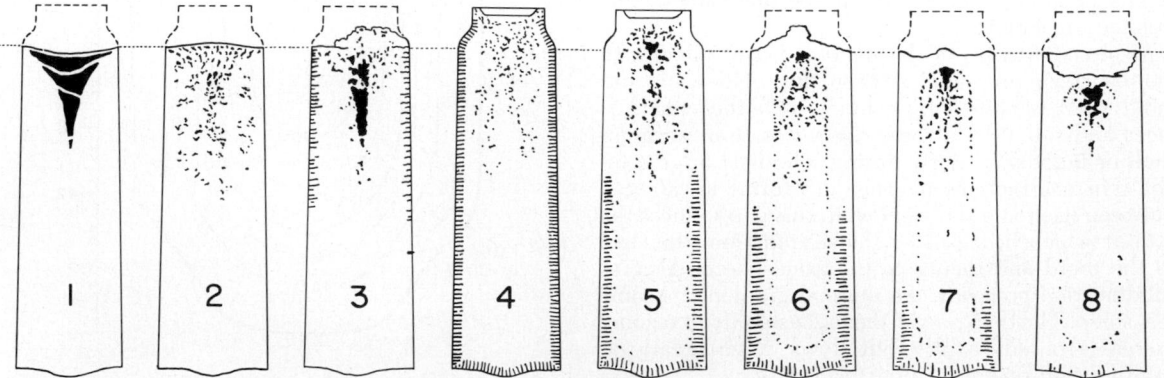

FIG. **18**—3. Series of ingot structures.

Ingot No. 4 evolved so much gas that the top ingot surface could not solidify immediately after pouring. Instead, numerous honeycomb blowholes formed very close to the side surface of the ingot, extending from top to bottom. The evolution of gas caused the steel to rise after pouring and produced a boiling action that is commonly called **rimming action**. This action was stopped by a metal cap secured to the top of the mold.

Ingot No. 5 represents a typical capped ingot. It evolved so much gas that the resulting strong upward currents along the sides in the upper half of the ingot swept away the gas bubbles that otherwise would have formed blowholes. Even in the lower half of the ingot, the blowholes could not form until the gas evolution had moderated somewhat. The result was that a thick solid skin formed first that was then followed by the zone containing the honeycomb blowholes. An ingot of this type would not have the interiors of its blowholes exposed to oxidation by scaling of the ingot surface during heating and soaking. Because this ingot No. 5 had fewer blowholes than did ingot No. 4, the steel rose less rapidly to the cap at the top of the mold.

Ingot No. 6 is a rimmed ingot, as are also ingots No. 7 and No. 8. In ingot No. 6, the evolution of gas, while greater than in ingot No. 5, was insufficient to prevent the honeycomb blowholes from exceeding in volume the amount required to offset solidification shrinkage. Therefore, the top surface of the ingot rose slightly as it froze in from the sides of the mold.

Ingot No. 7 represents a typical rimmed ingot in which gas evolution was so strong that the formation of blowholes was confined to only the lower quarter of the ingot. The apparent increase in volume due to blowholes offset the shrinkage that occurred during solidification. As a result, the top of the ingot did not rise or fall appreciably during solidification.

Ingot No. 8 illustrates a violently rimming ingot, typical of low-metalloid steel. Honeycomb blowholes could not form and the top surface of the ingot fell markedly during solidification.

The foregoing eight ingot structures were selected merely to illustrate a series of cast structures ranging from a fully killed steel to a fully rimmed steel. Included in the series were the four main types of ingots that are produced commercially: killed steel (No. 1), semikilled steel (No. 2), capped steel (No. 5), and rimmed steel (No. 7).

As was mentioned earlier, oxygen is the principal gas dissolved in steel that makes it possible to produce the various types of ingots. In the form of FeO, it reacts as follows with carbon during cooling and solidification:

$$FeO + C = Fe + CO \text{ (gas)}.$$

The reaction to the right of the equation may be explained as follows: at the tapping temperature, the iron oxide and carbon contents of the liquid steel are essentially in equilibrium; however, as the metal cools, the equilibrium is changed and the reaction proceeds toward the right of the equation in an attempt to restore the chemical balance of the system. Because cooling in the mold is continuous, a new state of equilibrium is not attained, and gases continue to be evolved. The last gases to be evolved may not be able to rise in the ingot, and may collect as bubbles to form blowholes.

Since the amount of oxygen dissolved in liquid steel decreases with increasing carbon content, it becomes apparent that rimmed or capped ingots, that require the evolution of large amounts of gas, cannot be produced if too much carbon is present. The practical upper limit of carbon content for such steels is 0.30 per cent. Killed and semikilled ingots can be produced in steels of low carbon and high oxygen contents by adding deoxidizers to the liquid steel to react with and remove the oxygen. However, in such low-carbon steels, the necessarily large amounts of deoxidizers to be added not only would add to the cost of the steel, but also would produce an excessive number of nonmetallic inclusions representing the products of the deoxidation reactions. Therefore, there are often practical advantages in producing the lower carbon steels by rimmed or capped practice, and the higher carbon steels by semikilled or killed practice.

Pipe—The shrinkage cavity, or pipe, located in the upper central portion of the ingot, is largest and most deeply located in the two extremes of ingot structure represented by ingots Nos. 1 and 8 in Figure 18—3. Less extreme structures such as No. 2 (semikilled) or No. 7 (strongly rimming) exhibit this tendency to a lesser extent, while the product of an ingot of intermediate structure such as No. 5 (capped) will be practically free from pipe after rolling. Big-end-down killed ingots (poured without a hot top) often have the lower, unoxidized portion of the pipe cavity below the bridges clean enough to be welded completely shut by pressure and deformation of the steel during rolling. This is particularly true for steels of higher carbon content or for steels that are extensively reduced during rolling, as in the lighter flat-rolled products. A satisfactory yield of sound rolled product often can be obtained with such steels without taking special steps to prevent the formation of pipe.

If assurance of complete freedom from pipe is required, it is accomplished best in killed-steel ingots by making them big-end-up with a hot top, as shown in Figure 18—4 (No. 1). This figure also illustrates the extent of pipe in hot-topped and non-hot-topped ingots of the big-end-down and big-end-up types. The refractory material with which the hot top is constructed or lined absorbs heat less rapidly than the cast iron of the mold, so that the top of the ingot remains molten until after the remainder of the ingot has solidified, thus furnishing an overlying pool of liquid steel that feeds down into the portions of the ingot below the hot top to overcome the shrinkage due to solidification. By using big-end-up molds, this feeding is made still more effective.

To improve the feeding of metal by hot tops, especially during the late stages of solidification, efforts are directed toward keeping the metal pool in hot tops liquid as long as possible. Several methods are used to do this. One method is to use a highly insulating refractory material in the hot top. Another method is to use exothermic materials as part of the

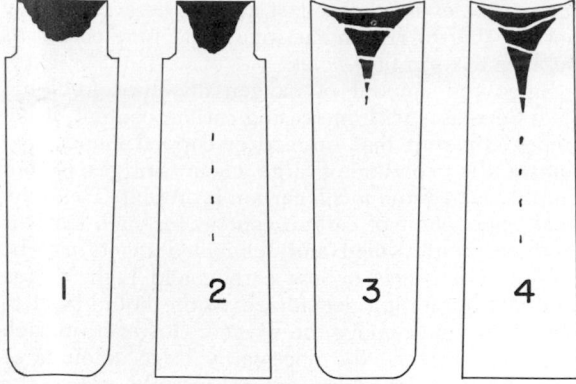

Fig. 18—4. Types of killed ingots.

1. Big-end-up, hot-topped.
2. Big-end-down, hot-topped.
3. Big-end-up, not hot-topped.
4. Big-end-down, not hot-topped.

hot top and as a covering over the top of the steel. Still another method is to employ an electric arc to provide heat to the top of a non-hot-topped ingot.

Blowholes—In all except killed-steel ingots, the evolution of gas produces cavities of roughly cylindrical shape (skin or honeycomb blowholes) or spherical shape (located deeper in the ingot). Except for the ones located within several inches of the top of the ingot, such blowholes tend to have interiors free of an oxide coating and clean enough to weld easily and completely during rolling. However, if the blowholes extend to the surface of an ingot, or lie at such shallow depth beneath the surface as to become exposed by scaling of the ingot surface during heating in the soaking pits, they can become oxidized and will not weld; instead, they may produce numerous seams in the rolled product. Properly made ingots, therefore, will have gas evolution during solidification so controlled that there will be a skin of adequate thickness over those blowholes closest to the surface. The fact that blowholes serve a useful purpose in diminishing or preventing the formation of pipe and improving ingot yield already has been mentioned.

Segregation—The amount of segregation found in an ingot depends upon several factors, some of which are the chemical composition of the steel, the type of ingot (killed, semikilled, capped, or rimmed), and the ingot size. A detailed explanation of segregation, crystal formation, and solidification rates of ingots is outside the scope of this discussion. In general, the metal that solidifies very rapidly close to the mold wall (the **chill zone**) has about the same chemical composition as the liquid metal entering the mold. However, as the rate of solidification decreases, the mechanism of solidification is such that crystals of purer metal solidify first: that is to say, the first crystals to form contain less carbon, manganese, phosphorus, sulphur, and other elements than the liquid steel from which they formed, and the remaining liquid is enriched by these elements that are continually being rejected in the crystallization process. Thus, the last material to solidify contains the largest

amount in total of the rejected elements. Segregation is frequently expressed as a departure from the average chemical composition. Thus, when the content of an element is greater than the average, the segregation is termed **positive segregation;** when the content is less than the average, it is termed **negative segregation.**

Some elements in steel tend to segregate more readily than others. Sulphur segregates to the greatest extent. The following elements also segregate, but to a lesser degree, and in descending order: phosphorus, carbon, silicon, and manganese. The tendency for elements to segregate while an ingot is solidifying increases with increased time for solidification, so that large ingots exhibit more severe segregation than do small ingots.

Also, when comparing ingots of the same cross-section, movement of liquid steel by convection currents or turbulence due to gas evolution in the steel in a mold during solidification increases the tendency of elements to segregate. Therefore, killed steels are less segregated than semikilled; and the semikilled less segregated than capped or rimmed steels. In a rimmed ingot, the rimmed zone exhibits negative segregation and the core zone exhibits positive segregation. The boundary between the rim and core zones of a rimmed ingot is very sharp, and these zones are so different with respect to chemical composition that they resemble different steels.

There are certain other special aspects of segregation in killed steel that are of interest, but can only be mentioned here; these include **axial porosity** (associated with the "**V segregate**" along the central axis of an ingot) and **ingot pattern** that may be due to the ingot being disturbed while solidifying, or to the type of segregation referred to as "**inverted 'V' segregate.**"

Columnar Structure—Steel after solidification is a crystalline material. The first molten metal to contact the comparatively cold mold wall freezes (solidifies) rapidly, with a structure characterized by small and randomly oriented crystals that form a chill zone about ½-inch thick. After this initial zone of randomly oriented crystals has formed, large crystals called **dendrites** that are characterized by a branching structure develop. Growth of the individual dendrites occurs principally along their longitudinal axes perpendicular to the surfaces of the ingot, and these large elongated crystals may extend all the way to the center of the ingot. An ingot possessing a preponderance of these large elongated crystals is referred to as having a **columnar structure** and, if the structure is exaggerated in extent, it is referred to as **ingotism.** Ingots exhibiting ingotism tend to crack excessively during rolling unless light drafts (small reductions in cross-sectional area per pass) are employed for the first few passes in the rolling mill. In most ingots, however, columnar structure gives way, toward the center of the ingot, to rather large, equiaxed, randomly oriented crystals that also are dendritic in character. The relative proportion of columnar and equiaxed dendritic crystallization appears to be dependent upon many variables, among which are: composition of the steel, mold temperature, pouring temperature, and gas content of the steel.

Internal Fissures—Tensile stresses in the interior of an ingot, arising during heating, cooling, or rolling may produce **internal fissures** or **internal bursts,** sometimes of a very large size. If these do not extend to the surface, they may weld completely during the rolling operation, provided that the amount of hot work (percentage of reduction) is sufficient.

Ingot Cracks—If the fractures produced by tensile stresses extend to the surface or originate at it, they produce the visible defects known as **ingot cracks.** The surfaces of such exposed cracks become oxidized and they will not weld together during rolling, thus producing large seams in the rolled product. This type of defect receives more attention in Chapter 22.

Nonmetallic Inclusions—All steel ingots contain nonmetallic inclusions that consist of oxidized material and lesser amounts of sulphides, in various combinations and mixtures with each other. They are derived chiefly from the oxidizing reactions of the refining processes and the deoxidizing materials added to the steel in the furnace, ladle, or molds. Some may result from erosion of ladle refractories during pouring.

Scabs—In top-poured ingots, the pouring stream first strikes the stool or the mold bottom, and splashes violently against the lower part of the mold walls. Many of these splashes adhere and solidify, forming a continuous layer on the lower portion of the mold walls. This splashing diminishes as a pool of liquid metal forms in the bottom of the mold. The adhering splashes cool rapidly, and their surfaces oxidize. If the cooling and oxidation have progressed too far by the time the liquid steel in the mold rises past them, they will not be incorporated into the ingot, but will remain as adhering and imperfectly bonded **scabs** on the surfaces of the ingot. If thin, scabs may be oxidized away by scale formation in the soaking pit. If thick, they remain and produce a similar defect on the rolled product, as will be discussed in Chapter 22. As the continuous layer of splashes cools, its upper edges tend to bend inward and, as the rising liquid steel overflows them, to become enfolded. Horizontal ingot cracks called **butt cracks** often occur below and parallel to such **folds,** and the folds themselves can produce surface laminations or seams in rolled product.

The defects associated with pouring splashes can be reduced by filling the mold more rapidly, so that the rising level of liquid steel covers the splashes before they can cool and oxidize. This is done by using larger or multiple nozzles, which practice, however, leads to various mechanical difficulties if carried to extremes. Bottom pouring also will minimize these defects, since the molten steel enters the mold from a runner through an opening in the mold bottom and there is little splashing as compared with top-pouring practice.

Mold Coatings—Another method of reducing the effects of splashing, and thereby improving the surface of ingots, is to coat the inside of the molds with a substance that will volatilize and tend to repel splashes. Many substances have been proposed or tried for this purpose, among which are tar, powdered pitch, gilsonite, graphite, and aluminum paint. Tar is probably the most effective splash repellant but, if used under unsuitable conditions, gives rise to annoying fumes. Powdered pitch has some of the effectiveness of tar, and the fumes are less objectionable. Gilsonite approaches tar in effectiveness and produces a minimum of fumes when properly applied. With carbonaceous coatings, such as tar, powdered pitch, or gilsonite, the temperature of the molds at the time they are coated is important. If they are too hot, the coating is decomposed and the residual charred film has no beneficial effect. If they are too cold, the coating is extremely heavy, and the excessive amount of gas accompanying its decomposition by the liquid steel gives rise to subsurface blowholes in the ingot.

SECTION 3

CONTROL OF INGOT STRUCTURE

The foregoing discussion has shown that the final structure of an ingot is determined almost entirely by the degree to which the steel from which it was cast has been deoxidized. The several types of steel require different steelmaking and deoxidation practices, which are described briefly in the following summary of the principal steps involved.

Rimmed Steels—For rimmed steels, proper rimming action in the molds has been described as necessary to produce the surface conditions and ingot structure desired. Slag control is aimed at adjusting the lime-silica ratio and iron-oxide content of the slag to give the desired level of oxidation of the bath of metal when the heat is ready to tap. The exact procedures followed depend upon whether the steel has a carbon content in the higher ranges (0.12 to 0.15 per cent), in the lower ranges (0.06 to 0.10 per cent), or under 0.06 per cent.

Rimmed steel usually is tapped without having made additions of deoxidizers to the steel in the furnace, and with only small additions to the molten steel in the ladle, in order to have sufficient oxygen present to give the desired gas evolution by reacting in the mold with carbon. Ferromanganese may be added to the furnace before tapping, or to the ladle, but it is usual to make the addition in the ladle. Aluminum, ferrotitanium, or other deoxidizers in small amounts may be added in the ladle, if needed. This type of steel, when properly made, can be cast into ingots having a minimum of pipe and a good surface, though they are subject to segregation. When the metal in the ingot mold begins to solidify, there is a brisk evolution of gas, resulting in an outer ingot skin of relatively clean metal. For many applications, particularly where the surface of the product is most important, this steel is used to a considerable extent.

The thickness of the outer skin and the absence of blowholes and oxides from it depends upon the skill of the steelmakers. When the temperature and the oxygen content of the steel as it is poured from the ladle are within the most desirable limits, the desired evolution of carbon monoxide from the steel in the molds is obtained. The rimming action of the first-cast ingot is observed, and if an adjustment of the rimming action is desired, this is obtained for subsequent ingots by making small additions of shot aluminum or gas-evolving materials depending upon whether the oxygen level is, respectively, too high or too low. If the steel is over-deoxidized (oxygen content too low), the rimming action will be incomplete because gas evolution is too small in volume and slow in starting.

Capped Steels—Capped-steel practice is a variation of rimmed-steel practice. The steel is poured into big-end-down bottle-top molds in which the constricted top or mouth of the mold facilitates the capping operation. The rimming action is allowed to begin normally, but is then terminated at the end of a minute or more by sealing the mold with a cast-iron cap. The addition of only a small amount of shot aluminum during pouring insures that the steel will rise to press against the cap. The oxygen level of the steel as poured into the mold is preferred to be not more, and possibly slightly less, than the level desired for rimmed steel. The capped ingot has a thin rim zone that is relatively free from blowholes, and a core zone that has less segregation than that for a rimmed-steel ingot of the same volume. In steels with a carbon content greater than 0.15 per cent, the capped-ingot practice is used with advantage. Steels of this type are applied to sheet, strip, skelp, tin plate, wire, and bars.

Semikilled Steel—Semikilled steel is deoxidized less than killed steel, and there is enough oxygen present in the molten steel to react with carbon and form gas after the steel is poured into molds. Semikilled steel finds wide application in structural shapes, plates, and merchant bar. This steel generally has a carbon content within the range of 0.15 to 0.30 per cent. The usual practice is to bring the carbon content of the steel in the furnace to the desired carbon content for tapping. Ferromanganese may be added to the furnace, to the ladle, or to both. If large additions are necessary, at least part should be added to the furnace. Carbon, ferrosilicon, and aluminum may be added to the ladle. Usually, most deoxidation is done in the ladle, so that only a few ounces of aluminum per ton of steel will be required as a mold addition.

Killed Steel—The term "killed" indicates that steel has been deoxidized sufficiently for it to lie perfectly quiet when poured into an ingot mold. There is no evolution of gas in the mold, and the top surface of the ingot solidifies with relative rapidity. Killed steel generally is used when a homogenous structure is required in the finished steel. Alloy steels, forging steels, and steels for carburizing are of this type, when the essential quality is soundness. In general, all steels

with more than 0.30 per cent carbon content are killed. In making killed steel, the usual steelmaking-furnace practice is to "catch the heat coming down," that is, to decrease the carbon content of the bath to the desired level and then either to **block the heat** (deoxidize it) by adding high-silicon pig iron (15 to 25 per cent silicon), 50 per cent ferrosilicon, or silicomanganese, or to tap the heat without blocking and depend upon ladle deoxidation. Blocking lowers the oxygen content of the liquid metal to prevent further oxidation of carbon; it also serves to protect alloying elements that are susceptible to oxidation and, consequently, are added after the heat has been blocked.

At the final part of the finishing period, the carbon will have been worked down until it is at a level within the range required for tapping and pouring. The phosphorus and sulphur contents should be below the specified maximum, the manganese usually will be below the minimum required, and the bath temperature should be proper for the composition and grade of the steel being produced. The steel is then ready for whatever ferroalloys need to be added.

The decision as to whether a ferroalloy addition is to be made to the furnace or to the ladle is determined largely by the susceptibility of the ferroalloy to oxidation. Manganese may be added to the furnace or to the ladle, or divided between them, but the additions to the ladle must not be so large as to chill the metal too much. The furnace additions are chosen and the timing of addition set so that maximum elimination of the solid oxides formed will take place by their floating up through the metal to the slag before the metal is tapped from the furnace. After tapping, other deoxidizing additions may be made to the steel as it runs into the ladle. These additions complete the deoxidation to the desired degree up to the pouring into molds. These ladle additions are usually ferrosilicon, aluminum, or some special alloys (calcium-silicon is an example) containing elements that have a strong affinity for oxygen. Additions containing such elements as manganese and silicon furnish part of these elements required to meet the chemical-composition specifications. Additions of deoxidizers may be made to the molds, depending upon the type of steel. In producing certain extra-deep-drawing steels, a low-carbon (under 0.10 per cent carbon) steel is killed, usually with a substantial amount of aluminum that is added in the ladle, in the molds, or in both.

Almost all killed steels are cast in hot-topped big-end-up molds. The type of hot top used will vary among different plants and even among various grades of steel cast in the same plant. The size of ingots cast will vary with limitations imposed by sizes and capacities of plant facilities, the amount of segregation that can be tolerated, and the application of the steel.

SECTION 4

VACUUM DEGASSING OF STEEL FOR INGOTS

Gases absorbed by liquid steel from the atmosphere and from raw materials used in steelmaking can cause flaking, embrittlement, voids, inclusions, and other undesirable or even harmful phenomena in the steel after it has solidified.

Hydrogen, in particular, has been recognized for a

considerable time to be the cause of flaking and embrittlement. Until relatively recently, necessary precautions during steelmaking to limit absorption of hydrogen by the molten metal were an effective boiling period and the drying of addition agents. Even with these precautions, the steel after solidification had to be subjected to lengthy and complicated heating and cooling cycles to promote the diffusion of hydrogen that the steel might have absorbed.

Oxygen and nitrogen combine with various addition agents and alloying elements to form oxide, cyanonitride, or nitride compounds that remain in the steel as inclusions that can only be removed by some remelting process.

The vacuum melting processes described in Chapter 17 provide means for eliminating gases and inclusions either from relatively small quantities of molten steel at reasonable cost or from larger quantities at considerable expense.

Several methods have been developed since about 1950 for degassing large quantities (up to 300 tons) of liquid steel produced in conventional open-hearth and electric-arc furnaces: the more common are referred to as (1) ladle degassing, (2) stream degassing, (3) the D-H (Dortmund-Hörder) process, and (4) the R-H (Ruhrstahl-Heraeus) process. The principles of these processes are shown schematically in Figures 18—5, 18—6, and 18—7. Hydrogen can be removed effectively by any of the processes, and some of them are also effective in removing oxygen from steel that has not been previously deoxidized with silicon or aluminum.

In **ladle degassing** (Figure 18—5A) the ladle of steel to be degassed is placed in a gas-tight tank that has an outlet connected to a vacuum pump. Evacuation of the space within the tank causes gases to escape from the steel with an accompanying boiling action. Hoppers in the tank top are provided for making additions to the ladle. An inert gas such as argon or helium may be injected into the steel in the ladle to agitate it and promote the boiling effect, or induction stirring may be employed for the same purpose (induction stirring necessitates the use of non-magnetic stainless steel for construction of the ladle shell). When degassing is completed, the tank is purged with an inert gas to remove possibility of ignition of flammable gas and metallic dust that may have accumulated in the tank before its internal pressure is raised to atmospheric to permit removal of the ladle. The degassed steel is teemed in the conventional manner.

Stream degassing is accomplished (Figure 18—5B) by placing an empty ladle in a tank. A bottom-pour ladle containing the molten steel to be degassed is set upon the evacuated tank: the bottom of the ladle and the top of the tank are equipped with mating seals to prevent entrance of air. When the stopper rod of the tapping ladle is raised, molten metal flows through the nozzle, melts a metal diaphragm that seals the opening to the tank, and passes into the ladle in the vacuum tank. As the stream of molten steel enters the evacuated space, it breaks up into tiny droplets, exposing an enormous surface to the degassing influence of the vacuum, and is received by the ladle in the tank. After purging the tank to remove any accumulation of flammable gases by replacing them with an inert gas, the tank is opened and the ladle of degassed steel is removed by a crane and teemed in the conventional manner.

In a variation of the foregoing method, the vacuum equipment is set up adjacent to an electric-arc furnace on the tapping side. The ladle to receive the degassed steel is equipped with a gas-tight cover with openings

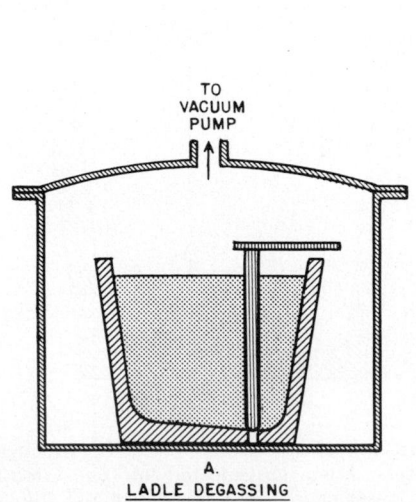

A.
LADLE DEGASSING

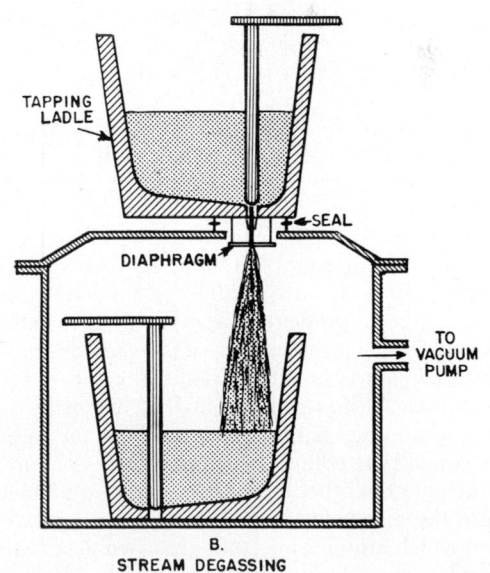

B.
STREAM DEGASSING

FIG. 18—5. Schematic arrangements of equipment used in (A) ladle degassing and (B) stream degassing of molten steel. In both methods, the degassed steel subsequently is teemed into ingot molds in the conventional way. Variations of (A) and (B) are discussed in the text.

for making additions from a hopper, for exhausting the space within the ladle, and for admitting molten steel. A stopper-equipped tundish is sealed to the top of the ladle cover. After the ladle is evacuated, steel is poured directly from the electric-arc furnace into the tundish and from thence, by raising the tundish stopper, into the evacuated space in the ladle through the opening provided in the ladle cover.

A stream degassing technique for casting large forging ingots is described later.

The **D-H (Dortmund-Hörder) process** for degassing liquid steel (Figure 18—6) accomplishes some refining and intensive mixing and permits additions of alloys to be made. The vacuum vessel is lowered until its nozzle extends through the slag into the molten steel in a ladle. Vacuum pumps then rapidly lower the pressure in the chamber to about 1 mm. Hg, and atmospheric pressure causes liquid steel to rise into the chamber. As the steel enters the evacuated space, there is a violent evolution of gas that exposes a very large surface area of the steel (in the form of droplets) to the vacuum. Raising the vessel without removing the nozzle from the liquid metal in the ladle permits the degassed steel to partially flow back into the ladle. By repeating this operation for the required number of cycles, the entire contents of the ladle can be degassed. Heat losses are compensated for by a graphite electrical resistance heating element in the upper part of the vacuum chamber. The following chemical changes occur during the operation: (1) hydrogen is removed; (2) the carbon content is lowered by reaction with oxygen in the steel to form carbon monoxide, and (3) some loss of manganese occurs. Steel of the desired composition is produced by compensating in advance for the carbon and manganese losses, or by adding replacement amounts through the addition hoppers that permit the additions to be made without breaking the vacuum. After degassing is completed, the vacuum vessel is purged with nitrogen before the nozzle is raised above the liquid steel to prevent ignition of any accumulation of flammable gases in the vessel.

The principle of the **R-H (Ruhrstahl-Heraeus) process** is shown in Figure 18—7. The equipment consists of a vessel equipped with two tubular extensions. One extension is provided with an inlet for the injection of an inert gas. The vessel is lowered until the ends of the two extensions are submerged beneath the liquid steel in a ladle, after which the vessel is evacuated. Atmospheric pressure causes the molten steel to rise through the extensions. Argon is injected into the one extension and, in effect, decreases the density of the column of liquid metal in that extension and causes a "pumping" action resulting from the imbalance between that column and the denser column of liquid metal in the other extension. As the liquid metal rises into the evacuated chamber through the extension into which argon is injected, absorbed gases leave the metal with a boiling action, and the degassed metal returns to the ladle by way of the other extension. The circulation of metal from the ladle into the evacuated chamber is continued until the desired low level of gas content in the steel is achieved.

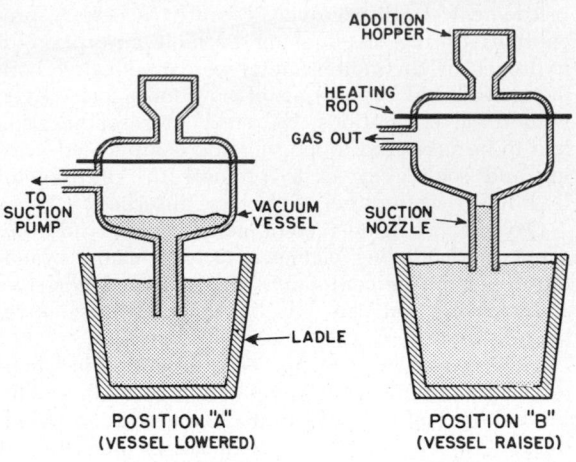

FIG. 18—6. Schematic diagram showing principle of operation of the D-H (Dortmund-Hörder) process. As the evacuated vessel is lowered and then raised, atmospheric pressure causes molten steel to rise into the evacuated space and then partially run back into the ladle.

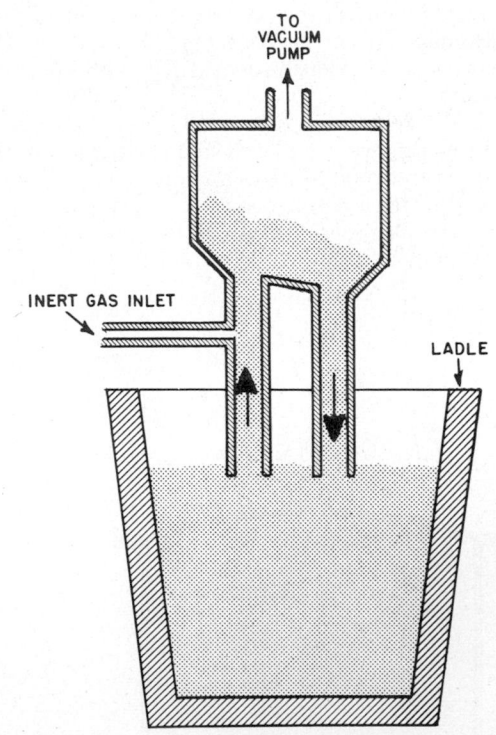

FIG. 18—7. Principle of operation of the R-H (Ruhrstahl-Heraeus) process. Argon gas injected into one extension or leg of the vessel causes molten steel to rise into the evacuated chamber with a boiling action that releases gases from the steel that then flows back into the ladle through the second leg. The continuous recirculation of steel is continued until the desired degree of degassing is attained.

Fig. 18—8. Vacuum casting of a large forging ingot at the Duquesne Works of United States Steel Corporation (see also Figure 18—9).

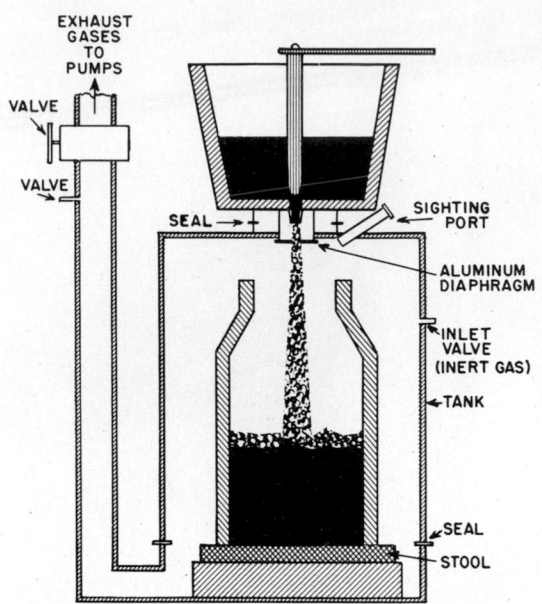

FIG. 18—9. Schematic arrangement of the vacuum-casting installation at the Duquesne Works of United States Steel Corporation, employing the stream degassing technique.

Vacuum Casting of Large Forging Ingots—Figures 18—8 and 18—9 show a vacuum casting installation at the Duquesne Works of United States Steel Corporation for producing large ingots for subsequent forging in which the hydrogen content has been lowered to a level at which the steel is insensitive to flaking. This installation employs the ladle-to-ingot mold stream degassing principle. Figure 18—8 is an overall view of the equipment in operation during the teeming of a large forging ingot. The general arrangement of the vacuum tank and pumping system is shown schematically in Figure 18—9.

With the pumping system functioning and the pressure in the vacuum tank at the required low level, the ladle containing the steel to be degassed is placed over the intermediate ladle and the pouring of steel is begun. When the intermediate ladle is about three-quarters full, its nozzle is opened, the molten steel melts a metal seal between the intermediate ladle and the tank, and the metal enters the low-pressure atmosphere in the tank. A refractory collar beneath the intermediate ladle nozzle confines the stream to prevent excessive spraying as gas evolution breaks the stream of steel into droplets. The molten steel is then collected in the ingot mold. The tank is purged with inert gas at the completion of casting, prior to breaking the vacuum to atmospheric pressure with air.

Factors Influencing Effectiveness of Gas Removal —Some of the variables that affect the amount of hydrogen that is removed from steel during vacuum casting are: the amount of gases dissolved in the steel; steel composition; absolute pressure during degassing; pouring rate; the moisture inside the tank; and the inleakage rate.

Steels made without the addition of aluminum, silicon, or other strong deoxidizers are subject to deoxidation by the reaction of carbon with oxygen when exposed to reduced pressures. Steels deoxidized with aluminum or other strong deoxidizers do not lend themselves readily to vacuum deoxidation because such deoxidizers form stable compounds with oxygen that could be removed only if the vacuum-casting pressure were lower than the dissociation pressures of the compounds.

CHAPTER 19

Plastic Working of Steel

SECTION 1

INTRODUCTORY

Plastic working of metal is the **permanent deformation** accomplished by applying mechanical forces to a metal surface. The primary objective of such working is usually the production of a specific shape or size (**mechanical shaping**), although in some cases it may be the improvement of certain physical properties of the metal (**mechanical treating**). Often these two objectives can be attained simultaneously.

The study of plastic deformation has been approached from two major viewpoints. The one, here called **microsopic**, is concerned with a physical explanation of plasticity. It considers such questions as the relation of plastic behavior to the crystal structure and the interatomic forces, factors which are important in the design of materials with improved plastic properties. The other, here called **macroscopic**, is concerned more with a phenomenological explanation of plasticity. It considers such questions as the relation of plastic behavior to applied stresses, temperature and rate of deformation, factors which are important in the design of metal-forming processes, and in the design of structures and machines.

The study of plastic deformation within each of these two major viewpoints may also be conveniently, if somewhat artificially, subdivided into areas called **cold working** and **hot working.** In hot working, the forces required to deform the metal are very sensitive to the rate of application of loads and to temperature variations, but the basic strength of the metal after the deformation is essentially unchanged. In cold working, on the other hand, the forces are relatively insensitive to the rate of application of loads and to temperature variations, but the basic strength is permanently increased.

In a book of this kind, it is possible to consider only the major aspects of this complex and extensive subject. An effort is made, however, to show the basic principles and present capabilities and limitations of both the microscopic and macroscopic studies of plastic deformation. An attempt is then made to show how these studies can be applied to the design of metal-working processes, and finally, the more important hot- and cold-working methods are summarized.

SECTION 2

MICROSCOPIC NATURE OF PLASTICITY

Metals generally consist of regions called **crystals** or **grains** where the atoms are arranged in more or less regular geometrical patterns, bounded by transition regions of irregular pattern called **grain boundaries.** The average diameter of the grains varies greatly with mechanical and thermal treatment but is usually in the range, 0.01 in. to 0.001 in. The geometrical pattern or **crystal lattice** consists primarily of repeated fundamental groups of atoms called **unit cells.** The unit cell of pure α-iron, for example, is shown in Figure 19—1. It is called body-centered cubic.

Plastic deformation of metals occurs by several processes including grain rotation. By far the most predominant process, however, is **slip** of adjacent planes of atoms within the crystals. This slip takes place only on definite crystallographic planes, usually those of most dense atomic packing, and only in definite crystallographic directions, also usually those of most dense packing, within these planes. A **slip plane** and **slip direction** of most dense packing for the body-

centered cubic structure are illustrated in Figure 19—1. Such a plane and direction constitute a **slip system.**

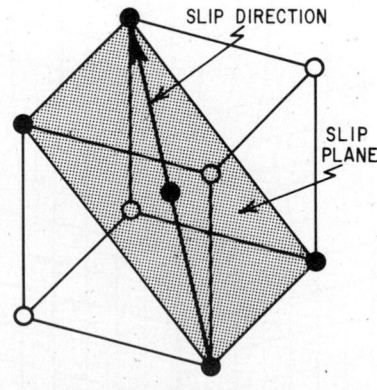

FIG. 19—1. Illustration of body-centered cubic cell and a common slip system.

Each particular crystal has its own characteristic slip systems. At least 48 are known for α-iron.

A force applied to the surface of a crystal is transmitted by interatomic reactions across each internal crystallographic plane. The force transmitted across a particular plane can, in general, be resolved into a component normal to the plane and a component tangent to the plane. The tangent component can in turn be resolved further into components corresponding to definite crystallographic directions in the plane. In this manner, a definite force component can be associated with each particular slip system. Many experiments have shown that slip in a particular system will occur if this force exceeds some critical value on a unit area of the slip plane. This is known as the **critical shear stress law**. The critical value, or **yield stress**, is essentially independent of the normal force on the slip plane, but it does depend on the particular type of slip system. When a system of forces is applied to the surface of a polycrystalline metal, slip first occurs in that crystal and that system where the critical shear stress is first attained. Complex plastic deformation occurs, however, by slip in several systems within each of many crystals.

Early efforts to predict the magnitude of the yield stress in perfect metal crystals, using laws describing interatomic forces, showed that **simultaneous slip** of an entire layer of atoms could occur when the shear stress in the plane was about 10^7 lb. per sq. in. Experiments showed, however, that the actual yield stress was several orders of magnitude lower. This apparent discrepancy was resolved when it was realized that metal crystals contain many imperfections in structure, called **dislocations**, which permit **consecutive slip** of one line or loop of atoms at a time in such a manner that the required shear stress is greatly reduced. Figure 19—2 shows a single dislocation line, BC, in an otherwise perfect simple cubic lattice. In a typical metal crystal there may be 10^7 to 10^9 such lines crossing a square inch of area everywhere in the crystal.

One of the characteristics of these dislocations is that they create internal forces between the atoms. These have been likened to the internal stresses that would appear in a perfectly elastic body by making a cut, such as ABC in Figure 19—2, displacing the upper portion one atom distance, b, and then cementing the cut together. In fact, an entire **mathemetical theory of dislocations** has been developed which equates these lattice imperfections to displaced surfaces within elastic bodies.

As mentioned above, the observed yield stress in a typical metal crystal is several orders of magnitude below the theoretical value for a perfect crystal. The yield stress of some iron whiskers, which are nearly dislocation free, however, is very high (about 10^6 lb. per sq. in.) approaching the theoretical value for a perfect crystal. The theoretical stress required to move a single dislocation, on the other hand, is very small, in fact much smaller than the yield stress of a typical metal crystal. This is explained by the fact that other imperfections in the typical crystal, i.e., vacancies, interstitial and substitutional foreign atoms, grain boundaries, or other dislocations, cause additional internal stress fields which oppose the motion of any dislocation. Finally then, a very simple picture of the effect of imperfections on yield strength can be constructed as shown in Figure 19—3. A perfect crystal has a very high yield strength, one with only a few imperfections has a very low yield strength, but as the density of imperfections increases, the yield strength again becomes large.

As plastic deformation proceeds beyond yielding, new imperfections are formed and old ones may be annihilated. At low temperatures, the overall effect is the creation of more imperfections, raising the stress required to cause further deformation. (See Figures 19—4a, 19—4b, 19—4c, and 19—4d). This phenomenon is known as **strain hardening** and is typical of **cold working**. At higher temperatures the thermal energy assists the movement of dislocations

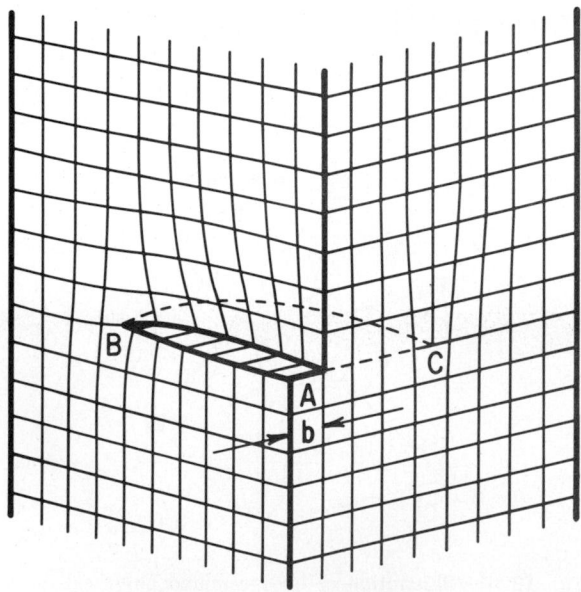

FIG. 19—2. Dislocation in a simple cubic lattice.

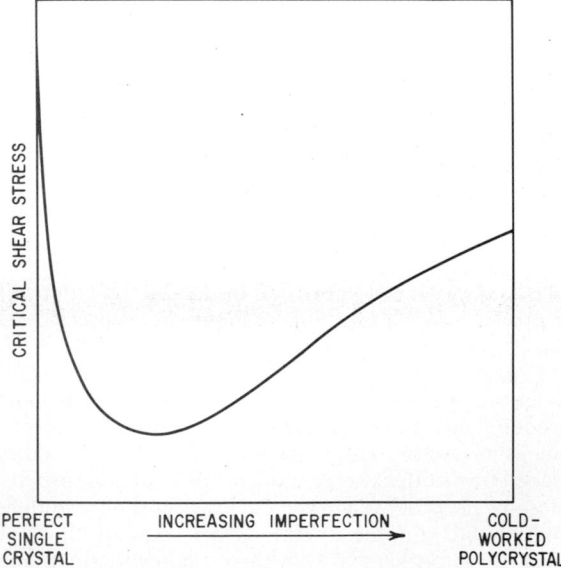

FIG. 19—3. Effect of imperfection on critical shear stress.

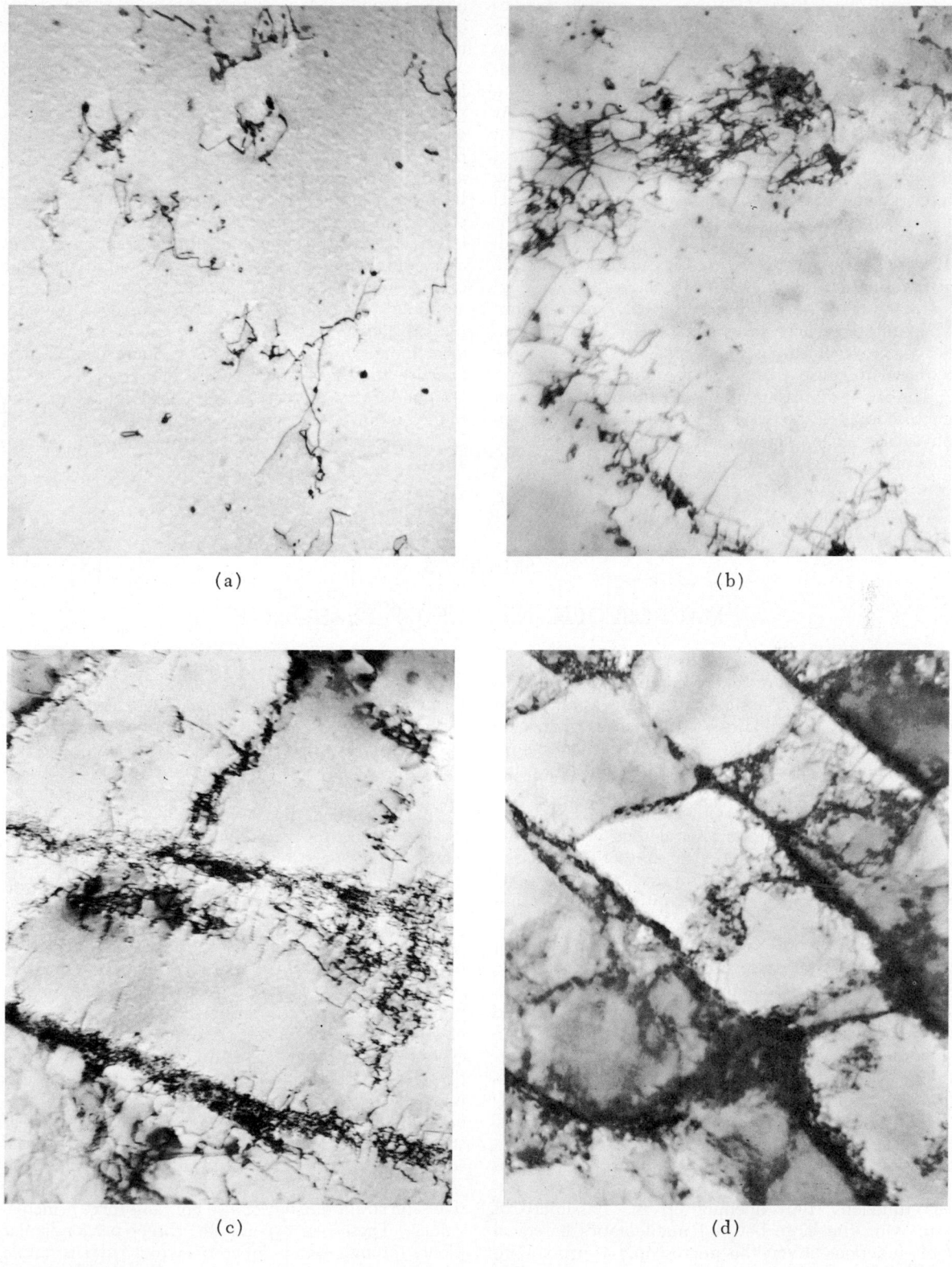

Fig. 19—4. Dislocation tangles in iron deformed at 25°C. (a) 1% strain, (b) 3.5% strain, (c) 9% strain, (d) 20% strain. (Transmission electron micrographs, approximately 25,000×.)

and tends to reduce the degree of imperfection to that of the annealed state. This phenomenon is known as **recovery** and is typical of **hot working.** Thus, two opposing factors are present in hot working, a tendency toward greater imperfection due to strain and a tendency toward less imperfection due to recovery. At high rates of deformation, the annealing is insufficient to overcome the strain hardening and the overall effect is one of a greater degree of imperfection. At low rates, however, the recovery may completely cancel the strain hardening, giving an essentially constant flow stress. Whereas the flow stress at low (cold-working) temperatures is quite insensitive to the rate of deformation, the flow stress at high (hot-working) temperatures is very dependent on this same factor. Thus, although it requires a relatively high stress to hot roll a steel bar, a much smaller stress may be required to cause creep at hot-rolling temperatures.

The above discussion may leave the impression that microscopic plasticity is now a closed chapter in physical science. This would be highly misleading. One of the gages by which to measure the true state of development of a branch of science is the ability of that science to make quantitative predictions within its own realm. This usually requires the development of a **mathematical statement of theory** of the laws of that science. The important role of imperfections in plasticity has been emphasized, and the development of a mathematical theory of these imperfections was briefly mentioned. This theory has been based primarily on the assumption that the crystal lattice may be represented as an isotropic, homogeneous elastic continuum with internal slips corresponding to lattice imperfections. It can predict the interaction stresses and equilibrium positions of certain regular groups of imperfections, but it is not yet capable of predicting a simple tensile stress-strain curve for even the simplest dislocation arrangement in a single crystal. For most metals the situation is even more complicated because they consist of many, many small crystals bounded by complex grain boundaries and containing highly involved dislocation groupings as illustrated in the electron micrographs of iron shown in Figure 19—4.

SECTION 3

MACROSCOPIC NATURE OF PLASTICITY

As mentioned above, microscopic plasticity begins with certain observations concerning the arrangement of atoms in the crystal lattice and proceeds to develop an understanding of the detailed mechanisms of plastic flow. Macroscopic plasticity, on the other hand, begins with certain observations concerning plastic deformation of polycrystalline metals in simple mechanical tests, such as simple tension tests, and proceeds to develop an understanding of gross plastic flow. Both viewpoints attempt to develop mathematical theories which enable quantitative predictions in their own realms.

In the macroscopic viewpoint, the metal is thought of as a **continuum** possessing properties like density, stress and velocity at all points within its outer surface. The detailed properties of the lattice structure and its imperfections including grain boundaries are smoothed out. Thus, although this viewpoint is particularly suited for situations involving the simultaneous deformation of many grains, it is completely unable to deal with the physical details of plastic flow. The great advantage of the continuum concept is that it enables the physical quantities, such as density, stress and velocity, to be treated as continuous functions, thus opening up the possibility of employing the large body of mathematics based on such functions. Even the microscopic viewpoint involving dislocation theory finds it necessary to adopt the continuum concept outside of the dislocation lines, i.e., in the more regular portions of the lattice.

Two quantities that play a central role in continuum theory are the quantities **stress** and **strain rate.** They describe in an average way the forces between the atoms in the crystal lattice and the deformation of the lattice respectively. Stress, as described before, is a quantity representing the force per unit area on an internal plane. Obviously, however, the stress at a point in a continuum cannot be described by a single number because it varies for different planes through the point. Strain rate represents the relative velocities of neighboring internal planes. Thus, it too varies for the different planes through a particular point. Quantities such as stress and strain rate are called **tensors.** They may be thought of as mathematical quantities like numbers, but with more complex properties. One of the special properties of tensors is that they have three **principal values** corresponding to three perpendicular planes through a point, that uniquely describe the tensor. In the case of stress these are called principal stresses and they correspond to three perpendicular planes on which there are no tangential or shear forces. Three such planes always exist through every point, and in general they are the only planes which have no shear stresses. Thus, the principal stresses are normal stresses, here denoted as σ_1, σ_2, and σ_3 such that $\sigma_1 \geq \sigma_2 \geq \sigma_3 \geq$, where tensile stresses are considered positive. The strain rate tensor also contains three principal values. These correspond to three perpendicular planes through each point across which there is simple stretching or compressing but no distortion or shearing. They are denoted $\dot{\varepsilon}_1$, $\dot{\varepsilon}_2$ and $\dot{\varepsilon}_3$, where stretching is considered positive.

The theory of macroscopic plasticity depends very largely on three macroscopic observations concerning stress and strain rate. The first of these is that the *volume remains essentially constant during gross plastic deformation.* This means that the sum of the principal strain rates, stretches and compressions, is zero, i.e.,

$$\dot{\varepsilon}_1 + \dot{\varepsilon}_2 + \dot{\varepsilon}_3 = 0.$$

This result is not really surprising since, as remarked above, the main mechanism of plastic flow is consecutive slip of adjacent rows of atoms, a mechanism that requires no volume change.

A second basic observation is that plastic flow or *yielding occurs at a point only after the maximum shear stress in some direction on some plane attains the critical value, k.* It is known from a study of the stress tensor that the greatest shear stress occurs on the two planes which are half way between the planes of greatest and least principal stress. Its magnitude is one-half the difference between the greatest and least principal values. Thus, the second observation is that, for gross plastic flow to occur,

$$\frac{\sigma_1 - \sigma_3}{2} = k.$$

As mentioned in the previous section, plastic flow in a single crystal requires the attainment of a critical shear stress in particular crystallographic directions. If one thinks of gross plastic flow as being the summation of many slips involving many crystals with all possible orientations, it is not surprising that the macroscopic critical shear stress is independent of crystal orientation.

The third basic observation of gross plastic flow is that *the directions of greatest shear strain rate coincide with the directions of greatest shear stress.* This

observation requires a more complex mathematical statement than those above and such treatment will not be given here. It is noted, however, that since shear straining is similar to slip, the observation is similar to saying that the most slip occurs in the directions of greatest shearing stress, a statement which certainly seems reasonable on the basis of microscopic plasticity.

The mathematical statement of the above three macroscopic observations forms the foundation of macroscopic or *continuum theory of plasticity.* One additional statement is necessary concerning k, the critical shear stress. For cold working, it is generally found to be an increasing function of prior work (**work hardening**) but not of strain rate. For hot working, it is taken to be a function of both previous work and strain rate. This is all in accord with the microscopic observations concerning the formation and annihilation of imperfections.

Before leaving this discussion of general plasticity it should be mentioned that the two viewpoints described here are extremes, the one specifically taking into account every crystal imperfection and the other averaging out even the individual grains. Several intermediate viewpoints are also possible. For example, one that has been considered is to use the properties of imperfections but to consider them continuously distributed over the lattice. Another is to consider the grains as individual continua treated with the same methods now applied to the polycrystalline body. Since all viewpoints are based upon experimental observation, they are mutually consistent, and are expected eventually to be merged into a single unified theory of plasticity.

SECTION 4

GENERAL PRINCIPLES OF METAL WORKING

In considering the application of the principles of plastic deformation to the design of metal-working processes, it is necessary to define the factors that can limit such deformation. These may be broadly classified into two types: **instability,** which is the creation of undesirable types of deformation due to small, but usually unavoidable, irregularities in the metal or in the load application; and, **fracture,** which is the creation of new surfaces such as holes, cracks, or actual separation into two or more parts.

Instabilities can be divided into two general types; those associated with compressive stresses and called **buckling,** and those associated with tensile stresses and called **necking.** The two types can be illustrated by considering a cup-drawing process such as shown in Figure 19—5. If the flange is too thin or insufficiently supported, the compressive circumferential stresses may cause buckling or wrinkling. If the walls of the cup are too thin, the tensile stresses in the axial direction may cause local thinning or necking. Instability is a very complex problem and not completely understood. It can be said, however, that *factors which tend to spread plastic deformation reduce the likelihood of instability.* These may be material prop-

erties such as work hardening, or they may be mechanical design factors such as shape and method of load application.

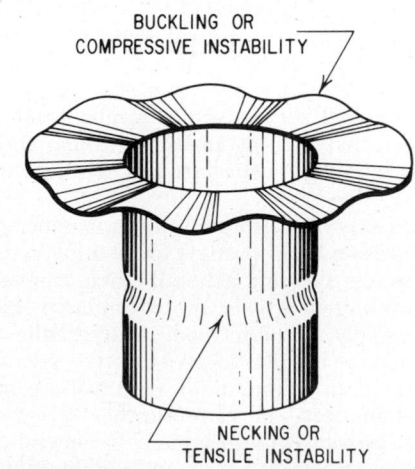

FIG. 19—5. Examples of forming instabilities in a deep-drawn cup.

Fracture may be considered as the separation of the crystal lattice due to tensile forces which overcome the interatomic cohesion. Exactly how this happens on the microscopic level is not completely clear. However, macroscopic observations show that fracture is generally associated with the attainment of some critical tensile stress within the metal. This leads to an important principle of metal working; namely that *the amount of plastic working is generally enhanced by using compressive rather than tensile methods.* This is why larger reductions are possible in forging operations than in stretching operations, in single-pass rolling than in single-pass drawing.

In addition to avoiding instability and fracture, a metal working operation may be designed to minimize forces or to increase efficiency. Since plastic flow depends upon achieving a critical shear stress, *forming forces are minimized in tensile-compressive operations;* that is, those which involve both tensile and compressive stresses. This is because the difference between the principal stresses, and hence the maximum shear stress, is large in these cases while the absolute magnitudes of the stresses remain small. It explains for example why roll-separating forces are reduced by the application of strip tensions. *Efficiency is enhanced by minimizing tool surface friction and by avoiding redundant work; that is, work that does not contribute to the final shape.* A drawing process is inherently more efficient than a rolling process because, unlike rolling, it does not depend on tool surface friction to transmit the work. Redundant work is quite difficult to avoid completely, but can be kept small by lubrication and die shaping.

Another factor which might be important in the design of metal-working operations is the achievement of some particular properties in the product. Thus, for example, it might be desirable to produce a product that has directional properties, or **anisotropy.** The rules for accomplishing this are not yet completely clear. It also might be desirable to produce a product that has no residual stresses, or one that has

certain prescribed residual stresses. *Residual stresses can be minimized by hot working which of course destroys the work hardening, or by die designing such that every portion of the metal goes through the same deformation history.* Figure 19—6 shows an

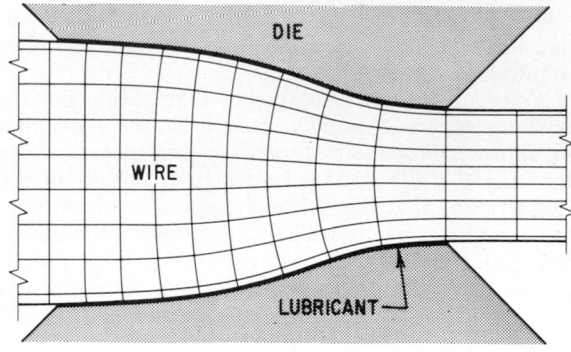

Fig. 19—6. Wire drawing with maximum efficiency and product uniformity.

example of an ideal wire-drawing die that forces each element of the wire to go through the same history as every other element. This die also avoids redundant work since all of the deformation done on each portion of the metal goes toward the shape of the final product.

Many other factors may enter into the design of a specific metal-working operation. In particular, some knowledge of the frictional conditions between the worked material and the forming tools is often essential for a complete design. The above examples, however, are believed to be representative of the major design factors involving the principles of plastic deformation, and to illustrate how a knowledge of these principles can be useful in designing such operations. The following two sections summarize the major hot- and cold-working methods now in use.

SECTION 5

PRINCIPAL METHODS FOR HOT WORKING

The principal methods of forming steel by hot working are hammering, pressing, rolling and extrusion. Hot working by the first two methods is called forging.

Forging may be performed under hammers, in mechanical presses and upsetters or by a method known as roll forging. Pressing generally includes the manufacture of forged articles in hydraulic presses. Extrusion usually is performed in hydraulic presses which force the hot plastic steel through a die. Rolling is performed in rolling mills of a variety of types described in detail in various other chapters. The present discussion will be limited to general descriptions of the various types of hot-working equipment and some of the principles of their operation.

Hammering—Hammering was the first method

employed by man in shaping metals. The first forging was done by hand hammers wielded by workmen.

The first known power hammer, called a **tilt hammer,** was built in England. It was driven by water power and consisted of a beam of wood, hinged at one end and provided with an iron hammer head or die at the opposite end. At an intermediate point between the hinged end and the free end carrying the hammer head, cams on the revolving shaft driven by the water wheel alternately raised the free end and allowed it to fall upon an anvil or die fixed upon a suitable foundation. This was a crude tool compared to the steam hammers now used.

The first steam hammer was built in France during 1842. It consisted of a two-piece frame, constructed so as to support a vertical steam cylinder, fitted with a piston and piston rod, directly over a die or anvil. To the piston rod of the steam cylinder was attached a **tup** or hammer head. By admitting steam to the cylinder below the piston, the hammer was raised for any desirable length of stroke and then allowed to drop upon the work piece supported on the anvil or bottom die.

In order to increase the striking force of the steam hammer above that derived from gravity alone, there was developed the **double-acting steam hammer,** in which steam can be admitted above the piston also and employed both on the downward stroke as well as for lifting the tup. This type of hammer is illustrated in Chapter 27, relating to the forging of axles. The first double-acting steam hammer was built at Midvale, Pennsylvania, in 1888.

A variety of other types of forging equipment employing the impact principle for forming hot steel have been developed but cannot be described here. Descriptions are available in reference works listed at the end of this chapter.

Pressing—The hydraulic forging press is an English invention dating from the year 1861. It was introduced into the United States about 1887. It consists (see Figure 19—7) essentially of a hydraulic cylinder supported by two pairs of steel columns which are anchored to a single base casting of great weight and strength. The piston or ram of the cylinder points vertically downward and carries the upper forging die, which is directly above a stationary die resting on the base casting to which the columns are attached. By admitting water under high pressure to the cylinder at its top, the ram carrying the upper die is forced down upon the material to be forged, which rests upon the lower forging die. Small auxiliary cylinders lift the ram after each application of pressure.

The pressure which must be very high if the forg-

ing press is to do effective work, is increased gradually and maintained until the metal yields. In practice, it has been found that the lowest pressure that can be effective in shaping steel at a full forging heat is about 1.2 tons per square inch, but the pressures employed in actual work often will exceed 13 tons per square inch.

Extrusion—The hot-extrusion process consists of enclosing a piece of metal, heated to forging temperature, in a chamber called a "container" having a die at one end with an opening of the shape of the desired finished section, and applying pressure to the plastic metal through the opposite end of the container. The metal is forced through the opening, the shape of which it assumes in cross-section, as the metal flows plastically under the great pressures used.

The equipment and methods for carrying out one type of hot extrusion are described in detail in Chapter 30.

Mechanical Forging—Many hot forgings are produced on mechanical presses. In machines of this type, pressure is applied to a vertical ram (carrying the upper forging die) through a connecting rod from a crankshaft. The heated work piece rests on the bottom die. The stroke of such a press is limited to the "throw" of the crankshaft.

Upsetting—A special type of mechanical press is the upsetting machine, in which the piece to be shaped is clamped between two dies with vertical faces and shaped by the action of a tool on a ram operated by a crankshaft. The ram of the upsetting machine operates with a horizontal, instead of vertical, stroke.

Hot Rolling—Of all the known methods of shaping steel, that of rolling, as introduced by Henry Cort in 1783, has come to be employed the most extensively. Though Cort is credited rightly with being the

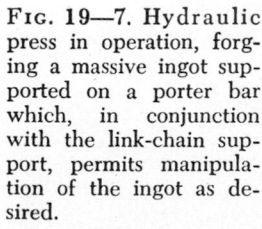

FIG. 19—7. Hydraulic press in operation, forging a massive ingot supported on a porter bar which, in conjunction with the link-chain support, permits manipulation of the ingot as desired.

"father of modern rolling," because of his successful development of mills employing grooved rolls, the use of this principle in shaping metal antedates his mill by many years. There are records, for example, to show that in the year 1553, rolls were employed in France to produce sheet of uniform thickness for the stamping of gold and silver coin. In Sweden, rolls were employed to produce certain sections prior to the year 1751, and even at that time assertion was made that as many as twenty times more bars could be reduced in a given time than could be shaped under the tilt hammer of those days. From the days of Cort to the present time, the rolling mill has passed through a rapid process of development, not only in the size, power and productive capacity of mills, but also in their design and in the increasing variety of shapes of sections that can be produced.

Mechanical Principle and Effects of Rolling—The process of shaping steel by rolling consists essentially of passing the material between two rolls revolving at the same peripheral speed and in opposite directions, i.e., clockwise and counterclockwise, and spaced so that the distance between them is somewhat less than the height of the section entering them (Figure 19—8). Under these conditions, the rolls grip the piece of metal and deliver it, reduced in cross-sectional area and increased in length. The extent of sideways or lateral spreading (called **spread**) is found to depend mainly upon the amount of reduction and the shape of the cross section entering the rolls; thus in rolling plates of considerable width, the actual total spread is independent of the width, and actually may be less than that resulting from the first pass in the reduction

of small, square billets, especially if the percentage reduction in cross-sectional area of the latter is great.

The turning of the rolls in contact with the work introduces a frictional force which acts along the arcs AB and A'B' of Figure 19—8, and is proportional to the pressure between the rolls and the piece. This pulls the work into the opening between the rolls, against the wedging action of the tapered section entering the rolls. The piece is delivered at a higher speed than the roll-surface speed; it enters at a velocity lower than the roll-surface speed. The ratio of the speed with which the work leaves the rolls to the surface speed of the rolls themselves is called the **forward slip.** Evidently, there must be some point between A and B and A' and B' where the speed of the bar is equal to the roll-surface speed. This point, indicated on the drawing by N and N', is called the **neutral point,** which coincides with the point of maximum pressure. The arc AB is called the **contact arc,** and its included angle AOB the contact angle or **rolling angle.** When this angle is the maximum at which the piece will enter (without pushing), it is called the **angle of bite.** The area of steel under the contact arc is called the **contact area,** which is projected to show the spreading that may occur. The force exerted against the rolls by the piece is called the **separating force.**

Effect of Work Temperature—The effects of rolling with respect to changes in physical dimensions of the piece are influenced very markedly by the temperature of the piece being rolled with respect to both degree and uniformity of heating. Additional plasticity imparted to steel by relatively slight increases

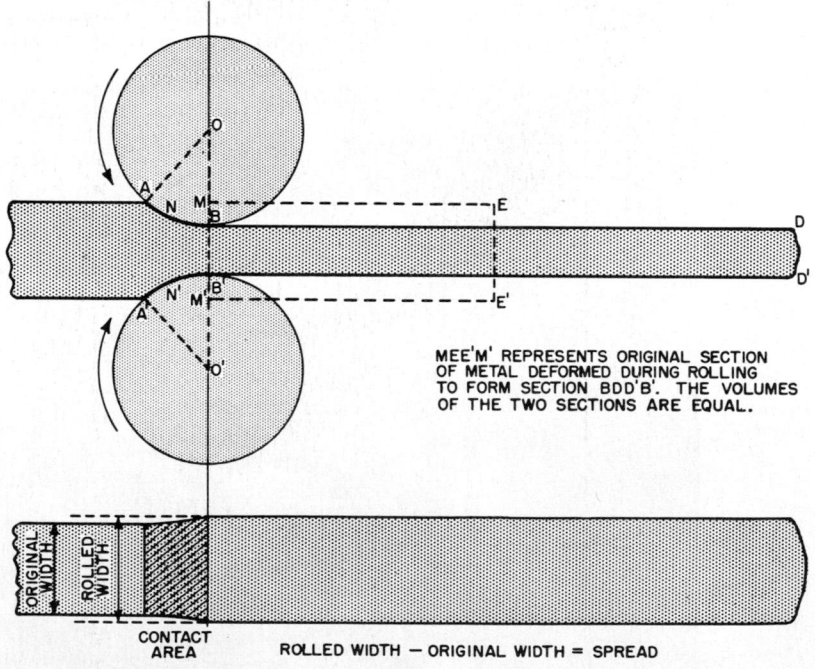

MEE'M' REPRESENTS ORIGINAL SECTION OF METAL DEFORMED DURING ROLLING TO FORM SECTION BDD'B'. THE VOLUMES OF THE TWO SECTIONS ARE EQUAL.

ORIGINAL WIDTH   ROLLED WIDTH   CONTACT AREA   ROLLED WIDTH — ORIGINAL WIDTH = SPREAD

FIG. 19—8. Diagram illustrating the action of plain rolls upon a piece of hot, plastic steel of originally square cross-section.

in temperature results in a reduction in the amount of power required for rolling and increases the ease with which it can be made to flow plastically in the desired directions. Chemical composition of a particular steel and the nature of the rolling operation to be performed may limit, respectively, the maximum and minimum rolling temperatures that are applicable.

Effects of Roll Diameter—Small diameter rolls require less force than rolls of larger diameter to effect a given reduction. Advantage is taken of this fact in four-high and other mills employing small-diameter work rolls backed up by heavier rolls that prevent the smaller rolls from bending. Smaller separating force is encountered with small-diameter rolls for two reasons: first, the area of contact is less so that, with a given pressure, the total force required is less; and second, the required average pressure is less because the smaller area of contact reduces the total frictional forces.

Miscellaneous Hot-Working Methods—**Rotary swaging** is performed to taper the end of bars, wires and tubes. The machine in which the work is done has two or four shaped dies, in opposing pairs, suitably mounted in a rotating ring. As the ring rotates, alternate pairs of dies are forced against the metal being swaged, the resultant pressure shaping the piece. Such a machine is illustrated in Chapter 30.

In **hot spinning**, which is limited to shapes symmetrical about the spinning axis, the heated piece to be shaped is mounted in a lathe or similar machine that can rotate it rapidly. A tool is then brought to bear against the spinning piece and, by manipulating the position and pressure of the tool, the work piece can be shaped. For example, bowl-shaped sections, such as flanged and dished heads, can be formed from flat, circular plates by spinning.

Many steel parts are formed hot from plates and sheets by **hot deep-drawing** operations that would be impracticable if the material were at room temperature. Roof ribs for railroad box cars, one-piece gates for hopper cars, deep bowls, etc., are typical. The heated steel is formed in hydraulic or mechanical presses equipped with forming dies that produce the desired shapes. Another example is the manufacture of closed-end cylinders by a combination of hot cupping and drawing operations, described in Chapter 30.

Roll forging, die rolling, and other hot-forming processes of limited use have not been included in the foregoing descriptions. Reference to these processes can be found in various handbooks.

COMPARISON OF METHODS FOR HOT WORKING

It is a very difficult matter to make a fair comparison between rolling and forging, or even between hammer and press forging. Each method has a field of its own with rather well-defined boundaries. Many irregular shapes are so intricate in design that rolling or extruding them is out of the question, and such shapes must be formed under the hammer or in the press. Certain crankshafts or a claw-hammer head serve as examples of these classes of shapes, which can be produced by no other form of mechanical working than by the forging method.

Tonnagewise, the hammer and the press are both slower and more expensive to operate than rolls. Special care must be given to all phases of the forging operation, including heating for forging. It is, perhaps, this meticulous care required to produce high-quality forgings that has given rise in some quarters to the belief that forged articles always are superior to rolled articles. Assuming that a given section can be produced by either rolling or forging, and that an equivalent amount of attention is given to all details of both processes with regard to heating, proper speed and amount of reduction, etc., the quality of rolled material can be equal to that of forged product.

With the complex stress-strain relationships involved in plastic deformation in hot working, and the basic differences in the nature of the major hot-working processes, direct comparison is difficult. However, studies have shown that the effects of rolling and pressing are comparable, provided equipment for carrying out both processes is of comparable capacity and the same sized pieces are being worked.

Rolls have the distinct advantage of speed of production where the shapes involved are of a nature suited to rolling. There is one field of operation in which rolling, hammering and pressing all can be applied; this is the shaping of blooms and billets from ingots.

SECTION 6

PRINCIPAL METHODS FOR COLD WORKING

Cold working, generally applied to bars, wires tubes, sheet and strip, is a process of reducing the cross-sectional area by cold rolling, cold drawing, or cold extrusion. Cold working is employed to obtain the following effects: improved mechanical properties, better machinability, special size accuracy, bright surface, and the production of thinner gages than hot work can accomplish economically. The present brief discussion will be supplemented in later chapters by

discussion of methods and effects of cold working various steel-mill products.

Cold Rolling—Cold working by cold rolling consists of passing unheated, previously hot-rolled bars, sheets or strip (cleaned of scale) through a set of rolls, often many times, until the final size is obtained. Methods and effects of cold rolling wide strip are discussed in detail in Chapter 32.

Cold Drawing—In this process a bar, wire or tube,

after being cleaned, is pulled through a die having an opening smaller than the entering piece to reduce the latter to the required size (see Chapter 29).

Cold Extrusion—The cold extrusion of steel is carried out in a manner similar to the hot-extrusion process, with two main exceptions: (1) The steel is at room temperature, and (2) the surface of the piece is treated by some chemical process such as bonderizing to assist in reducing friction between the steel and the container wall and die, in conjunction with special lubricants.

Bibliography

American Society for Metals, Metals Handbook, Cleveland Ohio, 1948.

A. T. Adams, Wire Drawing and the Cold Working of Steel, Sherwood Press, Cleveland, Ohio, 1936.

Zay Jeffries and R. S. Archer, Science of Metals, McGraw-Hill Book Company, New York, 1924.

F. W. Harbord and J. W. Hall, The Metallurgy of Steel, J. B. Lippincott Company, Philadelphia, 1923.

W. Lueg, Hot Rolling of Medium Hard Carbon Steels, Stahl und Eisen, Vol. 57, 1937. Translated by Henry Brutcher, Lansdowne, Pennsylvania.

W. Trinks, Roll Pass Design, Vol. I, Second Edition, 1933, Vol. II, Second Edition, 1934, and Supplement to Roll Pass Design (Vols. I and II) First Edition, 1937, The Penton Publishing Company, Cleveland, Ohio.

Louis Moses, The Flow of Metal Between Rolls, Iron and Steel Engineer, Vol. XV, No. 11, February, 1938.

L. R. Underwood, The Rolling of Metals: Theory and Practice, Chapman and Hall, London, 1950.

Sheet and Strip Metal Users' Association, First Report of Special Conference on Cold Extrusion of Steel, Sheet Metal Industries, Vol. 30, No. 314, June, 1953.

W. Naujoks, Forging Handbook, American Society for Metals, Cleveland, Ohio, 1939.

Morton C. Smith, Principles of Physical Metallurgy, Harper & Brothers, New York, 1956.

CHAPTER 20

Construction and Operation
of Rolling Mills

SECTION 1

TYPES OF MILLS

General Classification—The three principal types of rolling mills used for the rolling of steel are referred to as **two-high, three-high,** and **four-high** mills, shown schematically in Figure **20—1.** As the names indicate, the classification is based on the manner of arranging the rolls in the housings, a two-high stand consisting of two rolls, one above the other; a three-high mill has three rolls, and a four-high mill has four rolls, arranged similarly. When rolling is in one direction only on **two-high mills,** and the piece is returned over the top of the rolls to be rerolled in the next pass, the mill is known as a **pull-over** or **drag-over** mill. This type of mill formerly was used mainly for production of light sheets and tin plate; it still is used by merchant mills for rolling of tool and high-alloy steels. On **two-high reversing mills,** the direction of rotation of the rolls can be reversed, and rolling is alternately in opposite directions, with work done on the piece while traveling in each direction. The long mill tables of reversing mills make it possible to handle heavy pieces in long lengths that would be impractical to roll on ordinary two-high mills, or to handle on the lift tables of a three-high mill (see below). The reversing two-high type of mill occupies an important position in the industry and, with the use of manipulators, it is possible to produce on it slabs, blooms, plates, billets, rounds, and partially-formed sections suitable for later rolling into finished shapes on other mills. In all **three-high mills,** each roll revolves continuously in one direction; the top and bottom rolls in the same direction and the middle roll in the opposite direction. The piece is lifted from the bottom pass to the return top pass by mechanically-operated lift tables, or by inclined approach tables. Usually the large top and bottom rolls are driven, while the smaller middle roll is friction driven. This latter roll is about two-thirds the size of the other two rolls, in order to permit removal through the housing windows. **Four-high mills** are used for rolling flat material, like sheets and plates, and represent a special type of two-high mill for both hot and cold rolling, in which large **backing-up rolls** are employed to reinforce the smaller **working rolls:** either the working or back-up rolls may be driven. Four-high mills resist the tend-

ency of long working rolls to deflect, and permit the use of small-diameter working rolls for producing wide plates, and hot- or cold-rolled strip and sheets of uniform gage. These mills often consist of a number of stands spaced closely together in one continuous line and are known then as **tandem mills;** the product passes in a straight line from one stand to the next. In **cluster mills,** each of the two small working rolls is supported by two (or more) backing-up rolls. This latter type of mill is used for the rolling of thin sheets.

ARRANGEMENT OF MILLS

A single stand mill, which may be either two-, three- or four-high, and either reversing or non-reversing, represents the most common arrangement for rolling a wide range of products, including blooms, slabs, plates, sheets, and various sections. **Guide, loop,** and **cross-country** mills are made up of several two- or three-high stands, or a combination of both, and are used for rolling of merchant-bar sections. **Guide mills** are small hand mills consisting of several stands of rolls in a **train.** Mills in train have the rolls of separate stands in the same line, the rolls of one mill being driven from the end of the rolls of an adjacent stand. Guide mills take their name from the metal guides which support the piece in the correct position during its passage through the grooves of the various passes. For example, it is possible to roll from an oval section to a round in one pass, provided the oval is supported by metal guides. In many guide mills it is the practice of the catchers, in order to save time, to start the piece through each of the passes before it is through the preceding one, thus forming a loop, resulting in this arrangement being called a **looping mill.** The layout of a mill of this type is shown in Chapter 28. There originated in Belgium the plan of setting up an independent roughing stand preceding the finishing train of the looping mill. This arrangement became known as a **Belgian mill.** On looping mills, it was found that the loop could be made mechanically by a tube or horse-shoe type trough, called a **repeater,** and thus dispense with the hand catchers. Prior to the looping mill, the piece was rolled throughout the entire length

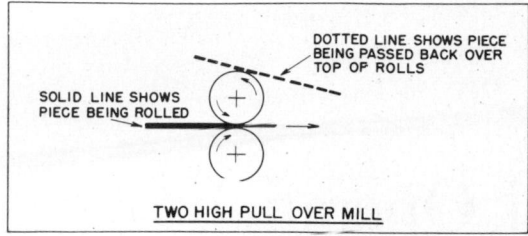

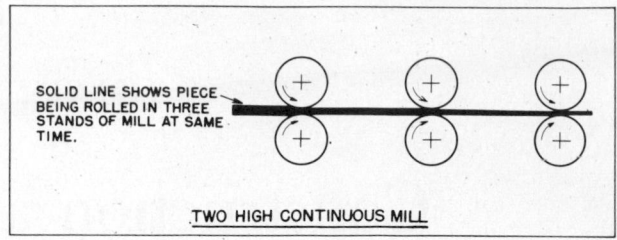

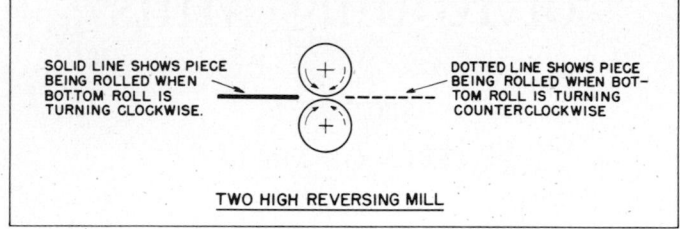

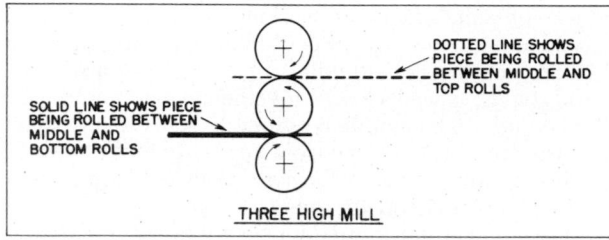

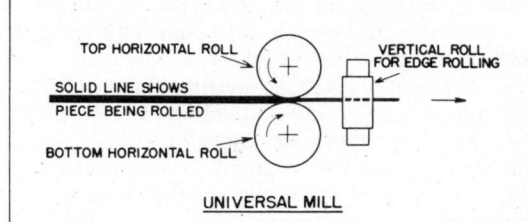

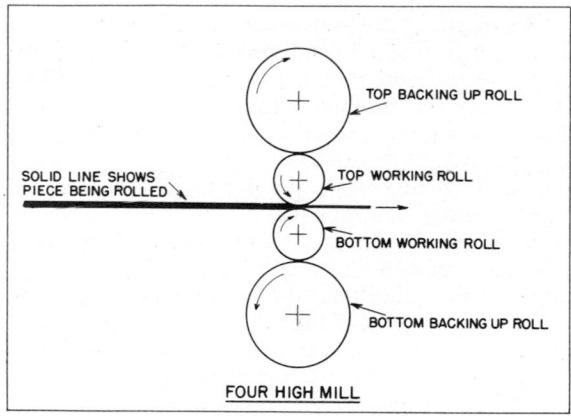

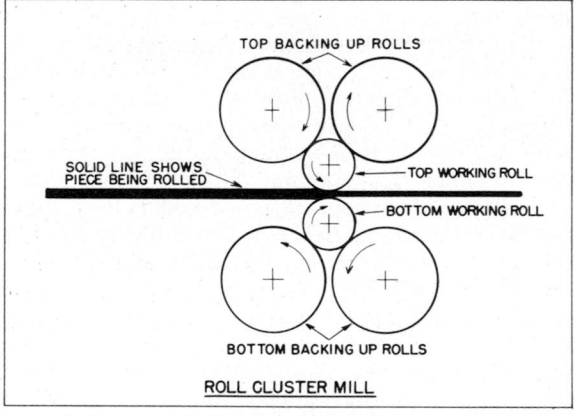

FIG. 20—1. Schematic representation of roll arrangements in the principal types of rolling mills.

in one pass before it could be entered in the next pass. The looping arrangement eliminates the temperature difficulties encountered with long lengths. The shapes produced range from simple rounds and squares to intricate special shapes, but must be relatively small in cross-section. The **cross-country mill** is so named because of the scattered location of its roll stands, and was developed for rolling sections that, due to size or shape, are not adaptable to loop rolling. These mills involve the continuous idea, but the stands are placed so far apart that the piece must leave one set of rolls before entering the next (see Chapter 28). To save space and to avoid complicating the drives, the stands

usually are arranged in two or more parallel lines, and the direction of travel of the piece is reversed during the rolling by employing transfer and skid tables. This arrangement results in a high-production mill of great flexibility, which may be used for a wide range of products, including structural shapes, rails, and splice bars. A **continuous mill** consists of several stands of rolls arranged in a straight line (in tandem), with each succeeding stand operating with roll surface speed greater than its predecessor. Such a mill is illustrated diagrammatically in Chapter 22. Reduction takes place in several passes at the same time until the piece emerges as a finished shape from the last roll stand.

This type of mill is in very common usage for rolling strip, sheet, billets, bars, rods, etc. A **semi-continuous mill** comprises also a four-high reversing roughing stand for reducing the piece prior to entering the continuous mill for reduction to the finished shape. This arrangement gives moderately high production with lower first cost than a continuous mill. **Combination mills** are those in which the roughing or major part of the reduction is performed in a continuous mill, and the shaping in a guide or looping mill.

SPECIALTY MILLS

The **universal mill** is a combination of horizontal and vertical rolls, usually mounted in the same roll stand (Figure **20**—1). The mill is made up of two-high (and occasionally three-high) horizontal rolls, with vertical roll sets on either or both sides of the horizontal stand. The vertical rolls also usually are driven. The direction of the piece is reversed after each pass in the mill. The universal mill is used to a limited ex-

tent also for plate product that requires rolled edges (see Figure **20**—2). A special type of universal mill, known as the **Gray mill** is well adapted for rolling beams and H-sections of great width and depth without taper on flanges (see Figure **20**—3). The horizontal rolls work on the web and flange thickness, while the idler vertical rolls in the same stand work simultaneously on flange thickness only. The roughing stands and intermediate stands are of the reversing type, and each has a separate stand of driven horizontal edging rolls which work on the flange height only. The finishing stand consists of the horizontal and vertical rolls in which the beams are given one pass only.

The **Wenstrom mill** is a similar modification of a universal plate mill, designed principally for rolling flats. Instead of acting upon the top and bottom and the two sides at different times, it docs this simultaneously. The top roll can be adjusted vertically, and the bottom roll transversely, whereby pieces of different thickness and width can be produced with the same set of rolls. The **Sack** universal mill, designed

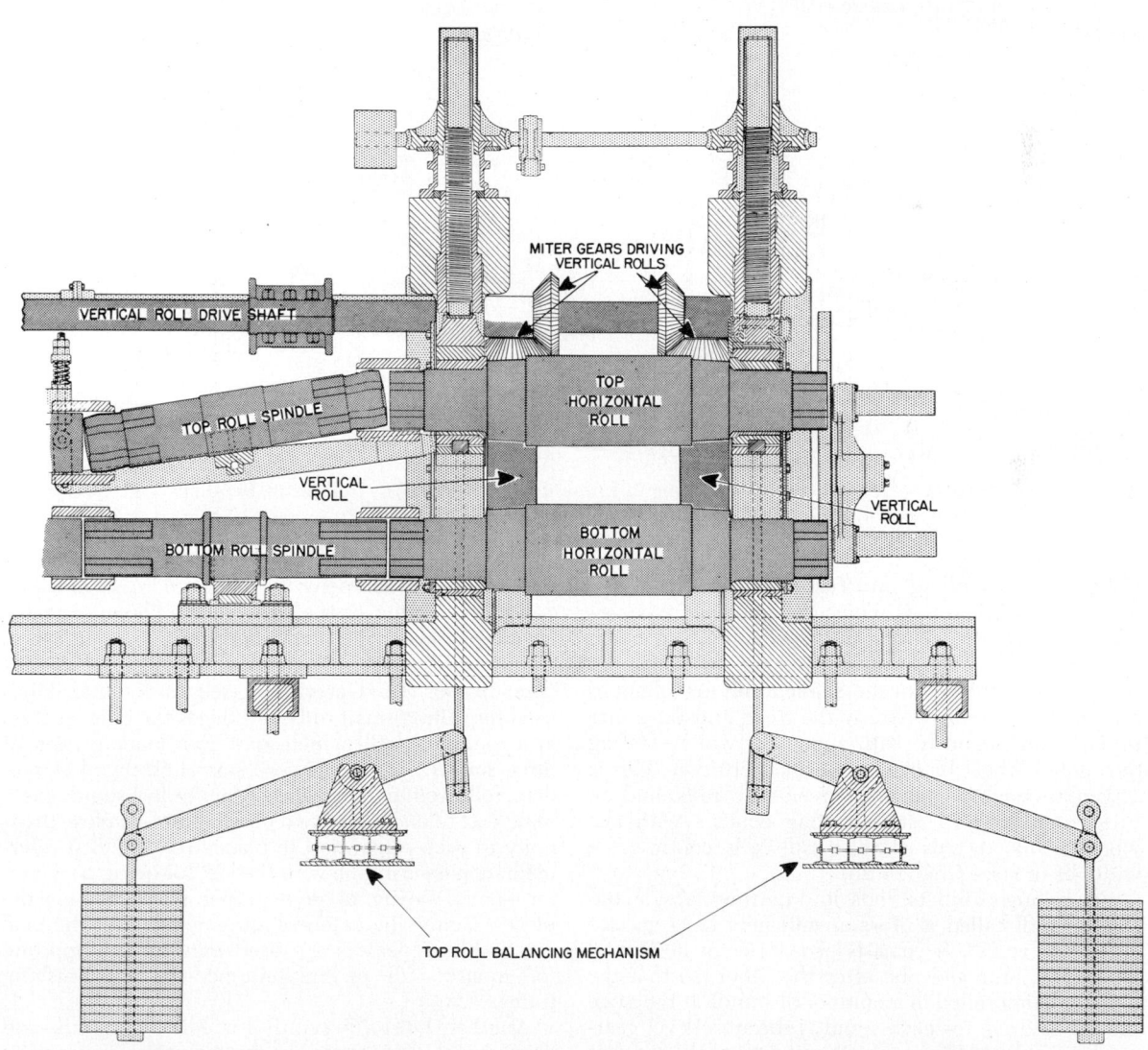

Fig. 20—2. Diagrammatic layout of the principal parts of a universal mill for rolling plates.

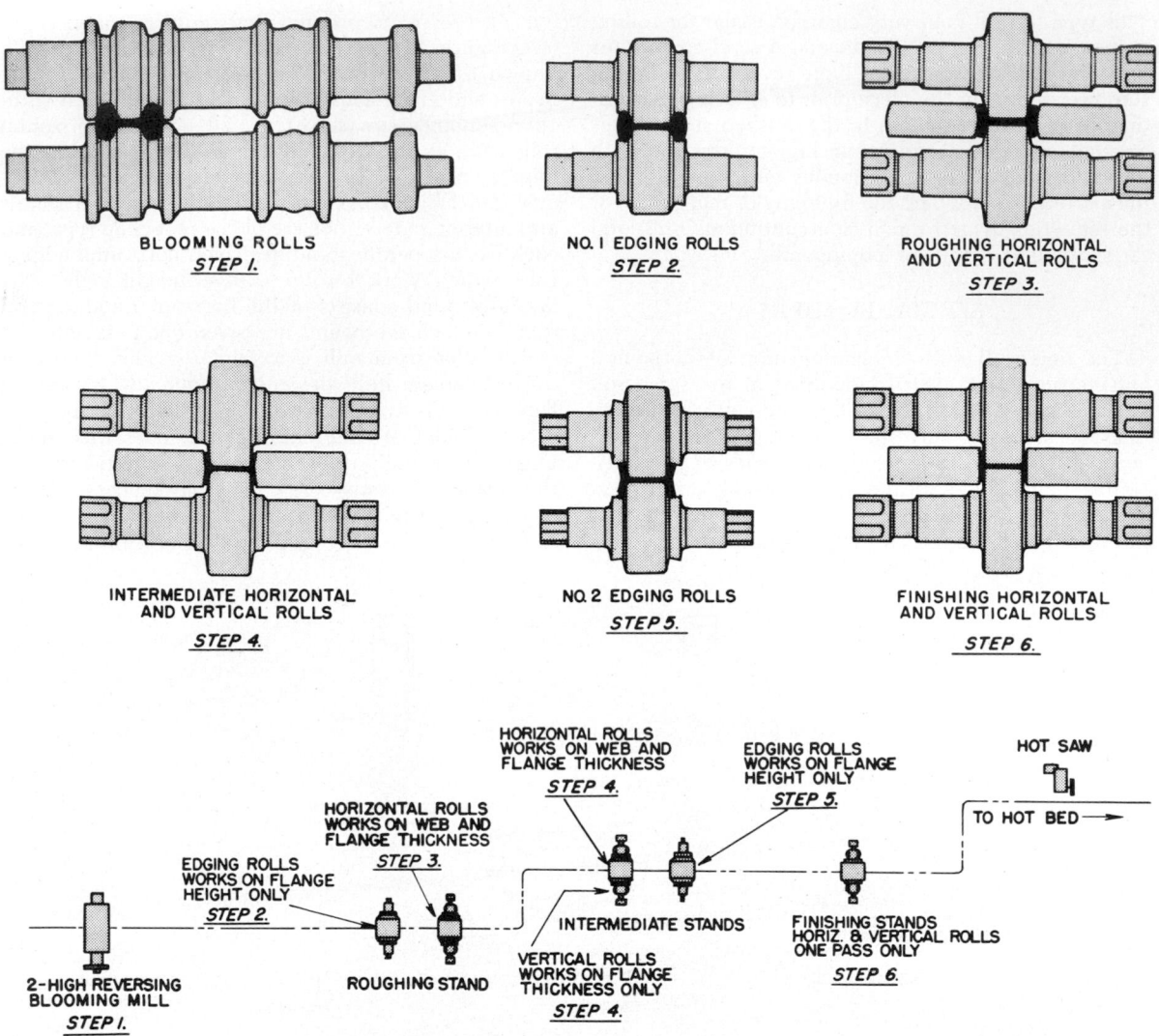

BLOOMING ROLLS
STEP 1.

NO. 1 EDGING ROLLS
STEP 2.

ROUGHING HORIZONTAL
AND VERTICAL ROLLS
STEP 3.

INTERMEDIATE HORIZONTAL
AND VERTICAL ROLLS
STEP 4.

NO. 2 EDGING ROLLS
STEP 5.

FINISHING HORIZONTAL
AND VERTICAL ROLLS
STEP 6.

HORIZONTAL ROLLS
WORKS ON WEB AND
FLANGE THICKNESS
STEP 4.

EDGING ROLLS
WORKS ON FLANGE
HEIGHT ONLY
STEP 5.

HOT SAW

TO HOT BED →

HORIZONTAL ROLLS
WORKS ON WEB AND
FLANGE THICKNESS
STEP 3.

EDGING ROLLS
WORKS ON FLANGE
HEIGHT ONLY
STEP 2.

INTERMEDIATE STANDS

FINISHING STANDS
HORIZ. & VERTICAL ROLLS
ONE PASS ONLY
STEP 6.

2-HIGH REVERSING
BLOOMING MILL
STEP 1.

ROUGHING STAND

VERTICAL ROLLS
WORKS ON FLANGE
THICKNESS ONLY
STEP 4.

FIG. 20—3. (Above) The rolls and their functions in forming an H section by rolling in two-high and Gray mills. (Below) Flow diagram showing layout of the mill utilizing the rolls shown above.

principally for rolling **cruciform sections,** has horizontal and vertical rolls which act upon the piece simultaneously, the general arrangement being much like that of the Wenstrom mill. A somewhat similar principle is employed in the **Schoen mill** for rolling of railroad car wheels, whereby the tread and flange are rolled simultaneously with the web, while rotating the forged wheel blank in a vertical position. This is accomplished by a pair of driven web rolls, and an idler tread roll in simultaneous contact with the wheel blank. A pair of idler rim rolls controls the width of rim (see Chapter 26).

For rolling of billets, rods, and narrow slabs, a continuous mill called a **Morgan mill** may be used (see also Chapter 29). It consists of a series of horizontal roll stands arranged one after the other, so that the piece is being rolled in a number of stands at the same time. The drive for each stand is through bevel gearing, with roll speed of each stand so proportioned that each set of rolls travels at a greater speed than neces-

sary merely to compensate for the increase in speed due to elongation of the piece in the preceding pass, in order to keep the piece under tension at all times. Twist guides may be used to turn the piece 90° between passes. The **Garrett mill** (see also Chapter 29) is used for rolling small rods; it reduces the billet section in a roughing mill, which may be a looping train of three stands, or two or more stands arranged in tandem, followed by two trains of four or five stands each, lying end to end along two parallel lines in close proximity to each other, and so placed that the first intermediate pass is in line with the last roughing pass, and far enough away to give proper clearance for the pieces. Generally, catchers are employed on the oval side, while repeaters are used only on the opposite (or square) side of the intermediate and finishing trains.

Another hot-rolling mill for billets, rounds and squares is the ingenious **Lamberton mill,** developed to avoid the need for a reversing motor. This mill (Figure

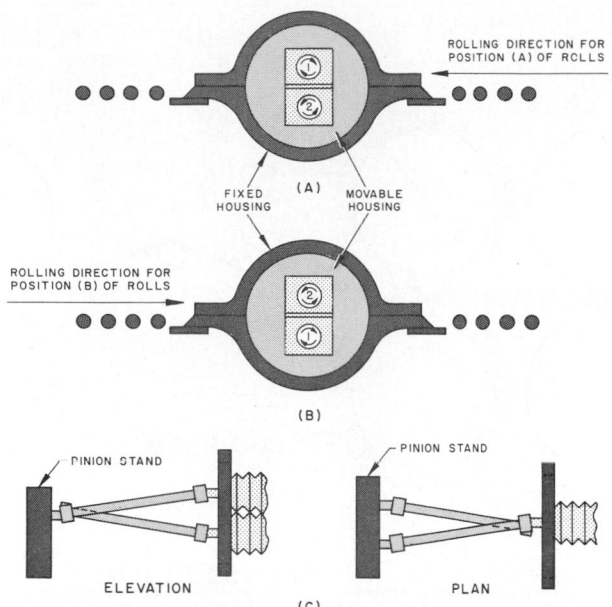

FIG. 20—4. Schematic representation of the principle of operation of a Lamberton mill. Turning the movable housing 180 degrees reverses the relative positions of the rolls without changing their respective directions of rotation. This is facilitated by having the pinion shafts in the same horizontal plane. The spindles on an actual mill are relatively longer than shown here, and are provided with separate support.

20—4) is a two-high unit, with the motor turning in one direction only. The roll housing has two horizontal rolls in the usual position, but the shafts of the mill pinions are in the same horizontal plane. The mill housing is arranged to revolve through 180°, so that the rolls exchange positions after each pass, thus reversing the rolling direction. The bottom roll becomes the top roll, and vice versa, without changing their directions of rotation; thus, bars may be rolled in either direction without reversing the motor.

The Sendzimir **planetary hot-rolling** mill (Figure **20—5**) was developed to reduce slabs to coiled hot-rolled strip in a single pass. Such a mill consists of the planetary assemblies proper, and feed rolls (one pair preceded by a pair of pinch rolls or two pairs of feed rolls) which push the slab (taking a small reduction) through a guide into the planetary rolls where the main reduction takes place. Other means than rolls have been used for pushing slabs into the mill. The mill is followed by a two-high or four-high planishing mill and coiler. The planetary assemblies consist of two back-up rolls surrounded by a number of small work rolls that are mounted in "cages" at their extremities. The cages are synchronized by external means so that each pair of opposed work rolls passes through the vertical center line of the mill at precisely the same time and so that the axes of the work rolls are always parallel to the axes of the back-up rolls. The angular velocity of the cage is somewhat less than half the angular velocity of the back-up roll. As shown in Figure 20—5, the cages rotate in the same direction as the corresponding back-up rolls, while the

work rolls rotate in the opposite direction (i.e., the work rolls turn clockwise when their back-up roll and cage turn counterclockwise). Mills are built with different ratios between back-up roll and work-roll diameters, and with different numbers of work rolls per back-up roll (18, 20, 24, 26, and 30 work rolls per back-up roll have been employed on different existing mills). The rolling process is cyclic. Work rolls make contact with the unworked portion of the slab, then work downward gradually, making a rolling pass in the deformation zone and finally breaking contact with the material where it has reached the final thickness but not before the next pair of work rolls has contacted the slab. Generally speaking, the temperature of the strip is higher at the exit side of the planetary mill than the temperature of the slab at its entrance, due to the energy of plastic deformation involved in the heavy reductions (as much as 98 per cent) that the mill is capable of effecting: this permits the rolling of slabs at lower entering temperatures than in conventional hot-strip-mill practice. Mills of this type can be designed up to 80 inches wide.

Sendzimir cold-rolling mills (frequently referred to as **Z-mills**) feature several roll arrangements, the predominant one of which is the 1-2-3-4 arrangement illustrated in Figure **20—6**, which is the only one that will be discussed here. In this design, each work roll is supported throughout its entire length by two first-intermediate rolls that are, in turn, supported by three second-intermediate rolls (of which the outer ones are driven) which transfer the roll-separating forces

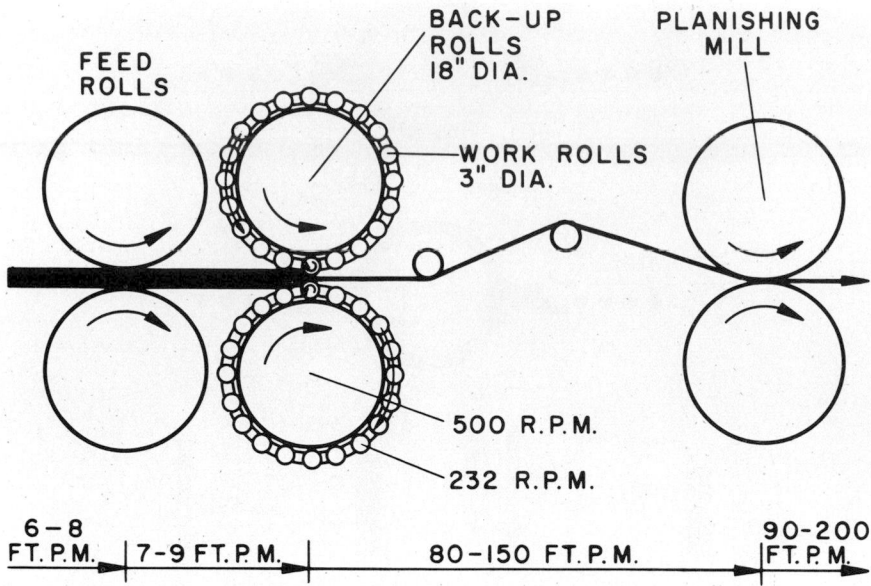

FIG. 20—5. Schematic representation of a planetary hot-rolling mill. Slab speed, roll speeds and product speeds were taken from a paper by H. W. Ward in the January 1958 issue of "Iron and Steel" and represent a typical set of operating conditions on an existing British mill.

to a rigid, one-piece cast-steel housing through four backing assemblies. The work rolls are driven by the four driven rolls through friction contact with the first intermediate rolls. Screwdown is controlled by rotation of the primary eccentric rings (see Figure 20—6) on the bearing shafts of the two top-center backing assemblies: hydraulic-cylinder-driven racks rotate the shafts by engaging pinion teeth mounted at both ends of each shaft. The two bottom-center bearing assemblies are similarly equipped to permit positioning of the lower work roll to balance the pass line. The two remaining pairs of eccentric shafts at the left and right of the diagram are also adjustable as pairs to maintain roll-opening capacity while compensating for roll wear. Depending upon the size of the mill and the roll arrangement, either mechanical or hydraulic means can be provided for crown adjustment by positioning individual secondary eccentric rings (see Figure 20—6) at the saddles. On most Sendzimir cold mills, such adjustment is possible during the operation of the mill. Lateral axial adjustment of the first-intermediate rolls (that are provided with minute crown or taper reliefs at opposite ends, as shown in Figure 20—6) enables the set-up of the mill to be changed quickly for rolling strip of various widths, thicknesses, and hardnesses.

The **Unitemper mill** is used as one means for temper rolling or skin rolling of finished cold-reduced strip. This mill consists of two stands of two-high mills, but with the second stand above the first in the same mill housing, to provide closer spacing between the two stands. With the motor of the first stand acting as a generator, and the motor of the second stand acting as a motor, the strip can be elongated a controlled amount between passes with only a very slight reduction in each stand due to rolling.

Die rolling is the process of rolling a string of blanks, each of which has varying cross-sectional area produced by heavy reductions, and specified center to center length. When sheared to length the blanks are of identical shape. Products such as automobile axles and crankshafts are produced satisfactorily by die rolling. The blanks are rolled with or without flashing, depending upon the particular product section.

For producing seamless tubing, the types of piercing mills include the **Mannesmann** or parallel-axis barrel-type roll piercing mill, the 60° **cone-roll** piercing mill, and the **Stiefel** or 180° disc mill. For the operating principles of these piercing mills, refer to Chapter 30. A **continuous tube rolling mill,** built in 1948 by United States Steel Corporation, consists of nine tandem individually powered stands of two-high grooved rolls. The rolls in the consecutive stands have their axes at 90° with each other. A cylindrical mandrel extends entirely through the pierced billet and passes through the mill with the work piece. The reheated tubes are processed in a tension reducing mill consisting of sixteen two-high roll stands, without the use of a mandrel. For producing buttweld pipe the **Fretz-Moon tube mill** may be used. The skelp on leaving the furnace enters the first pair of rolls which form the piece downward, with the edges still apart. The second pair form the complete circle and bring the edges of skelp together, and the welding of the edges by their own heat takes place. The mill actually consists of three pairs of horizontal rolls and three pairs of vertical rolls. The last four pairs reduce and size the pipe, and furnish traction for pulling the skelp through the furnace and forming rolls.

Opportunity will be given in later sections to become better acquainted with the operating details of most of these mills. The types of rolls used in the more common mills, and their manufacture, will be discussed in Section 3 of this chapter.

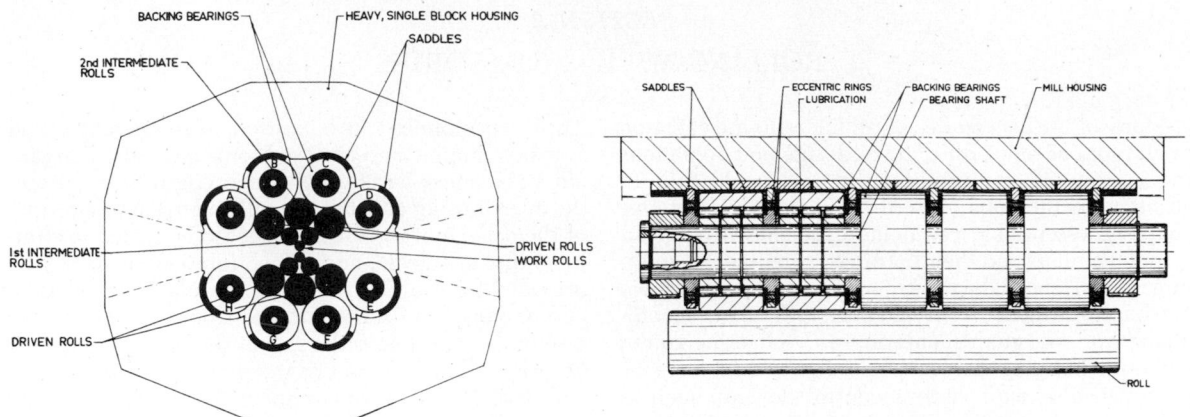

PRINCIPLE OF ROLL ARRANGEMENT AND SUPPORT
IN A SENDZIMIR MILL

TYPICAL BACKING ASSEMBLY OF A SENDZIMIR MILL

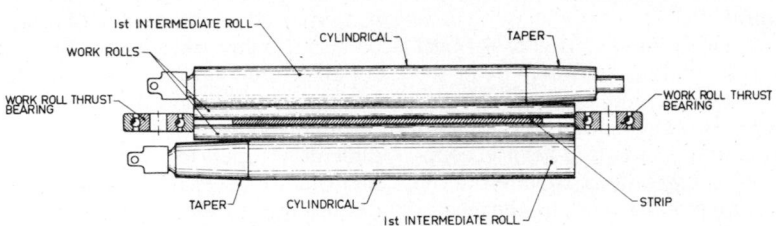

LATERAL ADJUSTMENT OF 1st INTERMEDIATE ROLLS ON A SENDZIMIR
MILL FOR STRIP SHAPE CORRECTION AND PROVIDING PRESSURE CONT-
ROL ALONG STRIP EDGES

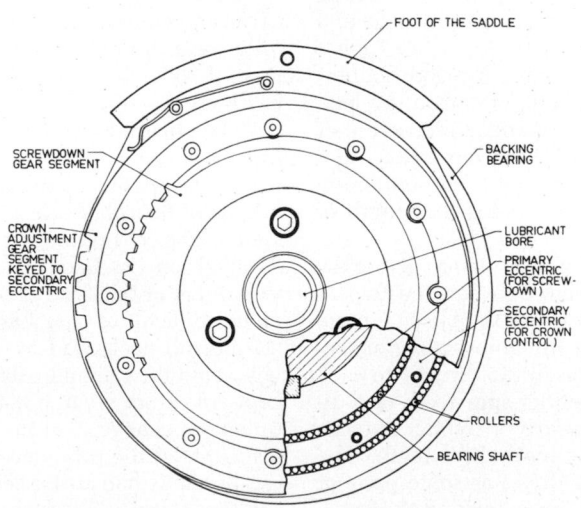

THE SENDZIMIR PRINCIPLE OF MILL SCREWDOWN AND
CROWN CONTROL
(END ELEVATION OF A BACKING ASSEMBLY WITH DOUBLE ECCENTRICS)

FIG. 20—6. Roll arrangement, details of backing assembly and lateral adjustment of first intermediate rolls on a Sendzimir cluster mill of the 1-2-3-4 type.

SECTION 2

ROLLING-MILL ACCESSORIES

Many of the accessories of rolling mills are common to all types of mills, differing in design and operations to conform with the conditions in a particular mill. In addition to the rolls (described in Section 3 of this chapter), essential parts include the mill **drive, lead spindle, pinions** and their **housings, spindles** and **coupling boxes, chock bearings, screws** and **screw-down mechanism, edgers, front** and **back mill tables, manipulators** and **side guards, entering** and **delivering guides** and **roll-changing devices.** The newer mills may be equipped also with various control devices, such as pressure meters and automatic roll-setting devices. Many of these parts are discussed in the description of particular types of mills in later chapters. In the following, a discussion is presented of those parts essential to the operation of the rolls. To aid in locating some of the various parts described below, Figure 20—7 shows a cross-sectional diagram of a high-lift reversing blooming mill.

Lead Spindle—The lead spindle is used to connect the prime mover with the pinions, and may be of the universal type, either short-coupled, or long with carrier bearings, depending on the position of the motor in the layout. If short-coupled, standard flexible couplings can be used. The lead spindle is attached to the bottom pinion of two-high mills, and to the center pinion of three-high mills. If the pinions are of the universal type, they can be of generous proportions, as their diameter is not limited by the space available. Lubrication of all working surfaces is important. Grease usually is applied through a system of holes drilled in the jaws, and connected to various designs of spring-loaded cavities in the spindle body. The connection at either end of the spindle may be made by a **coupling box,** which is a hollow cylindrical casting corresponding in section to the wobbler, with one end fitting the spindle and the other the pinion (see Figure 20—14). The coupling box usually is made deliberately as the weak spot of the mill, either on the lead spindle or the spindles on the roll end. In the event of extreme overloading of the mill, the box breaks and disconnects the motor from the mill. The minimum length of spindle is slightly over twice the length of the coupling box that is used.

Pinions—The pinions are gears serving to divide the power transmitted by the drive between the two or three rolls, driving the adjacent rolls in opposite directions. If twin-motor drives are used, no pinions are required, since the power is transmitted directly to each roll. The earlier pinions had either spur teeth or a divided face and staggered spur-type teeth, but the present practice is to use double helical teeth. The helical gears give a smoother drive, as some parts of the teeth are in contact at all times, making the transmission of power continuous. When rolling certain grades of materials, operation of the old type of pinion with spur teeth was characterized by jarring of the meshing teeth. This mechanical jarring was transmitted to the rolls and produced marks on the product being rolled. Pinions are made of cast or forged steel.

They are mounted in babbitted bearings and set in housings similar to those used for roll stands. The pinion stand must be of adequate strength to withstand the over-turning effect of the full and maximum torque of the drive motor. Housings should be sealed to eliminate dirt and scale, and forced lubrication should be provided for the pinions. Except in plate, direct-drive and universal mills, the distance from center to center of pinions determines the size of the mill. The pinions absorb about 6 per cent of the power transmitted.

Spindles are used to connect the pinions with the rolls if the mill is not a direct-driven type; in the latter case the spindle is connected directly to the motors. Spindles are made of cast or forged steel and are fitted at each end with wobblers similar to those on the rolls (Figure 20—14), or with the universal couplings, depending upon the type of mill. The bottom spindle runs in spring-balanced carriers, and the top spindle is supported at its center of gravity by carrier bars balanced hydraulically or by counterweights. The spindles are supported by babbitt or composition bearings, and should operate as nearly level as possible to prevent excessive power loss. It is very difficult to operate with a spindle more than 15 degrees out of level. This angle may be kept within the desired limits by increasing the length of the spindles. If the angularity is greater than 6 degrees or 7 degrees, a universal coupling should be used, in which case the ends of the wobbler are cut from a section of a sphere to give them the rounded form necessary to permit them to work at different angles, and the spindle is supported by saddle bearings in a carrier which rises and falls with the top roll and holds the spindle in place.

The Bearings—The bearings, which support the roll necks and align the rolls, may be of two general types; roller bearings or the older chock-type bearings. One type of roller bearing is illustrated diagrammatically in Figure 20—8.

Roller bearings first were used for rolling mills in Czechoslovakia in 1921 and in Sweden in 1922, where they were applied to small hot-rolling mills. In America, use of the roller bearing accompanied the development of the cold-reduction mill for strip and sheet, and its adoption has been extensive since 1932. The development of this type of bearing was slow on account of the difficulties that had to be overcome; namely, (1) the roll necks had to be of adequate diameter to withstand the rolling loads; (2) the roll necks had to be kept free from wear; (3) the bearings had to permit quick roll changes; (4) the bearings had to permit adjustments of the roll laterally as well as vertically; (5) the bearings had to be self-adjusting to take care of slight changes in the shape of the rolls caused by heating and bending; (6) the bearings had to have ample carrying capacity; and (7) in case of roll breakage, provisions had to be made to keep the bearings themselves from being damaged. Roller bearings are now common in new mills, although they have not replaced entirely the chock type of bearing, which possesses the

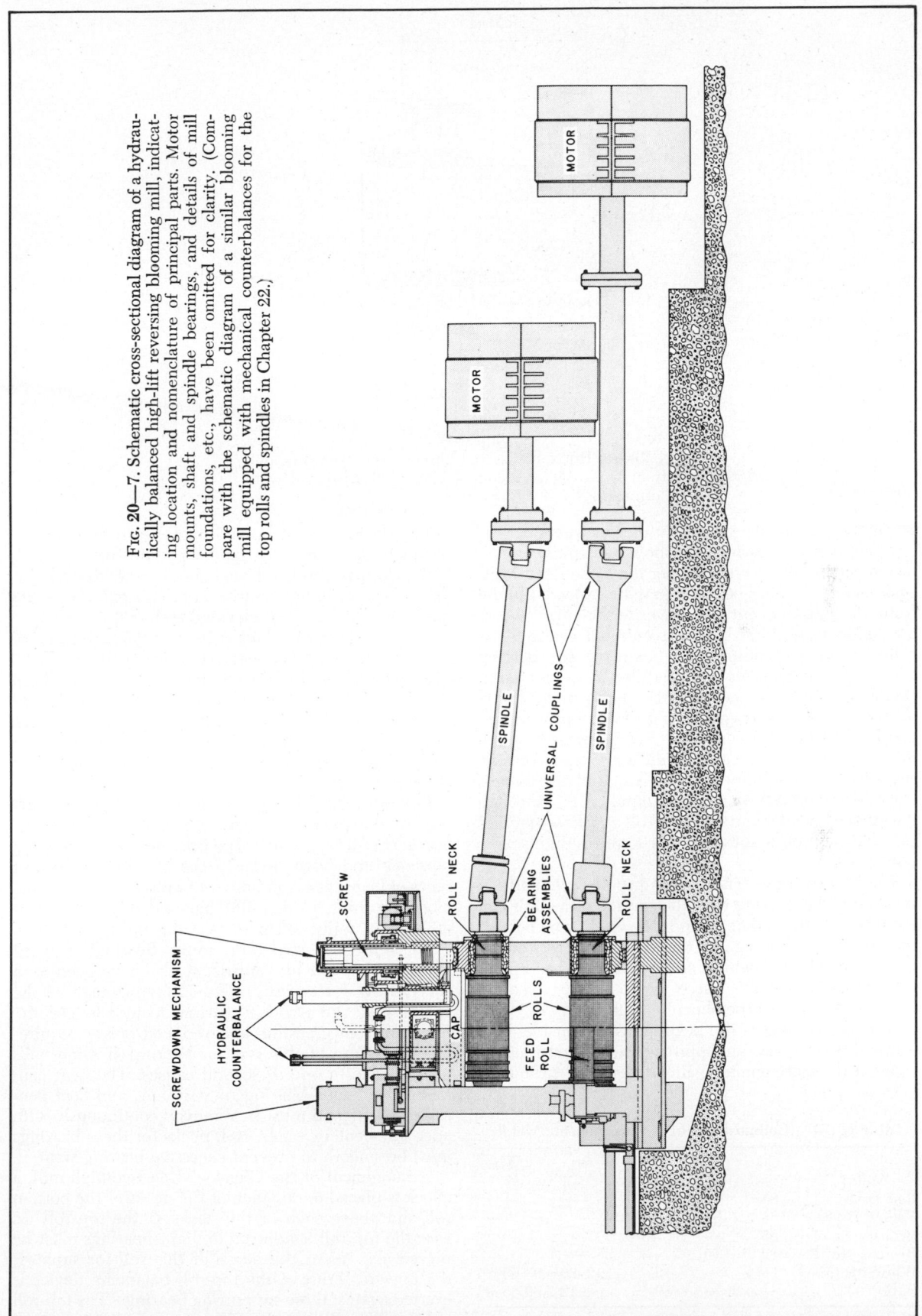

FIG. 20—7. Schematic cross-sectional diagram of a hydraulically balanced high-lift reversing blooming mill, indicating location and nomenclature of principal parts. Motor mounts, shaft and spindle bearings, and details of mill foundations, etc., have been omitted for clarity. (Compare with the schematic diagram of a similar blooming mill equipped with mechanical counterbalances for the top rolls and spindles in Chapter 22.)

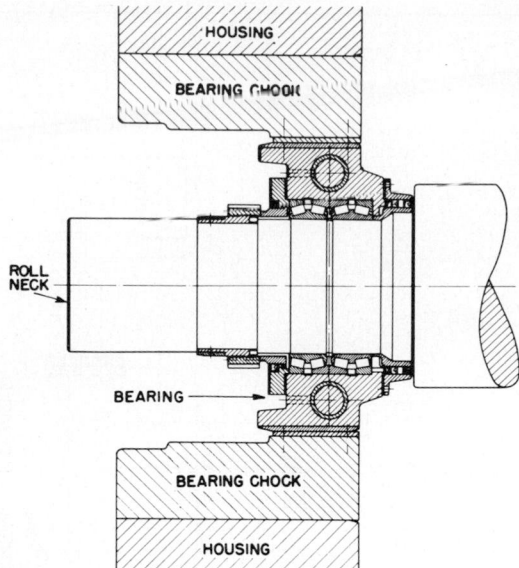

FIG. **20**—8. Horizontal section through the centerline of a bottom work-roll chock on a plate mill equipped with roller bearings.

advantage of greater simplicity of construction.

Modern roller bearings are showing extremely long life, with resulting lower cost per ton of product. Mills equipped with roller bearings may be expected to use from 15 to 20 per cent less power for the main drives than mills using bronze or conventional bearings. As roller bearings require no adjustment for bearing wear, greater tonnages can be rolled with less variation in section from piece to piece, permitting requirements to be met with greater ease and improved mill yield. Roller bearings also result in a general reduction in mill maintenance, and, as an automatic greasing system is used for lubrication, a clean mill operation is effected. Figure **20**—8 is a horizontal section through the center-line of a bottom work-roll chock (sometimes called chuck) on a 160-inch four-high reversing plate mill.

Chock Bearings—The chocks usually are made in two parts, the bearing with the surface of its lining in contact with the roll neck, and the chock, which holds the bearing in place against the roll neck. The bearings may be lined with babbitt or may be made with babbitt, brass or bronze inserts or they may be nonmetallic bearings of the phenolic-resin type.

The alloys used in the bearings vary considerably. Table **20**—I gives an approximate composition of some of the more common alloys used for bearings.

The tin in babbitt bearing metals can be replaced satisfactorily in most instances by substituting lead-base babbitts for tin-base babbitts and making, in some cases, additions of silver or arsenic to increase the hardness of the alloy at elevated temperatures.

As bearings made of all of these metals are soft and not very strong, it is necessary to insert them in supporting castings which are set into the housings. These castings are box-like in shape, each one containing on one side a semicircular groove corresponding to, but larger than, the necks of the rolls. In order to reduce weight, the castings are cored out, and may be of either iron or steel.

Reference has been made above to the use of bearings of the phenolic resin type. These composition bearings of a laminated type operate with water as a lubricant and have replaced the bronze and babbitt types of bearings on a number of mills, including some blooming mills, plate mills, bar and billet mills, rod mills, strip mills, skelp mills, tube mills, three-high sheet mills, and structural mills. Bearings of hard wood, with water as a lubricant also have been used successfully for certain mills. The advantage of the composition and wooden bearings include longer life, freedom from greasing, and reduced power requirements. Failure of this type of bearing in some mills may be due to one of several causes. The heat conductivity of such bearings is very low, and heat generated by friction must be removed continuously with adequate cooling water. Roll necks for these bearings must be smooth to prevent excessive bearing wear.

Arrangement of the Chocks—In a two-high mill, a chock is placed under each of the necks of the bottom roll and above each of the necks of the top roll. In case the top roll is adjustable, light bearings must be placed also under the necks of this roll for support; the upward thrust of the top-roll balancing device is exerted against these supporting bearings. The top-roll balance is for the purpose of keeping: (1) the top-roll

Table **20**—I. **Compositions of Typical Bearing Metals**

Metal	Cu (%)	Zn (%)	Sn (%)	Sb (%)	Pb (%)
Red Brass	85	15	—	—	—
Yellow Brass	65	35	—	—	—
Bronze, No. 1	85	—	15	—	—
Bronze, No. 2	82	15	3	—	—
White Metals	—	—	10–15	12–20	65–80
Babbitts*	—	—	59–91	4–12	0.35–26

*As, 0.1 max.; Bi, 0.08 max.; Fe, 0.08 max.

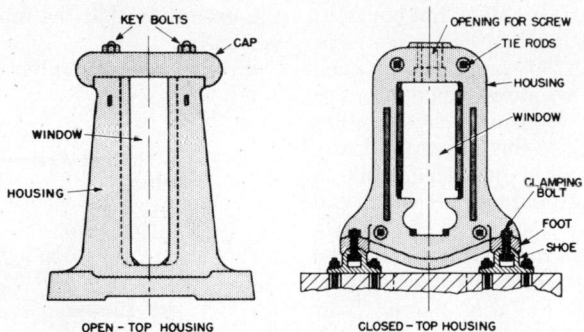

FIG. 20—9. Diagrams indicating principal parts and their names for (left) a closed-top housing and (right) an open-top housing.

necks in contact with the upper chock bearings; (2) the chocks tight up against the screw points; and (3) the screw-thread surfaces in contact. On heavy mills, the counterbalance may be of the overhead hydraulic-cylinder type connected to an accumulator system, or of the underneath counterweight-and-lever type; both types of counterbalances can be compared in Figures 20—7 and 22—7. On small mills, screw bolts extending through the housing serve the same purpose. The exposed half of the necks of the lower roll usually will be covered to protect them from scale, etc.

The arrangement of chocks in three-high mills is more difficult. The simplest way is to place double-groove chocks between the top and middle and the middle and bottom rolls, and then set them in the housings one above the other, so that all the adjusting made necessary by the wearing away of the bearings and the material of the rolls themselves may be made with large screws in the top of the housing that can be turned to move upward or downward. However, this arrangement causes the bottom bearing to wear down rapidly and increases the power required to drive the mill, owing to the additional friction induced on the bottom bearing by the weight of the upper two rolls and their chocks. This fault may be overcome in two ways: (1) by making the bottom roll fixed and supporting the weight of the upper two rolls and their chocks on the shoulders of the chocks themselves, the dis-

tance between rolls may then be regulated with shims, or "liners," by adding or removing the shims as the bearings wear down; (2) a better way, and the one most often employed in modern mills, is to make the middle roll fixed, in which case the bottom roll is raised or lowered by an adjusting wedge attached to a screw in the housing which permits it to be moved back and forth with a wrench from the outside of the housing.

In all mills, two-high as well as three-high, the top chocks are held down by two strong screws which work in threaded holes or nuts in the tops of the housings.

The functions of the chocks are not only to furnish vertical bearings for the rolls but also to prevent their movement laterally as well. This lateral displacement of the roll is prevented by the inner edge of the bearing which is formed to fit against the shoulder of the roll. Adjustment for wear in this direction is provided by adjusting screws which extend through the side of the housing and bear on the ends of the chocks. This lateral adjustment is a matter of great importance in rolling sections that require grooved rolls, the reason for which is self-evident.

Housings—There are two housings for each stand of rolls (see Figure 20—9). They may be made either of iron or steel, the choice of materials depending upon the size of the mill and the strength required.

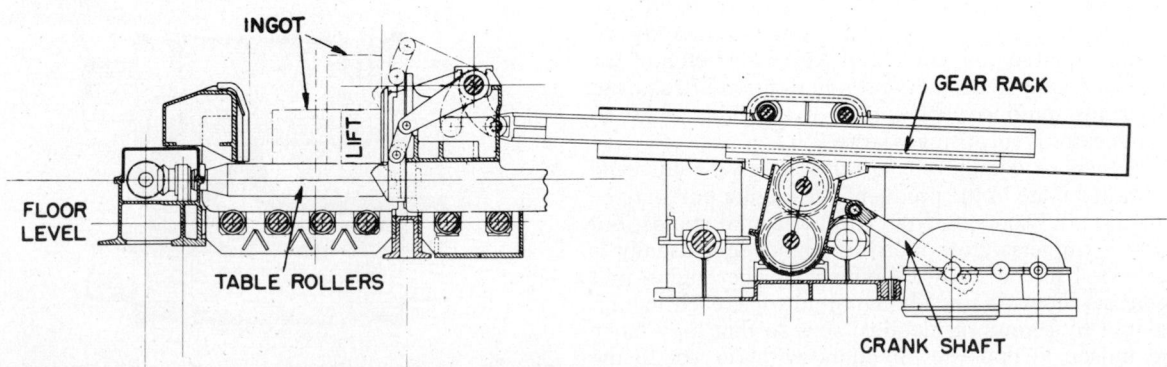

FIG. 20—10. Schematic diagram of the main operating parts of a typical manipulator, showing motion of the lifting fingers that raise ingot by a corner in the process of turning it 90 degrees.

Generally they are of annealed cast steel, but housings may be of welded steel construction, heavy plates or slabs. The housings are of an "O" or "U" form, each having an opening called the **window,** which serves as a receptacle for the bearings. Housings may be either **closed top** (O) or **open top** (U). In the former, the base, the two legs and the top are all in one piece, while in the latter, the top will form a separate part which can be removed. The base of the housing is cast with a projection on each side to form the **feet.** In the bottom of each foot is cut a groove which fits over a **shoe,** running parallel to the rolls. Suitably shaped bolts then serve to clamp the foot of the housing to the shoe, which is fastened firmly to the foundation by long bolts. This method permits the housing to be moved laterally, and facilitates the lining up of the mill. The tops of the two housings in a set are prevented from spreading apart by suitable **tie rods** or, in the case of open-top housings, the top for both housings may be cast in one piece. Similarly, tie rods usually will be placed at the bottom. Recesses or other openings are cast in the inside face of each housing to receive the supports for the guards and guides, these supports being usually in the form of square **rest bars** which extend from housing to housing in front of the rolls. The immense pressure applied to the rolls between the top and bottom of the housing acts as a stretching force on the uprights of the housings; the degree to which the housings resist this force is an important factor in determining the reduction that can be effected in one pass and also the exactness with which the thickness of the piece is controlled. The uprights of the housings sometimes are referred to as **posts.**

A **screw down mechanism** is used on mills to position the top roll for each pass through the mill, except on continuous and three-high mills where fixed passes are used. The top roll is adjusted by **screws** which extend through the top of each housing. The screwdown bearings are of roller or antifriction type. The transmission of power was first accomplished by hydraulic pressure, but in modern mills the speed of the operation has been greatly increased by electric drives. On one recent installation, the maximum rate of raising or lowering the top roll is 38 feet per minute, compared with 2 or 3 feet per minute on the older mills. On small mills where the adjustment is only occasional, the screws will be operated by hand with spanner bars. In all cases, compression of these screws is unavoidable and, combined with the stretch of the housings plus deflection and deformation of rolls and bearings, produces the **spring** of the mill, which in some cases is surprisingly large.

Edgers or **edging rolls** are used to give a universal or rolled edge to the product. The edging unit may be a roll stand separate from the horizontal stands, but in the universal-type mill the edging unit usually is attached to the main-roll housings. The edging unit consists of two vertically-mounted rolls, each manipulated by screws of identical size, so that they move in unison in opposite directions with respect to the centerline of the mill. Each roll is operated through a screw-down mechanism like that used on the top horizontal roll of a reversing or universal-type mill, with the exception that the motion is horizontal instead of vertical.

Front and back roller tables feed and receive the

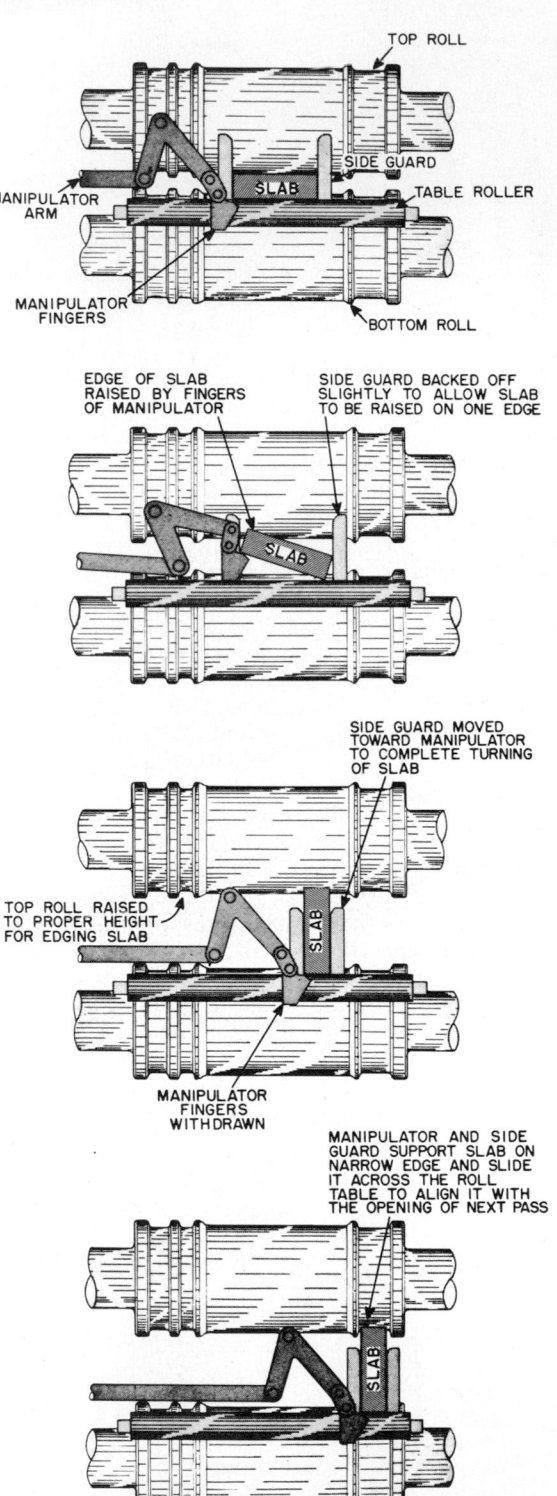

FIG. **20**—11. Schematic representation of the actions of the principal parts of a manipulator in turning a slab 90 degrees. The mechanisms have been simplified and exaggerated in size for the sake of clarity.

piece during each pass. Their speed should be matched closely to that of the rolls, and the width should be the same. On reversing mills these tables are subject to heavy usage due to impact from turning the piece, and should be of rugged construction. Forged steel generally is used today in making the rollers, which in new mills are mounted in roller bearings and equipped with automatic lubrication. In the older mills, bronze or babbitt bearings are lubricated by hand. The rollers usually are electrically driven by a line shaft through miter gears.

The **manipulator** consists of a pair of side guards, stroking laterally over the rollers of the front or back mill tables, usually on both sides of the mill (Figures **20—10, 20—11** and **20—12**). The manipulators operate to turn the piece between passes, to move it to another pass, and to straighten it when necessary. Most manipulators are constructed so that both horizontal and vertical motion is possible. In most mills, these units are operated by electric or hydraulic power. Depending upon the size of ingot or section to be manipulated, the height of side guards may run up to 48

inches. Lifting fingers, always on the front manipulator and sometimes on the back one also, are incorporated in the guard or guards toward the drive side. These have a vertical or nearly vertical stroke and serve to lift the piece by a corner in the process of turning it 90 degrees.

Guides and Guards—In order to prevent collaring and to insure that the piece enters and leaves the pass in the correct position, guides are employed. These guides vary in form and size to fit the conditions. In some cases, they are merely grooved fore-plates; in others, they are blunt-edged plates set up in front of the collars, dividing the space in front of the rolls into a series of pigeon holes; in large mills rolling heavy sections, they may take the form of grooved rollers; in the smaller mills like the guide mills, they are trumpet-shaped castings that fit close up to the roll and have exit openings to conform to the shape and size of the section of the entering piece; in continuous mills they may be constructed so as to twist and thus turn the piece between two successive passes. Guides may be employed on both sides of a pass, in which case they

Fig. **20—12**. Blooming mill in operation rolling a round section, showing location of manipulator with respect to stand.

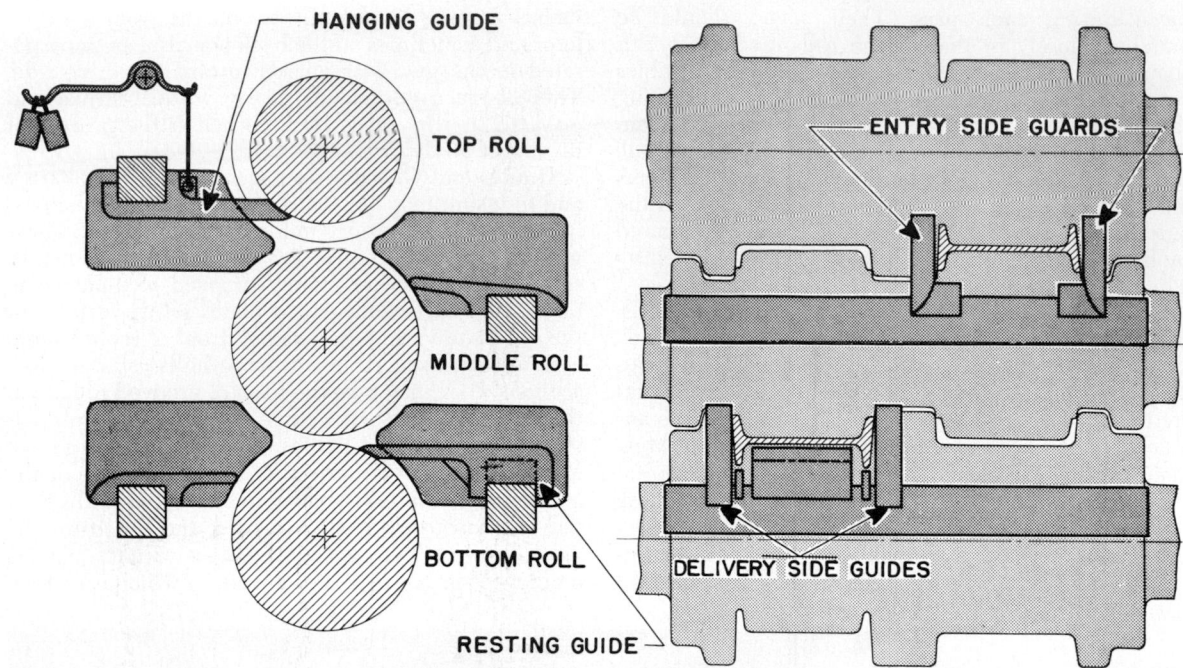

FIG. 20—13. Schematic representation of guides and guards applied to a three-high mill.

are designated as **entering guides** and **delivery guides.** They are held in place by means of the rest bars previously mentioned in connection with the housings. **Guards** are devices employed mainly on the delivery side of the mill to control the direction of the piece after leaving the pass. Reversing and three-high mills are provided with guards on both sides of the mill (see Figure **20—13**).

Roll-changing devices are dependent upon the construction of the mill housing. The rolls in an open-top housing are changed by removing the housing cap and picking out the rolls separately or collectively with crane slings. Roll changing in closed-top housings is accomplished through the window of the housing either: (1) by using a counterweighted porter bar,

(2) by a sleeve utilizing the ingoing roll as a counter-weight, or (3) by a "C" hook. All of these methods require overhead crane service to remove the rolls one at a time. The rolls are pulled out of the housing by attaching a socket fitting over the protruding roll necks. In some large modern mills, a roll-changing rig is used to remove worn rolls and install new ones. The rig is placed in a permanent mounting, level with the housing sill, and consists of a rack-and-pinion motor-operated crosshead mounted on a rail frame. It withdraws both top and bottom rolls with their respective bearings, all at one time. The old setup is removed from the rig by the crane and the new rolls and bearings are mounted on the rig to be pushed back into the mill.

SECTION 3

ROLLING-MILL ROLL DESIGN AND MANUFACTURE

Principal Parts of Rolls—Of the essential parts of the rolling mill, the rolls are of the greatest interest, as they control the reduction and shaping of the metal. There are three parts to a roll; namely, the **body,** or the part on which the rolling is done, the **necks** which support the body and take the rolling pressure, and the **wobblers,** where the driving force is applied through loose-fitting **spindles** and **boxes** which together form a sort of ingenious universal coupling. These parts are shown in Figure **20—14**.

A plain-surface or cylindrically-bodied roll is used (in pairs) for rolling sheets and plates, while for bars and shapes, grooves of suitable design are turned in the roll bodies. Such grooves are called **passes.**

Figure **20—15** shows two examples of grooved rolls:—a three-high set of rolls with 98 degree diamond passes, with the roughing-down operation from a billet indicated by the hatched lines, and a two-high set of rolls with grooves for rounds. Rolls are turned as required for a multitude of shapes. Figure **20—16** shows some of these grooves or passes and their nomenclature. The dotted lines over each pass show the cross-section of the piece leaving the preceding pass and entering the pass in question.

Procedure in Designing—When a new section has been approved for rolling, a detailed drawing of the section is sent to the roll designer, together with instructions to proceed with the design.

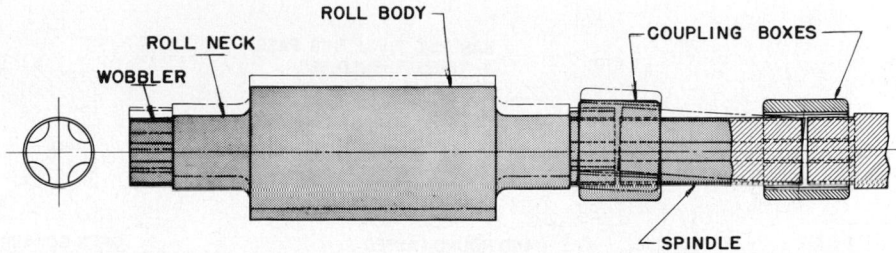

FIG. 20—14. Nomenclature of the parts of a rolling-mill roll and the units that connect it to the motive power driving the mill. The broken lines indicate position of the parts when the roll is raised.

In most cases, though not all, a cold-finishing **templet** of the section is made which is an exact cross section of the bar to be produced by rolling. This is the starting point in the design. The templet work is done by skilled artisans called **templet filers** who must work to very close tolerances. As the bars are finished hot, a certain amount of shrinkage takes place in cooling. To allow for this shrinkage it is necessary to prepare a hot-finishing templet to which the rolls are turned. The shrinkage varies with different finishing temperatures, but, on the average, is $1/64$ inch to the inch.

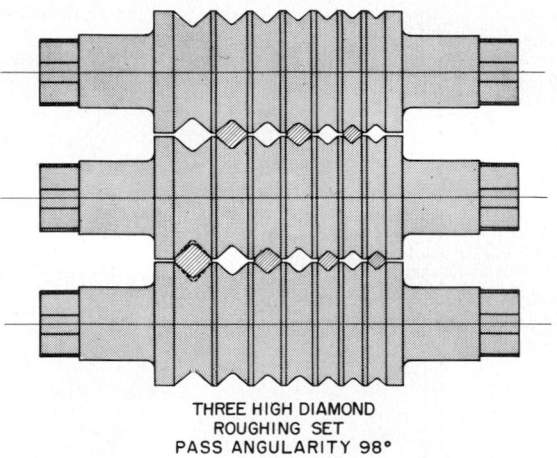

THREE HIGH DIAMOND
ROUGHING SET
PASS ANGULARITY 98°

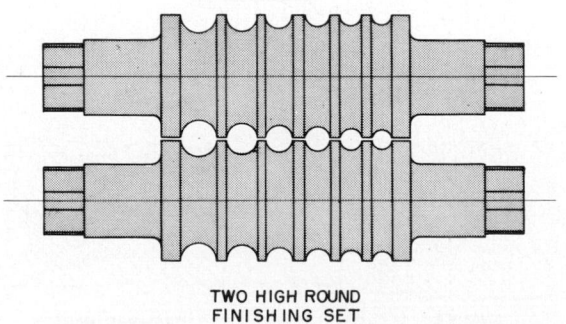

TWO HIGH ROUND
FINISHING SET

FIG. 20—15. (Above) Set of three-high rolls with diamond passes, showing the seven passes used in roughing down a billet to a round-cornered square section. (Below) Two-high set of rolls with grooves for finish rolling of rounds.

The passes in the design are drawn very accurately from the finishing pass to the starting billet, bloom or ingot. Where it is necessary to use a definite size of billet or bloom, the design must be shaped so that the available billet or bloom will be satisfactory.

Plants having primary blooming mills have an advantage in that special sized billets, blooms, or shaped blanks may be made exactly to the size required.

In designing the passes, it is customary to draw each preceding pass, from the finishing pass to the initial pass, over the succeeding one, and the roll designer judges the correctness of the design by this method, drafting the passes in the form which his knowledge and experience has shown to be proper. This part of roll design has been referred to as intuitive ability in design and is a faculty not readily transferred to others.

When the templets have been prepared, drawings are made and roll castings ordered from the drawings. When the castings have been received, the rolls are turned on special lathes to match the drawings and to an exact fit of the templets. As will be shown later, rolls are cast from either iron or steel, with or without alloying elements, depending upon the use to which they are to be put.

The **pass guides** usually are designed by the roll department and are a very necessary part of any successful roll design. Many shaped sections are so cut in the rolls that they would have a tendency to wrap around the rolls unless stripped from the pass by guides. Entering and delivery pass guides also serve their purpose in guiding and delivering bars into the proper pass in a straight line. Figure 20—13 illustrated the guide principles.

Elements of Good Roll Design—In the designing of rolls there are many points to be observed if the design is to be satisfactory.

In determining the number of passes, one point to be remembered is that the fewer the passes, the smaller the roll expense. Drafts (amounts of reduction per pass), however, must be suited to roll diameters and plant heating capacity so that roll breakage will be small, and excessive use of power will be avoided.

The passes must be designed with liberal tapers on the various parts so that they may be dressed to templet with the minimum possible reduction in diameter.

A successful design also takes yield into consideration. A minimum of section variation, giving a bar uniform in size from the front to middle and back, insures

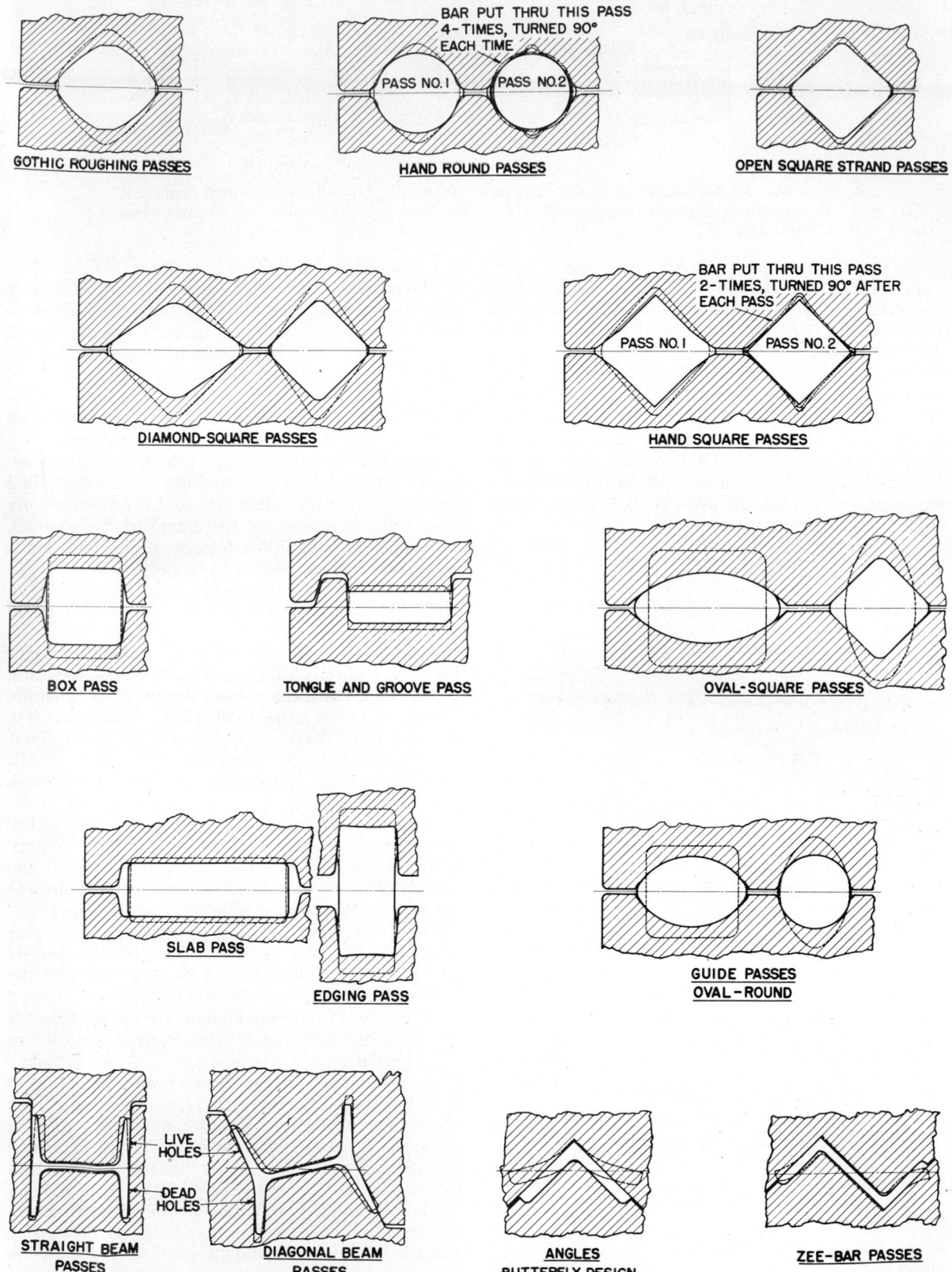

Fig. 20—16. Diagrammatic representation of some common types of roll grooves or passes. The cross-hatched portions are axial sections of the roll bodies. Dotted lines indicate cross section of the piece entering each pass.

good yield. Yield is defined as a measure of good product made from a given quantity of starting material.

The tonnage which may be obtained from the rolls also is important. The design which permits the greatest tonnage to be rolled before it is necessary to scrap the rolls because of their reduction in size, due to dressing to eliminate the effects of wear, gives the lowest roll cost.

In roll design, the fact that material being rolled elongates and also spreads in proportion to the draft must be given the most careful consideration, as this is the fundamental principle in rolling, and the proper directing of this elongation and spread is vital to the success of a roll design.

Spread of the various kinds of material must be taken into consideration, as there is a great deal of variation in spread of steels. Roll speeds must be considered in the design. High speeds in many cases restrict spread and low speeds increase it. Low speed permits heavy drafts, while high speed requires lighter drafts.

Temperature of the steel is also a factor. High temperatures permit heavy drafting, while low temperatures call for lighter draft.

Roll diameter also is important. A roll of large diameter is strong and permits heavy drafts without roll breakage, and also, because of the large diameter, the area of contact of roll on bar is large, permitting easy entrance (see Chapter 19). Rolls of small diameter require less power to drive, reduce spread and increase elongation, but are more easily broken, and heavy reductions cannot be taken readily on them as the area of contact between the work-piece and roll is small.

All these points and many more must be given full consideration in any successful roll design.

CASTING OF ROLLING-MILL ROLLS

The selection of the proper grade of roll to be used in any of the various stands of the rolling mills is most important. In general, primary mills such as blooming or slabbing mills require a roll in which strength is paramount. Such rolls are subject to tremendous shock and extreme pressures in the rolling of large ingot masses with heavy reductions. The heat from the ingots transmitted to the roll also has a tendency to cause surface or fire cracks through differential expansion of the surface, and the strength and toughness of the rolls must be such as to resist the further development of these cracks. The original plain-carbon steel roll containing 0.30 per cent to 1.50 per cent carbon, used in the past for such applications, now has been supplanted largely by the alloy-steel roll of greater strength and durability.

From the primary mills through the secondary and so on to the finishing mills, the required rolls generally become smaller and harder and any of a variety of roll grades may be used; carbon-steel or alloy-steel rolls for roughing, iron or alloy-steel rolls for intermediate work, and the various grades of iron-base rolls for the finishing stands. Specifically, however, each roll must be custom made to suit the requirements of the individual mill by a procedure within the limits of the manufacturer's equipment. For this reason, no two

manufacturers use exactly the same procedure for the same roll and each must apply his own specifications for a given requirement.

Steel-base rolls, as now produced, generally are cast from steel made in acid open-hearth furnaces, while iron-base rolls are usually made from metal melted in reverberatory-type air furnaces. In some cases, both types of rolls are made of material melted in electric-arc furnaces, either acid or basic. Although the fundamentals for making steel and iron rolls are similar in many respects, important differences exist.

STEEL-BASE ROLLS

In the casting of steel rolls, as indeed in the casting of any shape, the greatest importance must be attached to the control of directional freezing of the molten metal in the mold after casting. To insure soundness in the casting, solidification must occur progressively from the smallest to the largest cross section. Shrinkage occurring in each step of solidification must be compensated for by still-molten metal drawn from adjacent unfrozen regions. Shrinkage of the interior of the largest section, which is last to freeze, is compensated for by a feed-head or sink-head of large volume provided to act as a reservoir for molten metal (see Figure 20—19). To obtain the advantage of gravity feed during this freezing-feeding process, as well as to satisfy mechanical requirements, the feed-head is always placed on top of a roll mold which has been set vertically on end, as shown. The effective cross-sectional pattern thus obtained should approach the shape of an inverted cone. Due, however, to the required design of the roll and the general rule that the drive end is best placed down, this optimum arrangement is often distorted or even inverted. In these cases provision must be made to control the freezing pattern by artificial means. This may be done in several ways, one of which is "padding" or adding extra thickness of metal to sections which are too small to solidify in the proper manner in relation to the balance of the casting. Increasing the rate of freezing by inserting heavy metal blocks, rings, or segments, called chills, in the mold, close to the surface contacted by the molten metal, is still another means for controlling the freezing pattern. Consideration must be given also to the fact that, in addition to increasing the freezing rate, chilling in the manner described also promotes formation of a dense, refined outer skin of the roll at the contact areas, which in most cases is very desirable. Although rolls are made with meticulous care in both molding and pouring, particles of the mold sand frequently are entrapped accidentally on the surface and, in order that these or other surface defects will be removed properly during subsequent machining, rolls are cast slightly oversize. The extra stock thus cast on a roll must be of such thickness that, in those instances where heat treatment precedes the other processing, the tough, heat-treated skin will not be removed during subsequent machining.

The initial step in the manufacture of steel rolls is that of examining the blue print of the roll; the composition and heat treatment are determined from the requirements indicated. The pattern is designed after applying the metallurgical and mechanical considera-

FIG. 20—17. Illustrating use of a sweep in preparing a mold for casting a steel roll. (Courtesy, Pittsburgh Rolls Corporation.)

tions discussed above. This pattern is generally in the form of a **sweep;** that is, a flat board carved on one edge to conform to the longitudinal contour of the roll as modified for casting, with provision on the other edge for fastening the sweep securely to a spindle or axle (Figure **20—17**). Then the plan of manufacture is given to the operating section.

The steel flasks or containers for roll molds are cylindrical in shape, and designed to separate into two longitudinal halves. Proper molding sand is first ram-

med into each half, after which the sweep mounted on the spindle is attached to the half flask and rotated, cutting the sand before it to the shape of the sweep contour. The same procedure is used on the second half-mold. Figure **20—17** shows a mold used for casting a large-diameter universal-beam mill roll. After molding, the half-molds are baked in drying ovens at temperatures somewhat above 400° F to drive out moisture and bond the mold thoroughly. Figure **20—18** shows the two halves of a mold being put to-

FIG. 20—18. Assembling the two halves of a mold for a steel roll. (Courtesy, Pittsburgh Rolls Corporation.)

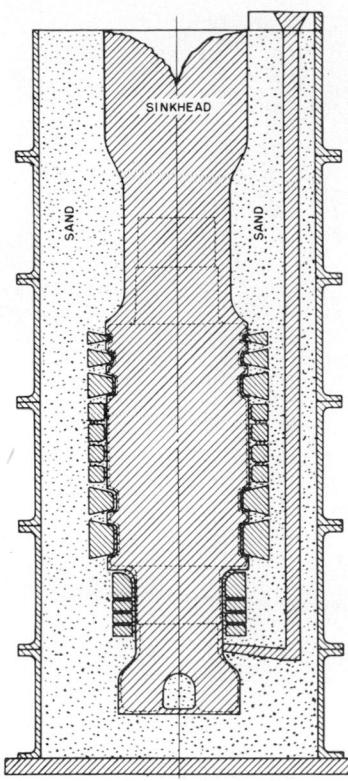

FIG. 20—19. Schematic section of a mold for an alloy-steel blooming-mill roll.

gether. Figure 20—19 shows the vertical section of a mold for an alloy-steel blooming-mill roll in position for pouring. Rolls are bottom poured and the metal enters the bottom neck through a gate tangent to the periphery of the neck. This is to set up a swirling motion of the metal as it enters the mold. This centrifugal action concentrates dirt and foreign particles in the center of the rising molten metal in the roll mold, and as the metal continues to rise, they are carried to the top into the sink-head. The dotted lines seen in **Figure 20—19** show the outline of the finished roll. The excess of metal at the top is either burned off before, or cut off during, the machining operation. The cavity in the sink-head is formed by feeding molten metal in the head to the roll body to compensate for shrinkage during solidification.

Figure **20—20** shows cooling or chilling rings being placed in a roll mold and Figure **20—21** shows the mold being smoothed over and near completion. Figure **20—22** shows some structural-mill rolls having the chills removed. In this type of mold, the chill rings located in the passes play their most important part by imparting a fine-grained structure to those parts of the roll which form the major wearing surface.

After the alloy-steel rolls are taken out of the molds, by an operation called **shaking out,** they are ready for heat treatment. An example of this heat treatment is that used for a chromium-molybdenum alloy-steel roll for a blooming mill, containing 0.80 to 0.90 per cent carbon, 0.70 to 0.80 per cent manganese, 0.25 to 0.30 per cent silicon, 1.00 per cent chromium, 0.25 to 0.30 per cent molybdenum, and a maximum each of phosphorus and sulphur of 0.04 per cent. After shakeout, the roll is brought to the heat-treating furnace and placed in the furnace in a manner to allow full access of heat to all parts. It is brought up slowly to 1700° F and allowed to cool in the furnace to 1000° F, and then is reheated to 1550° F. At this point, the roll is removed from the furnace and air-cooled to 1000° F, replaced in the furnace and brought back up to 1250° F, after which it is allowed to cool to 300° F and removed from the furnace. The heat treatment varies with the size and chemical composition of the roll.

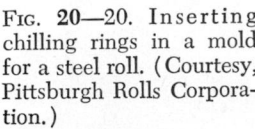

FIG. 20—20. Inserting chilling rings in a mold for a steel roll. (Courtesy, Pittsburgh Rolls Corporation.)

Fig. 20—21. Smoothing over the face of one-half of a roll mold, after insertion of chilling rings. (Courtesy, Pittsburgh Rolls Corporation.)

After heat treatment, the roll goes to the roll lathe for removal of extra stock on the top neck and thorough testing of the roll body. Any defects which cannot be removed by the rough turning result in rejection and scrapping of the roll.

A special type of alloy-steel roll is the **built-up roll.** These are used for backing-up rolls on four-high plate and strip mills. The solid backing-up roll as used on large four-high mills is a difficult one to cast. The large volume of the casting induces strain during cooling due to the unequal cooling between the roll surface and its center. Due to this unequal cooling, cracks are very apt to occur in the casting. In the built-up roll, the center arbor or mandrel is relatively small in diam-

Fig. 20—22. Removing the chilling rings from steel-roll castings after they have been shaken out of the molds. (Courtesy, Pittsburgh Rolls Corporation.)

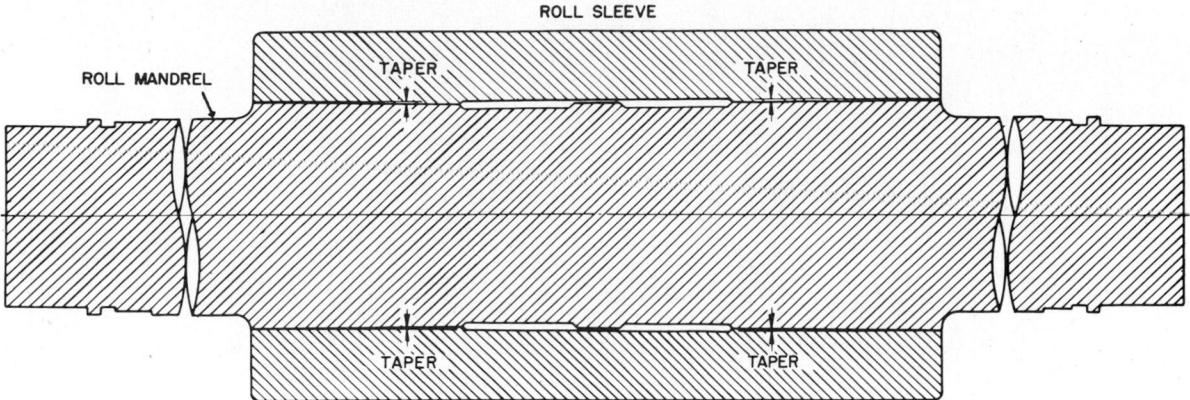

FIG. 20—23. Cross-section of a built-up roll.

eter and easier to cast. It also cools more uniformly than a large-diameter solid roll, and is less liable to strain and cracking. The outer shell also is easy to manufacture and, due to its construction, can be heat treated to be much harder than the arbor. Figure 20—23 shows a built-up roll of special construction. In some cases, solid rolls which have been dressed down repeatedly in service are reduced further and fitted with sleeves and returned to service.

Another type of roll is the **forged-steel roll.** This roll is forged from an ingot of suitable size and, after being normalized in a heat-treating furnace, is turned close to the finished size. A hole is then bored longitudinally through the center of the roll to facilitate hardening by quenching after heating to the proper temperature. This type of roll is used mostly for the cold rolling of flat material. One of the favored compositions for a roll of this kind is: carbon, 0.85 per cent; manganese, 0.25 to 0.30 per cent; phosphorus and sulphur, below 0.05 per cent; silicon, 0.25 to 0.30 per cent; chromium, 1.60 to 2.50 per cent; molybdenum, 0.25 per cent; and a trace of vanadium.

IRON-BASE ROLLS

The iron-base roll differs from the steel-base roll principally in per cent of carbon, the steel roll containing from 0.30 to 2.50 per cent carbon, whereas iron rolls contain from 2.50 to 3.50 per cent. The material for iron rolls usually is melted in an air furnace using powdered coal as fuel. The flame is less oxidizing than that used in open-hearth operation and there is less loss of elements.

In the manufacture of iron rolls, a wide range of composition is employed to obtain the desired characteristics such as hardness, strength, resistance to spalling, and depth of dense, refined grain structure. Table 20—II summarizes the general range of elements for various types of rolls, and rolling-mill applications.

The normal charge for the melting furnace in the manufacture of iron rolls contains 25 per cent pig iron and 75 per cent worn-out rolls, heads and gate scrap. If lower carbon content is desired, a certain percentage of low-carbon-steel scrap makes up a part of the charge. Alloys, such as nickel, chromium and molybdenum, if required, are also added with the charge.

When the iron is melted and sufficiently hot, two samples are taken, one for chemical analysis and the other for a test block which is cooled and broken. From the chemical analysis and the test coupon, the roll metallurgist determines the necessary additions of alloys for the type of roll being cast. The metal is tapped in a ladle and, when the correct temperature is reached (2425° to 2650° F), poured into previously prepared roll molds. After cooling from one to four days, the rolls are shaken out, heat treated if necessary, and machined to specifications.

Chill Rolls—Figure 20—24 shows a roll-mold ar-

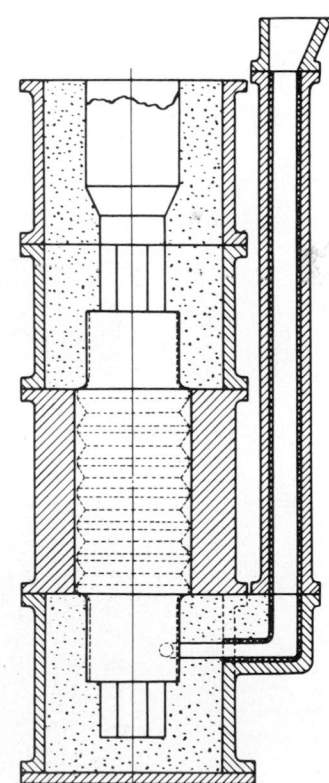

FIG. 20—24. Vertical section of mold for casting a plain-bodied roll, or a shape roll in which grooves are machined from the solid (dotted line).

Table 20—II. Types, Compositions and Uses of Iron Rolls

Type	Carbon (%)	Manganese (%)	Silicon (%)	Phosphorus (%)	Sulphur (%)	Chromium (%)	Nickel (%)	Molybdenum (%)	Scleroscope Hardness	Uses
Plain Chill	2.90–3.30	0.20–0.25	0.60–0.70	0.45	0.08	......	......	0.25	58–70	Sheet, Merchant, Plate and Rod Mills.
Nickel Chill—Regular	2.90–3.30	0.18–0.25	0.40–0.60	0.35	0.08–0.12	0.25–0.50	2.50–3.00	0.25	65–70	Finishing; Bar, Rod, Skelp and Intermediate Stands of some Strip Mills.
Nickel Chill—Hard	3.30	0.18–0.25	0.40–0.50	0.35	0.08–0.12	0.75–1.00	3.50–4.50	0.25	80	Finishing Stand; Strip and Band Mills.
Sand Iron (Low-Alloy Grain)	2.50–2.80	0.40–0.50	0.80–1.25	0.15–0.25	0.08–0.12	0.50	0.50	0.25	45–55	Roughing and Intermediate; Merchant, Structural and Rail Mills.
Medium Alloy Grain	3.00–3.25	0.40–0.50	0.90–1.25	0.10–0.20	0.08	0.70–1.20	0.50–1.00	0.25	55–65	Intermediate, Finishing; Merchant, Bar, Rod, Structural and Pipe and Skelp Mills.
High-Alloy Grain (Regular)	3.15–3.40	0.40–0.50	0.80–1.10	0.10–0.15	0.06	1.50–1.75	4.00–4.50	0.25	65–75	Intermediate Stand; Hot Strip Mills.
High-Alloy Grain (Hard)	3.40	0.90–1.50	0.80–1.00	0.10–0.15	0.06	1.50–2.00	4.50–5.00	0.25	80–90	Finishing Stand; Strip Mills and Cold Reduction Mills.
Ductile Iron	3.20–3.40	0.30–0.50	1.50–2.25	0.04–0.15	0.01–0.02	0.75 max.	1.50–2.50	0.25–0.50	40–65	Roughing or Intermediate Stands; Rod, Structural and Bar Mills.

rangement for casting a plain-bodied roll, or a shape roll in which the grooves are machined from the solid. The wobblers and necks are cast in sand but the body of the roll is formed by heavy-walled cast-iron cylinders, known as chills. The purpose of these chills is to cool the molten iron quickly after it has been poured into the mold, while the necks and wobblers, being molded in sand, are not subjected to fast cooling. The carbon in molten iron is in solution. If the molten iron is allowed to cool slowly, the carbon in excess of 0.82 per cent separates as graphitic carbon and is distributed throughout the mass. But if iron of the proper composition is cooled rapidly from the liquid state, the carbon combines with the iron to form cementite (Fe_3C), which is very hard and white in color. The depth of case on the body of the roll, induced by the fast cooling of the molten iron in contact with the chill mold, depends upon the chemical composition of the iron (see Chapter 38). As the mold loses its chilling effect, carbon starts to come out of solution to form a mottled area immediately below the hard case. This mottled area consists of a mixture of graphite, cementite and iron. Since the interior of the roll cools slowly, gray iron forms therein. Another factor controlling the depth of chill is the diameter of the roll being cast. As the diameter increases, the chilling rate is retarded due to greater cross-sectional area. On a 30-inch diameter roll, the following composition would give a clear chill about ¾ inch in depth, and a mottled area about ¾-inch deep before reaching the portion composed uniformly of gray iron:

Element	Per Cent
Carbon	3.00
Silicon	0.65
Phosphorus	0.40
Manganese	0.25
Sulphur	0.08

To improve the finish of the mill product and reduce spalling and wear, various alloys are added such as: nickel, chromium, molybdenum and vanadium in balanced proportions to control chill depth and roll structure.

Since the case or chill on the rolls is hard and brittle, there is a practical limit to the depth a roll can be chilled without causing failure through breakage. In general, chill specifications will vary between ½ and 1½ inches in depth, depending upon the product to be rolled and the amount of diameter reduction through dressing expected to be permissible before the roll is scrapped.

Grain-Iron Rolls—For certain applications, such as the intermediate stands of some hot-strip, plate, rod and merchant mills, where shock, temperature and extremely heavy loads frequently result in spalling, firecracking and breakage, chill rolls are not practical. This applies also to rolls for billet, rail and structural mills, with deep grooves or passes. To meet these requirements, an iron composition commonly referred to as **grain iron** is used. Sufficient alloys, such as chromium and nickel, are added to control hardness and to

increase strength while silicon or other graphitizers are used to resist formation of a definite chill. While these rolls do not give the quality of finish obtained from a true chilled-type roll, they have deeper penetration of the refined structure, with increased strength. The grain-type rolls become softer and the gray iron coarser progressing inward from surface to center, and this less desirable structure is encountered as the deeper passes are cut in a roll. To overcome this characteristic, rolls calling for deep working passes are molded similar to steel rolls, as shown in Figures **20—20**, **20—21** and **20—22**. The inserted iron rings promote a finer structure and better wearing metal in the passes.

Composite or Overflowed Rolls—High-alloy rolls (1.50 to 2.50 per cent chromium and 4.00 to 5.00 per cent nickel with 75 to 90 Scleroscope hardness) used in cold-reduction mills and finishing stands of some hot-strip mills, would, if cast solid, have hard, unmachinable necks. Casting strains are quite severe in this type of roll. To overcome these objectionable features, a different method of pouring has been developed as shown in Figure **20—25**. The mold is made in the regular manner, except that a spout is connected to the top neck cavity a few inches above the body of the roll. Metal of high-alloy content is poured until the metal reaches the run-off spout. Pouring is stopped and a small amount of metal of a composition that produces much "softer" iron than the first high-alloy metal is poured down the runner to keep the ingate from freezing. After a predetermined time, pouring of the "soft" iron is continued, washing out through the

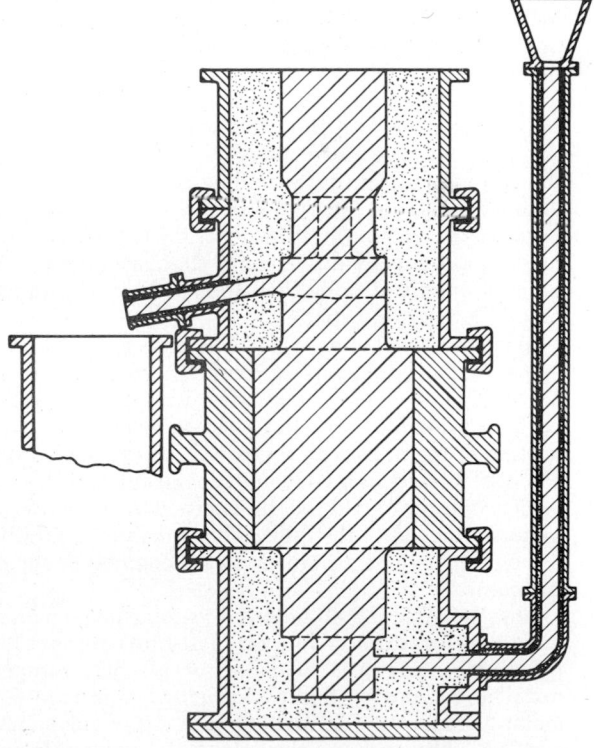

FIG. **20—25**. Schematic representation of the vertical section of a mold for casting a composite iron roll.

spout connected to the top neck and into a "nugget pot" the still-molten hard roll metal that has not been chilled and solidified by the iron mold which forms the body of the roll. When sufficient "soft" iron has been introduced into the mold to wash out the still-fluid iron in the center of the roll, the pouring is stopped, and a plug inserted in the overflow spout. The same iron used to flush out the molten hard iron from the interior of the roll is introduced into the top neck either by pouring directly down through the neck or through a gate attached to the top neck just above the run-off spout.

A roll poured by this method will have an extremely hard fine-grained structure for a depth of 1 to 2 inches.

The necks will be machinable and the central part of the roll will be strong, the hard brittle iron having been replaced or diluted by the soft "flush iron."

Ductile-Iron Rolls—With the recent development of "ductile" or "nodular" cast iron, some manufacturers have produced rolls of this material which is made by the addition of magnesium or rare earth compounds to iron of restricted composition.

The remarkable strength and toughness of this iron results from the nodular shape of the free graphite in the structure as contrasted with the flake graphite common to gray iron. This iron, if properly made and heat treated, develops properties which approach the strength and ductility of steel.

SECTION 4

MILL DRIVES AND POWER REQUIREMENTS

DEVELOPMENT OF MAIN MILL DRIVES

During the first part of the nineteenth century, rolling mills were driven by water wheels and low-pressure steam engines. The power was transmitted to the mills by direct mechanical connection, through suitable shafts, gears and couplings. Because of the low steam pressures used, short steam lines were necessary. As a result, many small boiler houses were built adjacent to the mills. Most of the engines were of the simple non-condensing type and this factor, together with the small, hand-fired boilers used, resulted in high-cost operation. Coal had to be delivered to the boiler houses, ashes disposed of, and steam lines maintained. In some plants, compound condensing engines were used, requiring a supply of cooling water and a sewer system. When the mills were shut down over the weekend, the steam lines had to be kept hot, as the contraction set up by cooling the line resulted in leaks at the joints. Nearly all of these early mills have been replaced, during the last thirty years, with modern electrically-driven mills that, while fewer in number than the mills they replaced, have a much greater combined capacity.

With the development of the electric generator and motor in the latter part of the nineteenth century, a new and more efficient method of driving rolling mills became available. Instead of direct mechanical connection of the mills with the power source, generators could be placed in a convenient central location, and electric power could be transmitted over wires to motors attached to the mills. The generators could be driven either by gas engines, steam engines, or steam turbines.

Shortly after 1890, internal combustion engines were developed to operate on blast-furnace gas. This by-product fuel was available at all blast-furnace installations and at this period either was used for making steam or was wasted. The gas engine could use this fuel direct and thus eliminate the investment for a boiler house required for a steam engine. These gas engines were used as the prime movers for blast-

furnace-blowing equipment and also for driving electric-power generators. This type of drive was selected for both the blowing units and the generators at the Gary Steel Works when this plant was designed in 1908. At that time, gas-engine-driven generators were available in sizes having outputs up to 2000 kw, and fifteen such units were installed. A few years later, the size was increased to 3000 kw, which equalled the largest generator driven by a reciprocating steam engine at that time. The gas-engine-driven generator installation at Gary was the first sizeable steel-mill power house in the United States, and made possible the use of 6000-horsepower motors to drive the mills. At a later date, the maximum size of the gas-engine-driven generators was increased to 6000 kw and three units of this size were installed in the South Works, Chicago, Illinois.

While the development of the gas engine was progressing, another prime mover had entered the field —the steam turbine. Both the steam engine and the gas engine were slow-speed machines and, when used to drive electric generators, the speed limitation resulted in a physical limitation of the generators. The 5000-kw generators, which were about the largest built, had a diameter of over 30 feet. On the other hand, the steam turbine is inherently a high-speed machine and the early generators of 5000-kw capacity that were driven by steam turbines required only a fraction of the space needed by other types of units.

Developments in boiler practice whereby steam pressures could be increased to 250 pounds at first, then 500 pounds and then, by 1948, over 2000 pounds per square inch, all favored development of turbine designs and the size of turbine units increased until 275,000-kw generators now are available. While these developments in electric-power-producing facilities were taking place, iron-silicon alloy steel in sheet form for transformer cores was being developed and improved and better insulating materials developed, with the result that larger quantities of electric power could be produced and, further, it could be transmitted economically over greater distances to the motors that used it.

Such improvement in both the generation and distribution of power were required before electrification of mills became possible. Figure 20—26 shows the growth of the installation of main-drive motors in steel mills, taken from the Proceedings of the Association of Iron and Steel Engineers, and indicates a growth from zero in 1905 to 9,600,000 horsepower in 1962.

Many steel plants, especially the smaller ones, are not self-contained in that they have no coke plant or blast furnaces. Such plants buy their electric-power supply from the power companies and, since they may impose large loads such as strip mills create, the power producer has the problem of providing sufficient generating and distribution capacity to serve such loads.

If a map showing the electric transmission lines in the United States is studied, it will be found that the various utility generating sources are interconnected by high-voltage lines to provide a pooled power supply. These interconnecting systems have many advantages, and are favorable to steel mills in that heavy peak loads caused by electric furnaces or strip mills do not necessarily have to be absorbed by a single generating station but, usually, are distributed among many units that are connected to the system. The growth of these interconnecting systems has followed the growth of electric-power consumption and today, with forecasted arrangements, it is possible to purchase power for all types of steel-mill electric loads.

The growth in generating capacity plus the interconnecting systems have made possible the large motor-driven installations in modern mills. Prior to about 1930, it often was a problem to obtain 6000 kw

to drive a proposed blooming-mill reversing motor. Today, purchased-power contracts often cover the supply of power for loads of 100,000 kw, and additions to the supply are limited only by the time required to install additional generating capacity.

In 1905, two 1500-horsepower, 230-volt, 100/125 r.p.m., direct-current motors were installed on the light-rail mill at the Edgar Thomson Works in Braddock, Pa. They were supplied with power from two 1000-kw, steam-engine-driven, direct-current generators in a nearby power house. In the same year, the first reversing direct-current main-drive motor was installed on the 36-inch universal-plate mill at South Works in Chicago. Power for this latter motor was furnished at 575 volts, direct current, from a 2200-volt, 25-cycle, motor-generator set.

At about the same time, another type of main drive, suggested by European developments, was installed on the light-rail mill at the South Works. This consisted of two 1500-horsepower, 2200-volt, 25-cycle, 80/120 r.p.m., variable-speed, wound-rotor motors. The rotor windings of these motors were connected to the stator of a second wound-rotor motor on the same shaft; this is known as a cascade connection. By varying the resistance in the rotor circuit of this second motor, the speed of the main drive could be varied between 80 and 120 r.p.m.

About the same time (1908–1910), the Gary Works, designed to be the largest steel plant in the world, planned to use slow-speed, wound-rotor induction motors on the heavy rolling mill drives. Some of these had windings that, by external contactors, could be connected to change the number of poles and thus provide what is known as a two-speed motor. Other than this, the main drive installations were designed to

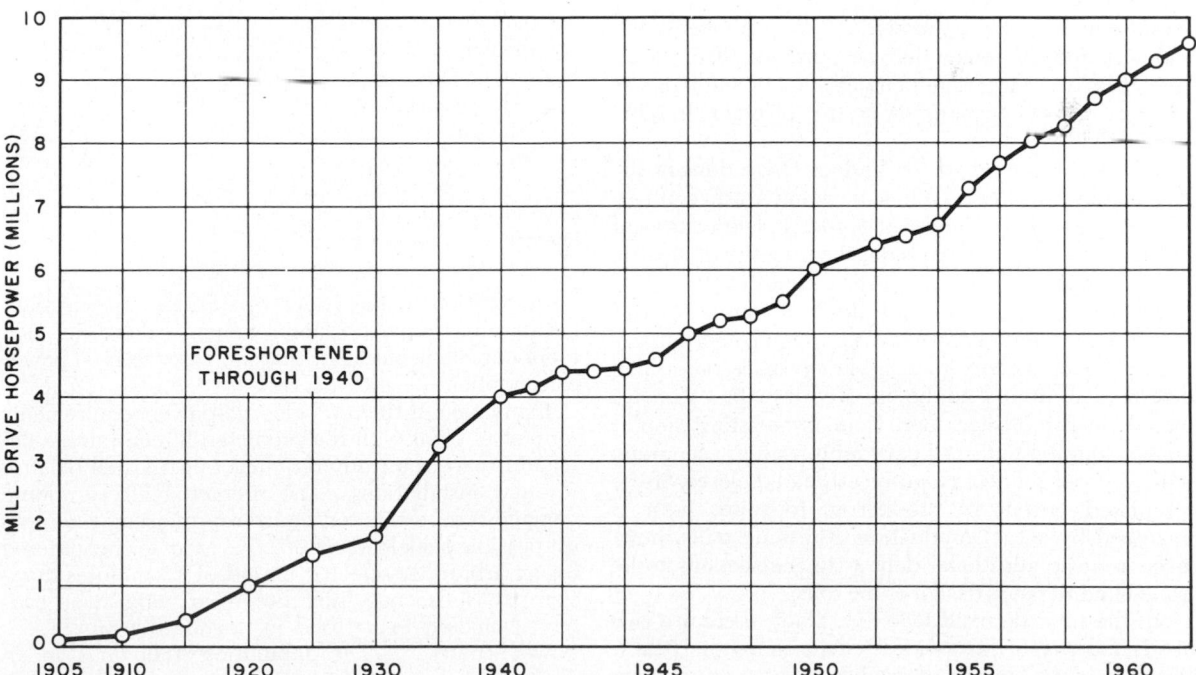

FIG. 20—26. Accumulative curve of main drive motors (over 300 horsepower) installed between 1905 and the end of 1962. (Courtesy, Association of Iron and Steel Engineers.)

operate at constant speed, except for the variations that could be obtained by changing the resistance in the secondary circuits of the wound-rotor motors.

This type of drive was satisfactory for some types of mills but, for the merchant mills in particular, greater ranges of speed variation were needed and this led to the development of variable-speed controls. With these systems, speed variations up to 50 per cent were made possible.

The demand for wider speed ranges, better regulation and a more simplified control led to the development of large, variable-speed, direct-current motors, which are now preferred drives on practically all new installations.

While these developments were progressing, another problem confronted the steel industry—the alternating frequency of the power systems. In the period 1905–1910, practically all steel companies generated their own power and were not interconnected with utility systems. Slow-speed, direct-connected drives were needed, since high-efficiency gears such as now used were not available. For this purpose, 25-cycle motors offered an advantage and were adopted in the mills and, as late as 1910, all main drive motors in the steel industry had a 25-cycle source of power. Today, while there are many 25-cycle drives representing many thousands of horsepower still operating, new installations using 25-cycle power are very few and 60 cycles has become the standard frequency of the industry.

POWER REQUIREMENTS IN THE STEEL INDUSTRY

According to a report of the American Iron and Steel Institute, the iron and steel industry used 31.2 billion kwh of electric power in 1962. Of this amount, about one third was generated in power houses in the industry and the remainder was purchased from utilities. With an ingot production of 98,300,000 tons, the average power consumption per ton of ingots in 1962 was 317.4 kwh.

Power Requirements for Various Operations in the Production of Steel—When new mills are contemplated in existing works or new plants planned, one of the questions to be answered is the quantity of electric power required to operate the new facilities.

Data on existing mills are the best source for this information. Actual power consumption by certain operations such as coke plants, blast furnaces and open hearths are found to be in accord with estimates based on established data from pre-existing similar units. Requirements of heavy mills such as blooming, slab and rail mills also can be estimated closely if the predicted output of product in tons per hour is matched by actual production. Finishing mills, however, require additional data as to the sections to be rolled and the pass design of the rolls.

In the total demand load of a plant, there are two loads that have the greatest effect on power peaks: those from the electric melting furnaces and the wide-strip mills. There are available data for power requirements of both of these operations, and the total

power required for new installations has to be estimated by using these data in conjunction with proposed operating schedules.

The following tabulation gives the average kwh consumption per ton of steel for some of the major operating units in a modern plant.

Operating Unit	Kwh Consumed per Ton of Product
Coke Plant	17, based on coal charged
Blast Furnaces	10, based on pig iron
Open Hearth	8, based on ingots
Bessemer (with motor-driven blowing equipment)	92, based on ingots
Blooming Mill	13–15, based on blooms
Slabbing Mill	10–12, based on slabs
Plate Mill (Reversing)	30–40, based on plates
Merchant Mills	40–80, based on product
Wide Strip Mills	45–65, based on product

The preceding tabulation for mills covers the power used by the main drive motors, and does not include that used for auxiliaries such as tables, fans, lighting, and so on. On some mills, this auxiliary power amounts to as much per ton as the power used by the main drive.

The following tabulation indicates how power requirements are increased as the finishing operations are continued. These figures are averages taken from the records of a modern strip mill whose end products are tin plate and sheets:

Facility	Kwh per Ton
80-Inch Mill (including all auxiliaries)	63.0
Continuous Pickling	6.3
5-Stand Cold-Reduction Mill (including auxiliaries)	86.0–100.0
Electrolytic Cleaning	8.8
Tin Mill Annealing	20.0
Tin Mill Temper Rolling	18.0
Electrolytic Tinning	100.0
Hot-Dip Tinning	38.0
3-Stand Tandem Mill	35.0
Sheet-Mill Galvanizing	30.0

In addition to the above operations, such a plant has pumps, shops, air compressors, yard lighting and other miscellaneous loads that increase the total power consumption.

Estimation of the total electric-power requirements for a steel plant with the predicted fifteen-minute demand is part of a study required to get a fuel balance for new installations. (The predicted fifteen-minute demand is an estimated figure representing the highest possible peak load expected ever to be encountered for an arbitrarily-selected period of 15 minutes duration.) It is also necessary before arriving at an estimated amount to be used in negotiating purchased-power contracts. The tabulation following is an example of the estimation of the annual kwh requirements for an integrated plant planned to produce 1,500,000 tons of open-hearth ingots per year.

Mill or Department	Annual Production (Tons)	Kwh/Ton of Product	Total Kwh Per Year
Coke Plant..........	826,000	17	14,042,000
Blast Furnaces.......	1,000,000	10	10,000,000
Open Hearth.........	1,500,000	8	12,000,000
Blooming Mill*......	1,235,000	26	32,110,000
Billet Mill*..........	458,000	28	12,824,000
Wheel Mill*.........	34,000	110	3,740,000
12-Inch Bar Mill*....	221,000	65	14,365,000
16-Inch Bar Mill*....	200,000	55	11,000,000
Structural and Rail Mill*.........	353,000	60	21,180,000
Plate Mill*..........	244,000	87	21,288,000
Splice Bar and Mine Tie	37,000	70	2,590,000
Miscellaneous (Pumps, Air Compressors, Lighting, Etc.; due load 7000 kw × 8760 hours).....................			61,320,000
Total........................			216,399,000

*Including auxiliaries.

The above represents an average consumption of 18,000,000 kwh per month or, in a 720-hour month, of 25,000 kw per hour. In this example, however, it is not the average power consumption in any hour but the peak hour that has to be determined, as this latter quantity determines the size of the generators required if a power house is to be built, or the peak demand that will be made on the utility system if power is to be purchased.

FACTORS AFFECTING SIZE AND TYPE OF MAIN-DRIVE MOTORS

The selection of the proper motor to be used on mill drives is a very important item in the design of a mill.

Its size and characteristics must be based not only on tonnage requirements and rolling schedules, but also on displacement, reductions, temperatures, composition of product, speed of rolling, and finish. The accepted methods for calculating loads when rolling a product at a specific speed and definite temperature, with specified reductions per pass, are based on data taken from tests on existing mills.

The most common main-drive motor is that used on reversing primary mills. For these drives, the size and shape of the ingot are known, also the size of the finished bloom or slab, the composition and temperature of the steel, the roll size, and the efficiency of the machinery. It has been determined from existing reversing primary-mill units that the total power required is divided approximately into the following components:

Power Required for Rolling.................	59.00%
Friction of Pinions and Mill.................	5.90
Loss in Reversing Motor....................	10.84
Loss in Electrical Connections...............	0.75
Loss in Generators........................	11.44
Loss in Flywheel..........................	1.32
Loss in Slip Regulator.....................	2.69
Loss in Induction Motor....................	6.40
Loss in Exciters, Blowers, Etc..............	1.66
Total.............................	100.00%

The part of the total torque required of the motor shaft of a single-motor drive for a reversing blooming mill that is used in (1) deforming the metal being rolled; (2) overcoming the increase in roll-neck bearing friction during rolling; and (3) other mechanical losses, may be approximated from the following formula (see "The Modern Soaking Pit and Blooming Mill," by T.

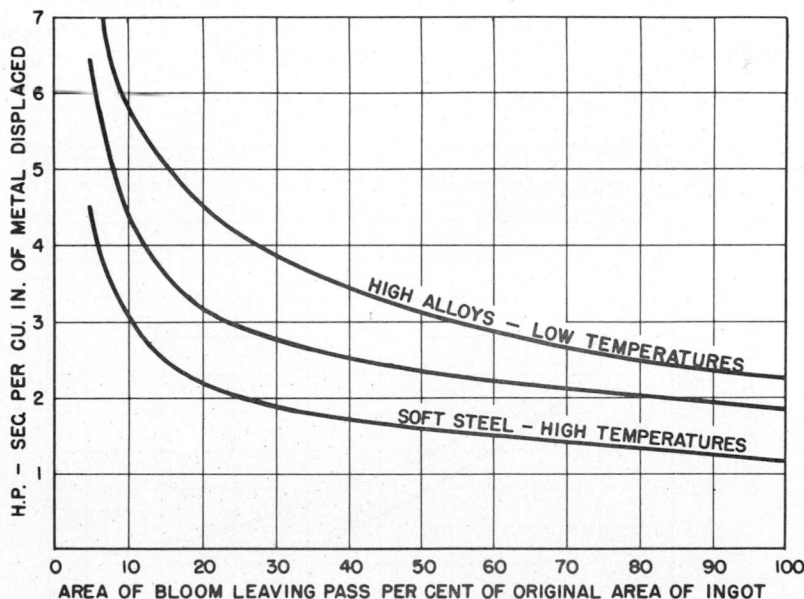

Fig. 20—27. Curves showing amount of work for displacement of one cubic inch of metal including all increases in friction during the pass in a single-motor-driven reversing blooming mill. (See "The Modern Soaking Pit and Blooming Mill," by T. J. Ess, and "Main Roll Drives for Blooming and Slabbing Mills," by R. H. Wright: both in the 1943 Proc. of the Assn. of Iron and Steel Engineers.)

J. Ess and "Main Roll Drives for Blooming and Slab-bing Mills," by R. H. Wright, both of which appeared in the 1943 Proc. of the Assn. of Iron and Steel Engineers):

$$(1) \qquad T = 275 \times C \ (A_1 - A_2) \times D\frac{A_2}{A_1},$$

where T = Motor torque in pounds-feet
　　　C = Factor for cubic inches of metal displaced (ordinate of Figure 20—27).
　　　A_1 = Area of section in square inches before pass
　　　A_2 = Area of section in square inches after pass
　　　D = Diameter of roll at base of pass in inches.

From this formula, which applies only to the type of mill mentioned, the rolling schedule can be calculated pass by pass, and to the figures so obtained must be added the idling friction torque for the mill which may amount to 20,000 to 25,000 pounds-feet.

To obtain the maximum torque requirements for the motor, it is necessary to add the torque required for acceleration. The inertia of the mill parts and the armature for a 7000-horsepower motor is about 4,250,000 lb.-ft.[2] If the rate of acceleration is 20 r.p.m. per second per second, and the time required for acceleration is 2 seconds, then from the formula:

$$(2) \qquad T_a = \frac{0.003255 \times WR^2 \times r.p.m.}{t},$$

where
　　　T_a = Torque required for acceleration (pounds-feet)
　　　t = Time required for acceleration (seconds)
　　　WR^2 = Inertia of moving parts,

$$T_a = \frac{0.003255 \times 4,250,000 \times 20}{2} = 138,000 \ \text{pounds-feet}$$

Another factor to be considered is selection of a motor of ample capacity to prevent excessive heating of the motor during operation (see Ess paper referred to in caption of Figure 20—27).

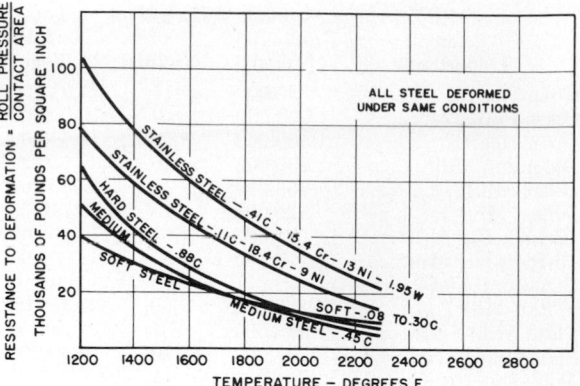

FIG. 20—28. Effect of temperature of steel on resistance to deformation. (After Trinks.)

Figure 20—28 shows a group of curves for five different steels in which the resistance to deformation is plotted against temperature of the steel in degrees F. Figure 20—29 shows similar curves for two grades of carbon steel, where rolling temperatures are plotted in relation to power consumption. From these curves it may be seen that a drop in temperature from 2300° F to 1750° F will double the power requirements for rolling. This indicates the necessity for considering steel temperature when calculations of power for rolling are being made.

Another factor to be considered is the number of horsepower-seconds required per cubic inch of metal displaced during the various passes. Temperature again must be considered in this case as the bloom or slab cools off during the rolling operation. Figure 20—27 shows curves giving the specific power for motor torque for displacement of metal plus all increases in friction during the pass. From these curves, it will be noted that as the bloom becomes smaller the horsepower-seconds increase rapidly, especially

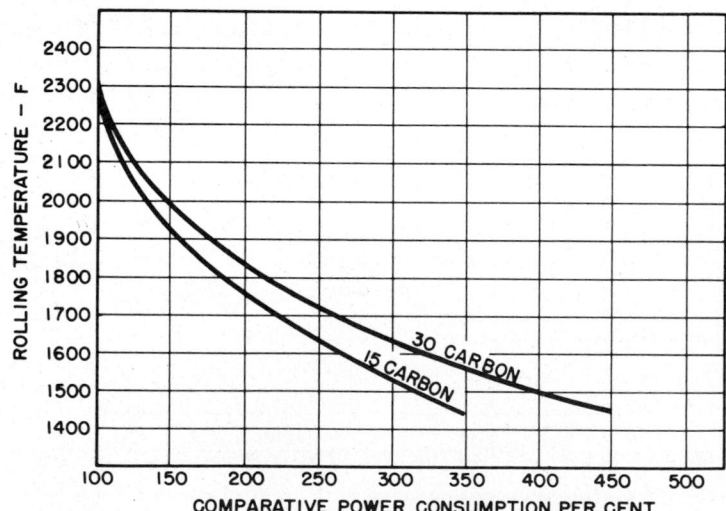

FIG. 20—29. Effect of temperature on power consumption during rolling steels containing 15 and 30 points (0.15 and 0.30%, respectively) of carbon. (Courtesy, Iron and Steel Engineer.)

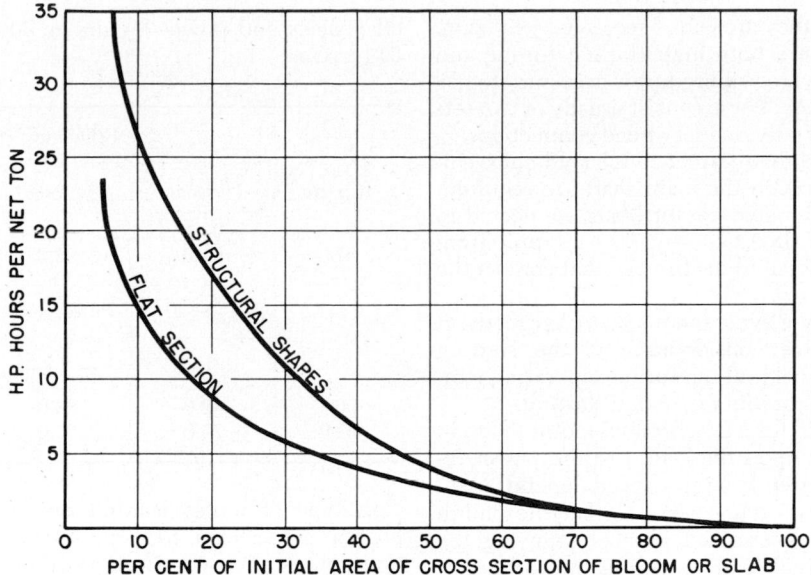

FIG. 20—30. Curves showing relation of horsepower-hours per net ton of steel rolled to per cent reduction of cross-section for shapes and flat sections.

after 25 per cent of the original area is reached. The constant "C" used in formula (1) was taken from this chart.

Another form of these power curves is shown in Figure 20—30. These curves, for flat and structural sections, show that power requirements do not increase in direct proportion to per cent reductions, and that the smaller the section the larger the increase in power in terms of reduction.

The speed at which the piece is rolled affects the power requirements in two ways. Theoretically, the power requirements should be directly in proportion to speed; however, with increase in speed the temperature of the piece being rolled has less time in which to drop; therefore, the higher the rolling speed, the higher the finishing temperature and, consequently, the lower the power required by the mill. For this reason, it is sometimes possible to increase the speed and not increase the motor loading to any great extent.

In order to meet the surface-quality requirements on certain products, it is necessary to roll them in the finishing pass at relatively low temperatures—sometimes as low as 1400° F. On mills where this practice is to be used, the horsepower requirements for the motor should be determined on the basis of the reduction and temperature required for such sections.

TYPES OF MOTORS FOR MAIN DRIVES

There are four general classifications of motors that can be used on mill drives: synchronous, squirrel-cage, wound-rotor, and direct-current. All but the last-named operate on alternating current. Each of these has characteristics which make it suitable for definite applications. The cost of each type also differs and is often the factor determining the type to be used.

The synchronous motor, if an exciter is not required, usually costs the least and, in certain speed ranges, may be used interchangeably with the squirrel-cage design. Wound-rotor motors cost more than either the

synchronous or squirrel-cage, and direct-current motors are the most expensive of all. With the latter, a supply of direct current is needed, which necessitates the use of a motor-generator set or suitable rectifier to convert the alternating-current power supply of the plant to direct current, and these have to be considered as a part of the installation.

In the following paragraphs, short descriptions of the four general classifications of motors are given, along with suggestions for possible applications. It is assumed that the reader is familiar with the general design of such units, if not, details of their design and construction are available in the literature.

Synchronous Motors—The synchronous motor has the stator or stationary part wound with core and coils in the same manner as the squirrel-cage and wound-rotor motors. However, the rotating part or rotor has salient poles, positive and negative, wound for direct current. The power supply for these poles usually is furnished by a small direct-current generator called the exciter. This may be mounted on the main motor shaft, be belt driven by same, or be driven by a separate motor in a motor-generator set. In addition to the direct-current coils on the pole pieces, another winding which is buried in the pole faces is required. This is called the squirrel-cage winding and controls the necessary starting and pull-in torques of the motor and also the uniformity of the accelerating torques between starting and pull-in. When driving reciprocating machinery, the squirrel-cage winding also develops a damping torque.

This winding consists of a number of round or rectangular rods or bars that pass through the pole shoes in the axial direction. The material used may be copper, brass, or bronze, of such electrical conductivity as to suit best the particular requirements of starting and pull-in torques. The ends of these rods or bars project sufficiently beyond the poles to allow making connections to the short-circuiting end-ring segments to which they are joined securely by brazing. In some cases, where both high starting torque and high pull-in torque are required, it is necessary to use double cage windings. These consist usually of two sets of damper bars but only one set of end connections.

To conduct the direct current to the field coils, collector rings mounted on the main shaft are required, the terminals for the field circuit being connected to these rings and the direct-current power supply from the exciter is connected to the brushes that contact the rings.

In order to apply a synchronous motor correctly, it is necessary to give consideration to the starting torque, pull-in torque, pull-out torque, operating temperature, power factor and method of starting.

The time required for a synchronous motor to attain full speed depends upon the load, and the power required to pull into step from this speed depends upon the inertia of the revolving parts, so that the pull-in torque cannot be determined without knowing the inertia of the external load as well as the torque required to overcome it.

The permissible starting-power input will vary with different localities, being affected by local power company regulations, capacity of feeders, or the capacities of individual, isolated power stations.

These motors can be designed with considerable range of starting, pull-in and pull-out torques. Some applications require a starting torque of 150 to 200 per cent, a pull-in torque of 110 per cent, and a pull-out torque of 175 per cent.

A synchronous motor usually has a higher efficiency than that of a comparable induction motor, it is less expensive in first cost, and it has the ability to correct power factor. They have been built in sizes up to 10,000 horsepower for mill drives. It must be remembered that they are a constant-speed motor and are locked in step with the frequency of the power system. For this reason, there is no cushion afforded by a drop in speed for a sudden peak load, and the pull-out torque must be high enough to handle the highest peak load encountered. Synchronous motors often are used to drive motor-generator sets, air compressors, pumps and other types of equipment where constant load conditions exist.

Squirrel-Cage Motors—Squirrel-cage induction motors are the most simple with respect to design, and can be built in a wide range of sizes and torques. By varying the design resistance in the rotor winding, the starting torque can be low, normal, or high, as desired. It has become customary to start these motors "across the line" in the usual sizes, which necessitates strong bracing for the stator coils to withstand the powerful magnetic forces involved.

In the larger sizes, these motors have been designed for use in certain speed ranges in capacities up to 10,000 horsepower, and for speeds as low as 100 r.p.m., operating on 60-cycle power.

This motor has the lowest initial cost per installation, but its efficiency is less than that of the synchronous induction motor, and at the lower speeds the power factor is lowered. For instance, a 500-horsepower, 60-cycle, squirrel-cage motor has the following

efficiencies and power factors at 900 compared with 514 r.p.m.:

R.p.m.	Efficiency (%)		
	½ Load	¾ Load	Full Load
900	91.1	92.9	93.1
514	91.3	92.3	92.3
	Power Factor		
	½ Load	¾ Load	Full Load
900	82.0	88.0	90.0
514	75.0	83.0	86.5

This type of motor is used on fans, pumps, compressors and shears, to name a few common applications, but is not used normally on main drives.

Wound-Rotor Induction Motors—This type of induction motor has a wide range of use in the steel industry. The difference between it and the squirrel-cage type is that the rotor winding consists of coils with the phase connections brought out to collecting rings mounted on the motor shaft. Connections can be made from these rings through external resistance boxes or a slip regulator; hence, the secondary resistance can be varied. By this means, the starting-power input and accelerating time can be controlled and, if the motor is used in connection with a flywheel, various divisions of the load between the motor and the wheel can be obtained.

These motors are available over the complete output and speed ranges required for mill drives, for operation on voltages up to 13,200. As in the case of squirrel-cage motors, the efficiency and power factor decrease with the base speeds.

Wound-rotor induction motors are standard for flywheel-equipped motor-generator sets, and usually have been designed for a speed of 360 r.p.m. in medium sizes and 300 r.p.m. for the largest sets. However, several large installations have been designed for 514 r.p.m. One such unit consists of an 8000-hp motor with a 65-ton, 215,000 hp-sec. flywheel, driving four 2500-kw and two 1750-kw direct-current generators.

Direct-Current Motors—Due to the demand for wide speed ranges for mill drives, many large direct-current motors are being used for this purpose. They are designed with flat speed characteristics, to operate usually on 600 volts. The largest size, about 8000 horsepower, has been used on reversing mills. These motors require forced ventilation due to the heat generated by operating conditions involving frequent reversals. The normal speed range is 2:1, but higher ranges can be obtained. On mill drives, it is not uncommon to have a maximum torque of 240 per cent of the full-load torque.

The trend toward the use of variable-speed direct-current motors on main drives began in the 1930's. The operating advantages of this type of drive overbalanced the added cost. Table **20**—III, taken from

Table 20—III. Main Drive Motors Installed 1939-1961.*

Year Installed	Alternating-Current Motors		Direct-Current Motors	
	Number Installed	Total Horsepower	Number Installed	Total Horsepower
1939	9	18,900	54	81,500
1940	13	6,850	72	112,000
1941	31	39,350	93	101,100
1942	14	20,000	97	263,650
1943	7	10,000	5	10,750
1944	14	14,200	17	34,100
1945	15	12,700	123	155,700
1946	16	41,650	191	286,650
1947	20	31,850	125	201,325
1948	11	29,900	93	107,900
1949	11	33,500	78	160,100
1950	32	77,750	236	451,450
1951	30	34,950	174	304,250
1952	8	7,200	41	64,600
1953	8	28,700	67	92,550
1954	13	16,100	106	159,605
1955	30	37,400	290	469,909
1956	28	93,350	226	381,510
1957	19	30,400	179	271,605
1958	13	32,100	84	140,550
1959	14	55,850	226	461,220
1960	7	11,800	133	211,866
1961	11	14,350	191	299,920
Totals	374	698,050	2901	4,818,810
	(11.41%)	(12.65%)	(88.59%)	(87.35%)

*Total horsepower of main-drive motors installed since 1905 (both AC and DC) = 9,553,925.

the Proceedings of the Association of Iron and Steel Engineers, shows this trend in motors (over 300 horsepower) installed on main drives from 1939–1961.

The speeds of synchronous and induction motors are a function of the number of poles in the motor windings. These speeds are determined by the formula:

$$N = \frac{60 \times F}{\frac{1}{2} P}$$

where,

N = Speed (r.p.m.)
F = Frequency
P = Number of poles

Table 20—IV shows the possible speeds that can be obtained in both 25-cycle and 60-cycle motors. These are synchronous speeds and apply to synchronous motors. For induction motors, the full-load speeds are a few per cent less due to slip.

Although it is possible to build motors with more than 40 poles, they become very expensive, and the above table shows how it was advantageous to build the slow-speed, 25-cycle motors used in some of the early mills and why it would have been necessary to use gear sets if 60-cycle frequency had been specified.

Table 20—IV. Synchronous Speeds of 25-Cycle and 60-Cycle Motors

Number of Poles	Speed	
	25-Cycle (r.p.m.)	60-Cycle (r.p.m.)
2	1500	3600
4	750	1800
6	500	1200
8	375	900
10	300	720
12	250	600
14	214	514
16	187½	450
18	166⅔	400
20	150	360
22	136	327
24	125	300
26	115	277
28	107	256
30	100	240
32	93.75	225
34	88.23	212
36	83⅓	200
40	75	180

PRINCIPLE AND APPLICATION OF FLYWHEELS

Many main-drive applications are on mills that have short-time peak rolling loads. Blooming mills, slabbing mills, and reversing plate mills are in this classification.

For such mills, it is often economical to use a wound-rotor induction motor having an adjustable secondary resistance in conjunction with a flywheel, to drive the generators that supply direct current to the main mill motors that are subject to peak loads. By this means, it is possible to select a motor having a capacity ⅓ to ½ of the value of the maximum load requirements of the mill, and so control its "slip" that the flywheel energy supplies the greater proportion of the energy to meet the peak loads. Some typical questions related to motors and flywheels of mill drives, and the methods of finding their answers, are given in the following examples.

1. Energy Stored in a Flywheel—Assume a large flywheel having a momentum $(WR^2) = 15,000,000$ lb.-ft.^{2} (that is, an effect of 15,000,000 lb. at a radius of gyration of 1 ft., or 3,750,000 lb. at a radius of 2 ft.), and a wheel speed of 83 r.p.m. What is the total amount of energy stored in the wheel?

The energy (E) possessed by any body of weight W lb. moving with a velocity of V ft. per second is:

$$(1) \quad E = \frac{W \times V^2}{32.16 \times 2} \text{ ft.-lb.}$$

In this expression, 32.16 ft. per second per second is the rate of acceleration due to gravity, usually expressed by the symbol, g. The rotating flywheel with a given WR^2 and running at N r.p.m. may be considered as a body with weight W moving with the same velocity as the end of its radius of gyration R; this velocity in feet per second for the case under consideration is:

$$(2) \quad V = \frac{2 \times 3.1416 \times R \times N}{60}$$

Substituting this value of V in (1), it becomes:

$$(3) \quad E = \frac{WR^2 \times N^2}{5865} \text{ ft.-lb.}$$

Then, for the present example,

$$(4) \quad E = \frac{15,000,000 \times (83)^2}{5865} = 17,500,000 \text{ ft.-lb.}$$

This energy is equal to the amount of work required to bring the flywheel from rest to a speed of 83 r.p.m.

Since 1 horsepower-second = 550 ft.-lb.,
E = 31,900 horsepower-seconds.

From the foregoing formulas, it may be seen that the stored energy in a flywheel is proportional to the WR^2 of the wheel and to the second power of its speed.

2. Amount of Energy Available for Regulation— The energy calculated above is the total energy stored in the wheel at a certain speed. How much of this energy may be used for load equalization in case this flywheel is installed on a mill drive?

If it is assumed that a speed variation of more than 15 per cent is not permissible, the wheel speed could be varied from 83 r.p.m. to 70.5 r.p.m. At 70.5 r.p.m., the stored energy in the wheel would be:

$$E_2 = \frac{15,000,000 \times (70.5)^2}{3,230,000} = 22,950 \text{ horsepower-seconds.}$$

Thus the energy given up by the wheel in slowing down from 83 to 70.5 r.p.m. would be:

31,900 − 22,950 = 8,950 horsepower-seconds, or approximately 28 per cent of the total stored energy.

From this it is evident that the per cent of energy given up by the wheel is not directly proportional to the per cent of speed reduction.

Suppose the speed of the flywheel is lowered from N_1 to N_2 r.p.m. The speed reduction (8) expressed as a fraction of the maximum operating speed (N_1) is:

$$S = \frac{N_1 - N_2}{N_1}$$

or, the minimum speed is:

$$N_2 = N_1 \times (1 - S)$$

Now, the total amount of energy stored in the wheel at speeds N_1 and N_2, respectively, are:

$$E_1 = \frac{WR^2 \times N_1^2}{3,226,000} \text{ horsepower-seconds}$$

$$E_2 = \frac{WR^2 \times N_2^2}{2,226,000} \text{ horsepower-seconds}$$

Hence, the energy given out comprises the following portion of the total:

$$\frac{E_1 - E_2}{E_1} = \frac{N_1^2 - N_2^2}{N_1^2} = \frac{N_1 - N_2}{N_1} \times \frac{N_1 + N_2}{N_1}$$

$$\frac{E_1 - E_2}{E_1} = S \times \left[\frac{N_1 + N_1 (1 - S)}{N_1} \right]$$

$$= S \times (2 - S) = 2S - S^2$$

Giving S various values from 0 to 100 per cent, the corresponding values of energy given up by the wheel in slowing down may be calculated. For instance, if the speed reduction is 12 per cent (S = 0.12), the flywheel will give up 22.5 per cent of the total energy available at the maximum speed. Further calculations would show that at 50 per cent speed reduction, 75 per cent of the total energy is given up by the wheel.

3. Acceleration and Retardation of the Wheel— Assume that the wheel should be accelerated at a uniform rate from N_2 r.p.m. to N_1 r.p.m. in t seconds; then, the rate of acceleration (a) would be:

$$a = \frac{N_1 - N_2}{t}$$

If the inertia of the wheel is WR^2 lb.-ft.^{2}, then there will be required during this period a uniform accelerating torque (T_0), equal to:

$$T_0 = \frac{WR^2 \times a}{308} \text{ ft.-lb.}$$

For instance, if the same wheel as was considered above $(WR^2 = 15,000,000$ lb.-ft.$^2)$ is to be brought from rest $(N_2 = 0)$ to $N_1 = 83$ r.p.m. in 10 seconds, then the required torque, T_0, equals:

$$T_0 = \frac{15,000,000}{308} \times \frac{83}{10} = 405,000 \text{ ft.-lb.}$$

If the flywheel is brought up to this speed by an 83-r.p.m. motor, the latter will have to develop during the acceleration a torque (in addition to frictional torque) which corresponds to a load of:

$$\frac{405,000 \times 83}{5250} = 6440 \text{ horsepower}$$

4. Induction-Motor Characteristics—The majority of all mills equipped with flywheels are driven by induction motors. Within the operating range, the speed-torque or the slip-torque curves for these motors are very nearly straight lines. This is the basis for the assumption that the motor torque is proportional to the slip. If the secondary resistance of the motor is changed, the slope of the speed-torque curve is changed, but the breaking-down torque for the motor is not affected.

The torque developed at the motor shaft is proportional to the speed, and the difference in power between the input power and this torque goes into losses in the rotor windings, the core, and external secondary resistance.

The total power, P_s, can be expressed as:

$$P_s = \frac{T \times N_s}{5250}$$

where N_s is the synchronous speed and T the torque.

Starting from rest and drawing normal current from the line, the motor at first does not develop any power at the shaft because the speed is zero, but the secondary losses are high. With increasing speed, the losses are reduced and the mechanical power increases.

If the motor is running and more resistance is introduced in the secondary, maintaining constant line input, it will be observed that the speed, N, and the mechanical shaft power, P, both decrease in the same proportion, which means that the torque, T, is not changed.

This is an important conclusion, since it shows that when an induction motor drives a mill without any flywheel, and is called upon to develop a certain torque nothing is gained by increasing the secondary resistance as long as the torque requirements are the same.

rolls, and this imposes a combined torque, T_1. The torque developed by the motor will increase gradually along some curve (Figure **20**—31). What will the motor torque be after "t" seconds?

According to an expression called Gasche's formula:

$$T = T_1 - \frac{T_1 - T_0}{e^{At}}$$

where

T = motor torque to be determined
T_1 = combined (external) torque
T_0 = frictional torque
e = 2.718, the base for Naperian or natural logarithms
A = a constant for a given motor and flywheel (provided the secondary resistance is constant), and

equals $\dfrac{308 T_n}{W R^2 N_s S_n}$, in which latter expression:

T_n = normal torque
S_n = normal slip
N_s = normal speed
W = weight of the flywheel, and
R = radius of gyration of the wheel.

Figure **20**—31 shows curves of the division of load between a motor and flywheel, calculated according to the foregoing formula. It can be noted that at point "4," where the steel enters the mill pass, the load rises to point "5," or 7000 horsepower. At this point, the flywheel carries the entire load and the motor is running at almost synchronous speed. During the succeeding seconds, the motor picks up load according to the curve "1–2," while its speed slows down according to curve "1–7." The flywheel load decreases during the four seconds the piece is in the mill, and when the piece leaves the mill, the flywheel load is 2500 horsepower ("2–6") and the motor load is 4500 horsepower ("3–2"). The shaded area denotes the flywheel load during the pass.

As the steel leaves the pass, the motor speed has decreased to 93.6 per cent. Before the next piece of steel enters the mill, the motor must regain its no-load speed of 99½ per cent and, in so doing, restores the full momentum (WR^2) to the wheel. This is indicated

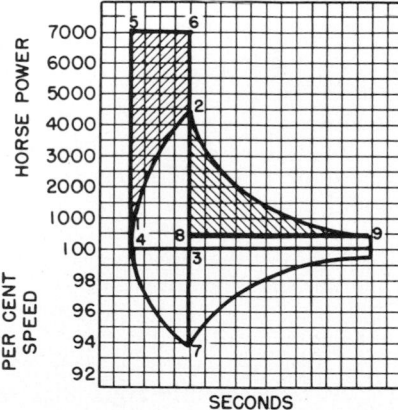

FIG. **20**—31. Effect of flywheel energy on load and speed, showing division of load between motor and flywheel. Each horizontal division equals 1 sec. (Courtesy, Iron and Steel Engineer.)

5. Motor Load Curves—Assume a mill with a flywheel being driven by an induction motor of P horsepower, at a speed of N_s r.p.m. (synchronous speed). The mill is running light and the motor is developing only frictional torque, T_0. Then the metal enters the

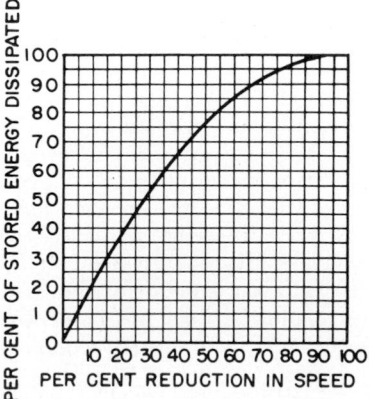

FIG. **20**—32. Relationship of stored energy given up by a flywheel to per cent reduction of speed of a motor operating in conjunction with it. (Courtesy, Iron and Steel Engineer.)

by the shaded section ("8–2–9") and requires 12 seconds. This shaded area is greater than the area "1–5–6–2" (the energy given up by the wheel) because friction and windage losses in restoring the wheel to speed must be taken into account.

Figure **20—32** shows the relation of the energy given up by a flywheel to per cent reduction in speed of a motor.

VARIOUS MEANS FOR OBTAINING ADJUSTABLE SPEEDS

A. CONTROL OF TWO-SPEED AC MOTORS

It is possible to design induction motors that will operate on two or more speeds with a single winding, the slower speed being one-half of the higher. This is done by bringing out the groups of phase leads to switches, by means of which the number of poles in the stator winding can be regrouped to give half the number of poles. Thus, a motor can be designed to operate at either 600 r.p.m. or 300 r.p.m. on 60-cycle power. Such a motor will cost 30 per cent to 40 per cent more than a standard motor, and would be a constant-torque machine, or, at the lower speed, would have only half the horsepower rating.

A variation of this design can be built using two stator windings with which two, three, or four speeds can be obtained.

In some of the older mills, two-speed, wound-rotor motors were installed so that the first passes on a reversing mill could be rolled at half speed; and, as the piece became longer, the contactors changed the winding connections to operate the motor at full speed and hence deliver its full horsepower.

B. AC-MOTOR SPEED CONTROL BY SECONDARY RESISTANCE

When resistance is added to the secondary circuit of a wound-rotor induction motor, and a load imposed, the speed of the motor is lessened, and this drop in speed is called "slip." The slip increases with increasing load, hence, it is a function of both load and secondary resistance. For example, if with a given load and secondary resistance the motor has a slip of 10 per cent, which means it is operating at 90 per cent synchronous speed, and the load is doubled, the motor will then have 20 per cent slip and operate at 80 per cent synchronous speed. These statements illustrate why speed control by varying secondary resistance is not satisfactory for mill operations, as each load has a definite corresponding motor speed and as soon as the load changes, the speed changes.

This type of control, however, has wide application on flywheel sets where the secondary resistance is controlled by a slip regulator which can be set to control automatically the amount of slip. This, in turn, controls the relation between the momentum given up by the flywheel and the torque of the motor.

C. VARIABLE-SPEED CONTROLS FOR AC MOTORS

Two common methods have been employed for controlling the speed of wound-rotor induction motors in mill drives. These are known as the Kraemer and the Scherbius systems. In the **Kraemer system**, slip rings of such a motor are connected to a rotary converter (plus auxiliaries) so that the slip energy of the main motor is transformed to DC power, and the latter is either returned to the main drive shaft (to maintain constant horsepower output), or converted to AC power and returned to the line (to maintain constant torque). The **Scherbius system** employs an auxiliary regulating machine which converts the slip energy of the main drive motor into mechanical power on the shaft of that motor to maintain a constant horsepower output. The main difference between the two systems is that, while the Scherbius system uses an AC commutation machine to convert slip energy of the motor to mechanical power on its shaft, the Kraemer system accomplishes this by using a rotary converter and a DC motor. Both systems are largely of historical interest, so far as main drives for rolling mills are concerned, as none have been installed in this application since about 1930.

D. VARIABLE-SPEED CONTROLS FOR DC MOTORS

Ward-Leonard Control—In the Ward-Leonard system of control the voltage of a DC generator is varied from zero to full voltage and this power supply connected to a DC motor or motors. The speed of a DC motor with a given load and the shunt field kept constant is proportional to the impressed voltage. Hence, if the armature voltage is varied from zero to full voltage, the motor speed will vary from zero to base speed (full field). During this period, the motor exerts constant torque and operates as a constant-torque machine. This is the essence of the Ward-Leonard system of control, and is the method used to start large DC motors as well as to control speeds up to the base speed. Such motors can be accelerated and decelerated very smoothly and rapidly without drawing an increased amount of power from the system, contrary to the case with AC motors.

For speeds above the base speed, DC motors in standard types have a 2:1 speed range. Higher speed ranges, up to 4:1, can be obtained in certain sizes and designs. An example of the higher extreme is the type of motor employed for driving the reel on cold-reduction mills. For speed control of such DC motors above the base speed (usually 200 per cent of the base speed or higher), the Ward-Leonard control is not applicable because at base speed, the system is delivering full voltage that already is producing maximum armature current. Speed control of such DC motors above base speed is accomplished by adding resistance in the field circuit that results in weakening of the shunt fields; during operation under these conditions the motor becomes essentially a constant-horsepower machine.

The direction of rotation of DC motors is controlled by reversing the direction of the flow of current irrespective of the method of speed control employed.

Relay and Continuous-Feedback Systems—During the past twenty years, various electrical control schemes have been developed for maintaining constant speeds, speed relations between different motors, and divisions of load in a tandem train. These methods have the basic principle of sensing very small variations in some function such as speed, load, voltage, current or tension and amplifying them so that the regulating equipment has large quantities to work with in maintaining close control. These systems also eliminate many contactors by employing the principles of rotating regulators, magnetic amplifiers or electronic equipment.

The choice of regulating system for mill drives requires a thorough knowledge of the requirements of the process and an appreciation of the proper function or combination of functions to be controlled to satisfy these requirements.

In general, there are two distinct regulating systems: (1) the **relay system** and (2) the **continuous-feedback system.** The relay system is usually applied to reasonably small power units, while the continuous-feedback system may be applied to any size power unit. The relay system has the disadvantage of applying full power to correct a small error, and is, therefore, not very useful where high accuracy is required; while with the continuous-feedback system the correcting effort is nearly proportional to the error and permits smoother operation and greater accuracy of control. Rotating, magnetic-amplifier and electronic regulators are examples of control elements utilizing the continuous-feedback principle. These systems have been described by Miller and Rothe (see reference at end of chapter) as follows:

Rotating Regulating Systems provide a high power-amplification ratio and respond very quickly to a change in input power. These characteristics have been obtained by a system of field and armature connections on a machine very similar to a conventional DC generator. The rotating regulator combines two stages of amplification into one machine, each stage of which has a very short time delay. The first stage of amplification is from the load axis. The second stage is from the short-circuit axis to the load terminals. For purposes of approximate analysis, it is as though two DC generators were used, with the first generator just as large as the second as regards voltage-output characteristics.

The Magnetic-Amplifier Regulating System differs from the rotating-regulator system in that the control element is a static rather than a rotating device. This static power-control unit combines a saturable-core reactor in a self-saturated circuit.

The reactor somewhat resembles a transformer with several windings linking one or more laminated iron cores. However, it differs from the transformer in that the core is designed to be operated in the region of magnetic saturation during part of each cycle. Selenium and germanium crystal rectifiers are most commonly used with the reactors. The output current of this combination which flows through the output winding of the reactors has a DC component and produces the bulk of the magnetizing force on the core of the reactor. The magnetizing force supplied by the DC control winding or windings is usually only a small fraction of that supplied by the output winding, but holds the "balance of power" in saturating the core. When the core becomes saturated, the imped-

ance of the output winding is practically eliminated, thus permitting a large direct current to flow to control the operation of the system.

It should be noted that the magnetic amplifier performs as a current amplifier, while the rotating regulator acts as a voltage amplifier. The rotating regulator is inherently reversible, while the magnetic amplifier has the irreversible characteristics of the rectifier. For reversing applications, either two generator fields and two magnetic amplifiers must be used, or efficiency must be sacrificed in the magnetic-amplifier units to convert them from current amplifiers to a reversing-voltage amplifier. In either case, two sets of reactors and rectifiers are required. Even when two fields are used on the generator, each magnetic amplifier unit may need to be larger than that required for non-reversing operation if a very rapid reversal of generator voltage is required. The forward field and the magnetic-amplifier rectifier circuit tend to behave as a short-circuited winding and will act to slow down the flux change called for by the increasing current in the reverse field. Each application of self-saturating magnetic amplifiers for reversing duty must be completely studied; first, to determine the suitability of the application and, second, to determine the most suitable means of obtaining reversing operation for that particular application.

Electronic Control Elements are used in steel-mill regulating systems when the characteristics of the application are favorable to this type of control. Electronic control is used where great accuracy and speed of response are needed. It is also used when the input signal from the drive must be controlled from a very low power level. On very small drives, electronic equipment may be considerably less expensive, and sometimes there is no other way to solve the problem. In several recent installations, electronic control has been used as an addition to rotating-regulator or magnetic-amplifier equipment. A recent development in electronic controls is the transistor, a tiny simple device that employs the unique electrical properties of germanium crystals for rectifying and controlling the flow of current.

Rotating regulators have a broad field of application. The main and auxiliary drives of blooming mills are good examples of applications requiring a large number of rotating regulators. They are used at the Fairless Works, for example, for regulating the drives for the skin-pass or temper mill, a cleaning line, the finishing stands of the hot-strip mill, the main drive and auxiliaries for the 45-inch slabbing mill, and the main drive for the 40-inch blooming mill. On the main drive of a blooming mill, rotating regulators are used to regulate and reverse the generator voltage, force fast response of the motor fields, limit the main armature currents to predetermined values, and for load-balance control where two or more armatures are operated in parallel (see Harris reference at end of chapter).

The magnetic-amplifier regulating system has been applied in considerable numbers in the steel industry. It has been used for controlling tandem cold-reduction mills, reel drives for cold-reduction mills, speed control for high-speed side-trimming line tension reels,

FIG. **20**—33. Twin-motor drive for a 44-inch slabbing mill consisting of two 5000-horsepower, 40/80 r.p.m., direct-current motors.

speed regulation for the bridle rolls on cleaning lines, tension-reel drives for processing lines, tensiometer-type tension regulators for skin-pass or temper mills and as a voltage regulator for ignition rectifiers (see Harris reference at end of chapter).

Electronic regulators have been used for applications where the regulator has to "see," such as edge control for slitting and cleaning lines, and where very precise and fast-acting regulator components are required, such as rod-mill droop regulators and electric flying-shear regulators. To obtain the required speed regulation, such as required on tube and rod mills, combination electronic-rotating regulating equipment has been used.

REVERSING-MILL DRIVES

On motor-driven primary mills, such as slabbing, blooming, or single-stand plate mills, it is customary to use a reversing mill drive. A few of the older mills still are driven by steam engines which were retained for economic reasons. Since the installation of the first motor-driven reversing mill in 1915, very few engine drives have been installed and, today, only motor drives are given consideration. Electric-motor

and steam-engine drives for primary mills are compared in some detail in Chapter 22.

For modern reversing-mill service, the main-drive DC motor is of rugged design, with a welded frame of rolled steel, horizontally split. The pedestal for the bearing next to the mill is cast steel and is provided with a thrust bearing. These motors, being connected directly to the mill pinion stand, necessarily must be of slow speed. One of the normal speed ratings is 0/40/80, which represents speed control from zero to 40 r.p.m., which is the constant-torque range, on voltage control, and from 40 to 80 r.p.m., which is the constant-horsepower range, on field control.

One of the original design problems on these motors was commutation and, in sizes above 4000 horsepower, they were built with two armatures on a single shaft. In recent years, however, the designs have been developed so that an 8000-horsepower, 0/50/100 motor has been built with a single armature. Sizes and speeds of some typical installations of these motors are shown in Table **20**—V.

This table indicates that the most popular size is about 7000 horsepower. Some of the characteristics of such a motor are:

Table 20—V.   Typical Installations of Reversing Mill Motors*

Company	Location	Size Mill	Motor Horse-power	Motor Speed (r.p.m.)	Motor Voltage Rating
Armco Steel Corp	Butler, Pa.	48″	7000	50–120	700
	Middletown, Ohio	45″	2–5000	40–80	700
Bethlehem Steel Company	Steelton, Pa.	44″	6000	40–120	600
	Sparrows Point, Md.	54″	7000	50–100	650
	Sparrows Point, Md.	40″	7000	50–100	650
	Lackawanna, N. Y.	54″	7000	40–80	750
Crucible Steel Co. of America	Midland, Pa.	46″	2–5000	40–100	750
Great Lakes Steel Corporation	Ecorse, Mich.	46″	7000	40–100	700
Inland Steel Company	Indiana Harbor, Ind.	46″	7000	50–120	700
Jones & Laughlin Steel Corp	Aliquippa, Pa.	44″	2–6000	70–140	750
Republic Steel Corporation	Warren, Ohio	36″	6500	50–120	600
	Canton, Ohio	35″	5000	40–120	600
	Gadsden, Ala.	40″	7000	50–120	700
United States Steel Corp.	Duquesne, Pa.	46″	2–5000	40–80	750
	Homestead Pa.	44″	7000	50–120	700
	Homestead, Pa.	45″	2–5000	40–80	700
	Gary, Ind.	44″	8000	40–100	800
	Gary, Ind.	40″	6000	40–90	600
	South Chicago, Ill.	54″	2–5000	40–80	700
	South Chicago, Ill.	40″	7000	40–120	700
	Fairfield, Ala.	46″	7000	50–100	700
	Morrisville, Pa.	45″	2–6000	40–80	700
Wheeling Steel Corp.	Steubenville, Ohio	45″	6000	50–120	700
Youngstown Sheet & Tube Co.	Youngstown, Ohio	44″	2–6000	50–120	750
	Indiana Harbor, Ind.	45″	2–5000	40–80	750

*Courtesy of "Iron and Steel Engineer."

Frame Diameter	197 inches
Armature Diameter	148 inches
Length of Shaft	295 inches
Diameter of Shaft	32 inches
Weight of Complete Motor	416,000 pounds
Approximate Reversing Cycle	50-0-50 r.p.m.—2 seconds / 120-0-120 r.p.m.—5 seconds

A motor of this type was installed on the reversing roughing stand of a 132-inch semi-continuous plate mill of United States Steel Corporation. This 7000-horsepower, 0/25/60 r.p.m. motor is really two 3500-horsepower motors mounted as a single unit. The armatures are of unusual construction in that they have no conventional shaft. The spiders are bolted to stub flanged shafts at each end and the complete unit assembled at the mill. This design solved some of the shipping problems for the heavy pieces.

When the power requirements for a reversing mill exceed 7000 horsepower, problems in motor and pinion design arise that suggest the use of two separate motors, one to drive the top roll and one to drive the bottom roll, connected together electrically. This is known as the twin drive (Figure 20—33). The first installations of the twin-drive type were made at the 54-inch blooming mill and the 44-inch slabbing mill in United States Steel Corporation's South Works in 1928.

This type of drive has a lower inertia than the single-motor drive of comparable power, eliminates the pinion stand, and represents about the same proportion of the cost of the complete mill as a single-motor drive. It has the advantage also of being able to operate with rolls of different diameters in the mill, and also to equalize loading of the two rolls.

One of the design problems involved in laying out a twin-motor drive is the determination of the length of the connecting spindles. The diameter of the main-drive armatures is a fixed distance for a given size and speed of motor, and this dimension, plus that of the field pole and the yoke, give the vertical distance between centerlines of the two drive shafts at the motor bearings. The diameter of the mill rolls, plus the maximum roll opening, set the condition at the mill end of the drive. The problem then is to use a length of spindle that results in a drive angle that will transmit the full torque without deflection or whipping. On some modern drives, each motor is rated at 5000 horsepower 0/40/80 r.p.m., and has a maximum torque of 1,970,000 foot-pounds.

On the 54-inch reversing blooming mill referred to above, the maximum angle with the horizontal for the spindle was limited to four degrees.

On reversing slabbing mills, an edger drive usually is required, the motor of which must perform in relation to the main-drive motor or motors. This drive should not push a slab into the main rolls or exert a pulling action on it in opposition to the main motors. One means of preventing this is to space the edger far enough away from the mill so that the slab is never in the edger and the mill at the same time. Several modern installations, however, have the edger as part of the main mill so that the slab can be edged and rolled simultaneously. Such an installation requires a coordinated motor and control design to distribute motor loads properly.

The Flywheel Motor-Generator Set—In all types of DC reversing drives, the motor receives the power from a flywheel motor-generator set. Since the practical size for generators of this type is limited to about 4000 kw, there may be two or three generators on a continuous bed plate, driven by a wound-rotor induction motor, whose combined output will meet the mill requirements. The generator capacity is in the ratio of 1.15 to 1.35 of the motor capacity in order to meet the requirements of the maximum torque of the motor, plus losses. The induction motor driving the generator or generators, plus the flywheel, has a capacity equal to about the average net output of the drive motor (which may be only 50 per cent of the capacity as limited by heating effects), plus the electrical losses of the generators, slip regulator and the friction and windage losses of the flywheel.

In practice, these motor-generator sets are proportioned as follows:

Generator Capacity (kw)	Induction-Motor Horsepower
6,000	5,000
7,500	6,000
9,000	7,000
10,500	7,500
13,500	8,000

The flywheel is of hot-riveted, steel-plate construction and, as indicated in Table 20—VI, may be fifteen feet in diameter, weigh from 140,000 to 200,000 pounds, and be driven at a peripheral speed of about 22,000 feet per minute. A slip of about 15 per cent in speed, which will make available about 30 per cent of the flywheel energy, is the maximum desirable. To obtain the benefit of this stored flywheel energy, a slip regulator is connected in the secondary circuit of the wound-rotor induction motor. This device consists of

Table 20—VI. **Reversing Drive Motors***

Motor Horsepower	3750	5000	6350	7000	8000	10000
Motor Speed (r.p.m.)	0–50–120	0–50–120	0–60–120	0–50–120	0–40–80	0–40–80
Continuous Rating Torque, Ft.-Lbs.	395,000	525,000	557,000	735,000	1,050,000	1,310,000
Max. Torque, Field Breaker, Ft.-Lbs.	890,000	1,185,000	1,250,000	1,660,000	2,300,000	2,950,000
Max. Torque, Main Breaker, Ft.-Lbs.	1,090,000	1,450,000	1,535,000	2,020,000	2,890,000	3,600,000
Generator Capacity, kw	2 × 1800	2 × 2200	2 × 2700	2 × 3000 / 3 × 2500	2 × 3500 / 3 × 2500	3 × 3000
M-G Set Drive, Horsepower	3000	3650	4350	5000–6000	5000–6000	6500–7500
M-G Set Drive Speed (r.p.m.)	514	514	400	360	360	360
Flywheel Diameter	13′0″	13′0″	14′6″	15′0″	15′0″	15′0″
Flywheel Weight, Lb.	75,000	75,000	100,000	110,000	150,000	180,000
Flywheel WR^2, Lb.-Ft.²	1,650,000	1,650,000	2,700,000	3,200,00	4,300,000	5,200,000
Flywheel Stored Energy, hp-sec.	135,000	135,000	134,000	130,000	175,000	210,000

*Courtesy of "Iron and Steel Engineer."

three vertical electrodes with their lower ends immersed in a salt solution, and raising or lowering the electrodes inserts more or less resistance in the secondary circuit, which causes the motor to slow down or slip as the load is thrown on, permitting the flywheel energy to be used.

A torque motor that responds to the amount of current in the primary circuit of the induction motor acts to raise or lower the electrodes. These slip regulators generally are set to restrict the input to the induction motor at some value between 125 and 150 per cent of full-load rating. The regulator also is used as the starting resistor when the set is put in the line.

The drive motor of the motor-generator set often has another feature incorporated in its control scheme; that is, means for dynamic braking. This consists of a circuit that, by means of circuit breakers, can be connected to a DC source, in order that after the AC source is disconnected, these circuit breakers close and DC flows in two of the motor phase windings. The purpose of this is to shorten the time required for the set to drift to a standstill. Without the dynamic braking feature, the drift time for an average flywheel set is 30 to 40 minutes.

THREE-HIGH MILL DRIVES

Motors to drive three-high mills usually are of the low-speed, direct-connected, wound-rotor induction

type. Often, the rotor is designed to take advantage of the flywheel effect. In other cases, a flywheel is mounted on the same shaft with the rotor. The motor speed is usually a compromise—slow enough to permit the slab or bloom to enter the mill, and fast enough to enable the mill to produce the specified tonnage.

Since the motor of a three-high mill operates continuously in one direction only, the proportion of total time the piece is in the rolls depends on the speed of (1) the screw-downs and (2) the tilting tables. There are some installations where DC motors are used, which have the advantage of variable speed, and these mills can produce higher tonnages than comparable mills using constant-speed motors because of more favorable operating characteristics.

The chief applications for wound-rotor induction-motor drives have been on three-high plate and structural mills. The motors are controlled by slip regulators or notch-back control to limit the power peaks. The notch-back control consists of secondary grid resistors which are cut in or out in fixed steps by load relays and function in the same manner as the slip regulators. The chief difference is that the notch-back control resistance is in fixed steps while the slip regulator, with electrodes moving in and out of the salt solution, makes it possible to increase or decrease resistance in a continuous manner without steps, giving smoother operation.

FIG. 20—34. Interior partial view of a motor room showing some of the drive motors and auxiliaries for an 80-inch hot-strip mill.

CONTINUOUS-MILL DRIVES

Wide Hot-Strip Mills—The major development of continuous-mill drives was associated with the wide strip mills.

The conventional layout for these mills has a long, narrow motor room paralleling the hot-strip mill, between the mill and the slab yard. This motor room houses all of the main-drive motors, the motor-generator sets or rectifiers, the gear-reduction units, control and switching equipment. Figure 20—34 shows a section of the motor room in one of the modern mills.

The drive motors for continuous mills follow a fairly uniform pattern, with the scale breaker and roughing stands being driven by synchronous motors, and the finishing stands driven by variable-speed DC motors.

The roughing stands are spaced so that the slab is in only one stand at a time.

The basic data for calculating the horsepower requirements per stand for a continuous mill are based upon actual test. Composition of the steel, its temperature, speed of rolling, and width are variables in these data. In addition, allowance has to be made for the judgment that has to be exercised by the roller, who is given a certain size slab to be reduced in a number of stands to a product meeting close dimensional tolerances and high surface-quality standards. To do this, the theoretical reductions per pass may have to be varied, and it may be necessary to increase or decrease the draft on certain passes as compared with the calculated reductions.

The DC finishing-mill motors are designed to operate on 600 to 700 volts. At this voltage, they will run at the base speed. These motors are started by the Ward-Leonard system, the armature voltage being increased gradually until the motors are at the base speed. If lower speeds are required, the DC voltage is reduced, which also decreases the horsepower output but does not change the torque. Higher speeds are obtained by weakening the DC fields in the motors by the field rheostats or, in the more modern installations, by changing the field voltage by means of rotating or static control. The standard speed range for these motors on field control is 2:1 or more and they are designed to have approximately flat speed characteristics.

When operating, the motors must function as a unit and maintain their speed relationship regardless of load. Usually, a master control is installed so that, once this relationship is established, the speed of the stands can be raised or lowered as a unit. Table 20—VII gives installed horsepower, speeds, etc., for five modern hot-strip mills.

Tandem Cold-Reduction Mills—Another type of continuous mill is the cold-reduction tandem mill. Mills of this type have three, four, five or six stands, with a reel to wind up or coil the cold-reduced product. The electrical problem here is more difficult than on the hot-strip mill, because tension maintained in the product between the stands must be controlled within close limits. The speeds on this type of mill have been gradually increased, several mills having a top finishing speed of over 7000 feet per minute. Table 20—VIII gives motor and generator data on some modern tandem cold-reduction mills.

Continuous Billet Mills—Modern continuous billet mills are provided with individual motor drives at each stand. On the 30-inch mill at Fairless Works, each stand (three vertical and three horizontal) is driven through gearing by a 1750-horsepower, 300/-600 r.p.m., 600-volt, direct-current shunt motor. They are supplied with power from a motor generator set consisting of four 2000-kw generators driven by an 11,200-horsepower, 514 r.p.m., 13,800-volt synchronous motor. The 21-inch billet mill at the same plant consists of two vertical and two horizontal stands, each individually driven by a 1250-horsepower, 400/-600 r.p.m., 600-volt, direct-current shunt motor through gears. The power for these drives is supplied by a motor-generator set consisting of two 2000-kw generators driven by a 5600-horsepower, 514 r.p.m., synchronous motor.

Continuous Bar Mills—Individual motor drives are also provided for the separate stands of modern continuous bar mills. At the 10-inch mill at Fairless Works, there are 18 two-high stands, all in line. Ten have horizontal rolls and eight have vertical rolls. Each stand is driven by a 600-volt, direct-current motor, in sizes ranging from 400 to 700 horsepower. Power is supplied by a motor-generator set composed of three 2500-kw generators, one 150-kw exciter, and a 10,500-horsepower, 514 r.p.m., 13,200-volt synchronous motor.

Continuous Rod Mills—Continuous rod mills consist of numerous stands arranged, for drive purposes, in groups with an individual motor driving the two or more stands in each group. The selection and distribution of motors in such a mill is dependent upon roll speed, roll diameter, amount of reduction in each stand, the horsepower required, and the degree of flexibility of control of the mill as an operating unit. The new straight-line continuous rod mill at Cuyahoga Works of United States Steel Corporation rolls 3¼-inch square billets, 30 to 34 feet long, into coiled rods from about ¼-inch to 1⅛-inches in diameter. The motors with their speed ranges were selected as shown in Table 20—IX.

Continuous Seamless Tube Mill—In the continuous seamless tube mill at Lorain Works of United States Steel Corporation (separate mills of which are described in Chapter 30), the piercing mill is driven by a 4500-horsepower, 225 r.p.m., 13,800-volt, synchronous motor through a reduction gear having a ratio of 2.25:1. The nine continuous stands of the mandrel mill are individually driven by direct-current motors with a combined rated capacity of 8500 horsepower. The product from the mandrel mill, after reheating, is further processed in either the stretch-reducing mill or the sizing mill. The stretch-reducing mill is made up of twelve two-high, overhung roll stands; each roll stand is individually driven by a 200-horsepower, 850/1700 r.p.m., 600-volt, shunt motor. The sizing mill consists of twelve overhung roll stands, each with an individual drive consisting of a 76-horsepower, 850-1700 r.p.m., shunt motor.

Table 20—VII. Installed Horsepower, Speeds, Etc.—Hot-Strip Mills

	U.S.S. Corp. Fairless Works—80" Mill	Great Lakes Steel Ecorse Works—80" Mill	Inland Steel Co. Harbor Works—80" Mill	Wheeling Steel Corp. Wheeling Works—80" Mill	Republic Steel Corp. Warren Works—58" Mill
Vertical Scale Breaker—Roll Size	45" x 32"	45" x 18"	45" x 20"	45" x 14"	—
Motor HP, RPM, Type	1000, 514, WR	1500, 514, Syn.	1250, 450, —	1250, 257, —	— — —
Gear Ratio, FPM	31.21/1 194	30.0/1 202	30.3/1 175	— 250	— —
Horizontal Scale Breaker—Roll Size	38" x 80"	—	48" x 80"	—	44" x 58"
Motor HP, RPM, Type	2000, 150, Syn.	—	5000, 300, Syn.	—	3500, 350, —
Gear Ratio, FPM	7.39/1 202	—	17.4/1 216	—	15.69/1 257
No. 1 Rougher—Roll Size	40" & 54" x 130"	44" x 81"	48" x 80"	46" x 80"	4-High Reversing Rougher 36" & 35" x 56"
Motor HP, RPM, Type	3500, 150, Syn.	5000, 450, Syn.	5000, 300, Syn.	5000, 450, Syn.	2-4000 HP
Gear Ratio, FPM	7.81/1 201	25.8/1 201	17.4/1 216	23.88/1 226	40/100 RPM
No. 2 Rougher—Roll Size	38" & 53½" x 81"	44" & 60" x 80"	48" x 80"	44" & 60" x 80"	377/942 FPM
Motor HP, RPM, Type	6000, 240, Syn.	5000, 450, Syn.	9000, 360, Syn.	5000, 450, Syn.	
Gear Ratio, FPM	6.49/1 368	25.8/1 201	17.4/1 260	23.7/1 219	
No. 3 Rougher—Roll Size	38" & 53½" x 81"	44" & 60" x 80"	38" & 60" x 80"		
Motor HP, RPM, Type	6000, 360, Syn.	10000, 450, Syn.	9000, 360, Syn.		
Gear Ratio, FPM	7.49/1 478	15.7/1 330	10.4/1 344		
No. 4 Rougher—Roll Size	34" & 53½" x 81"	44" & 60" x 80"	38" & 60" x 80"	44" & 60" x 80"	
Motor HP, RPM, Type	6000, 360, Syn.	10000, 450, Syn.	9000, 360, Syn.	10000, 450, Syn.	
Gear Ratio, FPM	5.24/1 612	11.7/1 442	5.75/1 620	9.92/1 522	
No. 5 Rougher—Roll Size	34" & 53½" x 81"	44" & 60" x 80"	38" & 60" x 80"	44" & 60" x 80"	
Motor HP, RPM, Type	6000, 360, Syn.	10000, 450, Syn.	10000, 450, Syn.	10000, 450, Syn.	
Gear Ratio, FPM	5.24/1 612	9.25/1 561	5.75/1 755	7.93/1 655	
Scale Breaker Motor HP, RPM, Type	500, 300/600 DC	500, 350/875 DC	—	300, 300/600 DC	—
Finishing Mill Roll Sizes	27" & 53½" x 81"	28½" & 60" x 80"	28½" & 60" x 80"	28½" & 60" x 80"	25" & 54" x 58"
No. 1 Finishing Stand Motor HP & RPM	5000 125/250	7000 200/400	9000 125/312	6000 175/410	5000 150/370
Gear Ratio and FPM	4.27/1 207/415	7.91/1 188/376	3.27/1 287/712	5.42/1 241/565	4.27/1 230/567
No. 2 Finishing Stand Motor HP & RPM	5000 125/250	8000 125/275	9000 125/312	6000 175/410	6000 100/230
Gear Ratio and FPM	2.47/1 358/757	2.98/1 313/680	1.96/1 477/1190	3.34/1 391/915	1.95/1 335/770
No. 3 Finishing Stand Motor HP & RPM	5000 80/160	8000 125/275	9000 125/312	6000 175/410	6000 100/230
Gear Ratio and FPM	1/1 565/1130	1.93/1 486/1060	1.402/1 665/1660	2.307/1 568/1325	1.35/1 485/1120
No. 4 Finishing Stand Motor HP & RPM	5000 100/220	8000 125/275	9000 125/312	6000 175/410	6000 100/230
Gear Ratio and FPM	1/1 706/1553	1.33/1 700/1545	Direct 934/2330	1.586/1 824/1930	Direct 655/1510
No. 5 Finishing Stand Motor HP & RPM	5000 125/270	8000 125/275	9000 125/312	6000 175/410	6000 125/300
Gear Ratio and FPM	1/1 883/1906	1/.833 930/2050	1/1.402 1308/3265	1.212/1 1078/2525	Direct 820/1970
No. 6 Finishing Stand Motor HP & RPM	4000 150/330	8000 175/350	9000 125/312	6000 175/410	5000 150/370
Gear Ratio and FPM	1/1 1060/2330	Direct 1300/2600	1/1.672 1560/3884	Direct 1307/3061	Direct 982/2420
No. 7 Finishing Stand Motor HP & RPM	— —	7000 200/400			
Gear Ratio and FPM		Direct 1500/3000			
Finishing Motor DC Supply by—	Mer. Arc. Rectifiers	Mer. Arc. Rectifiers	Mer. Arc. Rectifiers	Motor-Generator Sets	Mer. Arc. Rectifiers

Table 20—VIII. Installed Horsepower and Generating Capacity—Tandem Cold-Reducing Mills*

	Youngstown Sheet & Tube Co.—6-Stand	U.S.S. Corp. 6-Stand	U.S.S. Corp. 6-Stand	Midwest Steel Co. 5-Stand	Wheeling Steel Corp. 5-Stand	U.S.S. Corp. 5-Stand
#1 Stand Motor Horsepower	23" & 56" x 52" 2—1500 S.A.	23" & 56" x 52" 2—2000 S.A.	23" & 56" x 52" 2—1500 S.A.	23" & 56" x 52" 2—1500 S.A.	21" & 53" x 48" 1—2000 S.A.	23" & 60" x 80" 2—1750 S.A.
Motor R.P.M.	125/375	80/280	160/480	115/400	90/270	80/300
Gear Ratio & F.P.M.	1.363/1 553/1656	1/1 480/1680	1.686/1 570/1710	1.438/1 482/1680	Direct 495/1485	1/1 480/1800
#2 Stand Motor Horsepower	2—2500 S.A.	2—2000 S.A.	2—2500 S.A.	2—2500 S.A.	1—4000 D.A.	2—3500 D.A.
Motor R.P.M.	212/520	225/563	175/437	125/375	150/375	225/620
Gear Ratio & F.P.M.	1.438/1 888/2175	1.5967 850/2123	1.15/1 920/2300	1/1.11 846/2520	Direct 825/2060	1.512/1 895/2470
#3 Stand Motor Horsepower	2—2500 S.A.	2—2500 S.A.	2—2500 S.A.	2—2500 S.A.	2—2000 S.A.	2—3500 D.A.
Motor R.P.M.	212/520	225/530	175/437	125/375	150/375	225/620
Gear Ratio & F.P.M.	1/1 1276/3130	1.0833/1 1250/2946	1/1.22 1288/3220	1/1.51 1140/3420	1/1.51 1242/3120	Direct 1350/3733
#4 Stand Motor Horsepower	2—3000 D.A.	2—3000 D.A.	2—3000 S.A.	2—3000 D.A.	2—2500 S.A.	2—3500 D.A.
Motor R.P.M.	255/637	350/700	122/305	200/485	250/518	225/620
Gear Ratio & F.P.M.	1/1.108 1700/4255	1/1.0882 1937/3874	D. Bk. R. Dri., 1789/4472	1/1.51 1820/4410	1/1.51 2080/4300	1/1.293 1752/4827
#5 Stand Motor Horsepower	2—3000 D.A.	2—3000 D.A.	2—3000 D.A.	2—3500 T.A.	2—3000 D.A.	2—3000 T.A.
Motor R.P.M.	255/637	350/700	161/402	200/500	275/550	350/840
Gear Ratio & F.P.M.	1/1.516 2325/5820	1/1.2828 2703/5406	D. Bk. R. Dri., 2360/5894	1/2 2410/6025	1/2 3025/6050	Direct 2107/5058
#6 Stand Motor Horsepower	2—3750 T.A.	2—3500 D.A.	2—3500 D.A.	—	—	—
Motor R.P.M.	300/635	350/700	773/520	—	—	—
Gear Ratio & F.P.M.	1/1.863 3365/7140	1/1.6904 3562/7124	D. Bk. R. Dri., 2536/7624	—	—	—
Reel Motor Horsepower	2—1200 D.A.	1—2100 T.A.	2—1500 T.A.	2—1800 T.A.	1—1500 T.A.	2—1400 D.A.
Motor R.P.M.	200/1000	300/1500	250/1250	200/1000	300/1120	260/1160
Gear Ratio	1/1.768	1/1	1/1.42	1/1.31	Direct	Direct
Total Horsepower	34,900	32,100	35,000	29,600	22,500	33,300
MG Sets Motor Horsepower	#1 15000 / #2 12000 / #3 12000	#1 18000 / #2 18000	#1 19000 / #2 19000	#1 17000 / #2 17000	#1 12000 / #2 12000	#1 18000 / #2 18000
Generator K.W. #1	2400 / 2000 / 2000	1600 / 2000	2000 / 2000	1440 / 1440	1600 / 2000	2800 / 2800
Generator K.W. #2	2400 / 2000 / 2000	1600 / 2000	2400 / 2000	1440 / 1440	1600 / 2000	2800 / 2800
Generator K.W. #3	2400 / 2000 / 2000	2400 / 2000	2400 / 2000	2000 / 1440	1600 / 1600	2800 / 2800
Generator K.W. #4	2400 / 2000 / 2000	2400 / 2000	2400 / 2800	2000 / 2000	1600 / 1600	2800 / 2800
Generator K.W. #5	2400 / 2000 / 2000	2400 / 2000	2400 / 2800	2400 / 2000	1600 / 1600	2800 / 2400
Generator K.W. #6		2400 / 1600	2400 / 2400	2400 / 2400	1600	2400 / 2400
Generator K.W. #7		2400 / 1600			1250	

*S.A. indicates Single Armature, D.A. indicates Double Armature, T.A. indicates Triple Armature, D.Bk.R.Dri. indicates Direct Back-Up Roll Drive.

Table 20—IX.   Motor Drives for Modern Continuous Rod Mill.

	Horse-power	Speed (r.p.m.)
Roughing Train		
Drive No. 1–Stands 1 and 2	600	300–950
Drive No. 2–Stands 3, 4 and 5	1250	225–675
Intermediate Stands		
Drive No. 3–Stands 6, 7, 8 and 9	1750	200–550
Finishing Stands		
Drive No. 4–Stands 10 and 11	1500	225–580
Drive No. 5–Stands 12 and 13	1250	225–620
Drive No. 6–Stands 14 and 15	1250	225–620
Drive No. 7–Stands 16–23, incl.	4500[a]	690–960
Drive No. 8–Stand 16a[b]	700	200–690
Drive No. 9–Stand 17a[b]	700	250–790

[a] Motor set consists of one double-armature and one single-armature motor.

[b] Looping stands 16a and 16b are used for rolling $\frac{3}{8}$-inch to $1\frac{1}{8}$-inch diameter rods. In this case, Stands 16 to 23 are not used.

MOTOR-ROOM VENTILATION

A very important feature of the motor rooms for large electrical installations is the ventilating system. It is necessary to supply sufficient clean air to maintain normal operating temperatures for the equipment. Several installations have been designed that employ down-draft recirculating systems, where the air which passes into the motors and generators is discharged into the basement, pulled or blown through surface-type water coolers, and sent back to the motor room. Since there is always some leakage, a certain amount of make-up air is required, and this is introduced into the basement through a cleaning system.

Several installations have allowed for only 10 per cent make-up air, which may have been adequate when the building was new but, as cracks developed and loose joints appeared in the structure, this quantity of make-up air was too small and, as a result, outside air infiltrated into the building. These recirculating systems also have the detrimental effect of picking up the carbon dust from the brushes of the motors and generators and, in the recirculating process, this dust is deposited in the windings since no cleaning equipment is included in the indoor system. If a closed system is specified, the make-up air provided for should be at least 25 per cent.

The other type of ventilating system supplies 100 per cent new air which is blown into the basement through a cleaning system, then forced up through the motors into the motor room, where a positive pressure is maintained that prevents infiltration. This system requires larger fans and motors than the recirculating system, but requires no cooling-water system and is less costly to maintain. Usually, there are three or four fans operated as needed so that, in winter time, the heat from the motors can be used to warm the room.

In the recirculating system, the cooling system has to be designed so that the difference in temperature between the cooling water and the outgoing air is not less than 10° F. Since the air delivered to the machines should not be above 104° F, the cooling water should not be warmer than 94° F. The following table indicates the amount of air required for cooling per kw loss in each machine:

Cubic Feet of Air Per Minute Per KW Loss	Rise in Air Temperature (Degrees F)
100	32.9
110	29.9
120	27.4
130	25.3

For cleaning the air, various types of filters have been used. The oil-immersed traveling-screen type, one of the early designs, did not remove the fine particles of soot and smoke from the air, and the oil was a fire hazard. Later installations favor the electrostatic type and/or dry-type filter media.

AUXILIARY DRIVES

The auxiliary drives on mills are as important as the main drives, and require proper application and co-ordination of types and sizes of motors. Both AC and DC motors are used, the former being the accepted ones for driving fans, pumps, and, occasionally, shears and run-out tables. The majority of the motors, however, are mill-type DC units, because of their ruggedness and the many operating characteristics that can be built into them. These mill-type motors were developed by the steel industry in cooperation with the electrical-equipment manufacturers for use in the rough service of driving mill tables, heavy-duty cranes, manipulators, etc. The ratings and principal dimensions have been standardized by the Association of Iron and Steel Engineers into fourteen frame sizes, ranging from 5 horsepower to 500 horsepower, based on the 1-hour rating. They can be obtained with several designs of windings from straight series to shunt, and with various types of ventilation. The designs are very rugged, and the armatures have low inertia in comparison with general-purpose motors. Table 20—X describes motors for various auxiliary-drive applications.

Table Rollers—The early strip-mill run-out table rollers were equipped with variable-speed AC motors, one per roller, and speed variations were obtained by varying the frequency of the power supply by a variable-speed motor-generator set. Since 1937, the DC mill-type motor has been used for this application.

Schloemann rollers, a German design, in which the movable part of the table roller is the rotor of the motor and the stationary part wound to form the stator of an induction motor, have been used on some mills. When such rollers handle hot products, they must be water cooled. Speed variations are obtained by frequency control from a motor-generator set.

In modern mills, the rollers may be driven by individual, small direct-current motors of 3 to 4 horsepower, or they may be arranged in consecutive groups with each group driven separately by a direct-current motor of ample size through a line shaft and gearing. Variable-voltage control is used to regulate the speed of the table rollers. The current generally is supplied by a motor-generator set.

Screw-Downs—Proper selection of motors for

Table 20—X. Motor Sizes on Screws, Manipulators, Shears, Etc., on Some Blooming and Slabbing Mills*

Company and Size of Mill	Great Lakes 46-inch	U. S. Steel Morrisville, Pa. 40-inch	U. S. Steel Braddock, Pa. 45-inch	Inland Steel 46-inch	Jones & Laughlin 46-inch	Youngstown Sheet and Tube 45-inch
Screw Motors (No. and hp.)	2–150	2–150	2–200	2–150	2–200	2–200
Screw Motor Control	Variable Voltage	Variable Voltage	Variable Voltage	Variable Voltage	Variable Voltage	Variable Voltage
Manipulator Motors (No. and hp.)	4–150	4–100	4–150	4–150	4–200	4–150
Lift Fingers (No. and hp.)	4–50	2–100	4–150	4–150	2–150	1–150**
Manipulator Control	Variable Voltage	Variable Voltage	Variable Voltage	Variable Voltage	Variable Voltage	Variable Voltage**
Front Table Drive (No. and hp.)	2–150	2–100	2–150	2–150	2–200	2–150
Front Table Control	Variable Voltage	Variable Voltage	Variable Voltage	Variable Voltage	Variable Voltage	Variable Voltage
Back Table Drive (No. and hp.)	2–150	2–100	2–150	2–150	2–200	2–150
Back Table Control	Variable Voltage	Variable Voltage	Variable Voltage	Variable Voltage	Variable Voltage	Variable Voltage
Shear (maximum size cut)	64 in. x 6 in.	16 in. x 22 in.	60 in. x 9 in.	40 in. x 8 in.	800 sq. in.	600 sq. in.
Shear Motors (No. and hp.)	2–275	2–250	2–250	2–275	Hydraulic	2–500
Shear Motor Control	Variable Voltage	Variable Voltage	Variable Voltage	Variable Voltage	Pressure Pumps	Variable Voltage

*Courtesy, "Iron and Steel Engineer."
** All auxiliaries under variable-voltage control.

screw-down drives on the various mills is very important. In some mills, such as blooming and slabbing mills, a maximum roll lift of 66 inches may be required, with lifting speeds of up to 645 inches per minute. On strip mills, a maximum operating lift of only a few inches may be required, but the opening must be controlled within a few thousandths of an inch.

Regardless of the speed or distance involved, the screw-down motor and control must be capable of positioning the rolls within close limits. The inertia of the armature and brake wheel makes this a difficult problem, even with a compound-wound motor, and has resulted in the adoption of the Ward-Leonard system of control. This system has an added advantage in that it limits the amount of torque that can be applied to the motor, thus preventing damage to the screws by jamming.

On primary mills, modern screw-down drives usually consist of two 230-volt, DC motors of 100 to 200-horsepower rating. If operating under variable-voltage control, they are shunt motors with shunt brakes. If magnetic control is used, they are compound wound with reversing, plugging, dynamic braking, series-parallel control. The parallel connection is used to obtain higher speeds for long screw-down travel.

Manipulators and Side-Guards—Mill tests have shown that steel being rolled on primary mills is in the rolls only from 25 to 70 per cent of the total rolling time, the remainder of the time being required for screw-down, manipulator, and table operation. In a typical slabbing mill, the maximum opening of the side-guards is 115 inches, with an overtravel of 40 inches to permit changing of the table rollers. Each of the side-guards is driven by a 150- or 250-horsepower motor. Due to the heavy plugging service required for these devices, and the heavy moving mass that has to be controlled, modern installations are using shunt-wound, variable-speed motors with Ward-Leonard control for this service.

The lift fingers on the manipulators are required to make four-foot lifts and complete the cycle in two seconds. They always must stop below the top of the rollers, and represent another application for variable-voltage control. Where magnetic control is used, compound-wound mill-type motors with reversing, plugging, dynamic-braking features, plus a jamming resistor and arranged to operate two motors in series with series brakes, should be specified.

Blooming-Mill Shears—Blooming-mill shears can be driven either electrically or hydraulically. Many of the older installations were driven by an induction motor with high secondary resistance to allow the flywheel to supply the peak power for the cut. The motor ran continually and the shear was actuated through a clutch. Some of the more recent shears are of a start-stop type, driven by two shunt-wound motors of 200 to 300 horsepower, each equipped with a shunt brake and variable-voltage control.

FUTURE DRIVES

This résumé on drives for steel mills is indicative of the ever-changing design in electrical apparatus. It is no longer a problem to add loads of many thousands of horsepower to existing systems. Motors have been improved in design and increased in rating so that they can be obtained for all types of service. Improved controls, too, have kept pace with motor improvements, so that it is possible to maintain close relationship between individual large motors on successive continuous-mill stands rolling product at rates above 6000 feet per minute.

The present trend is toward still greater flexibility in drives. Recent continuous mills have been designed with separate generators for each drive motor; this allows the greatest range in speed.

In the near future, silicon-controlled rectifiers can be expected to succeed mercury-arc rectifiers or motor-generator sets as a source of DC power. With associated solid-state electronic control, this device can regulate voltage or speed within very close limits and increase overall efficiency.

The story of motor drives for mills is one of continual improvement in design to obtain higher speeds and closer regulation, to provide for more and better products from the mills.

SECTION 5

AUTOMATIC CONTROL OF ROLLING OPERATIONS

The continuing trend toward more powerful mill drives and higher rolling speeds developed as a result of efforts to obtain larger output of better quality product from each stage of the rolling processes. A necessary corollary of this trend has been the development of improved electrical equipment and controls, coupled with the application of automatic process-control systems. Automatic control of some or all of the functions of a rolling mill can result in more consistent operating practices that improve product quality and uniformity while increasing the degree of utilization of the equipment.

PRINCIPLES OF PROCESS-CONTROL SYSTEMS

The general form of a process-control system is one is which a multiplicity of inputs, such as the physical and chemical characteristics of the raw materials, the energy levels, the machine settings, and so forth, are used to provide desired outputs such as product quality, productivity, and minimum cost, or some selected combination of these. In addition, there may be other outputs required; for example, processing information for supporting functions such as accounting and evaluation.

One of the most effective ways to exercise process control is through **feedback control.** By this method, the actual output is compared to the desired output, and the necessary actions are taken to eliminate any discrepancies. In a relatively simple system an operator may observe the value of an output, determine the extent and direction of any discrepancy from a desired value, and manually adjust some process variable or combination of variables to arrive at the desired output value. In the past, many such systems have been made automatic by continually comparing the output to the desired value and making corrections automatically as required. These systems have been applied extensively to speed control, position control, and temperature control. As the scope of the control system increases, there comes a point at which a simple comparison and logic function is no longer sufficient. This may be due to the fact that a relatively complex calculation may be required before a decision can be made on the necessary corrective control action. It is the control of systems of this latter type that is facilitated by what is generally termed **computer control.** Therefore, a computer controlled system primarily denotes a degree of complexity of control rather than a basically new concept.

Because most processes in the steel industry employ feedback control, whether the loop is closed by an operator or automatically, it is important that corrective actions be determined and executed in times that are short compared to the major delays of the process. This is important because the delays in applying corrective action should not substantially add to the inherent process delay and thus unnecessarily prolong any off-standard production. Therefore, computer control would evidently be indicated for consideration when the following process conditions prevail:

(1) Complex calculations and decisions are required that exceed both the operator's capabilities and his ability to react sufficiently fast. In this case the loop would be closed automatically and would represent the greatest potential for computer control.

(2) Complex calculations and decisions are required that exceed the operator's capabilities, but his reaction time is adequate if he has this information. In such a case the loop could be closed by the operator, but the overall feedback time delay would be reduced substantially.

(3) A large number of simple comparisons and decisions are required, but corrective action must be made quickly.

(4) A large amount of operating data and summarizing information is required for operational reasons.

Before a computer controlled processing system can be engineered properly, the following items must be available:

(1) Mathematical equations that adequately describe the process.

(2) Instrumentation to measure the required variables of the system.

(3) Control equipment to perform the required functions for control of the system.

Process Equations—Because a computer controlled system, and for that matter any control system, has no intelligence of its own but can only follow orders, it is necessary to instruct the computer as to what to do under any set of operating conditions. This instruction is provided by programming the computer in accordance with mathematical formulations that describe the relationships between the process variables. The mathematical form of the relationships used will be different depending upon the specific application. They might include the differential equations derived from theoretical considerations, empirical equations developed from experimental data, statistical analysis, or some combination of these. Regardless of the approach used, there must be assurance that such treatment of the processing data will provide the desired degree of control. In addition to the computational instructions, the computer must also be instructed in the logic to be used: this is accomplished by programming the computer to establish the time sequence of events required, priorities of several possible control actions under certain circumstances, and other decisions that must necessarily be made for proper process control.

Instrumentation—A computer-controlled system accepts the quantitative values of the many processing variables and executes its control function based on these values. A prime requisite of such a system is adequate instrumentation for translating a process variable from its physical or chemical units to a form suitable for use by the computer. Many instruments are presently available to measure such variables as position, force, temperature, and flow. In general, instruments that will measure the physical and chemical properties of both raw materials and finished products have not been developed as extensively. However, high-speed computers have made it possible in some cases to circumvent a direct measurement with an indirect one for which it may not be possible to provide direct instrumentation. For example, the thickness of a slab during rolling may be calculated quickly from measurements of screw setting and mill loading, making it unnecessary to measure thickness directly. Because the decisions made by a computer control are not better than the information with which it works, the importance of reliable instrumentation is obvious.

On-line process computers are beginning to appear in various operations, such as sintering, continuous annealing, and electrolytic tinning, as well as in rolling. Some of these applications are or will be primarily data-processing, while others will include varying degrees of control.

Because the field of automatic control of rolling operations is both wide and relatively new, there has been little unanimity of opinion as to the best methods for solution of control problems inherent in mills of the same classes. For this reason, some automatic features that have been applied to existing mills, or incorporated into the design of new mills, will be discussed here only in the most general of terms.

CONTROL OF PRIMARY ROLLING

Progress in the area of control of primary rolling can be demonstrated by first considering the manual operation of a typical reversing primary mill. In the manual system, all operations and decisions are made by the operator from the control station. Feedback is through the operator who receives process information from observations and instruments and from this information makes all process adjustments as required.

In the recent past, several reversing primary mills have been equipped with a control system in which all mill operations such as main-drive acceleration and reversal, screw setting, manipulator and roll-table operations, and other functions are performed automatically in accordance with instructions previously prepared on punched cards. The feedback in such a system is through the operator, who makes modifications to the programming on a relatively long-time basis as average performance dictates. Although this might not normally be considered a computer control system because there are no computations involved, in the broad sense it is one in which the stored program contains only the logic function. In this system, decisions for each piece are made by the operator, but the execution is automatic. This is a satisfactory procedure when process variability is small and changes at a relatively slow rate.

PLATE-MILL CONTROL

When selecting the computer control system for the 160/210-inch plate mill described in Chapter 23, it was apparent that a control of the type just described for a reversing primary mill would not be adequate for a reversing mill for rolling plates. More stringent requirements for finished dimensions and shape, and the extremely large number of combinations of finished product to be handled by the plate mill, indicated the need for a more comprehensive control system. Consequently, a control system was installed that includes not only all of the logic functions provided by previous card-programmed mills, but also the continuous determination and execution of the best schedule during rolling consistent with existing workpiece conditions and mill limitations. In this system, the only information provided the computer is the general instructions and limitations for all rolling and the dimensions of the slab, the grade of steel, and the desired dimensions of the finished product. The feedback does not include the operator, and the time delay is shortened considerably because after each pass a completely new rolling schedule is derived if a discrepancy exists between observed performance and predicted performance for that pass. Here, both decision making and execution are both automatic. The control system initially included all operational functions from entry of the slab to the scalebreaker to delivery of the rolled plate to the leveler, with provision for increasing the scope of the control as operational experience might dictate.

HOT-STRIP MILL CONTROL

Roughing—Semi-continuous hot-strip mills employ

a reversing roughing stand that reduces slabs, in a series of passes, to the desired starting thickness for hot rolling in six finishing stands (in tandem) to the desired final hot-strip thickness. Continuous hot-strip mills consist of a series of four or five roughing stands in tandem that perform the same function as the reversing rougher of a semi-continuous mill. Factors affecting selection of one type of roughing operation over the other are discussed in Chapter 31.

Punched-card programming of reversing roughers for hot-strip mills follows the same general principles as have been discussed earlier for reversing primary mills under "Control of Primary Rolling." Continuous roughing trains also have been adapted to operate from punched cards to control roll openings, edger-roll adjustment, and edger speed (the last-named to adjust for changes in draft in the main rolls).

Finishing—Incorporation of automatic speed regulators as standard equipment on finishing-mill stands, the development of automatic gage control, and automatic regulation of looper and sideguard positions, each in itself contributes to improved operation of a continuous finishing mill. Data logging and processing equipment provides a means for measurement of process variables and quality control, and may range in complexity from simple gage-logging instruments to more elaborate systems that record strip width, width deviations in tolerance bands, coil weight, strip composition, temperature, history of slabs from melt to finished product, and so on, in addition to the information recorded by simple gage loggers that usually includes coil identification, turn, crew, time, and thickness-gage settings.

Computer Control—All of the foregoing elements relating to automatic control of stand speed, sideguard position and product gage are valuable production aids in themselves as separate regulating systems. Each element must be considered an essential part of any integrated system of computer control of the entire operation of a hot-strip mill. In addition to the sensing devices (tachometers, load cells, x-ray gages, and so on) and actuating mechanisms required for successful operation of each individual control system, an overall system controlled by a computer requires further instrumentation. The additional instrumentation is required to enable the computer to accept, analyze and correlate data describing conditions at various stages in the process, perform any necessary calculations, and develop a new set of operating conditions to correct any deviation at any stage of the actual process from the program stored in the computer's memory by operating regulators and actuating mechanisms that will bring the process within the desired control limits.

The 68-inch continuous hot-strip mill at Spencer Works of Richard Thomas and Baldwins, Ltd., in Llanwern, South Wales, is controlled by a digital process computer. This mill exemplifies application of computer control to the entire hot-strip rolling process from reheat furnaces to downcoilers. Other plants have applied computer control to the same extent as Spencer Works, while others have adopted such control to a lesser degree considered to be better suited to their type of operation.

Throughout the hot-strip rolling process at Spencer

Works, the computer makes the decisions and performs actions based upon a mathematical model of the process. The computer also determines the optimum throughput for any given mill conditions, and accumulates and logs operating and quality data for mill production and accounting records. Input data to the computer system consists of slab dimensions, rolling schedule and metallurgical data from punched tape or cards. The identity of each slab is established and maintained in the computer from the time it is charged into the furnace until the finished coil has passed the weigh station. Data on the furnace into which the slab is charged is communicated to the computer so that at all times there exists a complete record of all slabs in each furnace.

After discharge from the furnace, each slab is tracked through the mill by hot-metal detectors located to establish zones which can contain no more than one entire slab at a time. The slab-tracking function is the executive function that ties the computer to the process in real time. It establishes when calculations must be made and when references to subsystems must be transmitted, maintains correct slab identities in the various operating-pulpit displays, and correlates all production and process data for logging.

A second function of the computer is to set the rate at which slabs are processed in order to obtain maximum utilization of the mill. This takes into account the physical limitations imposed by mill design and mill components and other functions of the computer control. The program maintains a minimum separation between slabs which just avoids collision at any point.

The mill set-up function of the computer determines a compatible set of stand speeds and roll openings for the entire mill and transmits them to the proper regulating sub-systems at the appropriate moment in time for each change in rolling schedule. Within the limitations of the mill, main-drive power and specified rolling practice, the computer distributes drafting through the mill to establish desired finished gage at the head end with desired stand-load distribution in such a way as to achieve maximum production rates.

Since uniformity of grain size and mechanical properties of hot-rolled steel are influenced by the temperatures at which finish rolling and coiling occur, the computer exercises further control over the mill operation through both the mill pacing and mill set-up functions to maintain the temperatures of these points within specified limits over the entire length of each coil. With the assistance of temperature-measuring sensors at several points in the mill, the finish mill-delivery speed together with all roll openings in both the roughing and finishing mills are modified as required. Runout-table sprays are also subject to computer control, with spray patterns varied according to rolling conditions.

A further computer function is width control. For given incoming slab dimensions, the computer determines the roll settings for the edgers, distributing reductions in a predetermined fashion. Feedback from width determinations by gages at strategic locations corrects roll settings as well as compensates for roll wear or other changing mill conditions. In the overall

system design, the regulating sub-systems such as speed regulators and screw-position regulators have been separated from complete dependence upon the computer in order to provide flexibility and assure reliability. Such modular approach permits the mill to be operated with various degrees of automatic control.

The mill also features automatic crop shearing, designed to reduce cobbles and scrap and increase mill capacity by making it unnecessary to decelerate the strip for shearing.

CONTROL OF COLD-REDUCTION MILLS

Reversing Mills—Reversing mills for the cold reduction of steel strip can be provided with accurate controls for both front and back tensions to enable the operator to roll a wide variety of materials with comparative ease. Since tension control is most effective in controlling thickness of thinner and harder forms of strip, screwdown positioning is employed for gage control when rolling the thicker gages. For example, in the early passes of rolling a coil when the strip is relatively thick, adjustment of screwdown position is employed because the reel drive cannot exert enough torque to affect strip thickness to a significant degree, nor can the steel strip withstand the excessive tension that would be required. When the strip has become thinner and harder from progressive rolling, undesirably large screw movements would be necessary to effect the desired reduction. Thus, a system for automatic gage control on a reversing cold mill should combine screwdown positioning and tension control, preferably in such a manner that back tension would provide the major element of control, with screwdown positioning used to keep the back tension within a desired range. Built-in limiting devices control tension to within safe limits to prevent breakage of the strip. On heavy strip, the upper tension limit is quickly reached, and the screwdown control takes over: with light-gage strip, gage corrections are made almost entirely by controlling tension, and the screwdowns operate seldom if at all.

Tandem Mills—Automatic gage control for tandem cold-reduction mills (i.e., a five-stand continuous mill) employs screwdown positioning on the first stand for a coarse control element to minimize the effects of gage variation in incoming strip, using an x-ray gage after the first stand to compare actual thickness with the desired gage setting. An off-gage indication to the automatic gage regulator on the first stand actuates the screwdowns to correct the variation to within narrow limits. With a proper mill set-up, the variations in thickness out of the first stand are reduced in the second, third and fourth stands to improve the accuracy of thickness of strip entering the last stand. A second x-ray gage following the last stand detects gage variations out of that stand, and any error in gage causes the speed of the last stand to change automatically in the proper direction so as to alter interstand tension by an amount that will produce a final gage of the desired accuracy.

Some other important advances in the automatic control of tandem cold-reduction mills have been the incorporation in new mills of means for automatic coil handling, automatic threading, and automatic slowdown for welds and tail ends.

Computer Control—A computer can be programmed to automatically set up a tandem mill from pre-calculated schedules whenever a product change occurs. Roll openings, mill speed and side-guide positions can be set for each stand, reel-motor current can be established, interstand tension limits can be set, and the components of the automatic-gage-control system can be set.

The computer can be employed for logging production and quality control data, such as: identification of coils by manual input; shift-summary log, including crew, coils rolled, tons rolled, and total feet rolled (the latter classified by gage bands, if desired); calculation of coil weight from nominal thickness, width and length; location of welds or other major defects; or other information. The computer can also log process data, which may include recording of roll openings, speeds, and separating forces for each stand, interstand tensions; motor currents; pressure, flow, and temperature of roll coolants and strip lubricant; and so on.

BIBLIOGRAPHY

Allison, F. H., Jr., and C. E. Peterson, Modern manufacture and use of cast rolling mill rolls. Iron and Steel Engineer **31**, No. 12, pages 68–77, December 1954.

American Foundrymen's Association, Cast metals handbook (latest revision).

Anon., Rod mill rolls formed by grinding. Iron and Steel Engineer **36**, No. 4, page 156, April 1959.

Antrim, M. B., The application of the mercury arc rectifier to large reversing mill drives. Iron and Steel Engineer **37**, No. 8, pages 71–80, August 1960.

Bailey, W., Manipulating equipment, guides, guards and strippers for rolling mills. Journal of the Iron and Steel Institute **173**, No. 10, pages 198–213, October 1953. Discussion **174**, No. 6, pages 249–255, June 1954.

Beadle, R. G., Characteristics of tandem mill drives. Iron and Steel Engineer **32**, No. 5, pages 97–103, May 1955.

Bradd, A. A., Material and design defects in forged steel rolls. Iron and Steel Engineer **38**, No. 1, pages 85–98, January 1961.

Briggs, C. W., The metallurgy of steel castings. Mc-Graw-Hill Book Company, Inc., New York (1946).

Brown, H. S. and A. P. Baines, Developments in electrical equipment for reversing plate mills. Journal of the Iron and Steel Institute **194**, No. 1, pages 225–240, February 1960.

Browning, E. H., Electrical drive systems for modern rolling mills. Blast Furnace and Steel Plant **44**, No. 3, pages 299–308, March 1956.

Browning, E. H. and H. G. Frostick, Process programming of automatically controlled rolling mills. The part played by the electrical manufacturer, by E. H. Browning; The role of the steel mill engineer, by H. G. Frostick. Iron and Steel Engineer **36**, No. 7, pages 107–117, July 1959.

Browning, E. H., Modern electrical systems in the steel industry—new concepts in design and maintenance. American Iron and Steel Institute Regional Technical Meetings 1959, pages 19–51.

Cook, J. W., Tandem cold mill control. Blast Furnace and Steel Plant **47**, No. 11, pages 1187–1190, 1194–1195, November, 1959.

Cramer, F. W., Twin motor drives for hot reversing mills. Iron Age **156**, No. 15, October 11, 1945, pages 58–61.

Ess, T. J., Fairless Works. Iron and Steel Engineer **31**, No. 6, pages F62–F92, June 1954.

Harris, W. R., Operating experience with regulating systems for the steel industry. Iron and Steel Engineer **29**, No. 10, pages 113–122, 124, October 1952.

Harris, W. R., Developments in electrical drives for steel mill applications. Iron and Steel Engineer **29**, No. 12, pages 69–74, December 1952.

Holman, R. W., R. G. Beadle and W. E. Miller, Card programming control of rolling mills. Iron and Steel Engineer **35**, No. 6, pages 113–119, June 1958.

Hurme, E. A., Factors involved in the selection of direct connected and geared main roll drives. Iron and Steel Engineer **2**, No. 5, pages 189–222, May 1925.

Hyams, W., Automatic contour turning of large mill rolls. Iron and Steel Engineer **35**, No. 3, pages 82–89, March 1958.

Jones, R. and R. Hawley, Trends in rolling mill drive design. Iron and Steel Engineer **38**, No. 9, pages 121–128, September 1961.

Kaufman, G. A. and A. S. Smith, Electrical design and operation of a modern 46-inch high lift slabbing-blooming mill. Iron and Steel Engineer **30**, No. 10, pages 61–68, October 1953.

Kenyon, A. F., Factors involved in the selection of electrical drive ratings for metal rolling mills. Iron and Steel Engineer **38**, No. 11, pages 121–129, November 1961.

Koss, G. S. and L. E. Ringger, Application of speed regulators to the Geneva Works hot strip finishing mills. Iron and Steel Engineer **37**, No. 1, pages 53–63, January 1960.

Krummel, W. M., Hot strip mill electrical system design trends. Iron and Steel Engineer **38**, No. 5, pages 97–105, May 1961.

Larson, H. E., Mercury arc rectifiers for main roll drives. Iron and Steel Engineer **29**, No. 11, pages 61–73, November 1952.

Lindberg, V. H. and J. E. Duffy, Automated structural rolling facilities at South Works of United States Steel. Iron and Steel Engineer **38**, No. 11, pages 87–99, November 1961.

Mayer, J. H., Mechanical design and operation of a modern 46-inch high lift slabbing-blooming mill. Iron and Steel Engineer **30**, No. 10, pages 55–63, October 1953.

McGaughey, E. R. and R. J. Beeswy, Inland's new automatic slabber. Part I, The mill (E. R. McGaughey). Part II, Electrical (R. J. Beeswy). Iron and Steel Engineer **38**, No. 2, pages 105–125, February 1961.

Miller, W. E., The magnetic amplifier and its application in the steel industry. Iron and Steel Engineer **30**, No 5, pages 65–79, May 1953.

Miller, W. E., Trends and developments in electrical automation systems for steel plant processes. Blast Furnace and Steel Plant **47**, No. 1, pages 64–71, January 1959.

Miller, W. E. and F. S. Rothe, Selection and analysis of regulating systems for mill drives. Iron and Steel Engineer **29**, No. 12, pages 81–97, December 1952.

Moran, R. J. and H. N. Snively, New techniques in mill control gives better hot strip. Iron and Steel Engineer **38**, No. 1, pages 107–116, January 1961.

Morgan, M. H., Adjustable speed main roll drives. Iron and Steel Engineer **5**, No. 10, pages 429–448, No. 11, pages 467–489, October and November 1928.

Peck, P. E., Electrical drives for reversing hot mills. Journal of the Iron and Steel Institute **169**, No. 3, pages 309–323, March 1951: discussion **169**, No. 10, pages 169–174, 168, October 1951.

Perry, W. A. and W. B. Snyder, Performance of blooming mill auxiliary drives with Ward-Leonard control. Iron and Steel **16**, No. 3, pages 42–51, March 1939.

Petraske, K. A. and R. M. Sills, Developments in drive systems and gage control for reversing cold mills. Iron and Steel Engineer **38**, No. 11, pages 151–157, November 1961.

Scheer, G. B., Rectifier applications on steel mill drives. Iron and Steel Engineer **29**, No. 10, pages 107–112, October 1952.

Sendzimir, M. G. and L. Zdanowicz, A mill for cold rolling metals to close tolerances. Iron and Steel Engineer **33**, No. 11, pages 65–70, November 1956.

Sendzimir, T., The planetary mill and its uses. Iron and Steel Engineer **35**, No. 1, pages 95–101, January 1958.

Snively, H. N., Electrical equipment for metal rolling mills. Blast Furnace and Steel Plant **50**, No. 10, pages 961–969; No. 11, pages 1086–1092; No. 12, pages 1173–1179, October, November and December 1962.

Snyder, W. B., Electrical equipment for merchant, bar and rod mills. Blast Furnace and Steel Plant **38**, No. 4, pages 427–437, April 1950.

Starling, C. W., An introduction to the theory and practice of flat rolling—8. Sheet Metal Industries **38**, No. 4, pages 247–252, April 1961.

Steel Founders' Society of America, Steel castings handbook (latest revision).

Steel Publications, Inc., Watkin's cyclopedia of the steel industry (ninth edition), Pittsburgh, Pa., 1963.

Thomas, C. C., Electric equipment for reversing hot strip mills. Iron and Steel Engineer **32**, No. 12, pages 92–109, December 1955.

Thurman, A. L., and D. Hancke, A new approach to continuous mill drives. Iron and Steel Engineer **33**, No. 2, pages 76–85, February 1956.

Umansky, L. A., Flywheels for steel mill drives. General Electric Review **26**, No. 10, pages 688–707, October 1923.

Umansky, L. A., Adjustable speed drives for rolling mills. Iron and Steel Engineer **1**, No. 9, pages 515–532, September 1924.

Vonada, E. E., Multiple generators for processing lines. Iron and Steel Engineer **29**, No. 11, pages 77–86, November 1952.

Wright, R. H., Modern reversing mill drives. Iron and Steel Engineer **6**, No. 5, pages 210–217, May 1930.

Wright, R. H., Twin motor drives. Iron and Steel Engineer **8**, No. 6, pages 246–250, June 1931.

Wright, R. H., Main roll drives for blooming and slabbing mills. Iron and Steel Engineer **20**, No. 11, pages 55–61, November 1943.

Wright, R. H., Steel mill drives; past, present and future. Iron and Steel Engineer **34**, No. 1, pages 76–81, January 1957.

Wusatowski, Z., Fundamentals of roll design for steel sections. Iron and Steel **36**, No. 10, pages 499–503; No. 12, pages 596–599, October and December 1963.

CHAPTER 21

Heating Steel For Hot Working

SECTION 1

PRINCIPLES OF FURNACE DESIGN

Objectives and General Metallurgical Requirements—A heating furnace is utilized to raise the temperature of steel for hot working (shaping) and for heat treating. Heating furnaces may be divided into three general classes:

1. Soaking-pit furnaces
2. Reheating furnaces
3. Heat-treating furnaces (see also Chapter 39)

The function of soaking pits and reheating furnaces is to raise the temperature of steel in the course of processing until it is sufficiently hot to be plastic enough for economic reduction by rolling or forging to the desired section. The function of heat-treating furnaces is to heat the steel to some specific temperature for the purpose of obtaining the desired mechanical properties, which may be developed either by: (a) regulating the speed of cooling of the steel in the furnace; (b) by removing the hot steel from the furnace and permitting it to cool in still or agitated air; or (c) immersing the work directly from the furnace into some liquid to cool it suddenly and thus develop maximum hardness after which, usually, the hardened steel is tempered by further heat treatment.

Heating furnaces must be constructed of suitable materials to withstand the effects of the temperature levels at which they must operate. They must be provided with charging facilities which are adequate for the material size and handling rate, and with the proper means for heating the steel at the specified production rate. From the metallurgical standpoint, all three types of furnaces must be constructed to heat the steel uniformly and, by suitable temperature and combustion control instrumentation, hold it at the desired temperature for a specified length of time. Heat-treating furnaces (Chapter 39) also may be designed to cool at controlled rates to a predetermined level, and be provided further, in many cases, with extra equipment by which special requirements, such as the control of furnace atmosphere for developing or maintaining the desired surface condition of the steel, may be met.

Basic Elements of Furnaces—There are many different designs for each of the three general furnace classes noted above, but each design (exclusive of salt-bath or lead-bath furnaces, which are discussed in detail in Chapter 39 of this book) consists of certain common parts, as:

1. The heating chamber; an enclosure to contain the material and retain heat.
2. A hearth or support in the furnace for carrying the charge.
3. Facilities for the development of heat to raise and maintain furnace temperature.
4. Means for the distribution of heat and the removal of spent gases from the furnace.
5. Means for the introduction of work to be heated and removal of heated stock.

The enclosure to contain the material and heat generally is called the furnace proper. It usually is constructed of refractory material, although furnaces for operation at relatively low temperatures may be fabricated exclusively of steel. The furnace hearth or support for the charged material also may be constructed either of refractory or metallic material. In high-temperature furnaces, metallic supports generally are water cooled. Furnace hearths are constructed to permit the charge either to remain in a fixed position in the furnace or to be moved during the heating process. An example of the first type of hearth is the conventional batch-type or **"in-and-out"** furnace. Examples of the second general type are found in **roller-hearth furnaces** in which the material moves as the series of rollers that constitute the hearth rotate, and in **continuous furnaces** in which a continuous line of material is pushed over skids. The combustion of fuel usually is employed to develop the required furnace temperature, but the conversion of electrical energy into heat is used also in some important heat-treating furnace installations. The circulation of heat in the majority of furnaces is accomplished by natural convection and stack draft; in others, by forced circulation.

Facilities for the introduction and removal of heated stock vary with the type and size of furnace, the size and shape of the stock to be handled, and the general layout of the furnace and auxiliary facilities. Roller tables, conveyors, charging machines, overhead cranes, furnace pushers and pinch rolls are the principal kinds of equipment used for this service.

Furnace Size and Capacity—The size of a heating

furnace usually is described by its hearth area. The hearth areas of the various types of the three general furnace classes differ greatly. Soaking pits may have a hearth area of from 10 sq. ft. to something over 300 sq. ft. Reheating furnaces may have hearths ranging in area from only a few square feet, as in a small forge furnace, to over 2000 sq. ft. in large, continuous slab-heating furnaces. Heat-treating furnace hearths vary in size from the laboratory type of furnace of only a few square feet to areas of 1600 sq. ft. or more found in some of the larger continuous normalizing or annealing furnaces. The productive capacity of a heating furnace often is related to its hearth area, and figures of from 2 pounds to 250 pounds per sq. ft. of hearth area per hour are quoted for the various types. The low rate may apply for some conditions in heat treating steel and the high rate to pit furnaces when heating already hot ingots to a higher temperature. The capacity of a furnace is determined primarily by the area of the surface of the piece to be heated which is exposed to the furnace temperature, and the shape, thickness and composition of the material, its temperature and that of the furnace, and the emissivity of the heat source and of the material to be heated (e.g., surface-ground or machined stainless steel). The desired rate of heating is regulated by manually or automatically controlling the rate of heat input to the furnace.

High-carbon steels and heat-resisting alloys require longer heating cycles to attain uniformity of heating at the same temperature levels, as compared to low-carbon steels. Selection of the time required for properly heating various grades and sizes of steel is based largely on experience with given furnaces heating specific types of products. Figure 21—1 shows the normal time for heating various sizes of cold mild steel and medium-carbon steel blooms and square billets to rolling temperature. The heating time for high-carbon steel is about one-third longer and for heat-resisting grades about twice that shown.

The flow of the heat through a thick body of steel is relatively slow compared to surface absorption in high temperature furnaces and, therefore, caution must be exercised in regulating the supply of heat to prevent the surface from "sweating" (partial melting) while bringing the temperature inside the material up to the required level. Figure 21—2 shows the average rate of heat absorption for an entire cycle as generally practiced in heating mild, or medium-carbon grades of steel from atmospheric to rolling temperature. During the early stages of the heating cycle, the heat-transfer rates are considerably above the average shown, while during the latter part of the cycle the rate is very low. In heat treating steel, considerably lower average heat-transfer rates are practiced than those shown in Figure 21—2.

Furnace Type and Shape—There are many types of each of the three general classes of heating furnaces. The selection of type is determined by its suitability for heating economically particular grades, shapes and sizes of the material at the rate and to the temperature level desired. For instance, batch-type furnaces are especially suitable for heating blooms of mixed sizes and lengths in thicknesses over 8 inches; continuous

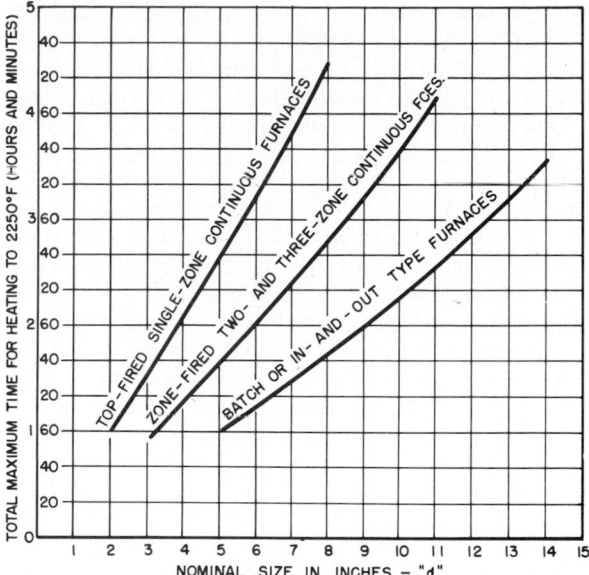

FIG. 21—1. Normal average time for heating various sizes of square mild-steel (low-carbon) and medium-carbon steel billets from room temperature to rolling temperature of 2250°F.

furnaces are used for heating slabs or billets for large orders of uniform length and thickness, and car-bottom furnaces are used for annealing miscellaneous shapes and sizes. The general shape of a furnace depends upon a number of factors, such as capacity desired, space available, auxiliary equipment and metallurgical requirements in heating. Refinements in furnace lines depend within rather wide limits on the kind of fuel used and on the grade and size of steel to be heated. The desired combustion space, tempera-

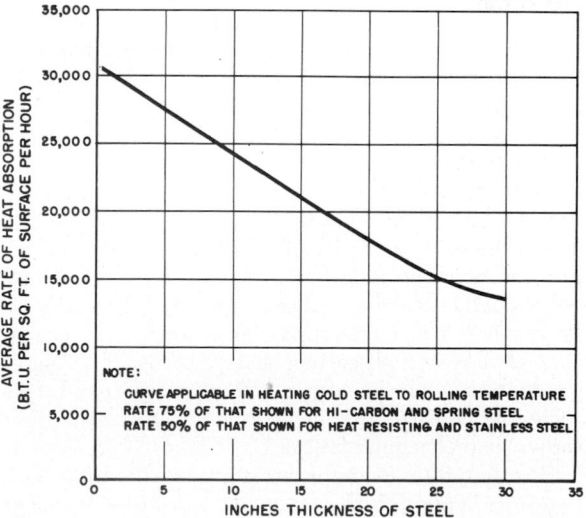

FIG. 21—2. Curve showing average rate at which heat is absorbed during an entire heating cycle by mild-steel and medium-carbon steel in heating from room temperature to rolling temperature in reheating furnaces.

ture level requirements, uniformity of heating and fuel flow are major considerations in furnace design.

Thermal Efficiency—The thermal efficiency of heating furnaces varies considerably because of differences in the temperature level of the heated stock and of the charged material, in the provision of heat recovery equipment such as regenerators and recuperators, in furnace insulation, in operating schedules, and in heating requirements. To cover the full range of all common types of heating furnaces, the thermal efficiency may fall anywhere between 5 per cent and 60 per cent. Large production-line furnaces, such as continuous furnaces equipped with recuperators and insulation, generally give 30 per cent to 40 per cent thermal efficiency over an average month's period of operation. Small shop furnaces, poorly loaded, with no insulation or heat-recovery facilities, have low thermal efficiency. The heat requirement per ton of heated product from heating furnaces for the production line varies from 300,000 to 3,000,000 Btu. The lower figure is obtained when heating hot steel, the higher one with poorly-loaded furnaces heating cold steel.

The sensible heat lost in stack gases is the principal source of heat loss in a fuel-fired furnace. Other losses include the heat loss by conduction through furnace walls, hearth and roof; radiation through furnace openings and from the outer surface of the furnace proper; the heat absorbed by water-cooled furnace parts; and the latent heat and unburned combustibles in stack gases.

In Chapter 3, dealing with fuels, the means employed for reducing furnace losses and the salvage of heat in waste gases already have been reviewed. Regenerators are provided usually for batch furnaces operated at high-temperature levels. They provide, in addition to heat salvage, a reservoir of potential heat for equalizing the temperature of steel during the soaking period. Ordinarily, in regenerative batch-type furnaces, the actual time for firing fuel amounts to only 50 per cent of the total time from charge to charge; the balance of time is taken up by charging, drawing and soaking. Firing in regenerative furnaces is usually at a constant rate with intervals of soaking, which occur more frequently as the charge approaches rolling temperature.

The heat stored in thick furnace walls of ordinary firebrick at high hot-face temperatures is considerable. When the so-called **flywheel effect** of hot walls and regenerators is not desirable, such as in furnaces which occasionally must be cooled as quickly as possible to lower than usual operating temperatures to receive special alloy or high-carbon heats, a material saving in production, fuel economy and maintenance can be effected by constructing the walls and roof of insulating rather than of regular firebrick.

Recuperators generally are supplied for high-temperature heating with continuous reheating furnaces and soaking pits, and in some instances for batch-type furnaces. They are more desirable than regenerators when the control of atmosphere and a constant flow of fuel into the furnace is important. They usually are de-signed to provide a lower preheat temperature than is obtainable with regenerators.

Materials of Construction—The temperature level carried in various parts of the furnace determines the kind and grade of construction materials that must be used. The hot end of continuous and regenerative batch furnaces, which employ burners or a fuel developing intensive combustion, may reach temperatures up to 2800° F. For this level, it is customary to construct the walls and roof of first-quality or super-duty firebrick and to water-cool any metallic parts which are exposed to high temperature. In high-temperature furnaces, there are applications for the use of special refractories. Hearths are constructed usually of refractories resistant to abrasion, slag attack or adherence to the steel being heated. Door jambs are made of refractories with non-spalling characteristics. Pier walls, such as those used in top- and bottom-fired continuous furnaces, use refractories with good hot-load-bearing properties. In pit furnaces, slag-resistant refractories are used in the lower wall areas to combat chemical attack by cinder.

Flue temperatures, especially following recuperators or regenerators, seldom exceed 1600° F, and for this application second-quality firebrick generally is used. Cast iron or heat-resisting steel is used for constructing dampers up to this temperature level; in flues subject to higher temperatures, the dampers are water-cooled. Annealing and normalizing furnaces seldom are operated in excess of 1700° F, and tempering or drawing furnaces normally operate at even lower temperatures. In these furnace types, insulating firebrick is used generally, especially when the operations are intermittent. In many heat-treating furnaces which require a careful control of the furnace atmosphere, particularly in those where special inert gas is used for this purpose, the heating chamber proper consists of a leakproof muffle of heat-resisting steel in which the work is sealed and surrounded by the controlled atmosphere, while heat is supplied to the outside of the muffle and transferred to the work through the muffle walls.

Besides the refractories and metallic parts directly exposed to internal furnace temperature, many furnaces contain a number of other essential parts which must be given careful consideration due to the temperatures to which they will be subjected. Cast-iron doors and door frames usually are lined with refractory material for protection; roof hangers are cast of heat-resisting metal; furnace casings and steelwork usually are constructed of ordinary grades of carbon steel; regenerators generally utilize refractories; recuperators are constructed either of refractory or metal, depending upon the temperature level at which they are to operate. Various grades of insulating material are used, dependent upon load, location and temperature level. Insulation for reheating-furnace walls, roof and hearth, not only provides a saving in fuel but also aids in maintaining a uniform temperature within the furnace, reduces stresses in furnace brick and steelwork, and improves working conditions around the furnaces.

SECTION 2

SOAKING-PIT FURNACES

Introductory—The modern soaking pit has been developed to provide uniform heating of ingots to the desired temperature with a minimum of over-heating of the surface. In most modern designs, this is accomplished with automatic controls. The normal range for heating ingots is between 2150° F and 2450° F. The proper temperature level varies with grades of steel and sizes of ingots and characteristics of the rolling mill. Low-speed mills with many passes require the higher level of heating for certain grades of steel. Soaking pits serve the dual function of heating and acting as a reservoir to correct irregularities in the flow of ingots between the steelmelting shop and the primary rolling mills. Briefly, soaking pits are deep chambers, or furnaces, of square, rectangular or circular shape, into which ingots are placed in an upright position through an opening at the top (Figure 21—3). A removable cover closes the pit opening. A series of pits, installed usually in rows, are placed under cover of a building adjacent to the entering side of the blooming or slabbing mill to be served. The top of the pit is usually several feet above ground level. The pits are spanned by one or more electrically operated traveling cranes equipped with a traveling hoist for charging the ingots into the pits and for lifting them out as they are needed by the mill. The lower end of this hoist is provided with adjustable tongs, by which an ingot may be grasped at the top and moved vertically a distance greater than the depth of the pit. This crane is used to transfer the ingots to the pits from the cars on which they were brought from the stripper, moving on tracks usually located along the side of the pits. For heated ingots, a pot car or ingot buggy is provided, which usually is propelled electrically along a track leading to the primary-mill tables, upon which it automatically deposits the ingots.

Types of Soaking-Pit Furnaces—There are several modern designs of soaking pits. Each design has special heating characteristics. The oldest of the modern types is the regenerative pit. In this type, the ingots are heated by alternately burning the gas through a port in the pit wall on one side, permitting the products of combustion to pass across the pit and out through the regenerator flues and stack to the atmosphere. The air, after each reversal, is passed through the hot regenerators to provide preheat for combustion of the fuel. If fuels of high calorific value, e.g., fuel oil, natural gas, or coke-oven gas are burned, they are introduced either through pipes in the top of the checker chamber and directed toward the bridgewall, or through a well in the checker brickwork adjacent to the port bridgewall. In some installations, particularly when cold blast-furnace gas is used, burners have been installed in the rear walls of the checker chambers.

Fig. 21—3. Schematic cross-section through a soaking-pit furnace building. (Courtesy, Amsler-Morton Company.)

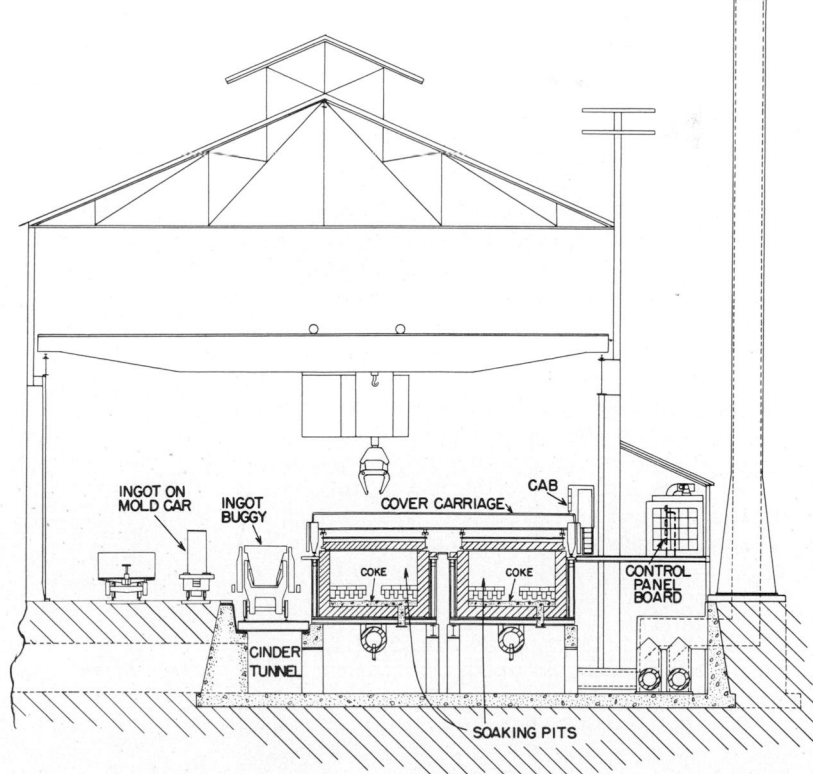

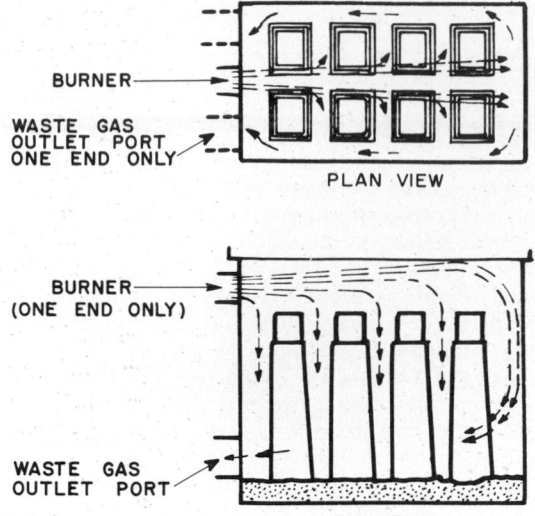

FIG. 21—4. Diagrammatic elevation and plan view illustrating principle of continuous firing and flow of hot gases in a "one-way fired" soaking pit. Hot gases from outlet ports pass to recuperators (not indicated).

Since the ports are located in the endwalls of the pit, the ingots are exposed to conditions of unequal heating on their opposite sides. To equalize ingot temperature, the practice of firing and dampering is generally followed. This practice provides uniformly-heated steel at a relatively-fast heating rate, but generally causes high scale losses, due to the flow of air through openings in the flues or checker chambers into the pit proper and out through holes in the pit cover or through faulty cover seals each time the pit is dampered. Corrective measures have been applied in modern regenerative pits by careful sealing of the checker-chamber brickwork and the installation of self-sealing covers. Difficulties from scaling are not confined only to regenerative-fired pits, but also may be met in recuperative-fired pits if there are leaks in the recuperators.

One of the first major steps towards improvement in pit-furnace design was to provide sufficient space for the combustion of fuel. Pits of a continuous-fired design, known as **one-way fired pits** (Figure 21—4), equipped with recuperators, were designed to provide combustion space above the ingots, where the space available for combustion was not affected by **ingot coverage.** "Ingot coverage" is a term used to denote the tonnage or number of ingots charged into a pit. Instead of the horizontal flow of gases through the pit as in the regenerative type, the flow in this type is vertical in accordance with hydrostatic principles. Utilization of one-way top-fired pits has become very popular, and, when installed in banks of three or four with common-wall construction, such pits make possible a high ratio of pit-hearth area to building area.

In another type, designated as the **bottom center-fired** or **vertically-fired** pit, a section of which is shown in Figure 21—5, the fuel is fired vertically through a port, centrally located in the bottom of the pit, around which the ingots are placed. As the products of combustion rise in the combustion zone, some of the spent

gases which are moving downward around the ingots and next to the furnace walls are drawn into this inner column of hot rising gases, and the resulting good circulation equalizes furnace temperature. Flues are located at the bottom corners of opposite sides of the pit to remove products of combustion and to aid in heat distribution. This design was introduced with recuperators and a full quota of controls for carrying out program heating. Adequate provision for combustion of fuel and careful sizing of pits, of nearly square shape, to suit loading conditions are incorporated in the design.

Another type, which is called the **circular pit** (Figure 21—6) employs tangential firing from a series of recessed burners located in the lower periphery of inclined side walls, to permit unusually long travel of the gases and to induce recirculation of the spent gases before they leave the pits through a centrally-located exit port at the bottom of the pit. This design utilizes a method for tempering the flame and securing uniform pit temperatures through gas circulation. These pits normally are fired with a high-calorific fuel and cold air in premix or nozzle-mix type burners to obtain complete combustion of the fuel before the gases come in contact with the ingots.

Still another pit is a refinement of the continuous-fired pit furnace, known as the **bottom two-way fired pit** (Figure 21—7). In this design the pits are fired by burners located in opposite endwalls about two feet above the bottom of the pit. The waste-gas ports are located in the same endwalls at each of the four pit

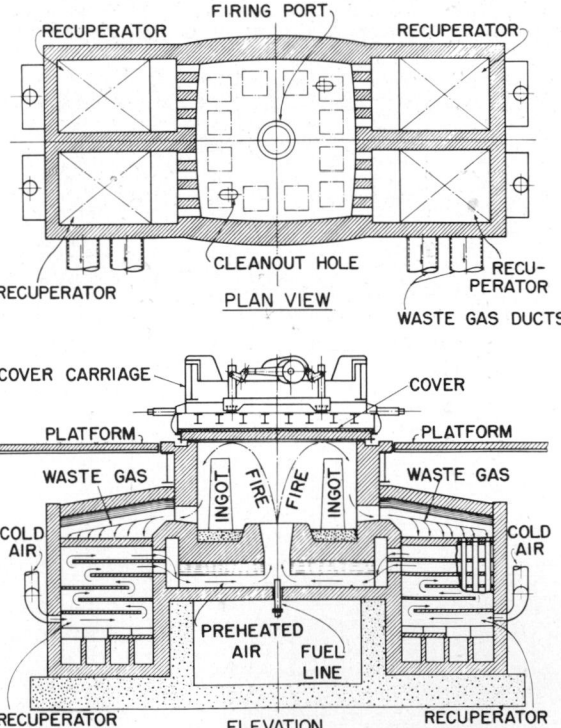

FIG. 21—5. Schematic elevation and plan view of a "vertically-fired" soaking pit, with the burner opening in the center of the pit bottom. (Courtesy, Amsler-Morton Company.)

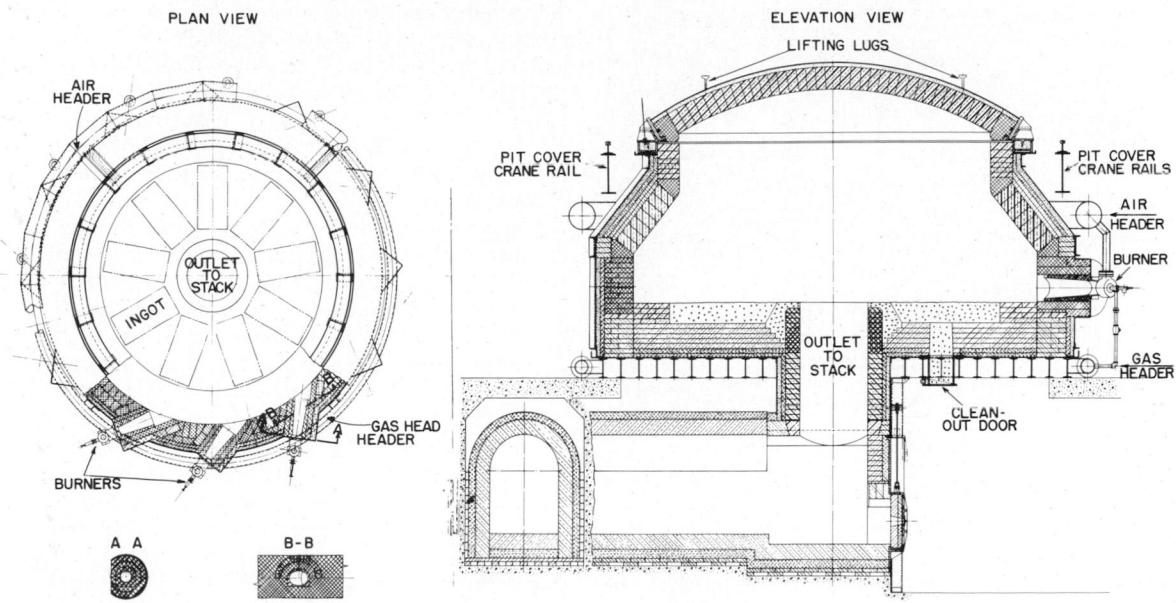

FIG. 21—6. Simplified section and plan view (not to same scale) of a tangentially-fired soaking pit. (Courtesy, Salem Engineering Company.)

corners and the gases on each end go directly to a recuperator. Combustion of the fuel takes place in a centrally located aisle, at the sides of which the ingots are placed. The method of firing and the position of the burners and waste-gas ports provide turbulence to the flow of gases in the pit, and results in improved heating of the ingot bottoms.

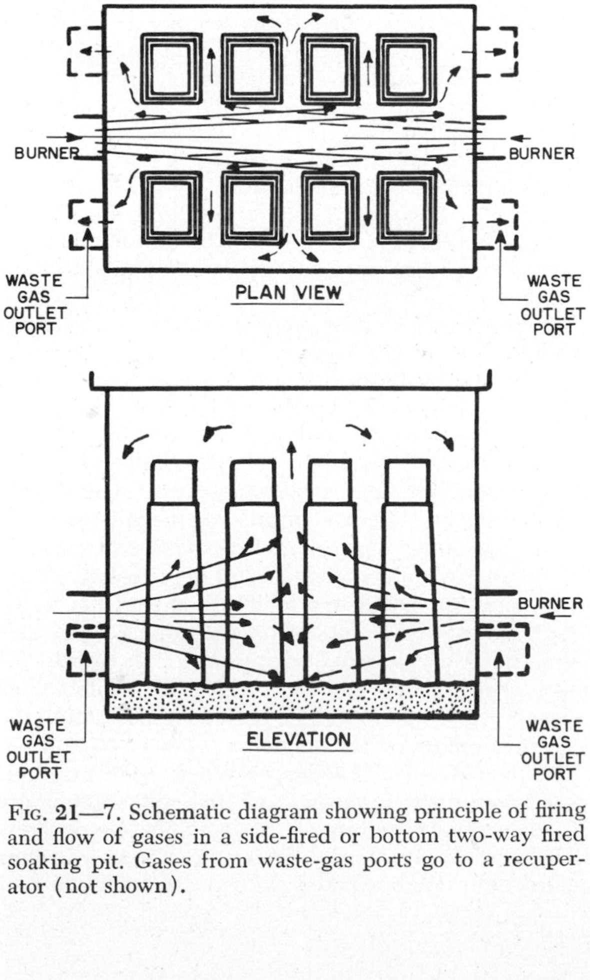

The **top two-way fired pit** is a deep rectangular pit in which the fuel is fired from opposite ends into a combustion space above the ingots (Figure **21—8**). The burners are set to fire horizontally at an angle to the centerline of the pit to obtain a swirling motion of the gases. Outlet ports are located in the endwalls just above the cinder line. Long-flame burners are used generally to distribute properly heat from combustion above and between the ingots. The flow of gases is vertical, similar to that in the one-way fired pits. In this design, the method of firing allows the pit shape to be selected that will give the desired coverage; it may be built long and narrow or square. Curved (elliptical) sides and endwalls, now common to the design of most square and rectangular types of pits, are utilized also in these pits.

Electric soaking pits were developed to meet special requirements, such as the control of scaling and the maintenance of controlled atmospheres during the heating of stainless-steel and alloy-steel ingots. An electric soaking pit installation is very simple, consisting of the pit proper and electrical equipment. The pit itself consists of a rectangular steel casing heavily bound in rolled-steel sections and containing a refractory lining and insulation to form a closed unit. Internal brickwork divides the pit into a number of cells, each of which may hold one or more ingots, depending upon ingot size. The cells are provided with individual covers that are handled with a special cover-lifting machine. The heating elements are coke-filled refractory troughs that run the entire length of the pit through arched openings in the walls that separate the cells. Power is applied to the heating elements by

FIG. 21—7. Schematic diagram showing principle of firing and flow of gases in a side-fired or bottom two-way fired soaking pit. Gases from waste-gas ports go to a recuperator (not shown).

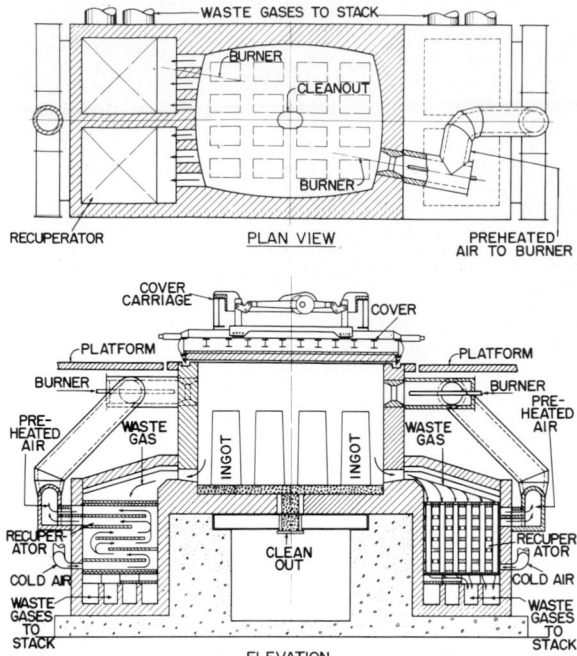

FIG. 21—8. Diagrammatic elevation and plan view of a top two-way-fired soaking pit. Left-hand section of plan view is through waste gas ports; right-hand section through one of the burners. Left-hand half of elevation is section through air passages of recuperator; right-hand, through waste-gas passages. (Courtesy, Amsler-Morton Company.)

electrodes that are led through the pit walls at each end. Temperature is controlled by adjusting the secondary voltage from transformers.

Auxiliary Facilities—The principal pit-furnace auxiliaries are pit covers, ingot pit cranes, facilities for ingot delivery to and from the pits and for cinder removal, along with the necessary instrumentation and controls for fuel and air supply and draft regulation.

Pit covers are constructed in various ways, the essential parts being a metal framework to support the refractories and means for quickly removing the cover then replacing it upon the pit. In the older pits, the metal framework usually was made of cast iron, and the bricks were slightly arched for support. The covers were supported upon rollers or wheels which moved over tracks, originally by the use of hydraulic cylinders and later by electric motors. A depression in the track permitted the cover to drop, when in position directly over the pit, and seal the pit opening. This design, however, seldom provided a tight seal at all points and leakage of gases caused high cover maintenance. More modern design consists essentially of a heavy steel frame which supports a suspended arch of high-grade firebrick, or a rammed or cast plastic refractory material held in position by refractory hangers. They are equipped with either self-actuating motors for lifting the cover vertically to free it from the sand seal and then move the cover sideways to the desired pit opening, or with a cover crane to effect similar movements. The cover crane spans a row of pits and serves several.

The steel frame of the modern pit cover is protected on its under side by heat-resisting-alloy castings. These castings are provided with a lip which penetrates into the sand seal. The sand seal, located around the periphery of the top of the pit, is a gutter-shaped space filled with sand. The suspended arch of a modern cover usually is backed up with insulation to reduce radiation losses.

Ingot Pit Cranes—In modern plants, the ingots are handled from the ingot delivery cars to the pits and from the pits to the ingot buggy by pit cranes. These cranes are of the conventional electric overhead design except for the trolley and position of the crane cab. Instead of the conventional hoist drum or drums, the trolley consists of the usual track wheels and a frame supporting a vertical housing in which travels a ram equipped at the bottom with mechanically operated tongs. The crane cab is attached to the lower end of the vertical housing and moves with the trolley. This arrangement of the crane cab is to provide maximum vision for the operator in order that the ingots may be placed in proper position in both pits and ingot buggy without damage to either. The modern pit crane also is used to handle coke breeze for bottom making and in many installations for actually making bottom.

Ingot delivery facilities consist usually of a track and ingot buggies. The ingot buggies which deliver the ingots to the pit are the same ones which held the molds for casting at the steel melting shop. The ingots usually are stripped of molds at the stripper, but in some cases where big-end-up ingots are used, the molds are only loosened at the stripper and are later removed by the ingot pit cranes, thus reducing heat losses enroute to pits. The layout of ingot-delivery tracks to avoid crossings and switches which interfere with other plant movements is very important. Minimizing delay in the delivery of ingots from the steel-making furnace pouring platform through the stripper and the pit furnace building into the pit furnace not only conserves heat but provides better metallurgical control of quality and less conditioning cost of the mill product.

Mill delivery facilities consist usually of an electrically-operated ingot buggy or pot car which runs directly between the pits and the mill approach table. There are two modern types of ingot buggies. On one type, the contact of the buggy with a cam arrangement at the mill approach table tilts the cradle of the buggy and throws the ingot from its vertical position in the buggy to a horizontal position on the mill approach table. The other type, in order to avoid battering the mill tables with heavy ingots and the necessity of approaching the tables at a high rate of speed to throw the ingot onto the table, is a self-tipping type. This design has a motor for driving the track wheels, for tilting the cradle, and for turning the table rollers which deliver the ingot in a horizontal position to the approach table.

Cinder-Removal Facilities—Where coke breeze is used as a bottom-making material, pit bottoms are made up with coke breeze to a depth of approximately 12 inches to 16 inches. When this breeze becomes burned or contaminated with scale, refractory or other material, it is removed through cinder holes, of which there are usually two, located in the bottom of the pit. In modern practice these holes, provided with gates at the outer end, discharge the cinder into a box located in the cinder alley under the pit bottom. The cinder box often is supported by a lift tractor or car which carries the box through the cinder tunnel to a hoist where it can be lifted to yard level and dumped into broad-gage cars for disposal. Some plants are equipped with an underground narrow-gage track system for moving the car to the cinder hoist. Bottoms for the older pit designs generally are made up each day; in modern pits they are made up only every 5 to 7 days under normal conditions. A recent trend is to utilize what is known as a **dry-bottom** practice, in which dolomite or magnesite is used as a 3-inch to 4-inch thick covering on the pit hearth. This material can be removed periodically in a manner similar to coke-breeze bottoms.

Fuel, air and draft facilities of a soaking pit are extremely important as these control furnace temperature and atmosphere. In modern pits the quantity of fuel, the desired fuel-air ratio and the draft or pressure in the pits are controlled automatically. The rate of fuel input is controlled by temperature measurement to maintain some predetermined level. The air is proportioned to the amount of fuel fired at a ratio that will give a slight excess or deficiency of air as desired. The furnace draft or pressure is controlled by automatically raising or lowering the stack damper to maintain the desired furnace draft. Pit-furnace burners are of various designs to provide the type of flame most suitable for heating in each particular pit design. In the regenerative pit the port acts as a burner. Some pit designs utilize a long-flame burner in which the air and gas are not mixed intimately in order to develop slow combustion and a longer path of heat release. In others, the mixing is very rapid and a short non-luminous flame is developed. Some burners are designed to inspirate either the gas or air. Low-pressure inspirating burners usually employ gas at a low pressure to inspirate air for combustion. With high-pressure inspirating burners, either the gas or air is carried at sufficient pressure to inspirate the required volume of the other that is at low or atmospheric pressure. Modern pits are provided with accurate means for measuring and controlling the air volume required for the combustion of fuel. Generally, motor-operated fans are used to supply the air. Fans are used for delivering either hot or cold air to the burners. If recuperators or regenerators are not installed, the fans deliver cold air. Fans may be installed in some designs on either the cold or hot side of the recuperator. If on the cold side, the fan construction is simple and does not require special features such as alloy blades and an insulated casing, as is the case with hot-air fans. Cold-air fans, however, subject the recuperator to a high pressure differential across its tubes and joints which sometimes causes excessive air losses and lowered recuperator efficiency.

Objectives in Modern Soaking Pit Design—The principal requirements of modern pit furnaces are:

1. Uniform heating of all ingots in the pit with no localized overheating of any ingot.

2. Heating rate equal to the ability of the steel to safely absorb heat.
3. Sufficient holding capacity to accommodate the required number of ingots without overcrowding.
4. Low operating cost.
5. Control of furnace atmosphere.
6. Ability to duplicate heating practices.
7. Minimum expenditure of ground space.
8. Minimum capital expenditure.

The first objective noted above is the most difficult to attain. Many different types of pits have been introduced to solve this problem. Uniform heating of all ingots in a pit with no localized overheating of any ingot permits holding the highest possible temperature in the pit compatible with the ability of the steel to absorb heat without sweating the surface or injuring the steel from severe temperature strain. Optimum heating rates are obtained by holding the surface just below the sweating point. This permits the most rapid flow of heat by conduction into the body of the steel. Since the flow of heat from the surface decreases as the temperature of the center of the ingot rises, the rate of firing must be reduced as heating proceeds to prevent overheating the surface. Variations in firing rate introduce problems in pit furnace heat distribution, as the hottest part of the flame, or the length of travel of heat release of the fuel, changes with the fuel volume and air-fuel ratio. Experience with various pit types generally dictates the proper adjustments necessary for variation in firing rate. In some cases alterations in fuel-air ratio or furnace draft are the remedy chosen. In many instances, when heating with regenerative pits, and occasionally with other types, adjustment for lack of uniform temperature distribution is secured by firing at a uniform rate for a period of time followed by a period during which the pit is dampered and no fuel is admitted. During the latter period, the steel is "soaked" to equalize the temperature between ingots in the pit and between the surface and the interior of individual ingots. This practice, known as "**firing and dampering**," provides a product with a uniform temperature at high production rates even though uneven heating developed during the firing period.

In order to aid uniform heating, circulation of the gases in the pit furnace has been given considerable thought in modern design. Entrainment of cooler, spent gases with the hotter products of combustion, especially near the burner, dampens the tendency of the flame to develop a hot spot, lengthens the time for full release of heat from the fuel and aids in uniform heating. Other effective methods utilized for obtaining uniform temperature distributions are: (1) designing the burner to release the heat of combustion of the fuel over as great an area in the pit as possible to avoid concentration of heat, (2) developing the flame sufficiently distant from the ingot surface to control radiation within safe limits, (3) reducing flame emissivity by using non-luminous-flame type burners or the equivalent, and (4) use of higher pit pressure. A cause of uneven heating in pit furnaces is the fact that the top of an ingot is exposed to heat from all sides while the bottom rests on a relatively cold unexposed surface. It is necessary to compensate for this either by proper distribution in the flow of gases in the pit, or, as is done in some designs, by maintaining higher effective flame radiation at the pit bottom. In some cases, as noted above, uniform heating is secured only by "soaking." Since the corners of ingots are heated from two adjacent sides, these parts reach the desired temperature first and, therefore, prevent the carrying of an otherwise permissible higher furnace temperature during a considerable part of the heating time.

The modern trend in pit design has been to construct larger holes than the two to six ingot capacity size formerly used. However, the over-all economy of using large pits for small ingots is not favorable for some mills and careful study of cycles is required in the selection of the proper size of pit.

Fuel consumption and the maintenance of modern pits have been reduced considerably by improved design, the installation of automatic controls and better materials of construction. Fuel-air ratio control for combustion and furnace atmosphere have reduced scale losses and the frequency of bottom making. Temperature measurements associated with automatic fuel-input control have made it possible to duplicate heating practices.

Modern Heating Practices—The time required to heat a charge of ingots in soaking pits generally is associated with transit time. The heat content of the ingot when charged into the pit is related to transit time, and it obviously requires less time to heat hotter steel. Transit time is the elapsed time beginning with the "start to pour" of ingots at the steel-producing source and ending with the charging of the first ingot of the heat into the soaking pit. The heating time required for ordinary carbon steels is approximately 1½ times the transit time when the track time is not excessive. Heating cold ingots usually requires from 8 to 12 hours, but, if the ingot is unusually large or of some particular type of steel which requires special treatment, it may require up to 18 hours.

Modern instrumentation has made it possible to estimate the relative state of temperature difference between the surface and center of the ingot from the temperature-time and fuel-input readings. Formerly, the heater, by careful observation of the ingots through sight holes in the cover and his knowledge of temperature requirements for each particular type of steel, determined when the charge was ready for rolling. While this practice is still common with old regenerative-type pits, the heating in continuous-fired pits is governed largely by automatic controls which carry out the heating program desired.

In heating ordinary grades of hot carbon steel in modern pits with automatic control, the operator sets the control dial at the temperature level desired for drawing. A full, or maximum, head of fuel automatically is fired into the pits in the early stages of heating. The fuel input is cut back gradually as the heat soaks into the ingot until it is finally reduced to a minimum, just sufficient to cover pit radiation losses. When the fuel input has remained at this low level for some spe-

cific time, such as a half hour or more, as experience dictates, the ingots are drawn. With high-carbon steel and many alloy grades which are cold or have had a long transit time, it is customary to cool the pit down to the temperature of the charged steel before placing these grades in the pits. They are then brought up rather slowly to some fixed temperature below the rolling temperature. After the ingots have been soaked at this lower temperature, most types of steel may be heated rapidly to rolling temperature. A common practice in heating certain alloy steels is known as **step heating.** Step heating consists in heating ingots to rolling temperature through several levels, each level being held for some specific time to permit equalization of temperature through the ingot. This procedure eliminates stresses due to severe temperature gradients in the ingots and provides slow, uniform heating. With step heating, it is customary to reduce the fuel-rate input considerably below the maximum setting permitted for heating ordinary types of steels. The best practice for heating each type and size of steel may be duplicated with modern control facilities. The fuel-air ratio control affects the flame characteristics and the furnace atmosphere. Flame characteristics have an important bearing on temperature distribution in the pit, and furnace atmosphere affects scale formation and character of the scale. By controlling the furnace atmosphere to advantage, the frequency of bottom making may be reduced, and minor surface defects on the ingot (from cooling, pouring or deoxidation practice) may be corrected or prevented from becoming more serious.

Operating Statistics—The principal operating data, aside from quality of heating and maintenance, relate to production output and fuel consumption. For comparative purposes, production is based generally on "live" pit area since there are so many different sizes and types of pits. The live pit-hole area is the area available in the pits on which ingots can be placed for heating. With proper loading this coverage of live pit area amounts to approximately 35 to 40 per cent (never more than 50 per cent) in modern pits. An average month's practice with modern pits is heating 30 to 100 tons of ingots per hour per 1000 square feet of live pit-hole area. This wide variation is due principally to the temperature at which the ingot is charged and to the type of steel. Other important factors causing the wide spread in pit furnace productivity are differences in the size and length of ingots, irregularity in mill operations and melting-shop pouring schedules, and the portion of live pit area occupied by the ingots.

The amount of fuel consumed per ton of steel heated varies from approximately 400,000 to 2,000,000 Btu. This variation also is due largely to variations in the temperature of the charged steel. Other factors contributing to fuel economy are careful design, proper use of insulation, reduction of stack-gas losses with recuperators and regenerators, proper installation of controls, utilization of the maximum percentage of hearth, controlled metallurgical practices, and regularity of melting shop and rolling-mill schedules.

SECTION 3

REHEATING FURNACES

Furnace Types—Reheating furnaces are divided into two general classes:

1. Batch type.
2. Continuous type.

Batch furnaces are those in which the charged material remains in a fixed position on the hearth until heated to rolling temperature. Continuous furnaces are those in which the charged material moves through the furnace and is heated to rolling temperature as it progresses through the furnace. Batch furnaces are the older type and are used for heating all grades and sizes of steel. However, small billets seldom have been heated in this type since the introduction of continuous furnaces. Batch furnaces are fired with either gaseous or liquid fuel, with preheated or cold air for combustion. The air may be preheated by regenerators and the furnace firing reversed from one end to the other, as in open-hearth furnaces. Batch furnaces, in which the air is preheated by recuperators, are not reversed and firing is continuous from one or both ends, depending upon the location of the gas outlet port (Figure **21**—9). The steel to be heated in a batch furnace commonly is charged and drawn through front doors by a charging machine. Batch furnaces vary in size from those with hearths of only a few square feet, with a single access door, to those twenty feet in depth by fifty feet long, with five or six doors.

Continuous furnaces were designed initially for heating billets and small bloom sections. The hearths were relatively short in length and were sloped downward longitudinally towards the discharge end to per-

mit an easy movement of billets through the furnace. In early designs, the furnaces were fired by burners located at the discharge end and the billets were heated by the hot gases flowing through the furnace above the top surface of the steel toward the charging end. Pushers were used to push forward the charge of cold billets. The flow of gas and steel in the furnace were counter-current. The modern continuous furnace has been altered in many respects from those of early design, although a large number of the older ones, particularly billet-heating furnaces, are still used. Longer furnaces generally are constructed now. Some have hearths 80 to 90 feet long, with top and bottom firing, and contain preheating, heating and soaking zones. The hearths usually are constructed level. A transition from the early designs to the modern five-zone slab heating furnace is illustrated in Figure **21**—10.

The steel to be heated in a continuous furnace can be charged either from the end or through a side door. In either case, the steel is moved through the furnace by pushing the last piece charged with a pusher at the charging end. As each cold piece is pushed into the furnace against the continuous line of material, a heated piece is removed. The heated piece is discharged either through an end door by gravity upon a roller table which feeds the mill, or it is pushed through a side door to the mill table by suitable manual or mechanical means. Figure **21**—11 shows a section through a modern triple-fired furnace using counter current flow of gases and steel.

A distinctly different type of continuous reheating

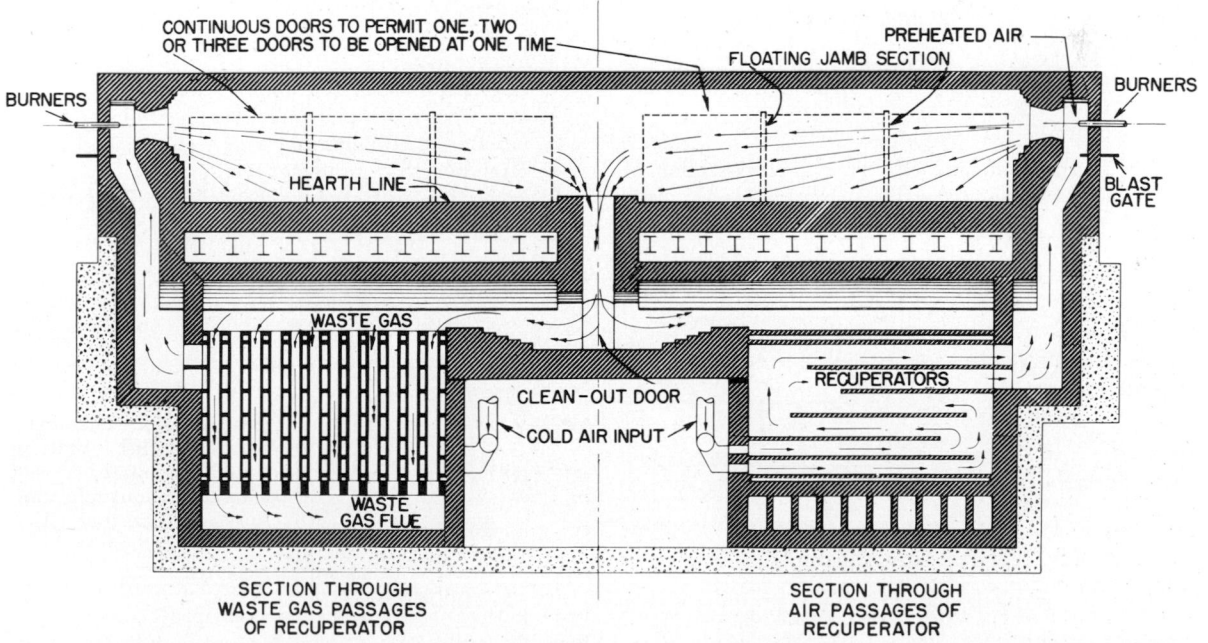

FIG. **21**—9. Schematic longitudinal section through a recuperative batch-type reheating furnace. (Courtesy, Amsler-Morton Company.)

ONE ZONE – END CHARGE SIDE DISCHARGE

TWO ZONE – SIDE CHARGE SIDE DISCHARGE

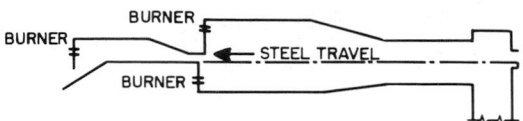

THREE ZONE FURNACE

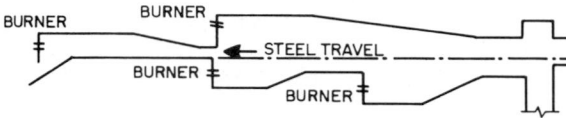

FOUR ZONE FURNACE

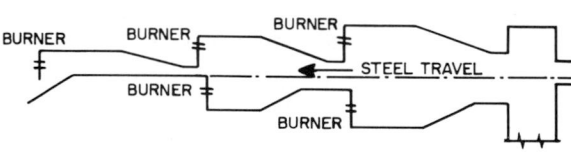

FIVE ZONE FURNACE

FIG. 21—10. Diagrammatic steps in the evolution of the modern five-zone slab-heating furnace from earlier designs.

furnace is the rotary-hearth type, a cross-section of which is shown schematically in Figure 21—12. It is

used frequently for heating rounds in tube mills and for heating short lengths of blooms or billets for forging. The rotary-hearth type permits the external walls and roof to remain stationary while the hearth section of the furnace revolves.

General Considerations in Furnace-Type Selection —Some of the particular advantages of batch-type furnaces are:

1. They provide means for heating steels of various types and sizes, which can be heated more properly in separate batches than when mixed with other types in the same furnace, especially when specific heating practices are required.

2. They are suitable as a reservoir for holding hot steel directly from the primary mill for later rolling in the finishing mills.

3. They can be operated to heat steel to temperatures above 2400° F more satisfactorily than a continuous furnace. Steel can be given a "wash heat," when desirable, without trouble from the pieces sticking together. (Steel is sometimes "washed" or heated until an earlier oxide scale is melted and a new scale formed, to reduce surface defects.)

4. They provide excellent means for soaking steel.

Some of the important disadvantages of batch furnaces are:

1. High capital investment per unit of production.

2. Low hearth area efficiency. That is, the hearth in the conventional type is not utilized fully because of interference of door jambs and clearance required inside the furnace for handling the stock with charging machines.

3. High man-hours per ton of heated steel.

4. Lack of flexibility for heating steel slowly in the lower temperature range. Furnaces must be cooled to charge high-carbon steel and some alloy steels.

5. Length of pieces to be heated is limited by tendency to bend when they are removed.

The advantages of the conventional continuous-type furnaces are:

1. High production per dollar of investment.

2. Low man-hours per ton of steel heated.

3. Greater ease in charging and drawing steel.

4. High hearth area efficiency.

5. Better means for controlling the rate of heating

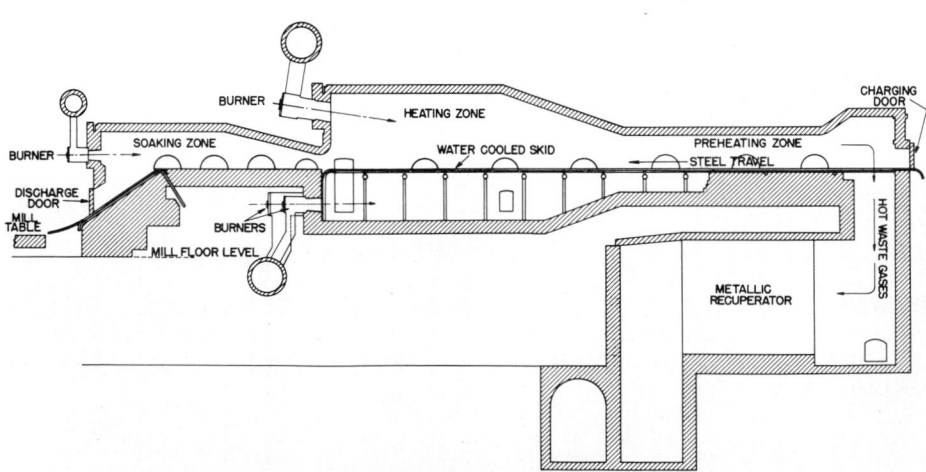

FIG. 21—11. Schematic longitudinal section through a counter-current fired continuous reheating furnace. (Courtesy, Rust Furnace Company.)

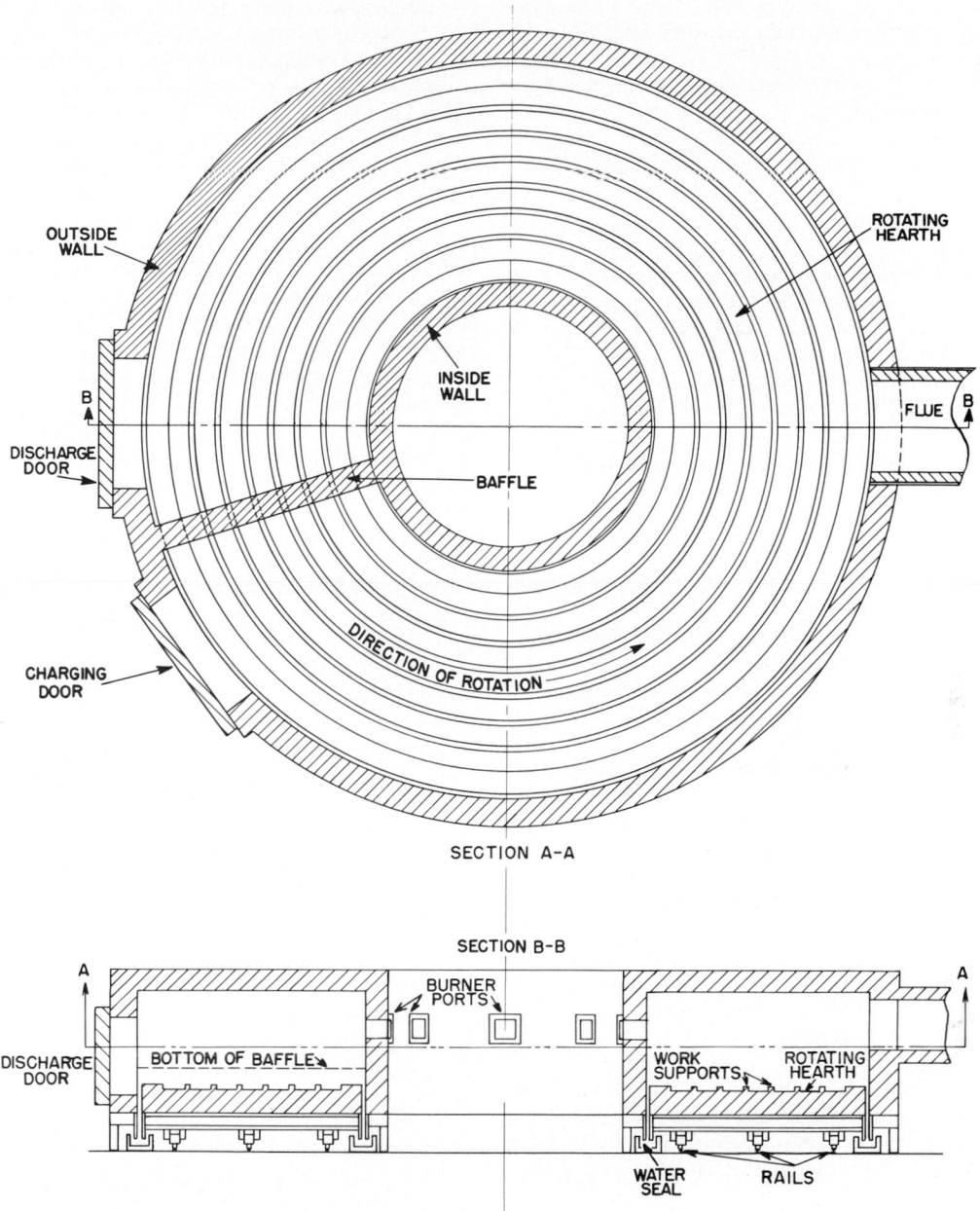

FIG. 21—12. Schematic arrangement of a relatively-small continuous rotary-hearth heating furnace. The plan view (above) shows a section above the hearth near the bottom of the baffle. Larger furnaces of this type have burners firing through both inside and outside walls above the hearth. (Adapted from a Salem Engineering Company drawing.)

at all temperature levels. Gradual rise in temperature permits charging all grades of cold steel without cooling furnace.

6. Less trouble from temperature inequalities between each succeeding piece drawn.

7. High production per square foot of ground space occupied.

8. Can be built for any reasonable length of piece to be heated, resulting in higher mill yield, because of fewer crop ends from lengths beyond batch-furnace possibilities.

Some of the important disadvantages of conventional continuous furnaces are:

1. Lack of flexibility for heating efficiently small orders of different lots of steel or thicknesses. Heating time must be increased to suit the heating cycle of the piece, requiring lower heat transfer rate which may be detrimental to the heating of the other grades and sizes in the furnace.

2. Trouble from water-cooled skid maintenance, and from building up of scale on hearth, which results in piling of steel in furnace, due to climbing of pieces

over each other, because of lack of square contact between adjacent pieces, when pressure is applied by the pusher.

3. Face of contacting surface of stock must be square to prevent piling.

4. Expensive to empty furnace at end of schedule.

5. Difficulty in pushing mixed sizes through furnace.

Some of the important advantages of rotary-hearth furnaces are:

1. They eliminate either the manual labor required for rolling rounds forward on horizontal or moderately sloped hearths, or the disadvantages of excessively sloped hearths in continuous furnaces.

2. They have better means for controlling the rate of heating at all temperature levels than batch-type furnaces.

Some of the important disadvantages of the rotary-hearth furnace are:

1. High capital cost per unit of production.

2. Low hearth area efficiency.

3. Large ground space required per unit of production.

Some features in both batch and conventional continuous furnaces are worthy of note:

1. Regenerators or recuperators act as a reservoir of heat supply, which is especially valuable for efficient soaking of steel.

2. Continuous furnaces provided only with top firing require longer hearths for equal production than those with top and bottom firing, but do not require a special soaking zone to eliminate cold spots on the work caused by contact with water-cooled skids.

3. Continuous furnaces with single-zone firing have higher scale losses and greater tendency to cause decarburization of high-carbon steel than the top-and-bottom fired furnaces, since the steel is in the furnace longer. Decarburization is caused primarily by hydrogen and water vapor combinations in furnace gases, and increases almost directly with the time the steel is at elevated temperatures. Free air and carbon dioxide in the furnace atmosphere cause decarburization to a lesser degree. The scaling of steel is practiced sometimes deliberately to remove the decarburized surface layer.

4. A level hearth in a continuous furnace eliminates the stack effect of hearths sloping upwards towards the charging end. This stack effect draws cold air into the furnaces at the hot end causing higher fuel consumption and scale losses.

5. Batch-type furnaces used for heating in a production line require supplementary furnaces for preheating certain grades of alloy and high-carbon steels for transfer into the hotter furnaces. The preheating zone of a continuous furnace makes this unnecessary.

6. Side-discharge continuous furnaces have less air infiltration at the hot end than end-door discharge furnaces. End-door discharge of the usual gravity type induces cold air into the furnace by the stack effect at the discharge section of the furnace. End-door discharge, however, is mechanically simpler for removing the heated stock, particularly slabs and heavy blooms.

Furnaces have been developed to raise the temperature of steel for hot shaping by exposing the piece to be heated to intense radiant energy from gas burners of special design, set very close to the path of the steel. This method of heating has been very effective in obtaining fast heating for small round sections. The barrel-type furnaces in tandem shown in Figure 21—13 are used for reheating pierced tubes for sizing in seamless-tube mills. This method has recently been applied to soaking pits.

The trend in reheating furnace design is towards the continuous type, with increased attention to refinements to satisfy conditions pertinent to each mill or forge shop, or the types of steel being heated.

Operating Statistics—The production rate of furnaces varies widely. Batch furnaces, as a general class, produce much less tonnage per furnace operating hour than the continuous type. While batch furnaces often are used for heating hot charges, as in structural and rail mills, continuous furnaces usually are used for heating cold steel. Batch furnaces heating cold charges for rolling mills are designed to heat from 5 or 6 tons up to 25 tons per furnace hour. When heating a hot charge, the production is much higher, and the rate depends largely upon the temperature of the charged material and the size of the furnace.

The production of a continuous furnace depends principally upon the hearth size of the furnace and whether the material is heated from more than one side. Many continuous furnaces heat over 50 tons of steel per furnace hour. A modern three-zone slab-heating continuous furnace, 20 feet wide, with an effective hearth length of 80 feet, top and bottom fired, is capable of heating 110 tons of slabs per hour to a rolling temperature of 2250° F. Five-zone furnaces are capable of heating rates up to 250 tons per hour. The productive rate of a furnace for a fixed thickness of steel is directly proportional to the surface exposed to the flame, other conditions remaining the same. For comparison of furnace performance, the relative number of pounds heated per effective square foot of hearth area per hour is used as a common factor. By this comparison, furnaces heat from 30 to 150 pounds per square foot of hearth area per furnace hour. The variation in heating capacity is due principally to the difference in the total surface of the steel exposed to heat in the furnace, which the hearth area does not measure. Other factors are the temperature of the heated product and the grade of steel. In many batch furnaces, the material receives heat from three sides and in continuous furnaces from two sides. Heating from more than one side decreases heating time and, therefore, increases production rates. The production and fuel rates of furnaces are affected by continuity of operation. A furnace will not provide high production rates and fuel economy if it is operated for only short intermittent periods. It also must be fully loaded to provide optimum production and fuel economy.

The fuel consumption of reheating furnaces varies from 300,000 to 3,000,000 Btu per ton. When hot steel is heated, very little additional heat may be required to attain rolling temperature. If the steel charged is at a temperature of 1800° F, only about 140,000 Btu per

FIG. 21—13. Barrel-type furnaces in tandem for continuous reheating of pierced seamless tubes for sizing. Conveyor rolls between adjacent furnaces support the work in its travel. Temperatures are automatically controlled by radiation-type pyrometers.

ton must be added in the furnace to heat to 2250°, while with cold steel about 700,000 Btu must be added in the furnace. If the hot steel requires 500,000 Btu per ton input to the furnace and only 140,000 Btu are absorbed, the furnace fuel efficiency is $\frac{140,000}{500,000}$ x 100, or 28 per cent. If cold steel is heated with a fuel con-

sumption of 2,000,000 Btu per ton, as obtained in many modern furnaces, the furnace fuel efficiency is about $\frac{700,000}{2,000,000}$ x 100 = 35 per cent. The best fuel efficiency is obtained in continuous furnaces that are relatively long, have hearths fully covered with steel, and are operated at a high rate of continuity. In both batch and continuous furnaces, the length of gas travel and the velocity of the gases through the furnace have an important effect on fuel economy. An excessive velocity of furnace gases tends to increase the exit temperature of the gases leaving the furnace and, therefore, low fuel efficiency results. Fuel efficiency is improved by providing features in design that reduce the inherent furnace losses. The greatest losses usually are represented by the heat carried away in the stack gases. Reduction of this loss can be obtained by the installation of recuperators, regenerators or waste-heat boilers, and by designing the furnace cross-sectional area for proper gas velocities. Automatic fuel-air ratio and furnace-pressure control reduce stack losses by reducing the volume of gases from excess air for combustion, or from air infiltration. Radiation losses are reduced by insulation of the furnace walls, roof and hearth. Losses from water-cooled skids in continuous furnaces can be reduced by eliminating any unnecessary exposure of them to hot furnace gases, and to some extent by use of refractory pipe covering.

CHAPTER 22

Production of Steel Blooms, Slabs and Billets

Introductory—There is no widely accepted precise definition for the terms bloom, slab, or billet, and local applications of the terms are used somewhat on a traditional basis. Distinctions are made according to general appearance, influenced by overall size and the proportions of the three linear dimensions and also by intended use. The distinction between **blooms** and **billets** is principally a distinction of size, billets being smaller than blooms in cross-sectional area, and both having a length several times greater than their maximum cross-sectional dimension. The distinction between blooms and **slabs** is principally one of cross-sectional dimension proportion, blooms tending to be round, square, or nearly square, and slabs being always oblong and tending to be relatively wide, thin, and (until recently) of short length. There are many exceptions, and there are special names for pieces intended for special uses.

For example, any piece to be rolled into a plate is called a slab, regardless of size or of dimension proportion. Likewise, any piece produced on a billet mill is termed a billet, regardless of shape and size, with the exception of round billets. Blooms in short lengths are sometimes called **blanks** or **blocks**, and special-shape blooms for structural sections frequently are called blanks regardless of length.

A rude guide using only the cross-sectional characteristics as the distinguishing features which may serve in place of definitions is shown schematically in Figure 22—1.

Until recently, steel in the form of blooms, slabs and billets was produced chiefly by hot rolling of ingots to produce blooms and slabs: these procedures are discussed in Section 1 of this chapter. Billets resulted from the further hot rolling of blooms (see Section 2). Some blooms and slabs were (and still are) produced by other means of hot working, such as forging by hammering or pressing.

Since the end of World War II, continued research and development have resulted in the perfection of methods for the **continuous casting** of molten steel directly into the form of slabs and billets, by-passing the ingot stage and the necessity for hot-rolling operations formerly required to produce such products (see Section 3). Another process known as **bottom pressure casting** is also employed to produce slabs and billets directly from molten steel (see Section 4).

Blooms, slabs and billets intended exclusively to be subjected subsequently to further hot deformation may develop a variety of defects arising from heating, rolling and casting that may have to be removed to prevent their affecting the surface quality of finished products made from them. These defects usually are detected and removed from the blooms, slabs and billets after they have cooled to ordinary temperatures. These cold steel products are referred to as **semi-finished steel**. After inspection and removal of defects by operations known by the collective name of **conditioning** (see Section 5), the semi-finished

TYPICAL CROSS-SECTION
AND
DIMENSIONAL CHARACTERISTICS*

SLAB

ALWAYS OBLONG
MOSTLY 2 TO 9 INCHES THICK
MOSTLY 24 TO 60 INCHES WIDE

BLOOM

SQUARE OR SLIGHTLY OBLONG
MOSTLY IN THE RANGE 6" X 6" TO 12" X 12"

BILLET

MOSTLY SQUARE
MOSTLY IN THE RANGE 2" X 2" TO 5" X 5"

* DIMENSIONS USUALLY GIVEN TO NEAREST ROUND NUMBER.
ALL CORNERS ARE ROUNDED, AS SHOWN.

FIG. 22—1. Comparison of the relative shapes and sizes of rolled steel governing nomenclature of products of primary and billet mills. (Cast sections produced by the continuous or bottom pressure casting methods are similarly designated when of the same general proportions and dimensions as their rolled counterparts.)

products are converted into finished products by re-heating and further hot working by rolling or forging coupled, in some instances, with cold-working operations that follow the secondary hot working.

As will be observed in the subsequent discussion, there are some important variations from the sequence of events described above: however, these steps are the ones usually followed in the production of the bulk of the steel products discussed in this book.

SECTION 1

PRODUCTION OF BLOOMS AND SLABS BY ROLLING

Prior chapters have described the several processes for making steel and the production and treatment of steel ingots. This section relates to the first stages in forming useful products from ingots (production of blooms and slabs) by hot rolling: Section 2 will extend the discussion to the production of billets by hot rolling. Hot working of ingots by other means, such as hammering or pressing, was discussed briefly in Chapter 19, and will be covered in more detail in Chapter 37.

These early stages in the production of useful objects from ingots consist of a series of operations, whereby the ingot cross-section is reduced to a square, oblong, round, or other simple shape, all having rounded corners, and of dimensions approximate to nominal specified size. The length of the ingot is increased, corresponding to the decrease in cross-section. The concluding operations cut a relatively short length called **crop** from each end of the rolled piece as scrap, and cut the remaining long piece, if necessary, into multiples to suit the required lengths or weights for subsequent operations.

GENERAL FEATURES OF BLOOMING AND SLABBING MILLS

It is possible, and often quite economical, to roll ingots directly through the bloom, slab, or billet stage into more refined and even finished steel products in one mill, of varying numbers of stands from one to about twenty, in a continuous operation, frequently without any reheating. Large tonnages of standard rails, wide-flange beams, and plates, and a lesser proportion of wide hot-rolled coiled strip are produced regularly by this practice from ingots of medium to large size. A few very small plants follow a similar practice in rolling small ingots, such as 4-inch to 6-inch squares, directly into wire rods, concrete-reinforcing bars and other bar products.

However, most of the ingot tonnage is rolled into blooms, slabs, or billets in one mill, following which they are cooled, stored, and eventually rolled in other mills or forged. The reasons for this more common practice are primarily economic; sometimes size or shape of product and certain quality requirements peculiar to the final article to be manufactured determine the steel-rolling method.

A variety of names for mills rolling ingots has come into common use to differentiate between them in reference to the particular kind of product intended or generally produced, the basic mechanical design features, or the general layout of the mill. For a long time, the term **blooming mill** was used rather commonly for all such mills, but, with the increasing variety, it has come to be restricted by many to a mill producing blooms, and the term **primary mill** has gained acceptance as a generic term to cover both blooms and slabs. In addition to a name, these mills are designated as to size, expressed in inches, with the result that almost every mill is known by a combination of size and descriptive name which, taken together, with the size always expressed first, indicate a rough mental picture of the mill; for example, 54-inch blooming mill, or 43-inch three-high mill, or 45-inch slabbing mill.

The composite name applies specifically to the roll stand, or to the first roll stand if the mill is a multiple-stand one. However, the name is used as an abbreviation for the entire group of facilities needed to produce blooms, slabs, or billets and for the organization operating them, known more properly as a mill department.

PRIMARY-MILL ACTIVITIES

The activities of all primary mills are the same, and it follows that the facilities for carrying out these activities are fundamentally the same in all mills, but they differ in detail according to the particular requirements of each mill. The primary operation is the conversion of a steel casting (the ingot) into rolled steel product; the secondary function of the rolling operation is to produce this rolled steel product in pieces of the desired cross-sectional dimensions and weights. Auxiliary operations, outlined below, include cropping, conditioning, cutting to length, and the collection and assorting of crops, roll scale and other by-products that are subsequently delivered to the steel-producing and blast-furnace departments.

The primary operation is carried out in a sequence of thermal and mechanical operations:

(a) Heating the ingots (discussed in Chapters 18 and 21).

(b) Breaking up the coarse crystalline structure of the ingot into a refined structure by heavy rolling pressure and recrystallization during hot working.

(c) Closing solidification voids by the same means as in (b).

(d) Cutting off such portions of steel as are metallurgically (both physically and chemically) unsuited for the intended final purpose.

(e) Cutting off test specimens.

(f) Cooling to atmospheric temperature those

products not destined for immediate further hot working.

The secondary function is performed in conjunction with operations (b), (c), and (d), above, since they can be carried out with the same facilities. The essential steps in performing the secondary function are:

(a) Positioning the rolls, which have been shaped to produce the desired cross-section.

(b) Cutting the rolled piece to measured length or to specified weight per piece.

(c) Weighing individual pieces, or weighing and measuring test specimens.

The auxiliary operations pertain to the rolled product and the by-products.

(a) Conditioning the steel products by removing injurious surface imperfections, removing portions containing injurious internal defects, and by correcting physical conditions by straightening bent pieces, cutting overlength pieces to proper length, and so on.

(b) Collecting identified crops, other ferrous scrap, roll scale, and cinder and delivering these by-products to steel-producing and blast-furnace departments.

In order to carry out these activities, all primary mills have the same general kind of facilities and all are operated in the same general manner, but no two are exactly alike, although there are a few instances of close similarity. The differences among mills are due to the sizes of ingots and product, the particular kind of product and the quantity required to be rolled in a given time, as well as to the date when the mill was built or subsequently altered, and to the most economical kind of fuel and power available at that time. The differences are in size, in details of design, in the auxiliary equipment provided, and in the arrangement with relation to other facilities, especially those producing the ingots and those rerolling the products of the primary mills.

In a large number of present-day mill arrangements, the primary mill supplies hot steel products either directly or through reheating furnaces to other mills producing semi-finished products such as billets and coiled strip, or finished products such as rails or structural shapes, and the number of such mills supplied by one primary mill is from one to three in various tandem and parallel combinations. When the product coming from the primary mill is rolled, while it is still hot and without reheating, directly in a succeeding mill, rolling capacities must be considered. In the ideal case, the primary mill will just keep the succeeding mill or mills busy, without loss of time in either the primary mill or the succeeding mills. The arrangement of the mills determines the material-handling facilities and the size and location of the mill buildings.

The basic operation in a primary mill is the gradual compression of the steel ingot between the surfaces of two rotating rolls, and the progression of the ingot through the space between the rolls. The physical properties of the ingot prohibit making the total required deformation of the steel in one pass through the rolls, so that a number of passes in sequence are always necessary. There are several ways in which a sequence of passes can be made, and some particular way is selected by choosing one which is suited to the quality of material to be produced and also likely to be the least expensive. This choice determines the general type of mill. The elements of pressure, motion, weight, and time, together with the sizes of ingots and sizes of products, plus the quantity of product desired in a given time period, determine the size and design of the mill.

Each type of mill has been developed to meet a definite need, and, in performing this one task, it is superior to other types. However, mills are expensive to install and are capable of long life, while changing conditions in the steel industry sometimes result in a number of changes in the needs to be met by a primary mill during the period of its useful life. This results in adapting existing mills to new needs, frequently with alterations to some of the facilities, and many of the present-day primary mills are rolling ingots and producing products that were not contemplated when the mills were built.

A relatively recent development has been the adaption of automatic program control to new and existing primary mills, as discussed in Chapter 20. Briefly, this type of control (under supervision of the mill operators who can exercise their trained judgment to interject manual control when necessary) automatically performs, in pre-set sequence, the numerous functions that formerly were initiated by manual control.

The general characteristics of each of the types of primary mills are outlined below.

TWO-HIGH REVERSING MILL

In the phrase "two-high reversing mill," the term "two-high" refers to the fact that the mill consists of two rolls, one over the other, as in Figure 22—2. "Reversing" means that after the piece has gone through the rolls in the direction of the first pass, the rolls are brought to a standstill and then caused to rotate in the reverse direction shown in Pass No. 2, so as to impose the next reduction on the piece (the next pass), and so on until the piece has been reduced by the desired amount. This type of mill has maximum flexibility in size range of ingot and product, as well as wide range of adjustment in the amount and rate of steel deformation in any pass. The majority of primary mills are manually operated in order to permit instant variations in practice, the crew on electrically-driven mills consisting of two men. A very high degree of skill is essential in each man in his own duties and, in addition, there is the necessity for complete coordination between the crew members of all motions of the equipment if the highest production rate is to be attained, since each individual is controlling a part of what is, in effect, one machine working on one piece of steel. As mentioned above, automatic program controls installed on some mills perform the coordinated functions without human intervention unless, in the judgment of the mill operator, it is necessary to resort to manual control of some function or functions to correct deviation from the program.

For the same size ingot rolled to the same size

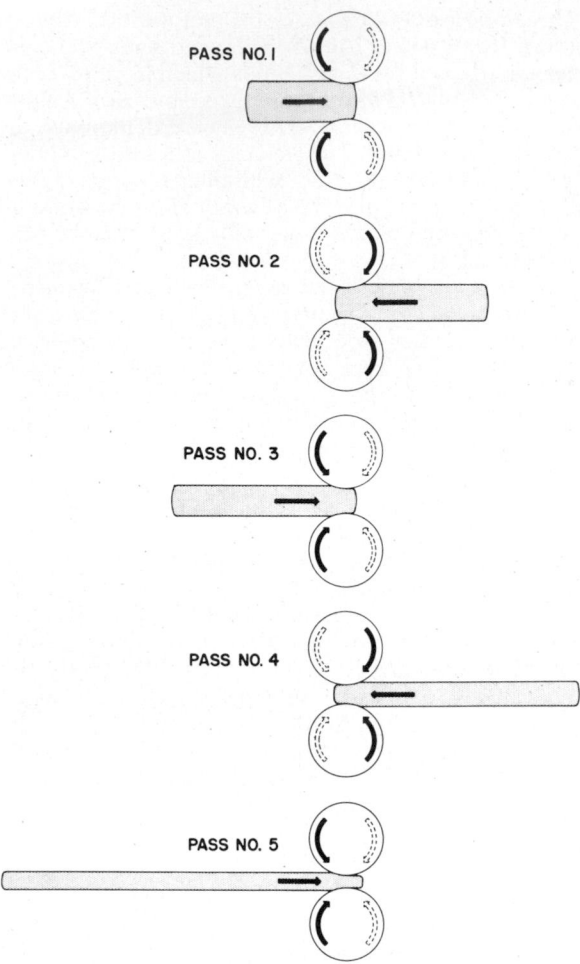

PASS NO. 1

PASS NO. 2

PASS NO. 3

PASS NO. 4

PASS NO. 5

FIG. 22—2. Diagrammatic representation of the sequence of rolling operations involved in reducing an ingot to a slab on a reversing two-high mill.

product, the two-high reversing mill has a lower production rate, in terms of tons per unit of time, than any of the others, and it was due to this relatively low output rate that the other types were devised. However, the two-high reversing mill remains the principal type in use, exceeding in numbers all other types combined, by a wide margin. Its chief characteristic, flexibility, is so valuable that this type of mill is combined frequently with other types to compensate for low production rate, the extreme being two two-high mills of different sizes arranged in tandem. Many such combinations are in operation at this time.

While there is no limit to the size or weight of ingot for which this type of mill is used, there is an economic limit to the length of piece which should be rolled from one ingot on one mill. It is determined by two factors: inertia of moving parts of equipment, and size of building to house the mill. The ingot is a relatively short casting, mostly from five to nine feet long. Mill parlance refers to length of ingots as their height, because they are poured vertically and this dimension is height at first, but the mill operates on the ingot when the latter is in a horizontal position. In the early passes,

the length of the piece is so short that one to three revolutions of the rolls is sufficient to complete a pass, and the rolling speed is preferably very slow. Reversals can be rapid, power loss in reversing is relatively slight, and impact among moving parts is light. As the piece becomes longer in successive passes, the rolling speeds must be increased if the steel is not to lose too much heat. At high speed, the motion in one direction is only a few seconds in duration, but reversals at high speed consume excessive power and subject all the moving parts in the mill tables as well as in the mill and the mill drive to severe shock, even with the best electrical controls. The mill table should be as long on each side of the mill as the rolled piece, plus adequate clearance for manipulation. Any appreciable increase in length of the rolled piece requires the combined length of the tables on both sides of the mill stand to be increased by twice that amount and requires a corresponding increase in length of building for proper accommodation. This economic limit of length of an uncropped piece rolled from an ingot seems to be about 90 feet.

The two-high reversing mills in use today are of three forms. The predominating form, known simply as a **blooming mill**, is provided with one pair of horizontal rolls in which several grooved passes provide the means of controlling the shape of the piece during rolling, and particularly of working the corners of the piece. This form of mill exists in a wide range of sizes and is designed to roll ingots of square or nearly square cross-section with a maximum thickness of about 34 inches, and can edge vertically, in a grooved pass, a piece of about 40 inches maximum width. A typical modern example is the 46-inch blooming mill in the Lorain Works of United States Steel Corporation, shown in Figure 22—3.

A variation of this form, designed for edging pieces up to about 78 inches wide resting on their narrow edges, is known as a **high-lift blooming mill and occasionally as a blooming and slabbing mill**. It differs from the more conventional form in being provided with higher mill housings to permit greater elevation of the top roll for the edging passes on **wide pieces**. The roll body is usually longer and has **fewer grooved** passes, and the motors which operate **the screws for** controlling top-roll elevation are usually larger in order to provide faster raising and lowering of the top roll. This latter feature is provided since edging passes are few in number but require excessive time unless the top-roll travel is accomplished in no longer than that required for the manipulator to turn the ingot 90 degrees. This form of mill can be provided with interchangeable sets of rolls so that it can produce not only wide slabs but also blooms and, for this reason, it has been installed rather widely since around 1940. It has the greatest range in sizes of ingots and products of all three forms. The 53-inch high-lift blooming and slabbing mill at South Works of United States Steel Corporation, shown in Figure 22—4, is a modern example of this type.

A third form, actually a special-purpose mill limited to the production of wide slab sections, is the **universal slabbing mill**, often referred to simply as a **slab**

Fig. 22—3. The 46-inch two-high reversing blooming mill in the Lorain Works of United States Steel Corporation. Relationship of this mill to other mills in the No. 4 Blooming, Bar and Billet Mill is shown in Section 2 of this chapter.

mill. It is designed to increase the production rate for wide slabs avoiding expenditure of the time required for vertical edging passes in a blooming mill, and is provided with a pair of vertical rolls in addition to the pair of horizontal rolls, the vertical rolls performing the edging. In this arrangement, no grooves are used in either pair of rolls. This lack of grooves prevents support of the ingot corners during rolling, and also limits the mill to production of slab sections, since it is incapable of avoiding consistently the inadvertent production of a diamond-shaped product in square or nearly square sections. The slab product rolled on universal mills has relatively sharp corners compared to that of the other mills. Figure 22—5 illustrates the 45-inch universal slabbing mill at Fairless Works of United States Steel Corporation.

Rolling a certain size ingot to a certain size bloom is done at the same rate in the conventional and the high-lift blooming mills. The installation cost of the latter is slightly higher. Rolling the same size ingot to the same size slab is done at a somewhat faster rate in the universal slab mill than in the high-lift blooming mill, but the installation cost of the universal slab mill is substantially higher due to the cost of the vertical roll assembly and the additional prime mover to drive it. Before the high-lift mill was developed, the universal mill was the means for producing wide, heavy slabs for plate mills, and it has been built in sizes to produce widths to about 78 inches, maximum.

Two-High Tandem Mill—This mill consists of several single stands, each containing one pair of rolls, spaced one following another at such distances as to permit the rolled piece to be free between stands. Normally, the piece is rolled one pass in each stand, as shown in Figures 22—13 and 22—14.

Because each stand rolls only one pass, there is no time lost in reversing the travel of the piece, with the result that this type of mill has the maximum output rate of all types. In addition, each stand can be designed for the almost ideal draft and rotating speed for each of the successive rolling passes. This is a great advantage in the early passes where the weakening effect of the ingot crystal structure exists. Opposed to these three very desirable features is the narrow limit of ingot and product cross-sections which the mill can roll without sacrificing the advantages by excessive idle time to change rolls and by compromise on roll-pass designs. For these reasons, the tandem mill is used as a roughing mill to supply hot steel to succeeding mills which permit flexibility in product sizes, but is confined to a narrow limit in ingot cross-section dimensions.

Two installations have been built in which a tandem mill was followed by continuous billet mills, and the entire mill in each case sometimes was called a continuous mill. This designation is slightly misleading with respect to the tandem roughing mill.

Due to the large amount of equipment in a tandem mill, it is the most expensive mill to build for a given ingot-to-product reduction but, when scheduled to full capacity, its operating cost per ton of product is lower than that of any other type mill rolling the same-sized

FIG. 22—4. The 53-inch, high-lift, two-high, reversing blooming and slabbing mill at the South Works of United States Steel Corporation.

ingot to the same product. A tandem mill can roll any size of bloom or slab for which it is designed, but its application has been chiefly to the medium and small sizes, since these were the only sizes in which sufficient orders could be obtained to provide the quantity of production to match the capacity of a tandem mill designed to roll them.

Three-High Mill—This type of mill consists of one stand containing three horizontal rolls, one above the other, each of which has grooved passes, and an ele-

vating table on each side of the mill so that the piece being rolled can be passed alternately between the bottom and middle rolls and between the top and middle rolls. In order to keep the roll dimensions and mill and table dimensions from being prohibitive in size, a compromise pass design is used wherein the grooves in the middle roll are used for rolling both with the top and with the bottom roll. This method limits the reduction possible in the second pass through each middle-roll groove to less than that possible in single

FIG. 22—5. Overall view of the 45-inch universal slabbing mill in the Fairless Works of United States Steel, designed and operated solely for producing slabs.

passes. The rotating speed of the mill is also a compromise, since each pass should be progressively faster than the one preceding, but, with all passes in one set of rolls, that is impossible. The speed selected is usually too fast for the early passes and too slow for the last ones. There are normally five or seven passes, so

that it is often necessary to employ heavy ragging in at least the first two passes to prevent slippage of the steel both in entering the pass and during rolling.

Because the rolls rotate in one direction only and at constant speed, a relatively simple and inexpensive constant-speed prime mover, aided by a flywheel, is

FIG. 22—6. A 40-inch, three-high blooming mill, forming an intermediate stand that rolls roughed down ingots (from another mill stand) to blooms that are supplied to the 28-inch billet mill in the far left background. (Courtesy, United Engineering and Foundry Company.)

used as the main drive. No power is lost overcoming inertia as there is no reversing. Raising and lowering the tables to guide the piece into successive passes can be accomplished in less time than the corresponding manipulations in a reversing mill. For these reasons, a three-high mill is less expensive to build and has a higher output rate than a two-high reversing mill rolling the same ingot to the same product.

Opposed to these favorable features are certain disadvantages. Like the tandem mill, the three-high mill with its fixed passes is rather inflexible with regard to size of ingot cross-section and product, except at the expense of serious operating delays due to roll changing. Then, too, its usual rather fast rolling speed in the first few passes makes it less desirable generally for the rolling of ingots in these passes.

The three-high mill is best adapted to a place as an intermediate stand (Figure 22—6) where it can be supplied with bloomed-down ingots (ingots which have received a few heavy reduction passes), or large blooms, and where it can supply smaller hot blooms of one or two sizes directly to a following mill. Its rather simple design permits a rolling schedule among three mills in sequence which can be balanced within reasonable limits by alterations in the pass design to adjust the entering bloom and the product bloom sizes to control the production rate of the preceding and following mills.

It finds a use as an ingot-rolling mill in those plants whose standard ingot sizes are very small, on the order of 14-inch square or less in cross-section, and whose total ingot-producing capacity is also quite modest. In these applications, the three-high mill functions more as a billet mill or as a roughing stand for a directly connected finishing mill. The 43-inch three-high blooming mill at Ohio Works of United States Steel, which uses an ingot of medium size in a large tonnage operation, is an exceptional use of the three-high type.

Operating Units Comprising a Blooming Mill—To avoid frequent digression, the physical layout will be described here for rolling ingots on a two-high reversing mill. Essentially the same auxiliary equipment is used in rolling on other types of primary mills. The

main parts of the rolling mill itself are shown diagrammatically in Figure 22—7.

Two men are required to operate the controls of an electric-motor-driven two-high reversing mill, the **roller** and the **manipulator,** whose functions are defined by their titles; their **pulpit,** or control station, is placed on a bridge over one of the mill tables. (A steam-engine-driven mill requires a third man in the pulpit, the **engineer,** to operate the engine controls.)

Rolling—A **pot car** or **ingot buggy** (Figure 22—8) transfers a heated ingot from the soaking pits to the **ingot receiving table,** which delivers it to the **mill approach table.** The receiving table, in some mills, is equipped with an **ingot turner** so the ingot may be rolled butt-end first (Figure 22—9). This practice aids the shearman in cutting the proper discard from the butt end of the rolled piece.

The mill approach table transports the ingot to the front mill table or roller table in preparation for rolling. It can move pieces at speeds of 200 to 400 feet per minute on modern mills. A few mills have a scale in the ingot receiving table or mill approach table for weighing the ingots before rolling (Figure 22—9).

During the complete rolling cycle, the hot steel is transported by reversible, live rollers in the **mill tables.** These rollers are subjected to high temperatures, heavy loads and impact. Depending upon the size of the mill they serve, rollers range in size from 12 to 21 inches in diameter, of whatever length is required for the particular service, and are spaced 2 to 3 feet apart. Forged steel generally is used in making the rollers which, in new mills, are mounted in roller bearings having a circulating lubricating system. Rollers on modern tables usually are driven electrically through a line shaft by miter gears; in some cases, they may be driven separately. As the pieces move along the tables, or are turned over by the manipulating equipment between passes, any loose scale falls between the rolls into a trough or depression beneath the tables and is removed to a settling pit with the aid of a stream of water.

Front and back roller tables alternately feed and receive the piece during each pass through the rolling

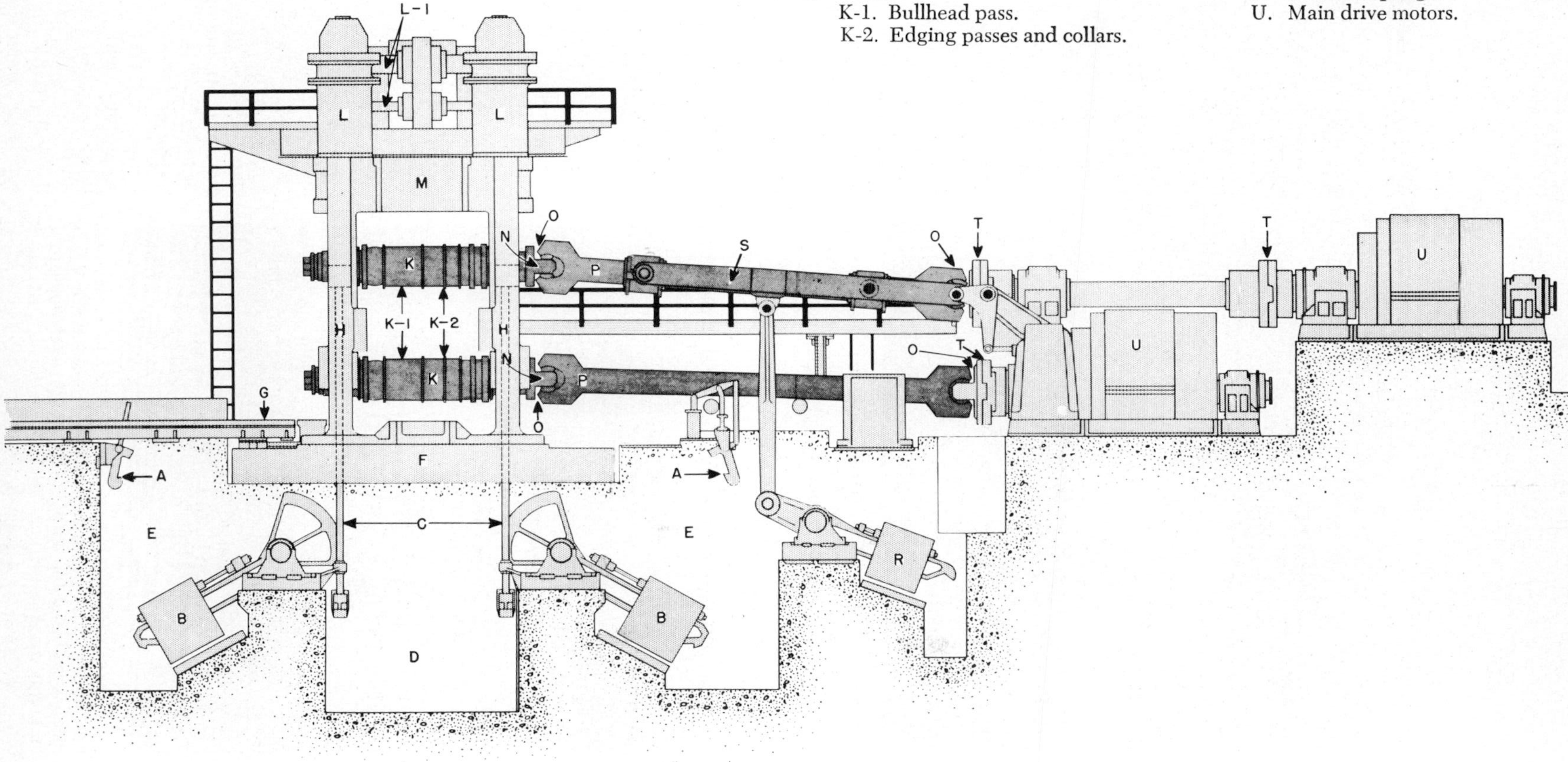

FIG. 22—7. Diagrammatic sketch of a high-lift, two-high, reversing blooming mill, with the main constructional details indicated. (Manipulator, roll tables and control elements not shown.)

LEGEND

A. Counterweight latches.
B. Roll-balancing counterweights.
C. Steelyard rods.
D. Scale pit.
E. Counterweight pits.
F. Housing shoe.
G. Roll-change rig rail.
H. Housings.
K. Rolls.
K-1. Bullhead pass.
K-2. Edging passes and collars.

L. Screwdown drives.
L-1. Crossover shafts.
M. Housing separator.
N. Wobblers.
O. Universal couplings.
P. Main-drive spindles.
R. Spindle counterweight.
S. Top-spindle carrier.
T. Motor couplings.
U. Main drive motors.

FIG. 22—8. Ingot buggy (pot car) transferring an ingot heated in the soaking pits in the background to the ingot-receiving table of the 46-inch blooming and slabbing mill in the Duquesne Works of United States Steel Corporation. Second pot car (empty) is on parallel track.

FIG. 22—9. Ingot being turned 180 degrees at the ingot-receiving table of the 46-inch blooming and slabbing mill in Duquesne Works of United States Steel. The ingot turner incorporates a scale for weighing ingots.

mill, and mechanical units called **manipulators** rotate the piece through 90 degrees as required and move it from pass to pass. Some of the precautions to be observed in rolling are discussed later in this chapter.

Shear approach tables carry the rolled product from the back roller table of the mill to the **shear.** These tables have side guards that line the piece at right angles to the shear so that square cuts can be made. Some mills have a **hot-scarfing machine** in the mill delivery table or in the shear approach table for "skinning" the surface of the hot piece to remove, in part, some of the surface defects.

Shearing—The shear, generally called the **crop shear,** usually is located 100 to 200 feet from the rolls, and in line with the mill. Live rollers transport the rolled pieces between the mill and the shear. Primary function of the crop shear is to remove from the rolled piece sufficient of the back and front ends (corresponding to the top and bottom of the ingot, or vice versa), so that the sheared piece remaining will meet chemical and metallurgical specifications. Secondary functions are to cut the remaining piece into desired semi-finished lengths and to shear test pieces.

Shears may be operated with electric or hydraulic power. A typical modern slab shear has an 80-inch wide knife, and a cutting-pressure capacity of 1200 tons; it can make straight cuts up to 8 inches thick and 60 inches wide, at a rate of 10 cuts per minute. It is driven by two 350-horsepower air-cooled motors. The top knife comes down to act as a gag and hold the piece while the bottom knife moves upward to make the cut. This principle of operation has caused this type of shear to be designated as a **down-and-up-cut shear.**

The **after shear tables** which receive the cut product are designed according to the type of shear. Modern down-cut shears have a table that can move vertically to compensate for the action of the material during shearing. Either kind of shear (down-and-up-cut or down-cut) may have a shuttle motion for the after-shear table, which permits it to move back so the scrap may drop onto a conveyor beneath the shear. A **crop pusher** on the front side of the shear facilitates pushing the last crop end from the shear. Most after-shear tables have adjustable guards for lining up the last piece to insure a straight cut.

The **shear gage** measures the length of pieces to be cut. It is operated by a motor-driven screw. The gage head stops the bloom or slab at the desired point between the shear knives.

Sheared-off discards are moved by the **crop conveyor** to transportation facilities for return to the steel-making departments where they are charged into the furnaces as scrap.

Located adjacent to and operating with the after shear tables are mechanical stamping devices or platforms for hand stampers to mark pieces for exact identification. A scale also usually is provided for weighing sheared pieces.

Transfers move sheared product from point to point, and may be of the continuous chain type with pusher dogs that engage and move the pieces over skid bars, or of the reciprocating-beam type which moves pieces progressively from one set of supports to another. Transfer buggies or cars also are used to move finished products from the runout table onto the pilers or transfer. Mechanical pilers separate the product into desired classifications as to weight, size of piece and type of cut, or other characteristics. Where the type of product permits, the sheared pieces may be moved by roller table from the shear to a piler, from which the piles may be removed by a "C" hook on an overhead crane, or moved by rollers onto a transfer car.

COMBINATIONS OF CONVENTIONAL-TYPE MILLS FOR SPECIAL PURPOSES

Two Two-High Reversing Mills in Tandem—A recently constructed primary mill at Duquesne Works of United States Steel Corporation was designed to provide a train of mills capable of rolling product ranging in size from 1¾-inch square billets up to and including 50-inch wide slabs in whatever mix of sizes might be required at any given time. The installation consists of stripping facilities, soaking pits, a 46-inch blooming and slabbing mill, a 36-inch blooming mill, and a four-stand continuous 21-inch billet mill, all in tandem and enclosed in one building (see Figure 22—10). A scrap- and scale-handling area and a shipping building were included, along with slow-cooling facilities and auxiliary equipment designed to handle the wide range of mill products. A wet-scale-handling flume system covers all areas under the entire mill and auxiliary equipment, including hot beds. An information-broadcasting and data-collecting system provide necessary rolling information and collect desired control data throughout the mill.

Stripping facilities consist of two stripping cranes, ground stripper, and a stool-coating station. The soaking pits comprise seven banks of one-way top-fired pits (Figure 22—8), fired with high-velocity multi-directional burners of new design. Metallic recuperators are employed: eight pits being equipped with both convection and radiation recuperators operating in series to preheat air to a maximum temperature of 1350° F, while the remainder are equipped with recuperators employing the convection principle only and designed for a maximum air-preheating temperature of 1150° F. Two cable-driven ingot buggies (Figure 22—8) transfer ingots from the pits to the mill receiving tables. Following delivery to the receiving table, the ingot passes through the overhead ingot turner that weighs and turns the ingot 180 degrees, when desired, and returns it to the mill approach table (Figure 22—9).

The 46-inch by 110-inch blooming and slabbing mill (Figure 22—11) is a high-lift reversing mill with individual roll drives. Each roll is powered by a 5000-horsepower motor with speed points of 20, 40, 55, 70, 85 and 100 rev. per min. and capable of reversal in 1½ sec. The rolls are equipped with four-row roller bearings. Maximum lift of the hydraulically balanced top roll is 70 inches, with a maximum screw speed of 600 inches of travel per minute. The mill is equipped with manipulating fingers on the front side only, with positioning side guards on each side of the mill stand. Table rolls adjacent to the mill are individually driven, and two feed rollers are incorporated into the housing on both the entry and delivery side of the mill.

The 46-inch mill is programmed and can be operated either (1) automatically, (2) automatically except for manual control of manipulation, (3) with roll position established by automatic screw control and other operations manually controlled, or (4) with all operations manually controlled when circumstances make this necessary. The program is actuated by punched cards, with two card readers to accommodate the rolling of alternate ingots of different size or grade of product. Eventually, the card system will be improved and supplemented by a system of supplying stored information that will permit the proper program to be initiated immediately when mill conditions arise that require a sudden change in plan.

Product sizes from the 46-inch mill include: slabs up to 52 inches wide with a minimum thickness of 3½ inches; blooms up to 20 inches square; and various breakdown sizes for subsequent rolling in the 36-inch mill. Product down to 8 inches square is finished on this mill when the 36-inch mill is rolling to the smaller sections to balance output of the two mills.

A four-sided scarfer following the 46-inch mill is capable of scarfing the complete range of products from this mill on the edges only, top and bottom only, or on all four sides.

The 46-inch-mill shear is an electrically driven up-and-down cut shear capable of parting 600 square

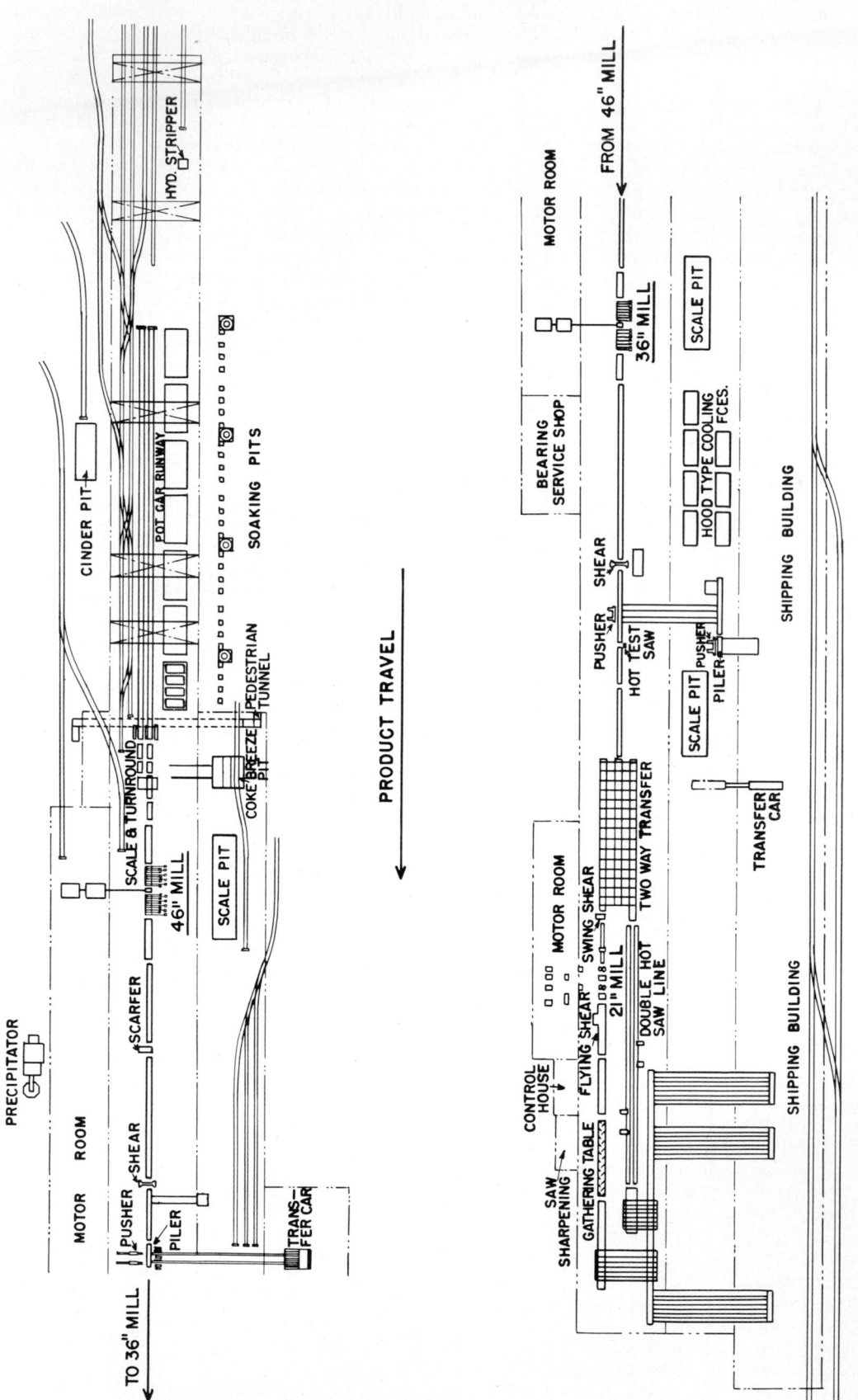

FIG. 22—10. Schematic arrangement (not to scale) of the recently constructed primary mill at Duquesne Works of United States Steel Corporation, consisting of two two-high reversing mills in tandem, followed by a 4-stand 21-inch billet mill. (Mill tables for both mills are in same straight line: drawing has been divided for convenience in printing.)

FIG. 22—11. General view of the 46-inch two-high reversing high-lift blooming and slabbing mill at the Duquesne Works of United States Steel Corporation.

inches of mild steel and 400 square inches of stainless or high-carbon grades. An elaborate crop-handling system maintains proper segregation of steels of the wide variety of compositions rolled on these mills. Revert scrap is loaded into charging boxes at the mill.

The slab piler and transfer, next in line, is the outlet for slabs and larger bloom sizes finished on the 46-inch mill. The elevator-type piler can pile product on a transfer car to a maximum height of three feet. The transfer car travels to the shipping bay where it is unloaded by a crane equipped with a "C" hook. A pneumatic impact stamping machine, remotely controlled by the piler-transfer operator, is used to mark rolled pieces with heat number, ingot number, and cut letter.

The 36-inch by 78-inch two-high reversing blooming mill (Figure 22—12) is next in line. Products rolled on this mill range from 3⅞-inch square billets to 15-inch square blooms, in sheared lengths from 5 to 20 feet. This stand is powered by two 3000-horsepower motors with a speed range of 60 to 150 rev. per min., individually driving the two rolls. This mill also is equipped with four-row roller bearings and hydraulic roll-balancing equipment. The maximum lift of the top roll is 40 inches and maximum screw speed is 400 inches of travel per minute. The controls for this mill are similar to those described on the 46-inch mill

with provisions for both automatic and manual operation. Positioning side guards are on both the entering and delivery sides of the mill, with finger manipulation on the entering side only. An auxiliary bar turner, capable of turning 8-inch by 8-inch and smaller sections, is provided on both sides of the mill stand and are used when the piece being rolled is too small in section and, consequently, too long to be turned effectively by the fingers.

The shear following the 36-inch mill is electrically driven through an air-operated clutch and flywheel combination. The relatively small amount of revert scrap accumulated at this point is handled in self-dumping boxes, with a diverter in the scrap chute to guide the scrap to the desired box.

Sheared product finished on the 36-inch mill is pushed onto a rope transfer and conveyed to a table running at right angles to the transfer that permits product to be moved in one direction to a ratchet-bar transfer for pickup by crane and "C" hook for placement in one of the slow-cooling furnaces, or in the opposite direction to a piler and ratchet-bar transfer that moves the product into the shipping building.

The slow-cooling furnaces for controlled cooling of rolled product are gas-fired furnaces with removable hoods, capable of holding 60-ton loads.

Fig. 22—12. General view of the 36-inch two-high reversing blooming mill at Duquesne Works of United States Steel Corporation, showing control pulpit in right background.

Just beyond the 36-inch-mill transfer is a 72-inch hot saw for securing metallurgical-test samples up to 15 inches by 15 inches in cross-section. Blooms are routed into the saw by an air-operated diverter and returned to the transfer after test pieces have been cut.

Product placed on the 21-inch-mill transfer table may be moved in one direction to the hot-saw line equipped with one stationary and one movable 60-inch hot saw with suitable stops and gages for cutting product from the 36-inch mill that requires hot-sawed ends: sections up to 7 inches by 7 inches square can be sawed into lengths of 8 to 34 feet, following which it is transferred to the hot-bed run-in table and discharged onto one of the three hot beds. In the other direction, the 21-inch-mill transfer table moves blooms to the 21-inch-mill run-in table. As the pieces approach the 21-inch mill, a swing shear with a section limitation of 36 square inches is used to crop their front ends. Immediately preceding the first stand of the 21-inch mill is an air-operated billet turner that turns pieces 45 degrees to position them for proper entry into the first diamond pass of the mill.

Continuous billet mills will be discussed in detail in Section 2 of this chapter: however, a brief descrip-tion of the 21-inch mill at Duquesne Works will be included here to complete the description of the new primary mill at that plant.

The 21-inch mill is a four-stand continuous mill with alternate vertical and horizontal stands (see Section 2). Each stand is driven by a 1500-horsepower motor. The alternate vertical and horizontal mill stands eliminate the necessity for twisting billets between stands. The ability to adjust the position of the mill housings and rolls makes possible the maintenance of a straight pass line through the four successive stands. Through proper pass design, it is possible by changing the pass line through housing adjustments to roll 1¾-inch square to 4½-inch square billets in size increments of ¼ inch. The complete range of sizes can be rolled from one set of rolls for each of the first three stands and two sets for the fourth stand. Product rolled on this mill is cut to length by an electrically driven flying shear in lengths from 22 to 34 feet. A double-skew table collects the billets in gangs after shearing and moves them to a rope transfer that carries them to the hot-bed run-in table that discharges them to one of three hot beds that extend into the shipping building.

Another example of the versatility obtainable by

using two two-high reversing mills in tandem to supply succeeding continuous billet mills is the No. 4 Blooming, Bar and Billet Mill at Lorain Works of United States Steel Corporation. Typical rolling schedules of the 46-inch and 38-inch reversing mills and the succeeding six-stand and four-stand continuous billet mills are illustrated in Figure 22—33 in Section 2 of this chapter, to demonstrate how a wide range of sizes of square and round billets and narrow slabs can be rolled at high production rates.

Tandem and Three-high Mill in Tandem—Figure 22—13 shows the arrangement of blooming mills in tandem supplying blooms to the Gary rail mill. The installation comprises four 40-inch, non-reversing, two-high roll stands, in each of which the ingot receives a single pass, and a three-high mill in which five passes are given, the ingot being turned 90 degrees between passes on the latter mill. Stands Nos. 1 and 2 are driven at 5 r.p.m. by a 2000-horsepower motor, and Nos. 3 and 4 by another 2000-horsepower motor. A 6000-horsepower motor drives the three-high mill. This arrangement provides for reduction of a 23¼-inch by 23¼-inch ingot to an approximately 8-inch by 8-inch bloom which, after cropping and cutting to lengths, is rolled directly, without reheating, on the rail mill.

Four-Stand and Five-Stand Tandem Mills in Tandem—The Gary billet mill produces billets, narrow slabs, and small blooms. The blooming-mill section of this mill is described here to illustrate the extreme case of utilization of tandem mills.

The blooming mill, shown in Figure 22—14, consists of four 40-inch, two-high, non-reversing stands, followed in line by five similar 32-inch stands. The first two 40-inch stands are driven by one motor, with the third and fourth stands being driven by a single second motor. All five of the 32-inch stands are driven by a single motor through a line shaft and miter gears. The increasing distance between successive 32-inch stands allows for increase in length of the piece being rolled as it is reduced in each pass. No screw-down mechanism is required on these stands, because all of the passes are fixed. The mill is restricted to practically one ingot size, but can be set up to produce a variety of shapes, as indicated in Figure 22—15. Manipulation is effected by the proper design and application of table rollers, collars, and side guards.

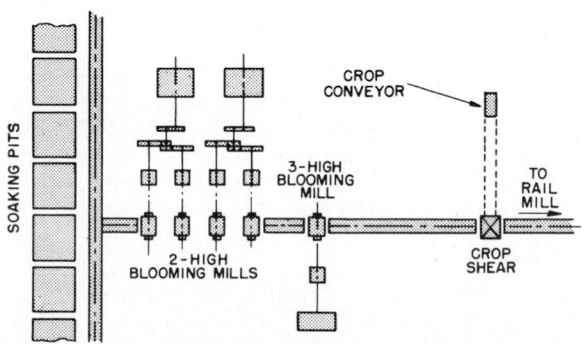

FIG. 22—13. Schematic arrangement of blooming mills in tandem, supplying blooms to the Gary Rail Mill.

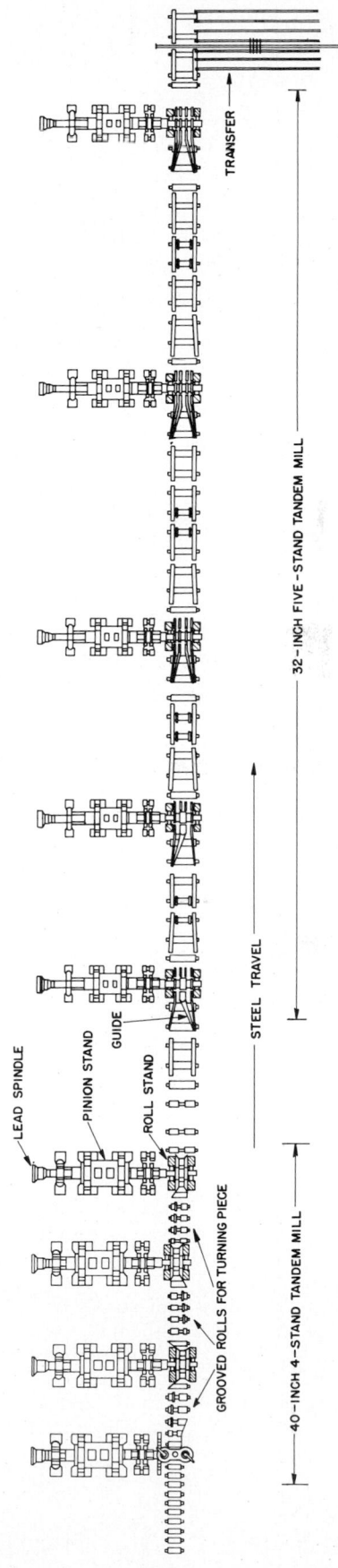

FIG. 22—14. Blooming-mill section of the Gary Billet Mill, that produces billets, narrow slabs, and small blooms. This illustration is schematic only.

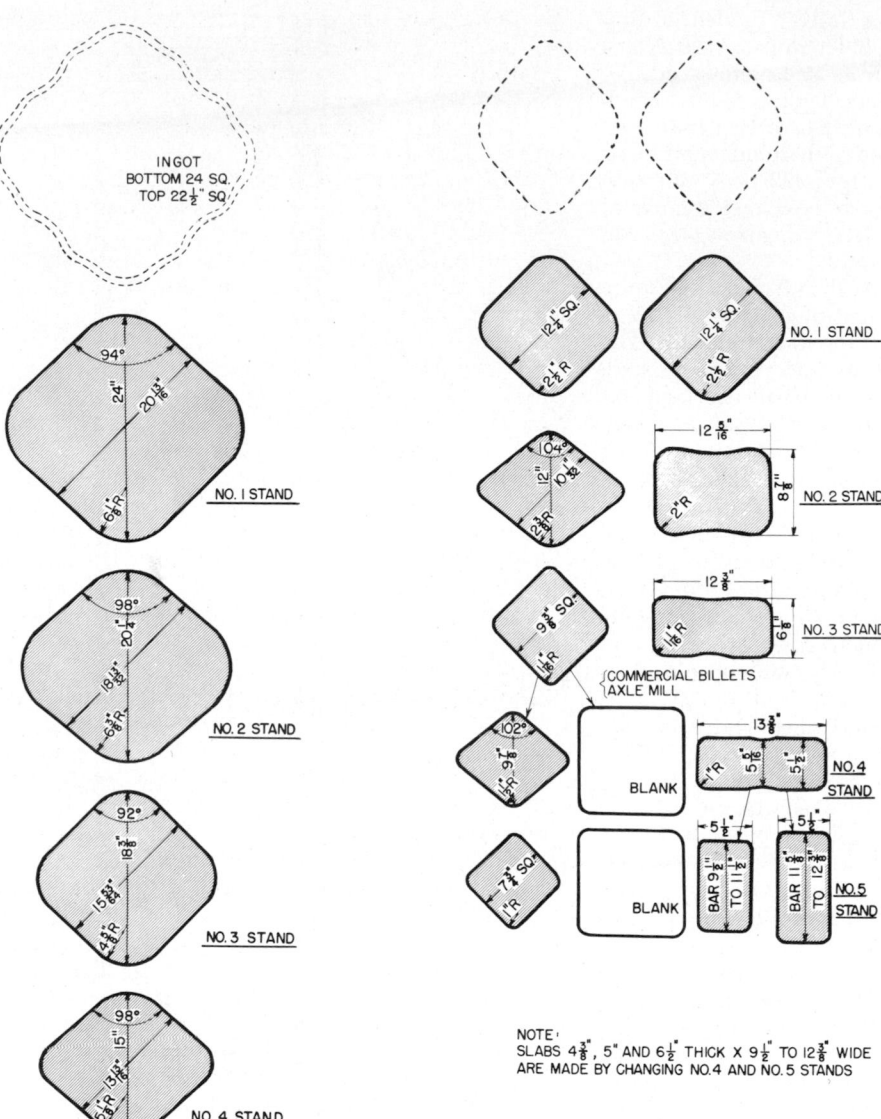

FIG. 22—15. (Left) Arrangement of roll passes in the four 40-inch stands and (right) arrangement of passes in the five 32-inch stands of the Gary Billet Mill, in a typical set-up for producing a variety of shapes from a single ingot size.

NOTE:
SLABS 4⅜", 5" AND 6½" THICK X 9½" TO 12⅜" WIDE
ARE MADE BY CHANGING NO.4 AND NO.5 STANDS

DESIGN OF BLOOMING-SLABBING MILL ROLL STANDS

The design of primary rolling mills is based on the work to be done, the size of material to be handled, and the length, weight, and shape of the sections to be produced. It is necessary in all cases to have all parts of the roll stand designed to survive the severe service conditions imposed by the inherent nature of the operations performed.

Foundations for primary mill stands are proportioned to the size and weight of the mill, and are built to withstand any tendency to settle or distort. On modern units, foundations are anchored to bedrock by piling to increase their ability to withstand the shocks and blows common to primary rolling operations. In counterweight-balanced mills, such as that shown in the diagram represented by Figure 22—7, foundation design is complicated by the space needed for this mechanism. Design of foundations for two-high continuous mills is simplified by the type of housing and

roll arrangement used. Three-high mill foundations must provide room under and adjacent to the mill for the mechanisms of lifting and manipulating devices that lift and turn pieces between passes.

Foundation design also must provide for the draining of water, oil, and greases to low spots, or sumps, from which they can be removed by pump or siphon if natural drainage cannot be provided. Passageways giving access to the equipment beneath the mill, sluice ways for handling scale that drops off pieces during rolling, and electric-cable tunnels also must be provided in the foundations of a modern mill.

Stand Design—The essential parts of rolling mills were discussed in Chapter 20, and need not be discussed again here for the particular case of the primary mills. The point should be made, however, that the component parts and auxiliary equipment for primary mills are extremely rugged and of very large size as compared to most other mills. Mention might be made of the fact that, in primary mills, two-high tandem and three-high mills generally are constructed with open-top housings, while two-high reversing mills, high-lift reversing mills, and universal mills are built with closed-top housings.

Front and back feed or housing rollers are required to move the ingot or piece between the mill tables and the horizontal rolls of the mill, because housings of two-high reversing, high-lift two-high reversing, and universal mills are so bulky in design and the tables for these mills are laid out in such a way that there is an open space between the last roller of the mill tables and the horizontal rolls of the mills. (Post and table construction of two-high continuous and three-high mills make it possible in these cases only for these rollers to be eliminated from their design.) These feed rollers have separate electric motor drives in modern mills. They must be designed with heavy bodies and necks to withstand pressure and impact, and should have carefully designed, well lubricated bearings that are protected from scale and water.

In universal-type primary mills, one of the feed rollers must be omitted between the vertical rolls, since these rolls must move in and out with respect to the center of the table. This one roller is replaced by a short dummy roller. If a piece "stalls" on this dead roller, the vertical rolls must be run in to contact the piece to move it onto the live table rollers on either side of the vertical rolls.

ROLL DESIGN AND ROLLING PROCEDURES

Roll Design—Roll sizes for blooming-slabbing operations are determined by the type and size of mill and the product being rolled. In most two-high reversing mills, roll diameters are usually 2 to 5 inches less than the size of the mill (based on the pinion drive). Rolls for a two-high tandem mill usually are short and heavy, since usually only one pass is made in each roll stand and diamond passes predominate.

In most three-high mills, the train-line diameters of the rolls are all different, the bottom roll being the largest, with the middle roll next in size and the top roll the smallest in diameter. These rolls are all of the same length body and neck.

Effect of Pass Design on Rolling Procedures—Drawings of rolls for various types of blooming mills are shown in Figures 22—16 and 22—17. Figure 22—16A shows rolls designed to produce a great number of sizes; this is typical of general practice. Since a large number of sizes must be produced on one set of rolls, it might be supposed that it would be well to roll on flat rolls without grooves. However, such procedure would produce blooms that were far from square. Grooves are provided, therefore, to produce the most popular sizes.

It is best practice to get the ingot into a box (grooved) pass as soon as possible in rolling, since any great amount of reduction of a piece without protection on the sides would cause the steel to crack. The spreading of the metal in these grooves causes wear of the rolls. Therefore, the sides of the grooves are tapered so that, with the dressing of the rolls, the pass may be made to approach its original width. The taper is made as great as possible for this purpose. However,

if too much taper is allowed, the piece being rolled will have a tendency to turn down as it emerges from between the rolls. Tapers up to 15 degrees per side have been used effectively.

Figure 22—16B illustrates rolls designed for a more specific purpose, while allowing a certain degree of flexibility. The largest proportion of product made on this set of rolls consists of 4-inch by 4-inch square billets. To use these rolls, it is necessary to provide grooved table rollers for the diamond passes. This also restricts manipulation and, consequently, full use of the roll body.

Rolls for a three-high, single-purpose mill are shown in Figure 22—17. In this case, the ingot size, bloom size, and number of passes is fixed. On this type of mill, much heavier reductions are given in the early passes than would be used in general practice on the two-high mill using the rolls of Figure 22—16A. With the rolls of Figure 22—17, edging occurs after each two passes. Since the ingot is protected on all corners and spreading is somewhat suppressed, and edging is done so frequently, it is possible to roll with the heavy reductions required to produce a bloom from an ingot in so few passes.

Figure 22—16F illustrates the pass arrangement for the production of shaped blooms called beam blanks. This type of roll, like the blooming-mill rolls of Figure 22—16A, usually lacks the necessary space for the most desirable arrangement of passes. Considerations involved in the design of rolls for beam blanks include: (1) reduction of the ingot to a smaller rectangle or square; (2) provision for an edging pass to aid in the reduction of an ingot; and (3) web and flange proportioning in the beam-blank pass. Available roll length usually limits the design to one pass for each of these three steps in the rolling operation. For the smaller sizes of blanks, it is possible to include a second shape pass in the rolls. Shape blanks to be rolled on universal mills producing beams are made in this type of rolls. For the larger beam sizes, a beam-shaped ingot is used. This permits a more uniform reduction that results in a better flange build-up in rolling.

Figures 22—16C and E show two sets of high-lift blooming-mill rolls. While the Method D of employing vertical and horizontal rolls is fastest for producing slabs, use of the horizontal rolls for edging, as in Figures 22—16C and E, is advantageous from the standpoint of surface of the semi-finished product of the mill. The edging pass, using horizontal rolls with the piece resting on its narrow edge, cracks the scale from the wide faces of the slab (which are in the vertical position) permitting the scale to fall off the piece and between the table rollers into the sluice-way beneath the mill. With the flat-rolling method using both vertical and horizontal rolls, the piece is not turned and some means must be employed to blow off the cracked scale; various ways are used, which will be discussed later.

Convexity of Passes—The convex shape (belly) of some passes will be noted in the illustrations; this convexity serves a double purpose. One is to prevent the formation of fins. If a straight-sided piece is edged in a succeeding pass, spreading causes the metal to

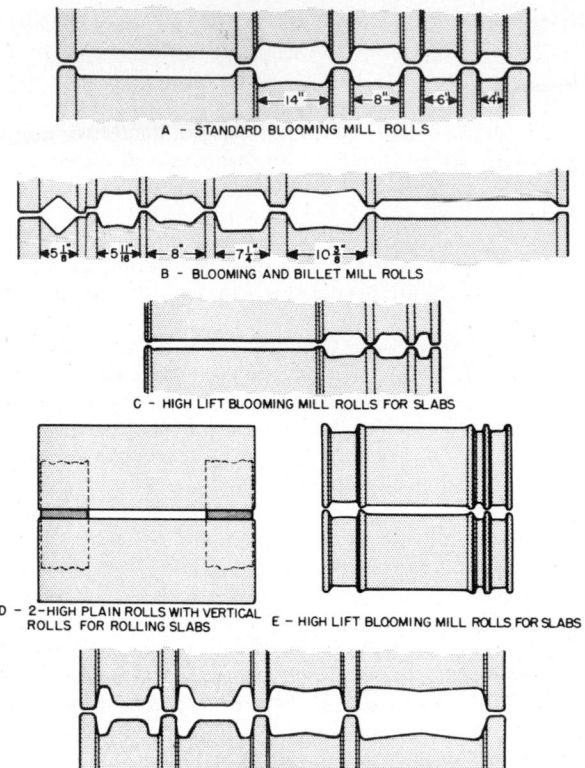

A - STANDARD BLOOMING MILL ROLLS

B - BLOOMING AND BILLET MILL ROLLS

C - HIGH LIFT BLOOMING MILL ROLLS FOR SLABS

D - 2-HIGH PLAIN ROLLS WITH VERTICAL ROLLS FOR ROLLING SLABS

E - HIGH LIFT BLOOMING MILL ROLLS FOR SLABS

F - BLOOMING MILL ROLLS FOR BEAM BLANKS

FIG. 22—16. Schematic representations of rolls for various types of blooming mills. In Sketches A, B, C and F, only part of each roll is shown to indicate the shapes of the pass openings. Sketches D and E show elevations of entire roll bodies.

squeeze out between the collars of the roll, as shown by the dotted lines in Figure 22—18A. Convexity of the passes produces a shape with concave sides, allowing considerably more spread in succeeding passes before a fin can occur. Fins, when a piece is turned 90 degrees then rolled in a succeeding pass, are rolled over and produce what is known as a **lap**, and no amount of further rolling can eliminate this defect. It is impossible for fins to roll back into the parent metal because an oxide forms on them which prevents clean metal-to-metal contact between the fin and the parent metal that would be essential to welding the two integrally together. Laps (or seams) also may result if the sides of a piece are excessively concave (Figure 22—18). Laps must be chipped or scarfed out before the bloom or billet can be rolled on finishing mills for further conversion.

The permissible amount of convexity is dependent upon the draft. It might seem that the convexity should be made very great to eliminate all possibility of fin formation. However, if the convexity is made too great, as illustrated by the dot-dash lines of Figure 22—18A, the reduction, in penetrating to the center, will not be able to push out the metal in the center and folding will occur that ultimately will form laps, as indicated in Figure 22—18B.

It will be seen from Figure 22—16F, showing the beam-blank roll set, that the box passes have a deep convexity; this is desirable in this case because of the shaping effect which is helpful in producing the shaped bloom.

The second purpose of convexity is to provide a convenient place for the ragging which is put on rolls for primary mills to increase their "bite."

Depth of Passes—The depth of any pass other than the bullhead pass in blooming-mill rolls is governed by two factors: (1) the maximum draft to be taken on any piece rolled in that pass, and (2) the minimum thickness to be produced in that pass. The relationship between the depth of any pass and the bullhead or barrel pass diameter must be such that the bottom of

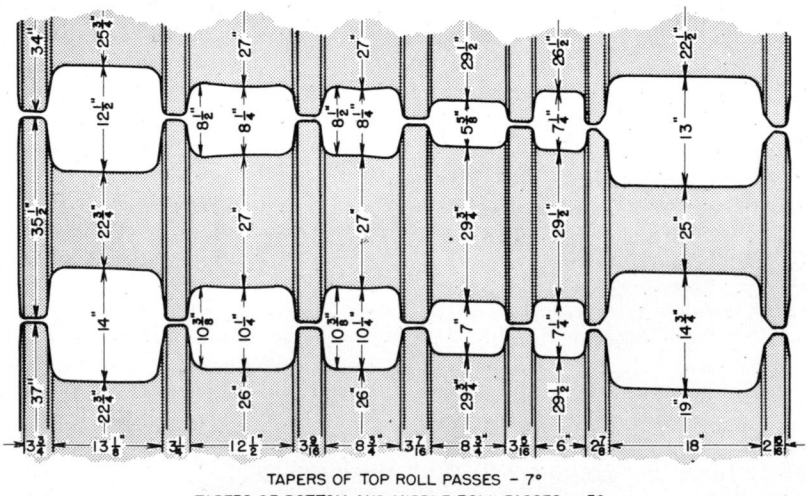

TAPERS OF TOP ROLL PASSES - 7°
TAPERS OF BOTTOM AND MIDDLE ROLL PASSES - 5°

FIG. 22—17. Schematic representation of rolls for a three-high, single-purpose mill. Only part of each of the top and bottom rolls are shown, sufficient to indicate the shape and size of the pass openings. The diameters of the rolls in the various passes, however, are given, to fix the size of the top and bottom rolls.

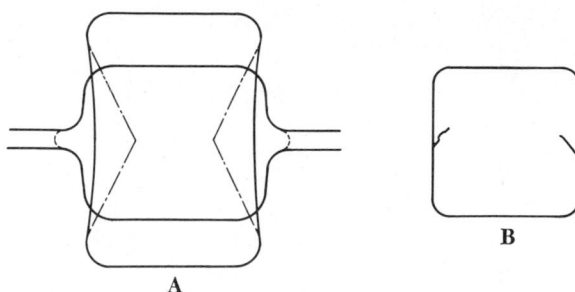

FIG. 22—18. (Left) Schematic representation of the effect of concavity of ingot sides in preventing the formation of fins. The large round-cornered shape is that of the piece entering the pass; the smaller shape represents the cross-section of the piece in the pass, with dotted lines indicating fins formed in the openings between the rolls if the ingot is straight-sided or has insufficient concavity. The dot-dash lines indicate extreme concavity which, as indicated at right, also will cause laps during rolling.

the bullhead pass is not elevated too high above the table rollers. If the bottom of the bullhead or barrel pass is too high above the table rollers, there would be excessive impact from the piece each time it passed through the mill and was discharged onto the rollers. Passes should be made as deep as possible, consistent with these considerations, however, because deep coverage of the bloom helps to guide the piece and also aids in preventing the formation of fins.

High-lift reversing mills require rolls of extraordinary length; most mills of this type have rolls 100 to 120 inches in body length. This is necessary to provide sufficient width for the grooved edging passes, along with a barrel or bullhead pass at least 6 inches in excess of the maximum width of slab to be rolled. Mills of this type may operate in conjunction with a separate vertical roll stand having relatively short, heavy rolls, located at the end of the mill runout table, to give a square edge to the finished product.

Universal-mill roll sizes are dependent directly upon the width of material to be rolled, along with the desired product size. In a typical mill, the bodies of the horizontal rolls are 45 inches in diameter and 80 inches in length.

Ragging, or grooves cut into blooming-mill rolls to prevent slippage when using heavy drafts, should be shallow and parallel to the axis of the rolls. Otherwise, it may prove injurious to the surface of the semi-finished steel by causing slivers and laps. Sometimes, ragging will be designed to protrude from the roll, instead of consisting of grooves cut into it. In general, the less ragging the better.

Bearings—Most of the newer primary mills are equipped with totally enclosed roller bearings or oil-film bearings, although many mills are still equipped with composition bearings of the laminated-fabric phenolic types. In earlier mills, the roll-neck bearings were mostly babbitted with brass-grid inserts.

Roll-Opening Indicators—On mills where the distance between the rolls is varied at the will of the operator to suit the particular rolling operation, some means must be provided for indicating visually the position of (i.e., the distance or opening between) the rolls. The conventional type of indicator is a large, calibrated dial with clock-like hands. The shaft that drives the hands is connected mechanically by rods, gears and cables to some rotating part or shaft on the screw-down mechanism, so that the position of the hands on the dial changes in unison with the movement of the rolls. The dial usually is mounted at the top of the mill, where it can be seen from the pulpit.

More recently, electrically operated devices have been developed that sense and measure some mechanical movement related to changing of the roll setting and transmit a signal to the control pulpit where it is translated into movement of a pointer on a dial where the roll setting can be observed.

Roll-Changing Devices—Rolls in open-top housings are changed by removing the housing cap and picking out the rolls separately or collectively with crane hooks.

With closed-top housings, roll changing is effected through a window of the housing by a counter-weighted porter bar, by a sleeve using the ingoing roll as a counterweight, or by a "C" hook. Any of these methods requires the use of an overhead crane to remove the rolls one at a time. The rolls are pulled out of the housing by attaching a socket fitted over the protruding roll necks.

In modern mills, a **roll-changing rig** removes worn rolls and installs new ones. It is set in a permanent mounting, level with the housing sill, and consists of a motor-operated crosshead mounted on a rail frame and driven by a rack and pinion. It withdraws both top and bottom rolls, with their respective bearings, one at a time. The old set-up then is removed from the rig, on which the new set-up is placed and positioned in the mill housings.

Cooling Water—During operation of a blooming or slabbing mill, a liberal supply of cooling water should be distributed carefully and uniformly over the rolls. If possible, the rolls always should be warm, never chilled, since the sudden contact of the surface of a hot ingot with a cold roll will cause too rapid a differential expansion of the roll surface, and cracks called **fire cracks** may develop. Water should be turned off when the mill is not rolling. If water is kept flowing when the mill is not rolling, the rolls should be kept turning to avoid uneven cooling which is one of the most common sources of cracks in rolls. Rolling without water at first and then putting water on the heated rolls is also a cause of cracking.

In some mills, great care is taken to warm up rolls before they are used in primary rolling operations. In one plant, the rolls are warmed by steam coils in a special pit before use. This practice minimizes fire cracking and roll breakage.

Manipulators—The rate of rolling steel in the blooming or slabbing mill depends upon the auxiliary equipment to a marked degree, as well as on the speed of the rolls. The importance of the auxiliaries is demonstrated by consideration of the fact that, in normal good rolling practice, a piece being rolled is in actual contact with the rolls only 25 to 40 per cent of the total rolling time. The remaining time is consumed in handling or manipulating the piece, emphasizing the importance of rugged, efficient equipment for performing this work. Transfer of the work from one point to another and away from the mill stand and between the different work stations is performed by the various live-roller arrangements discussed earlier.

Turning of the piece between passes, moving it sideways on the roller tables from one pass to another and, when necessary, straightening it, is the function of the manipulators. Usually, they are built to have both horizontal and vertical motion and, in most mills, are operated by electric or hydraulic power.

Location of blooming-mill and slabbing-mill manipulators depends upon the type of mill. In most three-high mills, the manipulators are located under the table, on the entering side of the rolls, the fingers coming up between the rollers to engage the piece as the table is lowered. The principle of operation is shown in Figure 22—21, as applied to a three-high billet mill. In other mills, they are located on side guards, stroking laterally over the tables on one or both sides of the mill. These side guards are equipped with retractable manipulator fingers or arms, which have a vertical or near vertical stroke and serve to lift the piece by a corner in the process of turning it 90 degrees.

SECTION 2

PRODUCTION OF BILLETS BY ROLLING

Development of the Billet Mill—It already has been described how, as the technique of pouring larger and larger ingots progressed, it became necessary to adopt the use of blooming mills to roll blooms of sizes which could be handled by separate finishing mills, either directly, or after reheating. A further step in the trend became necessary as ingot sizes increased still further, in that many reversing blooming mills are capable of producing satisfactory billets in sizes down to 4 inches by 4 inches, but this size is still too large for rolling a great part of the products rolled in finishing mills. About half the steel now produced is rolled into material of small section, and to finish these products with one heating, mills rolling these sections start with small billets. Hence, an intermediate mill between the blooming and finishing mills is required for rolling billets.

Blooms from 6 inches by 6 inches to 10 inches by 10 inches usually are taken to the billet mill from the blooming mill directly without reheating. The ends of the bloom are cropped, and it is often necessary to cut the remainder of the bloom into two or more pieces, as will be explained later. Hot scarfing also may be performed at this time. These operations must be performed rapidly to retain as much heat as possible in the bloom to keep its temperature high enough for good rolling in the billet mill. In this connection, billet mills capable of handling large blooms not only save time on the blooming mill, but also receive hotter steel, because the smaller surface area per unit of

weight exposed by pieces of heavy cross-section lessens heat losses.

Although most billets are rolled directly from blooms without reheating, there are some plants that provide reheating furnaces between the blooming and billet mills (Figure 22—23). The older blooming and billet mills generally did not provide for reheating since the grades of steel then produced could be rolled through a greater temperature range without harmful effects. Since the more critical grades of steel, with their restricted range of rolling temperatures, have become more widely used, some of the newer primary-mill installations provide reheating facilities between the blooming mill and the billet mill. These mills are arranged sometimes so that the ordinary grades of steel can be sent direct to the billet mill without reheating.

Since the billet section is a simple one and the requirements in the way of accuracy as to finish and dimensions of section are not exacting, the first requirement of the billet mill is that it be heavy enough to handle fairly large blooms, and speedy enough to reduce the piece to the desired size before it becomes too cold. Most billets, however, must be straight, square, and free from surface defects. Billets that are twisted, bent, or not square, will not charge into or push through reheating furnaces properly, causing pile-ups in the furnace; this due to the fact that billets lie on the hearth side by side, and depend, for their movement through the furnace, on pushing against the ex-

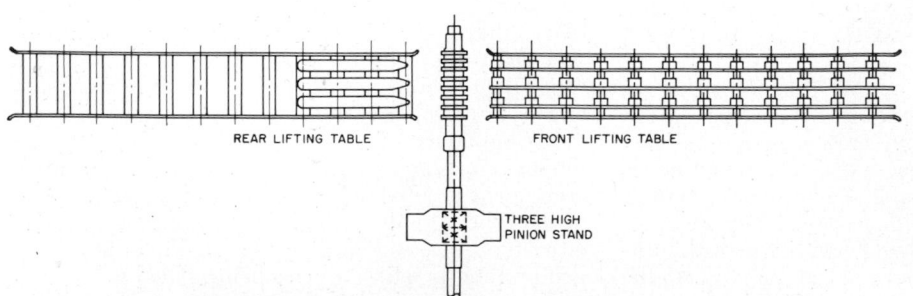

REAR LIFTING TABLE   FRONT LIFTING TABLE

THREE HIGH PINION STAND

TO DRIVE

Fig. 22—19. Schematic layout for a three-high billet mill, using the rolls shown mounted in their housings in Figure 22—20.

posed side of the last billet charged to move all the billets forward through the heating chamber. Poor surface causes excessive conditioning or even losses due to rejections.

In this section of the chapter, only the rolling of billets will be discussed. The rolling of sheet bar and skelp will not be considered, for, although these are both considered as semi-finished products, their production on billet mills has been abandoned almost completely in favor of using products of the continuous hot and cold strip mills as raw materials for the production of sheets, welded pipe, and tubes.

TYPES OF BILLET MILLS

Three-High Billet Mills—Billet mills may be of several types. One is the three-high mill with lifting or tilting tables. This type of mill consists of three rolls mounted one above the other in a single roll housing. Billets are rolled in one direction between the bottom and middle rolls, and through the middle and top rolls in the opposite direction. The lifting or tilting tables move the billet to the two different pass levels. Mills of this type have fixed drafts, and only a few limited sizes of billets can be rolled with a given combination of rolls. To produce various sizes of billets on this type of mill would necessitate numerous roll changes, which are costly.

Figures 22—19 and 22—20 show the layout for a three-high billet mill and the rolls used in the mill. It can be seen that alternate passes are used in the top and bottom rolls while every pass is used in the middle roll. On this mill, four rolls comprise a set, consisting of a top, bottom, and two identical middle rolls although only three rolls are used at one time. When the middle roll becomes worn to the extent that it must be replaced, the mill is changed; that is, the rolls are removed from the housing and the worn top roll is placed in the bottom position, the fourth roll or second middle is placed in the middle position and the worn bottom roll is placed in the top position. This presents a whole series of new passes and permits the same tonnage to be produced with the set of four rolls that otherwise would require two sets of three, or six rolls. Since the piece is rolled in one direction between the bottom and middle rolls and in the opposite direction between the middle and top rolls, the use of lifting or tilting tables is necessary to transfer the piece between the bottom and top pass lines. The table on the side of the mill from which the bloom enters (the side nearer the blooming mill) is called the front table, while that on the opposite side of the stand is called the rear or back table. Manipulators must be used in conjunction with these tables to turn the piece between passes and move it into line with the next pass. Both tables on a three-high mill are raised and lowered as a unit. The lift type table is more common and will be described along with only one of the many possible arrangements of manipulators.

Figure 22—21 shows diagrammatically a three-high mill lift table in raised, intermediate and lowered position. The front table contains twelve cast-steel rollers, each of which has five collars for turning the billets. These collars create four grooves extending from end

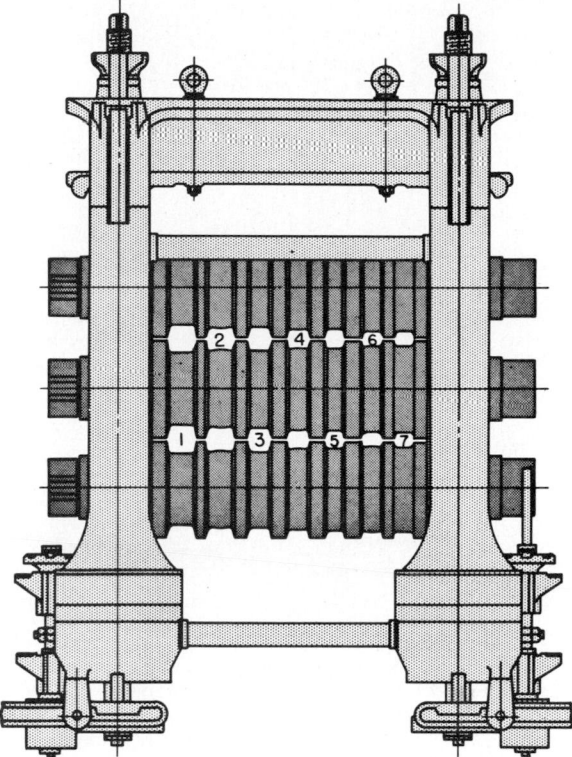

FIG. 22—20. The rolls (mounted in the housings) of a three-high billet mill. Numerals in the pass openings indicate the sequence of passes used in rolling (see also Figure 22—22).

to end of the table. The rollers are driven by an electric motor. There are side guards on the edges of the table and at the front end are side guards for putting the bloom into the proper pass. The front table is equipped with a stationary manipulator for advancing the billets from pass to pass which consists of fingers bolted to a pedestal on the foundation of the mill. These fingers are flat, cast-steel plates mounted vertically and with their tops shaped at an angle giving a 45-degree slope toward the outside of the mill. The fingers do not reach above the level of the roll passes when the table is elevated and the billets run out on the collars of the rolls. When the table is dropped, the billets encounter the stationary fingers and slide down into the grooves in position for the next pass. The rear table is operated through the same shaft as the front table but owing to the fact that it not only must raise the billets from the bottom pass line to the top pass line, but also must advance them one pass toward the outside, it has to travel through an arc in rising to bring the billet in line with the next pass. This is done by causing the table to slide toward the next pass as it is raised, by the use of pull-over rods attached to pedestals on the proper side of the scale pit. When lowered, the table slides back into place again. This table consists of twelve cast-steel rollers driven by a motor similar to the one used on the front table. Three heavy cast-steel side guards between the four passes that are used on the bottom roll divide the table into

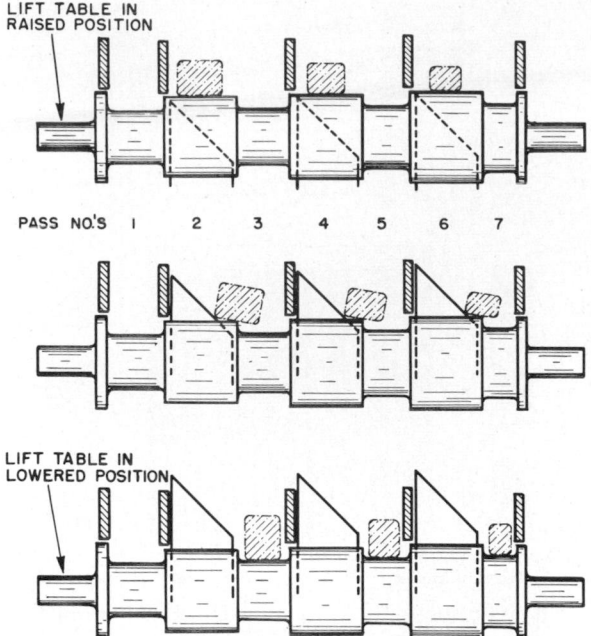

LIFT TABLE IN
RAISED POSITION

PASS NO.'S   1   2   3   4   5   6   7

LIFT TABLE IN
LOWERED POSITION

FIG. 22—21. Diagram showing the action of the fingers of a stationary-type manipulator for advancing the piece from pass to pass, while simultaneously turning it 90 degrees. The fingers remain stationary, and their action is performed by the motion imparted to the piece as the table is lowered from the raised position. The middle diagram represents the lift table in intermediate position.

four grooves. There is a manipulator in the first groove that consists of five forged-steel fingers. The upward motion of the table draws the fingers with it and causes them to turn the piece and, as stated before, the sideward motion of the table advances the billet to the next pass. This manipulator lies below the table when the billet is delivered from the bottom roll and acts only to turn the billets 90 degrees from the first to the second pass.

The mechanical operation of these tables leads to high maintenance for, when the piece drops into a groove, it causes severe shock to the bearings and other parts of the equipment, and when the tables are

lowered, they may strike the stops with rather high speed. These severe service conditions make necessary considerable maintenance and repair work to maintain the tables in good operating condition.

Since the piece being rolled must be entirely out of the rolls for the lift table to transfer it between the top and bottom passes, its length must be limited to that which the tables will accommodate. This requires cutting the blooms from the blooming mill into the correct lengths so that when they are elongated, due to draft in the three-high mill, they can be handled properly on the tables. Cutting the blooms into pieces reduces the yield considerably as the ends of each piece usually are cropped after rolling.

The roll housings generally are cast steel, although some mills use cast-iron housings. The middle roll is not adjusted, but the top and bottom rolls are adjusted toward the middle. Cast-steel guides and side guards are held in guide cages or on rest bars which are bolted to the receiving and delivery sides of the housings. The pinions preferably are made with double helical or herringbone teeth. The three-high mill ordinarily is driven at a constant speed by a steam engine or electric motor. Methods of calculating power requirements for mills were discussed in Chapter 20.

The three-high billet mill shown in Figures 22—19 and 22—20 rolls four sizes of billets, which are reduced further in size on a smaller billet mill. As noted previously, the blooms are turned only once on the rear table and from one to three times on the front table, depending on the number of passes taken in the mill.

Figure 22—22 shows the shape of the piece out of each of these roll passes. The rolls used are cast alloy steel, 30⅜ inches in diameter with a 76½-inch roll body. Box passes, as shown in Figure 22—20, are used generally on three-high mills for rolling billets. Slightly greater reduction can be taken using a diamond and square series but, since in passes of this shape the piece is rolled on the diagonal, the overall height of the piece is greater, requiring a deeper groove in the roll than for box passes. Such deeper grooves weaken the roll and increase the rolling or contact angle. Generally speaking, billets produced in box passes do not have as uniform diagonals as those

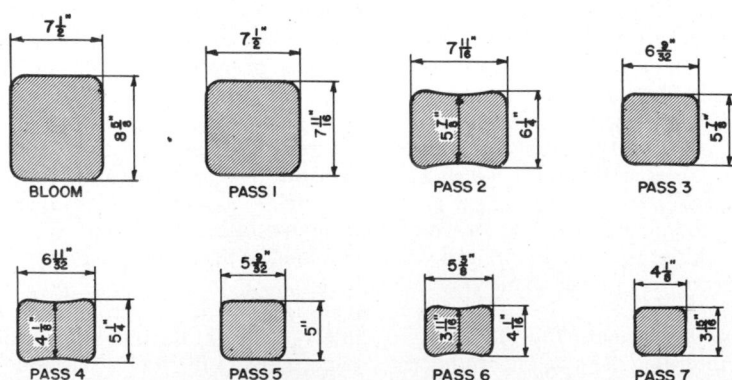

FIG. 22—22. Cross-sections of the pieces out of each pass when billets are rolled on the mill shown diagrammatically in Figures 22—19 and 22—20.

rolled in diamond passes. If the box pass is narrow enough to restrict spreading, the action of the steel attempting to spread wears the sides of the pass and it rapidly becomes too wide. When the pass wears wide, the stock entering the pass will "float" to opposite sides in the top and bottom of the pass and, hence, produce a **diamond** billet. The stock cannot be adjusted very easily to control this condition since the three-high mill is a fixed-draft mill, and any adjustment for one pass affects all passes. Another reason for not using too heavy reductions on the three-high billet mill is that the rolling or contact angle must be small enough to assure the entry of the piece in the roll pass. When several pieces are rolled at once, the failure of one to enter the pass causes the others to be held up until it enters. This delay results in loss of temperature by the steel, with its resultant harmful effects; it also reduces output, since it can affect the production of the blooming mill as well as any mills following the three-high mill.

Billets from a three-high mill usually are cut by stationary shears or, in the larger sizes and for special purposes, by hot saws. This type of mill usually is used where only a few sizes of billets are produced, or in conjunction with smaller billet mills that further reduce the billets from the three-high mill.

Cross-Country Billet Mills—Another design of mill is the cross-country mill. This type of mill is composed of several stands of rolls, so arranged that the piece to be rolled is never in more than one stand at the same time. The roll stands may be placed side by side and the piece transferred to the various roll tables, the direction of rolling being reversed in each stand; they may be arranged with two or more stands rolling in one direction, with the piece transferred to roll tables and then rolled through several other stands in the opposite direction, and so on. This type of mill is faster than the three-high, but as in the three-high, the piece from the blooming mill must be cut into several lengths before entering the mill. The cross-country mill is much more flexible than the three-high billet mill in that, in order to roll a complete range of billet sizes, it not only can take the product of the blooming mill during a greater percentage of the operating time, but also can roll various sizes of billets with only one complement of rolls throughout the mill, with only a few minutes delay necessitated by changing guides for the various passes. Quite frequently, production on the blooming mill is not affected by roll changes on the cross-country mill, except when they occur in the first two stands. Some cross-country mills are so arranged that a single pass is taken in each stand while others are composed of a combination of single-pass and multiple-pass stands.

In contrast to the three-high mill, the finishing pass in the cross-country mill can be faster than the first passes, provided separate drives or gear ratios are used. Since the piece being rolled is only in one stand of rolls at a time on a cross-country mill, tables must be provided to carry the piece from stand to stand. Some mills are provided with diagonal tables to direct the piece from one train to another, while other mills provide transfers at the end of each line of stands for moving the piece over to the next train line. The roll passes of a cross-country mill can be any shape required for good rolling practice and quality of product. The piece can be turned as desired between stands by manipulators, guides, transfers, turn-up rolls, and other devices.

Advantages of Cross-Country Mills—The production of any mill is governed by the speed of the finishing pass and the percentage of the operating time during which it can be kept full. In the cross-country mill, the speed of the finishing pass can be greater than in the three-high mill, but pieces have to be spaced far enough apart in going through the mill so that each table is clear of one piece before receiving the following one. It should be possible to keep the finishing pass of this type of mill full for more than half the time (as opposed to the three-high mill) and this, together with the higher speed possible, enables such a mill to reach higher production rates than the three-high mill.

Cross-country mills, where the piece can be turned at will after every pass, and particularly those mills where the direction of rolling is reversed after every pass, are admirably suited for the rolling of quality steels.

Figure **22—23** shows the layout of the cross-country billet mill at Republic Steel Corporation's plant at South Chicago, which is part of an integrated installation designed for the production of electric-furnace alloy steels. A 44-inch blooming mill supplies blooms to a 36-inch two-high reversing roughing mill, which in turn feeds three 32-inch two-high stands. The major part of production when this chapter was written was being rolled from hot-topped ingots, 25 inches square, weighing 12,000 pounds, and open-type steels from 23-inch by 25-inch ingots weighing 11,500 pounds. The 44-inch reversing mill produces blooms, for subsequent rolling into billets, bars, etc., in the following sizes: 7 by 7-inch, 8 by 8-inch, 9 by 9-inch, 10½ by 10½-inch, 12 by 12-inch, and 13 by 15-inch, depending on the finished size of the re-rolled product. It is driven by a 7000-horsepower motor at 40 to 100 r.p.m.

Delivery tables, transfers and reheating furnaces of the 44-inch blooming mill are so arranged that the blooms may be disposed of in any one of three ways. They may be sent without reheating directly to the 36-inch roughing mill and then on to the 32-inch and 21-inch mills; they may be kicked off on a transfer and then directed through one of two continuous reheating furnaces from which they are discharged onto the same table that leads directly from the 44-inch mill to the 36-inch mill, or they may be removed from the transfer table and placed in slow-cooling pits after which they are conditioned and shipped or are charged cold into the reheating furnaces and re-rolled on the billet mills.

The 36-inch two-high reversing mill is driven by a 50 to 120 r.p.m., 5000-horsepower motor. It is equipped with 36-inch by 82-inch rolls, laid out to use either 5 or 7 passes in roughing blooms down in preparation for rolling in the 32-inch mill. It is possible, however, to vary this practice by coordinating the work of this mill with that of the 44-inch mill, which

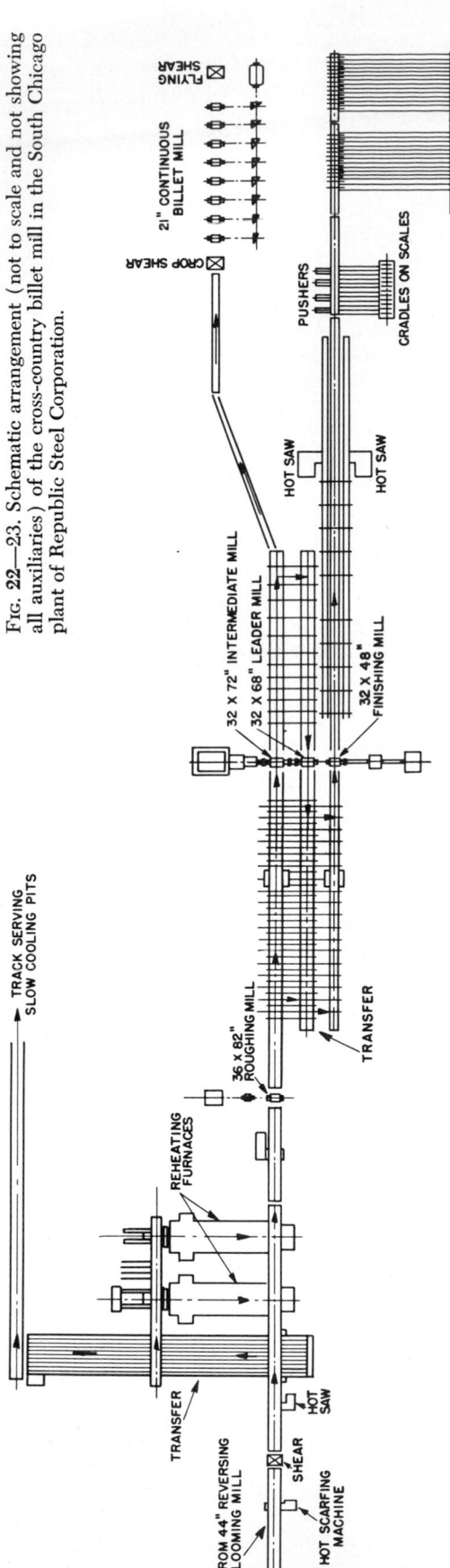

FIG. 22—23. Schematic arrangement (not to scale and not showing all auxiliaries) of the cross-country billet mill in the South Chicago plant of Republic Steel Corporation.

is the practice usually followed. Manipulators and side guards on both sides of the 36-inch mill permit turning the blooms after each pass. Delivery tables and transfers are arranged so that, by reversing the 32-inch finishing stand (see Figure 22—23), squares from 5 to 9 inches and some narrow slabs may be finished on the 36-inch mill and sent to the saws, while the 32-inch mill is undergoing a complete roll change, thereby permitting uninterrupted production. The three 32-inch two-high stands are located 225 feet beyond the 36-inch two-high reversing roughing mill. The three stands are placed side by side. The first, or so-called intermediate stand, contains 32-inch by 72-inch rolls; the second, or leader, stand, has 32-inch by 68-inch rolls; and the third, or finishing, stand has 32-inch by 48-inch rolls. The three stands are spaced 14 feet, 6 inches, and 21 feet, 3 inches apart, respectively. All stands are electrically driven, are provided with electric screw-downs, and the roll necks rotate in composition bearings. The first two stands are driven by a single 5000-horsepower reversing motor, while the third stand is driven by a 2500-horsepower motor. The intermediate stand is equipped on either side with an electrically operated manipulator to carrying tilting fingers. The leader and finishing stands each have one manipulator on the entry side, incorporating a manually operated turning device. Blooms from the 36-inch mill are given one or three passes in the first or inter-

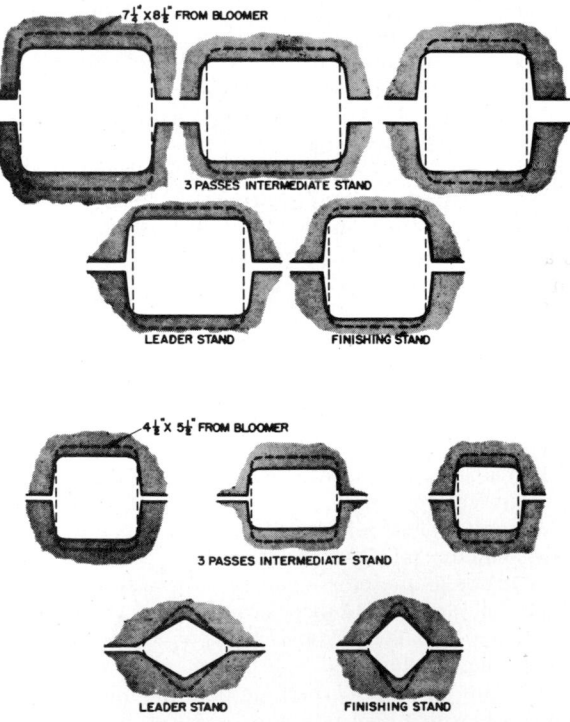

FIG. 22—24. Two typical sets of passes used in the mill shown diagrammatically in Figure 22—23. The five passes shown in the top set produce 5½-inch square billets. The lower set of five passes produce 3-inch square billets. In each pass, the dotted line shows the rolled shape which is received from the preceding pass. The solid line shows the new shape produced, which consequently appears dotted in the next pass.

mediate stand of the 32-inch mill, and one each in the leader and finishing stands, depending upon the finished size of the billet (Figure 22—24). The intermediate and leader stands, being coupled together with a common drive, are reversed together from pass to pass. The finishing stand, being separately driven, operates in only one direction. This mill rolls billets 3 inches to 7 inches square, and rounds 3 inches to 9½ inches in diameter, from blooms and billets varying in size from 4½ inches by 5½ inches to 10¼ by 11½ inches. Two tables, each containing a 60-inch hot saw with a 5-foot, 6-inch stroke, parallel the run-out table from the finishing stand of the 32-inch mill. The double saw arrangement enables cutting the billets to standard mill lengths without slowing up the mill.

It will be noted that a 21-inch continuous mill composed of eight horizontal stands is located beyond the first stand of the 32-inch cross-country mill. A 6⅛-inch bloom from the first stand of the 32-inch mill can be rolled into square billets ranging in size from 4 by 4 inches to 2 by 2 inches on the 21-inch mill. The bloom is cropped before entering this latter mill, and the finished billets are cut to length by a steam-operated flying shear. The eight stands of the 21-inch mill are driven by a single electric motor through bevel gears from a main drive shaft, and all roll necks rotate in composition bearings. The billets are twisted between stands by twist guides and twist rolls. These devices are discussed in the ensuing section dealing with continuous billet mills.

It has been mentioned previously that some plants are equipped to reheat blooms between the blooming and billet mills. The above-described mill is so arranged, as shown in Figure 22—23.

Continuous Billet Mill—The continuous mill consists of a series of roll stands, arranged one after the other so that the piece to be rolled enters the first stand and travels through the mill, taking but one pass in each stand of rolls and emerging from the last set as a finished product. These stands may be all horizontal, and may include one or more vertical edgers, or the stands may be alternately horizontal and vertical. In the continuous mill, where the piece is being rolled in several different stands simultaneously, the peripheral roll speeds must be such that the elongation which occurs as a result of reduction in cross-sectional areas of the piece is taken care of by increasing the speed of each successive roll pass. On mills where all of the various stands are driven through gears by one motor or engine, the elongation is compensated for in the original design of the mill by choosing gear ratios that drive each set of rolls at a higher speed than the preceding set. The diagram of such a mill appears as part of Figure 22—23, where it is designated a 21-inch continuous billet mill. Any deviation from the originally designed elongation must be compensated for by varying roll diameters and thus changing peripheral speed. The rolls usually are installed in sets and are all dressed together. However, excessive wear on one set of rolls requires excessive dressing on the remaining rolls in the train. Various means have been adopted to gain longer roll life. Some plants will carry

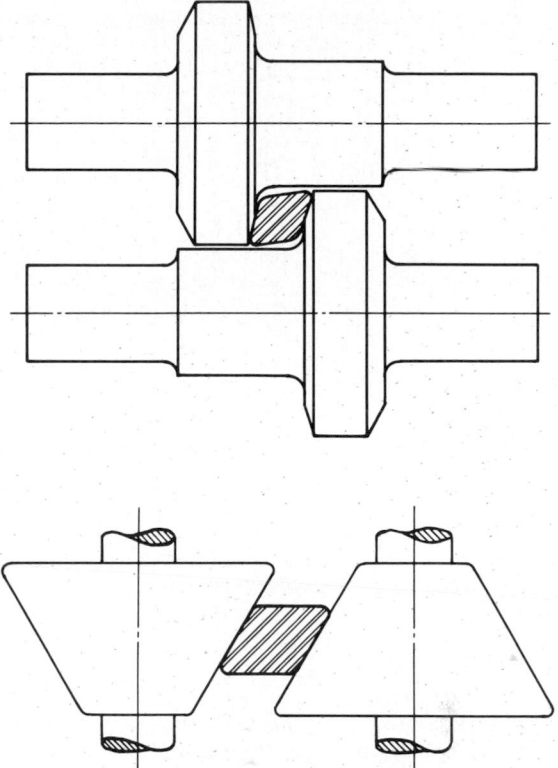

FIG. 22—25. Sketches illustrating two types of friction driven twist rolls, as used on a continuous billet mill to turn pieces 90 degrees between passes. Twist rolls such as those shown in the bottom diagram are called "cone-type" twist rolls.

extra rolls for those stands that receive the most wear, and thus save excessive dressing on the remainder of the train, while others change the rolls around from stand to stand. As an example of the latter methods, a 2½-inch square in No. 4 stand can be changed to a 3-inch square without reducing roll diameter, and used on No. 2 stand.

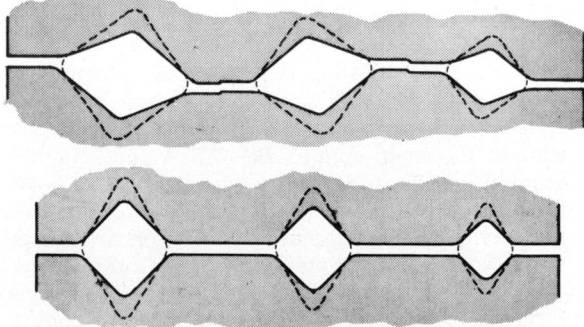

FIG. 22—26. Diagram of oblique roll passes designed to provide a twisting action on billets between stands when being rolled on a continuous mill. In each pass, the dotted line shows the rolled shape which is received from the preceding pass. The solid line shows the new shape produced, which consequently appears dotted in the next pass.

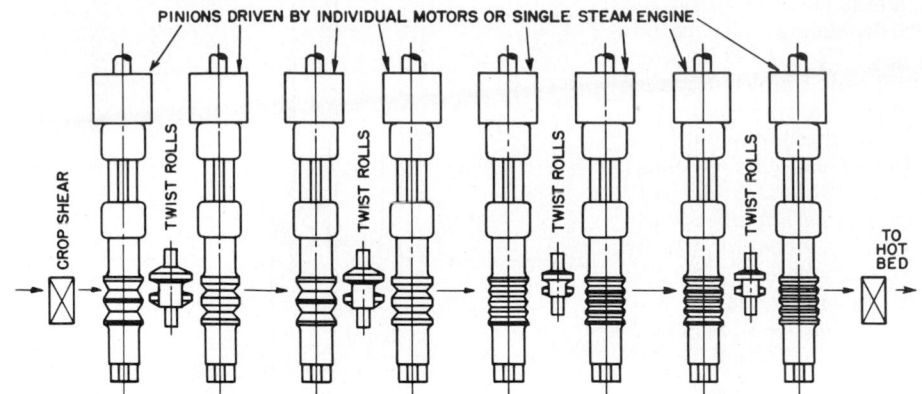

Fig. 22—27. Schematic arrangement of the roll stands and twist rolls for an eight-stand continuous billet mill.

The use of individual drives for each stand in a continuous mill is a great improvement over the single-drive type. With this drive, roll diameters need not be matched and the speeds of the individual motors can be regulated to give the correct peripheral speed for each set of rolls. The speed ratio on continuous mills must be maintained closely to prevent the piece from pushing or pulling between stands.

Since the piece being rolled in a continuous mill is in several stands simultaneously, the piece cannot be turned between passes in successive horizontal stands but, rather, it must be twisted. (The necessity for twisting, however, is eliminated in mills composed of alternate horizontal and vertical stands.) Various methods have been devised for obtaining this twist, one of which incorporates the use of twist delivery guides. These guides are iron or steel castings, and are designed so that the piece is twisted gradually by the action of the guide which is contacted by two surfaces of the piece being rolled; the other surfaces have clearance in the guide. The twist in the guide is designed so that the piece being rolled is rotated to the correct degree for entry into the succeeding roll pass.

Another method uses friction-driven twist rolls, mounted in housings, between the various stands of work rolls. Some plants use twist delivery guides that are designed with a slight over-twist, to start the twisting action, in conjunction with twist rolls. The twist rolls relieve the twisting slightly, thus reducing the pressure on the twist guide and minimizing guide scratches on the product. Two different types of twist rolls are shown in Figure 22—25. A third method accomplishes the twist as shown in Figure 22—26. With this latter method, the passes are cut in rolls obliquely, and the difference in diameters in the pass causes the twisting action. This method, however, requires the use of twist guides to insure the proper twist, since temperatures and the chemical compositions of steels being rolled are not always constant and can cause a variation in the degree of twist. This method of twisting causes excessive roll-pass wear.

High output is one of the chief advantages of the continuous mill. Scrap losses are low, due to the fact that blooms of any length can be rolled, making it unnecessary to cut the bloom after it leaves the blooming mill, except to discard pipe or any other flaws that might be present. Flying shears are placed after the finishing stand on a continuous billet mill, and are synchronized with the speed of the stand on which the billet is finished.

It should be stated, however, that sometimes breaks occur in the steel due to the twisting of the billet, and that when the billet is deflected from one pass line to another, it is more subject to scratching by the guides. These defects increase the amount of conditioning required by the steel. The continuous mill composed of alternate horizontal and vertical stands, which eliminate twisting and arranged so that it is never necessary to deflect the bar from one pass to another, produces a product with much better surface quality.

Figure 22—27 shows a schematic diagram for a continuous billet mill; Figure 22—28, the passes used on a 14-inch mill for rolling two different sizes of billets.

Six-Stand Continuous Mill at Lorain Works—This embodies many features uncommon to billet mills. Its relationship to the other facilities of the mill of which it is a part is shown diagrammatically in Figure 22—29.

Designed to produce a wide variety of semi-finished products from 9-inch by 8-inch blooms, the mill is equipped to roll 4-inch square billets, 5⅝-inch by 4-inch, 7-inch by 4-inch, 8-inch by 4-inch, and 9-inch by 4-inch skelp slabs, 4¾-inch and 5½-inch tube rounds, on the same roll and guide set-up, with the ability to alternate quickly on any of the above sizes by push-button-operated controls. Additional skelp slabs up to 12 inches wide also may be rolled on the same set-up from 12-inch or 14-inch slabs received from either the 46-inch or 38-inch mills.

The mill consists of three vertical roll stands numbered Nos. 1, 3 and 5, and three horizontal roll stands numbered Nos. 2, 4 and 6, set in tandem on 10-foot centers (Figure 22—30). Each stand is powered individually by a 1750-horsepower, direct-current motor (300 to 600 r.p.m.), making a total of 10,500 horsepower for the six stands combined. Suitable gear reduction sets provide for a finishing speed of 346 to 692 feet per minute at No. 6 stand. All vertical mills are of sufficiently rugged construction to enable drafting equal to the horizontal stands. The main ver-

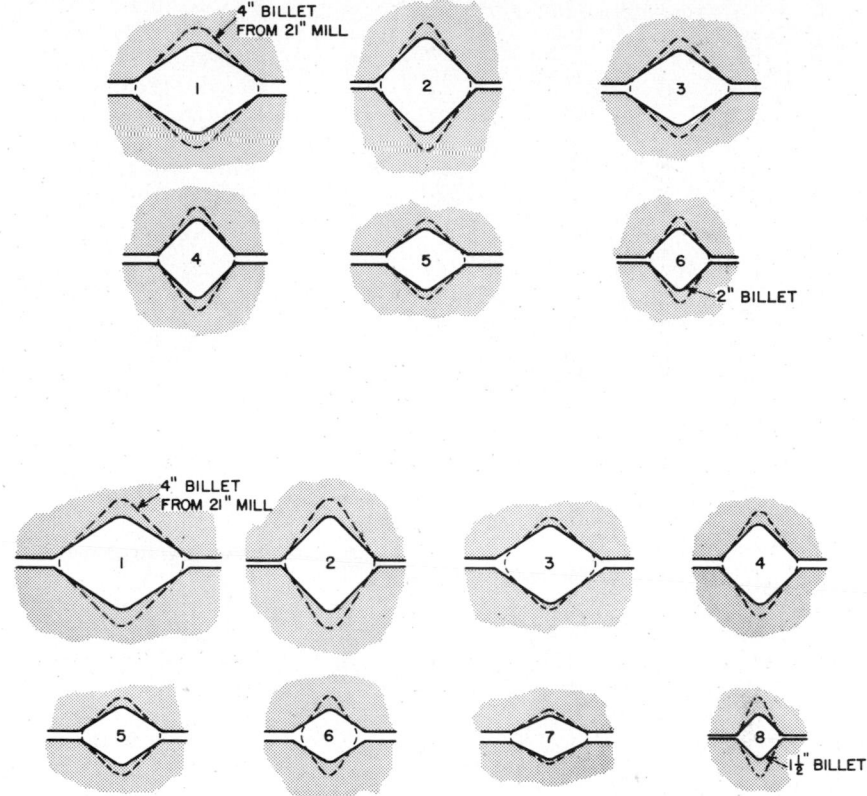

Fig. 22—28. (Above) Six successive roll passes employed in the production of 2-inch square billets from 4-inch square starting material on a 14-inch billet mill. (Below) Method of rolling 1½-inch square billets on the same mill, using the same starting material, in eight passes. In each numbered pass, the dotted line shows the rolled shape which is received from the preceding pass. The solid line shows the new shape produced, which consequently appears dotted in the next numbered pass.

tical housing containing two 30-inch by 48-inch rolls is a self-contained, integral unit and resembles a horizontal stand laid over on its side. A fixed outer roll held securely by hydraulic pressure against the housing seat, and a movable inner roll hydraulically balanced against motor-driven screws, plus anti-friction roll-neck bearings and thrust units, comprise the roll-adjusting mechanism. Screw speed is 6 inches per minute, and screw travel is sufficient to permit operating the rolls with the distance between their centers set at any point between 35¾ and 27¼ inches.

Power for the vertical mill rolls is transmitted from the main gear drive (Figure 22—31) through a horizontal shaft to an intermediate bevel-gear drive, through a shaft inclined at 40 degrees to a combination bevel-gear drive and fully-enclosed 30-inch pinion stand. Universal couplings and spindles equipped with anti-friction thrust bearings, suspended and attached beneath the main mill housing, complete the drive. The main housing is enclosed within a secondary housing supported on the shoe plates. The secondary housing carries the screw-up mechanism and guiding slides for controlling the vertical movement of the main housing with respect to the horizontal-mill pass line. The motor-driven screw-up mechanism operates by push-button control at 10½ inches per minute, and provides for a maximum vertical movement of the main housing of 36 inches. Thus, a set of vertical rolls may contain several passes within this range, each of which may be aligned properly with the horizontal mills. The male coupling end, transmitting motive power from 30-inch pinions through universal

couplings to the rolls, is forged in one piece with the spline shaft that telescopes with the pinions. This arrangement permits maintaining the drive connection during upward movement of the rolls. The three vertical mills are of similar design, having all parts interchangeable, including intermediate bevel-gear drive. Rolls with complete bearings are changed in pairs, using double roll-changing hooks.

Vertical-mill roll and guide equipment is of such design that changes are unnecessary when rolling any of the previously mentioned sizes. The useful proportion of rolling time on the mill is thus increased, since it is necessary to change rolls only when worn or in the event of possible breakage. The entry guide unit is attached to the secondary housing in a fixed, pre-leveled position, to accommodate the upper pass in the rolls. The remaining passes may be utilized by adjusting the screw-up mechanism upwards, thus positioning the desired pass in front of the guide.

Delivery guides are set up within a swinging integral unit, including guides for all passes in the vertical-roll set. Once set in position, they seldom need adjustment, fixed-roll guides remaining stationary while the movable-roll guides are carried along with the roll during adjustment. Upon changing rolls, the entry guide retracts clear of the rolls by a hydraulically operated mechanism. Delivery guides are manually swung clear of the rolls. The rolling operations of the three vertical mills in conjunction with the three horizontal stands will be described subsequently.

The three two-high horizontal roll stands (Nos. 2, 4 and 6) resemble strip-mill stands in their construc-

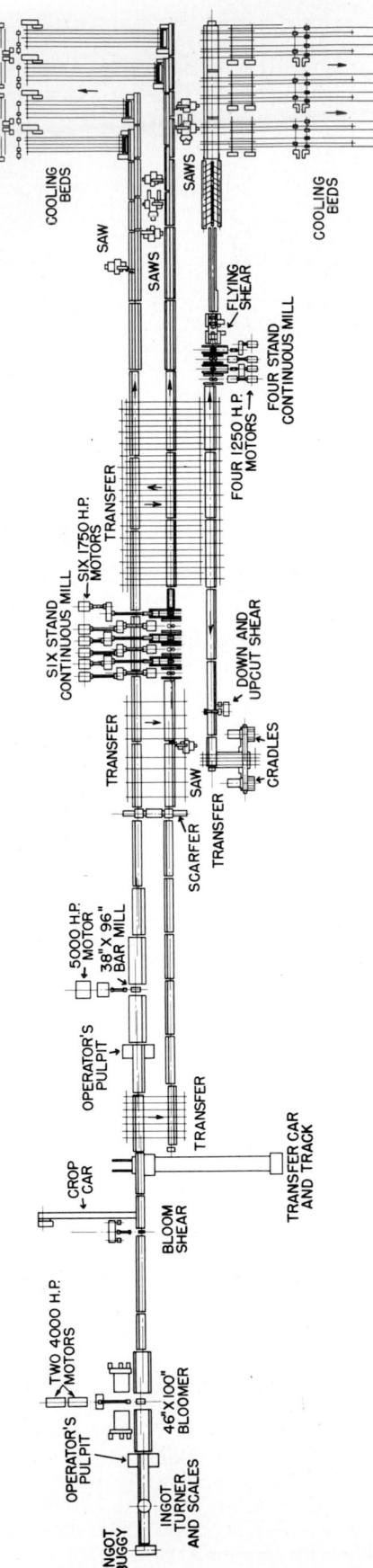

FIG. 22—29. Diagrammatic layout (not to scale) of the No. 4 Blooming, Bar and Billet Mill in the Lorain Works. Flow of material through this mill is illustrated schematically in Figure 22—33, which also indicates typical sizes produced.

tion features, having been designed for stability, smoothness of operation, accurate roll settings, and ease in roll changing. Housings are of cast-steel, closed-top construction. The top roll is hydraulically counter balanced against motor-driven screws. The screw-down permits the screws to function independently or in unison. The bottom roll is fixed, with provision on the outward chuck for endwise adjustment. The top-roll outward chuck is fixed, while both drive-side chucks are free to "float" in the housing. The 28-inch diameter by 48-inch body length rolls are mounted on anti-friction bearings of the radial thrust type, all preassembled with fully-enclosed chucks. Rolls thus can be quickly changed by use of a "C" hook similar to those used in changing strip-mill rolls. Horizontal roll stands Nos. 2 and 4 each are driven independently through a double reduction-gear drive and a 27-inch pinion stand. No. 6 horizontal roll stand is driven through a single reduction-gear and 27-inch pinion stand. Universal couplings and spindles mounted on carriers connect the pinion stands with the rolls.

A feature essential to the flexibility of operation of this mill is the endwise movement provided for the horizontal roll and pinion stands. To utilize all the grooves provided in the horizontal rolls for various product sizes, provision was made for rapid alignment of horizontal-roll grooves with respect to vertical-roll grooves to maintain a straight line of product travel throughout the desired grooves of all six stands. This was accomplished by mounting the roll stand, spindle-carrier base, and pinion stand as a unit on the bed plate. By using the bed as sliding ways, the entire unit can be moved endwise horizontally 42 inches through power supplied by a 14-inch diameter hydraulic cylinder operating at 1250 pounds per square inch. To maintain the drive connection during such movement, the main drive shaft telescopes a spline-type flexible coupling at the pinion stand. Hydraulically operated quick-release clamps anchor the assembly to the bed plate, obviating the use of foot bolts.

As in the case of the vertical mills, the roll and guide equipment of the horizontal stands was designed to roll all of the previously mentioned sizes without roll or guide changes. Entry and delivery guides are mounted as integral units on sliding rest bars which, in turn, are supported by the main rest bar attached securely to the roll housings. All main rest bars are adjustable vertically by jack screws mounted on the housings. Rolls must be changed after excessive wear occurs. To minimize roll-changing time and increase efficiency, all guide equipment is mounted on a retractable mechanism operated hydraulically, which makes it possible to move the guides clear of the housing window to permit rapid and simple removal or insertion of the roll-and-chuck assembly.

To thoroughly understand the functions of all the foregoing features on the six-stand mill, a discussion of a typical roll-pass arrangement and the sequence of operations is advisable. These are as follows:

Vertical roll set V-1 (Stand No. 1) consists of rolls 30 inches in diameter with a 48-inch body. It is pro-

FIG. 22—30. General view of the six-stand continuous billet mill in the Lorain Works of United States Steel.

vided with three duplicate 8⅜ by 7-inch box passes, all of which are set up complete with the necessary guides. Either pass may be used at any time, the 7-inch dimension varying with finished bar size and adjusted by mechanical screws on the movable roll. In the event of a worn-out pass, the roller may, by push-button control, quickly raise or lower the entire main housing unit to the desired position so that an unworn pass can be utilized. A gage attached to the secondary housing post, and a pointer on the movable housing, indicate within easy view of the operator the proper level of the pass.

Horizontal roll set H-2 (Stand No. 2) has rolls 28 inches in diameter and 48 inches in body length. It has two duplicate passes, 7¼ by 6¼ inches, plus a 13-inch wide bullhead pass used when rolling skelp slabs. The normal setting as used for 4-inch by 4-inch, as well as 4¾-inch and 5½-inch rounds, is 6¼ inches and is also subject to variation by use of the top roll mechanical screw-down. All three grooves are completely equipped with the necessary guides. The roller also may select any groove rapidly by operating the hydraulic valve controlling the mechanism which moves the entire roll-housing unit endwise. A gage on the housing shoes indicates the proper position for the horizontal groove with respect to the vertical to assure straight line travel of the piece being rolled through the mill.

Vertical set V-3 (Stand No. 3), with rolls 30 inches in diameter and 48 inches in body length, also has three 6⅝ by 5-inch duplicate grooves, and functions in a manner similar to the V-1 set. The 5-inch setting is variable for finished product size.

Horizontal sets H-4 and H-6 have rolls 28 inches in diameter with 48-inch bodies. Each has its designated passes for 4-inch by 4-inch squares, and 4¾-inch and 5½-inch rounds, plus a skelp-slab pass, and have operating controls similar to H-2. Vertical set V-5, with rolls 30 inches in diameter and 48-inch body length, which is the leader pass, also has its designated passes. Two leader passes for the 4-inch by 4-inch square, and one each for the two sizes of rounds, have been provided in sets V-5 and H-6. Vertical set V-5 utilizes the 4-inch by 4-inch passes for edging skelp slabs, with operating controls similar to V-1 and V-3.

The run-out table from the six-stand mill delivers all product to transfer equipment designed to handle bar lengths up to 160 feet. Rounds may be delivered direct to either one of two saw lines, each equipped with stationary and movable saws for cropping and cutting to required lengths. Each of the saw lines converges to its own independent chain-conveyor cooling bed. Or, product may be transferred to the double saw line which normally handles product (rounds) from the 38-inch mill, each line having a single saw with individual cooling bed. Thus, the finishing equipment for tube-round product from the 38-inch mill and the six-stand mill comprises altogether six saws, four saw lines, and four cooling beds. All products 4 inches by 4 inches to 12 by 4 inches delivered from the six-stand mill for skelp conversion are transferred to a roller line that carries them to shearing facilities and inspection and storage. For further reduction to smaller billets and tube rounds, 4-inch by 4-inch or 4½ by 4½-inch billets are delivered from the six-stand mill and transferred to a roller line directly preceding the four-stand continuous mill.

The Four-Stand Continuous Mill at Lorain—This mill (Figures 22—29 and 22—32) is similar in design and employs all the advanced features of the six-stand

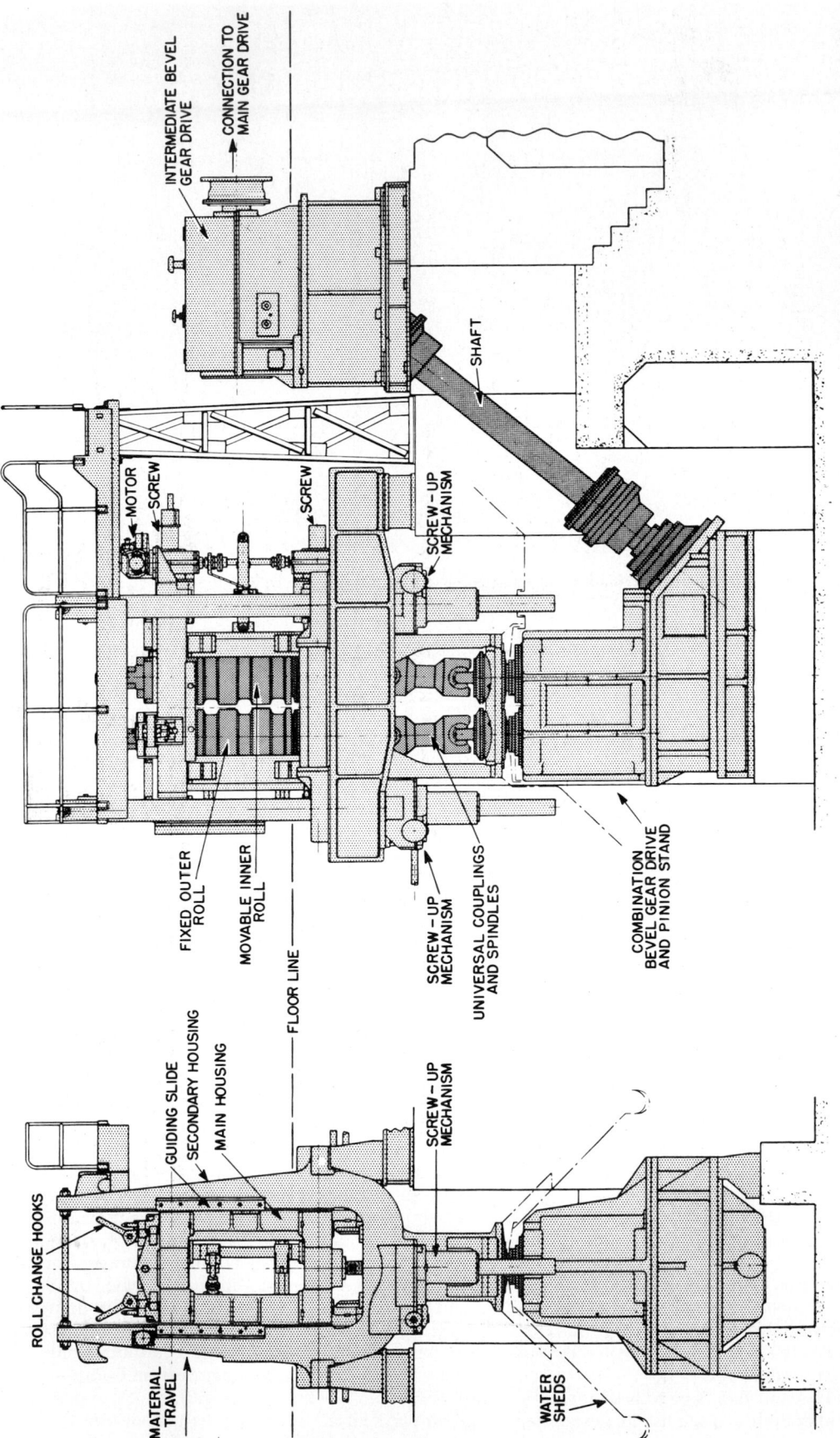

Fig. 22—31. Schematic arrangement of the principal parts of one of the vertical stands of the six-stand continuous billet mill in the Lorain Works of United States Steel Corporation.

FIG. 22—32. General view of the four-stand continuous billet mill in the Lorain Works of United States Steel.

mill. It comprises four sets in tandem; V-1 vertical, H-2 horizontal, V-3 vertical, and H-4 horizontal. Each set is powered individually by 1250-horsepower, 400 to 800 r.p.m., direct-current motors, with reduction gear drives designed for a finishing speed of 430 to 860 feet per minute. All mill rolls are 20 inches in diameter, with body length of 36 inches, and to meet original requirements, were set up to produce 3¼ to 3¾-inch rounds and 2½-inch square billets, with sufficient space available for rolling other sizes. Billets delivered from the six-stand mill lie flat on the roller feed table and, prior to entering the No. 1 vertical (V-1) pass of the four-stand mill, are turned 45 degrees on the fly, by an air-operated turning device, to permit finishing the 2½-inch square billets in diamond passes on their diagonals.

Billets of 4½-inch square size enter the V-1 pass on the flat for alternate flat and edge reduction to lead-oval and finished rounds. No. 4 horizontal set delivers billets to the flying shear for cropping and cutting to length. A specially designed double skew table with disappearing stops receives the product from the flying shear. Here the product is gaged, then conveyed in groups to the roller line opposite the cooling beds. The roller line has disappearing stops that position

these groups opposite either one of the three adjacent cooling beds, over which the product travels to the cradles and storage bays. This completes the cycle of operations beginning with the 32½-inch ingot on the 46-inch blooming mill, as described in Section 1 of this chapter. Figure 22—33 is a flow chart summarizing a typical series of operations possible with this modern mill.

Hot-Scarfing Machines—The increased demand for conditioning of semi-finished products (see Section 5 of this chapter) has led to the installation of hot-scarfing machines in many primary mills. Such machines may be placed immediately after the bloom shears or, when multiple units are fed from the same blooming mill, they can be installed after the roughing or the first billet mill.

The scarfing head of the machine contains oxy-acetylene burner nozzles and is designed to be adjusted rapidly to accommodate several different sizes of billets. The head also can be moved laterally to permit the scarfing of blooms or billets from different passes in a set of rolls, or to remove it entirely from the line to permit the passage of steels not to be scarfed. The machine desurfacing process can remove defects within ⅛ inch of the surface, which is usually sufficient

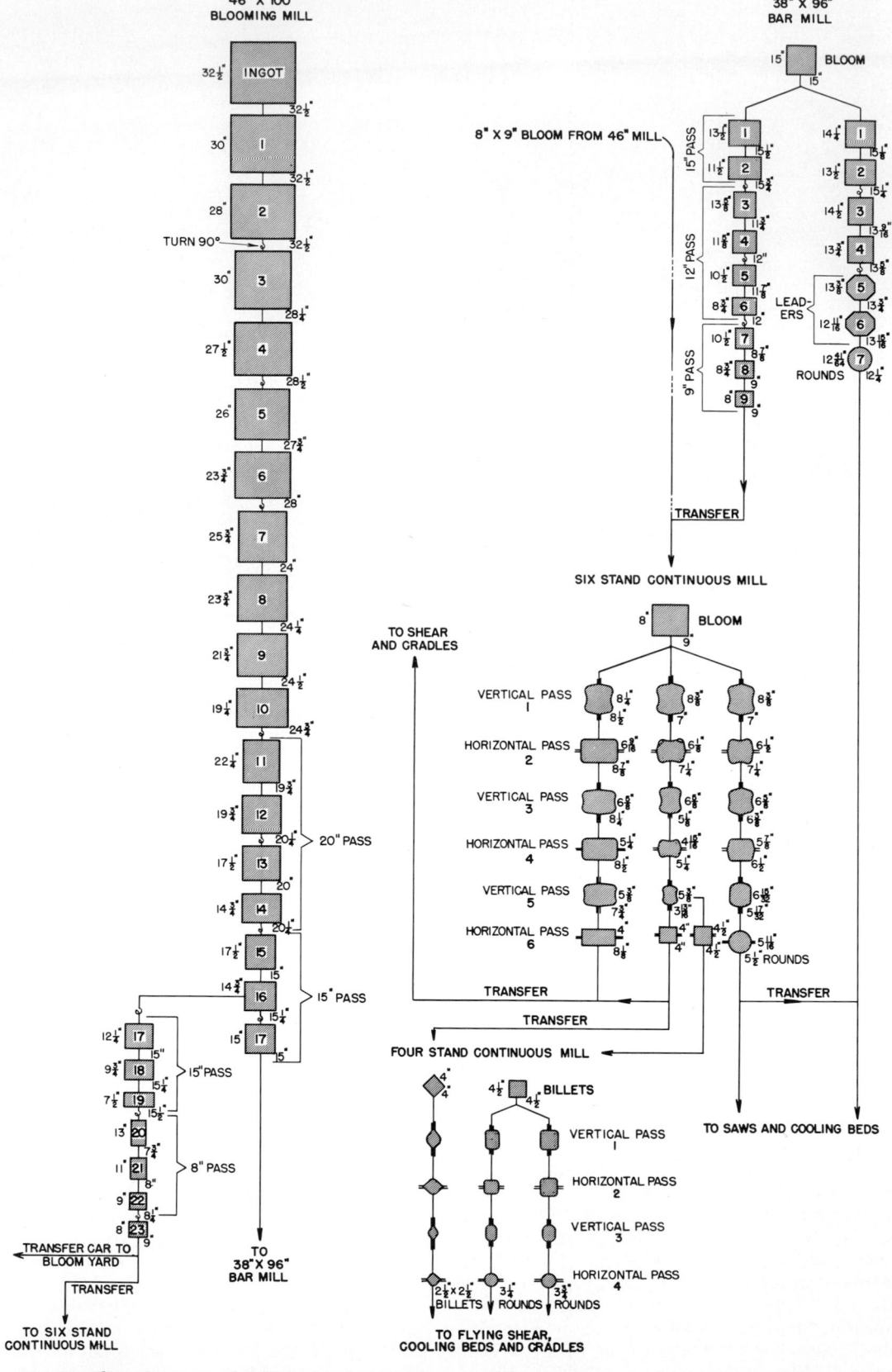

Fig. 22—33. Flow chart summarizing typical series of operations possible due to the extremely flexible arrangement of the modern No. 4 Blooming, Bar and Billet Mill in the Lorain Works.

to remove such defects as rolled seams, light scabs, checks, etc. It is not always economically advisable to cut at depths necessary to remove the deepest defects. General practice in those mills using the process is to desurface each grade of steel to the depth which strikes the right economic balance between loss in yield due to removal of metal and processing costs on one hand, and savings in lessened rejection loss on the other hand. This depth will vary with different materials, but the metal loss is generally 2 to 3 per cent of the product.

Roll Adjustment—There are several different methods for adjusting rolls on two-high mills (in addition to the one described earlier for three-high mills). One is a simple method of using a rider bearing on the bottom roll neck. The top-roll carrier bearing rests on liners on the bottom rider bearing. A wedge is placed between these liners to vary the distance between the rolls. Another method of adjustment consists of supporting the top roll by springs from the housing cap. Turning of the housing screw compresses the springs, and thus the space between the rolls is varied. Still another method of adjustment in which the top roll remains stationary and the bottom roll is moved up or down is used in a good many mills. This is accomplished in the following manner: a cast-steel screw box in which the threads have been babbitted to prevent excessive wear is placed on the sill of each housing. A screw bolt is placed in each of these, the outside one containing a left-hand thread while the inside one has a right-hand thread. The two screws are joined together by a cast coupling. Above the screw bolts, and resting upon them and the screw boxes, cast-steel wedges are mounted containing the same number of babbitted threads as the screw box. The bottom chocks are wedge-shaped and rest on the screw wedge. Since the two screws are coupled together, turning of the screw on the outside of the mill causes both screw wedges to move in or out and, due to the wedge shape of the bottom chock, the bottom roll is raised or lowered. This method of adjustment is used on many continuous mills. One of the newer methods of adjusting rolls on billet mills makes use of an electric screw-down. With this type of adjustment, the top roll is supported by two hydraulic cylinders through steelyard rods in each housing, reaching up to the top-roll carrier bearings. The top roll is held down by screws reaching through the cap to the breaker blocks on the rider bearings. An electric motor mounted on the housing cap actuates the two housing screws.

Shears—The product from the blooming mill must be cropped to discard pipe before entering the billet mill and the finished product from the billet mill must be cut to length. The bloom-crop shears, however, usually are considered part of the blooming mill rather than the billet mill. When the primary mill set-up consists of several billet mills fed one from the other, and all or part by the same blooming mill, crop shears usually are placed before each unit. Crop shears assure a clean end entering the mill and also enable cutting of the stock to the right length to accommodate the various mill tables. These crop shears usually are

stationary, and may be steam, hydraulically or electrically driven.

Billets of large cross-section generally are cut by **stationary shears.** Such billets are usually short enough to be handled on tables and transfers, and there are comparatively few cuts to the finished piece. These shears cut one or more pieces at the same time. The length of cut is determined by an adjustable stop on the shear table and the shears usually can cut accurately to within ¼ inch of the desired length.

Another form of shear is the gang shear in which several shears are placed in line in such a manner that any length of billet may be sheared by moving the position of individual shears within the limits of the first and last shear in line. They may be made to cut in unison, or separately, as desired.

The **flying shear,** as opposed to the stationary shear, cuts the piece as it travels in a continuous operation. These shears are used for the smaller sizes that would require excessively long tables and transfers and would, of course, consume too much time in handling, if cut on stationary shears. This is obvious when it is realized that an 8,000-pound ingot, rolled into a 1½-inch by 1½-inch billet, would be over 1000 feet long. By the use of flying shears, this piece can be cut effectively into shorter lengths as it leaves the finishing stand.

Billets also may be cut to length by saws or flame cutters to eliminate distorted ends produced by shears. Sawing is usually slower and more expensive than shearing, and saws are more costly to maintain.

Flame cutting, while entailing a comparatively small initial investment, is costly in that it is slower than shearing and also requires the use of relatively expensive gases.

Identification—It is of primary importance that every billet be identified properly. Every billet should be stamped with its heat number, and some orders require that top and bottom cuts from the ingot be identified. The steel must be followed closely through the mill, especially in those mills composed of several units, to make certain that the correct steel is coming for which the stampers already have received instructions. This tracing of the steel can become quite complicated at times, and must be adhered to rigidly in order to prevent costly errors in identification. Some mills identify all products by the use of special hand or pneumatic hammers having suitable heads for containing the stamps. Heat numbers can be machine stamped on billets after leaving the finishing stand by the use of a wheel, suitably mounted and containing the proper marking devices or stamps, contacting the steel. These wheels can be held in a stationary housing, so arranged that the height above the table can be varied for different sized billets, or they may be moved by a manually controlled hydraulic cylinder to contact each piece as it passes over the table. Usually, heat numbers only are applied in this manner.

After leaving the shears, billets are delivered usually to **cooling beds,** or **hot beds** as they are sometimes called, where they are cooled before shipping. In many mills, the above mentioned hand stamping is done on billets on the hot bed. The hot beds are at right angles to the direction of delivery from the mill and are wide enough to handle the longest billet length regularly produced on the mill. These beds are composed of skids placed close enough together to support the billet, but not too close to permit air to circulate around them. The skids may be composed of rails or of a series of specially designed castings. The castings give much better results than rails since they do not bend so readily with prolonged use. After cooling, the billets are pushed off the hot beds into **cradles**, from where they can be loaded easily into cars for shipment, or transferred to the conditioning area where they are handled as described in Section 5 of this chapter.

SECTION 3

CONTINUOUS CASTING OF BLOOMS, SLABS AND BILLETS

Principles of Continuous Casting—Sir Henry Bessemer about 1860 conceived the idea of casting molten steel continuously into plate form by pouring it into the opening between two relatively closely spaced horizontal rolls (Figure 22—34). Flanges on the rolls prevented escape of metal at the sides of the opening. Because of the inadequacy of engineering materials of his day, the principle failed of success and, indeed, cannot be made to work with steel even today with improved materials of construction.

The attractiveness of casting molten steel continuously into useful shapes, however, led to a long series of attempts by many investigators using various designs of machines. The possibility of successfully casting shapes equivalent in section to conventional semi-finished shapes would eliminate the ingot and primary-mill stages of rolled-steel production, and could be expected to afford important economies.

The high melting point, high specific heat, and low thermal conductivity of steel made most of the attempts abortive or only partially successful in the case of ferrous metals, although the continuous-casting principle proved practicable for non-ferrous metals. Success in the non-ferrous field spurred continuing study of the problem of applying continuous casting to steel and, eventually, the problem was solved.

Although the continuous casting of steel (and even metals of lower melting point) appears deceptively simple in principle, many difficulties are inherent in the process. Figure 22—35 illustrates schematically one of the problems inherent in the continuous casting of steel. When molten steel comes into contact with the walls of the water-cooled mold, a thin solid "skin" forms. However, due to the physical characteristics of steel mentioned above, and also because thermal contraction causes the skin to separate from the mold

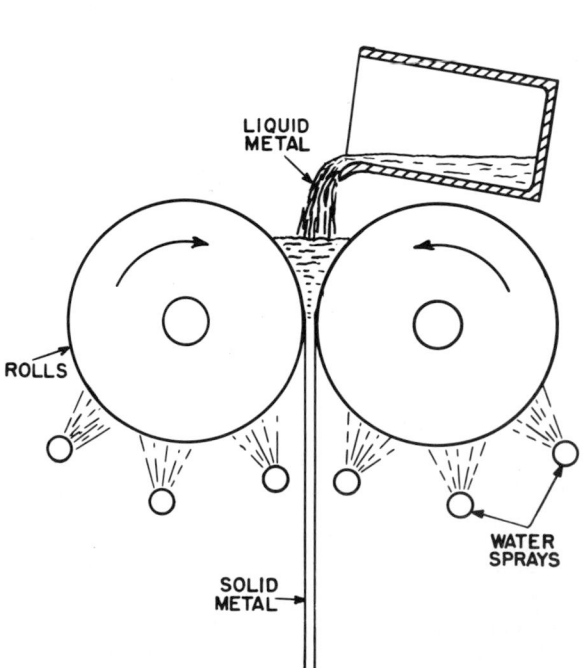

FIG. 22—34. Schematic diagram of a method suggested by Sir Henry Bessemer for the continuous casting of steel into the form of plates.

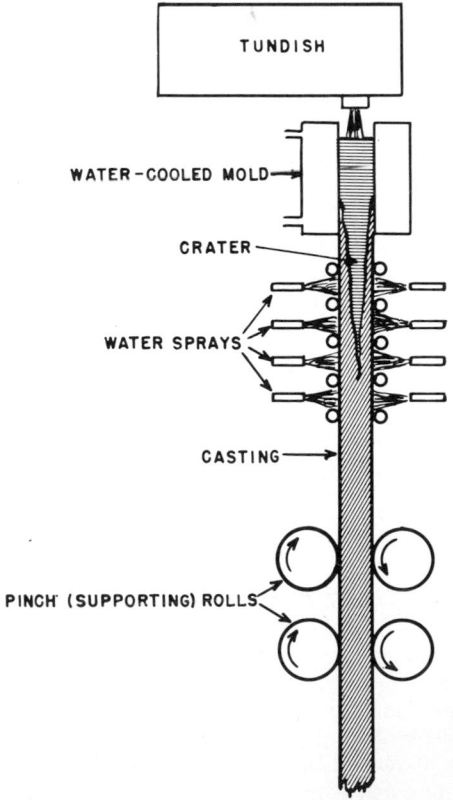

FIG. 22—35. Schematic diagram depicting how liquid metal persists in the center of a continuous casting for a considerable distance after the casting leaves the water-cooled mold, forming a so-called "crater."

wall shortly after solidification, the rate of heat abstraction from the casting is so low that molten steel persists within the interior of the section for some distance below the bottom of the mold. The thickness of the skin increases due to the action of the water sprays as the casting moves downward and, eventually, the entire section is solid.

The mass of the solid steel casting is supported as it descends by driven pinch rolls that also control line speed by controlling the rate of withdrawal of the casting from the mold. Any tendency for the casting to adhere to the mold wall may cause the skin to rupture due to the tensile forces exerted by the pinch rolls. With proper mold design, a rupture of the skin within the mold may not be serious since, under proper conditions, it may "heal" itself before the piece leaves the mold. However, a rupture that occurs below the mold will result in a "break-out" that releases molten steel and forces a shut-down of the operation. The use of oscillating molds that move up and down for predetermined distances at controlled rates during casting have practically eliminated sticking of the casting in the mold. Space does not permit a detailed discussion of mold design here.

There are several variations of the method of arranging the principal components of existing continuous-casting machines (Figure 22—36). It should be noted that the machines in that illustration are confined to designs that are constructed beginning at ground level: this necessitates building a tall structure that requires hoisting of the steel ladle to considerable heights. Other machines have been designed and built with their foundations in a deep pit that minimizes the height to which the steel ladle must be raised: such machines require some sort of conveyorized inclined plane or hoist arrangement to raise the product to plant-floor elevation for further processing.

The principal difference in Machines A and B in Figure 22—36 is that in Figure 22—36A the continuous length of casting is parted by gas cutting while the casting is supported in a vertical position and the cut-off piece is received by a tilting basket mechanism that lowers it to a horizontal position. In Figure 22—36B, the continuous casting is bent by a series of rollers from the vertical to the horizontal position, and cutting is performed on the horizontal casting.

Figure 22—36C represents a design of machine referred to as a semi-horizontal unit. By the use of an oscillating mold of special design and a curved cooling chamber, the height of the machine is reduced to about one-third that of machines of the types in Figure 22—36A and 22—36B.

Conservation and control of temperature of the

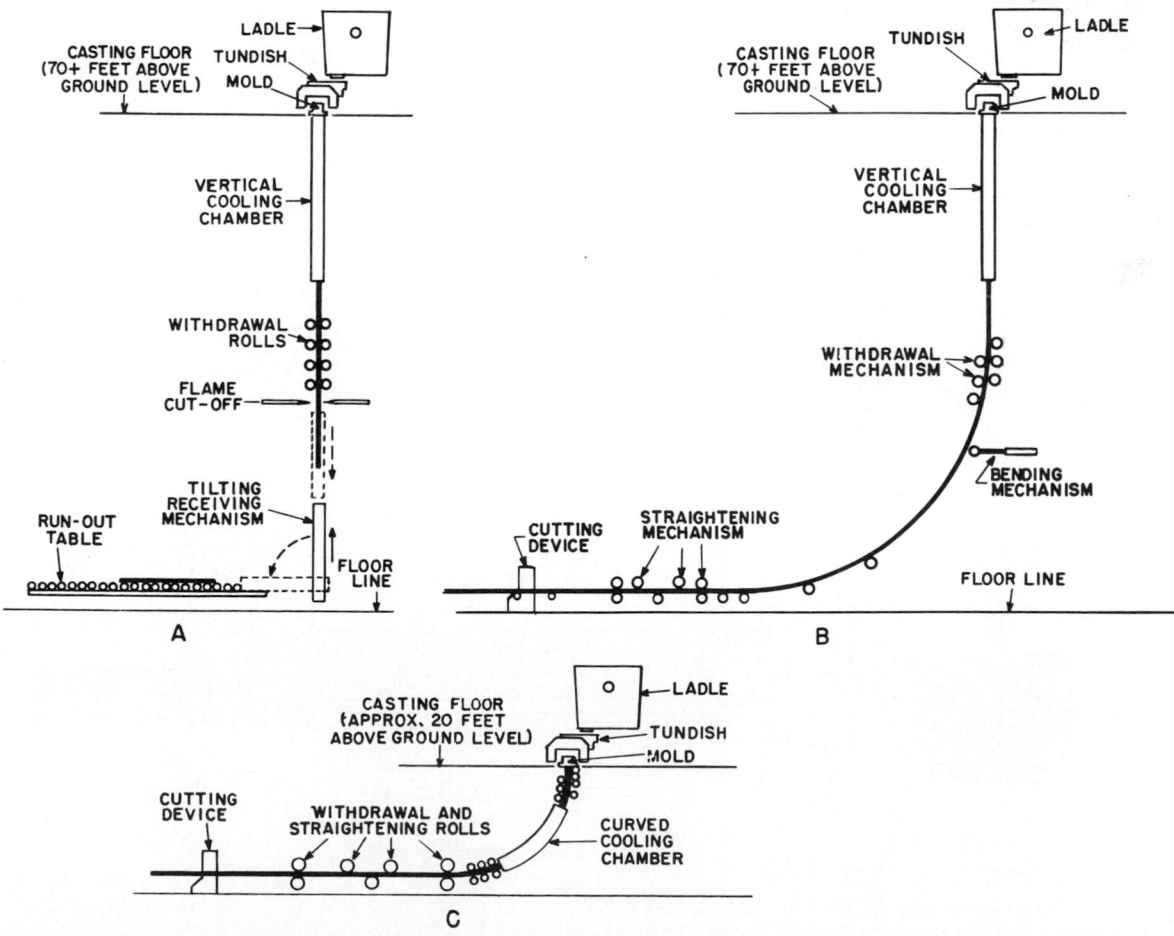

FIG. 22—36. Three methods that have been successfully applied to the continuous casting of steel.

molten steel requires the use of preheated and insulated ladles and preheating of the tundish. Small ladles may even be fired to compensate for heat loss. The molten metal is poured into the tundish from either a stoppered or tilting ladle. The tundish may be equipped with one or more nozzles that feed the metal to the mold or molds (in the case of smaller sections such as billets, multiple molds make it possible to cast more than one strand simultaneously).

The molds are made of copper, fabricated from a solid block or by assembling plates, and are cooled by the internal circulation of copious amounts of water.

Only a small amount of solidification takes place in the mold and water sprays below the mold perform the major cooling of the exposed casting.

Continuous-casting techniques have been used successfully in the production of shapes corresponding to all of the basic semi-finished sections—squares from 2 in. by 2 in. to 12 in. by 12 in., and slabs up to 8 in. by 60 in., and while some small rounds are being produced, larger rounds such as tube rounds have presented some difficulty although one plant successfully produces 8⅝-inch rounds. Stainless, tool, alloy, and carbon steels all have been successfully cast.

SECTION 4

BOTTOM-PRESSURE CASTING OF BLOOMS, SLABS AND BILLETS

Another attempt to by-pass the ingot and primary-mill stages in the production of wrought steels is represented by the bottom-pressure casting method of producing shapes equivalent to the products of the primary mills.

The principle of operation of the bottom-pressure casting method is illustrated in Figure 22—37. A ladle filled with molten steel is placed in a pressure vessel. The pressure vessel is covered with a lid in which has been inserted a pouring tube that dips down into the molten steel, almost to the bottom of the ladle. A

gooseneck connects the pouring tube to the mold in the casting position.

When air pressure is applied to the pressure vessel, the pressure of the air on the molten steel causes it to rise in the pouring tube and gooseneck and enter the mold. The vertical rise of the molten metal is determined by the increase in air pressure; increasing the pressure 1 lb. per sq. in. will cause the metal to rise vertically almost 4 inches. The height to which the metal must be raised is that of the highest point to be filled with metal. The highest point depends on the

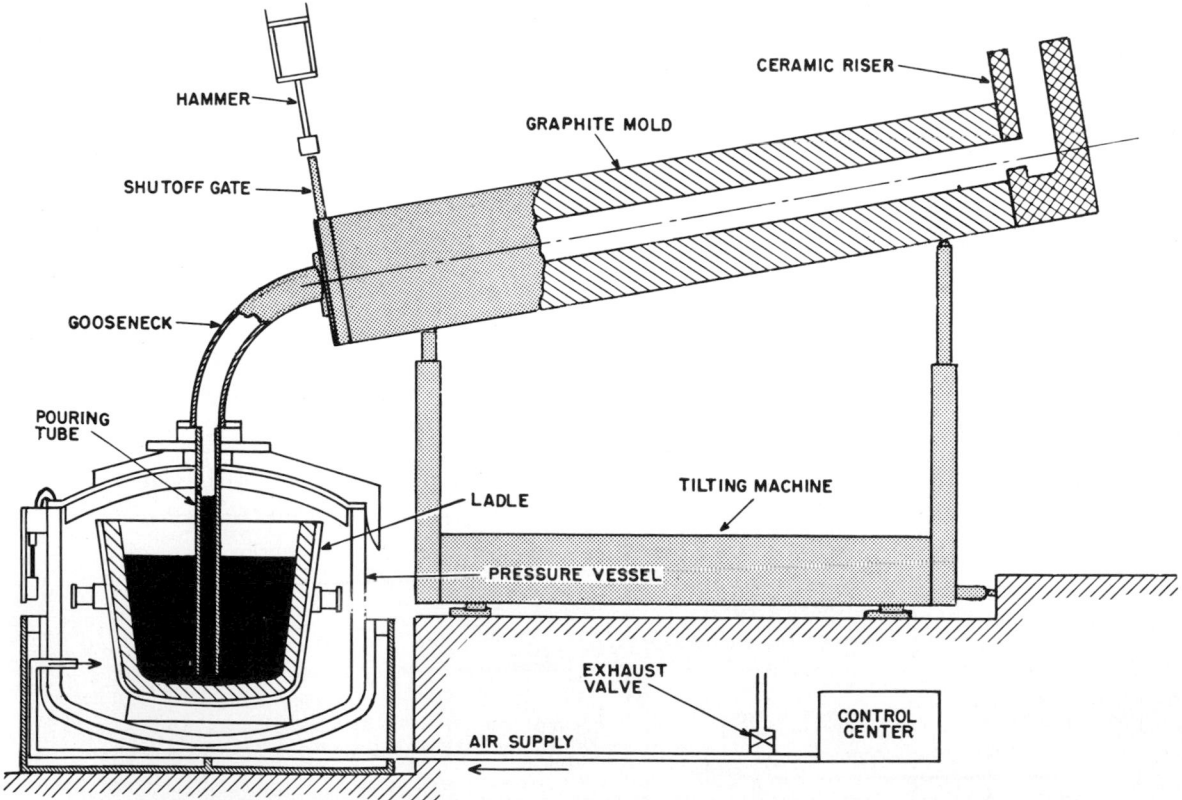

FIG. 22—37. Principle of operation of the bottom-pressure casting method as applied to slabs.

length of the mold and riser, the height above the level of the metal in the ladle, and the angle above the horizontal at which the mold is set. The casting rate is controlled by regulating the pressurizing equipment to increase air pressure in the desired increments.

Each mold is enclosed in a flask, equipped with a gate that retains the molten metal in the mold after the cast is completed. Graphite molds are employed. An insulating ceramic (sand) riser is installed in the mold flask at the end opposite the inlet gate to feed metal into the shrinkage cavity and thus minimize the formation of voids. A sensing wire is placed inside the riser. When molten metal reaches the wire, it completes an electrical circuit that actuates an electrically powered hammer that drives the gate closed and thus shuts off the flow of metal. The air pressure is maintained momentarily, and then the pressure vessel is exhausted to drain the gooseneck tube back into the ladle.

Typical products that have been cast in equipment of the type shown schematically in Figure 22—37 are: 2½-inch square billets, 8-inch diameter rounds, and slabs 6 inches by 30 inches and 17 feet long, although these sizes are not to be considered limitations of the method.

The mold flask is placed in casting position by a combination elevating and tilting machine. When the mold is filled, the gate closed, and the pressure vessel exhausted to the atmosphere, the mold is lowered onto a conveyor that moves it to the stripping table. After the casting has solidified, the mold is removed in a stripping machine where the drag and the casting are separated from the cope. The casting is then separated from the cope by special machines and placed on the cooling conveyor. The cope and drag are then transferred to the preparation table for readying for the next casting. In the meantime, a second mold has been moved into position in preparation for the next casting operation.

SECTION 5

SURFACE DEFECTS ON SEMI-FINISHED STEEL

Semi-finished steel is previously hot-worked cold steel intended exclusively to be subjected subsequently to further hot deformation. When steel is rolled from ingot to semi-finished forms, such as blooms, billets and slabs, a variety of ingot defects and some defects arising during heating and rolling may be carried through to appear on the surface of the semi-finished product. It often is necessary to remove these defects before the steel is converted further into finished products by forging, rolling or other hot forming operations. The removal of these defects, which operation is known as **conditioning,** will be the subject of the earlier parts of the present section; a discussion of the principles and practice of controlled cooling of certain grades and sizes of semi-finished products from rolling temperatures will be presented later in this section.

Surface defects on semi-finished products may be caused by defects on or in the ingot or by improper handling after pouring or by variations in heating and rolling practice.

The major surface defects which generally are attributed to defects on the ingot are:

1. **Ingot Cracks**—These defects occur as both transverse and longitudinal ruptures in the ingot wall, and normally are observed first while the ingot is being rolled on the primary mill, although some are apparent on the surface of the ingot itself, especially if it becomes cold. Ingot cracking has been the subject of numerous investigations, and some of the causes have been brought to light, although many still remain obscure. Excessively high pouring temperature (a temperature considerably above the solidification temperature) has been established as one definite cause of ingot cracking. During solidification a dendritic crystalline structure is developed in the ingot and interdendritic zones of weakness are formed which extend from the ingot surface toward the center. The larger the dendrites, the more pronounced are these zones. Lower pouring temperatures will help eliminate cracking from this origin by limiting the size while increasing the total number of individual dendrites. **Folds** due to surging of the molten metal in the mold form discontinuities in the ingot wall that lead to transverse ingot cracking. This type of defect has been minimized by use of mold coatings and improved mold design. Steels of the 0.15 to 0.25 per cent carbon grades, especially the fine-grained killed types, have the greatest tendency toward transverse cracking. Generally, the higher carbon steels have the least tendency toward this transverse rupturing. **Hanging** of hot-topped ingots by fins forming over the edge of the mold wall usually produces a transverse crack approximately 6 inches below the hot-top junction, easily recognizable and termed a **hanger crack.** Hanger cracks from this source can be prevented by use of properly designed hot-tops. Plain-sided molds are more prone to produce or at least accentuate transverse cracking than the fluted type. Longitudinal cracks generally are related to the flute or corner design of the mold.

Other and more obscure causes and corrective measures for ingot cracking are a constant subject for study by practically all steel-mill personnel.

2. **Scabs**—This type of defect is caused by splash of metal against the mold wall when an ingot is being teemed. Rapid solidification and oxidation of the metal on the mold wall causes it to stick to the ingot surface and finally appear as a scab on the surface of the rolled product. A picture of a scabby surface on a bloom is shown in Figure 22—38. This defect can be minimized by bottom pouring, use of mold coatings, and

proper mold design, as well as by proper attention to pouring speed and technique, as discussed in Chapter 18. A "cold" heat usually causes difficulties in pouring such as inability to obtain a tight closure of the ladle nozzle; the resulting leakage of molten metal when the ladle is positioned over the mold generally results in an ingot surface covered with scabs. Properly prepared mold coatings not only will minimize scabs but also will improve the surface condition generally. Many types of coatings have been employed with varying success, such as graphite, tar, aluminum paint, oil, and others. However, it might be noted that a poor coating is often worse than no coating at all, becoming a better adherent for splashes than the original mold wall itself.

3. **Seams**—This term is used to denote the straight-line longitudinal cracks or openings that may appear on the surface of semi-finished steel. Generally, they may be divided into two classes:

(a) A long deep seam usually is the result of ingot cracks, either longitudinal or transverse. A transverse crack in the ingot is elongated during rolling, and the seam so produced often has a "steeple" at the head, drawing out into a long straight line or a pair of parallel lines on the product. A deep seam on the semi-finished product surface such as originates in an ingot

crack is shown in Figure **22**—39. The basic causes of these defects in the rolled steel are obviously the same as those outlined above for ingot cracks.

(b) Short seams, usually light and in clusters, may be due to a number of causes. Surface pits on the ingot, or subsurface blowholes which become exposed and oxidized during heating, will produce this defect. Some other causes include poor heating practice, and rolling outside the proper temperature range. Clustered seams are illustrated in Figure **22**—40.

Those surface defects which originate at the soaking pits and on the primary mill and other mills rolling semi-finished products are:

1. **Cinder Patch**—This defect is the result of pick-up of material from soaking-pit bottoms, and generally has the appearance of a very scabby bottom. Cinder patch can be overcome to a great extent by proper attention to bottom making. Some plants charge hot-top ingots of the big-end-up type upside down in the pits, thus causing the cinder patch to be confined to the hot-top or discard portion of the ingot.

2. **Burned Steel**—This defect is very often the result of flame impingement on the surface of ingots, usually on their corners, as they are heated in the soaking pits, causing penetrating oxidation at the grain boundaries with a resultant tearing or rupturing of the ingot

FIG. **22**—38. Scabby surface on a bloom, showing the effects of roll collars on the pre-existing scabby surface on the ingot from which it was rolled.

FIG. **22**—39. Deep seam on the surface of a semi-finished rolled product, originating with an ingot crack.

FIG. 22—40. Clustered seams on the surface of a semi-finished rolled product, pickled after rolling to facilitate detection of defects.

FIG. 22—41. Surface of a "burned" steel bloom.

FIG. 22—42. A lap on the surface of a rolled steel billet.

on the primary mill. A burned bloom is shown in Figure 22—41. Burned steel seldom can be salvaged and normally must be scrapped. Some steels are more sensitive to burning than others.

3. **Laps**—Laps are the result of overfilling in the mill passes that causes fins or projections which turn down as the material rolls through succeeding stands in the mill train.

A lapped billet is shown in Figure 22—42. Laps us-ually are deep and the product often cannot be salvaged economically.

The foregoing list of defects is not all-inclusive, but presents merely the more important causes of surface defects that require removal in conditioning. There are numerous other defects, such as: twist, guide marks, collar cut, diamond, bent, crop ends, and so on, the names of which are self-explanatory. Most of these will receive attention at various points in the text.

INSPECTION

Conditioning is that function of steel manufacture which, by removal of defects, renders steel more suitable for subsequent hot- and/or cold-forming operations. Of primary importance is the detection and proper removal of the defects where required. It is neither economical nor always necessary (and, strictly speaking, probably not possible) to remove all of the imperfections.

What, if anything, is removed is determined by the prospective subsequent operations and final end use of the product. The following paragraph is an example of the method for determining the conditioning practice in a plant producing semi-finished steel for bar products.

Using an arbitrary classification, product end uses can be grouped to include under one class semi-finished products which require the removal of all surface defects visible after pickling or skinning. As an example of this class of material, if the steel is intended for alloy-steel bars of high hardenability and the bars are further quenched in oil after reheating, it is obvious that any light seams may result in quench cracks, so that all defects should be removed from the semi-finished steel. In a second example, where the material is to be rolled or forged to some finished form, but not heat-treated, oxidation during the reheating for rolling or forging will eliminate, in many cases, slight surface imperfections, and semi-finished products for this use could be placed in another class for which removal of only those defects visually detectable without pickling would be required. If material is to receive considerable work in further hot rolling or cold machining, even medium-sized seams can be acceptable, offering another classification which might be defined as a class of material requiring the removal of only major defects such as scabs, ingot cracks, laps, and deep seams. Finally, the remainder of the product can be placed in a class from which only those defects need be removed such as large scabs or ingot cracks, deep laps, and burned steel which might be damaging to either or both the final product or the operation (such as subsequent hot rolling where large scabs might cause cobbles on the mill, tear out the guides or cause other damage). Thus, it can be seen that the basis for inspection is predicated both on the end use of the product as well as upon the operations employed to shape the steel into its final form.

Pickling for Inspection—Pickling, as applied to surface inspection and conditioning, consists of immersing the steel in a chemical solution for the purpose of removing the scale on the outside surface so that defects will be exposed. The usual solution for ordinary steels is composed of 5 to 8 per cent sulphuric acid in water, used at temperatures between 150 and 180° F. A good, clean surface is desired for optimum results in inspection, and to attain this, relatively close control of temperature and acid concentration is necessary. A thorough rinse after pickling is required, either by immersion in clean, hot water or washing with high pressure nozzles. The time required for pickling varies with the grade of steel; for example, a 10-ton lift of blooms of plain-carbon steel may re-quire pickling for around 45 minutes, while the same quantity of constructional alloy steel may require treatment for from 1 to 2½ hours.

Pickling generally has been associated with hand chipping, as a dual operation. In those plants where hand scarfing has replaced hand chipping, the pickling practice has been abandoned, too. Modern practice for the same specifications is: for rectangular sections, to skin by scarfing and then spot scarf where needed; for round sections, to peel mechanically and then spot scarf.

REMOVAL OF DEFECTS

Hand Chipping—Until a few years prior to the First World War, the practice of extensive conditioning of semi-finished steel was almost unknown except for seamless tubes and special forgings. For most purposes, the use of a cold chisel and hand hammer was about all the work that was done, and this only to knock off such things as large slivers or scabs that might tear out the guides in rolling on a secondary mill. For the most part, steel was either accepted or scrapped in the semi-finished form. It is not to be assumed from this that a good deal of unusable material was produced, for it must be borne in mind than, in those days, a great deal of stock-removal in machining was accepted as commonplace and the tolerances for finished work were much wider. This was the only method of steel preparation used to any great extent until the early 1930's.

Hand chipping, as it is known today, consists of using a pneumatic hammer with a cold chisel placed in the barrel, so that the reciprocating action of the piston on the chisel causes the chisel to cut into the steel and remove the surface to the desired extent. Figure 22—43 shows a close-up view of a chipper at work.

Machine Chipping—There are available several large machines built specifically for the purpose of removing imperfections from the surface of steel blooms and billets. These machines fall into two general types: the planer and the milling machine.

The **planer type**, illustrated in Figure 22—44, is constructed with a large table which can be moved longitudinally and a tool holder which can be moved to any position in a plane vertical to the table motion. The steel is clamped onto the table by mechanical or hydraulic vise-type jaws. The table then is operated to move in a horizontal direction, back and forth in a reversing motion, so that the steel passes under the tool. The tool can be adjusted while the machine is in operation. The distance of travel and the depth of cut are governed by the operator. Speeds are varied in accordance with the hardness of the steel and the depth of cut desired. In this manner, any length of cut or repeated cuts in depth can be made, so that either complete skinning or partial surface removal can be accomplished.

The **milling machine**, typified in Figure 22—45, is constructed with a multiple set of tools in a revolving head. The steel is clamped in a stationary position, and the tool head can be moved in a horizontal as well as a vertical direction so that surface removal can be

FIG. 22—43. Chipper using a pneumatic hammer equipped with a cold chisel for removing selected portions of steel billet surface.

restricted to selected spots or the piece being conditioned can be skinned completely. The entire frame of the machine carrying the tool is capable of traveling the entire length of the pieces processed.

Scarfing—Scarfing in the steel mill consists of surface removal by the use of oxygen torches (Figures 22—46, 22—48 and 22—51). The oxygen rapidly oxidizes the steel surface, generating elevated temperatures that cause the oxidized product to become liquid. The process can be carried out on hot steel between stages of rolling, when hot scarfing machines are used, or on cold steel in the conditioning area by the use of the hand torch. In principle, the tip of the scarfing torch is similar to the regular oxygen-gas torches used for the burning of steel. As early as 1919, surface-defect removal on semi-finished steel was at-

tempted by hand scarfing, but because of lack of knowledge of proper torch design and the difficulties encountered with the fuel gas, the results obtained were unsatisfactory. During the 1920's, some attempts at specialized uses of torches met with success, but it was not until 1929 that a determined effort was made to procure fuels and equipment to perform satisfactorily the function of defect removal from the surface of semi-finished steels. Promotion of the chemical reaction that forms the melted iron oxide is not the only function of the oxygen; its kinetic energy must also force the liquid, oxidized metal from the path of the torch.

Hand Scarfing of Cold Steel—As might be expected, the first hand torches, though successful, were cumbersome and slow, but since 1929 many outstand-

FIG. 22—44. Planer-type machine for removing surface imperfections from surfaces of semi-finished steel.

FIG. 22—45. Milling machine adapted to the removal of surface imperfections from semifinished steel.

ing improvements have been effected so that the bulk of semi-finished steel now is conditioned by the scarfing method. So far, only oxygen has been mentioned, but fuel gas, too, is necessary to the functioning of the scarfing torch. The gas acts as a preheating agent to elevate a spot on the steel surface to such a temperature that the oxygen and the steel will begin to combine chemically. Once this preheating has been accomplished, the heat of reaction between oxygen and iron produces sufficient heat in front of the torch tip to maintain the reaction and fuel gas is no longer a necessary part of the operation. An interesting development with respect to this spot pre-heating is the so-called **starting rod,** which is a small rod of steel

that extends into the flame and is heated until a small drop of melted rod falls onto the steel surface, thus instantly kindling the reaction. The melting of this steel rod is a matter of a fraction of a second as opposed to the 6 or 8 seconds required to heat sufficiently a spot on the steel surface with the flame alone. Many different types of torches and many different kinds of fuel gases are employed currently.

Perhaps the largest tonnage of all conditioned steel is processed by hand scarfing. Scarfing can be used for both small and large sizes down to about 2 inches by 2 inches, below which a bowing effect is produced.

A factor present in scarfing cold steel which is not present in other types of conditioning previously de-

FIG. 22—46. A scarfing torch in use removing surface imperfections from a rolled steel slab.

FIG. 22—47. Surface cracks resulting from scarfing to remove surface imperfections from a rolled steel billet.

scribed might be termed the metallurgy of scarfing. When a relatively small portion of a large piece of steel, such as the area adjacent to a cut made by the scarfing torch, is heated to a high temperature and the source of heat is suddenly removed, a **quenching effect** is produced by the rapid extraction of heat from the hot area by conduction of heat into the surrounding relatively cold areas. This rapid cooling of a heated portion of steel from a temperature above its critical temperature range causes it to harden, to a degree proportionate to its carbon content and to some extent also to the hardenability of the particular steel being scarfed. In plain low-carbon steel, this ef-

fect is not noticeable, but as the content of carbon or alloying elements increases, the effect becomes more and more severe, producing, in the extreme case, a hard, martensitic layer on the surface where scarfing has been performed.

This hardened surface will crack upon cooling if no preventive measures are taken. Scarfing cracks on a billet are shown in Figure 22—47. To prevent scarfing cracks, preheating before scarfing to temperatures between 300 and 500° F normally will suffice, although in highly critical grades, such as SAE 52100 (1.0 per cent carbon, 1.3–1.6 per cent chromium), postheating for stress relief after scarfing also should

FIG. 22—48. View of a hot scarfer in operation at a slab mill.

be employed. To eliminate completely the hardened surface, a normalizing or annealing heat treatment is necessary. Ordinary brick pits, gas fired, can be used for routine preheating before scarfing, where a sufficient tonnage of sensitive steels is involved. Conventional car-bottom or continuous heat-treating furnaces are employed for complete softening of the steel by heat treatment. The necessity for proper preheating of some steels cannot be over-emphasized, since scarfing cracks cannot be tolerated in finished products.

Mechanical Scarfing of Hot Steel—The **mechanical hot scarfer** (Figure 22—48) originated about 1930. It is installed directly in the mill line, and is composed of a number of scarfing torches so designed that they form a pass on the mill. The torches are used in exactly the same manner as the hand torch. A starting rod is not used because the high temperature of the product being rolled is enough to obtain quick starting action. The working speed of the machine must be coordinated with the mill so that no delay in rolling production is encountered. Only a moderate amount of metal can be removed but very satisfactory results can be obtained in conditioning some products. This equipment is not confined to four-side removal, but has been employed for two-side removal (of slab edges and the like). Such machines can be designed to meet the needs of individual mills.

Grinding—Conditioning by grinding also is in general use. For semi-finished steels, the **stationary** or **swing-frame grinder** is employed. This machine consists of a large grinding stone, up to 24 inches in diameter, electrically driven. The machine is suspended so that it can be raised or lowered readily to suit the product being ground. When the material is positioned properly and held firmly, the operator grasps the handle bars and, by body pressure, forces the revolving stone against that portion of the surface to be removed, moving the stone with a slight back and forth horizontal movement until the defect is gone (Figure 22—49). The grinding wheel can be considered as a revolving cylinder carrying many sharp tools, which are the abrasive grains. When revolving at a proper speed, the grains cut very small chips from the material being ground. It is, therefore, the cumulative effect of the action of a very large number of cutting points which produces the result. Grinding cracks can result from the heat generated by grinding unless the proper wheels are used; this occurrence is related to the quenching effect discussed under "Hand Scarfing of Cold Steel."

Grinding is a more or less specialized process, being particularly adaptable to stainless steel and other products which cannot be scarfed or chipped.

Material Handling—New developments in the material handling field are being employed in increasing numbers to simplify the handling and stocking of material for conditioning. The use of **straddle carriers** (Figure 22—50), in some plants which have large conveniently located vacant areas, has revolutionized the transporting of semi-finished material, permitting flexibility and simplification of stocking areas, improved scheduling and better control of inventory. **Bloom-turning machines** (Figure 22—51) safely and efficiently position material automatically for hand scarfing, permitting increased tonnage to be conditioned. These machines are designed to be loaded and unloaded by fork lift trucks, eliminating the need for cranes.

CONTROLLED COOLING OF SEMI-FINISHED PRODUCTS

Blooms, billets and slabs are rolled at temperatures well above the critical temperature range of the steel

Fig. 22—49. Two swing grinders in operation conditioning the surface of a steel slab.

FIG. 22—50. Straddle carrier in right foreground facilitates the transporting and stocking of semi-finished material.

FIG. 22—51. Overall view of a bloom-turning machine showing a bloom on the supporting arms being scarfed.

and thus, in cooling to atmospheric temperature after rolling, must pass through its transformation range. Depending upon the chemical composition of the steel and the size of product rolled from it, it may be necessary to retard the rate of cooling by artificial means for two reasons:

(1) To prevent the formation of small internal ruptures, called flakes.

(2) To minimize development of internal stresses.

Some steels are relatively very sensitive to rapid changes in temperature, and this **thermal sensitivity** requires that great care be exercised during both heating and cooling to avoid physical damage to the steel due to high internal stresses.

Nature and Prevention of Flakes—Flakes are small internal ruptures that usually occur some distance away from the end of a piece and often midway from the surface to the center of a section. Although there is not complete accord as to the relative importance of the various factors contributing to flaking, it generally is considered that hydrogen dissolved in the molten steel makes it more susceptible to flakes and that proper retardation of cooling from forging or rolling temperatures effectively will prevent their formation.

More recently, the development of methods for degassing molten steel has provided an effective means for preventing flaking (see Chapter 18).

Development of Controlled-Cooling Practices—The earliest method employed for retarding the rate of cooling after forging or rolling was to bury the steel, as it came from the press or mill, in ashes or some other insulating material such as sand or slag. The purpose of this was not to prevent flakes, but to retard the cooling sufficiently to lessen the hardness developed by the steel on cooling and to minimize the development of internal stresses. Rates of cooling varied greatly, depending upon the type of insulating material used and the depth to which the steel was covered. No positive control of cooling rates was pos-

sible with such crude methods, and the time required before the steel safely could be removed usually was two to ten days. Another method of slow cooling involved the use of unfired pits, lined with brick to provide insulation. After the steel was placed in these pits, they were covered with insulated lids, and the charge cooled at a rate dependent upon the mass of the charge and the rate at which heat was lost by radiation. In another method, steel boxes were inverted over piles or bundles of hot steel as it was delivered from the mill. Because of the space and long time required, and the difficulties involved in handling, the burying processes proved entirely inadequate as increased tonnages of alloy steel came to be produced. Consequently, it became imperative to develop more suitable means for slow cooling.

In recent times, use has been made of automatically controlled furnaces, insulated and heated railway gondola cars with covers, and heavy pits equipped to control temperatures during slow cooling. With such equipment, it has been possible to take advantage of cooling cycles of considerably shorter duration with better control of results. When using equipment that makes possible close control of rate of cooling, the temperature of the steel can be lowered rapidly and arrested at the desired temperature which improved knowledge of heat-treating procedures has established as effective for each particular type of steel. After a suitable holding time, measured in hours instead of days (as was the case when the steel was simply buried in ashes), the steel can be removed and air cooled in the open, permitting prompt placement of the next charge in the furnace or pit.

Much experimental work has been done to determine the proper holding temperature for the different grades of steel. Figure 22—52 shows the cooling curves for AISI 4340 and 52100 steels superimposed on the isothermal transformation curves for these steels. The latter curves, formerly called "S" curves,

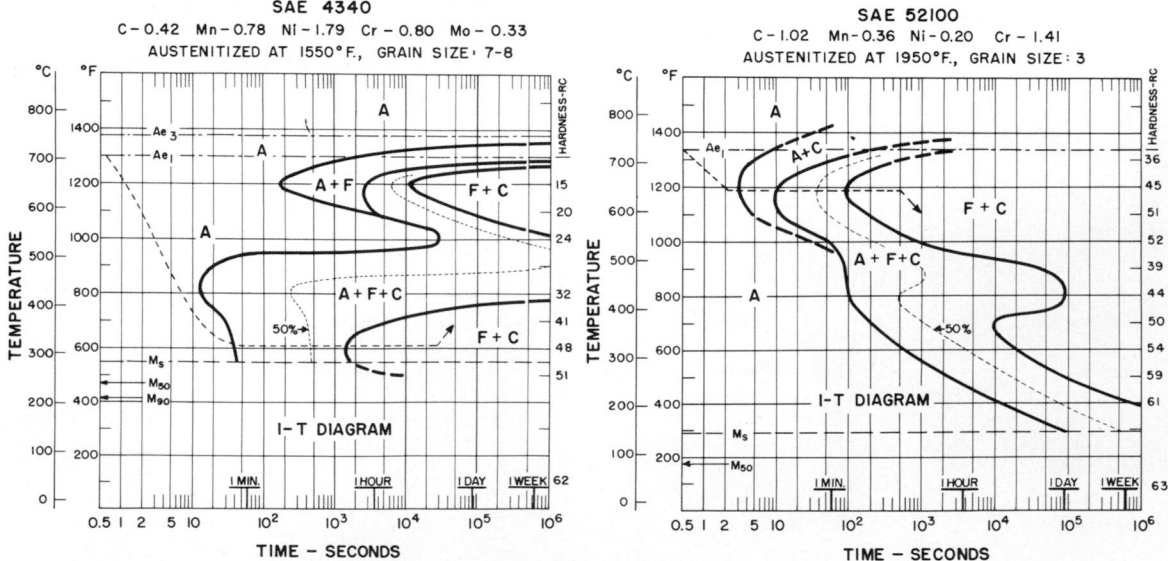

FIG. 22—52. Cooling curves superimposed on isothermal transformation diagrams of two steels, showing cooling cycles employed to effect transformation in a minimum of time while still avoiding flake formation.

show the time required to complete transformation at various temperature levels, and a more detailed description of their derivation and use will be found in a later chapter. The objective in selecting the holding time for each of these grades was to determine what temperature would require the minimum holding time to obtain transformation and still give a product free from flakes. In the case of the 52100 steel, 1200° F was selected as the temperature from which the billets could be air cooled. For the 4340 steel, holding at 1200° F was not feasible, as excessive time would be required for transformation. Since 600° F corresponded to the minimum time of holding, this was the temperature selected. Transformation in this range would result in an appreciable amount of internal stress which might result in flakes on cooling in air to atmospheric temperature. Hence, instead of air cooling immediately after the end of the holding period, this particular steel should be heated instead to a temperature just below the critical range to relieve these stresses after which it may be cooled.

These two types of cycles are applicable to a large number of different grades of steel, and the holding temperature for a particular grade can be determined from the proper isothermal transformation diagram. In general, the higher holding temperatures followed by air cooling can be used for the carbon and lower alloy grades of steel; the use of lower holding temperatures, followed by immediate reheating to just below the critical temperature range, is applicable to the more highly alloyed deep-hardening steels.

BIBLIOGRAPHY

Association of Iron and Steel Engineers, Roanoke Electric Steel Operates First U.S. Continuous Steel Casting Plant. Iron and Steel Engineer 40, No. 6, June 1963, 141-144.

Am. Iron and Steel Institute, Steel Products Manual. Alloy Steel: Semifinished; Hot Rolled and Cold Finished Bars. The Institute, New York, 1955.

Am. Iron and Steel Institute, Steel Products Manual. Carbon Steel: Semifinished for Forging; Hot Rolled and Cold Finished Bars. The Institute, New York, 1957.

Beynon, R. E., The rolling of semifinished steel. Assn. of Iron and Steel Engrs., Proc., 1944, 427-444.

Brittain, Marshall and Frostick, H. G., The blooming mill programmed. Iron and Steel Engineer 38, No. 3, March 1961, 99-106.

Cardwell, G. P. and W. J. Reilly, Features of Lukens' 140-inch roughing and slabbing mill. Iron and Steel Engineer 40, No. 3, March 1963, 133-143.

Clifford, T. D., Operational features of 45-inch slab mill and 80-inch hot strip mill. Iron and Steel Engineer 35, No. 9, September 1958; 198-200; discussion, 201.

Cramer, R. E. and E. C. Bast, Production of flakes by treating molten steel with hydrogen and the time of cooling necessary to prevent their formation. Am. Society for Metals, Trans. 27, 433-445; discussion, 446-457 (1939).

Curtin, J. J., Design of a mill for rolling semifinished products. Am. Iron and Steel Institute Yearbook, 1947, 495-509.

Daniels, F. C. T. and D. L. Eynon, Bloom and billet mills and their rolls. Assn. of Iron and Steel Engineers, Proc., 1944, 301-313.

Doyle, E. A., Hot scarfing of billets, blooms and slabs. Assn. of Iron and Steel Engineers, Proc., 1941, 260-268.

Fleming, D. H., Powder cutting and scarfing. Welding Engineer 32, 66-70 (1947).

Gray, A. C., and J. G. Mitchell, Operating and mechanical features of new 46-inch by 110-inch high-lift blooming mill at Stelco. Iron and Steel Engineer 35, No. 8, August 1958; 123-131.

Henderson, G. A., Bethlehem Steel Co.'s 45-inch slabbing mill at Lackawanna Plant. Iron and Steel Engineer 40, No. 2, February 1963; 63-78.

Hultgren, A., Flakes or hair cracks in chromium steel, with a discussion on shattered zones and transverse fissures in rails. Iron and Steel Inst. J. 111, 113-148; discussion and correspondence, 149-167 (1925).

Johnson, E. R., S. W. Poole and J. A. Rosa, Flaking in alloy steels. Am. Inst. Mining and Metallurgical Engineers, Open Hearth Proc. 27, 358-368; discussion, 369-377 (1944).

Kingsley, P. S., Prevention of flakes in steel forging billets. Metal Progress 47, 699-703 (1945).

Laidlaw, J. L. and J. H. Walshaw, Algoma's 46-inch blooming and plate mill. Iron and Steel Engineer 38, No. 1, January 1961; 67-77.

Lavette, R. F., Republic's 44-36-32 in. mills at Chicago. Assn. Iron and Steel Engineers, Proc., 1948; 717-721.

Lindberg, V. H., and J. E. Duffy, Automated structural rolling facilities at South Works of U. S. Steel. Iron and Steel Engineer 38, No. 11, 1961; 87-99.

Linde Air Products Co., Oxy-acetylene handbook. New York, The Company, 1943.

Marrs, R. E. and P. E. Perrone, Operating experience with the automated slabbing mill. Iron and Steel Engineer 40, No. 4, April 1963; 105-116.

McBride, D. L. and T. E. Dancy (editors), Continuous casting. Proc. of Tech. Sessions of Iron and Steel Div., Am. Inst. of Mining, Metallurgical and Petroleum Engineers, Detroit, Mich., Oct. 24, 1961. Interscience Publishers, New York, 1962.

Miller, David H. and Dr. Terence E. Dancy, Continuous casting—past, present and future. Iron and Steel Engineer 40, No. 5, May 1963; 97-110.

Montgomery, A., Jr. and J. K. Magee, New primary mills at Duquesne Works, United States Steel Corp. Iron and Steel Engineer 40, No. 6, June 1963; 80-86.

Reid, Warren and R. H. Wright, Electrical features of universal slabbing and hot strip finishing mills at Fairless. Iron and Steel Engineer 32, No. 1, January 1955; 97-104; discussion, 104-105.

Schlesinger, Kurt, Selection and economy of equipment for blooming and slabbing mills. Iron and Steel Engineer 34, No. 7, July 1957; 63-74.

United States Steel Corporation, Isothermal transformation diagrams; 3rd ed. 1963. Pittsburgh, The Corporation.

Winlack, G. D., Scarfing high carbon and alloy steels. Assn. Iron and Steel Engineers, Yearly Proceedings, 1942; 208-216.

CHAPTER 23

Production of Steel Plates

SECTION 1

PLATE-MILL PRODUCTS

Plates are classified, by definition, according to certain size limitations to distinguish them from sheet, strip, and flat bars. According to this classification, plates generally are considered to be those flat, hot-rolled, finished products that come within the following dimensional and weight limitations:

Width (In.)	Thickness (In.)	Weight (Lb. per Sq. Ft.)
Over 8 to 48, incl.	0.2300 and thicker	9.62 and heavier
Over 48	0.1800 and thicker	7.53 and heavier

There are a few exceptions to the above classification. Flat, hot-rolled, semifinished products such as slabs, sheet bar and skelp are not classed as plates, although their dimensions and weight may be within the foregoing limits. Also, the dimensional limitations for stainless-steel plates differ slightly from those listed above (see AISI Steel Products Manual entitled "Stainless and Heat-Resistant Steels").

Principal end uses for plates include such fabricated structural and plate products as bridges, trestles, storage tanks, pressure vessels and penstocks; railroad freight and passenger cars; shipbuilding; line pipe; industrial machinery and equipment; weldments and many special applications.

Plates are produced by hot rolling, either from reheated slabs or directly from ingots. The terms applied to plates to differentiate between the several kinds (without regard to the chemical composition of the steel) are based upon the types of mills used in their production, e.g., **sheared plate** or **sheared mill plates** when rolled between straight horizontal rolls and later trimmed on all edges. Mill edge is the normal edge produced by hot rolling between horizontal finishing rolls: **mill edge plates** have two mill edges and two trimmed ends. Plates are called **universal plates** or **universal mill plates** (abbreviated **U.M. plates**) when rolled simultaneously between both horizontal and vertical rolls and trimmed on the ends only: grooved rolls are sometimes substituted for the plain horizontal rolls used for universal plates.

Carbon-steel **rolled floor plates** are also flat, hot-rolled, finished steel products that come under the plate classification. Floor plates are hot-finished in the final pass or passes between one or more pairs of rolls. One roll of each pair has a pattern cut into it so that one surface of the plate passing between the rolls is forced into the depressions on the pattern roll to form a raised figure at regular intervals on the surface of the plate. Individual floor-plate patterns are produced exclusively by each manufacturer, the patterns differing in both dimensions and appearance.

The majority of steel plates produced are rolled from carbon steels. In addition to carbon steels, the complete range of steel-plate production includes high-strength, alloy, and stainless steels.

The as-rolled product of plate mills is rectangular in form, and a considerable proportion is shipped as **rectangular plates. Circular** and **semi-circular plates** and **sketch plates,** including **rings,** are produced by shearing or gas cutting hot-rolled rectangular plates to specified shapes.

A considerable proportion of plate-steel production is subjected to some form of heat treatment prior to shipment from the mill, especially in the case of alloy-steel plates, to develop the desired mechanical or physical properties. Heat treatments employed include: annealing, spheroidize annealing, stress relieving, normalizing, accelerated cooling, quenching, and tempering. The principles and purposes of carrying out these treatments are discussed in Chapter 39. A modern heat-treating installation designed specifically for plates is described in Section 4 of this chapter.

The same rolling mills and auxiliaries are common to all plate-steel production. There are, however, for both carbon- and alloy-steel plates, special manufacturing and quality requirements that have been adopted by the industry. These are not discussed here, but are given in two Steel Products Manuals issued by the American Iron and Steel Institute under the following titles: "Alloy Steel Plates," and "Carbon Steel: Plates; Structural Sections; Rolled Floor Plates; Steel Sheet Piling."

PLATE-MILL OPERATIONS

The sequence of operations for plate mills is covered by the following general subdivisions:

1. Heating slabs for rolling
2. Descaling
3. Rolling
4. Leveling or flattening
5. Cooling
6. Shearing or cutting

These major steps in the production of steel plates will be discussed in the order in which they are listed above.

HEATING SLABS FOR ROLLING

Batch-Type Heating Furnaces—Early plate-producing plants were laid out so that the slabs from the primary mills could be transported to the heating furnaces of the plate mill as hot charges. The continuous-type heating furnace had not yet been developed, and batch-type furnaces were used. Such layouts were motivated by the considerations: (1) that the small ingots then generally produced were not so susceptible as present-day large ingots to being the source of major surface defects that carried though to the finished product; (2) that economical, intermediate-conditioning processes had not yet been developed; and (3) that the economies of increased production rates from hot charges would more than offset the surface rejections which might be incurred.

Heating in a fuel-fired batch furnace is essentially a process of transmitting heat by radiation and convection from the combustibles to the top slab surface and by conduction through the thickness of the slab to the bottom surface and the hearth. Even where the temperatures of both the hearth and the charge are high in relation to the drawing temperature at the beginning of a cycle of charges and draws, the heating rates per square foot of furnace area are low in contrast with continuous slab-heating furnaces. When the cycle involves cold charges, the initial abstraction of heat from the hearth, which must be restored later in the cycle, slows the process to the point where continuous operation is impracticable, if the heating capacity was installed initially for hot charges. The process of heating from top to bottom through the thickness, in itself, suggests the existence of a temperature differential which can be minimized only by soaking. Changes which have occurred in the industry in the past thirty-five years have created a trend in the direction of cold charges and have confronted many plants with the necessity of determining whether to operate mills on an intermittent basis, add heating capacity, or build new mills.

Continuous-Type Heating Furnaces—Most of the existing continuous slab-heating furnaces were designed for and are operated on cold charges. The slabs are charged into the low-temperature end of the furnace and progress toward the high-temperature end by being pushed progressively forward on water-cooled skids. Burners located above and below the skid level furnish heat by radiation and convection to both the top and the bottom surfaces of the slabs until they reach the high-temperature zone, which is, in effect, a soaking zone. Only top burners are provided for the high-temperature zone. The slabs are at approximate rolling temperatures when they arrive in this zone, and elimination of **skid marks** (visibly colder "stripes" on slabs caused by contact with the water-cooled skids) and other temperature non-uniformities, plus making up radiation losses to maintain the desired furnace temperature, are the principal heat requirements to be met.

Furnace Control—Furnace-control equipment is intended not only to effect fuel economies, but also to improve the quality of heating. Slab heating is improved if slabs are brought to the plastic state most satisfactory for rolling, with a minimum of temperature variation in each slab without any part ever attaining an excessive temperature, and with the production of a scale coating conducive to the best surface finish. The thickness and the type of scale formation is dependent on temperature, time at temperature, and availability of oxygen. The temperature that must be used is dependent upon the required plastic state of the heated steel; time of heating is controlled by the heating capacity of the furnace; therefore, control of the fuel-air ratio is the only flexible practical determinant of the types of scale that may be formed, which may vary from extremely adherent to loose. Automatic furnace-control equipment was not available when the bulk of existing batch furnaces was designed. Some were modified later to permit installation of controls. Several furnaces, such as at Homestead District Works, built during World War II, were designed for and equipped with automatic furnace controls. The preponderant number of batch furnaces still in operation are dependent on manual control. Slab-heating furnaces of the continuous type either had furnace controls included in the original design or they were added later, inasmuch as such furnaces are very adaptable to automatically controlled operation. Scale formation, consequently, can be controlled closely with respect to both thickness and type.

DESCALING

Prior to the introduction of the modern hydraulic pressure sprays, various expedients were resorted to for primary scale removal. Moistened burlap thrown on the slab at the entry side of the rolling mill embodied the same scale-removing principle as the more common use of salt. In both instances the materials were used to get moisture between the work rolls and the stock, where it vaporized instantaneously with explosive effects and removed the scale. Of all flat, hot-rolled products, hot-rolled sheet and strip must meet the most stringent surface finish requirements, and it was natural that scale-removal methods and equipment would first reach their maximum development in connection with those product classifications which were rolled on continuous mills. The trend of development moved in the direction of the use of a leading roll stand in which light drafts were taken for the initial breaking of the scale. Hydraulic sprays, impinging on both top and bottom surfaces, were placed on the delivery side of the scale breaker and on the entry side of the roughing stands and the first finishing stand. Hydraulic pressures were increased with various installations from the 600 to 800 pounds per square inch which prevailed for general plant hydraulic equipment, up to 1,500 pounds per square inch. It was found, however, that with proper heating, spray pressures of 1,000 pounds per square inch were adequate for the production of surface finishes to meet consistently the most stringent requirements. The continuous hot-strip mill method of scale removal was, therefore, adopted for new plate-mill installations.

PLATE ROLLING

Plate-Rolling Variables—The rolling of plates is subjected to a number of variables. Control of temperature, if not properly effected, may cause variations in mechanical properties in steel from the same melt or lot of material. Inherent characteristics of equipment permit one mill to roll plates to closer limits than another with respect to thickness, weight, width, length, camber (the greatest deviation from a straight line along a longitudinal edge), and flatness of plate after mill finishing-pass delivery and ordinary roller-leveler treatment.

Other variables affecting rolling are the **mill spring** (the total looseness under load of all mechanical parts) between the roll necks and the housings, which makes it necessary to increase spring allowances for light mill construction as compared with heavier or more rigid mill construction for the same loading.

Bending of rolls and resultant **crown** in the plates are also variables which affect the accuracy of rolling. When the rolls are subjected to the separating force of a plate being rolled between them, they are equivalent to beams supported at the bearing centers and subjected to a uniformly distributed load over the length. Uniformly loaded beams have maximum deflection in the center and a similar condition exists in the rolls. For the same drafts, small-diameter rolls are subject to less separating force than large-diameter rolls but the latter have greater resistance to deflection. The minimum roll deflection and plate crown are found in a mill with small-diameter work rolls backed up by large-diameter rolls. Crown (increase in thickness of the rolled center of the plate over its edges) is related to the amount of bending or deflection in the rolls. A minimum crown and uniform thickness of plates are desirable for many applications, especially forming operations.

Roll wear is an important factor in rolling plates. There is only one point in the arc of contact of the rolls with the stock at which the linear speed of the rolls and the stock is identical. As mentioned in Chapter 19, this is called the neutral point. There is backward slippage of the stock on the entry side and forward slippage on the delivery side of the neutral point. Slippage contributes to roll wear, and as the central portion of the roll face comes in contact with the stock on all widths, it is subject to the most wear and gradually develops a hollow contour across the roll face, accompanied by a surface roughness.

The effect of roll wear on plate crown and surface finish can be visualized readily. An additional effect relates to plate flatness and becomes more pronounced with the thinner plate gages. Roller levelers operate on the principle of imposing a slight extension, through the bending-roll action, on each increment of constricted plate surface as it goes through each bending action in the leveler. The extensions which can be imposed by the bending action are relatively slight and, even for these to be accomplished in one pass, a minimum state of plasticity (corresponding to that which obtains at the lower transformation temperature) generally is required.

Because edges of rolled plate cool faster than the center, the desired shape for entry into the leveler, particularly for light gages, is one with a slight edge wave. A mill which is too full will deliver light-gage plates with center buckles that require excessive edge extensions in the leveler to secure flat delivery. Conversely, a hollow mill will deliver light-gage plates with more edge wave than can be compensated for by the limited extension of the central portions of the plate which can be accomplished in the leveler.

Temperature variation in the plate from the front end to the back is also a problem in rolling plates. Every roll pass involves a time interval for its accomplishment. In initial passes, when the stock is relatively thick and short, the time interval has no practical effect in creating a temperature differential from front to back. If the stock is being reduced to wide, light gage, and is elongated to long, thin lengths in the last several passes, the time interval will cause temperature differentials of such magnitude that the consequent gage differential must be anticipated in mill settings in order to retain the gage within tolerances. Differentials are minimized by shortening the time required for rolling.

LEVELING (FLATTENING)

The amount of flattening required by the plate after leaving the rolls generally increases with decreasing thickness of the plate. The effectiveness with which flattening can be accomplished by a leveler increases with decreasing roll diameters and spacing and with increasing temperatures. For light-gage plates, therefore, a roller leveler with small-diameter rolls and with close roll spacings should be located near the mill finishing stand.

Heavier-gage plates, at corresponding temperatures, require greater strength and rigidity of rolls than lighter-gage plates. The heavier gages usually are delivered from the rolls at higher finishing temperatures and require accelerated cooling prior to leveler entry or the leveler must be located at a greater distance from the finishing stand to permit proper cooling before leveler entry. A compromise in roll diameters and leveler location may be satisfactory if the range of gages produced does not include extremes.

Levelers with small-diameter bending rolls backed up by short, rigidly supported backing-up rolls are used for cold releveling. They provide the requisite combination of severe bending and roll rigidity.

COOLING

Plates delivered from the roller leveler must be cooled uniformly to avoid localized stresses that again would set up permanent localized distortions. As more heat is given up by the plate on contact with another metallic surface than by exposure to the atmosphere, it is necessary that cooling conveyors be so constructed that only momentary, staggered contacts are made with the bottom surface of the plate and cooling of the bottom side is effected primarily by radiation, similarly to the top surface. This cooling condition should be maintained until temperatures are reached at which the plates are no longer susceptible to distortion as a result of non-uniform cooling.

SHEARING AND CUTTING

Shearing—All plates are sheared above atmospheric temperature in normal production. The most important factor in shearing plates to the desired size is the proper allowance for shrinkage. The cooling rate of plates decreases as they approach atmospheric temperature, consequently, extremely long cooling lines would be required to permit plates to cool sufficiently for accurate shearing to be done without the necessity for making allowance for shrinkage.

Manual layout of plates for shearing introduces some degree of deviation from theoretical accuracy. Mechanical layout machines and calibrated dials integral with the shearing equipment reduce the frequency and extent of deviations. The fundamental characteristics of the shearing equipment itself influence the degree of accuracy that can be attained consistently.

Cutting—The chemical composition of the steel limits in a general way the maximum thickness of steel plate that can be produced by shearing.

Rectangular plates, circular and semi-circular plates, sketch plates, and rings all may require gas cutting or special cutting on machine-tool type equipment in certain combinations of chemical composition and thickness.

Special cutting equipment, such as circle shears, is used for cold-shearing shapes from rectangular plates whenever the composition and thickness of the plate permits.

IDENTIFICATION, INSPECTION AND LOADING

Except for material in the lighter gages or narrower widths, each plate is marked by hand-stamping, painting or writing with chalk to show the heat number and any other necessary identification marks. It also is inspected for possible defects. If the order calls for special treatment such as annealing or other forms of heat-treatment, the plates are sent to the heat-treating department. Samples cut from the plates are usually subjected to the specified mechanical tests. If the plates meet the requirements, they then are loaded in railroad cars in accordance with standard loading practice.

SECTION 3

GENERAL TYPES OF PLATE MILLS

Plate-rolling mills are generally considered in two very broad design classifications. One type includes the **universal mills,** which are characterized by vertical rolls preceding and following the horizontal rolls. The horizontal and the vertical rolls are integrated into a single mill unit and work the stock simultaneously. The purpose of the vertical rolls is not only to work the edges of the stock in the process of reduction, but also to produce a rolled width in conformance with specified standard tolerances.

The second type includes the **sheared-plate mills,** some of which may include edge-working equipment. While some installations use the edging equipment for both edge working and approximate width sizing, final widths are attained by edge shearing. Sheared-plate mills, in turn, may be subdivided into the following mill types: (1) the single-stand two-high pull-over mill, (2) the single-stand two-high reversing mill, (3) the conventional single-stand three-high mill, (4) the single-stand four-high reversing mill, (5) the tandem mill, (6) the semi-continuous mill, and (7) the continuous mill.

A. TWO-HIGH PULL-OVER, TWO-HIGH SINGLE-STAND REVERSING AND THREE-HIGH PLATE MILLS

Two-High Pull-Over Mills—The two-high pull-over plate mills were essentially an adaptation of the then existing sheet mills to plate rolling. Prior to the development of mechanical passers, single-stand hot sheet mills were drafted in one direction only, and the sheet packs were returned for successive passes by being lifted manually on to the top roll and pulled over by hand to the starting or entry side with the aid of the tractive friction of the top roll. Roll settings were altered after each pass by hand operation of levers, which rotated the head screws. Plates rolled on these mills were limited in size and weight by the ability to handle manually. This restricted their utility and soon rendered these mills obsolete for producing finished plate. Two-high non-reversing mills still are in operation, however, in the form of single-pass units, such as scale breakers and roughers, in tandem arrangements in which the finishing-mill unit is either a three- or a four-high mill.

Two-High Single-Stand Reversing Mills—Hot-rolled sheet production by the pack method anteceded volume tonnage production, and recognition of the impracticability of handling heavy plates on two-high pull-over mills prompted the introduction of reversing engines for two-high mills for rolling plates. These mills, likewise, soon reached their practical limit of application, particularly for the production of wide, lighter-gage plate. The fact that all passes from slab to finished plate were made on the same set of rolls accelerated roll wear, which is always greatest in the central portion of the roll body and in itself imposes a restriction on the gage that can be finished satisfactorily. Roll deflection also is an important factor and, for the same roll diameter, increases with the body length for like reductions. An increase in the roll diameter to provide more strength and stiffness increases the separating force between the rolls for the same draft, because of the greater area of contact between the stock and the rolls. The lessening of roll deflection, therefore, progresses at a diminishing ratio with increasing roll diameters.

The art of casting massive rolls developed gradually. Increased roll separating forces for like reductions meant greater power requirements for rolling, as well as to overcome greater resistance to acceleration and deceleration. The design of reversing engines of increasing power also was a gradual development. Neither of these developments progressed sufficiently to meet expanding requirements for plates prior to the invention of the three-high mill.

Two-high, single-stand, reversing plate mills are obsolete in this country, and a detailed description of any installation would have historical value only.

Three-High Plate Mills—The invention of the three-high mill provided design features which, to a degree, overcame some of the principal limitations of the two-high reversing type. In the three-high mill, the top and the bottom rolls are of large diameter, whereas the middle roll is friction-driven and usually about two-thirds of the diameter of the top and bottom rolls. The top roll can be raised and lowered in the housing by power-operated screws, and the middle roll can be brought into contact alternately with the top and the bottom rolls. In making the bottom pass, the stock passes between the middle and the bottom roll while the top roll serves as a backup roll. The stock is raised on the delivery side by a tilting table for a return pass between the middle and the top roll, while the bottom roll serves as a backup roll. The sequence of alternate passes is continued until the stock is reduced to the desired finished plate thickness.

The middle roll is changed when combined roll wear produces a crowned plate which approaches the permissible tolerance limits. The replacement roll is itself crowned to compensate for the wear which already has taken place on the top and the bottom rolls. Successive replacements in the course of a week's rolling schedule are turned with progressively increased crowns to compensate for the continued wear of the top and the bottom rolls. During the weekly mill-repair shutdown, the top and the bottom rolls are either turned in place to their original contours or are replaced with newly dressed rolls. The cycle of replacement of middle rolls with progressively increased crowns is repeated in the following week.

The fact that one of the rolls in contact with the stock on each pass is of smaller diameter than is required for strength (the requisite strength being provided by the roll serving as a backup) reduces the total roll separating force for like drafts in contrast with a two-high mill. This principle, when applied to wide plate production, served to solve the problem of providing rolls of the required strength without being too massive. The fact that only one smaller-diameter roll needed to be replaced in the course of a rolling schedule for wear compensation, eased the roll-changing problem. The three-high roll arrangement, with tilting tables on entry and delivery sides, eliminated the necessity for using reversing engines. The tilting tables and the undirectional main drives permitted a shortening of the rolling-time cycle and provided a temperature advantage in the finishing of light-gage plates. Continued trade demands for improved finishes, lighter gages, and closer and more uniform rolling to desired dimensions (width and thickness) for many applications, which the three-high mill could not meet consistently, hastened the development of the other plate-mill types.

The era of the predominance of three-high plate mills was coincident with the development of open-hearth furnaces in which furnace capacities were relatively small, ranging from 40 to 100 tons. Ingots, with the exception of those poured for armor plates, were also relatively small and 40-inch maximum width dimensions were about the largest produced. The three-high mills, however, were not as restricted in the production of plate-size ranges as might be inferred from the restricted ingot sizes. Slabs were conveyed to the mill in a broadside position and after the requisite number of passes were taken to attain plate widths, turning hooks attached to rigid masts were employed to turn the stock 90 degrees by utilizing table traction. The stock was then reduced to final thickness in successive passes.

B. FOUR-HIGH REVERSING PLATE MILLS

The development of the four-high reversing plate mill further increased the advantages which the three-high mill possessed when compared with the two-high reversing mill. The backup-roll to work-roll diameter ratios were increased to over two-to-one as compared with the three-to-two ratios prevailing in three-high mills. For like reductions, therefore, not only is the total roll separating force less, but also strength is provided for each pass by the backup rolls on both top and bottom sides. A four-high reversing plate mill was in operation in 1917 at the Coatesville, Pennsylvania, plant of the Lukens Steel Company; but the general adoption of the type for plate rolling was retarded until antifriction bearings for the rolls became available. Such bearings were developed for the hot-strip mills and the cold-reduction mills and their use was extended to four-high reversing plate mills. A concurrent development was the designing of multi-armature reversing motors for primary mills. The de-

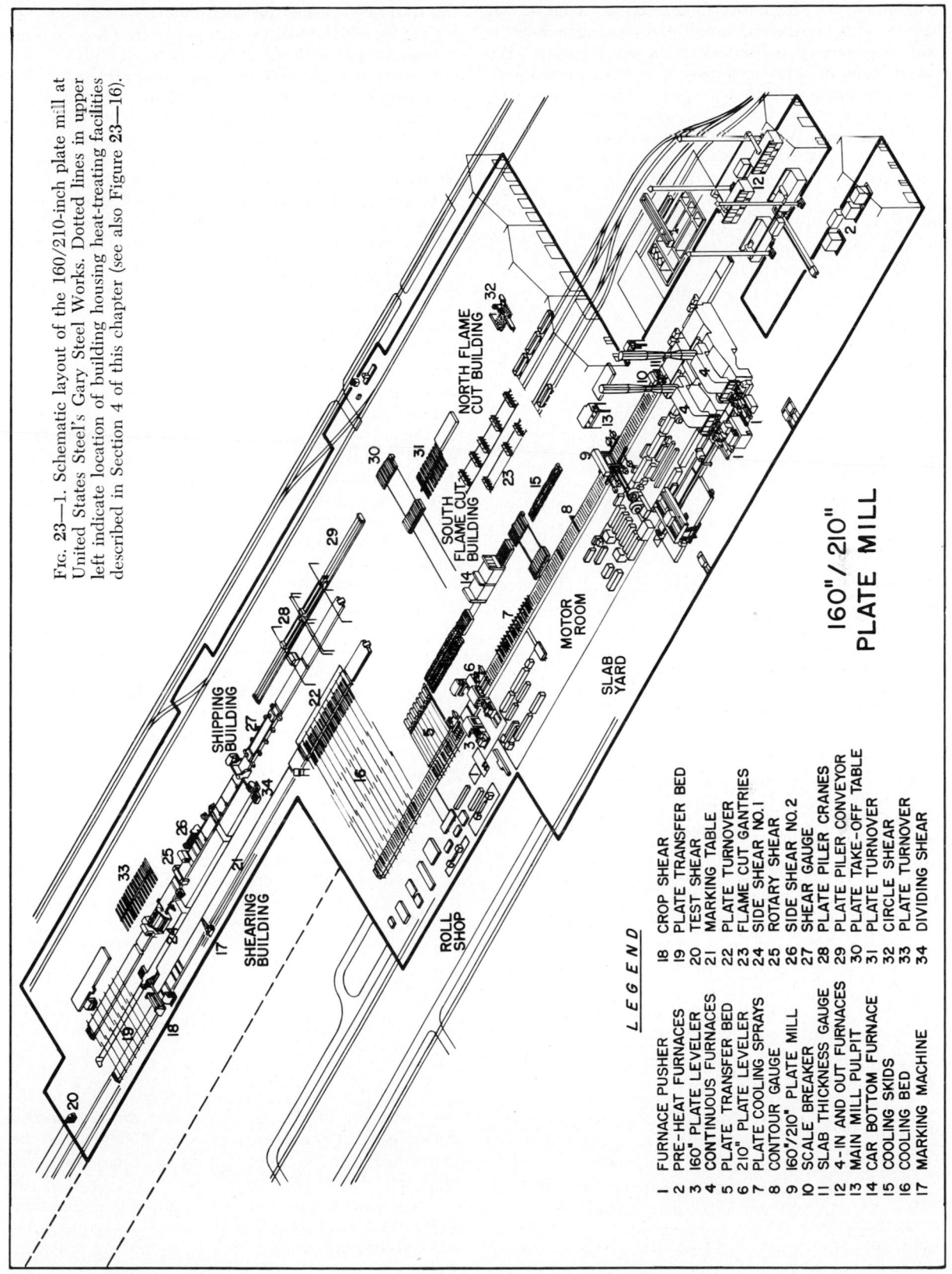

FIG. 23—1. Schematic layout of the 160/210-inch plate mill at United States Steel's Gary Steel Works. Dotted lines in upper left indicate location of building housing heat-treating facilities described in Section 4 of this chapter (see also Figure 23—16).

160"/ 210"
PLATE MILL

LEGEND

1 FURNACE PUSHER
2 PRE-HEAT FURNACES
3 160" PLATE LEVELER
4 CONTINUOUS FURNACES
5 PLATE TRANSFER BED
6 210" PLATE LEVELER
7 PLATE COOLING SPRAYS
8 CONTOUR GAUGE
9 160"/210" PLATE MILL
10 SCALE BREAKER
11 SLAB THICKNESS GAUGE
12 4-IN AND OUT FURNACES
13 MAIN MILL PULPIT
14 CAR BOTTOM FURNACE
15 COOLING SKIDS
16 COOLING BED
17 MARKING MACHINE

18 CROP SHEAR
19 PLATE TRANSFER BED
20 TEST SHEAR
21 MARKING TABLE
22 PLATE TURNOVER
23 FLAME CUT GANTRIES
24 SIDE SHEAR NO.1
25 ROTARY SHEAR
26 SIDE SHEAR NO.2
27 SHEAR GAUGE
28 PLATE PILER CRANES
29 PLATE PILER CONVEYOR
30 PLATE TAKE-OFF TABLE
31 PLATE TURNOVER
32 CIRCLE SHEAR
33 PLATE TURNOVER
34 DIVIDING SHEAR

velopment of the latter motor types reduced the inertia effects of massive mill parts and their relation to acceleration and deceleration on reversals. The multi-armature motors replaced reversing steam engines as prime movers.

160/210-INCH PLATE MILL AT GARY STEEL WORKS

This new mill, located at United States Steel's Gary Steel Works, is the world's largest plate mill. General layout of the mill is shown in Figure 23—1.

Slab Yard—All slabs for the new plate mill are produced on a 46-inch universal slabbing mill.

The slabs, after being conditioned either by hand scarfing or by machine scarfing at the conditioning area, are delivered to the 160/210-inch mill slab yard by one of three transfer cars. Two of the cars are arranged to transfer slabs directly from the conditioning area to the slab yard after machine scarfing. Three electric overhead traveling cranes, equipped with slab tongs, are used to place the slabs into stock for later transfer to the continuous-furnace assembly area or the in-and-out furnace charging area. At this point the slabs are identified with a serial number in accordance with a pre-determined schedule, and placed on the slab-charging table.

Slab-Reheating Furnaces—Heating facilities consist of two double-row continuous-type furnaces and four batch-type in-and-out furnaces.

The continuous furnaces each have six water-cooled skids, with a pusher for each group of three skids. Slab sizes range from 4 inches to 12 inches thick and from 72 inches to 144 inches in length. A television receiver indicates to the pusher operator the slab position at the drop-out end of the furnace. The furnaces are quadruple fired, with four heating zones. The steel enters the primary or preheating zone cold. As it is pushed through this zone, it is heated to between 800° and 1200° F. It then passes through the two heating zones (the first bottom-fired and the second top- and bottom-fired) where it is heated to its rolling temperature of approximately 2400° F. In the final or soaking zone, slab temperatures are equalized with the slabs supported on a dry hearth.

The four in-and-out batch-type furnaces normally are used to heat slabs under 4 inches thick, over 12 inches thick, or less than 72 inches in length, and slabs for small orders or other slabs requiring special heating. An electric overhead traveling "peel"-type crane charges and draws the slabs and places them directly on the mill-approach roll table.

Coke-oven gas with a heating value of 535 Btu per cu. ft. is normally used for firing both the continuous and the in-and-out furnaces, with auxiliary facilities provided for firing fuel oil.

Three hood-type preheating furnaces are located in the slab yard, adjacent to the in-and-out furnaces.

Scalebreaker—The scalebreaker is a two-high mill with 40-inch diameter grooved rolls. A slab measuring gage is located ahead of the scalebreaker to prevent overdrafting. This mill is equipped with water sprays operating at 1500 lb. per sq. in. for descaling on both the entry and exit sides. In addition to scale breaking,

this stand establishes the slab thickness for slabs entering the four-high mill.

Slab Turnaround—A slab turnaround with a mushroom-type lift is used for turning slabs 90 degrees before broadsiding at the four-high mill. The lift is operated by pressure supplied at 2400 lb. per sq. in. by the hydraulic roll-balance system, and has a double-acting cylinder for positive return. The rotating drive is powered by a non-reversing electric motor.

Four-High Reversing Stand—The four-high reversing stand where the actual rolling of plates is performed (Figure 23—2) has adjustable housings that permit operation as either 160-inch or a 210-inch mill. This is accomplished by shifting the housings to the proper positions and installing rolls of the proper length. In order to move the housings, all mill rolls, bearings, feed rolls, spray headers and stripper plates are removed, and hydraulic clamps holding the housings at the shoe-plate elevation are loosened. A center tapered pin that keys the upper portion of the housings together is lifted from position, and hydraulic pressure from the roll-balance system is applied to slide the housings into the new position. A four-high set of rolls of the proper length is then installed and the mill accessories are replaced.

Two 6000-horsepower, 40/80 rev. per min., single-armature, direct-current motors drive the two work rolls with a separate motor driving each roll. To permit the same drive spindles to be used with rolls of either 160- or 210-inch length, the 160-inch rolls have a 25-inch integral extension on the drive ends.

A roll-changing sled is used for changing both the work rolls and back-up rolls. The roll assemblies are retracted on the sled and there are disassembled and handled with an electric overhead traveling crane.

The back-up rolls are ground truly cylindrical and the work rolls are crowned 0.008 inch on the diameter when a complete set of four new rolls are installed. Work rolls are replaced from time to time without changing the back-up rolls until wear of the latter has become excessive. As wear on the back-up rolls increases, work-roll crowns are gradually increased to 0.016 inch, after which new back-up rolls are installed.

Load cells and thickness gages are mounted in the mill as sensors for automatic operation, and controls are included for full manual operation.

Plate sizes produced by the mill are $3/16$-inch to 15 inches in thickness, 30 inches to 200 inches in width, and 10 to 70 feet in length. Longer lengths may be rolled, depending upon slab weights, physical rolling characteristics and transfer-equipment problems for the particular plate size. Most slabs are reduced in thickness at the scalebreaker, turned 90 degrees on the mushroom-type lift, rolled to proper width on the four-high mill, turned 90 degrees on the spin table at the delivery side of the four high mill, and then rolled straightaway to gage. Some plate product requires additional turning during rolling to obtain optimum yield.

Scale removed from slabs at the scalebreaker is collected by dry-type shuttle conveyors up to the entry end of the scalebreaker stand; after this point, all

Fig. 23—2. Delivery side of the 160/210-inch plate mill at the Gary Steel Works of United States Steel Corporation. In this illustration, the mill is operating as a 160-inch mill.

scale is sluiced by water to conventional retention pits that are equipped with oil-skimming devices.

Automatic Operation—The 160/210-inch main mill can be operated manually or programmed on a computer with automatic control of the scalebreaker, mushroom-type turnaround, and the four-high mill. The automatic-control system combines sequencing operations, computing, and correction monitoring (based on roll-force measurement, length gage measurement, and a profile gage) to produce plates within close tolerances of specified thickness, width, and length. The automatic control is operated from input data provided by cards fed into an automatic card reader in the same sequence as the slabs are delivered to the mill roller-table line. The input data include: (a) the grade of steel, (b) the slab dimensions and (c) the desired finished gage and width, including side and end crop allowances. From this input data, and permanently stored instruction data, the computer determines the necessary number and sequence of passes; the position setting of scalebreaker centering guides, scalebreaker screwdown adjustment, mushroom turnaround, mill front centering guides, mill screwdown and mill back centering guides for each pass; passes on which the spin turn is required; and passes on which the scalebreaker and mill descaling sprays are to be used, before and after spreading. This computed program may then be corrected at any time as the monitoring devices recognize that the feedback does not correspond to those calculated by the computer.

A rolling pulpit with all necessary instrumentation including the programming equipment is located just to the entry side of the mill, approximately 30 feet above floor level.

Tables—All mill tables are individually driven, with adjacent rollers driven from opposite sides of the table. The plate-spin table, comprised of 11 alternately tapered rolls, turns the plate by having adjacent rollers rotate in opposite directions.

Transfer Tables and Cooling Sprays—A long run-out table is located between the mill and the levelers where an electric overhead traveling crane, equipped with a cradle, has access between the rolls to remove heavy-gage flame-cut product, over 10 inches thick, to a transfer buggy. This buggy travels to the south flame-cut building, where they are removed by a plate "take-off table." Also located over these tables is a system of cooling sprays comprised of inverted L-shaped pipes that are motorized to swing out of line in case of a cobble on the roller line. These sprays cool plates in two separate spray patterns, 130 inches and 210 inches in width, respectively.

The No. 1 flame-cut transfer cooling bed is located after the levelers for transfer of 3-inch to 10-inch thick flame-cut product into the south flame-cut building. The cooling bed is of the link-and-dog type and can handle plates up to 720 inches in length. The plates are removed by electric overhead traveling cranes equipped with a spreader beam having either multiple "C" hooks or magnets, and are placed on cooling skids or directly on the brick floor when cooling in piles is required.

All other plates, under 3 inches thick, pass over the main cooling-bed transfer that will handle plate with a maximum length of 1500 inches. The transfer is of the chain-link, disappearing dog type, with a sprocket drive having five sections, with a cast-iron grid design that affords maximum support for $3/16$-inch thick plate and excellent cooling for heavier gages.

Levelers—There are two levelers: the 160-inch leveler which normally levels plates less than 150 inches wide and the 210-inch leveler for plates from 150 inches to 210 inches wide. Since the 210-inch leveler has three 9-inch back-up rolls for each leveler roll, it is also a good supplementary leveler for lighter-gage plates that are narrower than 150 inches wide. Both levelers are of the retractable type with attached roll table. The levelers are designed to level hot plates from $3/16$-inch to 2-inch thickness, and both have sufficient opening to pass plates up to 6 inches thick.

Plate-Inspection Turnovers—There are three plate-inspection turnovers of the multiple-arm scissors type that permit turning plates 180 degrees to permit complete bottom-side inspection.

The first turnover is part of the cooling-bed transfer where plates up to 1500 inches long can be turned and inspected. Any defect can be marked for possible cutting out at the shears or, if the plate requires minor spot grinding, that particular surface may be left in the upward position. After this inspection, plates over $1\frac{1}{2}$ inches thick are removed to the north flame-cut building by magnet-equipped electric overhead traveling cranes. All sheared plate is transferred on the roller line to the plate-marking tables.

Two additional plate turnovers, designed to turn plates up to 720 inches in length, are located in the finishing end to facilitate final inspection of plates.

Plate Marking—At the plate-marking tables, the layout crew checks the rough plate for pattern size, stencils necessary slab identification, customer requirements and shipping destination on the plate. Test specimens are also sketched out and stamped at this point.

The plate-marking machine traverses the full length of the table on rails, with an arm extending out over the entire roller line. Attached to the arm are three marking heads: two to mark the ordered width of the plates for side-shear cutting, and one as an auxiliary head to mark a guide line (24 inches from the left edge line) for the shearman's use. The machine is adjustable to mark plates from $3/16$ inch to $1\frac{1}{2}$ inches thick, up to 210 inches wide and 125 feet long.

Crop Shear—The crop shear can cut a $1\frac{1}{2}$-inch carbon steel plate, 210 inches wide. This shear (as are the dividing and side shears) is of the motor-driven start-stop crank type with open throat and has a raked guillotine-type moving upper knife. The hold-down is independently mounted on the top knife. Usually, both front and back end crops are cut with this shear. It also performs any multiple cutting required by the rough plate length being greater than that of the transfer bed. After cropping, the plate is transferred 90 degrees across an 1140-inch transfer of the chain-link disappearing-dog type to the side-shear line.

Side Shears—Plate-positioning magnets mounted below the top of the table rollers position the front end of the plate under the No. 1 side-shear knife. A traverse pusher and a hold-down maintain plate alignment during shearing to assure a straight sheared edge. Knife length is 210 inches.

The No. 2 side shear is equipped with almost identical features as the No. 1 side shear but, of course, is located on the opposite side of the shear line. The edge cut by the No. 1 side shear is pushed by a straight edge to provide a straight cut at the No. 2 side shear. No. 2 side shear is equipped with a motor-driven plate-width gage, used for remote indication of plate width. A digital readout is located in the No. 2 side-shear pulpit for the operator to set the desired sheared width. At this point, it can be determined how close to ordered plate size the shears have trimmed. With the extended travel of the plates during the cooling cycle, accurate width and length tolerances can be met.

Dividing Shear—The dividing shear has a dual function of dividing the plate into ordered lengths and of accurately cutting the ends of the plate. Plate-positioning magnets and movable edging rollers move and hold the plate edge snugly against the fixed side guard. There are two shear-gage stops, one used for short cutting and one used for long cutting, thus minimizing the time required for setting plate-cutting lengths. This shear features motorized upper-block adjustment wedges which alter the knife gap at the operators' discretion to obtain optimum shearing of both light and heavy plates.

Scrap Shears—Each product shear is equipped with an individual pallet-type scrap conveyor and scrap shear. All crop scrap is cut to open-hearth charging-box size, and transferred by chutes to a system of shuttle conveyors at basement level. The shuttle conveyors discharge to self-dumping boxes remote from the immediate work area for transfer to rail cars.

Test pieces are cut by the scrap shearman and transferred to the operating floor by apron-type conveyors.

Inspection and Piling—After shearing, each plate is weighed on a roller-type scale table of the load-cell type, gaged, and inspected for dimensional accuracy. The plates are then transferred to the piling tables in the shipping bay by two magnet-equipped transfer cranes. At this point, the plates either are loaded directly into cars or assembled and stored in piles for later loading.

Flame Cutting—The flame-cutting operation is performed in two adjacent building bays. The light flame-cutting area usually handles plates up to 3 inches thick, 210 inches wide and of lengths up to 1000 inches. This burning bed consists of five motorized gantry-type burning machines, each equipped with five torches. The usual operation consists of one gantry machine making four parallel length cuts while alternate machines are making and cutting the end crops. Crop scrap is prepared simultaneously by hand torch. A car-bottom furnace is provided in this area for various heating, stress-relieving and normalizing operations.

The heavy flame-cutting bed is similarly equipped with three motorized gantry-type burning machines, and usually handles plates 4 inches to 15 inches thick, up to 160 inches wide.

Flame-cut plates are inspected, weighed, and shipped by rail and truck in the immediate area.

Heat-Treating Facilities—A complete continuous heat-treating department has been provided to heat treat certain grades of plates rolled on the 160/210-inch mill: the layout and equipment are described in Section 4 of this chapter.

Roll Shop—The roll shop has facilities for handling the rolls and bearings of the 160/210-inch mill and the 46-inch slab mill that supplies the 160/210-inch mill. The equipment includes roll lathe, roll grinder, bearing extractors, degreaser, and shear-knife grinder, with adequate storage and working area served by an electric overhead traveling crane.

160-INCH FOUR-HIGH PLATE MILL AT HOMESTEAD DISTRICT WORKS

The 160-inch mill at Homestead District Works, Figure 23—3, has a cold-slab storage yard that provides for stocking approximately 15,000 tons of slabs in accordance with a predetermined rolling sequence. Six gas-fired preheating pits are located in this yard; each has a capacity of approximately 10 slabs (50 tons) and is capable of heating cold steel to a temperature of 1200° F in 24 hours. Three gas-fired pre-heating hoods, each with a capacity of approximately 120 tons, can heat cold steel to a temperature of 1600° F in 24 hours. Slabs are transferred to the reheating-furnace areas by two standard-gage shuttle-car transfers, powered by Diesel-electric locomotives.

The slab-heating equipment consists of two continuous-type furnaces and two batch or in-and-out type furnaces. The batch-type furnaces are designed to heat slabs of a maximum size of 144 inches long by 20½ inches thick. They are two-zone-controlled, end-fired, recuperative-type furnaces, designed to operate on a mixture of coke-oven and natural gas and have a rated heating capacity of 15 tons per hour from cold to 2250° F. These furnaces are served by a charging crane which charges the cold slabs from the transfer car into the furnace and draws the heated slabs and delivers them on to the furnace delivery table.

The continuous-type furnaces are designed to heat slabs from 3 to 12 inches thick, 44 to 60 inches wide and 70 to 120 inches long. They are conventional two-zone-controlled, triple-fired, end-charged-and-discharged, recuperative-type furnaces. The top and the bottom burners of the primary heating zone are designed to burn a mixture of coke-oven and natural gas as a primary fuel and also can burn fuel oil as an alternate fuel. Only the gas mixture is burned in the holding zone. The heating capacity of each furnace is approximately 70 tons per hour from cold to 2250° F with full hearth coverage.

The continuous furnaces are served by an electric overhead traveling crane which takes the slabs from the transfer cars by magnet or slab-handling tongs, and places them on the furnace charging table. The slabs are fed through the furnaces by double rack-type

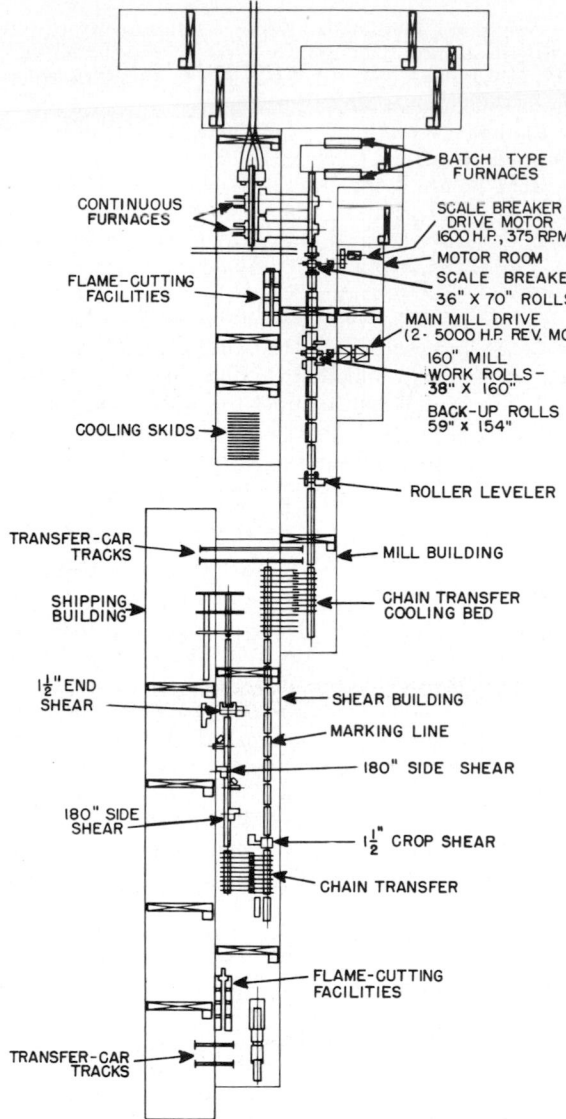

FIG. 23—3. Diagram (not to scale) of the physical layout of equipment comprising the 160-inch mill at Homestead District Works.

pushers arranged to feed two rows of slabs through each furnace (Figure 23—4). Slabs are discharged from the delivery end, and slide down the furnace dropout skids to the furnace delivery table against spring-backed bumpers.

Heated slabs are conveyed on a roller table from the furnaces to a scalebreaker stand (Figure 23—5) which is a two-high mill with fluted alloy-steel rolls, operating in water-lubricated composition bearings.

The top roll is balanced by carrier bars supported from a yoke which is actuated by hydraulic jacks and accumulator to hold the top roll against the housing screw. The screws are operated by 50-horsepower motors through worm reduction gearing at a lineal vertical speed of 11 inches per minute. The rolls are changed at approximately one-month intervals under normal operating conditions. Approximately four

hours are required to make the roll change with the use of a "C" hook and an overhead crane.

The mill is driven through a double-reduction flywheel gear drive, a universal leading spindle, mill pinions and universal mill spindles, resulting in a lineal roll speed of 295.6 feet per minute. A meter in the pulpit gives the operator a reading of the opening between rolls at all times. Drafts of ½ inch may be taken on this stand, and the passage of the slab is guided to and from the mill by twin adjustable side-guides. Primary descaling is completed on the delivery side of the mill as the slab is passed through top and bottom hydraulic sprays operating at a pressure of 1,500 pounds per square inch.

The distance between the 160-inch reversing-mill stand (Figure 23—6) and the scale breaker is spanned by 40 feet of 72-inch-wide table and 120 feet of 168-inch-wide table. All table rollers in this mill are journalled in antifriction bearings. A lift-and-turn table device is located on the reversing-mill side of the junction between the narrow and the wide table sections. The turntable is elevated and lowered by oil-hydraulic pressure and turned by a motor-operated rack and pinion. This permits either straightaway or broadside slab entry into the reversing mill. When spreading is required in the first pass, the slab may be entered following the preceding plate without a turning delay.

The crowned (0.024-inch maximum) alloy-iron work rolls of the four-high reversing stand are equipped with four-row tapered roller bearings. The alloy-steel backup rolls employ oil-film bearings through which the roll-separating force is transmitted. Thrust is taken by two-row steep-angle tapered thrust bearings. The top rolls are balanced by hydraulic jacks mounted in the bottom backup chucks. An automatic forced-feed lubricating system is connected with all wearing surfaces on the mill other than the oil-film bearings.

Three sets of work rolls are used in the course of a normal weekly rolling schedule. Approximately one hour is required for a work-roll change, which is accomplished by an overhead crane-suspended "C" hook, equipped with a motor-driven shifting device that positions the hook suspension over the center of gravity of the unloaded or loaded hook. The average time between complete roll changes, including the backup rolls, is three weeks. The complete roll change requires approximately ten hours, with the backup rolls being moved in and out of the mill on a motor-driven slide.

The reversing motors are each directly connected to a work roll through universal spindles. The motor speed range is from 40 to 80 r.p.m., which provides a roll surface speed of 400 to 800 feet per minute. The mill screws are operated by two 150-horsepower mill-type motors, supplied by a variable-voltage motor-generator set. A pre-set automatic screw-down control, with optional manual control, is provided for this mill. Provision is made to set up one schedule while another is being run. The control is operated by the screw-down operator, who also reverses the mill drive and who can make manual adjustments to the screw

Fig. 23—4. General view of the charging end of continuous-type reheating furnaces supplying hot slabs to the 160-inch plate mill at Homestead District Works.

settings by interrupting any automatic setting without affecting the accuracy of the following automatic stop. The mill is capable of producing the minimum gage of $\frac{3}{16}$ inch to sheared widths of 120 inches. Auxiliary facility limitations restrict the sheared-plate gages to a $\frac{3}{16}$ to $1\frac{1}{2}$-inch range, widths to a $38\frac{1}{2}$ to 144-inch range and lengths to a 720-inch maximum. Flame-cut plates range from $1\frac{1}{2}$ to 15-inch thickness and a maximum of 144 and 480 inches in width and length, respectively.

The front and the rear mill tables have tapered table rollers. Even-numbered rollers all are tapered in the same direction and driven as a unit. Odd-numbered rollers are tapered in the opposite direction and also are driven as a unit. By rotating the alternate roller units in opposite directions, it is possible to turn a slab 90 degrees as desired. Heavy, powered side-guards are on each side of the mill for squaring and centering the slabs and holding the plates during the rolling operation. Hydraulic sprays on both sides of the mill, operating at a pressure of 1400 pounds per square inch, are utilized for top and bottom secondary scale removal.

The remainder of the distance between the four-high mill and the leveler is occupied by a conveying table. Top and bottom water sprays facilitate the cooling of heavier-gaged plates prior to leveler entry and retard secondary scale formation. A section of the table on each side of the leveler is designed to permit plate removal by a "C" hook suspended from an overhead crane. The plates may be transferred to either one of two motor-driven transfer cars and subsequently transferred to the cooling area of the adjacent flame-cutting building or to the controlled-cooling facilities located in the shipping yard.

The leveler has two entry pinch rolls and 6 top and 5 bottom bending rolls. The machine is driven by a 250-horsepower, 400 r.p.m. motor, and positioning is accomplished through a selective screwdown assembly which is equipped with drum indicators located at all four corners of the leveler housing. The leveler can level structural-grade plates of $1\frac{1}{2}$-inch thickness and can be raised to a maximum passage opening of 6 inches.

From the leveler, the plates travel to a chain-transfer cooling bed. This grid-type bed delivers the plates from the mill building onto a disc-roller marking table located in the shear building. A motor-propelled automatic measuring and marking machine moves parallel with this table. Indexed longitudinal and transverse movements enable the operator to measure and mark off mechanically any desired size and shape of a rectangular plate, and scribe a reference line which is used by the side-shear operator in the trimming of the side scrap. Beyond the marking machine, all required identification stamping and painting of the plates and test coupons are performed manually prior to entry in the crop shear.

The crop shear or end shear is capable, in common with the main line shear units, of cutting $1\frac{1}{2}$-inch gage to the maximum width produced. Powered mechanical manipulators are available for the square positioning of the plate. Oil hydraulic hold-down gags furnish positive clamping for the shearing stroke. The shear operates on the oil-hydraulic principle, and has a self-contained pump with motor drive. The crop shear is used for dividing plates that are too long to pass over a second transfer, and for front-end shearing of heavy, wide plates, which must be free of shear bow.

Plates from the crop shear are delivered either to

Fig. 23—5. Close-up view of the scalebreaker stand of the 160-inch plate mill at Homestead District Works.

another chain transfer or to a table section beyond the transfer, which is equipped with roll-off lifting arms and a side piling bed. This run-off and piling bed is utilized to divert flame-cut plates of such size and composition that will permit their conveyance to this point without the necessity of slow-cooling cycles. Plates to be finish-sheared are moved across the transfer to the transfer run-out tables, which double back through the shear building and are parallel to the marking line.

The main shear line consists of two side shears and one end shear. These shears are similar in design and construction to the crop shear, with the exception that the side shears have longer knives. The side shears are staggered on either side of the table. The side crop is sheared at the first side shear by positioning the plates to the reference line. A series of electromagnets with hydraulic vertical motion and screw drive transverse motion are utilized to position the plate so that the reference line is matched with a positioning line on the shear block. A mechanical width-gage guide is provided at the second side shear, which facilitates the positioning of the plate by working against the finished

sheared edge; and its position in relation to the shear knife is recorded on a dial located on the shear housing. The end shear is a duplicate of the crop shear and is equipped with squaring pushers located on the entry side, and two motorized gage stops on the delivery side, which gage plates mechanically to predetermined lengths. One stop is used for short and the other for long lengths in the 60- to 720-inch sheared-length range.

Crop and end shear auxiliary equipment consists of motor-driven scrap shears. A butterfly chute arrangement diverts test coupons, "block sheared," to a test box in which they are periodically delivered to a test-cutting shear for final handling. The test-cutting shear is also motor-driven. The side shears are provided with motor-driven scrap shears to which side scrap is fed by conveyors located below the table level, and the cut scrap is guided to removal buckets through gravity chutes.

Plates are delivered from the end shear to a scale table, where they are weighed individually. They then proceed to a table section spanned by two transverse, selective, electromagnetic-type piling cranes. One

FIG. 23—6. The 160-inch reversing mill stand of the 160-inch plate mill at Homestead District Works, showing powered side guards for squaring and centering slabs and holding plates during the rolling operation.

crane can handle a 360-inch plate length, and the two cranes working together can handle a 720-inch plate length. Lifting force of the magnets can be regulated at will to provide a wide range in the lift combinations. The cranes transfer the plates into the shipping building and deposit and pile them on gravity conveyor tables. The piles are moved by a conveyor-chain dog into positions from which they can be picked up by the overhead shipping cranes.

The shipping building is equipped with a shipping track extending its entire length. A connecting spur track of an 8-car capacity is located in an adjoining lean-to section of the building. This track is not serviced by overhead cranes and is used for preparing cars which require special blocking, either prior to or after loading. The shipping building is serviced by four electric overhead traveling cranes of the double-hoist type. This building also is equipped with controlled-cooling hoods. Two additional inlets into this yard, other than the piling cranes just mentioned, are provided in the form of motor-driven transfer cars located at the extreme ends of the building. One car delivers directly from the mill building, and the other car delivers from the flame-cutting unit located in the end of the shear building.

The flame-cutting unit, located at the end of the shear building, is equipped with a flame planer, three pantographs, and sketch-cutting machines. The flame planer is designed primarily for side and end trim-

ming as well as splitting rectangular-shaped plates. The pantograph machines are designed primarily for intricate shape cutting, although they can be used efficiently for cutting rectangular shapes. Magnetic tracing mechanisms, traveling over templates or operated manually over sketch drawings, guide the torch through the course desired.

Another flame-cutting unit is located in a building parallel and adjacent to the mill building. A continuation of this building merges with the end of the continuous-furnace building, and the two cranes servicing this unit operate on a common runway with the crane servicing the continuous furnaces. This unit is equipped with three pantograph sketch-cutting machines, two large heat-treating ovens, and a heat-treating pit. The heat-treating facilities are used extensively in preheating, stress-relieving, normalizing and the controlled cooling of flame-cut products requiring these treatments. The heat-treating ovens also can be used for preheating slabs prior to charging in the slab-heating furnaces when such practice is necessary. Cooling skids are provided in this area for heavy-gage plates which are transferred hot from the mill by a transfer car previously mentioned.

The greasing system for all table bearings, spindles, spindle carriers, jacks, slide joints, etc., is of the automatic "single-line" reversing type and contains eleven major pumping units.

Oil lubrication for the majority of the equipment,

such as table line shafts, gears and bearings, leveler drives, screw-down drives, reduction gears, pinions, backup-roll bearings, and motor-room equipment, is accomplished by circulating systems of the single- and double-tank types.

C. TANDEM MILLS

Many of the original single-stand plate mills have been supplemented by an additional stand to form a tandem plate mill. The various tandem-mill arrangements represent a wide variety of mill unit combinations, which achieve two principal objectives. When the total work of reducing slab to plate is divided between two mill stands, satisfactory surface finish and shape of rolls can be maintained for longer periods between roll changes. Secondly, since the work is divided between two units operating simultaneously, the required time interval for the reduction of a slab to a plate is reduced and the overall capacity of the unit is increased correspondingly.

A wide variety of tandem arrangements exists because they represent modifications of original rather than new installations, and because they were accomplished by the maximum utilization of existing equipment, the minimum expenditure for new equipment and a minimum of alteration to auxiliary facilities. The tandem arrangements, consequently, may include a two-high reversing rougher with a three-high finisher; a two-high reversing rougher with a four-high finisher; a three-high rougher with a three-high finisher; or a three-high rougher with a four-high finisher.

The two principal advantages of the tandem mills over the corresponding single-stand mills have been stated. No specific installation has mill or auxiliary equipment of engineering interest which is not covered in descriptions of more standardized arrangements.

D. SEMI-CONTINUOUS AND CONTINUOUS MILLS

These plate mills constitute the plate-mill groupings which include multipass, reversing, roughing units for the semi-continuous mills, and non-reversing roughing units for the continuous mills, coupled with two or more single-pass continuous units in which the plate is reduced simultaneously. Two-, three- and four-high stands with or without scale breakers, broadside stands, squeezers, and edgers are used as roughing units, while four-high stands are used as finishing units. The semi-continuous mill arrangement, although requiring a larger capital investment, has a number of operating advantages over both the single-stand and the tandem-mill types. The total reduction work is divided between individual stands to an even greater extent than in the case of the tandem mills. The roll wear of individual stands is, therefore, less than that of the prior mill types. The total time increment for reduction from slab to plate also is less, and the tonnage capacity per unit of time correspondingly is greater. The decreased time element permits sheets as well as plates to be rolled on these units.

THE 100-INCH SEMI-CONTINUOUS PLATE MILL AT HOMESTEAD DISTRICT WORKS

The 100-inch Semi-Continuous Plate Mill at Homestead District Works—The 100-inch semi-continuous plate mill at Homestead District Works (Figures 23 —7 and 23—8) has a slab-storage yard with a capacity of 18,000 tons stocked in rolling sequence. Two gas-fired, insulated, fabricated-steel preheaters, each having a capacity of 70 tons, are located in this yard. Slabs are placed in lifts on a yard table which delivers them to a magazine feeder located in the slab-storage yard which serves as an intermediate unit between the yard and the furnace tables. These tables, as well as all others in this mill, are equipped with anti-friction bearings.

FIG. 23—7. General view of the 100-inch semi-continuous plate mill at the Homestead District Works.

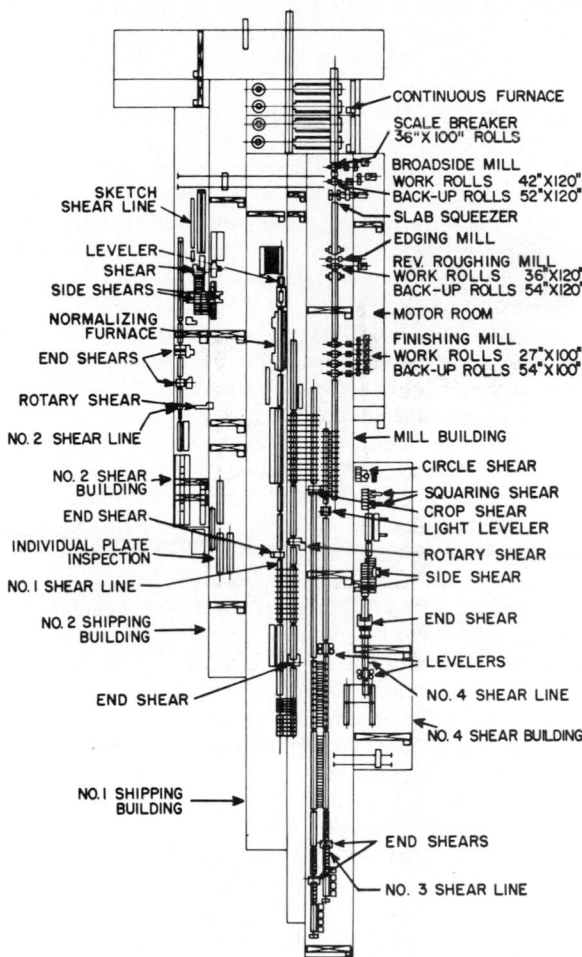

SKETCH
SHEAR LINE

LEVELER-
SHEAR

SIDE SHEARS

NORMALIZING
FURNACE

END SHEARS

ROTARY SHEAR

NO. 2 SHEAR LINE

NO. 2 SHEAR
BUILDING

END SHEAR

INDIVIDUAL PLATE
INSPECTION

NO. I SHEAR LINE

NO. 2 SHIPPING
BUILDING

END SHEAR

NO. I SHIPPING
BUILDING

CONTINUOUS FURNACE

SCALE BREAKER
36" X 100" ROLLS

BROADSIDE MILL
WORK ROLLS 42" X 120"
BACK-UP ROLLS 52" X 120"

SLAB SQUEEZER

EDGING MILL

REV. ROUGHING MILL
WORK ROLLS 36" X 120"
BACK-UP ROLLS 54" X 120"

MOTOR ROOM

FINISHING MILL
WORK ROLLS 27" X 100"
BACK-UP ROLLS 54" X 100"

MILL BUILDING

CIRCLE SHEAR

SQUARING SHEAR
CROP SHEAR
LIGHT LEVELER

ROTARY SHEAR

SIDE SHEAR

END SHEAR

LEVELERS

NO. 4 SHEAR LINE

NO. 4 SHEAR BUILDING

END SHEARS

NO. 3 SHEAR LINE

Fig. 23—8. Schematic arrangement (not to scale) of the production units comprising the 100-inch semi-continuous plate mill at Homestead District Works.

The feeder raises each pile of slabs to the level of the furnace charging table and discharges them one at a time onto the furnace table by an endless chain pusher. The slabs then are positioned in front of the furnace doors for charging by two pushers which can be operated independently or in unison for each furnace. The mill is served by four conventional, continuous, triple-zoned furnaces with non-metallic recuperators. A mixture of natural and coke-oven gas is the primary fuel, although fuel oil can be burned as an alternate. The furnaces are equipped with combustion and temperature controls. They have heated, on a continuous basis, 68 tons an hour per furnace from cold to 2250° F. Slabs charged vary from 24 inches to 60 inches in width, 3¼ inches to 12 inches in thickness, and 65 inches to 92 inches in length.

The slabs slide down the furnace dropout against inclined spring-loaded bumpers or an improved shockless bumper onto the furnace tables. A skew table with movable side guards permits straightaway entry or may be used as a turnaround for broadside entry to the scale breaker. This is a two-high stand with smooth rolls, operating in bronze-insert babbitt bearings. The

mill is driven by a 1000-horsepower, 500-r.p.m. motor, transmitting power through a reduction gear and pinion stand. Top and bottom descaling sprays operating at 1000 pounds per square inch are located at the delivery side of the scale breaker and at the entry sides of the reversing rougher and the first finisher.

The distance between scale-breaker and broadside stand is spanned by a roller table into which is incorporated an electrically-operated lift-and-turn platen at the broadside entry. The broadside mill is a four-high nonreversing stand. Both work and backup rolls operate in bronze-insert babbitt bearings. The mill is driven by a 4500-horsepower, 370-r.p.m., AC motor, transmitting power through a 22-to-1 gear ratio and conventional pinions to give a lineal speed of 185 feet per minute at the work-roll face. Movable side guards on the entry side permit centering of the slab. Pushers on entry and delivery sides facilitate entry and return for another spreading pass if required.

A duplicate of the turn-around on the entry side is located on the delivery side in the table leading to the slab squeezer. The squeezer is a two-ram width-sizing machine. The rams are supported above the mill table rollers and are positioned for the squeezing stroke in conformance with the plate widths being rolled. A 500-horsepower motor, through gearing and mechanical linkage, actuates the forging rams. A hydraulic hold-down prevents bowing of the slab as the edges are subjected to the squeezing action.

On the entry side of the four-high reversing roughing mill are movable side guards which guide the slab into a vertical edging mill. The vertical rolls have a 40-inch diameter and an 11-inch face with a 5-degree downward taper. They are driven by a 600-horsepower, 125 to 406-r.p.m., variable-speed motor.

The reversing roughing mill is connected directly through mill pinions to a 7000-horsepower, 40 to 80-r.p.m., variable-speed motor which provides a lineal speed range at the work-roll face of 376–752 feet per minute. Both work and backup rolls operate in anti-friction roller bearings. Heavy ram-type guides on entry and delivery sides and a turn-around on the delivery side permit the finish rolling of plates wider than could be finished through the continuous stands.

The four, four-high, continuous finishing stands are exact duplicates of each other. Both work and backup rolls operate in anti-friction roller bearings. The finishing stands designated as No. 4 to No. 7 are each driven by a 5000-horsepower motor. No. 4 to No. 6 stands have a speed range of 110–250 r.p.m. and No. 7 has a speed range of 125–265 r.p.m. Reducing-gear ratios for No. 4 to No. 7 are, respectively, 2.32, 1.77, 1.46 and 1.35. Corresponding lineal speed ranges at the work-roll faces are: 333–760, 440–1000, 530–1200 and 655–1386 feet per minute. Pull-back chutes with a variable opening up to a 100-inch maximum guide the rolled plate through the individual stands. Steam top-side blow-offs are provided between stands in addition to the hydraulic sprays at No. 4-stand entry.

The scale-breaker top roll and the top work and backup roll of all the other stands are balanced by hydraulic jacks and accumulators. Overhead cranes and counter-balances are used to change scale-breaker rolls and the work rolls of the broadside and the finishing stands. A roll-changing rig is used to change the reversing-rougher work rolls, and the broadside, the reversing-rougher, and the finishing-stand backup rolls.

The first section of the run-out table is equipped with a series of cooling sprays. The far portion of the table is a part of a transfer, over the cooling grids of which the plates are moved laterally by a rope-and-carriage transfer. Located immediately beyond the transfer is the light leveler with 17 bending rolls. A cooling table with individually-driven disk rollers spans the distance between the light and the heavy levelers. The heavy leveler is an 11-bending-roll machine. After leveling, the plates may progress through either one of two alternate routes, to the No. 3 shear unit or toward the rotary-shear line.

No. 3 Shear Unit—The No. 3 shear unit consists of two similar shear lines, each one of which is a continuation of the dual transfer table. Each line consists of a shear approach table, a motor-driven guillotine shear, a powered gage and gage table, and a "kick-off" table with a stacking bed. A scrap shear serves both end shears.

As all the kick-off tables and the stacking beds in this mill are of similar design, a brief description of one will suffice for all. The kick-off mechanism consists of a series of arms which, during a plate delivery from the shear, are positioned between and below the table rollers. The arms are of a double-bar design with small idler rollers free to rotate in the space between the bars. The stacking-bed ends of the arms are keyed to a pivot shaft which, on being rotated through a partial arc, will lift the arms correspondingly through a partial arc and permit the plates to slide down along the idler rollers.

The stacking beds consist essentially of a series of double beams between which movable stops may be shifted and secured in a position to correspond with the widths of plates to be received. A series of beams is fastened to a bed frame and constitutes a stacking-bed section. The sections can be raised individually or in unison to receive the first plate of a stack and are then lowered in consecutive increments as the stack is built up. The stacks are removed from the beds by overhead cranes equipped with sheet carriers or spreaders.

The No. 3 shear unit is utilized for cutting sheet and light plate gages up to ⅜ inch. The mill is capable of rolling material to thicknesses of approximately 0.10-inch minimum, 72 inches wide. The sheets and the plates sheared on the No. 3 unit generally are cut into multiples of the ordered lengths in order to keep ahead of the mill rolling rates. The mill has rolled a maximum of 2,137 tons in an 8-hour period. The multiple-length, side-untrimmed sheets and plates are transferred to the No. 4 shear unit by a transfer car or by placing them on a gravity-feed table, which moves them under a magnetic depiler.

No. 4 Shear Unit—The No. 4 shear unit is housed in a building adjacent to and parallel with the mill building on the motor-room side. Two gravity con-

veyor tables, one located in the shear building and one in the mill building, move the stacks under a magnetic depiler. The stacks are depiled, and the plates are placed singly on the approach table of a backed-up roller leveler. The leveler has two pinch rolls, nine bending rolls and eleven backup rolls. A marking mechanism attached to the delivery side of the leveler scribes the ordered width on the plates.

The plates progress from the leveler to an end shear equipped with a powered gage which can be set in the range of 48 inches to 510 inches. Delivery from the shear gage table is made to the caster bed of a left-hand side-trimming shear and from there to the caster bed of a right-hand shear of otherwise identical design. A scale table and a kick-off table with a 60-foot stacking bed complete the main shear line.

Beyond the main shear line are located a squaring shear and a circle shear serviced by gravity conveyors and a jib hoist. The circle shear can cut 8-inch to 96-inch diameter circles from ³⁄₃₂-inch to ⅜-inch, 0.30-carbon steel at a cutting speed of 50 to 100 feet per minute. A scrap shear serves both the resquaring and the circle shears, and a similar shear serves each of the side shears.

Rotary Shear Line—No. 1 Shear Unit—Heavier-gage plates, after moving across the dual transfer, continue their travel in a reverse direction to the mill rolling direction, over spool-type marking and inspection tables toward a crop shear. The distance traveled by a plate from the finishing stand to this crop shear is approximately 1,200 feet. The plates are cropped and are divided into multiples of the ordered lengths at this point and progress to a roller-chain lift transfer located immediately beyond the shear. Required painting and stamping identifications are applied as the plates travel over this transfer.

Sketch plates and other plates which are beyond the capacity of the rotary shear are diverted from the delivery side of the transfer by a table extension and stacking beds. They are moved by overhead crane and transfer car to the No. 2 shear unit for cutting. Plates within the capacity of the rotary shear resume travel in the rolling direction toward the unit.

The rotary-shear approach table is equipped with magnetic manipulators to position the plates for the shear entry. The shear is driven by a 300-horsepower motor. Scrap from each side is guided from the main cutters through chutes to the scrap cutters located below the large knives. The scrap is cut by a rotary, eccentric motion and is dropped through chutes into disposal buckets. The shear has a capacity for cutting 20-inch to 90-inch widths, ³⁄₃₂-inch to ¾-inch gage, of 0.30-carbon material at a cutting speed of 79 to 237 feet per minute. The cutters may be set to ¹⁄₁₆-inch increments within the width range.

The trimmed plate may be sent to either one of two end shears for final cutting to ordered length. The near or No. 2 end shear, located in the shipping building, is reached by traversing a rope-and-carriage transfer located immediately beyond the rotary-shear delivery table. The far or No. 3 end shear approach table is immediately beyond the transfer referred to, and is reached by direct, continuous travel from the rotary shear. Both shears can handle material ¾-inch thick by 100 inches wide, and each is driven by a 150-horsepower motor. They are followed by gage tables equipped with motor-operated, tilting, and traveling plate stop-gages with a 48-inch to 720-inch travel range from the knife edge. The gage carriage travel speed is 50 feet per minute. Each end shear is serviced by a scrap shear.

The sheared plates from the No. 3 end shear are transferred into the No. 1 shipping building by a roller-chain lift transfer. Travel direction is reversed to move over a scale table with an automatic weight-recording device and continue on to a kick-off table and stacking bed. Plates from No. 2 end shear travel over a similar scale table and on to a kick-off table and stacking bed. The kick-off table connects with the conveyor feed table of the continuous normalizing furnace.

Continuous Normalizing Furnace—Plates to be heat treated in the normalizing furnace are placed in stacks on a gravity feed table which moves them under an unpiler. The unpiler is a motor-driven traverse bridge and hoist with five selective magnetic lifters having a total capacity of ten tons. It operates on a structural framework runway. The runway extends over a gravity conveying table which also connects the No. 1 shear line kick-off table with the normalizing furnace.

The furnace is of the straight conveyor type, divided into five zones. All zones, with the exception of the entrance or heating zone, are equipped for recirculation to improve temperature uniformity. There is an alloy baffle between the heating and the recirculating zones. The furnace is 130 feet long, 9 feet wide, and the roof is 2 feet 10 inches above the conveyor. The conveyor consists of 5 sprocket-driven chains with vertical flights. A variable speed range with a maximum of 75 feet per minute is provided. Pressure burners for all zones, burning a mixture of coke-oven and natural gas, with temperature and fuel-air ratio controls, provide the heat input. A stack at each end of the furnace provides natural draft.

Plates emerging from the furnace may be quenched in a quenching hood prior to leveler entry. The backed-up leveler is a duplicate of the one in the No. 4 shear unit. Plates from the leveler traverse a cooling bed and are stacked in conventional stacking beds at the far side of the traverse.

No. 2 Shear Unit—The No. 2 shear unit has two main shear lines, consisting of a rotary shear line housed entirely in the No. 2 shear building, and the sketch shear line, which has the feeding table and two shears in the shear building and one shear, scale table, and stacking beds in the No. 2 shipping building.

The sketch shear line, as its designation implies, is used to shear irregularly shaped plates. It also is utilized to shear structural-grade, rectangular plates heavier than ¾-inch gage, and alloy plates of thinner gage which, because of composition, are beyond the cutting capacity of the No. 1 shear line. Such plates are diverted from the No. 1 shear line beyond the No. 2 transfer and moved to the No. 2 shear unit by transfer car, as previously described.

Plate stacks for the sketch shear line are placed on a gravity feed table by an overhead crane. An overhead, selective, magnetic unpiler puts the plates singly on a marking and layout, five-chain conveyor table. Both sketch and rectangular plates are laid out manually on this table. The first shearing unit in the line, an end shear, cuts the plates to length. The plates may be turned 180 degrees on the caster beds immediately beyond and returned, if necessary, to have both ends front-end cut for the elimination of shear bow. A continued, manually propelled movement over caster beds brings the plate to a side shear for edge trimming. A lateral movement into the shipping building brings the plate to an opposite hand but otherwise identical shear for the trimming of the opposite edge. Further manual propulsion opposite to the original travel direction moves the plate back to powered traction on a scale table and a kick-off table and stacking beds. Two scrap shears serve the three major shearing units in this line.

When the mill rolling rate on ⅜-inch to ¾-inch gage plates exceeds the capacity of the No. 1 shear line, the excess multiple-length plates are diverted at the same point and are transferred to the No. 2 shear unit in the same manner as sketch plates. The plates are spread on a chain-conveyor marking table and move over an approach table to a rotary side-trimming shear. In general design features, the shear is similar to the one in the No. 1 shear line. The capacity ranges from 30 inches to 96 inches in width and $\frac{3}{32}$ inch to ¾ inch in gage at a cutting speed of 50 feet per minute. The scrap cutters are of the revolving-drum type. A duplicate of the end shear in the sketch shear line serves the rotary shear. It is followed by a back shear table, a scale table and a kick-off table with stacking beds. A guillotine scrap shear serves the end shear.

Auxiliary shearing equipment in No. 2 shear unit consists of a resquaring shear, a circle shear, and a test-cutting shear. The squaring shear is a motor-driven unit. The motor-driven circle shear has a capacity ranging from 20-inch to 150-inch diameter, $\frac{3}{32}$-inch to 1¼-inch gage, in structural grades at a cutting speed of 56 feet per minute. The test-cutting shear has a capacity equivalent to cutting 20-inch by $1\frac{3}{16}$-inch thick plates.

An individual plate inspection unit is made available by feeding from the No. 2 shear building and repiling in the No. 2 shipping building. It includes two parallel sections of gravity table for plate entry and two parallel sections for plate delivery. Each section employs pipe rollers operating in roller bearings. Located between the gravity table lines is a motor-driven roller table over which individual plates are moved and are tilted for inspection by eight lifting arms to an angle of 75 degrees. The unit is served by one unpiling unit and one piling unit. Each traverse and hoist, with five selective magnetic lifters, operates on a structural framework.

THE 96-INCH FOUR-HIGH CONTINUOUS PLATE MILL AT SOUTH WORKS

The four-high continuous plate mill which will be described in detail was placed in operation in the early part of 1931 and, therefore, represents an early stage in the development of the wide four-high continuous mills. The wide, four-high, continuous hot-strip mills, which have been placed in operation in the intervening period and which are described in another section of this book, are more representative of the potential productive capacities, the surface finish, and the width and gage uniformity which can be achieved with a modern mill of this type designed primarily for plate production.

The 96-inch continuous plate mill at South Works, Figures 23—9, 23—10 and 23—11, receives the bulk of its charge in the form of cold slabs from a multi-purpose slab-yard building running at 90 degrees to the mill center line and serviced by four overhead cranes. The 96-inch plate mill and its supplying unit, the 44-inch slab mill, have a common and continuous center line. The slab mill shear delivery and piler tables form a continuous table line with the 96-inch mill furnace and mill approach tables so that hot slabs may be table-conveyed directly from the slab-mill shears into the 96-inch mill. A pusher and chain transfer adjacent to No. 1 reheating furnace permits the diversion of hot slabs from the mill table and their transfer to the charging ends of the reheating furnaces. It also is utilized for the recharging of furnace kick-outs.

The slab mill has a rated capacity of 140,000 product tons per month. It supplies all of the slab requirements of the 96-inch mill, with the bulk of its excess productive capacity allocated to the slab requirements of the 80-inch hot-strip mills at Gary Sheet and Tin Mill, and a smaller percentage allocated to the 30-inch universal plate-mill slab requirements and semifinished trade-slab requirements. Virtually all the slab-mill production is removed from the run-out tables by three sectional pushers and pilers located in the slab yard. Slabs in ingot stacks are removed from the pilers by overhead cranes.

All 96-inch plate mill slabs are placed in the central portion of the slab yard, adjacent to the pilers, for cooling. After cooling, they are conditioned, and piled in rolling sequence in an area near the pilers. This area has a storage capacity of 5,000 tons. A portion of the slab tonnage produced for other applications and cooled in the central area also is conditioned here and is loaded out on standard-gauge tracks. Cool slabs in excess of the yard conditioning capacity are sent to other yards for conditioning.

The plate-mill furnace-charging tables extend into the slab yard. The slab charger is a side unpiler consisting of a skidded deck with a vertical screw motion and a pusher operating transversely to the table travel direction and at the table-top elevation. Slab stacks are placed on the unpiler deck in its down position, and the slabs are pushed singly on the charging table as the unpiler is moved upward in slab-thickness increments. The slabs are positioned at the furnace

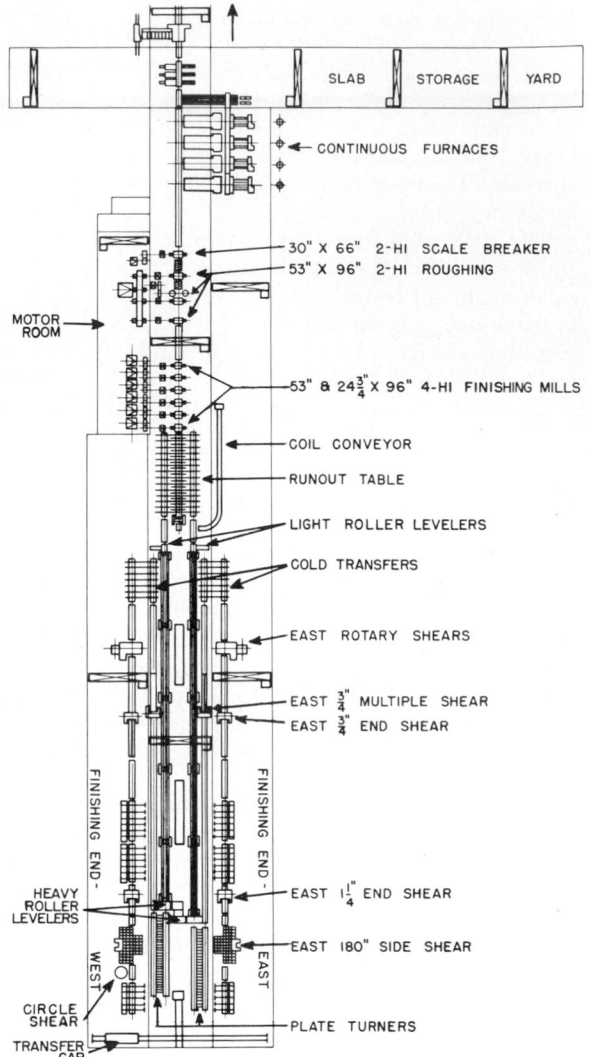

FIG. 23—9. Diagram (not to scale) of the layout of the mills and auxiliary equipment comprising the 96-inch four-high continuous plate mill at South Works.

charging doors and are charged into the furnaces by double-row pushers which can be operated singly or in unison.

The heating equipment for this mill consists of four continuous-type, two-zone, triple-fired furnaces equipped to burn natural gas or fuel oil through all burners. One of the originally installed furnaces is manually controlled, is not equipped with either recuperators or regenerators and is only used for standby service. When this furnace is used, it is single-row charged with slabs of 83-inch maximum length. Three furnaces are equipped with automatic heating controls and metallic recuperators. Slabs charged into these furnaces vary from 3½ to 6½ inches in thickness, from 28 to 60 inches in width, from 50 to 83 inches in length for a double-row charge and up to a maximum of 178 inches for a single-row charge. Each of these furnaces has a rated heating capacity of 50 slab tons per hour.

FIG. 23—10. General view of the 96-inch continuous plate mill at South Works.

The two-high scale-breaker stand is driven by a 600-horsepower, 488-r.p.m. motor, driving through a gear reducer and pinions. The steel rolls operate in bronze-insert, babbitt bearings. The top roll is counter-weight balanced. Drafts on this stand are limited to ⅜-inch maximum. Top and bottom hydraulic sprays operating at 1000 pounds per square inch are located on the delivery side of the mill.

The roughing train consists of three duplicate two-high stands. All three stands are driven by a 6000-horsepower, 370-r.p.m. motor, driving through a special gear-reduction set with two flywheels on the high-speed shaft and through conventional pinion stands. No. 1, No. 2, and No. 3 stands operate, respectively, at 8.5, 10.1 and 15.15 r.p.m., corresponding to lineal surface speeds of 116, 138 and 206 feet per minute. Only one slab can be undergoing reduction in the roughing train at any time. The cast-steel rolls for these stands operate in bronze-insert, babbitt bearings. The top roll is balanced hydraulically. The screw-

FIG. 23—11. General view of inspection and marking operations on plates at the delivery end of the 96-inch continuous plate mill at South Works.

downs are operated by two motors tied in with a magnetic clutch so that they may be operated in unison for draft settings or individually for roll alignment. High-pressure hydraulic sprays are located at No. 1 and No. 3 delivery and at No. 4 entry.

Motor-driven sectional side guards on the skew roller table between the scale breaker and No. 1 stand may be positioned to permit either a straightaway entry to No. 1 stand or to form a turning pivot for a 90-degree turn and a broadside entry to No. 1 stand. Therefore, No. 1 stand may be utilized as either a straightaway or a broadside mill. A rack-type carriage pusher operating on a structural framework above the table provides for a square entry for the broadside pass. Powered side guides at the entry of each roughing stand, as well as the first finishing stand, permit centered entry.

A similar arrangement of side guards and skew table on the delivery side of No. 1 stand makes possible either continued straightaway progress of the slab or a 90-degree turn after a broadside pass.

The finishing train consists of six duplicate four-high stands. Each mill is driven by a 3500-horse-power, 165–330-r.p.m. motor through a gear-reduction unit, conventional pinion stand and wobbler-type spindles. The speeds of the work rolls of the various stands in r.p.m. and f.p.m. are listed below:

Speed Range

Stand No.	Rev. per min.		Ft. per min.
4 Finishing	20	to 49	128 to 315
5 Finishing	30	to 72	193 to 463
6 Finishing	39	to 94	250 to 600
7 Finishing	49	to 118	315 to 760
8 Finishing	54.5	to 132	350 to 850
9 Finishing	60	to 146	385 to 940

Grain-iron work rolls are used in No. 4 and No. 5 stands, and chilled-iron work rolls in the remainder of the stands, with steel backup rolls. Both work and backup rolls operate in antifriction roller bearings. The top backup and work roll are balanced hydraulically as an assembly, with the work roll being held against the backup roll by two spring suspension take-up rods positioned through yoke extensions. Draft settings are made by motors driving the screwdowns through worm reduction gearing. The two motors for each stand are connected by magnetic clutches and are operated in unison for draft settings and singly, when the stock is in the mill, for camber correction.

The spacings between the mill stands are each occupied by a two-sectional retractable table which in a normal operating position presents a continuous, smooth iron liner surface to plate travel. Adjustable, powered side guides center the plates for admission at the point of entry, and top and bottom stripper-guide assemblies are attached to the delivery section. A looping roll normally is positioned below the table surface and is raised in an arc by pneumatic cylinders when it is necessary to take up stock slack while speed adjustments are being made. Prior to a roll change, the two table sections are retracted so that the liners and the supports of one section overlap the other in the center of the spacing. In this position both the

entry- and the delivery-guide assemblies are free of the rolls.

An overhead-crane-suspended sleeve, into which a work roll is fitted as a counterweight, is used for work-roll changes. The frequency of work-roll changes is extremely variable and is dependent on the particular roll stand as well as on the preponderance of product gages rolled. In the rolling of sheet gages, the leader and the finisher may require changing at four-hour intervals. When the schedule includes only plate rolling and the preponderance of the tonnage is in the heavier plate gages, the work rolls in No. 4 and No. 5 stands may last out the weekly schedule or require changing only once to meet wide-plate rolling requirements in the latter part of the week. Work-roll changes are made in 25 minutes.

A cast counterweight secured on an integral arm and sleeve which fits over the roll-neck extension, is used for the changing of the backup rolls, whereas a sleeve and another roll as a balancer are used for changing the roughing rolls. The frequency of backup-roll changes is also variable and dependent on the roll-stand position and gages rolled. Since one roll is changed per week, the average time interval amounts to 12 weeks. No. 3 roughing rolls are changed each week, No. 2 at weekly or bi-weekly intervals dependent on schedules, and No. 1 at 3 to 4-week intervals. Backup-roll changes require an average of 2½ hours per roll, and roughing rolls require 3½ hours a set.

Product is delivered from the finishing stand onto a central runout table, consisting of individually-driven disk rollers which protrude through openings in cast alloy-iron aprons. Plates are stopped on the runout table by raising the lifting aprons above the table rollers. The plates are moved laterally over iron gridwork by a cable-carriage dog transfer to either one of two duplicate, parallel finishing lines.

The leveler-approach tables convey the plates to the light levelers, the first processing units in each line. They are located immediately beyond the hot transfer and have seventeen bending rolls. Delivery from the leveler is made to the first of five 125-foot sections of sprocket-driven chain spool conveyors. These conveyors span the distance to the heavy levelers and also serve as cooling and top surface inspection tables. The heavy leveler is a 13-roll machine with seven top and six bottom, 14-inch diameter by 100-inch long, rolls. From the leveler the plates are discharged on a 132-foot combination table and turnover device. The turnover consists of two series of arms keyed to pivot shafts located between two parallel roller tables. In an idle position both sets of arms are below the roller-top levels of the two tables. When the plate is delivered from the leveler, the arms are moved toward each other in an arc, with the sending arms passing through a greater arc. This results in a transfer of the plate to the receiving arms as they approach a vertical position. The lowering of the arms transfers the plate to the adjacent parallel table which reverses travel direction toward the multiple shear.

Approach tables for the multiple shears serve as a bottom surface inspection and marking table. The first identification is made by chalking on the plate surface.

Multiple lengths to be sheared are also marked on the plate with allowances for necessary tests. The multiple shear is a ¾-inch by 100-inch, motor-driven, open-throat, downcut shear. A chain scrap conveyor is common to the multiple and the adjacent end shear and carries the scrap from both to an alligator scrap shear.

Continued table travel brings the multiple plates to a cold transfer. This is a chain lift transfer. During the crosswise travel, physical identification of product and test pieces is completed by manual painting and stamping. Routing information for placement in the shipping area or direct car loading also is indicated on the plates.

Travel in the rolling direction is resumed on the approach table to the rotary shear. The finish-shear lines are located in the shipping buildings which are adjacent and parallel to the mill building. Three magnetic manipulators traveling in a direction transverse to that of the table are available for positioning the plates for the rotary-shear entry. An electromagnet, traveling with the table direction, holds the plate in a fixed lateral position. Cutting capacity of the rotary shears ranges from ⅛-inch to ¾-inch gage and 20 inches to 96 inches in width at a cutting speed of 79 to 158 feet per minute. Width settings may be made in 1/16-inch increments. Side trimmings are guided to rotary scrap cutters, cut into short lengths and dropped into a hold for removal by magnet.

Two table sections that serve as delivery and entry tables for the rotary and the end shears respectively have powered side guards to guide the delivery from the rotary shears and facilitate square entry into the end shears. The end shears are duplicates of the multiple shear. A motor-operated lift plate gage with a travel speed of 50 feet per minute can be set from a 6-foot to a 60-foot distance from the shear knife. The delivery table is followed by a scale table and two sections of 64-foot push-off tables and side pilers. The side pushers travel in transverse ways across the tables to stack the plates in the pivoted side pilers, the table ends of which are lowered in conformance with the height of the plate stack.

Plates heavier than ¾-inch and up to 1¼-inch gage are laid out manually on the push-off tables and continue over short approach tables to end shears. The shears are conventional motor-driven downcut type followed by a short depressing table and a delivery table. The plates then are moved manually over caster beds to a side shear. The plates are turned 180 degrees on the caster beds and moved back to the side shear to trim the opposite edge. Side-trim scrap is moved manually to an alligator scrap shear for cutting into short lengths.

A circle shear is located beyond the side shear of the west shear line. The shear has a cutting capacity of ⅛-inch to ¾-inch gage and 16-inch to 84-inch diameter at a cutting speed of 20 to 60 feet per minute. A transfer car at the extreme end of the building permits the transfer of circles and plates between the various buildings.

E. UNIVERSAL PLATE MILLS

Universal plate mills are single-stand units which roll plates to width within standard tolerances. Al-though universal plate mills producing widths up to 60 inches have been in operation, the bulk of the installations has been of 48-inch width and under. The number of installations and the capacity has decreased rather than increased in the past several decades. This may be attributed to the development of the narrow as well as the wide continuous hot-strip mills, and to the development of the wide-flanged beam mills. The former mill types, particularly in the narrower widths, have displaced directly considerable universal-mill tonnage, owing to the improved surface finishes that can be obtained with the continuous hot-strip mills. The production of deep wide-flange beams displaced a large tonnage of fabricated beams and columns that formerly had utilized universal plates for the web portions. Consequently, the universal plate mills which are in operation today date back several decades to their installation dates; and the unit which will be described in detail is typical in spite of its early construction date.

THE 30-INCH UNIVERSAL PLATE MILL AT SOUTH WORKS

The 30-inch universal plate mill at South Works, Figure 23—12, was erected in 1907 to produce rolled-edge plates ranging from 3/16 inch to 6 inches in thickness and 6 inches to 30 inches in width. Slab sizes utilized to produce this range vary from 2½ inches to 11½ inches in thickness, 5 inches to 31 inches in width and 55 inches to 120 inches in length.

The conditioning and slab-storage yard serving this mill is under an open crane runway serviced by two cranes. The yard consists of four sections, for slab receipt, conditioning by hand scarfing, stock storage, and current charge storage. Charge slabs are piled in upright racks in the proper sequence. Forty-five hundred tons can be stored in the charge and stock racks.

Reheating Furnaces—Two single-zone, end-fired, hydraulic-pusher-charged, continuous reheating furnaces service the mill. The burners located above the discharge doors are designed for changing quickly to natural gas or oil for combustion. Neither gas nor air is preheated. Air for combustion is provided under pressure by a fan which draws directly from the atmosphere. Fuel-air ratio and furnace pressure controls are operative for natural-gas combustion. The furnaces are rated at 20 tons an hour per furnace for full hearth coverage and a cold charge. Heated slabs and billets slide down the dropout skids onto the mill approach table.

30-Inch Universal Plate Mill Stand—The single-stand two-high reversing mill, with vertical edgers front and rear, has chilled alloy-iron horizontal rolls and chilled-iron vertical rolls. The top roll is balanced by counterweights, and is positioned for draft settings by a motor driving both vertical screw-downs through worm reduction gearing. The maximum available horizontal roll opening is 10 inches. Initial roll alignment is provided by placing liners as required under the fabric bearing chucks of the bottom-roll.

Additional roll-alignment adjustment required in rolling is obtained by the manual operation, during pass intervals, of a device which varies the distance between one screw and bearing chuck.

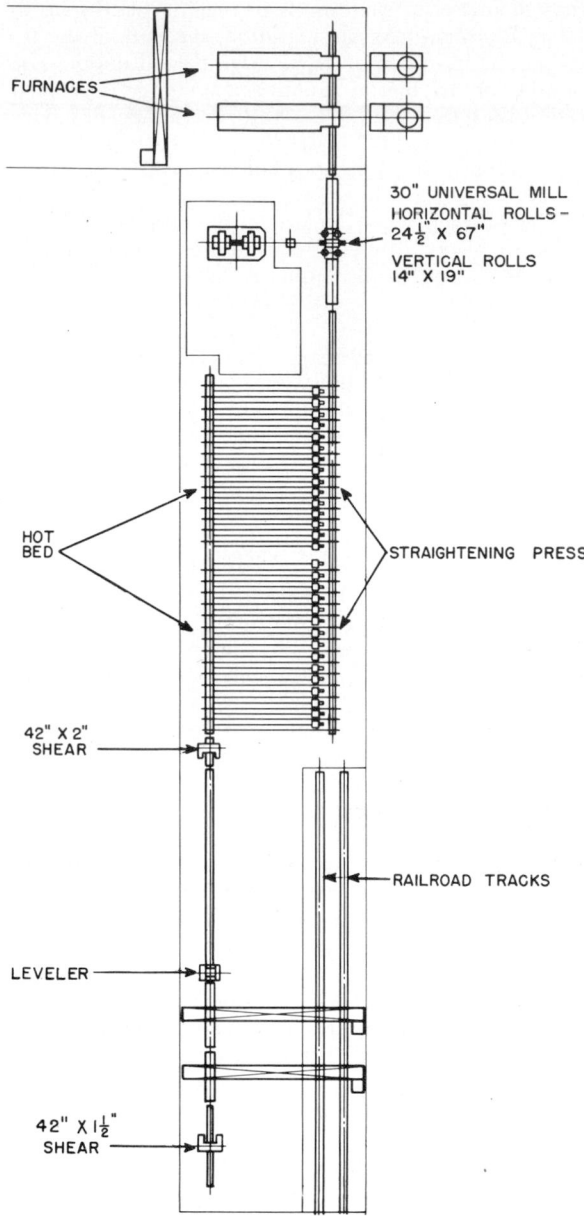

FIG. 23—12. Layout (not to scale) of the 30-inch universal plate mill at South Works.

The vertical-roll assemblies at each side of the mill are positioned by a motor driving a shaft that extends across both main housings and has pinions meshing with a spur-gear train on the outer vertical face of each housing. Bronze nuts, driven by the gearing, move upper and lower screws transversely, which in turn move the vertical-roll housings. A yoke connects the outer square ends of the screws to prevent their turning. It also has an adjustable rod attached with a nut to the yoke center that extends through an opening in the housing and is pinned to the vertical-roll yoke. The yoke and the rod serve as a pull-back when the roll spacing is widened. Available roll opening varies from a 5-inch minimum to a 31½-inch maximum. The weight of the vertical-roll assemblies is

supported on an inverted V slide at the base of the main housings.

The mill is driven by a 4000-horsepower, 150-r.p.m. reversing motor, the first reversing-mill motor to be built and placed into successful operation. Power is transmitted through a leading spindle to the bottom pinion of a five-pinion, three-high, cast-herringbone pinion stand. The bottom and second pinions, of sixteen teeth each, are connected directly through spindles to drive the top and the bottom horizontal rolls. The top pinion of fifteen teeth meshes with the middle pinion below it and with one fifteen-tooth pinion at each side of it with a common center-line elevation. All five pinions are journalled in babbitt bearings in the pinion housing. The side pinions drive the vertical-roll square shafts on which the square bores of the bevel driving gears for the vertical rolls slide for roll positioning, and which transmit power to the mating gears keyed to the vertical rolls.

Rolling—Slabs intended for bars in the 6-inch to 8-inch width range are provided 1 inch narrower than the finished plate width. A slab 6 inches thick and 8 inches wide rolled down to 1-inch gage will finish 9¾ inches wide on this mill if it is allowed to spread freely. Therefore, on the basis of slab provision for a 1-inch-gage, 8-inch wide bar, a 1-inch spread is allowed; and the edges actually are worked down ¾ inch. Slabs provided for over 8-inch to 12-inch widths are ½ inch narrower than the finished size; slab and finished widths are equivalent in the over 12-inch to 17-inch range; and slabs ½ inch over finished size are provided for the over 17-inch to 30-inch range. Edging drafts are taken alternately with the vertical rolls on the delivery side of the horizontal-roll drafting passes. As the horizontal-roll drafts are variable, vertical and horizontal-roll diameters must be kept matched so that the peripheral speed of the vertical rolls exceeds that of the horizontal rolls. Main-roll changes average three per week for a normal schedule and require 55 minutes to complete. Vertical rolls are changed at three-week intervals and require 3½ hours to change both sets. Spray nozzles operate at 650 pounds per square inch pressure for descaling on both sides of the mill.

Hot Bed—The finished plate is delivered by a roller table to a two-section lift chain hot bed. When delivered to the hot bed, the plate is moved off the table by the transfer chains and positioned against fixed raised castings or anvils which are parts of a straightener-press used to remove delivered camber, and to prevent camber resulting from the initial cooling stages. The straightener-press contains 30 individual blocks, each of which consists of a worm screw, a bronze nut, a head casting attached to the worm screw, and the fixed table casting that serves as the anvil. The blocks are located between the transfer chains and adjacent to the hot-bed entry table. Two worm line shafts drive the individual worm screws. Each line shaft, in turn, is driven by a motor through reduction gearing. The castings which serve as anvils are integral parts of troughs through which cooling water circulates. When the worm screws are operated, the movable heads push against the edge of the plate and press it straight against the anvil castings.

Plates are delivered to the two hot-bed sections alternately. When the plates are released by the straightener-press, they again are picked up by the lift transfer chains and moved across the bed in plate-width space increments. In the course of their traverse progress the plates are identified by painting and stamping and laid out for the lengths that are ordered. Required tests also are laid out and identified. The final chain movement places the plates on the combination bed-delivery and shear-approach table.

Finishing—The end shear is located immediately adjacent to the hot bed. A chain conveyor moves crop scrap to a chute which guides it into a scrap box for disposal. The sheared plates go over a table to a roller leveler which has 6 top and 5 bottom bending rolls. Plates up to 2-inch thickness are pulled off the table line on the delivery side of the leveler. They are pulled off manually by the use of hooks into stacking cradles. Heavier plates are pushed manually on an idler table to a horizontal gag in which they are straightened and pulled off in a similar manner on the delivery side.

Auxiliary equipment includes flame-cutting equipment for heavy plates, hand-grinding tools and powered hack saws. Storage racks are provided for carload-accumulation storage in the combination shearing and shipping building. Additional storage and shipping facilities are available in an adjacent building.

SECTION 4

HEAT-TREATING FACILITIES FOR STEEL PLATES

Types of Heat Treatment—Depending upon the grade of steel and the intended end use of plates, they may be subjected to annealing, normalizing, stress relieving, spheroidize annealing, accelerated cooling, quenching, tempering, or certain combinations of some of these treatments. Heat treatment of carbon-steel plates usually is confined to annealing, normalizing and stress relieving.

While the purposes and principles of these heat treatments (and the types of equipment in which they can be performed) are discussed in detail in Chapter 39, each will be defined briefly here.

Annealing consists of a single thermal treatment, intended to place the steel in a suitable condition for fabrication. The steel is heated to a temperature in or near the critical temperature range and is cooled at a predetermined rate or cycle. Plates are generally annealed in "open" furnaces without atmosphere control.

Normalizing consists of heating the steel above its critical temperature range, and cooling in air. This treatment refines the grain size and improves uniformity of microstructure and properties of the hot-rolled plate.

Stress relieving consists of heating the steel to a temperature below the critical range to relieve stresses induced by flattening or other operations such as cold working, shearing, or gas cutting. It is not intended to alter the microstructure or mechanical properties significantly.

Spheroidize annealing is performed by prolonged heating of the steel in a controlled-atmosphere furnace at or near the lower critical point, followed by retarded cooling in the furnace, to produce a lower hardness than can be obtained by regular annealing. The purpose is usually improvement of performance of the steel in severe cold forming, such as deep drawing.

Accelerated cooling is employed to improve resistance to impact (toughness) and refine the grain size of certain grades and thicknesses of plate. Such cooling is accomplished by fans to provide circulation of air during cooling, or by a water spray or dip.

Quenching consists of heating the steel to a suitable austenitizing temperature, holding at that temperature for a sufficient time to effect the desired change in crystalline structure, and immersing and cooling the steel in a suitable liquid medium that will depend upon the composition of the steel and its cross-section.

Tempering is carried out by preheating previously quenched or normalized steel to a predetermined temperature below the critical range, holding for a specified time at that temperature, and then cooling under suitable conditions to obtain the desired mechanical properties.

Furnaces for Heat Treating Plates—The size, thickness and grade of steel determine to some extent the type of furnace employed for the heat treatment of plates. In-and-out batch-type, car-bottom and semi-continuous roller-hearth furnaces are among the types employed.

PLATE HEAT-TREATING EQUIPMENT AT HOMESTEAD DISTRICT WORKS

United States Steel has assembled what is believed to be the most complete and flexible steel-plate heat-treating equipment in the steel industry at its Homestead District Works. With installations in the 160-inch and 100-inch plate mills, the Harvey Shop and the Forgings Division, the plant can heat treat carbon-, alloy-, and stainless-steel plates ranging from

$\frac{1}{10}$-inch to 6 inches thick and heavier. Facilities consist of the following:

Location	Maximum Thickness of Plate Treated
160-Inch Mill	
No. 1 Plate Treating Line	2 inches and under
No. 2 Plate Treating Line	2 inches and under
Stainless-Steel Furnace	2 inches and under
100-Inch Mill	
Normalizing Furnace	¾-inch and under
Harvey Shop	
Car-Bottom Furnaces	Over 2 inches
Forgings Division	
Car-Bottom Furnaces	Over 2 inches

160-Inch Mill Heat-Treating Facilities—The heat-treating facilities of the 160-inch plate mill comprise: (1) a preliminary inspection and conditioning area; (2) a classification and shipping building; and (3) the heat-treating and shearing building in which are located the No. 1 and No. 2 plate treating lines and the furnace for heat treating stainless-steel plates, arranged as shown in Figures 23—13 and 23—14. These facilities are designed to slow cool, inspect and heat treat plates up to 156 inches wide and 514 inches long, and up to 2 inches thick, that have been produced by hot rolling on the 100-inch and 160-inch plate mills, and to shear all such plates that are no more than one inch in thickness.

Plates are delivered to the inspection building directly from the rolling mills. The inspection area has hoods for slow cooling of heavy plates. All plates are inspected top and bottom, with the assistance of a turnover rig. Those having defects revealed by the

inspection are taken to grinding beds for conditioning. A gantry crane handles the product throughout the various operations. When inspection and any necessary conditioning are completed, the plates are loaded onto mobile trailers and delivered to the classification building by a diesel-powered tractor.

In the classification building, the plates are unloaded from the trailers, grouped for most efficient heat treatment, and then moved by gantry crane onto the charging table of the appropriate furnace in the heat treating and shearing building.

As shown in Figure 23—13, the No. 1 and No. 2 plate heat treating lines are situated on opposite sides of the heat treating and shearing building. The furnace for heat treating stainless steel is located between the two plate treating lines. Operating data for the various furnaces are given in Table 23—I.

Plates to be processed in the No. 1 and No. 2 plate treating lines are placed on the charging tables of the continuous hardening furnaces (Figure 23—15), whose function is limited to heating the plates to a hardening temperature. The individual plates are carried through these furnaces, by the motor-driven high-alloy steel rollers that form the hearths. Speed of travel of plates through a furnace is regulated according to the thickness of the plate, with thinner plates moving through more rapidly than thicker ones. Each plate heated for hardening is delivered to the water quench (Figure 23—13), which is sized to accommodate the largest plates. A fast runout section of table at the delivery end of each hardening furnace rapidly moves heated plates into the quench, with only an anticipated 20 seconds of elapsed time until the water is applied.

When a plate is in position in the quench, the transfer rollers are lowered so that the plate rests on a fixed platen. The hydraulically operated top platen is then lowered until it comes in contact with the top surface of the plate. Both platens have ribbed surfaces extend-

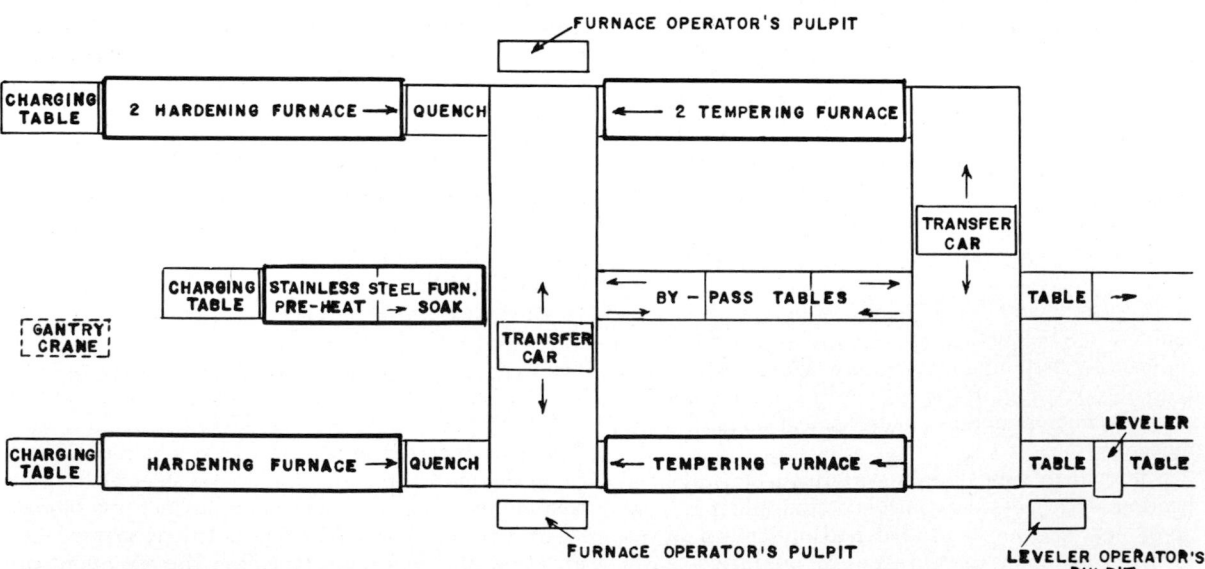

Fig. 23—13. Schematic layout (not to scale) of the plate heat-treating lines in the 160-inch mill at Homestead District Works of United States Steel Corporation. (See also Figure 23—14.)

Table 23-I. Operating Data for Furnaces in the 160-Inch Plate Mill at Homestead District Works.

Characteristic	No. 1 Hardening Furnace	No. 2 Hardening Furnace	No. 1 Tempering Furnace	No. 2 Tempering Furnace	Stainless-Steel Heat-Treating Furnace
Temperature Limits (°F)	1250–1750	1250–1750	750–1250	750–1250	1250–2100
No. of Temperature Control Zones	6	11	10	12	3
Connected Fuel Input (cu. ft. per hr.)	67,000	67,000	62,400	68,400	52,800
Average Fuel Consumption at Max. Capacity (cu. ft. per hr.)	34,000	40,000	31,000	48,000	32,000
Roller Speeds (ft. per min.)					
Charging	0.3 to 7.5	0.5 to 12.5 or 20 to 80	75	0.5 to 12.5 or 87.5 to 175	50
Through Furnace	0.3 to 7.5	5.0	0.35 to 87.5	5.0	1 to 2*
Discharging	175	87.5 or 175	175	87.5 or 175	175

*Oscillating.

ing across the width of the quench, and water pipes are located in the recesses between the ribs. With the plate in place and the platens exerting pressure over the entire surfaces of the plate, water sprays from the pipes play on the steel from above and below. Quenching time is approximately three minutes per inch of plate thickness.

From the quench, the plate is rolled onto an electrically operated transfer car that delivers it to the by-pass roller tables, parallel to the tempering furnaces. The plate is then transferred by another car to the entry end of the tempering furnace in which it is to be processed. The tempering furnaces, like the hardening furnaces, are equipped with heat-resistant steel rollers that move the plates through the furnace and into the quench when treating plates of certain grades that must be rapidly cooled after tempering. Direction of travel of plates through the tempering furnaces can be reversed when treating plates that do not require water cooling after tempering.

Some carbon-steel plates are normalized. In this operation, the steel is heated to the proper temperature in a hardening furnace but, instead of being quenched, is cooled on roller tables in the open air.

Stainless-steel plates, as contrasted with others, are not tempered. They are heated in the stainless-steel furnace and then quenched, following which they are delivered to the roller leveler for flattening.

Plates that have been tempered or quenched and tempered are delivered by the transfer cars and by-pass tables to the delivery end of the roller leveler. With the exception of stainless-steel plates, roller leveling is rarely necessary and the plates simply pass through the rollers of this machine to the cooling tables. A transfer car at the exit end of the cooling tables returns the plates to the classification building, where test coupons are removed and sent to the metallurgical laboratory for tests. Plates that conform to test requirements are returned by transfer car from the classification building to the approach table of the shear line. Individual plates pass through a turntable to the side shear where one side of each plate is sheared. The roller table is reversed to return each plate to the turntable where it is then turned end for

end and returned to the shear for shearing the other side. Plates continue down the roller table from the side shear to the end shear, where both ends are sheared. After shearing, plates are removed from the table and loaded for shipment. Plates over 1 inch thick cannot be sheared on this shear line and are sent to heavy shearing or gas-cutting facilities elsewhere in the plant.

100-Inch Mill Hardening-Tempering Furnace— This furnace is an integral part of the 100-inch mill facilities. It is located in the shipping building and plates to be heat treated can be transferred from the normal travel of product to its approach table. This combination semi-continuous hardening and tempering furnace is similar in design to the furnaces of the No. 1 and No. 2 plate treating lines of the 160-inch mill. It is designed to heat treat plates and sheets up to a maximum of 96 inches in width and 30 feet in length, with thicknesses ranging from 0.10 inch to 0.75 inches. Operating-temperature limits of the furnace are from 550° to 1750° F, and temperature-control zones make very uniform heating possible. Plates move through the furnace at speeds ranging from 1.3 to 13 ft. per min., depending upon the thickness of the product being treated. Heating cycles are established by metallurgical requirements dictated by grade of steel, thickness of the plate, and the treatment desired. After heating to either hardening or tempering temperature, the plate can be conveyed into a platen-type water quench.

Car-Bottom Heat-Treating Furnaces—For heat-treating plates too thick for the continuous lines (product over 2 inches and up to approximately 8 inches thick) large, direct top-and-bottom-fired, car-bottom furnaces with operating temperatures ranging between room temperature and 1940° F are utilized. Seven of these furnaces are located in the Harvey Shop and six in the Forgings Division. The Harvey Shop also is equipped with an 18-foot by 60-foot water-quench tank, 8 feet deep with a working depth of 4½ feet. Stools, 3½ feet high, are placed at the bottom of the quenching tank on which to lay the plates.

FIG. 23—14. General view of the heat-treating lines in the 160-inch mill at Homestead District Works of United States Steel Corporation, seen from the charging end. No. 1 plate-treating line is at the right, No. 2 line at the left, with the stainless-steel heat-treating furnace between. (See also Figure 23—13.)

Fig. 23—15. Alloy-steel plate entering the hardening furnace of the No. 2 plate heat-treating line of the 160-inch mill at Homestead District Works of United States Steel Corporation.

PLATE HEAT-TREATING EQUIPMENT FOR GARY STEEL WORKS 160/210-INCH MILL

A continuous plate heat-treating line operates in conjunction with the 160/210-inch plate mill at Gary Steel Works of United States Steel. It is capable of heat treating plates up to 200 inches wide and up to 3 inches thick, the actual combination of dimensions being related to the sizes of plate that can be rolled on the mill.

The plate heat-treating department was installed as a continuation of the South Flame Cut Building of the 160/210-inch mill, parallel to and extending beyond the Shearing Building (see Figure 23—1). It is equipped to normalize or quench and temper carbon-steel, alloy-steel and high-strength low-alloy steel plates as required by the grade of steel and the mechanical properties desired in the final product. The arrangement of the equipment is shown in Figure 23—16.

The gas-fired roller-hearth hardening furnace and tempering furnace are 156 feet and 208 feet in length, respectively. Following the delivery end of the hardening furnace is the quench, equipped with platens that exert pressure against both surfaces of a plate while it is spray quenched with water. The roller leveler is a four-high unit capable of flattening alloy-steel plates up to ¾-inch thick.

Electric overhead traveling cranes, transfer cranes, transfer cars, roller tables and other handling equipment facilitate movement of plates from one work station to another.

Plates thicker than about 1 inch are removed from the transfer table located beyond the roller levelers in the 160/210-inch mill line (item 5 in Figure 23—1) and transported by overhead crane to the slow-cool area of the heat-treating department. Alloy-steel plates are placed in unfired hoods for slow cooling and then inspected, checked for layout, and conditioned by grinding if necessary, prior to heat treating. Plates approximately 1 inch thick and lighter that do not require slow cooling progress across the cooling bed (item 16 in Figure 23 —1) to the marking and crop shear line (items 21, 18 and 17, Figure 23 —1) to be inspected, checked for layout, cropped, and parted if necessary. The transfer crane of the heat-treating department, operated remotely by the crop-shear operator, transfers plates into the heat-treating area where they receive further inspection and test grinding.

The plates then are scheduled for treatment, stacked in schedule order in the single-leg gantry area by overhead crane, and placed individually by the gantry on the charging table of the roller-hearth hardening furnace. Plates to be quenched and tempered

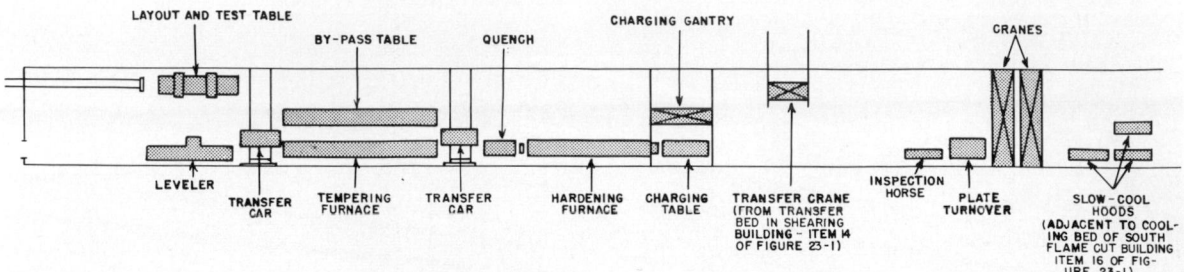

LAYOUT AND TEST TABLE

BY-PASS TABLE

QUENCH

CHARGING GANTRY

CRANES

LEVELER

TRANSFER CAR

TEMPERING FURNACE

TRANSFER CAR

HARDENING FURNACE

CHARGING TABLE

TRANSFER CRANE (FROM TRANSFER BED IN SHEARING BUILDING – ITEM 14 OF FIGURE 23-1)

INSPECTION HORSE

PLATE TURNOVER

SLOW-COOL HOODS (ADJACENT TO COOLING BED OF SOUTH FLAME CUT BUILDING ITEM 16 OF FIGURE 23-1).

FIG. 23—16. Schematic arrangement (not to scale) of the heat-treating facilities that operate in conjunction with the 160/210-inch plate mill at Gary Steel Works of United States Steel. Location of the heat-treating department in relation to other mill facilities is shown in Figure 23—1.

are heated progressively while proceeding through the furnace by continuous or indexing movement and, after attaining the proper temperature, are rapidly moved into the platen quench press where they are quenched by water sprays.

Normalized plates are heated in the same manner, but are "dummied" through the quench press, and then transported to the by-pass table by the transfer car adjacent to the press.

Quenched or normalized plates requiring tempering are moved from the by-pass table and charged into the tempering furnace by the transfer car that operates at the other end of the tempering furnace (adjacent to the leveler).

After tempering (or after heating, in the case of normalized plates), the plates are air-cooled on the by-pass table (some grades are quenched in water after tempering), transferred to the leveler (if necessary) and then to the layout and test-cutting tables where the plates are marked for shearing or flame-cutting and test samples are removed. All plates then are moved by overhead crane from the tables and stacked in the storage area pending results of metallurgical tests.

After test release, the heat-treated plates are moved by over-head crane to either the transfer-crane area or south flame-cut areas of the mill. Sheared plates are placed on the mill shear line by transfer crane, trimmed to finished size, and transferred to the shipping building for final inspection, conditioning and shipment. Flame-cut plates are cut to final size, inspected, conditioned and shipped.

CHAPTER 24

Railroad Rails and Joint Bars

SECTION 1

ROLLING OF RAILROAD RAILS

Dating from the invention of the steam locomotive, the railroad rail represents one of the first sections to be rolled. The railroad rail is a most vital part in railroad operations and represents a difficult section for the roll designer and roller. With the advancement in speed of travel and weight of loads carried, more and more has been required of the rail, until today no product is subject to more severe service conditions. Exposed to the weather at all times, it is subjected, under constantly varying conditions, to high compression and bending stresses, impact, vibration, friction and wear.

The railroad rail should be designed to have the greatest possible transverse strength, to provide an abundance of metal for wear, to present a wide base for fastening to the cross tie, and, for the sake of economy, it should be of the lightest section possible. The American Tee Rail best meets all of these requirements and represents the accepted design.

Historical Development of Rail Sections—The history of rail development is indicated in the sketches of Figure 24—1. The first running surfaces for the early railroad rolling stock consisted of strap rails comprised of cast-iron plates approximately 4 inches by 1¼ inches by 5 feet long, which were attached to a wooden base. The first strap rails were used around 1767. Various types of cast and malleable iron rails were used until about 1820 when the first iron rails were rolled. These were supported by cast-iron holders, called chairs, attached to stone supports. In an effort to eliminate use of the expensive chair required for this type of iron rail, a rail with a wide and relatively heavy flange on the bottom was rolled in 1831. The difficulty of rolling the flange led to the better balanced Locke rail of 1837, the bull head and U-shape rails of 1844, and the pear head rail of 1845. Then came the compound rail of 1856 (not shown in Figure 24—1) and another form in 1858, which was the U-shape of 1844 with the lower parts closed in and welded to form a web. As neither of these forms proved serviceable, a demand for more metal in the head for wear forced a final return in 1858-1868 to the tee shape with wide thin flanges. Subsequent to 1858-1868 the quality of the steel, the design of the rails and rolls, and the equipment of the mills have improved continuously. Present standard railroad rails are rolled in various sizes ranging in weight from 65 lb. up to and including 140 lb. per yard. Rails 60 lb.

per yard and lighter are classed as light rails. Representative chemical compositions for rails are shown in the American Railway Engineering Association (A.R.E.A.) tabulation given in Table 24—I.

Mills for Rolling Rails—There does not seem to be much accurate information available about the first mills which rolled rails. It is probable that existing mills designed to roll bars were utilized with such al-

Table 24—I. Representative Chemical Compositions for Rails

Constituents	Nominal Weight in Lb. per Yard		
	81/90	91/120	121 and Over
Carbon	0.64–0.77%	0.67–0.80%	0.69–0.82%
Manganese .	0.60–0.90	0.70–1.00	0.70–1.00
Phosphorus (Maximum)	0.04	0.04	0.04
Silicon	0.10–0.23	0.10–0.23	0.10–0.23

terations and additions as were necessary. Credit for rolling the first steel rail in 1857 is given to the Dowlais Plant, Wales, while the credit for rolling the first steel rail in this country is given to Captain Ward's North Chicago Rolling Mills, where the first Bessemer steel rails were rolled experimentally in 1865 from blooms made of hammered ingots produced at Wyandotte, Michigan.

Rails were originally rolled on the pullover mill, and later on the reversing mill. In this country rails have been rolled for many years on the three-high mill, which was usually made up of a single train of three stands driven by one engine. Sixty-nine mills were reported to be rolling rails of various weights in 1874. During this great railroad-expansion period, rails were in such demand that even this large number of mills could not supply the demand. These mills were scattered around the country with one as far west as Laramie, Wyoming. The tonnages produced on the old mills were small in comparison to present-day tonnages. Since about 1900, rail mills have undergone many changes because of the ever-increasing requirements of the railroads with respect to quality of the steel, size of the rail section, length of rail, freedom from internal and surface defects, exactness as to dimensions, and a variable demand as to quantity. At the end of 1961, there were five mills in the United

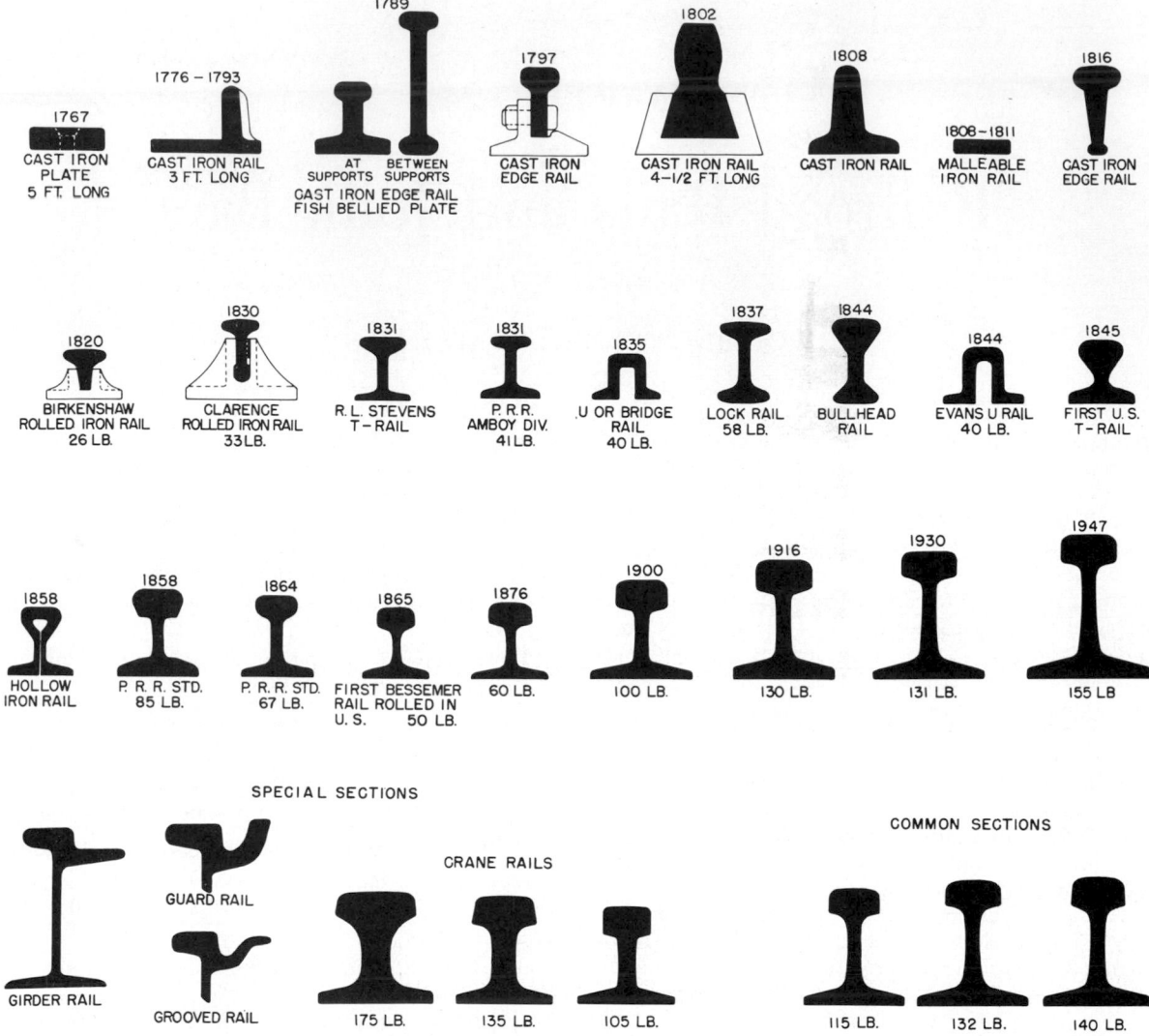

FIG. 24—1. Sketches of cross-sections of rails from the earliest periods of railroading until the present, showing the evolution of the modern railroad-rail design. Certain special rail sections are shown at the lower left.

States that were producing railroad rails. These mills are far from standardized in layout. Some have a large number of stands, others only a few; some are two-high throughout, while others are three-high. No one rail mill may be cited as an example typical of all, but a brief general description of a rail mill which rolls rails directly from ingots will illustrate operating conditions of a rail mill. This mill is the largest rail mill in this country: its layout is somewhat similar to the cross-country type of rolling mill.

The mill starts with four tandem stands of 40-inch, two-high rolls. In these stands, the ingot is given one pass per stand, and is turned after each pass. The passes are of diamond, diamond-square, and box-pass design. After the initial passes, there is a 40-inch three-high mill with five box passes, the final pass being slightly shaped to give the hitherto rectangular bloom a form more suitable for subsequent rolling. Following this three-high blooming stand is the bloom shear and then the cross-country arrangement of seven stands of rolls arranged in two groups of three stands each and one separate stand. The leader stand has a vertical roll working on the head of the rail; the finishing stand one for the rail base.

Rails are formed by two general methods of rolling, known as the **tongue-and-groove, flat** or **slab-and-edging,** and the **diagonal** or **angular** method. Several of the rail mills combine these two methods, some of the passes being designed to form by the first method and the remaining passes to roll the section by the second method. In the tongue-and-groove, flat or slab-and-edging method, illustrated by the second roughing stand in Figure 24—2, the axis of symmetry of the rail coincides with the pitch line and is parallel to the train line of the rolls.

The diagonal or angular method of rolling is represented by the roughing stand shown in Figure 24—3. It differs from the slabbing method in that the shaping of the rail is begun with the first pass in the roughers and instead of first compressing the bloom to a smaller

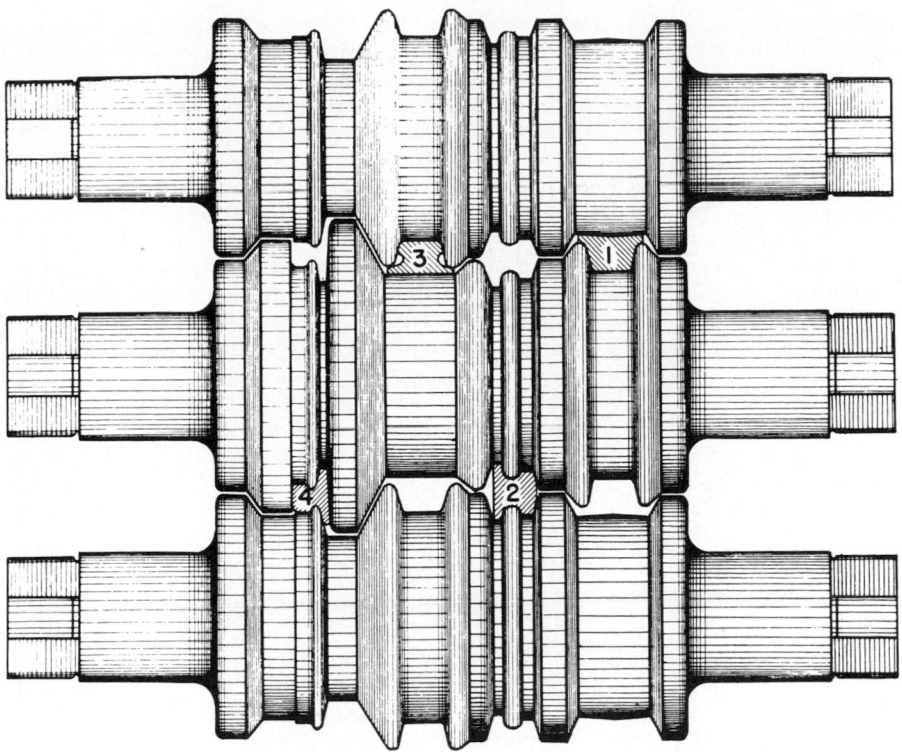

Fig. 24—2. Sketch of rolls used in second roughing stand of a rail mill rolling by the tongue-and-groove, flat, or slab-and-edging method, showing shape produced in each of the four passes.

size and then forming the section partly through compression and partly by spreading, the process is one of compression from beginning to end.

DESIGNING THE ROLLS FOR RAILS

The first consideration in designing the rolls for rails is to produce a finished piece of the correct size and

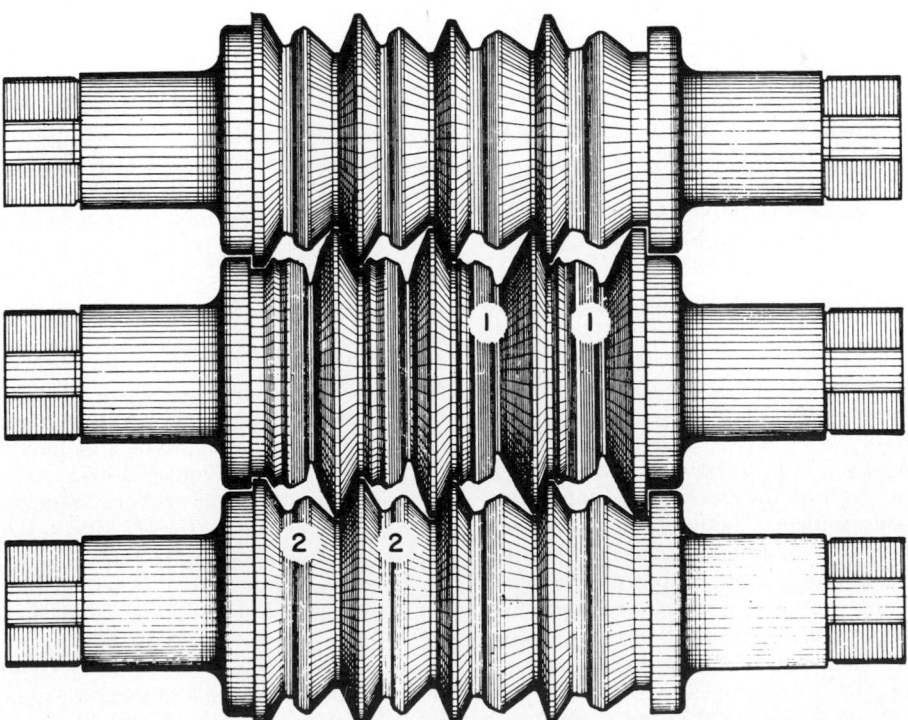

Fig. 24—3. Sketch of rolls used in the roughing stand of a rail mill rolling by the diagonal or angular method.

form. This objective can be accomplished only by directing and controlling the flowing, spreading and bending of the steel. The ease with which this forming is done depends on the plasticity of the metal, which in turn is affected by the temperature. With the speed of the rolls fixed, the temperature confined to a narrow range, and the grade of steel given, the only means of control remaining to the roll designer is the size and shape of the passes, and in part of these, at least, the size will be governed by the size of the bloom. In designing the passes, a good designer will endeavor to work the steel in such a manner that the quality of the product will be benefited, and no defects will be developed. The defects that should be carefully avoided are fins, laps, overfills, and underfills. Laps may result from fins or a collaring of the piece in the rolls; overfills, from worn rolls, poor or improper design; and underfills either from poor design or incorrect adjustment of the rolls.

Stages of Reduction—The formation of the rail from the bloom may be considered as taking place in three steps or stages. The first stage, called the **roughing**, is merely one of preparation; in it a large amount of work is done, but this work is expended mainly in reducing the size of the section and elongating the piece. The intermediate stage proceeds with the forming of the rail and involves a combination of **slabber, dummy, former, edger** and **leader passes**, dependent on the mill layout. The **finishing pass** completes the formation of the rail.

The Section—No original designing of section is done by the roll designer. The first requirement in the rolling of a new section is that the roll designer be supplied with a drawing or print of the section, which must be accompanied with all the dimensions, preferably indicated on the print. The weight of rail desired or expected should also be given. Here the matter of dimensions is of extreme importance, for the designing of the templets cannot be started until each and every dimension required is given. These dimensions not only include linear measurements, such as height of rail, width and thickness of parts, but also the radius of all curves, and amount of slope on inclined surfaces expressed in degrees or percentages.

Roll Preparation—With all the necessary information available, the first step taken by the roll designer is to prepare a drawing for the cold templet. This drawing is constructed on the axis of symmetry of the rail, which is the vertical line drawn through the center of the head, of the web, and of the flange. On this line the section of rail is symmetrically constructed to the dimensions given on the drawing, all the dimensions being made with extreme care and accuracy. Upon completion of this very accurate drawing, the area of the section is measured with a planimeter in order to check the weight of the section, after which the cold templet is prepared from either brass or steel.

The next step, which is really the first step in designing the roll passes, is the making of the hot templet. This templet is similar to the cold templet, but larger in size, as it represents the section of the rail at the finishing temperature of rolling.

From the hot templet the various passes are designed successively as the experience and judgment of the designer dictates. Roll designers may prepare the various pass templets by several methods. Usually the pass templets from a similar section are used as a guide, since many of the sections currently being rolled have been perfected through many modifications from initial designs for the passes. Frequently, the designer constructs each pass outline in a drawing showing the different passes superimposed upon each other. As a preliminary step toward designing passes back to the bloom from the finished templet, a table is usually prepared. This table will consist of various passes, cross-sectional area of the head, web, and base, per cent reduction, and spread in inches. The designer must constantly keep in mind the danger of forming fins. In order to avoid these defects, the designer may arrange the passes so that each side of the piece alternately enters an open and a closed side of the groove when rolling by the tongue-and-groove, flat or slab-and-edging method. Even with this arrangement, fins would still be formed if the passes were not properly designed. To avoid the possibility of forming fins, two modifications of design may be used. In the leader pass, the corner of the head, which is to come opposite the openings between the rolls in the finishing pass, is well rounded off, so that the spread or flow of the metal will be taken up in filling out this rounded corner and none will remain to be forced into the clearance. For the same reason, that half of the flange on the same side of the rail is left much shorter. This provision is made in many of the passes. Great care is necessary in distributing the reduction of each part to prevent the metal flowing away from parts where it is needed. For example, if a too great reduction in the web takes place in one pass, it will produce a flow of metal away from the head, causing the latter to be underfilled. The cause for much of the trouble of this kind lies in the different diameters of the pass, which cause a different roll-surface speed for head, web, and flange, and hence different rates of elongation. If the elongation produced through compression is at the point of less speed, the section will be imperfectly formed, or cracks will result. The accompanying illustration (Figure **24—4**) will help in understanding this point.

The roll designer strives to keep the roughing passes of such shapes and sizes that the same set may be used for a large number of different rail sections. The pass contours for producing the 132-pound RE rail are illustrated in Figure **24—5**.

Upon completion of the pass templets, including both male and female for the cold templet, they are sent to the tool shop where they are used as patterns in making a set of tools for turning the rolls for the section. As many as 24 different tools may be required for the last six passes of each size rail. After shaping these tools a little over-size, they are heat treated and then redressed to exact size before they are used to turn the rolls. When ready, templets and tools go to the roll shop, where the work of turning the rolls is done. Rail-mill rolls may be sand iron, alloy iron, or

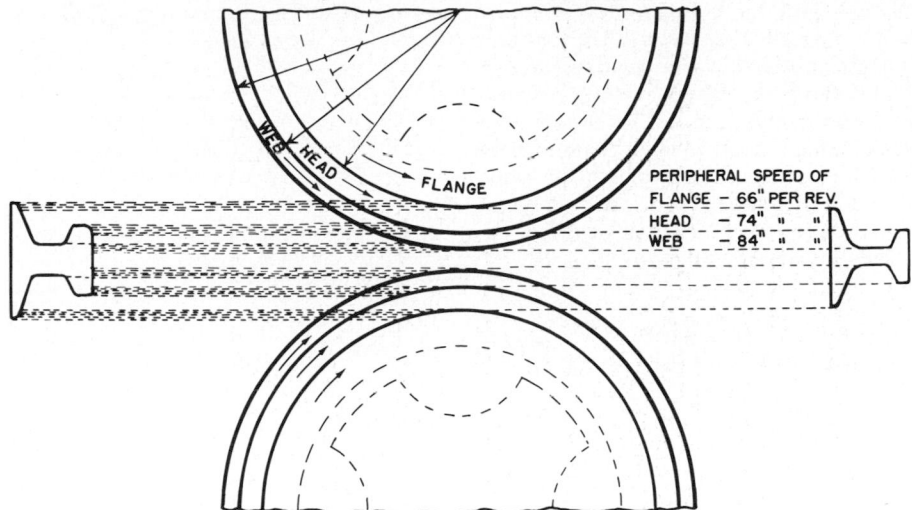

FIG. 24—4. Differences in peripheral speeds at various points in the roll pass contacting, respectively, the flange, head and web of a rail during rolling.

alloy steel rolls. Frequently more than one grade of rolls will be used on the same mill.

ROLLING PRACTICE

After the rolls have been properly turned, they are placed in the housings in their proper position and carefully lined up. A trial rolling with one bloom will then be made with the roller checking the piece

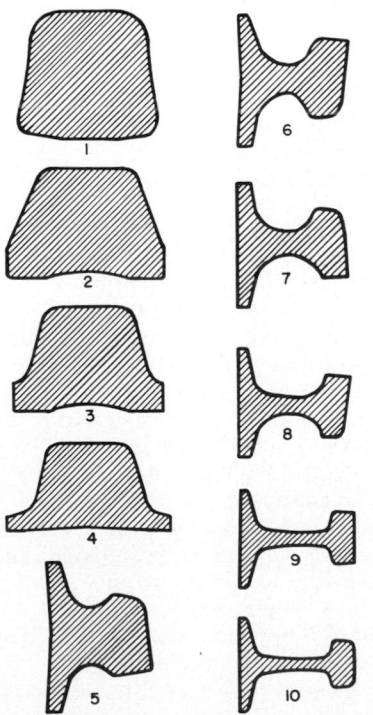

FIG. 24—5. Roll-pass contours for producing a 132-pound RE rail.

closely to see that it goes through the mill in a satisfactory manner. The trial rail thus produced is gaged by templets which permit checking of base over-all, head width and contour, flange length and thickness, head radius and **fish**. (Fishing is a mill term for the dimensions of the theoretical contour of the under side of the head, the side of the web, and the upper side of the base.) By comparison with a master or cold templet the height and web thickness can be checked. If this section is found to be correct, the mill is then ready to begin the rolling. At frequent intervals, the rails are gaged and examined for defects such as collar marks, underfills, roll marks, overfills, guide marks, cracks, seams or pickups. One of the things that cannot be avoided in the rolling is the wear of the rolls which is aggravated by the slippage associated with the irregular section. The grooves tend to wear down rapidly, which will produce a "loose fish." "Rocking base" rails may result from worn rolls.

Standard specifications for rails require that the cold templet shall conform to the specified section as shown in detail on the drawing and shall at all times be maintained perfect. The rail section shall conform as accurately as possible to the templet or drawings. A variation of $1/64$-inch less or $1/32$-inch greater than the specified height is permitted. A variation of $1/16$-inch in the width of either flange is permitted, but the variation in total width of base shall not exceed $1/16$-inch. No variation is permitted in dimensions affecting the fit of the joint bars, except that the fishing templet may stand out not to exceed $1/16$-inch laterally.

Crane Rails—Crane rails, in three sections of 105 pound, 135 pound, and 175 pound, are produced. These rails in general have a heavier head and web than the railroad rail in order to withstand the heavy loads imposed in service. These rails are rolled on rail mills and are made by the same manufacturing practices as railroad rails.

Light Rails—Light rails are rolled on several types

of mills—bar mills, light structural, and, in some cases, mills built and operated exclusively for light rails. Light rails are produced from standard rails or from billets. In the rerolling of light rails from standard rails, either passes of the edge and flat design or of the diagonal design may be used. The rolling of light rails from billets is accomplished in much the same manner as the rolling of standard rails. An average of nine passes is generally used, although in a few extreme cases as few as five passes have been used.

FINISHING OPERATIONS FOR STANDARD RAILS

Cutting and Cambering—Railroad rails are ordinarily cut to produce the standard 39-foot rail. Lengths of 30 and 33 feet, which represent the old standard lengths, are seldom produced. The rails are cut to desired lengths by hot saws operated singly or in gang, mounted over the runout table beyond the finishing stand. In cutting the hot rails, proper allowance must be made for linear thermal contraction, which, for a 39-foot rail, is approximately 6 inches. The exact amount of the contraction depends upon the temperature at which the rail is sawed. It is necessary to set the saws very accurately as the first rail from an ingot as well as the last rail from the same ingot must be within the length tolerance of plus or minus 3/8-inch. Vertical alignment of the saws must also be accurate and the saws must be maintained in sharp condition in order to meet a 1/32-inch maximum off-square tolerance. Drop-test and the nick-and-break samples are obtained from the crop ends cut at the hot saws. After sawing, the rails pass under a stamping machine which marks the heat number, ingot number and position of the rail in the ingot. The latter is designated by letters beginning with A at the top of the ingot. Between the stamping machine and cooling beds is a cambering machine which consists of a set of horizontal rolls with a vertical roll on each side, all in one housing and set to bend the rail slightly so as to make the top surface of the rail convex from end to end. This bending is done to compensate for the camber produced in a straight rail as it cools on the cooling bed, this camber being caused by the different rates at which the head and the base cool. A scale located near the end of the delivery table is used for checking the weight of the rails as often as desired, before they are advanced to the cooling beds. Rail specifications state that a variation of 0.5 per cent from the calculated weight of section as applied to the entire order is permitted.

Marking and Branding—One of the mandatory requirements for standard railroad rails is that each rail shall be legibly marked for complete identification. So far as practicable, this branding is done by numbers, symbols and letters cut in the bottom finishing roll to give raised characters on one side of the web of the rail. Markings that cannot be thus rolled into the web are marked intaglio on the opposite side of the web by a hot stamping machine following the hot saws. The

nature of the information required and the methods of marking are as follows:

Method of Marking	Kind of Mark	Nature of Information
Engraving on bottom finishing roll	Raised characters	Weight or section number Type CC (for control cooled) Manufacturer's brand Year rolled Month rolled
Hot stamping	Intaglio	Heat number Rail letter Ingot number

Controlled Cooling—Controlled cooling of rails on a production basis was begun in 1937.

Present specifications for rails intended for railroad service require controlled cooling of the rails within the temperature range between 725° and 300° F. This is a process especially developed to prevent the formation of shatter cracks, also called internal thermal ruptures, flakes or internal thermal cracks. In mill operations, the rails are allowed to cool to under 1000° F and then are placed in either stationary or movable insulated containers. The rails must be placed in the container within the temperature range between 1000° and 725° F, which is checked by a pyrometer. One or more thermocouples of the chromel-alumel type are placed between tiers of rails in the slow-cool container in order to obtain temperature readings during cooling. The containers are insulated to meet the specified cooling cycle of not dropping below 300° F in 7 hours for rails 100 lb. per yard in weight or heavier, from the time that the bottom tier is placed in the container, and 5 hours for rails of less than 100 lb. per yard in weight. Rails must remain in the cooling container for a minimum of 10 hours. Complete records of the cooling cycle to 300° F are maintained on each container.

Testing of Standard Rails—Testing of standard railroad rails includes chemical, mechanical and internal tests. Two ladle test samples, representing the composition of one of the first three and one of the last three ingots applied, are obtained for chemical analysis. The drop test is relied upon to supply the only mechanical-test information required. Crop ends 4 to 6 feet long are cut from the top end of the "A" rail from the second, middle, and the last full ingot of each heat. ("A" rails are those rolled from the upper portion of the ingot, "B," "C," "D," etc., rails being rolled from steel in successively lower parts of the ingot.) These specimens are placed upon supports and subjected to the impact of a tup weighing 2000 lb., falling from a height of 17 to 22 feet, depending upon the weight of the section. For rails 106 lb. per yard or less in weight, the supports are placed 3 feet apart and for rails over 106 lb. per yard this distance is increased to 4 feet, with the tup striking the rail midway between the supports. If a specimen breaks, all the "A" rails of the heat are rejected and the "B" rails must be similarly tested. Failure of a "B" rail specimen causes all "B" rails to be rejected in addition to the "A" rails and similar tests must be made in "C" rails. Failure of a "C" rail specimen is cause for rejection of the whole heat. One specimen from a heat is given a number of blows to determine the ductility.

The nick-and-break test is a fracture of the rail adjacent to the top end of the top rail of each ingot rolled. If the fracture of any test specimen exhibits seams, laminations, cavities or foreign matter, the top rail represented is classed as an "X-Rayl."

Finishing Operations—Finishing operations for standard rails include preliminary inspection upon unloading from slow-cool cars or containers, removal of saw burrs, straightening, drilling, grinding or milling of ends, beveling of heads when specified, inspection, classification, and painting. The purpose of the preliminary inspection is to check identification and lengths and to locate harmful surface defects and thus save the expense of finishing a rail that would be rejected. The removal of burrs made by the saws on the ends of the rails usually occurs prior to the straightening, although in some instances burr removal occurs after the straightening operation. The burrs are cut off with chisels and subsequently smoothed with a file or a grinder.

The rails are straightened on gag presses, each of which is provided with two bottom supports located in the table proper on which the rail rests, and a top block with die attachment which moves up and down with a fixed stroke between the supports. The stroke of the block is of such length as not to touch the rail by about two inches at its lowest point. On each side of the press at spaced intervals are located two or three stands, each with a roll, to allow bringing the rail to the press and manipulating the rail back and forth while it is being straightened. The die has a double face, each side of which slopes to the center line. The gag, a rectangular block of steel slightly beveled to fit the die, is inserted between the rail and the die. The die form, in combination with the different dimensions of the gag, makes it possible to control the amount of bend the rail receives and to adjust the press to the several rail dimensions. To straighten a rail, one man called a gagger is stationed in front of the machine and a second referred to as a straightener at the end. By sighting along the rail, the straightener at the end locates the areas of rail which require straightening and brings them under the blocks while the gagger before the machine, acting under directions from the straightener at the end, inserts the gag in such a way that the stroke of the machine will bend the rail enough to straighten it, which requires that the rail be bent beyond its elastic limit in order to give a permanent set.

The rails for bolted track are next moved to the drilling machines, which are arranged in pairs and so spaced that when one machine has completed the drilling on one end of the rail, it is moved under the other machine which drills the holes in the opposite end. These machines are provided with three drilling spindles, the middle one of which is fixed, and the outside two adjustable, and may be made to drill from one to three holes at one time. After drilling,

the rails are moved to inspection beds where they are walked, or inspected, ends checked, ends beveled when specified, classified, painted, and separated for loading. When rails are for welded track, the ends to be welded are not drilled. The finished rail inspection is made by mill and purchasers' inspectors to satisfy themselves that the rails are according to specifications. The rails are inspected twice, one time with the base up and the second time with the head up. The location of defects or rails not satisfactorily straightened are marked with chalk. If these defects are located near the end, that portion of the rail may be sawed off and the rail still applied on the order as a short of first grade; shorts are accepted in limited quantities. If the defects are many or are near the center, the rail is either classed as a number two, or scrapped. Number two rails may contain slight imperfections which do not make them unfit for service. Number one rails must be free of injurious defects and flaws of all kinds. Rails which are not straight are transferred to a restraightening press for restraightening whereas rails required to be sawed are transferred to a recut unit which is equipped with slow-speed saws. Off-square ends are corrected either by use of end-milling machines or hand grinders. Rails are classified into the following groups and each group is loaded in separate cars.

Classification	Painting on Rail Ends
No. 2 rails	White
"X-Rayls"	Brown
"A" rails	Yellow
No. 1 rails of less than standard lengths.....	Green
No. 1 rails of a heat in which both the carbon and manganese contents are above the mean of the specified range....	Blue

End Hardening—End hardening is a heat treatment given to the top end surface of a rail head that makes it more resistant to batter and wear. The heating of the rail end is accomplished by either gas hoods or gas burners. Compressed air is used for quenching. Usually the hardened pattern, including the hardened and transition zones, is about ¾-inch in depth at the rail end, tapering to zero depth at a distance approximately 3¾ inch back from the end of the rail.

Production-control testing on end-hardened rails includes the Brinell test made on representative samples.

Finishing and Inspection of Crane Rails—Crane rails are processed about the same as standard railroad rails. In addition, they may be heat treated by quenching in oil and tempering with very satisfactory service results where heavy loads are involved. Crane rails in the control-cooled and the heat-treated conditions are in common use.

Finishing and Inspection of Light Rails—The finishing and inspection of light rails are different from the same operations for heavy rails. Because of the relatively small tonnage of most orders, light rails cannot be handled as separate heats and many light rails are rolled from billets of lower carbon content than heavy rails. Light rails are supplied in 15-foot and 30-foot lengths and are usually straightened on a machine straightener. Bolt holes may be punched or drilled.

SECTION 2

THE ROLLING OF RAIL-JOINT BARS

Types of Rail Joints—Paralleling the development of rails to present-day standards has been the development in rail-joint bars and new techniques, such as welding for joining rails. Through the years, rail-joint bars have been known by various names, such as splice bars, angle bars, and fish plates. A great number of rail-joint bar designs were in use around 1925, such as: the Duquesne rail joint; the 100 per cent rail joint; the Weber rail joint; the Hatfield rail joint; the Wolhaupter rail joint; the Barschall rail joint; the Bonzano rail joint; the Abbott rail joint; the Williams reinforced rail joint; and the reinforced angle bar. Only a few of these rail joint bars are in use at the present time. In recent years there has been a trend toward standard designs of joint bars.

Present Rail-Joint Bars—Even with one type of joint bar, there must be many different designs, for the joint bar must fit accurately between the head and the base of the rail, and each change in these dimensions of the rail requires a change in the joint bar. The most popular rail-joint bar type at the present time is the short-toe joint bar of either the head-free or head-contact design. A sketch of the conventional rail-joint bar of the head-free type (with short toe) is shown in Figure 24—6. The head contact type of conventional rail-joint bar is identical with the sketch shown in Figure 24—6, except there is contact of the under surface of the head of the rail with the head of the joint bar. The head-free design is considered to have some advantage with respect to a lower rate of bolt-tension loss and lower resistance to expansion movement of rail ends. The principal advantage of the head-free design, however, is the fact that its use permits the desired thickening of the upper web and lengthening of the fillet radius. Nomenclature for the present conventional rail joint (with long toe) and the older type of continuous rail joint is shown in Figure 24—7. The continuous joint bar shown is in very limited use. This section is rolled with the lower base flared, the flare being pressed into a size to fit the rail base when the bar is punched. Other types of joint bars, with or without reinforcements in the web, are in very limited use at the present time.

Problems in Rolling Rail-Joint Bars—Passes for rolling three typical joint bars are shown in Figure 24—8. Joint bars are usually rolled from billets or blooms within the carbon content range of 0.30 to 0.60 per cent, although a lower carbon range has application for the cold-worked joint bar. The conventional joint bar and the joint bar with long toe present rolling problems because of their irregular section and lack of symmetry. In the conventional joint bar, the angles at which the section is rolled are limited by possibility of undercuts, and the shape of the passes in which the piece is necessarily reduced are favorable to the formation of laps and seams. If the joint has a depending flange, or long toe, these difficulties are multiplied, while the excessively protruding parts of a joint, such as in the continuous section (Figures 24—7 and 24—8), often prevent the piece from entering the pass properly, by striking the rolls first or being a trifle colder than the rest of the piece. For similar reasons, it is difficult to make guides that will properly handle such sections, and they are prone to become cobbled or caught in the rolls of the tables. The rolled section of joint bar is cut into convenient long lengths for handling and sent to the joint bar shop for processing into finished joint bars.

FINISHING JOINT BARS

In general, rail-joint bars may be finished in one of three ways: First, all the operations of shearing to length, straightening, punching and slotting may be performed upon the cold pieces without heating in any way; the finished pieces then are referred to as **cold-worked joint bars**. Second, the bars may be heated, after shearing to length, and the work of punching and slotting be done while they are hot, after which they are allowed to cool in air. In this case they are called **hot-worked joint bars**. Third, instead of cooling the bars in the air after hot working they may be quenched by immersing them in oil, when they are designated as **hot-worked and oil-quenched bars**. It will be observed that in this latter method, as in the other two methods, the bars are sheared to length

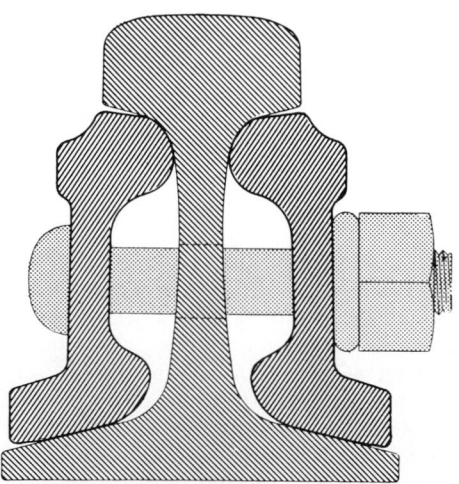

FIG. 24—6. Cross-sectional diagram of the head-free type of conventional rail-joint bar.

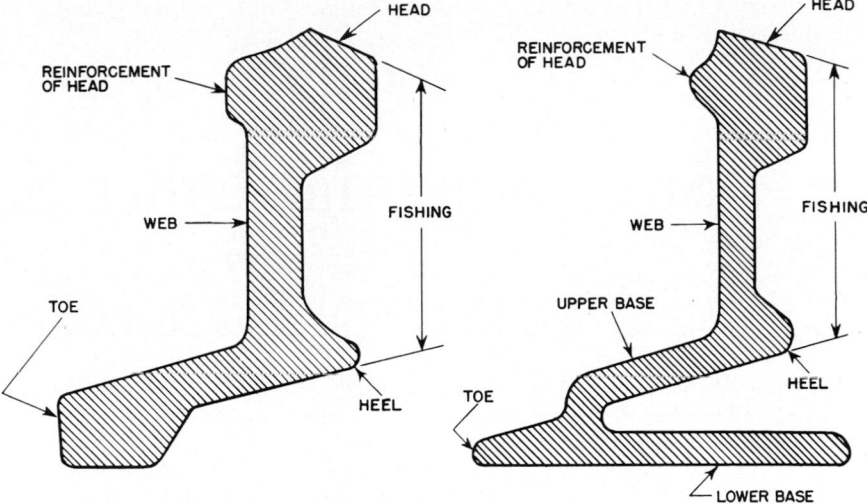

FIG. 24—7. Diagrammatic cross-sections of two types of rail-joint bars, with nomenclature of principal components.

CONVENTIONAL JOINT BAR

CONTINUOUS RAIL JOINT

cold, hot shearing being impractical, and hot or cold sawing too expensive. The hot-worked and oil-quenched joint bars possess such superior mechanical properties that practically all joint bars used on trunkline railroads are finished by this process.

WELDED RAIL JOINTS

The joining of rails by welding the joints is used by practically all railroads. The Thermit process, the electric-flash method, and the gas-heated butt-pressure method have all been used, with the latter two methods being most generally accepted for railroad installations.

A typical example of the gas butt-pressure method for welding rail joints as practiced by one of the major railroads in this country is as follows: Rails to be welded are held together end to end and a saw cut is made at the junction of the two rails to produce parallel, clean and smooth end faces. After end preparation, the rails are placed end to end in the welding unit under high pressure. A gas-fired heating head with multiple orifices brings the two ends to a temperature resulting in plastic deformation from the pressure, giving an upset fusion weld. After welding is completed, the upset metal at the weld is scarfed or sheared off. Subsequent to the removal of the welding flash, a normalizing treatment generally is applied to the weld area.

An electric flash-welding process that was developed in Europe has been adopted by many railroads in the United States for the fabrication of continuous rail. Rail ends to be joined are properly cleaned and then clamped in the heads or platens of a welding machine, and electrical current is applied. One of the platens is movable, and is repeatedly moved back and forth to make and break the electrical contact between the two rail ends. This "flashing" operation heats the rail ends to the plastic state, at which they are brought together under high pressure and an upset weld is produced the same as under the butt pressure method that employs gas for heating the rail ends. Upset metal is removed by shearing and grinding and the weld is tested to assure complete soundness.

Bibliography

"Rail Mills and Rail Mill Roll Design" by Ross E. Beynon. Pages 53 to 80 of June, 1946 issue of Iron and Steel Engineer.

"Specifications for Open Hearth Steel Rails." Issued by American Railway Engineering Association.

"Standard Specifications for Open Hearth Carbon Steel Rails." Issued by American Society for Testing and Materials.

"Specifications for Quenched Carbon-Steel Joint Bars." Issued by American Railway Engineering Association.

"Railway Track Materials." Steel Products Manual; American Iron and Steel Institute.

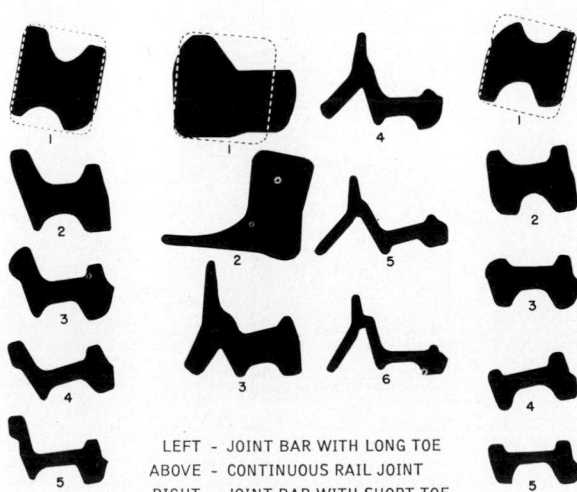

LEFT - JOINT BAR WITH LONG TOE
ABOVE - CONTINUOUS RAIL JOINT
RIGHT - JOINT BAR WITH SHORT TOE

FIG. 24—8. Successive roll passes for the production of three typical rail-joint bars.

CHAPTER 25

Structural And Other Shapes

SECTION 1

EQUIPMENT FOR PRODUCING SHAPES

In rolling-mill parlance, the word "shape" is used interchangeably with the word "section" in describing forms of rolled material (except for geometrical shapes, which are known as rounds, squares, hexagons, etc.). Shapes, or sections, are normally divided into two classes, **structural** and **other sections**. **Structural sections** include standard items, such as I-beams, channels, angles, and wide flange beams, and special sections such as zees, tees, bulb angles, and car-building center sills. **Other sections** include such miscellaneous shapes as steel H-piles, sheet piling, tie plates, cross ties, and those for special purposes.

The production of shapes, as enumerated above, involves a number of processes which are generally common to all of them. These processes include heating of the bloom, rolling to proper contour and dimensions, cutting while hot to lengths that can be handled, cooling to atmospheric temperature, straightening, cutting to ordered lengths, inspecting, and shipping.

The heating of the bloom for large sections is done in either of two types of furnaces, the in-and-out, or the continuous, which are described in Chapter 21. The in-and-out furnace is the more common of the two and serves nearly all of the older structural mills. A typical mill uses three furnaces of this type, having hearth areas about 18 feet by 36 feet. The newer mills tend to use continuous furnaces because of the greater economy, one or two continuous furnaces being sufficient. Practical widths of this type furnace can accommodate blooms up to 30 feet long, and one furnace of proper length, designed according to the cross-section of blooms to be heated, can have sufficient capacity to supply a mill. To hold heat loss to a minimum, furnaces are usually located adjacent to a bloom-storage yard, or the delivery table from a blooming mill, or both, and at a minimum distance from the first stand of the mill on which shapes are to be rolled.

A typical mill for the production of structural sections is shown schematically in Figure 25—1. It has a two-high reversing breakdown stand in which the initial shaping is accomplished, followed by a group of three stands, arranged in train, where the rolling process is completed. The first of these three stands, known as the rougher, is three-high. The middle stand, which is known as the intermediate, is also three high, and continues the formation of the shapes

to almost finished dimensions. The finishing stand, which is usually two-high, establishes the final shape of the rolled section. Under some conditions it is desirable to have a three-high stand for the finisher. The two-high breakdown stand is fitted with rolls of cast steel, either carbon or alloy, with pitch diameter typically 36 inches, and body length 80 inches. The roughing, intermediate, and finishing stands, which are sometimes referred to collectively as the finishing mill, usually employ rolls with a pitch diameter between 28 inches and 33 inches, and a body length of 68 inches. Cast rolls are used on these three stands, usually of carbon or alloy steel, grain or sand iron (see Chapter 20), the selection being based on service requirements.

In modern mills all of these rolls are driven by electric motors, with direct-current variable-speed reversing motors being essential for the breakdown stands, and preferred for all stands. On breakdown mills, the motor drives through a flexible connection to a two-

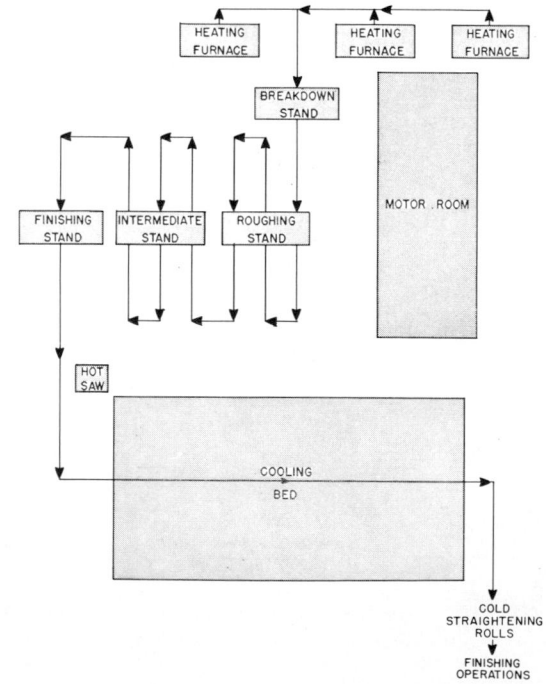

FIG. **25**—1. Diagrammatic layout (not to scale) of a typical mill for rolling structural sections.

high set of pinions, and through spindles to the rolls. Most structural finishing mills drive the three stands from a single motor, through a single three-high set of pinions, the drive being carried by spindles from the pinions to the roughing rolls, and by other spindles from the roughing rolls to the intermediate rolls. Two more spindles, connected to the middle and bottom rolls of the intermediate stand, drive the finishing rolls. Horsepower requirements vary, with 5000 horsepower being typical for breakdown stands, and 6000 horsepower typical for the finishing mill.

The breakdown stand is normally served by stationary roller tables equipped with mechanical manipulators. The shape is conveyed into, and received out of, the finishing mill passes by traveling, tilting roller tables.

The mill equipment for the production of wide-flange beams and H-piles is substantially different from that used in the production of other shapes. The distribution of metal in the web and flanges of wide-flange beams is such that beams of this type have maximum resistance to bending moment with minimum weight per foot length of beam, and the thickness of metal in the web is usually less than that in the flanges. On the other hand, the bearing piles, known as steel H-piles, while essentially wide-flange beams, are produced with an equal thickness of metal in the web and flanges to provide: (1) ruggedness to resist driving forces; and (2) the same thickness of metal in all parts to provide uniform life under corrosive conditions, for the entire cross-section. Two or three groups of roll stands may be used, with each group containing more than one set of rolls. Figure 25—2 shows the schematic arrangement for a typical mill. This mill has a roughing group of stands which consist of a two-high roughing edging stand, closely

associated with a roughing main stand, which has two horizontal main rolls and two friction-driven vertical rolls in a single vertical plane. The rolls in the roughing edging stand have a nominal diameter of 30 inches at the working zone and a body length of from 20 inches to 48 inches varying according to the depth of section rolled. The roughing main rolls have a nominal body diameter of 52 inches with a body length matching the edging rolls. Vertical rolls in the roughing stand, having a nominal diameter of 42 inches and a face width of 18 inches, are friction driven by the shape about a roller bearing in their bore. The intermediate group of stands is identical in all of the above particulars to the roughing group, with the exception of the edging stand being on the opposite end of the main stand. The finishing stand resembles the roughing and intermediate main stands in that it has main and vertical rolls of the same size in like arrangement, but does not have edging rolls. The general arrangement of the mill is such that the hot shape from the blooming mill or reheating furnace enters first into the roughing edging stand and before clearing that stand enters the roughing main stand. The intermediate group of stands is placed a minimum distance to the side and one maximum shape length beyond the roughing group. The main intermediate stand is on the side toward the rougher and is closely followed by the intermediate edging stand, again arranged so that a single shape is in both stands of the group simultaneously (12½ foot centers). The finishing stand is in line with the intermediate group and 186 feet beyond the intermediate edging stand. Stationary roller tables are provided throughout with a short transfer mechanism to move the shape from the line of the roughing group of stands to the line of the intermediate group. All of these stands are driven by direct-current reversing motors, each individual stand having a separate motor, two-high pinions, and the necessary spindles. The roughing and intermediate main stands are driven by 7000-horsepower motors, and their respective edgers by 2000-horsepower motors. The finishing-stand motor is rated at 4000 horsepower.

Rolled shapes are further processed with equipment which is substantially the same for shapes produced on the standard type of structural mill as on the wide-flange-beam mill.

Removing ends not filled to proper section, commonly called "crop ends," and cutting the hot shape into lengths which can be handled in further processing, is done with a hot saw. This equipment consists of a toothed circular saw blade mounted on a sliding frame and driven at high speed by an electric motor. Blades range up to 66 inches in diameter and copious water cooling helps maintain the cutting edges. The saw and its drive are moved on a sliding base at right angles to the hot shape so that the revolving blade cuts through the stationary shape.

Cooling of the rolled shapes is accomplished by placing them on a cooling bed which is a steel structure, arranged to support a continuous layer of shapes, while providing for a maximum circulation of air upward around them. A mechanism is provided to pull the shapes sideways into place and to slide them across the bed onto the discharge table.

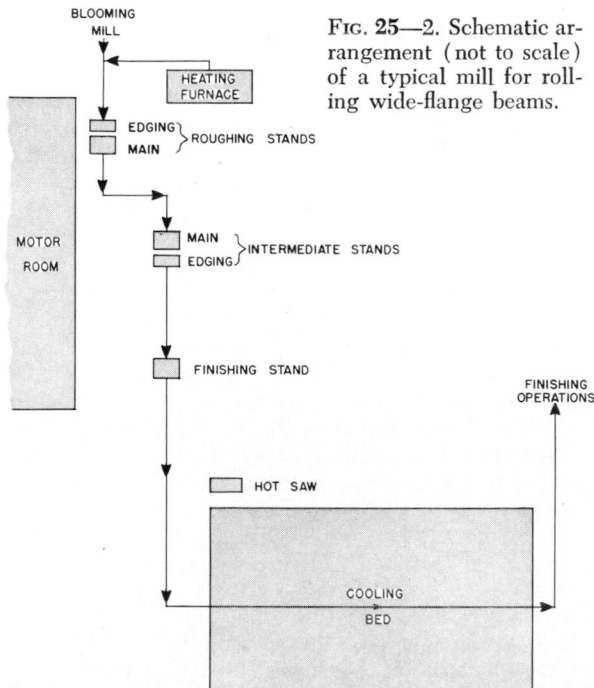

FIG. 25—2. Schematic arrangement (not to scale) of a typical mill for rolling wide-flange beams.

Large shapes are straightened by roller-type straightening equipment, or a gag press. The former normally consists of seven or eight cast-iron or cast steel rolls assembled in a single housing with a single drive, driving either part or all of the rolls. The top rolls are placed midway between the bottom rolls and may be moved vertically by screws. All rolls are arranged for axial adjustment. The gag press consists of a horizontally-reciprocating ram midway between two support points on a platen which is so arranged that it can be moved closer to or further away from the ram, thereby varying the amount of bend made in the shape.

Cold cutting to final length is accomplished by shearing or cold sawing. The shears consist of a stationary bottom blade over which the shape is positioned, and a top blade which is forced down on the top of the shape to cut it through, either with a single shearing action, or by punching a slug, or short piece, out of the shape. The cold saw is similar in design and action to the hot saw, but is fed at a substantially slower rate.

SECTION 2

ROLLING METHODS AND PROCEDURES

The practice of heating blooms for rolling into shapes varies with the quality of the steel, the size of the bloom, and the temperature at which the blooms are charged. A typical mill charges ordinary carbon-steel blooms received from the blooming mill at about 1800° F and heats them to 2250° F in approximately 45 minutes. On a mill using three in-and-out type furnaces, normal operations find one furnace being charged, one heating, and the other being drawn, at a given time. Charging of the single layer of blooms in a furnace is begun as soon as the drawing has been completed. When steel at atmospheric temperature is charged, the heating to 2250° F requires about 2½ hours for the average size bloom. Handling the blooms into and out of the furnaces is accomplished by charging machines which grip the blooms on their sides. This necessitates a space between adjacent blooms of some six or eight inches as clearance for the charging-machine tongs.

Rolling—Heated blooms are deposited by the charging machine on the breakdown-stand approach table, which conveys them to the rolls. The manipulators, on the entry side of the mill, are brought into play to align the bloom with the first pass and to turn it about its longitudinal axis, if necessary. When properly aligned, the table rollers are revolved to feed the bloom into the first pass of the rolls. The rolls for the breakdown-stand generally have three or more pass grooves, some of which may be rectangular blooming passes. The number of different shaped grooves in the rolls, and the number of passes made in each groove, vary with the section being rolled. After making the required number of passes through the first groove, the bloom is re-aligned for subsequent passes by the manipulators.

Blooms processed through the breakdown-stand progress over the stationary rollers of the delivery table to the traveling tilting table which carries the bloom into line with the first pass of the roughing stand. Since the finishing-mill rolls are not reversed during operation, only a single pass is made through each groove. Similar tables on the opposite side of the finishing mill receive the shape from the first groove and enter it into succeeding grooves. Roughing- and intermediate-stand rolls usually contain from two to five pass grooves, while finishing-stand rolls are generally limited to a single pass on a shape. Finishers usually have duplicate grooves for the same section, or provide grooves for a variety of sections.

The type of section resulting from the rolling process is determined by the shape of the various pass grooves through which the material progresses, with optional groups of pass shapes frequently being available for the production of a given section. In the case of standard beams, at least three different systems of passes may be used.

The most common pass shapes used in rolling standard beams are those of the straight-flanged method which are shown in Figure 25—3. This method owes its popularity to the large range of web thicknesses which can be produced from a single set of rolls, the ability to use the early passes for the production of channels as well as beams, and the small thrust loads transmitted by the rolls to the bearings. The versatility of the weights produced results from the relatively small total taper in the live or open flanges which permit rolls to be separated to produce heavier webs with a minimum thickening of the live flange. The most undesirable feature of this method is the relatively slight taper in the pass sides which reduces the gain on dressing and results in passes getting progressively wider and flanges relatively heavier when dressed, thereby limiting the life of the rolls.

The butterfly method of rolling beams closely resembles the straight-flanged method. The outstanding difference is the fact that the live flanges are bent out to a much greater degree in all passes preceding the finishing pass. This results in greater ease of restoring the open flanges by dressing, but imposes a serious limitation on the range of web thicknesses that can be produced in a given set of passes.

Figure 25—4 illustrates the passes used in the diagonal method of rolling beams. This method makes good provision for the restoring of both flange thickness and pass width by dressing, but involves serious restrictions in the web thicknesses that can be satisfactorily produced from a single set of rolls, and vastly increases the thrust loads that are imposed on the bearings which support the rolls. Since thrust-bearing wear permits longitudinal motion of the rolls with corresponding changes to the thickness of the open flanges, rolling difficulties result.

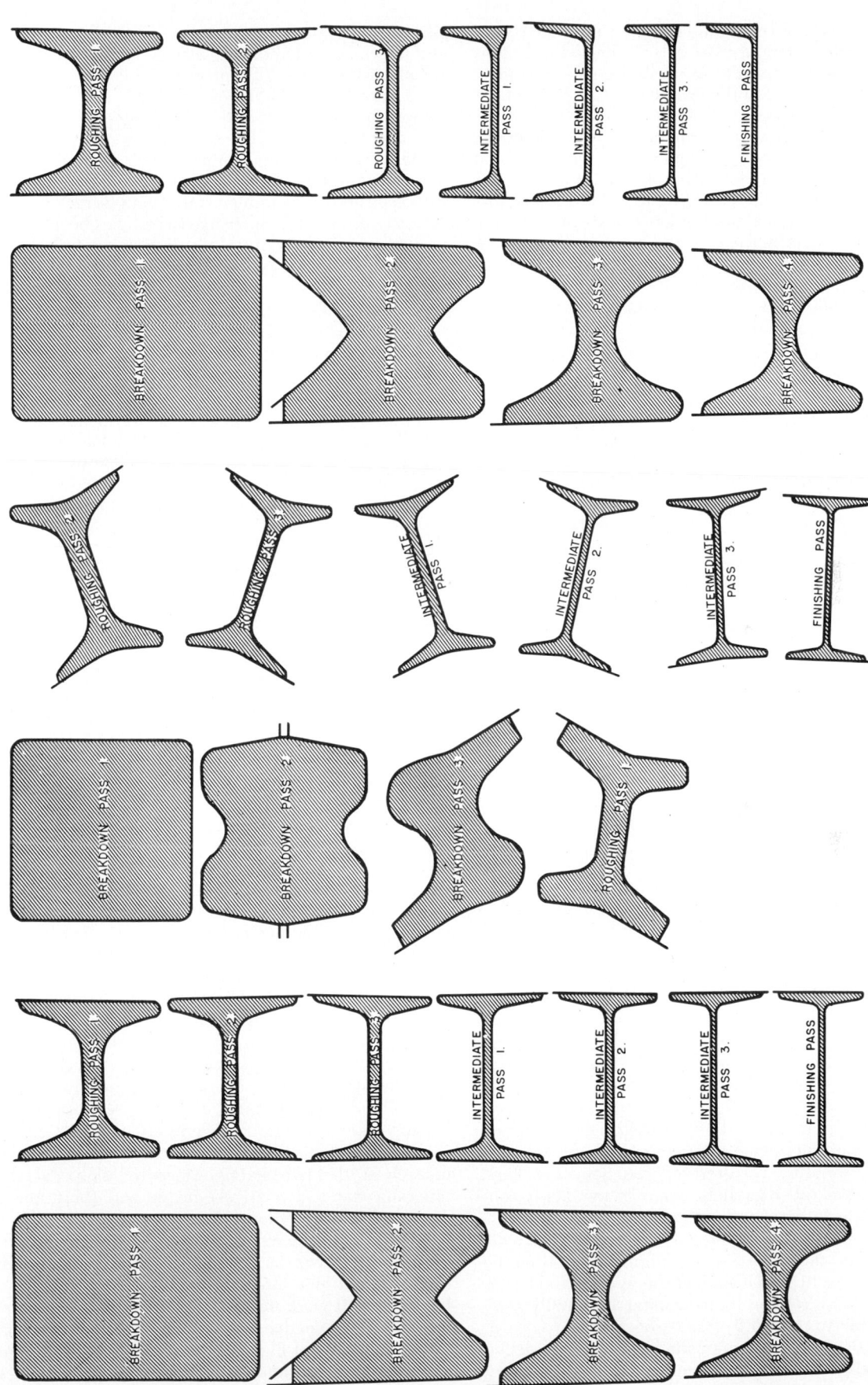

FIG. 25—5. Roll passes for producing a channel, using early passes shared for rolling beams.

FIG. 25—4. Roll passes for rolling beams by the diagonal method.

FIG. 25—3. Roll passes for rolling standard beams by straight-flanged method.

The method of rolling a channel using early passes shared with a standard beam is illustrated in Figure 25—5. This plan results in a smaller roll inventory, good flange control in the production of a large range of weights, narrower passes and stronger collars than can be had if the butterfly method is used. Figure 25—6 shows the butterfly design. It has the advantage of producing channels which are filled to proper section very close to the ends of the rolled bars. However, this method of production results in relatively thin weak collars on the rolls and almost precludes the rolling of multiple weights. This is caused by the extreme thickening of the flanges in the early passes when the rolls are separated to produce a thicker web.

Angles also offer the roll designer a choice between a number of proven rolling methods. Those most generally approved today may be referred to as the butterfly and the flat-and-edge methods. Typical passes for the butterfly angle are shown in Figure 25—7. The current popularity of this method is due to the relatively small crop loss on the shapes, the absence of vertical rolls or turning for edging, and the ease of controlling the bending, which is slight in any one pass. Undesirable features of the design are the lack of proportional thickening of the various parts of each leg when rolls are separated to make heavy weights, and somewhat poorer control of leg length.

The flat-and-edge type of design can be seen in Figure 25—8. This method is popular on those mills having vertical edging rolls and is sometimes used where the shape is turned 90° for edging in a pass in horizontal rolls. Leg lengths are readily controlled in the edging passes and thicknesses remain uniform when rolls are set to produce heavy weights. These advantages are frequently offset by the difficulty in maintaining proper entry alignment of the section in the later passes where bending is drastic. Turning long lengths of hot, flexible steel for edging, where that is necessary, is also difficult.

The special structural sections include shapes rolled rarely or for a single purpose. The passes used for the production of zee bars involve the same principles as the rolling of angles by the butterfly method, with each half of the pass resembling an angle pass, and with the two halves being fitted together reversed. The half center-sill section, used in making modern railroad cars, is a special type of zee bar, being irregular in both thickness of the members and flange lengths. Passes for its production are included here (Figure 25—9) because of the relatively great demand for the section.

Modern practice tends towards the production of tees by splitting a beam of proper size through its web to make two of the required sections. Some tees, however, are still rolled as such. The rolls are unduly complicated and the actual rolling is difficult. Where a choice is offered, the rolling of tees is usually avoided because of the necessity of turning the section between passes to permit each of the two tapered flanges and the parallel stem to be worked alternately so far as possible, in open and closed grooves.

One of the most interesting groups of sections produced upon standard structural mills is the sheet-piling group. (Steel sheet piling of domestic manufacture is produced almost exclusively to ASTM specification A-328.) Usually produced in three general types, known as straight web, arch web, and zee, these sections have been adapted as wall members in both permanent and temporary structures requiring strong vertical walls for lateral support, such as coffer dams, piers, dykes, breakwaters, etc. In the rolling of piling sections, the usual problems are complicated by the necessity of bending the flange (which has been rolled straight) to form the interlock. Precise control of the bend is necessary since proper clearance within the interlock must be maintained and the resulting opening between flange tip and thumb must be within close limits. The particular arch web section for which passes are shown in Figure 25—10 accomplishes this bending of the flange in two steps in the leader and finishing passes. Attention should be given to the fact that the shaping of the section starts in the blooming mill. This is typical of most piling sections and large beams, and is the result of the large size of the sections coupled with their intricate shape which precludes getting enough passes into the limited space of the breakdown and finishing mills to properly form the section.

While the rolling procedure for a section on the standard type of structural mill does not normally employ the same pass groove for more than one reduction in the shape, multiple passes being limited to the breakdown stand and seldom exceeding three passes in a groove, the opposite situation exists on the wide flange beam mill. Here as many as fifteen successive passes are taken through the main and edging stands of the roughing group. In a typical layout, the main and vertical rolls of the roughing main stand and the rolls of the roughing edging stand are moved to new settings with respect to each other by an automatic screwdown control. With this mechanism, the operator sets in advance of rolling the reduction to be taken on each pass. Then, pass by pass, he advances the lever of the master control switch a notch, with each of the three sets of rolls of the roughing group moving closer together simultaneously to the new settings. The control equipment is so designed that each of the three sets of rolls can be made to move different amounts, thus permitting proportional rather than like reductions on flange and web.

The equipment of the intermediate group of stands is practically the same as the roughing equipment. As in the rougher, fifteen passes are provided for in the control equipment. In practice, the passes are divided between the roughing and the intermediate stands in a proportion that gives equal duration of rolling cycle in each of the two stands. Since the shape at the roughing stand is relatively heavy and short, more passes are required there to balance the relatively few passes made on the elongated shape at the intermediate stands. Passes in actual use range from fifteen roughing and nine intermediate on sections requiring heavy overall work, to five roughing and three intermediate on the sections requiring a minimum of work; nine roughing and five intermediate passes represent the average condition. In all cases the intermediate

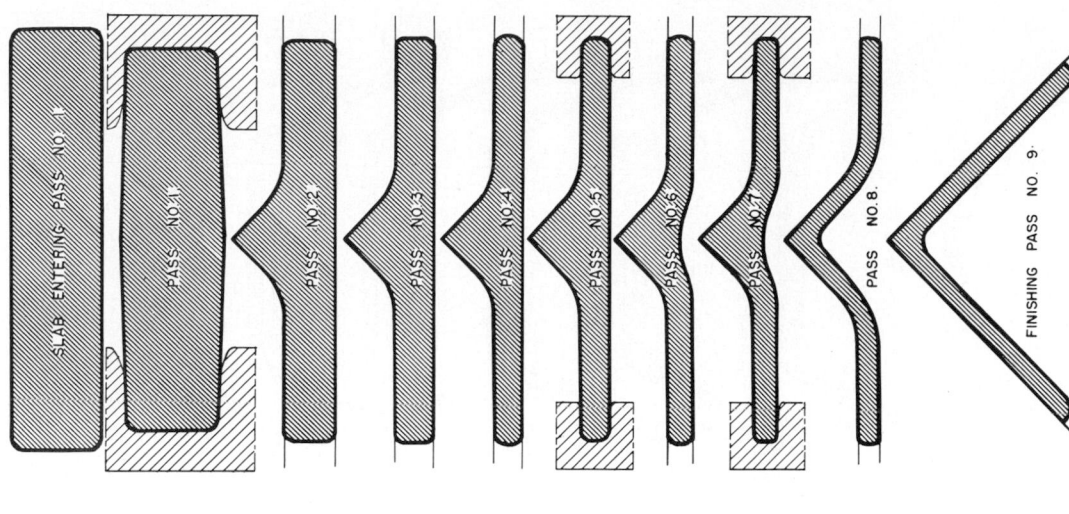

Fig. 25—8. Roll passes for producing an angle by the flat-and-edging method.

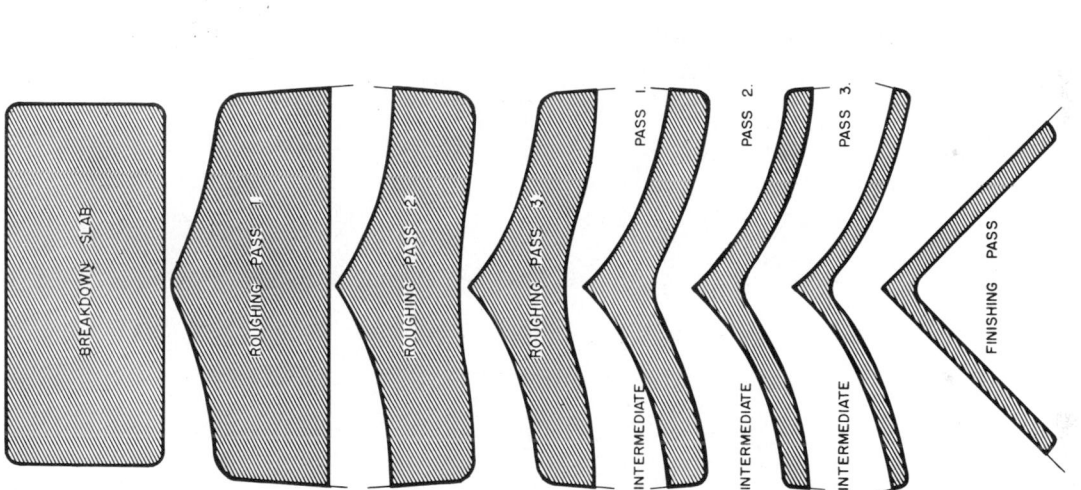

Fig. 25—7. Roll passes for rolling an angle by the butterfly method.

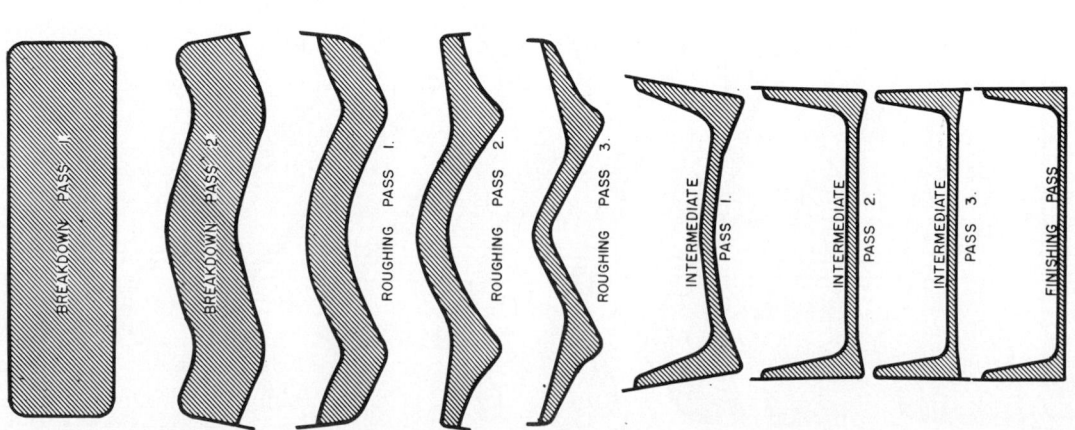

Fig. 25—6. Roll passes for rolling a channel by the butterfly method.

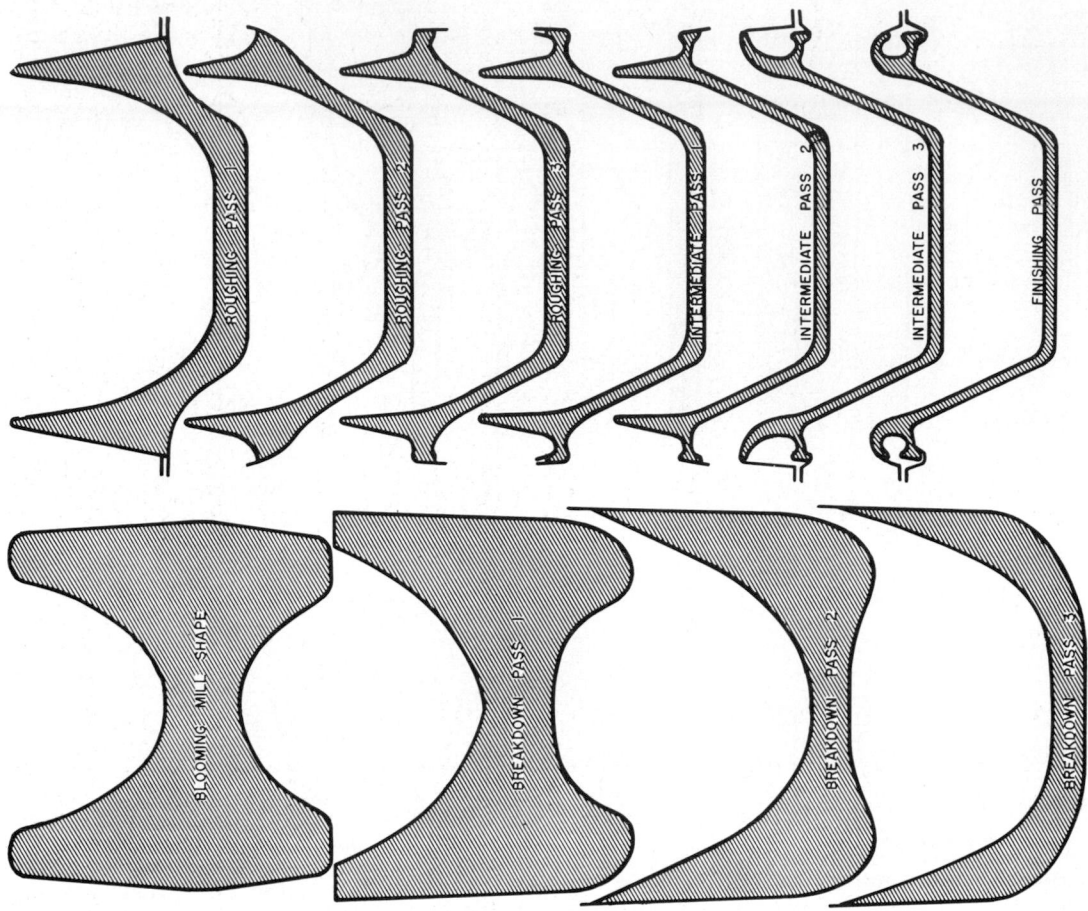

Fig. **25—10**. Roll passes for rolling an arch web section of sheet piling, showing how flange is bent to accurate configuration in the leader and finishing passes.

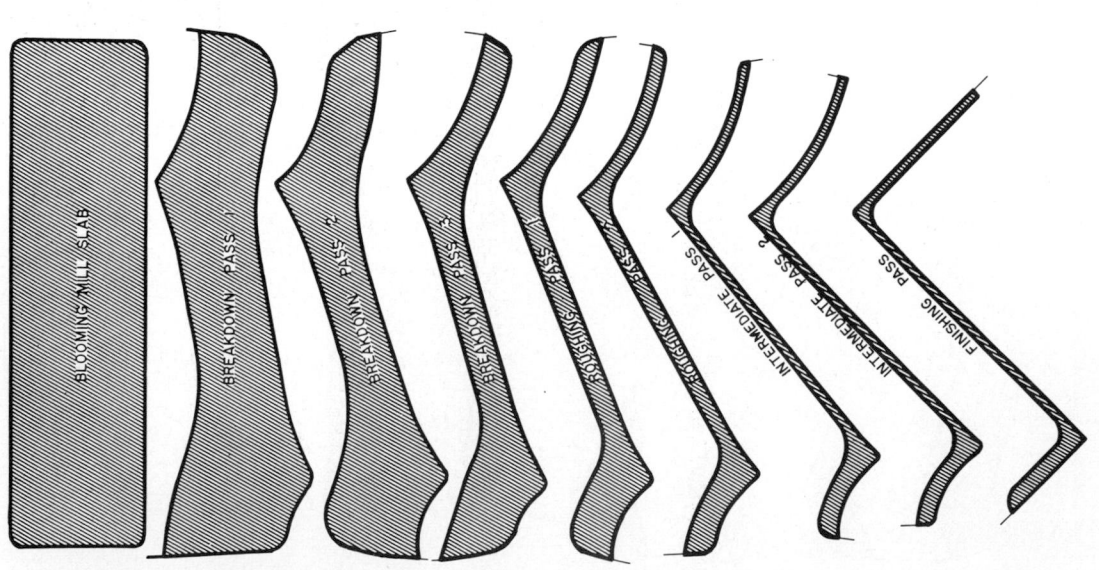

Fig. **25—9**. Roll passes for the production of a half center-sill section, a special type of zee bar.

passes are followed by a single finishing pass. In rolling wide-flange beams it is customary to roll a bloom which has, as nearly as possible, the same proportions as the finished beam. Each succeeding pass in the rolling cycle strives to maintain these proportions, resulting in reduction, pass by pass, being proportional. Since at no time after leaving the blooming mill are the flanges rolled in a closed groove, the loss in flange length is very small, and the rolling of beams with extremely high flanges is entirely possible.

Rolled material from either of the described structural mills is delivered by roller table to the hot saw. The blade of the saw is normally revolved in such a direction that the cutting edge is moving downward toward the shape. The action of the rapidly revolving toothed blade combines a mechanical sawing and melting of the steel, the chips when thrown clear frequently being molten. Cuts are usually made at the hot saw to remove the crop ends, to part the usable material into lengths that can be handled for further processing, and to provide short test pieces. Tests are cut for the guidance of the roller in correcting defects in the section and for various mechanical tests which are part of the inspection procedure.

Cooling is accomplished by the natural circulation of air about the shapes on the cooling bed. The rate of cooling can, to some extent, be controlled, and is of relative importance. Cooling can be accelerated by maintaining space between shapes on the bed, and by providing ample space below the bed for the passage of cool air. Retarding of the cooling cycle results from putting the hot shapes on the bed in a solid touching layer. If cooling is too drastically retarded, the size of the hot bed must be increased or rolling delays will result. On the other hand, too rapid cooling may result in mechanical properties outside the ordered range. Non-uniform cooling results in warpage of the shapes as they cool. This must be avoided in symmetrical shapes, if possible. Most non-uniform shapes warp during cooling, sometimes to the point that they are difficult to convey to the straightening machine.

SECTION 3

FINISHING AND INSPECTION

When the shapes have been properly cooled they are conveyed again by roller table to the straightening machine. For the products rolled on the standard type of structural mill and the smaller wide-flange beams, a roller straightener is normally used. The first shape to be straightened is stopped in the machine while the rolls are adjusted laterally to it. The top rolls are then moved downward to deform the shape with each successive top roll making less deformation than the preceding one. This shape is backed out of the machine and then run through for most of its length. If not straight to the eye of the experienced operator it is again reversed in the machine. Further adjustment is made with this process being repeated until a straight shape is obtained. Subsequent shapes will require only slight alteration to the setting of the machine to compensate for wear and other variables. The larger wide-flange beams and some few standard mill products are straightened in the gag press. Here the process consists of advancing the stationary platen and the shape towards the reciprocating ram until a bend is accomplished in the shape. The operator has full control of the point on the shape at which the bend will be made, the amount of the bend, and by turning on the table, the direction of the bend. Bending strives only to offset initial crookedness.

Cutting to final length is accomplished by one of several means. Hot shearing or hot sawing are most commonly used, wherever the class of product permits. Cold sawing is the next most frequently used method. Flame cutting is available for extremely heavy sections and unusual applications. Where overall length must be accurate, as in the case of columns, the ends may be milled: this results not only in close length tolerance, but in a reduction in the ends' out-of-square allowance as well.

Before the products rolled on the various mills may be shipped, they must be inspected for defects and tested for certain mechanical properties. This is accomplished by two general methods. First, the test cuts taken at the hot saw are sent to the laboratory where tests are made to determine the mechanical properties of the material, such as tensile strength and yield point. The other method of inspection is visual inspection of the material on an inspection bed where the shapes are inspected for metallurgical defects, such as pipe, blister and scabby surface, and for dimensional variations such as length, straightness, and out-of-square condition. Dimensions such as web or flange thickness, flange height, weight per foot, etc., are checked on tests taken at the hot saw by the mill inspector, and the roller then adjusts the mill to correct improper conditions. Special sections may require additional inspection. An example is the slot and thumb on sheet piling. Chemical composition of all material is known, as a record is kept of all rolled products showing the number of the heat from which it was rolled.

The final steps are to separate and assemble for shipment. The material then is loaded in freight cars, river barge, or truck, and shipped to its destination.

CHAPTER 26

Production of Wrought-Steel Wheels

Introduction—Classified according to methods of manufacture, steel wheels are either fabricated from several pieces joined by riveting or welding, or they are made in one piece and designated as solid iron or steel wheels. Very light wheels, such as automobile wheels, and extremely large wheels generally are fabricated. Solid steel wheels are either cast from liquid metal or wrought from a solid block of metal. According to modern practices, therefore, the term **wrought-steel wheel** is applied to wheels formed from a suitable block of metal by forging alone or by forging and rolling operations. This chapter describes the production of wrought-steel wheels by both forging and rolling.

Parts and Classification of Wrought-Steel Wheels —Wrought-steel wheels generally are used in heavy traction service. Such wheels are designed with contours which are considered as being composed of five parts, namely, the **hub**, the **web** or **plate**, the **rim**, the **tread** and the **flange**. These parts, for the case of a railroad wheel, are illustrated in Figure 26—1. The flange may be single or double, and the hole in the hub into which the axle is fitted is called the **bore**. The tread is the outer surface of the rim on which the wheel rolls or makes contact with the rail. The flange keeps it from leaving the track. The **dishing**, or **coning**, refers

to the offset of the hub with regard to the rim and the resulting slanting of the web section. The flange, the rim, the service to which they are applied, the methods of forming, the finish, and the finishing treatments are all bases for classifying wheels. Thus, they may have a single flange (a flange on the inside only) or a double flange (a flange on both sides) and a rim thickness that will permit worn treads and flanges to be machined one or more times to restore their original contours. The term **one-wear wheels** implies that only one major period of wear is generally obtained. However, with wrought-steel one-wear wheels, it is often possible to machine the worn tread and flange to obtain additional life. **Multiple-wear wheels** have a rim thickness of 2½ inches or more, and may be machined two or more times to the original tread and flange contour.

Classifications based upon the service to which the wrought steel wheels are to be applied are defined as:

(1) **Industrial car wheels** are single-flange wheels designed for "application" under cars used for industrial purposes, such as mine cars, railroad hand cars, and cars or buggies used in steel mills.

(2) **Industrial locomotive wheels** are single-flange wheels designed for use under electric and other

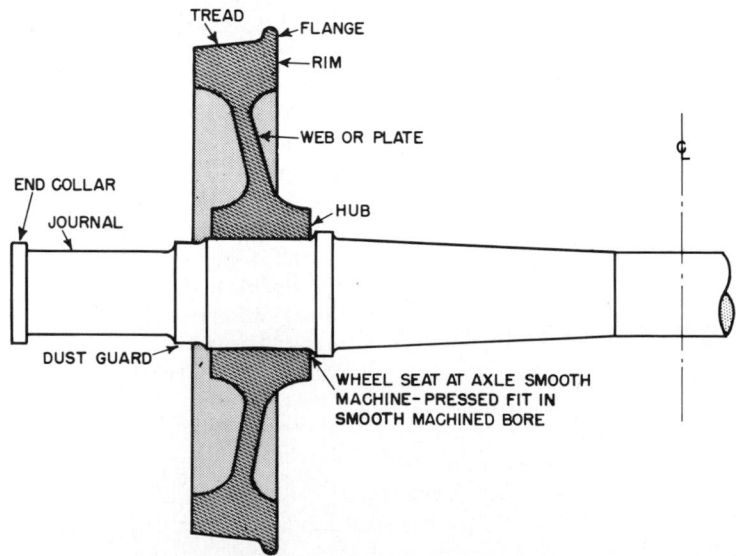

Fig. 26—1. Sketch showing cross-section of a wrought-steel railroad wheel mounted on an axle, giving nomenclature of the principal parts of each.

types of locomotives used in mines, and in industrial plants.

(3) **Crane track wheels** may have either a single or a double flange, and are used under such equipment as traveling, gantry and bridge cranes, transfer and turn tables, and floor-type charging and drawing machines.

(4) **Railroad freight-car wheels** are machined on treads and flanges, and generally have hub faces as-forged when one-wear or two-wear types are involved. Multiple-wear wheels for freight service are machined to the same tolerances as other high-duty wheels.

(5) **High-duty wheels** are manufactured to closer tolerances than one-wear or two-wear freight-car wheels and are used under railroad, electric street-railway, and rapid-transit passenger cars, as well as under locomotives.

Wrought-steel wheels are completely covered by standard specifications including the type and kind of steel used, the design of the wheels, the dimensional tolerances, and the inspection and tests. While alloy steels are used in some circular shapes, wrought-steel wheels have generally been made of carbon steel. The remainder of this chapter will be devoted to the manufacture of freight-car and high-duty wrought-steel wheels.

Classified according to methods of manufacture, wrought-steel wheels may be forged, or forged and rolled; as well as machined on tread, flange, and hub faces, or machined all over. With respect to heat treatment, wheels are no longer **air cooled** from forging or rolling temperatures, but are always **controlled cooled, rim toughened,** or **oil-quenched and tempered** by processes to be described later.

Classes of Wrought-Steel Wheels—Wrought-steel wheels are generally manufactured to Association of American Railroads or American Society for Testing and Materials specifications. These specifications call for four classes of wrought-steel wheels. The four classes differ in chemical composition and hardness and were developed after extensive research followed by many studies of wheels in different types of railroad service. Each class is processed and treated for a definite service and it is important that wheels of the proper class be used in the service for which they are intended.

American Association of Railroads specification M-107 and American Society for Testing and Materials specification A-57 cover one class of untreated wheels (Class U) and three classes of heat-treated wheels (Classes A, B and C) grouped according to carbon content, as follows:

Element		Per Cent
Carbon	Class U	0.65–0.77
	Class A, not over	0.57
	Class B	0.57–0.67
	Class C	0.67–0.77
Manganese		0.60–0.85
Phosphorus, not over		0.05
Sulphur, not over		0.05
Silicon, not less than		0.15

Classes A, B and C are heat treated to the following hardness requirements:

	Brinell Hardness Number	
Class	Minimum	Maximum
A	255	321
B	277	341
C	321	363

These specifications state:

"The Brinell measurement shall be made on the front face of the rim with the edge of the impression not less than $3/16$ inch from the radius joining face and tread. Before making the impression, any decarburized metal shall be removed from the front face of the rim at the point chosen for measurement. The surface of the wheel rim shall be properly prepared to permit accurate determination of hardness."

These specifications require that heat-treated wheels be stamped with the class letter A, B or C, together with the letter E for wheels entirely quenched, and the letter R for wheels that have the rim quenched as follows:

	Significance	
Mark	Class	Treatment
AR	A	Rim Treated
BR	B	Rim Treated
CR	C	Rim Treated
AE	A	Entire wheel treated
BE	B	Entire wheel treated
CE	C	Entire wheel treated

Outline of Methods for Forming Solid Wrought-Steel Wheels—All methods for forging and rolling solid wrought-steel wheels require a cylindrical, or nearly cylindrical, block of steel for the initial forming operations. Originally, the blanks were sheared from slabs, but this method located the central portion of the ingot diametrically across the wheel, so that the line of segregation terminated at opposite points in the tread. The objections to this method are obvious. Therefore, the procedure was changed, as shown in Figure 26—2, so that metal in the line of segregation, or central portion of the ingot, would be punched out in forming the bore.

To accomplish this, the steel blocks may be prepared in any one of three ways, namely, (1) by casting the metal for each wheel as an individual ingot, (2) by cutting the blanks from ingots, or (3) either by hot shearing or cold cutting the blanks from a round bloom. The United States Steel Corporation uses the third method. After the blocks have been press forged to the general form of a wheel, called the **wheel blank,** the shaping is completed by rolling the blank in the **wheel mill** which may be one of two types, designated from the position in which the blank is held in the mill during the rolling, as a **vertical mill** (Figure 26—3) and a **horizontal mill** (Figure 26—4). The practice will be described in detail as an example of the manufacture of wheels.

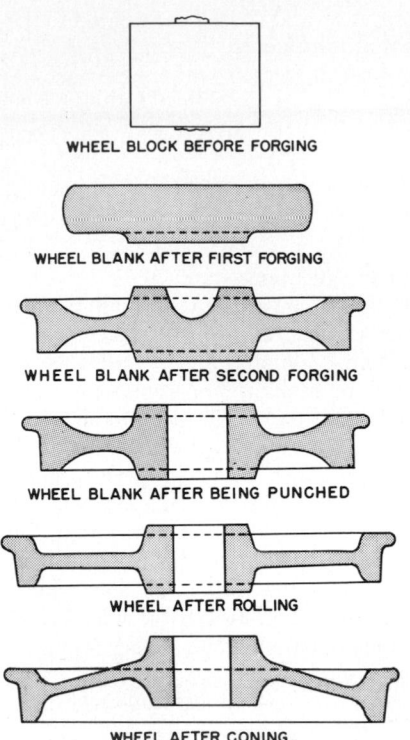

FIG. 26—2. Cross-section showing steps in the procedure of making a wrought-steel wheel by a combination of forging, rolling and pressing operations.

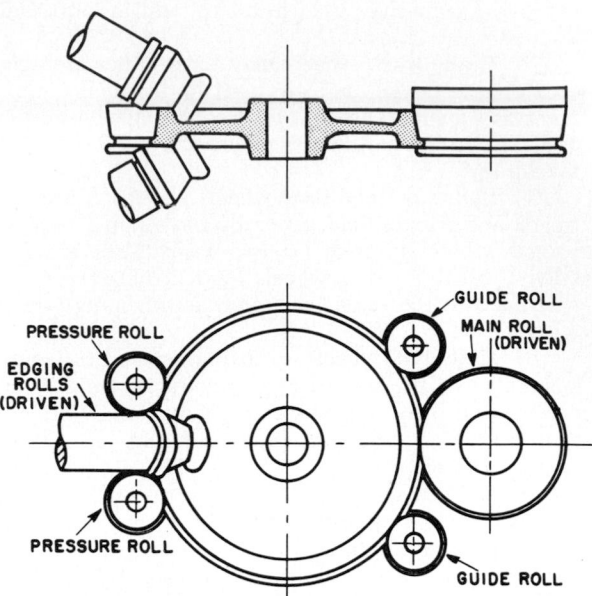

FIG. 26—4. Elevation (above) and plan (below), showing disposition of the rolls in a horizontal mill for rolling wheels.

PREPARATION OF BLOCKS

Wheels are produced by the United States Steel Corporation at Gary Steel Works and at the Wheel and Axle Division of Homestead District Works. While the practices of these two plants differ some-

what as to equipment and details of manipulation, this difference is not of a fundamental nature. Both plants are equipped for controlled cooling of wheels and for heat treating by the approved methods. At Homestead the steel to be rolled into round blooms for wheels is cast in 25-inch by 25-inch hot-top molds with rippled or corrugated walls, and rolled on either the 54-inch or 44-inch mills into round blooms either 15 inches or 17½ inches in diameter, according to the weight of the wheels to be made. With proper allowance for discard, these rounds are generally hot

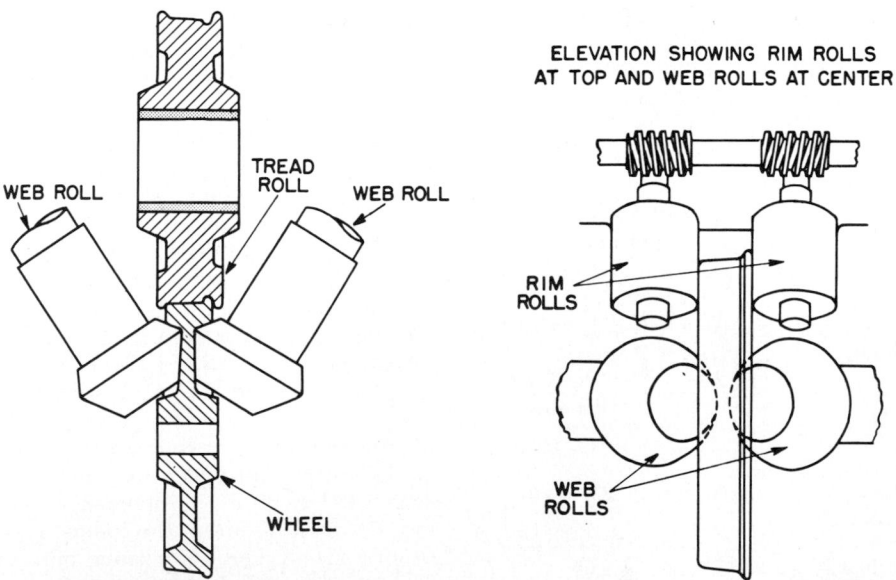

FIG. 26—3. Schematic arrangement of the rolls in a vertical mill for rolling wheels.

sheared into blocks to form a wheel of the desired weight and dimensions by a special shear which cuts the bloom almost in two but leaves a central core about 5 inches in diameter to be fractured when the bloom has cooled to atmospheric temperature. Instead of air cooling, however, the partially sheared blooms from the shears are put into special, insulated containers and allowed to cool slowly to 300° F. The cooling is thus controlled as a precaution against the possible formation of minute internal cracks in the blocks. The balance of round blooms are cold cut on special multiple-tool lathes after controlled cooling. The blooms are then unloaded at the shipping yard, inspected, surface conditioned, and fractured. At Gary, the steel is cast in 25-inch by 25-inch big-end-up hot-top molds and rolled into 18-inch round blooms on the 40-inch mill. While still hot, these blooms are sliced into blocks by a special shear which cuts to the center of the bloom, and the blocks are individually inspected and surface conditioned as may be necessary. As each block is separated from the bloom, it is hammer stamped with numbers to identify it. At both plants the smallest wheel that can be rolled is about 26 inches in diameter, and the maximum sizes are 40 inches in diameter at Gary and 46 inches at Homestead.

FORGING OF WHEEL BLANKS

Heating the Blocks for Forging—This operation is carried out in two stages, referred to as the "preheat" and the "forge heat." Hence, at the wheel plant the blocks are first placed in a gas-fired preheating furnace where they are slowly and uniformly heated to a temperature of 800° F in a period of 6 hours or longer. The object of this slow heating is to avoid abrupt temperature gradients and resulting high internal stresses that occur in a block when its surfaces are suddenly exposed to a high temperature while the central portion is cold. The preheating furnaces are preferably of the continuous type in which the blocks may move from the cold end to the hot end, but it is possible to obtain similar heating effects in sand-bottom furnaces, in which the blocks remain stationary, by charging a number into the furnace when it is relatively cool and gradually raising the temperature.

After preheating, the blocks are transferred by charging machine (Figure 26—5) to the forge furnace, which is of the sand-bottom type. This furnace is held at a uniform heating temperature so that the blocks reach a forging temperature in about 2½ hours, and the blocks are charged and drawn in a definite order, so that none will be overheated or underheated. Full control of the heating combines automatic pyrometric control with skill and judgment of the heaters, who become expert in estimating both steel and furnace temperatures.

First Forging of the Block—As indicated in Figure 26—2, the forming of the wheel blank preliminary to the final forming in the rolling mill is carried out in three steps spoken of as the **first forging**, the **second forging**, and **punching the bore**. However, in the forging operations it is essential that the block or bloom be free of scale formed during the reheating. In some plants this scale is removed by mechanically-operated chain beaters; in others various procedures are used. An effective method is carried out as follows: When the block is removed from the forge furnace and delivered by the charging machine, the scale on the ends is knocked off with long handled steel scrapers. The block is then placed in the bottom die of the press and held in a vertical position, while the press is started slowly. When the top die contacts the block, the first deformation cracks off the scale, which is immediately blown out of the die by jets of compressed air. The press then continues the stroke to complete the first forging. From this point, the

FIG. 26—5. Operator of a charging machine drawing a heated wheel block from furnace preparatory to transfer to the forging press.

practices at different plants vary somewhat. Thus, the first forging may be merely an upsetting of the block and punching of the bore to form a circular bloom. At present, the practice at the United States Steel Corporation is to do some forming in the first forging, and punch out the bore after the second forging (Figure 26—2). However, this procedure is subject to some variation, for the forging may be done in one heat, or in two heats and on one press or on two different presses.

When two heats are used, two presses are usually employed for the forging. In this method, the scale is removed from the two ends of the block and it is then placed vertically in the first press, where it is first centered by two arms which engage it from opposite sides of the press and so support it until the top die has descended upon it (Figure 26—6). In this press, the bottom die corresponds to the outside face

of the wheel, while the top die is not contoured, but may be slightly convex to cause a radial flow of the metal in taking the shape. The pressure, applied in successive steps through accumulators and intensifier, starts with about 700 pounds per sq. in., then increases to 2500 pounds per sq. in., and finally, to as much as 5000 pounds per sq. in., if needed. In general, the presses used for forging wheel blooms and blanks vary from 5000 to 12,000 tons capacity. This pressing is, in itself, a severe test upon the metal, and any occasional flaws, such as seams or cracks, are generally exposed. The blanks are now placed in a second reheating furnace, where their temperature is equalized and they are again brought to forging temperature.

Second Forging—If both the first and second forgings are performed on one heat, sometimes designated as **double forging**, the press is provided with

FIG. 26—6. Hot wheel block in position between the dies of a forging press at the start of the first operation in forging a wheel.

two top dies, one plain or slightly convex and the other conforming to the inside of the wheel. These dies are mounted upon a top crossslide in such a manner that either may be brought beneath the ram of the press, thereby dispensing with one forging press and permitting the forging to be accomplished in one operation when the conditions are favorable. Generally, however, the plain die is used first, then the inside die is moved into position and the pressure applied, thus forming the blank in two stages, but with a single heating. With this press, the procedure can be varied to permit reheating if necessary, but the object is to accomplish the forging of the blank in one heat. When the forging is done in two steps with intermediate reheating, the procedure is about as follows: When the temperature of the blank formed in the first forging has been restored and equalized, the blank is brought to the press, cleaned of scale, placed in the bottom die which is lubricated to prevent sticking, and formed by a stroke of the press, the top die of which conforms to the inside of the wheel (Figure 26—7).

Punching the Hub Bore—By the process described, the next step consists of punching the bore in the hub. This operation is carried out with a small press such as that shown in Figure 26—8. During punching, the outside of the hub of the wheel is supported in neatly fitting dies in order to avoid forcing this part of the wheel out of shape.

ROLLING OPERATIONS ON WHEELS

Reheating the Blanks for Rolling—The forging now resembles a wheel and is called a wheel blank.

Fig. 26—7. This shows the wheel blank after the second forging operation. Note indentation formed in center of hub to facilitate punching of the bore.

However, a great deal of work must still be done on the blank to produce the finished wheel. While in general the blank may lack tread and flange, these parts have been partly formed in the forging operations. As to dimensions, the forged blank is 3 to 5 inches undersize in diameter, some three-fourths of an inch oversize in that part of the web near the rim, and considerably oversize in the rim. These oversize parts contain metal for the working and shaping to be done in the rolling mill, and dimensions will vary with different sizes of wheels and the method of rolling. The hub and a small annular section of the web next to the hub are forged to correct size for the finished wheel. In some processes the forged blank is not reheated for the rolling, but when forged as described above, certain parts, such as the web, are liable to become cooled to a greater extent than other parts, and temperature equalization becomes desirable. This reheating is done in flat-bottomed gas-fired furnaces, similar to the reheating furnaces mentioned in connection with the forging. These temperature equalizing furnaces, as well as the reheating furnaces, are equipped with recording pyrometers as an additional precaution against improper heating of the blanks.

The Rolling Mill—Mills for rolling wheels are of two types, vertical and horizontal, already shown diagrammatically in Figures 26—3 and 26—4. The following description, however, is confined to mills of the vertical type used at both the Homestead and Gary plants of the United States Steel Corporation. Even these two mills vary somewhat as to details of construction and operation, and each represents a somewhat complicated piece of machinery in which 5 or 7 rolls are made to bear on the wheel during the rolling. These rolls consist of one **tread**, or **back roll**, two **web rolls**, and two or four (2 sets) **rim rolls**, which are supported, together with all of their bearings, pinions or gears, adjusting screws, levers, etc., in a single pair of horizontal housings. These housings are large steel castings placed one above the other. The bottom housing lies directly upon the mill foundation and forms the support for the rolls and for the top housing some four feet above it.

The housings, between which the rolls are located, are held apart by suitable pillars or posts and are bound firmly together by large bolts. The rolls may be described as follows: The largest roll is the back roll, which resembles a wheel in form, approximately 33 inches in diameter, and is located in the same vertical plane as the car wheel blank, to the rear of the central axes of the housings. This roll is either driven or revolves by friction, bearing on the rim of the wheel, forming the tread and flange. The Homestead mill is equipped with a variable-speed motor, while the Gary mill uses a constant-speed motor.

On the opposite sides of the tread roll are located the two web rolls. They are about three feet in length, lie in a horizontal position and extend inward, so that their center lines form nearly 30 degree angles with the mill center line and intersect at a point near the center of the wheel that is being rolled. On their

FIG. 26—8. Forged steel wheel after the operation of punching the bore.

front ends they carry the rolling heads, or surfaces, which conform to the shape of the wheel beneath the rim, while their rear ends are anchored in rotating coupling boxes. Light steel spindles, some five feet in length and provided with suitable wobblers, connect these couplings to the two bevel gears, one of which stands on each side of the mill at the rear. These gears mesh into similar gears mounted on the driving shaft of a 750-horsepower, direct current motor (130 r.p.m.), used to drive these rolls. This motor is located at the rear and on the center line of the mill. Just back of the rolling heads, these rolls are supported in sliding bearings which permit them to be spread as desired. The pressure for rolling is transmitted to these bearings through radial levers, the long arms of which are each attached to the same screw above the housings (see Figure 26—9). By this arrangement, with the same motion, but in opposite directions, equal pressures are imparted to the two rolls at the same time. This screw, which corresponds to the adjusting screws on ordinary mills, is actuated by a 15-horsepower, direct-current motor (550 r.p.m.). By this means, the power of the motor is multiplied many times and is capable of exerting sufficient pressure on the web rolls to roll or form the

web plate to its proper thickness and diameter. As to the orientation of these three rolls, they are so placed that their lines of contact with the wheel in rolling,

FIG. 26—9. Steel wheel being rolled in a vertical-type wheel mill.

and the axis of the wheel itself, all lie in the same horizontal plane. The friction driven rim rolls are located below the web rolls, so that all the rolls lie within an arc of 180 degrees of the circumference of the wheel being rolled. In mills using four rim rolls, one set is located above the web rolls. These rolls are approximately twelve inches in length and nine inches in diameter and are so placed that the projected axis of rotation of the roll on either side of the wheel intersects the axis of rotation of the wheel. They are mounted upon sliding frames attached to the front of the mill housings. These frames are moved by horizontal screws connected by vertical worm shafts and gears to a common shaft, which extends in front of and beneath the housings, and is operated by an electric motor set eight or ten feet to the right of the housings. In this way the spread of these rolls is made uniform. However, the bottom set of rim rolls, due to the manner of rolling, do nearly all the work. An indicator, mounted on the upper horizontal screw attached to the sliding frame on the right side of the mill, is in plain view of the operator, who is able, by this means, to read the spread of the rolls and thus control the width of the rim. These rolls may be so formed that they will roll the sides of the rim at a slight angle to the vertical, so that these surfaces will lie in parallel planes after the dishing, or coning process. Two shelves attached to the housings in front of the tread and web rolls and separated by a space a little greater than the thickness of the wheel at the hub, give support for the wheel, which is mounted on a loosely fitting mandrel during the rolling. This mandrel is provided with removable bearings, which rest, unattached, upon the shelves, thus leaving the wheel free to move forward after the rolls have gripped it.

The Rolling Process—After the forged blank has reached the proper temperature for rolling, it is removed from the furnace and carried to the mill by a charging and drawing machine, where it is gripped beneath the rim by tongs suspended from a small jib crane standing on the housing above the rolls, or by a floor crane especially designed for the purpose. The wheel, held vertically, is guided between the two supporting shelves, and the mandrel is inserted through the punched bore. Then the wheel, resting on the mandrel, is pushed back against the tread roll into position for rolling. The web and rim rolls are then brought to bear on the wheel, the latter rather lightly at first. The large driving motor is started, and the wheel is made to revolve by the action of the roll or rolls upon it. The web rolls, working upon both sides of the web and the under side of the rim, force the metal back into the grooves of the tread roll with considerable pressure, until this part of the wheel has reached the dimensions for which the mill is set, or the diameter desired, while the spread of the metal and the width of the rim is controlled by pressure applied to the rim rolls. The diameter of the wheel is ascertained by a gage, or caliper, one end of which is attached to the tread-roll housing, so that it is moved simultaneously with this roll, in the same direction and through the same

space. The other end of the caliper projects in front of the mill, and is provided with a hinged arm or pointer, so that it may be raised out of the way for inserting the blank or removing the wheel. The end of this pointer is curved toward the mill at right angles to its length. At the beginning of the rolling, the roller lowers this pointer to rest on the left hand shelf, in which position its curved end extends toward the tread roll and is opposite its line of contact with the wheel, the pointer having been adjusted so that the distance between its point and the tread roll is equal to the diameter of the wheel desired. The wheel increases in diameter during the rolling and moves forward on the loose sliding mandrel until a circle on the center of its tread comes in contact with this pointer, when the roller stops the mill and spreads the rolls for the release of the wheel. During the rolling, jets of water are directed against the surfaces being rolled to remove the scale and give a smooth finish to the wheel. The actual rolling process requires about one minute, so that the maximum capacity of the mill is high.

Effect of the Rolling—All the work of the rolling is concentrated upon the outer part of the web, the rim, the flange and the tread, where the additional grain refinement due to rolling is most needed. This refinement is marked as is shown by the visible difference in the structure of the metal in the hub and in the tread.

FINISHING WROUGHT-STEEL WHEELS

Stamping—After each wheel has been rolled, it is taken on a small buggy to a stamping press, where markings fully identifying it are stamped on the inside rim face. Stamping practice, however, varies at different plants. For example, at Gary the stamping is done in the coning press. These markings include the brand, the month and year of manufacture, the serial and heat numbers, and occasionally other markings such as type of heat treatment.

Coning—The wheel is taken from the punching press, or from the rolling mill, to the coning press for dishing. In this operation the form of the web, or plate, is changed from that of a flat ring to that of a truncated cone sloping from the hub to the rim. This form of the plate is important for it serves to prevent the development of the high internal stresses that would be set up by the cooling of the wheel if the plate were left flat. Coning presses are of various designs, but essentially they consist of a set of two dies, the top one of which is attached to the ram of the press. In the generally preferred method of coning, the hub is held rigidly and coning accomplished by the use of top and bottom dies shaped to contact the outer diameter of the hub and the underside of the rim. The top die descends a fixed distance, exerting pressure on the underside of the rim until contact is made with the bottom die. It has been found that, with this method of coning, improved control of geometry of the wheel is obtained.

Controlled Cooling—After coning, the wheel is allowed to cool to a temperature below the critical

FIG. 26—10. Wrought-steel wheel undergoing finish machining on a lathe of special design, employing carbide cutting tools.

range. It is then control cooled under proper conditions to 300° F. Various methods of controlling the cooling are in use and have been found to give satisfactory results. The requirement is that every part of the wheel must be kept at the same temperature until the heaviest portion has cooled to 300° F or lower.

Inspection of wheels is very rigid and may be said to begin with the making of the steel and to continue through every step of manufacture until the wheel is ready for shipment. For example, the wheels are inspected after rolling and, when cold, each wheel is again inspected for surface defects, location of the hub, rotundity of tread, and the size, which is measured in standard **tape sizes.** These tapes are graduated in eighths of an inch, beginning with seven feet for a zero mark for wheels 28 inches and over in diameter, and with four feet for wheels under 28 inches in diameter. The surface defects consist principally of overfills, underfills, slivers, scale pits, and block marks, and as they are seldom deep, they may be removed by machining. The tape size is plainly marked on each wheel.

Machining and Final Inspection—After this inspection, the tread, flange, rim, and bore of the wheels are machined. The lathes used for machining wheels are massive and include many ingenious features of design, as indicated by Figure 26—10. The wheels are then rolled back to the platforms for final inspection, which is even more rigid than the previous. In this inspection, the wheels are measured for size, eccentricity and size of bore, position and size of hub, thickness and height of flange, radius of throat, thickness of rim, coning, and rotundity. After being stenciled with tape size and marks requested

by the customer, such wheels as come within the allowable tolerances are mated and sent to the shipping platform.

Machining includes either rough machining or rough and finished machining operations. Extra machining not covered by standard specifications includes:

1. **Finish boring** covers machining of the hub bore to a smooth finish and to permissible variations in dimensions, so that the wheel may be mounted on the axle.

2. **Semi-machining** consists of machining the back and face of the rim and hub, the tapered surfaces on the diameter of the hub and on the inside diameter of the rim and the fillets joining these surfaces to the web, or plate, of the wheel.

3. **Finish machining hub faces** refers to finish machine work on a hub face when a hub projection or depression is machined to closer tolerances than required by standard specifications.

4. **Fully-machined** or **machined all over** is applied to a wheel the dimensions of which must be close to the nominal dimensions and the weight of which must be distributed symmetrically about the axis. All surfaces of the hub, the plate and the rim are machined.

5. **Hub recessing** consists of counterboring or turning a recess in the face of the hub for installation of a bearing plate to prevent hub wear from lateral pressure.

6. **Turning outside of hub** is performed on wheels for electric railways, and consists of turning the end portion of the outside hub to a cylindrical section for a gear casting seat.

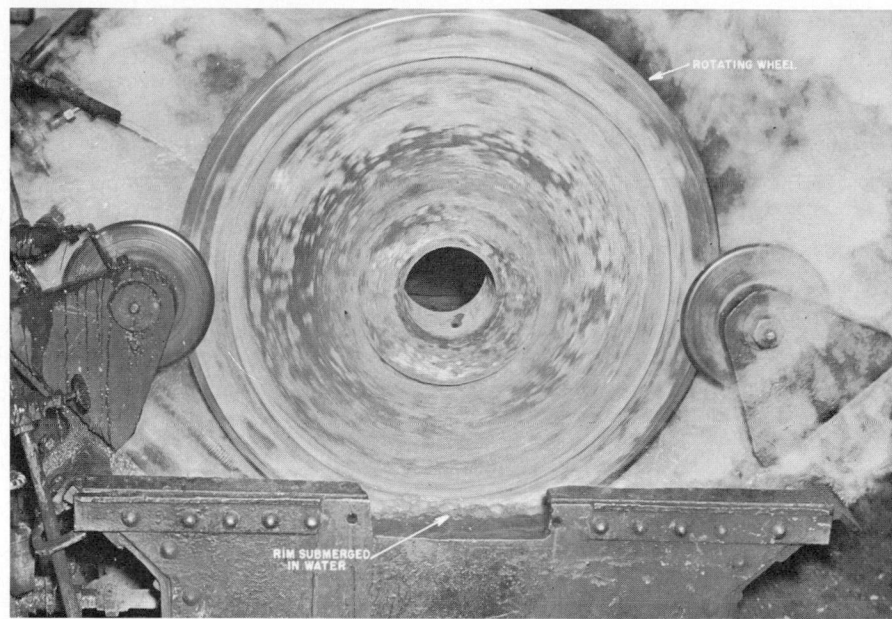

FIG. 26—11. Wheel undergoing quenching of the rim by being rotated in a special machine designed so that only the rim of the wheel contacts the quenching medium.

HEAT TREATMENTS FOR WROUGHT-STEEL WHEELS

In addition to the controlled cooling mentioned above, two methods of heat treating wheels are used. They are **rim toughening,** and **oil quenching and tempering.**

For **rim toughening,** the wheels are cooled below the critical range and then reheated above the critical range. Upon removal from the furnace they are immediately placed in a special quenching machine (Figure 26—11) and rotated at a uniform rate with part of the rim submerged in water. This method prevents the water from coming in contact with either the plate or the hub of the wheel. After the rim has beeen quenched in this manner for a given period, the optimum duration of which has been predetermined, the wheel is removed from the quenching machine, transferred to a furnace and heated to a proper tempering temperature to remove internal stresses and obtain the hardness desired. The wheel is then placed in pits and control cooled to 300° F or below. This treatment leaves the hub and the plate in a normalized condition, and increases the hardness of the wearing zone of the rim.

To **oil quench and temper** the wheels, they are heated as described above, withdrawn at a temperature slightly above the critical range of the steel, and totally immersed in oil contained in a tank constructed to permit the wheels to be rotated for the period of the quench. The wheels are then placed in a reheating furnace, heated to the required tempering temperature, and control cooled to 300° F. or below. This treatment refines the grain structure and toughens equally all parts of the wheel, developing the hardness to about the same extent as in the rim-toughening treatment.

Bibliography

"Wrought Steel Wheels." Steel Products Manual, American Iron and Steel Institute, New York.

Specifications A-57 and A-186; American Society for Testing and Materials, Philadelphia.

Specifications M-103 and M-107; Association of American Railroads.

CHAPTER 27

Production Of Railroad Axles

Axles are important because of their functions and the number in service. They form vital parts of every kind of vehicle and vary in size from a few ounces to several thousand pounds. The larger sizes manufactured by the United States Steel Corporation include axles for railroad freight and passenger cars, Diesel locomotives, electric locomotives, subway and elevated rapid transit cars, electric street cars, and industrial axles. The Homestead District Works is an example of a plant manufacturing these larger axles, although they are also produced at Gary Steel Works and the Fairfield Steel Works of the United States Steel Corporation.

Some typical axle forms are shown in Figure 27—1.

Composition and Heat Treatments—Axles are generally made of carbon steels of various grades, ranging from 0.40 to 0.55 per cent carbon and 0.60 to 0.90 per cent manganese, with phosphorus and sulphur each under 0.05 per cent.

They may be ordered untreated; normalized; normalized and tempered; double normalized and tempered; quenched and tempered; or normalized, quenched and tempered, according to the size of axle, the kind of steel, and the mechanical properties desired. The carbon content may vary depending upon the heat treatment involved.

THE AXLE WORKS

The essential equipment of the plant includes continuous gas-fired furnaces for heating the blooms; double-acting steam forging hammers; manipulator; gag press straighteners; double cutting-off, facing and centering machines; as well as rough-turning and finishing lathes, and a complete heat-treating plant.

The layout of the plant provides for the most economical handling of the materials. The blooms start at one end of the plant and continue in one direction, progressing step by step through the various operations, until arrival at the other end of the plant where they are ready for shipment.

METHODS OF FORMING AXLES

In general, axles are formed by a combination of rolling and forging operations, and the practices of different plants vary somewhat. Thus, with a suitable mill properly equipped for the work and located near the forge shop, it is possible, by starting with an ingot of proper size, to roll the bloom and complete the forging in one heating. The axle bloom is rolled either round or square and the forming is completed by forging. In other plants, where it is necessary to start with cold steel after it has been rolled into blooms (which must correspond in dimensions and weight to the size of the axles for which it is intended), the various steps in the process of manufacture are as follows:

Inspection of the Blooms—The blooms are sub-

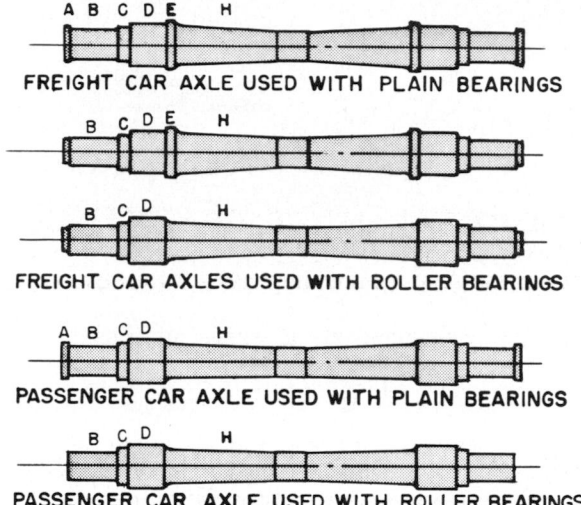

FREIGHT CAR AXLE USED WITH PLAIN BEARINGS

FREIGHT CAR AXLES USED WITH ROLLER BEARINGS

PASSENGER CAR AXLE USED WITH PLAIN BEARINGS

PASSENGER CAR AXLE USED WITH ROLLER BEARINGS

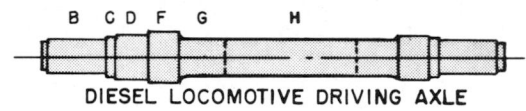

DIESEL LOCOMOTIVE DRIVING AXLE

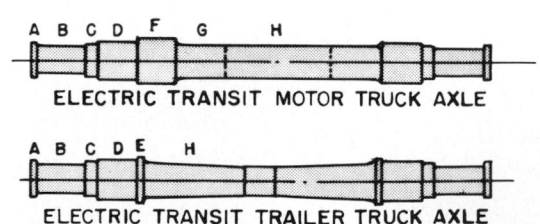

ELECTRIC TRANSIT MOTOR TRUCK AXLE

ELECTRIC TRANSIT TRAILER TRUCK AXLE

FIG. 27—1. Some typical forms of steel axles. Legend: (A) End Collar, (B) Journal, (C) Dustguard Seat, (D) Wheel seat, (E) Wheel-seat collar, (F) Gear seat, (G) Motor-support bearing, and (H) Body.

jected to a rigid inspection before the steel is shipped to the axle works. Those blooms that show any signs of pipe or insufficient discard at the blooming mill shears are rejected. Surface defects, such as seams, slivers, and surface cracks, are eliminated by surface-conditioning treatments. Blooms passing this inspection are shipped to the axle works, where they are stored until needed.

Heating the Blooms—Proper heating of the blooms for forging requires that they be uniformly heated throughout and brought gradually to the forging temperature. The importance of heating slowly is obvious; rapid heating may cause the outside of the bloom to become somewhat hotter than the core, which condition would prevent uniformity in grain structure and in the flow of the metal during the forging operations. In addition, high internal stresses would be developed. Slow heating gives the heat a chance to "soak" into the bloom and thus produce that uniformity in temperature from center to surface so necessary to secure a finished forging of the best quality. Reheating furnaces of the continuous type are used, and these are equipped with recording pyrometers. In addition, the temperature of the steel is periodically checked with an optical pyrometer as the bloom is drawn from the furnace. With this type of furnace, the bloom is placed in the furnace at the cold end and is slowly pushed or rolled toward the hot end. The bloom reaches forging temperature only a short time before it is drawn from the furnace.

The Forging Operation—After heating to the proper temperature for forging, the blooms are pushed out of the hot end of the heating furnaces upon a conveyor, and are carried by it to a roll table that distributes the blooms to the hammers. Adjustable deflecting rails built in the side guards of the roll table serve to divert the blooms to small receiving tables, of which there is one for each hammer. The blooms are handled by a manipulator, as shown in Figure 27—2, and forming begun as described below.

Tongs having been quickly clamped on, the bloom is swung around between the forging dies of the hammer. These dies are provided, when desired, with one or more grooves; one, the plain groove used to do the greater part of the forging, is located directly under the piston rod, while the other grooves, used to form special sections, such as the journals, are placed beside the plain groove. The forging is begun at the middle of the bloom, which is rapidly reduced by heavy blows of the hammer, the forging progressing toward the free end of the bloom. Here, the journal or other special section is formed by the special grooves in the die in a few blows. The piece is again placed in the plain groove, and the forging is smoothed up and brought, by light blows of the hammer, to correct diameter, which is determined by caliper. The forging is withdrawn and reversed end for end. The other end of the axle is then forged down like the first, except that, in addition to diameter, the length is also fixed. The axle is then placed on the hot bed.

FINISHING PROCESSES FOR AXLES

Straightening—The next step after the forging is straightening, which is accomplished in gag presses while the axles are still hot. From the hot beds, the forgings are carried by overhead cranes to similar

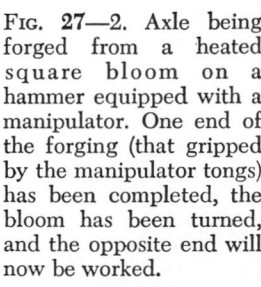

FIG. 27—2. Axle being forged from a heated square bloom on a hammer equipped with a manipulator. One end of the forging (that gripped by the manipulator tongs) has been completed, the bloom has been turned, and the opposite end will now be worked.

FIG. 27—3. General view of a special lathe, known as a double combination cutting-off, facing and centering machine, for machining forged axles.

beds in front of the presses. Here each axle is inspected for straightness, and those which require it are straightened before their temperature drops below 950° F. At this temperature, the axles are placed on cradles and put into pits for controlled cooling to below 300° F. Heat-treated axles are straightened after treatment.

Cutting-off and Centering—After removal from the controlled-cooling pits, the forgings are moved forward by overhead cranes and distributed to the cutting-off lathes. These lathes are double combination cutting-off, facing and centering machines (Figure 27—3) and are designed to work on both ends of the forging at the same time. Upon being inserted in this machine, the forging is grasped at the wheel seats by adjustable revolving centering clamps, which hold it firmly to the central axis of rotation. Cutting tools adjusted to the correct length then are brought to bear and cut off the excess metal at the ends. Ends are faced in this operation, a tolerance of one-eighth inch over length and nothing under being permitted. When these tools have cut to within about 1/16 inch of the center the crops drop off and, with the forging still held by the centering clamps, the revolving centering tools are brought to bear at each end. These tools are shaped to cut a 60-degree cone-shaped centering hole (to the dimensions shown in Figure 27—4) with a five-sixteenths inch in diameter clearance hole for points at the bottom of the centering hole.

Rough turning before shipment is of decided advantage to both the shop and the customer, because certain flaws can be detected more easily after rough turning, and a considerable saving can be effected in handling and transportation by holding excess weight to a minimum. Lathes of the type shown in Figures

27—5 and 27—6 are used for this work. Rough turned material falls into two classes, known as "rough turned on journals and wheel seats," and "rough turned all over." Axles of the first class are put into service with the center portions between the wheel seats "as forged." In the case of axles rough turned all over, the center portions are forged slightly over size to provide for the metal removed in turning to size; in such case, the center portion is furnished with body

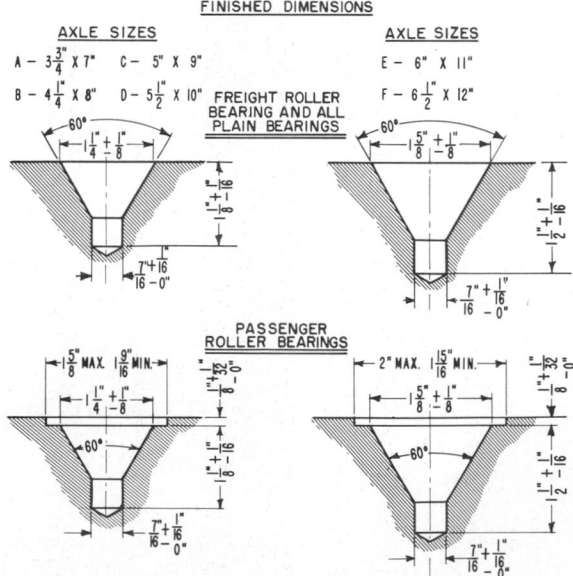

FIG. 27—4. Standard dimensions of centering holes cut in the ends of axles in United States Steel Corporation plants.

FIG. 27—5. Lathe of the type used for rough turning only journals and wheel seats of forged axles, after cutting-off, facing and centering (Figure 27—3).

finish when no further machine work is to be done by the customer. In the case of car axles or other axles with a tapered body, this metal is removed at the same time (or after) the journals and wheel seats are rough turned in a lathe (Figure 27—6). In finishing rough turned axles, the wheel seats are finish-turned only, while the dust guards, journals and collars are finish-turned and burnished or ground. In order to provide the excess metal required for this work, these parts are rough turned one-eighth inch over size on their diameters.

AXLE HEAT-TREATING PLANT

The heat-treating plant is housed in the same building with the hammers and lathes and consists of furnaces for heating forgings, a quenching tank containing water, a tank holding quenching oil, and all the necessary supplemental equipment for handling and testing the material.

Heat-Treating Furnaces—The inside working space of each of the furnaces is twenty-one feet in length and eight and one-half feet in width, and is designed to heat forgings uniformly. The furnaces are provided

FIG. 27—6. Lathe of the type used for rough machining of the entire surface of forged axles after cutting-off, facing and centering in the machine shown in Figure 27—3.

with removable bottoms of the car type, which facilitate the charging and drawing operations. This bottom is moved into and out of the furnace by a toothed rack attached to the bottom of the car and a stationary pinion actuated by an electric motor, the car itself resting on rollers that move over a double track. The doors of the furnace are of the vertically lifting type, and are hydraulically operated. These features, together with the close proximity of the quenching tanks, permit the drawing and quenching of a charge in the least possible time. In order that the entire surface of the material may be exposed to heat of the same intensity, the charge is supported at a height of about eighteen inches above the floor of the car bottom by two stools that extend the entire length of the car. These stools are spaced about four feet apart. The floor of the car bottom is constructed of brick laid upon a bottom of steel plates, and is of a thickness that will give the plates ample insulation from the heat of the furnace. The bottom is made to fit the furnace neatly, and the escape of hot gases from the heating chamber is prevented by sand seals. Means are provided for taking the temperature of the charge at regular intervals during the heating. Recording pyrometers are used throughout the heating cycle.

Advantages of Heat Treating Axles—With proper equipment, care, and judgment, heat treating provides a way in which the grain structure of the as-forged axle can be refined and made uniform. In doing this, variations in the as-forged grain structure which result from the heating and working of the bloom are overcome. Stresses remaining in the piece after forging are also reduced. The principal advantage is the control of and improvement in mechanical properties effected through correct heat treatment. For example, normalizing refines the grain of the as-forged axle and increases both its strength and ductility; and quenching and tempering refine the grain to give maximum control over the final mechanical properties. The latter treatment offers the only positive means of markedly increasing the strength as well as the torsional and shock-resisting properties that are very desirable under modern conditions of road traffic.

Testing equipment includes all the latest devices for testing materials. In the shop, hollow drill machines are provided for cutting out tests. A drop-testing machine, adapted for testing axles in accordance with standard specifications, is provided. Other mechanical tests are made in the physical laboratory, which is equipped with all the necessary appliances for accurate testing in accordance with standardized methods.

Bibliography

"Forged Railway Axles." Steel Products Manual, American Iron and Steel Institute, New York.

Specifications A-21, A-236 and A-238, American Society for Testing Materials, Philadelphia, Pa.

Specifications M-101, M-126 and M-127, Association of American Railroads.

CHAPTER 28

Merchant-Bar Production

SECTION 1

MILLS AND THEIR PRODUCTS

The name "merchant mill" is said to have been given in the early days of rolling to those **bar mills** which carried a stock of their product from which merchants selected bars at their convenience. The name has been carried over from that time and is still applied in the designation of modern bar mills, particularly those on which some of the small shaped sections are rolled. In other plants, the mills are designated simply as bar mills. Other designations sometimes used are "**hand bar mills**" and "**guide mills.**"

In the early mills, rounds and sharp-cornered squares were rolled by hand, that is, the bars were prevented from turning over in the passes by a tongsman, who forcibly held the bars in the proper position in the grooves throughout their passage through the rolls. As a general rule, the finishing stand of rolls was two-high in these mills, though in rare instances a three-high stand was used. In the two-high mill, the bar delivering from a given pass was returned over the top roll for entering into the next pass, and so on until the section was finished. This type of rolling was arduous and the length of bar that could be rolled under these circumstances was limited to about 16 to 20 feet.

This limited length that could be rolled, in combination with the heavy labor involved, led to the adoption of the so-called guide mills, in which rounds and sharp-cornered squares were held in the passes by close-fitting entering guides. To do this for rounds, it was necessary to devise a new pass design in which a square (or gothic square) was entered into an oval pass and the resulting oval was then entered on edge into a round finishing groove. By using an oval, closely fitting entering guides could be used that would hold the oval section in its proper position as it passed through the round groove.

In the older hand-round method, bars entering the finishing groove were so nearly round that no entering guide could be devised which would prevent the bars from turning over in the grooves. Thus the guide-round design permitted the rolling of long lengths and this method has practically superseded the hand method, although, for various reasons, there are mills in which rounds still are rolled by hand. Figure 28—1 illustrates both the hand and guide method of rolling rounds.

The mills in which rounds and squares were rolled by hand were referred to by the early operators as "bar mills," whereas the mills using guides to hold up the bars were referred to as "guide mills." What can be called the first bar mill was the two-high mill designed by Henry Cort in the latter part of the 18th century. Many of the early mills were driven by water wheels, and it is known that two water wheels were used in some cases, one for each roll. Later, steam-engine drives became common.

Crude as these early mills were, they were vastly superior to those in use prior to Henry Cort's time. With these early mills as a start, the bar mill gradually became a more and more finished machine until, to-day, a modern bar mill can turn out in one day more tonnage than one of the pioneer mills could roll in a year.

Evolution of the Bar Mill—As indicated, the first bar mills consisted of one two-high stand of rolls. The number of stands was gradually increased and in time four to five stands in line (in train*), driven by the same engine, became the popular design. Various names were given to the stands of a mill of this kind, such as **roughing** for the first stand, **strand** for the second, **pony** or **leader** for the third, and **finishing** or **planishing** for the fourth. In a typical layout the roughing (first) stand was three-high; the strand (second) stand, three-high; the leader was two-high in a three-high housing; and the finishing stand was two-high. The leader was in a three-high housing to permit driving the leader rolls through the top and middle strand rolls, with which they were in line, while the top finishing or planishing roll was driven through the bottom leader roll, and the bottom finishing roll was driven by a spindle from the bottom strand roll. This spindle passed through the three-high housing of the two-high leader in the space where the bottom roll would have been if the leader had three rolls. Such an arrangement permitted the leader and finishing stands to operate with opposite rolling directions. After the development of three-high stands, the number of stands for a bar mill was increased to as many as seven in line (in train).

The drawback to this type of mill was the limited roll speed. The mill could be run only as fast as the

---

* Rolling mills are "in train" when they are set relatively close together, side by side, and the rolls of one stand are driven by connecting them to those of an adjacent stand, as in Figure **28—1**.

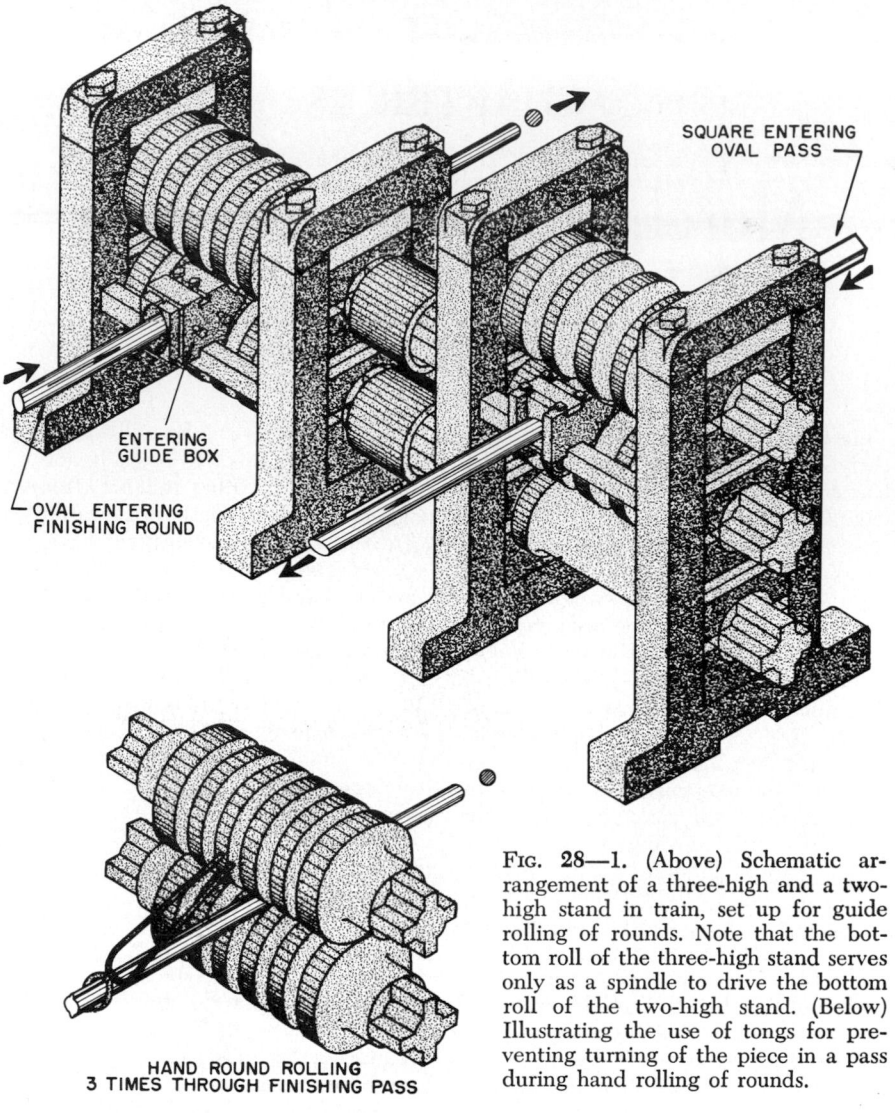

FIG. 28—1. (Above) Schematic arrangement of a three-high and a two-high stand in train, set up for guide rolling of rounds. Note that the bottom roll of the three-high stand serves only as a spindle to drive the bottom roll of the two-high stand. (Below) Illustrating the use of tongs for preventing turning of the piece in a pass during hand rolling of rounds.

roughing-stand tongsmen could catch the bars. At this stand the bar was caught on the front end as it emerged from the rolls in order to return it into the next pass, and beyond a certain speed of rolling the momentum of the bar would tend to push the men off their feet. In the succeeding stands, the bars were smaller in section and longer, and the tongsmen caught the bar on the back end as it emerged from the rolls. Thus the bars could have been delivered faster for these men, but since the speeds in these stands were governed by that of the roughing stand, this could not be done. As a result of this limiting speed, tonnage was limited.

In 1838, a separate roughing stand was added to the mills and this innovation became popular. A typical layout of this kind of mill is shown in Figure 28—2. In this design, the three-high roughing mill could be independently operated at a speed suitable for the best roughing practice, while the finishing train could be run at a much higher speed. This combination mill was referred to as a **Belgian mill**, as it was said to have originated in Belgium. The mill could roll

longer lengths and finish them at a higher rate of speed and, consequently, could produce greater tonnage than earlier mills.

As the next innovation, the Belgians and Germans introduced the looping of bars. In this practice, the bars in the finishing train, when they reached a stage in their reduction at which they were relatively flexible, were caught by the tongsmen on the front end as they emerged from the rolls and pulled around in a half circle and entered into the next pass. As a result of this practice, rolling time for a bar was appreciably reduced and more bars could be rolled per hour, producing greater tonnages. Some of the more improved mills of this kind had two or three roughing stands in train, on the same housing shoes, which permitted still greater production because the roughing passes could be divided among the two or three stands.

After the looping of bars became common practice, means were sought to eliminate, so far as possible, the manual looping of bars. A trough called a **repeater** was devised to conduct bars from one stand to anoth-

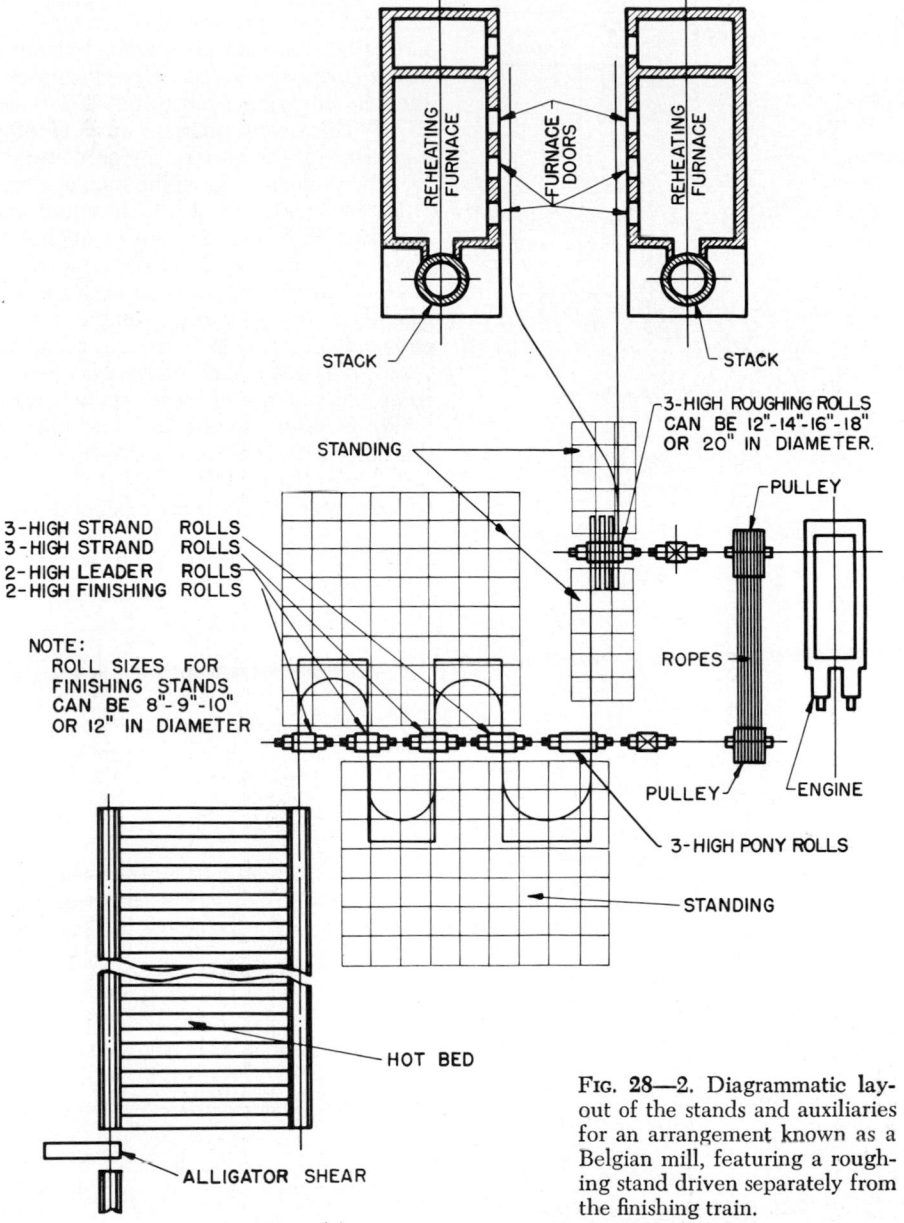

FIG. 28—2. Diagrammatic layout of the stands and auxiliaries for an arrangement known as a Belgian mill, featuring a roughing stand driven separately from the finishing train.

er. The first successful repeater was put into use by W. McCallip, superintendent of a small bar mill in Columbus, Ohio, in 1877. For the most part, repeaters are used to direct the bar out of a square pass into the succeeding oval pass, while the tongsmen direct the ovals into square passes. Some mills also use repeaters for oval into square, in which case the oval must be twisted so that its longer axis is in a vertical position as it goes around the repeater; otherwise it will jump out of the trough.

In Europe, the production of the Belgian-type bar mills was further increased when two Austrians perfected a repeater for three-high roughing stands. This repeater was a trough which conducted the bars, as they emerged from the passes, around a half circle and back into the next groove in the same roll stand,

obviating the use of a tongsman who could not, in any case, work in such close quarters as would be necessary on these roughing stands. The repeaters were used on the last two or three passes in the roughing operation, when the bars were small and long enough to provide the necessary flexibility. Figure 28—3 shows a three-high mill repeater in use on the roughing stand of a mill in which the finishing stands have been divided into two groups, the second group being run faster than the first for increased production. The finishing stands employ two-high repeaters for looping square into oval. Some mills in the United States use three-high repeaters of this type.

Further improvement of the bar mills became possible with the introduction of the continuous roughing principle in 1882. Mills employing this principle con-

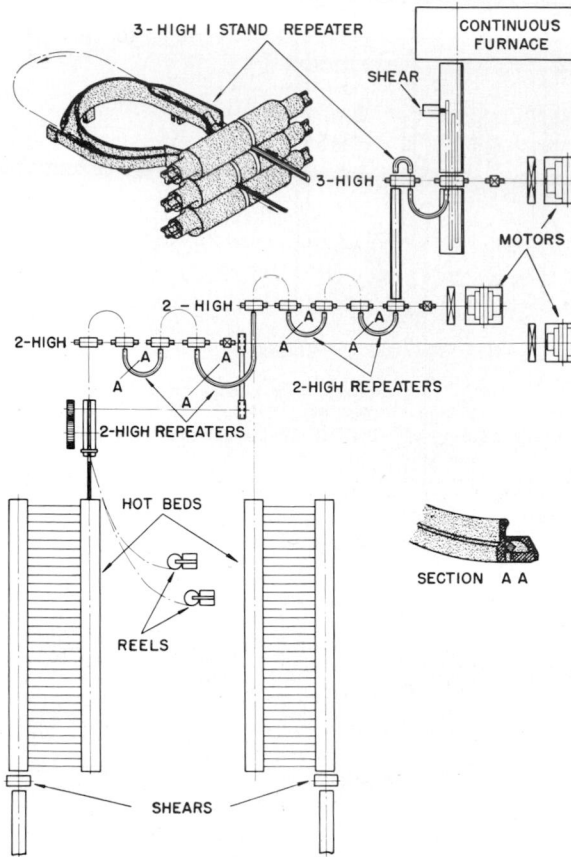

FIG. 28—3. Schematic arrangement of the stands and auxiliaries for a looping mill, employing repeaters of the type
shown in the inset at the upper left on the three-high
roughing stand as well as the two-high finishing stands.
The three-high roughing stand is driven separately from
the two trains of two-high finishing mill stands.

sisted of an eight-stand tandem* continuous roughing
mill and four finishing stands in line. Although such
mills were first built for the rolling of rods, about 1900
several were built to roll bars from a 4-inch by 4-inch
billet. Figure 28—4 shows an improved type of this
mill with two additional stands added for the rolling of
smaller bars.

The early mills of the type shown in Figure 28—4
had some serious disadvantages. As discussed in
Chapter 19, since the cross-sectional area of a piece is
reduced during rolling, the piece leaving the rolls has a
higher velocity than that at which it entered, due to its
being elongated. The continuous roughing stands of
the early mills had fixed speeds, with each successive
stand running faster than the preceding one by an
amount calculated to compensate for bar elongation.
The fixed speeds made it imperative to have perfect
balance between speed and elongation among the
several stands, otherwise either the bars would be
stretched or a loop would form between stands, either

* Rolling mills are said to be "in tandem" when they are
  arranged so that the rolled piece can progress from one
  stand to the next in a continuous straight path, as in the
  continuous roughing stands in Figures 28—4 and 28—5.

of which was undesirable. At the same time, the distances between stands were relatively short, causing
heavy pressure on the delivery guides used to twist
the bars 90 degrees for entrance into each succeeding
stand. This heavy pressure often resulted in injurious
scratching of the bars by the guides and these scratches, when rolled in, gave the bars a seamy appearance.

In the finishing mill the four roll stands, being in
one line (in train), are driven at the same speed. As
there is a reduction in cross-sectional area of the bar
in each succeeding pass through the mill, and consequently a corresponding elongation of the bar, a successively longer loop forms between each stand. As a
result, the back end of the bar becomes colder than the
front end because of more contact with the floor and
longer exposure to the air, a condition which introduces a variation in size of the ends of the bar as compared with the middle.

A number of mills were designed to overcome these

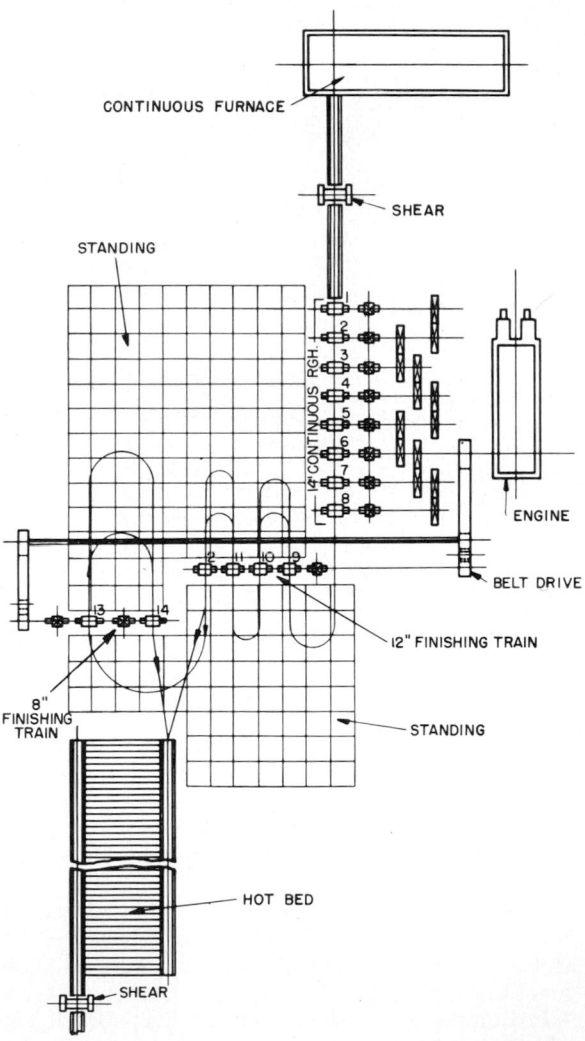

FIG. 28—4. Layout of the stands for a bar mill employing
the continuous roughing principle, comprising an 8-stand
tandem continuous roughing mill supplemented by a 12-
inch four-stand and an 8-inch two-stand finishing train.
All stands are two-high.

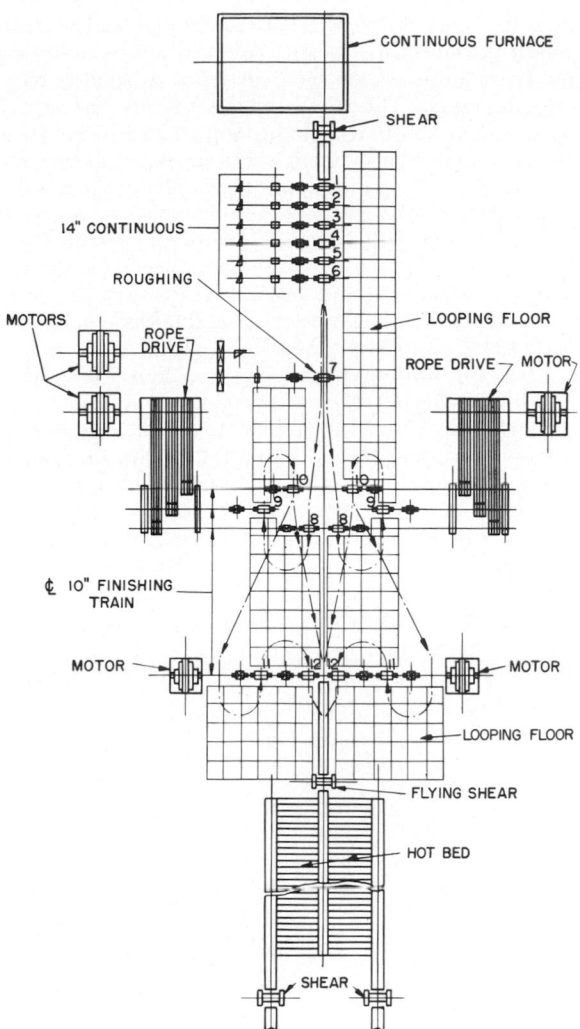

FIG. 28—5. Arrangement of a bar mill employing a 6-stand tandem continuous roughing mill, followed by a double finishing train. All stands are two-high.

supply both finishing trains, thus increasing production. Two billets can be sent through the roughing train, one for each finishing train.

Figure 28—6 shows a mill with a semi-continuous roughing arrangement in which the first two stands are driven by one motor and the bar runs free after each stand. These two stands are followed by four continuous stands driven by individual variable-speed motors. The finishing unit is comprised of four stands, each one driven by an individual variable-speed motor at a successively increased speed. This mill, through the use of separate motors, permits excellent control over push and pull in the roughing stands, except in the first two, and, as the stands are a good distance apart, the heavy pressure on the guides experienced in the older close-coupled mill is relieved. In the finishing stands, the speed control provided by the separate motors permits close control of the length of the loop between any two passes. This mill was a considerable improvement over the older types.

Figure 28—7 shows a bar mill of the cross-country

disadvantages. Some had the roughing line split into two or three groups so that the bar would run out to its full length between the groups. The finishing stands were also separated into groups of two or more roll stands, each group being separately driven and at a higher speed than the preceding one. Thus, between each group of rolls, the loop could be kept at a minimum, though they still formed between the stands which were in train. Space does not permit showing all of the arrangements devised to eliminate long loops.

A mill designed to overcome some of the disadvantages of these older mills is shown in Figure 28—5. In this mill, which has a double finishing train, the finishing stands have been divided into groups, with no more than two roll stands driven at the same speed. In each of these groups of two stands driven at the same speed, the second stand has rolls of larger diameter than the first in order to keep the loop between stands at a minimum. In a mill of this type the continuous roughing mill has sufficient capacity to

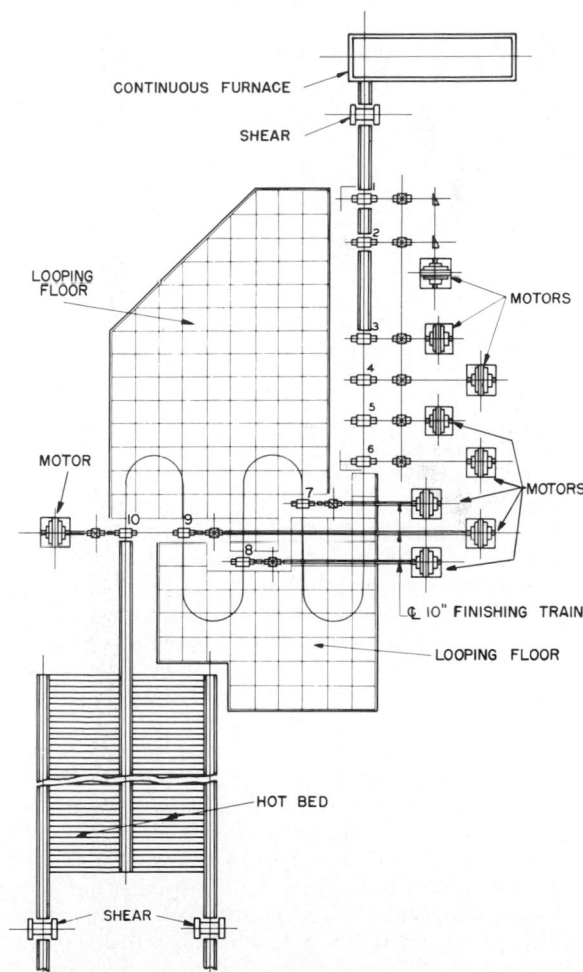

FIG. 28—6. Bar mill designed with a semi-continuous roughing arrangement followed by a four-stand continuous roughing mill, supplying roughed-down billets to the four stands of the finishing mill. All stands are two-high, and each is separately driven except for the two stands of the semi-continuous roughing set-up.

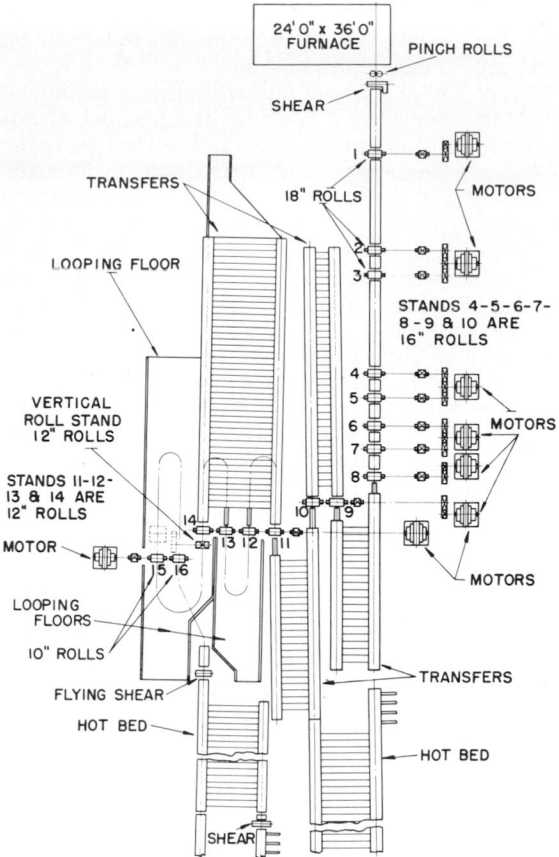

FIG. 28—7. Schematic layout of the stands and auxiliaries for a bar mill of the cross-country type, employing the continuous principle in the latter roughing stands.

type which rolls a wide range of products. The mill has two hot-beds and finishes the large sizes out of stand No. 10. The smaller sizes are finished in stand No. 14 or No. 16. The mill is further distinguished by having a vertical roll stand immediately following stand No. 14 and continuous with it. The vertical stand provides the means for rolling off all over-sizes or shoulders formed in the horizontal stand, giving a more perfect round. So-called precision rounds, which are rounds rolled to approximately one-half standard tolerances, are finished through these two stands. The vertical stand is removed when finishing in stand No. 16 or when rolling to standard tolerances.

Figure 28—8 shows another cross-country design. This layout does not have any continuous stands and the bars run out free after each pass. The sections rolled on this mill range from ½-inch to 5⅛-inch rounds, squares in corresponding sizes, flats from 1 inch to 9 inches in width and other products of comparable dimensions. The larger size products are finished from stand No. 9-A, which has 16-inch rolls, and the smaller sizes are finished from stand No. 12, which has 12-inch rolls. The distinguishing feature of the mill is that each stand has a variable-speed motor.

The most modern of all the bar mill designs is the continuous mill with alternate horizontal and vertical rolls, an arrangement which, curiously enough, was embodied in the first continuous mill built by Bedson

in 1862. The use of alternate horizontal and vertical stands obviates the necessity for twisting the bars, and the twist guides, with their tendency to scratch bars, are eliminated. The stands of the mill are spaced far enough apart so that a slight loop can be formed between stands. Individual variable-speed drives for practically every stand permit regulation of speed relationships to take care of bar elongation between stands, and the slight loop eliminates all push and pull between stands. The general principle of employing alternate horizontal and vertical stands was discussed in the description of the continuous billet mill at Lorain Works of United States Steel in Chapter 22.

Mills for Rolling Light, Narrow, Flat Material— Flat thin material of narrow width is produced on various types of bar mills. This material is known as **narrow strip, band iron, hoop,** and **cotton tie.** When first produced, this type of product was rolled on mills similar to the one shown in Figure 28—2, but as mills of this type could not roll any large tonnage of such light weight material, better mills were soon developed for the purpose.

Figure 28—9 shows a modern mill designed to roll this thin material. This continuous mill produces comparatively large tonnages of hoop, cotton tie, and nar-

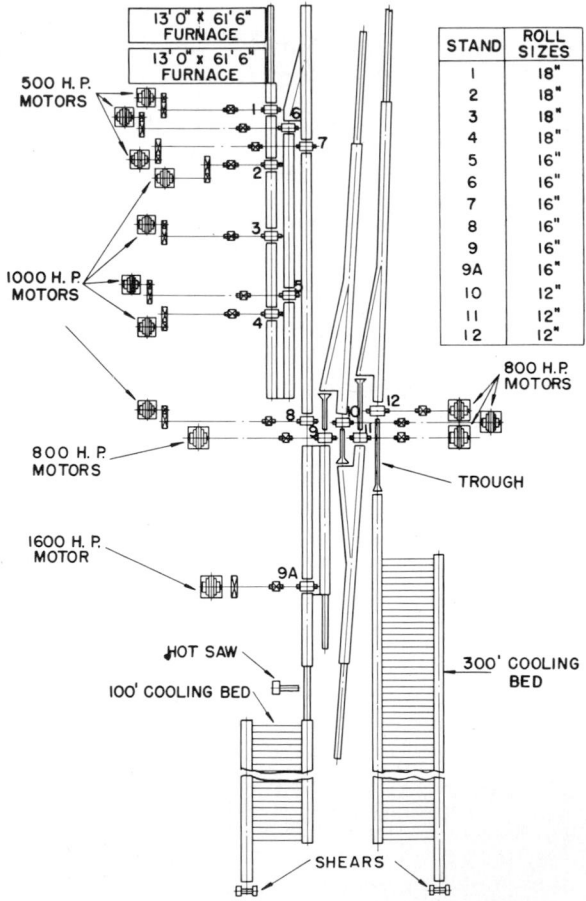

STAND	ROLL SIZES
1	18"
2	18"
3	18"
4	18"
5	16"
6	16"
7	16"
8	16"
9	16"
9A	16"
10	12"
11	12"
12	12"

FIG. 28—8. Bar mill of the cross-country type differing from that of the preceding illustration in that no continuous stands are used and the bars run out free after each pass.

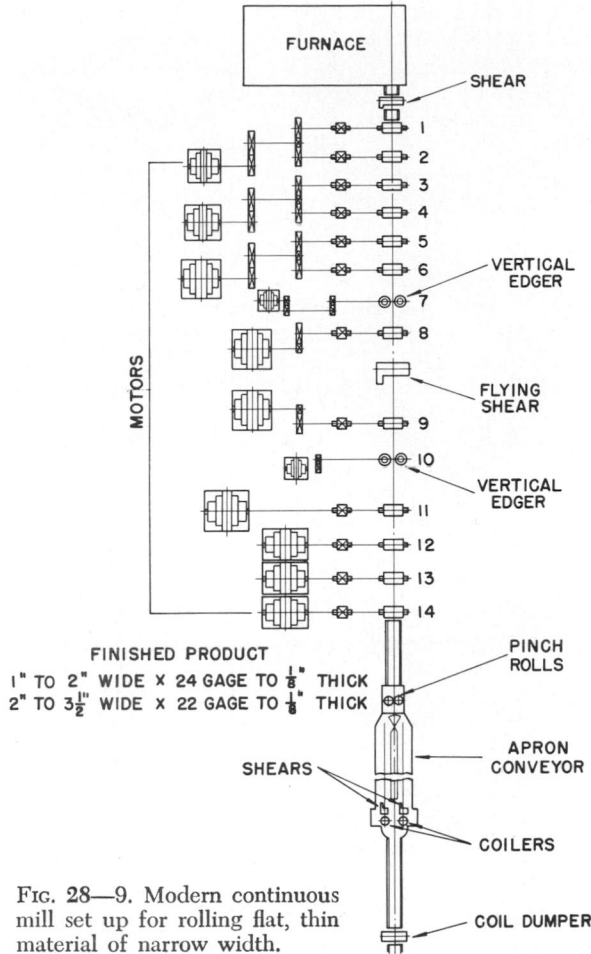

FIG. 28—9. Modern continuous mill set up for rolling flat, thin material of narrow width.

ROLL DESIGN FOR BAR MILLS

The first roll designs for bar mills were very simple. They consisted of box passes, gothic passes, tongue-and-groove passes for flats, and so-called hand-round grooves for rolling rounds.

Figure 28—11 shows a design of passes and a sketch of the rolls for rolling a hand-round, using gothic passes in the roughing and hand-round grooves in the finishing rolls. Figure 28—12 shows a typical series of passes for rolling guide-rounds, using gothic roughing passes, strand open-square passes, and oval and round finishing passes. These two methods were extensively used in the older bar and guide mills.

The gothic roughing rolls are not used to any great extent today. The design has been superseded in most hand mills by the diamond roughing set. Figure 28—13 shows one of these sets, which are also used for roughing passes for hand-guide rounds. Figure 28—14 shows a line of passes for a guide round using diamond

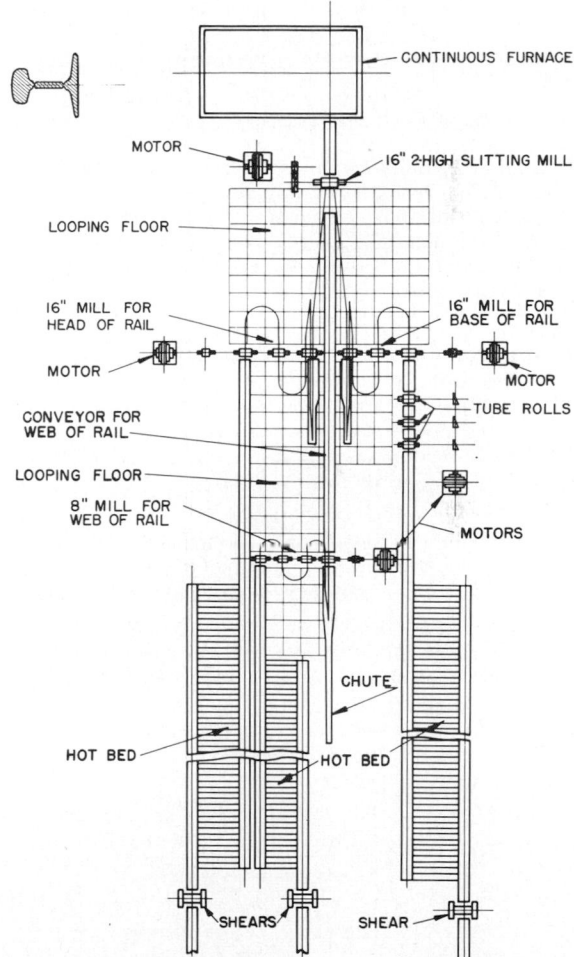

FIG. 28—10. Schematic arrangement of the slitting mill and roll stands of a rail-slitting mill. Inset at upper left shows how the head, web and base of the heated rail are separated in the slitting mill prior to rolling each, without reheating, into a bar. This particular mill has three continuous stands (marked "tube rolls") for forming a tube as described in the text.

row strip. In mills of this kind, the very narrow widths of the thin gauge materials are obtained by rolling a multiple width of the material and then slitting the rolled piece (after it is cold) into the desired widths. This permits the mill to maintain a rate of production that could not be realized if very narrow widths were to be rolled.

Rail-Slitting Mills—Rail-slitting mills were first developed when Bessemer rails were being rolled in large quantities and before open-hearth furnaces were common. Bessemer rail scrap was a drug on the market, as it could not be used in any quantity in the Bessemer vessel. The rail-splitting mills, a number of which are still in use, solved the problem of utilizing this scrap by rerolling it into other and useful sections.

Figure 28—10 illustrates a rail-slitting mill. These mills take a heated rail, usually 10 to 16½ feet long, and run it through a two-high stand of rolls with sharp collars which cut through and separate head, web, and base. Each one of these parts is then rolled into a bar of some kind directly after it is slit. The products include rounds, squares, fence posts, angles, concrete-reinforcing bars, flats, and a variety of other small sections. The continuous stands shown on the drawing are used to bend and form a flat, rolled from the base of the rail, into a cylinder which is then welded at the joint to make a tube or pipe.

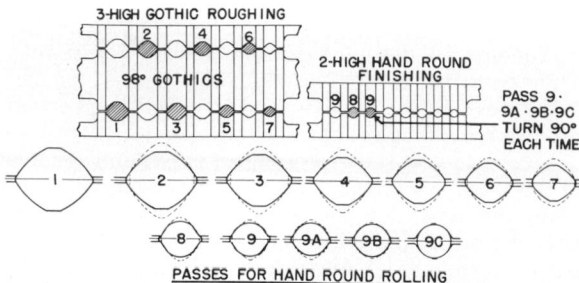

Fig. 28—11. Rolls and passes for rolling a hand round, using gothic passes in the roughing and hand-round grooves in the finishing rolls. The numbers of the sketched passes correspond to the cross-hatched and numbered pass openings between the rolls above.

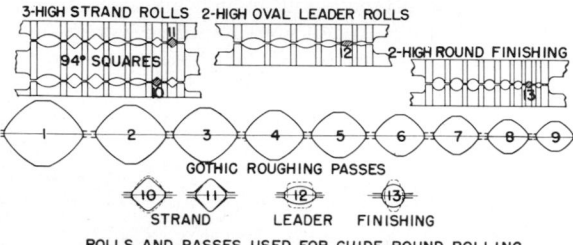

Fig. 28—12. Rolls and passes for rolling guide rounds. The roughing rolls containing the nine gothic roughing passes are not shown. Numbers on the sketched strand, leader and finishing passes correspond to the cross-hatched and numbered pass openings in the respective sets of rolls shown immediately above.

roughing grooves, oval and square strand grooves, and oval and round in the leader and finishing passes. The three-high strand rolls shown in Figure 28—12 have a

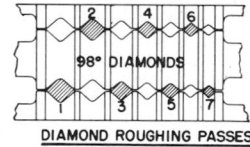

Fig. 28—13. Rolls with diamond roughing passes of the type which has largely superseded gothic roughing passes for rolling rounds by either the hand or guide method.

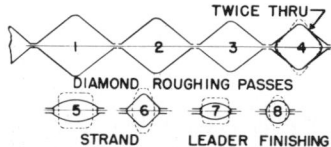

Fig. 28—14. Diamond roughing passes, oval and square strand passes, oval leader pass, and round finishing pass for guide-round rolling. Dotted lines indicate shape of piece entering pass, corresponding to shape of piece out of preceding pass turned 90 degrees.

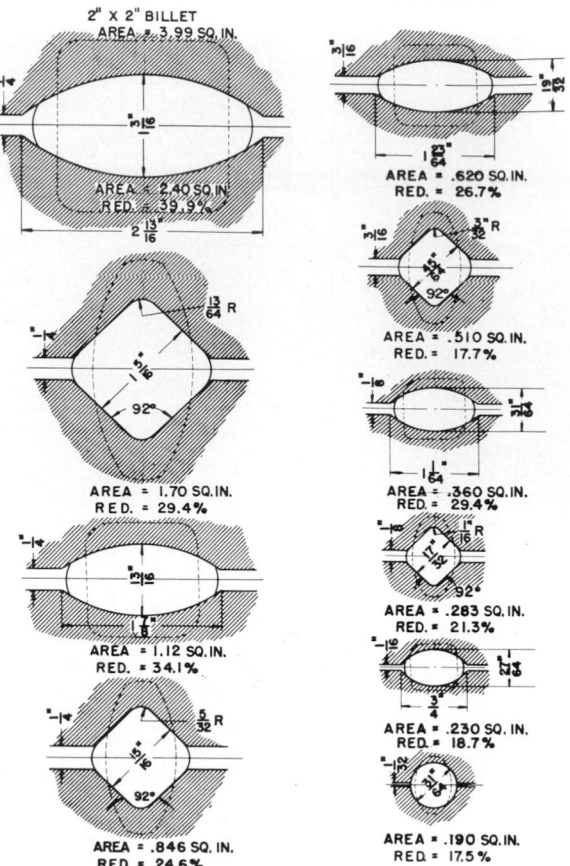

Fig. 28—15. Series of passes for rolling a 2-inch square billet into a $^{31}/_{64}$-inch round in ten passes, using an alternate oval and square reduction down to the finishing oval and round. Dotted lines indicate shape of piece entering pass, corresponding to shape of piece out of preceding pass turned 90 degrees. Per cent reduction of the piece in each pass has been calculated from the cross-sectional areas, as shown.

combination of oval and open-square passes, also diamond passes. The open-square passes referred to are of 94-degree angularity. To make a 90-degree square using these grooves it was customary to go twice through the same size groove.

The mill with the eight-stand continuous roughing arrangement and the looping finishing mills shown in Figure 28—4 used a 4-inch by 4-inch billet of not over 225 pounds. The continuous stands were close together and a roll design was provided which would require the least possible twisting of the bars. The roll design on this mill provided for a $^{15}/_{32}$-inch round in 14 passes. The first and second passes were both flat ones in box grooves. The bar then was twisted 90 degrees into a hexagon-shaped groove (pass No. 3) and then on into pass No. 4, which was a square in the diagonal position. By using this design, only one twist of the bar was required in the first four grooves. After pass No. 4, the bar was twisted 45 degrees to enter pass No. 5, which was an oval, and from there on the passes were alternately square and oval, the bars being twisted 90 degrees in the oval form and 45 degrees

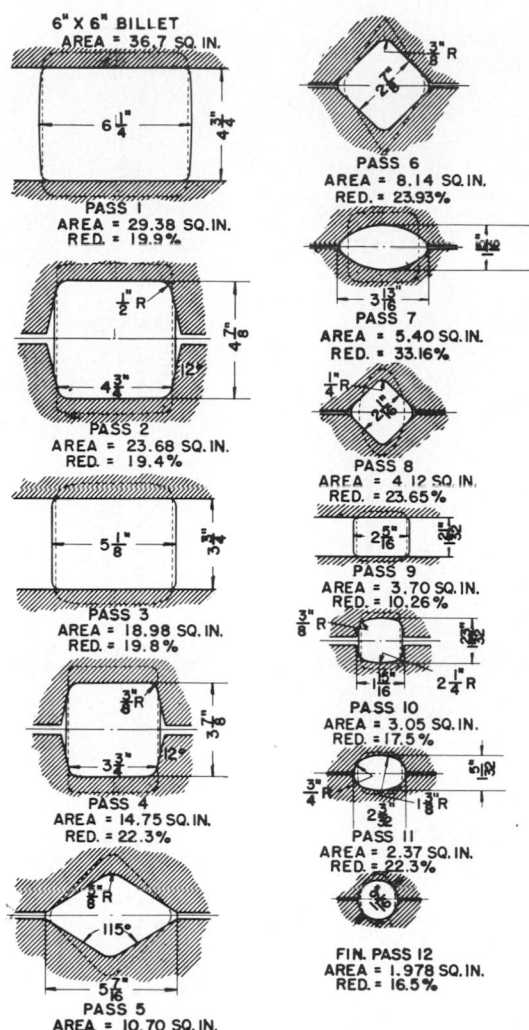

6" X 6" BILLET
AREA = 36.7 SQ. IN.

PASS 1
AREA = 29.38 SQ. IN.
RED. = 19.9%

PASS 2
AREA = 23.68 SQ. IN.
RED. = 19.4%

PASS 3
AREA = 18.98 SQ. IN.
RED. = 19.8%

PASS 4
AREA = 14.75 SQ. IN.
RED. = 22.3%

PASS 5
AREA = 10.70 SQ. IN.
RED. = 27.46 %

PASS 6
AREA = 8.14 SQ. IN.
RED. = 23.93%

PASS 7
AREA = 5.40 SQ. IN.
RED. = 33.16%

PASS 8
AREA = 4.12 SQ. IN.
RED. = 23.65%

PASS 9
AREA = 3.70 SQ. IN.
RED. = 10.26 %

PASS 10
AREA = 3.05 SQ. IN.
RED. = 17.5%

PASS 11
AREA = 2.37 SQ. IN.
RED. = 22.3%

FIN. PASS 12
AREA = 1.978 SQ.IN.
RED. = 16.5%

FIG. 28—16. Steps in the reduction of a 6-inch square billet to a $1\frac{9}{16}$-inch round in twelve passes on the cross-country mill shown in Figure 28—8. Dotted lines indicate shape of piece entering pass, corresponding to piece out of preceding pass after turning the required number of degrees for proper entry.

in the square form, before entering the next pass. The last pass, naturally, was round. Passes Nos. 9, 10, 11, 12, 13 and 14 were looped by hand on this mill.

As mentioned earlier, mills of this type rolling short 4-inch by 4-inch billets, with their close coupled roughing stands and long loops, were not able to roll bars of close tolerance on the front and back ends of the bars. These disadvantages led to the adoption for modern continuous mills of 30-foot billets of 1½-inch to 3-inch squares. Rolling 30-foot billets produces bars more uniform in section throughout their lengths because the back end of such a billet is still in the furnace and retaining heat while the front end is emerging from the continuous roughing mill and, as the mills generally have good speed adjustment in the finishing stands, mill loops are kept at a minimum to insure uniformity of size throughout the rolled piece.

Figure 28—15 shows the pass design for rolling a 2-inch by 2-inch billet on a modern-type mill into a $^{31}\!/_{64}$-inch round in 10 passes, using alternate oval and square reduction down to the finishing oval and round.

In the cross-country mill types, somewhat different roll designs are used. Figure 28—16 shows a roll design for the mill shown in Figure 28—8, which rolls many different grades of alloy steel, including stainless steel. The design shows the steps in reducing a 6-inch square billet to a $1\frac{9}{16}$-inch round in 12 passes. The first four passes are flat and edge, the flat passes being in plain rolls and the edging in box passes. The principal object in using these flat and edge passes is to break and free the bar of the scale that formed in the furnace during heating. In the first pass the roll pressure is on the top and bottom of the piece; the sides are free and, being compressed, crack the scale and allow it to drop off. In the next pass, the other two sides are free and the scale drops off here also. The

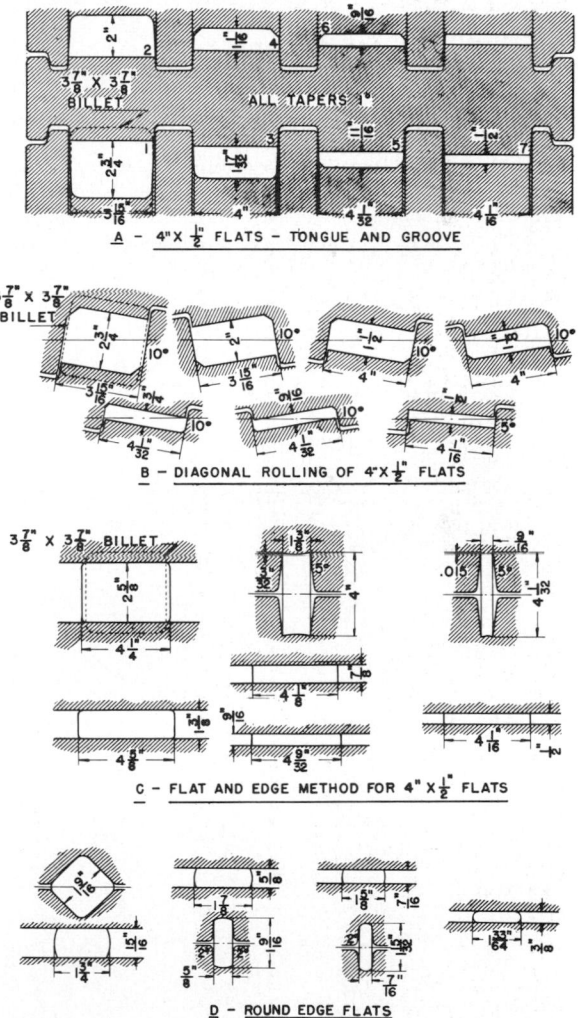

A - 4" X ½" FLATS - TONGUE AND GROOVE

B - DIAGONAL ROLLING OF 4" X ½" FLATS

C - FLAT AND EDGE METHOD FOR 4" X ½" FLATS

D - ROUND EDGE FLATS

FIG. 28—17. Diagrams A, B, and C show, respectively, bar-mill roll-pass designs for rolling square-edge flats by the tongue-and-groove, diagonal, and flat-and-edge method. Diagram D shows a typical set of passes for rolling round-edge flats.

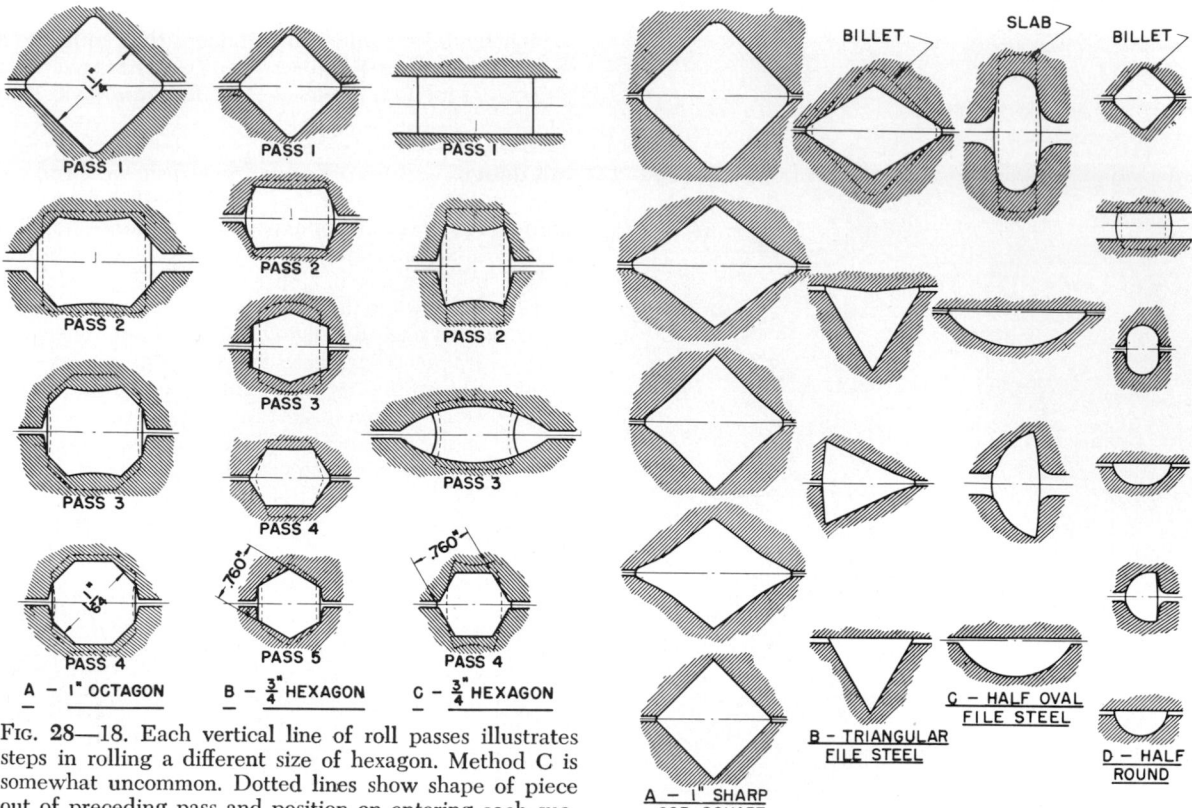

FIG. 28—18. Each vertical line of roll passes illustrates steps in rolling a different size of hexagon. Method C is somewhat uncommon. Dotted lines show shape of piece out of preceding pass and position on entering each succeeding pass.

FIG. 28—19. Steps in rolling (A) one-inch sharp-cornered squares, (B) triangular file steel, (C) half-oval file steel, and (D) half-rounds on a merchant bar mill.

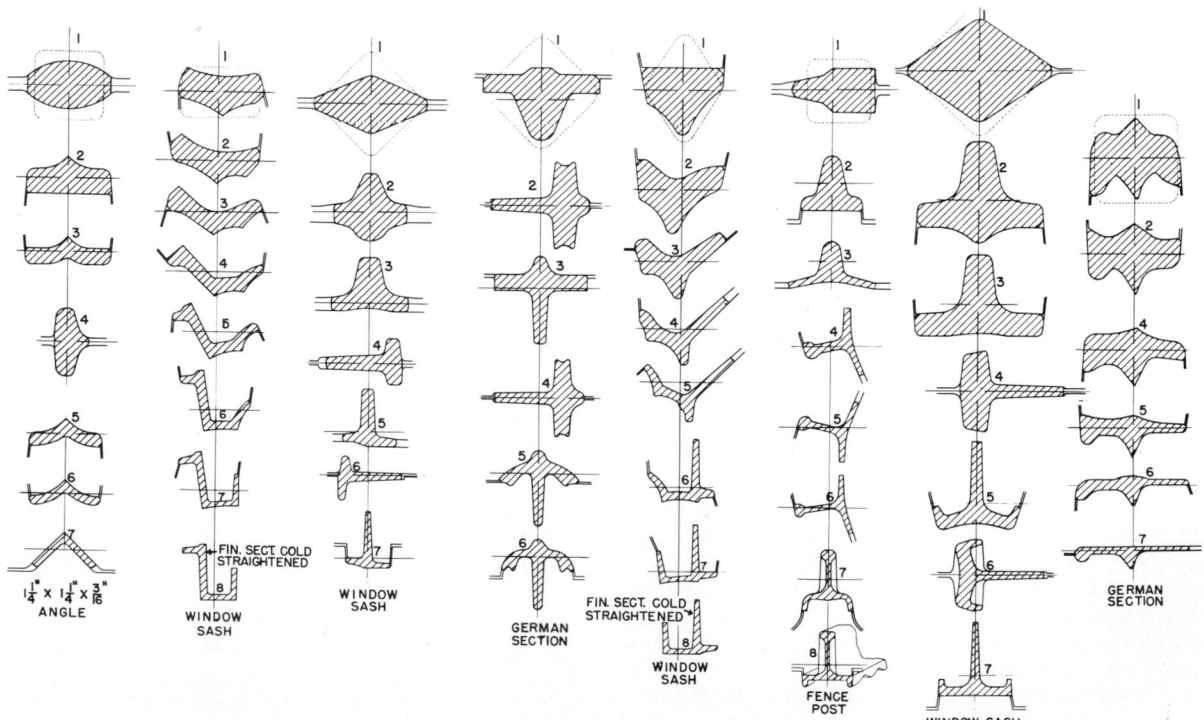

FIG. 28—20. Steps in rolling various small sections from billets or slabs on merchant bar mills.

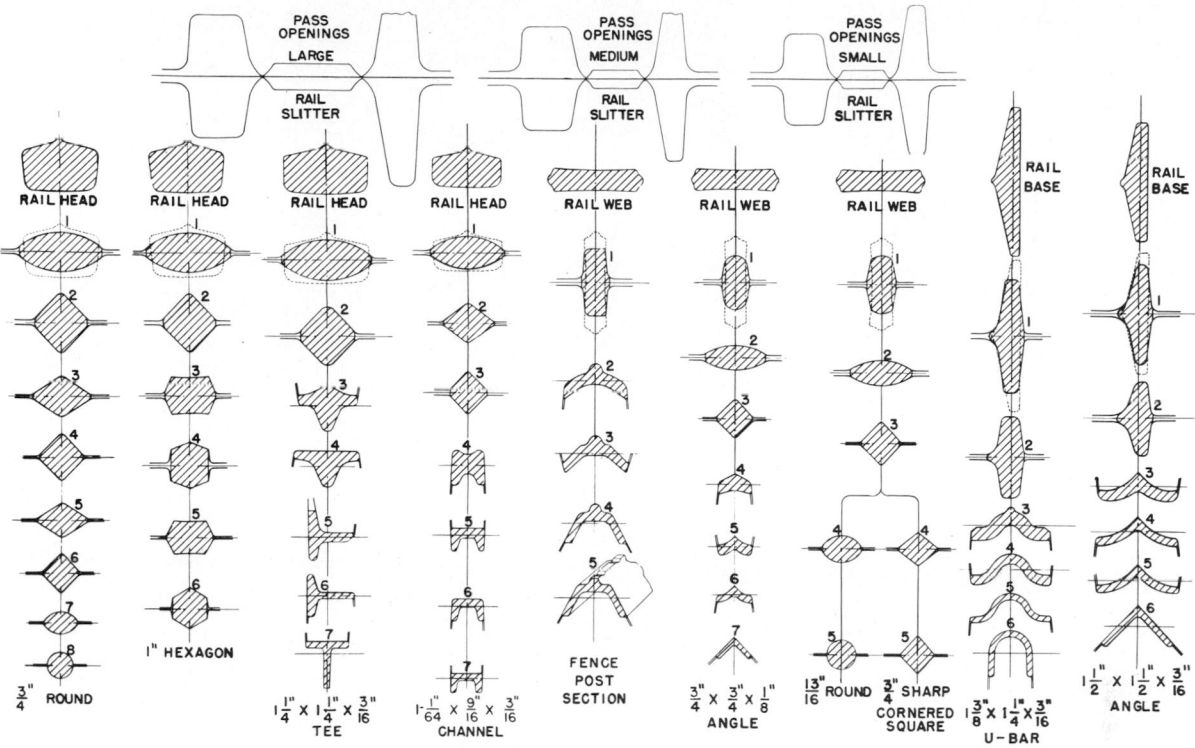

FIG. 28—21. Roll passes for producing various bars and shapes on a rail-slitting mill such as shown in Figure 28—10.

next two passes repeat the same procedures. It is not practical to use this type of pass throughout the mill because box passes are not efficient in drafting in the smaller sizes, and for this reason the next two passes are diamond and square, a form of pass which effects substantial reduction in cross-sectional area and also has the merit of contacting all sides of the bar at once. In the next two passes, oval and square are used as it is desired to have a heavy reduction in order that passes Nos. 9 and 10 may be more lightly drafted. Pass No. 9 is a slabbing or flatting pass which reduces the $2\frac{1}{16}$-inch square to a rectangle measuring $2\frac{5}{16}$ by $1\frac{21}{32}$-inches. Pass No. 10 is called a "former" pass. The function of this pass is to round the upper and lower edges so that the following oval will be well-rounded on the sides, for when the oval is rounded at the roll parting, scale will not readily adhere to it at this point. When scale is present, it is rolled into the finished round. In some mills, a square is used to enter the round oval and, when so used on some grades of alloy steel, scale sticks to the bar at the roll parting and is rolled into the bar.

Figure 28—17 shows three roll-pass designs for rolling square-edge flats, and one design for round-edge flats, as used on bars mills. Figure 28—17A illustrates a tongue-and-groove design used on a simple four-stand old-style bar mill. Figure 28—17B shows a diagonal design used on some mills, while Figure 28—17C shows the most popular design, one used on many modern bar mills, consisting of a flat and edge layout

wherein the widths of the flats are regulated by edging grooves which at the same time give the section a square edge. This design permits the rolling of several sizes in the same grooves. Round-edge flats are commonly rolled as shown in Figure 28—17D.

Octagons are often produced as illustrated in Figure 28—18A, but the most popular design for hexagons is shown in Figure 28—18B. Figure 28—18C shows an uncommon hexagon design used in one mill.

Figure 28—19A shows a 1-inch sharp-cornered square design and Figure 28—19B a design used for rolling triangular file steel. Figure 28—19C illustrates a half-oval design also used for file steel and Figure 28—19D an arrangement for rolling half-rounds.

On many merchant bar mills, small shapes are rolled, such as angles, channels, small beams, tees, small agricultural shapes, window sash, etc. Figure 28—20 shows a number of small sections and steps in their formation from the billet or slab.

Rail-slitting mills, such as shown in Figure 28—10, roll a variety of bars and shapes. These mills, of course, must confine their product to material which can be rolled from steel having the chemical composition of rail steel. Figure 28—21 shows a number of typical bars and shapes produced from the various parts of a rail.

Hoop and cotton-tie passes on the older mills were made by the tongue-and-groove method. The tongue-and-groove passes restricted the spread of the bar somewhat and also regulated the width. A series of

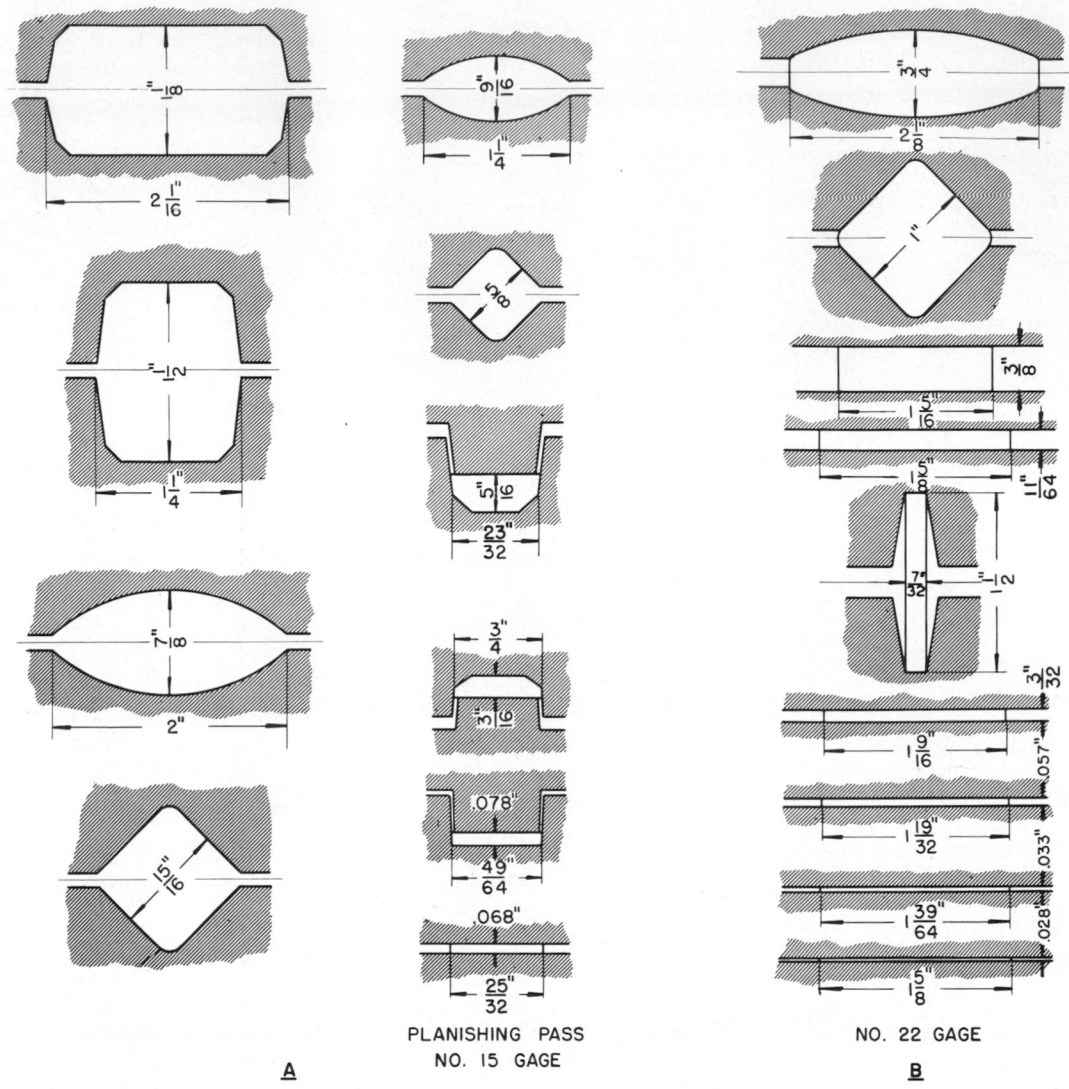

FIG. 28—22. Roll passes for producing hoop and cotton tie on a merchant bar mill.

passes using tongue-and-groove in the next to the last three passes is shown in Figure 28—22A. A later design is shown in Figure 28—22B. In this design the flattening is done in plain rolls and the width is regulated by a vertical edging stand. These passes represent the design used in the first continuous hoop and cotton-tie mill of 1895. The passes used in the most modern mills are of this same general design.

SECTION 2

FINISHING AND SHIPPING MERCHANT MILL BAR PRODUCTS

Coordination of Finishing and Shipping Functions —The operations involved in finishing and shipping merchant bar products are essentially the same in all plants, and the coordination of these functions differs only as to location of the rolling mill or mills, the type of products, arrangement of equipment, mode of transportation, etc. The functions of finishing and shipping merchant bar products are: (1) To provide a method of identification, cutting, bundling or coiling the product at the rolling mill as a preliminary to its delivery to the finishing departments. (2) To straighten, surface condition, heat treat, inspect or otherwise prepare the product for shipment in the finishing departments, in accordance with specifications and in compliance with transportation regulations.

BAR FINISHING PROCEDURES AND EQUIPMENT

Relation of Mill Delivery Equipment to Subsequent Finishing Operations—The type of rolling mill delivery equipment used has a very significant bearing on the straightness of the bar delivered for shearing. Most modern mills have certain features in the design of the hot beds—straight edges, kick-off equipment, roller tables and guides—to minimize bending and kinking that result in the necessity for subsequent straightening. When rolling-mill design permits, straightening units should be installed in the hot-bed delivery roll train ahead of the shears. Such an installation generally eliminates straightening as a finishing operation and necessitates fewer material handling steps prior to loading.

METHODS OF CUTTING PRODUCT TO LENGTH

The cutting of merchant bar product in most plants is performed by one of the following methods or by combinations of these methods: (1) Cutting by mill shears, directly to ordered lengths if practicable, or in multiple lengths if necessary to facilitate mill delivery, the latter requiring subsequent recutting to a variety of shorter lengths in the finishing departments. (2) Recutting by a finishing-department shear to meet ordered requirements, or for salvaging of portions of the product which may have surface or end defects. (3) Hot sawing of large rounds or sections which are not adaptable to hot shearing. (4) High-speed friction sawing where recutting is necessary after the straightening operation on a product previously cut by a mill shear or hot saw. (5) Machine cutting, which consists of the use of an abrasive cut-off machine, a hack saw, a cracker shear, or a slow-speed saw (Figure 28—23), where the closest tolerance on end-squareness is required, or where, by the nature of the product, recutting cannot be done satisfactorily by other methods. (6) Flame cutting, where the nature of the product and specifications permit the application of heat for rough cutting.

MACHINE STRAIGHTENING

Many merchant bar products require straightening after hot shearing at the mill. Straightening is necessary so that the product may meet either standard commercial tolerance specifications or any special specifications. In the finishing departments this is usually accomplished by roll-type machines, or by gag presses. The selection of the type of straightening equipment depends on the characteristics of the product and the end-use requirements. There are numerous commercial types of straightening machines, but they all are similar in principle and are fundamentally designed to process a specific shape within certain dimensional limitations. On this basis, straightening equipment can be divided into three main classifications:

(1) **For flat product.** This equipment includes multi-roll units for flats, squares, hexagons, etc.; and two-way roll units for straightening in planes at right angles in one pass.

(2) **For round products.** This equipment includes roll units which rotate the product through either a two-roll (cross-roll) or a multi-roll unit, and gag presses. Figure 28—24 illustrates a two-roll straightening machine.

(3) **For standard shapes and special sections.** This equipment includes both light and heavy multiple-roll units having grooves to fit each separate section, gag

FIG. 28—23. Slow-speed saw for recutting steel bars.

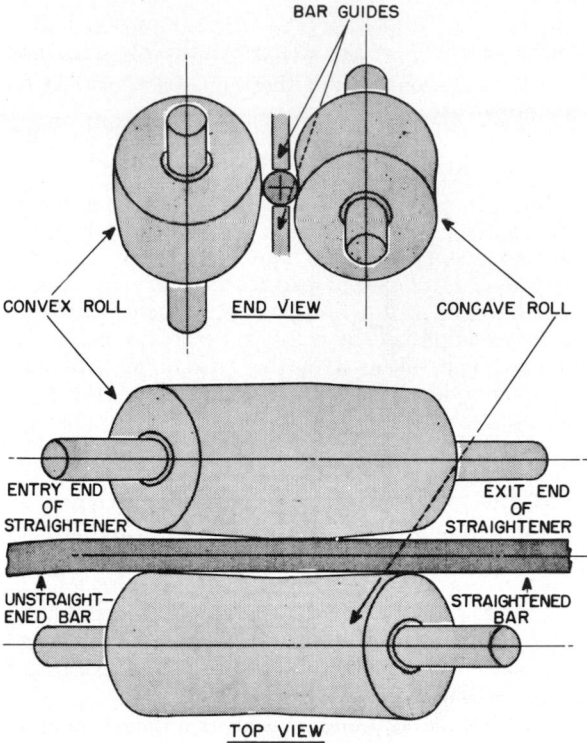

FIG. 28—24. Sketch showing end and top views of a typical two-roll unit for straightening rounds.

presses (both vertical and horizontal, with interchangeable guides and adjustable stroke), and roll units for shaping such products as small channels or U-bars which are hot rolled in an open form and then closed by cold forming before the straightening operation.

SIZING, TURNING AND CENTERLESS GRINDING

In the manufacture of merchant bar products, the design and type of rolling mill or the characteristics of the steel frequently preclude the possibility of hot-rolling a round to within precise sectional or out-of-round limitations, or to roll a round with a surface suitable for later fabrication requirements. When such requirements must be met, rounds are further processed in the finishing departments by such operations as sizing, turning, centerless grinding, or by combinations of the latter two. Bars to be processed by any one of these methods are hot-rolled over-size by an amount predetermined by experience.

Sizing is applied to bars when a moderate reduction in section or an improvement in out-of-roundness is desired. It is performed by passing the bar through a two-roll or cross-roll straightening machine in one or more passes as required. Sizing can impart a cold-drawn appearance to the surface of the bar if the rolls are new and properly adjusted; however, it is not generally used for the purpose of improving the surface appearance. As sizing elongates the bar, due to reduction of cross-sectional area, re-cutting to length must follow.

Turning improves the surface of a bar by the removing of undesirable defects that may be present in the surface. It is applied on those types of steel, predominantly the alloy type and particularly the stainless steel group, where, due to the inherent characteristics of the product, it is very difficult and in some cases impossible to obtain a hot-rolled surface which can be utilized by the customer without the removal of a portion of the "skin" of the bar. Turning is accomplished by passing the bar through a turning machine or lathe, using one or more passes depending upon the amount of material to be removed. There are several designs of turning machines used in producing merchant bar products, but they all are constructed according to a fundamental principle. They differ only in the arrangement of the revolving heads or the manner in which the bars are supported and fed to the revolving heads. In all types, a suitable cutting oil is fed to the tool or tools in the revolving head by a pressure system. In one type of machine, two cutting heads are mounted very close together, in tandem, between two guide bearings. In another type, the revolving heads are a considerable distance apart, separated by guide bearings. Due to the arrangement of the revolving cutting heads, the former type is more adaptable for bars of short length, while the latter is more suitable for bars of long length. Turning machines are made in various sizes and can handle rounds in sizes up to and including six inches and in lengths up to forty feet. The amount of metal removed per pass is dependent on the type of steel, and the diameter and the length of the bar. Removal of approximately ⅛ inch on the diameter per pass is considered normal for bars of medium or large diameter. Speeds of twelve inches to fifteen inches per minute are normal when removing this amount of metal.

In finishing some grades of alloy and stainless steels, surfaces and dimensions are required that can be met only by **centerless grinding.** Centerless grinding differs from turning in that a grinding wheel is used for removal of metal instead of a cutting tool, and more accurate dimensions and better surface finish are obtained. The centerless grinding machine is constructed so that the bar is supported under the greater portion of its length as well as under the grinding wheel, rather than at the ends. This design enables the machine to operate to close tolerances by elimination of axial thrust, always present when a bar is supported at the ends. A suitable coolant is used on the grinding wheel or wheels. Most commercial centerless grinding machines are constructed to handle round bars up to four inches in diameter, in ranges of approximately one inch in diameter. When the diameter of the bar must be reduced materially, it is more economical to remove a large portion of unwanted metal by the turning machine before centerless grinding. Standard centerless grinding machine tolerances are ±0.002 inches on bar sizes up to two inches in diameter and ±0.003 inches on larger sizes up to four inches in diameter.

In some cases a highly polished bar is desired rather than the standard centerless ground finish. The polished finish is produced by passing centerless ground bars through a polishing or lapping machine. This machine is similar to the standard centerless grinding machine except that the grinding wheels are composed of a fine grit and the bar-supporting apparatus is constructed to operate within very narrow limits of accuracy. Polishing or lapping tolerances are one-half of those for standard centerless grinding. In precise polishing or lapping of long bars, it is very difficult to keep within these tolerance limits because of the wear of the grinding wheel and the spring of the metal. For these reasons, more precise tolerance limits than those stated above are not considered practical for commercial products.

Processing Bar Coils—There are some manufacturers, such as bolt, rivet or cold-drawn steel fabricators, who find it more convenient and economical to obtain bars (either rounds, squares, hexagons, or flats) in coil form rather than in straight lengths. As most of the smaller bar and rod mills are not equipped with flying shears to crop the front and back ends of a coil, it is necessary to complete this operation in the finishing department of the mill. Variations in the process for cropping coils, depending upon available equipment, will be found at the various plants. The most widely used equipment is a long conveyor, sometimes over 1,000 feet in length, equipped with hooks spaced approximately ten feet apart, which pick up the coils from the mill coiler and carry them to the end of the conveyor. While the coils are moving along the conveyor, the ends are cropped either by a small shear or by flame-cutting. As the coils proceed further, they cool considerably, and then can be inspected and wired or banded securely. A shipping tag is attached, following which spark testing of material representing the beginning and end of each order item is performed as a final check of identification. By the time the coils have reached the end of the conveyor, they are cool enough to be loaded into the railroad cars for shipment. In some plants having high speed mills, where cutting to length would seriously retard output of the mills, bars which finally are to be shipped in straight lengths first are rolled in coils; subsequently, in the finishing department, they are then uncoiled, straightened, and sheared to length on a processing line designed for the purpose.

PICKLING

Stationary or Vat Pickling—Pickling is the term given the descaling process by which the hard black oxide formed on the surface of a bar during hot rolling is removed by chemical action. The removal of hot-rolled scale by pickling may be performed in order to: (1) prepare the surface of the bar for inspection, (2) prepare the product for ultimate end use. Pickling is also used, though to a much lesser degree, to remove the slow-forming red rust that develops on bar products after long exposure to air. Stationary or vat pickling in its simplest form consists of immersing the steel bars in a dilute acid bath, which is held at a predetermined temperature, and permitting them to remain stationary until the pickling action is completed. Most modern instal-

lations have improved the method by including means of keeping the bath in motion or agitation. Stationary or vat pickling is one of a number of pickling methods which are classified according to the manner in which the operations are conducted. Other methods of pickling and equipment are described elsewhere in the text.

The stationary or vat pickling method for descaling bars has been used with success and reasonable economy where the best established procedures are followed. A number of variables, both chemical and physical, determine the procedure to be followed, the design and capacities of equipment, and the layout to be used in the construction of a unit. Beginning about 1935, considerable data have been published concerning the pickling process, many of these being more or less empirical. Study of these data indicates that there is considerable difference of opinion as to what actually takes place as the iron oxide is removed. One theory proposes that the scale or oxide layer is relatively less soluble than the iron underneath and that the acid solution, passing through tiny cracks or fissures in the scale (formed by differences between the cooling rates of the metal and scale), reacts chemically with the bonding structure between the underside of the scale and the true metallic surface of the bar. In this reaction hydrogen gas is liberated which, it is claimed, dislodges the scale particles. A second theory proposes that the acid solution attacks the iron oxide or scale, resulting in its actual dissolution in the pickling bath. A third theory, a combination of the first and second, proposes that there is a preferential dissolution of the surface of the scale by the acid, followed by the penetration of the acid solution through tiny cracks or holes to the base metal, where it attacks the bonding structure and liberates hydrogen gas. The hydrogen gas, as in the first theory, is said to serve as an agent in lifting the scale in small particles from the surface of the bar.

A large majority of the various types of steel bars can be pickled by the stationary or vat method, providing all factors pertaining to the physical and chemical variables of the process are taken into consideration. The efficiency of scale removal by pickling varies considerably. The scale on some types of steel bars can be removed readily, while on others, considerable difficulty is encountered. The pickling of hot-rolled low-carbon steels, for example, is done with little difficulty and the scale can be removed readily by the use of a sulphuric-acid solution. On hot-rolled high-carbon steels or alloy steels, however, many difficulties are encountered in the removal of scale. On high-carbon steels, a bad discoloration in the form of a black smudge of carbonaceous, insoluble material is the chief difficulty. The black smudge is particularly undesirable when close inspection must follow. On alloy steels, the hot-rolled scale is not removed as uniformly as in the case of the low-carbon steels. This condition can be attributed to the differences in chemical composition of the scale. By proper selection of acid or acids, by the selection of the most effective acid concentration, by adequate agitation, by use of proper bath temperature and the inclusion of an effective inhibitor, the pickling of high-carbon and alloy steel bars can be accomplished successfully. On the very high-alloy steels, such as the stainless group, pickling cannot be accomplished successfully in sulphuric-acid solutions alone, even at high acid concentration and elevated bath temperatures. Stainless steels are pickled in baths containing sulphuric plus another acid, another acid alone, or by a combination of other acids. The choice of the acid combination and concentration depends upon the characteristics of the steel to be pickled and the finish desired. The most commonly used acid for pickling is sulphuric. Other acids used in this method are hydrochloric (muriatic), nitric, and phosphoric.

Another factor affecting scale removal on hot-rolled high-carbon or alloy steels is the thermal treatment, such as normalizing or annealing, to which the bars may have been subjected. Bars so treated are difficult to pickle and, in some cases, the attendant pitting of the product is so severe that other methods of removing the scale must be employed.

The equipment for stationary or vat pickling consists of three tanks. The first tank is used for the dilute acid solution or pickling bath; the second contains only water, for washing the steel bars after immersion in the pickling bath; the third tank contains an alkaline liquid (lime water), for neutralizing any acid which remains on the bars after washing.

Tanks or vats containing the dilute acid solution or pickling bath can be of several types and are constructed of various materials. They must be water tight and capable of resisting attack by the acids used in the pickling solution. They are constructed either of wood, concrete, brick or metal lined with wood. When wood is used for the tank or when it is

used as a lining, cypress has been found to be the most durable. Recently, improvements in tank construction have been realized by using acid-resistant brick or terra-cotta tile as a lining for either wood, concrete or metal tanks. The acid-resistant brick or tile is laid in courses, with an acid-resistant mastic cement as a binder. Rubber is also used for lining tanks and has given excellent service. The practice of lining stationary or vat pickling tanks with sheets of lead is no longer looked upon with favor, because experience over the years has indicated that the lead lining is susceptible to cracking under the rapid temperature changes which are prevalent in this method of pickling.

In addition to the three tanks required for the pickling operation, bar-mill finishing-department equipment usually includes a steel tank, containing a rust-preventative oil into which the bars are dipped in order to provide adequate protection against subsequent rusting.

As a coating of lime may be specified on bars, particularly those to be cold drawn, an additional tank for this purpose is generally part of the equipment. The lime coating serves as a lubricant in the cold-drawing process and reduces wear on the dies. It is applied after the washing and neutralizing stages of the pickling process. The tank for lime coating generally is constructed of steel and, as the lime should be kept in suspension in the water, a means of providing continuous agitation is usually a part of the installation. Pickling, washing, neutralizing, and liming tanks should be equipped with proper means of heating the bath and provision must be made for proper means of disposing of the waste solutions.

The efficiency of a stationary or vat pickling unit depends in a large measure upon the manner in which a multiplicity of similar pieces can be arranged and immersed in the pickling solution or in the

FIG. 28—25. Loaded pickling rack, showing how combs keep bars separated to allow free circulation of acid solution.

washing, neutralizing, oiling or liming baths. The entire surface of each individual bar must be exposed if the best results are to be obtained. For this reason, various designs of crates and racks have been developed, one of which is shown in Figure 28—25. The steel bar product to be pickled is placed in tiers on the crates or racks. In the tiers, the bars are kept apart by separators which are called **combs**. These combs are designed to permit adequate spacing between each bar to allow for free circulation of the acid solution around them. The racking or placing of the steel bars on the fixtures for pickling is done manually. The materials used in the construction of the crates, racks, separators, and combs must be of acid-resisting metal and of a strength sufficient to carry the weight of the load.

When conditions and specifications permit, steel bar product that has been coiled is pickled by passing a chain through the open center of a group of coils, and attaching the ends of the chain to the hook of an overhead crane. Such a group of coils is referred to as a "lift," and is suspended in the pickling tank by the crane. This practice is referred to as chain pickling. Chains used in this work also must be made of acid-resisting metal. Monel metal or aluminum-bronze alloys are used in many parts and fixtures, including the chains.

Steam has been the most widely used for heating pickling baths, but, the submerged gas burner method, a relatively recent development, has become popular with many operators. Where steam is used, suitable piping for conducting the steam into the bath is necessary. Adequate and convenient steam-input controls must be provided in the form of valves, either hand operated or automatic in action, in order to maintain the bath as nearly as possible at the proper temperature. When steam is introduced directly into the bath, care must be taken to avoid direct impingement against the sides or bottom as this will result in rapid erosion and damage to the tank. Also, the introduction of steam directly into the pickling bath results in an increasing dilution of the bath, which requires the addition of more acid to maintain the solution at the proper concentration.

The submerged gas burner provides for burning gas and air under automatic control in submerged burners. The hot waste gases from the burners are conducted into lead tubes which run the length of the tank on the bottom. This method heats the pickling bath quite efficiently, and the waste gases, which are forced out under pressure through holes located throughout the length of the tubes, provide the desired agitation of the bath. When this type of heating equipment is used, however, care must be taken to avoid accumulation of sludge and scale in the bottom of the tank. If the lead tubes become completely covered with sludge and scale, they are shielded from the pickling solution in the tank, become overheated, and are destroyed.

When a new pickling bath is to be prepared, the tank first is filled to approximately three-fourths capacity with water. Acid in an amount to provide the proper concentration is run into the tank, and then enough water is added to bring the solution to an operating level. The heat is then turned on and the bath is brought to the operating temperature. When placing products in the pickling bath, care must be taken to avoid any rapid or irregular movement that may splash acid solution over the sides of the tank, where it rapidly attacks the outer tank shell, concrete floors and tank foundations. It is very important that wash tanks be emptied frequently, as acid in damaging amounts builds up in the wash water and interferes with the proper function of the washing operation.

The surface of steel bars to be pickled must be free from oil or grease, as these materials protect the surface from the action of pickling solution. Any substance on the bars which may serve to contaminate or neutralize the acid solution must be removed before they are immersed in the pickling bath. After the steel bar product is washed and dipped into the neutralizing bath, it is further safeguarded against rusting by being thoroughly dried. Live steam and sometimes air, blown against the bars as they hang suspended in the rack, are used for this purpose.

Summarizing, the factors controlling the rate of pickling and the iron loss are: (1) acid concentration, (2) temperature, (3) time in bath, (4) percent of iron (ferrous) sulphate in the bath, (5) presence of inhibitors, and (6) agitation of the bath. Frequent tests of the bath should be made. Not only will the testing of the pickling solution reveal the concentration of the acid bath, but will also show the rate of iron dissolution into the bath, thus giving a good indication of the efficiency of the pickling operation. If the rate of iron increase in the solution is rapid, it indicates that the true metal is being attacked severely. Under such operation, not only is the wastage of acid high, but also the loss in weight of the steel bars becomes excessive. When the iron content of the pickling solution reaches approximately 0.5 lb. per gallon, the bath is considered to have little further use and is ready to be dumped. Testing the pickling solution for acid and iron can be done very readily by titration.

Temperature of the Pickling Bath—The significance of this factor should be understood clearly. By raising the temperature of the pickling bath the action of the acid solution upon the scale can be increased greatly, for the particular pickling job at hand. It should be remembered, however, that while increasing the temperature of the acid solution speeds up the pickling action on the scale, it also increases the tendency of the acid solution to attack the steel itself. When the metal is attacked, the iron reacts with the acid and goes into solution in the form of the salt of the particular acid or acids used. As the amount of iron salts in solution increases toward the point of saturation, the efficiency of the process decreases very rapidly. This may necessitate the addition of more acid to the bath, or, possibly, the complete replacement of the bath with a new acid solution. The trend with some operators is toward the use of lower acid concentrations and lower bath temperatures. The practice requires more time per ton of steel pickled, but the quality of the work is improved. Less metal is lost from the surface of the bar and less acid is consumed in the process.

An **inhibitor** is an agent added to the pickling solution for the purpose of protecting the exposed surface of the metal of the bars, by inhibiting or retarding acid attack upon the metal without affecting, to any appreciable degree, the pickling action which removes the scale. The inhibiting action is not understood clearly but is generally explained by the electrolytic theory of corrosion. Inhibitors show little change and lose little of their efficiency during the pickling operation. However, they may be broken down and their function destroyed by overheating. Many different substances are used as inhibitors in acid pickling. They range from vegetable or animal matter to complex synthetic organic chemicals. The prime requirements of an inhibitor are that it must **disperse** colloidally in the bath, prevent hydrogen evolution and not leave a smudge or film on the surface of the steel. Many inhibitors contain substances that cause foaming, and the floating layer or blanket of foam on the bath prevents the escape of acid with escaping gases and vapors. As inhibitors are expensive and only a small amount is needed for desired results, less costly foaming substances are added separately by many operators when increased foaming activity is desired.

Common difficulties encountered in pickling are **over-pickling, under-pickling, smudge** and **pitting.** Over-pickling may be defined as the etched appearance of the surface of a product caused by over-activity of the acid solution. Conversely, under-pickling may be defined as incomplete removal of the scale due to limited activity of the acid solution and/or the use of too low a pickling temperature. Smudge is a carbonaceous precipitate or stain which forms on bars of high carbon content. Pitting may be defined as the appearance of crater-like indentations on the surface of the bar, which may result from over-activity of the acid solution on the metal in areas where scale has been loosened mechanically or removed prior to the pickling operation, or as the result of an electrolytic action taking place in areas where there are concentrations of dense scale on the surface.

GRIT-BLASTING

Grit-blasting or blast-cleaning is a mechanical process used for removing scale and rust on merchant bar products. It consists of eroding or abrading away the scale from the surface of the bar by impinging an abrasive substance like sand or aluminum oxide, or a metallic substance like cast-iron shot. The abrasive material may be directed against the work by air under pressure or by a mechanical apparatus utilizing centrifugal force. All types of steel bar products and shapes can be cleaned successfully by this method. As a result of the difference in economy of operation between the grit-blasting and the pickling method, the former generally is confined to the cleaning of one of the following types of products: (1) those which must have certain physical characteristics essential to subsequent processing; (2) those which

cannot be cleaned satisfactorily by the pickling method after such thermal treatments as normalizing or annealing; (3) those with high alloy content whose scale cannot be removed satisfactorily by ordinary pickling methods.

The principal difference between the various types of grit-blasting equipment is in the means employed for throwing the grit or shot against the work. One type of grit-blasting machine makes use of centrifugal force generated by a rotor or impeller which rotates at a very high speed. Grit in the form of metal shot is fed from a hopper into the revolving rotor through an opening in the center of the rotor housing. The shot, on entering the revolving rotor, is picked up by the rotor vanes and is thrown by centrifugal force away from the center of the rotor toward its periphery. From the periphery, the shot is directed outward to impinge on the work at the angle desired for the best abrasive effect. Since this type of machine develops its abrasive characteristics on the basis of the velocity and the weight of the particles, lighter grit, such as sand, cannot be used satisfactorily.

Another type of machine employs compressed air or forced air from a blower for throwing the grit particles. There are several modifications of this principle, but in each type the grit is permitted to entrain in a fast-moving air stream and is directed upon the surface of the work through a hose having a nozzle designed for the purpose. The lighter grit is used most effectively with this type of equipment. The material used for, and the size of, the grit or shot in blast cleaning are dictated by the requirements for a given job and, as previously noted, by the type of equipment in which it is to be used.

From the standpoint of density, grit can be divided into: (1) the light, and (2) the heavy. Light grit is a non-metallic inorganic material with excellent abrasive characteristics. It is purchased according to particle size. Examples of light grit are the widely used natural abrasive known as Ottawa sand and the synthetic abrasive, aluminum oxide. Heavy grit is principally of the metallic type such as cast-iron shot. Like the light grit, it is purchased according to particle size. Metallic grit is the type most generally used on merchant bar product.

The chief advantages of grit blasting are: (1) it leaves the surface of the bar with a bright metallic finish without any adhering scale; (2) it is capable of cleaning a number of types of products that cannot be cleaned successfully by pickling; (3) it does not produce such physical or chemical conditions as over-pickling, under-pickling, smudge or pitting which may attend the pickling process. The disadvantages of grit blasting are: (1) only a few bars can be processed at one time in the blast machine; (2) as the grit or shot builds up with the scale the efficiency of the cleaning effect is decreased; and (3) the bars are difficult to inspect for surface defects because of the peening action of the grit or shot.

Grit blasting does produce minute indentations on the surface of the product which are more beneficial in some subsequent fabrication operations than they are detrimental. The size of these indentations and their shape serve to produce a surface sheen or finish determined somewhat by the particle shape and size of the grit. The character of this sheen or finish is very important where cold-drawing operations are to be performed. As a grit-blasted steel surface is very susceptible to rusting, bars cleaned by this method must be protected immediately from moisture and alkaline or acid vapors. Also, when a bar is grit-blasted with cast-iron shot, particles of the shot have a tendency to adhere to the product and will cause rapid rusting or corrosion on some types of steel if they are not removed immediately. In such cases the grit-blasting operation must be followed by a light pickling operation.

BAR INSPECTION AND TESTING

Inspection—In order to produce satisfactory bar products it is important that an adequate quality control system be established and maintained. This system should include mechanical and metallurgical testing as required, and the inspection for surface or other defects. The procedures for making mechanical and metallurgical tests and the inspection of steel prior to rolling in the merchant mills are covered in other chapters of this book. The inspection of merchant bar product in the majority of plants is carried out along the same general lines and can be divided into two divisions; (1) mill inspection, and (2) finished product or final inspection. The duties and responsibilities of the inspection forces in these divisions must be thoroughly co-ordinated to accomplish the best results.

Mill inspection is performed during the rolling process and is the means of minimizing or preventing discrepancies at the source. The duties of the inspector at the mill are: (1) to check the identity of the steel being rolled, (2) to inspect the surfaces of the product to determine its suitability for further processing in the finishing departments or in its final intended use, (3) to check section and length of the product to determine its suitability for application on a particular order, and (4) to procure necessary samples for mechanical or metallurgical tests. The inspection of the finished bar products, on the basis of commercial standards or for dimensions, straightness, surface defects, and other items of form as may be required, is carried out upon completion of the finishing end operations at designated units.

The duties of the final inspector are in a measure a repetition of the duties of the mill inspector, with the additional responsibility of checking and posting heats. The checking and posting of heats is a method of reporting the amount of product accepted or rejected (per heat) on an order, with reasons for further processing or for rejections. The final inspector must lay particular emphasis on surface quality if the product has been conditioned and straightened. Various tools are required for inspecting merchant bar product. A list of these tools and a brief description of their use follows: (1) micrometers and calipers, for measuring the section of rounds, flats, and squares; (2) snap gages, for precision rounds; (3) tape, for measuring length; (4) slide scales, for measuring width; (5) protractors, depth gages and radius gages, for shapes; and (6) the square tool for measuring off-squareness.

Surface defects, as well as other defects which cause the rejection of merchant bar products, may be the result of steelmaking practices which carry through from the ingot or may be caused by the rolling mill equipment used to produce the product. A list follows giving the general mill terminology of the most regularly occurring types of mill defects and a brief description of each:

1. **Fins and overfills** are protrusions formed when the section is too large for the pass it is entering, or when proper allowance has not been made for lateral spreading in the rolls. Overfills are broad and less sharp than fins. As a rule, overfills occur more frequently than fins and in many cases are associated on the same bar with underfills.

2. **Underfills** are the reverse of overfills, that is, they are areas in which the section is incompletely filled. They are formed by permitting the bar to be rolled scant in certain dimensions. Underfills appear most frequently on rounds and channels.

3. **Slivers** are loose or torn segments of steel rolled into the surface of the bar. They may be caused by a bar shearing against a guide or collar, incorrect entry into a closed pass, or a tear from other mechanical causes. Sometimes slivers are present in the billet and are carried through to the hot-rolled bar or shape.

4. **Laps** can be said to be a rolled-over condition caused by a bar having been given a pass through the rolls after a sharp overfill or fin has been formed, causing the protrusion to be rolled into the surface of the product.

5. **Seams** are crevices in the steel that have been closed but are not welded. They are a type of a defect very difficult to detect on certain types of steel products. Seams are caused by blow holes and cracks in the original ingot, or by faulty methods of rolling in both semi-finishing and finishing mills.

6. **Fire cracks and roll marks** are impressions in the product, of varying degree and pattern, caused by mill rolls becoming overheated, and cracking or spalling.

7. **Scratches** are long nicks or indentations in the product caused by the surface or surfaces of the bar rubbing against sharp or pointed objects such as guides on the mill, chutes, "dead" conveyor rolls, chain hoists or other mechanical equipment.

8. **Rolled-in scale** is a defect in the surface caused by scale, formed during a previous heating, which has failed to be eliminated during the rolling operations. It is one of the most prevalent surface defects.

9. **Buckle and kink** is a corrugated or wrinkled surface condition caused either by worn out pinions on a roll stand or uneven cooling beds.

Buckle is an up-and-down wrinkle, whereas kink is a side wrinkle.

10. **Burned steel** appears as a rough area with checked or serrated edges. It is caused by steel being exposed to an excessive temperature and is always scrapped.

11. **Camber** is the deviation of the side edge of a bar from a straight line. It is caused by improper heating of the billet, uneven dimensions causing differential expansion or contraction, or improper alignment on the hot beds.

12. **Hook** is a short bend or curvature caused either by improperly adjusted delivery guides or by any obstruction which may halt momentarily the forward motion of the bar from one roll stand to another.

13. **Pipe** is a steel-making defect carried through from the ingot. The presence of pipe is detected as a small round cavity located in the center of an end surface.

14. **Shear distortion** is a mashed or deformed end on a bar caused by defective or improperly adjusted shearing equipment.

15. **Twist** is a condition wherein the ends of a bar have been forced to rotate in relatively opposite directions about its longitudinal axis. It may be caused by excessive draft, faulty setting of delivery guides, or lack of uniform temperature in the bar.

Testing—Numerous tests are made during the finishing operations, the purposes of which are to reveal defects otherwise impossible to detect during surface inspection. The tests most commonly employed are described as follows:

1. **The pickling test** consists of immersing short pieces of product for several minutes in dilute sulphuric acid. The acid removes the scale from the bar and exposes to view such surface defects as may be covered or hidden by the scale.

2. **The upset test** consists of heating small test pieces to a forging temperature and then subjecting them to severe compression under a hammer. The compression or upsetting action will force open any defects which could not be detected while the steel was in the as-rolled condition. A sound steel will be indicated by the absence of areas which open up.

3. **The magnaflux test** is used on certain types of steel for which there are very rigid surface requirements. It is carried out by placing the steel to be tested in a powerful magnetic field. A fine magnetic powder is then sprinkled over the surface. The particles of the powder seek out and cling to the local magnetic poles which may be developed by any sort of metal discontinuity at or slightly below the surface. Any irregularity in the metal surface will cause a distinct magnetic pattern to be set up, thereby disclosing any hidden defects.

4. **The file test** consists in removing the scale, by filing, on any surface area which may be suspected of containing a hidden defect. The file test is a quick method employed by inspectors for determining the extent and depth of seams in bars.

5. **The bend test** is made on certain classes of material to determine the soundness of internal structure and to denote the degree of ductility. The test consists merely in bending a standard test specimen through a certain specified arc. Examination of the bend will disclose surface defects.

6. **The etch test** is one which is used repeatedly in standard manufacturing and fabricating processes to determine the soundness of internal structures. A test piece is cut from the desired location in a bar and from this test piece a specimen of the size required for etching is removed. The surface to be examined is polished and then dipped in a solution of hydrochloric, sulphuric, nitric or picric acid. For some products, solutions of iodine, copper ammonium sulphate, ferric chloride, cupric chloride or cupric sulphate are used. Directions for etching various products may be found in "Metals Handbook."[*]

7. **The grit-blasting test** is used for much the same purpose as the pickling test. The grit removes the hot-rolled scale so that the surface of the test piece can be visibly inspected. It is not recommended for detecting fine seams on certain types of steel because of the peening action of the grit.

CONDITIONING METHODS AND EQUIPMENT

It has been noted that bars which are free from surface defects cannot always be produced. Some of these defects are common to all steel products, whereas others are more or less peculiar to merchant bar product. In order that the product may meet required quality standards, these defects must be removed by chipping or grinding. Their removal by either of these methods is known by the term "conditioning." Thorough inspection must precede conditioning. In a large number of cases pickling before inspection is necessary in order to reveal all the defects that may be present. The product requiring conditioning must be marked properly with a suitable chalk or crayon in the areas showing defects.

Conditioning is carried out by either chipping or grinding, depending upon the characteristics of the product. Conditioning by chipping is confined to soft and medium-hard steels and to those products on which subsequent fabrication procedure will permit the presence of grooves from chipping. Well-maintained pneumatic hammers operated by an adequate air supply, and chisels which have been properly heat-treated and dressed, are the principal equipment necessary for chipping. Conditioning by grinding is confined to those steels with a high hardness, or to bars or shapes whose contours would be changed by chipping grooves. The grinding operation is accomplished by: (1) pneumatic grinders, or (2)

---

[*] Metals Handbook, 1948 Edition; American Society for Metals, Cleveland, Ohio; pages 384-399, inclusive.

high cycle electric grinders. The choice of grinder depends upon local conditions such as air and power supply, or upon the suitability of the machine to perform the required task. Each type of grinder possesses certain advantages and disadvantages. The pneumatic grinder has the advantage of being lighter in weight and has a minimum of moving parts, which facilitates repairs. Its major disadvantage is its inability to maintain full speed on all loads. It also must have an adequate air supply (90 to 100 lb. per sq. in.) without a large drop in pressure from source to point of use. The high cycle electric grinder, because of its special construction, has the advantage of being able to maintain full speed at all loads. It has the disadvantages of being somewhat heavier to handle, of having many complicated working parts, and of requiring a frequency changer adjacent to the work. The grit, bond, shape and speed of the grinding wheels are dictated by the characteristics of the steel and by the shape of the product being worked. Of the two types of conditioning, chipping is the most economical and, when conditions permit, is most generally used.

NARROW FLAT-ROLLED PRODUCTS

Band, Hoop and Cotton Tie—Band for use in commercial packaging is usually rolled in coil form in multiple width on the rolling mill, and then slit to narrow widths on multiple slitting units installed in the bar finishing departments. Edge conditioning is necessary to eliminate the sharpness of the slit edge, before final coiling and shipment. The usual sizes are ¾ by 0.028, ¾ by 0.035, 1¼ by 0.035, 1¼ by 0.050, and 2 by 0.050 inches. It is made from a steel in the 0.50 to 0.60 per cent carbon content range, with 0.80 per cent manganese and 0.15 to 0.30 per cent silicon.

Hoop—There are four general classifications of this type of product: (1) tight cooperage hoop for barrels to hold liquids, (2) slack barrel hoop for barrels to hold dry products, (3) tobacco barrel hogshead hoop, and (4) special hoop for special packages.

Hoop (except tight cooperage hoop) is made from steel in the 0.08 to 0.10 per cent carbon content range. Tight cooperage hoop is generally made from open-hearth steel having a carbon content of 0.30 to 0.35 per cent carbon, but may also be produced from Bessemer steel having a carbon content of 0.19 to 0.24 per cent.

Hoop is made either by slitting coiled strip, rolled in multiple width, into narrow coiled strip of the desired width; or, from narrow coiled strip with a hot-rolled or mill edge. The type and width of hoop being produced influences the choice of method used.

Hoop is produced in widths increasing in increments of ⅛ of an inch, beginning with a minimum of 1⅛ inches and extending to and including 2 inches. It is made in thicknesses between 0.025 to 0.049 inches. It is prepared in cut lengths for making hoops ranging from 2 feet 8½ inches to 8 feet 6 inches in circumference. Automatic machines are used in the fabrication of hoop (Figure 28—26). These machines are so designed that the strip from the coil, passing through a machine in a horizontal position, is first run through rolls in which a slight bend is made on the edge to be beaded. This is followed by a beading operation, done in forming dies that operate horizontally at approximately 400 strokes per minute. The beaded strip next moves into a combination shear and rivet-hole punching die, where it is sheared to a specified length, and where the rivet holes are punched. Hoop is produced as "curled hoop" or a "straight length." Curled hoop is made by a pinch-roll and curved guide-shoe arrangement that permits the hoop to take a circular form. A straight length hoop is produced merely by removing the curved guide shoe.

Cotton tie is a light, narrow, hot-rolled strip used, as the name implies, to bind bales of cotton, hemp, jute, etc. It is fabricated in a manner quite similar to hoop. After being finished in pinch rolls and a vibrator it is delivered onto apron conveyors. From the apron conveyors, the strip is coiled and delivered on a coil conveyor to cold shears where it is sheared to

FIG. 28—26. Automatic hoop-forming machine in operation. Finished hoops are on stand in right foreground.

a length of approximately 12 feet. It is then bundled by hand at which time buckles are inserted. The bundles are then dipped into a tank containing an asphalt base paint if desired. Cotton tie is shipped in bundles consisting of 30 ties and 30 buckles, either painted or unpainted. Two sizes of bundles are produced; the standard, weighing about 45 lb., of 15/16-inch wide and 0.042-inch thick (19 gage B.W.G.) cotton tie, and a special bundle, weighing approximately 60 lb., of 15/16-inch wide and 0.049-inch thick (18 gage B.W.G.) cotton tie.

CONCRETE REINFORCING BAR

Concrete reinforcing bar is a merchant-bar product consisting of plain rounds and deformed rounds. It is used to furnish tensile strength to concrete sections subject to bending loads and to furnish additional compressive strength in sections where unreinforced concrete would prove too bulky.

All types of concrete structures are commonly reinforced with either deformed or plain bars. Concrete reinforcing bars are usually deformed and this discussion will be confined to that type of bar. Deformed concrete reinforcing bars are bars in which the surface is provided with lugs or protrusions (called "deformations") which inhibit longitudinal movement of the bars relative to the surrounding concrete. The surface deformations (Figure 28—17) are hot formed in the final roll pass by passing the bars between rolls having patterns cut into them so that the surfaces of the bars are forced into the depressions in the rolls to form characteristic deformations. Deformed bars are produced in accordance with the specifications for minimum requirements for the deformations of deformed steel bars for concrete reinforcement (ASTM designation A305). Table 28—I furnishes dimensional data on these bars.

Deformed concrete reinforcing bars are produced to standard specifications for new billet-steel bars for concrete reinforcement (ASTM designation A15), rail-steel bars for concrete reinforcement (ASTM designation A16), axle-steel bars for concrete reinforcement (ASTM designation A160), special large-size deformed billet-steel bars for concrete reinforcement (ASTM designation A408), high-strength deformed

FIG. 28—27. Photograph of a deformed concrete-reinforcing bar, showing protrusions produced by rolling the bar between rolls having a pattern cut into them.

Table 28—I. Deformed Concrete-Reinforcing Bar Designation Numbers, Unit Weights, and Nominal Dimensions.

Bar Designation Number*	Unit Weight (lb. per ft.)	Nominal Dimensions		
		Diameter (In.)	Cross-Sectional Area (Sq. In.)	Perimeter (In.)
3	0.376	0.375	0.11	1.178
4	0.668	0.500	0.20	1.571
5	1.043	0.625	0.31	1.963
6	1.502	0.750	0.44	2.356
7	2.044	0.875	0.60	2.749
8	2.670	1.000	0.79	3.142
9**	3.400	1.128	1.00	3.544
10**	4.303	1.270	1.27	3.990
11**	5.313	1.410	1.56	4.430
14-S	7.650	1.693	2.25	5.32
18-S	13.600	2.257	4.00	7.09

* Bar numbers are based on the number of eighths of an inch included in the nominal diameter of the bars. The nominal diameter of a deformed bar is equivalent to the diameter of a plain bar having the same weight per foot as the deformed bar.

** Bars of designation Nos. 9, 10, and 11 correspond to the former 1-in. square, 1⅛-in. square, and 1¼-in. square sizes and are equivalent to those former standard bar sizes in weight and nominal cross-sectional areas.

Note: The above table including the footnotes is in agreement with U. S. Department of Commerce Simplified Practice Recommendation 26-50 covering Steel Reinforcing Bars.

billet-steel bars for concrete reinforcement with 75,-000 lb. per sq. in. minimum yield point (ASTM designation A431), and deformed billet-steel bars for concrete reinforcement with 60,000 lb. per sq. in. minimum yield point (ASTM designation A432). These classifications are largely self-explanatory.

Three grades of steel are produced under specifications ASTM designations A15 and A408 for billet-steel bars and ASTM designation A160 for axle-steel bars: classification of the three grades, referred to as structural, intermediate and hard, is based on different mechanical-property specifications for each.

Referring to Table 28—I; bar sizes 3 to 11, inclusive, are produced to ASTM designation A15 and A305. Bar sizes 14-S and 18-S are produced in accordance with ASTM designation A408.

Concrete reinforcing bars produced to ASTM designations A431 and A432 (high-strength billet-steel bars and bars with 60,000 lb. per sq. in. minimum yield point, respectively) are manufactured with rolled-in identification marking.

Concrete reinforcing bars are shipped from the mills in straight lengths, either cut to design length in the mill shears or in long lengths to be recut for fabrication, as required in specific applications.

Engineers' and architects' designs and specifications are prepared in accordance with the Manual of Standard Practices of the Concrete Reinforcing Steel Institute. Bar fabricators furnish concrete reinforcing bars either straight and cut to the proper length or bent or curved in accordance with plans and specifications.

PACKAGING AND LOADING

The packaging of merchant bar products in most plants is performed according to: (1) standard practices, or (2) special practices as required by the customer. Standard practices are controlled by such factors as: (1) the weight of the bundle or lift, (2) the means of binding or fastening the bundles or lifts, (3) the means of identification, (4) the means of protecting the product in transit, and (5) the geographical location of the customer. Special practices are predicated upon the type or capacity of handling and processing equipment used by the customer.

Either wiring or banding may be applied for binding or fastening bundles or lifts, depending upon the shape, size and length of the product. Special practices for binding or fastening bundles or lifts are applied only when specified. Wiring is used generally on large rounds and heavy sections, whereas bands are used most generally for small sections or for flat products. Standards have been established which specify the spacing and the number of wires or bands to be used for various sizes of bundles. Additional wiring or banding, either for domestic or export shipment, is handled as special practice. Special practice also applies when stack piling is required, as the number of pieces and the dimensions of the bundle are limited as well as the weight. Wiring and banding is accomplished by such special tools as stretchers and sealers.

Identification of merchant bar products requires that each bundle or lift for domestic trade be identified by a standard manila tag, approximately three inches by five inches, attached to one end. Where coils are involved the same type of tag is used on each coil. The information on the identification tag will vary somewhat in different plants but it generally contains a part or all of the following information: customer's name, destination, customer's order number, mill order number, part number or special markings, number of pieces, section, length, weight, heat number, bundle or lift number, and the grade of steel. On products for export, additional identification is required on each bundle or lift in the form of duplicate manila tags on opposite ends and a metal tag attached to the center of the bundle. This is necessary because of the possible loss of a single manila identification tag when the product is rehandled at railroad terminals, shipping docks, or aboard ship. In addition to the standard manila tag, as mentioned above, the identification of merchant bar products may involve the die stamping of heat numbers on the ends of bars of certain dimensions. These specifications are as follows: heat numbers are stamped on one end of all bars (round, squares or hexagons) of 2½ inches or above, and on all flats three inches by one inch and above. When special practices are involved, bars are stamped with codes or symbols as specified. When product in sizes 3-in. or over (or of equivalent cross-section) consigned for export is to be shipped loose, each piece is stenciled with the necessary information for proper identification.

Color marking may be specified on one end of each lift or bundle or may be specified on one end of each bar, depending on the product size. In special practices, either for export or domestic trade, special marking is applied only when required by the customer.

Bundles or lifts are loaded in open cars without protection from the weather. When shipping carload lots, bars and bar shapes are shipped loose or in large lifts in open cars. When special practices are required, lifts may be wrapped or shrouded individually, or the entire carload may be shrouded as a unit. Loading, like packaging, is divided into (1) standard practice, or (2) special practices as required by the customer. The gondola car is the standard means of transit, either for magnet, chain, or crane unloading. Standard practice for loading and bracing is conducted in accordance with the rules of the American Association of Railroads. Special practices as requested by the customer generally fall into one of the following categories: (1) modified methods of gondola-car loading for chain or crane unloading, or magnet unloading alone; (2) flat-car loading for chain or crane unloading, magnet unloading, or tractor unloading; (3) box-car loading for either tractor unloading or hand unloading; (4) double loads or sets for chain or crane unloading; (5) other methods of special blocking. Double loads are used principally for long lengths of structural material which exceeds the length of a single standard gondola car. Box-car loading generally is used on products which cannot be exposed to the weather and which require the best handling methods.

Material-Handling Equipment—Numerous and varied types of handling equipment are used in the finishing and shipping of merchant bar products, depending upon the type of product and the arrangement and design of the finishing department equipment. The types of handling equipment most generally used are: (1) overhead electric cranes, (2) tractors (principally the lift or peel type), (3) transfer buggies, (4) jib cranes, (5) box-car loading machines, (6) conveyors, and (7) such auxiliary apparatus as coil hooks, spreaders, package lifters, chains, and slings.

SECTION 3

HEAT TREATING CARBON AND ALLOY BAR STOCK

Heat treating may be defined as an operation or combination of operations in which a metal or alloy in the solid state is heated and cooled, under controlled conditions, according to a predetermined schedule, to obtain desired properties.

The purpose of heat treatment is to develop the full effect of the various elements in the steel as related to desired properties, through structural or phase changes. "As-rolled" bars vary in hardness and microstructure in relation to the chemical composition of the steel and, therefore, usually require some form of heat treatment to obtain a physical condition best suited for the final product. Low- and medium-carbon bars often are used in the as-rolled condition, but higher-carbon steels and most alloy steels require heat treatment. This treatment consists of some form of annealing, normalizing, or quenching and tempering, or a combination of any two or even three of these.

It has been found that the results of heat treating conform to certain definite principles, a detailed discussion of which will be found in Chapter 39. Application of these principles makes it possible to obtain transformation of a particular steel at a stipulated temperature by controlling the rate of cooling from temperatures above its critical range of temperature, and thus obtain desired mechanical properties. More detailed descriptions of how this is accomplished will be given in the following discussion of the various types of heat treating.

PROCESSES AND THEIR EFFECTS

Annealing—The term annealing is used rather loosely to describe several types of heat treatment which differ greatly in procedure yet all accomplish one or more of the following effects:

1. Remove stresses
2. "Soften," by altering mechanical properties
3. Refine the grain structure
4. Produce a definite microstructure

In most commercial operations, more than one of these effects usually are obtained simultaneously, although only one may be desired specifically. Therefore, the selection of a specific annealing process is dependent on the particular predominant or overall effect desired and the grade of steel being processed.

Full Annealing—If, for example, it is desired to refine the grain structure and produce a lamellar pearlite, a full annealing cycle should be used. This consists of heating the steel to a temperature above the transformation range, holding for one to two hours, and then cooling at a predetermined rate to obtain the desired microstructure (see Figure 28—28A). Grain refinement is accomplished in this instance by the recrystallization of the steel in passing through the critical range both in heating and in cooling, as explained in greater detail in Chapter 39. The microstructure obtained in cooling any steel from above the critical temperature range is dependent both upon the temperature range in which transformation occurs and the time required for completion of transformation in that range. Thus, it is obvious that the rate at which any steel is cooled determines the final microstructure, since the degree of transformation will depend on the amount of time allowed for it to occur. Therefore, the slower the rate of cooling and the higher the temperature at which complete transformation occurs during full annealing, the coarser the pearlite will be with correspondingly lower hardness. Such treatment is performed usually on steel of 0.30 to 0.60 per cent carbon content which is to be machined.

Isothermal annealing is a type of full annealing in

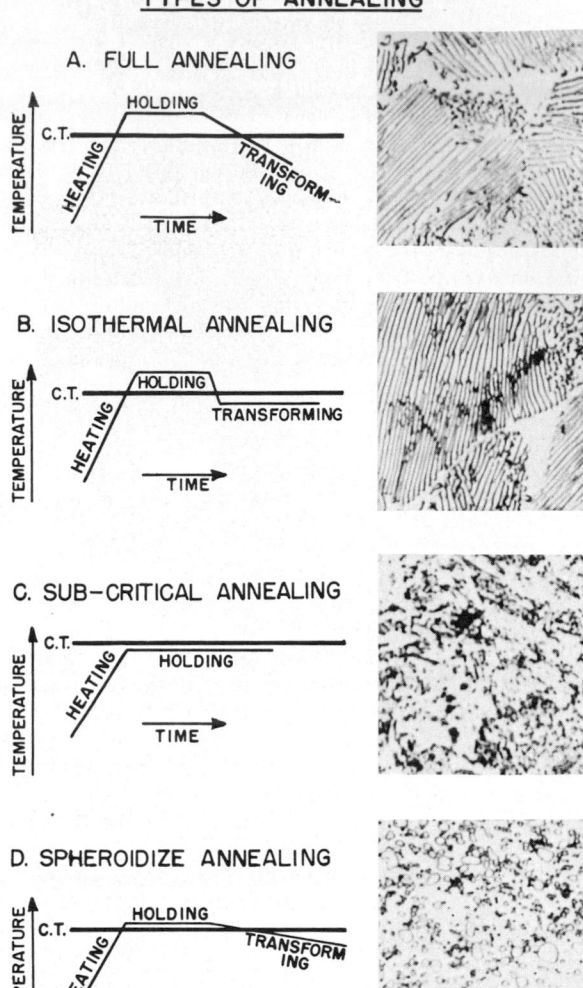

TYPES OF ANNEALING

FIG. 28—28. Thermal cycles and resultant microstructures obtained from the four basically different types of production annealing.

which the steel first is cooled to the temperature at which it is desired to have transformation occur, at a rate sufficiently rapid to prevent any structural change above that temperature. The steel then is held at the selected temperature for the time necessary to complete such transformation (see Figure 28—28B). Thus it is possible, with this process, to obtain a more uniform microstructure than could be expected by continuous cooling. However, since it is necessary to drop the temperature rapidly to prevent any transformation above the desired temperature, there are definite limitations as to the mass that can be so treated. It is applicable, therefore, only to smaller sections and would not be suitable for large bars or large loads in batch-type furnaces, since it would be impossible to cool them at a rate sufficiently rapid to prevent some transformation.

A modified application of isothermal annealing is possible, however, in which the charge is heated in one furnace and transferred to another, which has been set at a temperature somewhat lower than the desired temperature of transformation, in order that the temperature of the charge will drop rapidly to that required. The selection of the temperature of the second furnace will be governed by the temperature to which the charge first is heated, the mass of the charge and the desired transformation temperature. Suitable handling equipment must be available to transfer the entire charge rapidly, since any undue delays might result in portions of the charge being cooled to too low a temperature. Continuous furnaces also are applicable to this type of cycle.

Process or Subcritical Annealing—Another type of annealing called process or subcritical annealing consists of heating the steel to a temperature just under the lower critical (Ac_1) and holding at this temperature for the proper time (usually 2 to 4 hours) followed by air cooling (see Figure 28—28C). This type of annealing results in softening the steel due to a partial coagulation of the carbide to form spheroids or small globules of carbide. It is not suitable when a close control of hardness or structure is desired, because the prior structure of the steel determines to a marked degree the extent of spheroidization which will occur. For example, an originally coarse lamellar structure may show very little evidence of spheroidization after this treatment, whereas an originally fine lamellar or martensitic structure would show a marked degree of spheroidization. The treatment is, however, quite satisfactory for rendering bars more suitable for cold sawing or shearing, and is used to a great extent for these purposes. Since the temperature to which the bars are heated is somewhat lower than in a full anneal, there is less scaling, and warping can be controlled.

Spheroidization—Spheroidization is a type of annealing which causes practically all carbides in the steel to agglomerate in the form of small globules or spheroids. There may be a wide range of hardness with such a structure for any grade of steel since the size of the globules has a direct relation to hardness, i.e., the larger the globules the lower the hardness. Spheroidizing may be accomplished by heating to a temperature just below the lower critical and holding for a sufficient period of time. However, as pointed out in the discussion under subcritical annealing, the prior structure of the steel affects to a marked degree the final result of such a treatment. Therefore, if a well spheroidized uniform structure is desired, such a treatment is not suitable because too many uncontrollable variables are encountered. A more desirable and commonly used method for spheroidizing is to heat to a temperature just above the critical and cool very slowly (about 10° F per hour) through the critical range (see Figure 28—28D) or to heat to a temperature within the critical range but not above the upper critical and cool slowly.

This treatment is used for practically all steels containing over 0.60 per cent carbon that are to be machined or cold formed and for bearing steels such as AISI-52100 prior to machining. For the latter, the size and distribution of the spheroidal carbide particles is extremely important since they all are not dissolved in subsequent heating for hardening but remain in the condition obtained in the annealing process. Small well-defined spheroids are the most desirable and coarse elongated carbides should be avoided at all times.

Normalizing—Normalizing is a process wherein the steel is heated to a temperature about 100° to 150° F above the transformation range and cooled in air. The resulting structure will differ greatly for steels of different chemical composition, since no attempt is made to regulate the temperature at which transformation on cooling occurs. It is used for the purpose of producing a more uniform structure and removing the irregularities caused by high or low rolling or forging temperatures for large sections. It also is applicable to a wide extent in treating low-carbon steels of all sections to produce a more uniform structure, and is preferred to full annealing for these steels as the more rapid cooling minimizes banding (marked segregation of carbide and ferrite) which is very undesirable for machining.

Quenching and Tempering—The heat treating processes described so far have all been for the purpose of "softening" the steel by regulating the rate of cooling so that transformation occurs at relatively high temperatures. Such processes are necessary to render the steel suitable for further operations such as machining and cold cutting. However, this condition does not represent the optimum mechanical properties which can be developed in the steel, and a further treatment termed quenching and tempering is employed to develop these properties. When the amount of machining or cutting to be done is not great, steel sometimes is given this treatment in the bar form in preference to an annealing treatment.

The combination of quenching and tempering consists of first heating the steel above the critical range, and then cooling it rapidly by immersing it in a liquid cooling medium such as oil or water. If the rate of cooling is sufficiently rapid, transformation does not occur until the lower temperature ranges are reached with the resultant formation of martensite or martensite and bainite. These structures are much harder than the structures obtained by transformation at higher temperatures. Martensite, however, is quite brittle and would be unsuitable for most applications where the steel may be subjected to shock. Therefore, the steel is given a tempering treatment which consists of heating it to an intermediate temperature, very seldom higher than 1200° F and usually somewhat lower. This treatment reduces the hardness by coagulation of the carbide and increases the toughness or shock resistance of the steel. A schematic illustration of quenching and tempering with the resultant microstructures after each operation is shown in Figure 28—29. It is possible to obtain any desired hardness within a wide range, with corresponding variations in strength and ductility, by selecting the proper tempering temperature. This can be seen readily by examining the chart in Figure 28—30.

Tempering is sometimes called **drawing**. Tempering is the preferred nomenclature. In ancient times

HEAT, QUENCH AND TEMPER

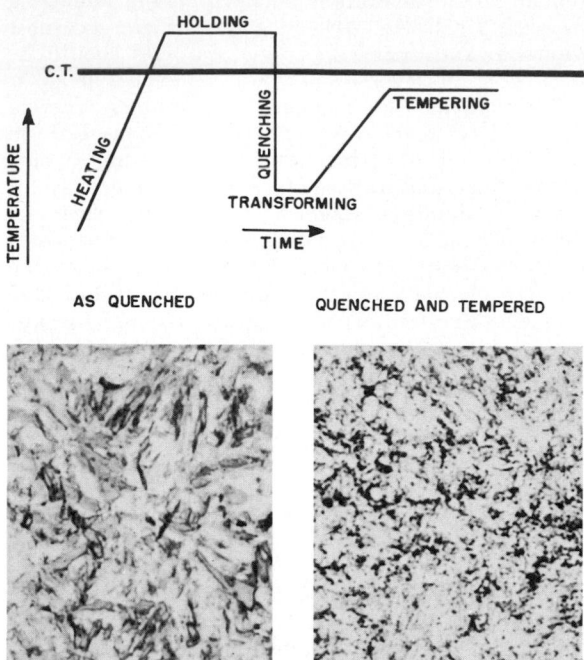

FIG. 28—29. Thermal cycle and microstructures obtained in (a) quenching and (b) quenching and tempering.

and in the early days of relatively modern steelmaking practices, steel for swords, tools, etc. was said to be "tempered" after it only had been hardened. Since the hardened steel was too brittle, some of its "temper" was "drawn" by suitable heat treatment, giving rise to the term "drawing." At present, temper is considered as describing the final condition of hardened and tempered steel, and it is more logical to give the operation that regulates the final condition the name "tempering."

HEAT-TREATING PLANTS

Modern heat-treating plants vary widely with respect to type of furnaces, auxiliary equipment and general arrangement. No matter how widely they may differ in these general aspects, all must have adequate and reliable means for controlling and checking temperatures and have handling facilities suitable for transferring the heated steel from the furnace to the quenching tanks with a minimum of delay. These are factors which must be given careful consideration when planning new units or additions to existing units, and will be governed to a great extent by the type of product to be processed and the heat treatment to be given.

Another important factor to be considered is the provision of adequate space for accumulating and building up charges so that they may be ready to load into the furnace as soon as it is available. This lessens time lost in charging the furnaces and increases the efficiency of these units.

Furnaces—In general furnaces which are suitable for annealing are not the most desirable for quenching and tempering, nor are the most desirable furnaces for quenching and tempering entirely suitable for annealing. This can be shown by analyzing the basic requirements for furnaces considered most suitable for these operations.

A furnace to be suitable for quenching and tempering must be capable of maintaining uniform temperatures over a rather wide range throughout the entire charge. It can be heated by either gas or electricity, and possibly oil, although the latter fuel is not too desirable at temperatures below 1200° F.

Since uniform temperatures must be maintained in furnaces to be used for quenching or tempering, and rapid cooling of the charge in the furnace is not required, such furnaces usually are insulated heavily to minimize heat losses due to radiation. Since only single-layer loads are charged for quenching, the height of the heating chambers need not be very great. This enables a more uniform temperature to

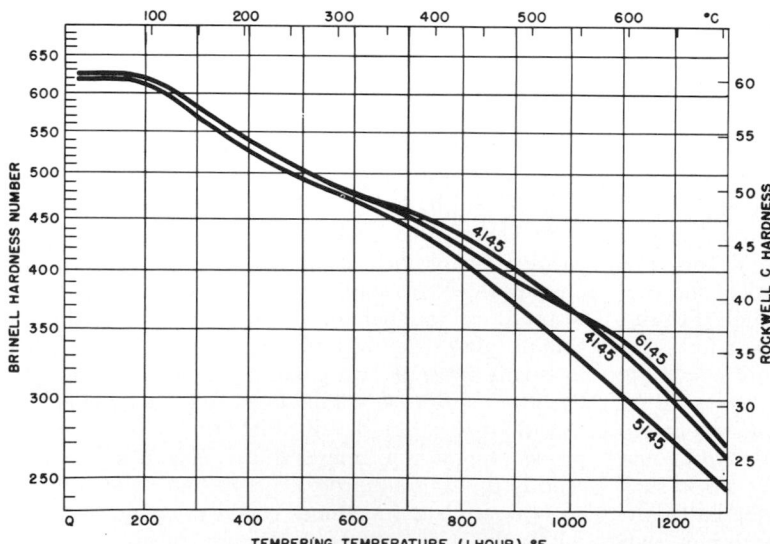

FIG. 28—30. Effect of tempering temperature on the final hardness of three grades of steel after quenching and tempering.

FIG. 28—31. Partially-loaded car-bottom of a heat-treating furnace, showing use of spacer bars between layers of the load, which is supported above the refractory hearth on heat-resisting alloy castings.

be maintained throughout the charge since the differential in temperature between the top and bottom of the furnace is much less than would be the case in a larger heating chamber.

Uniformity of temperature is also very desirable in furnaces used for annealing, but the requirements are not necessarily as exacting as for furnaces used for quenching and tempering. However, it is essential that a rather wide range of cooling rates be attained. Therefore, furnaces that cool too slowly, such as the heavily insulated type referred to in the discussion on furnaces for quenching and tempering, are not

suitable for very many annealing cycles. A furnace which will lose heat at a fairly rapid rate can be adapted to a wider range of cycles because various rates of cooling can be attained by control of the heat input. Thus, if the heat input is cut off entirely, the furnace and charge will cool rapidly; by firing at reduced rates, the heat losses from the furnace and charge can be balanced to any desired degree to control the net heat loss and, consequently, the overall rate of cooling. Possible methods for increasing the rate of cooling in a heavily-insulated furnace would be to blow air into the furnace or to open it. This is

FIG. 28—32. Car-bottom batch-type heat-treating furnace with bell-type cover in operating position.

FIG. 28—33. The bell-type cover (upper left corner of illustration) of the heat-treating furnace of Figure 28—32 has been raised and hot load is being moved on furnace car bottom toward crane carrier arms.

not very desirable, however, because it is extremely difficult to regulate the temperature drop uniformly throughout the charge and erratic, non-uniform results may be obtained. Furnaces have been developed which are equipped with large fans that circulate the furnace gases over water-cooled pipes, thus reducing the temperature to around 800° to 900° F. The partially-cooled gases are then forced into the furnace chamber at the bottom and up through the charge, causing a rapid drop in temperature. Such equipment has many potential advantages but care must be exercised in its use to avoid non-uniform cooling.

Since annealing cycles are usually rather long and tie up a furnace for some time, it is desirable that they be large enough to accommodate the maximum size load that can be cooled uniformly. For this reason, furnaces designed for annealing have a great deal more height in the heating chamber than those designed exclusively for quenching. Consequently, there is more danger of greater differential in temperature between the top and bottom of the chamber. This affects selection of the type of furnace to be used.

Control of Temperature—As stated previously,

FIG. 28—34. Hot steel bars, supported on crane carrier arms above the quenching tank in the foreground (see also Figure 28—35).

Fig. 28—35. Looking down on a load of hot steel bars supported on carrier arms above quenching tank.

adequate and reliable control and checking of temperature is absolutely essential for all types of heat treating. Furnaces equipped with automatic temperature-control devices are generally more reliable and can be operated more economically than manually controlled units. Thermocouples to indicate and control temperature generally are located near the top of the heating chamber, as this location will be the first to reach the desired temperature on heating; placing the controlling thermocouples in this position prevents overheating. In the case of furnaces designed primarily for quenching and tempering, these couples will be close to the charge (which consists of only one layer of bars or other sections) so that additional couples should not be needed to assure uniform heating. However, in the case of furnaces designed primarily for annealing, in which the chamber height is much greater and in which there is a correspondingly greater possibility of temperature differentials, provision should be made to insert couples in the charge also, being sure that some are located so that they indicate the temperature of the bottom layer. With couples so located, the temperature throughout the charge will be known and sufficient time can be allowed to attain uniformity.

Methods of Loading—As stated previously, loads to be quenched should consist of only one layer; if there is more than one layer the load would not be uniformly quenched because the efficiency of this operation is dependent on the entire surface of the bar being in contact with the quenching medium. The same principles apply to normalizing, since uniform properties are dependent on attaining a uniform rate of cooling along the entire length of the bar, which can only be obtained by having the entire surface exposed to the air and not in contact with other hot bars.

Loads for annealing are generally more than one layer high but care should be taken to avoid having a load that is too compact, as this would prevent uniform cooling throughout the entire charge. A common practice is to separate the load into layers by the use of spacer bars, as shown in Figure 28—31. The load also may be separated lengthwise down the middle, leaving an open space approximately six inches wide. These methods of loading provide for better circulation of gases throughout the charge, thus enabling the operator to cool the entire charge at a reasonably uniform rate.

Auxiliary Equipment—Effective quenching is dependent on immersion of the steel in the quenching medium while the temperature is still above the critical range. If there is too great a delay in moving the load from the furnace to the quench tank, it may air cool below the critical range, especially at the ends of the bars. Thus, there is the danger of obtaining some products of transformation in the higher temperature ranges. To offset this hazard the quench tanks should be located close to the furnace and cranes or lifting devices should be provided which are capable of moving the entire load to the tanks at a rapid rate. By moving the entire load at one time, all bars will receive the same treatment. If only one bar or any portion of the load is quenched at a time, there is always danger that the last bars quenched will have cooled below the critical temperature before reaching the quenching tank.

Figure 28—32 shows a car-bottom batch-type furnace equipped to handle loads rapidly from the quench tank to the furnace. This is a rectangular bell-type furnace with a car bottom. To discharge the load,

Fig. 28—36. Hot steel bars in position on elevator roll-table section above quenching tank, ready to be lowered into the quenchant. This is furnace "C" in Figure 28—37.

the furnace bell is raised (there are no doors on this furnace) and the car is moved out from under it, alongside the quenching tank which is in front and to one side (see Figure 28—33). The entire load then is picked up by a crane, equipped with carrier arms or bales as shown in Figures 28—34 and 28—35, which moves it quickly into the quenching medium. Agitation is obtained by alternate raising and lowering of the load in the tank through a travel distance of approximately four feet. This particular unit is equipped with automatic controls so that the entire sequence of movements of the equipment is initiated by closing a single control switch. This eliminates delays which might be caused by improper timing in closing successive switches by the operator. The time required from the instant the bell of the furnace is lifted until the load is immersed in the quenching medium is one and one-half minutes.

A roller-hearth furnace with similar handling equipment is shown in Figures 28—36, 28—37, 28—38 and 28—39. In this furnace, the bars in single layers are placed on the charging table indicated in Figures 28—37 and 28—38. From here they progress through the three separate chambers of the furnace, where they are pre-heated to about 1200° F in the first chamber, then progressively heated above the critical temperature range and soaked in the other two. Progress is not continuous through these chambers, the bars being held for a sufficient period of time in each chamber to be heated throughout to the prescribed temperature. The time required in each chamber, of course, is determined by the size and number of bars being treated. After the bars have been soaked properly in the last chamber, they are run out on the delivery table, which is suspended over the quenching tank (Figure 28—36), and immediately are im-

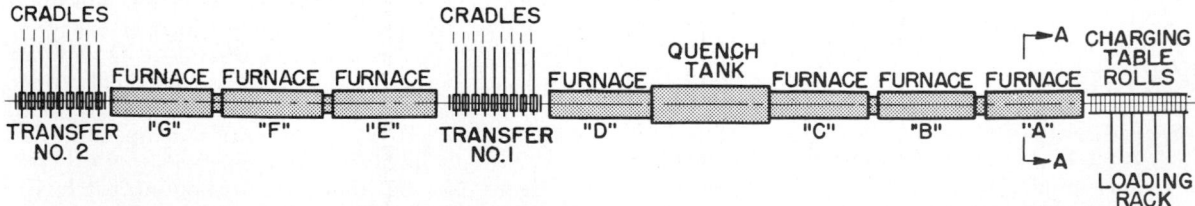

Fig. 28—37. Layout of the various units comprising a typical continuous heat-treating line for bar products. Work travels from right to left. See also Figures 28—38 and 28—39.

Fig. 28—38. Perspective view of most of the actual continuous heat-treating line shown diagrammatically in Figure 28—37.

mersed in the quenching medium. When bar temperature has fallen sufficiently, they are raised from the tank and run into the succeeding furnace for stress relieving, after which they may be removed from the transfer table to continue through the remaining three furnaces for tempering.

Facilities should be available for quenching in either oil or water. The choice of quenching medium is to be determined by the grade of steel and the section, as explained in greater detail in Chapter 39. Facilities also should be provided for cooling the oil between the quench loads to maintain a uniform temperature of the quenching medium, because variations of an appreciable magnitude in this temperature will have a marked effect on results. Storage facilities for the oil also should be provided since a reserve supply is necessary to replenish that lost through dragout. One quenching tank can be used for either oil or water, the oil being pumped back to the storage tank when it is necessary to use water in the quenching tank. However, this is not the most desirable arrangement since there is always danger of contaminating the oil with water. It is more desirable to have separate tanks for oil and water when the size of the unit warrants such an installation.

Bibliography

"Principles of Heat Treatment," by M. A. Grossmann. Published by the American Society for Metals, Cleveland, Ohio. (1953 Edition.)

"Steel and Its Heat Treatment," (Fifth Edition), by D. K. Bullens. John Wiley and Sons, Inc., New York, N. Y., Vols. I, II and III (1948-1949).

"Suiting the Heat Treatment to the Job." United States Steel Corporation (1947).

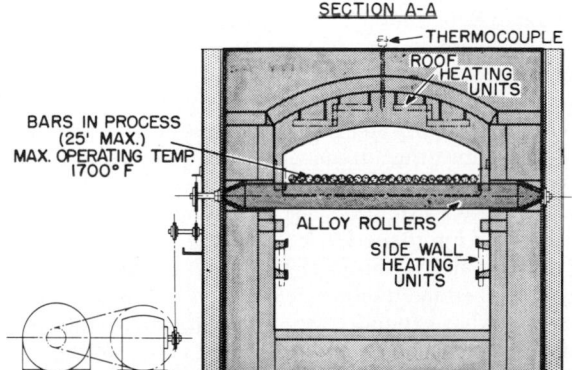

Fig. 28—39. Schematic cross-section of one of the high-temperature furnaces in the line shown in Figure 28—37.

CHAPTER 29

The Manufacture of Steel Wire and Steel Wire Products

HISTORY AND IMPORTANCE OF STEEL WIRE

Historical—In general, wire is a term that may be applied to any metallic shred, thread, or filament, or to any exceedingly slender rod or bar of metal having a uniform cross section. Considering the term in this sense, wire is of very ancient origin. Gold wire is mentioned in the Bible in connection with the sacerdotal robes of Aaron, and was used to form part of a necklace, found at Denderah, which bears the name of the Pharaoh who reigned in Egypt about 2750 B.C. Evidences of the use of wire by the Assyrians and Babylonians as far back as 1700 B.C. have also been found.

As to the methods of manufacture used by these ancient peoples, practically nothing is known. The specimens of ancient wire that have been found so far are flat, and it is probable that they were produced solely by hammering.

How, when or of what material round wire was first made is not known. No doubt it was first produced by hammering, but the difficulty of forming a fine round wire by this method probably caused the metalworkers, early in the history of the art, to seek some better method. An old Latin manuscript written by Theophilus sometime during the 8th and 9th centuries describes a method of making wire of an alloy of lead and tin, which was cast into an ingot, hammered into a long slender bar and drawn through holes in a wire-drawing plate.

The draw plate, itself, is described as "a piece of iron three or four fingers wide, smaller at the top and bottom, rather thin and pierced with three or four rows of holes through which wire may be drawn." However, there is reason to believe that the art of wire drawing was known and practiced before this time.

The chain armor used by the knights in the great crusades against the Saracens and Turks is thought by many to have been made of drawn wire. Other authentic records are available to show that wire drawing on a commercial scale was practiced in France in 1270, in Germany in 1350 and in England in 1465. The first wire-drawing mill in this country was built in 1775 by Nathaniel Miles at Norwich, Conn. But, though three

other mills, two of which were in Pennsylvania, were started during the next twenty years, none of these appear to have been very prosperous, for in 1820 practically no wire was being made in this country. In 1831, however, the industry was reestablished in this country by Ichabod Washburn of Worcester, Mass., who, with Benjamin Goddard, founded the firm of Washburn, Moen and Company.

Present Importance of Steel Wire Industry—From that date, 1831, the wire industry grew very rapidly. Aside from the great quantities of wire made from other metals, such as copper and brass, the present annual production of steel wire alone is astonishing. For normal years, the production of steel wire rod now is about 5,500,000 tons. This tonnage represents about one-twentieth of all the steel produced in the country, and if it were all drawn into No. 12 gage wire, which is about average, it would have a total length of more than 70,000,000 miles or enough to girdle the earth about 2,800 times. The causes contributing to this growth were many and cannot be discussed in detail here, but they may be grouped or classified about as follows: (1) The great number of purposes to which wire, particularly steel wire, is adapted. (2) Development of inventions requiring great quantities of wire. (3) Improvements in the methods of producing steel and steel wire. It need not be pointed out that these causes are interdependent.

Principal Uses of Steel Wire—The adaptability of wire to the manufacture of household articles of common use has expanded until it has become known as the steel product of 150,000 uses. These articles, including such items as pins, needles, brooms, strainers, hooks, egg beaters, toasters, etc., are almost indispensable to our comfort. Of the many inventions developed since 1820 that make use of large quantities of wire, only a few of the most important can be mentioned here. The first of these was wire rope. Rope made of bronze or brass wire is known to be of ancient origin, while iron wire rope was used in Europe as early as 1820. The first wire rope manufactured in this country was made in 1840 at Saxonburg, Pa., by John A. Roebling, founder of the firm of John A. Roebling's

Sons Company. In 1844 the first telegraph line, extending from Washington to Baltimore, was completed by Professor Morse, but for more than ten years the growth of the telegraph was hampered because the wire essential in the construction of the lines could be produced only in short lengths, which required much time and labor for splicing.

The use of crinoline wire, a high-carbon heat-treated wire, for hoop skirts has been cited by some as a novel use of the product and as a great boon to the industry, but is better as an example of the unstable character of a business that depends on fashions. Starting about 1860, this business, for the next ten years, consumed about 1500 tons of wire annually, but suddenly collapsed with the passing of the hoop skirt in 1870. This was not to be the last time that feminine fashions would play a part in the wire industry, for in 1916 some 15,000 tons of wire were being consumed annually in the manufacture of corsets and several hundred tons for hair pins, but these have largely disappeared as did the crinoline wire.

The collapse of the crinoline-wire business was replaced by more staple articles, for in 1868 the first patents were obtained on the use of wire for bale ties and barbed wire for fence. Both these articles came quickly into wide use, the latter article being especially useful in fencing the great unwooded lands west of the Mississippi River, which were rapidly being brought under cultivation about this time. By 1876 the development of the telephone had reached the practical stage, and began to create a demand for more wire of the same type used by the telegraph. It was in 1879 that the beneficial effect of sulphur on machinability was discovered, and the manufacture of high-sulphur screw stock was begun. Chas. H. Morgan also began the manufacture of coiled-wire springs in this year. In 1884 woven-wire fence was first made by machinery. This fence, of which there are now several types, fulfilled all needs that could not be met with barbed-wire or straight-wire fence and possessed all the advantages of any fence that could be constructed of wood, hence it was soon being used in all parts of the country. In 1851 the first American-made wire-nail machine was built by Thomas Morton; in 1875 the first steel-wire nails were made; and in 1888 the production of the wire nails exceeded that of the cut nail for the first time. Today, more than fifty times as many wire nails as cut nails are made, and about 10 per cent of all the steel wire produced is made into nails.

Early Method of Manufacture—The methods employed at the time of the introduction of wire drawing into this country were wholly inadequate to meet the demands that were soon to arise. As the Bessemer and open-hearth processes for making steel were then unknown, practically all wire was made from wrought iron, or the softer metals like copper, brass, bronze, etc., though crucible steel in softer tempers was also used. Practices varied somewhat in different localities, and detailed descriptions of the operations are lacking but, from information gleaned from different sources, the process and operations for drawing wrought-iron and steel wire appear to have been

about as follows: Starting with a small square bar or billet, the metal was heated and hammered into as small a round as practicable, say $\frac{1}{4}$ to $\frac{3}{8}$ inch in diameter and some 6 to 10 feet in length. One end of this rod was tapered to a size a little less than the hole in the die through which the rod was to be drawn. The rod was then scoured bright with a piece of sandstone or other abrasive. In the case of iron and steel, it was early discovered that this cleaning of the rod was not only essential to good work but was well worth the trouble, for the hard scale, when not removed, soon scored the die. Then, the tapered end of the rod was inserted in the proper hole of a draw plate made of cast iron or hard steel, where it was grasped with a pair of tongs attached to a lever, and the rod was drawn through the hole a few inches at a time, about 5 inches at each stroke being the common practice. The lever could be operated either by hand or by water power, and the rod, as it passed through the hole, was generally lubricated with butter or other grease, to facilitate the drawing and save the die as much as possible. After the first draft, the operation was repeated through progressively smaller holes in the draw plate until the wire was drawn to the size desired or until it became too hard and brittle for further drawing. If the wire was to be drawn to still finer sizes, it was annealed at a red heat, generally in an oven sealed off from the air, after which the thin coat of oxide thus formed was removed by tumbling with a mixture of sand and water, or by immersing the wire for some time in sour beer or fermented barley water. The machine for drawing this fine wire differed somewhat from that used for drawing the rod. The draw plate was mounted on a table or bench in front of a drum or block that could be revolved by a hand-operated crank and gear drive.

Improvements in the manufacture of iron and steel wire have kept pace with the demands. In connection with this statement, it should be noted that the basic principles of wire making have remained unchanged. As already indicated, the process consists essentially in drawing a rod or a slender piece of the metal through a tapered hole in some harder materials, or successively through a series of such holes. It involves the application of force in the simplest manner, a straight pull, and the use of one of the simplest tools, the wire-drawing die. The efficiency of the latter and the simplicity of both these elements have left little room for improvement, and many doubt the possibility of finding a substitute for the process that will do the work so well. The improvements that have been made pertain to the accessory equipment and to the complementary operations, rather than to the process of wire drawing itself. Thus, the need for long lengths was met not by any radical change in the wire-drawing process, but by changing the method of producing the wire rod. As long as the rod was made by hammering, it was too short to coil, or draw with a block; but when the need for long lengths began to be felt, efforts were made to roll the rod. About 1840, Washburn succeeded in adapting the wire-drawing block to coarse-wire drawing. This block was power driven, and provided a means not only of applying a greater pulling force continuously to the rod, but also of storing the wire as it was drawn through the die. This development made it desirable to use very long rods, and this demand was met first by the invention of the three-high mill about 1857, which was succeeded by the Morgan continuous mill about 1875 and the Garrett rod mill in 1882.

Another important development was the substitution of soft steel for wrought iron, made possible by the invention of the Bessemer and the open-hearth processes for steelmaking. This change was inaugurated in this country by the Washburn and Moen Manufacturing Company at Worcester, Mass., in 1871. Important improvements in methods for handling, cleaning, coating, or lubricating the rod, and in heat treating and finishing the wire, were also made.

SECTION 2

CLASSIFICATION OF STEEL WIRE

Bases for Classification—Steel wire products are classified in various ways, as indicated in Table 29—I. From the standpoint of a manufacturer, the factors of greatest interest are the kind and grades of steel; the size, shape and mechanical properties of the wire; and the methods of drawing and treatment. In commercial transactions, classifications based upon mechanical properties of the wire, its treatment and finish, and its commercial applications are of most interest. The following brief descriptions are intended to assist the reader to a better understanding of the classes listed in the table.

Table 29—I.   Kinds and Classes of Steel Wire

Classification, according to:

Method of making the steel—Open hearth, basic oxygen and electric-furnace processes.

Compositions of steel—Low carbon (C1006, C1008, C1010, C1012, C1108 and C1110), medium low carbon (C1013 to C1022, inclusive), medium high carbon (C1025 to C1041, inclusive), high carbon and alloy steel.

Shape—Round, half-round, oval, half-oval, square, rectangular, hexagonal, crescent, triangular, etc.

Method of drawing—Dry-drawn, wet-drawn, single-draft drawn and continuous drawn.

Size—Coarse wire, fine wire.

Treatment and finish —Bright (hard dry-drawn), bright soft (annealed in process; processed wire), normalized (pre-normalized), spheroidized, extra smooth clean bright, sull coated, annealed, black annealed (pot annealed), strand annealed (lead annealed), bright annealed, lime bright annealed, patented, oil tempered, liquor finished (coppered or bright coppered wire), galvanized, tinned, aluminum coated.

Uses or commercial applications—Armor wire, bale-tie wire, bolt wire, scrapless-nut wire, recessed-head screw wire, broom wire, cold-heading or cold-extrusion wire, concrete reinforcement, fence wire, music wire, piano wire, poultry netting, rope wire, valve-spring wire, upholstery-spring wire, mechanical-spring wire, telephone wire, telegraph wire, tire wire, welding wire, wool wire (for steel wool), special wires, miscellaneous wires.

Kinds and Composition of Steel Used for Wire—The steel for wire is produced by all the modern processes, including the basic open-hearth, Bessemer, and electric-furnace processes. Plain carbon steels chiefly are produced by the basic open-hearth and basic oxygen processes; stainless steels and alloy steels for certain special-purpose wires are made in electric furnaces. The alloy steels known as constructional alloy steels (see Chapter 41) generally are made in open-hearth furnaces.

By properly selecting and handling the plain carbon steels in drawing and heat treating, it is possible to develop a wide range of mechanical properties. Ordinarily, sulphur and phosphorus are kept within the usual limits for each grade of steel, while the silicon, manganese, and carbon contents are varied according to the mechanical properties desired. Occasionally, the sulphur content will be increased to improve the cutting qualities (machinability) of the steel.

In recent years, there has been a constantly increasing demand for wire possessing properties that cannot be obtained by cold working and heat treating plain carbon steel. This demand has been met by the addition of alloying elements, such as nickel, chromium, manganese, silicon, vanadium, molybdenum or combinations of them. Many of these alloy steels can be produced satisfactorily by the basic open-hearth process. For those that cannot and for the stainless steels containing large percentages of chromium and nickel, electric furnaces of the arc type are commonly used and, to a decreasing extent, the induction type of electric furnace is sometimes used. Each of these processes produces steel having the best properties for certain purposes or kinds of wire.

Wire Shapes—While wire is ordinarily thought of as being round, it may have any one of an infinite number of sectional shapes, as required by the particular use for which it is desired. After the ordinary round wire of circular section, the most common shapes are square, hexagon, octagon, oval, half-oval, half-round, triangular and flat. Besides these regular, or symmetrical, shapes, wire is also made in various odd and irregular shapes for specific purposes.

The American Iron and Steel Institute (AISI) Steel Products Manual entitled "Carbon Steel Flat Wire" defines a flat wire as a cold-rolled product, with a prepared edge, rectangular in shape, ½-inch or less in width, under ¼-inch in thickness. "Low-carbon steel flat wire is generally produced from hot-rolled rods or specially prepared round wire, by one or more cold-rolling operations, primarily for the purpose of obtaining the size and section desired and for improving surface finish, dimensional accuracy and varying mechanical properties. Low-carbon steel flat wire can also be produced by slitting cold-rolled flat steel to the desired width. The width-to-thickness ratio together with the specified type of edge generally determine the process which will be necessary to produce a specific flat wire item." Those edges, finishes, and tempers obtainable in flat wire are similar to those furnished in cold-rolled strip.

Sizes of Wire—The size of round wire is determined by its diameter, which is expressed in absolute units, or decimal parts thereof, or by gage numbers. In this country the absolute unit is the inch, and the diameter is obtained by a micrometer capable of making measurements accurate to at least one thousandth of an inch. As stated in Chapter 48 on gages, there are several different gages in effect for the measurement of wire. The size of music wire is expressed in gage numbers of a system known as the Music Wire Gage (M.W.G.), which is the standard for this wire. For iron and steel telephone and telegraph wire, the standard gage is the Birmingham Wire Gage (B.W.-G.), while for copper electrical wire the Brown and Sharpe Gage (B.&S.G.), also known as the American Wire Gage (A.W.G.), is largely employed. With these notable exceptions the gage used by United States Steel and by many other manufacturers of steel wire, is the United States Steel Wire Gage (U.S.Stl.W.G.), or the Steel Wire Gage (Stl.W.G.), and all unidentified

Table 29—II. United States Steel Wire Gage
(Decimal Sizes and Feet Per Pound)

U.S. Steel Wire Gage No.	Deci-mally	Feet Per Lb.	U.S. Steel Wire Gage No.	Deci-mally	Feet Per Lb.	U.S. Steel Wire Gage No.	Deci-mally	Feet Per Lb.	U.S. Steel Wire Gage No.	Deci-mally	Feet Per Lb.	U.S. Steel Wire Gage No.	Deci-mally	Feet Per Lb.
1—	0.283	4.68	10—	0.135	20.6	19—	0.0410	223.0	28—	0.0162	1429.	37—	0.0085	5189.
¼	0.278	4.85	¼	0.131	21.9	¼	0.0394	241.6	¼	0.0159	1483.	¼	0.0084	5313.
½	0.273	5.03	½	0.128	22.9	½	0.0379	261.1	½	0.0156	1540.	½	0.0083	5443.
¾	0.268	5.22	¾	0.124	24.4	¾	0.0363	284.5	¾	0.0153	1602.	¾	0.0081	5714.
2—	0.2625	5.44	11—	0.1205	25.8	20—	0.0348	309.6	29—	0.0150	1666.	38—	0.0080	5858.
¼	0.258	5.63	¼	0.117	27.4	¼	0.0340	324.3	¼	0.0148	1712.	¼	0.0079	6007.
½	0.253	5.86	½	0.113	29.4	½	0.0332	340.2	½	0.0145	1783.	½	0.0078	6163.
¾	0.248	6.10	¾	0.109	31.6	¾	0.0325	355.1	¾	0.0143	1833.	¾	0.0076	6491.
3—	0.2437	6.31	12—	0.1055	33.7	21—	0.0317	373.1	30—	0.0140	1913.	39—	0.0075	6665.
¼	0.239	6.56	¼	0.102	36.1	¼	0.0309	392.7	¼	0.0138	1969.	¼	0.0074	6846.
½	0.235	6.79	½	0.099	38.3	½	0.0301	413.8	½	0.0136	2027.	½	0.0073	7037.
¾	0.230	7.09	¾	0.095	41.5	¾	0.0294	433.7	¾	0.0134	2088.	¾	0.0071	7437.
4—	0.2253	7.39	13—	0.0915	44.8	22—	0.0286	458.4	31—	0.0132	2152.	40—	0.0070	7652.
¼	0.221	7.68	¼	0.089	47.3	¼	0.0279	481.7	¼	0.0131	2185.	¼	0.0069	7874.
½	0.216	8.04	½	0.086	50.7	½	0.0272	506.8	½	0.0130	2218.	½	0.0068	8110.
¾	0.212	8.34	¾	0.083	54.4	¾	0.0265	533.9	¾	0.0129	2253.	¾	0.0067	8352.
5—	0.207	8.75	14—	0.080	58.6	23—	0.0258	563.3	32—	0.0128	2288.	41—	0.0066	8607.
¼	0.203	9.10	¼	0.078	61.6	¼	0.0251	595.1	¼	0.0126	2361.			
½	0.200	9.37	½	0.076	64.9	½	0.0244	629.7	½	0.0123	2478.			
¾	0.196	9.76	¾	0.074	68.5	¾	0.0237	667.5	¾	0.0121	2561.	42—	0.0062	9753.
6—	0.192	10.2	15—	0.072	72.3	24—	0.0230	708.7	33—	0.0118	2693.	43—	0.0060	10415.
¼	0.188	10.6	¼	0.070	76.5	¼	0.0224	747.2	¼	0.0115	2834.			
½	0.185	11.0	½	0.067	83.5	½	0.0217	796.2	½	0.0111	3043.			
¾	0.181	11.4	¾	0.065	88.7	¾	0.0211	842.1	¾	0.0108	3215.	44—	0.0058	11145.
7—	0.177	12.0	16—	0.0625	96.0	25—	0.0204	901.	34—	0.0104	3466.	45—	0.0055	12394.
¼	0.173	12.5	¼	0.060	104.2	¼	0.0198	956.	¼	0.0102	3605.			
½	0.170	13.0	½	0.058	111.5	½	0.0193	1007.	½	0.0100	3749.			
¾	0.166	13.6	¾	0.056	119.6	¾	0.0187	1072.	¾	0.0097	3985.	46—	0.0052	13866.
8—	0.162	14.3	17—	0.054	128.6	26—	0.0181	1144.	35—	0.0095	4154.	47—	0.0050	14997.
¼	0.159	14.8	¼	0.052	138.7	¼	0.0179	1170.	¼	0.0094	4243.			
½	0.155	15.6	½	0.051	144.2	½	0.0177	1197.	½	0.0093	4335.			
¾	0.152	16.2	¾	0.0491	155.5	¾	0.0175	1224.	¾	0.0091	4527.	48—	0.0048	16273.
9—	0.1483	17.1	18—	0.0475	166.2	27—	0.0173	1253.	36—	0.0090	4629.	49—	0.0046	17718.
¼	0.145	17.8	¼	0.0459	177.9	¼	0.0170	1297.	¼	0.0089	4733.			
½	0.142	18.6	½	0.0443	191.1	½	0.0168	1329.	½	0.0087	4953.			
¾	0.138	19.7	¾	0.0426	206.6	¾	0.0165	1377.	¾	0.0086	5069.	50—	0.0044	19366.

gage numbers used in this chapter will refer to this gage, which is shown in Table 29—II.

The size limits for the product commonly known as wire range from approximately 0.005 inch to under 1 inch for round sections, and from a few thousandths of an inch to approximately ½ inch for square sections. Larger rounds and squares, and all sizes of hexagonal and octagonal shapes are commonly known as bars.

Classification of Common Round Wire According to Size—As wire may include a wide range of sizes, its classification has been governed somewhat by manufacturing equipment and methods of handling. It normally is separated into two broad groups known as **coarse** and **fine** wire. The fine-wire classification is usually recognized as including 16 gage and smaller wire, normally produced in 8-inch diameter coils. Coarse wire includes sizes 20 gage and coarser, normally drawn on 16-inch, 22-inch and 26-inch or 30-inch blocks. The distinction is not clearly drawn for 16 to 20 gage, inclusive, as this range is commonly regarded as coarse wire for some end uses, and as fine wire when made by a different manufacturing practice for other end uses. The most commonly used wire sizes are those drawn from a 7/32-inch rod to 8 to 20 gage, inclusive.

Surface Finishes of Wire—A variety of finishes on the wire may be obtained by controlled processing in manufacture. The more common finishes are usually designated as bright, black annealed, liquor finished, coppered, tinned, galvanized, aluminum coated, and painted or enameled. For certain specific uses, a drawn aluminum coated or a drawn galvanized finish is sometimes produced, by cold drawing the wire one or more drafts through a die after coating. The bright finish is obtained by dry drawing, liquor finish by wet drawing, black annealing finishes by oxidation of the surface in heat treatment, while the tinned, galvanized and painted finishes are produced by subjecting the wire to a coating process as a final operation. The methods used in producing these different finishes will be developed more fully in the description to follow.

Temper of Wire—In the wire industry, temper is a word used in referring to the hardness, stiffness and strength of wire. The temper is affected by the amount of carbon, manganese and phosphorus, or other alloying element present in the steel, the amount of cold drawing without annealing, and the heat treatment given the wire. Thus, increasing the carbon content of the steel or submitting the wire to drawing operations increases the temper, while heat treating may either harden or soften the metal, according to whether it is heated to the hardening-temperature range and quenched, or annealed. The strength and hardness of low-carbon, medium-low carbon and medium-high carbon wires are regulated by drawing and annealing operations, and of high-carbon wires by drawing and patenting operations. The tempers of low-carbon wires are usually expressed as hard, medium hard, bright soft, soft and extra soft. Thus the **hard temper** is obtained by drawing through several dies in succession without annealing to obtain considerable reduction, **medium hard** by drawing (usually fewer drafts) to obtain somewhat less reduction or, in some instances, by subjecting hard temper wire to a partial or "slack" annealing, **bright soft** by giving the wire one light pass through the die after annealing, and soft and extra soft by annealing after drawing to size. Thus it will be seen that by properly correlating all these factors—composition, drawing, and heat treatment—the mechanical properties of steel wire may be varied over a wide range of hardness, strength, toughness, ductility, or softness. As an illustration of the possibilities in varying these properties, there may be cited the strength of steel wires, which are regularly made with tensile strengths varying from 50,000 to as high as 500,000 pounds per square inch for the smaller gages of high-carbon wire. It must be remembered, however, that, with but one exception, whatever is done to strengthen the metal will decrease its ductility, and vice versa.

The exception refers to the special heat treating process known as patenting, which may, under certain conditions, increase both the strength and ductility of the wire.

SECTION 3

ROLLING THE WIRE ROD

The Wire Rod—The slender rods or bars of metal from which wire is drawn are known as wire rod, and, as already indicated, all steel wire rod is now produced by hot rolling. It may be made in various shapes and sizes, but for common wires and fine wires, i.e., No. 8 and finer, 7/32-inch round rod may be considered as the standard. This size rod is the smallest round that is practicable to produce on a rolling mill and, while the diameter may vary, it is nominally 0.218 inch. For large wires the rod will, of course, be somewhat larger than the wire to be made from it. As the rod comes from the rolling mill, it is wound into coils.

These coils are usually about thirty inches in diameter inside and weigh from 300 to 1200 pounds each. Each coil represents the rod made from a single billet, and its weight, therefore, is determined by the weight of the billet used. While the wire rod represents a finished product of the rolling mills, it constitutes the raw material used in the wire mill and should be considered as the first step in the making of wire, for upon the kind and quality of the rod depend largely the kind and quality or grade of wire drawn from it. Physical defects in the rod will either cause failures in drawing or remain as more minute defects in the wire. While some wire mills obtain their rods from outside sources, many mills, especially the larger plants, roll their own rods.

Types of Rod Mills—After it has been made according to specifications, the steel for wire is cast into ingots and rolled on the blooming mill in the usual manner. In most cases, the blooming mill is succeeded by a billet mill, and the blooms are rolled into billets 4 inches square or less in size. These billets are cut into lengths to give the weight desired, allowed to cool, inspected, conditioned if necessary, re-heated, and then rolled directly into rods. As pointed out in the first section of this chapter, the demand for wire in exceedingly long lengths and in large quantities has led to the development of special mills for rolling the rods. These mills are of four different types, known as: (1) the Morgan, or continuous, rod mill, (2) the Garrett, or looping rod mill, (3) the combination, or combined continuous and single Belgian, rod mill, and (4) the double Belgian rod mill. Of these the first two employ fundamentally different principles of roll arrangement, hence will be described somewhat in detail.

The Continuous Rod Mill represents a development which in this country began about 1870. At that time the mill most generally employed for rolling rods was the single train **Belgian**, or **looping, mill.** This mill, while it represented a great improvement over the single-stand three-high mill, was comparatively inefficient and was limited as to the length of rod it could roll. Since all the rolls were run at the same speed, the billets could be roughed down much faster than the rod could be finished, and, owing to the loops formed and the length of time required for the piece to pass through the finishing rolls, the rod would become too cold to finish if its length exceeded certain limits. In 1869, however, the Washburn and Moen Manufacturing Company erected at their Grove Street Works, Worcester, Mass., an entirely new type of mill, which had been patented in 1862 by George Bedson of Manchester, England. This mill consisted of a number of pairs of horizontal rolls and an equal number of vertical rolls arranged in a series so that the first, third, and succeeding stands of odd number were horizontal, while the second, fourth, and other stands of even number were vertical. This arrangement of the rolls made the draft in any stand at right angles to that in the succeeding stand, and overcame the necessity of giving the piece a quarter turn between passes, as in the looping mill. Then, by placing the stands as close together as possible, he was able to drive the mill through two long shafts, on each of which was mounted a system of gears, whereby the rolls of each stand beyond the first was made to revolve at a rate definitely faster than the stand preceeding. This system of driving was to regulate the speed of the different stands so that the peripheral speed of the rolls in each would be the same, or nearly the same, as the linear speed of the bar, which increases after each pass due to the elongation. In this way the looping of the rod between passes was avoided, and a billet once started in the first stand was rapidly carried through the mill in a straight line, being thus rolled into a rod in one continuous operation. This mill met all expectations as to speed and length of rods rolled, but its output was restricted at first, because the rods could not be coiled and taken out of the way as rapidly as the mill could produce them. But C. H. Morgan, who was then general manager for Washburn and Moen, soon overcame this difficulty by devising a power traction reel for coiling the rods. This was the beginning of the development of the automatic reels, which will be described later.

The Morgan Mill—While the Bedson mill represented a great advance in rod rolling, it possessed certain mechanical features which were objectionable. Its chief faults were found to be due to the vertical rolls. They were not easily kept in adjustment, and the shaft and gears for driving them were all beneath the mill floor. The scale and water from the rolls fell upon these gears and bearings and caused excessive wear, which, combined with the difficulty of getting to them under the floor, made them a source of much trouble. After a few years' experience with the Bedson mill, therefore, Morgan and his associates developed the twisting guide, by means of which the vertical rolls could be eliminated and horizontal rolls substituted for them. This was a closed delivering guide in which the grooves were cut in a spiral, so that with this guide properly mounted after any pass the piece was forced through it and twisted a quarter turn before it entered the next pass. Besides overcoming most of the disadvantages of the Bedson mill, this Morgan plan presented the additional advantage of more than one rolling line, that is, of rolling two or more rods side by side at the same time and on the one set of rolls. This plan of increasing the capacity of the mill, however, increases the difficulty of keeping such mills in adjustment, and was not taken advantage of until some years after the erection of Morgan's first mill. Even with a single rolling line, the development of the mill to a practical basis of operation presented some difficult problems. It is evident that such a mill requires very fine adjustment of the draft, roll diameter, and speed of rotation, for these factors are brought into close relation. The relations of all these factors can be determined by proper mathematical calculations, but as the draft fixed by the grooves in the rolls is affected by the adjustment of the rolls, the temperature of the bar, composition of the steel, and changes with the wearing of the grooves and bearings, much difficulty was at first experienced in getting the mill adjusted so that the piece would not loop or jam between the different stands of rolls. This was particularly true in the case of the last few roll stands of the high-speed finishing mill. This difficulty was finally solved by increasing the speed of the rolls enough to keep the rod under slight tension at all times, and by making the bottom as well as the top roll adjustable as explained under the heading of continuous billet mills.

Modern Continuous Rod Mills—Since the time of Morgan's first mill, various improvements have been made, not so much in the mill itself as in the auxiliary equipment. These improvements have made it possible to produce a more nearly perfect rod in greater and greater tonnages. The delivery speed of modern continuous mills rolling 7/32-inch rod ranges from 3700 to 6000 feet per minute. The actual output of a mill depends upon conditions and the number of rolling lines, which was formerly one or two, and in recent years has been increased to three or four. The number of stands of rolls in a mill and, to a considerable extent, the general layout of the mill, depends upon the size of the billets used and rod size to be rolled therefrom. There are several standard sizes of billets, 1¾, 2, 2½, and 3¼ inches square.

Layouts for Rolling Small Billets—From the standpoint of general efficiency, accuracy, and uniformity in size of the product, continuous rod mills are designed, preferably, to roll billets from 1¾ to 3¼ inches square and approximately 30 feet in length. This length fits the former standard railroad freight car, while the section is about the largest that can be rolled satisfactorily without a reheating or increasing the speed of the mill beyond the limits of safety and practicability. To work these sections into a 7/32-inch rod (0.218-inch) without unduly increasing the danger of developing rolling defects, requires from 16 to 23 passes. For straight continuous rolling, that is, where the rolls are all in the same straight line, these passes are split into two groups, known as the roughing and the finishing sets (Figure 29—1). The roughing set consists of 6 to 9 stands of rolls, the first of which is set as near to the discharge door of the heating furnace as possible, usually within 6 to 12 feet. Since the furnace is of the continuous side-discharge type, this arrangement makes it possible, without removing the billet entirely from the furnace to push one end into the rolls, which then withdraw it no faster than it is being rolled. Immediately following the last roughing stand is a flying shear, which permits the cropping of bad ends before the billet enters the high-speed finishing sets. To provide space for these and also for a little slack between the two groups of rolls, so as to make it easier for the roller to keep the mill in proper adjustment, the first stand in the second group is placed about 20 to 30 feet from the last roughing stand. The second group of rolls contains 10 or 12 stands, the last of which is known as the finishing stand. Following the finishing stand, tube-like pipe

guides are provided for conducting the rod to the reeling machines which are located some 20 to 60 feet beyond and usually number twice the number of rolling lines or strands. The chief advantages in this arrangement lie in its compactness, which aids in maintaining uniformity of rolling temperature and provides for a choice of different methods of driving. The control of temperature possible is evident from the fact that at the time the forward end of the rod reaches the reels, about one-half of the billet is still in the furnace. For driving the mill, two motors, one for each group or rolls, may be used, but some mills of this type are driven through two shafts connected by gears to a single motor or steam engine.

The Looping Continuous Mill—To provide greater flexibility and make it easier to keep the mill adjusted, in some recent installations of continuous rod mills, the finishing group of rolls also has been split up into three smaller groups of four, two and four stands each. The two-stand group is both preceded and followed by 180-degree loops. The roughing rolls and the first four intermediates are in the same straight line, and driven in the usual way by a single motor, while the next two groups, driven by another motor, stand in two separate lines parallel to the first line, with the two-stand group a little in advance of the finishing stands. Since the roll speeds are adjusted to the elongation of the piece being rolled, the loops, once formed, increase very little in size, and cooling of the rod through this exposure is very slight and uniform for each unit of its length. Also, this placing permits ironing out some of the effect of tension in the early part of the mill.

Layouts for Rolling 4-Inch by 4-Inch Billets—Although the continuous mill is best adapted to roll small long billets, local conditions frequently make it desirable or necessary to start with a larger size of billet. To meet such conditions, many continuous mills have been designed to use 4-inch by 4-inch billets. In designing these mills, the engineers have developed two plans. In one of these an additional group of roughing or breaking-down rolls is provided, and the rod is rolled directly from the billet, as in the straight continuous plan for small billets. The plan has some drawbacks, the chief of which may be noted as follows: If all the rolls are speeded to correspond to the

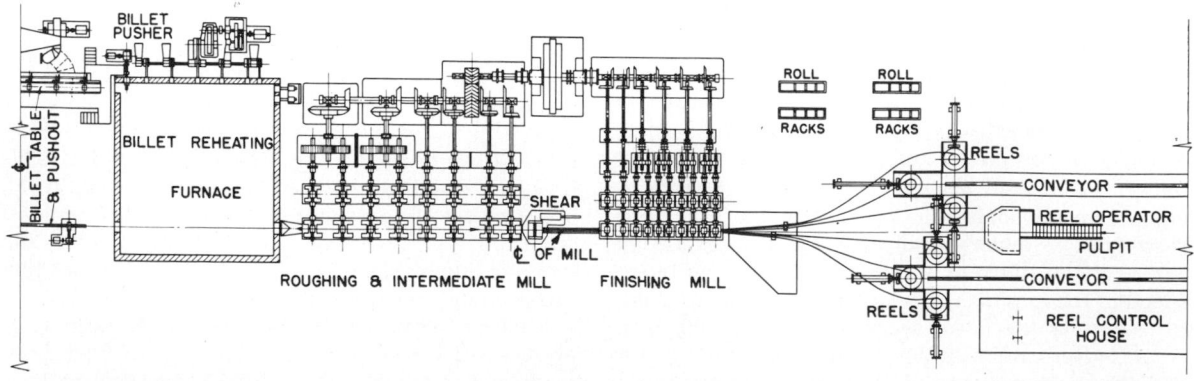

Fig. 29—1. Plan and layout of continuous rod mill for 2-inch billets, including reels and part of the rod bundle conveyor.

elongation of the bar, the speed of the first roughing group is very slow. Even with the finishing roll revolving at the rate of 1350 r.p.m., the speed of the first roughing rolls, with a roll diameter of 14 inches, would be close to 3 r.p.m. The long time the piece is thus kept in contact with the cold rolls results in cooling it to a point where it becomes difficult to finish. If the first roughing group is speeded up, then the piece must be held ahead of the first intermediates and is cooled even faster and more unevenly than in the former instance. In some cases a solution to this difficulty has been sought by placing a heat retainer, a long narrow brick chamber heated by gas, between the roughing and intermediate groups. By passing the billet through this chamber slowly some of the heat lost in the previous rolling may be restored before it enters the intermediate sets of rolls. But the best plan involves the use of a reheating furnace between these two groups of rolls. In this plan, which is in effect equivalent to placing a billet mill before the usual straight continuous rod mill, the first group of rolls, consisting of several stands driven by a separate motor or engine, breaks the 4 by 4 by 72-inch billet, for example, down to a more suitable size billet about 30 feet long. This long billet is immediately charged into the continuous reheating furnace, where its rolling temperature is fully restored before being rolled to finished size. From this point the arrangement of the mill does not differ materially from the straight continuous plan already described.

Operation of Continuous Mills—With the mill properly designed and erected, its efficient operation depends largely upon the skill of the operating crews, headed by the roll turner and roller. For best results the roll diameters for the different stands must be carefully selected and maintained in proper proportions; the roll passes, especially for the finishing group of rolls, must be skillfully adjusted and accurately turned; the rolls and guides must be carefully set in the housings; and there-after the draft must be regulated through the mill screws to suit the conditions. The uniform heating of the billet is also a matter of importance, as is seen from the following facts: Under a given pressure, a hot bar or rod will elongate more than a colder one. Translated into operating terms, this statement means that if the mill is adjusted to roll the colder rod properly, the hotter rod will buckle between passes and cause cobbles. The mill must, therefore, be adjusted to the hottest bars, and if the draft on the different passes is regulated to keep this bar under slight tension the same adjustment will produce a pull of considerable force on the colder bars. Thus pull is the cause of the longer "finny" ends which are characteristic of rods rolled on straight continuous mills, and it also produces a difference in section between the ends and the middle of the rod, causing it to exhibit a tendency toward flatness in the middle. This matter is especially important in the case of mills rolling more than one line, or strand, at a time. In such a mill, any adjustment of the screws to correct a fault in one pass affects the draft on the corresponding pass of the other strand also, and it is practically impossible to overcome any variation in temperature of the two strands through adjustment of the rolls only.

The Garrett Mill—Up to 1882 the continuous rod mill had no competitor as to speed, length of rod, and tonnage produced. On the Belgian, or looping mill, which was the only other type of mill used for rolling rods, the longest lengths that could be rolled would not exceed 300 feet, the heaviest coils weighed less than 50 pounds, and the tonnage produced daily would not, in case of small rod under 0.2-inch diameter, much exceed 20 tons. On such mills the best rolling practice of that day for steel involved the rolling of the ingots to 4-inch by 4-inch blooms, which were cut into lengths convenient for hand rolling and allowed to cool. These blooms, or billets, were then reheated and rolled on a three-high billet mill to a 2-inch square or its equivalent in rectangular section. These small billets were again sheared into lengths to give the weights required and allowed to cool, when they were reheated and rolled into rods on the looping mill. In endeavoring to overcome the advantages enjoyed by the owners of the continuous rod mill, William Garrett, who was then superintendent of the plant of the Cleveland Rolling Mill Company, conceived a plan whereby the looping mill could be modified to roll No. 5 rod in long lengths and direct from 4-inch by 4-inch billets without reheating. In formulating this plan, he reasoned that, since a large section loses heat less rapidly than a small one, the 4-inch by 4-inch billet could be rolled in the roughing mill to a size suitable for the rod mill in so short a time that it would still retain enough heat to be finished if it were not exposed so long in the looping mill. So he combined the three-high billet mill with the rod mill, and split up the latter into three groups or trains of rolls, which he arranged in echelon and drove at progressively increasing rates, so as to rough at low and finish at high speeds. By this arrangement the speed of the finishing trains could be adjusted to the elongation of the rod, so that not only could a given length be rolled in a shorter period of time, but the size of the loops could be controlled and their length reduced. Garrett erected his first mill in 1882, and at once he was able not only to roll rod in much longer lengths, but also to double, and more than double, the output of the older looping mills.

Accessories to Garrett's Mill—After the erection of his first mill, Garrett was able, from time to time, to add certain improvements. One of the most important of these improvements was the use of repeaters. As pointed out in connection with merchant mills, these are semicircular trough-like guides placed so as to guide the end of the piece from one pass to the next. As the repeaters are open at the top, a loop once formed is free to rise out of the trough, and enlarge to correspond to the elongation, or otherwise adjust itself to any difference in the speeds of the two passes. A looping mill fully equipped with repeaters is practically as automatic as a continuous mill. In the case of the earlier looping rod mills, however, repeaters did not work equally well on both sides of a mill. In these mills, the passes from the first few roughing stands to the finishing are alternately oval and square, the squares coming out on one side of the mill and the ovals on the other. On entering the square passes, the ovals must be turned on edge, and the use of guides for doing this work generally resulted in the production of much scrap, due to their frequent failures to edge the ovals properly. In some present-day Garrett mills, however, oval repeaters have been perfected and catchers are necessary only at points where cropping must be done.

Number of Strands—Another improvement introduced by Garrett, who was the first to employ the scheme, was the practice of finishing more than one rod at a time. Due to the shortness of the billet, the roughing train was able to break down the billets much faster than the finishing train could roll the rod in a single strand, even when the latter was speeded up to 550 r.p.m., which is the maximum speed at which it was practicable to run this train. Since the rod makes only one pass in the finishing and most of the intermediate stands, there was a great amount of roll space unused in rolling a single strand. By adopting power reels, and reeling each strand on independent reels, Garrett found no difficulty in finishing two strands at once in the same trains and thus doubling the output of the mill. In present-day Gar-

rett mills, four, and even six, strands may be rolled simultaneously. The number of strands rolling in a mill has considerable effect upon the forming of the rod, and it is considered good practice to keep the mill as full as possible.

Floors—Another characteristic of looping rod mills is the sloping floors, which, though a simple device, play an important part in their operation. Since it is necessary to run the rolls in each finishing train at the same rotative speed, and it is not practicable to take up all the elongation of the piece, or equalize the rolling time of the different passes by using rolls of different diameters, it is necessary to allow the loops which are formed after catching or repeating, to grow upon loop floors. If these floors are level the frictional resistance soon becomes so great that it stops the forward motion of the loop, when the rod will pile up and become hopelessly twisted. In the old days, boys were employed to draw the loops back with hooks or tongs, but in Garrett mills this frictional resistance is overcome by laying the looping floors at an incline, sloping from the rolls, except on the oval side where a narrow level space is left to provide standing room for the catchers. When more than one strand is being rolled, as in all present-day mills, these floors must

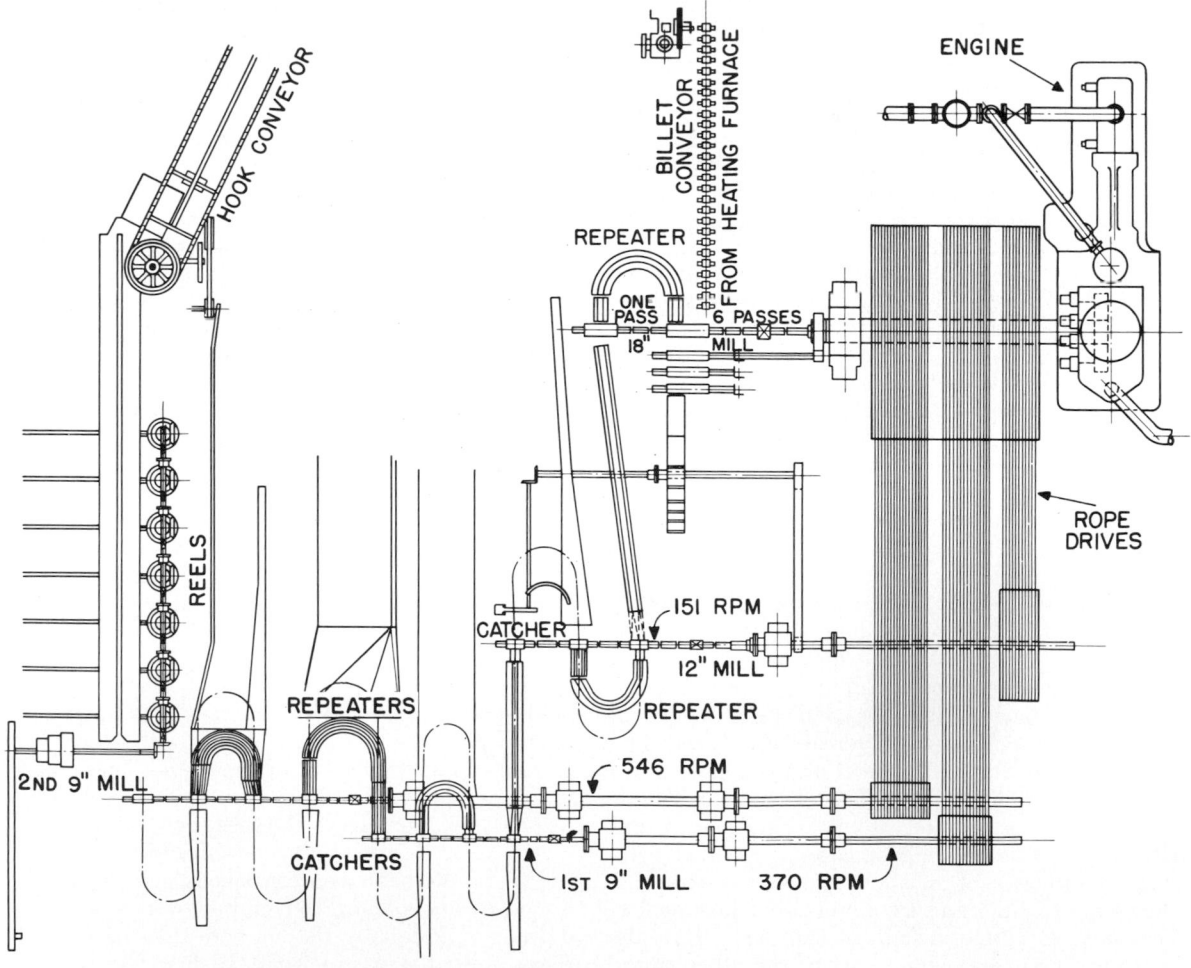

FIG. 29—2. General layout of Garrett rod mill.

be provided with guiding channels and other facilities to prevent the different loops from becoming entangled.

Layouts of Garrett Mills—The arrangement of the roll trains in later looping mills has been subjected to considerable variation. A typical layout is shown in Figure 29—2. As originally planned by Garrett, the three-high billet mill was placed near the heating furnaces, which are now mainly of the continuous end-discharging type with floors sloping downward from the charging end. Two or more of these furnaces may be used to heat the billets, which are conveyed to the mill by roll tables. Following the billet mill, at a distance great enough to permit the piece from the last pass to clear the billet-mill rolls, is the roughing mill which, in present-day mills, may be a looping train of three stands or two or more stands arranged in tandem. Then come, with their looping floors sloping in opposite directions from the narrow level standing, the intermediate and finishing rolls, arranged, usually, in two trains of four or five stands each, lying end to end along two parallel lines in close proximity to each other, and so placed that the first intermediate pass is in line with the last roughing pass and far enough away to give proper clearance for the piece. In some mills especially designed to roll small rods, the finishing and last intermediate stands are coupled together in a third and separate train, which is driven at the highest speeds practicable, to reduce the size of the loops and make it possible to finish the rod at a higher temperature.

Combination Mills—In roughing down the 4-inch by 4-inch billets on the three-high mill, considerable time is consumed in making the necessary five to seven passes back and forth through the rolls. Not only does this delay tend to cool the steel somewhat, but these operations require some heavy hand labor. To overcome these disadvantages as far as possible, some looping mills make use of a group of continuous rolls for roughing purposes. This group usually consists of eight stands, and displaces not only the billet mill but the roughing train as well. With such a group, the work of roughing can be done much faster than the looping trains can dispose of the material even when four strands are rolled at once. Consequently, one continuous roughing mill is used to feed two looping finishing mills, one of which is placed on the right and the other on the left side of the roughing mill. By locating these finishing trains at a suitable distance beyond the roughing mill, the sections from the last roughing stand are carried forward or looped into the first intermediate pass by guides similar to the repeaters previously described. This type of mill is sometimes referred to as the Garrett semi-continuous mill.

The Double Belgian Mill, which is also designated by the name of Boecker's wire mill, represents another attempt to apply the combined continuous and looping methods of rolling, in this case, to the finishing mill. It consists, usually, of seven or nine stands of rolls, six or eight of which are arranged in two parallel lines or trains of three or four stands each, so that the corresponding stands in each line are opposite each

other, thus forming three or four continuous groups of two stands each. The mill is driven from a central shaft lying between the two parallel lines of stands, and from this shaft the power is transmitted to the rolls through three sets of gears. In this way the speed and direction of rotation of the various rolls is so regulated that a rod, passing through the mill, can be looped by catchers or repeaters from one continuous set to another, and from the last continuous set into the single finishing stand, which is two-high. A mill of this design offers some of the advantages of both the looping and continuous types, but also possesses some of the limitations of both. Thus, while it is capable of producing rods that are exceptionally uniform in section, the complicated system of shafting and gearing makes its upkeep expensive and tends to offset its advantages.

Continuous and Looping Mills Compared—A just comparison of the continuous mill and the looping mill is difficult to make. Local conditions and a great number of other factors must all be considered. For example, there is the matter of raw material. The small billet of full standard length, i.e., 30 feet, cannot be rolled on a looping mill because of the long exposure on the looping floor, which cools it below the temperature for hot finishing. On the other hand, the continuous mill is particularly suited to rolling these long billets, and, when combined with the special heating furnace previously referred to, presents a layout by which the rolling can be done at higher and more uniform temperatures, which saves power and minimizes the variation in section of the rod from between the first and last end.

As already pointed out the large, or 4-inch by 4-inch, billet may be rolled on the continuous, the Garrett, or the combination mill. Mills of the Garrett type with looping trains for all except the first roughing, or billet mill, are limited to a billet weight of about 175 pounds for small rod, because, with a larger billet, the last end of the rod becomes so cold that excessive power is required to roll it, and the variation in size of the rod from end to end is too great to be tolerated. Continuous mills and combination mills can roll, without a second reheating, 3¼ by 3¼-inch billets weighing up to 1200 pounds. On billets of these weights, the continuous mill requires less power and fewer operators than mills which are chiefly of the looping type; also the repair costs per ton on modern continuous mills are less than on looping mills. The heavier the rod bundle the better, on account of the longer length of the wire that can be drawn from it in one piece, which reduces the handling required and the scrap produced in the drawing and finishing operations.

As to other differences made in the product by these two methods of rolling, these are of such a character as to leave little from which to choose. The tendency exhibited by the continuous-mill rod toward flatness in the middle is offset by the variation in section from end to end of the looping-mill rod when rolled in long lengths. Since the continuous mill cools the rod during the rolling less than the looping mill and uses no hand labor for catching, it permits the use of a greater number of roll stands and passes. This great number of passes makes it possible to use better-shaped passes with smaller reductions from pass to pass, and thus avoid overfills, which frequently cause surface defects in the rod—defects that are of very serious character in many wire products.

New Rod Mills—All of the rod mills installed in this country during recent years employ both continuous and looping features. These mills have a considerable number of their stands arranged in a straight line similar to continuous-type mills. However, instead of these stands being driven by one motor, the stands are arranged in units of one, two, three, or more stands, each unit driven by a separate variable-speed motor. This provides single-Belgian, double-Belgian, and continuous-mill features. The variable-speed motors give some of the benefits obtained from the loops in the original single- and double-Belgian types of mills, and considerable of the benefit of a continuous mill is retained by having a large number of stands arranged in a straight line. The length of these mills is greater than that of a continuous mill, but shorter than if loops were used instead of variable-speed motors. In addition to using separate drives for the single stands or groups of stands that together make up the straightaway part of the mill, these mills employ two to five loops, using either single or double Belgian stands driven by variable-speed motors to maintain short loops. Heat loss in the loop is thus reduced to a minimum. These loops assist in correcting the variation in section that occurs in the early part of the rolling operation, and also provide a means for carrying the sections to a position where pouring-type reels can be installed close to the stand where coarse rod is finished. Rod sizes approximately 3/8-inch and smaller are finished in a 6- to 8-stand continuous finishing train. Very high finishing speeds can be used on small rod without the difficulties encountered with high speed in loops. High finishing speed is essential on small rod to obtain heavy-weight coils.

The No. 1 rod mill at the Cuyahoga Works of United States Steel incorporates the principal features of modern rod mills that have just been described. A schematic layout of this mill is shown in Figure 29—3. A maximum of 23 stands is used for continuous-rolling operations, and 17 stands maximum for semi-continuous or looping operations. The size ranges produced continuously are No. 5 rod through $^{27}/_{64}$-in., and $1^{5}/_{32}$ through $1^{1}/_{2}$-in.: these two groups represent the finest and coarsest rods rolled on the mill. Intermediate sizes from $^{7}/_{16}$-in. through $1^{1}/_{8}$-in. are finished on the semi-continuous or looping stands. A speed of 6400 ft. per min. is possible when rolling continuously.

Because of the very high investment cost required for a rod mill, all of the newer rod mills are designed to roll the full range of rod sizes. They employ finishing speeds of 5000 to 6000 (or higher) ft. per min., and roll 3 or 4 strands simultaneously. Coil weights of No. 5 rod rolled on these mills range from 600 to 1000 lb. Production rates of 300 to 500 net tons per 8-hour turn are obtained. The advancement represented by these modern mills is not all due to the general mill layout. Improvements have been made in heating, rolling, shearing, coiling and handling equipment. Motors, controls and drives also have been improved, and automation is playing a part. All these things, together with ever-increasing knowledge of steelmaking have contributed to the advancement made in recently installed rod mills.

Rolls for Rod Mills—As to size, the rolls used for rolling rods are subject to considerable variation according to the type of mill and the purpose for which they are used. Thus, in Garrett mills the rolls are long, and vary in diameter from 16 or 18 inches for the first roughing rolls to 9 to 12 inches for the intermediate and finishing rolls, while in continuous mills using 3¼ by 3¼-inch billets they vary from about 18 inches for the roughers to about 11½ to 12 inches for the finishing groups. The roughing rolls may be cast steel or cast iron. However, cast steel is only used where it is

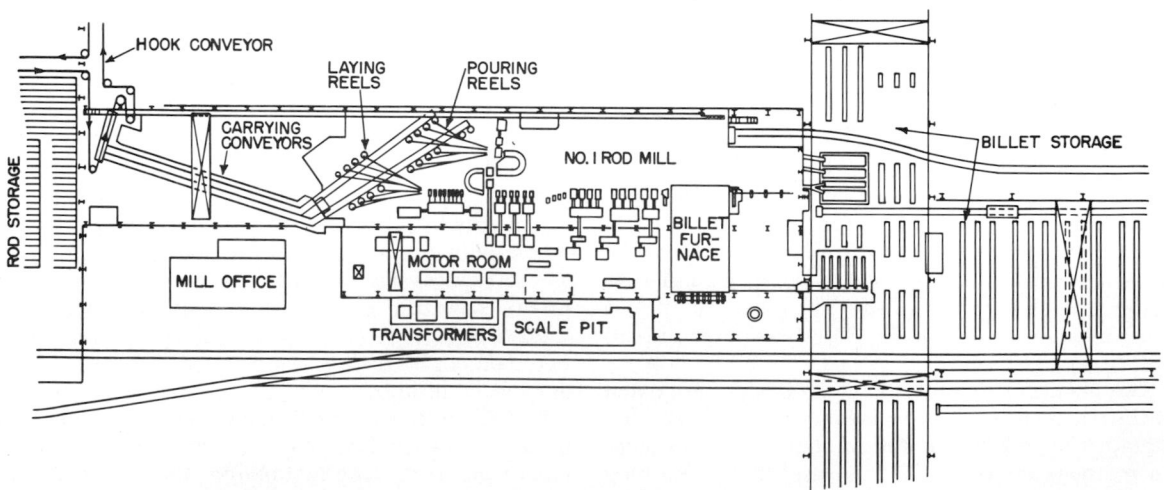

Fig. 29—3. General arrangement of the four-strand No. 1 rod mill at the Cuyahoga Works of United States Steel. The main sections consist of a 5-stand first roughing mill, a 4-stand intermediate roughing mill, a 6-stand intermediate finishing mill, and an 8-stand finishing mill for continuous rolling or a 2-stand finishing mill for semi-continuous rolling.

required for strength because of the poorer pass life obtained. Most mills at present use grain iron rolls in the roughing stands.

In the intermediate and finishing stands, the rolls are either grain iron or chilled iron with the practice being, until very recently, to use chilled iron wherever possible because of the longer pass wear. However, recent development of grain rolls has improved the pass life to the point where they are now being used even in the finishing stands of some mills. As to the roll passes, these are simple in form but of a design to give the necessary reduction without developing defects in the material. In Garrett mills and continuous mills using 4-inch by 4-inch billets, the first roughing passes are rectangular or box passes, or diamond and square passes, but in all other rolls except the finishing, the passes for round rods are arranged to give alternately squares and ovals, etc. For round wire, the last oval feeds the finishing pass which, of course, must be circular. To reduce the number of roll changes otherwise necessary, a number of duplicate grooves are cut in each set or pair of rolls, so that when one set of grooves becomes defective or too badly worn a new set can be made available for use merely by resetting the guides. When all the grooves in a set of rolls have thus been used, they must be replaced by a new set while the worn rolls are being redressed, so that duplicate rolls as well as duplicate grooves are required.

Designing the Passes—Here, the matter of chief concern is the proper regulation of the draft in each pass. The highest drafts are made in the roughers, where the reduction in any one pass may be as high as 45 per cent though a limit of 35 per cent represents better practice. In the intermediate sets of rolls, a maximum draft of about 30 per cent may be attained in the first passes, but as the rod approaches the finishing pass the amount of the reduction permissible gradually diminishes, until in the final pass it is well under 15 per cent. Within the limits mentioned, the drafts will be determined largely by the number of passes provided by the mill, which in turn will depend upon the type of mill, the size of billet used, and also the size of rod to be rolled. For rolling 4-inch by 4-inch billets to No. 5 rod, Garrett mills usually provide from 18 to 20 passes; some continuous mills use 21 passes, while others provided with an intermediate reheating furnace may use as many as 24; and combination and double Belgian mills may use 18 to 24 passes. Nearly all the mills are so arranged that the size of the finished rod can be varied, that is, made coarser than No. 5, either by "opening up the mill," thereby producing larger sections in each pass, or by omitting the use of some of the stands immediately preceding the last. In the latter case the finishing is done on one of the stands used as an intermediate when rolling No. 5 rod.

Housings and Guides—The construction of housings, with their mechanism for making necessary adjustments of rolls and guides, differs in the different mills, but is the same in principle as described elsewhere in this book for corresponding types of billet and merchant mills. The setting and adjustment of the rolls and of the receiving and delivery guides require a great deal of experience and, upon the efficiency of making these adjustments depends, in great measure, the quality of the rolled rod as well as the tonnage of the mill.

Rod Reels—The daily output of rod mills in use today varies from 450 to 1500 net tons, which tonnages, translated into linear units of No. 5 rod, are equivalent to about 1500 and 5000 miles, respectively. From this statement it is evident that this enormous output would have been impossible without adequate reeling facilities. As previously pointed out, this need caused the early adoption of automatic reels, the first practical development of which was introduced about 1880. The rod reels now in use are mainly of two types, known as the **pouring reel** and the **laying reel**. The pouring reel consists essentially of a horizontal steel disc or pan mounted upon a vertical shaft so that it may be revolved at a speed corresponding to the delivery speed of the rod. Near the circumference of this pan are two circular and concentric rows of pins, or spokes as they are often called. Into the annular space bounded by these spokes the rod pours from the end of a pipe which conducts it from the finishing rolls, and since the rotative speed of the reel is adjusted to the linear speed of the rod, the latter is laid in a neat coil within this space, a single ring of the coil being formed at each revolution of the machine. In the laying reel, the receptacle is stationary, while the end of the delivery pipe, itself, is made to revolve in a circle, thus laying the rod within the annular space provided by a motion similar to that in coiling a long rope by hand, so that the rod is given a twist at each revolution of the pipe, or as each ring of the coil is formed. The laying reel, therefore, can be used only with small round sections; however, pouring reels can only be used up to about 4200 feet per minute. Laying reels provide a better coil on small rod. Hence, most modern mills rolling both small and coarse rod have both laying and pouring reels. In both types the diameters of the coils are determined by the relation between the delivery speed of the rod and the rotative speed of the reel, for the peripheral speed of the coil being formed must equal the rod delivery speed. As these two factors cannot always be kept in exactly the same relation, the diameters of the coils vary somewhat. In all cases the reels are designed to raise the coil or lower the spokes, and deliver the product upon a conveyor, which carries each coil to some designated point where it may be disposed of as desired. In case of wire manufacturers who roll their own rods, the rod mill is located very near the wire mill, and the coils are carried by the conveyor directly into the cleaning or heat treating departments of the latter. Most wire mills, whether they roll their own rods or not, are provided with covered yards where rods of various kinds of stock may be stored for use as required.

Defects in Rods—To produce a satisfactory rod requires that proper care be exercised in every department concerned with its preparation. To begin with, the steel must be properly made and its composition should be as uniform as possible; also, it is essential that the ingot be properly cast and rolled at a suitable temperature, and that the billet be free from pipe, seams, and slivers. Even with perfect billets, considerable care and skill are required to produce satisfactory rods. Assuming that the rod mill, itself, has been properly designed and speeded and equipped with all the necessary accessories, unsatisfactory rod may still be produced by improper heating, by the use of improperly designed ragging on the roughing rolls, by improperly adjusting the rolls and guides, or by using the grooves too long. In order to finish the rod correctly, every pass in the mill should be made to produce, as near as possible, the section it was originally designed to produce, and to bring about this result all the passes must be kept full but none may be allowed to overfill.

Great emphasis is to be laid upon all these features of operation, because, from the point of view of the wire mill it is most essential that the rod be uniform in composition, and also in section, that it be close to the size and shape required, and that it be free from such surface defects as slivers, seams, and fins. These defects, as well as the composition, are matters of importance to both the consumer and the wire mill, for none of the subsequent wire-drawing operations or finishing processes will eliminate them or reduce their capacity to do harm in the final product.

SECTION 4

OUTLINE OF WIRE-DRAWING PROCESSES

The rolling of the rods is a fairly well standardized process. The primary object of rod rolling is, of course, to put the steel into such shape that it can be most efficiently cold drawn into wire. Using steel of the required composition, the rod is rolled to the desired size and shape by following a standard practice on a standard rod rolling mill. From this point, however, the method for manufacture into wire depends entirely upon the end use to which the wire is to be put. These uses are many and varied, and the wire drawing practices necessary to provide the wide ranges of required wire characteristics vary accordingly. Obviously, it would be impossible to cover all the practices in detail here. However, a brief summary of the various operations necessary to process the rod to finished wire will be outlined.

Preparing the Rod for Drawing—In order to prepare the rod for drawing, it is first given some necessary preliminary treatments. In general, these consist of acid cleaning and coating following a heat treatment when required. The heat-treating process is usually one of the following: patenting, annealing, or normalizing. These processes will be described in more detail later. Low-carbon rods which are to be drawn into wire usually do not require any heat treatment and are cleaned and coated after rolling. In the process of rolling, the rods acquire a mill scale or oxide on the surface. Oftentimes, it is necessary to store the rods for some time before drawing. In storage they may pick up either some additional oxide in the form of rust or just plain dirt. All mill scale, oxide, or dirt must be removed before the rods are drawn into wire. This is accomplished by placing the rods in a solution of hot dilute sulphuric acid for from fifteen to thirty minutes. The action of the acid loosens the scale and frees the rod of all rust or dirt, leaving the surface of the rods perfectly clean. The rods are then removed from the acid and given a thorough rinsing in a spray of high-pressure water. This removes all the acid from the surface and from between the various strands. The next step is to give the rods a suitable coating, usually lime. The purpose of the coating is threefold: first, to protect the surface of the cleaned rods from rusting in the atmosphere; second, to neutralize any traces of acid left from the cleaning; and, third, to serve as a carrier for the lubricant used in drawing the rod to wire.

For many years it was customary to coat rods which were to be drawn into ordinary finished wire with a sull coating. This is accomplished by placing the cleaned rods on a rack or a traveling conveyor and spraying them with a fine mist-like spray of water. The rods are then dipped in a tank containing hot milk of lime. In recent years the practice of sull coating has been discarded, and the rods are coated with the milk of lime directly after the water rinse. Sull coating is used now only on a few kinds of wire; in some instances for manufacture of cold-headed bolts.

Borax is another coating which has been used quite extensively in recent years with good results. After the coating is applied, the rods are baked in an oven or other type of baker to dry the coating. This function will be described later in more detail.

Drawing the Rod—After the rods are properly cleaned, coated, and baked, they are delivered to the wire-drawing equipment. Today, most wire which is drawn three or more drafts is produced on continuous machines. Wire which is to be drawn one or two drafts is produced on single or double-deck motor blocks. Wire in sizes ⅝-inch and coarser is drawn on horizontal bull blocks. However, there is still a considerable amount of wire produced on the so-called wire drawing frame. This frame, in the type most generally used for drawing rods, supports a single **die** and the power driven **block** for drawing the rod through the die, also a **drawbar** for drawing the first few feet of the rod. One end of the rod is now pointed, or tapered, so that it may be threaded through the die hole, which is somewhat smaller than the rod in section. Next the die holder, on the entering side of the die, is filled with a specially prepared grease, or some other suitable lubricant, so that in passing through the die the rod must first pass through the lubricant. The pointed end of the rod is now inserted through the proper die hole, where it is grasped by tongs attached to the drawbar, and drawn through far enough to be attached to the draw block. When this block is started revolving, it coils the wire about itself and thus continuously draws the rod through the die, thereby bringing about a fixed decrease in its sectional area and a proportional increase in its length.

Draft, Drawing and Process Wire—The amount of the reduction in the sectional area, as in the case of rolling, is expressed in per cent of the original area and is known as the **draft,** while the operation itself is called **drawing.** In general the draft on the rod varies from 10 to 45 per cent according to the kind of wire to be made. As soon as a rod has been given a draft, it is thereafter designated as a wire, though many more drafts and various other treatments may be necessary to work it into wire of the size, finish and temper desired. In wire-drawing plants, any wire which, following the initial drawing from the rod, is to receive further work or treatment before it is finished is designated as **process wire.** After the first draft from the rod, process wire may be finished in various ways.

Dry Drawing and Wet Drawing—There are two processes for drawing wire. These are designated as dry drawing and wet drawing. Mechanically, the processes are the same; that is, the wire is drawn through a die and wound up on a block. The difference in the processes is in the coating applied to the wire and the lubricant used. All wet-drawn wire is first given one or more dry drafts from the rod. This process wire is then thoroughly cleaned, rinsed, and immersed in a dilute solution of copper or tin sulphate or a mixture of both of these salts. A chemical reaction takes place which results in the deposition upon the wire of a thin metallic coating from the solution used. After coating, the wire is usually kept under water to protect it from the influence of the atmosphere.

In subsequent wet drawing, the pay-off reel containing the wire is placed in a tub of water. To this water a special type of soap is usually added to act as a lubricant. In recent years special coating solutions have been developed which are applied to the wire after the copper or copper-tin solution treatment. These coatings protect the surface from the atmos-phere and are also quick drying, so it is possible to store the wire without keeping it under water and also to permit drawing from a dry reel. In drawing, the copper or copper-tin solution imparts a characteristic metallic color to the wire which is known commercially as **coppered wire** or **liquor-finished wire.** The latter term designates the brass-colored finish obtained from the copper-tin coating mixture.

Types of Wire—For all practical purposes, wire may be described as being low-carbon or high-carbon. Although there are additional classifications in the American Iron and Steel Institute Steel Products Manual entitled "Wire Rods and Wire, Carbon Steel," 0.30 carbon may be considered the dividing point and, broadly speaking, wire under 0.30 carbon is referred to as low-carbon, while that which is 0.30 carbon and higher may be considered as high-carbon. The end uses of the various types of wire require different characteristics in the finished wire as to physical properties, finish, gage tolerance, electrical conductivity and many others. These requirements are met by designing manufacturing practices which employ various amounts of cold work (drawing), various types of heat treatments, or combinations of both. All of these practices are carefully worked out and are designed to provide wire which will adequately meet consumer requirements and at the same time make the most efficient use of producing equipment.

A general discussion of wire manufacturing follows which is divided into six sections, namely, "Preparation of Rods and Wire for Drawing," "Wire-Drawing Equipment," "Wire-Drawing Processes and Operations," "Heat Treatment of Wire," "Protective Metallic Coatings for Wire," and "Some Fabricated Wire Products."

SECTION 5

PROCESSES AND EQUIPMENT FOR PREPARING RODS AND WIRE FOR DRAWING

Importance of Cleaning—All of the hard, brittle oxide commonly called mill scale, which forms on hot-rolled rods or on heat-treated rods, and also the slow-forming red rust which forms on long exposure to the air, must be entirely removed before drawing. If these oxides remain on the surface of the rods, they result in very rapid wear on the wire-drawing dies and also cause scratched and off-gage wire. Proper cleaning and coating is largely responsible for success in the wire-drawing operation.

Method of Cleaning—As already stated, the method generally employed for cleaning the material preparatory to drawing consists in dipping the coils into a vat of hot, dilute sulphuric acid. The action by which this acid removes the scale is for the most part mechanical rather than chemical, for ferrous-ferric oxide, Fe_3O_4, which is the chief constituent of the scale, is but slightly soluble in sulphuric acid. The acid, however, is able to penetrate to the metal beneath the scale, where it reacts with the iron forming iron sulphate, a soluble neutral salt, and liberating a mixture of gases, mainly composed of hydrogen. This action results in loosening and detaching the scale from the surface of the metal, when it sinks to the bottom of the vat where it accumulates and must be removed at frequent intervals. Unlike the black scale, the red rust (which is a hydrated sesquioxide of iron of the general formula $XFe_2O_3 \cdot YH_2O$ or a double compound of ferric oxide and ferric hydroxide, $Fe_2O_3 \cdot 2Fe(OH)_3$), is readily soluble in sulphuric acid, and under the conditions of pickling this action results in the formation of iron sulphate, also. This salt remains in solution, and as concentrated acid is added from time to time to replace that neutralized, the solution eventually becomes saturated to such an extent that it is no longer fit for pickling. The exhausted solution must then be replaced.

Manner of Handling the Material—When the rods are removed from the hook conveyor in the rod mill, they are loaded into standard-gauge gondola cars. The coiled rods are loaded in an upright position to facili-

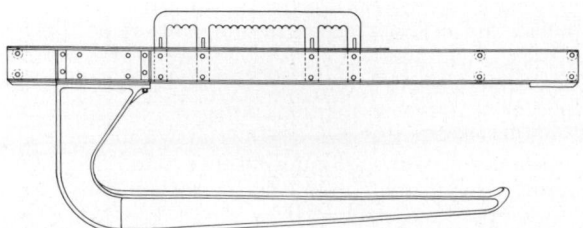

FIG. 29—4. Open-type "C" hook for handling coiled rods and wire.

tate unloading with a so-called "C" hook (Figures 29—4 and 29—5).

From the rod mill, the rods are transported to the rod storage where they are unloaded by an overhead crane. The crane is equipped with the "C" hook referred to above, which has a capacity of two to three tons. Facilities for storing rods consist of large bins or racks. Each gage and steel composition is stored in a separate bin in order to avoid confusion and possible misapplication.

In modern integrated mills, the rods may be moved directly from the rod storage to the cleaning crane by the rod-storage crane. In other mills, the rods are set down in racks by the rod-storage crane and then moved to the cleaning crane by ram tractor or on rod trucks. In either case, the rod-storage crane sets up the exact amount of rods which the cleaning crane can handle in one lift, so that there is a minimum of handling.

The "C" hook or hairpin hook, as it is sometimes called, is a specially designed device for handling coiled rods and wire. It is designed to lift as a unit the number of coiled rod bundles which the cleaning crane was designed to handle in one lift. There are two types, the open-end type and the latch type. Both are made by using a section of extra-heavy pipe, or I-beam, which is long enough to span the cleaning tank. This pipe has a metal eye attached at the approximate center, or balance point, into which the crane hook is inserted for lifting. From the pipe, a very heavy hanger is suspended. In the open type (Figure 29—4), this

hanger is in the form of a large letter "C" with the bottom section straightened horizontally and made long enough to lift the proper number of coils.

In the latch type (Figure 29—5), the hanger is made more in the shape of the letter "L," and the horizontal section is pivoted to the vertical section which allows for a slight movement of the cross piece. At the opposite end of the pipe, a second hanger is suspended. This hanger is pivoted to the pipe allowing it to swing freely. When the hook has been threaded through a lift of rods, this second hanger is swung down and latched to the free end of the cross piece. This gives support to both ends of the cross piece. All of the parts which come in direct contact with the acid are made of phosphor bronze, aluminum bronze, or other acid-resisting material.

A hook with its load is referred to as a "pin" or "stem" of rods or wire.

Types of Cranes—There are two types of cranes generally used in cleaning, namely, the circle crane and the overhead electric traveling crane. One type of circle crane consists of an upright standard set in bearings to allow the upright standard to turn 360°. A horizontal boom is placed on the upper part of the standard. This boom or arm is built long enough to reach the center of the cleaning and coating tanks which are placed in an arc around the base of the standard. Power for lifting the material to be cleaned is supplied by a steam piston which is placed on the boom or standard. Power for turning the standard and boom is supplied by placing a ring gear around the upright standard. This ring gear is then driven by an electric motor which is connected by the proper gearing and shafting.

Use of the circle type of crane requires the cleaning and coating tanks to be placed in an arc around the upright standard. The number of tanks is then limited by the radius of the boom.

When the electric overhead traveling crane is used, the cleaning and coating tanks may be placed in a straight line or sometimes two lines are used.

The gantry crane is another type of electric crane in use. This crane requires all the tanks to be in one line as the crane has no cross travel, and the crane hook moves in relatively the same horizontal line at all times. This type of crane has value where there is a large volume of work and few varieties of product.

Construction of Tanks—The rectangular acid tanks are constructed of welded steel plate, and are usually large enough to hold two stems of rods. The bottom is reinforced with channels and angles, and the interior is lined with a $\frac{3}{16}$-inch thick membrane of rubber or neoprene to protect the steel from the acid. Inside the rubber lining a layer of acid-proof brick is placed completely covering the sidewalls and bottom of the tank. The brick lining is bonded to the rubber or neoprene with acid-resisting sulphur-base cement. Acid-resisting synthetic-resin cement is used in the brick joints. All unprotected exterior surfaces of the tank are covered with a black vinyl-resin-base acid-resisting paint.

Water-rinse tanks are also usually rectangular and constructed of welded steel plate. Such tanks usually

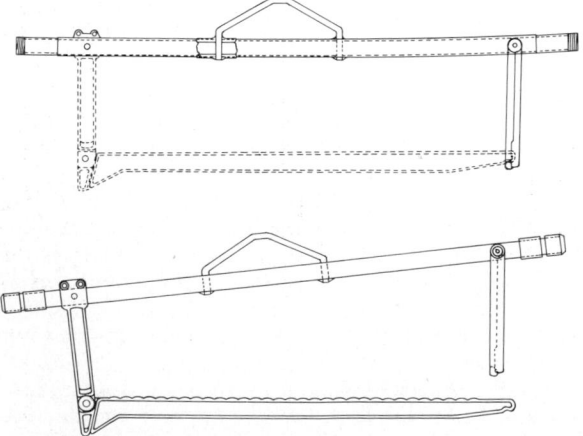

FIG. 29—5. Latch-type "C" hook for handling coiled rods and wire.

FIG. 29—6. General view inside a straight-line cleaning house. Rods can be cleaned in acid, coated with borax, lime, or sulphur, dried and baked in one continuous operation.

are of one-stem capacity. All surfaces are coated with a black vinyl-resin-base acid-resisting paint. The upper section of a water-rinse tank is provided with a series of high-pressure water nozzles, while the lower part of the tank contains fresh running water for rinsing.

Lime tanks are also rectangular and constructed of welded steel plate, and usually have a capacity of one stem.

Arrangement of Tanks—As already indicated, when a circle crane is employed, the number of tanks is limited by the radius of the boom of the crane. When an overhead traveling crane is used, the number of tanks is unlimited. Figures 29—6 and 29—7 show typical arrangements for so-called straight-line cleaning. In general, the acid tanks are used first in the cycle, then the water-rinse tank, and finally the coating tanks. Sull coating today is in very slight demand,

but usually a small section is provided where the rods can be treated for formation of this coating.

Concentration of Acid—There are three factors which affect the cleaning operation, namely, time, temperature, and concentration of acid. In operation, the tanks are first partially filled with water. Then the acid is added in the required amount and the steam for heating the bath is turned on. By the time the tanks are filled by the addition of more water, the steam has raised the temperature to the required point, usually about 180° F, and the acid concentration has been adjusted to the required amount.

Certain kinds of steel require longer time for cleaning than others. Low-carbon rods which may be finished at a high temperature on the rod mill will have a very heavy scale. Also, rod coils which are very compact, as is usually true with the coarser gages, are more

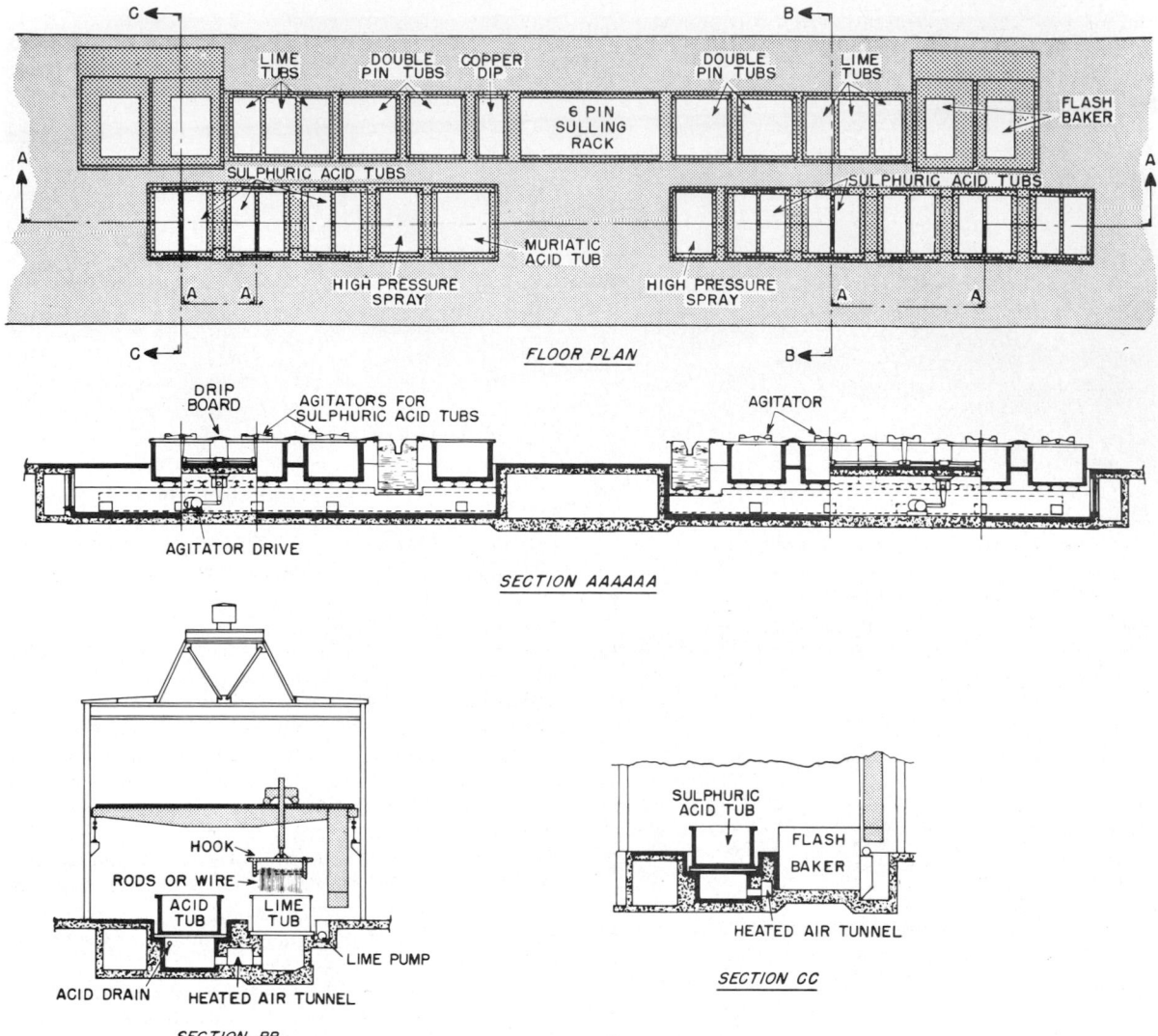

FIG. 29—7. Typical arrangement for so-called straight-line cleaning of rods in preparation for drawing.

difficult to clean. Bessemer and high-carbon steels re-act much faster to the acid, and the time of cleaning is shorter. This is particularly true of high-carbon pat-ented rods which have the scale broken up by the sheaves on the take-up frame of the patenting furnace. The acid concentration, then, is varied according to the kind of steel being treated, the low-carbon heavily-scaled material requiring a solution having a higher concentration of acid, with the higher-carbon steels and patented material requiring a lower concentration.

Temperature for Cleaning—The control of tem-perature in the cleaning operation is very important since the rapidity of the reaction between acid and steel is greatly affected by temperature. It is known that the reaction is 100 times as fast at 190° F as at room temperature. Too high a temperature, therefore, can be very wasteful. It causes rapid and high usage of the acid, develops unnecessary fumes which, in turn, can cause excessive corrosive action on the steel-work of the building. What is more important, it

causes pitting action on the surface of the steel being treated. The tanks in most modern cleaning houses are equipped with thermostatic controls so that a uniform pickling-solution temperature is maintained.

Inhibitors are used to aid in preventing pitting or over-cleaning. These usually have a nitrogenous hy-drocarbon base. The theory of the use of inhibitors is that when the scale has been removed from the steel, the inhibitor forms a protective film on the cleaned surface and minimizes any additional attack by the acid.

Time of Cleaning—The time required for cleaning will vary according to the amount of scale to be re-moved and the type of steel being treated. This may vary from as little as 10 minutes for high-carbon patented rods to 30 or 35 minutes for low-carbon heavily-scaled rods. Another factor which affects the time of cleaning is the change in specific gravity of the acid solution. As the work proceeds and more and more scale is removed, the iron content of the bath builds up. This is reflected in a change in specific gravity of the solution, which is usually measured by a hydrometer that provides a Baumé reading. As the Baumé figure increases, the action of the acid is retarded and the cleaning process gradually slows down. When the Baumé reading reaches about 20, the acid in the tanks is discarded, after which the tanks are washed out and refilled. In modern cleaning houses, where the tanks hold from 5000 to 7000 gallons, it is customary to have one extra acid tank. This tank is filled and heated to temperature, ready to operate when one of the other tanks is being emptied of its spent acid. By rotating the use of the tanks in this way, continuous operation can be maintained.

Rinsing—It is very important to have the cleaned rods or wire thoroughly rinsed after the acid cleaning. The cleaned material is dipped into a tank of fresh running water. There is a series of high-pressure sprays placed around and at the top of the water tank. When the cleaned rods are dipped in the water, a switch automatically turns on a high-pressure pump. As the crane moves the rods up and down, the high-pressure sprays wash them thoroughly and remove all traces of acid or acid residue.

Coatings—After the rods are thoroughly cleaned and rinsed, it is necessary to apply a coating. The purpose of the coating is three-fold: First, it prevents oxidation or rusting of the surface; second, it neutralizes any traces of acid which may be left on the steel; third, it acts as a carrier for the lubricant used in drawing. For dry drawing, dry slaked lime or hydrated lime have been found to be the best materials for coating. Lime is a low-cost material and is easily applied. Borax is another coating which has been used for dry drawing in recent years. It is a little more costly than lime, but it offers some advantages. It dries very quickly, it does not pick up moisture, and it does not flake off or form a dust in the wire-drawing room, thereby making conditions much cleaner in the mill.

Process for Lime Coating—The lime coating is applied to the rods simply by dipping the cleaned rods into a tank of hot milk of lime. The temperature is kept between 190° F and 200° F. The rods should be kept in the solution long enough to bring them up to bath temperature. This aids in drying the coating and also makes it adhere better to the steel. Formerly, it was customary for the mills to purchase the burned lime and slake and age it before use. In recent years, very good grades of so-called quick-slaking lime and hydrated lime have been developed commercially. These are packaged in paper bags of about 50 pounds each.

By using a special recirculating pump and an auxiliary small tank, the lime can be kept in motion so that "settling out" cannot take place. This results in a more-adherent fine-grain coating.

Coatings for Dry Drawing—In practice, several coating tubs are served by one cleaning crane. There may be three or four lime tubs. In these tubs, the lime is kept at various consistencies. This allows the several coatings which may be required in the wire-drawing operations to be kept in readiness. Rods which are to be drawn one or two drafts to produce a clean bright finish are given a very light lime coating. For three- and four-draft wires, a medium lime coating is applied,

and for wires which may be drawn five and six drafts, a very heavy lime coating may be used. In fact, where many drafts are required, it is often customary to give the rod two or three dips in a very heavy lime.

Where borax is used, a separate tank must be provided. This solution is adjusted to a consistency depending upon the number of drafts the wire is to be given.

Phosphate Coatings—Recently, this type of coating has become quite popular, primarily for wire to be subjected to cold heading or cold extrusion, where a chemical rather than a mechanical bond between the coating and the metal is desirable. Either a zinc-phosphate or an iron-phosphate solution may be used, and both are applied by immersing the wire in the heated solution (at about 180° F) for from 2 to 10 minutes depending upon the weight of coating desired.

After suitable hot- and cold-water rinsing, the phosphate coating is neutralized with lime or some other suitable agent, baked, and drawn through the normal dry-drawing lubricants (calcium- or aluminum-stearate and lime mixtures) or coated with a neutral sodium tallow soap.

This type of coating, when heavy enough, gives excellent results for heavy cold extrusions as well as long shelf life.

Baking—After the rods or wires are properly cleaned and coated, they must be thoroughly dried before drawing. The drying or baking is done in ovens or bakers. In the cleaning process, hydrogen is liberated by action of the acid upon the steel, and sometimes this hydrogen is absorbed by the steel. This can cause the drawn wire to be brittle, a condition known as "acid brittleness." The baking process has two purposes: one, to dry the coating so that it will function properly in dry drawing and, two, to remove any hydrogen that may have been absorbed by the steel.

There are several types of bakers. The **flash type** is the most popular. This is a baker of about the size and shape of a lime tub. One pin of rods is placed in the baker for from five to fifteen minutes, depending upon the weight of coating to be dried. The temperature is usually kept between 450 and 600° F. The **tunnel type** is another baker used. This is a long, rectangular oven with a roll or chain conveyor running through its length. In operation, the rods are placed on the con-

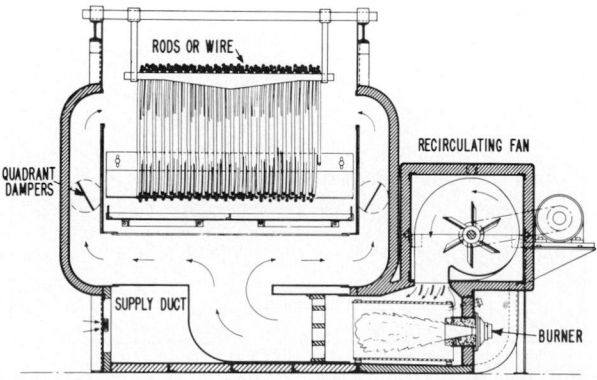

FIG. **29**—8. Cross-section of a flash baker for drying rods and wire after cleaning.

veyor and pass slowly through the baker. The time may be one or two hours at temperatures from 400 to 500° F. **Compartment-type** bakers are still used to a limited extent. In these bakers, the rods are loaded onto steel buggies which are pushed into the oven on tracks running throughout its length. The temperature is usually between 250 and 325° F which requires a longer baking time. This may be from three to eight hours. The flash and tunnel bakers are fired with oil or gas and are equipped with high-velocity fans which rapidly recirculate the heated air. Figure 29—8 shows a sketch of a flash baker.

SECTION 6

WIRE-DRAWING EQUIPMENT

Dies—The wire-drawing die is one of the most efficient tools used in industry. It has no moving parts; it does not remove any of the metal; yet it uniformly reduces the cross-sectional area of the steel and at the same time improves the finish and physical properties. Over the years many different materials have been used for wire-drawing dies. Chilled iron, steel plates, alloy steel, all have been used, but in the late 1920's tungsten carbide was developed and tried out. This material was an immediate success, and in a comparatively few years it replaced all other materials except the diamond. Diamond dies are still used for very fine sizes of high-carbon and alloy steels but even in this range the tungsten-carbide die can be used. Tungsten carbide is a very hard material and has great wearing characteristics but does not have very great resistance to impact. It must have some outside reinforcing when put to use. This is accomplished by pressing a small section of tungsten carbide, called a "nib," into a cylindrical steel casing, as shown in Figure 29—9.

Die Holes—The shape of the die has been found to be very important. There are four distinct zones in the die as shown in Figure 29—10. The first zone, on the entering side of the die, is somewhat larger in diameter than the rod or wire to be drawn; its purpose is to afford room for the die lubricant that adheres to the rod or wire to be drawn into the hole. This is called the **bell and entering angle** and gradually tapers into the second zone. The second zone is called the **approach angle** and is the section where most of the actual re-

duction takes place. The next zone is called the **bearing zone** and it may have a very slight angle of taper. The exit zone or **back relief** is in the form of a countersinking of the back part of the hole. This is done as a strengthening to prevent the circular edge of the hole from breaking away.

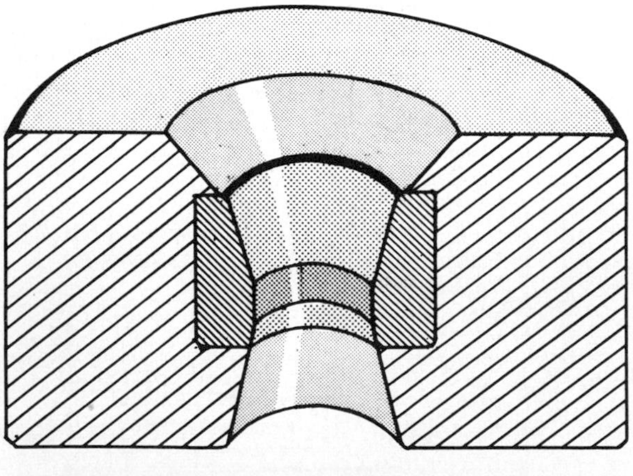

Diamond Dies—Diamond dies are frequently used when accuracy and uniformity of section are required in the finer sizes of wire, especially in the process of continuous wet drawing. In the construction of diamond dies, a diminutive flat crystal of diamond is securely fastened in a center opening of a small circular metal disc, then a hole of required diameter is worked through this diamond by special drills and diamond dust. Diamond is one of the hardest substances known and has great wearing qualitites. Long lengths of fine wire can, in consequence, be drawn through these dies with little or no change of sectional area due to wear of the die.

The Block—Wire was first drawn in very short lengths and was merely pulled through the die in straight pieces. As the lengths grew longer, some means of storage became necessary. The wire-drawing block serves this purpose. The block is a steel casting in the form of a cylinder the sides of which have a slight taper. The base of the cast cylinder is solid and there are enough cross members inside the casting to give adequate support to the sides. At the base, there is also a flanged section extending horizontally outward around the cylinder. The juncture of this horizontal flange and the vertical sides of the block is machined to a definite radius. This is called the **fillet** of the block. In the center of the block, a vertical cylindrical hole is left to allow for the drive shaft to be keyed to the block.

In operation, the wire is threaded through the die

Fig. 29—9. Schematic cross-section (not to scale) of a single-hole wire-drawing die employing a nib of sintered carbide mounted in a circular steel holder.

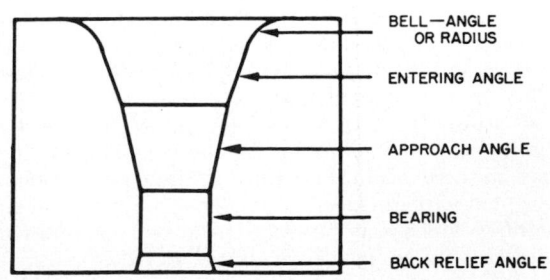

BELL—ANGLE OR RADIUS

ENTERING ANGLE

APPROACH ANGLE

BEARING

BACK RELIEF ANGLE

Fig. 29—10. Enlarged cross-section of die hole showing names of parts.

and attached to the block by a vise or clamp. The block revolves and pulls the wire through the die. As the wire is wound around the fillet of the block it is forced upward. At each revolution of the block the wire moves upward approximately one diameter of the wire being drawn. The sides of the block may be six or eight inches high. At the top of the block four vertical pins are placed. As the wire feeds upwards and reaches the top of the block, it is stored around these four pins. The result is a uniformly wound, compact coil of wire.

DRAWING MACHINES

There are several types of drawing machines. These may be grouped as follows: drawbench, bull block, motor block, multiple-draft machines, drawing frames. These will be briefly described.

Drawbench—A drawbench is a mechanism used to give a single draft to heavy material, which is afterwards usually straightened and cut to a definite length. It handles the largest sizes drawn and is especially adapted for drawing shapes, screw stock and small shafting. The machine itself consists of a horizontal framework 50 to 100 feet long, along the center line of which runs a heavy roller chain driven by heavy sprocket wheels. The die through which the material is drawn is located at the opposite end of the frame from the drive. A carriage mounted on wheels, and arranged to travel along the upper surface of the frame or bench, has suitable jaws for gripping the ma-

terial and pulling it through the die, and also a heavy hook for connection with the roller chain. This equipment is similar to that used for drawing seamless tubes (see Chapter 30).

Bull Blocks—Sizes ½-inch to 1-inch are usually drawn on horizontal blocks called bull blocks. These are very heavy machines built to pull these coarse sizes (Figure 29—11). They are driven by an individual variable-speed motor. The blocks are usually 36 inches in diameter. The horizontal block makes it easier and safer to handle coils of drawn wire in these coarse sizes.

Motor Blocks—These are also driven by an individual motor, but the blocks have a vertical spindle (Figure 29—12). The size range drawn on these machines is usually ³⁄₁₆-inch to ½-inch. The blocks may be 26, 30 or 36 inches in diameter. Motor blocks may also be equipped with double-deck blocks. This is an arrangement whereby one block is placed above the other, both being mounted on a common spindle. The lower block is made smaller in diameter than the upper block. In drawing, the wire is pulled through one die and wound around the lower block several times, then it passes around a sheave and into a second die and onto the second or finishing block. Thus two drafts are drawn on the one spindle. Sizes from ³⁄₁₆-inch to ⅛-inch are usually drawn by the double-deck method. Due to the heat developed, only low-carbon wire is drawn in this manner.

FIG. 29—11. Heavy machines employing horizontal blocks called "bull blocks" for drawing coarse (½-inch to 1-inch) sizes of wire.

FIG. 29—12. Motor block, with vertical spindles, for drawing wires.

Continuous Machines—Wire which requires three drafts or more from the rod is usually drawn on continuous machines. The tungsten-carbide die, due to its long-wearing characteristic, makes it practical and economical to use continuous machines for the so-called multiple-draft work. There are two general types of machines used in dry drawing. These may be described as the cumulative and non-cumulative types.

In the cumulative-type machine, the wire is drawn on a conventional type block and is allowed to build up around the block pins. At the top of the pins a ring is placed. The first end of the wire is threaded through a loop on this ring and then is fed over a dome and down through the center shaft of the block which is hollow. From here it is led around sheaves and into the next die and onto the next block. In another type of cumulative machine the wire passes from the ring up over a sheave, which is mounted above the center of the block, and then down around another sheave and into the next die. In this type of machine the blocks are usually geared so that the speed of each block is increased as the diameter of the wire is reduced. In drawing it is customary to lay out the drafting so that each block draws a little more wire than the succeeding block. This results in a gradual buildup on each block. When the blocks are filled up, the machine is shut down and all the blocks, except the finishing block, are de-clutched. The machine is then started again and the finishing block removes the accumulation from the block next to it. The slip ring at the top of this block revolves and keeps the wire paying off uniformly. When this block is nearly empty, the machine is stopped and the nearly empty block is re-clutched. This process is repeated until the build-up is worked down from all blocks. Figure 29—13 shows a cumulative-type machine and Figure 29—14 shows a closeup of the blocks.

On the non-cumulative type of machine, the wire is drawn through the die and wrapped around a block in the conventional manner. This block will be about six to eight inches in height. When the wire reaches the top of the block, it passes around the sheave. This sheave is mounted at the end of an arm which is attached to a rheostat, which in turn controls the speed of the block. From this sheave, the wire passes to another sheave and into the next die. Each block of this type of machine has its own individual motor. The drafting is usually laid out to meet the nominal speeds for which the machine is designed. If, however, this drafting should get out of line and one block draws more wire than the preceeding block supplies, the arm

FIG. 29—13. Overall view of cumulative-type continuous wire-drawing machine. (Courtesy of Morgan Construction Co.)

FIG. 29—14. Closeup view of the blocks of a cumulative-type continuous wire-drawing machine. (Courtesy of Morgan Construction Co.)

FIG. 29—16. Closeup view of a block of a non-cumulative type of continuous wire-drawing machine. (Courtesy of Vaughn Machinery Co.)

moves forward and actuates the rheostat so that the speed of the preceding block is increased. By this means the production of each block is kept in balance with all the other blocks and there is no great amount of build-up on the blocks.

Both types of machines are equipped with means for cooling the wire between each draft. In drawing higher-carbon wire (0.30 carbon and over) it has been found that the wire will become brittle if the heat developed in drawing is not removed between drafts. Both types of machines use a blast of air directed at

the wire to cool it, but the non-cumulative machine also employs a water spray inside the block. This is necessary because the time the wire is on the block is much shorter than on the cumulative machine. Figure 29—15 shows the non-cumulative machine, and Figure 29—16 a closeup of a block.

Intermediate Machines—It is usually economical to use the continuous machines which draw from the rod for not more than six or seven drafts. This produces sizes down to 0.072-inch or 0.062-inch. For sizes finer than 0.062-inch down to 0.030-inch an intermediate-size machine is used. This machine is usually the same in design principles as the rod machines but its construction is lighter and speeds are usually faster to take care of the smaller-gage wire.

Fine-Wire Machines—Sizes finer than 0.030-inch

FIG. 29—15. General view of a non-cumulative type of continuous wire-drawing machine. (Courtesy of Vaughn Machinery Co.)

FIG. 29—17. General view of a cone-type fine-wire drawing machine.

are usually drawn by the wet process on specially designed machines. There are several types of these machines. The **tandem type** uses horizontal spindles and the drawing blocks are vertical. The wire is drawn through the first die and given a few wraps around the block and passes directly into the next die. The **step-cone type** uses horizontal spindles and has several blocks of different diameters mounted on each spindle, giving the appearance of a cone. The coarser wire is drawn on the smaller block and passes around an idler sheave and into the next die and onto the next larger block. The diameters of the blocks are designed to take care of the normal elongation of the wire. Another type is the **circular tandem type** in which the blocks are arranged in a circle, with a die between each block. Each block is geared to draw enough faster than the preceding block to take up the increase in length. The finishing block is usually eight inches in diameter, but many of these machines are equipped to take up the wire on spools.

In wet drawing, the drawing lubricant is a soap solution diluted with water. This solution is pumped from a tank on the machine or from a central tank supplying several machines. The solution is piped directly to a nozzle which sprays the lubricant into the bell of the drawing die. There is enough surplus to spray the drawing block also. In this manner the die, the wire, and the drawing block are kept well lubricated. The surplus lubricant falls to the bottom of the machine where it drains out to the supply tank or into a filter system for recirculation. Figure 29—17 shows a cone-

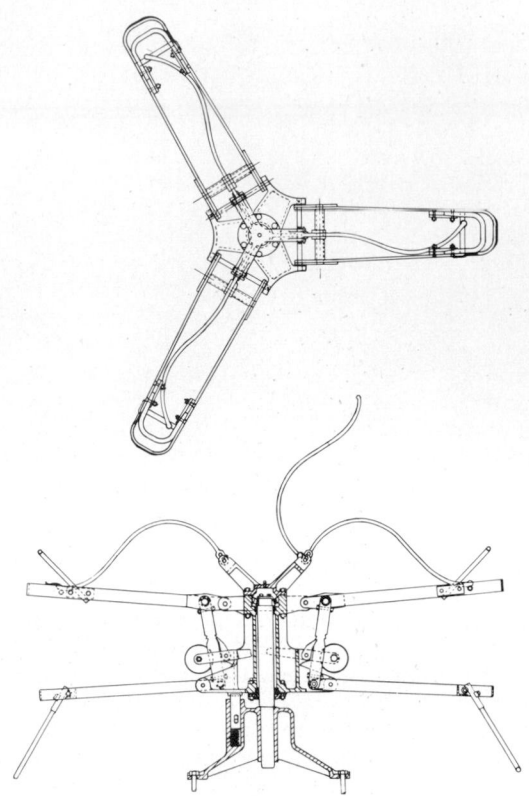

Fig. 29—19. Plan and elevation sketch of a three-arm pay-off reel. (Courtesy of Morgan Construction Co.)

type machine and Figure 29—18 shows the circular tandem type.

Drawing Frames—Before the development of continuous machines, all wire was drawn on what are known as **frames,** and a large percentage of wire still is drawn by this method. A frame is equipped with several wire-drawing blocks, all capable of being driven from a common shaft, either singly or in unison. The horizontal shaft extends the length of the machine, usually below floor level. From this shaft, vertical spindles are geared, and at the top of each spindle a drawing block is mounted. A separate clutch for each block permits the individual blocks to be started, operated or stopped without affecting the others on the frame. The blocks are usually 22 or 26 inches in diameter and the spindles set at about 5-foot centers. The blocks are about 25 to 30 inches above the floor level and all gearing and other moving parts are enclosed. Each block has a die holder or die box which also holds the drawing lubricant. Each block is also equipped with a pull-out mechanism, which is geared to the main shaft. In operation, the rod is placed on a pay-off reel and one end is pointed. This pointed end is then threaded through the die. The pointed end is then grasped by a pair of pincer jaws which are attached to the pull-out mechanism. About three feet of wire is then pulled through the die. The pincer jaws are released and the wire is attached to the block by a clamp on the side of the block. The block is then started by attaching it to the spindle by actuating the jaw clutch which is operated by a foot lever. When the coil

Fig. 29—18. General view of a circular-tandem type of fine-wire drawing machine.

has been drawn, the block is declutched and the coil is removed by an overhead hoist. The coil is then placed on another pay-off reel and the process is repeated on another block until the required size is produced.

Obviously, there are disadvantages to this method. Each coil must be handled separately for each draft. All blocks on a given frame turn at the same speed and as the diameter of the wire is reduced, the length of the wire and, consequently, the running time increase, and more blocks must be provided for drawing wire to the smaller sizes in order to keep pace with the blocks drawing coarser wire through the early drafts.

AUXILIARY EQUIPMENT

Pay-Off Reels—For rods $11/32$-inch and smaller, a flipper-type reel is used. This consists of two horizontal arms placed one above the other, both extending from a vertical standard. The arms are hinged so that they may be moved up or down. In use the arms are collapsed and the rod coil is suspended on the upper arm. Both arms are then moved to the horizontal position and the rod is held vertically. In this manner each convolution of the rod coil can be paid off or flipped and pulled up to the die. Some reels are made with three arms set at 120°. While one coil is paying off, the other arms are loaded and the ends are welded so there is no stoppage necessary between rod coils. Figure 29—19 shows a 3-arm reel. Another method is the stem pay-off, Figures 29—20 and 29—21. By this method the full stem of rods from the cleaning operation is placed on a special holder. A long bar or U-shaped rod is placed through the center of the coils and acts as a hold-back to keep the convolutions paying off uniformly. The coils are welded as in the flipper pay-off.

Welders—For continuous drawing, electric butt welders or flash welders are used. These have been developed to perform very well on high- and low-carbon steel. For welding high-carbon steel, the welders are equipped with annealing jaws to give the steel

Fig. 29—20. Stem of rods from the cleaning house being loaded by tractor into the stem-type pay-off.

the proper structure for drawing after the weld is made. Grinders are also provided to quickly remove the "burr" or upset formed by the weld.

Safety Stop—All machines and frames are equipped with stops to cut off the power quickly in case of trouble. Between the flipper reel and the first die a snarl stop is placed which will stop the machine or block in case of a tangle or snarl before the rod is broken. All machines are equipped with bars around all working parts. By merely pushing against these bars the machine can be stopped. The motors are also equipped with dynamic brakes so that there is immediate response to the stop signal and there is no tendency for the machine to "coast."

Pointers—Several methods are used for pointing the rods or wire for the initial threading of the dies. The fine sizes are literally pulled apart and the "necking down" forms a point. The intermediate sizes are pointed by means of a "roll pointer" as shown in Figure 29—22. This consists of a pair of oscillating rolls with grooves of varying diameters. The rod end is worked down to smaller sizes by successive rolling in the

Fig. 29—21. Battery of wire-drawing machines (left) being fed by stem pay-offs in the right foreground.

Fig. 29—22. "Roll pointer" for pointing rods or wire for initial threading through the dies. (Courtesy of Morgan Construction Co.)

grooves of decreasing size. The larger sizes are swaged or hammered on rotary swaging machines or are machined by specially designed cutting machines.

"Turks-Head" Shaped-Wire Drawing Machine— Common four-sided shaped wire, such as squares, oblongs or keystone shape, are frequently produced on cold-rolling equipment known as a "Turks-head" machine. This consists of four hardened-steel rolls set in

planes at right angles to each other. The narrow face of the rolls, as set in the framework, is adjustable on the same plane so that the assembly of the overlapping roll edges facing each other will project the contour of the opening so formed, into the desired shape of the cross-section of the wire to be made. The process wire, of a size somewhat larger than the finished size desired, is pointed and pulled through the Turks-head, being thus rolled to shape and size, after which it is coiled on a regular wire-drawing take-up block.

Heating Effect in Wire Drawing—The plastic deformation involved in drawing wire will induce internal heat, and this rise in temperature of the wire will be dependent on the composition or hardness of the steel and the amount of cold work or reduction of cross-sectional area of the wire. In the ordinary dry drawing of frame or individual drafting, the wire will cool somewhat between successive drafts, but on continuous drafting, the heating of the wire may be cumulative resulting in temperatures frequently detrimental to the quality of the wire. This rise in temperature may be restricted by several methods, such as air or water cooling of the wire-drawing capstans or blocks and the use of water-cooled dies, the latter being more of a secondary rather than a direct effect. The effect of the wire-drawing temperatures is not as detrimental to low-carbon steel wires as to high-carbon wires. The toughness and uniformity are adversely affected, and in drawing high-carbon wire of high tensile-strength requirement, by either single or continuous drafting, the temperature must be controlled and kept as low as possible. The efficiency of lubricants used in the wire-drawing die, and carried on the wire in continuous drafting, is adversely affected by excessive wire-drawing temperatures. Without the cooling devices, the present high wire-drawing speeds could not be attained and die life would be considerably reduced.

SECTION 7

WIRE-DRAWING PROCESSES AND OPERATIONS

Results of Cold Drawing—The results attainable by the wire-drawing process may be summarized as follows:

1. Metal may be elongated and reduced in section to an extent not attainable by other methods.

2. A greater degree of accuracy as to size and section can be attained than is possible by other methods excepting cold rolling, which is not applicable to common sizes of wire.

3. A uniformly smooth and highly polished surface can be produced.

4. The process serves as a test for the detection of hidden flaws in the metal. The fact that a wire has satisfactorily withstood the drawing operation may be taken as an indication that the metal was originally sound and free from defects liable to cause it to fail in service. This statement does not mean that the wire itself is free from all flaws or defects, for it is possible to produce certain flaws by improper drawing.

5. Finally, the process affects the mechanical prop-

erties of the metal, which fact, as noted under the heading of tempers, makes it possible, by employing this process in conjunction with heat treatment, to produce many wires from the same steel having different mechanical properties.

Effect of Drawing Upon Mechanical Properties— Wire drawing, like any cold working of metals such as iron or copper, will increase the hardness, stiffness, tensile strength and elastic limit. The ductility, as indicated by the elongation and reduction of area, will be correspondingly decreased. The extent of these changes in mechanical properties is not always directly proportional to the amount of drafting or cold work done upon the metal, as it is affected by various factors such as the total amount of drafting, number of drafts, per cent draft per draft and the type of material itself. However, for each set of conditions, the change in mechanical properties has been determined, and the processing necessary to produce the required grade of wire may be regulated accordingly. The gain

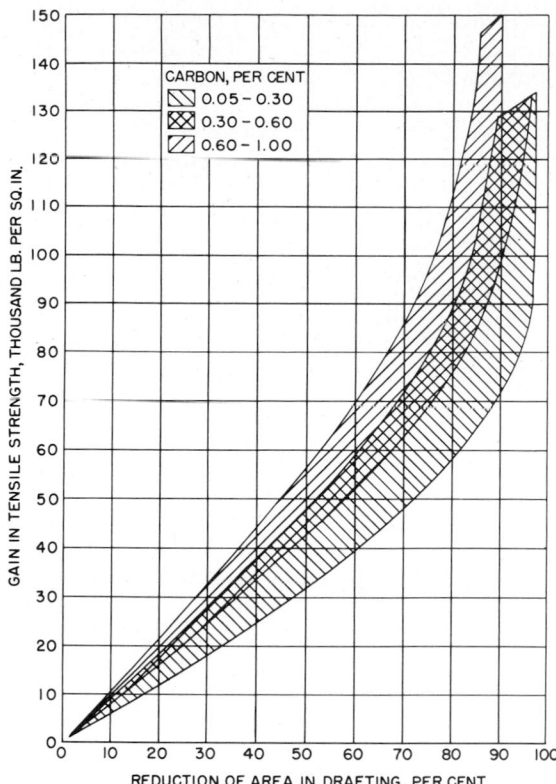

Fig. 29—23. Gain in tensile strength on drafting steels of carbon contents from 0.05 to 1.00 per cent.

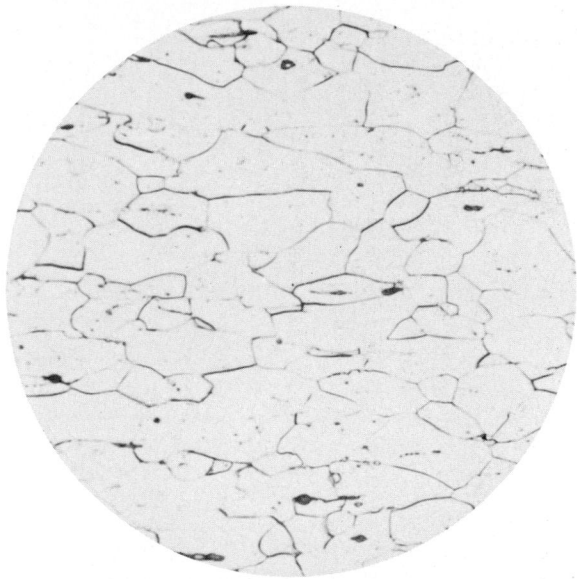

Fig. 29—25. Structure of 0.06 carbon-steel wire after one draft. Longitudinal section. Magnification: 500X.

in tensile strength in drawing of various carbon steels under standard conditions is shown in Figure 29—23 and indicates the hardness increase as the cold reduction of the wire increases.

The Cause of These Changes—These changes in the characteristics of the metal brought about by cold working are to be attributed to the changes in grain structure such working produces. In a hot-rolled rod or in an annealed wire the grains have a polygonal form and are arranged about as shown in Figure 29—24. The microstructure of an annealed low-carbon steel wire is shown in the photomicrographs of Figures 29—27 and 29—28. All photomicrographs shown represent longitudinal sections, parallel to the direction of drafting. Figure 29—24 exhibits grains in the steel before drafting. Figure 29—25 shows the condition of

Fig. 29—24. Full-annealed 0.06 carbon-steel wire. Longitudinal section. Magnification: 500X.

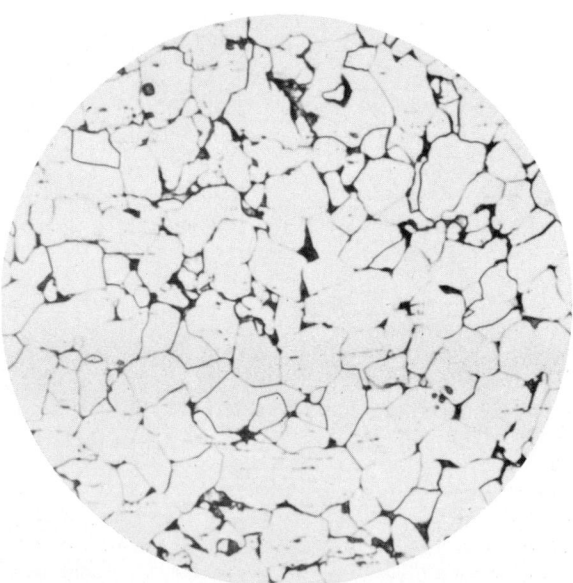

Fig. 29—26. Longitudinal section of hard-drawn 0.15 carbon-steel wire. Magnification: 500X.

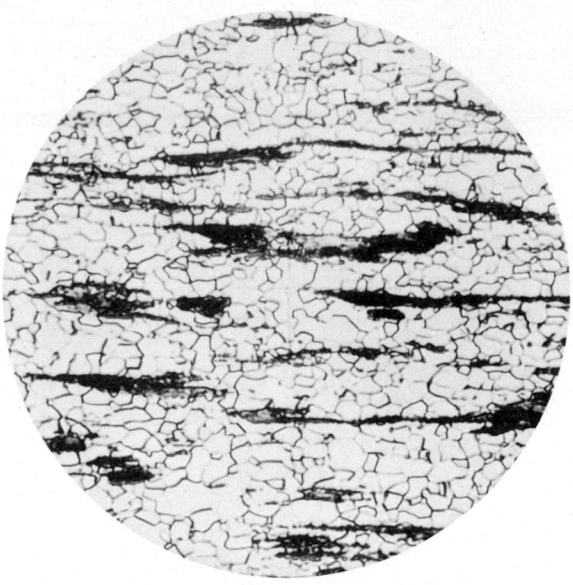

FIG. 29—27. Structure of 0.15 carbon-steel wire after short-time-cycle sub-critical anneal. Longitudinal section. Magnification: 500X.

the grains after the material has had one draft. Here it can be seen that, as the wire is being elongated while passing through the die, the grains in the steel actually become elongated, also. The grains elongate in the direction of the drafting and become correspondingly narrower at right angles to that direction. Figure 29—26 shows the same wire after having had a number of drafts. Here the grains have been elongated to a considerable extent. Due to the stretching of the wire in drawing and the crushing effect produced by the pressure exerted by the die in all directions towards the center of the wire, the structure has become so

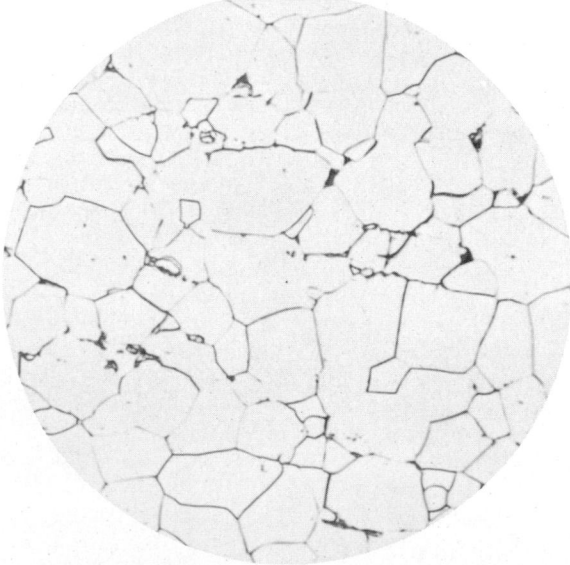

FIG. 29—28. Structure of 0.15 carbon-steel wire, full-annealed after hard drawing. Longitudinal section. Magnification: 500X.

altered that it is difficult, if not impossible, to locate the exact boundaries of the individual grains in their strained and distorted condition.

Limitations of Drawing—Steel may be drawn several drafts further than the state illustrated by Figure 29—26, but when wire has been put into this highly strained condition by drawing, it loses its ductility to such a degree that it is not practicable to submit it to further drawing, and if required to be reduced in section still more, it becomes necessary first to restore the grains to the form and arrangement characteristic of the unworked (not strained) condition. This changing back of the grains to a non-distorted form simultaneously restores the properties that existed in the wire before it was subjected to drawing. The processes employed for restoring the grain to strain-free formations are annealing and patenting. The effects of these processes will be discussed in the section on "Heat-Treatment of Wire." Enough having been said to explain the reasons for them, some of the chief features of wire-drawing practice will now be considered.

DRY DRAWING

Dry Drawing of Low-Carbon Wire—Most low-carbon wire is drawn directly from the hot-rolled rod. In producing sizes coarser than 0.1875 in. in diameter, it is normal practice to roll the rod 1/16-in. larger than the required finished-wire diameter. After proper cleaning, coating, and baking, the wire is drawn to size in one draft.

Sizes 1/2-in. to 1-in. are drawn on horizontal bull blocks.

Sizes 0.1875-in. to 1/2-in. generally are drawn on single-spindle motor blocks.

Wires having diameters smaller than 0.1875-in. are drawn from a 7/32-in. (0.218-in.) diameter hot-rolled rod, which is the smallest hot-rolled rod size that it is commercially feasible to produce.

Low-carbon wire finer than 0.1875-in. down to 0.140-in. is drawn usually on double-deck motor blocks. Sizes finer than 0.140-in. are drawn on multiple-spindle machines that, as previously described, may have 3, 4, 5, 6, or 7 spindles. Ordinarily, wire of 0.0625-in. diameter (16 gage) is the smallest-diameter low-carbon steel wire that is drawn from the hot-rolled rod in one series of operations on a multiple-spindle machine: although it is possible to draw finer sizes, experience has proven that sizes smaller than 0.0625-in. should be finished on other pieces of equipment called **intermediate machines.** The so-called intermediate machines are built with 6 or 7 spindles and usually are equipped with 16-in. finishing blocks. Wire to be finish drawn on an intermediate machine is first drawn to a **process size** that is determined by experience to provide the most efficient starting material for the intermediate machines. Since total reduction in cross-sectional area of the wire effected in the series of drawing operations on an intermediate machine is approximately 90 per cent, the "process size" is set at about 90 per cent larger than the desired finished size.

Under favorable conditions, low-carbon wire can be drawn to reduce the cross-sectional area 95 per cent in a series of drafts without intervening heat treatment, starting with a hot-rolled rod of 7/32-in. diameter.

Uses of Low-Carbon Wire—In the fastener-manufacturing industry, low-carbon wire is used in the production of bolts, nuts, screws, studs, rivets and many other items—some of a highly specialized nature. Baling wire, barbed wire, and wire fence are among the important agricultural uses of steel wire. In the field of communications, low-carbon wire is used for telegraph and telephone wire. Nails and concrete reinforcing are only two of the very numerous prime uses of low-carbon wire in the construction industry.

High-Carbon and Specialty Wire—High-carbon and other specialty wire are also produced by the dry-drawing method. As the designation implies, these wires are intended for use in applications of a particular special nature. It is important for the wire manufacturer to know the intended use of the wire and how it is to be fabricated or processed in attaining its end-use form, so that the wire-making practice can be adjusted to produce wire that will perform satisfactorily during the customer's manufacturing operations and in service.

Some of the items in this category produced in large quantities are the various types of rope wire, bridge wire, valve-spring and other automotive-spring wire. Other important types include: tire-bead wire, tire-cord wire, music spring wire, hose-binding wire, and strand for reinforcing concrete; as well as wire for the many types of springs used in the bedding and furniture industries.

In most cases, the wire is drawn from a patented rod. The patenting process, described in more detail later, is a special heat treatment used only on high-carbon steel and peculiar to the wire industry alone: it imparts uniformity of microstructure, hardness and strength to steel so treated, thereby overcoming any non-uniformity that may have resulted from the hot-rolling operation by which the rod was produced.

After patenting, cleaning, coating and baking of the rod, the drawing operation on high-carbon wire is similar to that of drawing low-carbon wire, except that the reduction in cross-sectional area per draft is smaller for high-carbon wire and the cooling of the wire between drafts becomes an important factor in controlling the properties of the finished wire. If the wire is not cooled properly between drafts, the cumulative build-up of heat in the wire has an embrittling effect in the finished product that cannot be overcome by subsequent treatment. Therefore, all motor blocks and wire-drawing machines are equipped with water-cooled or air-cooled blocks, or both, as required to prevent embrittlement of the wire by the cumulative heating effect.

As previously mentioned, the cross-sectional area of a low-carbon hot-rolled rod may be reduced as much as 95 per cent in a series of drafts without intervening heat treatment but, as a general rule, the total reduction in cross-sectional area in drawing high-carbon wire from a patented rod does not exceed 75 to 80 per cent before another patenting operation is performed.

Sometimes, a hot-rolled, unpatented rod may be drawn one or two drafts to a process size before it is patented and drawn to finished size. This practice promotes greater uniformity in the finished wire because the roundness of the cold-drawn wire before patenting is improved, compared with the relatively non-uniform cross-section of the average hot-rolled rod.

By selecting the right combination of steel composition, heat treatment, and amount of cold work, the wire producer can manufacture wire that can meet almost any of the many and varied requirements of the wire-consuming industries. End uses of high-carbon wires range from springs actuating delicate miniature electronic-computer parts or opening and closing valves on an automobile engine to the fabrication of the load-carrying cables that support the colossal weight of modern suspension bridges.

WET DRAWING

The wet-drawing process is used to produce wire for decorative purposes or for special applications where extra-clean finish is required. In order to produce satisfactory wet-drawn wire, good cleaning and coating facilities and practices are required. Wet drawing is more costly than dry drawing; therefore, it is customary to dry-draw wire to a process size and then clean and coat the process wire prior to wet drawing to finished size.

Cleaning of the dry-drawn process wire prior to coating and wet drawing is usually effected by immersing the wire in a cold muriatic-acid or hot sulphuric-acid solution, or both. The objective is to remove all of the surface film resulting from dry drawing, so that clean metallic surface is ready for plating.

The plating solution consists of copper and tin sulphates in a liquid solution made by mixing with cold water and a small amount of sulphuric acid. By adjusting the proportions of copper sulphate and tin sulphate in the bath, various shades of color ranging from a typical reddish copper color to a nearly metallic-white tin finish can be obtained as required.

After cleaning, the coils are spread out on a stem or hair-pin hook and dipped into the plating solution. The plating is accomplished by deposition, and the thickness of coating and its uniformity are dependent upon duration of immersion and degree of agitation of the bath. After plating, the wire is washed thoroughly in fresh, cold water. At this point, the wire is either dipped in a special hot coating solution and baked, or placed in barrels and kept under water until it is delivered to the wire-drawing machines.

In principle, the wet-drawing process is identical with dry drawing. The equipment and actual practices, however, are entirely different. As a rule, lighter drafts (around 15 per cent) are taken.

With the older "underwater" method, the wire is placed on a submerged "wet reel" in a tub of water, pointed and pulled through a die onto the block. No lubricant is used in the die box; however, lubricant is added to the water.

The more modern method of using coated and baked wire paid off from a "dry reel" requires the use of additional lubricant in the die box.

For single-draft work, a single-spindle motor block may be used as well as frames. Block diameters are usually 26, 22, 16, or, in some cases, 12 inches. Finished wire sizes range from 20-gage (0.0348-in. diameter) to ¾-inch diameter.

Wet Drawing—Multiple Drafts—This is done on continuous machines that differ from those used for dry drawing. In general, they are cone-type machines with the drawing blocks mounted adjacent to each other on the same horizontal shaft. Naturally, the first block has the smallest diameter. After a sufficient length of wire has been pulled through the first die, a few wraps of the wire are taken around the first block and the wire is then passed back around a sheave and through the next die onto the next block, and so on. The second and each succeeding block is made sufficiently larger in diameter than its immediate predecessor to take care of the increased length due to the decrease in diameter of the wire after each draft. After the required size is reached, the wire is gathered on an 8-in. diameter block.

Wet-drawing machines are usually capable of making 10 to 14 drafts, and are completely enclosed, with a mixture of lubricant in water being sprayed continuously on the blocks and dies. In some cases, the blocks and dies are completely submerged in a water-and-lubricant solution that is constantly recirculated by a pump from a reservoir adjacent to the machine.

Drawing Limits and Tolerances—Although every effort is made to draw the wire as true to the required shape and size as possible, exactness in these respects is almost impossible under commercial conditions, and all wire produced under such conditions will vary somewhat in diameter and section. These variations may be due to a varying degree of hardness in the metal being drawn, to somewhat rapid wearing of the die, or, in the case of wet-drawn wires, to unsuitable or imperfect coatings. Some tolerance is necessary therefore, but it is important that these tolerances be kept within certain limits defined by the use to which the wire is to be put. The tolerances used by the wire industry are divided into four groups of allowable variations in the diameter of the common grades of round wire, other than special grades, and designated as **standard, semi-special, special,** and **extra special** drawing. Each of these sets of tolerances contains the variations allowable, which are adjusted to the size of the wire as indicated in Table **29**—III. The **standard** tolerances are those adopted by the American Iron and Steel Institute (AISI) and are given in their Steel Products Manual, Carbon-Steel Wire.

All wire is gaged carefully in two or three places around the circumference, just after the first end of the coil is pulled through the die and at the finished end to insure that it is of the correct size and shape. Wire ordered by gage number, by decimal, or by fraction of an inch, is gaged with a micrometer gage.

SPECIAL FINISHING OPERATIONS

Straightening and Cutting Wire—With the exception of the largest sizes, all wire, both round and shape, is drawn on a block and, therefore, at the finished size, is still in the form of a coil. But for certain purposes it is desired to have the wire furnished in short straight lengths, rather than in coils. This straightening and cutting work is usually done on some type of machine.

Whirls—For common round wire, automatic machines are employed for straightening and cutting the wire. These machines are required to perform three operations simultaneously or in very rapid succession, namely, pull the wire forward, straighten it, and cut it into the lengths desired. The mechanism for straightening the wire is known as a **head** or **whirl.** It contains a number of staggered dies which bend the wire slightly, as it passes through, in reverse directions so as to remove the bends and kinks and leave it straight. The wire to be straightened is automatically fed through the whirl and onto an apron, where it actuates a mechanically or electrically driven cutting tool which cuts the wire into uniform short pieces of the length desired.

Roll Straighteners—For shapes and flats the **roll straightener** is used. This machine consists of a set of vertical and also of horizontal rolls which can be so adjusted that pressure can be brought to bear on the

Table 29—III. Standard Size Tolerances for Wire

Size Tolerances for Uncoated Coarse Round Wire in Coils

Size, in.	Tolerance, Plus and Minus
0.500 and larger	0.003
Under 0.500 to 0.076, incl.	0.002
Under 0.076 to 0.035, incl.	0.001

Out-of-round is customarily one-half the total gauge tolerance.

Size Tolerances for Coarse Round Galvanized Wire in Coils

Size, in.	Tolerances, Plus and Minus, in.			
	Regular Coating	Type 1 Coating	Type 2 Coating	Type 3 Coating
0.500 to 0.251, incl.	0.004	0.004	0.005	0.006
0.250 to 0.148, incl.	0.003	0.003	0.004	0.005
0.147 to 0.076, incl.	0.003	0.003	0.003	0.004
0.075 to 0.035, incl.	0.002	0.002	0.002	0.003

Size Tolerances for Uncoated Fine Round Wire in Coils*

Size, in.	Tolerances, Plus and Minus, in.
0.0625/0.0348	0.001
0.0347/0.0271	0.0008
0.0270/0.0200	0.0006
0.0199/0.0151	0.0005
0.0150/0.0101	0.0004
0.0100/0.0060	0.0003
0.0059/0.0044	0.0002

Size Tolerances for Galvanized Fine Round Wire in Coils*

Size, in.	Standard Tolerances, in.			
	Type 1 Coating		Type 3 Coating	
	Plus	Minus	Plus	Minus
0.0625/0.0348	0.0015	0.0015	0.002	0.002
0.0347/0.0271	0.0015	0.0010	0.002	0.001
0.0270/0.0200	0.0013	0.0005	0.0015	0.001
0.0199/0.0151	0.0010	0.0005	—	—
0.0150/0.0101	0.0008	0.0004	—	—
0.0100/0.0060	0.0005	0.0003	—	—

* These tolerances do not apply to special wires which have been annealed as a separate operation following cold drawing or immediately prior to coating.

sides, top and bottom of the wire. On these machines the first sets of rolls put a considerable bend in the material to remove the kinks, and succeeding sets of rolls reverse this bend just enough to leave the wire perfectly straight. Squares, rectangles and hexagons, narrow flats that are not too thin, most shape wires, and also very fine wires, can be straightened on this type of machine provided the machine is properly designed for them.

INSPECTION AND TESTING

Importance of Inspection—Of equal importance with the various processes in making wire is the thorough system of inspection and testing to which the material is subjected during its progress through the mill and after finishing. Beginning with the hot-rolled rod, the material undergoes frequent and careful inspection during manufacture and is subjected to whatever tests are necessary to determine its fitness for the service required.

Final Tests on Wires—Wire for shipment to customers is regularly inspected and tested at both ends of each bundle for size, finish, and temper. For temper, small sizes are tested by a kink test, medium sizes by a bending test, large sizes by hardness tests. Certain grades of wire are subjected to a machine test for determining tensile strength and elongation, and some of it may be given severe torsion tests. All telephone and telegraph stock is tested also for electrical conductivity. Cold-heading and cold-forging wire is subjected to upset testing and/or etch and file tests for surface-quality evaluation. All exact-weight bundles are net weight of wire, excluding wrapping material. Wet-drawn wires are always packaged; that is, bundles are covered with paper, but may also be wrapped in burlap when so ordered.

DEFECTS IN WIRE

After the wire has been drawn, it may be found defective or unsuitable for the purpose for which it was intended, and every effort is made to detect and discard all such wire. The chief sources of trouble can usually be placed under one of the following headings: off size or shape, internal defects, surface defects, and improper mechanical properties.

Size and Shape—The reasons for wires being off size or shape have been already given. While every effort is made to draw the wire to the tolerances given, the tolerances themselves may be too great to permit use of the wire in an exacting application. Where extreme dimensional accuracy is needed, proper specifications should be established before the wire is drawn so that product can be made to suit the special requirements.

Internal Defects—Pipe and segregation are the most common types of internal defects, and are detected by deep etching of a cross-section of the wire, or by making a nick-and-break test.

Pipe and/or segregation cause uneven temper, brittleness and what is known as **cuppy wire.** Cuppiness (cup and cone fracture) may also be caused by overdrafting.

Surface Defects—Sometimes the finish of the wire does not meet requirements. If the finish is not satisfactory it may be due to poor cleaning, to the use of improper coatings or other causes. In the case of liquor-finished wires, especially, the color may not be of the particular shade desired, or it may vary too much in different bundles. When these features are of special importance, they should be stated on the order, so that special attention may be given to meeting requirements in this respect. Other surface defects in wire are scratches, slivers, and seams. Scratches are caused by using a die in poor condition, or they may result from improper lubrication or from pieces of metal or other gritty substances being drawn into the die with the wire. Slivers, as the name indicates, are sharp pointed projections of metal that rise from the surface of the wire. They may be caused from any one of a number of sources, including the ingot and rolling practice. Seams are longitudinal cracks in the surface of the wire and are generally traceable to lack of proper care in billet preparation, conditioning, and rod rolling. In general, seams are relatively shallow and are detected by upset testing, etching, magnetic-particle inspection or eddy-current testing.

MECHANICAL PROPERTIES

The mechanical properties of any wire will depend upon the chemical composition and quality of the steel as well as the exact nature of the drafting practice and of the heat treatment it has undergone. The particular application or method of fabrication determines the grade of wire necessary. A finished wire taken at random will not be suitable for all purposes, as the strength and ductility may vary from a 50,000 lb. per sq. in. tensile strength for an annealed low-carbon tie wire to 480,000 lb. per sq. in. tensile strength for a high-carbon music wire. If the wire manufacturer is fully informed both as to the desired properties of the wire and its application, the requirements can be met by proper selection of composition, heat treatment and predetermined amount of hardening by cold working in wire drawing. Many products such as upholstery springs, rope, telegraph wire, etc., are recognized in the industry as regular grades of wire for standard applications, being covered by standard specifications, and may be ordered as such.

SECTION 8

HEAT TREATMENT OF WIRE

Heat-treating processes used in the wire industry include **subcritical** or **process annealing, patenting,** and **hardening and tempering.** Of these, patenting may be described as a special toughening process used only in the wire industry, while annealing, hardening, and tempering play such an important role in the industry and the methods of applying these processes have become so highly specialized that, although their general principles and their application to other branches of the steel industry have been thoroughly discussed in other chapters of this book, a brief account of their specific application to the wire industry is included in this chapter. These processes are briefly described and discussed in the order of their importance, which is the order in which they were first mentioned above.

Importance and Purposes of Annealing—Of the three wire heat treatments mentioned above, subcritical or process annealing is the most common, and it is practically the only heat treatment given to the soft, or low-carbon, steel wires, which constitute by far the bulk of wire production. In general the process is employed in the wire industry to accomplish any one of the following objectives: (1) to refine, soften, and make uniform the grain structure of rods or wire; (2) to obtain a specific structure in, and thus impart special properties to, process wire or the finished material, and (3) to soften the wire after cold-working, i.e., drawing or cold-rolling.

Normalizing—Normalizing consists of heating the rods or wire to above the transformation temperature and cooling in still air at room temperature. This practice is usually followed when treating medium-carbon steels of about 0.25 to 0.45 per cent carbon to obtain uniformity of structure and hardness. Normalizing imparts the proper ductility or flowability as required for certain cold upsetting and forging applications, and much of the medium-carbon bolt wire is therefore normalized in the regular course of manufacture. This normalizing process consists of passing full coils of rods or wire on a moving conveyor through a furnace made up of three zones, "preheating," "soaking" and "cooling" zones, the temperatures of which are automatically controlled. In the soaking zone, a temperature of approximately 1600° F is maintained. Combinations of several variables permit variations in the heating and cooling cycles and the cooling rate is usually retarded. By the use of controlled atmospheres in the furnace, decarburization and scaling may be held to a minimum.

Annealing for Definite Structures—This type of annealing is applied to the higher carbon steel wires, i.e., those with a carbon content of 0.35 per cent or more, in order to obtain certain definite structures, and is similar to the treatment given carbon tool steels and other high-carbon steels in order to make them easy to machine. If steel having a pearlitic (lamellar) structure is heated to 1300° F (704° C), and is held at that temperature for a sufficiently long period of time, the iron carbides slowly coalesce, changing from a platelike form to a granular, globular, or spheroidal form. By properly regulating the temperature of the treatment, structures intermediate between these two extremes and best suited to the purpose for which the wire is to be used may be obtained with temperatures in excess of 1330° F yielding a correspondingly greater percentage of pearlite as the temperature increases. These structures are sought in high-carbon wires mainly to enhance their machinability. Close regulation of the

temperature is imperative in this type of annealing, for in heating the steel to a point so near the critical range, a difference of 50° F in the temperature often means the difference between obtaining the spheroidized carbide structure sought and the lamellar (pearlitic) structure which it is desired to efface.

Process Annealing to Soften Hard-Drawn Wires—In the previous section, it was pointed out that each successive draft in drawing a wire has a certain hardening effect upon the metal; that the grains become elongated in the direction of drafting; that, as the drafts are repeated and the wire becomes progressively harder, a point is reached at which the wire will break if subjected to further drafting; and that well before such a condition of brittleness is reached, it is necessary to heat-treat the wire in order to put it in a condition that will permit further processing without injury. For reasons which have already been stated or will be made apparent in the discussions to follow, high-carbon wires are generally patented, while low-carbon wires are annealed.

For softening wires in process of manufacture, process annealing at sub-critical temperatures is usually employed. This type of annealing is used mainly to restore the ductility of hard-drawn low-carbon wires at process size so that they may be drawn to finer sizes, although it is also employed to adjust the mechanical properties of some wires at finished size as required by their application. To accomplish these results, it is only necessary to heat the wire to below the lower critical range, as a temperature between 1000° F and 1250° F is sufficient to soften the steel to such an extent that the material is almost as ductile as it was before any drafting was done. The reason for this is illustrated by a comparison of the photomicrographs of wire in Figures 29—24 through 29—28 (Pages 795 and 796). Figure 29—24 shows the form, arrangement, and size of the grains in the full annealed steel. In this condition, this steel exhibits a tensile strength of approximately 48,000 lb. per sq. in. and an elongation of approximately 33 per cent in 10 inches. Figure 29—25 shows the structure after a single draft; the grains are somewhat elongated in the direction of drafting. Figure 29—26 shows the structure of the wire after it has had about five drafts, and it will be observed that the grains have been generally elongated into a stringer-like or fibrous structure, greatly changed from the original equiaxed grains of Figure 29—24. This wire would have a tensile strength of about 125,000 lb. per sq. in. and an elongation of about one per cent. At an elevated temperature, such as 1000° F, the grains recrystallize, thereby forming new grains. The greater the amount of plastic deformation, the lower the recrystallization temperature. Such incipient recrystallization or forming of new grains is indicated in Figure 29—29. Grain size is shown in the photomicrographs to increase as the temperature of annealing and the time the wire is held at temperature increase. The grain size obtained after the long time annealing cycle and recrystallization at 1200° F is similar to that of the original structure, although certain remnants of the structure produced by drawing still remain, with some residual directional properties.

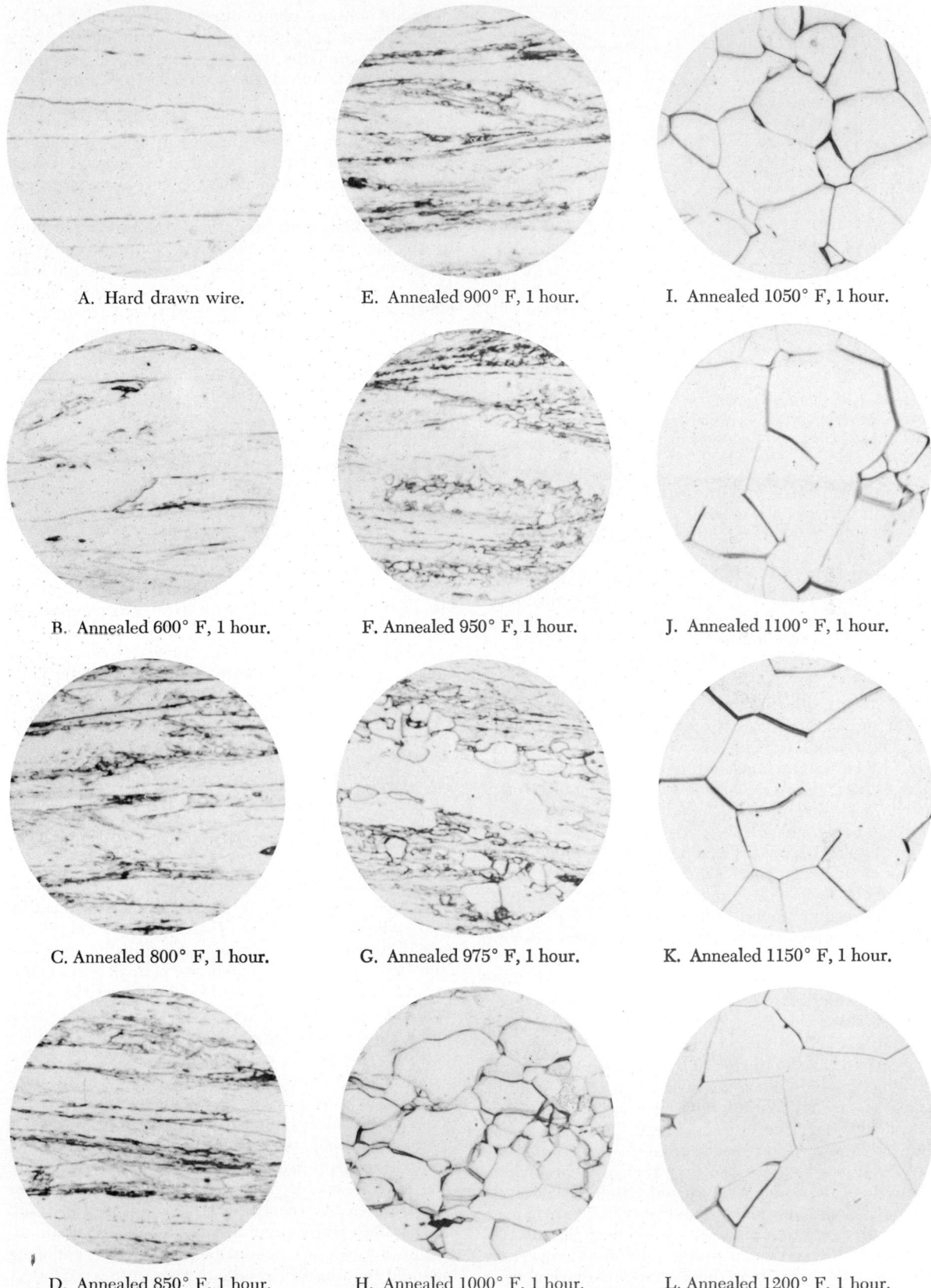

A. Hard drawn wire.

E. Annealed 900° F, 1 hour.

I. Annealed 1050° F, 1 hour.

B. Annealed 600° F, 1 hour.

F. Annealed 950° F, 1 hour.

J. Annealed 1100° F, 1 hour.

C. Annealed 800° F, 1 hour.

G. Annealed 975° F, 1 hour.

K. Annealed 1150° F, 1 hour.

D. Annealed 850° F, 1 hour.

H. Annealed 1000° F, 1 hour.

L. Annealed 1200° F, 1 hour.

FIG. 29—29. Series of 12 photomicrographs illustrating the changes in microstructure of a hard-drawn wire after annealing at various temperatures. All longitudinal sections. Magnification: 1000X.

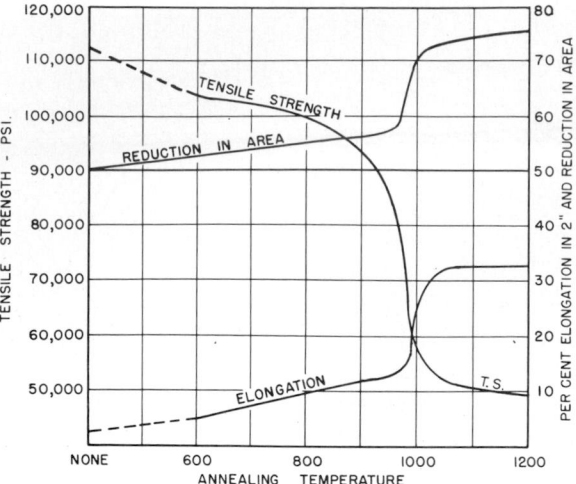

FIG. 29—30. Curves showing changes in mechanical properties of hard-drawn low-carbon steel wire after annealing at various temperatures up to 1200° F.

The mechanical properties obtained by annealing hard-drawn low-carbon wires at various temperatures up to 1200° F are shown in the graphs of Figure 29—30.

Sizes of Grains—While the preceding paragraph shows the effect of grain distortion upon the mechanical properties of steel, nothing is said about the effect of grain size on these properties, and in all annealing, as well as other forms of heat treatment, the matter of grain size is of considerable importance. Large grains lower the tensile properties of the metal somewhat, while small grains make it not only stronger but tougher. The reasons for this, as well as the effects of cold working, are to be found in the structure of the grains themselves. Structurally, each grain is in reality a small crystal in which the atoms of which it is composed are arranged in regular rows and "layers," as described elsewhere in this book. Crystals deform through movement of adjacent parts along definite planes, called **slip planes,** whose location and direction within the crystal are determined by the positions of the atoms within the space lattice. Anything that interferes with this movement will make the metal more resistant to deformation, while anything that promotes slip will lower its resistance to deformation. Small grains offer greater interference to slip than large grains, because the slip planes in different grains lie at different angles, and in any one of such small grains the slip cannot progress far before it is stopped by an adjacent grain. Each grain offers considerable resistance to the force causing the slip, because the direction of possible slip movement may differ greatly from the direction of the applied force. In a small section, such as a wire, where the ratio of the diameter of the wire itself to that of the crystals is relatively small, the effect of large grains on lowering the tensile properties is likely to be very noticeable. The increase of strength due to drawing may also be explained from the standpoint of slip interference, for, as the grains are distorted, the slip interference becomes greater and greater until most of the grains have been drawn into parallel stringers and

there are no more planes of easy slip on which further motion can take place. In this condition, the force required to pull the wire apart should approach the force of attraction of the molecules or atoms themselves, since the wire no longer can adjust itself to the load by deforming, but it never does because some of the grains begin to break before the others. The resulting ferrite grain size is referred to as "structural grain size," and is not to be confused with austenitic grain size.

The conditions for process annealing involve three factors, namely, strain, time, and temperature. Without strain no change in the crystalline structure takes place on heating below the critical range. As to the effect of the amount of the strain in causing grain growth, or rearrangement, below the critical range, Sauveur has shown that, in the case of steel containing from 0.04 to 0.12 per cent carbon, very slight straining followed by annealing at 1200° F for 7 hours produces no grain growth, but that moderate straining (approximately 15 per cent), such as might be effected by a single light draft, and annealing cause the grains to grow to very large size resulting in "orange peel" surface if the wire is deformed; over-straining, or severe distortion, and annealing at the same temperature and for the same length of time produce grains of small size, comparable with the structures shown in Figures 29—24 and 29—25. The condition of strain producing large grains is seldom met with in process annealing of wire, because the grains of such wires are usually distorted far beyond that point. However, when a consumer expects to anneal wire, this fact should be made known to the manufacturer; it will then be possible, except in a few cases, to supply wire that will not form large grains under any annealing conditions. In the case of pure or almost pure iron, and steel containing more than 0.12 or 0.15 per cent carbon, the amount of strain, according to Sauveur, has no effect in producing large grains on annealing, but others have shown that the same tendency persists in 0.20 to 0.30 per cent carbon steel.

Time and Temperature for Annealing—From what has already been said, and the evidences supplied by Figure 29—29, it is evident that, for the best results in annealing, careful regulation and adjustment of the time and temperature are necessary. In all types of annealing, sufficient time must be allowed for the whole charge to reach the required temperature, and in low-temperature annealing additional time is required for the development of the structure desired. Process annealing requires careful adjustment of time and temperature in order to avoid the formation of large grains, and, at the same time, eliminate the effects of the cold working, because at a low temperature the atoms or molecules move at a slower rate, and more time is required for their adjustment than at higher temperatures. As to temperature, the fact that full control and careful regulation of this factor in all annealing is necessary to satisfactory results cannot be too highly emphasized. If the temperature is too low, it may fail entirely to accomplish the results desired in process annealing. In some cases adjustment of the temperature to the size of the wire is also necessary.

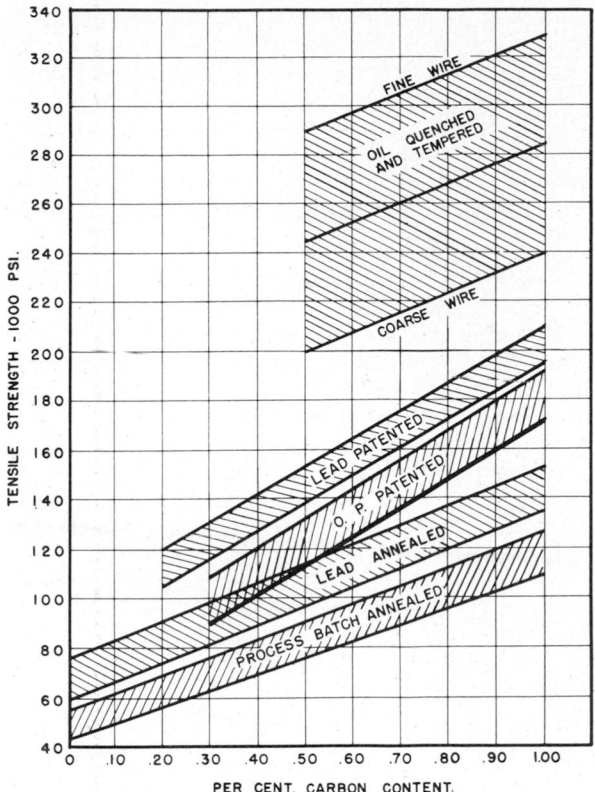

Fig. 29—31. Curves showing approximate effect of carbon content and heat treatment on tensile strength of steel wire.

Fine wire in coils, for example, is generally annealed at as low a temperature as practicable, in order to avoid the sticking of the wire in the coils. After these remarks it is scarcely necessary to say that accurate and carefully standardized pyrometers form an essential part of any equipment for the proper annealing of wire.

The tensile strength (at various carbon levels) of wire full-annealed or recrystallized by annealing above the upper critical point, followed by slow cooling, is shown in Figure 29—31, as well as that of wire subjected to annealing in a molten lead bath (one form of a "subcritical anneal" involving a short time cycle of heating and cooling). It should be noted that it is possible for sub-critical annealing to produce approximately the same tensile strength values obtained by full annealing, providing the long time cycle of heating and cooling used in the former treatment is observed. A comparison of the effects of full annealing on recrystallization and grain size with short time sub-critical annealing of hard-drawn wire is indicated by the photomicrographs of Figures 29—27 and 29—28. These differences in structure are reflected in the lower tensile properties of full-annealed wire shown in Figure 29—31.

METHODS OF ANNEALING WIRE

While it is possible, theoretically at least, to anneal wire in any apparatus in which the proper conditions of time and temperature can be maintained, the efficient handling of the material calls for, and some of the finishes and conditions to be met demand, equipment specially designed for the purpose in mind. These conditions, in general, call for differences in the time of annealing, and differences in the methods of applying the heat, and usually require that the material be protected against oxidation. To meet these conditions, several different methods requiring entirely different equipment for each are employed: these are known as **controlled-atmosphere annealing, salt-bath annealing, continuous lead annealing,** and **tube annealing.**

Controlled-Atmosphere Annealing—Controlled atmosphere annealing is the most recently adopted method of annealing used by the wire industry. Both batch-type and continuous-type furnaces are employed. The protective gas or controlled atmosphere maintained in the heating chambers or muffles of these furnaces is prepared by the partial combustion of natural gas to produce a "neutral" atmosphere gas (consisting principally of nitrogen with controlled amounts of methane, carbon monoxide and carbon dioxide) that will prevent oxidation and decarburization of the steel rods or wire undergoing heat treatment. Both types of furnaces are heated by gas-fired radiant tubes. Further details about controlled-atmosphere furnaces, the means for heating them, and the generation of controlled atmospheres will be found in the section of Chapter 39 dealing with heat-treating furnaces.

Furnaces referred to as bell-type or cover-type are employed for **batch-type annealing** of rods or wire under a controlled atmosphere. Coils of rods or wire are "threaded" on vertical stems placed on a lattice-work cast-steel base. A stainless-steel inner cover or hood is lowered over the charge. A high-velocity fan in the base circulates controlled atmosphere within the inner cover during the annealing cycle. The bell, with radiant-heating tubes installed on its inner surfaces, is then lowered over the entire base and inner cover that encloses the charge.

Radiant-tube-heated continuous furnaces for annealing rods and wire in coils under a controlled atmosphere are of the pusher type. The furnaces are zone-controlled to provide connecting zones for heating, soaking and cooling of the charge. The wire or rods are loaded onto mesh-type trays that are pushed, one following another, into the entry end of the furnace. As a tray is pushed into the entry end, a tray of annealed wire is pushed out of the furnace at the exit end, the thrust being transmitted from tray to tray through the continuous line of trays in the furnace. Escape of controlled-atmosphere gas is minimized by a vestibule with inner and outer doors at each end of the furnace.

For annealing rods and wire, the continuous-type furnace is believed to possess some advantages over batch-type furnaces, notably: shorter annealing cycles and better uniformity of heating of the coils. However, the efficient operation of a continuous furnace requires that large tonnages of similar material be available for heat treatment to minimize changes in the operating cycle of the furnace, and operation of the furnace should be uninterrupted for the longest possible periods, since down time resulting from cycle changes or lack of or delays of stock to be annealed can increase operating costs considerably.

When annealing hot-rolled rods by either the batch or continuous method, the rods should be cleaned and lightly coated with lime, since scale or rust will cause decarburization of the rods by reacting with carbon in the steel in spite of the presence of a controlled atmosphere.

Salt-Bath Annealing—Molten salt-bath annealing is sometimes practiced for process annealing of common sizes of wire. The wire, in coils, is immersed for one-half hour to one hour in gas-fired pots containing molten salt which is held at some predetermined temperature between 1000° and 1300° F, depending on steel composition and structure or physical properties desired. Advantages over other methods are that small amounts of wire may be quickly annealed at closely controlled temperatures without scaling the surface on the wire. Such annealing is somewhat limited as to its application in wire processing.

Continuous lead annealing consists merely in drawing the wire through a bath of molten lead heated to the proper temperature. The molten lead is contained in a shallow rectangular steel pan, some 10 to 15 inches deep, 3 to 4 feet wide, and 15 to 25 feet long, the exact dimensions depending upon conditions. (Sometimes two pans are used, the first known as the cold pan and the second as the hot pan, and the wire is drawn through each in succession.) The pan is heated from below usually by gases from an oil or gas fire and is supported by a brick setting adapted to the method of heating. In practice several strands of wire are drawn through the bath in parallel. For this purpose the coils of wire to be annealed are placed on free-running reels before the annealing furnace, and the wire from each coil is drawn through the bath by a take-up block placed at a convenient distance from the other end. For keeping the wires immersed in the molten lead, devices of various forms, known as **sinkers,** are used. To obtain bright annealing by this process, it is necessary to cool the wires without their being in contact with the air. Consequently, when such a finish is desired, the wires from the hot lead bath are conducted directly into long tubes which are kept as nearly sealed as possible.

The advantages of lead annealing are obvious. In addition to protecting the material from the air, the bath of molten metal is readily maintained at a uniform temperature throughout its mass, and its temperature can be accurately ascertained at any time by a pyrometer. Also, since the process is continuous, it eliminates much handling of the material.

The principal use of lead annealing is in connection with galvanizing plants, where it is employed to anneal process wire. In these plants, layouts are provided that permit the wire to be annealed, cooled, cleaned, washed and dried, or dried and galvanized or tinned, all in one continuous operation. In continuous annealing and cleaning, when the wire is not to be galvanized or tinned, the wire, after passing through the lead bath, is conducted through crushed coal or sand banked at the end of the lead pan; this bank of coal or sand is known as a **header**. The wire then passes successively through a water bath, a weak acid bath, a cold water bath, and a hot water bath, thence to the take-up blocks, which are located several yards beyond the hot water bath to permit the wire to dry. This elimination of the customary process of dip-cleaning with cranes is very desirable in the case of process wire.

PATENTING

Patenting is a heat treatment applied to rods and wire having a carbon content of 0.40 per cent and higher, the term being peculiar to the wire industry. The object of patenting is to obtain a structure which combines high tensile strength with high ductility and thus impart to the wire the ability to withstand heavy drafting to produce the desired finished sizes possessing a combination of high tensile strength and good toughness.

Methods of Patenting—Patenting is always conducted as a continuous process and consists in first heating the material to a point well above the upper critical temperature, then cooling through the critical temperature at a comparatively rapid rate to a predetermined temperature level at which the transformation will yield the desired microstructure and mechanical properties. In practice, there are three ways of carrying out the treatment. Thus, the wire may be heated by passing it through alloy-steel tubes arranged in an open muffle or in an open flame without tubes and be cooled by pulling it from the furnace into the open air, which method is now referred to as "O.P." (old process or air) patenting. In a second method, the wire may be heated as in the first method, then cooled by passing it into a lead bath held at a relatively low temperature; this process is known as the **metallic hardening process.** The wire, in the third process, can be heated in a bath of very hot lead and cooled in another bath of lead at a lower temperature, as in the **double lead process.** In this last process the temperatures of both baths can be readily controlled and accurately measured. These features make it possible to obtain any desired structure even in wires of highest carbon content, a condition not easily attainable in "O.P." patenting. The third method is also more advantageous in that less scale is formed than in the other two methods. In the wire industry, both the metallic-hardening process and the double-lead process are generally referred to as "lead patenting."

Properties of Patented Wires—The structure obtained by patenting is extremely tough and possesses the best characteristics for drawing to high tensile strengths. As indicated in Figure 29—31, the tensile strengths of air- or lead-patented rods or wire are considerably higher than the same steels in the annealed condition. The lead patenting process is definitely required in the production of any exceedingly high strength and tough wire such as music wire. As an illustration, by properly patenting and drawing 0.75-carbon steel, a wire is produced having a tensile strength of 375,000 lb. per sq. in. or over. In spite of the great amount of drafting required to raise the tensile strength to this point, such wire will be tough enough to wrap around itself (i.e., can be wound around a pin of the same diameter as the wire) or can be hammered flat to one-half its original thickness without cracking.

HARDENING AND TEMPERING

In other branches of the steel industry, hardening and tempering are usually considered as separate operations, but in wire-making they are more often conducted in a single continuous operation. As in the case of tools and other products of steel, the object in hardening and tempering wire is to control the hardness, or "temper," in order to adapt the material to the use for which it is intended. Hardening and tempering are applied to a great variety of wires, such as typewriter wire, umbrella wire, dress-stay wire, curtain spring wire, and wires for measuring tapes, clock and watch springs, automobile-engine valve springs, door-check springs, etc. Wires for such purposes are generally treated in wire form by a continuous process, but many kinds of springs, tools, and miscellaneous special products, are heat-treated after the wire has been formed into the article desired, when it is not always possible to use a continuous hardening and tempering process.

Methods of Hardening and Tempering Wire—For greatest efficiency in hardening and tempering, it is necessary to adapt the method of treatment to the nature of the material and the size and form of the article. Therefore, because of the great variety of steels and of articles produced by the wire industry, various methods of treatment involving the use of various kinds of apparatus and of various heating and cooling media, are employed. Thus, for hardening, the material may be heated in muffle, tube or electric furnaces, or in molten lead, and be quenched in water, oil, molten lead, or some other liquid. For tempering, the material may be reheated in open furnaces, in baths of molten lead or hot oil, or by bringing it in contact with hot sand or with hot plates or discs of iron or steel. In continuous hardening and tempering, the heating for hardening may be accomplished in a manner similar to that for patenting, and the quenching may be accomplished by passing it quickly into a tank of water or oil; in the tempering operation, the material may then be drawn through a suitable bath, such as molten lead, the wire being in continuous motion throughout the process.

AUSTEMPERING

Austempering, described in Chapter 39 on "Heat Treatment," is a method adapted to the heat treatment of wire, and particularly formed parts. It is employed to develop the highest combination of strength and toughness in certain kinds of wire, particularly for fabrication into springs. In this process the transformation of austenite is effected at some preselected and constant subcritical temperature, which usually requires a longer time than does the regular continuous oil tempering operation; consequently this process is preferably used for batch or semi-continuous operation on high-carbon springs or small articles made of steel of $\frac{1}{4}$-inch maximum thickness or diameter.

SECTION 9

PROTECTIVE METALLIC COATINGS

Kinds of Coatings—Probably more than one-third of all the steel wire drawn is given some kind of metallic coating, either for decorative or protective purposes. This phase of the industry has reached huge proportions and is of great importance. As already indicated, appreciably large quantities of the medium and larger sizes of wire are given a light coating or "liquor finish," varying in color from that of copper through the various shades of brass to the color of tin, for decorative purposes only, and practically all soft fine wires have to be given this coating for lubricating purposes. This coating, which may consist of copper or tin or a combination of the two, is very thin and has but little value as a protection against corrosion. As is well known, all of the common grades of steel will rust sooner or later when exposed to atmospheric conditions unless their surface is covered with some substance that will protect it from moisture and air. To afford such protection, it is the practice to galvanize wire, i.e., coat it with zinc, or to tin it, or to coat it with aluminum, or, for certain purposes, to give it a coating of paint, lacquer or japan. While it is also possible to coat steel wire with copper, lead, nickel, and the precious metals, these metals are seldom used for coating wire, except in a few particular cases, so they need not receive any further consideration here. The remainder of this section will, therefore, be devoted to galvanizing, tinning, and aluminum coating.

WIRE GALVANIZING

Advantages of Galvanizing—As a protective coating, zinc offers several advantages over other metals: (a) Zinc is electropositive to iron, which means that if the steel of a galvanized wire should be exposed to corrosive influences, owing to defective or damaged coating, the zinc will corrode first, and its presence will protect the iron from corrosion until after a considerable area has been exposed. Just the opposite reactions might occur with other metals, such as tin, which are electronegative to iron. The presence of tin alone under the same conditions would hasten the corrosion of the iron, but, for specific purposes, tin is added in small amounts to zinc for galvanizing to improve adherence of the metallic coating, and the size and appearance of the spangle, without affecting corrosion resistance. (b) Zinc may be obtained in a comparatively pure state at a relatively low cost. (c) With zinc, it is easy to obtain a hard, smooth coating with relatively good resistance to abrasion. (d) The color of the zinc coating is satisfactory for general purposes.

Methods of Galvanizing—There are two common methods in use for galvanizing wire, known as (1) the hot galvanizing process and (2) the electro-galvanizing process, but the second is the less widely used. In both processes, some 30 (more or less) parallel strands of wire pass first through certain preparatory processes, thence through the galvanizing bath to take-up frames on which each strand of wire is separately coiled, all these operations being made by attaching the last end of each coil to the first end of the succeeding one. As the wires pass through the various baths required to clean and coat them, they are submerged by suitable forms of sinkers (either of the stationary or rotary type) or, in the case of electro-galvanizing, under contact fingers in the electrolytic or plating solution.

Processes Preliminary to Hot Galvanizing—In nearly all cases, wire to be galvanized must be annealed to remove the effects of cold working, and, in order to minimize handling of the wire, it is common practice to do this work in conjunction with the galvanizing operations by one of the continuous annealing processes. For this purpose, a molten-lead pan will be built in front of the cleaning and galvanizing apparatus. The lead pan also serves to burn off the wire-drawing lubricant. Since the rate of cooling in process annealing has little effect upon the physical properties of the wire, the wires are cooled in air, or, if the space is limited, low-carbon wires will be cooled by conducting them from the annealing furnace into a vat of water. Following annealing, the next step is cleaning, for which purpose the wire is conducted into a bath of hot muriatic (hydrochloric) acid at predetermined con-

centration. This acid is used instead of sulphuric, which is the acid commonly employed for cleaning in the galvanizing of sheets and tubes, because it acts much more quickly than sulphuric, and is much more effective in removing traces of lime remaining from the drawing operations. The iron chloride formed by the action of the acid, as well as any particles of loosely adhering scale, must next be removed and these objectives are accomplished by passing the wire through a bath of hot water.

While the wire is now perfectly clean, it must also be perfectly dry before it is brought into contact with the molten zinc, but in drying, any exposure to the air, which in practice it is impossible to avoid, results in the formation of a light coat of oxide, or rust. This difficulty is overcome by the use of a flux. In galvanizing sheets, tubes, and various wire products, this flux consists of fused ammonium chloride, commonly known as sal ammoniac, which lies upon the surface of the zinc bath, but for the continuous galvanizing of wire, better results are obtained by passing the cleaned and thoroughly washed wires directly through a hot solution of zinc chloride or zinc ammonium chloride flux at predetermined concentration or Baumé; and then through or over a dryer into the molten zinc. The wire thus becomes coated with a thin film of zinc chloride, which tends to protect it from oxidation during drying and also removes any traces of rust that may be formed.

Apparatus for Hot Galvanizing—From the dryer, the wires are drawn at once into the molten zinc, or **spelter,** as it is commonly called. This molten metal is contained in a **spelter pan,** which is usually made of boiler plate and is supported by a brick setting of suit-

Fig. 29—32. Overall view of the apparatus employed in the continuous hot-dip galvanizing of steel wire.

able construction for firing with the most satisfactory fuel available. Figure 29—32 shows the general form of the pan and the furnace commonly used. The dimensions of these pans are subject to much variation, and depend upon several conditions. Thus, the width will vary according to the number of strands it is desired to galvanize at once, which is usually about 30. The length is dependent upon the size of the wires, the speed of travel, and the thickness of the coating desired. Pans designed for galvanizing coarse sizes of wire may reach a length of thirty feet. The depth of the pan must be sufficient to prevent the wires from coming into contact with the **dross** which settles and collects upon the bottom. This dross is an alloy of iron and zinc containing from 3 to 7 per cent iron, which is solid at the temperature of molten spelter, forms a pastelike mixture, and is very harmful to the coating. As molten zinc oxidizes rapidly, the pan is provided with some form of covering medium, which rests upon the molten spelter and protects it from the air, except at the ends where the wires enter and leave the bath. Here, the surface of the metal must be kept free from oxide by frequent skimming. The mixture of zinc and zinc oxide thus obtained is known as **zinc skimmings**; these skimmings, together with the dross, represent a considerable loss, for the proportion of these waste products to the total zinc used is relatively large, and, although both are refined, the cost of recovering the zinc they contain is relatively high.

Wiping the Wire—As the wires emerge from the galvanizing pan, some of the zinc they carry remains in the molten state for a brief period, and, unless prevented from doing so, tends to flow downward on the surface of each wire, making the coating rough and uneven. Such a coating makes the wire hard to handle, and renders it unsuitable for many purposes, especially when it is to be fabricated by machinery. Further, such a coating represents an actual waste of zinc, for the durability of an unevenly applied coating is determined by the thinnest part of the coating, not by the thickest parts. It is plain, therefore, that the removal of this excess zinc is a matter not only of economy, but of expediency as well. It is also evident that in order to form a smooth, evenly distributed coating, the surplus zinc must be removed while it is still in a fluid state. This is accomplished by passing the wire, just after it emerges from the zinc bath, through either one of two devices known as **wipes** and **headers**. In the case of wipes, the parts in contact with the wire are made of asbestos, and the type most commonly used is known as the **split wipe**. It consists essentially of two balls, or molds, of asbestos fibers held together by some suitable binding material, or stranded asbestos rope of suitable diameter formed into wiping pads. In service, these two balls are pressed lightly against and about the wire, and are held securely in place by cup-shaped holders. The aim in the split wipe is to make it possible for the operators to separate the two halves in order to permit the splices joining two coils of wire to pass, as otherwise the wipe is torn out entirely or badly damaged. Headers are employed for wiping only when extra heavy coatings are desired. A header consists of crushed charcoal of definite mesh,

blended with a certain wax, beef tallow or certain oils and arranged so that the wires shall pass upward through it. In any of these cases the wipe thus artificially provided acts as such only for a short time, for a hollow cone of solidified spelter soon forms about the wire, either within or in front of the wipe, and this cone of zinc then becomes the real wipe.

Cooling the Coated Wire—After passing the wipes, the coating of the wire is completed, but the manner in which it is cooled should also be given some consideration. If the wire is allowed to cool naturally in the air, the coating, because of the formation of a thin film of zinc oxide on the surface, will be dull and lusterless in appearance, known as air-cooled galvanized wire, but if the coating is cooled suddenly, as by immersing the wire in cold water as soon as possible after leaving the wipes, it will have a bright lustrous surface. However, since the real value of the coating as a protection against corrosion depends upon the thickness of the coat and the completeness with which it excludes moisture from the iron, it is clear that the luster, which is a characteristic of suddenly cooled coatings, is no indication of the quality of the coating, and since this luster can be preserved only for a short time in any natural atmosphere, its attractive appearance is of little value.

Coiling the Wire—The wire, which is delivered to the galvanizing department in coils, is drawn through the annealing, cleaning and galvanizing apparatus by blocks, which form it into coiled bundles again (Figure 29—32). The blocks commonly used for this purpose are of the so-called continuous type, and are similar to a wire-drawing block except that their spindles are mounted in a horizontal position. With these blocks, bundles of wire may be removed at any time without stopping the blocks, so that the speed of travel of the wire through the annealing and galvanizing baths may be uniformly maintained.

Some Features of the Operations for Hot Galvanizing—To the novice the galvanizing of wire may appear to be a simple process. The wires being drawn through the various pieces of equipment and recoiled on the blocks apparently require little attention from the operator. As a matter of fact, however, the process demands considerable experience and skill in order to obtain uniformly good results. For example, the firing of such long shallow pans requires not only a properly designed furnace, but constant care and observation on the part of the operator to keep the temperature of the spelter uniform and constant and to avoid injury to the pan. Similar statements apply also to the annealing and cleaning equipment. Some of the factors that determine the quality of the zinc coat are as follows:

The quality of the zinc coat, by which is meant its effectiveness in protecting the wire from corrosion and its adaptability to the intended use of the wire, depends upon the completeness with which the zinc covers the iron, the thickness, uniformity, physical properties, structure, and chemical composition of the coat. The completeness with which the iron is covered by the zinc depends upon the thoroughness of cleaning and fluxing and also upon the aftertreatment of the wire. Attention has already been called to the effects of the manner of cooling the wire as it is leaving the spelter bath. It should also be noted that the coating may be injured in fabricating the wire. If the cooled wire is bent at sharp angles or otherwise severely deformed, the coating is likely to be cracked or peeled off, especially if the coating is a heavy one. As to the thickness of the coat and the uniformity with which the spelter is distributed over any given wire and adherence of the zinc coating, these features depend upon the type of steel used, thoroughness of cleaning, the methods of wiping, the temperature of the molten spelter, and the time of immersion of the wire in the spelter bath. Up to certain limits, the thickness of the spelter coat increases as the temperature of the bath increases and as the time of immersion is prolonged. The time of immersion is controlled by the length of the spelter pan and the speed of travel of the wire through the bath. In this connection it should be pointed out that the thickest coat is not always the best, for, as the thickness of the coat increases, its brittleness and its tendency to peel or crack also increase. Some of the brittleness is to be attributed to the fact that zinc itself is a comparatively brittle metal. This brittleness might be lessened somewhat by alloying with other metals, but as these might decrease the resistance of the zinc to corrosion or otherwise affect it adversely, it is the practice to keep the spelter as pure as possible. The composition of the spelter is checked repeatedly by chemical analysis, and close limits are fixed for all the impurities it may contain. Another reason why the brittleness increases with the thickness of the coat is the fact that the conditions necessary to produce a heavy coat are also likely to affect the structure of the coat itself, for the coat obtained by hot galvanizing is not wholly composed of pure zinc.

The Structure of the Zinc Coat—The structure of the zinc coating as obtained on hot-dipped galvanized wire is shown in the photomicrograph of Figure 29—33. It will be seen that the spelter coating is made up of three different layers. The lower portion of the photomicrograph represents a section of the steel base, and the zinc layer represents the outer layer of spelter, which may be considered pure zinc. The alloy layer is made up of two different alloys of iron and zinc, the one next the steel base containing slightly more iron in solution than the other. Formerly it was thought that when iron is brought in contact with molten spelter, two compounds, having the formulas $FeZn_3$ and $FeZn_7$ are always formed. More recent studies indicate that the constitution of these coating layers is not precisely represented by these formulas. Assuming for the present that the formulas are substantially correct, however, the alloy next to the steel base consists of the compound $FeZn_3$, while the remainder of the alloy layer is composed of the compound $FeZn_7$. The dark lines separating different areas in the photomicrographs are not cracks, but the result of grain boundary effect in etching, similar to that observed in developing the structure of pure metals.

Electrogalvanizing—Electrogalvanizing is the name applied to the process of covering any metal with a coating of zinc by means of an electric current. It is sometimes termed "cold" or "wet" galvanizing to distinguish it from the more common method of hot galvanizing. For galvanizing flat wire and also strip steel, this cold process has certain advantages over hot galvanizing. For example, in hot galvanizing such materials, the edges, especially of strip steel, tend to destroy wipes, and special care is required to secure a smooth uniform coating, whereas the thickness of the zinc coating may be readily controlled in electrogalvanizing. The thickness of an electrodeposited coating depends primarily on two factors, namely, current density and time. By current density is meant the number of amperes flowing per unit of surface of the metal exposed in the electrolyte. The coating, when well applied, adheres firmly to the metal and will stand severe bending without flaking off. But many features

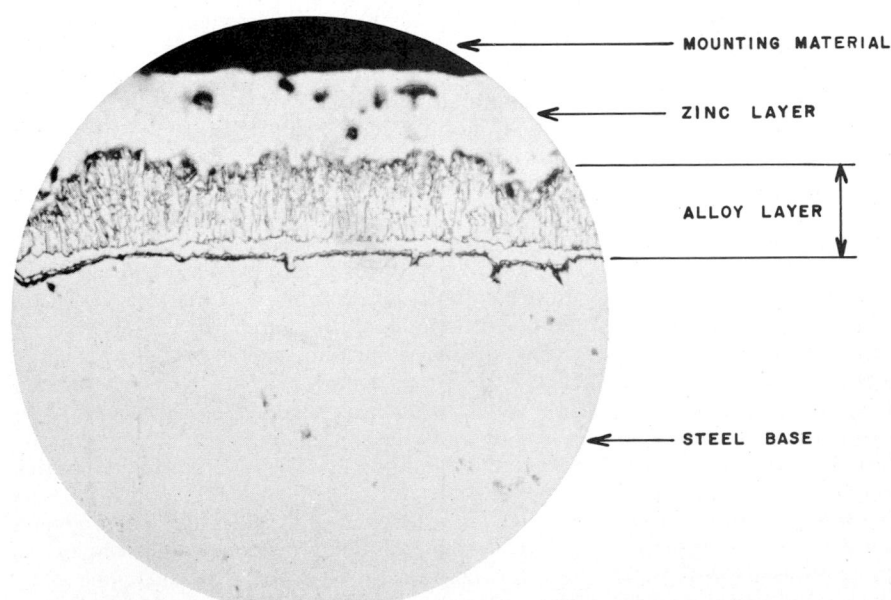

MOUNTING MATERIAL

ZINC LAYER

ALLOY LAYER

STEEL BASE

Fig. 29—33. Structure of the zinc coating on a steel wire galvanized by immersion in molten zinc. Magnification: 250X.

of the process require special attention, because the quality of the coat depends upon the condition of the electrolyte, the cleanliness of the surface, and on general working conditions.

The equipment for electrogalvanizing consists of a long shallow horizontal vat, known as the plating vat, which is usually made of steel lined with rubber or a synthetic mixture. Attached to one outer side of this vat are the positive bus bars, or feeders, connected to the plating generator, while on the other side are similar negative feeders. As considerable time is required for suitable electroplating, the vats are usually from 100 to 200 feet long in order that the speed of the wires or strips through the vats can be maintained at a reasonable rate for production and still remain submerged in the electrolyte long enough to receive the desired coating. Since the working voltage is low and the amperage high, the conductors consist of heavy copper bars. In addition, there are needed a low-voltage direct-current supply source, and means for making and storing fresh electrolyte.

Operation of the Process—The vat is nearly filled with the plating liquid, called the **electrolyte,** consisting of a solution of some zinc salt, such as zinc sulphate. This solution must be continually agitated to maintain a uniform density, and it must also be kept clean and at a fairly constant and suitable temperature. For **anodes,** slabs of zinc are submerged at selected locations in the electrolyte and are electrically attached to the positive bus bars. Alternating with the anodes are strong copper contact bars which are placed across the vat, immersed a few inches below the surface of the electrolyte, and connected with the negative bus bars outside the vat. These contact bars support the wires being plated, which collectively form the **cathode.** The wires to be electrogalvanized are generally annealed, thoroughly cleaned in acid, then rinsed before they pass through the plating vat. From the vat the wires pass through or over some simple form of wipe and onto take-up blocks placed far enough away from the wipe to permit the wires to dry in air.

Factors in Controlling the Thickness of the Coat—Theoretically, about 2.5 pounds of zinc can be deposited per hour per 1000 amperes of current. In practice, the amount of zinc deposited will be somewhat less, as no electrochemical operation can be carried on at 100 per cent efficiency. The practical maximum current density varies and must be determined experimentally for each set of working conditions. Having determined this and also the efficiency to be expected, it will be possible to calculate the required total current needed to deposit a required amount of zinc in a given time. The current flowing from the zinc anodes through the electrolyte into the cathode wires cause the zinc to dissolve into the solution at the same rate that the zinc is deposited on the wires, so that the solution, if it is continually and correctly agitated, will remain at a uniform density, and only pure zinc will be deposited, although the slabs used usually contain some impurities. As the zinc ions traveling through the electrolyte actually carry the current, the amount deposited will be directly proportional to the current strength and to the time of current flow. Since

the former factor is fixed, the latter must be increased as the required weight of coating becomes greater.

Tests for Galvanized Coatings—The whole galvanizing process is placed in the hands of experienced operators, who keep constant watch over each phase of the process and at frequent intervals make certain tests to determine the fitness of the material for the purpose for which it is to be used. With respect to the galvanized coatings, these tests are both physical and chemical. The more common of the physical tests are known as the **button test** and the **mandrel test,** each being applied to different classes of wire to meet different requirements. In the button test, the wire is wound tightly about its own diameter, while in the mandrel test the wire is similarly wound about a smooth mandrel having a diameter that is some multiple of its own diameter. The object in both these tests is to determine if the coating will crack or flake under these conditions and, if so, to what extent. For determining the thickness of the coat and whether or not the zinc has been uniformly distributed, two chemical tests are employed. One of these, called the **antimony hydrochloride test,** is a laboratory test used chiefly for determining the exact quantity of zinc per unit of surface galvanized. The other, known as the **Preece** or **copper sulphate test,** though only qualitative, is the best known and most generally used chemical test for galvanized coatings. This test, when made under properly standardized conditions, will determine whether or not the coating is uniform in thickness and whether the thinnest portion will dissolve in a certain solution of copper sulphate in one, two, three, four or more minutes. The terms "one minute wire," "two minute wire," etc., are based on this test, and mean that the coating will successfully withstand immersion in a standard neutral copper sulphate solution for one, two, or more minutes.

Methods of Carrying Out the Copper Sulphate Test—The standard solution used in the test is prepared by dissolving approximately 36 parts of crystallized commercial copper sulphate in 100 parts of distilled water, adding an excess of pure cupric oxide (CuO), and filtering. The concentration of the solution is then adjusted, by adding water or a stronger solution, so that its specific gravity is exactly 1.186 at 65° F. The samples to be tested are thoroughly cleaned before making the test by dipping in benzene or gasoline, or rinsing in water, and wiping with clean white cotton waste or cloth. A clean test jar, 5 inches high and 2 inches in diameter, is then filled to within one inch of the top with the standard solution at a temperature between 62° F and 68° F, which temperature must be maintained throughout the test. The sample is now immersed in the solution by lowering it endwise into the jar, where it is allowed to remain for exactly one minute; it is then removed, rinsed immediately in water of the same temperature, and wiped until dry with the clean cotton waste or cloth, so as to remove the dark deposit of copper which forms on the surface. These operations are then repeated, the wire being immersed for exactly one minute at each trial, until traces of bright metallic copper begin to appear on the surface of the steel, indicating removal of the zinc, or until the number of one-minute immersions exceeds the number required by the specifications. In case more than one wire is tested at the same time, the samples, numbering not more than seven, are immersed simultaneously in the same jar, and these must be kept well separated. The lower inch of each sample, being adjacent to the cut exposing the iron, is disregarded in the test. A fresh portion of the standard solution must be used after each complete test of seven wires or less.

Principles of the Test—The principles upon which the copper sulphate test depend may be explained as follows: The copper sulphate dissolves both zinc and iron, these two elements displacing the copper in the solution of copper sulphate according to the following reactions:

$$Zn + CuSO_4 = ZnSO_4 + Cu.$$
$$Fe + CuSO_4 = FeSO_4 + Cu.$$

From these reactions it will be seen that copper is precipitated, or thrown out of solution, in each case. Since the reaction can take place only where the wire is in contact with the solution, this liberated copper is deposited upon the surface of the wire, and the test depends wholly upon the difference in the manner in which this deposit is made upon zinc and iron. In the case of zinc, the deposited copper is in a finely divided form, and appears as a black flocculent coating completely covering the wire. As this coating increases in thickness, it tends to shield the wire from the solution, thus retarding the reaction, hence the necessity for removing the wire from the test jar and cleaning its surface at regular intervals of one minute. In the case of iron, however, the copper, if all the conditions of the test are properly observed, is deposited upon the surface in the form of a bright metallic coating which cannot be wiped off and is similar in appearance to that obtained in electroplating. Thus, as soon as the zinc has been removed from any part of the surface of the wire, this bright coating appears on that spot.

Value of the Copper Sulphate Test—The chief merit of the copper sulphate test is that it reveals any unevenness in the thickness of the coat. Although the test is not directly quantitative, it provides a relative measure of the amount of zinc at the thinnest point of the coating, provided the surface condition, composition and structure of the coatings being compared are the same. This information is important, for the corrosion resistance of the coat depends not only upon the weight of the zinc on a given surface but also upon the evenness with which it is distributed. In service, corrosion of the steel begins where the zinc coating first disappears, so that for a given total weight of zinc applied, the best protection to the steel is offered by the most uniform distribution of zinc. The test can be quickly made with simple apparatus, and the effect is very apparent, but each phase of the test must be carefully performed under standard conditions to obtain fair comparative results. The latter fact is not generally recognized, the impression being that almost anyone can make the test without instruction as to the points to be observed. In this connection it should be noted that the copper will plate out upon an alloy of zinc and iron as well as upon pure iron or steel, but the coat of copper on the former does not adhere firmly to the surface and may be brushed off with a fine steel brush.

WIRE TINNING

Because of the high cost of tin, and of the difficulty of entirely avoiding pin holes in tinning steel wire, only a small amount of steel wire is tinned, and that largely for decorative purposes. As already explained, tin is cathodic to iron. Consequently, in the case of steel wire coated with tin and exposed to the atmosphere, the destruction of the steel base will be accelerated by the presence of tin when corrosion begins. The tinning process is very similar in principle to the hot galvanizing process and need not be described at length. The wire has to be thoroughly cleaned and fluxed before entering the bath of tin, and as it emerges from this bath it passes through a wipe of wicking wound about the wire, after which it goes to the take-up blocks, either with or without an intermediate water cooling. The tin must be maintained at a fairly constant temperature (500° to 550° F), for if the bath temperature is too low, the coating will be rough and uneven, and if too high, it will be discolored by the yellowish tin oxide formed on the surface.

ALUMINUM COATINGS

In recent years aluminum coatings have been applied to steel products for resistance to corrosion in marine, industrial and the usual environments. The aluminum is applied to steel wires by the hot-dip process, where the cold-drawn wires are cleaned prior to immersion into a molten aluminum bath. Aluminum forms alloys with steel in a manner similar to zinc, and the process must be carefully controlled; otherwise, a brittle alloy layer will form which will cause cracking and spalling during subsequent forming operations.

The aluminum bath is operated at a temperature of approximately 1225 to 1250° F. This temperature is sufficient to soften carbon steels with a corresponding loss in tensile strength. Aluminum-coated wire can be cold drawn after coating to improve or raise the tensile strength. Also, by drawing after coating, very bright finishes can be produced which make the wire suitable for many decorative applications.

Wire which can be coated with aluminum for corrosion protection includes: field fence, barbed wire, chain-link wire, netting wire, tie wire, welding wire, strand wire, telephone wire and A.C.S.R. core wire.

SECTION 10

TYPICAL FINISHED WIRES FOR MANUFACTURING PURPOSES

The object of this section is to list according to their common trade names the different kinds and grades of wire used for manufacturing purposes and indicate the uses of each.

COMMON WIRES

Bright Bessemer Wire—Wire of this grade is hard or stiff wire, ordinarily drawn from a rod to finished size without an intermediate annealing. It is not well suited for purposes involving special finishes or specific mechanical properties.

Bright Basic Wire or Bright Hard Basic Wire—Wire of this classification receives the same treatment as Bright Bessemer, is slightly softer wire than Bright Bessemer Wire, has a finish obtained by regular dry drawing and is used in applications not requiring specific physical properties.

Bright Soft Basic Wire is a soft grade of bright wire for manufacturing purposes, and is adapted to difficult forming, severe twisting, swaging, crimping, etc.

Medium Classifications—Medium hard and medium soft Bessemer and basic wires are finer gradations between the "bright" and "bright soft" grades. They are common only to the finer sizes, 8¾ gage (0.152-inch) and finer, and their use depends upon the severity of the bending and forming operations which are to be performed.

Annealed Wires—Annealed wire is the softest grade that can be produced. Because of differences in chemical composition (assuming the carbon content is the same), annealed basic wire is softer than annealed Bessemer wire of the same size. In producing annealed wire, the coarser sizes must be given a special draft before annealing, otherwise brittle wire known as "crystallized wire" will be obtained after the annealing. The finer sizes are drawn the same as the bright (hard) grade and then annealed. "Annealed," or "annealed, cleaned and limed basic" Cold-Heading Quality wire is used largely for extremely severe upsetting, such as special bolts, certain kinds of rivets and for any purpose in which the wire is severely deformed by pressing or heading operations. If maximum softness is essential, the use of annealed basic wire is indicated.

Cold-Heading Wire—Wire for cold heading or cold forging has become one of the large production items in the wire industry. Wire of this grade is used for bolts, rivets, screws, and similar applications requiring, in many instances, severe plastic deformation. For common fabrication, low-carbon steel may be used, but with the advent of highly stressed parts as in automobile and aviation applications, higher carbon, low-alloy and stainless steels are now required. As upsetting the head on the bolt or screw will readily accentuate surface defects of the wire such as seams or slivers, bolt wire must necessarily be a high quality product with great uniformity of structure and composition. Production of higher carbon and alloy wire for heat-treated bolts requires close control at all stages: melting the steel, rolling the rod, heat treating and drawing the wire. In addition to the above prerequisites, the surface coating of the wire, which is controlled primarily by the wire-drawing lubricant, is important as a factor in the cold-heading operation. The type of upsetting die and whether or not the bolt shank is extruded in the operation determine the type of wire coating required; the coating, in turn has a significant bearing on the life of the heading die and the quality of the finished bolt. The finished hardness and chemical composition of bolt wire both are definitely controlled according to the severity of the deformation required in forming the bolt. As the hardness increases with increasing carbon and/or alloy content of the steel, the final hardness will be regulated by normalizing, process annealing or spheroidizing the steel. Machinability requirements and the ability of the wire to respond to heat treatment may also be factors influencing selection of the manufacturing processes to produce wire having the proper microstructure and hardness, particularly in steels over 0.35 carbon. The finished product is rigidly inspected, and includes adequate mechanical, chemical and metallographic testing.

Liquor-Finished Fine and Weaving Wire—Some of this grade of wire, which may be used for weaving household window-screen cloth, is made in very fine sizes, 0.0118 inches and 0.0104 inches being the common sizes. Wire for this purpose is usually made from low-carbon basic steel and to reduce the wire from a 7/32-inch rod (0.218-inch) to such fine sizes requires annealing in process and 22 to 24 drafts, depending on composition and requirements.

Welding Wire—Various steels, both carbon and alloy, are used to produce welding wire for the manufacture of electrodes and rods for electric and gas welding, and these range from 0.05 carbon to about 1.0 per cent carbon. While considerable gas welding is still employed, by far the greater proportion of welding operations are performed by the electric-arc process. Wire for gas welding is copper coated and used in straight lengths, composition being governed by properties required in the weld metal.

Electric-arc welding is divided into two classifications: manual welding and automatic welding.

Wire for manual welding is furnished in straightened and cut lengths with surface as free from wire-drawing lubricant as possible to enable electrode manufacturers to apply a flux coating by an extrusion method. Welding steels are made especially for this application, and selection of heats or portions of heats is mandatory to conform to required composition limits and ranges. Low sulphur, not exceeding 0.035 per cent, is generally preferred. Most of the grades of steel made for welding electrodes are of the rimming type, with carbon in the neighborhood of 0.10 to 0.15 per cent. However, there is also some demand for rimming-type steel with 0.31 per cent carbon as the maximum of the range. Killed steels of 0.55 to 0.65 per cent carbon and 0.90 to 1.10 per cent carbon are also used to some extent, along with some alloy grades for special purposes such as resistance to abrasion. Composition of the steel is governed by composition of the flux coating, the combination being designed to provide certain welding characteristics and specific properties in the deposit metal.

The wire thus serves as the core of the coated electrode and is expected to provide good welding characteristics and a dense, sound deposit. Wire sizes in popular demand are ⅛-inch, 5/32-inch, 3/16-inch, and ¼-inch. Tolerances for diameter, length, camber, and burrs in the straightened and cut wire are listed in the AISI Products Manual for Wire.

The flux coating on the electrode provides a blanket which surrounds the arc during welding and serves as a protection against oxidation from the atmosphere. In automatic electric-arc welding, there are two main processes: submerged-arc and inert-gas. In the former, the welding is shielded by a blanket of fusible material, usually referred to as flux which is fed on to the work. In the latter, shielding is obtained from inert gas such as argon or helium. Both automatic and semi-automatic equipment is used for each process.

Wire compositions vary for submerged-arc welding according to requirements in the deposit metal. The wire is produced with a bright copper finish to improve the contact surfaces and so facilitate the introduction of the relatively high currents used. It is important that the surface of the wire be as free as possible from wire-drawing lubricant which would tend to clog the nozzle through which the wire is fed. Wire for submerged-arc welding is furnished in layer-wound coils with cardboard cores. Dimensions of these coils are designed for insertion into a reel from which the wire is fed through the welding machine. Wire sizes in demand range from about ³⁄₃₂-inch up to about ⁵⁄₁₆-inch.

The inert-gas welding process calls for smaller wires ranging from 0.045-inch to around 0.125-inch. Wire for this application is furnished with a bright, clean copper coating for the same reason as mentioned above and is wound on spools of the dimensions necessary for insertion in the welding equipment. The required wire compositions vary according to requirements of consumers.

Brush Wire—Untempered brush wire is used for bristles in wire brushes. There are three grades: Low-Carbon Brush Wire; Scratch Brush Wire and High-Strength Brush Wire. Brush wire is supplied in the following finishes: straw liquor finish, steel bright, coppered, tinned, galvanized, or cadmium coated. The Low-Carbon Brush Wire is usually produced in sizes under 0.008-in. from low-carbon steel to an approximate tensile strength of 140,000 lb. per sq. in. Scratch Brush Wire is generally produced in sizes 0.035-in. and under from carbon steel of approximately 0.45 to 0.60 per cent carbon content, in tensile strengths from 230,000 to 290,000 lb. per sq. in. High Strength Brush Wire is usually produced in sizes 0.035-in. and under from steel of approximately 0.55 to 0.75 per cent carbon content in tensile strengths ranging from 300,000 to 380,000 lb. per sq. in.

HIGH-CARBON OR SPECIAL WIRES

To select the proper grade of wire for any given purpose, it is necessary to know the mechanical properties required to meet the demands of that particular service. As a result of work correlating a large number of experiments in the wire mills with data collected from actual experience, it is now possible to supply wire meeting various combinations of mechanical properties, including tensile strength, torsional strength, toughness, etc. These studies have led to the discovery of the principles governing the behavior of high-carbon stocks, and these principles determine the processes to which the wire must be subjected to obtain the desired results. Other elements of uncertainty have been removed by careful standardization, so far as possible, of the manufacturing practices for producing the various classifications and grades of high-carbon steel wires.

Rope Wire—Rope wire is made from high-carbon steel produced by the basic or acid open-hearth or electric-furnace processes. Carbon content ranges from 0.45 to 0.80 per cent. The various grades, namely; Mild Plow, Plow, and Improved Plow Steel, require very exacting processing to produce wire to meet the tensile-strength and torsion-test requirements. At least one and perhaps three patenting heat treatments at various stages of reduction are necessary to produce the various sizes of wire down to 0.005-in. diameter. Practically every size and grade of rope wire must be produced from a different final patenting size in order to obtain the proper mechanical properties in the finished wire.

Rope wire is generally made in any of the following finishes:

A. Bright—Dry drawn in coarser sizes, wet drawn in finer sizes.

B. Drawn galvanized.

C. Galvanized at finished size.

Music Wire—Music wire is the term applied to wire having the physical requisites necessary for use in musical string instruments. Although commonly known as music wires, these wires are generally referred to as piano wire, harp wire and mandolin wire, depending upon the purpose for which it is used. In conjunction with the manufacture of music wire, there is a grade of wire manufactured known as music spring wire. This wire is not quite as high in quality as piano wire and is used for high-grade, cold-wound, high-tensile-strength springs.

Piano Wire—Piano wire has rightly been called the "speciality of specialties." It represents the highest attainment in the art of wire manufacture. The wire possesses the highest tensile strength of any form in which carbon steel is used for purely stress-resisting purposes. It is made from the finest quality of steel, having a carbon content of from 0.80 to 0.95 per cent. Different grades and sizes require varying drafting and heat-treating practices to develop the proper tensile strength and toughness.

In addition to the mechanical properties required, piano wire must possess acoustic properties. Attainment of this requirement is dependent upon the accuracy of the size, the soundness of the steel and the finish of the wire. Furthermore, the tension required for different pitches and lengths means that high elastic limit with uniform tensile strength is imperative for a given wire. The toughness must be developed to a maximum for the tensile strength to permit forming the wire into loops or eyes by the bass-string manufacturers. The bass strings must also be flattened locally on the ends to form an anchor for the covering wire. Tensile strengths for the highest grades of piano wire are given below, from which data it should be noted that the higher strengths are obtained in the finer sizes.

Kind of Wire	Diameter in Inches	Tensile Strength (Lb. Per Sq. In.)
Bass Strings	0.035 to 0.067	290,000 to 351,000
Treble Strings	0.029 to 0.049	319,000 to 390,000

Bronze Finish Tire Bead Wire—Tire wire is used in the beads of automobile tires. This product receives special care at every stage of its manufacture to be sure it will meet requirements, which are very exacting. It therefore receives a rigid inspection. It must be perfectly round and true to gage, and possess the proper tensile strength, torsion and elongation qualities. Practically all consumers require this wire to stand a torsion test under tension of a five-pound weight, usually in a length of six to eight inches. Some demand only a minimum breaking weight while others specify both a maximum and a minimum. A wire having the high tensile strength demanded, that will withstand a minimum of 58 twists in 8 inches, must be free from injurious steel defects, such as pipe, seams, and segregation.

Spoke Wire—Satisfactory spoke wire to be used in the manufacture of automobile wire wheels must possess special mechanical properties. It is made from sound stock, free from all imperfections, so that a good finish can be obtained on the final product. The method of manufacturing spokes requires that the wire shall be capable of being swaged, headed and threaded. It is stiff enough to withstand the loads to which it is subjected and yet it possesses considerable toughness and ability to withstand the shocks and vibration that are imposed on it in service. The increase in strength obtained by heat treatment, plus that developed in the wire by drawing to the finished size, results in a tensile strength ranging from 140,000 to 160,000 pounds per square inch. It is furnished in sizes ranging from 0.0645 to 0.2045 inch, either in bright or liquor-finished grades. Bicycle-spoke wire (usually 0.0795 inch in diameter), also follows this general requirement, but is normally supplied with a drawn galvanized finish.

Baby carriage and similar types of wire wheels do not require the high tensile strength developed in the wire for automotive wheels. A bright or tinned low-carbon basic wire, drawn direct to finished size from the rod without any intermediate heat treatment, is furnished for this purpose. It has a tensile strength of 90,000 to 110,000 pounds per square inch and is usually supplied in sizes ranging from 0.0625 to 0.162 inch.

Valve Spring Wire—In early automobile engines, operating at speeds around 2200 rev. per min., any good commercial-quality hard-drawn or oil-tempered spring wire would make a satisfactory valve spring. However, modern engines, designed for speeds from 3800 to 4200 rev. per min. require valve springs made from special wire. Higher-horsepower motors require greater energy storage in the springs. At higher speeds, the effect of inertia in the valve-spring system becomes much more pronounced, and the spring designer must employ the highest design stresses possible to obtain the desired load without excessive weight in the valve springs. High speeds also tend to introduce considerable amounts of dynamic stress,

in addition to the high static stress mentioned above. The designer usually attempts to keep these dynamic stresses to a minimum by adding dampener coils to the spring or by using a separate dampener spring inside the main valve spring. If the stresses encountered in service exceed the fatigue limit of the material, or if significant surface or internal defects that can cause localized concentrations of stresses are present, fatigue failures may take place, often in the first few hundred miles of operation.

By careful selection of materials at all stages of wire manufacture, the use of the best processing equipment and practices available, and very rigorous inspection, all the requirements of valve spring wire for modern high-speed high-power engines can be met. Some of the precautions taken with this material are: (1) Use of basic open-hearth steel of exceptional cleanliness; (2) Generous cropping from both top and bottom of the ingot; (3) Inspection and conditioning of billets; (4) Special rod-rolling equipment and practices; (5) Extra heat treatments from rod to finished wire; (6) Careful control of processing to produce high, uniform tensile strength and coating satisfactory for uniform spring coiling; (7) Special tests, including tensile-strength, twist tests, and surface inspection by acid etch and examination under binocular microscope on both ends of every bundle; and (8) Special tests and investigations to determine fatigue limit of wire samples or test springs coiled from the wire.

Most of the valve springs produced in this country are made from wire that has been oil tempered at finished size. However, within the past few years, a substantial percentage of valve spring wire has been used in the hard-drawn condition, with tensile strength built up by a combination of process heat treatment and cold drawing. Wire diameters usually range from 0.162- to 0.192-inch, and tensile strength from 210,000 to 250,000 lb. per sq. in.

Tempered Wire—Tempered wire is made in rounds, flats and rectangles. The most important feature of this class of material is its temper, which depends upon both the composition and heat treatment. The tensile strength of this product may ordinarily be required to range from as low as 160,000 pounds per square inch to as high as 300,000 pounds per square inch. Occasionally, strengths in excess of 300,000 pounds per square inch are required. The tempering is accomplished by passing the wire through a continuous tempering furnace in which the wire passes successively through a heated muffle or heated tubes or a hot lead pan, an oil quenching bath and a cold lead pan.

The temperatures of the muffle, tubes and lead pans are controlled automatically by pyrometers which hold each of these at a very uniform temperature and consequently give uniform temper to the wire within very close limits.

Tinned armature-binding wire is another specialty wire. It is made in several grades, which differ in tensile strength. The specifications require a product having high elastic limit and high elongation combined with toughness. To obtain this combination, important essentials are: first, steel of the proper composition; second, proper heat treatment; third, a uniform drafting practice; fourth, a tinning temperature which will give a good finish and will aid in obtaining the desired physical properties in the finished wire.

Metal-stitching wire was developed for fastening non-stressed parts in automotive assembly operations and is now also used in the assembly of non-stressed aircraft structures as well as in a multitude of other types of assemblies. In this application, the wire is fed from a spool through a stitching machine which cuts the wire to length, forms it into a staple and drives the legs of the staple through the material to be fastened. In most cases, the legs are folded back or clinched after penetrating the two or more layers being assembled. This wire is frequently used to unite metal to metal or metal and non-metal parts, such as rubber, fiber, felt or plywood. The tensile strength of wire for these applications may range from 200,000 to 330,000 pounds per square inch, depending on the thickness and type of metal required to be penetrated by the fasteners. For this purpose, it is evident that the wire must be very uniform in temper and possess great toughness. Metal-stitching wire is made with several different finishes, according to whether a protective or decorative finish is desired.

Other Special Wires—Besides those already mentioned, there are numerous other grades of drawn high-carbon wires produced. In practically every case, the various grades differ from each other in one or more respects, such as stock, temper, quality of toughness, finish and coating. Practically all of the high-carbon wires are classified as "special wires." By special wires is meant wires made to uncommon specifications, either as to finish or mechanical properties. The range of stocks used for special wires may include basic open-hearth steel from the lowest carbon steel up to a steel having a content of 1.20 per cent carbon. There are at least twenty-five different carbon grades, and these are further increased by variations in manganese and other elements. Following selection and rolling of the stock, preliminary testing of the rods is usually necessary to prevent unnecessary work on stock which will not give the desired qualities in the finished wire. Extreme care must be used in the cleaning, coating, and every step of the manufacture. Special drafting, various heat treatments, both before and after the complex drawing processes, special testing and extraordinary precautions must be followed to secure the unusual properties and degree of uniformity that may be required.

STAINLESS-STEEL WIRE

Stainless-steel wire has become an established commodity for many purposes because of its utilitarian nature, its stainless and heat resisting characteristics, and its ability to withstand a variety of forming operations. Among the established products are cold-heading wires for the manufacture of bolts, rivet pins, and screws; tinned non-magnetic armature-binding wire for use in highly-powered motors for Diesel engines, and other motors which require a high-tensile non-magnetic wire; welding wires furnished for all methods of welding; spring wires to be used where resistance to chemical solutions and atmospheres is a necessity; weaving wires for a wide range of screens from very fine mesh flour sifters to coal and coke screens and continuous high-temperature conveyor belts; rope wires for specialized purposes such as mine sweeping, aircraft-control cables and strands for yachts and ships. The unusual properties of stainless steel which permit a lasting bright finish to be developed, combined with its utilitarian nature, give it great intrinsic value when used as display racks, dishwasher and refrigerator racks.

While Types 430, 410, 302, 304, and 305 may be considered the more popular grades, almost the entire list is drawn to wire for a great variety of uses.

The processing and drawing of these steels are similar, in general, to that of the carbon-steel wires. They will differ somewhat in individual practices because of the inherent nature of the alloys, such as resistance to some acids and activation by others, all of which combine to make the coating and lubricating problems in drawing stainless-steel wires one of meticulous control.

STAINLESS COLD-ROLLED STRIP STEEL

Stainless cold-rolled strip steel is manufactured from hot-rolled annealed and pickled strip by cold rolling in mills equipped with ground or ground and polished rolls, depending upon the surface finish requirements. Strip steel is normally supplied up to and including $23^{15}/_{16}$-inches wide in a great many of the more common types of stainless steels.

A range of mechanical properties can be provided by taking advantage of the possibilities offered by combining the influences of chemical composition, cold work (cold rolling), and heat treatment. These are varied according to the mechanical properties desired. Physical properties developed in this manner are referred to as tempers and are associated with the capacity each temper level possesses in regard to resistance to cold deformation. In the straight chromium grade (400 series), only three tempers are generally recognized by the industry, viz., full hard (Rockwell C 20 minimum), No. 4 Temper (approximately Rockwell B 80–90), and No. 5 Temper (approximately Rockwell B 83 maximum). In the chromium-nickel steels (300 series), No. 4 Temper will show approximately 80–90 Rockwell B and No. 5 approximately Rockwell B 83 maximum. In addition to these soft tempers, a variety of hard tempers is available classed as ¼, ½, and ¾ hard and full hard. These are based on minimum values for tensile strength or yield strength or both.

Finishes—Various surface finishes are possible in cold-rolled stainless strip steel although they are gradations. For example, a dull finish without luster can be produced by rolling on rolls roughened by chemical or mechanical means. A luster finish can be produced by rolling on rolls having a moderately high finish. For the very best or high luster, all of the treatments must be carefully done and the rolling performed on highly-polished rolls.

Basically only two finishes are recognized in the stainless steel strip industry:

> No. 1 Finish, which is cold rolled, annealed, and pickled, and

No. 2 Finish, which is cold rolled, annealed, pickled, and rerolled.

Because of the difference in the alloy contents between the straight chromium and the chromium-nickel steels, it is possible to anneal the former so that a bright finish results, while the annealed and pickled chromium-nickel steel will be dull. In the chromium-nickel steels, No. 1 Finish is classed as dull, while the hard tempers are relatively bright as will be the No. 2 Finish, No. 4 Temper.

Since the annealed and pickled straight chromium steels result in a bright No. 1 Finish, it is possible to change the processes to enhance this finish in making a No. 2 so that it is even brighter. Dull finishes are also available in these grades where the requirements are necessary.

There are three edges available in stainless strip depending upon the width and thickness:

No. 1 Edge is a rolled edge, either round or square as specified, and is recommended when a very uniform width is required. It is limited to strip of approximately 5 inches in width and under.

No. 3 Edge is an approximately square edge produced by slitting. This edge is not burr free. Width is not a limiting factor in furnishing this edge.

No. 5 Edge is an approximately square edge produced by rolling or filing for the primary purpose of removing burr originating in the slitting operation. Width is not a limiting factor in furnishing this edge.

COLD-ROLLED CARBON-STEEL STRIP

Cold-rolled carbon-steel strip is manufactured in a variety of finishes, tempers, and edges, all depending upon the end use. By common custom, cold-rolled carbon-steel strip is made in a width range of over ½ inch to 23¹⁵⁄₁₆ inches and up to 0.2499 inch thick. It has a carbon content of 0.25 per cent maximum; material of this form containing more than this amount of carbon is considered as cold-rolled carbon spring steel.

Cold-rolled strip is produced in coils on any of the conventional reversing mills, tandem mills, or by single-stand rolling. While the strip may be supplied in coils, it can be furnished in cut lengths by the straighten-and-cut process.

Before cold rolling, the mill scale is removed from the hot-rolled strip, usually by pickling. From this point, the strip may be cold reduced to final thickness or to some intermediate gage where it is annealed and further cold reduced to obtain the desired temper and gage.

Temper—Many degrees of temper are possible in the manufacture of cold-rolled strip by controlling the combinations of cold rolling and annealing. However, many years of use have brought certain ranges of temper into common usage, and these have come to be recognized by number, as follows:

Temper	Maximum Carbon Content (Per Cent)*	Rockwell Hardness Minimum	Rockwell Hardness Maximum**
No. 1 (Hard Temper)	0.25	B-84[a] B-90[b]	
No. 2 (Half Hard)	0.25	B-70	B-85
No. 3 (Quarter Hard)	0.25	B-60	B-75
No. 4 (Skin Rolled)	0.15	—	B-65
No. 5 (Dead Soft)	0.15	—	B-55

* Ladle analysis
** Approximate
[a] For thicknesses 0.070 inch and greater
[b] For thicknesses less than 0.070 inch.

No. 1 Hard Temper is a very stiff springy strip intended only for flat work where no bending is required.

No. 2 Half Hard Temper is less stiff than No. 1, but is intended for limited cold forming and will only withstand 90 degree bends made across the direction of rolling around a radius equal to the thickness.

No. 3 Quarter Hard Temper is intended for limited bending and cold forming and can be bent 90 degrees in the direction of rolling around a radius equal to the thickness and 180 degrees across the direction of rolling over its own thickness.

No. 4 Skin-Rolled Temper is intended for cold forming such as bending flat upon itself in any direction and for deep drawing. The purpose of the skin pass is to prevent the formation of stretcher strains.

No. 5 Dead Soft Temper or annealed temper is intended for severe cold forming and deep drawing where the formation of stretcher strains is not objectionable.

Three finishes have come to be recognized as standard within the industry, again by common usage.

No. 1 Dull Finish does not have any luster and is actually made rough intentionally by rolling on rolls roughened either mechanically or chemically. This finish is suitable where paint adherence is desired, or in deep drawing since the lubricant will stick to it.

No. 2 Regular Bright Finish is cold rolled on rolls having moderately smooth finish. It is suitable for many requirements, although it is not generally applicable to plating.

No. 3 Best Bright Finish is the highest luster finish produced by cold rolling and is particularly suited for electroplating.

Cold-rolled carbon-steel strip in No. 1 Dull Finish, No. 2 Regular Bright Finish, and No. 3 Best Bright Finish is also available with "rolled-in" designs produced through the use of embossed rolls.

Six types of edges have become recognized as standard.

No. 1 Edge is a prepared edge of a specified contour (round, square, or beveled) which is produced when a very accurate width or edge finish is required.

No. 2 Edge is a natural mill edge carried throughout the cold rolling from the hot mill without additional processing of the edge.

No. 3 Edge is an approximately square edge produced by slitting.

No. 4 Edge is a rounded edge produced by edge rolling either the natural edge of the hot-rolled strip or the slit-edge strip. This edge is produced when an approximate round edge is desired and when the finish of the edge is not important.

No. 5 Edge is an approximately square edge produced by rolling or filing of a slit edge to remove the burr.

No. 6 Edge is a square edge produced by edge rolling the natural edge of the hot-rolled strip or slit-edge strip when the width tolerance and finish required are not so exacting as for No. 1 Edge.

COLD ROLLED CARBON SPRING STEEL

Cold rolled carbon spring steel is furnished either untempered or hardened and tempered in a variety of finishes, tempers, and edges. It is produced in coils in a manner similar to cold rolled strip and it can also be supplied in cut lengths by the straighten-and-cut process.

Tempered cold rolled carbon spring steel is customarily produced with a No. 1 edge. Untempered cold rolled carbon spring steel is customarily produced with edge Nos. 1 to 6, inclusive, as described above for cold rolled strip.

Untempered cold rolled carbon spring steel is commonly furnished with a No. 2 finish as described above for cold rolled strip. The following types of finishes are commonly produced on hardened and tempered cold rolled spring steel:

> Black Tempered
> Scaleless Tempered
> Bright Tempered
> Tempered and Polished
> Tempered, Polished and
> Colored (Blue or Straw)

Table 29—IV. Expected Rockwell Hardness for Different Ranges of Carbon Content and Thickness of Soft Type Cold Rolled Spring Steel.

Carbon Content (Maximum of Range—Per Cent)	0.040 In. and Over ("B" Scale)	Under 0.040 In. to 0.025 In., Incl. ("30T" Scale)	Under 0.025 In. ("15T" Scale)
0.30	74	67	84
0.35	76	68	84
0.40	78	70	85
0.45	80	71	85
0.50	82	72	86
0.55	84	73	87
0.60	85	74	87
0.65	87	75	88
0.70	88	76	88
0.75	89	76	88
0.80	90	77	89
0.85	91	77	89
0.90	92	78	89
0.95 and over	92	78	90

Temper—As with cold rolled carbon steel strip, many degrees of temper are possible in the manufacture of cold rolled carbon spring steel. Untempered spring steel is commonly furnished to the temper designations of Hard, Intermediate, and Annealed.

Hard type cold rolled carbon spring steel is a very stiff, springy product intended for flat work and not for cold forming. It is furnished to a minimum Rockwell hardness value of B-98.

Intermediate type cold rolled carbon spring steel is intended for applications where hardness ranges are required, the maximum being higher than that customarily obtained by annealing at finish thickness. The Rockwell hardness ranges commonly specified vary according to the maximum of the carbon range involved, the maximum of the required hardness range, and the thickness of the material.

Soft type cold rolled carbon spring steel is intended for moderately severe cold forming requiring low hardness and is produced to a specified maximum

Table 29—V. Rockwell Hardness Range Limits for Hardened and Tempered Cold Rolled Carbon Spring Steel for Various Ranges of Carbon Content and Strip Thickness.

Thickness, Inch	Rockwell Scale	Per Cent Carbon, Maximum						
		0.75	0.80	0.85	0.90	0.95	1.00	1.05
		Limits of Rockwell Hardness Range*						
Over 0.115 to 0.125, incl.	C	32-44	37-45	38-46	39-47	40-48	41-49	42-50
Over 0.100 to 0.115, incl.	C	33-45	38-46	39-47	40-48	41-49	42-50	43-51
Over 0.085 to 0.100, incl.	C	34-46	39-47	40-48	41-49	42-50	43-51	44-52
Over 0.070 to 0.085, incl.	C	35-47	40-48	41-49	42-50	43-51	44-52	45-53
Over 0.055 to 0.070, incl.	C	36-48	41-49	42-50	43-51	44-52	45-53	46-54
Over 0.035 to 0.055, incl.	C	37-49	42-50	43-51	44-52	45-53	46-54	47-55
Over 0.015 to 0.035, incl.	30N	57-68	62-69	63-70	64-71	64.5-71.5	65-72	66-73
Up to 0.015	15N	78-84	80.5-84.5	81-85	81.5-85.5	82-86	82.5-86.5	83-87

* By common usage, a Rockwell hardness range is the arithmetical difference between two limits. It is customary to specify Rockwell range requirements within the above limits for each grade of hardened and tempered cold rolled carbon spring steel in accordance with the following:

Rockwell Hardness Scale	Specified Range
C	Any 4 points
30N	Any 4 points
15N	Any 3 points

Rockwell hardness value only. This type is produced by performing the final annealing at finish thickness. The Rockwell hardness values indicated in Table 29—IV are commonly expected for the indicated ranges of carbon content and thickness.

Hardened and tempered cold rolled carbon spring steel customarily has a carbon content over 0.60 per cent. It is commonly produced to the Rockwell hardness ranges given in Table 29—V, dependent upon the maximum per cent carbon content of the range and the thickness of the strip.

FLAT WIRE

Flat wire is ordinarily cold rolled from a drawn round wire, properly annealed and treated to permit additional reduction in rolling and to produce a reasonably bright surface. Natural round, smooth edges are produced by this method of manufacture. Flat wire can be made up to ½ inch wide, with ratio of width to thickness being in accord with good manufacturing practices. Normally, flat wire is best produced in sizes up to ⅜ inch in width with roughly a 5-to-1 ratio in thickness. However, this ratio can in some instances be as high as 10-to-1 or 15-to-1. Flat wire is available or can be made to include soft or medium or hard rolled tempers. This material has a variety of uses: some typical applications are in window-shade roller springs (Curtain Spring Wire), leaf-type feeler (thickness) gauges (Feeler Gauge Steel), electricians' tools for "fishing" wires between walls and through conduits (Fish Tape Wire) and staples for many fastening operations involving stapling machines (Flat-Preformed Staple Wire). Flat wire can be formed into flat wound springs. It also is used in miscellaneous products where spot welding is required in assemblies. Types 302 and 430 are grades of stainless steel which have been most commonly furnished in the form of flat wire, although flat wire can be produced from many of the other grades.

SECTION 11

SOME FABRICATED STEEL-WIRE PRODUCTS

Importance of Fabricated Wire Products — Steel wire is fabricated into thousands of different kinds of articles, which are used for a great variety of purposes. In a list of such articles will be found many items of common use, such as automobile and bicycle spokes, hoops, rivets, bolts, chains, buckles, cotterpins, sifting screens, wire netting, wire cloth, and a host of others, each of which consumes large amounts of wire. Since even the briefest description of the fabrication of all these articles would require a great deal of space, only a few of the more important commodities, in the fabrication of which great tonnages of steel wire are consumed annually, are briefly discussed here.

WIRE NAILS

The wire nail has almost entirely displaced the old-style cut nail, being better in all respects and much cheaper. A review of any modern nail catalogue will show that there are many varieties as to length, size and style, ranging all the way from the tiniest tack to the long heavy spikes. The common finish on nails is obtained by tumbling. Recent developments in the nail industry have combined the tumbling with caustic cleaning and vapor chemical cleaning. Large quantities are hot galvanized, zinc coated, tinned, coppered or cement coated. In the last-named process, the nails are given a light coating of a resinous compound that to some degree increases the holding power.

Nail Machines—All steel-wire nails are made in automatic machines. These machines differ greatly in size and in design, but the principle of operation is much the same in all of them. Nails are made on a machine by five distinct operations; namely, (1) forming the head, (2) feeding the wire, (3) pinching the wire, (4) cutting off the wire and forming the point, (5) expelling the nail.

The head of the nail is formed by compressing and flattening against a die the portion of the wire which projects beyond this die and remains after the previously-formed nail has been cut from the wire. This compressing and flattening is done by a hammer which is attached to a reciprocating member, called a hammer stock, which in turn is actuated usually by a crank and pitman. The amount of wire which projects beyond the die governs the size and thickness of the head and is regulated by adjusting the cutting knives to the proper distance from this die. The various shapes of heads are obtained by cutting the desired depression in the die. This die is split, that is, made in two parts, one fixed or stationary and the other movable.

Feeding—After the head is formed, the hammer moves away from the die, and the die opens up and allows the feed mechanism to push the wire, with a nail head on the end, the correct distance through the die to give a nail of the length required. The feeding mechanism is driven by an adjustable crank on the flywheel of the machine, and, by adjusting this crank, various lengths of nails can be obtained. This feed mechanism also pulls the wire through a series of staggered rolls, as it leaves the reel, to straighten it.

Pinching—When the hammer has reached the end of the stroke, the wire has been fed the correct amount for the nail required and the die closes to pinch the wire. This pinching action is motivated by a cam on the crankshaft.

Cutting—Immediately after the wire is pinched, two knives, each attached to a lever, move together and cut the wire. These cutting knives are ground to form the point on the nail at the same time that the cut is made. This point is formed by pressing the wire into the shape required, and, in doing so, some of the metal is squeezed out or protrudes between the knives and is cut off by them. These cutoff particles are called whiskers. The cutting levers to which the knives are attached are actuated by various forms of mechanisms deriving their motion from the crankshaft.

Expelling—Sometimes, because of dull knives or insufficiently close adjustment, the nail will still adhere to the wire when the cutting knives open up. The cutting knives open up on the return stroke of the hammer, and, in order to remove this adhering nail, an expeller comes into action, knocking the nail downward out of the path of the hammer and breaking it off. The hammer on the return stroke forms another head on the wire for the next nail, the wire being pinched during this stroke. The finished nails drop into a pan placed on the floor beneath this mechanism.

Finishing Common Nails—The nails in these pans are collected and placed in a tumbler, care being taken to have nails of only one kind in the tumbler at a time in order to avoid mixing. Into this tumbler some sawdust is also placed. The tumbler has projections on the inside, causing the nails to be churned when it is rotated. This churning polishes the nails and removes any whiskers which may have adhered to the nail by a thin fin of metal. The sawdust absorbs the grease and oil which the nails collected during their manufacture. The cover of the tumbler has perforations or a screen which allows the whiskers and sawdust to pass through but holds back the nails. After the nails are tumbled sufficiently they are packed in kegs ready for shipment.

WIRE FENCE

An increasing amount of steel wire is used for fence purposes. Today an enormous tonnage of galvanized steel wire is fabricated into woven-wire fence and barbed-wire fence.

Woven-Wire Fence—There are a great many types of woven-wire fence, varying in style or design, and each may be made up in many different sizes. In a general way, the various styles resemble one another in that they have several **horizontal** or **lateral wires** which are secured in position with vertical or diagonal **stay wires,** the former being stronger and stiffer than the latter and provided at frequent intervals with **tension curves,** to take care of expansion and contraction due to temperature changes. The crossing of stay wires, with the horizontals, form the meshes, which may be quite large, as in cattle fences, or very small, as in poultry netting, and may be of any one of four forms, namely, triangular, rectangular, hexagonal, or diamond-shaped. They are also fastened together in various ways. In the **cut-stay fence** there is a short piece of stay wire for each space, having its ends twisted about the laterals. The stays may be electrically welded to them, or the two wires may be woven together. In any case, the work is done by specially constructed and rather complex machines from which the coils of fence will emerge all ready for the market (Figure **29—34).** In the making of these fences, a most rigid system of inspection and tests is maintained, not only in the drawing and galvanizing of the wire, but also in the weaving room, in order to turn out as perfect a product as possible. These same fences made of extra-strong wire constitute exceptionally good reinforcement for concrete work. The leading fence manufacturers also produce a line of gates, special fittings, steel posts, and other articles used in fencing.

Barbed-Wire Fence—In this fence, two wires, usually galvanized, and known as **line wires,** are twisted together, and, at regular and frequent intervals (3 to

FIG. **29—34.** Battery of machines producing various types of woven wire fence.

6 inches apart) either two or four **barbs,** which may be round, flat or oval in section, are wound about one or both of these line wires. The barbs are diagonally cut so as to produce a long sharp point extending at right angles to the line wires. Here again, a great variety of styles and sizes of fence are made by fast-running and rather complex machines. The bulk of barbed wire, however, has the two line wires of No. 12½ wire, while the barbs are usually made of No. 14 wire. The fence is furnished to the market in 80-rod, or in "catch-weight," spools.

CONCRETE REINFORCEMENT

Concrete reinforcement is a steel fabric which, as the name implies, is used to reinforce concrete work in its numerous applications. Although concrete offers great resistance to compressive stress, it is lacking in tensile and bending strength unless reinforced by some material which possesses these characteristics to a marked degree. In this respect steel excels, particularly cold drawn steel, because of its high tensile strength and high yield point. Concrete-reinforcing wire fabric is electric welded: the longitudinal and transverse wires are fixed in position by an electric-welding machine designed to space the wires accurately and weld them together at the contact points.

The accurate spacing of the longitudinal and transverse members is important, since it not only enhances the reinforcing value of the fabric by placing the steel exactly where it is designed to be, but also facilitates handling of the material. Furthermore, each welded intersection develops a positive anchor in the concrete.

Electric-welded wire-fabric reinforcement has a varied application. It is used to reinforce concrete roads, buildings, dams, etc. As a matter of fact, every type of concrete construction should be reinforced. This fabric is used in such precast concrete products as pipe, posts, and slabs. It is supplied in flat sheets or rolls of desired length and width. Standard rolls are 60 inches wide by 150 feet long. Welded wire fabric which is too heavy to be rolled must of necessity be supplied as flat sheets.

PRESTRESSED CONCRETE

Prestressing of concrete is the introduction of desirable compressive forces into a concrete member. These compressive forces are designed to offset or neutralize any subsequent tensile forces which occur when the concrete member is loaded. Since concrete has very little tensile strength, prestressing permits a concrete member to withstand tensile forces without cracking.

Prestressing is done by two general methods:

(a) **Pretensioning.** Steel wire or strand is tensioned on a precasting bed and then concrete mix is poured around the steel. When the concrete has attained full strength, the strand or wire is released from its tensioning apparatus, and the tensile forces of the steel induce equal and opposite compressive forces in the concrete. The bond between the concrete and steel continues to hold the steel in tension and the concrete in compression.

(b) **Postensioning.** Postensioning is a method of prestressing in which tension is not applied to the steel members until after the concrete has attained sufficient strength to carry the compressive forces imposed upon it. This can be accomplished in several ways. Tensioning members may be introduced through holes formed in the concrete, or they may be located entirely outside of the concrete section. The most common method, however, is to enclose steel in flexible metal hose and place it in forms before depositing concrete. In any of these three methods, there is no bond between steel and concrete prior to applying tension to the steel; instead, mechanical anchorage is utilized to transfer prestressing force to the concrete section. After tensioning, bond is desirable since it protects the steel from corrosion. This bond is usually provided by pressure-grouting spaces around the wires. Grouting has the additional advantage of improving performance of the member at high overloads.

The most commonly used strand sizes are ⅜-in., ⁷⁄₁₆-in., and ½-in. diameter seven-wire strand, generally used in pretensioning, in such members as bridge beams, piling, deck and roof trusses, etc., in which a sufficient number of similar members are required to justify the building of a tensioning bed, and the members are of such size that they can be transported from the tensioning plant to the construction site. Individual wires, usually 0.192-in., 0.196-in., 0.250-in., or 0.276-in. diameter, are generally used in postensioning, when a limited number of similar members, unusually large members, special design, or other considerations make construction on the job site more economical. For certain applications, special products such as two- or three-wire strands made from wires about 0.080-in. to 0.120-in. in diameter or deformed wires of various diameters are employed in either pretensioning or postensioning.

Wire (or wire to be made into strand) for prestressed concrete is made from heat-treated high-carbon rods (approximately 0.70 to 0.85 per cent carbon content), with multiple cold drafting to produce the required mechanical properties. It must have high tensile strength (usually on the order of 250,000 lb. per sq. in. minimum); have high yield strength (at least 80 per cent of the tensile strength); adequate ductility for placement, anchorage and tensioning; and uniform stress-strain characteristics within the elastic range so that tensioning loads can be checked against theoretical values calculated from measured elongation. The pre-stressing steel must also be relatively straight, to facilitate placement in concrete, and free from excessive amounts of foreign material on its surface that might have an adverse effect on bonding properties. These desirable properties are enhanced by stress relieving. After the final cold draft or stranding, the material is heated in molten lead, in a hot-air muffle furnace, or by means of an induction coil. The temperature employed is generally in the range of 600° to 800° F, depending upon the heating medium used and the mechanical properties required in the finished product.

In certain cases, hard drawn high-carbon wire, not stress relieved, is employed. One of these is prestressed concrete pressure pipe, used for conveying liquids under pressure. It is made by forming a steel plate into a liquid-tight cylinder with a welded seam. After the cylinder is subjected to a severe hydrostatic test to assure freedom from leakage, a layer of centrifugally cast concrete is deposited inside the steel shell. When this has attained the desired strength, the assembly consisting of concrete core and steel cylinder is wrapped with a helix of wire under tension maintained by friction drums. Wire of ⅛-in. to ⁵⁄₁₆-in. diameter, having a minimum tensile strength of from 210,000 to 174,000 lb. per sq. in., depending upon size of the pipe, is employed. After wrapping, the entire pipe is covered with a mortar coating to protect the wire from corrosion. Tensioning the wire places the concrete and steel in compression. In service, the bursting pressure caused by liquid carried by the pipe acts to overcome the compressive forces in the pipe. With suitable design, no tension will occur in the concrete core.

Another application of non-stress relieved wire is in prestressed concrete tanks. Wire is helically wrapped around a concrete tank. While being wrapped, the wire is drawn through a tapered die that reduces the wire diameter (e.g., from 0.162 to 0.142 in.). The force required to reduce the wire diameter induces the necessary tension. Concrete is compressed so that the liquid pressure will be unable to cause any tension in the concrete tank wall. Wire is carried around the tank at a constant speed by a wire-wrapping machine. This machine is pivoted at the center of the tank and suspended from the top so that it can travel upward or downward at a variable rate. Since bursting pressure increases toward the bottom of the tank, more prestressing force (and more wire) is required there. This is accomplished by decreasing the pitch of the wires, using multiple layers, or both. Wire of 0.162-in., 0.192-in., or 0.236-in. diameter, having a minimum tensile strength of 210,000 lb. per sq. in., is employed. After wire-wrapping is complete, a layer of cement mortar is applied pneumatically to protect the wire from corrosion.

BALE TIES

Large quantities of wire are used annually for tying or bundling bales, bundles, boxes, or packages of every description. While there are several styles of bale ties, each, however, is made of wire that is high in tensile strength and fairly pliable, a goodly percentage of this commodity being made of annealed medium-carbon steel having a light oxide finish. The wires are cut to length, and one end is fabricated to form a means of fastening the two ends together. Lengths and sizes vary between wide limits, but tie wires are made of sizes No. 13 to 16½, inclusive, plain or galvanized. They are put up and sold in bundles of 250 and 500 per bundle, the ends of the bundles being wrapped in burlap.

WIRE ROPE

A single, solid bar of steel, for example a bar one inch in diameter, is very stiff and will stand relatively little "back-and-forth" bending before breaking, but if this same bar of steel is drawn and then formed into a twisted bundle, or "strand," of small wires having the same aggregate sectional area of metal, it will be found to have gained greatly both in flexibility and life, and usually, also, in tensile strength. These reasons account for the large amount of steel-strand wire rope that is used as haulage rope, hoisting rope, hawsers, guys, etc., and for such purposes as oil-well drilling, ships' rigging, tramways, elevators, and so on. These ropes consist of steel wires ranging in tensile strength from 85,000 to 280,000 pounds per square inch or even more, the wire of very high strength being made from high-carbon steel. Wire for ropes used for guy or standing purposes is generally galvanized.

Fabrication of Wire Rope—A full description of the fabrication of wire to form the various types and kinds of rope would be very lengthy, indeed. Consequently, only a few of the simplest examples can be cited here to illustrate a few of the principles involved in steel wire ropemaking. The first wire rope was made of straight wires held together by fine wires which were wrapped about them at intervals, but this construction was unsatisfactory for obvious reasons. The first great improvement consisted in twisting a number of wires together to form what was called a strand, and then twisting a number of these strands together to form a rope. At first both the strands and the rope consisted only of wire, and the strands in the rope were few in number, with the result that it lacked flexibility and bending qualities. But this lack was soon remedied by the introduction of the hemp core, which, together with an increase in the number of strands and the number of wires in a strand, marked the beginning of really successful wire rope manufacture—from the standpoint of the user, at least. So, a steel wire rope, as it is made today, may be defined as a group of strands, usually in one layer, twisted together helically and symmetrically, with a uniform pitch and direction, around a central core of hemp or wire, each strand in turn consisting of a group of steel wires similarly twisted, in one or more layers, around a central core of wire or hemp. The principal operations of ropemaking are two in number and are known as **stranding** and **laying**.

Stranding—Stranding consists of bringing the individual wires together in a predetermined pattern, and twisting or "stranding" them uniformly in concentric rings about a central wire, in either a clockwise or counterclockwise direction, to form the completed strand (Figure 29—35).

Many types and geometrical patterns of wire-rope strands are possible and are made for special uses. Most wire-rope strands, however, fall into three classifications or basic types: 7-wire, 19-wire, and 37-wire. The 7-wire strand is made by covering a center wire

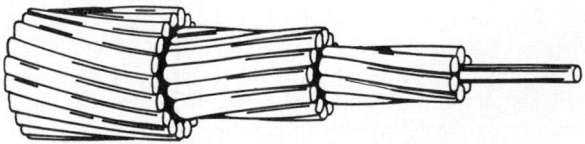

FIG. 29—35. Arrangement of wires in a galvanized bridge strand. Note the increasing number of wires, starting at the right, are 1, 7, 19, and 37, respectively.

with a layer of 6 wires stranded or twisted about it in uniform helices. Strands of this kind made of uncoated wires are closed about a fiber core to form a 6x7 haulage rope (Figure 29—36, Diagram A). When made of galvanized wires, this construction is a 6x7 guy or standing rope. If a cover of twelve wires is twisted about a 7-wire strand, a 19-wire strand is formed. There are several modifications of the basic 19-wire strand used in the fabrication of 6x19 hoisting ropes, the most widely used of all wire ropes. Adding another cover of 18 wires to the 19-wire strand produces the 37-wire strand, which is also fundamental in design. Modifications of this basic pattern are used by manufacturers in wire ropes of special flexibility, such as crane ropes and other wire ropes which operate over relatively small sheaves.

Laying or Closing—The final operation in rope making is the closing of the strands around the core. More wire ropes are composed of six strands than all the others combined, as the 6x19 and 6x37 classifications are the most common types. Eight-strand ropes, 8x19 classification, are extensively used on passenger elevators. There are ropes of three, five and other numbers of strands, but these are comparatively few in number. The largest number of strands in any standard wire rope is eighteen in 18x7 non-rotating hoisting rope.

The cores around which the strands are closed are usually either sisal or synthetic fiber or wire. Fiber cores are standard for wire ropes which are not subjected to heat, crushing and/or heavy loads. Wire cores, usually independent wire-rope cores, are employed where greater strength or greater resistance to distortion and/or heat are required. Other substances, such as plastics, are used to limited extents to meet specific service requirements.

The direction of lay of a wire rope may be either right or left, although practically all wire ropes are right lay. In a right lay wire rope, the strands form a helix about the core similar to the threads on a right-hand screw. If the direction of the lay of the wire in the strands is opposite to the direction of lay of the strands in the rope, that rope is **regular lay.** If the lay of the wires in the strands and the strands in the rope are of the same direction, that rope is **Lang lay.** Regular lay ropes are in greater demand than are the Lang lay ropes because of greater inherent stability. Lang lay ropes, however, possess greater resistance to abrasion than do regular lay ropes because of the greater distance that each outer wire in a Lang lay rope is exposed to surface wear.

Types of Wire Rope—By changing the number and arrangement of wires in each strand, by varying the number of strands in the finished rope, by making ropes both with fiber cores and with independent wire-rope cores, by closing the ropes so that they are regular lay and Lang lay, right lay and left lay, by producing wire ropes in several grades of steel and in sizes from 1/16-inch diameter through 4 inches in diameter, the number of possible wire ropes becomes legion. However, only a small fraction of the possible constructions are sufficient for industrial purposes.

A. 6 x 7 Classification Haulage Rope, consisting of 6 strands of 7 wires in each strand and one fiber core.

B. 6 x 19 Classification Hoisting Rope, with 6 strands of 19 main wires in each strand and one main fiber core.

C. 8 x 19 Seale Elevator Hoisting Rope, consisting of 8 strands of 19 wires in each strand - arranged in Seale construction - and one fiber core.

D. 8 x 19 Classification Hoisting Rope, consisting of 8 strands of 19 main wires in each strand - plus 6 filler wires and one fiber core.

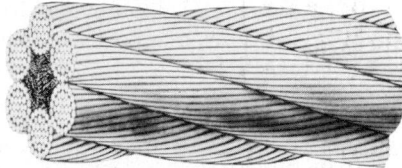

E. 6 x 37 Classification Hoisting Rope, with 6 strands of 37 main wires in each strand and one fiber core.

F. 18 x 7 Non-Rotating Hoisting Rope consisting of 12 strands of 7 wires each over a core of 6 strands of 7 wires each and one fiber core.

FIG. 29—36. Different types of steel wire rope.

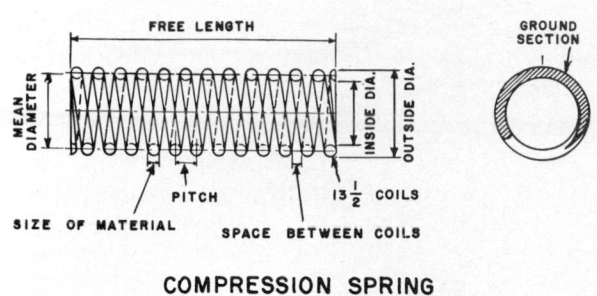

COMPRESSION SPRING

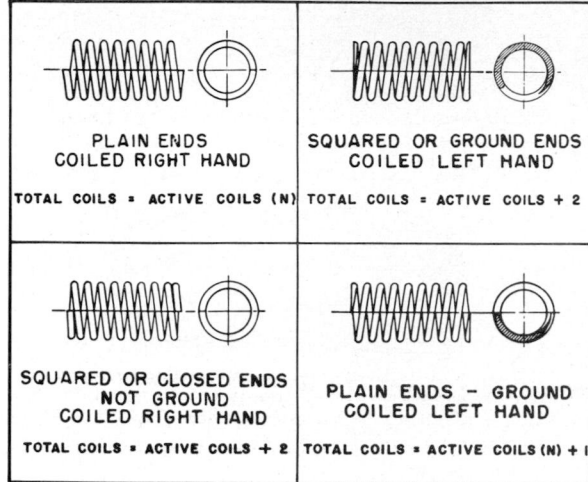

FIG. 29—37. (Above) Illustrative sketch of a compression spring. (Below) Types of end finishes for compression springs.

WIRE SPRINGS

There is a wide diversity in types, shapes and sizes of springs, ranging from the tiny watch hairspring to the large buffer springs used for railroad equipment. The majority of springs are manufactured from medium-carbon or high-carbon steel; such springs are furnished in the annealed, hard-drawn or pretempered state. As to shape, they may be round, flat or rectangular. Special applications may require stainless steel, and many non-ferrous metals such as brass, phosphor bronze and the nickel alloys are likewise employed for certain classes of use. The following classifications indicate the springs in most common use.

1. **Compression Springs**—These springs are open wound with varying space between the coils and are provided with the ends plain, plain and ground, squared, or squared and ground. They are furnished in a wide range of wire sizes, diameters, lengths, shapes and each and every one must be designed to meet certain load requirements. Figure **29—37** illustrates typical springs of this class.

2. **Extension Springs**—Generally, extension springs are close wound, usually with specified initial tension and, as they are used to resist pulling forces, they are provided with hook or loop ends to fit their varied applications (Figure **29—38**). These ends may be an integral part of the spring itself, or may be specially inserted forgings, castings or wire forms to meet individual requirements.

3. **Helical Springs**—The term "helical" springs although literally applying to any spring which is helically wound, is generally considered as a trade name for extension springs used in great volume by manufacturers of spring beds, couches, and cushions. Many sizes and shapes of this particular category are in general usage.

Any one of the three foregoing types of spiral springs may be strengthened by increasing the wire size, or by decreasing the mean diameter of the helix, but in any case the ability of the material to withstand the load must be of prime consideration.

4. **Torsion Springs**—This type of spring (Figure 29—39) is one in which work is required to wind up the spring about its own axis—never to unwind it. The ends may be finished in a number of ways, the type of end being generally dependent upon the particular requirements.

5. **Upholstery Springs**—These are almost invariably made from hard-drawn high-carbon wire, with slight modifications of mechanical properties for the various types of springs manufactured, to provide the best balance between high elastic properties and toughness or ductility to withstand the forming operations involved. Springs for box springs or furniture frames are usually single-cone, with the larger end "knotted," that is, twisted about the wire at the beginning of the second coil. The smaller, free end is turned around intersecting wires of a gridwork of crimped wire, to position the upper ends, and the lower end is stapled to the wooden frame. Springs for mattresses or cushions may be of the "Marshall type," free-end, uniform diameter, inserted in muslin pockets in assembling into a construction; "Bonnell type," knotted-end, double-cone (having a smaller diameter at the center than at either end); "High Count," knotted-end, uniform diameter; or "Holland type," free-end, double-cone. In assembling constructions of the last three types of springs, rows of springs are positioned properly in an assembly bench or machine, and joined by the applications of lacing helicals which enclose adjacent portions of springs in both rows, by clinching loops preformed in straight lacing wires to join adjacent portions of springs, or by some other means. Sometimes crimps or offsets are formed in the base coils of springs to keep them from turning in the construction.

6. **Zig Zag, No Sag, or Formed Wire Elements**—High-carbon, high-tensile-strength hard-drawn wires are corrugated in a sinusoidal pattern or in a series of right-angle bends with varying lengths of straight wire between bends. Lengths of these corrugated members, with crown and end formations as required, are fastened side-by-side to form seat and back-cushions for automobiles or furniture. These constructions require less wire and provide lower-contour cushions than coil-spring constructions.

7. **Clock and Motor Flat Springs**—These springs are made of cold-rolled high carbon strip steel of proper width and thickness to meet specifications and

HOOK OPENING
WIRE DIAMETER
OUTSIDE DIAMETER
INSIDE DIAMETER
LENGTH OVER COIL
LENGTH INSIDE HOOKS

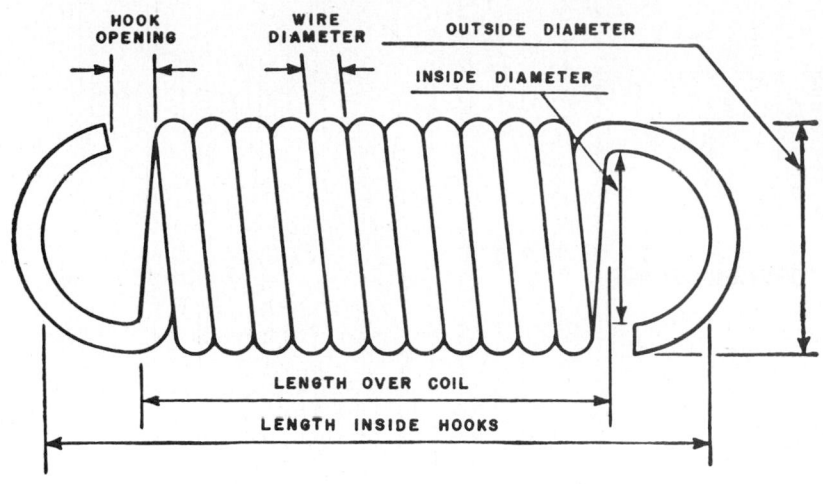

EXTENSION SPRING

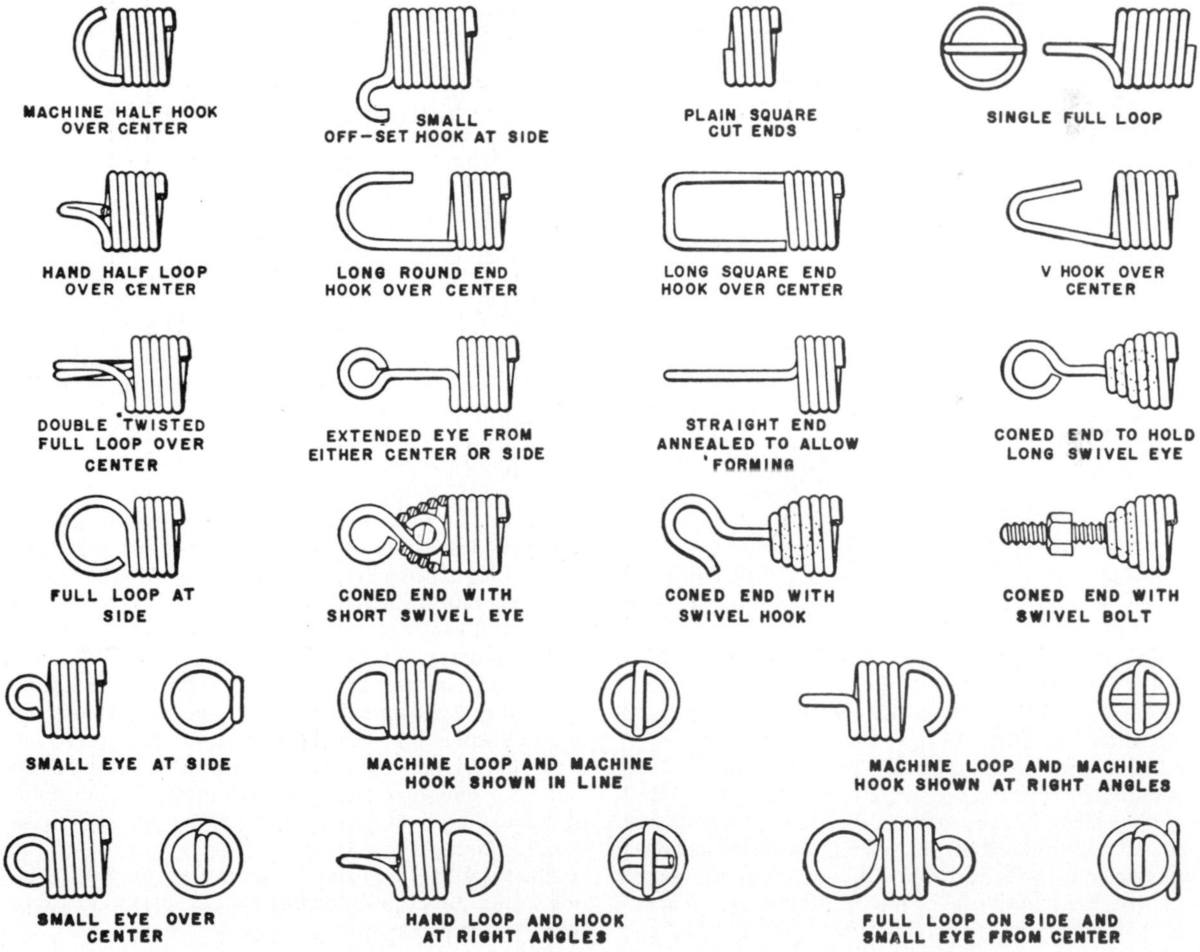

MACHINE HALF HOOK OVER CENTER
SMALL OFF-SET HOOK AT SIDE
PLAIN SQUARE CUT ENDS
SINGLE FULL LOOP
HAND HALF LOOP OVER CENTER
LONG ROUND END HOOK OVER CENTER
LONG SQUARE END HOOK OVER CENTER
V HOOK OVER CENTER
DOUBLE TWISTED FULL LOOP OVER CENTER
EXTENDED EYE FROM EITHER CENTER OR SIDE
STRAIGHT END ANNEALED TO ALLOW FORMING
CONED END TO HOLD LONG SWIVEL EYE
FULL LOOP AT SIDE
CONED END WITH SHORT SWIVEL EYE
CONED END WITH SWIVEL HOOK
CONED END WITH SWIVEL BOLT
SMALL EYE AT SIDE
MACHINE LOOP AND MACHINE HOOK SHOWN IN LINE
MACHINE LOOP AND MACHINE HOOK SHOWN AT RIGHT ANGLES
SMALL EYE OVER CENTER
HAND LOOP AND HOOK AT RIGHT ANGLES
FULL LOOP ON SIDE AND SMALL EYE FROM CENTER

TYPES OF ENDS USED ON EXTENSION SPRINGS

FIG. 29—38. (Above) Illustrative sketch of an extension spring, giving nomenclature of parts. (Below) Types of ends used on extension springs.

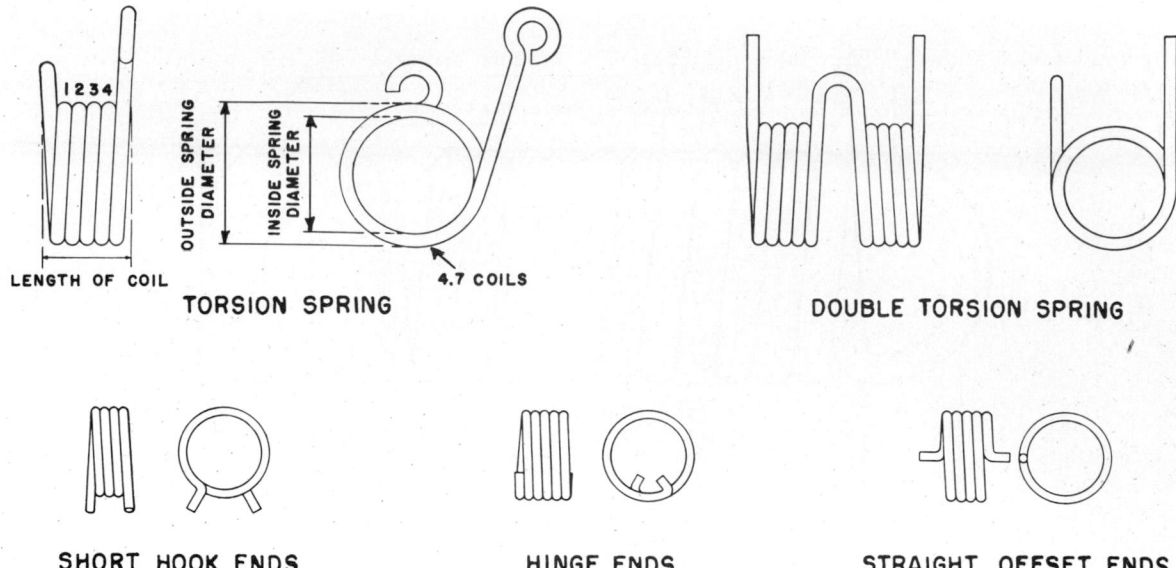

FIG. 29—39. (Above) Illustrative sketches of (left) a torsion spring and (right) a double torsion spring. (Below) Types of ends for torsion springs.

are tempered, tempered and polished, or tempered, polished and colored. The ends are formed as desired, and the coils are wound spirally and held in compact shape by a retaining clip or ring.

8. **Jig Springs and Specially-Formed Wires**—These represent a group, covering an endless variety of odd shapes and sizes, made or formed in jigs, on automatic wire-forming equipment, or with small hand tools. Springs of this type are generally used to serve as more or less simple parts of mechanisms.

SPRING TERMS

The manufacturers of springs, in common with every other industry, have used terms frequently misunderstood. The most common of these are:

Bluing—A low-temperature heat treatment of springs after fabrication, to relieve the cold-working strains created by coiling and forming.

Tested Spring—A spring which has had its set removed as a result of one or more compressions to solid height.

Scale Testing—A spring which has been tested for load at a given height or heights.

Pitch—Center to center distance between adjacent coils at free height.

Active and Inactive Coils—Two types of coils are present in compression springs, namely, active and inactive. This is prevalent in squared springs where the end coil squared on the next adjacent coil becomes inactive due to its contact with said coil and, consequently, the inactive coils are omitted when computing spring load and stress data.

Initial Tension—Indicates the force or load necessary to cause the coils to start to open. This force or load must be considered as part of the total spring load for stress calculations. This initial tension factor applies only to the close-wound extension type of spring.

BRIDGE WIRE

Bridge wire is the term commonly applied to high-grade rope wire used in the construction of cable suspension bridges, in which the main cables consist of parallel wires compacted to act as a unit. These bridges are remarkable for their graceful beauty, the absence of heavy superstructures, and their extraordinary long spans. Some of the largest bridges in the world are of this type, including the George Washington Bridge in New York, the Golden Gate and San Francisco-Oakland Bay Bridges in California, the Mackinac Bridge in Michigan, and the Narrows Bridge in New York.

Interesting data on the Narrows Bridge are: main span, 4260 feet, the longest and heaviest span in existence; total length, including two side spans of 1215 feet each, the Staten Island toll plaza and the Brooklyn approach ramps, approximately 13,700 feet. The bridge has two decks, each accommodating six lanes for vehicular traffic, with navigational clearance of 228 feet at the center of the main span. Width of the bridge (center to center of outer cables) is 112 feet. Total width of the suspended structure is 115 feet; the towers are somewhat wider. The roadway structure is suspended from the four main cables, two on each side of the deck. Each main cable is about 36 inches in diameter and is composed of 26,108 cold-drawn extra galvanized wires, each having a diameter of 0.196 inch.

The total length of the bridge cable wire is 142,500 miles, totaling 38,500 tons; the 1048 suspender ropes total 74 miles in length.

Bridge wire requires steel of high quality and extreme care in every step of its manufacture from melt to finished wire. Specifications for the finished wire have required: (1) The wire to be heavily coated with zinc to protect it from corrosion—galvanized to withstand 5 immersions in the standard Preece test. (2) A minimum tensile strength of 225,000 lb. per sq. in. (3) A minimum elongation of 4 per cent in 10 inches. (4) A coating that will permit wrapping without peeling about a round mandrel of a diameter equal to 1½ times the diameter of the wire.

At one time, specifications required the steel to be made by the acid open-hearth or the crucible processes, but it is now generally accepted that steel equally as satisfactory or better can be made by the basic open-hearth process. The wire is made from selected high-carbon steel, the composition of which is held within close limits. The composition of the steel used heretofore has usually been held within the following limits: carbon, 0.75 to 0.85 per cent; manganese, 0.55 to 0.75 per cent; phosphorus, under 0.03 per cent; sulphur, under 0.03 per cent; silicon, 0.15 to 0.30 per cent, with maximum limits for other elements that may be present in small amounts. Some of the more important requirements of the manufacturing practice are listed as follows: The manufacturing processes in the production of bridge wire are very closely controlled in order to produce the required mechanical properties of high tensile strength, toughness, and resistance to fatigue. The bright wire is produced in two common wire sizes, No. 6 and No. 8, the former being more frequently used. The bright wire is usually hot galvanized. In order to prevent undue bending, and to supply wire which is straight, as required for the subsequent spinning of the cables, the wire is finished in five-foot diameter coils. Coils are coupled together to form long, continuous lengths of wire, and are shipped to the bridge site on large reels, from which the wire is unreeled during the process of spinning the cables.

The following notes cite one example of metallurgical, rolling, drawing and coating practice. Heats must be kept separate, from casting of the ingots to the finished wire. The steel should be made in heats of about 150 tons or less, cast into hot-top ingot molds, and held till completely solidified before stripping. The ingots should be soaked to a uniform temperature throughout, and rolled on the blooming mill at a temperature of 2200° F, with reduction in each pass limited to avoid cracks and other rolling defects. The crop from the top of the bloom should not be less than 12 per cent, and billets (usually 2 in. by 2 in. by 30 ft.) should be carefully inspected on the ends for pipe and segregation and on the surface for other defects and chipped and surfaced to remove seams, laps, slivers, etc. The billets should be rolled at temperatures between 1900° F and 2000° F to a rod of specified diameter with a minimum amount of water used on the rolls and none on the reels, to avoid hard

spots on the rod. The rod should be carefully inspected before it is treated. For the latter operation, the rod is uncoiled continuously and passed through a 50-foot or longer continuous furnace held at 1625° F to 1675° F to heat the rod above the critical temperature of 1325° F, after which it is passed into an 18-foot lead pan held between 900° F and 950° F, the exact temperature to give the desired structure being determined by preliminary tests on each heat. Lead adhering to the rod must be removed, a result usually accomplished by a header of coke breeze on the exit end of the lead bath.

To clean the rod, it is pickled in a bath, the acidity of which is maintained between 5 and 8 per cent with 66° Baumé sulphuric acid, and the temperature of which is held at not over 110° F to avoid acid embrittlement that cannot be removed by the subsequent baking. A suitable inhibitor is used to reduce the amount of acid consumed, prevent overpickling, or pitting, and help avoid acid embrittlement.

The rod is then washed with water, submerged repeatedly in a water suspension of slaked lime, and baked 10 to 12 hours at 400° F to 450° F.

The rod is then drawn on a specially-built 6-draft continuous machine or on powerful 30-inch diameter blocks at a speed of 16.5 r.p.m. or 130 feet per minute, using powdered soap mixed with grit-free hydrated lime as a lubricant and uniform light-reduction drafts of 0.384, 0.334, 0.290, 0.252, 0.219, and 0.192. Each wire should be inspected front and back and tested. Requirements are: minimum tensile strength, 240,000 lb. per sq. in., 40 per cent reduction of area; and 2 per cent elongation in 10 inches. It has been demonstrated that wire cold drawn to finish in this way is far superior for bridges than a heat-treated wire of about the same strength.

Galvanizing operations are continuous, the wire passing through the following baths: (1) molten lead at 850° F, momentarily, to remove lubricants, (2) a cleaning box containing a 4 to 6 per cent solution of hydrochloric acid at 150° F to 170° F, (3) a hot water wash at 200° F, (4) a flux box of zinc chloride (ZnCl₂) or 1 per cent hydrochloric acid at 150° F to 175° F, (5) the galvanizing tank filled with especially pure zinc at 880° F to 900° F, equipped with an exit sinker of the roller type and a charcoal header filled with a mixture of charcoal and beef tallow.

Bridge Strands—For cable suspension bridges where the size of the main cables does not justify the stringing of individual wires, parallel bridge strands are used to form the main cables. These strands are compacted in the same manner as are the main cables composed of individual, parallel bridge wires.

CHAPTER 30

Manufacture of Steel Tubular Products

SECTION 1

HISTORY AND CLASSIFICATION OF STEEL TUBULAR PRODUCTS

The Present Importance of the Steel Tubular Industry and of steel tubular products is apparent to all observers. This growth was due to many things, chief of which is the diversity of uses to which steel tubular products may be and are applied. The mere mentioning of the names, oil, gas, air, water, plumbing, heating, ammonia, dry-kiln, greenhouse, boiler tubes and bedstead tubing are sufficient to call to mind industries almost wholly dependent upon steel pipe or tubing. In addition to these uses, we find it in service as trolley poles, flag poles, lighting poles, telephone and telegraph poles, columns, conduits, automobile axle housings, airplane fuselage, motor mounts, and many other items too numerous to list here.

DEVELOPMENT OF THE BUTT-WELD PROCESS

About the year 1815, William Murdock, a Scottish inventor, introduced at London the use of coal gas for lighting purposes. For conveying this gas, Murdock collected old musket barrels and screwed them together to form continuous tubes. The popularity of this lighting system created a demand for tubes, and stimulated inventors to seek some means of producing the tubes more rapidly and at a lower cost. The first to succeed in this undertaking was James Russell, who filed patent papers describing his process as "an improvement in the manufacture of tubes for gas and other purposes" in 1824. In his method, the tube was formed by butting the white-hot edges of a bent plate together. The initial welding was done with a tilt-hammer provided with round grooves in the head, and the rough tube thus formed was finished by reheating it and passing it through a round groove in a rolling mill and over a mandrel which was supported in the pass, or opening, between these rolls. The next year, however, Russell's work was overshadowed by the invention of Cornelius Whitehouse, who succeeded in forming a commercially perfect tube by merely drawing the flat plate, heated to a proper temperature, through a "bell" or die. This invention, which became the basis of one of the butt-weld processes used until recently, made it possible to produce tubes of superior quality much more cheaply than before. Shortly after this invention, about 1832, the first shop for making butt-weld pipe in the United States was established in Philadelphia by Morris,

Tasker and Morris. Four years later, this firm built the works afterwards known as the Pascal Iron Works. Following their success, other plants appeared in Eastern Pennsylvania, Eastern New York, New Jersey and Massachusetts, but no plants were built west of the Allegheny Mountains until after 1860. The idea that pipe could be butt-welded continuously was conceived by John Moon in 1911. Later, with S. F. Fretz, Jr., he built the first experimental mill. This equipment proved successful and in 1921 and 1922 the Fretz-Moon Tube Company was formed and continuously butt-welded pipe was made on a production basis. Modern continuous butt-welding methods are discussed in Section 2 of this chapter.

DEVELOPMENT OF SEAMLESS TUBES

Concurrent with these developments in making welded tubes, inventors turned their attention to the production of seamless tubes. At first they attempted to duplicate with iron or steel the method (extrusion) used to produce tubes of lead and some other metals, namely, forcing the hot metal through an orifice formed by a mandrel or punch located and supported in the center of a circular die. In 1836 such a process was patented by Hanson in England, but this method proved impracticable. Two other methods were brought out in 1840 and 1845. They involved the cupping of a plate or the piercing of a round billet in a press, and subsequently elongating the rough tube thus formed by drawing or rolling. While practicable, these methods were costly, and for fifty years the use of seamless tubes was restricted on that account. The modern developments beginning about 1890 are described in Section 5.

In the piercing process, developed around 1840, a round hole was first made along the central axis of a round billet which was then rolled and drawn over mandrels to form a tube. The mill for lengthening such hollow billets was first patented in England by Church and Harlon about 1841. The rolling mill and the draw bench afforded simple and comparatively cheap methods of elongating the hollow billet, but the development of a method for piercing it proved a difficult matter. The oldest and simplest method was to heat the billet to a high forging temperature and hydraulically force a punch through its center while in this hot state. As it was essential that the hole be exactly concentric with the billet throughout its entire length, a feat that is hard to accomplish with a billet more than a foot or so in length, recourse was had to drilling a small hole in the cold billet, then heating the billet and enlarging the hole by piercing in a press. About 1888 a patent was granted for a process whereby a small ingot was cast about a core of refractory material, which hollow ingot was to be treated as described for hollow billets.

In the cupping process, which was first used about 1845, a circular sheet or plate was forced by successive operations through several pairs of conical dies, each pair being deeper and more nearly cylindrical than the previous one, until the plate took the form of a tube, or cylinder with one end closed. This method is still in use for certain sizes.

The Mannesmann machine, employing the principle of helical rolling for piercing round billets for making seamless tubes, was patented in 1886: its design and operation will be discussed later (in Section 5). The Pilger process for making seamless tubes was developed later but, for economic reasons, was employed only to a limited extent in this country and will not be discussed in detail here: it utilized a rolling mill with a pair of grooved rolls with shaped passes that exerted a forging force on the piece as it was forced into the roll pass rather than drawn into the pass by the action of the rolls. Other processes employing special machines and techniques, including the Stiefel disc piercer, the Assel mill, and the Diescher mill, along with the methods known as plug rolling, double piercing, rotary rolling and reeling have been introduced over the years and will be described in succeeding sections of this chapter.

Innovations by Briggs and Riverside Iron—Besides these developments in methods of manufacture, two other events should be mentioned because of their far-reaching effects on the industry as a whole. About 1862 Robert Briggs, then superintendent of the Pascal Iron Works, formulated the dimension of pipe (tube) threads, and compiled a table giving the nominal sizes, the exact diameters and the number of threads per inch for all sizes of pipe and tubes up to 10 inches. These formulae and tables were subsequently adopted as standard for the manufacture of all tubes and pipes up to 15 inches in size and are widely known as "Briggs Standards," but the name now officially adopted is American Standard (A.S.A.) Pipe Thread. In 1887 the Riverside Iron Works, Wheeling, W. Va., began making butt- and lap-welded pipe of soft Bessemer steel. Up to that time, wrought iron had been the only material used for welded pipe and tubes. Riverside proved that steel was not only equal to wrought iron for this purpose, but actually superior to it in many respects.

Classification of Steel Tubular Products—The many uses to which steel tubular products have been applied have led to a great variety of products and to the use of a large number of more or less descriptive terms in designating the products used for different purposes. Use, therefore, may form a basis for classifying steel tubular products, as shown in Table **30**—I.

Another classification is based on methods of manufacture. On this basis all steel tubular products may be classified under the two main headings of welded and seamless, with subclasses, as shown in Table 30—II.

Modern Methods of Manufacturing Welded Tubular Products—A butt-welded pipe or tube is made from hot-rolled skelp with square or slightly beveled edges, the width and thickness of the skelp being selected to suit the various sizes to be made. The coiled skelp is uncoiled, heated, and fed through forming and welding rolls where the edges of the skelp are pressed together at a high temperature to form a weld.

In the electric-weld process, hot-rolled strip or plate, of a gage corresponding to the thickness of the wall of the pipe desired, but of an overall width slightly greater than its circumference, is first edge-trimmed to obtain parallelism and accurate width. To produce fusion-welded pipe, the plate is then bent into cylindrical shape with the beveled edges abutting to form a "V" into which the electrode is melted. Fusion welding, which is particularly adapted to large-diameter pipe, is a term used to distinguish this method from electric-resistance welding used in the manufacture of smaller sizes of tubing. By the latter process, union of the seam is effected by the application of pressure and heat, the heat being generated by the resistance to current flow (either transformed or induced) across the seam during the welding.

Seamless Tubular Products—Seamless tubular products are made by three basic methods:

(1) Rotary piercing of a solid round bar or billet, followed by various methods of refining to produce the wall thickness and size required.

(2) Piercing a bloom or section of steel in a vertical press, leaving one end closed, and then further processing to the required size in a hot-draw bench.

(3) Extruding a short, large-diameter round in a hydraulic extrusion press.

Pipe—Applied in a general sense, pipe is a term used to designate any long hollow body used for conducting gases or liquids, and may be of clay, cement, wood, lead, brass, cast iron, or steel. Restricted to the steel industry, the term is one that is applied to all tubular products intended for the purposes for which such products are ordinarily used, as for conducting water, fuel, gas, steam, air, oil, etc. The term "wrought" distinguishes forged iron or steel pipe from cast-iron pipe.

Varieties of Pipe—Since the pipe should be adapted to the kind of service it is expected to give, there are different varieties of pipe. Thus, **welded pipe** is regularly made in three separate classes, which are distinguishable by characteristic differences in the wall thickness of each class of pipe as a class. These classes of pipe are known as **standard weight, extra strong,** and **double extra strong.** Standard weight pipe is pipe made and threaded to the American Standard (A.S.A.). The weights or wall thicknesses of this pipe are suitable for all ordinary purposes, such as water and gas lines for plumbing and heating, etc. **Extra strong pipe** is characterized by heavier walls in all sizes than the standard weight pipe, and is used where higher internal pressures or greater column loads are to be sustained. **Double extra strong pipe** is used for extremely

Table 30—I. Steel Tubular Products Classified According to Use

1. Standard Pipe.
   a. Standard Weight Pipe (Black and Galvanized)
   b. Extra Strong Pipe (Black and Galvanized)
   c. Double Extra Strong Pipe (Black and Galvanized)
2. Special Light Weight Pipe.
3. Conduit Pipe.
4. Drive Pipe.
5. Dry-Kiln Pipe.
6. Refrigeration and Ammonia Pipe.
7. Large-Diameter Pipe.
   a. Water Mains
   b. Gas Lines
   c. Penstocks
8. Line Pipe.
   a. Gas Lines
   b. Oil Lines
   c. Water Transmission Lines
   d. Slurry Lines
9. Nipple Pipe.
10. Tubular Piling.
11. Tubular Poles.
    a. Line Poles
    b. Signal and Safety Poles
    c. Flag Poles
    d. Masts and Booms
12. Rolls and Roller Piping.
    a. Paper- and Textile-Mill Rolls
    b. Printing-Press Rolls
    c. Conveyor Rolls
13. Pressure Piping.
    a. High-Pressure Steam Lines
    b. Hot-Oil Lines
    c. High-Pressure Chemical Lines
14. Signal Pipe.
15. Structural Pipe.
    a. Railings
    b. Fence Posts
    c. Scaffolds
    d. Columns
    e. Bridge and Roof Trusses

16. Water-Well Pipe.
    a. Water-Well Casing
    b. Water-Well Pump Pipe
    c. Water-Well Drive Pipe
    d. Water-Well Reamed and Drifted Pipe
    e. Driven-Well Pipe
17. Oil-Country Tubular Products.
    a. Oil-Well Casing
    b. Oil-Well Tubing
    c. Drill Pipe
    d. Drive Pipe
18. Pressure Tubes.
    a. Boiler Tubes
    b. Superheater Tubes
    c. Economizer Tubes
    d. Water-Wall Tubes
    e. Locomotive-Boiler and Superheater Tubes
    f. Arch Tubes
    g. Air-Heater Tubes
    h. Soot-Blower Tubes
19. Oil-Still Tubes.
20. Heat-Exchanger and Condenser Tubes.
    a. Galvanized Tubes
21. Mechanical Tubes.
    a. Airplane Tubes
    b. Automotive Tubes
    c. Precision Pump Tubes
    d. Working Barrels
    e. Stainless Steel Tubes
    f. Ball- and Roller-Bearing Race Tubes
    g. Rolls
    h. Shafting
    i. Bushings
    j. Special Shapes for Structural Purposes
    k. Upset, Swaged and Special Formed Tubes
    l. Axle Tubing
22. Stainless Steel Pipe and Tubes.
    a. Ornamental
    b. Mechanical
    c. Pressure

Table 30—II. Steel Tubular Products Classified According to Methods of Manufacture

A. Welding Process.
  I. Butt-Weld Process. This process is used in the manufacture of pipe, ⅛ inch to 4 inches, nominal diameter.
  II. Electric-Weld Process. This process is employed to produce pipe and containers in practically all sizes.

B. Seamless Process.
  I. Piercing Processes – Roll-Piercing and Disc-Piercing. These processes are used to make pipe and tubes up to 26 inches in diameter.
     a. Hot Finished.
        (to 26 inches, outside diameter)
     b. Cold Drawn.
        (any size up to 10¾ inches outside diameter)
     c. Cold Expanding.
        (sizes 16 inches to 26 inches outside diameter)
  II. Vertical Piercing Process. This process is applied in the manufacture of tubes and cylinders, 3 inches to 20 inches outside diameter.
     a. Hot Drawn (Finish).
        (3 inches to 20 inches, outside diameter)
  III. Extrusion Process. Used primarily for small sizes of stainless or high alloy pipe for cold reducing.

high-pressure purposes, such as hydraulic lines for operating hydraulic machinery or apparatus. **Line pipe,** used for the higher pressure oil, gas and water lines, and **drive pipe,** used in drilling oil and water wells, differ from each other and from standard pipe mainly in the manner in which the different sections of pipe are coupled together. **Air-line pipe,** for railroad train and electric car air-brakes, and **drill pipe,** used for oil-, gas- and water-well drilling, are further examples of the different varieties of pipe. In addition to these varieties, pipe is also made to conform to the British Standards. Pipe may be used for many structural purposes, such as columns, railings, piling and poles for telegraph, telephone and electric power lines, also railway signal and safety devices.

Sizes of Pipe—As a whole, pipe is made in sizes that range from ⅛-inch nominal inside diameter to 96 inches outside diameter. Up to a diameter of 12 inches, pipe is commonly known by the inside diameters, and is spoken of as three-quarter-inch pipe, one-inch pipe, two-inch pipe, etc. These terms are but nominal, because, in order that different pieces of pipe may be coupled together conveniently, the outside diameters must be standardized, and any variation due to differences in gage, or thickness of the wall, occurs in the bore. However, care is taken to make these differences for any one kind of pipe as small as possible, so that in the case of standard pipe these nominal diameters approximate as closely as possible the inside diameters. Exceptions may be cited in the case of 8-inch, 10-inch, and 12-inch standard line pipe, which are made in different weights to adapt the pipe to different purposes. For example, 8-inch standard line pipe is made in two standard weights, namely 24.696 pounds per foot and 28.554 pounds per foot, the difference in weight being represented by a difference in the wall thicknesses. Standard line pipe, drive pipe and pipe over 12 inches internal diameter, and practically all pipe over 12¾ inches in diameter, are known by their outside diameters.

SECTION 2

BUTT-WELD PROCESS (CONTINUOUS)

The continuous butt-weld is a true continuous process starting with coiled skelp and ending with finished pipe. Figure 30—1 shows an arrangement that is typical of many of the continuous butt-weld mills in use today.

Production of Skelp—The skelp mill operated by the United States Steel Corporation at its Fairless Works is an example of a modern mill designed primarily to roll skelp to meet the requirements of the modern continuous butt-weld pipe mill. This mill normally rolls skelp in coils up to 56 inches in outside diameter, weighing up to 550 pounds per inch of width, at the average rate of approximately 700 tons per 8-hour turn on a monthly basis, from slabs 36 to 40 feet in length. Typical widths and thickness of skelp for the production of pipe of various sizes and wall thicknesses are as follows.

Skelp Width (In.)	Skelp Thickness (In.)	Pipe Size (In.)
8¾	0.120	½
8¾	0.165	½
9½	0.125	¾
9½	0.165	¾
11	0.150	1
11	0.190	1
12½	0.150	1¼ & 1½
12½	0.215	1¼ & 1½
13¾	0.155	2
13¾	0.225	2
14¾	0.195	2½
14¾	0.205	2½
14¾	0.275	2½
17½	0.180	3, 3½, & 4
17½	0.205	3, 3½, & 4
17½	0.215	3, 3½, & 4
17½	0.300	3, 3½, & 4
17½	0.327	3, 3½, & 4

The incoming slabs are delivered to the open slab-storage yard on specially built standard-gauge slab cars. The slabs are removed from the cars in 10-foot wide tiers by a 30-ton electric overhead traveling crane equipped with two rectangular magnets carried on a rotating trolley. This makes it possible to pile the slabs in alternate tiers, rotated 90 degrees to se-cure piling stability, and provides for the stocking of unusually large piles of slabs separated into their proper sizes and grades of steel. Slab-separating skids 38 feet wide by 25 feet long and the furnace-charging conveyor are located in the slab yard. The separating skids consist of both stationary and movable skids arranged to provide a cascade effect that separates and aligns individual slabs and deposits them singly onto the 110-foot long furnace-charging conveyor. In conjunction with the charging conveyor is a chain-driven ram-type charging car for pushing slabs into the furnace.

The slab-heating furnace (Figure 30—2) is of the side-charge and side-discharge, zone-controlled, double-fired type. The effective heating length of the furnace is 60 feet, its inside width is 43 feet, and its maximum heating capacity is 120 net tons per hour. The furnace has a suspended roof throughout its length, and the hearth is sloped upward from the point of discharge. Zone-controlled heating, utilizing primary and secondary heating zones, is employed. After a slab has passed through the primary heating zone, it enters the secondary zone where heating to rolling temperature is completed and temperature throughout the slab is equalized. The furnace is top-fired in both zones, and is equipped to burn either coke-oven gas or oil. Combustion air is preheated in a refractory-tile recuperator located beneath the furnace. Located on the charging end of the furnace is the slab cross pusher that operates at right angles to the furnace-charging conveyor and pushes slabs off the conveyor and advances them through the furnace. The cross pusher has a 42-inch stroke and a maximum speed of 3.04 strokes per minute and is mounted on its own independent foundation that is not attached in any way to the furnace structure.

A pushout bar and a pair of pull-out rolls remove heated slabs from the furnace. The pushout bar assembly, located entirely outside the furnace, consists of the pusher bar and a pair of driven rolls: the bar is clamped between the rolls and is driven by friction. The complete unit can be shifted by a hydraulic mechanism to align the bar with slabs in the furnace. The bar has a maximum speed of 206 ft. per min. and a maximum travel of 48 feet. A pair of pullout rolls located outside the furnace-discharge door aids the push-out bar in delivering slabs to the mill-ap-

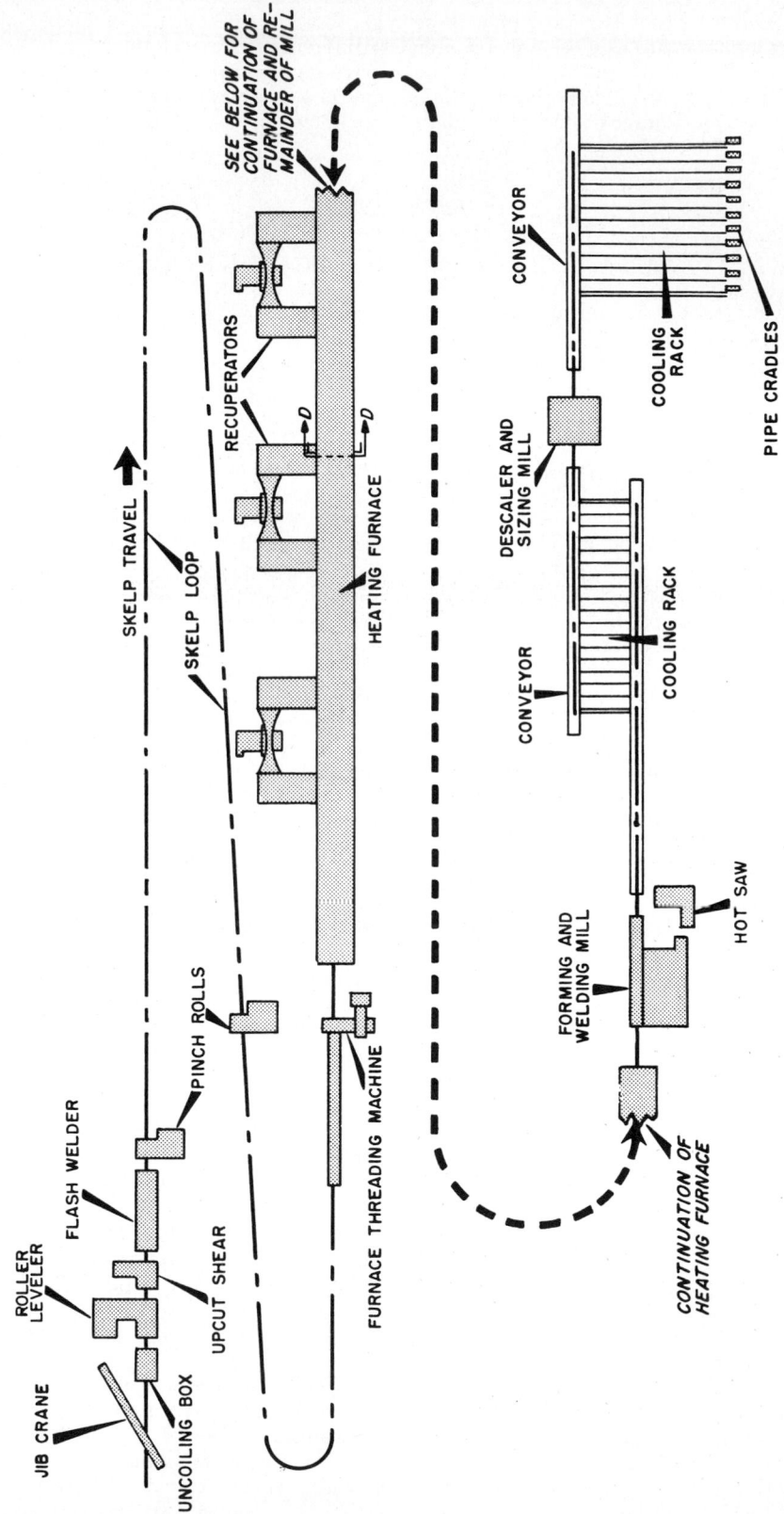

Fig. 30—1. Schematic plan of the layout of a typical continuous butt-weld pipe mill.

FIG. 30—2. General view of furnace for heating slabs for rolling in a skelp mill.

proach table: the bottom roll of the pair is driven by an adjustable-speed motor so that the speed of delivery of slabs from the furnace can be matched approximately to the speed of the mill-approach table.

The mill-approach table, which conveys heated slabs to the mill, is approximately 65 feet long and has a speed range of 32 to 96 ft. per min. A hydraulically operated slab turnover and discard permits slabs to be presented to the mill with the heavy scale on the bottom or to be removed from the approach table when desired.

A general arrangement of the skelp mill proper is shown in Figure 30—3: a general view of the mill in operation is shown in Figure 30—4. Table 30—III

provides data with regard to the capacity of the main drives and other features of the mill.

The mill proper consists of ten 19-inch closed-top roll stands, one 16-inch scale-breaking edging stand, and four 12-inch edging stands. The ten horizontal stands are of heavy cast-steel construction with the windows equipped with liners. All horizontal rolls are carried by oil-film-type sleeve bearings. The top rolls are carried on hydraulically supported rails that extend through the front and back housing windows, enabling the supports to serve also as guide rails when changing rolls. The bottom roll-neck bearing on the operating side of each mill is located axially by a parallelogram adjusting device that not only clamps the roll

1. SEPARATING TABLE	12. MILL APPROACH TABLE	23. VIBRATORS
2. DISCARD CRADLES	13. DISCARD CRADLES	24. APRON CONVEYORS
3. CONTROL HOUSE	14. 16" EDGING MILL	25. SHEAR
4. CHARGING CONVEYOR	15. 19" HORIZONTAL MILL	26. COILERS
5. CROSS PUSHER	16. 12" EDGING MILL	27. REEL CONTROL HOUSE
6. FURNACE CONTROL HOUSE	17. COBBLE SHEAR	28. COIL CONVEYORS
7. HEATING FURNACE	18. CROP PIT	29. COIL SCALES
8. FURNACE PUSHOUT	19. MILL PULPIT	30. COIL UP-ENDERS
9. CONTROL DESK	20. MILL RUNOUT TABLE	31. CONTROL HOUSE
10. FURNACE PULLOUT	21. TWIST TROUGH	32. COIL ASSEMBLY CONVEYOR
11. CONTROL DESK	22. PINCH ROLLS	33. COIL DISCHARGE

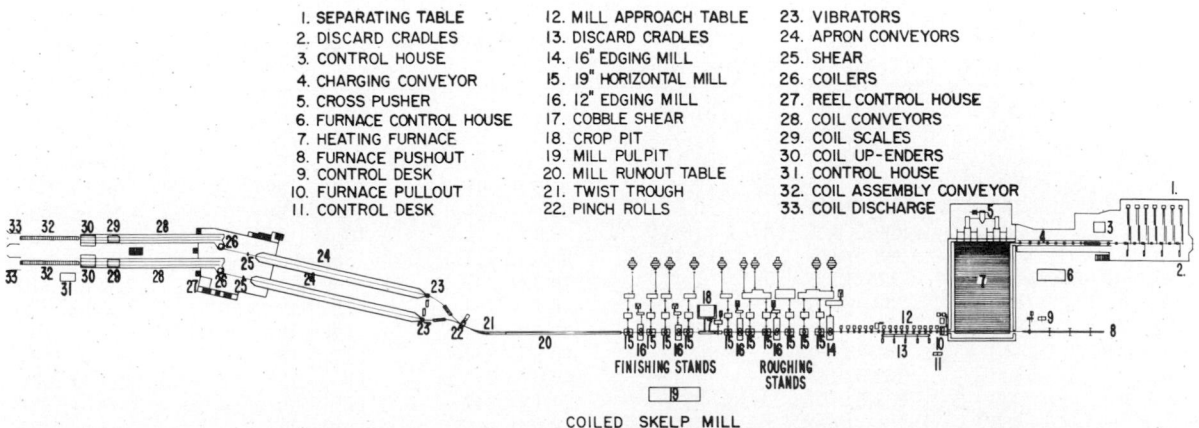

FIG. 30—3. General layout of a skelp mill for producing coiled skelp. (See also Figure 30 —4)

Fig. 30—4. General view of skelp mill rolling coiled skelp for use in the continuous butt-weld process for pipe. Product travel is from the vertical 16-inch edging mill at the right toward the left of the illustration. (See also Figure 30—3.)

to prevent axial movement, but also provides for limited axial adjustment if required. The bottom rolls may be adjusted vertically by a screw and wedges accessible from the operating side of each mill. The first five horizontal roll stands are equipped with hand-operated screwdowns since, in normal operation, very little screw adjustment is required on these stands. The last five horizontal roll stands are equipped with single 15-horsepower motor-driven screwdowns, so arranged that the top screws may be adjusted in parallel or individually.

The heavy-duty 16-inch scale-breaking edging stand is located ahead of No. 1 horizontal-mill stand and, to maintain close control of product width, the 12-inch edging stands are located ahead of horizontal stands Nos. 4, 6, 8, and 10.

A rotary cobble shear, situated between horizontal stands Nos. 5 and 6, disposes of strip leaving the roughing stands in the event of a cobble occurring in the finishing portion of the mill.

Air-operated loopers are provided between stands Nos. 5 and 6, 7 and 8, 8 and 9, and 9 and 10 to assist in width control.

High-pressure-water descaling boxes are provided both ahead of and following the edging scalebreaker to chill the scale on the slabs entering the edger and to remove it following the edger.

The runout table of the mill is approximately 80 feet in length and contains 39 individually driven rollers on 24-inch centers. This table has a speed range to match the mill delivery speed of 523 to 1570 ft. per min.

To turn the finished-rolled skelp on edge, polished cast-iron twist troughs are provided, preceded by a horizontal pinch-roll unit and followed by a vertical pinch-roll unit and a strip switch. The strip switch, automatically operated by a photoelectric system, is a

Table 30—III.   Drive and Mill-Speed Data for Skelp Mill—Fairless Works.

Stand Number	Motor hp	Motor Speed Range (r.p.m.)	Total Gear Reduction	Roll Speed (r.p.m.)	Roll-Pass Diameter (In.)	Delivery Speed (ft. per min.)
Edger 1	200	225/1200	51.77	4.3 to 23.2	$12\frac{1}{2}$ - 15	14 to 91
No. 1	600	225/900	33.95	6.6 to 26.5	$17\frac{5}{16}$ - $19\frac{1}{16}$	30 to 132
No. 2	600	225/900	25.54	8.8 to 35.2	$17\frac{5}{16}$ - $19\frac{1}{16}$	40 to 176
No. 3	800	262.5/875	17.68	14.8 to 49.5	$17\frac{7}{8}$ - $19\frac{5}{8}$	69 to 254
Edger 2	150	225/1200	9.50	23.8 to 126.8	9 - 12	56 to 398
No. 4	800	262.5/875	11.56	22.7 to 75.7	$18\frac{1}{2}$ - $19\frac{7}{8}$	108 to 394
No. 5	800	262.5/875	7.85	33.4 to 111.5	$18\frac{5}{16}$ - $20\frac{1}{16}$	160 to 586
Edger 3	150	225/1200	4.83	46.8 to 249.6	9 - 11	110 to 719
No. 6	800	262.5/875	5.69	46.1 to 154	$17\frac{3}{16}$ - $18\frac{15}{16}$	207 to 764
No. 7	800	262.5/875	4.74	55.4 to 184.8	$17\frac{5}{16}$ - $19\frac{1}{16}$	251 to 922
Edger 4	150	225/1200	3.67	60.8 to 324.4	12 - 13	191 to 1104
No. 8	800	262.5/875	4.07	64.6 to 215.2	$17\frac{3}{8}$ - $19\frac{1}{8}$	294 to 1077
No. 9	800	262.5/875	3.54	74.1 to 247	$17\frac{3}{8}$ - $19\frac{1}{8}$	337 to 1237
Edger 5	150	225/1200	2.85	78.6 to 419.2	12 - 13	247 to 1427
No. 10	800	262.5/875	3.19	82.2 to 274.4	$17\frac{1}{2}$ - $19\frac{1}{4}$	377 to 1381

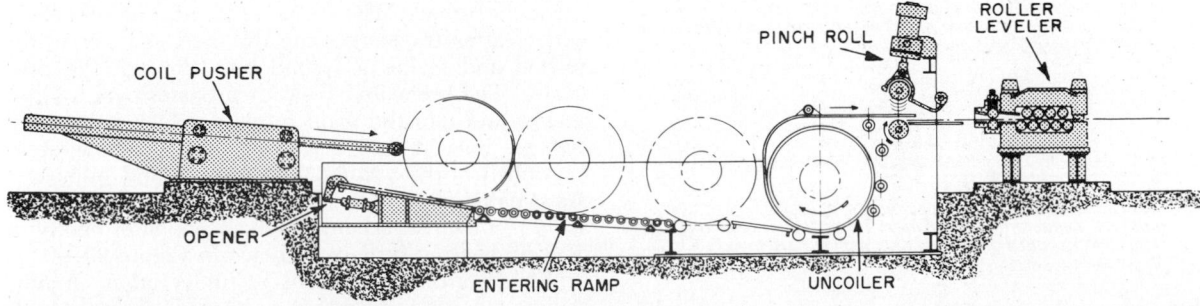

FIG. 30—5. Finish-rolled skelp fed in serpentine pattern onto apron conveyor that carries it to reel.

mechanical guide trough that is swiveled about its entry end while its delivery end is free to move to direct the skelp alternately to either of two vibrators that feed the skelp in serpentine pattern onto an apron conveyor. From the strip switch through to the unloading of coils in to storage, dual facilities have been provided to handle the mill output.

The serpentine-formed skelp is fed directly onto the apron-type conveyor, which is 110 feet long and 7 feet wide between side guards, at a speed of from 54 to 162 ft. per min. (Figure 30—5). The conveyor will hold a maximum of about 1600 feet of skelp. The skelp is held on the conveyor until the leading end is trimmed square and then fed by an adjustable-speed vertical pinch roll into the reels for coiling. The trimming shears are of the vertical alligator type and can shear skelp up to 18 inches wide.

Two vertical-type skelp reels receive the skelp delivered from the apron conveyors. The reel centers are of the collapsible type and, upon completion of a coil,

FIG. 30—6. Schematic elevation of coiled-skelp handling equipment at the entry end of a continuous butt-weld pipe mill.

are collapsed automatically and withdrawn downward from the coil. Centers are designed to form coils with an inside diameter of 20 inches. The reels have a speed range of 122 to 244 rev. per min. Each reel has a coil pushoff for pushing the coils onto the coil conveyors. This method of coiling avoids telescoping and produces coils much less subject to edge damage in handling to storage or from storage to subsequent processes.

The coil conveyors are of the double roller-chain type, with the coils riding on the chains on 6-foot centers. The conveyors are approximately 90 feet long and have a maximum speed of 15.5 ft. per min. Scales in each conveyor weigh the coils.

To facilitate the handling of coils to storage in 15-ton lifts by either the 25-ton electric overhead traveling coil-storage crane with rotating trolley or by a 15-ton capacity self-propelled ram truck, there are a coil upender and coil assembly conveyor after each of the conveyors that carry coils from the reels. The upender is hydraulically operated and raises the coils to a vertical position and pushes them onto a 40-foot long assembly conveyor where the coils are assembled into approximately 15-ton lifts.

The coiled skelp is stored in a large building in

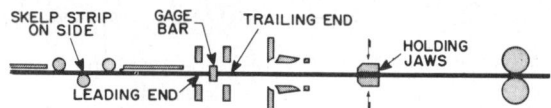

A. TRAILING END OF SKELP STRIP IS HELD STATIONARY BY HOLDING JAWS, WHILE LEADING END OF INCOMING STRIP IS BROUGHT AGAINST GAGE BAR.

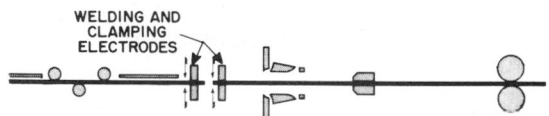

B. WELDING AND CLAMPING ELECTRODES GRIP BOTH ENDS OF SKELP. GAGE BAR IS REMOVED.

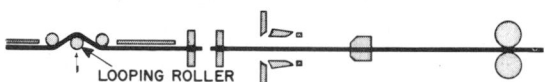

C. LOOPING ROLLER MOVES UP TO ALLOW SLACK IN SKELP FOR NEXT OPERATION.

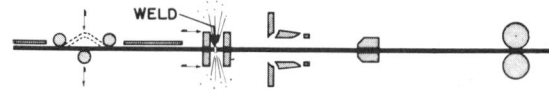

D. POWER IS APPLIED TO ELECTRODES. LEFT HAND ELECTRODES MOVE TO RIGHT BRINGING ELECTRIFIED ENDS TOGETHER FORMING ARC, UPSETTING AND WELDING.

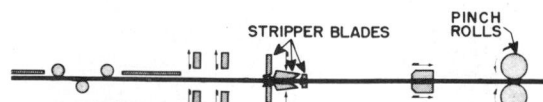

E. WELDING AND CLAMPING ELECTRODES RELEASE. SKELP IS PULLED THROUGH FLASH STRIPPER. STRIPPER JAWS RELEASE AND PINCH ROLLS PULL WELDED AND CLEANED SKELP TO CONTINUOUS LINE.

FIG. 30—7. Welding cycle for a typical flash-type skelp welder.

which are located the discharge end of the apron conveyors, the two coiling reels, the two coil conveyors, two coil upenders and assembly conveyors. All floor areas within the building are paved and suitable for storing the coils three high. The building is served by a standard-gauge railroad siding. A transfer car is provided for delivering stored coils as required to the continuous-weld pipe mills.

Production of Continuous Butt-Welded Pipe—In a modern continuous-weld mill, coiled skelp is formed into high-quality butt-welded pipe at speeds of 150 to 1100 feet per minute. The automatically controlled equipment assures a uniformity of wall thickness and diameter of finished product never before attained. The continuous mills produce pipe in the full range of sizes from ½-inch to 4-inch nominal diameter from only a few different widths of skelp.

Coils of skelp from storage are loaded on the arms of a turntable that provides a continuous supply to the mill. The coils are removed from the turntable, one at a time, and placed on a cradle car. Each coil is rotated on the cradle car until it is in the right position for the coil peeler, which opens the coil and bends the end of the skelp so that it can be fed into the pinch rolls of the uncoiler-leveler. When the skelp is started through the leveler, the coil is transferred to an expanding mandrel for payoff into the mill. Figure 30—6 illustrates one type of coil-handling equipment at the entry end of a continuous butt-weld mill.

An upcut shear squares the leading end of each coil and the trailing end of the coil preceding it so that the ends can be joined by flash welding. A flash welder is designed to position and clamp the two coil ends, heat them, and force them together to form an upset weld. After welding, the joint is reheated to relieve stresses, and a drawcut planer removes the flash formed in the welding operation. The principle of operation of a flash welder is shown in Figure 30—7.

Pinch rolls and the uncoiler-leveler push the strand of skelp away from the welder. The steel is guided to the floor and formed into a large storage loop that provides skelp for continuous mill operation while end welds are being made. Four magnet-roll units help to feed skelp into the storage loop. At the end of the storage loop, a horizontal pinch-roll unit moves skelp into a secondary loop, then feeds it into the preheater or upper main furnace chamber (Figure 30—8). Pinch-roll speed is varied by automatic controls that maintain the extent of the secondary loop within set limits.

The preheat chamber is heated by waste gases from the main furnace. The skelp is fed into the preheater where, after traveling some distance, it reverses direction and makes a second pass through the preheater. The preheated skelp then passes over a large sheave and into the main furnace, which is fired by 434 gas burners and is divided into four separately controlled heating zones. The furnace and preheater are capable of heating 70 tons of 0.225 by 17½-inch skelp per hour. A schematic cross-section of one type of skelp-heating furnace is shown in Figure 30—9.

When starting operations or under other circumstances when it is necessary to "thread" skelp through the furnace, a furnace-threading machine installed in

Fig. 30—8. Skelp from storage loop in right foreground being fed into furnace extending into center background that heats the skelp for continuous butt welding. The roller leveler and flash-welding machine are visible at the left of this illustration.

the line (Figure 30—10) is employed. This machine has driven pinch rolls, one convex and one concave, to give the skelp a dished shape that imparts sufficient stiffness to permit it to be pushed through the furnace. As soon as the skelp is entirely through the furnace and is being pulled by the forming and welding unit, the threading rolls are opened up and become inoperative until the mill must again be threaded.

An air blast cleans the surfaces of the hot skelp

before it enters the forming, welding, and reducing stands.

The functions performed in the forming and welding mill are shown schematically in Figure 30—11.

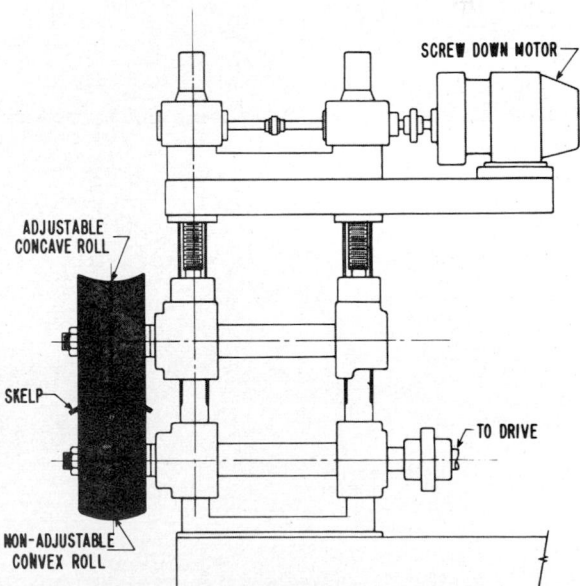

Fig. 30—9. Cross-sectional diagram showing design of a furnace used on a continuous butt-weld pipe mill for heating the edges of the skelp prior to welding. (This sketch corresponds to Section D-D of Figure 30—1.)

Fig. 30—10. Schematic elevation of a furnace threading machine.

Skelp passes through the forming stand that forces it into an arc of about 270 degrees. Then it goes through a welding horn and into the welding stand, where the edges are pressed firmly together. The last five stands of the welding mill provide for reduction of diameter and wall thickness. An overall view of a forming and welding mill is shown in Figure 30—12.

A seven-stand stretch-reducing mill brings the welded pipe to its finished size. As the name implies, this mill is used for reducing the diameter of, and simultaneously applying tension to, the tube being produced. By this method, and without the use of supporting mandrels, the wall thickness of a tube can be maintained or even decreased while the diameter is being reduced. Figures 30—13 and 30—14 illustrate some of the principles of design of a stretch-reducing mill; further details are given in Section 5 under "Continuous Seamless Process." Multiple-pass rolls permit rolling of six pipe sizes without changing rolls. This minimizes downtime for size changes and roll wear.

Roll shafts of the multiple-pass stretch-reducing mill are at 45 degrees from horizontal, and roll axes on successive stands are perpendicular. Each stand is mounted on a steel sled that houses the pinion stand; sleds are moved by hydraulic cylinders and positioned by adjustable stops. Hydraulic clamping mechanisms hold the sleds in position.

The drive system insures compatible speeds for the last six stands of the forming and welding mill and all seven stands of the stretch-reducing mill. Each stand has a controllable variation of 30 per cent above or below its normal speed with an accuracy of 0.1 per cent.

All forming, welding, and reducing stands are driven by a 1000-horsepower direct-current motor through a common lineshaft. Except for No. 1, stands receive power through differential gear units that are connected to the main lineshaft by right-angle gear boxes. The differential gearing permits variation or adjustment of stand speeds without changing the speed of the lineshaft. Such variation or adjustment is

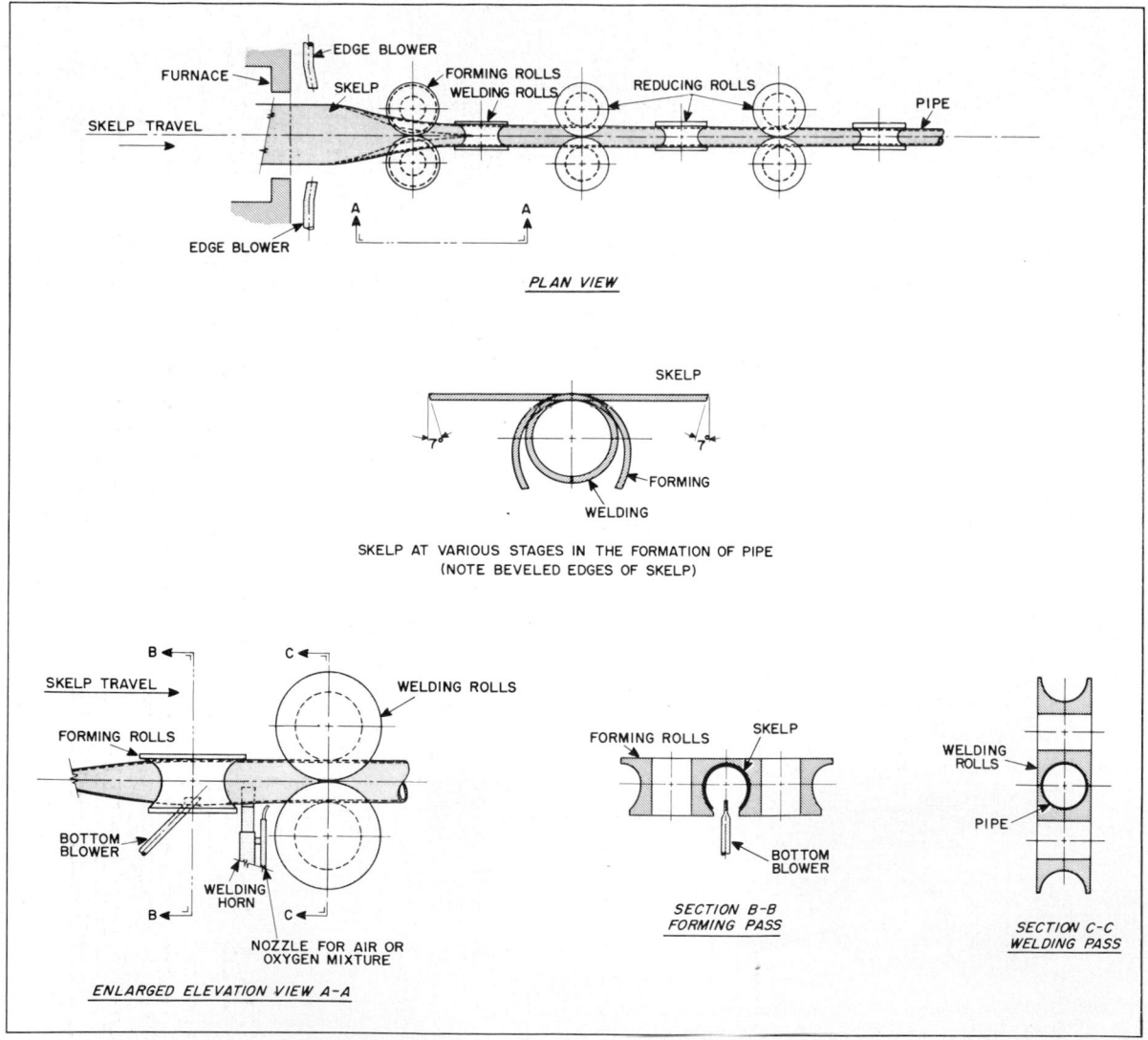

FIG. 30—11. Diagram depicting schematically the operations performed in a continuous forming and welding mill.

FIG. 30—12. Overall view of forming and welding stands of continuous butt-weld mill.

accomplished by rotating the differential gearing independently. Rotation of the gearing in one direction increases output-shaft speed, and rotation in the opposite direction decreases output-shaft speed. A hydraulic motor drives the differential gearing in the desired direction at the desired speed.

The hydraulic motors are operated by fluid from variable-displacement pumps that receive power di-

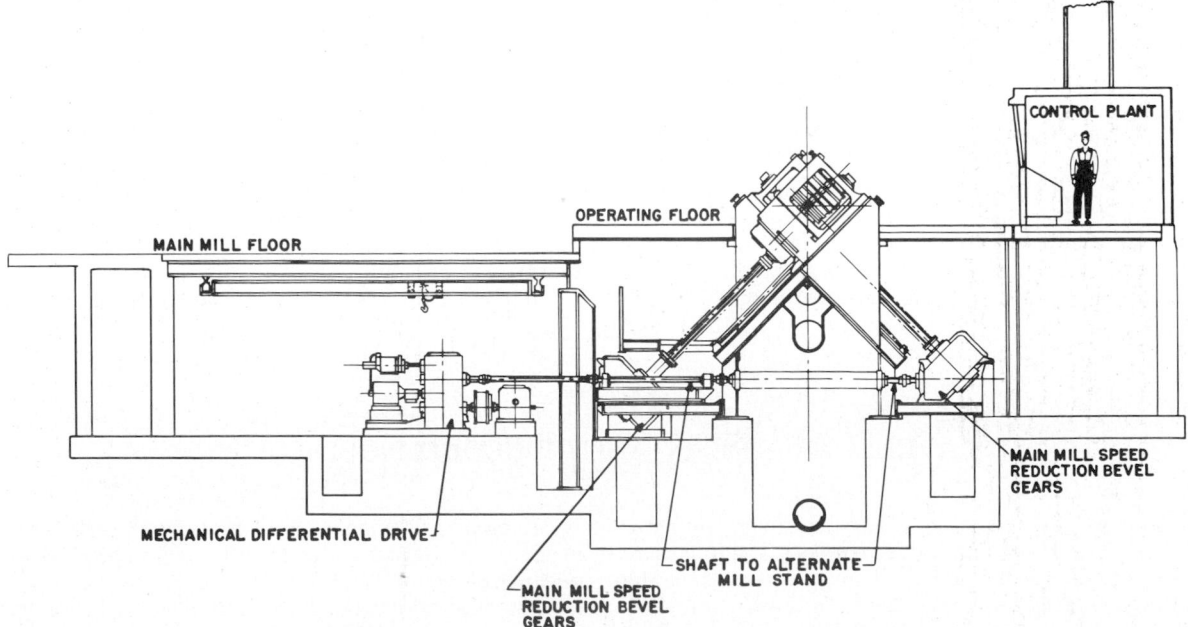

FIG. 30—13. Schematic cross-section of two typical stands of a stretch-reducing mill, illustrating components of the differential drive system that insures a constant interstand speed ratio.

Fig. 30—14. Close-up view of two active stands (right) of a stretch-reducing mill. Two stands at left have been retracted. Welded pipe leaving active stands passes through tubular guide in the left foreground.

rectly from the differential-input gears. Control of the hydraulic-pump discharge and the direction of fluid flow between the hydraulic pump and motor permits mill rolls to run at an infinite number of speeds—30 per cent above or below the predetermined base speed.

Hydraulic tachometers automatically control and regulate a metering device that governs oil flow from the hydraulic pump to the hydraulic differential-drive motor.

If skelp thickness varies and off-gage pipe is delivered to the stretch-reducing mill, over-all elongation can be distributed among the stands by available controls to bring wall thickness to its standard value.

A rotary flying saw cuts the continuous pipe into predetermined lengths at maximum mill-delivery speeds. Hydraulic saw-drive equipment is separately powered but controlled by an extension of the main mill shaft. Controls, using the lineshaft speed as a reference, cause the saw cycle to coincide with the product speed.

Cut lengths are reduced to the required hot size on a three-stand sizing mill, delivered by a kickout mechanism to a middle-cut saw, and dropped on a cooling bed. Crop saws at opposite ends of the cooling beds trim the pipe ends.

Pipe passes from the cooling bed to a water bosh tank for fast cooling; then it is taken to conveyors that feed rotary straighteners in the finishing bay.

The pipe is then ready for finishing operations.

SECTION 3

ELECTRIC-RESISTANCE-WELDED TUBING

The art and processing equipment for manufacturing electric-resistance-welded tubing, sometimes referred to as ERW tubing, has improved considerably during the recent past. These improvements have widened the range of available ERW tubular products from small diameters and thin walls to permit the manufacture, in installations now under construction, of tubing up to 20 inches in diameter with wall thicknesses up to 0.500-inch. The development of non-destructive testing methods such as ultrasonic, eddy current, and fringe flux has been a major factor towards promoting ERW tubular product acceptance. These non-destructive testing devices are normally placed directly into the welding-mill line to check

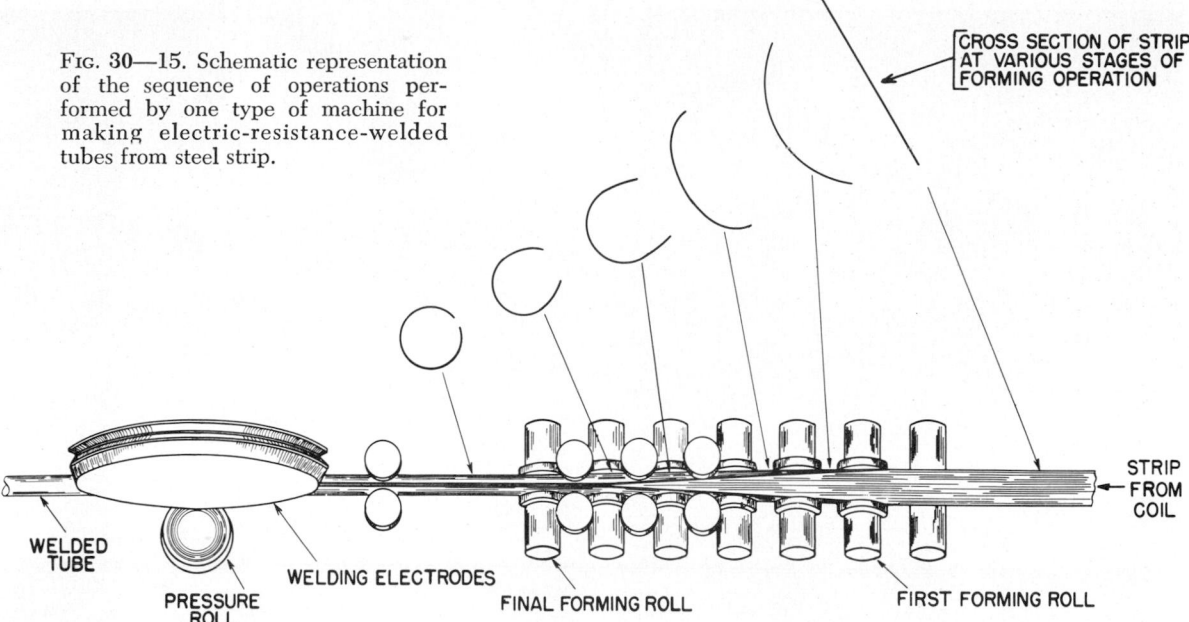

Fig. 30—15. Schematic representation of the sequence of operations performed by one type of machine for making electric-resistance-welded tubes from steel strip.

CROSS SECTION OF STRIP AT VARIOUS STAGES OF FORMING OPERATION

STRIP FROM COIL

WELDED TUBE

PRESSURE ROLL

WELDING ELECTRODES

FINAL FORMING ROLL

FIRST FORMING ROLL

steel quality and also weld integrity. The steel product used as starting material for making ERW tubing is generally strip, sheet or plate in coil form (some mills are designed to use uncoiled plate) produced from either rimmed or killed steel; either hot rolled or cold rolled; with pickled, grit blasted, or mill surface.

Steps in Manufacturing Electric-Resistance-Welded Tubing—The sequence of operations required in the fabrication of electric-resistance-welded tubing are: slitting (when multiple-width strip is used), forming, welding, sizing, cutting, and finishing.

Slitting—Frequently, tubing is manufactured direct from single-width strip: i.e., strip the width of which will equal the perimeter of the tubing to be welded. However, many manufacturers of tubular goods purchase wide-width coils which are subsequently slit into the desired widths.

The wide coils are loaded onto a ramp from which they are permitted to roll, as required, onto a charging buggy which moves the coils to the pay-off reel of the slitting machine. The buggy is provided with an elevator by which it is possible to center the coil on the reel before the retaining bands on the coil are removed. The reel, which is motor driven, is rotated to slowly unwind the strip which is threaded into a set of breaker rolls that flatten it sufficiently to facilitate threading through pinch rolls into the slitter knives. These knives, which may take .the form of tool-steel discs, are mounted on arbors above and below the strip and are spaced with rings to slit to the desired width. From the slitter, the strips pass to the recoiler where they are wound between thin, steel disc spacers. The narrow strips of scrap from the edges of the wide strip pass over the recoiler onto the scrap winder.

After the strip has been threaded completely through the line, the recoiler and slitter motors are adjusted to pull it through the slitter knives with any desired tension. The slitter, recoiler, scrap winder, breaker rolls and pay-off reel are not synchronized

with the others as they are used only when threading the strip.

When the entire coil has been slit and wound on the recoiler mandrel, steel bands are placed around each of the narrow coils. An unloading buggy is elevated under the coils which are then pushed off hydraulically onto the buggy. The banded coils are weighed, and are then ready for the welding mill.

Forming—Although the range of sizes handled by any mill is limited, the process of forming and welding the tubing is generally similar in mills of this type.

Coils are fed either directly into forming rolls or into a "looper" to permit continuous forming of strip welded end-to-end in the smaller sizes. The strip first passes through an edge trimmer where the desired width is established and the edge is made smooth and clean for good welding.

ERW mills normally make use of three types of rolls to progressively form the flat steel section into the round form prior to welding. These three types of rolls are: (1) Breakdown or forming rolls, (2) Idler the rolls are horizontal and are driven either by uni-

In the cases of the breakdown and fin pass sections, the rolls are horizontal and are driven either by universal line shaft or by individual drives to allow perfect speed control of each stand. Breakdown rolls provide the initial shaping of the strip towards the round form. These are followed or interspersed by idler rolls which further close and guide the strip into the fin pass rolls. The fin pass rolls provide perfect guidance into the welding section and in addition coin the strip edges to provide the precise circumference.

Welding the Tube—After forming has occurred, the open tube passes directly into the welding section of the mill. Here the tube is held in squeeze rolls at the correct pressure to provide the desired weld as the edges are heated at this point to welding temperature.

The heat for welding is provided either by low-frequency power through electrode wheels (Figures 30—15 and 30—16), or radio-frequency power.

FIG. 30—16. Tube passing under welding electrodes.

through sliding contacts or coil induction. Typical radio-frequency power for welding is supplied at 450,000 cycles per second.

The welded tube then passes under a cutting tool which removes the outside flash resulting from the pressure during welding. Inside flash is likewise removed by cutting tools in this area. After removing the flash, the tube is subjected to proper post-weld treatment as metallurgically required: e.g., such treatment may involve sub-critical annealing or normalizing of the welded seam or normalizing of the full cross-section of the tube.

Sizing the Welded Tube—After cooling, the tube is sized to obtain a round finished product of the de-sired diameter. The sizing mill consists of several driven horizontal rolls and several idle vertical rolls.

Finishing—After the tube leaves the sizing mill, it is cut to determined lengths by suitable cut-off machinery. Cutting may be performed by discs, parting tools, shears, or cold saws which travel with the tube while cutting.

The cut tubes are then transferred to the finishing floor where they are straightened, if required, using standard facilities either continuous or of the gag-press design.

Also on the finishing floor, special cutting and end finishing is performed when needed. After finishing, tubes are inspected and packed for shipment.

SECTION 4

ELECTRIC-WELDED LARGE-DIAMETER PIPE

Applications of the Process—Large-diameter pipe in sizes beyond the practical limits of the seamless process is fabricated by electric welding. This type of pipe, which is employed for water lines, gas mains, oil lines, tanks, pressure vessels, etc., may be made from rolled-steel plate of any weldable quality. The size of the pipe which can be made by this process is practically unlimited, since, when the circumference of the desired pipe exceeds the plate width capacity of the rolling mill, two or more plates may be welded together longitudinally to provide the necessary width or, if only a short length is desired, the plate may be bent lengthwise, permitting it to be formed with only one longitudinal weld. Where long-length, large-diameter pipe is required, the desired length may be made by welding together two or more pieces circumferentially.

Steps in the Manufacture of Electric-Welded Pipe —The sequence of operations required to make plates into pipe by the electric-weld process are shearing, planing, crimping, bending, welding, expanding and finishing.

Shearing and Planing—Plates employed in the manufacture of electric-welded pipe are rolled on either a plate or strip mill as described elsewhere in this book. The plate is transferred to the edge-planing machine where it is aligned so that the two edges will be parallel and square with the ends after planing. A clamping bar, hydraulically operated, holds the plate during the edging operation. Along the full length of both sides of the table, lead screws drive carriages carrying a series of cutting tools which trim the edges of the plate.

The series of cutting tools are arranged so that no single tool will be required to remove more than a reasonable amount of stock from the rough edges of the rolled or sheared plate.

Crimping—Forming plate into the circular shape required for pipe is usually performed in three operations. The first operation, called crimping, consists of bending the edges of the plate so as to avoid a flat surface near the longitudinal seam of the pipe.

Crimping may be performed in a large crimping press which deforms the edges of the plate for a distance of approximately 6 inches in a hydraulically operated press. Crimping may also be performed by crimping rolls which roll the edges to the desired radius as the plate is drawn through the roll pass.

Bending—The crimped plate is then conveyed to what is called the "U"-ing machine (Figure 30—17). In this operation, the plate is centered over a series of parallel rocker-type dies which lie along the axis of the plate. A large "U"-shaped die, which is as long as the longest length of plate fabricated and which is operated by a 2000-ton press, is moved down on the plate, forcing it between the dies which automatically conform themselves to the operation and assist in forming the plate into the "U" shape. The plate is then transferred to what is called the "O"-ing machine. This machine consists of two semi-circular dies which are as long as the plate to be formed. Rollers mounted on vertical spindles prevent the "U"-shaped plate from falling and keep it in correct alignment as it enters the "O"-ing machine. The "U"-shaped plate rests in the bottom die, and the top die, operated by an 18,000-ton hydraulic press, is forced down, deforming the plate until it is the shape of an almost closed circle which is then ready for welding.

Welding—Welding may be performed by any one of the numerous methods. However, the most common is the submerged-arc method. In this method, coalescence is produced by heating with an electric arc or arcs between bare-metal electrode or electrodes and the work. The welding is shielded by a blanket of

Fig. 30—17. The "U"-ing machine forming the crimped plate in a "U" shape.

granular, fusible material or flux on the work. Pressure is not used and filler metal is obtained from the electrode and sometimes from a supplementary welding rod.

It is extremely important that the gap in the formed pipe be properly positioned for outside welding. Two steel archways supporting a longitudinal guide are located over the conveyor approaching the welding machine. As the pipe moves over the conveyor, the guide enters and continues along the gap, guiding it into the welding machine. Figure 30—18 shows a pipe emerging from an outside-welding machine.

The welding operation is started by striking an arc beneath the flux on the work. The heat produced melts the surrounding flux so that it forms a subsurface conductive pool which is kept fluid by the continuous flow of current. The end of the electrode and the work piece directly under it become molten and molten filler metal is deposited from the metal electrode onto the work. The molten filler metal displaces the flux and forms the weld.

The specially designed welding heads used for this process perform the triple function of progressively depositing the flux along the joint, feeding the electrode, and transmitting welding current to the electrodes. The flux is supplied from a hopper connected

Fig. 30—18. Pipe beginning to emerge from the outside welding machine.

to the head by tubing. The bare electrode is fed into the welding head from a coil mounted on a reel.

After the pipe is welded on the outside, the weld is inspected and conditioned on the ends when required. At this time, square pieces of metal are welded to the pipe at the ends of the weld to enable the inside-welding machine to start at the end of the pipe.

The automatic machine which does the internal welding is similar in design to the outside welder, and is mounted on the end of a long cantilever arm and the pipe is drawn over this arm by a carriage.

After welding, the scaly deposit left from the flux must be cleaned out. This is accomplished by running the pipe over a series of rollers and, at the same time allowing the entry of a cantilevered tube which is attached to a vacuum system. The weld is then carefully inspected and defects corrected with manual welding equipment.

Sizing or Expanding—The final pipe diameter is obtained by hydraulically expanding the welded shell against a retaining jacket. The pipe is placed in an expanding machine (Figure 30—19) and mandrels are forced into each end to expand the pipe to the required diameter at the ends only. Retainer jackets

then encircle the body of the pipe which is filled with water and expanded by hydraulic pressure to the limits of the jackets. The pressure is then reduced and serves as a hydrostatic test. In addition to obtaining close diameter control, this method cold works the metal, resulting in higher mechanical properties, and is a good test of the weld.

Attention is continuously given to non-destructive inspection of weld quality. This is accomplished by X-ray examination of the weld at both ends of the pipe at suitable intervals. In addition, the entire longitudinal weld can be subjected to X-ray examination by viewing a fluoroscopic screen followed by photographic X-ray inspection of any points wherein fluoroscopic examination suggests further inspection is in order.

Finishing—Following the rounding-up or expansion operation, the pipe is placed in special machines which face the ends. This operation insures that the ends will be smooth and accurately within a plane at right angles to the longitudinal axis of the pipe. If the pipe is being prepared for welded joints, the ends are beveled in this operation.

FIG. 30—19. Hydraulic expanding machine for final sizing of diameter of electric-welded large-diameter pipe. The ribbed sections are retaining jackets.

SECTION 5

SEAMLESS STEEL TUBULAR PRODUCTS

In the decade preceding the twentieth century, the bicycle became a very popular vehicle, and the growth of the bicycle industry created a demand for high-class seamless tubes in very large quantities. The early methods of seamless tube manufacture were slow and tedious, and orders aggregating millions of feet of tubing for bicycle construction could not be filled. In 1895 the first American seamless tube plant using the principle of rotary piercing was constructed in Ellwood City, Pennsylvania, and operated successfully for many years in the manufacture of bicycle tubing. The equipment at this plant consisted of a Stiefel disc piercer, a Pilger rolling mill, and cold-drawing benches on which the tubes were finished.

After 1900 the automotive industry began to grow and soon caused a great decrease in the manufacture of bicycles, with a consequent loss of seamless-tube business. On the other hand, the great increase in the use of automobiles created an immense demand for motor fuels and lubricants, which greatly stimulated expansion in the oil industry and thus developed a new and enormous market for seamless tubes. In the transition period, the seamless-tube manufacturer turned to the boiler industry, and the next step in the development of the seamless process related to the production of all forms of stationary- and locomotive-boiler tubes. The seamless tube soon displaced the wrought-iron and lap-welded steel tubes which had previously been standard in boilers.

After World War I, the discovery of enormous oil pools with flush production created a demand for pipe for wells and transmission lines. The later discovery, after 1920, of huge natural-gas reservoirs in remote districts, from which the gas could be transported to consuming markets only in steel pipelines, sometimes over 1,000 miles long, resulted in another large market for seamless pipe. Some idea of the size of the oil and gas industry in the United States may be gained from the fact that there are over 500,000 producing oil wells and over 550,000 miles of pipe lines in existence.

The seamless-tube mills prior to 1920 were scarcely able to make pipe over 6 inches in diameter and longer than 25 feet.

In the year 1925, the United States Steel Corporation developed the so-called double-piercing process, which consisted of piercing a heavy-walled shell and then expanding this in a second piercing operation to a larger diameter tube with a lighter wall. This development made possible the production of tubes up to 16 inches in diameter. The Pilger process had also reached a production stage at this time, but a thorough study of this method caused its rejection for American manufacturing conditions. Further study of the double-piercing and expanding process later led to the rotary-rolling process, by which it was possible to produce seamless tubes up to 26 inches in diameter and in lengths exceeding 40 feet.

Scope and Requirements of Seamless Tube Products—The expansion of the seamless-tube industry described above was also greatly influenced by the adaptation of the piercing process to the many different types of steels which were developed during this period. Steels melted by many processes can now be successfully converted into seamless tubes. In general, killed steels made by open-hearth, electric-furnace and basic oxygen processes are used. Considerable quantities of deoxidized acid-Bessemer steel have also been converted into seamless tubes with excellent results.

Because of the severity of the forging operation involved in piercing, the steels used for seamless tubes must have good characteristics with respect to both surface and internal soundness. A sound, dense cross-section, free from center porosity or ingot pattern, is the most satisfactory for seamless tubes. For this reason steels of the thoroughly killed types and in some cases semi-killed steels are to be preferred to strongly rimming steels. Although rimming steels have been successfully converted into seamless tubes, the results are not always uniform, either because of a poor inside surface, due to internal porosity, or because of high losses from external seams, caused by surface defects. Metallurgical developments in recent years have contributed greatly to the improvement of steels for seamless tubes.

As a result, the seamless process has been extended to include practically all of the regular and alloy grades of steel. At the present time all of the ordinary carbon steels, even those containing as much as 1½ per cent of carbon, are processed in commercial quantities. Some of the high-sulphur and leaded steels developed for machining are also manufactured into seamless tubing.

All of the constructional alloy steels, such as those listed in the specifications of the American Iron and Steel Institute and the Society of Automotive Engineers, are available in tubing.

In the last twenty years, many steels of special compositions that impart resistance to heat and corrosion have been developed. Seamless tubes are now satisfactorily made from most of these steels. These include the chromium steels containing from 1 to 30 per cent chromium and numerous other alloyed steels containing chromium with additions of such elements as molybdenum, nickel, manganese, columbium (niobium), silicon, and titanium. In general, it can be stated that all of the alloys which are ferritic or pearlitic in structure are satisfactory for piercing. The alloy steels which are generally of the austenitic type can be successfully pierced if the austenite remains stable at forging temperatures. A few of the austenitic steels which have a considerable proportion of ferrite at forging temperatures are difficult to pierce. For exam-

ple, an alloy such as the 25 per cent chromium-10 per cent nickel, which is partially ferritic, may be difficult to pierce, whereas an alloy with 25 per cent chromium and 20 per cent nickel can be pierced satisfactorily. However, seamless tubes of alloys containing free ferrite may be produced by the extrusion process.

Seamless pipe with a variety of special properties has been developed to meet the needs of the oil industry. In this field the pipe employed for rotary drilling must possess great torsional strength and high resistance to fatigue stresses. An idea of the stresses to which the pipe is exposed in drilling service may be gained from the realization that the power for the rotation of the drill bit on the lower end of the pipe is applied at the upper extremity, which, in some cases, is more than three miles distant. The string of drill pipe itself may weigh up to 370,000 lb., and rotate at 200 rev. per min. or more, so that only material of the highest strength and toughness will perform satisfactorily. Drill pipe is usually made with heavy upset ends, and the full lengths of pipe are normalized on the completion of the forging operations.

The casing for such deep oil wells requires seamless pipe having a high resistance to collapse to withstand the high external pressures. Casing has been set to depths of over 20,000 ft. under very high hydrostatic heads. Other classes of seamless pipe and specialty tubing made for the oil industry include oil-well tubing, pump tubing, and line pipe.

The oil-refining, chemical and high-pressure-steam industries also demand special seamless pipe. Satisfactory alloy-steel tubing and pipe are made to withstand temperatures up to 1200° F coincident with pressures as high as 5000 lb. These industries also use high-pressure pipe lines at temperatures as low as −450° F, and steel pipe which is tough and strong at these low temperatures is now produced in considerable quantities.

Sequence of Seamless-Pipe-Mill Operations—The sequence of operations in seamless-pipe mills varies slightly from mill to mill. At the Lorain Works of United States Steel it follows three general patterns determined by the size of the pipe to be produced. The round billets are first uniformly heated to piercing temperature in special gas- or liquid-fuel-fired furnaces. They are then processed through the various operations in the following order, depending upon the diameter of tube to be produced:

> Pipe Size—2-inch to 4½-inch diameter
> > Piercing Mill
> > Plug Rolling Mill
> > Reeling Machine
> > Reheating Furnace
> > Sizing Machine
>
> Pipe Size—3½-inch to 16-inch diameter
> > First Piercing Mill
> > Second Piercing Mill
> > Reheating Furnace
> > Plug Rolling Mill
> > Reeling Machine

Pipe Size—14-inch to 26-inch diameter
    First Piercing Mill
    Second Piercing Mill
    Reheating Furnace
    Plug Rolling Mill
    Reheating Furnace
    Rotary Rolling Mill
    Reeling Machine
    Reheating Furnace
    Sizing Mill

The operation of each of the above units will be described in detail in the remainder of this section. In the overlapping sizes of the range 3½-inch to 4-inch diameter, the heavier-wall pipe is processed through only one piercing operation whereas the two piercing mills are employed in producing the light walls. Also, in the overlapping sizes of the range 14-inch to 16-inch diameter, the lighter-wall pipe is rotary rolled, the heavier-wall pipe by-passing the second reheating operation and the rotary-rolling mill.

The Mannesmann Machine for piercing round billets for making seamless tubes (Figure 30—20) was patented in 1885. In this machine, the principle of helical rolling is employed. The two steel rolls, which bring into play the forces used to produce the cavity

in the work piece, are positioned side by side and have their axes inclined at opposite angles 6 degrees to 12 degrees with the horizontal centerline of the mill (Figure 30—21). These rolls measure from 20 inches to 30 inches in length and from 32 inches to 48 inches in diameter. The roll surfaces are contoured so that, in the horizontal plane through the centerline of the pass, the space between the rolls converges toward the delivery side for a length of from 5 inches to 15 inches to a minimum, called the **gorge,** and then diverges to form the pass outlet. The converging and diverging angles formed by the roll surfaces vary from 4 degrees to 12 degrees with 7 degrees as the usual standard. The shafts of these rolls are mounted in bearings which can be adjusted laterally in the housing to permit the space between the rolls to be properly set for the size of work piece being rolled. The inlet end of each roll shaft is fitted with a universal coupling which, through long spindles, connects with a common reduction gear powered by an electric motor. The size of this motor and reduction unit depends on the size range to be produced on the mill, varying between 750 and 5,000 h.p. These motors are designed for a pullout torque of 300 per cent. The rolls are cooled by water sprays. The elevation of the centerline of the pass is determined by two guides,

FIG. **30**—20. Mannesmann piercer in operation.

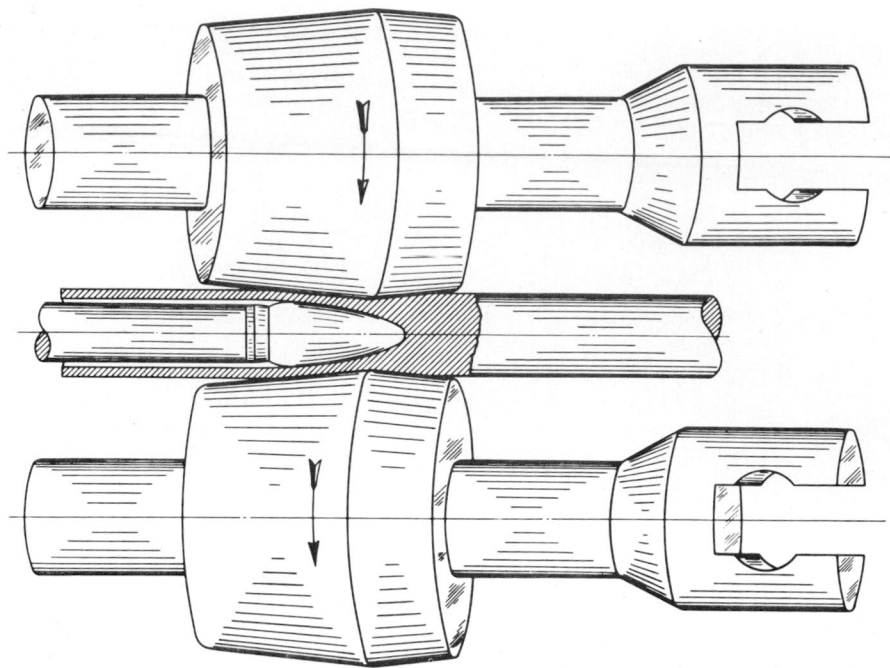

Fig. 30—21. Sketch illustrating action of different parts of Mannesmann piercer in the piercing of a solid billet.

one of which is mounted above and the other below the center of the mill in the space between the rolls.

Between these guides in the pass outlet a projectile-shaped piercing mandrel is held in position on the end of a water-cooled mandrel-support bar, located on the delivery side of the mill. The opposite end of this bar is mounted in a thrust bearing which is carried in a reciprocating carriage that is latched stationary during the piercing operation. The pointed end of the piercing mandrel extends just beyond the gorge toward the entering side of the rolls.

The Operation of Piercing—A solid round bar or billet of the proper length and diameter to make the size and weight of tube desired, is heated uniformly to the usual temperature for rolling light sections (2200 to 2300° F). With the rolls revolving at constant speed (800 to 1100 surface feet per min.), the heated billet is transferred to a horizontal trough, which positions the axis of the billet on the inlet side of the mill coincident with the centerline of the pass.

The heated billet is pushed forward into the space between the rolls, which has been adjusted so that the gorge is approximately 90 percent of the diameter of the billet. As soon as the leading end of the billet has contacted the rolls, the force of the pusher is removed. Because of the obliquity of the roll axes, the motion imparted to the billet between the rolls is one of rotation and axial advance. When the leading end of the billet has advanced to the gorge, it encounters the nose or pointed end of the piercing mandrel. The grip of the rolls is sufficient to continue the advance of the work piece against the retarding effect imposed by the piercing mandrel. When the rearward end of the billet is rolled clear of the piercer mandrel, the thrust-bearing carriage is unlatched and the mandrel withdrawn

from the billet, now a hollow shell, which is then conveyed to a reheating furnace in preparation for further fabrication into a finished tube. These shells are produced in lengths up to 26 feet in less than a minute.

The Action of the Rolls—It is evident that the forward motion of the billet is caused by the inclination of the axes of the rolls. How these two rolls, by exerting pressure only on a surface of the billet, are able to force the metal over the mandrel to form a tube from a solid billet is not so readily grasped. It is to be especially noted that the mandrel is not forced through the metal, but that the rolls cause the metal to flow over and about the mandrel. To bring about this result, the rolls must first draw metal away from the center of the billet, which action tends to form a central hole, or cavity, for the entrance of the piercer point. The truth of this statement is evident from the fact that a small, but somewhat irregular, hole may be formed in a billet without the use of the piercer point. In practice, the end of the piercer mandrel is placed sufficiently forward to prevent the formation of a cavity ahead of the point. Advantage is taken only of the tendency of the rolls to form this cavity.

The Principle Involved in Forming the Cavity—Indeed, such a hole can be opened up in the center of any solid cylindrically shaped plastic body by rolling it between, even, two flat surfaces. Steel workers, particularly hammermen, are familiar with the fact that, if a piece of steel in the form of a round be pressed or hammered into an oval form several times in succession, a rupture will occur in the center that will extend longitudinally through the middle of the bar. The reason for the formation of this rupture is plainly due to the fact that when pressure is applied to the round bar at diametrically opposite points sufficient to deform it, making one diameter shorter and that at right angles to it longer, the spreading of the metal, which takes place along the long diameter and in opposite directions, sets up a lateral tension that may cause its particles to be drawn away from the center (Figure 30—22).

Flow of the Metal in Piercing—As the billet, which is in a plastic state, enters the mill, the rolls grasp it at diametrically opposite points on its circumference. As they draw the billet forward in the converging portion of the pass, they continue to compress it at these opposite points and, since the billet is being revolved rapidly, these points are continually changing. As the compressive rolling or cross-rolling proceeds from the point of initial contact of the piercer rolls to the gorge, the diameter of the billet is reduced and the section is changed from a circle to an oval with the long diameter in a vertical position. Since the billet is rotating, the central portion is acted on by all of the forces which are applied around its circumference during successive contacts between the billet and rolls. If a sufficient reduction is effected in this manner, a cavity will be formed in the center of the billet even without the presence of a piercer mandrel. In practice, this cavity is not permitted to form in advance of the nose of the mandrel, since the rough surface of the self-formed cavity might not permit the inner surface of the shell to be subsequently rolled smooth by the action of the mandrel. It is for this reason that the end of the piercer mandrel is positioned in advance of the gorge so that it will actually effect the opening in the center of the billet, being assisted in its function by the cross-rolling action. To avoid the difficulty of ac-

curately centering the mandrel, the forward end of the billet is centered to insure that the point of the mandrel will penetrate the billet at or very near its axis. Centering is not absolutely necessary; however, it assists in starting the end of the mandrel in the center of the billet and reduces wear on the mandrel. If the end of the piercer mandrel is positioned too far in advance of the gorge, the cross-roll action on the center of the billet will not be great enough to reduce the resistance sufficiently to permit the grip of the rolls to advance the billet over the mandrel.

Once the end of the mandrel has penetrated the axial center of the billet, the piercer mandrel serves as a third roll so that, with the properly designed pass, the metal of the work piece is helically rolled over the piercing mandrel (rather than extruded) to produce the hollow shell. The grip of the rolls on the hollow in the diverging portion of the pass, due to the obliquity of the roll axes, tends to draw the billet forward as the reduction in wall thickness is being made, and, as a consequence, tends to increase the length of the pierced hollow shell at the expense of diameter.

Double Piercing—It is to be especially noted that the amount of metal displaced increases considerably as the O.D. size (outside diameter) is increased. In 1925, United States Steel Corporation developed the process known as double piercing. In this process the solid billet is first pierced to a comparatively heavy-walled shell, after which, without reheating, it is put through a second piercing mill. The second mill further reduces the wall thickness and increases the diameter and length of the piece. This practice has extended the permissible diameter range of the auto-

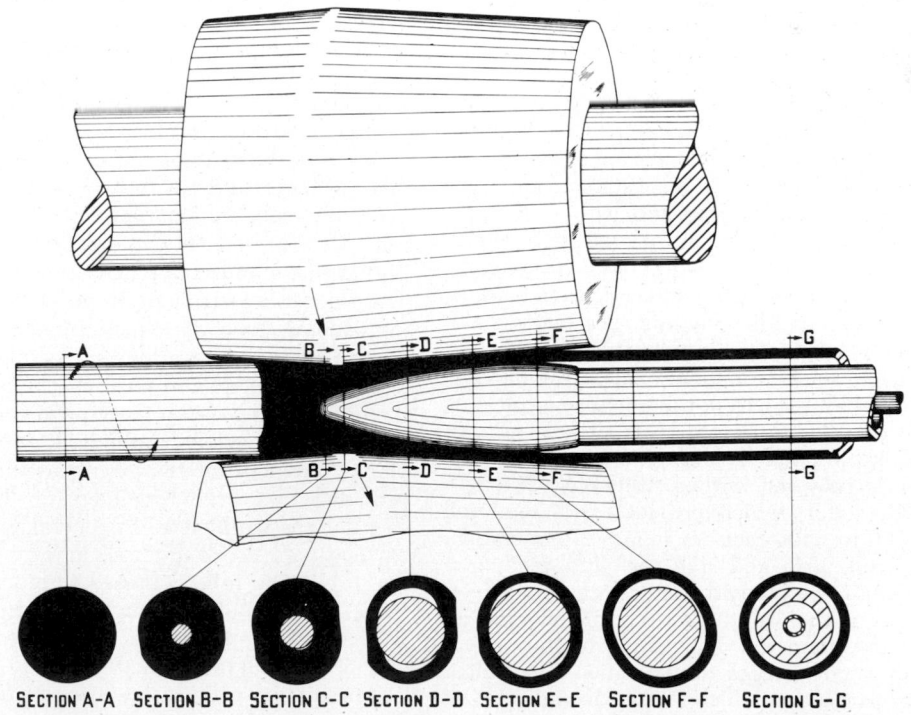

SECTION A-A   SECTION B-B   SECTION C-C   SECTION D-D   SECTION E-E   SECTION F-F   SECTION G-G

FIG. 30—22. Sketches illustrating action of rotary-piercing mill on the round billet.

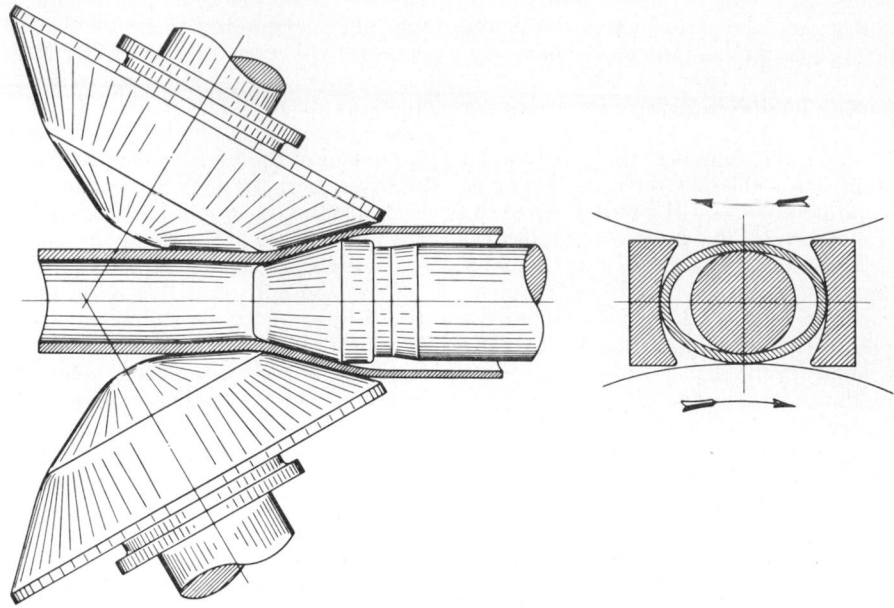

FIG. 30—23. Rotary-rolling mill.

matic-mill method of producing seamless tubes by dividing the requisite work of piercing in the two stages.

Rotary Rolling—The large demand for pipe between 16 inches and 36 inches in outside diameter for the transportation of natural gas for long distances raised a serious question as to the best manner of manufacturing such pipe. The lap-weld processes then used for making such pipe sizes were both costly and slow and also unsuited for the manufacture of lengths over 40 feet. It is also not feasible to roll pipe over 16 inches in diameter on the automatic rolling mill, and this feature made it questionable whether seamless pipe in these sizes could be economically made. The rotary-rolling mill was developed by United States Steel Corporation, which has made possible the production of pipe as large as 26 inches in outside diameter in lengths up to 45 feet and with wall thicknesses as light as 0.281 inch. Other large sizes are produced with wall thicknesses as light as 0.250 inch.

The rotary-rolling mill is a modification and enlargement of the cone-type piercing mill. The shafts of this mill, which drive the 74-inch (diameter) conical rolls, are in separated horizontal planes and are at an angle of 60 degrees with the axis of the pipe being rolled. A diagram of this mill is shown in Figure 30—23: an actual mill in operation is shown in Figure 30—24. Each shaft is powered with a 1500-h.p., 200-500-r.p.m., D.C. motor, which provides peripheral roll speeds of 800 to 2400 feet per minute. In operation, the conical rolls grip and spin the pipe, feeding it forward over a large tapered mandrel, thereby effecting a decrease in the wall thickness of the pipe and an increase in the diameter. The length of the tube is substantially unchanged by the operation. The rolling action is similar to that which takes place in a **tire-** or **ring-rolling machine**, except that in the rotary-rolling mill a forward helical advance is imparted to the tube,

which is supported on the inside by the tapered mandrel.

The Plug Rolling Mill is a motor-driven, non-reversing, single two-high stand, which resembles a reversing bar mill (Figures **30—25** and **30—26**). There are, however, several differences between the two. Instead of roll tables, the mill is equipped on the entering side with a movable trough and pusher and on the delivery side with a stationary guide table and mandrel-bar support. The guides on the latter table, two or more in number, are of the double-bell type and are mounted on cross beams and lined up one behind the other directly in back of the grooves in the rolls. The water-cooled mandrel bar, which is anchored in the support at the rear of the table, projects through a series of these guides with its opposite end terminating about ¼ inch short of the vertical centerline of the rolls. The free end of the mandrel bar provides support for the mandrel or plug during the working cycle. The work rolls, which are from 22 inches to 38 inches in diameter, depending upon the size of the mill, have several semi-circular grooves machined in their surface. With the rolls in position one above the other, the opening formed by the groove is not a true circle but is slightly oval with the long axis in a horizontal plane. This flare of the groove at the roll surface is provided to prevent the edge of the groove from shearing the work piece. In general, only one mandrel bar and one groove are used in the rolling of a given size tube. The tube is passed through this roll stand twice, being rotated through 90 degrees between the passes so that the entire surface receives an equal and similar treatment in the slightly ovalled groove. To permit the tube to be stripped rapidly from the mandrel bar, the top roll is supported by counterweights and arranged to be elevated mechanically for

Fig. 30—24. Rotary-rolling mill in operation.

a rapid opening of the pass. Stripper rolls, located just to the rear of the main rolls, are grooved to correspond with the main rolls. The lower stripper roll is also ar-ranged for mechanical movement for rapid closing of the pass. These stripper rolls rotate in a direction op-posite to that of the main rolls and function only

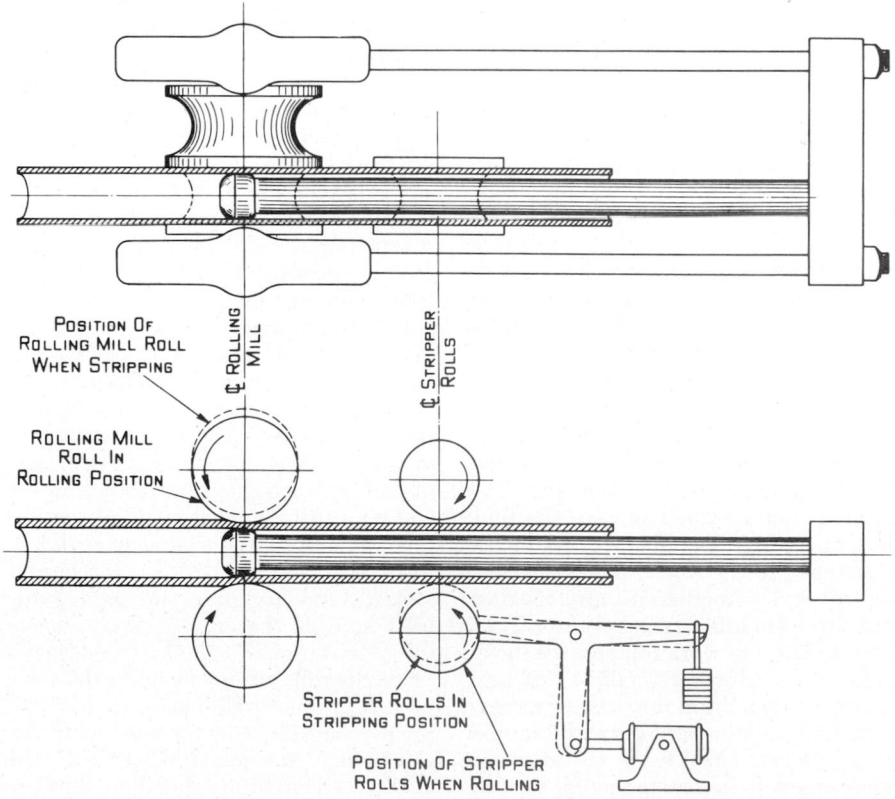

Fig. 30—25. Schematic plan view (above) and elevation (below) of a plug rolling mill.

FIG. 30—26. Plug rolling mill.

when the top main roll is in its elevated or open pass position.

The Operation of Plug Rolling—The pierced shell, except for the smaller pipe sizes, is reheated after the piercing operations. With the pierced shell lying in the feed or delivery trough, an alloy-steel mandrel or plug is attached to the end of the bar, the bar holding the plug at the correct position in the roll groove. The plug is somewhat larger in diameter than the support bar in order to provide clearance between the inside of the tube and the support bar. In order to start the shell over the plug and permit the rolls to secure a good bite upon it, the shell is shoved into the pass with considerable force by a compressed-air-operated ram or pusher. Once started, the force of friction due to the pressure exerted by the revolving rolls is sufficient to draw the shell rapidly over the plug, slightly reducing its diameter and wall thickness and increasing its length. As soon as the shell has passed through the groove, the mandrel is removed from the bar. The top work roll is elevated approximately 1½ inches. The lower stripper roll is then elevated to raise the tube clear of the bottom work roll and to grip it in the grooves of the stripper rolls, which return it to the entering side of the mill. Another mandrel is then placed on the bar, and the tube is rotated through an angle of 90 degrees. The top work roll and the lower stripper roll are returned to their original position, and the pusher again enters the tube in the pass. As soon as the tube has passed through the groove for the second working pass, it is returned again to the entering side of the mill, from which it is discharged for further fabrication. In this way the wall of the tube, supported by the mandrel on the inside and subjected to the ac-

tion of the rolls on the outside, is reduced in thickness to the gage desired. The pierced billet is proportionately lengthened and slightly reduced in outside diameter. The wall reduction normally made in the plug mill is approximately ⅛ inch to ¼ inch. After plug rolling, the tube has a uniform wall of the desired thickness throughout but is slightly out of round or oval shaped, not perfectly straight, and still at a bright-red heat.

The Reeling Machine (Figure 30—27) is similar in construction and operation to the Mannesmann piercer except that the rolls, which are about 30 inches long and 34 inches in diameter, are almost cylindrical in form. The rolls are adjusted laterally in the same manner as that described for the Mannesmann piercer and are separated by a space a little less than the diameter of the tube to be reeled. The rolls are motor-driven and are geared together to revolve in the same direction at a surface speed of approximately 900 feet per minute. In operation, a cylindrical mandrel, which is placed between the rolls, is supported on the delivery end by a water-cooled mandrel-support bar. Like the piercing mill, the opposite end of this bar is connected to a thrust bearing carried in a reciprocating carriage, locked stationary during the reeling operation. On the inlet side of the mill a conveyor carries the tube through stationary guides to contact with the rolls. Since the rolls are revolving in the same direction and with axes oppositely inclined, they cause the tube to revolve and helically advance over the mandrel. The elevation of the mandrel and tube during reeling is maintained in the proper horizontal position by stationary guides mounted between the reeler rolls above and below the pass. Owing to the fact that the total

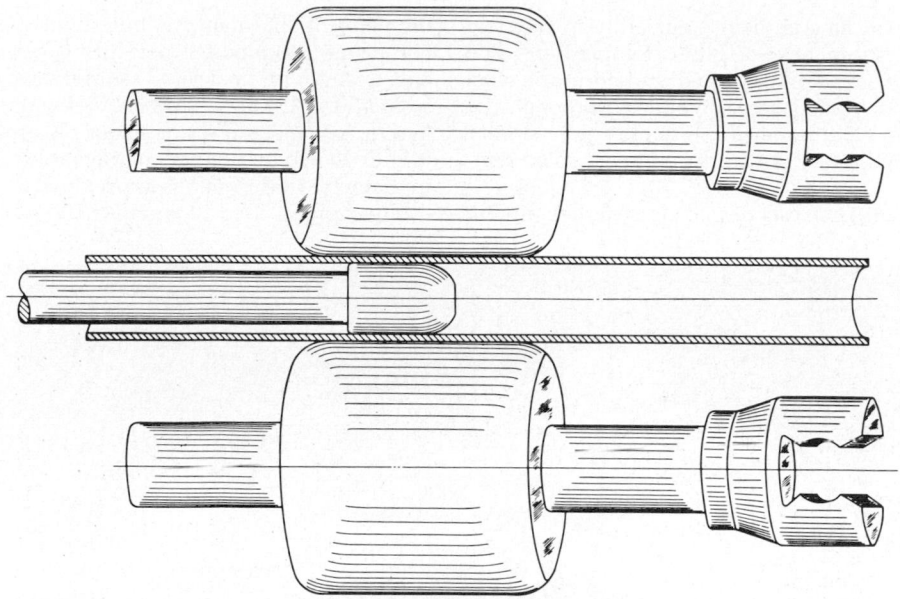

FIG. 30—27. Reeling machine.

space between the reeler rolls and the mandrel is a few thousandths of an inch less than twice the wall thickness of the entering tube, a slight reduction in the thickness of the wall is effected during the reeling operation. This slight reduction made in the reeling operation has the effect of burnishing the inside and outside surfaces of the tube and slightly increasing its diameter. The function of the reeler is, therefore, to round up and to burnish the inside and outside surfaces of the tube delivered from previous fabricating operations.

Sizing the Tube—The manner of sizing the reeled tube depends upon the diameter of the pipe that is being produced. For sizes from approximately 5½ inches and over, the sizing process consists merely of passing the tube, reheated in some cases, through two or three stands of sizing rolls the grooves of which are slightly smaller than the reeled tube. The diameter reduction effected is to insure uniform size and roundness throughout the length of the tube.

Seamless mills producing pipe from 3½ inches to approximately 7 inches outside diameter usually are equipped with a seven-stand gear-driven reducing mill where reductions up to ½ inch in diameter can be made. Such a reduction in diameter provides greater flexibility in operation and minimizes the change time of the mill by lessening the number of steel sizes and high-mill roll changes required for the size range of the mill.

Since it is not economical to pierce, roll and reel tubes of small diameter, the production of hot-finished tubes less than 3 inches in diameter requires a reducing and sizing process for which a special machine is employed. This machine is similar to a continuous rolling mill. It consists of 8 to 16 stands of two-high grooved rolls about 12 inches in diameter, arranged on the continuous plan and set about 2 feet apart, center to center. Instead of standing vertically, the housings for these rolls are inclined 45 degrees, so the

adjacent stands lie at right angles to each other and the loci of the centers of the pass openings formed by the grooves, which gradually decrease in size from the first to the last, are in the same straight line. The grooves in the initial stands are slightly oval in shape. However, the grooves in the last two stands on the delivery end of the mill are preferably round. As the tube from the reeling machine is too cold to be reduced in diameter, it is passed endwise into a long reheating furnace located at the entering end of the reducing mill where it is heated to a uniform temperature just below the scale-forming point. It is then pushed by a mechanical pusher directly into the first stand of the reducing mill, being drawn continuously through the successive stands in which it is elongated and reduced to the outside diameter desired. The smallest size to which tubes generally are reduced by this process is 1½ inches. The preferred maximum diameter reduction per stand in this type of reducing mill is 3 per cent. Since the relationship of wall change and elongation varies with the ratio of diameter to wall thickness (D/T), a medium condition is assured and the diameter of the rolls in successive stands is chosen to provide a linear speed as close as possible to the natural flow of the metal.

An improvement to the reducing mill is the stretch-reducing mill described later in connection with the continuous seamless process.

Warm Working—It has been known for some time that the cold working of steel pipe by various drawing, rolling, or compressing methods will raise the yield strength and in some cases increase the collapse resistance. Such material worked at room temperature loses a considerable amount of ductility. If steel which has a yield point of 60,000 lb. per sq. in. is cold worked to raise the yield point to 90,000 lb. per sq. in., a considerable amount of force must be exerted. A steel having a yield point of 60,000 lb. sq. in. at room temperature will have a yield point of approximately 30,000 lb. per sq. in. at some higher temperature. The amount of force or work required to deform the steel at this higher temperature is much less, although the increase in the yield point of the steel is quite similar to that obtained when the work is done at room temperature.

Warm working consists of making seamless pipe in the conventional manner, but slightly oversize. After hot sizing, the pipe temperature is equalized over its entire length to the desired temperature, which ranges from 650 to 1,000° F, and is quickly passed through a five- or seven-stand set of sizing rolls following which it is air cooled on regular cooling tables. The reduction in diameter in this pass is approximately 5 per cent.

The furnace used to equalize the pipe temperature

Fig. 30—28. Cut-off machine for the preparation of pipe ends for the cold-expanding operation.

is divided into two zones: a cooling, or heating zone if cold pipe is charged, and an equalizing zone. Air is heated, passed through the ducts into the furnace and recirculated. Thermocouples placed in the air ducts control the temperature within narrow limits.

As previously stated the mechanical properties are increased by warm working. Test results show that a carbon steel which, in the as-rolled condition, will average 65,000 lb. per sq. in. yield strength and 108,000 lb. per sq. in. ultimate strength with an elongation of 27 per cent in 2 inches will, after warm working, average 95,000 lb. per. sq. in. yield strength, 115,000 lb. per sq. in. ultimate strength with an elongation of 24 per cent in 2 inches. Resistance to collapse, one of the most important considerations in oil-well-casing design, is markedly increased by warm working. For example, 7-inch O.D. casing with a wall thickness of 0.317 inches will have its collapse value increased from an average of 4,370 lb. per sq. in. in hot-rolled pipe to 6,320 lb. per sq. in. after warm working, an increase of 45 per cent.

Spray-Quenched Deep Well Casing—When higher strength casing than that produced by the warm-working process is desired for deep oil wells, carbon-manganese steel pipe is heat treated by a special process. In this process, the hot-rolled pipe is heat treated in a continuous unit by water quenching from 1650° F and tempering at 600 to 1000° F. A series of barrel-type gas-fired furnaces are used for heating the pipe. During heating and quenching, the pipe is rotated. The total length of the eight-barrel continuous furnace is 47 feet, and the rate of heating, depending on pipe size, is 5 to 20 feet per minute. The capacity of this unit may be increased by the addition of more barrel furnaces. After heating to 1650° F, the pipe is quenched as it passes through a specially designed water-spray ring containing nozzles which spray water on the complete periphery of the pipe.

After quenching, the steel pipe is placed in a tempering furnace and heated in a 50-minute cycle to 600 to 1000° F, depending upon the final properties desired. The pipe is rotated during heating in the tempering furnace to maintain straightness and uniformity of heating. The continuous tempering furnace is fired with gas and the pipe temperature is checked with a radiation-type pyrometer as it leaves the furnace.

When the pipe leaves the tempering furnace, it immediately passes through a set of five stands of sizing rolls. Due to the formation of martensite during quenching, an expansion of the steel occurs which increases the outside diameter of the pipe, and introduces a limited amount of ovality and out-of-straightness. The sizing operation insures uniform size in the quenched and tempered product; however, the severity of the sizing pass must be limited.

Test results show that a carbon-manganese steel with average hot-rolled mechanical properties of 64,000 pounds per square inch yield strength, 100,000 pounds per square inch ultimate strength and 30 per cent elongation will, after spray quenching and tempering, exhibit average mechanical properties of 123,000 pounds per square inch yield strength, 136,000 pounds per square inch ultimate strength and 23 per cent elongation. A marked increase in collapse resistance also results from this heat-treating process. For example, 7-inch O.D. casing with a wall thickness of 0.408 inch will have its collapse resistance increased from 6,400 pounds per square inch in hot-rolled pipe to 12,290 pounds per square inch after heat treating—an increase of 92 per cent.

Cold-Expanded Seamless Pipe—One of the new developments in the line-pipe industry is the production of seamless cold-expanded pipe in sizes 16 to 26 inches O.D.

The hot-rolled seamless pipe produced in a Mannesmann-type mill from solid billets up to 12¼ inches in diameter is expanded in a rotary-rolling mill. After the pipe leaves the rotary rolling mill, it enters a pair of cut-off machines (Figure 30—28) which trim both ends. In these machines the pipe is held stationary as a six-tool cutting head revolves around the end, cutting through from the outside of the pipe. The new machines are controlled automatically by electronic devices.

The pipe is next conveyed to the cold expander shown in Figure 30—29, where it drops into the expander trough and one end is held firmly against a backstop. A 60-foot ram made of 14-inch O.D. seamless pipe is positioned at the opposite end of the pipe and an expander plug is fitted on the bar cap at the end of the ram. The expander plug is then forced through the pipe by a pressure of 300,000 pounds (1500 horsepower).

At the end of the stroke, the backstop opens to permit passage of the plug, which drops from the bar cap onto an elevator. The elevator lowers the plug to a conveyor which carries it back to the entry end. Here another elevator raises it to an automatic aligner which again positions it for fitting onto the bar cap and expanding another pipe. Five plugs of the same diameter are used in sequence to permit uninterrupted operations and cooling of the plugs between use. The expander plugs, are built-up discs fitted with nickel-chromium-iron alloy rings. The plugs to produce expanded seamless pipe of 24-inch nominal outside diameter are under 24 inches in diameter and 8½ inches thick. They expand the pipe to its nominal outside diameter. Power is supplied to the ram through an electrically driven gear-reduction unit. Two heavy chains, one on each side, are attached to a cross head to drive the ram. The plug is lubricated through a flexible pipe which feeds from a reel and leads through the ram to the bar cap. Clamps which hold the pipe in the expander are operated by an oil hydraulic system at 2000 pounds per square inch pressure.

After cold expansion, the pipe enters a rotary straightener and then is conveyed to an inspection table where it is rotated during visual inspection. Two rings are cut from each lot of pipe. One is flattened and prepared for a standard strip tensile test to determine ultimate strength and elongation and the other ring is hydraulically tested for transverse yield strength.

After the pipe ends are beveled, the finished pipe is again inspected for surface and end flaws, after which it is hydrostatically tested to a pressure that exerts a

FIG. 30—29. The mandrel bar at the lower left is inserted into the circular expanding plug that is then forced through the seamless pipe at the right to increase its outside diameter. Rated thrust is 300,000 lb.

fiber stress equivalent to 85 per cent of the specified minimum yield strength.

Pipe manufactured by this process is cold worked in the transverse direction. The operations involved in cold expanding a seamless pipe about 40 feet long may be performed in 60 seconds, using a ram speed of 175 feet per minute. Depending upon the size, cold-expanded seamless pipe is produced at the rate of about 50 tons per hour. The diameter of the pipe is increased during cold working and, although a water-soluble oil is used as a lubricant, there is a temperature rise in the pipe during expansion. The pipe length is reduced about 1½ per cent, with less than 1 per cent change in wall thickness. Cold working seamless pipe in the transverse direction increases the yield strength to a greater degree than the ultimate strength. Excellent transverse ductility is obtained due to the nature of the seamless process.

The Continuous Seamless Process—Two recently constructed seamless mills utilize equipment entirely different than that used in the conventional seamless process. The rolling mill and reelers of the conventional mill are replaced by a continuous rolling mill (Figures 30—30 and 30—31) with nine tandem individually powered stands of two-high grooved rolls. Figure 30—30 illustrates the method of reduction employed by this continuous rolling mill. The rolls in the

consecutive stands have their axes at 90 degrees to each other and are driven by motors which provide a total of 8500 horsepower. The pipe mill requires an internal mandrel against which the work piece is rolled to reduce wall thickness. This cylindrical mandrel extends entirely through the pierced billet and passes through the mill with the work piece. In the first two roll stands, the diameter of the pierced billet is reduced so that the inner surface is in substantial contact with the mandrel bar. Each of the next two stands makes a reduction in wall over a portion of the circumference, the two jointly completing the first increment of reduction. The next two stands, the fifth and sixth in this mill, make a similar complete reduction but of somewhat less magnitude. The next two succeeding stands (7 and 8) are designed to effect a very slight reduction, the purpose of which is to planish the tube surface. The shape of the tube which has been oval in the preceding stands is changed to approximately circular section in the ninth stand. The rounding up operation effected by this stand frees the inner surface of the tube from the mandrel bar to facilitate withdrawal of the mandrel.

In the operation of the mill, after a billet has been pierced by a conventional Mannesmann piercing mill, a lubricated mandrel, considerably longer than the pierced shell, is inserted and both pass through the

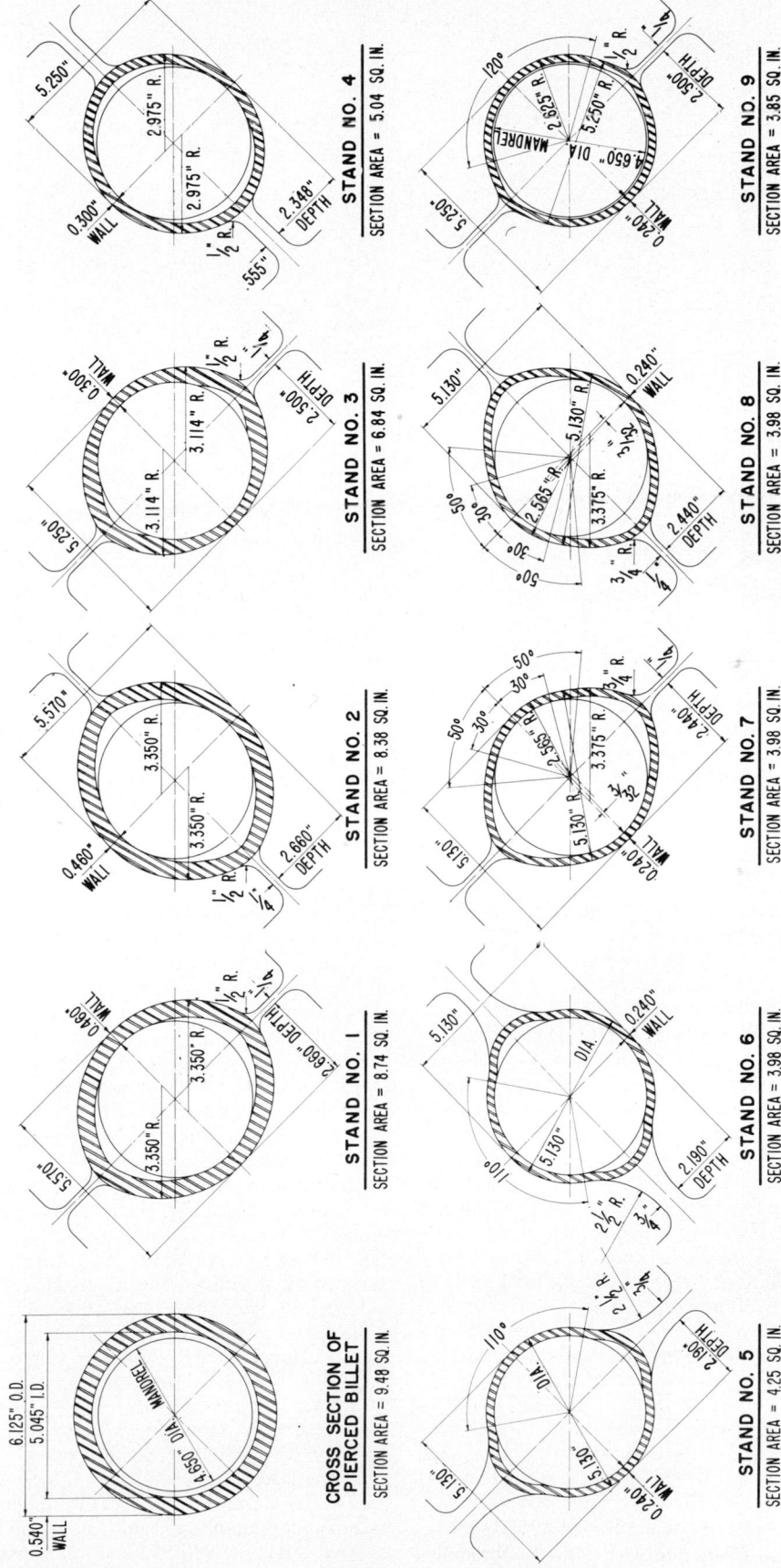

FIG. 30—30. Pass design for a nine-stand continuous tube-rolling mill when rolling 5.250-inch O.D. by 0.240-inch wall pipe shell.

FIG. 30—31. Over-all view of a continuous seamless-pipe mill, known as a mandrel mill.

rolling mill. The tube and mandrel are then kicked out of the pass line to a stripper which mechanically removes the mandrel. The rolled tube is then further processed by one of two methods depending on the desired product.

After withdrawal of the mandrel, the rolled tubes are reheated before being processed in either a sizing mill or a tension reducing or "stretch" mill. The stretch mill (Figure 30—32) which is similar in construction to the continuous rolling mill, consists of twelve two-high roll stands with the individual stands powered by 200-horsepower variable-speed motors. Tension re-

FIG. 30—32. Over-all view of 12-stand stretch-reducing mill, with tube emerging from tube-reheating furnace in the background.

ducing is unique in that without the use of a supporting mandrel the wall thickness is diminished while the diameter is reduced. This operation differs from the conventional reducing mill in which the wall thickness is increased as the diameter is reduced. In the tension reducing mill, the tension forces to which the tube is subjected between roll stands are not only effective in reducing wall thickness of the tube but the reduction in diameter performed in each stand can be tripled over conventional practice.

A typical schedule of roll-pass design for making 2⅜-inch outside diameter by 0.190-inch wall thickness by 140-foot length from a shell size of 5.156-inch outside diameter by 0.225-inch wall thickness by 54-foot length is shown in Table 30—IV for 14-inch diameter rolls.

Table 30—IV. Schedule of Roll-Pass Design for A Tension Reducing Mill with 14-inch Diameter Rolls.

Stand	Height of Groove (in.)	Cutter Diameter (in.)	Mean Diameter (in.)	Groove Depth (in.)	Reduction per Pass (Per Cent)	Roll Speed (r.p.m.)
1	4.630	5.560	4.970	2.300	3.5	115
2	4.310	5.170	4.620	2.140	7.0	123
3	4.010	4.730	4.270	1.990	7.5	132
4	3.692	4.320	3.920	1.831	8.1	154
5	3.362	3.900	3.560	1.666	9.1	167
6	3.062	3.520	3.230	1.516	9.1	181
7	2.798	3.190	2.940	1.384	9.0	204
8	2.542	2.900	2.672	1.256	9.0	240
9	2.445	2.640	2.514	1.208	6.0	265
10	2.414	2.500	2.447	1.192	2.7	275
11	2.414	2.414	2.414	1.192	1.3	275
12	2.414	2.414	2.414	1.192	0	275

Having both a sizing and stretch mill permits continuous production since it is possible to divert tubes to either unit, depending upon the desired size.

The pierced billet which is 5⅞ inches in outside diameter by 0.450-inch wall thickness and 22 feet long, pierced from a solid round that is 5½ inches in diameter and 8 feet long, will emerge from the continuous reducing mill as a tube with 5 inches outside diameter with 0.225-inch wall and 54 feet long. This tube, after passing through the stretch-reducing mill, if rolled into 2⅜-inch outside diameter tubing with 0.190-inch wall, will be 140 feet long.

The long tubes are cut into two sections by a rotary saw on the cooling table. The half sections then are cut into predetermined lengths by high-speed rotary-blade cutters before going to the finishing floors.

Cross Rolling of Precision Tubing—As an alternate to the conventional high mill and reeling machines, two processes are in use:

(a) The Assel Mill—When rolling heavy-wall tubing, a pierced shell can be diverted to an Assel mill (Figure 30—33) that is specifically designed to roll this product in a size range of 3 inches to 6 inches outside diameter with walls over 10 per cent of the diameter in thickness. It consists of three equally spaced rolls, approximately 18 inches in diameter, set at a feed angle of 8 degrees, which are driven by a variable-speed motor. A polished mandrel is inserted into the

shell and then introduced into the Assel mill where the billet is cross rolled over the freely revolving mandrel. The roll design includes a diverging inlet of an included angle of 7 degrees which grips the billet and rolls it down on the mandrel. The wall thickness is then reduced to the extent of the height of the hump. Roll positions are changed by motor-driven screwdowns that are tied together to give equal movement to each roll. The advantage of this process is that the cross rolling over a smooth mandrel improves concentricity and inside-surface quality. After removing the mandrel, the elongated shell is returned to the mill proper for reheating and sizing to the required tolerances.

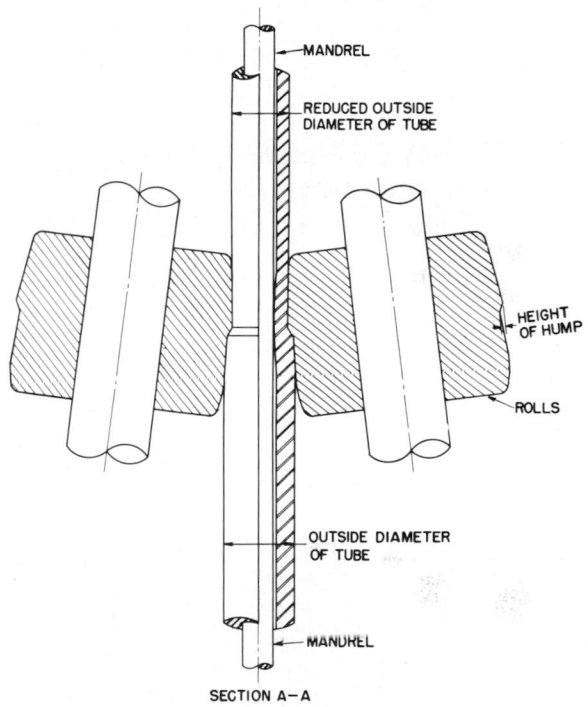

SECTION A—A

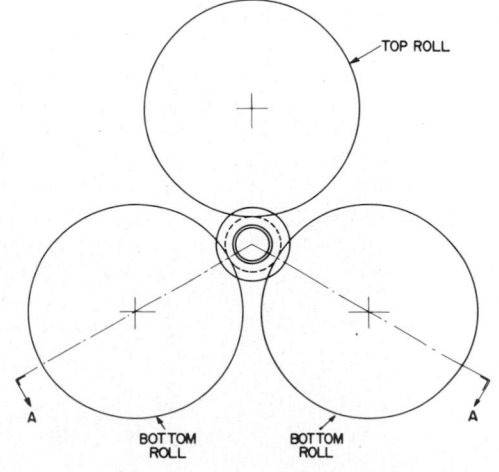

FIG. 30—33. Roll design, Assel mill.

(b) Diescher Mills—The Diescher process also involves cross rolling a pierced shell over a freely rotating mandrel. In this instance, however, the wall reduction and elongation is accomplished by two main rolls skewed at a 6-degree angle and, during the rolling operation, the billet is supported at the top and bottom by two revolving discs of 42-inch diameter with a surface speed of 2300 feet per minute. The discs' contour is such that nearly a closed pass is effected and an excellent inside and outside surface with a very close wall-thickness tolerance is obtained. The process is applicable for the production of both extremely light- and heavy-wall tubes. A diagram of the Diescher elongator pass design is shown in Figure 30—34. The mill size range is from 2½ inch to 4 inch (for the mill being described), from which the product can be further reduced in a sixteen-stand reducing mill to 1½ inch to 3½ inch outside diameter.

Seamless Fabricating Practices—In the discussion of the various phases of seamless tube manufacture in this section, the role of each unit was described. It was also indicated that the number of operations is dependent on the size of the tube to be produced. To further clarify these discussions, the following exam-

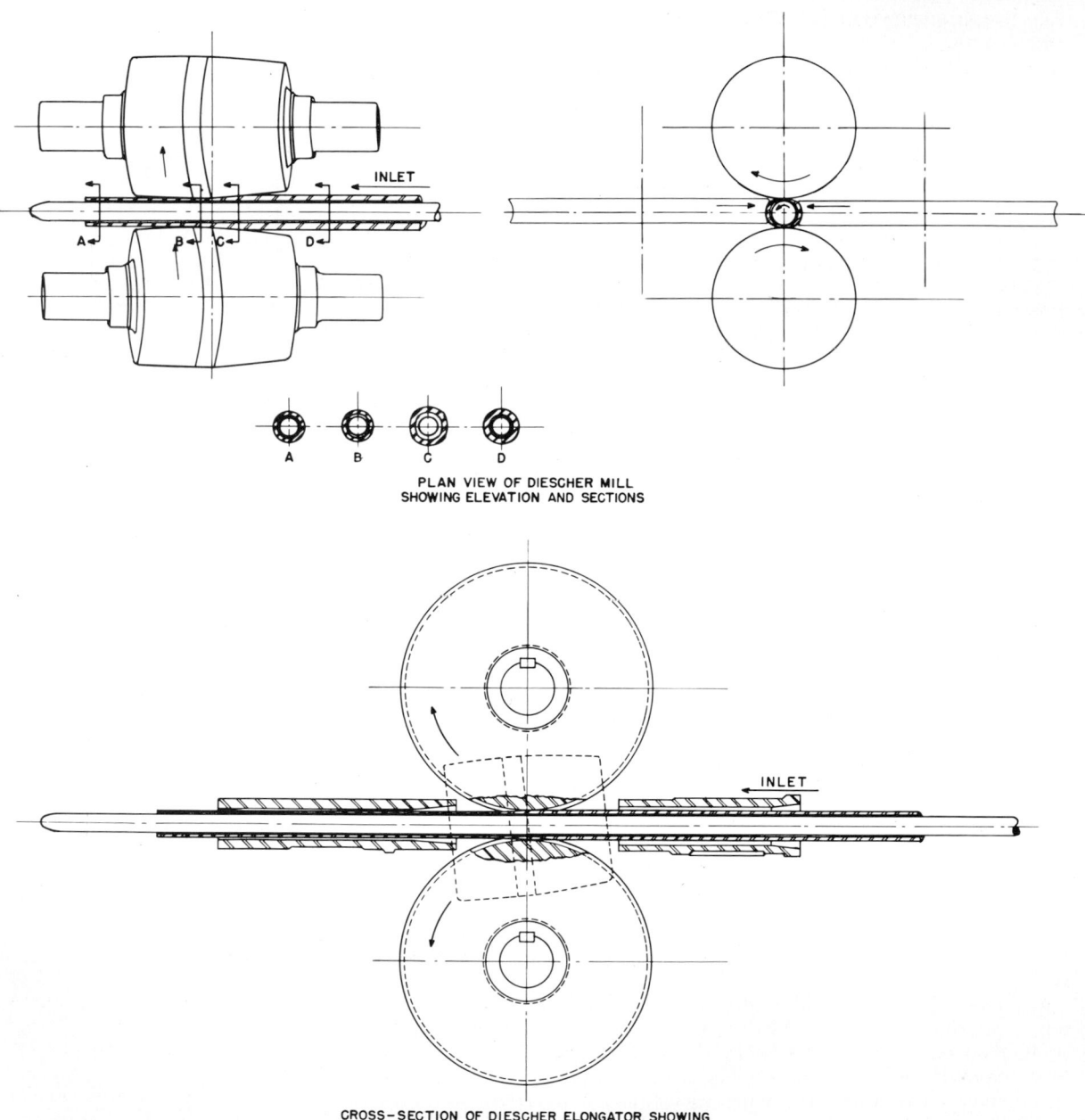

PLAN VIEW OF DIESCHER MILL
SHOWING ELEVATION AND SECTIONS

CROSS-SECTION OF DIESCHER ELONGATOR SHOWING
RELATIONSHIP OF GUIDES, DISCS AND ROLLS

FIG. 30—34. Principle of operation of a Diescher mill.

ples, which typify the variations employed in the manufacture of seamless tubes, are given to develop the operations step by step.

In producing a 2⅜-inch O.D. by 0.154-inch wall single-length hot-rolled tube, a solid billet 3¼ inches in diameter and weighing approximately 82 lbs. is pierced to a shell 3⁷⁄₁₆-inches O.D. with 0.215-inch wall, about 11 feet long. This pierced shell is passed, without reheating, to the plug rolling mill where it is plug-rolled in a 3¼-inch groove to produce a tube 3¼-inches O.D. with a 0.140-inch wall and 17 feet, 6 inches long. The plug-rolled shell is then reeled to approximately 3⁷⁄₁₆-inches O.D., 0.140-inch wall, and about 16 feet, 6 inches in length. After reeling, the tube is passed through a reheating furnace and into the reducing-sizing mill from which it emerges 2⅜-inch O.D. with 0.154-inch wall and approximately 22 feet, 3 inches long. From this tube, the crop-ends, and any test pieces that may be required, are cut in the finishing operations described in a later section.

In producing a double-length hot-rolled tube 8⅝ inches O.D. with 0.277-inch wall, a solid billet 8¼ inches in diameter, 6 feet, 5 inches long, weighing 1166 lbs. is pierced in the first piercer to a shell 8 inches O.D., wall thickness of 1¼ inches and 12 feet, 10 inches long. Without reheating, this shell is further processed in the second piercer to a shell 8⅝ inches O.D., with 0.470-inch wall, and approximately 28 feet long. The shell from the second piercer, after reheating, is plug-rolled in an 8⁷⁄₁₆-inch groove to 8⁷⁄₁₆

inches O.D., 0.227-inch wall and 46 feet, 9 inches long. The plug-rolled tube is transferred directly to the reeling machine which produces a tube 8¾ inches O. D., 0.277-inch wall, and 45 feet, 5 inches long. The tube then receives two or more passes in the two-high sizing mill from which it emerges 8⅝-inch O.D. with a 0.277-inch wall and approximately 46 feet long. It is then ready for end cropping and the other finishing operations.

To produce 26-inch O.D., 0.303-inch wall double-length hot-rolled tubes, a solid billet 12¼ inches in diameter, 10 feet long and weighing 4007 lbs., is pierced to a shell 14 inches in outside diameter, 1.640-inch wall, and 18 feet, 3 inches long in the first piercer. This shell, on the same heat, is entered in the second piercer where it is rolled to 17 inches O.D., 0.750-inch wall, and 30 feet, 2 inches long. After reheating, the shell is plug-rolled to form a tube 16¾ inches O.D., 0.500-inch wall, and 44 feet, 9 inches long. The plug-rolled shell is reheated a second time, after which it is rotary rolled to 26¼ inches O.D., 0.303-inch wall, and 45 feet, 8 inches long. Without reheating, it is then reeled to 26½ inches O.D., 0.303-inch wall, 45 feet, 3 inches long. The tube, after reeling, is again reheated in the tunnel-type reheating furnace, after which it passes through two stands of two-high sizing-mill rolls, forming a hot-rolled tube 26 inches O.D., 0.303-inch wall, and 46 feet long, ready for the finishing operations.

SECTION 6

COLD-DRAWN, OR COLD-FINISHED, TUBES

While the ordinary requirements for pipe and tubing can be met by the hot-rolling process just described, there are many requirements that demand greater accuracy, higher physical properties, better surfaces, thinner walls and smaller diameters than can be produced by hot-working methods. This demand is met by cold drawing the hot-rolled tubes as a finishing operation. This phase of tube production is analogous to the drawing of wire and the cold rolling of sheets described in other chapters.

In the early history of seamless tube production, cold drawing was employed in almost every instance as a finishing operation, but, as the art of hot rolling developed, the necessary finish and dimensional requirements have been met to a greater and greater degree in the hot-rolling operation. However, a substantial proportion of tubing is still cold drawn for the following reasons:

1. To produce tubes with thinner walls than can be hot rolled.
2. To produce tubes with smaller diameters.
3. To produce tubes longer than can be hot rolled in certain sizes.
4. To secure better surface finishes.
5. To obtain closer dimensional tolerances.

6. To increase certain mechanical properties, such as tensile strength.
7. To produce shapes other than round.
8. To produce tubes with varying diameters and wall thicknesses from end to end.
9. To make small lots of tubing of odd sizes and gages that do not justify a hot mill run.

One and five-sixteenth inches is about the practical minimum diameter produced by hot rolling, and 0.083 inch is the thinnest wall of commercial hot-rolled tube, which is available in the smaller diameters only. The diameter and wall thickness range of cold-drawn tubing produced by the United States Steel Corporation is from ½-inch O.D. by 0.035-inch wall to 10¾-inch O.D. by 2-inch wall.

The fact that hypodermic needles are seamless steel tubes that are cold drawn from hot-rolled tubing in small specialty plants conveys the idea of how far seamless tubing can be reduced by cold drawing.

Principle of Cold Drawing—Tube drawing is essentially the same as wire drawing, as explained in preceding chapters with two important exceptions: viz., the inside diameter of the tube must be supported while it is passing through the die to effect wall reduction and control the size of the hole, and

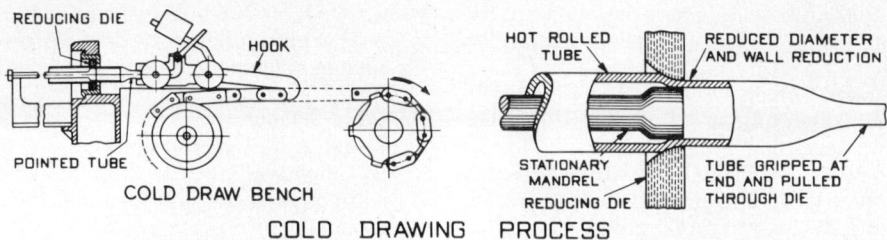

FIG. 30—35. Cold drawing a seamless steel tube.

comparatively short lengths are involved as in bar drawing. The process consists of pulling the tube through a die, the hole of which is smaller than the outside diameter of the tube being drawn, and at the same time supporting its inside surface by a mandrel anchored on the end of a rod so that it remains in the plane of the die during the drawing operation. Figure 30—35 shows the operation. The mandrel may be omitted if it is not necessary to make a reduction in the wall thickness, or if the dimensions and surface of the inside are not important. A modification of this method consists of drawing on a bar rather than over the mandrel, in which method the bar travels through the die with the tube and must be removed later. The resistance of the metal to passage through the restricted space between the die and the mandrel exceeds the yield strength of the metal at this section, thereby resulting in plastic flow. As a result of the reduced metal section leaving the die, the velocity is increased, the amount of increase being dependent upon the cross-sectional reduction. It is evident that the reduction or draft may be increased only up to a certain limit, depending on the ultimate strength of the section leaving the die, because, if the resistance and balancing pull exceeded the stress, the section leaving the die would break. In drawing tubes over a stationary mandrel, the maximum practical sectional area reduction does not exceed 40 per cent per pass, while, in drawing tubes on a bar which is free to move with the tube, the area reduction can be 50 per cent. As in wire drawing, all of the metal passing through the die is subjected to stress almost up to its breaking strength and is thus given a test of its physical fitness to withstand high stresses in its ultimate service. Any flaw or defect of consequence is brought to light under this severe treatment.

The Draw Bench—A cold-draw bench for tubes consists of a heavy steel frame or bench, in the middle of which is located a die head for holding the die. At one end of the bench is located an adjustable holder to anchor the mandrel rod. At its other end a shaft is mounted carrying a sprocket wheel over which passes a heavy, endless, square-linked chain. This chain lies in a trough on top of the bench, which extends from the sprocket wheel to the die head, where the chain passes around an idler and returns underneath the bench to the sprocket wheel. The sprocket wheel is driven by a variable speed motor through suitable reduction gearing. A carriage called a **plyer** runs on tracks on the top of the bench and over the chain that lies in the trough between the tracks. This plyer is

equipped on one end with jaws to grip the tube and on the other end with a hook to engage a link of the draw chain. The plyer is connected by cable to a motor-actuated drum by which means it is returned to the die head after drawing a tube. The jaws grip the reduced or pointed end of the tube which projects through the die about 6 inches. The closing of the jaws is effected by the motion of the hook in dropping into engagement with the chain. The whole action of gripping the tube and engaging the chain is automatic, once the operator pushes a button to return the plyer to gripping position. The mandrel-rod anchor is equipped with an air cylinder to push the mandrel into operating position inside the die after the pointed end of the tube is inserted in the die. Draw benches for small tubes are equipped with two mandrels with their supporting rods, so that a tube is being loaded on one mandrel while another tube is being drawn off the other. A motor-driven indexing mechanism places the anchor in the pass line so that the mandrel rod is in perfect alignment with the die and plyer jaws prior to the beginning of the draw. A friction-roller mechanism automatically loads the tubes on the mandrel rods. All controls for the draw benches are grouped at the operator's position near the die head so he does not have to move away from that position when operating the bench.

The total length of a bench is about 80 to 100 feet. The capacity of draw benches may be from 50,000 to 300,000 pounds pulling power. Chain speed may vary from 20 to 150 feet per minute and is automatically controlled so that the tube is started through the die at a slow speed, and, as soon as it is fairly started, the speed increases to the predetermined drawing rate. Dies are made with a conical outer surface which fits in a holder mounted in the die head. Dies up to a 3-inch hole size are made with tungsten-carbide inserts or nibs. Larger dies are made from hardened tool steel, chrome-plated on the wearing surface. Mandrels are chrome-plated, hardened tool steel and are either made in the form of a bar from 6 inches to 12 inches long with one end upset to form the working surface and the other end tapped for connection to the mandrel rod (see Figure 30—35) or, in the case of larger mandrels (2 inches and over), they are made in disc form with a central hole for engagement with the mandrel rod. In the drawing-on-the-bar method, hardened and ground bars of a diameter to correspond with the inside diameter of the drawn tube and somewhat longer than the drawn tube are used. As the bar-removal operation requires some time, three or more bars constitute a set, which permits the drawing of a tube during the interval required for inserting a bar in the next tube and extracting the bar from the tube previously drawn.

Preliminaries to Cold Drawing—The hot-rolled tubes after cooling are **pointed** on one end. This pointing consists of reducing the outside diameter, for a distance of about 6 inches, sufficiently to permit the reduced portion to enter the hole in the draw die freely, so that the jaws of the plyer can grip this end of the tube. If more than one cold-draw pass is to be given the tube, the point is made slightly under the final die size, if possible. Where large diameter reductions are made on small tubes, a point that would enter the final die may be too small and weak to stand the earlier reduction, in which case the original point may be further reduced after a few passes or, in the case of very small tubes, the pointed end may have to be cut off and a new point made on the reduced diameter and wall section. This procedure may have to be repeated several times in drawing very small tubing. Tubes with diameters 2½ inches to 3 inches and over are usually **open pointed** with a reduced section, 2 inches or 3 inches long, which has a rather sharp shoulder or offset joining the two diameters. A pulling pin with a cylindrical head is inserted in the tube so that the head engages the shoulder of the point and the stem of the pin projects through the die far enough to enter the plyer jaws. Pointing is done on rotary swagers or steam or air hammers after the end of the tube has been heated to a forging heat (see Figure 30—36). Tubes of certain grades of steel receive an annealing heat treatment, prior to cold draw-

Fig. 30—37. One step in the pickling operation for tubes.

ing. This treatment, which is usually confined to high-carbon and alloy steels of the air-hardening type, is necessary to obtain additional ductility. All tubes are pickled in dilute acid solutions to remove scale and oxides from the outside and inside surfaces. The pickling practice is quite similar to that employed in preparing wire for drawing or sheets for cold rolling. The pickle tubs are 40 to 50 feet long, about 4 feet wide, and 5½ feet deep (Figure 30—37). Steam for heating and agitating the bath is led into the bottom of the tubs and discharged through jets or perforated acid-resisting pipes. A wash tub of similar construction is located near the pickle tubs, and after the tubes are pickled free of scale they are dipped in the wash tub to remove the acid and any sludge or loose scale. A similar tub is provided for lubricant for cold drawing, in which great care is exercised in dipping to assure that lubricant reaches the entire interior surface of each tube. This lubricant, which is an emulsion containing flour, tallow, and water in proper proportions, is used for process-drawing all tubes and for finish-drawing large-diameter tubing which requires a heavy reduction. Where tubes with bright finish are required, a special oil-base emulsion is used. After being thoroughly coated with lubricant, the tubes are placed on a conveyor chain on which they are carried through a continuous gas-fired drying oven (about 200° F) where the excess lubricant is drained and the moisture is evaporated from the lubricant. Throughout these operations the tubes are handled in bundles up to 10 tons in weight. From the drying oven the tubes are then sent to the cold-draw benches or to stock piles near the benches.

Fig. 30—36. Rotary tube pointer and feeder mechanism. Tube-end heating furnace is at left.

The Cold-Drawing Operations—One cold-draw pass produces a cold-drawn tube of close dimensions, good surface, and of any mechanical property within the usual limits of cold-worked steel. Additional passes may be necessary to secure: (1) thinner walls, (2) better surface finishes, (3) smaller diameters, or (4) longer lengths. The bundle of pointed, pickled, inspected and lubricated tubes is laid on a table at the chain end of the bench, with open ends toward the mandrel-anchor end of the bench. The mandrel on its supporting rod is held so that the powered pinch rolls, into which a tube has been entered, drive the tube over the mandrel and rod until the mandrel is just back of the pointed portion. The operator then swings the tube into the pass line and operates the control for the push-up which advances the tube and mandrel to drawing position. The cable-driven plyer-return mechanism moves the plyer carriage toward the die head, in a direction opposite to that in which the draw chain is moving, until the carriage contacts a limit which releases the cable mechanism and permits the hook, which has been elevated, to drop into engagement with the draw chain. The engagement of the hook with the chain permits the grip jaws to close on the projecting point, and the motion of the carriage draws the tube through the die. When the open end of the tube clears the die, the plyer hook automatically disengages from the chain. Another tube is loaded on the mandrel and the cycle is repeated as before. When, after a series of draw passes, the inside diameter of the tube becomes too small to accommodate a substantial mandrel, the tube may be further reduced in both its outside and inside diameters by sinking it through a die without a mandrel or bar on the inside. Such a reduction results in a thickening of the tube wall which is uniform and predictable; how-

ever, the inside diameter cannot be held to the close tolerances produced with the use of a mandrel or bar support.

The Tube Reducing Process is used for the same purposes as conventional cold drawing; i.e., to produce tubing with smaller diameters and lighter walls, closer tolerances, better surface finish, higher mechanical properties, better machinability, etc., than may be obtained by hot rolling. Longer lengths than obtainable by either hot rolling or cold drawing—up to 100 feet or more—are possible, but such long lengths, especially in the smaller diameter range associated with material made by this process, may not be conveniently handled through finishing operations, hence little use is made of this feature. Production is generally confined to the smaller-diameter tubes although the upper limit is established only by capacity of existing machines. The tube reducing process has a slower production rate in feet per hour than conventional drawing, but accomplishes much greater reduction per pass so that the net effect is more or less equivalent production rates, particularly where a tube reducing machine performs the work of three or more cold-draw passes, as is usually the case. Advantages of the process over conventional drawing include improvement in the concentricity of the product, and elimination of certain intermediate operations (such as cutting, pointing, annealing, pickling, doping, etc.) required by the successive cold-draw passes used to accomplish the same total reduction; less material waste is also experienced because there is no point-crop to discard. Disadvantages include slower production rates than conventional drawing where small reductions are involved, and the time required for a size change is much greater. Additionally, the relative die costs of the two processes greatly

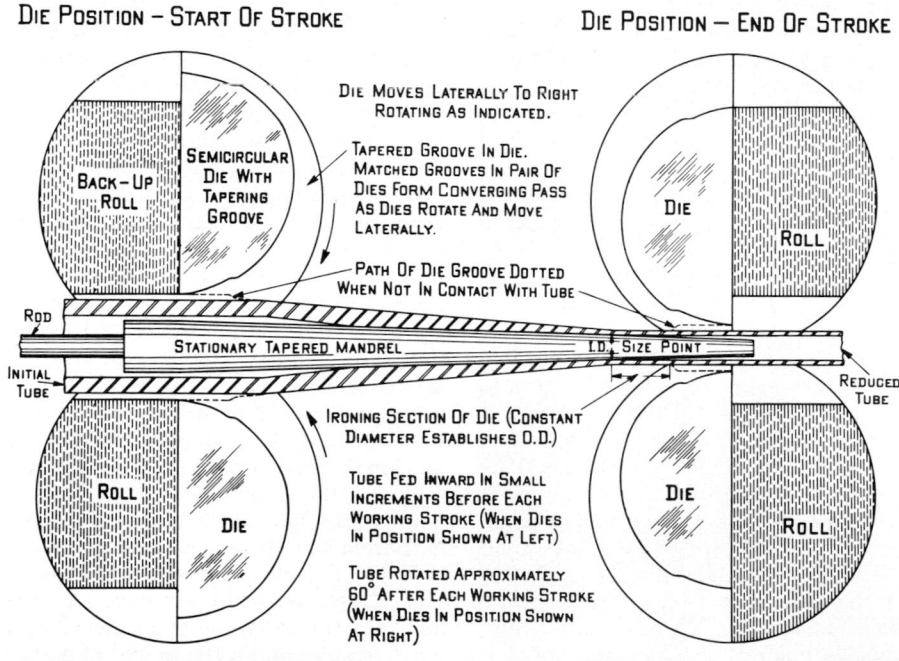

FIG. 30—38. Vertical section through tube reducer pass—showing dies at start and end of stroke.

favor conventional drawing when small production lots of odd sizes are to be made.

Principle of Tube Reducing Process—The process accomplishes simultaneous reduction of tube diameter and wall thickness by a cold-swaging action which utilizes compressive forces rather than the tensile forces employed in conventional drawing. This fact removes the reduction limitation present in the cold-draw process which is governed by the ultimate tensile strength of the reduced section. In the process, very large reductions in one pass are found feasible—as much as 85 per cent or more; this may be compared with the 40 per cent reduction per pass which is the practical upper limit in the drawing process. This comparison is even more striking when it is understood that four successive passes of 37.8 per cent reduction each are required to effect a total reduction of 85 per cent.

Of fundamental importance in the tube reducing process are two semi-circular dies which have matching, tapering, semi-circular grooves machined into their curved faces (Figure 30—38). In operation, one die is placed on top of the other so that the matching semi-circular grooves make a circular pass. The dies are geared to each other in such a fashion that they rotate in opposite directions when they are moved laterally (in the plane of the grooves), and a converging (or diverging, depending on the direction of lateral movement) circular pass is traced by the die grooves. When a tube is held stationary on the center line of this pass, the converging path of the die grooves reduces its diameters. If now a stationary mandrel of the proper taper is also positioned in the center line of the pass, the inside of the tube is supported and the tube wall is reduced and extruded or elongated by compression between the die and mandrel. In actual practice, the dies are in constant, lateral and rotary, reciprocal motion. Modifications in die contour permit repetition of the swaging action to reduce an entire tube of given diameter and wall thickness to one of smaller diameter and lighter wall thickness, with the length being increased in direct proportion to the amount of reduction in a cross-sectional area. Such modifications include contour-relief at both ends, and an ironing section of constant diameter at the smaller end. Contour-relief at the inlet or large end of the die grooves permits feeding the tube, in small increments, into the pass during the short interval when the dies are not in contact with the tube. Contour-relief at the outlet or small end of the die grooves permits rotation of the tube during the corresponding time interval at the end of the working stroke; this rotation serves to prevent the formation of fins to round up the finished section. The constant-diameter ironing section is of sufficient length to permit several working strokes on each increment of reduced tube, and serves to size and round up the reduced tube. The inside diameter of the finished tube is governed by the diameter of the mandrel at the point located directly beneath the beginning of the ironing section of the dies; this point is called the "size-point." It is obvious that minor changes in I.D. size may be made by axial movement of the mandrel. O.D. size may not be altered so simply, requiring regrinding and refinishing operations in existing dies.

The Tube Reducing Machine—Tube reducing machines are classed as continuous or intermittent, but the production mechanism is essentially the same in the two types. The machine proper consists of a heavy steel frame, some 30 to 40 feet long and 8 to 10 feet wide. The forward end of the frame contains the mechanism which actually swages the tubes. This mechanism, called the "saddle," is a housing containing the rolls into which the dies are keyed, and which slides back and forth on ways in short reciprocating strokes, being driven by connecting rods attached to cranks geared to the 40- to 100-horsepower main-drive motor. A stationary rack attached to the frame engages one of the intermeshed gears on the roll ends, and thus produces reciprocating rotation of the dies as the "saddle" moves back and forth. The tapered mandrel is located in the desired position in the pass by a long mandrel rod running back, inside the tube being processed, to a thrust block located at the rear of the machine frame.

The tube being processed is gripped at its back end in a vise carried in the "cross-head"—this last being the tube feeding and turning mechanism. A long screw—running from beyond the back end of the machine, through a suitable drive-nut in a stationary housing, up to the "cross-head"—advances the latter a predetermined amount during the time interval at the end of each back stroke of the "saddle" when the tube is not contacted by the dies. Similarly, a splined shaft—running from the back to the front end of the machine frame, and passing through the "cross-head" —rotates the "cross-head" vise, together with the tube it grips, approximately 60 degrees during the corresponding period each time the "saddle" reaches the forward end of its stroke. This splined shaft also drives an outlet friction vise which serves to rotate the tube being processed when its back end is no longer gripped in the "cross-head" vise.

The chief difference between the continuous and intermittent machine types is the method of charging a new tube. In the so-called continuous machine, two mandrel-rod locks, or thrust blocks, located some 20 feet apart, are employed. In use, assuming both locks closed and the machine in operation, the rear lock is opened and a new tube is charged over the end of the mandrel rod up to the forward lock; the rear lock is then closed and the forward lock opened, allowing the tube to be moved forward until it touches the end of the tube being reduced—in which position it remains to be gripped by the "cross-head" on its return to initial position. Suitable automatic controls open the "cross-head" vise at the forward end of its travel, actuate a high-speed return motor, and then close the vise again when the "cross-head" has returned to its initial position at which time the regular feed stroke is resumed. The "saddle" remains in motion during this entire cycle and the production time lost is negligible. In the intermittent machine, when the "cross-head" reaches the forward end of its travel, the "saddle" is stopped, the "cross-head" vise opened, the mandrel-rod thrust block unlatched, and high-speed return motors actuated to return the "cross-head," and back out the mandrel rod and mandrel. A new tube is then placed in position, the mandrel rod and mandrel returned to position and the mandrel-rod thrust block locked, then the "cross-head" vise is closed to grip the tube, and finally the "saddle" is restarted in motion. Since reduced tubes are too long to handle conveniently through finishing operations, a flying saw has been devised to cut shorter lengths as the reduced tube emerges from the machine.

Preliminaries to Tube Reducing—Hot-rolled tubes, or those which have been previously cold-drawn or reduced by the reducing process, may be cold-reduced by the tube reducing process. Tube preparation generally first involves an annealing operation to insure the ductility required by the swaging action; some plain low-carbon steels are ductile enough as received from the hot mill, but hot-rolled alloy steels and all previously cold-drawn tubes and tubes previously reduced by the tube reducing process must be annealed. Tubes are next pickled and straightened, then both ends cropped square with the tube body, and finally they are coated with an oil base or flour-tallow-water lubricant by immersing horizontally in the desired solution—this last operation is more commonly referred to simply as "doping." The pickling operation is employed to remove mill scale or annealing scale, and utilizes an inhibited sulphuric-acid solution, the same as employed in preparing tubes for cold drawing. The straightening operation is performed in a rotary straightener, and may be preceded by a so-called "break-down" pass through a press straightener when excessive camber necessitates this operation. Tube ends must be cut square because the trailing tube is used to feed the one preceding it when the forward tube is no longer gripped by the "cross-head" vise.

Tube Reducing Machine Operation — No more than one operator is required for each tube reducing machine, and in some instances one operator may handle two or more machines. The principal duty of the operator is charging new tubes and disposing of reduced material. In the case of intermittent machines, he must also start and stop the "saddle," and manually open and close the "cross-head" vise. A coolant solution is constantly poured onto the dies during the motion of the "saddle," and the operator must control its flow and be sure that it is adequate and continuous.

The number of strokes per minute made by the "saddle" is variable within limits (say 70 to 140 per min.), but this is generally fixed by supervision—depending on the steel grade being processed, amount of reduction, and rate of in-feed. The in-feed is also variable—from 0 to $\frac{5}{16}$ inch or more per stroke—but this is similarly controlled by supervision—depending on the steel grade being processed, the amount of reduction, and the class of product being manufactured. The amount of reduction is governed by the die and mandrel contour, and, except for minor mandrel adjustment (which alters the size of the finished product) is beyond the control of the operator. The stroke of the "saddle" is constant for any given machine size, and increases from about 15 inches to 2 feet and longer as the rated capacity of the machine increases.

Annealing and Redrawing—While a large proportion of tubes receive only one cold-draw pass, many require a number of passes for reasons previously noted. Because cold drawing hardens and reduces the ductility of tubes, it is necessary to anneal them after each cold-drawing operation. Before further cold-drawing, the annealed tubes must be pickled and

FIG. 30—39. Continuous annealing furnace.

Fig. 30—40. Car-bottom annealing furnace.

lubricated as previously described. All tubes, except bright-finished mechanical tubes, receive a final anneal or heat treatment after the last cold-draw pass. Many tubes receive a special normalizing treatment before the last pass in order to obtain the proper grain structure in the finished tube. This annealing is performed in either continuous tunnel or car-bottom batch furnaces fired with gas. The **continuous furnaces** are provided with heat-resisting driven rolls spaced about 3 feet apart, on which the tubes are carried through the furnace at a predetermined rate depending on the tube section, annealing temperature, time at temperature, etc. (see Figure 30—39). The **car-bottom batch furnaces** are arranged in a battery and are served by a special charging crane. Less than two minutes is required to discharge a 5-ton batch of annealed tubes and recharge the furnace with a new batch. The furnaces will accommodate tubes up to 50 feet long (see Figure 30—40). Both

types of furnaces are fully equipped with recording pyrometers. Each furnace is divided into four zones, and the temperature is automatically controlled in each zone. When extreme softness or freedom from scale or both are requested, the tubes are enclosed in a heat-resisting sheet-metal box and annealed in a car-bottom batch furnace. The final anneal or heat treatment is varied to produce tubing with the desired mechanical properties. Table **30—V** illustrates the effect of this heat treatment on AISI-C-1015 steel. The mechanical properties shown are representative expected values for all but the soft-annealed condition, where they reflect the approximate softest condition expected.

Finishing Operations on Cold-Drawn Annealed Tubes—After the final heat treatment, the cold-drawn tubes are finished in preparation for shipment. The principal finishing operations consist of straightening, cutting, inspecting and testing. Straightening

Table 30—V. Approximate Mechanical Properties of Hot-Rolled, and Cold-Drawn Low-Carbon Steel Tubing. Steel Specification AISI-C-1015

	Yield Strength (lb. per sq. in.)	Ultimate Strength (lb. per sq. in.)	Elongation (Per Cent)	Hardness	
				Rockwell	Brinell
Hot Rolled	33,000	55,000	40	B-64	107
Normalized	35,000	50,000	40	B-57	97
Soft Annealed	30,000	48,000	40	B-50	...
Medium Annealed	40,000	65,000	30	B-73	128
Finish Annealed	55,000	75,000	20	B-81	149
Hard Drawn	65,000	80,000	15	B-84	159

is performed on various types of straighteners, viz., press, rotary, continuous and post. The rotary type consists of rolls set with axes oblique with the pass line (see Figure 30—41). These rolls are somewhat smaller in the center than at the ends to afford a line contact with the tube, which passes between the two driven rolls on one side and the three idle rolls on the other. The tube is helically advanced by the rolls which are adjusted to bend the tube progressively as it moves through the machine. Initial bends in the tube are removed and a straight tube is produced. Care must be exercised to have the roll setting adjusted accurately, especially on light-walled tubing, to prevent crushing the tube. Some very thin-walled tubes can be straightened successfully only on a post set in the floor carrying grooved blocks which support the tube while it is sprung into straightness by hand. Where exact straightness is required, as in some mechanical tubes, gag press straighteners are used. Operators of these presses develop great skill in giving the tubes the proper deflections between the supporting dies so that the desired amount of permanent set remains. A proving table, on which the tube rotates, is equipped with dial gages, which provide a quick and accurate means of determining straightness. Each tube is spark tested as a final check to identify it as made of steel having the composition specified. The hardness is established by Rockwell or Brinell tests, and tension tests of samples indicate the mechanical properties. Microscopic examination of the grain structure is an essential phase of the inspection program. Each tube is given a visual inspection for surface defects, both inside and outside. Pressure tubing is hydrostatically tested to internal pressures in excess of service pressures that may be encountered. The usual range of test pressure is from 1000 to 5000 pounds per square inch. On pressure tubing, manipulation tests on coupons consist of flattening, expanding, flanging and crushing. All tubes are carefully measured for outside diameter, size and wall thickness. A protective coating of oil, or rust preventive, is usually applied before shipment. Light-gage tubes are boxed and small-diameter tubes are bundled to prevent injury during shipment.

Mechanical Tubing—Tubing for mechanical purposes is made in a wide range of sizes (³⁄₁₆-inch O.D. to 10¾ inches O.D.) and in many wall thicknesses in round and special sections. Some of these special sections are square, rectangular, oval, streamline, octagon, hexagon, etc. (see Figures 30—42 and 30—43). Square and rectangular sections are produced on a bench equipped with a Turk's head in place of the regular die. This Turk's head consists of a frame in which are mounted four rolls with their axes in one plane and so arranged around the pass line that the faces of the rolls form a square or rectangular hole through which the round tube of proper size is pulled, thus producing the desired section. Other special shapes are made in dies in which the bore corresponds to the outside contour of the finished tube, or in which shaped mandrels support and control the inside dimensions. Mechanical tubing has wide application and can be found in airplanes, automobiles, agricultural machinery, electrical equipment, household equipment, etc. Specific uses include ball- and roller-bearing races, gravity conveyor rolls, bushings, separators, hydraulic cylinders and hoists, oil-well pumps, bicycle frames, metal furniture, etc.

FIG. 30—41. Rotary-type straightener. (Courtesy, Mackintosh-Hemphill Division, E. W. Bliss Company.)

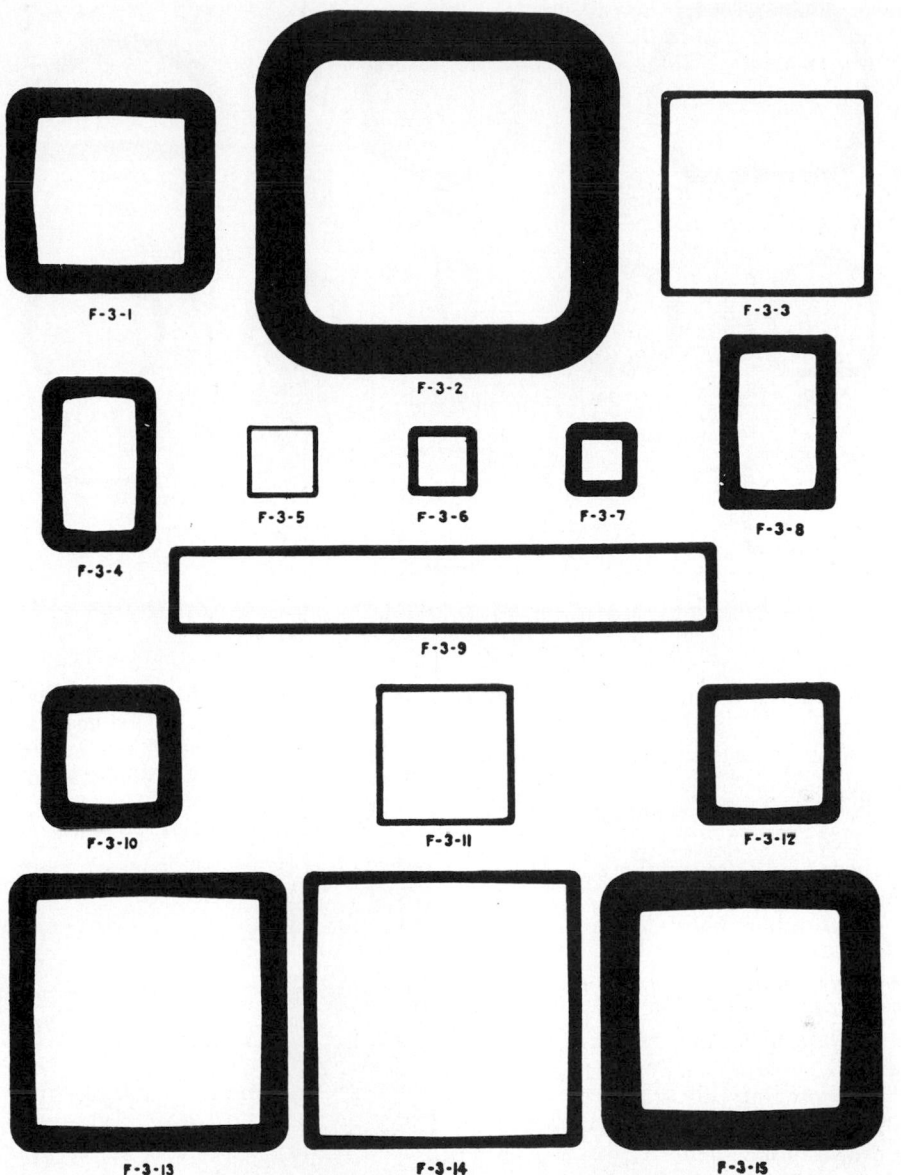

FIG. 30—42. Rectangular shaped sections of seamless tubing. Scale $1'' = 2\frac{3}{4}''$.

Hot-Rolled Carbon-Steel Hollow Structural Tubing —Hollow structural tubing is made in round, square, and rectangular shapes from both a continuous-weld product and seamless pipe in sizes ranging from 1-inch by 1-inch to 10-inches by 10-inches. This product is made as a step in the regular operating practice by the use of specially designed rolls in the reducing mill (Figure 30—44).

The product is made to applicable parts of structural specification A-7 and A-36 and proprietary grades of high-strength low-alloy grades used for construction (i.e., COR-TEN).

Pressure Tubing—Tubing used to withstand internal or external gas, steam or fluid pressure in refining, chemical, or evaporator apparatus is designated as pressure tubing and is usually furnished in the full-annealed state to assure ductility under service conditions. The most common applications of pressure tubing are in boilers, condensers, heat exchangers, evaporators, cracking stills, refrigerators, and air-conditioning apparatus. Many of these applications can be met by hot-rolled tubing, but the smaller-size, light-walled tubes can be produced only by the cold-drawing process or by the tube-reducing process.

Dimensional Tolerances of Cold-Drawn Mechanical Tubing—While dies for cold drawing mechanical tubing are held to the same exact sizes as wire- and bar-drawing dies, the fact that thin-walled sections will spring out of round while a solid section cannot, accounts for the somewhat greater tolerances required in tubing than with solid sections.

Surface Finishes—The various surface finishes in

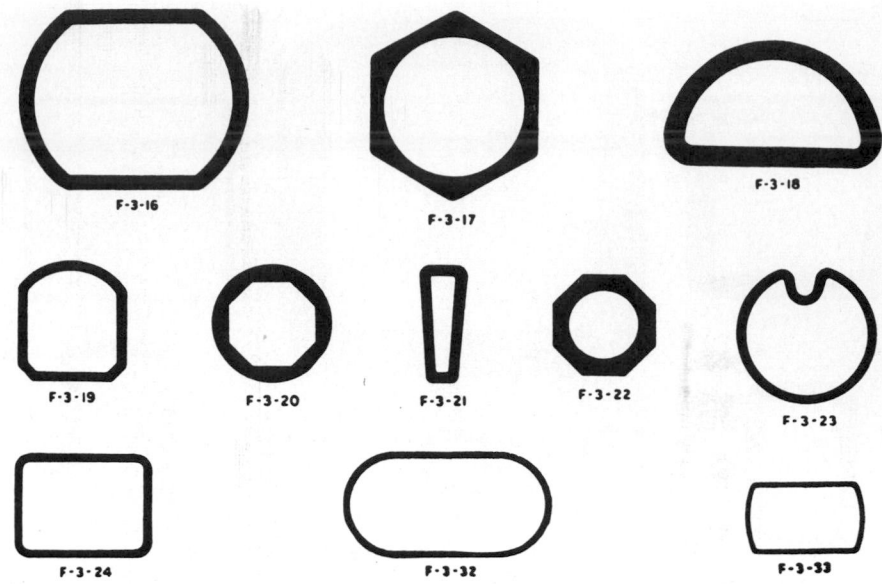

FIG. 30—43. Special shaped sections of seamless tubing. Scale 1" = 2¼".

both hot-rolled and cold-drawn tubing are as follows:

1. Hot Finished
   Hollow-forged billets and hot-rolled tubing.
2. Normalized
   Hot-rolled or cold-drawn tubing.
3. Soft Annealed
   Hot-rolled or cold-drawn tubing.
4. Medium Annealed
   Cold-drawn tubing only.
5. Finish Annealed
   Cold-drawn tubing only.
6. Hard Drawn (Unannealed)
   Cold-drawn tubing only.
7. Bright Finish
   Cold-drawn tubing only.
8. Bright Annealed
   Cold-drawn tubing only.
9. Specially Smooth (Cylinder Finish)
   Cold-drawn tubing only.
10. Pickled
    Hot-rolled or cold-drawn tubing.
11. Sandblasted or Shotblasted
    Hot-rolled or cold-drawn tubing.
12. Polished
    Cold-drawn tubing only.

1. **Hot Finished**—Hollow-forged billets have a surface appearance much smoother than hammered or pressed forgings, but may show a slight marking that will clean up with very little stock removal. Hot-rolled tubing has a surface finish comparable to plates or sheets of equal thickness. The thin-walled tubing, because of the high reduction in the rolling operation and the low finishing temperatures, will have a better surface than tubing with heavy walls. A light, tightly-adhering mill scale, blue-black in color, is found on both the outside and inside surfaces of hot-rolled tubing.

2. **Normalized**—Whether hot-rolled or cold-drawn, all normalized tubing will be coated with scale, the thickness of which depends upon the thickness of section and grade of steel. Thin-walled tubing can be

FIG. 30—44. Six-inch square hot-rolled carbon-steel structural tube emerging from a sizing mill in a National Tube Division plant.

brought to temperature and cooled rapidly, thus avoiding long exposure to oxidizing atmospheres at high temperatures, while heavy sections require a longer exposure. Scale formation is directly proportional to time and temperature. Some alloy steels, notably those containing chromium or nickel in small percentages (1 to 5), usually are more heavily scaled when normalized, due to the time-temperature effect.

3. **Soft Annealed**—Soft annealing, as commonly applied to pressure tubing, or mechanical tubing that is to be manipulated cold, leaves a light scale from reddish brown to blue-black in color that is comparable in thickness to the scale on hot-finished tubes, but is usually less tightly adhering and of a more porous nature. This surface may at times resemble that caused by rusting in storage or in transit. Oil used for protective coating may be absorbed by the oxide film, and the tubing may have the appearance of not being properly oiled, when fully protected against normal atmospheric corrosion.

4. **Medium Annealed**—Due to the lower temperature employed, medium annealed tubing is very slightly scaled and the loose scale can usually be rubbed off easily, leaving a black oxidized surface.

5. **Finish Annealed**—As the temperature at which tubing is finish annealed produces an oxide film of blue color, the tubing has a blue-black appearance and the smooth surface produced in the cold-drawing operation is not disturbed. The oxide film offers a slight protection against local rusting or discoloration.

6. **Hard Drawn (Unannealed)**—As the tubing has no heat treatment after the cold-drawing operation, the surface is more or less bright, depending on the number of passes through the die and on the nature of the lubricant used in cold drawing. Normally, thin-gage tubing will have a smoother and more uniform surface than heavy-walled tubing.

7. **Bright Finish**—Bright Finish is applied to hard-drawn tubing in the lighter gages and smaller diameters and is secured by special treatment in the cold-drawing processes. The appearance of this tubing is like that of cold-drawn bar stock.

8. **Bright Annealed**—Annealed cold-drawn tubing may be furnished with a scale-free surface, when so specified, by annealing the material in a controlled atmosphere or bright annealing furnace.

9. **Specially Smooth (Cylinder Finish)**—Cylinder finish is often required in oil-well-pump tubing, hydraulic jacks and hoists, air cylinders and similar applications where a smooth, dense inside surface is desired. Due to the surface hardness and the fact that there are no circumferential scratches, as in machined or ground bores, this finish is particularly valuable in cylinders using soft plunger packing. This finish can also be supplied on the outside surface when desired.

10. **Pickled Finish**—Where mill scale or scale from heat treatment is objectionable, tubing can be furnished with pickled surfaces, both inside and outside. This is often desirable when the tubing is to be machined, especially in automatic machines using formed cutters, as the tool life is materially increased. Pickling also permits close surface inspection.

11. **Sandblasted Finish**—The method of removing scale by blasting is usually confined to heavy-wall pressure tubes, but facilities are available for treating mechanical tubing on both inside and outside surfaces. Sandblasting gives a dull silvery finish, which is very susceptible to discoloration in handling and storage. A bright, smooth finish is obtained on heavy-walled, hot-rolled tubing, when sandblasted or pickled, and then burnished in a special finishing operation.

12. **Polished Finishes**—Polishing machines polish both the outside and inside surfaces of tubing. The polished finishes are classified as follows:

Grade "A" secured by use of No. 80 grit abrasive.
Grade "B" secured by use of No. 120 grit abrasive.
Grade "C" secured by use of No. 180 grit abrasive.

In the polishing operation, stock is naturally removed from standard-sized tubing, and, unless otherwise specified on the order, it will be assumed that O.D. tolerances may be under and I.D. tolerances may be over nominal dimensions.

Special Practices for Processing Stainless-Steel Tubing—The following special practices are employed in the processing of stainless-steel tubing:

(1) Deep Drilling of Solid Rounds for Piercing. Extruded hollow cylindrical sections are used as much as possible as the starting material for cold reduction. Sizes beyond the extrusion range (1½ to 4½ inches, outside diameter) are pierced on a Mannesmann mill. For this latter type of processing, the rounds are prepared for piercing by drilling an axial hole for the entire length of the round: this procedure improves concentricity as well as surface quality of the pierced rounds by helping to offset the inherent tendency for stainless steels to be difficult to pierce.

(2) Cold Reduction of the Extruded or Pierced Hollow. Cold reduction of the extruded or pierced hollow can be performed either by tube reducing or cold drawing: both of these processes have been described previously. Due to exacting quality demands by the trade, special practices are required in the preparation of the hollows prior to cold working. The hollows are first immersed in a molten salt bath which removes scale from both extruded and pierced hollows, and remnants of glass lubricant from extruded hollows, without harming the surface. Hollows for tube reducing are subjected to a preliminary cold working and then conditioned on the interior surface by honing and on the exterior surface by polishing to remove all defects prior to tube reducing to a finished size. When cold drawing is employed, the hollow is drawn to a size allowing sufficient stock to permit honing of the inside, and polishing of the outside, surfaces after drawing. Honing and polishing are necessary to obtain the extremely high quality finish needed to meet commercial requirements.

(3) Heat Treatment. The solution heat treatment of austenitic stainless steels of the 300 series may be carried out in a series of barrel-type furnaces with single tubes following each other, end to end, through the furnaces and then through a water-spray quench at the exit end of the last furnace; or in a conveyorized hearth-type furnace with quenching facilities at the exit end. Bright annealing is performed in a hydrogen atmosphere in controlled atmosphere furnaces under rigidly controlled conditions: the tubes emerge into

enclosed trays where they undergo a cooling process in the hydrogen atmosphere to retain their bright surface finish.

(4) Inspection Practices. Vapor degreasing is employed to remove grease, oil, dope, or other compounds used in the cold processing of stainless steels and thus provide clean surfaces for inspection. Besides the usual inspection techniques of checking size, wall thickness, length, and surface quality, special techniques are necessary to establish that stainless tubes are flawless. One means of insuring this quality is ultrasonic inspection, used to detect and evaluate the depth of imperfections on the surface under inspection or on the opposite surface and also imperfections that may lie invisibly between the two surfaces. This inspection method involves the use of an energy beam traveling at ultrasonic frequencies. The tube is simultaneously revolved and advanced axially into the path of the scanning beam and, if the beam encounters an imperfection or discontinuity, a back reflection occurs that, by suitably calibrated equipment, can be measured to indicate the severity of the imperfection. The combination of rotation and forward movement of the tube under the energy beam results in scanning of the entire tube.

Fluorescent-penetrant inspection is another nondestructive method for the detection of fine hairline imperfections on surfaces. A fluorescent penetrant is applied to the entire surface and then washed off. A developer is then applied that is permitted to dry and become an absorbent powder that draws out any penetrant trapped in a surface imperfection: under ultraviolet light, the fluorescent properties of the penetrant serve to indicate the location of surface imperfections in the tube.

Visual inspection of the inside of stainless-steel tubes is accomplished by a long cylindrical unit to the end of which illuminating devices are attached. With a high-powered lens in the eye-piece of the unit and the refraction of light in the interior of the tube, an inspector can detect surface imperfections on the inside of the wall of the tube.

(5) Marking and Packing. When requested, stainless tubing can be continuously marked with specified identification. Depending upon size and specification, all stainless tubing is individually wrapped or bundled and then wrapped with polyethylene. Bundles are secured with pressure tape to avoid damage to the tube surface.

SECTION 7

THE PIERCE AND DRAW PROCESS

Application of the Process—A considerable quantity of seamless tubular product is made by the process of piercing and drawing, starting with a bloom of steel of the required composition. The process is used primarily where special alloy steels, combined with non-standard pipe diameters and wall thicknesses, are the requirements for the particular product. This process is used at the Christy Park Plant of United States Steel, where a large quantity of special tubular products is processed and, although seamless-pipe requirements are met at this particular mill, the large use of this product is in the manufacture of cylinders for containing high-pressure gases. The continued increase in the use of steel cylinders for the storage and/or transportation of hydrogen, helium, and oxygen—as well as many unusual gases—has necessitated the use of steels of much higher alloy grade and of much greater wall thicknesses than are employed in the manufacture of the more-standardized types of seamless pipe and tubing, and has revived the original piercing process to meet the needs for special products in the high-pressure field. Walls up to 3½ inches thick and in diameters up to 20 inches are not unusual for pressure vessels for the containment of gases at pressures up to as high as 15,000 lb. per sq. in.

Chief Details of the Piercing Process—The piercing and drawing process requires skill and experience, although its principles are simple and easily understood (Figure 30—45). Depending upon the required end result, the starting material is a solid steel billet ranging in size from 14 to 20 inches square and from 40 to 60 inches in length. The billet is heated to a forging temperature of about 2300° F (Step 1 of Figure 30—45) and is preformed into a solid cylindrical form by forging in a closed die set in a forging press (Step 2). A following operation called piercing (Step 3) results in the forming of a hole in the center of the billet; the operation producing, in addition to the pierced hole, a substantial amount of back extrusion. The pierced billet is reheated to bring it back to forging temperature, after which it is placed on a mandrel of proper size in a horizontal draw bench (Step 5). The mandrel propels the piece through a series of dies in the form of rings which progressively reduce the outside diameter of the forging and elongate it on the mandrel, following which a stripper is inserted between the end of the forging and a stripper disc to hold the forging in place while the mandrel is withdrawn. Further operations to produce further reductions and elongations are performed in the same manner and on the same type of equipment. As tool changes in the draw bench are performed rapidly, it is possible to make a relatively small number of pieces of special size requirements economically as compared to the cost of producing the same specialty products on a standard high-speed seamless mill. After the drawing operations are completed, the closed end of the forged piece is removed, the ends are square cut, and the resulting tube is ready for use either as a piece of pipe or to be further processed into a forged-end cylinder.

Forming Cylinders—Where a high-pressure vessel is to be produced, one end of a tube produced in the

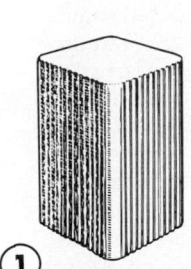

1 HEATING THE BILLET

A solid steel billet, already worked in rolling from an ingot, is heated to forging temperature.

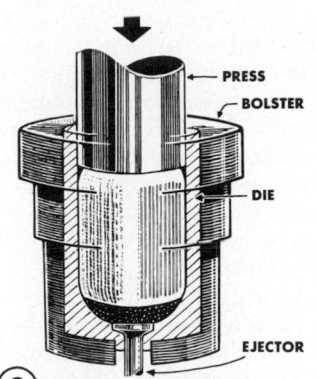

2 PREFORMING

In this initial forming operation, the heated billet is pressed and partially formed for the piercing operation in a cylindrical "die pot."

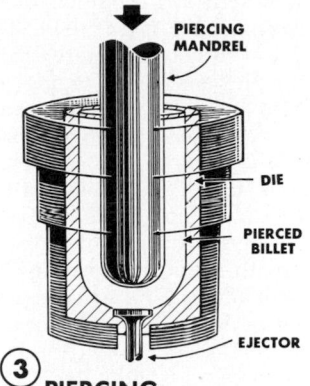

3 PIERCING

The billet, formed to fit snugly in the die pot, is pressed into a closed-end hollow forging by a piercing mandrel in a vertical press.

4 INSPECTION

The forged "cup" is given a thorough inspection of wall thickness and surface quality.

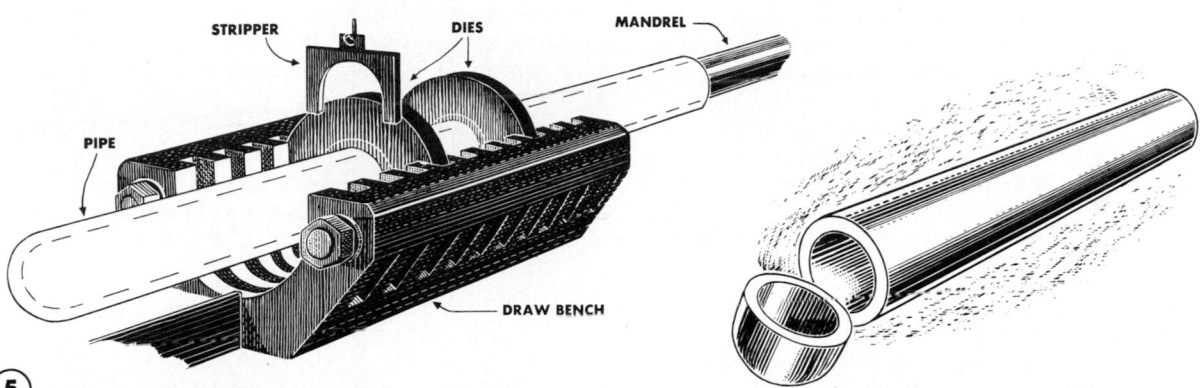

5 HEAT AND DRAW

The forging is pushed through a series of circular dies by a mandrel inserted in the open end. Multiple "draws" are made to reduce the wall thickness and diameter and increase the length. (The closed end may then be retained or removed depending on product application.)

6 HEAT TREAT

In heat treating, the pipe may be normalized, normalized and tempered, or quenched and tempered, depending on specification requirements.

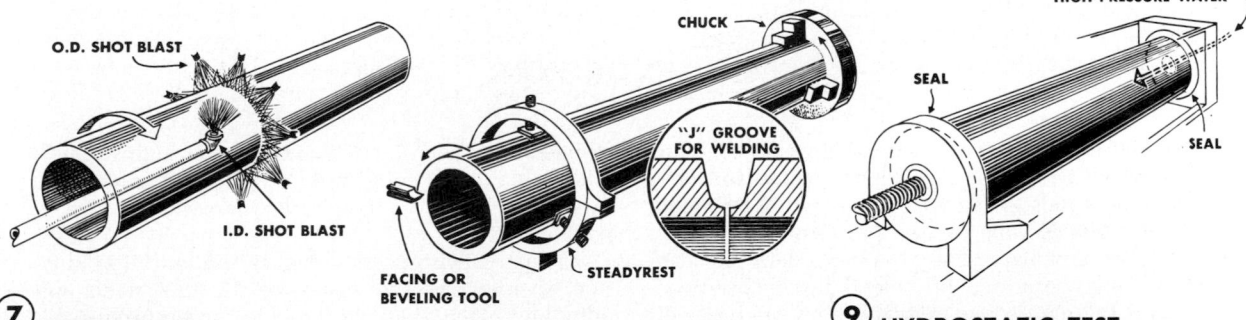

7 SHOT BLAST

The inside and outside surfaces of the pipe are subjected to high-velocity abrasive grit to disintegrate and remove scale. The surfaces are then inspected.

8 FACE OR BEVEL ENDS

The pipe is rotated in a chuck while stationary tools face the ends square or bevel them for welding.

9 HYDROSTATIC TEST AND INSPECTION

The pipe ends are sealed and high-pressure water is introduced to establish the test pressure. The pipe then receives a complete inspection of surface and all dimensions before marking and shipping.

FIG. 30—45. Steps in the production of seamless forged pipe.

manner just described is heated and hammer forged to convert it into a hemispherical closed end. The other end is then heated and forged to impart a conical shape without closing the end. The forging operation on either end is also known as **swaging.** Swaging is performed on an air- or steam-operated forging hammer. Hemispherical or conical-shaped cavities in two mating dies, one mounted on the solid bed of the hammer and one on the ram, impart the desired shape to the end being swaged. A series of properly tooled forging hammers with suitable reheating furnaces spaced between them allows for a succession of swaging operations to be performed to produce the desired end result.

Following the completion of all forging operations and heat treating, the open formed end section is machined and threaded for the required detail of piping or fixtures that will be assembled in the cylinder end.

To assure the degree of internal cleanliness required by the individual gases to be stored, the interior surface of the cylinder is first shot blasted to remove all scale that developed in the forging or heat-treating processes. In many cases, complicated chemical washing is also done to assure what is sometimes called "hospital cleanliness" for the interior of the cylinder. Special interior coatings of either the air-drying of baked types are often applied. The exterior of the vessel is shot blasted to insure a clean metal surface for the application of exterior coatings. Pipe fittings and flanges with seal welded connections

are often required, following the installation of which the entire assembly is tested with air at operating pressure to test the leak-proof qualities of the unit. Another function of inspection to fill the requirements of ASME or ICC specifications calls for hydrostatic testing of all cylinders made. Non-destructive testing beyond hydrostatic testing consists of ultrasonic testing of the entire vessel area: this becomes more necessary with increased service-pressure requirements.

The described method of producing pressure cylinders is used for vessels of ten inches or greater diameter and of half an inch or greater wall thickness. The operation called **spinning** is used to produce vessels of smaller diameters and lighter walls. The spinning operation (Figure 30—46) is performed by placing the pipe section in the hollow spindle of a lathe-type machine and rotating the piece at relatively high speeds (600 to 1200 rev. per min.), the piece having been heated to a dull red color prior to insertion in the hollow spindle. A tool holder is mounted on a carriage that permits longitudinal and cross feeding of a blunt spinning tool. The tool is fed against the work piece, moving from the outside diameter, and the sweep of the spinning tool is controlled to form the necks and ends of the cylinders. Sufficient heat is developed from friction of the tool against the work-piece to form a weld in the case of closing the end of a cylinder.

FIG. 30—46. Ends of a tube at different stages of the spinning process, showing the progress of the operation from the tube on the left to the closed cylinder on the right.

SECTION 8

HOT EXTRUSION

Historical—The hot extrusion process has been successfully used to shape non-ferrous metals for many years and has also been used to a limited extent for some years in Europe for the production of carbon-steel tubes and bars. The presses, usually mechanically driven, permitted little flexibility in speed control, and the grease and graphite lubricant used left much to be desired. Tool life was short and only rather low extrusion ratios could be used. This made the operating cost of the process too high for economical use in this country where labor costs are much higher than in Europe.

During the late 1940's, the French inventor Jacques Sejournet developed the use of glass as a lubricant at the Persan (near Paris) plant of Comptoir Industrial D'Etirage et Profilage de Metaux to the point where

stainless steel and other ferrous alloys of high strength and high melting point could be extruded much more satisfactorily and economically than was previously possible.

The extrusion process is well suited for the production of tubes or solid shapes of stainless steels and other high-strength alloys for which orders are usually for small quantities. With this process, it is possible to produce shapes which are difficult or impossible to form by other processes, to shape some steels which are difficult to roll or forge and some which previously could only be cast. Included in materials difficult to form are tubes of alloys known as non-pierceable because they cannot be produced on conventional seamless-pipe mills.

Advantages of Hot Extrusion—One of the advantages of the process is the ability to produce orders of small tonnage which cannot be rolled economically. The cost of dies for a special shape is insignificant in comparison with the cost of rolls and a size change can be made on the extrusion press in a few minutes except when it is necessary to change for a different size of billet to produce the required section. It is, therefore, a simple matter to make changes in the design of a section to be extruded, while the cost of such a change to a rolled section might be prohibitive. This ability to make changes is of particular advantage for new developments. Special formed sections can be extruded experimentally in small quantities until the best procedure for extruding and machining can be developed.

The extrusion process, which takes place at a substantially uniform temperature, with the steel under heavy compression in all directions, gives an end product with a fine and uniform structure well suited for further processing by cold drawing or machining. Some producers, particularly the French at Persan, specialize in precision sections which are cold drawn from extruded shapes.

All extrusions tend to be slightly greater in cross-sectional dimensions at the back end than at the front end. Several factors probably contribute to cause this effect. The glass coating is heavier on the front end of the piece, the die wears and its temperature increases as the extrusion is made. To obtain the accuracy of size usually required, it is necessary to cold reduce, cold draw, or finish machine the extrusion. In the production of alloy tubes, it is possible to extrude small tubes with lighter walls and better surface than it is practical to pierce and roll on conventional seamless mills and to produce them with a much better surface. This means that the amount of tube-reducing or cold-drawing work on small tubes can be greatly decreased.

The Extrusion Press—For satisfactory operation, the extrusion press must be ruggedly constructed to withstand the heavy forces involved and remain in accurate alignment. When extruding tubes, it is essential that the mandrel be accurately centered in the die or eccentric tubes will result. The dies, which are thin, must be well backed up to minimize deflection. The die holder must be accurately centered with the bore of the container.

The furnace must be able to heat the billets uniformly to a closely controlled temperature and supply them to the press substantially free of scale.

Before heating, the billets must be properly conditioned. For some non-ferrous metals, the condition of the surface is not of particular importance. For example, brass is extruded with a dummy block smaller than the container so that the billet is scalped and the surface layer is not extruded. With stainless steel however, the billets must be machined to a smooth surface.

The extrusion press at Gary Works of United States Steel embodies a number of new design features which were found to be desirable when the experimental work was being performed in France. It has a main ram of 2000 tons capacity and a separate piercing ram of 500 tons capacity which can be used separately or together. The stroke of the main ram is 100 inches. The container is movable so that the discard can be easily removed as will appear later.

The Extrusion Operations—The general plan of the extrusion plant is shown in Figure 30—47. Turned rounds in lengths up to 20 feet are received and stored in the yard until needed. They are transported into the building by straddle truck and distributed by overhead crane to the four saws for cutting into the desired billet lengths. As mentioned before, these bars already have been turned. The finish must be rather smooth as any undue roughness will affect the finished product. The saws are of the milling-cutter type in order to produce a straight cut with a smooth surface, perpendicular to the axis of the bar. The billets are piled on pallets, which can be handled by a fork truck or by overhead crane. If intended for the production of tubes, they are next delivered to the drill presses where holes about ¼ inch larger than the inside diameter of the extruded tube are drilled from end to end on the axis of the billet. It is important that the drilled holes be straight and on center, as otherwise the extruded tube will be eccentric. Three drilling machines using high-speed twist drills about 4 feet long have been provided for this work. Oil holes through the drills carry an ample supply of coolant to the cutting edges. Two of the machines are of the horizontal type which rotate the work while the drill is fed into it and the other machine is vertical and feeds the rotating work down over a stationary drill. The largest hole which can be drilled by any of these machines is 3 inches in diameter. Most of the stainless steel that is drilled and cut tends to work harden, and all sawing and drilling is performed at a slow speed and with a heavy feed.

The billets are then transferred to a lathe where one

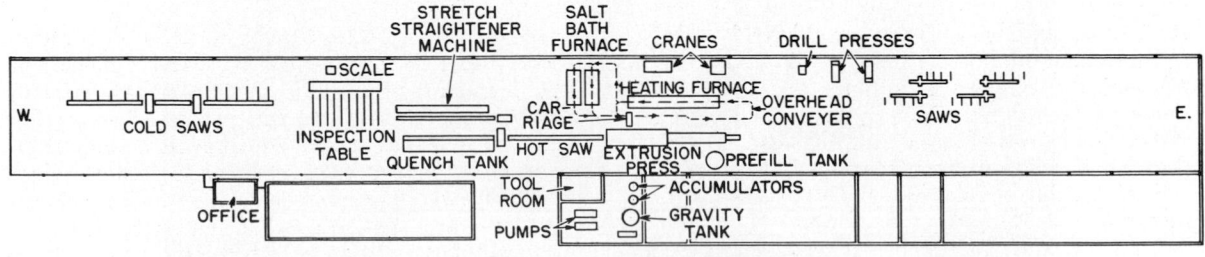

FLOOR PLAN — EXTRUSION DEPARTMENT

Fɪɢ. 30—47. General plan of extrusion plant.

end is chamfered. This chamfer is provided on the lead end of the billet, which contacts the die, and has been found necessary to eliminate a surface flaw known as "corner defect."

The billets are next taken to the stud welder shown in Figure 30—48. Here, each billet is upended and a ¾-inch carbon-steel stud with a round head is flash-welded to its end. Hangers on the overhead conveyor then pick up the billets and carry them through the gas-fired furnace where they are heated to about 1600° F. The furnace, which is shown in Figures 30—49 and 30—50, has a water-cooled slot in the top to permit the hangers to pass through. The slot is covered by over-lapping alloy seal-plates which travel with the hangers and ride on water-cooled rails. The furnace is fired with coke-oven gas and is equipped with 54 radiant burners in the side walls with three zones of control. It has a rated heating capacity of 8 tons per hour at 2300° F. It is operated at only 1600° F, however, in order to minimize scaling of the steel.

The billets leaving the gas-fired furnace are rapidly conveyed to one of the salt pots. These are electrically heated baths of barium chloride which are operated at 2300° F. Each bath is 14 inches wide by 10 feet long inside, and has four pairs of electrodes connected to two transformers of 200-kva capacity each. It is important that the billets be uniformly heated throughout and that they be free of scale as it will cause rapid die wear at the extrusion press. The salt-bath furnace has, to date, proved to be the most satisfactory equipment for achieving the desired results.

After moving through the salt bath, the billets are lifted by conveyor and quickly carried to a point near the extrusion press, where the supporting stud is removed by an air chisel. The layer of salt which adheres to the billet helps to prevent formation of scale. The billet falls into a trough on the charging carriage, as shown in Figure 30—51. As the carriage moves toward the press, the trough drops to a horizontal position and discharges the billet, which rolls across the table to a trough on the opposite end. As it rolls, it wraps itself in a fibre-glass veil which acts as a lubricant in the container of the press. Figure 30—52 shows a longitudinal section through the press. The tooling is shown in Figure 30—53.

Before the glass-wrapped billet is introduced, the stem is fully retracted, the mandrel is extended from the stem the proper distance to permit it to reach through the die when the extrusion is started, a dummy block is placed over the mandrel and against the stem, and the mandrel is covered with a woven-glass sock. The container is placed in its forward or closed position, a die and holder are placed in the die carriage, and the carriage is moved up against the container and locked in position. A glass cartridge of approximately the same diameter as the container is placed in the container and pushed back against the die (Figure 30—54a). This cartridge may be a pad of fibre glass or a cake of powdered glass, or both. This glass, or a substantial portion of it, melts in contact with the hot steel and flows to the die, thus lubricating the bearing surface. The portion of the glass which does not melt serves to insulate the die and die holder from the hot metal. This glass is the important factor in reducing friction, thereby increasing die life and permitting longer pieces to be extruded and greater extrusion ratios to be used.

FIG. 30—48. Stud welder which flash welds studs to ends of billets to enable them to be carried on hangers through heating furnace.

FIG. 30—49. Billets supported on conveyor are shown here entering the gas-fired furnace for preheating to 1600° F.

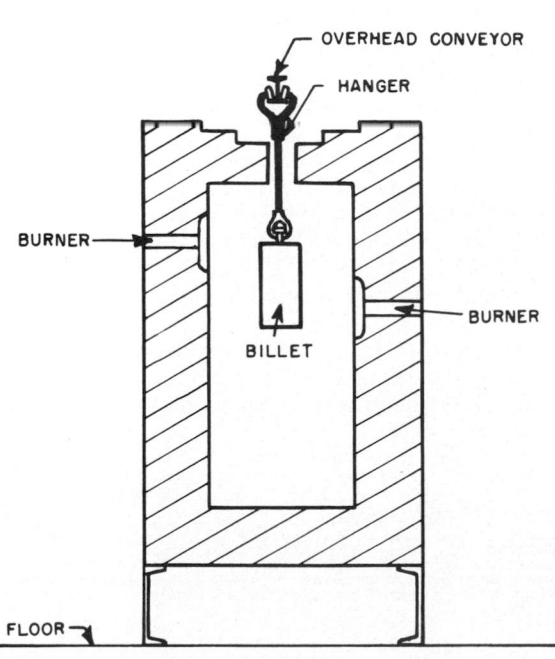

FIG. 30—50. Section through gas-fired billet-heating furnace.

The stem with the dummy block and the mandrel now move forward rapidly under pre-fill pressure. The mandrel enters the drilled hole in the billet and the dummy block presses against the back of the billet and compresses it until it fills the container (Figure 30—54b). The stem continues to move under high pressure and forces the hot steel through the die at a high speed (Figure 30—54c). The extrusion is usually performed in 2 or 3 seconds. It is desirable to perform this operation rapidly to avoid loss of heat from the piece and to minimize the temperature rise of the die and mandrel.

The traveling crosshead comes to rest against a split-ring stop on the container housing before the dummy block reaches the die face. This leaves a short length of billet unextruded. The dummy block has slots in its outer surface and its face is chamfered so that the hot steel tends to flow over and attach itself to the dummy block. The stem is then pulled back a few inches and the container also moves back a short distance. The unextruded piece of billet, or discard, and the dummy block stick to the container and the extruded piece pulls back through the die, thus leaving a gap between the container and the die. The hot saw then descends through this gap and severs the discard (Figure 30—54d). Another forward movement of the container then pushes the end of the extrusion through the die (Figure 30—54e) and it is removed by the outlet con-

Fig. 30—51. Heated billet sliding down trough to charging carriage.

veyor. The die and its carriage are retracted, the container again moves forward, the crosshead stop moves away, and the stem is moved in to push the discard and dummy block from the container (Figure 30—54f). They fall to a conveyor which carries them to the side of the press, where a small hydraulic press squeezes the discard from the dummy block. The dummy block falls to a chute from which it is picked up by a device which raises it into position where the mandrel will pick it up. There are always several dummy blocks in the system to permit cooling before reuse.

After the discard is pushed from the container, the stem is retracted and the mandrel retracts inside the stem where it is water-cooled. A rotating brush moves in and cleans the container of glass residue. The die and its holder are removed from the die carriage and another die and holder previously prepared are inserted. The die which has been used is cleaned and prepared for another extrusion. Normally, from three to six dies are used in rotation. Figures 30—55 and 30—56 show the inlet and outlet sides of the extrusion press.

Piercing Billets—Tubes with inside diameters of 2½ inches or larger and walls of not less than 5/16 inch can be made by piercing the billets on the extrusion press instead of drilling them as described previously. A piercing head is placed on the end of the

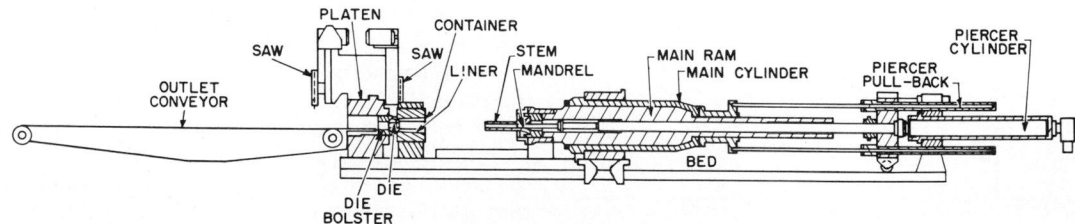

SECTION THROUGH EXTRUSION PRESS

Fig. 30—52. Schematic longitudinal elevation of an extrusion press.

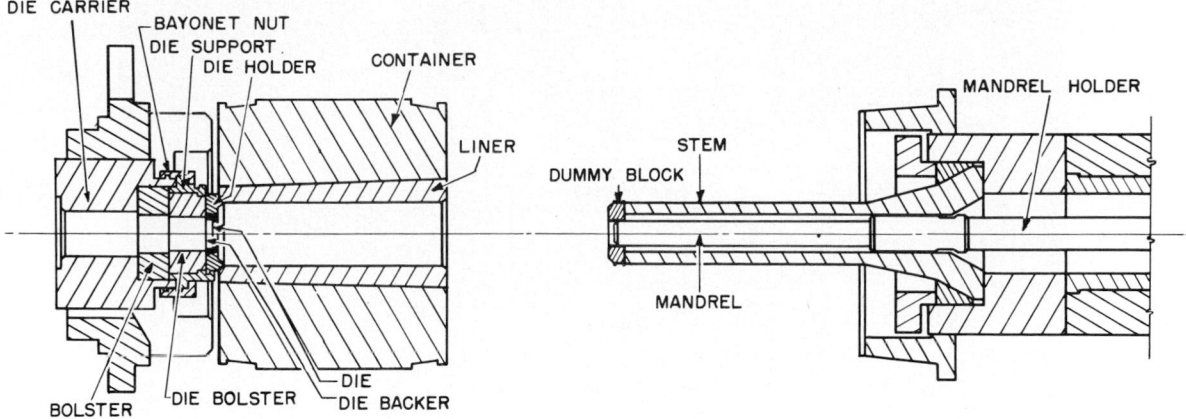

FIG. 30—53. Tool assembly for the extrusion press shown schematically in Figure 30—52.

mandrel and pushed completely through the billet and through the die. The piercing head and a short slug of metal sheared from the inside of the billet drop off and the stem with the dummy block then advances and extrudes the piece.

Other Billet-Piercing Methods—In other plants it is common to provide a separate vertical press for the piercing operation. A section of the tooling for one such press is shown in Figure 30—57. Here the billet is first compressed by the ram which then guides the piercing mandrel to the center of the billet. The piercing mandrel advances to a point near the bottom,

while the ram retracts and allows the billet to extrude backward. The back-up mandrel is then withdrawn and the piercing mandrel forces a small slug out as it completes its operation. Some use two presses and first pierce to a point near the bottom with a closed die pot on the first press, then complete the piercing on the second machine. In any case, it is necessary to reheat the billet before extruding.

There are other extrusion presses on which a closing plate is inserted between the container and the die while the mandrel pierces the billet to a point near the end, forming a closed cup. The closing plate is then

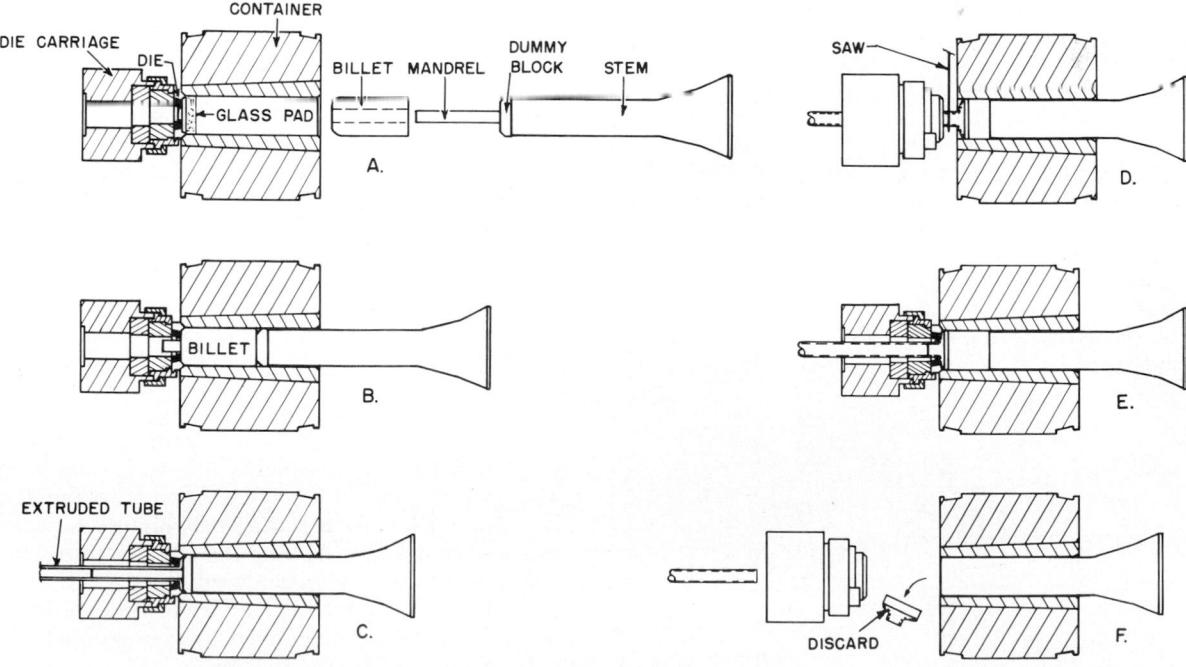

FIG. 30—54. Cycle of operations in the production of an extruded tubular section.

FIG. 30—55. View at the inlet side of the extrusion press.

FIG. 30—56. View of the outlet side of the extrusion press.

removed and the mandrel completes the piercing operation, forcing a small slug through the die, after which the stem moves ahead to make the extrusion.

When solid shapes are extruded there is, of course, no mandrel, and the stem and dummy block are solid. Otherwise, the operation is exactly the same as for extruding tubes.

Tooling—All the extrusion tools are highly stressed in operation and must be made of alloy steels which will withstand heat. The containers are 36-inch outside diameter forgings with a 14½-inch bore at the entry end. The bore has a slight taper to accommodate a liner of the desired inside diameter, which is pressed into the container. Liners are not removed until worn out; therefore, a container is provided for each liner. Stems, both solid and hollow, are provided to fit each liner with about ³⁄₁₆-inch clearance on the diameter. These stems are subjected to compressive stresses up to 160,000 lb. per sq. in.

Dies range from ¾ to 1½ inches thick and are of the general contour shown in Figure 30—58. They have a short bell-mouth, a straight bearing section which is usually about ³⁄₁₆ inch long, and a flared section on the outlet side. Dies of 10 per cent tungsten steel and 5 per cent chromium hot-work steel have given good service. At best, dies wear rather rapidly, due partly to the fact that their temperature is raised considerably during each extrusion. Long extrusions cause much more rapid die wear than short ones. Dies of harder materials, and steel dies with hard facings such as stellite, have been tried experimentally but have not as yet proved successful.

Dies for solid shapes present more problems than dies for tubes. Unsymmetrical shapes have a tendency to bow or twist when extruded because the metal flows more easily and therefore faster through the wider portions of the aperture and through the portion at the center of the billet. Also, it is difficult to lubricate the re-entrant corners. To minimize these difficulties, the aperture in the die should be located so that the sections more difficult to extrude are as near the center as possible. Bearings sections can be made longer on the sections where the flow is fastest, and the bell-mouth part of the die can be increased to encourage glass flow to certain sections.

Mandrels are made from 5 per cent chromium steel, hardened and ground to size. These mandrels must withstand the heavy compressive stresses transmitted by the billet under pressure and also the tension caused by friction of the extruded piece. Failure is usually due to necking-down near the back end where the stresses are greatest. Due to the heavy stresses, there is a minimum limit for the size of mandrel of any definite material and for any certain extrusion. In general, it has been found best to keep the mandrel diameter over 1 inch, although smaller ones have been used.

Dummy blocks are of the same steel or a similar steel as that used for mandrels, with the addition of about 1½ per cent tungsten.

Dies, mandrels, and dummy blocks are preheated to about 300° F in a small furnace before placing them in use. The container is kept warm with an electric heater when the press is not in use. If these things are not done, the tools may break due to thermal shock.

Power Supply—Power for the press is supplied by

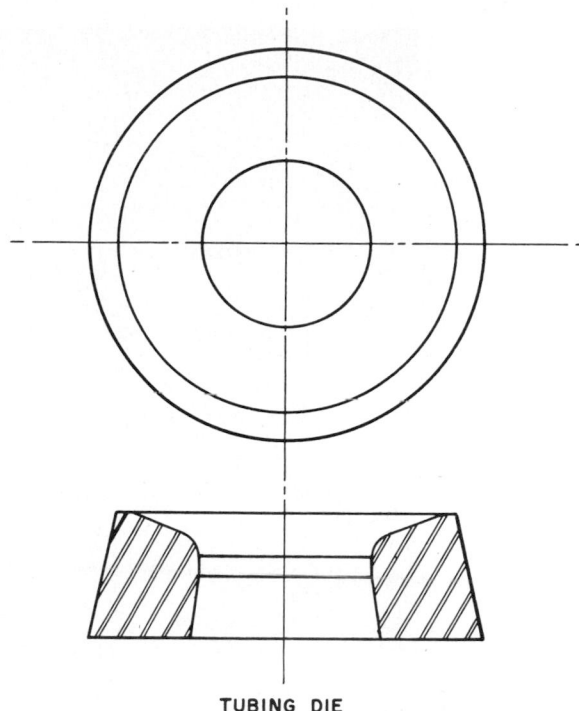

TUBING DIE

Fig. 30—58. Sketch of die used for the hot extrusion of tubular sections.

two 300-gallon per minute pumps. They supply water at 3600 lb. per sq. in. pressure through two air-hydraulic accumulators. An air compressor is available to charge the accumulators, when necessary. One pump and one accumulator supply water for the main ram only. The other pump and accumulator supply the piercer ram and auxiliary equipment, including the die carriage, the die locks, the discard separator, and the container shift. An oil-hydraulic system operating at 500 lb. per sq. in. supplies the power to operate the main control valves through servo-mechanisms, the saws, and the hydraulic motor for the charging-carriage travel.

Extrusion - Finishing Operations—The extruded piece is carried on the outlet conveyor past a hot saw which can be used to divide the length if desired. The extrusion is then submerged in a quench tank if it is of austenitic stainless steel. Steels which cannot be quenched are discharged onto skids to cool.

All extruded pieces are covered with a thin coating of glass which, due to its abrasive nature, must be removed before any cold work is performed. Quenching removes a portion of this glass, but the remainder must be removed by pickling. Before this de-glassing operation, special shapes are straightened on a stretch straightener, shown in Figure 30—59. This machine has a capacity of 100 tons, and one of the heads is rotatable so that any twist in the piece can be removed.

After straightening and de-glassing, solid shapes are cut to length. Tube hollows (a mill term for semi-finished tubes produced by hot extrusion), after de-glassing, are further processed by cold drawing or tube reducing.

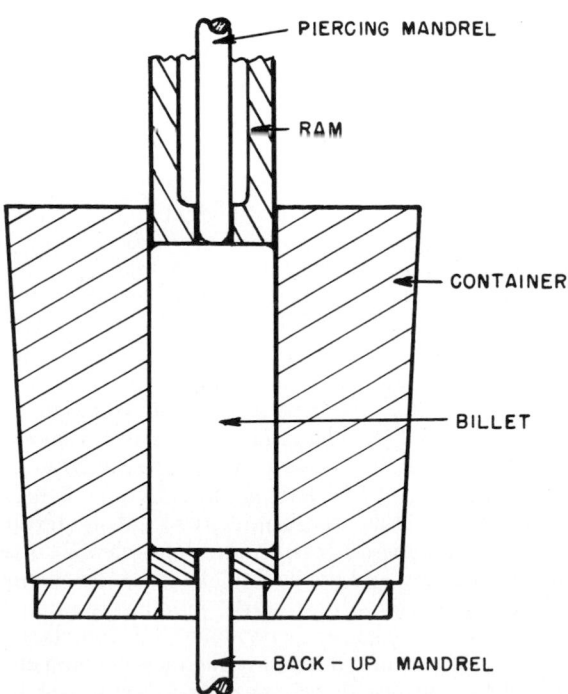

PIERCING MANDREL

RAM

CONTAINER

BILLET

BACK - UP MANDREL

Fig. 30—57. Tooling used in some plants for the piercing of hot billets for extrusion. Piercing is performed on a separate vertical press by the method shown schematically in this sketch. Pierced billets must then be reheated before transfer to the extrusion press.

Fig. 30—59. Extruded section clamped in rotatable head of stretch straightener for the straightening and removal of twist from the section.

SECTION 9

FINISHING OPERATIONS

Pipe made by the hot-rolling process described in previous sections must be subjected to many mechanical operations, such as: straightening; end cropping; plain-end machining for various mechanical uses; chamfering, reaming and facing for welded line pipe; chamfering and reaming for threaded line pipe or casing. These are some of the characteristic operations classified as "finishing," and each requires its own special technique.

Straightening—Pipe from the hot mills must be straightened either by continuous "in-line" processing through a skewed-roll machine, or by a press. Both units use the principle of supporting a pipe at two points while applying a deflecting force to the opposite side of the pipe at a point midway between the supports in a direction opposite to the bend.

In the continuous roll straightener, two pairs of skewed power rolls rotate and advance the pipe and serve as the fixed fulcrum points mentioned above. A single skewed roll located midway between these two sets is positioned ahead of the axial centerline to exert the deflecting force. Details of this general type of straightener vary. In some machines, power is applied to both rolls of each of the driver pairs; in others, to only one. Some use a pair of rolls in the deflection set; others, only one, with or without power. In one case, the deflection rolls are formed into a cluster that holds the pipe over approximately one-half of the pipe circumference.

In all straighteners, including the press, the deflection is selected that will straighten bent or bowed pipe, but will not exceed the elastic limit of the pipe that is straight before entering the machine.

Inspection and Cutting—When seamless pipe leaves the straightening rolls, it is delivered to a table where it is thoroughly inspected for straightness, size and external and internal surface defects such as seams, pits, etc. The pipe is then delivered to the cutting-off machine where the crop ends are removed and the ends are cut smooth and perpendicular to the pipe axis, beveled for welding, or if the pipe is to be threaded, the ends are chamfered to aid in starting the threading dies. The ends are then reamed to remove any burrs, and the wall thickness of the cut end is measured to establish that the pipe has the proper uniform wall thickness. Depending upon the class of pipe, a number of cut-off portions may be subjected to a flattening test to determine the ductility of the steel in the individual pipe.

Pipe Joints—A pipe joint is a means of connecting two or more lengths of pipe so as to permit transportation of liquids or gases under leak-proof conditions, or to permit the use of long lengths of pipe for mechanical or structural purposes. Generally speaking, joints may be divided into three classes:

(1) Joints with threaded ends for couplings or flanges.
(2) Special connectors or couplings for use with plain-end or flanged-end pipe; as, for example, Dresser, Victaulic, Vanstone, and similar joints.
(3) Welded joints, including plain-end pipe beveled for welding, slip-joint casing and line pipe, and double-belled-end line pipe with inserted chill ring for welding.

Joints with Threads and Couplings—Pipe to be used for oil- and gas-well casing is mostly finished to American Petroleum Institute (A.P.I.) specifications which specify that all sizes from 4½-inch to 20-inch outside diameter, inclusive, shall be threaded on both ends with round top and bottom sixty-degree threads. A.P.I. drill pipe and tubing are also provided with this type of thread. Threaded A.P.I. line pipe requires a modified Briggs thread. An increasing proportion of casing that is to be subjected to severe tensile stresses—as in deep wells—is threaded with the modified buttress thread that was developed by the United States Steel Corporation. This makes a joint that is practically equal in tension to the pipe that it joins. Standard pipe that is to be fitted with couplings or flanges is manufactured to the applicable parts of the American Standards Association Threading Specifications. The great increase in the loads and pressures to which many types of threaded joints have become subject in recent years has resulted in additional efforts to improve physical properties and threading practice. Thread form, thread depth, lead, and taper are maintained within the limits of the rigid tolerances given in the specifications of the American Petroleum Institute and other organizations, so that coupling threads will mate properly with the pipe threads when made up to the power-tight position.

Threading Pipe—To secure good threaded joints it is necessary to have clean, smoothly cut threads of the proper taper and pitch, and to secure such threads it is necessary to have threading dies made with full consideration for the following: lip, chip space, clearance, lead, lubricants or cutting oils, and, for power machines, number of chasers.

Lip—Figure 30—60 illustrates clearly what is meant by lip on a chaser. The lip forms a slanted cutting edge which promotes curling of the chips and gives an easy cutting action, similar to that of a properly ground lathe tool, instead of the pushing-off effect caused by chasers which have no lip; it also permits a higher cutting speed. The angle to which the lip should be ground depends upon the kind of material to be threaded and the style and condition of the chasers and chaser holder. For Bessemer-steel pipe, this angle should be from 15 to 20 degrees; for open-hearth steel, the lip angle should be from 15 to 25 degrees.

Chip Space—Chip space is the space required in the die holder in front of the chasers to prevent the accumulation or packing up of chips. If sufficient chip space is not allowed, the chips will rapidly pack in front of the chaser, causing rough, torn threads, and

creating a tendency on the part of the chaser to pick up stickers. The best design for this chip space provides an even curve for the chips to follow, with the back of each chaser well supported.

Clearance—Clearance is the space between the threads of the chaser and the threads on the pipe at a given distance from the cutting edge ("heel clearance" in Figure 30—60). This clearance is secured by die manufacturers in various ways. A simple method for getting clearance in the type of die known as "cutting-edge-on-center" or "center cut," consists of setting the chasers for machining with their cutting edge tangent with a larger circle than they are set for cutting threads. Clearance may be obtained on the "stock-on-center" type of chaser by machining in the same manner as a "cutting-edge-on-center" chaser, with the exception that their cutting edge is tangent to a smaller circle than when they are set for cutting threads. Stock-on-center chasers can also obtain their clearance by setting the chasers ahead of the center-line when they are being machined.

Lead or Throat—Lead is the angle which is machined or ground on the first three threads, more or less, of each chaser to enable the die to start on the pipe, and also to distribute the work of making the first cut over a number of threads. The lead may be machined or, as is more common, it may be ground after the chasers are tempered. The proper amount of lead is about three threads. As the heaviest cutting is done by the lead, this section of the chaser should have a slightly greater clearance angle than the rest of the threads, but care must be used to see that this angle is not excessive. Excess lead clearance will cause the die to feed too fast, and the half threads cut by the lead are consequently damaged by the full teeth of the chasers (see Figure 30—61).

Number of Chasers—To get good results in threading at one cut, the die head should have a suitable number of chasers. The number is determined by the size of the pipe. In some cases as many as eighteen chasers are required. The number necessarily depends upon the design, size, and operative principle of the die; hence, no exact rule can be laid down for universal acceptance. When an insufficient number of chasers is used, the die will chatter and cut a rough thread.

Dies—Dies usually are designed with the chasers evenly spaced and arranged either with the stock on center or with the cutting edge on center, as shown in Figure 30—60, in which case the face of the chaser is in the same plane as the central axis. A more recent development places the chasers at an angle of 24 degrees with a radial or center line and spaces them at varying angles around the pipe. An odd number of chasers is used. This has several advantages among which is the steadying effect the unequally spaced chasers have on the die thereby reducing chatter. Sharpening is simplified since the rake or lip angle is set at 24 degrees by the angle of the chaser with the center line and sharpening consists of merely grinding parallel to the face of the chaser.

Chaser teeth are usually designed to have the even-numbered chasers cut one flank of the thread and the odd-numbered chasers cut the other flank. This is

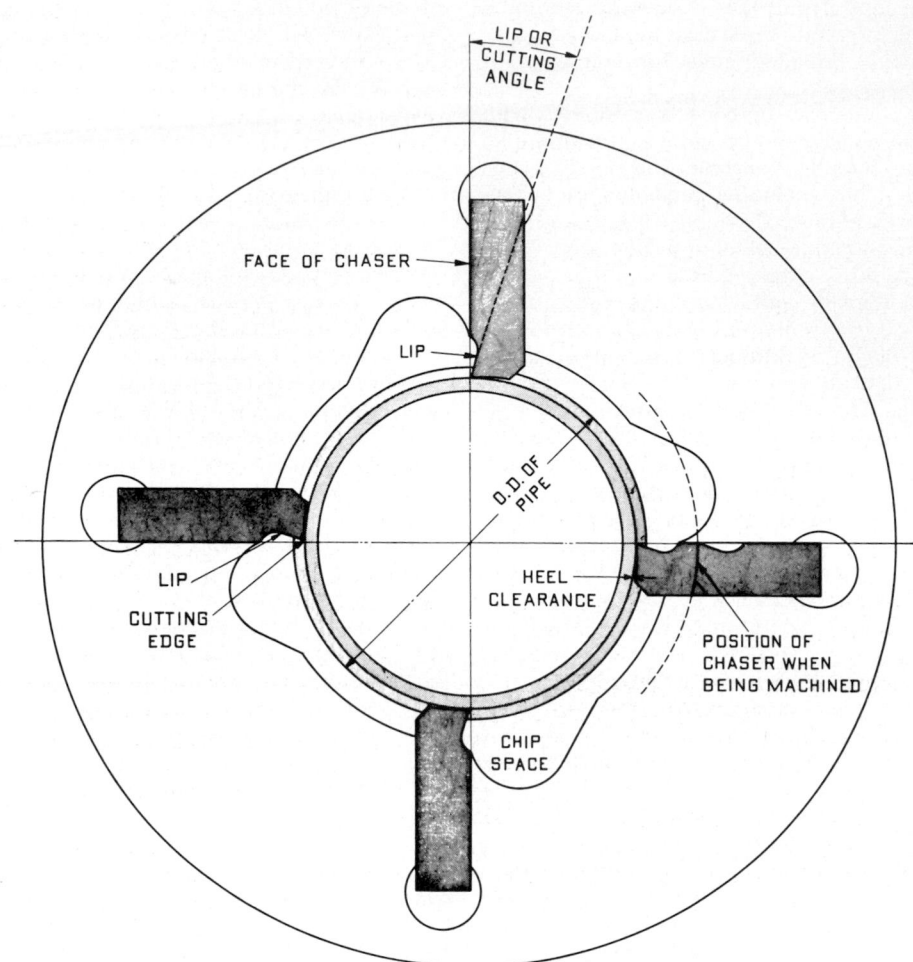

FIG. 30—60. Threading die showing lip, lip angle, chip space, clearance and cutting edge.

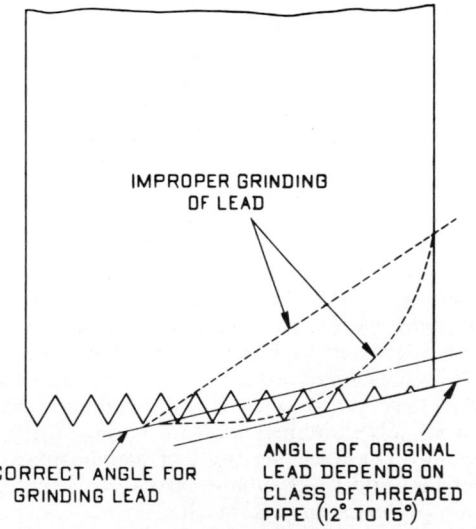

FIG. 30—61. Sketch showing correct angle for regrinding lead of chasers.

done so that the threads of any individual chaser will not cut both flanks and results in a smoother thread.

Lubricant—Care should be taken to provide the proper quality of threading oil, as the best die made will not produce good results with poor or insufficient oil. With hand tools or where the flow is intermittent, No. 1 lard oil can be used with success. Cottonseed oils have a tendency to gum if not used in a constant flow. Poor lubricants are destructive to dies, and more power is required to cut a thread when they are used. A good quality of sulphurized mineral oil should be used with a constant flow on power machines.

Gaging Pipe Threads—To keep pipe-threading practice at a high degree of accuracy, the mills maintain complete sets of standard gages with which the pipe-thread dimensions may be measured. For each size of pipe threaded, a master plug gage is kept at the mills, and these gages are returned periodically to the National Bureau of Standards for examination of accuracy. Except for the pipe-thread vanish angle, the threaded master plug gage represents a theoretically correct pipe thread as to pitch diameter, lead, taper, and thread form. The ring gage is the transfer medium, also certified for accuracy by the Bureau of Standards, and represents a theoretically correct coupling thread with reference to lead, taper, and thread form. The ring gage is threaded and sized so that it will screw onto the master plug gage a predetermined distance, known as the hand-tight position. On American Petroleum Institute gages, the hand-tight position is expressed as **standoff,** which is the distance from a scribed mark or notch in the master plug gage to the face of the ring gage. The standoff represents the advance from the hand-tight to power-tight position which has been determined as necessary to obtain a leak-proof and otherwise efficient joint. The working plug and ring gages used to verify the accuracy of the couplings and threaded pipe, respectively, are in turn compared with the master plug and ring gages, so that the makeup from hand-tight to power-tight position in the joint will be uniform and within the specification tolerance limits. In addition to plug and ring gages, the mills are provided with various other types of high-precision gaging instruments, each one serving its particular function in indicating the accuracy of thread depth, thread form or angle, taper of threads in a specified length, pitch diameter, and lead or pitch. A more complete description of thread inspection and gaging instruments may be had by reference to American Petroleum Institute Standards 5-B.

Coupling Forgings—All threaded couplings are made of seamless steel forgings of a grade of steel at least equal to that of the threaded pipe with which they are used. Seamless coupling forgings, also called **blanks,** are cut from lengths of seamless pipe, pierced and rolled to the required coupling diameter and wall thickness.

Finishing Steel Couplings—The blanks are stamped with the necessary identifying marks. They are then placed in machines which true up the ends, taper the bore to conform accurately with the taper of the thread and, if required, recess or chamfer the ends internally. This is all performed in the same operation to assure alignment of the two ends of the finished coupling. The preparation of the coupling blanks is of great importance and care is taken to see that all operations associated with their preparation are properly carried out. The prepared blanks are tapped on automatic tapping machines. After tapping, all couplings are inspected for pitch, taper and thread depth with precision instruments specially designed for this type of work. Size or pitch diameter is checked on hardened and ground, threaded gages.

To prevent galling of the threads, the couplings are electroplated with either zinc or tin, depending upon the type of thread and/or the yield strength of the coupling. As the first step in the zinc plating process, the couplings are first washed with a soda solution to remove the oil adhering from the threading operation. Thoroughly cleaned on the inside, they are placed, several at a time, in a specially constructed plating tank filled with a zinc solution. In this tank the couplings are supported so that they collectively form the cathode, while zinc poles project into the couplings to form the anode. Upon the passage of direct current through the apparatus, the zinc is deposited upon the inside of the coupling as a firmly adhering coat, the thickness of which depends upon current density and time. Since the coat will not adhere firmly if the current density is too great, this factor is limited and maintained to give a tight coat, and thickness is controlled by time.

As an additional safeguard against galling, to facilitate the tightening up of the couplings on pipe and also to prevent rusting of the threads in service, a special thread compound consisting of various metallic powders suspended in non-drying greases has been prepared for use with couplings.

Testing the Pipe—From the threading machines, or from the cutting-off machines if the pipe is plain end or beveled for welding, the pipe is moved over a final inspection table, where each length is carefully inspected for surface defects, end finish, size, etc., to the hydrostatic-testing machine. If the pipe is threaded, the threads are lubricated, after which the couplings are screwed up to the established hand-tight position, examined for standoff, and then brought up to power-tight position by a power screwing-on machine. The pipe is then filled with water and an internal hydrostatic pressure is applied. This pressure may be from 400 to as high as 15,000 pounds per square inch, depending upon the kind of pipe, the size, and the service for which it is to be used. Some pipe, such as butt-weld pipe for ammonia purposes is also given an air test while submerged in water. For the hydrostatic test a specially designed machine is provided, which consists of a bench mounted on one end with a water-tight head connected with a hydraulic line and with a similar head made adjustable to suit different lengths of pipe, mounted on the other. A number of clamps for supporting the pipe and an air hammer for tapping the pipe during the test are mounted between these heads. When being tested, welded pipe is placed between the heads, the supporting clamps are applied, and the adjustable head is moved forward to seal the ends of the pipe tightly with packing rings or gaskets. Water is admitted until the pipe is full and no air pockets remain. The pressure line valve is then opened until the gage indicates the specified test pressure, which is maintained for five seconds, during which time the pipe is jarred automatically with the air hammer. The face of the air hammer is brought to bear upon and vibrate against the pipe, which is thereby subjected to impact and vibration while under maximum internal stress. The pipe is then unclamped from the testing machine, and one end is elevated while the water flows out, carrying with it flakes of detached scale.

Because of the enormous head pressures encountered in testing pipe, the higher test pressures are usually applied by what is known as the "field testing" method, so called because it was originally used with portable equipment. The extremely high pressures are employed to test casing and tubing to be used in deep wells where very high working pressures are encountered. A cap is screwed onto the field end pipe threads and a plug, through which the water enters the pipe, is screwed into the coupling on the other end of the pipe. Since there are no restraining forces on the ends of the pipe, the internal pressure acting on the cap and plug hydrostatically test the pipe joint in tension. Because of the very high pressures involved in this test, safety precautions are an important factor when installing and operating this equipment.

A very important factor in setting oil-well casing is the amount of external pressure exerted on the casing. This pressure is usually directly proportional to the depth of the well and together with the bursting pressure and joint strength determines the grade of steel and wall thickness of casing required in deep wells. The resistance to collapse is proportional to the ratio between the outside diameter and the wall thickness of the casing which is usually expressed as D/t. It also varies with mechanical properties, especially the yield strength, below the range of elastic failure.

In order to assure a satisfactory level of collapse resistance, representative specimens of casing are subjected to external hydraulic pressure under laboratory controlled conditions. After outside diameter and wall measurements are recorded, the ends are sealed either with portable leakproof heads or by welded plugs and the specimen is inserted in a heavy-wall forged jacket which is sealed and closed with heavy bayonet-type heads. After filling the jacket and bleeding out all entrapped air, hydraulic pressure is applied to the outside of the pipe by a high-pressure electrically driven reciprocating pump until failure of the specimen occurs through collapse of the section. The hydraulic pressure applied during the test is indicated on a calibrated mercury pressure gauge. Open-end tests are made by sealing the specimen using suitable packing rings through openings in the heads of the collapse jacket. In this method, the length of the test specimen is fixed by the length of the collapse jacket and consequently the ratio of the length of specimen to its diameter varies with each size. The method of applying and registering the pressure during the test is the same as with the closed-end test.

The test results are recorded and used as a process control, and as part of the experimental work which is constantly being done to improve casing quality and manufacturing method.

Oiling—Each length of pipe as it leaves the testing pump is measured, and this information together with the necessary identification marks is stenciled on the pipe, which is then given a coating of protective oil as it passes through a spray machine. This oil is a hardening transparent oil that leaves a lacquer finish. Sizes 1½ inches and smaller are identified by stamping the necessary information on metal tags rather than stenciling, and these sizes, after oiling, are bundled to facilitate handling and shipment.

Types and Uses of Joints—The joints shown in Figures 30—62 to 30—72 represent those best known and most commonly used.

Upsetting—For severe service, it is often necessary to provide additional strength in the joint, and for this reason the ends of the pipe are upset before cutting the threads. To accomplish this upsetting, the end of the pipe is heated to forging temperature, then inserted endwise between two semi-circular dies of the upsetting machine. These dies clamp the pipe from the outside, while a mandrel, carrying a collar of the exact size of the outside diameter of the upset end, is inserted into the pipe. As the mandrel advances, the collar comes in contact with the end of the pipe and pushes the hot metal back to fill the ring-like space between the mandrel and the die. By changing the design of the dies, the upsetting may be controlled to displace the extra thickness either to the inside or to the outside of the pipe. Figure 30—62 shows internal upset casing.

A.P.I. Seamless Buttress-Thread Casing—Non-Upset—This joint (Figure 30—63) was developed to satisfy the petroleum industry's need for a casing joint which will safely and economically support the weight of casing designed for deep wells. The high tensile strength of the buttress-thread joint is due largely to the combined effect of the coupling threads completely engaging the casing thread throughout their entire length, including the vanishing threads, and the three-degree flank angle of the thread which support the weight of the casing in the well. Used on the A.P.I. casing grades and with full inside clearance, 4½-inch through 13⅜-inch O.D. casing combination strings of multiple weight can be designed for 20,000-foot depths and corresponding approximately 10,000 lb. per sq. in. bottom hole rock pressure.

A.P.I. Casing with Long Coupling—A.P.I. casing with long couplings is manufactured in sizes 4½ inches to 9⅝ inches outside diameter. The general outline of the joint is as shown in Figure 30—64. Casing with long couplings is intended for use in wells of somewhat lesser depths than the internal upset type and may also be used in the lower sections of casing strings where the internal upset shown in Figure 30—62 is not necessary to obtain the desired joint strength and safety factor against failure. When it is necessary to obtain added clearance inside a larger size of casing or in open holes, couplings of substandard outside diameter but otherwise having standard dimensions may be used.

A.P.I. Standard Casing—The A.P.I. Standard Casing Joint (Figure 30—65) was designed for oil-well depths of 5,000 to 7,000 feet with a safety factor of 2.0 against failure in tension based on minimum physical properties. However, this joint may be used in the bottom sections of longer strings of casing, thus resulting in some reduction to the cost of the string. This joint is available with a special clearance coupling outside diameter, where additional clearance is desired because of the necessity of its being run inside another string of casing or in open hole. The A.P.I. Standard Casing Joint is furnished in sizes 4½ inches to 20 inches outside diameter.

A.P.I. Line Pipe—The A.P.I. line pipe joints are similar in general outline to the A.P.I. standard casing joints (Figure 30—65). A.P.I. line pipe is threaded to American Petroleum Institute Standards 5-L, and the same rigid control of threading tolerances maintained as for A.P.I. casing and all other classes of threaded joints. Until recently, the essential differences between line pipe and standard pipe joints were in the coupling diameters and length and also

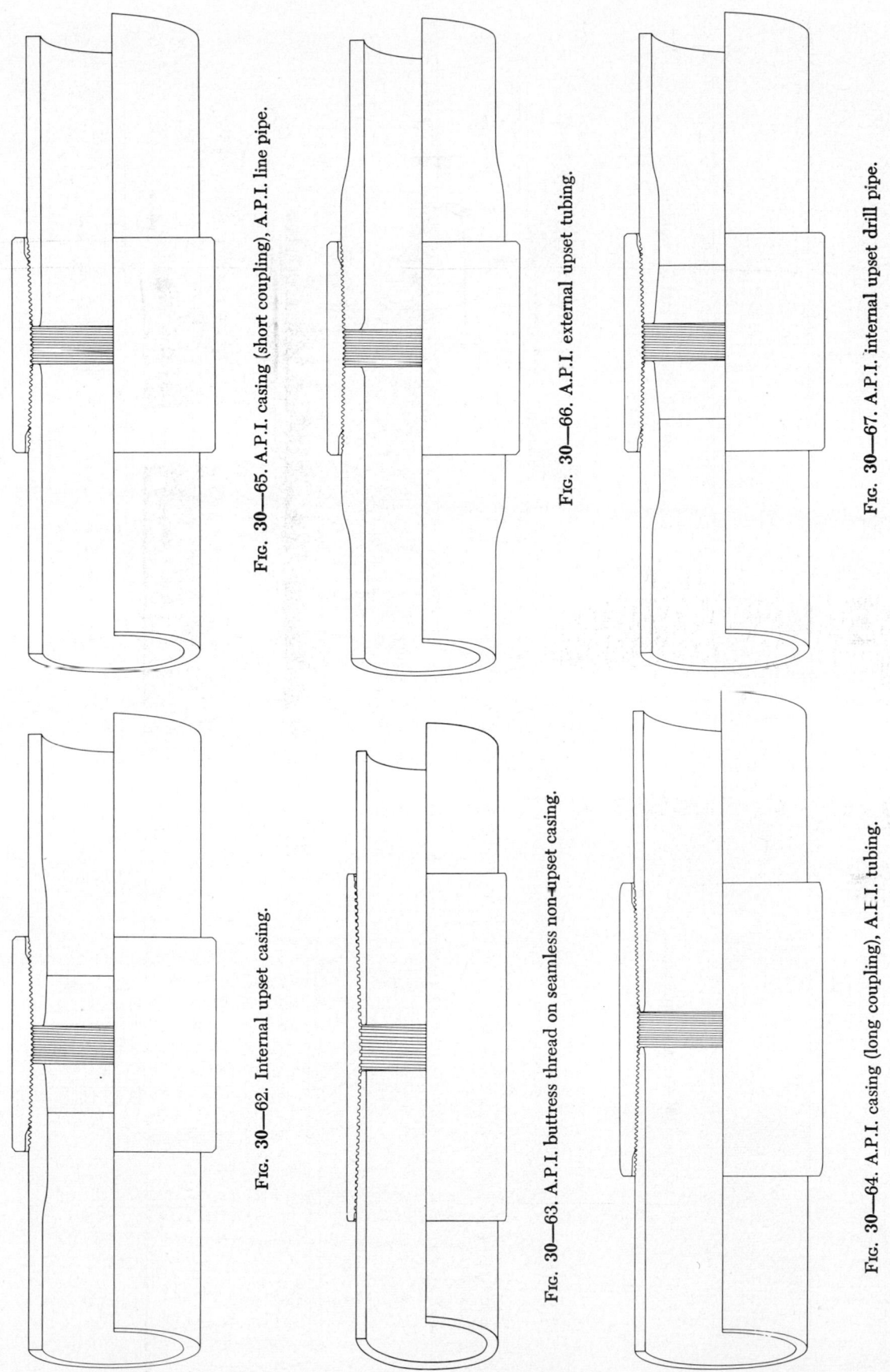

Fig. 30—65. A.P.I. casing (short coupling), A.P.I. line pipe.

Fig. 30—66. A.P.I. external upset tubing.

Fig. 30—67. A.P.I. internal upset drill pipe.

Fig. 30—62. Internal upset casing.

Fig. 30—63. A.P.I. buttress thread on seamless non-upset casing.

Fig. 30—64. A.P.I. casing (long coupling), A.P.I. tubing.

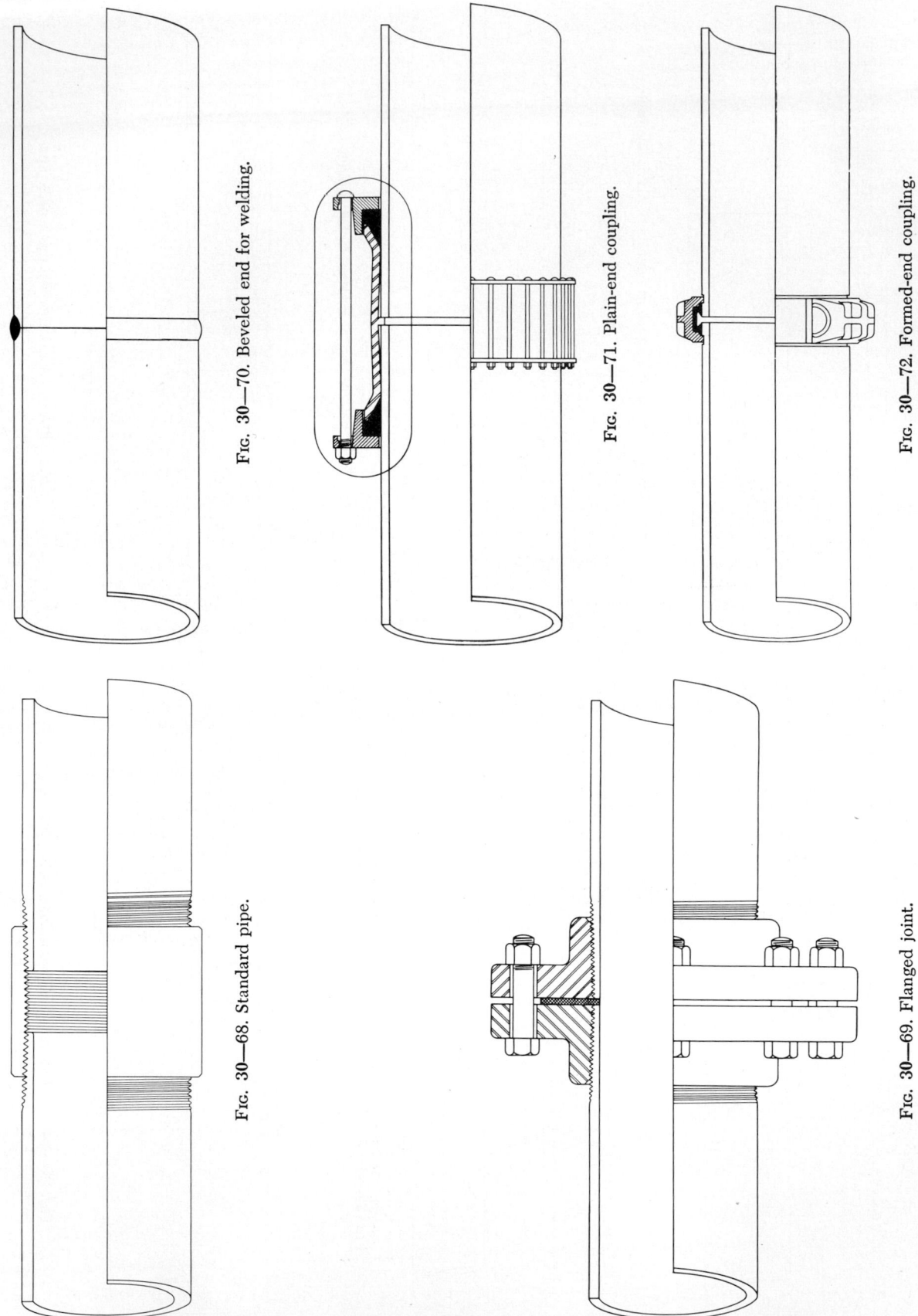

Fig. 30—70. Beveled end for welding.

Fig. 30—71. Plain-end coupling.

Fig. 30—72. Formed-end coupling.

Fig. 30—68. Standard pipe.

Fig. 30—69. Flanged joint.

in the thread length, each of these dimensions being greater in A.P.I. line pipe than in standard pipe. The American Petroleum Institute has since adopted the American Standards Association thread lengths for line pipe, thus eliminating the longer line-pipe threads. Line-pipe and standard-pipe couplings may now be used on pipe threaded to either the A.P.I. or A.S.A. specifications. The threaded line-pipe joint, however, is subject to higher test pressures since, in actual service, line pipe is generally subject to far higher working pressures than is standard pipe; the latter being more suitable for low-pressure work, such as piping for plumbing and sprinkler systems.

A.P.I. External Upset Tubing—A.P.I. external upset tubing (Figure 30—66) is desirable for deeper wells and for wells of any depth that are pumped. Both ends of the tubing are externally upset in order that the metal area at the root of the first exposed thread, when the joint is properly made up, may be at least equal to the metal area in the body of the pipe and thus of equal strength in tension. This tubing can therefore better absorb the dynamic stresses induced by pumping as the possibility of a fatigue failure in the threaded section is reduced to a minimum.

A.P.I. Standard Tubing—A.P.I. standard (or nonupset) tubing is generally used in open-flow wells and in shallow wells where tubing is pulled from the well infrequently and is a medium for pumping or otherwise raising oil to the well surface and thence to storage tanks. The A.P.I. standard tubing joint is similar in general outline to the A.P.I. casing (long coupling) joint (Figure 30—64).

A.P.I. Internal Upset Drill Pipe—The drill-pipe joint (Figure 30—67), which is manufactured with upset end, is subject to still greater and far more complex loading, since strings of drill pipe as long as 20,000 feet are supported by one joint which also transmits the torque from the rotary table to the body of the pipe and ultimately to the bit. The bit, in turn, revolving at high speed is subject to varying degrees of pressure, depending on the formation being drilled. Where cavings occur, the pressure on the bit, expressed in terms of column loading, is sometimes sufficient to induce very high stresses in the joints. Drill pipe is also subject to high internal mud pressure, which is required to wash cuttings to the surface and to act as a lubricant while drilling. While the joint as shown in Figure 30—67 is still the A.P.I. standard, most strings of drill pipe are now fitted throughout with tool joints; and the design of these tool joints is such that the greater part of the stresses incidental to drilling pass from the body of the pipe through the tool joint and into the next pipe section, thus reducing the possibility of V-notch failures through the threaded section of pipe. This is accomplished by flash-welding the tool joint to the upset, or by welding the tool joint to the body of the pipe back from the threaded end, or by shrink-fitting an extension in the tool joint to a special external upset and machined pipe end. Since it is not the purpose here to describe types and uses of tool joints, the reader is referred to A.P.I. Specifications 7-B and to the catalogs of various tool-joint manufacturers.

Standard Pipe—The standard pipe joint (Figure 30—68), while primarily intended for low-pressure steam, gas, and water lines, as found in buildings and industrial plants, is also used for structural purposes, as in hand railing, scaffolding, etc. This joint has been superseded for long transportation lines by the A.P.I. line-pipe joint and welded line-pipe joint.

Flanged Joints—While only one type of flanged joint (a threaded-flange joint) is illustrated in Figure 30—69, there are a number of other types of flanged joints that may be more suitably adapted to specific problems, and the fact that they are not described or illustrated does not in any way detract from their recognized merits.

Pipe to be fitted with standard screwed flanges is threaded to A.S.A. Standards (Briggs' threads). The flanges for use with steel pipe are generally manufactured from forged or alloy steel, depending on the temperature and pressure to which they are to be subjected. Joints of this type (Figure 30—69) are used for power plants, refineries, etc., where working pressures of 1,500 pounds per square inch and temperatures of 1000° F are quite common.

Dresser-Type Joint (Plain-End Coupling)—This joint (Figure 30—71) has been frequently used for transportation of high-pressure natural gas, also for low-pressure oil and water lines. It is easily and rapidly assembled and is made leakproof by tightening the bolts, thus exerting pressure on the gaskets and in turn on the pipe perimeter. The two gaskets are of rubber, or other suitable material, depending on the temperature to which the joint is to be subjected, and also upon the corrosive action of the fluid being carried in the pipe. The joint is designed to accommodate contraction or expansion due to temperature changes encountered in the line, and will also take care of a certain amount of misalignment. The ends of the pipe for Dresser-type couplings are gaged to specified diameter and roundness tolerances to insure proper assembly in the field.

Victaulic Joint (Formed-End Coupling)—Like the Dresser-type joint, the Victaulic joint (Figure 30—72) is quickly assembled and designed to take up expansion or contraction due to normal temperature changes. This joint will also absorb a certain amount of angular misalignment. Figure 30—72 shows the grooved-end type of joint, the pipe ends being grooved or machined out to provide a seat for the coupling. Other formed pipe ends used with Victaulic couplings are:

1. The shouldered end.
2. The expanded end.
3. The folded-back end.

Of these, the expanded end is most generally used. The pipe ends are expanded in an upsetting machine and finished to the specified dimensions. The joint is assembled by first lubricating the pipe ends, and then slipping the ring gasket over one pipe end, after which the second pipe end is brought into position and the ring moved over to cover both ends of pipe. The metal housing or coupling, made in two sections, is mounted over the ring gasket so that it fits into the grooves or over the expanded or shouldered pipe ends, and is made leakproof by tightening the bolts,

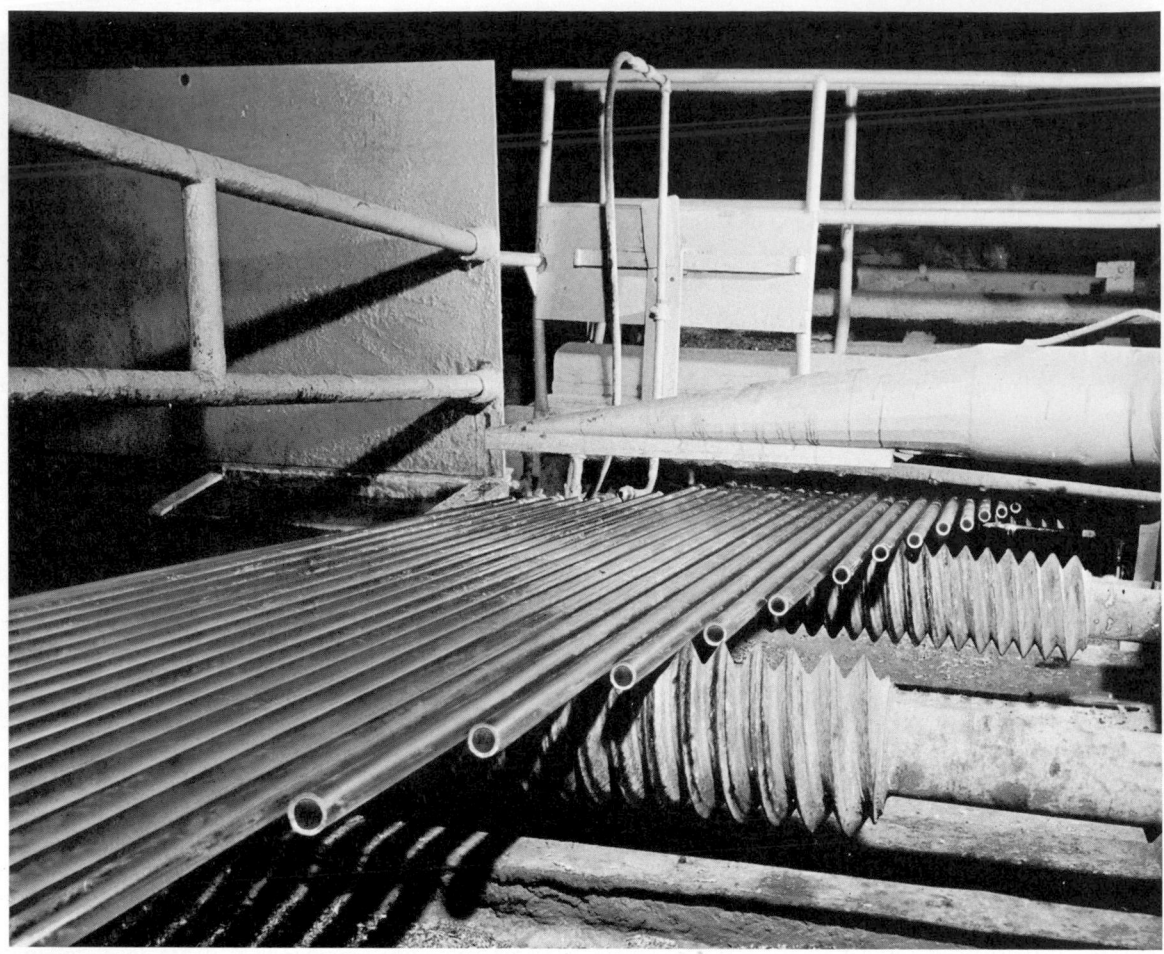

Fig. 30—73. Pipe discharging from a continuous galvanizing kettle.

thus forcing the gasket against the pipe face. As will be seen in the illustration, the gasket is so formed that pressure inside the pipe tends to increase the resistance to leakage.

Galvanizing—The hot-dip process of galvanizing is widely used for applying zinc coating to steel pipe for protection from corrosion. The pipe is first thoroughly cleaned by washing in a water solution of caustic soda to remove all traces of oil, paint and grease. It is then pickled in a hot, dilute sulphuric-acid solution (containing an inhibiting agent) to remove all rust and mill scale, after which it is washed free of adhering acid by immersing in a bath of fresh, clean water. The fluxing operation then follows and is accomplished by immersing the pipe in a hot solution of zinc ammonium chloride until the temperature of the pipe approximates that of the solution. Upon removal from the fluxing tank, the pipe is thoroughly drained, then placed on the charging table of the galvanizing kettle where it is introduced into a bath of molten zinc maintained at a temperature of about 870° F. When the pipe has been immersed for a time sufficient to permit its temperature to reach that of the molten zinc, it is withdrawn slowly in an inclined position to permit the excess zinc to drain from both the inside and outside. It·is

then conveyed through the cooling tanks, at which time it is given a special chromate treatment which aids in preserving the bright, metallic appearance of the zinc coating.

Several methods are employed for processing pipe through the galvanizing kettle. An outstanding development is the continuous method of processing pipe in the size range ½-inch to 2 inches inclusive, whereby the pipe are handled on a series of spiral-groove rolls which rotate the pipe with a screw-feed motion, imparting forward and lateral travel through the galvanizing kettle (Figure 30—73). This is accomplished by automatically charging the pipe on an inclined table equipped with spiral-groove rolls, the pipe moving on a downward slope of approximately 10 degrees and entering the kettle at the corner of one end. The pipe continues downward into the·kettle until it is completely immersed, the direction of slope is changed from downward to upward by pivoting the pipe on the center roll. The pipe continues traveling forward and laterally, leaving the kettle at the diagonally opposite corner. A low-pressure air blast is directed on the pipe on the outgoing table, as it emerges from the kettle, to set the coating and maintain a smooth surface and bright luster. The pipe is then discharged into a tank containing a dilute solution of sodium dichromate.

The continuous method of galvanizing pipe has the advantage of a high production rate and uniform and closely controlled operation, ½-inch standard pipe, for example, being galvanized at a rate of 1250 pieces per hour. With bath temperature and immersion time closely controlled, a decided improvement is obtained in the uniformity of the inside and outside coating of the pipe. A full coating is also obtained, as the pipe is not wiped. This provides a surface coating of almost pure zinc which is believed to have corrosion resistance superior to pipe which has been wiped.

Galvanized pipe in sizes over 2 inches is processed by the batch method wherein the pipe is charged into the galvanizing kettle in batches, the amount of the batch depending on the size of the pipe being processed. In this process, the pipe are submerged by a sinking-arm arrangement and after a short interval are withdrawn from the kettle by a magnet, the pipe being pulled out of the kettle on an inclined plane to provide drainage of the excess zinc from the inside and outside surface. No wiping operation is normally employed on pipe processed by the batch method; however, in galvanizing pipe in sizes smaller than ½-inch or pipe requiring an exceptionally smooth surface and a minimum weight of coating, the pipe is withdrawn from the kettle on single-draw magnetic rollers, the excess zinc being air-wiped from the outside and blown from the inside surface during withdrawal.

Value of Zinc Coating for Pipe—Though zinc coating is readily soluble in dilute acids, strong alkalies and some mineral-salt solutions, galvanizing affords effective protection against ordinary atmospheric corrosion, because the zinc, when exposed to the air, immediately reacts with oxygen to form zinc oxide. This reaction progresses only to a limited extent, however, for the oxide remains as a thin film on the surface of the zinc coating, and protects the zinc from further oxidation. Since this oxide is insoluble in water and since the film adheres rather tenaciously to the zinc, it protects the underlying coating of zinc against all ordinary types of weathering, and as long as the zinc remains intact, the steel beneath is secure from corrosive action. If the zinc coating is broken,

by bending or abrasion, and the underlying steel is exposed to corrosive influences, the zinc will still afford considerable protection. Being electropositive to the steel, the zinc is dissolved instead of the steel as long as any zinc remains closely adjacent to the exposed steel. In underground piping, where the pipe is in direct contact with the earth, galvanizing is not generally suitable as protection against corrosion, because it may be quickly destroyed either by certain acids or by certain alkali substances in the soil.

Bibliography

Am. Institute of Mining and Metallurgical Engineers, Tube producing practice (Institute of Metals Div. Symposium Series, vol. 4) N. Y., The Institute, 1951.
(Schroeder, J. W., The metallurgical factors affecting the production of seamless pipe, p. 57-68)

Am. Iron and Steel Institute, Steel products manual: Steel tubular products (Section 18) N. Y., The Institute, 1951.

Bray, T. J., Manufacture of welded steel tubing. Engineers Society of Western Pennsylvania Proceedings, 1888.

Brown, D. I., How National Tube hot extrudes stainless steel tubing. Iron Age 171, 129-133 (March 19, 1953)

Camp, J. M. and C. B. Francis, The making, shaping and treating of steel; 4th ed. Pgh., Carnegie Steel Co., 1925 (The lap-weld process, pp. 1043-1059)

Herb, C. O., Steel tubing made by resistance welding. Machinery 44, 1-5 (Sept. 1937)

Loewy, E., Latest developments in extrusion of metals. Assn. of Iron and Steel Engineers, Yearly Proceedings, 1952, p. 225-230.

New tube extrusion process at Babcock and Wilcox Co. Assn. of Iron and Steel Engineers, Yearly Proceedings, 1952, p. 338-342.

Sanders, E. N., Progress in steel pipe manufacture with particular reference to seamless pipe. Am. Iron and Steel Institute Yearbook, 1947, p. 446-454; Discussion, 454-458.

Sejournet, J., The extrusion of steel-equipment, operation, production. Assn. of Iron and Steel Engineers, Yearly Proceedings, 1953, p. 71-76.

Sutherland, W. C., The Pilger tube mill of the Pittsburgh Steel Products Company. Am. Iron and Steel Institute Yearbook, 1927, p. 117-131; Discussion, 132-134.

Thirty-inch pipeline. Steel 120, 74-75 (March 24, 1947)

Wilder, A. B., When stronger line pipe is needed . . . pipeliners will get it. Oil and Gas Journal 54, 130-133 (May 9, 1955)

Wright, E. C. and S. Findlater, Manufacture of seamless steel pipe in the plants of the National Tube Co. Iron and Steel Institute Journal 138, 109 P-124 P (1938)

CHAPTER 31

The Manufacture of Hot-Strip
Mill Products

SECTION 1

CLASSIFICATION OF FLAT-ROLLED STEEL PRODUCTS

The products of the hot-strip mill are classed among flat-rolled steel products. About half of the rolled-steel products now made in the United States may be classed as flat-rolled material. Flat-rolled steel products (including sheets, strip, tin plate, black plate, flat bars, slabs, plates, skelp and hoop) may be distinguished from other forms of rolled steel in two general ways. First, flat-rolled steel is produced on rolls with smooth faces in contrast with the cut or grooved roll faces employed in the manufacture of shapes and, second, in flat-rolled products the ratio of width to thickness is generally high as distinguished from other rolled products. The ranges of dimensions are wide, varying in thickness from 0.005 inch in light strip to 15 inches in heavy plates, and in width from 3/16 inch in narrow strip to 204 inches in wide plates.

Sheets, strip and tin plate comprise about three-fourths of the total tonnage of all flat-rolled steel products. Total net shipments of all grades of these commodities from mills in the United States in 1961, according to the Annual Statistical Report of the American Iron and Steel Institute for that year, were as follows:

Hot-rolled Sheet and Strip...........	8,240,000 net tons
Cold-rolled Sheet...................	12,153,000 net tons
Cold-rolled Strip...................	1,254,000 net tons
Galvanized Sheet...................	3,330,000 net tons
Other Coated Sheet.................	256,000 net tons
Electrical Sheet and Strip...........	527,000 net tons
Tin, Terne and Black Plate.........	6,122,000 net tons
Total	31,882,000 net tons

Flat-rolled steel products fall into two major categories: hot rolled and cold rolled. Hot-rolled products are reduced to final thickness by heating and rolling at elevated temperature. Hot rolling usually is conducted at temperatures between 2200° and 1200° F, except in the case of pack-rolled sheets for some purposes where the finishing temperatures may be as low as 900° F. In ordinary practice, virtually all hot rolling is conducted well above 1300° F, the "lower critical temperature" of plain carbon steel. Cold-rolled products are really "cold finished" products, since much of the reduction from ingot to final thickness is, of course, done while the product is hot, in a manner similar to that em-

ployed for hot-rolled products. Cold rolling is carried out on products which have not been heated immediately prior to the cold-rolling operation in which they are reduced to final thickness. However, the temperature of the steel is raised due to frictional effects of rolling. The temperature of the steel in coils immediately after cold reduction has been measured, and coil temperatures ranging from 250° to 450° F have been recorded: the temperature of the steel in the actual nip of the rolls is probably higher than this, but is quickly lowered by the coolants used in rolling. The important distinction is that cold-rolled products receive enough cold reduction in the final rolling operation to affect the surface and mechanical properties of the finished product.

Flat-rolled steel products include both semifinished and finished materials. Among the **semifinished** products are **slabs** (Chapter 22) and **flat bars** (Chapter 28). An important semifinished flat-rolled product of the hot-strip mill, which will be discussed later in this chapter, is **hot-rolled breakdowns for cold reduction, in coils.**

The chief hot-rolled **finished** flat products are divided into four major groups, namely, **bars, plate, hot-rolled strip,** and **hot-rolled sheets.** Dimensions, particularly thickness and width, are the principal bases of classification.

In this chapter, finished, flat-rolled carbon steel produced within the following dimensional limitations is considered to be **sheets,** whether in cut lengths or in coils:

Thickness Range (In.)	Width Range (In.)
0.2299 to 0.1800	Over 12 to 48, incl.
0.1799 to 0.0449	Over 12 to over 48

By common custom, finished flat hot-rolled carbon-steel **strip** is produced in the following dimensional ranges.

Width (In.)	Thickness (In.)
Up to 3½, incl.	0.0255 to 0.2030, incl.
Over 3½ to 6, incl.	0.0344 to 0.2030, incl.
Over 6 to 12, incl.	0.0449 to 0.2299, incl.

Size limitations of bars and plates are discussed in Chapters 28 and 23, respectively.

The chief cold-rolled products, all classified as **finished,** are divided into four major groups, namely, **bars, strip, sheets,** and **black plate.** The dimensional bases for differentiating between the three latter commodities are discussed in Chapter 32; dimensional limitations for bars are given in Chapter 28. Continuous hot-strip mills roll product in very long lengths, up to several thousand feet, according to the width and thickness of the strip and the size and equipment of the mill. The product of a continuous hot-strip mill is generally produced in coil form, although it can be cut to specified lengths after rolling, either directly on the mill or as a subsequent operation.

The distinction between the hot-rolled and the cold-rolled classes of these commodities lies, as mentioned above, in the methods used to attain finished thickness. The cold-reduction process, however, applied to the hot-rolled and pickled steel imparts, after proper heat treating and finishing operations, greatly superior surface and mechanical properties to the hot-rolled counterpart of each commodity. The starting material for the cold-reduction process consists of the semifinished product of the hot-strip mill designated as hot-rolled breakdowns in coil form.

Further sub-classification of sheets, strip and black plate is necessary to approach an understanding of the diversity of characteristics which enables steel in these forms to be applied to so many important uses. As one example, most black plate actually is not used as such, but is coated with tin to produce tin plate of many varieties for many uses, including the common "tin" can. Such group subdivisions are based on steel type, product treatment, characteristic properties, and final use, and will be discussed after description of the manufacturing methods used.

SECTION 2

HISTORICAL DEVELOPMENT

The mills used for rolling flat-rolled steel products include the following, named in the order of their development:

(1) The two-high mill for hot rolling sheets in packs.
(2) The two-high mill for rolling sheared plates.
(3) The universal mill for rolling plates.
(4) The three-high or Lauth mill for rolling sheared plates.
(5) The continuous or tandem hot-strip mill for rolling sheets, strip and hot-rolled breakdowns for cold reduction in coils.
(6) The cold-reduction (cold-rolling) mill for sheets and strip.
(7) The continuous sheared plate mill.

The plate mills mentioned above are described in Chapter 23.

The method for rolling sheets on two-high, single-stand mills (described in detail in a later part of this chapter) originated between 1720 and 1728 and antedates all other methods for rolling iron and steel. Up to about 1890, the finished flat-rolled steel products could be classed as sheets, plates and bars, although many thin products, such as pipe skelp, were rolled on the merchant-bar mills. The bar mills also rolled thinner sections, and about this time there developed such a demand for very thin flats that special mills were built to supply the material. The differentiation first took place in the narrower widths, ranging from ⅝ inch to 3 inches, and from 0.065 to 0.028 inch in thickness. The higher grades of this material were designated as **hoop;** a common grade was known as **cotton tie.** In 1890, **bands** 14⅝ inches by 0.14 inch were rolled at Warren, Ohio and, in 1892, a mill designed to roll sheets in tandem rolls was built in Austria. In 1893, a mill at Bridgeport, Connecticut produced thin sections up to 7 inches in width and, in 1895, a semi-continuous mill was built there to produce thin hot-rolled products up to 10 inches wide. In rolling on these first mills it was found that the limits as to width and thickness bore a certain relation to each other. In the Bridgeport mill, the ratios of width to thickness of product varied between 100 and 160. From these beginnings, the widths within the same range of thicknesses were increased at intervals by various producing mills until, in 1920, steel 22 inches wide and 0.105 inches thick was rolled successfully at Weirton, West Virginia. Some of the product of the successful strip mills subsequently was pickled and cold rolled, when it was designated as **cold-rolled strip steel,** but much of it was used as rolled and was known as **bands, band steel,** or **hot-rolled strip.** In 1920, therefore, flat-rolled products were classed commercially as sheets, plates, bars, bands and hoop, although the use of the term "strip" commonly was applied to the light products, which were somewhat narrower than the heavier sheets rolled on pack mills.

Up to 1920, it was customary to observe a certain width-to-thickness ratio in the hot rolling of strip, and the maximum ratio for successful hot rolling was considered at that time to be 250. In 1923, however, a continuous hot-rolling mill at Ashland, Kentucky, began rolling much wider strip, the widest and thinnest being 36 inches by 0.065 inch. This mill can be considered the forerunner of the modern continuous wide hot-strip mills described later in this chapter.

In 1926, at Butler, Pennsylvania, the first mill was built to combine successfully use of the following principles: (a) four-high finishing stands; (b) control of the direction of travel of steel through the pass line of the tandem finishing mills by progressively decreasing the product crown in successive mill passes, and (c) hot-coiling equipment at the discharge end of the mill. This installation was the first of the modern wide continuous hot-strip mills as known today.

SECTION 3

SOURCES AND TYPES OF STEEL FOR SHEETS, STRIP AND TIN PLATES

Chemical Compositions—Steel compositions used for the manufacture of thin, flat steel products range from so-called "pure iron," in which the sum of all elements other than iron in the product is less than one-third of one per cent of the total weight, to the high-alloy stainless and heat-resisting steels composed of as much as 50 per cent alloying additions. About four-fifths of the sheet, strip and tin plate tonnage rolled, however, is made from steel compositions within the following ranges (based on ladle analyses):

Element	Per Cent
Carbon	0.03 to 0.12
Manganese	0.20 to 0.60
Phosphorus	0.04 maximum
Other elements	Low as possible

This general range of compositions provides the best combination of rollability during manufacture and formability in most of the applications for which these products are used. Such compositions, too, are well suited for the production of rimmed steel, which is preferred for flat products because of the superiority of its ingot surface. Deviations from this basic composition range are deliberately employed to obtain specific desired properties in the steel, according to principles discussed later. Within the basic composition range, however, most steel plants further subdivide the indicated ranges for individual elements to fit particular production conditions or consumers' special needs. The end result of such adjustments of composition will differ from plant to plant; accordingly, most consumers' requirements are expressed best in terms of suitability for particular applications or of desired properties, with composition restricted only where a direct relationship between composition and performance is known.

Sulphur, silicon, copper, nickel and chromium generally are considered as the "other elements" of the basic composition given above. Except in the steels where they are added deliberately to produce alloy steels with definite properties, these elements offer no advantages and, when present in greater than certain amounts, may even be detrimental to the rolling or fabricating properties of steels for sheets, strip and tin plate. An effort is made to keep sulphur and chromium contents each below 0.05 per cent, and copper and nickel contents below 0.15 per cent. Silicon content naturally falls under 0.02 per cent in the rimmed and capped steels popularly used for sheets, strip and tin plate, but is present in amounts up to 0.15 per cent when this element alone is used as the deoxidizing agent in the manufacture of steel in the range of the basic low-carbon composition. Other elements seldom are found in undesirable amounts, although unusual local conditions affecting the scrap or ore supply may

result in the presence of enough molybdenum or tin, or both, in the steel to cause it to be somewhat harder in the finished condition than would be the case if these elements were absent or present in only very small amounts.

Steelmaking Processes—The steel for sheets, strip and tin plate is made in this country by the open-hearth, basic oxygen, Bessemer or electric-furnace process, each being used where it is best suited to produce steel having the desired composition and properties. Bessemer steel, for example, inherently contains larger amounts of phosphorus (totaling about 0.10 per cent) and nitrogen (about 0.015 per cent total) than open-hearth steel of otherwise similar composition; the additional stiffness imparted to certain products by the presence of these elements in the steel causes Bessemer steel to be selected for such limited applications. Stainless and some other alloy steels are melted in the electric arc or induction furnace for conversion to sheet and strip, the processes in these cases being chosen for their ability to produce alloyed grades of steel with minimum loss of valuable alloying elements in melting and finishing the steel in the furnace. However, about 95 per cent of the steel for sheet, strip and tin plate has been produced in the basic open-hearth furnace, for the following reasons.

The basic open-hearth process provides the most economical means for the utilization of scrap, pig iron and Bessemer blown metal, and for the positive control of phosphorus content of the steel by permitting its removal to the desired degree, while producing steels of suitable composition and properties for most flat-rolled products. Furnace charges vary from the duplex and "liquid metal" processes in which no scrap is used, to the opposite extreme of charging up to about 75 per cent cold scrap. Melting practices vary widely to produce steels which, although they may be made by different practices, possess closely similar characteristics when rolled into end products.

Increasing amounts of steel for flat-rolled products are being made by the basic oxygen steelmaking process.

Rimmed, capped, semi-killed and killed steels all are used for conversion to thin, flat steel products. Rimmed steels comprise more than half of the sheet, strip and tin plate tonnage made, since steel of the basic low-carbon composition given above, when properly refined, tapped and teemed, provides a naturally rimming steel that can be cast into ingots with sound surfaces and possesses a high degree of cleanliness and ductility. Mechanically-capped steel retains most of the surface qualities of rimmed steel and provides more uniformity of hardness throughout the cross-sections of rolled products, while increasing the yield of sound steel obtained from each ingot. This modification of rimmed steel by mechanical capping is, therefore, of importance in producing steel for such an application as tin plate where a controlled degree of uniform stiffness is desirable in the end product. Aluminum capping or top killing also is employed; in this practice, the rimming action is stopped after having progressed to the desired point by adding aluminum to the molten steel in the top of the mold. The aluminum killed ("special killed" or "fine-grained") extra-deep-drawing steel is a highly specialized modification of the low-carbon type, having virtual freedom from age-hardening and, hence, unique suitability for some types of drawing operations.

Rimmed, capped and even the "special killed" low-carbon steels are cast into ingot molds without hot tops. "Semi-killed" grades, usually made to possess somewhat higher carbon and manganese contents, still allow sufficient deoxidation control (with aluminum or silicon) of gas evolution and shrinkage to provide a sound ingot from an open-topped mold. Steels having high contents of carbon or alloying elements, those fully killed to attain certain desired end properties, and occasionally the "special killed" grade, are hot-topped to eliminate the formation of "pipe" resulting from the shrinkage characteristic of the solidification of such grades. The stainless steels are the best known hot-topped steels converted to thin flat-rolled products.

Slabs—Slabs are the raw material for the modern continuous hot-strip mill. A slab is defined as a rectangular steel section having a minimum thickness of 1½ inches and minimum width not less than twice the thickness. Slabs are generally provided in thicknesses of 2 to 7 inches, widths of 12 to 64 inches, and lengths of 60 to 240 inches, depending on strip-mill requirements. They must be accurate enough in dimensions and sound enough in structure to permit conversion in subsequent rolling operations with a minimum of difficulty, and their edges and surfaces must be free of injurious defects which would carry through to the finished product.

Two methods are practiced in converting steel from ingot form to slab and then to hot-rolled sheets, strip or breakdowns for cold reduction. By one procedure, the ingots may be heated in soaking pits and rolled on a blooming or slabbing mill to slabs of the required width and thickness, then sheared to length and immediately passed along to the hot-strip mill for final reduction to desired thickness, without reheating. The second and most generally used method is similar to the foregoing, except that the slabs are allowed to cool after being sheared to length at the slab-producing mill. The cooled slabs then are laid out for inspection to locate visible surface and edge defects which are marked for conditioning by the procedures described in Chapter 22. The conditioned slabs then are charged into reheating furnaces at the continuous hot-strip mill.

The first or single-heating method described above results in substantially lower fuel costs and minimizes handling and conditioning expenses, but does not provide sufficient flexibility in scheduling hot-strip mills rolling a widely varying product mix or a substantial portion of small orders. The reheating method

(the second described above) has proven more advantageous as it provides full flexibility of hot-strip mill scheduling, permits closer metallurgical control of steel-rolling temperatures and minimizes injurious steel-surface defects resulting from defective slab areas.

In accordance with the latter practice, conversion of ingots to slabs is effected by the following typical steps: After stripping, the ingots are charged in the soaking pits of a blooming or slabbing mill and brought to a uniform temperature, approximately 2400° F for the low-carbon steel grades which comprise the bulk of this tonnage. They then are removed by crane-borne tongs to ingot buggies that convey them to the entry roll table of the slabbing or blooming mill. Some mills are equipped with turntables at this point which automatically record ingot weight and place the ingots butt first with respect to the rolling stands and shears; this practice is advantageous as it provides a close check on ingot weight and efficient control of end scrap. Ingots then are passed along a roller table to the reducing stand, consisting of a slabbing mill or a blooming mill of the single stand, reversing type. The slabbing mill is equipped with both horizontal and vertical rolls that work on all four sides of the ingot simultaneously, while the blooming mill operates with horizontal rolls only (see Chapter 22). Greater tonnages and wide slab sections can be produced on the slabbing mills as a result of this difference in design. After reduction to the prescribed slab thickness and width, the elongated slab is advanced toward a shear at the end of the mill roller table. Some mills, at a point between the reducing stand and the shears, are equipped with automatic flame scarfing equipment for the purpose of removing all but the worst edge or surface defects from the slab. The shears cut the slab product to the designated lengths, cropping sufficient scrap from the two ends of the slab, corresponding to what originally was the top and bottom of the ingot, respectively, to insure elimination of pipe, porosity, mechanical end laps, slag deposits, and so on.

Immediately after hot shearing, the slabs are hot stamped with identification markings, such as heat number, ingot number and cut number. After shearing and stamping, the slabs are piled on cooling beds and permitted to cool to a workable temperature, then laid out individually for inspection and marking of surface and edge defects such as scabs, ingot cracks, spongy surface, breaks, tears, and so on which, if not removed, would result in surface slivers, scabs, skin laminations or cracked edges on the finished strip. The defects are removed by scarfing with an oxy-acetylene torch or, on stainless steels, by grinding with abrasive wheels or powder scarfing. The slabs then are repiled, and each is painted with identifying information normally including heat, ingot and cut numbers, thickness, width, weight and code letters or numerals representing chemical composition and steelmaking process.

The finished slabs finally are transported to the storage yard of the hot-strip mill, where they are stacked in orderly fashion according to size and steel grade to facilitate their selection and charging into magazines feeding the reheating furnaces of the hot-strip mill.

SECTION 4

CONTINUOUS HOT-STRIP MILLS

Development and Output—The terms "strip" and "sheet," as applied to the finished products, have definite reference to width and gage limitations, as shown in Section 1 of this chapter, and the term "hot-rolled breakdowns for cold reduction" defines a semifinished product for subsequent rolling by another process. These distinctions do not exist when the terms are used in connection with a continuous mill rolling such products; thus, a mill rolling continuous lengths of strip, sheet, or breakdowns commonly is known as a "strip mill." The history of development of continuous hot-strip mills was summarized in Section 2 of this chapter.

As of July, 1961, forty-two wide continuous hot-strip mills were in operation in the United States, their combined annual capacity being approximately 63,-651,000 net tons. As a group, the wide strip mills roll flat steel in thicknesses of 0.04 inch to 1.25 inches, widths of 24 to 96 inches, and lengths up to 2,000 feet. Each mill has its own limitations as to sizes of finished product though, as a general rule, no mill exceeds a product width-to-thickness ratio of 1000:1.

General Arrangement of Modern Mills—The modern wide hot-strip mill has become quite standardized in its general layout. Slabs are heated in two or more continuous reheating furnaces. A typical rolling train will consist of a roughing scalebreaker, four four-high roughing stands, a finishing scalebreaker, and six four-high finishing stands. Driven table rolls convey the steel from furnace to mill and also from stand to stand. If the mill is to produce strip, sheets or breakdowns of greater width than the maximum width of slab available, the first rougher or roughing stand is a broadside mill in which the width of the slab is increased in a single pass by cross rolling. In this case, turntables for manipulating the slab must precede and follow this stand. A slab squeezer also follows the broadside mill. The next three roughing stands usually are provided with integral vertical edgers in front of each stand. Separating the roughing train from the finishing train is a holding table, while the finishing end is a closely grouped tandem train composed of the finishing scalebreaker and six finishing stands.

High-pressure hydraulic sprays to remove scale from the hot slab are located after the two scalebreakers and perhaps at several roughing stands. Water is supplied to the spray nozzles by suitable high-pressure pumps.

Following the last finishing stand there is usually a flying shear for cutting the rolled product into lengths, if so desired. As the steel proceeds from the mill, it is carried over a long table called the runout table, consisting of individually driven rollers. Two or more coilers are located in this table; they operate to coil the material when continuous long lengths are required. If short lengths are cut at the flying shears, the coilers are inoperative and the steel passes over them and onto a piler at the end of the table. Additional tables may be installed parallel to the central runout table, with

suitable transfers for moving material to them; this equipment is used principally when the heavier gages are being rolled.

The most commonly used hot-mill arrangement just described, employing continuous roughing and continuous finishing trains, provides high rolling capacity and rapid steel travel with little loss of heat, but entails a high installation cost and a fixed number of passes, with some loss of flexibility in making rapid changes in the mill set-up when the size of product to be rolled is changed. An alternate arrangement, used in several instances, employs a reversing roughing mill and a continuous finishing train; this arrangement has a lower original installation cost, requires less floor space, and is flexible with regard to the number of passes available, but at a sacrifice in capacity and operating cost. Another modification of the conventional mill (the single-heating practice already described) provides for rolling the slab direct from the blooming operation, utilizing retained heat and by-passing the slab-reheating furnace; this practice saves fuel but sacrifices flexibility of scheduling rolling operations on the continuous hot mill.

Still another arrangement for continuous hot rolling of steel calls for the use of a reversing hot mill for finishing. This mill may have a conventional roughing train or single reversing stand for roughing, followed by the single reversing finishing mill. The reversing finishing mill has a pair of pinch rolls and a paddle-type coiler located on both sides (entry and exit) of the mill. The coilers operate inside of small heating furnaces which keep the steel hot and permit the finishing rolling operation to be carried out by repeated reversing of the finishing stand. This type of mill entails low initial cost and is highly satisfactory for the production of small orders or the rolling of alloy steels.

Control of Finished Product Quality—When an order is accepted for production by a particular mill, the first step taken is to determine the proper grade of steel and the size and surface quality of the slab necessary to make the order. The order is then grouped with others and scheduled in its proper rolling sequence. The principal factors taken into consideration at this important stage are rolling width, gage, and steel composition.

The next step in production requiring control is the operation of heating the slabs to rolling temperature. The slabs must be heated uniformly throughout, and also must have a uniform "scale jacket" that will "clean up" readily in rolling. Many rolling delays and mechanical difficulties are a direct result of poor heating practice; the steel may not be "soaked" sufficiently, may be too hot, too cold, or unduly hard to clean.

The third step is to rough down the slab to a predetermined intermediate thickness. As the slab leaves the last roughing stand, it should be flat, straight, free of furnace scale, true to width and of a cross-section suitable for further reduction on the finishing stands. The first rolling pass on the slab is done on a scalebreaker which is followed immediately with a high-pressure hydraulic spray to facilitate removal of the furnace scale. In addition, there are usually one or two more descaling sprays following the second or third roughing stands and numerous steam and air sprays available to remove any further scale that may be loosened during rolling or edging. Proper use of the broadside mill, slab squeezer and the three vertical edgers normally will guarantee the uniform width essential for all subsequent operations.

Next, the finishing train must be operated with careful regulation to obtain a finished hot-rolled product of prime quality. As mentioned later in this chapter and as discussed in Chapter 20 on "Rolling Mills," various automatic-control elements have been incorporated in mill design to assist the operators in producing strip of uniformly high quality. Surface, gage, width, finishing temperature and cross-sectional contour of the product, all are required to meet given standards depending upon the subsequent treatment or ultimate use of the material in question. As an example, metallurgical requirements may dictate a definite finishing temperature for a particular gage and width to be rolled. Time on the holding table prior to coiling, number of descaling sprays used during rolling in the finishing stands, speed of the finishing train, and method of drafting, all affect the finishing temperature and may be varied at the discretion of the operator to help meet requirements. Defects in the surface of the rolled steel, if not evident in the rough slab, usually can be traced to defects in the surfaces of the work rolls on the finishing stands and are corrected readily by substituting newly-surfaced work rolls. The principal factors affecting the overall dimensional accuracy of the finished hot-rolled product include contour of the work rolls and back-up rolls as installed, changes in the contour of the work rolls and back-up rolls due to intermittent heating and cooling, method of drafting (i.e., amount of reduction in successive passes), and rolling sequence of various gages and widths. Also involved in the occurrence of gage (thickness) variations in hot-rolled strip are: the difference in the speed of the strip leaving the last roughing stand and the entry speed of the strip entering the first finishing stand, which results in temperature variations along the length of the strip; and variations in the tension applied to the strip between stands. Many of these factors that affect product quality are amenable to control by automatic means to assist the mill operators in achieving the best results from the rolling operation by minimizing the number of elements that otherwise must be manually controlled. Some of the control principles are discussed in Chapter 20 on "Rolling Mills."

Figure 31—1 shows typical reductions per pass in the finishing train of a continuous wide hot-strip mill.

The final step in rolling an order on a strip mill is disposition of the hot-rolled product. On some mills, the product may be cut into shorter lengths on a flying shear located at the exit end of the mill, the sheared pieces progressing along the runout table to a hot piler. The greater portion of hot-rolled flat material, however, is handled by the hot-coiling method; this includes the semifinished product designated as hot-rolled breakdowns in coils for subsequent cold reduction, as well as hot-rolled sheets in coils which may be shipped as such or transferred to the finishing department where they are uncoiled and processed into the form of flat cut sheets. The essential requirements of the coiler are to receive the material at mill speeds and coil it tightly without excessive tension, telescoping, scratching or marking and, finally, discharge the finished coil quickly without damage.

An 80-inch Continuous Hot-Strip Mill—The 80-inch hot-strip mill at the Gary Sheet and Tin Mill of United States Steel Corporation serves as an example of the wide continuous mill. This mill, built originally in 1935, was modernized completely in 1948 and, through continuous additions and improvements, has maintained its position as a highly efficient production unit.

Slabs for the mill may range in size from 4 to 7½ inches in thickness, 18 to 64 inches in width and 80 to 216 inches in length. The conditioned slabs, as needed, are carried by overhead crane to the individual storage machine located in front of the charging end of each of the five slab-reheating furnaces, which extend at right angles to the hot-strip mill building. The slab pushers of each furnace travel under the corresponding storage magazine and push the bottom slab of the pile in the magazine onto the charging table. This table is equipped with driven rollers to position the slabs properly before the furnace doors. When the slabs are in position on the charging table, they are shoved over skids into the furnace by pushers (Figure 31—2) operated by 150-horsepower, 500 r.p.m., DC motors through worm reduction drives. These are controlled from an operating platform behind the charging end of the furnaces. The doors of the furnaces also are controlled from there and are arranged so that, when the charging door is opened to push a slab into the furnace, the door on the delivery end simultaneously opens, permitting a slab to be discharged over an apron onto a roller table (Figure 31—3).

The five furnaces all are of the zone-controlled, triple-fired, recuperative, continuous type. Each furnace is 80 feet long by 20 feet wide and is capable of heating approximately 105 tons of steel slabs per hour to a maximum of 2400° F. The furnaces normally are fired with coke-oven gas or fuel oil, and are equipped with automatic combustion and temperature controls. Natural gas also may be used or a mixture of natural and coke-oven gases. Approximately 340,000 cu. ft. of coke-oven gas per hour are required to heat each furnace. Preheated air at 700° F is obtained for combustion by passing the hot products of combustion from the furnaces through recuperators. Air is pushed through the recuperators for each furnace by a motor-driven fan, rated at 50,000 cu. ft. per minute. Flue gas is conducted through underground flues to individual stacks, 150 feet high, or can be diverted to be used on two waste-heat boilers.

The slabs move through the first 60 feet of the furnaces on water-cooled skids which permit heating on both tops and bottoms. These skids use about 60,000 gallons of cooling water per hour for each furnace. The last 17 feet of the furnaces, known as the "soak-

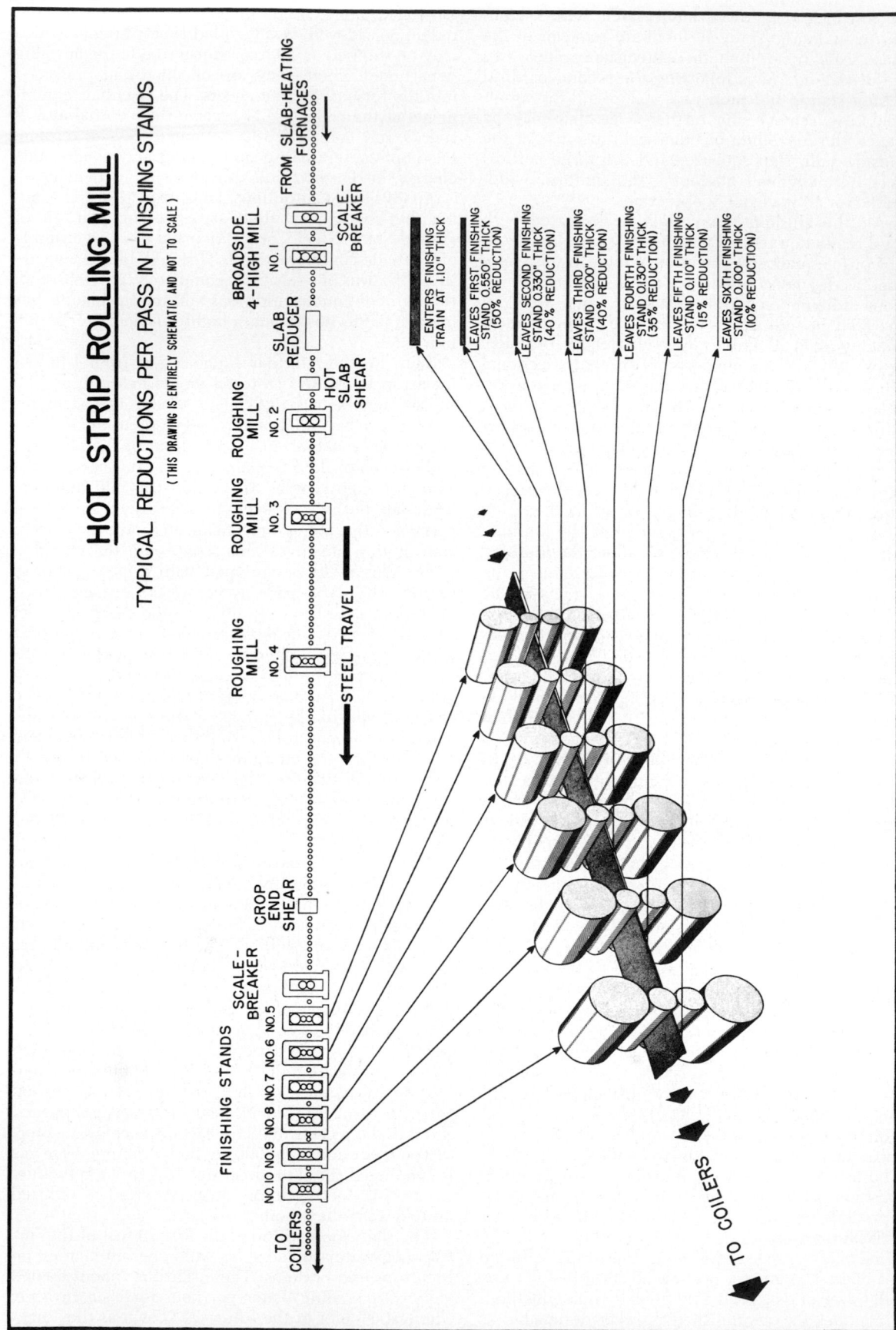

HOT STRIP ROLLING MILL

TYPICAL REDUCTIONS PER PASS IN FINISHING STANDS

(THIS DRAWING IS ENTIRELY SCHEMATIC AND NOT TO SCALE)

FROM SLAB-HEATING FURNACES

BROADSIDE 4-HIGH MILL

NO.1

SCALE-BREAKER

SLAB REDUCER

ROUGHING MILL

NO. 2

HOT SLAB SHEAR

ROUGHING MILL

NO. 3

ROUGHING MILL

NO. 4

STEEL TRAVEL

CROP END SHEAR

FINISHING STANDS

SCALE-BREAKER

NO. 10 NO.9 NO.8 NO. 7 NO. 6 NO.5

TO COILERS

ENTERS FINISHING TRAIN AT 1.10" THICK

LEAVES FIRST FINISHING STAND 0.550" THICK (50% REDUCTION)

LEAVES SECOND FINISHING STAND 0.330" THICK (40% REDUCTION)

LEAVES THIRD FINISHING STAND 0.200" THICK (40% REDUCTION)

LEAVES FOURTH FINISHING STAND 0.130" THICK (35% REDUCTION)

LEAVES FIFTH FINISHING STAND 0.110" THICK (15% REDUCTION)

LEAVES SIXTH FINISHING STAND 0.100" THICK (10% REDUCTION)

TO COILERS

FIG. 31—1. Typical reductions per pass in the finishing stands of a hot-strip rolling mill.

FIG. 31—2. Charging end of heating furnaces for an 80-inch mill, showing slabs in position before the furnace doors. In the foreground are the pushers which force the slabs through the nearest furnace.

ing zone," have a flat bottom (combination steel and brick) where the slabs are brought to a uniform temperature throughout. Accurate control of temperatures, furnace atmosphere composition, and pressure in all parts of the furnaces is facilitated by a battery of recording and indicating instruments. Doors are provided along the sides of the furnaces for observation purposes and to permit manual positioning of slabs if desired.

Slabs are discharged from the heating furnaces at temperatures ranging from 2000 to 2400° F, depending upon the grade of steel and thickness of finished product. They are carried to the mill by a roller table 245 feet long. This table is made up of six units, each

driven by a 50-horsepower motor. The table is reversible, so that, when necessary, slabs can be returned to slab storage by a transfer located parallel to the furnaces.

The first mill stand in the 80-inch hot strip mill is the No. 1 scale-breaker. This mill is a two-high, 36-inch by 80-inch stand, operated at 212 feet per minute, and driven by a 1250-horsepower, 490 r.p.m., AC motor through a double reduction-gear drive equipped with two 12½-foot flywheels. The descaling water spray following this stand operates at 1300 lb. per sq. in. pressure. Slabs travel 100 to 200 feet per minute over a 26-foot reversible table between this scale-breaker and the first roughing stand.

FIG. 31—3. Discharge ends of a group of three heating furnaces for an 80-inch mill.

The first roughing stand is a four-high 40-inch and 54-inch by 130-inch mill operated at about 182 feet per minute, driven by a 3500-horsepower, 6600-volt, 340 r.p.m., AC motor through a gear set and two 13½-foot flywheels. This stand is a broadside mill in which slabs up to 127 inches long can be spread to a maximum of 77 inches wide in a single pass, when it is necessary to produce widths greater than the original slab (Figures 31—4 and 31—5). A rack-type slab pusher on the entry side of this stand assures square and proper entry of the slab between the rolls. Slab turn-arounds are provided before and after this stand to rotate the slab through 90 degrees when the stand is used for broadsiding. Following the broadside mill, a slab squeezer serves to true up slab edges and widths and to flatten them for subsequent rolling. This squeezer has a 24-foot head with a maximum stroke of 6½ inches on a 6-inch thick slab. Slabs reach the squeezer and pass to the second roughing stand over a reversible roller table 100 feet long, in three independent sections, each driven by a 50-

horsepower, 550 r.p.m., reversible DC motor. Table speed is 120 to 240 feet per minute. A slab shear is located between the squeezer and the second roughing stand.

The second roughing stand is a 44-inch by 80-inch universal two-high mill with vertical edging rolls mounted on the entry side of the stand. This mill is driven by a 3500-horsepower, 490 r.p.m., AC motor. The gear drive is equipped with two 13½-foot flywheels. The edging rolls are driven through twin worm reduction sets by a 350-horsepower, 400 to 1000 r.p.m., DC motor. After leaving this stand, the slab passes over a reversible roller table 51 feet long, driven by a 50-horsepower, 550 r.p.m., DC motor at speeds of 178 to 356 feet per minute.

No. 3 rougher is a four-high 32-inch and 53-inch by 80-inch universal stand, as is No. 4 rougher, located 94 feet beyond No. 3. Both of these stands have vertical edging rolls mounted on the entry side, duplicates of those on the second roughing stand. Each mill is driven, through a gear set with two 13½-foot fly-

FIG. 31—4. Broadside stand of an 80-inch mill. Here slabs receive their first heavy reduction in thickness. The slab shown here has received a broadside (sideways) pass to extend it to the proper width. The turntable (slab turn-around) next will turn the slab 90 degrees before it goes on to the following roll stands.

Fig. 31—5. View of part of an 80-inch continuous mill from the operator's pulpit from which the speed of the roughing stands is controlled.

wheels, by a 3500-horsepower, 490 r.p.m., AC motor. A holding table, 200 feet long, lies between the roughing and finishing trains. This table is divided into two sections, each driven by two 50-horsepower, 550 to 1100 r.p.m., DC motors, providing table speeds from 100 to 400 feet per minute. The rolled product is cooled by holding on this table, if necessary, to attain proper finishing temperatures to meet requirements. A rotary crop shear is installed at the finishing end of the table, so that both the front and back ends of the material can be squared off before finishing.

A second scalebreaker, two-high, 36-inch by 80-inch, followed by high-pressure descaling sprays and driven by an 800-horsepower, 150 to 450 r.p.m., DC motor, precedes the finishing train. The finishing train is six four-high, 26-inch and 53-inch by 80-inch stands spaced on 22-foot centers (Figure 31—6). Each stand of the finishing train is driven by a 600-volt, DC motor. Numbers 5, 6 and 7 stand motors are of 4500-horsepower capacity, operate at 125 to 282 r.p.m., and drive through gear sets. No. 8 (4500-horsepower, 85 to 190 r.p.m.), No. 9 (4500-horsepower, 100 to 230 r.p.m.) and No. 10 (3000-horsepower, 110 to 255 r.p.m.) motors drive direct. Product speed leaving No. 10 stand reaches a maximum of 1960 feet per minute. Loopers are provided between the finishing stands, each driven through a worm reduction unit by a 200 pound-foot torque DC motor. Steam sprays are provided on the delivery side of each stand and tachometers are installed in control stations to indicate mill speeds.

The screwdown on each finishing stand in the mill is operated by two 75-horsepower, 575 r.p.m., DC motors equipped with magnetic clutches and dynamic brakes. Single 35-horsepower, 575 r.p.m., DC motors drive the screwdowns on the two scalebreakers and

the first two roughing stands through cutout clutches; two similar motors with magnetic clutches and dynamic brakes are used on No. 3 and No. 4 roughing stands. The top roll on all stands, except No. 2 scalebreaker, has a hydraulic roll balance. No. 2 scalebreaker has a spring balance.

Oil-film bearings are used on all back-up rolls in the four-high finishing stands. Grease-lubricated roller thrust bearings are used on Nos. 1 and 2 scalebreakers and 3 and 4 roughing mills, while fabric bearings are used on the back-up rolls of No. 1 roughing mill and the work rolls of No. 2 roughing mill. The mill is lubricated automatically by five separate recirculating oil systems servicing the oil-type back-up roll bearings, the pinion-stand gears and bearings of the large mill-drive motors and motor-generator sets. Grease requirements are maintained automatically by several central-station greasing systems strategically located throughout the mill.

Temperature of the product is watched carefully throughout its passage in the mill by use of one recording pyrometer and three recording-indicating pyrometers placed at the entry to No. 1 roughing stand, on the holding table, at the entry to No. 10 stand and at the entry to the coiler.

The hot-strip mill building is 95 feet wide and 2352 feet long; it is served by three 60-ton cranes with 10-ton auxiliary hoists, one 60-ton crane with 15-ton auxiliary and one 15-ton crane, all of 90-foot span. A building 92 by 624 feet, conveniently located alongside the hot mill, houses service and roll shops. The latter include roll lathes, roll grinders and special degreasing equipment for cleaning bearings. The hot-strip mill motor room, 65 by 644 feet, is served by one 50-ton crane having a 60-foot span. The twelve hot mill drives, with their reduction gears, control equip-

FIG. 31—6. General view of an 80-inch continuous hot strip mill. In the background are the roughing stands. In the center are the six finishing mills. The cooling sprays over the runout table are in the left foreground.

ment, switch-gear, etc., are located in this room (Figure 31—7). The motor room is equipped with a recirculating-type ventilating system forcing air through coolers located in the motor-room basement into the motor room proper. All make-up air is filtered before distribution. The ventilating system is designed to handle 525,000 cubic feet of air per min. at 95° F.

Power is supplied from the outdoor substation via a metal-clad bus system at 6600 volts to the switchboard and is distributed to equipment through conduit laid in the concrete floor. Variable-voltage direct current is supplied to the main motors driving the finishing train from three 3-unit, 6000-kw, 600-volt synchronous motor-generator sets, each consisting of two 3000-kw, 600-volt, DC generators driven at 360

r.p.m. by an 8600-horsepower, 6600-volt synchronous motor.

Product Disposition—After leaving the last finishing stand of a continuous hot-strip mill, the rolled product is delivered onto a long runout table where it is carried either in long lengths to coilers, or to a sheet piler in cut lengths. The 80-inch hot-strip mill being described produces only coiled product. It has a flying shear, spaced 11 feet 9 inches from the last finishing stand, which is used to crop either or both ends of product that is to be coiled as a single piece. The shear is driven by twin 150-horsepower, 450 to 900 r.p.m., DC motors.

After leaving the flying shear, the steel passes over a roller table 364 feet long, having 243 rollers, each

FIG. 31—7. Motor room of an 80-inch hot-strip mill. At the left are the motor-generator sets which supply direct current to the finishing-stand mill motors in the right foreground.

FIG. **31**—8. Coiled product leaving the coiler of an 80-inch continuous hot-strip mill.

driven by a 4-horsepower, 0 to 800 r.p.m., DC motor through rubber-ball couplings. The table is equipped with cooling sprays both above and below the rollers. Three mandrel-type coilers are installed at the end of this table, each driven by a 350-horsepower, 1200 r.p.m., DC motor. Coils with a maximum width of 77 inches, an inside diameter of 32 inches and an outside diameter up to 69 inches can be accommodated. Air-operated pushers remove the coils from the mandrels onto a coil tilter, which places coils on end onto a chain conveyor which carries them to the coil-storage building (Figure 31—8). Heavy-duty scales are installed in the hot-coil conveyor, giving an accurate check on production and yield figures.

Two 900-kw, DC generating sets and several smaller units furnish power for all of the product-disposition equipment. Two generator sets normally are allotted to flying-shear service, two to the three run-out-table sections between the flying shear and coilers and one to the three coilers. One generator is a spare which can be switched into any of the other services.

Metallurgy of Hot Strip—Wide hot-rolled strip from a modern continuous mill may be used in the as-rolled condition, in which case it is referred to as "hot-rolled sheets," with or without the application of such auxiliary treatments as pickling, shearing and flattening. When produced as hot-rolled breakdowns for cold reduction, it is pickled in coil form, cold reduced as much as 90 per cent of its original thickness, heat treated and further processed to cold-rolled sheets, strip, black plate, or the various coated sheet-mill and tin-mill products. In any case the metallurgical re-

quirements of the great bulk of the product are relatively simple and lend themselves to best operating conditions on the hot-strip mill and subsequent processing units.

The last hot-rolling operation (in the last finishing stand) should be conducted above the upper critical temperature on virtually all continuous hot-mill flat-rolled products. Such a practice permits the rolled steel to pass through a phase transformation after all hot work is finished and produces a uniformly fine, equiaxed ferritic grain throughout all portions of the steel. For the low-carbon steels generally used, proper finishing temperatures will have been attained when the apparent product temperature emerging from the last rolling stand is over 1550° F. This finishing temperature is practical over most thicknesses rolled on most modern mills at normal maximum rolling speeds.

If part of the hot rolling is conducted on steel which already has transformed partially to ferrite, the deformed ferrite grains usually will recrystallize and form patches or layers of abnormally coarse grains during the self-anneal induced by coiling or piling at the usual temperatures of 1200 to 1350° F. Such a structure is more likely to occur at the surface of the product, which is colder than the interior during rolling. Very thin hot-rolled material, inadvertently finished far below the upper critical and coiled or piled too cold to self-anneal, may retain microstructural evidence of hot-working. Neither condition is suitable for some types of severe drawing applications; both may be corrected by normalizing the sheet.

A special case occurs in the steels of the so-called

"pure-iron" or "enameling sheet" compositions, in which the sum of the carbon and manganese contents may be well under 0.10 per cent. Such compositions often exhibit a hot-short temperature range between 1650° to 1900° F, and normal hot rolling in that range may produce deep cracks on the edge of the product. Accordingly, it is the practice on many mills to complete the roughing operations above the hot-short range, to allow the steel to cool through the range by holding it on the conveyor table between the last roughing stand and the finishing train, and to resume rolling by passing the product into the finishing train below the hot-short range. By this practice it is impossible to finish above the upper critical temperature of these steels.

The runout table following the last rolling stand of most hot-strip mills is long enough and equipped with enough quenching sprays to cool the single thickness of rolled product 200 to 500° F below the finishing temperature before the continuous length or the hot-sheared sheets become a part of the 2 to 20-ton mass of steel being formed in the coiler or on the piler. In addition, some mills have auxiliary tables or holding beds which allow single-thickness cooling to a take-off temperature of 500° F or lower. The cooling practice employed largely determines the metallurgical properties of the steel, its suitability for further processing and its final applicability to the intended use.

On hot-rolled products properly finished above the upper critical temperature, a uniform ferrite grain has been established and the runout cooling practice determines the carbide characteristics and, to some extent, the grain size. The self-annealing effect of a large mass of steel coiled or piled at around 1350° F produces considerable carbide agglomeration, a coarse ferrite grain and a soft, ductile sheet. Coiling or piling around 1200° F yields a fine, dispersed spheroidal carbide in a finer ferrite matrix, resulting in a somewhat harder sheet, which still retains excellent ductility. Even more drastic quenching produces various transformation states of carbide, down to and including martensite. For most low-carbon steel made either for use as hot-rolled sheets or as breakdowns for subsequent cold reduction, coiling temperatures of 1200 to 1300° F are employed; this range provides optimum uniformity of mechanical properties without excessive scale formation or over-annealing. A few mills have resorted to quenching the hot coil in a tank of water to inhibit scale formation and provide a surface oxide which can be pickled very readily. Steels of 0.15 to 0.30 per cent carbon content and alloy steels often are quenched drastically to attain higher strength levels from finer carbide dispersions, or are coiled very hot to facilitate cold reduction.

As most heat treatment after cold reduction is carried out below the lower critical point, the cold-reduced, box-annealed microstructure usually bears a relationship to the microstructure of the hot-rolled material. In the somewhat unusual case of the aluminum-killed, cold-rolled deep-drawing sheet, coiling temperatures under 1200° F are employed when rolling breakdowns on the continuous hot mill to provide the best drawing properties in the finished cold-reduced, box-annealed sheet.

SECTION 5

HAND HOT MILLS

Development—Prior to the advent of wide continuous hot-strip mills, all sheet and tin plate products were rolled on single-stand sheet and tin plate hot mills. These mills were patterned after the crude water-power or horse-driven units used to roll lead and copper as early as 1600, which were adapted to rolling thin steel sheets for tin plating in England about 1728. Until the middle 1930's, mills of this type, designated "jobbing" mills, were used to roll heavy-gage sheets, and "pack" or "finishing" mills were used for light-gage sheets and tin plate. Except for a few isolated instances, the hand hot mill is now obsolete for the rolling of flat-rolled products. For this reason, the process will be described in the past tense.

Process—In the original manual process of hot rolling, sheet bars, a semifinished product rolled to a specified weight per linear foot and in various widths and thicknesses, were used to produce sheets. Packs made up of multiple thicknesses of steel first were prepared by "breaking down" or cross rolling sheet bars cut to the correct length to produce the width of sheet desired. The bars were heated in a bar or "pair" furnace to near the upper critical point for the steel, and then passed through the rolling mill repeatedly in pairs, one bar closely following the other through the

rolls of a two-high or three-high roughing mill. A number of final passes with the bars "matched," that is, placed one on top of the other, might be given the "breakdown" if desired to form a "pack" for finish rolling. For light gages, the pack usually was "doubled" or folded over prior to finish rolling. It should be noted that the term "breakdown," as now applied to a semifinished hot-rolled product of the hot-strip mill, does not describe the same physical type of hot-rolled product as in older practice, but does connote still an intermediate stage in the production of flat-rolled products.

In jobbing mills where sheets heavier than 16 gage and up to 90 inches wide were produced, packs or bar breakdowns, after roughing, might be rolled immediately on a two-high finishing mill, down to desired finished thickness. In plants equipped with wide continuous hot-strip mills, breakdowns and packs eventually were made from hot-rolled breakdowns produced on the continuous hot mill, thus eliminating the operation of breaking down sheet bars (roughing).

The number of sheets in the finished pack varied from two to eight according to the finished gage. While practices in different mills varied somewhat, a typical arrangement was for sheets of 14 to 18 gage to be finished in packs of twos; 19 to 22 gage, in threes; 23 to 27 gage, in fours; 27 to 29 gage, in sixes, 29 to 34 gage, in eights.

Light-gage sheets and tin plate were rolled from packs on two-high finishing mills. The packs were heated and then given successive passes through the mill until the desired thickness was obtained. Finished packs were allowed to cool, then side and end sheared to desired width and length and placed on the opening floor. During the rolling operation, the individual sheets of the pack became firmly stuck together. They were pulled apart manually with the use of tongs and "sticker-opener swords."

At this stage of production, the sheets were classi-

fied as hot-rolled only. For most uses they had to be heat treated, generally by box annealing. Additional treatments, such as pickling, cold rolling, and oiling, might be given to the sheets. The sheets also might be used as the base for galvanized, terne or tin coatings. For high-grade sheets, requiring a smooth surface free from all defects, the bars or the breakdowns might have been pickled prior to rolling. The pickling operation, in addition to removing scale, exposed defects which might have caused imperfections and rejection of finished product.

The processes and equipment required to convert ingots to finished rolled products by the foregoing methods are illustrated by the flow diagram, Figure 31—9.

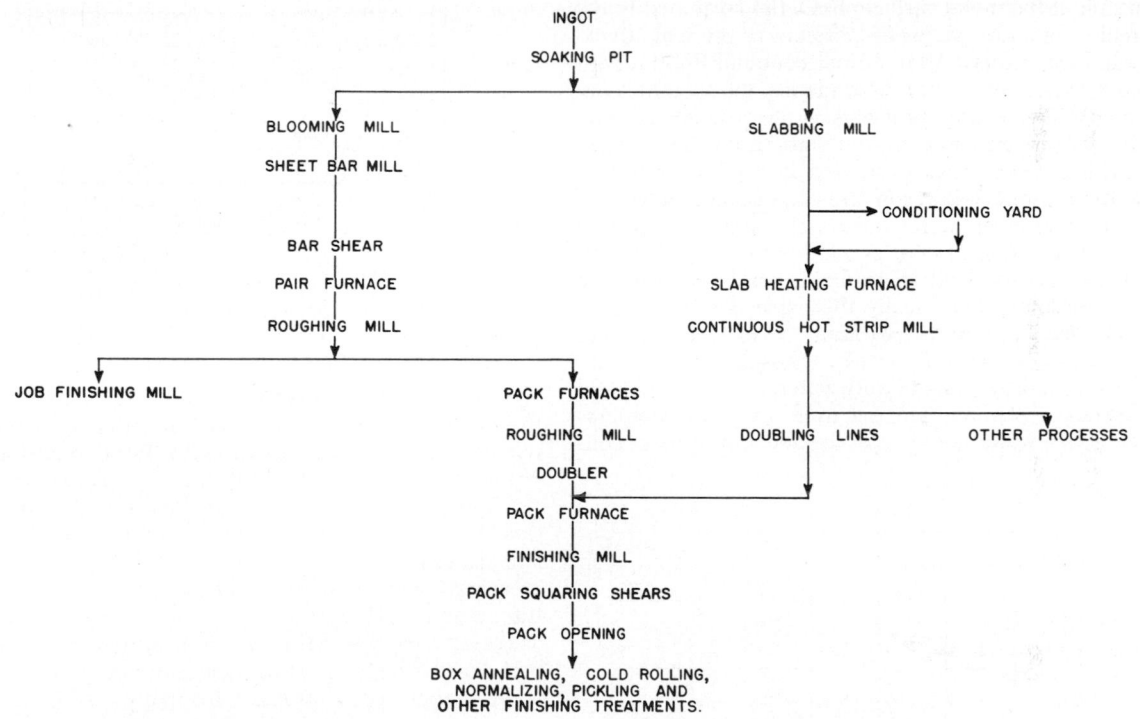

Fig. 31—9. Comparison of sequences of operations in the production of flat-rolled products.

SECTION 6

OXIDE REMOVAL

(Pickling and Shot Blasting)

Necessity for Removal—The presence of oxide (scale) on the surface of strip, sheet, or breakdowns, is objectionable when they are to be processed further. For example, the oxide must be removed and a clean surface provided if satisfactory results are to be obtained from the hot-rolled sheet or strip in any operation involving deformation of the material. If the sheets are for drawing applications, removal of the oxide is essential, as its presence on the steel surface tends to shorten die life, cause irregular drawing conditions and destroy surface smoothness of the finished product. Oxide removal is also necessary if the sheet

or strip is to be used for further processing involving coating in order to permit proper alloying or adherence of metallic coatings and satisfactory adherence when a non-metallic coating or paint is used.

In the production of cold-reduced steel sheet and strip, it is necessary that the oxide resulting during hot rolling the steel slab to breakdown form be removed completely before cold reduction to prevent lack of uniformity and eliminate surface irregularities.

Types of Oxide—The term "oxide" as used here refers generally to the chemical compounds of iron and oxygen formed on the surface of the steel by exposure to air while the metal is at an elevated temperature. "Scale" is specifically the oxidized surface of steel produced during heating for working and during hot working of steel. Hence, the oxide produced on steel surfaces in hot-rolling processes is known as **mill scale.** Chemical compounds thus formed are iron oxides FeO, Fe_2O_3 and Fe_3O_4.

The mechanism whereby mill scale is formed generally is considered to be of a dynamic nature, whereby alternate formation and reduction of the higher oxides of iron occur. Fe_2O_3 is formed first and then reduced successively to Fe_3O_4 and FeO by the availability of iron. Additional Fe_2O_3 is formed at the atmosphere-surface interface and the process becomes continuous; the final result is a scale composed of layers richest in oxygen at the scale surface and richest in iron at the metal surface. FeO, the layer next to the steel, constitutes about 85 per cent of the scale thickness, Fe_3O_4 about 10 to 15 per cent and Fe_2O_3 about 0.5 to 2 per cent. There is evidence, too, of a molecular or ionic diffusion process involving oxygen moving inward and iron moving outward through the scale.

The rate of oxide formation is dependent on the temperature, composition and physical characteristics of the steel, and temperature, character and rate of flow of the atmosphere, as well as the length of time the steel is exposed to oxidizing conditions. Figure 31—10 shows graphically the oxide development at temperatures of 1000° to 2200° F for a low-carbon steel exposed for two hours to atmospheres of oxygen, dry air, carbon dioxide and water vapor. It is noted that rate of scaling increases uniformly with temperature when water and carbon dioxide atmospheres con-

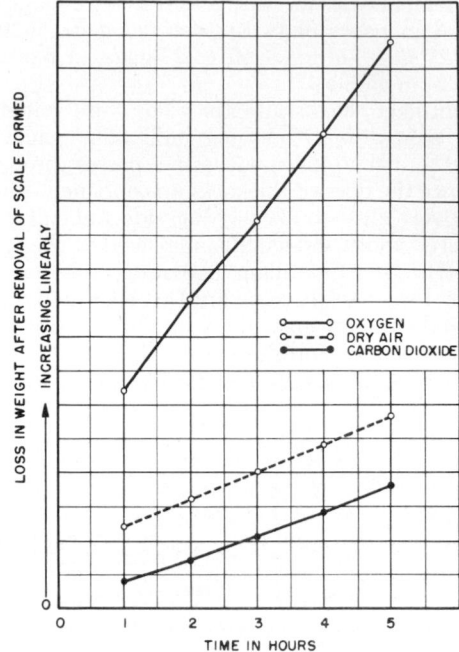

FIG. 31—11. Comparative effects of time of exposure and nature of the atmosphere on the scaling of plain carbon steels at 1520° F.

tact the steel surfaces and that interruptions occur in the rate of scaling when oxygen and dry air are employed. These interruptions are attributed to blistering of the scale which leads to pitting of the undersurface.

Figure 31—11, in which scale loss is plotted against time for samples of low-carbon steel exposed to carbon dioxide, air and oxygen atmospheres, shows increasing loss for an increasing time at a given temperature. Figures 31—10 and 31—11 also show relative oxidizing activity of the four atmospheres, with carbon dioxide the least oxidizing and dry air, oxygen and water vapor more strongly oxidizing in the order named.

PRINCIPLES OF PICKLING

Pickling is the process of chemically removing oxides and scale from the surface of a metal by the action of water solutions of inorganic acids. While pickling is only one of several methods of removing undesirable surface oxides, this process is used the most widely in the manufacture of sheet and tin mill products, due to comparatively low operating costs and ease of operation. Considerable variation in type of pickling solution, operation and equipment is found in the industry. Among the types of pickling equipment may be mentioned the batch picklers, modified batch, semi-continuous and continuous picklers.

The reaction occurring when steel or iron materials are immersed in dilute inorganic acid solutions includes the solution of metal as a salt of the acid and the evolution of hydrogen. Steel pickled in dilute sulphuric-acid solutions is an example of this reaction, with the end products of reaction being ferrous sulphate and

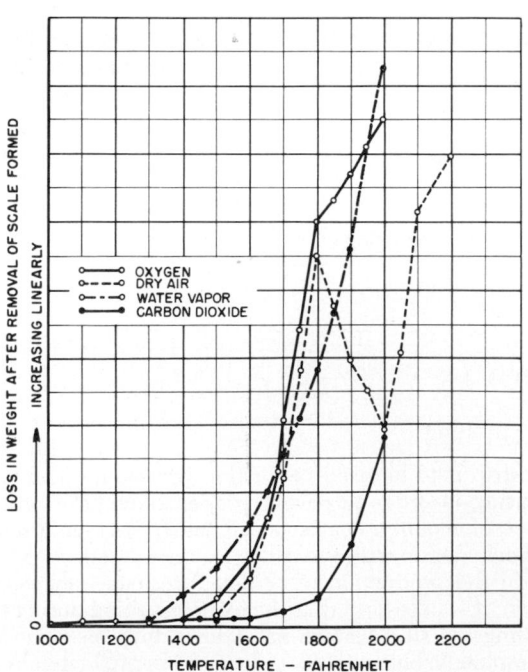

FIG. 31—10. Comparative effects of temperature and atmosphere on the scaling of plain carbon steels, all exposed for a constant time.

hydrogen. Adherent films of oxides are undermined by the acid attack through the pervious scale on the base metal. FeO is not dissolved as readily as the steel, but does have higher reaction rates than Fe_2O_3 and Fe_3O_4, both of the latter being soluble very slowly in the acid. Ferric sulphate is formed first and then is reduced to ferrous sulphate by the free hydrogen. Sulphuric-acid baths rarely contain significant amounts of ferric sulphate since this compound is unstable in the presence of reducing agents. Certain metals, such as copper, chromium and nickel, retard the rate of pickling when they occur in the steel base, since the scale bearing these alloying metals inhibits acid attack. Silicon and aluminum form refractory-type oxides, which in turn lower the solubility rate of the oxide in the acid.

The rate of pickling is affected by numerous variables, including the aforementioned steel-base constituents and type and adherence of oxide to be removed. Solution temperature and concentration, ferrous sulphate concentration, agitation, time of immersion and presence of inhibitors influence the rate of acid attack. While the rate of pickling increases in direct proportion to the concentration of the acid from zero to 25 per cent by weight, the influence of temperature is much more pronounced. For example, in 15 per cent sulphuric acid an increase in temperature over the range 70° F to 210° F doubles the pickling rate for each rise of 15° or 20° F in temperature. Rate of solution of iron at 180° F is about five times the rate at 140° and about 100 times greater at boiling than at room temperature. The trend in recent years in batch pickling of hot-rolled steels is to maintain temperatures at 150° to 175° F if possible and to increase or decrease pickling activity with adjustment of the concentration, thus affording some savings in fuel for heating and avoiding decomposition of the inhibitor. Acid concentration is varied over a relatively wide range in the industry, dependent on the amount of pickling required to prepare the surface for the succeeding process. Much higher concentrations are used in continuous pickling methods, as the desired surface must be secured in the shortest possible time; hence, temperatures are maintained at 200° to 220° F and concentrations at 12 per cent to 25 per cent. These specific examples pertain to the commonly-used sulphuric-acid baths. The required concentration is also a function of the kind of acid used; for example, hydrochloric acid can be used in concentrations of 5 per cent to 50 per cent.

The retarding or inhibiting effect of ferrous sulphate is recognized widely and provisions are made in every pickling operation for adequate control of the salt build-up in the bath. Continued use of the bath without replenishment results ultimately in complete ineffectiveness of the solution. It is usually considered good practice to permit build-up of ferrous sulphate to 25 per cent and work the bath until the free acid content is reduced to less than 5 per cent.

Agitation of either the work or the bath saves time, metal and acid and is a practice used widely throughout the industry. Several methods have been adopted, such as raising and lowering the work in the bath, agitating the bath with plungers or circulatory systems or passing the work through the bath horizontally.

Inhibitors—The effect of inhibitors has been known and used commercially for years. An inhibitor is any substance added to a solution that inhibits or lessens acid attack on the steel itself, while permitting preferential attack on the iron oxides. Originally such substances as wheat bran were used but in recent years complex synthetic organic chemicals have been manufactured for this purpose. For economic reasons, some of the by-products or waste materials of the agricultural and oil industries have been used with varying success; these still retain a competitive position with the synthetic inhibitors. The principal requirements of an inhibitor are that it must be effective in very low concentrations, its effectiveness must be constant at all bath temperatures and concentrations, it must not leave an oily or otherwise harmful film on the steel, and it must be economical for use on the basis of cost per ton pickled. Many inhibitors promote foaming to restrict acid and heat losses from the bath so blanketed.

Wetting agents, while often constituting a supplementary ingredient to inhibitors, in most cases are somewhat of an inhibiting agent in themselves and are used principally to improve rinsing and wetting of the surfaces. Wetting agents are organic compounds that lower the interfacial tension between the steel and the liquid. Some improvement in pickling rate is believed to result from their use and improvement in rinsing is definite.

CONTINUOUS PICKLING LINES

With the advent of continuous cold-reduction mills, it was necessary to design and develop suitable equipment to remove the oxides resulting from the continuous hot-rolling operation and prepare the hot-rolled breakdowns for cold reduction in coil form. This operation is performed in a continuous pickling line (Figure 31—12). The primary function of a continuous pickling line, as of other pickling processes, is the removal of oxide from the steel surface. This serves to promote maximum reduction with a minimum of power, to assure good roll life in the cold-reduction mills and to secure the increased surface density possible with cold work. Modern continuous pickling lines operate at speeds as high as 700 to 800 ft. per min.

The thickness of the oxide varies considerably on steel rolled on the hot-strip mill. Loose coiling permits greater atmospheric penetration into the wraps, with corresponding heavier oxide formation on the edge areas. Flexing of the steel in passing through the pickling line tends to break this scale or oxide film and permits more rapid attack by the acid bath.

The continuous pickler has other advantages or supplementary functions. The product of the hot-strip mill is subject to fluting (formation of creases when the steel is bent or otherwise deformed) due to lack of springiness. Continuous pickling lines usually are equipped with suitable apparatus for cold working the material so that severe local strains are eliminated and fluting largely is prevented. Another advantage is that they permit individual lengths to be joined into a single coil containing multiple lengths, often neces-

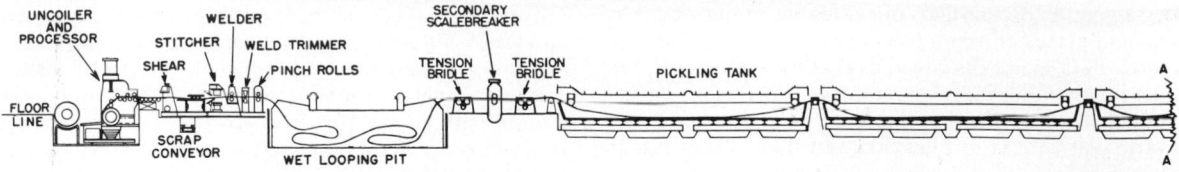

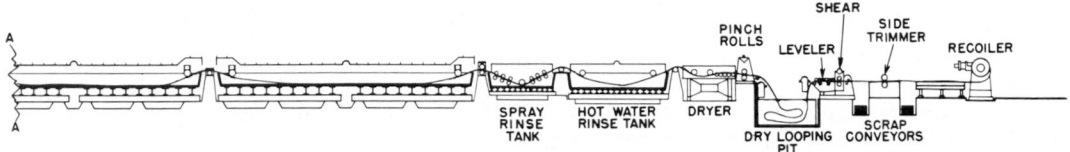

FIG. 31—12. Schematic arrangement of the equipment comprising a continuous pickling line. Although a two-high temper mill is indicated as the secondary scalebreaker in this sketch, a machine similar to the processing uncoiler at the entry end of the line may be used.

sary because of coil length limitations of the continuous hot-strip mill. The result is a much longer continuous coil for the cold-reduction mills. The pickling line permits inspection of the steel for defects and suitability for the next operation, and finally oiling of the steel as a protection against rusting and as an aid to cold reduction.

At the coil entry end of a typical continuous pickling line are facilities for handling and charging coiled product into the line. These usually consist of conveyors on which the coils are placed in proper sequence by overhead cranes, upenders in cases where the coil is delivered with the axis vertical, and a motor-driven integrated buggy and hoist for placing the coil in the uncoiling or pay-off equipment. The primary cold-working equipment called a "processor," integral with the uncoiling equipment, consists of a mandrel on which the coil is placed, a hold-down roll, and a series of smaller diameter rolls. After the coil is charged on the mandrel and the lead-end entered into the small diameter rolls, the hold-down roll is brought down and pressure applied to the material. This action alternately flexes the steel around the rolls, thus effectively "breaking" the surface scale into numerous fine cracks, and increasing the available sub-oxide area for pickle attack. This flexing also cold works the steel enough to eliminate, in large part, the fluting tendencies of the hot-rolled steel. The group of small driven rolls immediately following the hold-down or breaker roll applies tension to the steel and also serves to straighten and flatten it. A stationary shear is located immediately after the processor for the cropping and squaring of the coil ends for butt-welding or stitching.

While most of the pickling lines in the industry include stitchers for fastening coil ends for continuously processing hot-rolled product, many also have installed flash butt-welding as supplementary equipment. The main advantage of this method of joining

coil ends is that it provides a joint which can be cold reduced, whereas the lapped and stitched joint cannot.

Following welding, the flash, or excess metal resulting from the upsetting action of the welder, is trimmed off by a cutter designed for the purpose. The looping pit is next in line and provides a continuous storage space for material to compensate for short delays at the charging end and to permit a uniform rate of travel through the acid tanks. The looping pit is usually 10 to 12 feet deep and 20 to 40 feet long, depending on equipment speed. Construction is generally of concrete with adjustable wood side guides for retaining the lapped-over material and preventing twisting. Water is kept in the pit to minimize scratching and increase wetting action in the first pickling tank.

In some continuous pickling lines, an auxiliary or secondary scalebreaker follows the looping pit, to break the scale even further than was achieved in the processor at the entry end, and thus increase the speed at which the line can be operated and still produce satisfactorily pickled strip. The secondary scalebreaker may be a machine similar to the entry-end processor, or it may be a two-high temper mill preceded and followed by a tension bridle at the entry and exit sides of the mill.

The pickling zone consists of several individual acid-proof tanks located in a series, comprising an effective immersion length of about 250 to 300 feet. While most lines have from three to five tanks, each about 70 to 80 feet long, some modern lines have only one long tank, divided by weirs into four or five sections, thereby increasing effective immersion depth about 10 per cent to 15 per cent. The inside dimensions of these tanks has been more or less standardized at four feet in depth and about one foot wider than the maximum product width. A steel shell is used for support with layers of rubber bonded to the steel and the rubber is protected from abrasion by a lining of about 9 inches of silica-base acid-proof brick. For operating temperatures in excess of 200° F, a bakelite-base cement generally is used for bonding. In modern high-speed lines operating at 200° to 220° F, the brick facing gradually is eroded away, so that replacement is required after several years of operation. Occasionally, small leaks in the rubber lining and the steel tank require patching. However, if care is taken to prevent acid attack on the outside of the tanks, the tank assemblies may be regarded as permanent for the life of the line.

Following the acid tank are rinsing tanks consisting of a cold-water spray rinse and a hot-water tank. The cold water rinses the acid carry-over from the steel. The hot-water rinse is a tank with an effective product immersion length of 15 to 20 feet. This tank completes the rinsing and by warming the steel, promotes flash drying prior to entering the succeeding set of pinch rolls. Situated between the final rinse tank and the pinch rolls are one, two or three banks of hot-air dryers operating at low pressures. Pinch rolls at the exit end of the pickling tanks control the speed of product travel and, in conjunction with the pinch rolls which provide back tension at the entry end of the line, help to maintain the proper loops in the tanks.

The delivery end of the continuous pickling line has, in the order listed, a looping pit, pinch rolls, shear, oiler, recoiler and suitable supplementary equipment for conveying the finished product from the line. The pinch rolls preceding the shear are located so that product delivery to the shear is facilitated. Stitches are removed at this point, as well as short sections which inspection has shown to be inferior quality. Some lines are provided also with rotary side trimmers at the entry end or, more commonly, at the delivery end.

Control of acid concentrations in four separate tanks within one pickling line posed a critical problem for some time. Until recently, it was considered good practice to measure the free acid and ferrous sulphate concentrations about four times per eight-hour period and make raw-acid additions to each tank on the basis of these frequent tests, until iron salts had increased to a very high concentration, at which time the tank was dumped and a new pickling solution made up. It was developed, however, that high concentration of iron salts in the entry tanks was not particularly harmful to pickling performance but that a similar condition in the final tank resulted in extremely poor line performance. The practice of adding raw acid, water and inhibitor (the latter being optional) to only the last pickling tank was then developed, and this practice, or slight variations of it, is now in general use in most continuous pickling lines. Tanks are connected with large rubber-lined or acid-proof tubes so that the acid solution will flow countercurrent to the product travel from the last pickling tank to the first pickling tank. This practice is called "cascading." The acid and water are added continuously at a prescribed rate, usually about 35 to 50 pounds of acid per ton of steel pickled. Hence, if the line production rate is 50 tons per hour, acid flow into the make-up pickling tank would be equivalent to about one-half to two-thirds gallons per minute. Steam is used generally for heating the solutions and temperatures are controlled automatically.

Maintenance of coil identity through the pickling operation is essential. Schedules are made out showing the coil number and other unit identification opposite a pickling sequence number. The coils are then charged into the line in the sequence listed on the schedule and unit identity is reassigned to the coil in the same sequence following pickling. Product delivered to the cold-reduction mills carries complete identity as to coil number, heat number, width and gage. Means of transporting the pickled coil to the storage area ahead of the cold-reduction mill varies from plant to plant, depending on the plant layout, nature of transportation available and the most economical method. Occasionally, long gravity-type conveyors are installed to deliver coils to a central point, from which a tractor or overhead crane stores the coils in areaways adjoining the cold-reduction mills. Slat-type conveyor-tractors also are employed and where the distances involved become greater, rail transportation is resorted to.

Inspection of the raw pickled product is carried on continuously at the exit end of the pickling lines. Each coil is inspected for surface and edge quality, width and gage. Some of the defects commonly causing rejection or diversion are as follows: slivers, cracked edges, laminations, off gage, off width, roll marks, underpickling, overpickling, handling damage and pitting.

Underpickling results when the steel has not had sufficient time in the pickling tanks to become free of adherent scale and occurs when acid concentration, solution temperatures and line speed are not balanced properly. Variations in the oxide and composition of the steel are also factors in underpickled product, as well as such factors as coiling temperature off the hot-strip mill and inadequate amount of cold working through the processor. Overpickling results from line delays which permit sections of the steel to remain in the acid too long. The presence of an inhibitor reduces iron loss, but when an inhibitor is not used, iron loss during a short delay period appreciably reduces thickness of the steel and raises the hazard of hydrogen embrittlement. Pitting is related to overpickling, the presence of non-metallic inclusions near the steel surface and to rolled-in scale, slag or a refractory substance. While overpickling is not common in continuous pickling operations, its occurrence does have a very serious effect on cold-reduction performance and surface appearance of the finished product. Product damage from handling or improper equipment adjustment can render the steel unsuitable for further processing.

Prior to recoiling, the pickled steel passes between a set of oiling rolls which cover both surfaces with a small amount of oil. The type of oil used to lubricate the steel, and protect it from rusting during storage and from scratching during handling, is determined by the type of lubricating system on the cold-reduction mill unit. Hence, palm oil diluted with light mineral oil, is applied to the steel at the pickling lines when a straight palm oil or a solution containing palm oil is used on the cold-reduction mill. Finally, the

FIG. 31—13. General view of a mill department containing four continuous pickling lines.

pickled and oiled product is recoiled on a conventional up-type or down-type coiler.

Figure 31—13 shows a typical continuous pickling department consisting of four lines.

BATCH PICKLING

Pickling of steel sheets and other light-gage sheared lengths is performed with specialized equipment in which a batch of sheets are processed together. In general, there are two basic methods of batch pickling and several modifications of them, but the employment of agitation as a means of increasing pickling rate is common to both. One method is to employ a large wooden or acid-resistant concrete tank installed in the floor so that the top of the tank rises about two feet above floor level. The tank is divided into two sections by a wooden partition extending between 6 to 10 inches from the tank bottom; one section is smaller than the other. A large float is inserted in the smaller compartment and the material to be pickled is placed in the larger side. Forcing the float down into the bath displaces acid solution in the smaller section and raises the level of the acid solution in the other compartment. The wood float is attached to a gear-driven crank, making the motion quite rapid, and effectively agitating the bath. Sheets are placed in a near vertical position on an acid-resistant metal rack, and pins inserted between every few sheets to facilitate exposure of all surfaces. The rack is then placed in the bath by an overhead crane and allowed to remain for several minutes. After sufficient pickling, the sheets are rinsed in a cold-water tank to wash off any iron-salt residue. Acid concentration is varied from 4 to as high as 12 per cent, depending on the amount of surface etch required. Temperatures usually are maintained between 150° F and 190° F.

In the second general type of batch picklers, the work is agitated instead of the bath. Equipment consists of a minimum of two, and more often three, tanks recessed into the floor and located at 90 degree steps to each other on about a 15-foot radius. At the center is a vertical mast topped by a four-armed spider from which the holding racks are hung. The pickling sequence begins at the loading station, followed by a high-concentration acid bath and, in a two-tank system, succeeded by rinsing and unloading stations. In the three-tank system, the first pickle tank is followed by either a more dilute acid solution or a cold-water rinse, followed in turn by a hot-water rinse. Racks must be unloaded at the fourth station prior to loading. A variation of this method has the tanks installed in tandem, with the first tank containing the highly concentrated acid solution, followed by a very dilute acid or cold-water rinse and finally with a hot-water rinse. The racks are suspended from a sectionalized conveyor system which plunges the work in the bath, the section immediately above the tanks being separated from the return rack conveyor off to the side of the pickle tanks. In this manner, racks are never removed from the overhead conveyor system, except for maintenance, and the product flow assumes a more continuous aspect. When pickled sheets are furnished the customer for use in that condition, it is necessary to force-dry them to minimize rusting. Equipment for drying consists of a short hydrochloric-acid bath, water spray rinse, high-volume V-type dryers, and pilers. Roller leveling frequently is included to obtain standard mill flatness and a rotary brush scrubber may be incorporated in the drying sequence.

Figure 31—14 shows a plunger-type pickling machine used for "white pickling" of plate for tinning (Chapter 34).

Fig. 31—14. A rack loaded with black plate is being pushed into position before a plunger-type pickling machine for "white pickling" of the plate prior to tinning.

Adjustment of the pickling bath for batch-type picklers is accomplished by adding raw acid after the water has been brought to the correct level. Sulphuric acid is used for low- and medium-carbon steels in concentrations ranging from 1½ per cent to 4 per cent for tin plate and from 4 per cent to 8 per cent for sheet products, with the temperature maintained between 150° F and 190° F. During working of the solution the acid is depleted and fresh acid must be added periodically as indicated by suitable tests for free acid and ferrous sulphate. Inhibitors generally are used so that iron loss is low and the hazard of hydrogen embrittlement reduced to a minimum.

After pickling certain steels containing small amounts of copper or nickel, a "smut" or dark film appears on the sheet surface. As a rule, the film contains relatively high percentages of the alloying elements and a dilute solution of hydrochloric acid must be used to attain the necessary cleanliness.

SHOT BLASTING

Shot blasting is employed in the flat-rolled steel industry for cleaning and smoothing the edges of plate, and for the removal from sheet surfaces of mill dirt, scale and rust in the manufacture of sheet for special applications such as galvanized culvert stock, where service requirements demand good adherence of relatively heavy coatings. In this operation, hot-rolled product is fed continuously from coils or as cut-length sheets through the equipment, which consists usually of two separate shot blasters, one for each surface, interconnected with common abrasive feeding auxiliary equipment. The type of abrasive used for this application is crushed-steel shot, which is more effective than round shot in giving the desired

cutting action with a minimum of peening. Auxiliary equipment includes abrasive storage and feeding facilities and dust separators to eliminate the fines that result from the breakdown of the particles upon striking the sheet surface.

Shot blasting, or more correctly, grit abrasive blasting, has several advantages over pickling for preparing heavy sheet for galvanizing. The principal advantage is that of obtaining better adherence with heavy zinc coatings. Secondarily, hydrogen embrittlement in heavy-gage sheets presents a greater hazard than in lighter gages, hence this type of cleaning is preferred over pickling. Storage of blasted product in dry areas permits processing of product ahead of the galvanizing pot, while pickling must necessarily be tied in with pot operations as pickled product rusts rapidly after pickling. On the other hand, shot-blasting equipment requires considerable maintenance, as the wear of abrasives on all contacting parts is relatively high under a wide range of operating conditions, and production rates are relatively low on such units.

There are two modern cleaning lines, actually called "pickle lines," in the United States that use grit abrasive blasting as the basic means for removing scale from strip. The entry and exit ends of these lines are identical with standard continuous pickling lines such as those already described under "Continuous Pickling." In the processing section, abrasive cleaning machines designed to remove all of the scale are substituted for the first two or three acid tanks of a standard line. One or two full-length pickling tanks follow the abrasive cleaning equipment to remove any fine particles of abrasive or scale that might have been left on the strip surface, and to remove some of the sharp ridges of steel caused by the thrown abrasive. These lines operate at relatively slow speed, but effectively clean strip passed through them.

SECTION 7

FINISHING OF HOT-STRIP MILL PRODUCTS

In addition to shearing equipment for cutting coils into sheets of ordered length, a hot-rolled-strip finishing department is usually equipped with a temper mill for the temper rolling of coils, and sometimes with another mill for the temper rolling of individual sheets. Other equipment consists of either roller-levelers, stretcher-levelers, or both; resquaring shears for trimming sides and ends of individual sheets to more exact sizes than is possible in ordinary mill shearing practices; slitters for dividing wide coils into coils of narrower widths; and, in a few cases, a continuous furnace for heat treating cut sheets that are usually pickled, scrubbed and dried in the finishing department after heat treatment. To minimize coil handling, so-called combination lines are set up in some instances to perform a series of functions combining two or more operations, such as uncoiling, leveling, side trimming, temper rolling, slitting or cutting to length or recoiling with the strip passing from one processing unit to the next without intermediate handling.

As has been stated earlier in this chapter, material produced on hot-strip mills has been coiled or, in some instances, cut into lengths after it leaves the last finishing stand of a mill and passes over the run-out table. Improved coilers on hot-strip mills have made it possible to coil hot-rolled strip up to ⅜-inch in thickness. Consequently, the bulk (probably more than 99 per cent) of all of the hot-rolled strip that is produced is coiled. Only a very small percentage (less than 1 per cent) is sheared into 20-foot to 40-foot lengths and piled at the hot-strip mill for subsequent transfer to the finishing department, and this is all material in heavier gages produced on mills not equipped to coil heavy product.

About 75 per cent of the coils produced on hot-strip mills are pickled and oiled on continuous-pickling lines. The balance go directly to the finishing department for whatever processing may be required to convert the coils into ordered forms for shipment.

Of the pickled and oiled coils, many of which are side-trimmed in the pickling line, the majority are transferred to cold-reduction mills, where they are processed as described in the next chapter. A small proportion of the pickled and oiled hot-rolled coils goes to the finishing department of the hot-strip mill. A small tonnage of hot-rolled pickled material, in heavier gages that need not be cold reduced, may be sent directly to galvanizing lines or processed into sheet product for vitreous-enameling stock.

Products of the hot-strip mill that may be received by a finishing department, therefore, are: (1) flat lengths of unpickled hot-rolled strip of the heavier gages, 20 to 40 feet long; (2) unpickled coils of hot-rolled strip; and (3) coils of pickled and oiled hot-rolled strip that may or may not have been side-trimmed as part of the pickling operation. Flat-rolled material of type (1) is sheared to sheets or ordered lengths, after which the sheets are usually leveled and, sometimes, side-trimmed or resquared. Coils of types (2) and (3) may be: (a) shipped directly in coil

form; or (b) the steel may be uncoiled, temper rolled and recoiled; or (c) cut into sheets of ordered lengths, with or without temper rolling; or (d) slit into coils of narrower widths. As in the case of sheets from type (1) material, cut sheets produced from coils of types (2) and (3) may be roller-leveled or stretcher-leveled and side-trimmed or resquared.

Temper Rolling (Skin Passing)—Temper rolling or skin passing is a cold-rolling operation that effects a relatively light reduction in thickness of the rolled material as compared with the substantial reduction in thickness effected by cold reduction. In the case of hot-rolled sheet products, temper rolling may be employed to improve flatness, produce a desired surface finish, alter mechanical properties, or reduce tendency of the sheet to flute during fabrication.

Leveling (Flattening)—The principal operations for producing hot-rolled sheets of a flatness suitable for many purposes are roller leveling and temper rolling. Where sheets must have a higher degree of flatness, stretcher leveling or some other special flattening method is employed (Figure 31—15).

Roller leveling in its simplest form is performed in a machine consisting of two rows of several small-diameter horizontal rolls each, mounted in a housing so that the top and bottom rolls are offset, as shown in Figure 31—15. A sheet passing through the leveler is flexed up and down alternately, the rolls being positioned so that the amount of flexing decreases as the sheet travels toward the exit end of the leveler, with the rolls nearest the exit end performing chiefly a straightening function.

Stretcher leveling produces flatness by stretching a sheet lengthwise between jaws (Figure 31-15), the necessary force being supplied by a hydraulic piston. The sheet is elongated between 1 and 3 per cent so that the elastic limit of the steel is exceeded to produce some permanent elongation. Since the width of a sheet is contracted by stretcher leveling, a suitable allowance must be made so that the flattened sheet is of adequate width.

All of the flattening methods may disfigure the sur-

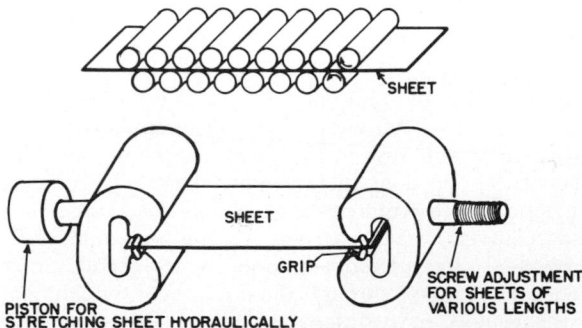

Fig. 31—15. (Above) Schematic representation of the disposition of rolls in a roller leveler. (Below) Diagrammatic sketch of the principle of operation of a stretcher leveler.

face of sheets at their ends with grip or entry marks and, where such marks are undesirable, the sheets are produced oversize and resquared by shearing to remove the objectionable portions.

Slitting—In its simplest elements, a slitting line consists of a coil-holding device, a slitter, and a recoiler. Depending upon production requirements, special auxiliaries may be added to the line for scrap disposal, coil handling and packaging, leveling, edge conditioning, and so on.

Circular slitting knives are packed on the slitter arbors with accurate spacing elements between them to establish the width of the slit material and to maintain proper cutting clearances between mating knife edges.

Slitting lines are of two types: pull-through and driven. In a pull-through line, all of the power for slitting is provided by the recoiler, which pulls the material from the uncoiler and through the slitter. Frictional force between the knives and the strip causes the knives to rotate. In a driven line, both the recoiler and the slitter are driven and sometimes also the uncoiler. Pull-through lines are employed for strip in the intermediate-thickness range, while driven lines are used when slitting very thin or relatively heavy gages, or for specialty products such as silicon steel.

Coils of slit material are built on the mandrel of the recoiler. Formerly, large thin discs of saw steel were spaced on the mandrel to keep the coils separated. In recent years, a device known as an "overarm separator" was developed to keep the slit coils separated on the mandrel. The overarm separator consists of an arbor on a hinged mounting. Steel discs of relatively small diameter, properly spaced, are positioned on the arbor which is lowered until the edges of the discs contact the mandrel. As the individual coils build up, their increasing diameter causes the arbor to be raised, but the edges of the discs still enclose the sides of the coils for a distance of several wraps. When winding of the slit coils is completed, the arbor is simply raised and the individual coils can be removed from the mandrel.

The slitting of wide hot-rolled material into narrower widths makes it possible to produce narrow hot-rolled strip for subsequent cold reduction more economically than equivalent tonnages of narrow hot-rolled strip can be rolled in single strands. Material produced by slitting wide hot-rolled coils also has, in some instances, replaced specially rolled "skelp" used in the manufacture of electrically welded pipe.

Shearing—Modern hot-rolled-sheet shearing lines employ a processing uncoiler as an uncoiling and feeding device. Larger processing rolls are used than on similar units incorporated in continuous-pickling lines, since scale breaking is undesirable in a shearing-line uncoiler; however, the shearing-line processor eliminates irregular coil breaks in the same manner as its pickling-line counterpart.

The frequent installation of a temper mill in hot-rolled-sheet shearing lines is a relatively recent development aimed primarily at improving the flatness of the material before shearing and thereby increasing the accuracy of the shearing operation. Temper mills

in shearing lines must be preceded and followed by a tension bridle.

In hot-rolled-sheet shearing lines for the lighter gages, flying shears are employed, while for heavier gages an upcut shear and gaging table are used, the choice being influenced by economic considerations.

Hot-rolled strip in coil form, accurately side-trimmed, can be cut to length on modern shearing lines with a degree of exactness that has resulted in the virtual disappearance of separate resquaring operations. When performed, resquaring of individual sheets employs guillotine-type shears.

Heat Treating—Continuous annealing or continuous normalizing of cut hot-rolled sheets has been performed chiefly in furnaces of the roller-hearth type, although furnaces equipped with either chain-type conveyors or walking-beam mechanisms have been used. Some features of such furnaces are described in Sections 8 and 9 of Chapter 32, along with some of the metallurgical principles involved in normalizing.

Bibliography

Am. Iron and Steel Institute, Steel Products Manuals:
"Carbon Steel: Plates; Structural Sections; Rolled Floor Plates; Steel Sheet Piling."
"Carbon Steel: Semifinished for Forging; Hot-Rolled and Cold-Finished Bars; Hot-Rolled Deformed Concrete Reinforcing Bars."
"Carbon Steel Sheets."
"Hot-Rolled Carbon Steel Strip."
"Cold-Rolled Carbon Steel Strip."
"Tin Mill Products."

Am. Society for Testing and Materials, ASTM Standards 1961, Part I, Ferrous metals specifications. The Society, Philadelphia, Pa.

Angle, John E., Maximum production on hot strip mills. Am. Iron and Steel Institute Regional Technical Meetings, 1953; pp. 29-44.

Assn. Iron and Steel Engineers, The modern strip mill. Pittsburgh, Pa., 1941.

Greenberger, J. S., Developments in scalebreaking and continuous pickling lines. Iron and Steel Engineer **33**, May 1956, pp. 69-79.

Hindson, R. D., Metallurgical factors in the hot working and cleaning of hot rolled strip and their influence on the cold reduced annealed product. Proc. International symposium on annealing of low-carbon steel, pp. 9-17. Lee Wilson Engineering Co., Cleveland, Ohio, 1958.

Iron and Steel Institute (British), Special Report No. 67, Production of wide steel strip (1960).

LeBas, J., Factors affecting the pickling rate of hot rolled steel strip. BHP Technical Bulletin, **2**, No. 2, Sept. 1958, pp. 10-16. Broken Hill Proprietary Co., Ltd., Melbourne, Australia.

Lyle, David, The reversing hot strip mill—its place in the steel industry. Iron and Steel Engineer **33**, April 1956, pp. 83-90.

Martin, E. D., Continuous strip pickling. Am. Iron and Steel Institute Yearbook, 1948.

McCollam, C. H., Pickling iron and steel products. Metals Handbook, 1948 Edition, Am. Society for Metals, Cleveland, Ohio.

Ride, John S., Analysis of operational factors derived from hot strip mill tests. Iron and Steel Engineer **37**, Nov. 1960, pp. 77-90.

Treasure, R. W., Continuous strip steel pickling. J. Iron and Steel Institute (British), **162**, No. 2. (June 1949), pp. 201-212.

CHAPTER 32

Manufacture Of
Cold-Reduced Flat-Rolled Products

SECTION 1

INTRODUCTION

Cold-Finished Flat-Rolled Products—The principal cold-finished flat-rolled products are **flat bars, cold-rolled strip, cold-rolled sheets,** and **black plate.** With the exception of black plate (a product made of low-carbon steel), these products may be made from carbon, alloy, or stainless steels as required by the intended end use. The present chapter will be devoted principally to the manufacture of the carbon-steel flat-rolled products designated as cold-rolled sheets and black plate, produced by the cold reduction of hot-rolled coils called "breakdowns" after the breakdowns have been descaled by continuous pickling.

As discussed in other chapters, cold-rolled carbon-steel sheets are the base material for such coated products as long terne sheets (Chapter 35), galvanized sheets (Chapter 36) and aluminum-coated sheets. Most black plate is subsequently coated with tin to produce tin plate (Chapter 34). A special variety of cold-rolled sheet is produced for porcelain enameling: some characteristics of the steel for enameling sheets were discussed in Chapter 31. Electrical (silicon-steel) sheets are discussed in Chapter 44.

The cold-finished flat-rolled products differ from each other principally in dimensions. In certain size and thickness ranges, surface finish and edge finish may determine their classification, as shown in Table 32—I.

COLD-FINISHED FLAT BARS

Cold-finished flat bars are commonly produced in the following dimensional ranges: ¼-inch and over in thickness, and up to 12 inches in width. These dimensions prevent the convenient use of cold drawing for the production of many such bars and, therefore, cold rolling is employed.

Hot-rolled bars of any suitable cross-section are cleaned of scale by pickling or other means, and then passed repeatedly through a set of driven rolls that reduce the section with each pass until the piece is worked down to the required thickness and surface finish. The edges of thin, flat sections are sometimes milled square after cold rolling. The cold working of the metal by this rolling process imparts to the bars a smooth surface finish and accurate thickness; and also increases the tensile strength, yield strength, and hardness, with a corresponding decrease in ductility. It is possible, by selecting the proper combinations of steel composition, degree of cold working, and heat treatment, to produce bars that will have mechanical properties best suited for intended uses.

Flat bars normally are furnished in straight lengths but, in sizes up to ⁹⁄₁₆-inch by ⅝-inch or others having cross-sectional areas not more than 0.30 sq. in., they may be supplied in coil form.

Table 32—I. Product Classification By Size of Flat Cold-Rolled Carbon Steel

Width (Inches)	Thickness, Inch		
	0.2500 and thicker	0.2499 to 0.0142	0.0141 and thinner
To 12, incl.............	Bar	Strip[1, 2]	Strip[1]
2 to 12, incl.............	Bar	Sheet[3]	Strip
Over 12 to 23-¹⁵⁄₁₆, incl.	Strip[2]	Strip[2]	Strip
Over 12 to 23-¹⁵⁄₁₆, incl.	Sheet[4]	Sheet[4]	Black Plate[4]
Over 23-¹⁵⁄₁₆	Sheet	Sheet	Black Plate

[1] When the width is greater than the thickness with a maximum width of ½ inch and a cross-sectional area not exceeding 0.05 sq. in., and the material has rolled or prepared edges, it is classified as **flat wire.**
[2] When a particular temper as defined in A.S.T.M. specification A109, or a special edge, or special finish is specified, or when single-strand rolling is specified in widths under 24 inches.
[3] Cold-rolled sheet coils and cut lengths, slit from wider coils with No. 3 edge (only) and in thicknesses 0.0142 inch to 0.0821 inch incl., carbon 0.20 per cent maximum.
[4] When no special temper, edge or finish (other than Dull or Luster) is specified, or when single-strand rolling widths under 24 inches is not specified or required.

COLD-ROLLED STRIP

Cold-rolled carbon-steel strip is produced in a single strand to a maximum carbon content of 0.25 per cent (by ladle analysis) in widths over ½-inch and up to $23^{15}\!/_{16}$ inches, with thickness 0.2499-inch and under, in a variety of tempers, edges, and finishes that are described in Chapter 29 on "Steel Wire and Steel Wire Products."

Cold-rolled strip may be produced on a single-stand straight-away (non-reversing) mill, or a single-stand reversing mill, or a tandem mill consisting of several stands in series. Hot-rolled breakdowns in coil form from hot-strip mills supply the semifinished material from which cold-rolled strip is made. Before cold reduction, the mill scale (oxides) that formed on the hot-rolled strip during and after hot rolling is removed, usually by pickling. The clean strip is then reduced to approximate final thickness by direct cold reduction, or with the inclusion of an annealing operation at some intermediate thickness to facilitate further cold reduction or to obtain the mechanical properties desired in the finished product.

COLD-ROLLED CARBON-STEEL SHEETS

Cold-rolled carbon-steel sheets are produced as either coils or cut lengths, within the dimensional limitations shown in Table 32—I. Their manufacture involves two distinct stages: (1) reduction of the product to the desired thickness (gage) and (2) the necessary finishing operations. At the present time, practically all cold-rolled sheets are produced by the cold reduction of hot-rolled breakdowns in coil form from the hot-strip mill.

Formerly, hot-rolled, pickled and annealed sheets that had been rolled on hand hot mills were cold rolled, one at a time, on two-high cold mills equipped with smooth rolls, to reduce the thickness to final gage and to impart a smooth finish and desirable mechanical properties to the cold-rolled sheets. Less than 1 per cent of all the steel sheets produced in this country are made by hand rolling methods, so that discussion of these methods will be limited to the description of hand hot mills and related finishing operations in Chapter 31.

BLACK PLATE

Black plate was the term used originally to designate small thin sheets produced by hand hammering. The term continued to be used when hot pack rolling was developed, and today the name is still retained for a product manufactured by the cold reduction of hot-rolled breakdowns in coil form from the hot-strip mill. As indicated in Table 32—I, black plate is produced in thicknesses of 0.0141-inch (29-gage) and thinner. Because of its classification as a tin-mill product, the uncoated black plate is specified in the same manner as tin plate; namely, by weight per base box (see Chapters 34 and 48).

Black plate originated as the starting material for the manufacture of tin plate, and by far the greatest part of all that is produced is still used for that purpose, as described in Chapter 34. The modern product manufactured by the cold-reduction method and sold uncoated with any metal is cleaned, continuously annealed or box annealed, and temper rolled after cold reduction to make it suitable for intended purposes. Heat treatment, and chemical or other surface treatments, may be applied. The product is available in coil form or as cut sheets.

Two general types of finish are commonly produced on black plate: dull finish and bright finish. Dull finish is produced by rolling the plate on rolls roughened by chemical or mechanical means: bright finish is a semi-luster finish produced by rolling on rolls having a moderately smooth surface. By varying the possible combinations of steel composition, degree of mechanical (cold) working and heat treatment, it is possible to produce black plate in a range of tempers to suit particular applications: these tempers are described in Chapter 34 on "The Manufacture of Tin Plate."

SECTION 2

PRINCIPLES OF COLD REDUCTION

Cold rolling is a generic term applied to the operation of passing unheated metal through rolls for the purpose of reducing its thickness; producing a smooth, dense surface; and, with or without subsequent heat treatment, developing controlled mechanical properties. Any single one or combination of these three effects may be the reason for cold rolling of a particular product. Actually, in terms of modern nomenclature of the steel industry, cold rolling implies a rolling operation in which the thickness of the material is reduced a relatively small amount—usually just enough to produce a superior surface or impart the desired mechanical properties to the rolled material.

Cold reduction is a special form of cold rolling in which the thickness of the starting material can be reduced by relatively large amounts in each pass through a single-stand cold mill or in a series of passes through a tandem cold mill. Thus, in the production of most cold-rolled sheets, cold-rolled strip, and black plate, the cold-reduction process is employed to reduce the thickness of the starting material (hot-rolled breakdowns) between 25 and 90 per cent. After cleaning and annealing, a large proportion of such products is subjected to a cold-rolling operation referred to as "temper rolling" that reduces the thickness of the material only a few per cent in the process of imparting the desired mechanical properties and surface characteristics to the final product.

The introduction of continuous methods for cold reduction of steel was the most recent step in the development of present-day rolling facilities for sheets and tin plate. As in the case of the hot-strip mill, cold reduction of wide hot-rolled breakdowns in coil form was developed from the rolling of narrow products.

The original purpose of cold rolling was, however, to achieve the desired surface and mechanical properties, and reduction in thickness was of incidental importance. Cold rolling of strip probably originated in Germany early in the nineteenth century as a process for cold rolling high-carbon wire to produce a flattened cross-section. Similar practices were adopted thereafter in this country. Low-carbon cold-rolled strip, the forerunner of today's cold-reduced strip sheets and tin plate, was first made in this country at the Stanley Works at New Britain, Connecticut. For years, the raw material for such strip was produced on merchant bar mills. Later, cold-reduction equipment developed rapidly, concurrent with the introduction of narrow continuous hot-strip mills and their evolution to the modern wide mills. Today, the narrow and wide cold-reduction mills provide the major outlet for hot-rolled breakdowns in coil form.

In the cold reduction of hot-rolled breakdowns in coil form, the prime objective is reduction in thickness of the material, since the modern hot-strip mill cannot reduce the steel to gages thinner than about 0.049-inch (18 gage). The development of the cold-reduction process for wide products has been even more rapid than that of the continuous hot-strip mill. The first efforts toward cold reduction of wide hot-rolled breakdowns in coil form were made in the 1920's and the process changed rapidly from single-stand non-reversing mills through single-stand reversing mills and then to the present-day high-speed tandem mills. Using tin plate as an example of the rate of change in the methods for reducing very thin flat-rolled steel, it is found that, in 1936, 24 per cent of the black plate for this country's tin plate production was cold reduced, with the balance made by the old hot pack-rolling method. By 1939, 75 per cent of all tin plate was made by the cold-reduction process and this figure reached 100 per cent by 1943.

Sequence of Operations in Cold Reduction—After hot-rolling, the hot-rolled breakdowns in coil form are uncoiled, passed through a continuous pickler, dried, oiled, and re-coiled. The oil serves as a protection against rusting and as a lubricant during cold reduction. There are several types of cold-reduction mills which vary in design from single reversing two-high, four-high or multiple-roll units to continuous four-high stands with up to six units in tandem. In rolling on any of the single-stand reversing mills, the product is rolled back and forth between the work rolls, through which very high pressures are exerted, until the desired thickness is reached. The steel may be forced through the roll pass by rotation of the power-driven rolls or may be pulled through non-driven rolls by tension reels in front and back of the mill or a combination of these effects may be used. In tandem rolling, the product is given one pass through three, four, five or six stands (Figures 32—1, 32—2, 32—3, 32—4 and 32—5), each contributing to thickness reduction and each driving the material being rolled, usually at speeds so synchronized that the steel is under tension at each of the stages between the payoff reel, the various sets of work rolls and the re-coil reel. Unlike hot-rolling, no scale is formed, but much greater pres-

sures and driving forces are required to effect a given reduction in thickness.

For any given pass in the cold-reduction process, the resultant of the compressive forces of the rolls on the steel and the tensional forces along its length between the reels and rolls must exceed the elastic limit of the steel to produce permanent deformation. For

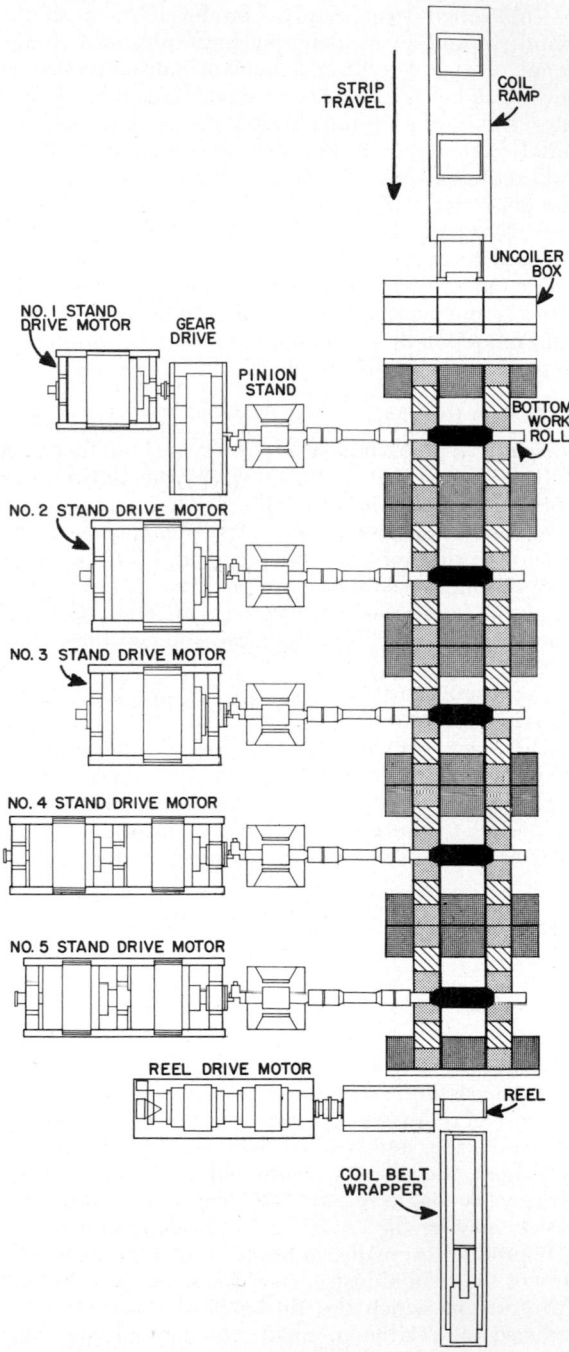

FIG. 32—1. Schematic arrangement of the mill stands and auxiliary equipment comprising a five-stand tandem cold-reduction mill. The shaded sections of the drawing represent the mill housings of the five four-high mill stands. Only one work roll of each stand is indicated in black; no other rolls are shown.

Fig. 32—2. An 80-inch, three-stand tandem cold-reduction mill. The motors and driving mechanism are in the left foreground, with the three four-high mill stands in the middle background.

the first pass after hot rolling, these forces are at their minimum, and for each succeeding pass they increase progressively, because the effect of the cold working through each pass is to increase the elastic limit sharply. The ultimate strength also is increased, but more slowly. As a result, much of the cold reduction is done on very hard steel having very little residual ductility.

The proper reduction of thickness which should be made at each pass of a reversing mill or in rolling on each stand of a tandem mill can be expressed only in very general terms. The work load should be distributed as uniformly as possible at the various stages without falling very much below the maximum capacity of any stage. The maximum is determined in each case by several factors, of which the most important are mill design, power available, steel width and total reduction to be taken, steel lubrication, steel cross-sectional contour, steel hardness, steel tension, steel surface, roll diameter and roll surface. Generally, the lowest percentage of reduction is in the last reduction pass to permit better control of the flatness, gage, and finish of the product. On the conventional wide four-high tandem mills used to cold reduce most sheet and

tin plate stock, the individual pass reduction will range generally between 25 and 45 per cent on all stands but the last, where it will fall between 10 and 30 per cent. The resultant total reduction on these mills from hot-rolled breakdowns in coil form to finished product will usually run 45 to 65 per cent for most sheet gages and 80 to 90 per cent for most tin plate.

Heavy reductions at high speed on any of the various types of mills generate considerable heat and not only raise the temperature of the product but also that of the rolls. The heat generated must be dissipated by a system of flood lubrication in which a water-soluble oil or a mixture of oils is directed in small streams or jets against the roll bodies and the surface of the steel. Some mills use palm oil on the steel and high-pressure water on the rolls. In any event, the resultant steel temperature generally runs between 150° and 250° F. On high-speed tandem mills rolling tin plate stock, the temperature of the steel may become as high as 400° F.

As discussed in Chapter 20, numerous automatic-control devices assist the mill operators in maintaining the optimum rolling conditions to achieve maximum quality of the rolled product.

FIG. 32—3. A 54-inch, high-speed, four-stand tandem cold-reduction mill. The delivery end of this mill is at the left of the illustration.

FIG. 32—4. A 48-inch, high-speed, five-stand tandem cold-reduction mill. Product being rolled travels through the mill from right to left in this view.

FIG. 32—5. A 52-inch six-stand tandem cold-reduction mill, used in the production of coils of steel for subsequent coating with tin.

SECTION 2

ROLL ARRANGEMENT FOR COLD REDUCTION

In reducing the thickness of steel, the action of a pair of rolls may be visualized as being somewhat similar to that of two very blunt knife edges in cutting partially through a stationary piece across which the knife edges are opposed under pressure. The smaller the roll diameter or the sharper the knife edges, the less pressure is required to do the necessary work. Other factors being equal, the force imposed across a set of work rolls to obtain a given reduction in thickness of steel varies with the square root of the roll diameter. To minimize the power requirements and mill size, it is, therefore, advantageous to use work rolls of as small diameter as possible.

The steel being rolled is necessarily narrower than the length of the work rolls. In a two-high mill, these rolls are supported only at their ends and rolling pressure is applied there. In view of this, it is obvious that rolls of some minimum diameter no longer will be sufficiently rigid to withstand the necessary pressures without bending. In extreme cases, this bending along the length of the roll might be sufficiently great to cause the rolls to touch each other at the ends. The tendency, of course, is for the bending to increase as the mill width (the roll length) becomes greater.

In order to overcome the difficulties arising from bending of work rolls of small diameter without sacrificing the advantage of the small diameter, the modern mill backs up the work rolls with rolls of larger diameter. These more massive rolls resist the bending force of the screw-down pressures applied to their ends, and the pressures are transmitted to the work rolls along their entire length. For example, four-high cold-reduction mills in the 42-inch to 98-inch width range, which produce nearly all cold-rolled sheets and tin plate, will have two work rolls of 16-inch to 21-inch diameter, each backed up by a roll of 42-inch to 56-inch diameter. The driving power is applied at one end of each of the work rolls of such a mill and screwdown pressure at both ends of the backing-up rolls.

While the widespread use of such conventional four-high mills, in single stands or, more commonly, in tandem arrangements, has long ago proved their economic suitability for producing most of the cold-rolled flat steel products, many departures from this type have been tried to obtain even smaller work-roll diameters. In the four-high Steckel mill, none of the rolls are driven and the steel is pulled back and forth between the 2 to 5-inch diameter work rolls by reversing power-driven reels. The back-up rolls in this case are 24 to 36 inches in diameter. Most Steckel installations are confined to the rolling of narrow strip. Other mills, known as the "six-high" or the "cluster" types, use two or more backup rolls for each work roll. The currently most successful of the multiple-roll class is the Sendzimir mill, with two work rolls of 1 to 2½-inch diameter. Each work roll is backed up by two rolls of twice that diameter, each of which in turn is backed up by two segmented rolls of even larger diameter. The intermediate backup rolls are driven and the outer segmented rolls, which are actually rows of bearings on common shafts, provide a caster-like support action and permit the application of screw pressure by rotating these shafts eccentrically (Chapter 20) a light, wholly-enclosed housing is possible and the entire roll system is immersed in lubricant. This mill appears to be well-adapted to taking heavy reductions on steels of the harder grades such as stainless and high-silicon steels.

Even with the rigidity provided by massive backup rolls, work rolls of the common four-high mills will flex or bend somewhat under the rolling pressures used; this tendency is greater in the wider mills. Accordingly, on mills rolling sheets and tin plate, work rolls are "crowned," that is, ground with roll diameters which increase very gradually from end to center. This convexity, which may consist of a diameter differential of 0.010-inch on the widest mills, compensates for normal roll flexure. On mills about 40 inches wide, the crown may be 0.001-inch or less, and on narrow cold-reduction mills it is usually unnecessary. The work rolls themselves are made of forged, hardened steel, surface ground to a high finish on specially-designed precision lathes. Work rolls for the last stand of a tandem mill, especially in a three-stand mill for sheets, generally are roughened slightly by shot-blasting to impress a matte pattern on the sheet as an aid in preventing sticking of stacked sheets in annealing. Work rolls for narrow cold-reduced strip, which requires a much brighter surface than sheets, are highly polished. Backup rolls on wider mills are generally made of cast steel and are always surface ground. They can be shaped "flat," that is, with no crown, or with up to 0.010-inch convexity.

SECTION 3

TYPICAL MILL LAYOUTS

Four-High Tandem Mills—The bulk of the cold-reduced flat steel made in this country is rolled on three-, four- or five-stand four-high tandem mills.

Most tin plate falls in the thickness range of 0.008 to 0.014-inch and requires 80 to 90 per cent cold reduction from the thinnest hot-rolled breakdowns in coil form available in the width range of 24 to 36 inches. Tin plate, therefore, usually is rolled on five-stand mills around 42 to 48 inches wide. A recently installed six-stand four-high mill rolls steel for tin plate in widths from 22 to 40 inches, with thicknesses ranging from 0.0035-inch to 0.024-inch.

Most cold-rolled sheets for automotive bodies, agricultural implements, architectural use, furniture and household equipment are required in thicknesses of 0.025 to 0.065-inch and widths of 30 to 72 inches. Material for these applications, most of which is given 45 to 65 per cent cold reduction, generally is rolled on three-stand mills producing material ranging from 54 to 98 inches in width. Four-stand mills, usually 48 to 56 inches wide, may be used to roll tin plate but are best adapted to produce 0.015 to 0.030-inch thick, 24 to 47-inch wide sheets for such applications as roofing, signs and containers. Maximum delivered cold-reduced strip speeds on such tandem mills may run as high as 1000 feet per minute on a three-stand, 3000 feet on a four-stand, 6000 feet on a five-stand mill, and higher than 7000 feet on a six-stand mill. The average operating speeds vary greatly throughout the industry.

All such mills have uncoiling reels, cradles, or boxes from which the coil is fed into the actual roll train, coil ends being started either by hand or by pinch rolls. At the discharge end the finished coils are recoiled on a mandrel, being started by a belt wrapper (a continuous driven fabric belt bearing against the mandrel), which guides the head end of the cold-reduced strip around the mandrel and is withdrawn when the re-coiling has been so started.

Mill housings are massive castings, similar to those on finishing stands of a hot-strip mill. On most tandem mills, both work rolls of each stand are driven through a pinion arrangement by a single motor, up to 5000-horsepower motors being used, although some of the latest mills have individual motors for each work roll on some stands. For the first stand or stands, in which the rolling speed is relatively low, motors are geared down; direct drive may be used for one or more of the remaining stands of such a tandem mill.

The 48-inch five-stand tandem mill at United States Steel Corporation's Irvin Works serves as an example of a unit of this type (Figure 32—4). This mills rolls a pickled, 12,000 or 24,000-pound, hot-rolled breakdown in coil form from approximately 0.085-inch thickness down to an average gage of 0.010 inch at a speed of 3300 feet per minute. The five stands, plus the reel, require a total of 11,000 horsepower for driving. From the moment when the head of the coil has been threaded through all stands until the mill reaches top speed, roughly 40 per cent of the horsepower is used for acceleration; the balance is required for reducing the metal. On this mill, the motors on No. 4 and 5 stands and also on the reel are of the double-armature type. Such motors provide a marked reduction in accelerating time and improve control at high speeds due to their lower inertia. The work roll and backup roll diameters are 21 inches and 53 inches, respectively. All work rolls are equipped with roller bearings while the back-up rolls are equipped with oil-film bearings. On an average, the work rolls in No. 5 stand are changed for redressing the surface after rolling every 150 tons; No. 4 stand, after 250 tons; and the first three stands after rolling somewhat over 1000 tons. Back-up rolls on the 5-stand tandem mill average approximately 20,000 tons between dressings. The cold-reduced strip tension reel at the delivery end is designed to pick up the end of the strip coming from the mill, grip it slowly and put it under tension without sudden or undue stress. The reel also winds the cold-reduced strip under constant tension, slowing down automatically with altering the tension as the coil increases in diameter. Such control is necessary to prevent tearing of the very thin, hard, cold-reduced strip. The reel is of the collapsible type and easily stripped by an air-operated plunger.

Four-High Reversing Mills—A typical four-high reversing mill consists of a single stand with reels located on each side of the mill. The mill itself is essentially the same in design and arrangement as the individual stands of a tandem mill. In the reversing mill, the steel must be passed back and forth until the required reduction is obtained. On the entry side of the mill, means are provided for uncoiling and feeding the coil through the mill to the tension reel on the delivery side. After the first pass, the tail end of the coil coming from the uncoiler is gripped by the second tension reel on the entry side of the mill. In each pass, the reel serving as the payoff unit is operated as a generator, providing back-tension to minimize rolling friction and feeding of current into the drive-reel motor. On the last pass, the tail end of the coil is released from the unwinding tension reel, completely wound on the winding reel and stripped in a manner similar to the action on the delivery reel of the tandem mill. For the rolling of tin plate product, a reversing mill usually requires five passes; for relatively heavy sheet product, usually three passes. All passes are considerably slower than the delivery pass of a tandem mill. From this it can be seen that a reversing mill is inherently flexible but cannot compete with a modern tandem mill from a pro-

duction or cost standpoint where large tonnages are involved. Low installation costs in comparison to tandem mills make reversing mills popular for the production of specialty items that vary widely in dimensions and are ordered in small tonnages for each specification.

Two-High Cold Mills—Two-high cold mills may be used singly or in tandem for the cold reduction of narrow coils. Low-carbon steel may be reduced as much as 50 per cent on such mills, usually in four passes. In practice, however, no more cold working is done than is necessary to obtain the finish desired, and it has been found that best surface finishes can usually be obtained in a four-gage reduction; i.e., from 16 to 20 gage. The general practice on two-high cold-rolling mills is to roll coils down to the finished gage but not less than 0.020 inch in thickness for widths up to the diameter of the rolls. For coils under 0.020 inch thick, this relation between width of steel and diameter of rolls decreases, until for a thickness of 0.010 inch, the width of steel is about half the roll diameter. Aside from surface finish and control of hardness, the chief object of cold rolling narrow coils on the two-high mills is to obtain product as free as possible from camber, buckles, ruffles and gage irregularities of the hot-rolled product. These defects are overcome to a high degree by the process of rolling under tension. Unwinding reels with sufficient drag capacity, together with a delivery reel of sufficient power to stretch the steel, are a necessary part of any modern two-high mill installation for the rolling of narrow coils. In addition, most mills rolling narrow coils are equipped with rolls to control the form of the edges of the steel and also to control its width. These edge rolls are relatively light in construction and are grooved to produce the required edge. They revolve on vertical axes and are mounted in housings immediately in front of the horizontal work rolls. Edge rolls may be power driven or the steel may be pulled through idle edge rolls by the horizontal work rolls.

SECTION 5

DISPOSITION OF PRODUCT

Cold-Reduced Product for Strip—Disposition of the cold-reduced hard product depends upon prior processing and ultimate use. Much narrow high-finish strip is sold as cold reduced, for "full-hard" applications, on which heavy cold reductions have been used; or as intermediate tempers, in which the cold-reduced strip has been reduced a predetermined percentage from hot-rolled breakdowns in coil form or intermediate-annealed gage to develop specified mechanical properties.

Cold-Reduced Product for Sheets—In the manufacture of cold-rolled sheets, the cold-reduced coils are either recoiled through a side trimmer or, if side trimming to width has been done on the continuous pickling line before cold reduction, the coil is conveyed directly to the annealing department from the cold-reduction mill. After annealing, most coils for sheets are temper rolled. An increasing amount of cold-rolled

sheet product is being shipped in coil form. However, the majority of coils are taken to continuous sheet-shearing lines, where they are sheared into sheets of ordered lengths. The latter may be subjected to one or more of the other finishing operations discussed in Section 10 of this chapter. Some coils may be slit into narrower widths as also outlined in Section 10.

For certain special products that are annealed in the form of cut sheets, the cold-reduced coils are taken to an uncoiling, side-trimming and sheet-shearing line, where they are cut to sheets of accurate size prior to heat treating. After annealing, the product in the form of individual sheets may be skin-passed or temper rolled, roller-leveled or stretcher-leveled, resquared, etc., as described in Section 10.

Cold-Reduced Product for Tin Plate—Cold-reduced coils for tin plate are uncoiled, cleaned and recoiled (Figure 32—6), to remove surface dirt and oil from the rolling operation, prior to annealing. For material that is to be box annealed, the cleaning is a separate operation. Material that is to be continuously annealed is uncoiled and passed through a continuous cleaning operation that is an integral part of the continuous annealing line before it enters the heat-treating section of the line: after continuous cleaning and annealing, the product is recoiled.

Annealed coils for tin plate generally are temper rolled, side-trimmed and recoiled and then delivered to the continuous electrolytic-tinning lines. A small proportion is uncoiled, sheared into individual sheets, and delivered to hot-dip tinning operations. In the manufacture of thin tin plate (see Chapter 34) annealed coils may be rolled in a two-stand or three-stand cold-reduction mill instead of being temper rolled prior to electrolytic tinning or, alternatively, may be rolled through a two-stand cold-reduction mill after the electrolytic-tinning operation.

SECTION 6

CLEANING OF COLD-REDUCED STEEL

In order to produce satisfactory tin plate by either the hot-dip or electrolytic process, or terne plate by the hot-dip process, it is necessary to clean the cold-reduced steel to remove the lubricant used in cold reduction since the lubricant left on the steel will decompose during annealing, and leave undesirable residues of carbonaceous material on the annealed product. Such residues are not removed satisfactorily in the subsequent pickling operations. Without exception, cold-reduced strip cleaners currently employ alkaline detergent solutions to remove the rolling-mill oils or solutions. The most commonly used reagents are caustic soda, sodium orthosilicate and trisodium phosphate; sodium metasilicate and sesquisilicate also have

found some application for certain types of product cleaning.

The type and amount of lubricant to be removed should be evaluated, as this may have a bearing on the required characteristics and operating conditions of the cleaning solution. Electrolytic action, while not universally employed, is believed to have merit. Figure 32—6 shows diagrammatically a continuous cold-reduced-strip cleaning line designed to employ the electrolytic principle. The detergent solution cleans the steel and serves as a conductor of electric current between the electrodes shown and the products being cleaned. Thorough rinsing of the steel after cleaning is essential to completely remove all contamination.

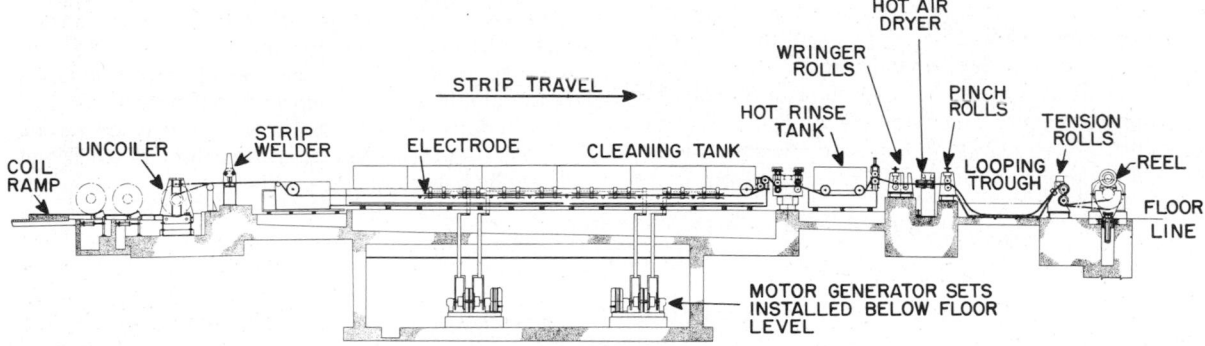

FIG. 32—6. Schematic arrangement of the equipment comprising a typical electrolytic cleaning line for processing cold-reduced steel.

SECTION 7

HEAT TREATMENT OF COLD-REDUCED STEEL

Purposes and Types of Heat Treatment—As is true of other steel products, sheets, strip and tin plate are heat treated primarily to effect changes in mechanical properties which will render the material suitable for the intended purpose. Other heat-treating objectives, involving relatively small tonnages of flat-rolled steel but highly important to the specialized commodities to which they apply, include: solution of chromium carbides to attain maximum corrosion resistance of

austenitic stainless steels; development of optimum magnetic properties and establishment of the thin insulating oxide on silicon-bearing electrical sheets; dispersion or spheroidization of carbides to influence later heat-treating characteristics of alloy and high-carbon sheets.

Except for the very small proportion of "full-hard" cold-reduced strip and sheets used in the as-cold-reduced state to take advantage of the high strengths developed by cold reduction, some form of heat treatment is applied as a separate operation to all cold-reduced flat products to restore the ductility lost in cold reduction. In the case of hot-rolled sheets and strip made on a modern continuous hot-strip mill, supplementary heat treatment is usually unnecessary because rolling practices are used which include definite finishing, piling and coiling temperatures as the steel leaves the last pass of the mill; the resultant "mill heat treatment" can be varied to provide mechanical properties in the as-rolled state which are satisfactory for most uses. This section will consider only those types of heat treatment conducted as separate operations.

Heat treatment of cold-reduced sheets, strip, and tin plate may be divided into: (a) "batch" operations such as **box annealing,** in which a large, stationary mass of steel is subjected to a long heat-treating cycle by varying the temperature within the furnace that surrounds it; and **open-coil annealing,** in which a tight coil is first rewound with a suitable spacer between each wrap of the coil to permit circulation of the furnace atmosphere between individual wraps to hasten and improve uniformity of heating and to permit the use of special atmospheres as described later; and (b) "continuous" operations that include **continuous annealing, strand annealing,** and **normalizing,** in which a single thickness or a few thicknesses of cold-reduced sheet or strip are passed through a furnace in a relatively short time and are subjected to a heat-treating cycle determined by the temperature distribution within the furnace and the dimensions and rate of travel of the steel.

Virtually all box-annealing practices on tight coils or piles of cut sheets slowly raise the steel to a temperature level at or below the lower critical temperature and "soak" it there for several hours, as discussed in Section 9. Such a cycle provides full recrystallization for steel in the severely deformed cold-reduced state and results in the softest possible finished product; accordingly, box annealing is the principal heat treatment applied to cold-reduced steel.

As usually practiced in the heat treatment of cold-rolled carbon-steel sheets, open-coil annealing is carried out in the same general type of equipment as conventional box annealing, with some modifications. However, the space between wraps of the open coils permits more rapid and uniform heating and cooling as well as some special treatments that are impractical with conventional tight coils. For example, it is possible to almost completely decarburize coils of steel for

special applications. It is also possible to alter the composition of the steel in other ways, such as by increasing the carbon content (carburizing), or by adding chromium to its surface (chromizing), or by adding nitrogen (nitriding) to change either the mechanical or physical properties of the steel or both. Spacing between wraps for open-coil annealing has been effected by rewinding tight coils on a second mandrel with a nylon cord or a formed-wire spacer between wraps: the former is removed before heat treatment, the latter is not.

Depending on the nature of the steel and the results to be obtained, in continuous heat treatment the steel may be heated quickly to a maximum temperature at or somewhat above the lower critical temperature (continuous or strand annealing), or it may be heated slightly above the upper critical temperature (normalizing). In any case, the time at temperature is only a few minutes and the cooling rate is fast as compared to the hours-long cooling cycle of a box-annealed charge. The ferrite and structures resulting from transformation in cooling are fine-grained and the finished steel is generally harder than that produced by box annealing; continuous heat treatment is used, therefore, to attain properties not attainable by box annealing, but usually the product is somewhat harder.

While the great bulk of flat-rolled steel products can be heat treated adequately at temperatures around 1250° F, a few because of their sluggish recrystallization tendencies after cold reduction, or their need for relatively quick cooling from the austenitic state to attain optimum properties, must be heated to temperatures ranging from 1400° to 2200° F. In such cases, continuous heat treatment is the most convenient method, as it avoids the hazard of pressure welding ("sticking") inherent in large masses of cold-reduced products held for hours at such temperatures. Continuous heat treatment is the only way to attain the quick cooling necessary to hold chromium carbides in solution in austenitic steels such as AISI Type 304 or to develop high strength levels in alloy sheets of the AISI 4130 type. It permits maximum reaction between a decarburizing atmosphere and the steel being treated (in single thicknesses) for such products as silicon-bearing sheets, whose magnetic properties require very low carbon contents. The controlled recrystallization possible in continuous heat treatment makes a fine-grained microstructure easy to obtain when such is desired, and minimizes the tendency for retention of directional properties of rolled steel which may be responsible for undesired irregular shapes in attempting to produce cylindrical stampings.

SECTION 8

EFFECTS OF HEAT TREATMENT ON MICROSTRUCTURE

Box Annealing—Prior to cold reduction, low-carbon rimmed steel in the form of hot-rolled breakdowns has more or less equiaxed ferritic microstructure, with the carbides visible as pearlite or cementite (depending on whether the product was coiled cold or hot); it is relatively free of internal stresses, particularly if coiled hot

and so "self-annealed." Cold reduction, however, elongates the grains from one- to ten-fold, greatly distorts the crystal lattice, and induces heavy internal stresses; the resultant product is very hard, with little ductility. This high degree of plastic deformation, however, renders the steel capable of returning to microstructural "equilibrium" by recrystallizing during heat treatment at temperatures well below those representing the thermal zone of conventional phase transformations. If such recrystallization is allowed to continue to completion by holding the steel at the proper temperature for sufficient time, the resultant structure again will consist of clearly-defined equiaxed ferrite grains with undistorted lattices and the steel again will be soft and ductile. In whatever state they were in the hot-rolled product, the carbides will have formed cementite, either small scattered spheroids (from hot-rolled breakdowns coiled cold) or massive agglomerates (from hot-rolled breakdowns coiled hot or from annealing slightly above the lower critical temperature).

Assuming sufficient time at the annealing temperature, steel given a heavy cold reduction will begin to crystallize at a lower temperature, will complete recrystallization more quickly, and finish with a finer ferrite grain, than steel given a light cold reduction. This is because the former material is more distorted before annealing and so has more centers of nucleation and higher localized stresses to induce the crystalline realignment. Similarly, those variations in practice during the hot-rolling of breakdowns which affect grain size of the product will affect similarly the microstructure of the cold-reduced, box-annealed steel, within the limits determined by steel grade, degree of cold reduction and annealing practice.

Recrystallization begins at each nucleation center with a return from distorted to "normal" atom alignment and is propagated by absorption of the surrounding distorted material into that alignment until the growth stops, establishing a single ferrite grain. Grain formation generally is stopped by the advancing fronts of differently-oriented adjacent grains. Within the practical range of recrystallization temperatures, however, the tendency of adjacent grains to assume the same lattice alignment, and to merge to form a larger grain, increases with increasing temperature. The maximum annealing temperature at which the steel is held for a significant time, therefore, determines the finished grain size for a given steel grade, hot-rolling practice and degree of cold reduction.

Beyond the period permitting full recrystallization —one to four hours at maximum temperature is sufficient for common steel grades and mill practices—time at subcritical temperature has relatively little effect on the grain size of the common steels. Extended "soaking" times do, however, lower the hardness for a given grain size, so that the annealing cycles applied generally hold the steel at temperature two to four times as long as is necessary for recrystallization.

A box-annealing practice developed to attain a given end result in grain size and physical properties, therefore, must balance several factors, some of them outside the annealing operation itself and invariable to any effective degree. Fortunately, minor variations in annealing practice have little effect on results and effective variations aimed at attaining lowest steel hardness values are not difficult to make or control.

Normalizing—The most common type of continuous heat treating employed at this time is normalizing, in which the sheet is heated above its upper critical temperature, around 1800° F for low-carbon steel, and cooled at a rate which permits the formation of the proper ferrite grain size. Normalizing is used only where box annealing is inadequate; typical applications include the heat treatment of alloy sheets to attain a fine pearlitic structure or the heat treatment of cold-reduced "pure iron" which recrystallizes sluggishly in conventional box annealing.

Continuous Annealing—Continuous annealing of light-gage cold-reduced steel in a deoxidizing atmosphere has received increasing study since the modern cold-reduction process has provided single lengths of material thousands of feet long; its potentialities for tin plate, which generally requires higher hardnesses than sheets, are very attractive. In this treatment, a single strand of steel, cold reduced to the thin section used for tin plate, travels at high speed through a heating zone having a controlled atmosphere, where it is brought to a temperature just above the lower critical in a very short time, recrystallizes almost instantaneously, passes through a cooling zone and emerges into the air cold enough to avoid oxidation.

Such an operation provides fully-recrystallized steel, ductile in spite of its relative hardness and nearly free of directionality in physical properties. The extremely short time at temperature is effective because recrystallization has been suppressed by the rapid temperature rise; the resultant increase in energy level at all potential nucleation centers causes the microstructure to "flash over" once recrystallization begins.

SECTION 9

HEAT-TREATING EQUIPMENT AND PRACTICES

Because of the wide range of flat-rolled products that receive heat treatment in their course of manufacture, and because the design of equipment is influenced by operators' preferences and the recommendations of those who design and build furnace equipment, heat-treating equipment and practices will be discussed here in general terms.

BOX ANNEALING

Box Annealing Equipment—Box-annealing equipment consists of annealing bases on which to place the steel charge, furnaces to apply the heat, and, generally, inner covers which fit over the charge in the furnace and contain the protective atmosphere that prevents oxidation of the steel (Figure 32—7). Each of these basic units may vary considerably in design, with little or much auxiliary equipment; in any steel plant several sets of units are grouped together into an annealing department, which is serviced as a whole by tracks, cars, tractors, cranes and atmosphere preparation equipment.

In most modern equipment, the bases are stationary

FIG. 32—7. A 500-ton capacity annealing furnace for coils. The furnace is being lowered by crane over the base loaded with eight stacks of coils. The burner tubes may be seen extending across the interior of the furnace. Note guide posts at the corners of the base.

and the portable furnaces are lowered by crane onto the loaded base and attached to fuel and control connections for the annealing operation. To attain maximum furnace utilization, two, three, or four bases and an equivalent number of inner covers are provided for each furnace. Thus, no furnace time is wasted while the bases are being loaded or cooled to handling temperature. Some plants use stationary "in-and-out" furnaces with doors at one end; the loaded bases, with inner covers in place over the charge, are pushed into and withdrawn from the furnaces on tracked rollers.

Annealing bases are usually rectangular, although circular bases (and furnaces) are not uncommonly used for coil annealing of cold-reduced products. A base consists of a shallow tray of cast iron or, more commonly, refractory-lined steel. For sealing the open down-end of the inner cover, the bottom of the base may be covered with a layer of sand or the sand may be contained in a trough around the periphery of the base. Where expensive protective atmospheres are used, such as cracked ammonia (to protect high-carbon steel against decarburization), the trough into which the edge of the inner cover fits is filled with oil or low-melting alloy for perfect sealing.

Annealing bases for cut-sheet charges generally have a steel plate, set on the sand or raised on rails or piers, on which the piles of sheets rest to permit circulation of the contained atmosphere. For annealing coils, rectangular bases have two to eight raised "stools," each capped with an annular plate and generally containing a motor-driven fan for atmosphere circulation and better heat transfer. In addition, most

bases are fitted with thermocouple inlets and atmosphere inlets and outlets.

The dimensions of a base are, of course, determined by the length and width of the furnace used on it. In the United States, they vary between 5 feet and 16 feet in width, 8 feet and 35 feet in length.

Inner covers are commonly open-bottomed thin-walled steel boxes or cylinders to fit, respectively, rectangular charges of cut sheets or cylindrical charges of stacked coils. These shells commonly are formed and welded either from $\frac{3}{16}$ to $\frac{1}{4}$-inch thick low-carbon steel, or $\frac{3}{32}$ to $\frac{1}{8}$-inch thick 18-8 columbium-bearing or 25-12 stainless-steel sheets. They may be strengthened by beading or corrugating the walls and the carbon-steel covers may be coated with aluminum oxide, sodium silicate or other protective compounds to reduce their oxidation rate.

The older in-and-out furnaces use thicker cast-iron covers to withstand the more severe oxidation conditions typical of open-flame firing.

Two innovations in inner covers are receiving some attention. In one design, the radiant tubes in which the fuel is burned are contained in the cover rather than in the furnace as in conventional equipment, and the "furnace" is simply a heat-insulating unit. This arrangement is intended to effect fuel economy and faster heating. Another new type of cylindrical cover has an inner shell to force the protective atmosphere being circulated by fans into better contact with the inner surface of the cover proper, and so effect better heat transfer and distribution.

Box-annealing furnaces are stationary or, more commonly, portable. **Stationary furnaces,** rectangular in shape, may be built singly or in batteries of two or four. Each furnace consists of a rectangular steel frame lined with 10 to 14 inches of fire-brick. Overall dimensions vary from 7 to 15 feet in width, 7 to 10 feet in height and 15 to 27 feet in length. Charging ends are fitted with hinged or counter-balanced doors, the latter traveling in vertical tracks. Floor tracks extend from the loading area into the furnace hearth and one or two charged bases are pushed into the furnace on cast-iron balls or carried in on a charging machine. Such furnaces may be fired with coal, oil, or gas.

Stationary furnaces are seldom used for annealing coils. Most of them employ heavy cast-iron inner covers and cast-iron bottoms, which together weigh as much as the 15 to 25 tons of sheets being annealed. The resultant fuel consumption of 2 to 4 million Btu per ton of sheets annealed represents very low efficiency. More modern in-and-out furnaces, with light steel inner covers over the charge, can anneal up to 150 tons per charge with a fuel consumption of 1.2 to 1.6 million Btu per ton of sheets.

Portable annealing furnaces consist of a structural-steel frame covered with steel plate and lined with 6 to 12 inches of refractory insulating brick. The rectangular furnace generally used varies greatly in size and in annealing load weight, depending on mill requirements, handling facilities and effectiveness of design in providing temperature uniformity. Dimensions of furnaces now in use range from 5 to 16 feet in width, 6 to 14 feet in height and 8 to 33 feet in length. Loads of sheared sheets vary from 25 to 150 tons and of coils from 50 to 500 tons; fuel consumption ranges between 0.8 and 1.5 million Btu per annealed ton and annealing rate from 1 to 10 tons of steel per furnace hour.

Such furnaces commonly are gas-fired, although any fluid fuel may be used and electrical resistance heating has been tried. Burners usually fire into "radiant tubes" of 25-12 stainless steel. These tubes are 3 to 6 inches in diameter and as long as the furnace size and desired temperature distribution dictate. They may run vertically or horizontally along the inner walls of the furnace or, in large furnaces for annealing coils, may span the distance between the walls for better temperature distribution. The tubes vent the products of combustion on the outside of the furnace.

Heating of the inner cover thus occurs by radiation. Proper tube location and the flexibility possible in having each tube served by an individual burner permit the necessary uniformity of heating of the large masses of steel contained in one annealing charge. For minor adjustments, burners can be controlled individually. They are manifolded together, however, and the fuel flow to the individual burners of one furnace is usually determined by the main fuel valve of the furnace which is controlled automatically by predetermined tube-temperature control settings and by charge-temperature controls.

Some use is made of tubeless furnaces, with the burner discharging into a refractory baffle which prevents flame impingement on the inner cover but permits circulation of the hot combustion gases between the furnace wall and the inner cover. Convection plays an important part in heating the inner cover in this design. The decision to use a tubeless furnace will be influenced by the relative importance of its possible fuel economy, freedom from radiant tube costs, higher inner-cover costs and different temperature-distribution characteristics.

Box Annealing Practices—To begin an annealing operation in portable furnace equipment, sheared sheets are loaded on the base in piles 3 to 5 feet high and coils on the base stools in stacks 8 to 12 feet high; loading is done by traveling overhead cranes equipped with hooks, slings, retractable racks or magnets. Thermocouples are inserted in standard locations in the charge. One rectangular inner cover is lowered over the entire sheet charge or an individual cylindrical "ash can" inner cover is lowered over each stack of coils and settled in the sand seal. The furnace is then lowered onto the base, fuel line and thermocouple connections are made, the flow of deoxidizing gas to purge the air from the space under the inner cover is begun, and the burners are ignited. Base fans, if available, are turned on to effect high-speed circulation of the atmosphere in the inner cover.

The subject of deoxidizing gas protective atmospheres is treated more fully elsewhere in this volume (see Index). It is sufficient to say here that it generally consists of the products of partial combustion of a fuel gas in a limited volume of air, these products then being treated to remove most of the resultant water vapor, dirt and carbon particles, and in some cases further treated to remove sulphur dioxide and carbon dioxide. The resultant mixture of 75 to 85 per cent nitrogen plus varying percentages of hydrogen, carbon monoxide, carbon dioxide and methane protects the bright steel surface from visible oxidation throughout the annealing cycle. Other effective atmospheres include dissociated ammonia and high-purity nitrogen.

During the heating-up period, fuel consumption is maintained at a constant rate until "tube" or "furnace" temperature, determined by a thermocouple connected to a recording-controlling instrument, reaches a predetermined level chosen to protect the equipment from damage. Fuel feed then is controlled automatically or manually so that this temperature is not exceeded. The next control point is reached when the thermocouple located in the hottest part of the load reaches a temperature preset to avoid overannealing or welding of the charge. Finally, the soak is begun when the "control couple" (either at the coldest spot in the charge or, if this is inaccessible, in a location bearing a known temperature relationship to the coldest spot) reaches the specified soaking temperature. Another fuel cutback takes place here, and the control-couple temperature curve flattens out through the specified duration of the soaking period. At the end of the soaking period, the fuel is shut off, the furnace is removed to begin a cycle on another base, and the charge is allowed to cool (still in a protective atmosphere under the inner cover) to about 300° F, when it can be exposed to air without oxidizing. The cooling period takes at least as long as the combined total time of heating and soaking.

The temperature and times specified for annealing practices vary greatly from plant to plant, even in the manufacture of the universally similar dead-soft low-carbon sheet. This is true because of inherent differences in the cold-reduced steel to be annealed and differences in furnace size and design, load size and piling pattern, and thermocouple locations. As an example of the effect of one of these factors, heat conductivity through a load of sheets parallel to the sheet plane is somewhat less than through a solid mass of steel, but four to seven times greater than heat conductivity perpendicular to the sheet plane. A stack of coils consists of a hollow cylinder with a 16-inch to 30-inch inside diameter and a 36-inch to 84-inch outer diameter, receiving inner-cover radiant heat perpendicular to the curved planes of the layers of steel comprising the coils. This handicap can be overcome in part by blowing the atmosphere at high speed through the spaces inside and outside the coil stack, and so transferring some of the heat from the inner cover to the inner diameter of the coils. Another means is to separate each pair of coils in a stack with "convector plates," resembling flattened doughnuts with passages for the hot circulating atmosphere between top and bottom surfaces. Thus, some heat is transmitted to the ends of each coil, from which it has an easier path to follow.

Regardless of the wide differences necessary in specified control cycles, the coldest spot of an annealing charge, whether or not actually accessible to a thermocouple under production conditions, will be found to have been annealed for 10 to 20 hours at a temperature in the range of 1225 to 1275° F in virtually all plants making deep-drawing rimmed-steel sheets, with the proper formula within these limits being determined by the prior history of the cold-reduced steel. Depending on furnace and load characteristics, the hottest part of the charge will have been at 1275° to 1350° F for 20 to 50 hours, and the furnace will have been under fire for 30 to 90 hours. When no steel decarburization occurs (as is the case with adequate prepared-atmosphere protection), the gross differences in time at temperature throughout an annealing load have little effect on sheet properties if the cold portion has been adequately annealed and so approaches the inherent limit of grain growth and steel softening.

Such temperature differences are more critical in annealing tin plate, where definite higher hardness levels are wanted. Partial protection against over-annealing exists in this case because the heavy cold reductions used limit the grain size to a relatively fine, and therefore relatively hard, structure, regardless of any annealing temperature employed below the transformation-temperature range. Such heavy cold reduction also induces full recrystallization at a lower temperature than is necessary on steel thicknesses given less cold reduction, and tin plate can be annealed fully in the slightly lower temperature range necessary to attain proper hardness.

For products other than low-carbon cold-reduced sheets, strip or tin plate, annealing practices can vary considerably from the outline given. Box-annealing furnaces are used occasionally at temperatures as low as 1000° F to stress relieve, rather than recrystallize, certain specialty steels, and temperatures up to 2000° F have been employed on other specialties.

Open-Coil Annealing—As has been stated earlier, open-coil annealing minimizes the difficulties inherent in box annealing in regard to uniformity and rapidity of heating. Open-coil annealing can employ protective atmospheres to prevent scaling, decarburization, or carburization of the charge equally as well as box annealing; however, by proper selection of the atmosphere, the open-coil technique can also be used to deliberately change the chemical composition of the steel, or to obtain desirable surface effects in a controllable manner. Obviously, time-temperature relationships as well as atmosphere controls are factors in obtaining the desired results from such special uses of the open-coil technique.

NORMALIZING

Normalizing furnaces are designed to heat and cool sheets singly or in thin packs of two, three, or four sheets. Therefore, they are built in the form of long low chambers, usually in three sections, known as the preheating zone (12 to 20 per cent of the total length), the heating, or soaking, zone (about 33 per cent of the total length), and the cooling zone, which occupies the remaining 40 to 50 per cent of the length. In modern furnaces of the conveyor type, the only type adaptable for treating short lengths, the sheets are carried successively through each of these zones upon disc rollers made of heat-resistant alloys with polished surfaces to avoid scratching the sheets, and with the discs staggered to assure uniform heating of the sheets. The discs are mounted upon water-cooled shafts, which are driven by variable-speed motors through chains and sprockets or shafts and gears. These furnaces are built up to 100 inches in width and vary from 120 to 200 feet in length; fuel consumption is 2.0 to 4.5 million Btu per ton and production rates vary from 3 to 12 tons per hour. A furnace of this type is illustrated in Chapter 39. Normalizing furnaces usually are heated with gas or oil and do not employ protective atmospheres. The sheets are, therefore, scaled during the heat treatment. Burners are arranged, along each side of the heating zone, usually above the conveyor rolls, but occasionally both above and below the conveyor. The roof, which is higher over the preheating and soaking zones than over the cooling zone, usually is built in sections. In most types, both the preheating and cooling zones are heated by the hot gases from the heating zone. This distribution of heat and gases within the furnace is obtained through two stacks, one being located at the entering end to draw the gases through the preheating zone and the other near the exit end to maintain a neutral atmosphere in the cooling zone. However, both the preheating and the cooling zones may be equipped with burners, the better to control their temperatures. Air is excluded by regulating the draft to maintain a slight pressure within all the zones. Heat losses are overcome by the generous use of heat-insulating materials. Furnaces designed to normalize sheared sheets are equipped with roller tables, one at each end, for charging and receiving the sheets.

The free-loop or catenary type of furnace is designed to normalize continuously cold-reduced steel unwound from coils, and neither rolls nor any other type of conveyor support material passing through the heating zone. The heating zones of these furnaces vary from 20 to 50 feet in length, and the preheating and cooling zones are usually shorter than in the conveyor type and may be omitted for some kinds of work. Such furnaces may have pickling or other descaling equipment at the exit end to remove, in the same operation, the surface oxides formed on the steel during normalizing. Catenary furnaces so equipped, but without a cooling zone, are widely used for the heat treatment of stainless steel, as the temperatures of 1900° to 2200° F used on the austenitic grades would result in short life for rollers used in the furnace. Steam or water quenching facilities are usually provided at the exit end of furnaces for heat treating stainless steel in this manner.

Assuming that the normalizing is to be done in a three-zone conveyor-type furnace, equipped with pyrometric controls, the operations appear extremely simple. If it is necessary to avoid all danger of scratching the sheets, they are brought to the charging table, and laid one or more at a time by hand upon a rider, or conveyor, sheet. The heaviest sheets (length, width and gage considered) are normalized singly, but lighter sheets may be laid two or more in a pile. Sometimes single sheets are laid upon a rider sheet and covered with another, called a cover sheet, to control heating and retard scaling. The sheets are carried by rolls into the preheating zone, where they at first absorb heat very rapidly because of the great temperature differential between them and the furnace interior. As the sheets become heated and this difference grows less, the absorption of heat becomes slower, so

that after traveling 15 to 20 feet, the sheets enter the soaking zone several degrees below the normalizing temperature. Heating is completed in the soaking zone, which is maintained at a constant temperature, and the sheets are at the necessary temperature for a time sufficient to convert the microstructure to austenite before they pass into the cooling zone. The sheet or sheets emerge from the cooling zone at a temperature which can be varied between 300° and 1000° F, and are conveyed for a short distance upon the run-out table, where they are cooled rapidly in contact with the air and carefully removed from the rider sheet. The trip through such a furnace is carried out at a uniform speed of 5 to 20 feet per minute and requires 5 to 20 minutes to complete.

Roller-hearth sheet-normalizing furnaces are sometimes modified by removing the cooling zone and substituting air, steam, oil or water quenching facilities, the latter two as sprays or tanks. Such facilities are utilized to retain the austenitic structure developed in the heating zone on sheared sheets of stainless or Hadfield manganese steels, and to develop a martensitic structure (for subsequent tempering) in the higher-carbon alloy steels of the AISI 41xx or 86xx types.

CONTINUOUS ANNEALING

From an engineering standpoint, the continuous-annealing operation is made practical by building the heating and cooling zones as towers and increasing their effective length by threading the steel back and forth around rolls at the top and bottom of the towers. This principle is illustrated in Figure 32—8, which

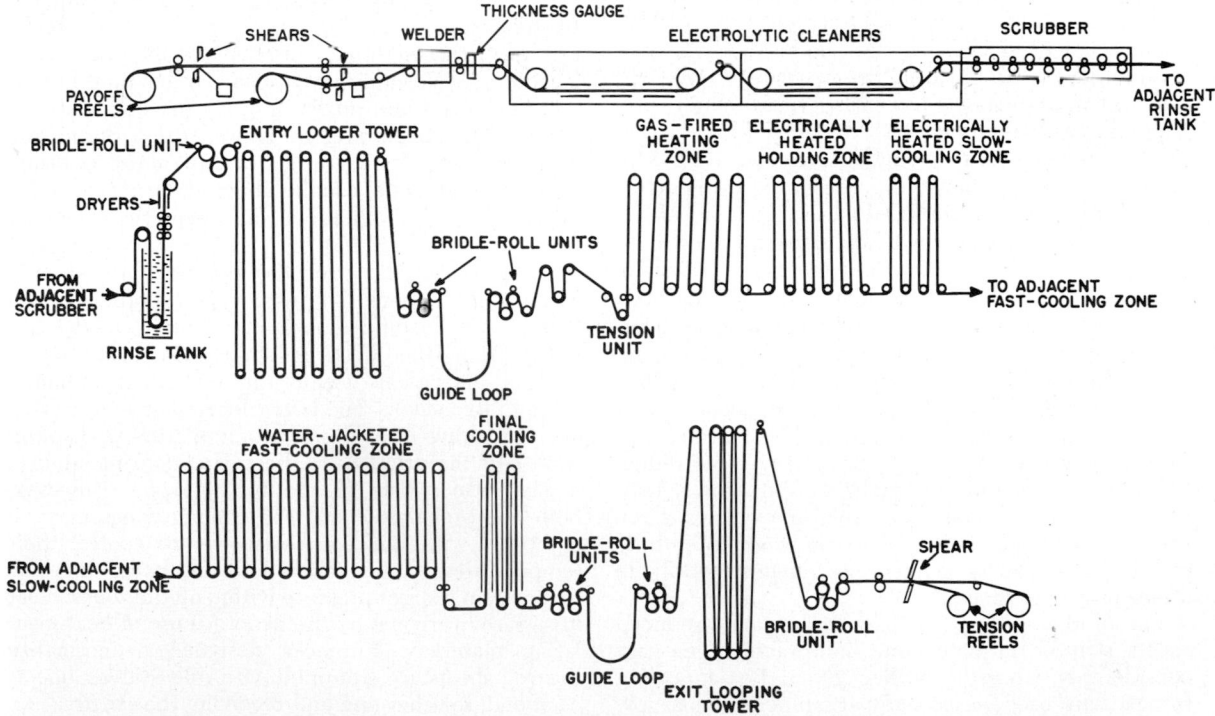

FIG. 32—8. Schematic diagram (not to scale) of a continuous-annealing line designed to operate at a strip speed of 1500 feet per minute.

shows schematically the path of full-width tin-plate stock passing through the line that consists, in the direction of strip travel, of a double payoff reel; shears for squaring the ends of coils for welding; a welding unit; an alkaline electrolytic cleaner with a brush scrubber, water rinse and drying unit; and an entry looping tower that can "store" 1000 feet of wide strip and from which strip is taken to maintain constant line speed when a weld is being made. This line was designed to operate at a speed of 1500 feet per minute. Following the entry-end equipment just enumerated is the furnace proper that consists of a gas-fired heating zone wherein the strip makes ten passes; an electrically heated holding zone of ten passes; an electrically heated slow-cooling zone of six passes; a water-jacketed fast-cooling zone of thirty passes; a final cooling zone of four passes; another looping tower; and two recoilers. Each pass consists of 50 feet of strip steel, and all passes are vertical. The strip is heated to approximately 1350° F in the heating zone in 20 sec. and maintained at this temperature for 20 sec. in the holding zone. Upon leaving the holding zone the strip is cooled to about 1000° F in 12 sec. in the slow-cooling zone and thence to about 240° F in 60 sec. in the fast-cooling zone. From its entry into the heating zone until it leaves the fast-cooling zone, the strip is protected from oxidation by a gas atmosphere containing 95 per cent of nitrogen and 5 per cent of hydrogen. Subsequent cooling is done in 8 sec. in air. At an operating speed of 1500 ft. per min., less than two minutes (112 sec.) elapse from the time a given section of strip enters the heating zone to the time it leaves the fast-cooling zone.

Two continuous furnaces of somewhat different design at the Vandergrift plant of United States Steel Corporation (Figure 32—9) were built for heat treating high-silicon electrical steels, which require precise recrystallization control at higher temperatures and very low carbon contents to attain optimum electrical properties. With a floor length of 175 feet, the furnaces utilize the tower principle to permit several hundred feet of steel to be treated at temperatures up to 1900° F for controlled lengths of time, and under atmospheres of varying decarburizing power, as determined by the desired magnetic properties of the product. Speeds up to 240 feet per minute and production rates up to 10 tons per hour are possible.

FIG. 32—9. Two tower-type continuous annealing furnaces for processing silicon steel.

TEMPER ROLLING

The purpose of temper rolling as applied to cold-reduced flat-rolled products depends upon the type of product. In some sheet products, the main purpose is to develop the proper stiffness or temper by cold working the steel in controlled amounts: this is also the primary purpose for temper rolling of tin-plate products. In addition, temper rolling tends to improve the flatness of annealed strip, to develop desired mechanical properties, and to impart the desired surface finish to the finished product. Temper-rolling mills are referred to as **sheet temper mills** or **coil temper mills,** depending upon the form of the product rolled on them.

Sheet temper mills are used only when it is necessary to process material in sheet form, such as in gages too heavy to be handled on a coil temper mill. The mechanical and stiffness properties imparted to steel by temper rolling are related to the degree of reduction in thickness effected by the cold working. Since an increment of length is added to each unit length that passes through the mill due to the reduction in thickness with the width remaining essentially the same, increase in length, referred to as **extension,** is used as the criterion for determining the relative reduction in thickness. Extension on a sheet temper mill is easily controlled by comparing sheet lengths before and after rolling. The temper rolling of sheet product on a coil temper mill involves back tension on the product between the uncoiling reel and the mill, and forward tension between the mill and the recoiling reel. Since coil temper mills operate at relatively high speeds, extension of the strip due to the combination of tension and roll pressure must be controlled by automatic measuring and control devices.

Sheet temper mills are of both two-high and four-high types, and consist of a single stand. Coil temper mills for sheets (Figure 32—10) consist of a single-stand four-high unit, while two-stand tandem coil temper mills are used to produce the harder tempers required for tin-plate product.

The finish of the rolled product is controlled by using rolls having a variety of surface finishes developed to impart the desired finish to the product. Roll finishes range from ground and polished rolls to impart a bright finish, to shot-blasted rolls that produce a dull, velvety finish on the steel surface.

Mechanical properties imparted by temper rolling vary with the amount of extension (which, as stated above, is proportional to the reduction in thickness). Sheets intended for deep-drawing applications receive about 0.25 to 1 per cent extension, which is sufficient to suppress the formation of stretcher strains during forming without significantly impairing ductility. Sheets having lesser ductility requirements are given about 1 to 1.5 per cent extension.

SHEARING, SIDE TRIMMING, SLITTING AND LEVELING

Although much less shearing is being done in sheet and tin mills than formerly, because an increasing tonnage of product is being shipped in coil form, shearing is still one of the most common and most important operations. There are two general types of shears: (a) those for making cuts across the width of the strip, and (b) those known as side-trimmers or slitters that make continuous cuts along the length of a moving strip

Shearing to Length—Practically all sheets produced by shearing from coils of cold-reduced material are cut to length on continuous-shearing lines employing **flying shears** that may be of either the guillotine type or the rotary type. As the name "flying shear" implies, both types perform the cutting operation on strip passing through the shearing line at some pre-set speed.

The guillotine-type flying shear operates on the same principle as a stationary-type guillotine shear, except that it is mounted in a movable housing that can move in the same direction and at the same speed as the moving strip while the knives perform the cutting operation. After each cut, the housing moves back to its original position in preparation for the next cut. Flying guillotine shears are used in lines capable of cutting strip moving at speeds up to 350 feet per minute.

Rotary-type flying shears consist of two horizontal cylinders, mounted one above the other in a housing, each carrying a knife that is parallel to the axes of the cylinders and that extends a suitable distance from the cylinder face. The cylinders can be operated so that the knife edges are brought together at intervals to achieve the proper length of cut. Lines employing rotary-type flying shears can operate at strip speeds up to 1000 feet per minute.

The speed advantage of the rotary shear is best realized on lines employed to cut large numbers of sheets of the same size. When small lots of sheets of different lengths are to be cut, it is possible to cut the same number of sheets per day on a line employing a guillotine-type flying shear.

Side Trimming and Slitting—As was stated in Chapter 31, most continuous-pickling lines have a side trimmer installed at the exit end. These trimmers employ mating circular knives, mounted on arbors, to remove continuously the desired amount from both edges of the strip, thereby establishing accurate and uniform width and producing parallel and reasonably smooth edges. Side trimmers have also been installed on continuous-tinning lines and continuous-annealing lines. Many sheet-shearing lines, however, do not have

FIG. 32—10. Single-stand four-high sheet temper mill, for temper rolling flat-rolled steel in coil form. Product travel through the mill is from right to left.

side trimmers because practically all sheet-mill strip is side trimmed at the continuous-pickling line and may not need a second trimming. Side trimming of strip for electrolytic tin plate may be done in separate lines called coil-preparation lines or, in some cases by trimmers incorporated in the tinning line itself or in the cutting-up line that follows the continuous-tinning line.

The principle of operation of the machines used for slitting was described in Section 7 of Chapter 31.

Leveling—Roller-leveling and stretcher-leveling of cold-reduced product for sheets are performed on equipment similar to that described in Section 7 of Chapter 31, and for the same purpose—to improve flatness of individual sheets to the degree required for the intended application.

Bibliography

Am. Iron and Steel Inst., Steel products manuals (Carbon Steel: Semifinished for Forging; Hot-Rolled and Cold-Finished Bars; Hot-rolled Deformed Concrete Reinforcing Bars. Also, Carbon Steel Sheets. Also, Cold-Rolled Carbon-Steel Strip. Also, Tin Mill Products. The Institute, N. Y.

American Soc. for Testing and Materials, ASTM Standards 1961, Part I, Ferrous Metals Specifications. The Society, Philadelphia, Pa.

Archibald, E. N., Modern techniques in the cold reduction of sheet and tin plate. Iron and Steel Engineer **34**, May 1957, pages 141–146.

Bauscher, J. A., Use of open coil process to change composition and improve sheet steels. Iron and Steel Engineer **39**, May 1961, pages 73–84.

Drever, Horace, C. E. Peck, H. W. Lynn, E. B. Fitzgerald, Symposium on continuous annealing of steel strip. Iron and Steel Engineer **34**, Feb. 1957, pages 69–94.

Ess, T. J., The modern strip mill. Assn. of Iron and Steel Engineers, Pittsburgh, Pa. (1941).

Helm, H. B., W. H. Swisshelm, W. F. Carter, John Soyring, Symposium on annealing furnaces. Iron and Steel Engineer **32**, March 1955, pages 73–81.

Johannsen, K. L., Operations of the wide strip rolling mills at Fairless Works. Iron and Steel Institute Special Report 67, pages 76–86 and 87–91. The Institute, London, 1960.

Mehl, R. F., Recrystallization. Metals Handbook (1948 Ed.), American Society for Metals (Cleveland, Ohio).

Miller, W. E. and R. G. Beadle, Automatic gage control of metal rolling. Automation **5**, Oct. 1959, pages 76–81.

Morrow, H. C., Continuous annealing of steel strip; controls for a high-speed line. Mechanical Engineer **76**, Dec. 1954, pages 990–994.

Rickett, R. L. and F. C. Kristufek, The microstructure of low-carbon steel. Trans. Am. Society for Metals, Cleveland, Ohio (1949).

Rickett, R. L., S. H. Kalin and J. T. MacKenzie, Jr., Recrystallization and microstructure of aluminum-killed deep-drawing steel. Trans. Am. Institute of Mining and Metallurgical Engineers, Metals Div., **185**, pages 242–251 (1949).

Roberts, William L. and Robert R. Somers. The cold-rolling lubrication of steel strip. Lubrication Engineering **18**, Aug. 1962, pages 362–368.

Seabold, E. J., Continuous strip annealing. Iron and Steel Engineer **23**, Dec. 1946.

Shedd, Robert R., Cold-reduction facilities at Fairless Works. Iron and Steel Engineer **32**, May 1955, pages 55–63.

Stelzer, J. M., Conventional instrumentation of a continuous annealing line. Proc. Eleventh Annual Conf. on Instrumentation for the Iron and Steel Industry. Instrument Society of America, Pittsburgh, Pa., 1961.

CHAPTER 33

Corrosion and Protective Coatings

SECTION 1

CAUSES OF CORROSION

The Mechanism of Corrosion—The corrosion of the common metals in usual environments is an electrochemical phenomenon. That is, it is associated with the flow of electric currents over finite distances. Electric currents associated with corrosion have been detected in numerous cases, and in a limited number of instances the amount of corrosion occurring has been accounted for quantitatively by the amount of electric current which passed.

Knowledge that corrosion is electrochemical is important, since it assists in the development of methods for combating corrosion. For instance, it is obvious that, in order for electrochemical corrosion to occur, there must be differences in potential between different areas of the corroding structure. Such differences can be caused by the use of dissimilar metals or alloys in contact with each other. However, differences in potential can be caused by heterogeneities of any kind in the metal surface or in the environment contacting the metal. Some of the most important of these heterogeneities will be discussed below.

FACTORS WHICH AFFECT CORROSION RATE

The fundamental reason why metals corrode is that the corrosion products are more stable than the metals themselves. Thermodynamically speaking, in order for metals to corrode there must be a decrease in free energy associated with the formation of the appropriate corrosion product from the metal. This free energy decrease is the **driving force** of the corrosion reaction. However, the magnitude of this driving force gives little information regarding the rate at which corrosion will occur. The rate of corrosion is determined by other factors which will be described later in this chapter.

An **electrolytic cell,** in its simplest elements, consists of an **anode** and a **cathode** in a conducting solution (electrolyte). **Polarization** consists of a behavior at an electrode and results in what might be defined as a "back e.m.f.," which has the effect of opposing the flow of current in the electrolytic cell. Polarization thus is a phenomenon analogous to mechanical friction. **Hydrogen overvoltage** is one of the components of the total effect of polarization, and results from the deposition of hydrogen on the surface of the cathode. It will be recognized that polarization (and hydrogen overvoltage) always retard current flow and tend to

lower rates of corrosion. Conversely, any factors that reduce polarization tend to accelerate corrosion.

Moisture—The presence of liquid or gaseous water is the factor of most importance in stimulating normal types of corrosion (although in special cases the presence of some moisture may retard corrosion). The reason for the customary stimulation in corrosion rate caused by the presence of moisture is that moisture generally increases the electrical conductivity of the environment contacting the metal surface. Since corrosion is commonly electrochemical in nature, an increase in electrical conductivity of the environment will permit flow of larger electrical currents and, therefore, result in higher corrosion rates for given potential differences from point to point on the metal surface. Examples of the effect of moisture in stimulating corrosion are so well known that it is hardly necessary to elaborate greatly on this point. It has been established that even unalloyed steels will remain uncorroded if they are exposed to air with a relative humidity less than about 30 per cent. At higher humidities appreciable rusting will occur. Similarly, contact between steel and dry cloth or paper causes no serious attack of the steel, whereas, contact with damp cloth or paper may.

Salts—Neutral salts may stimulate corrosion in the presence of moisture by either or both of two mechanisms. They increase the electrical conductivity of the solution and thus increase corrosion currents. In addition, certain salts may form complexes with the metal corrosion products, thus increasing the solubility of the metal ion. This also stimulates corrosion. Local differences in salt concentration in a liquid which contacts a metal surface can cause severe localized attack as a result of the formation of concentration cells. These will be discussed in greater detail later.

Acids—There are two broad classes of acids:—(1) oxidizing acids such as concentrated nitric acid and (2) the non-oxidizing acids such as hydrochloric acid. The non-oxidizing acids stimulate corrosion by permitting the more rapid evolution of hydrogen as a result of reduction of the hydrogen overvoltage. Oxidizing acids may or may not be corrosive, depending on whether they form thin protective films on the metal surface. The so-called **passivity** of steel in concentrated nitric acid is the result of the formation of a thin, insoluble film on the steel surface upon contact with nitric acid above a certain concentration. Very concentrated sulphuric acid also forms a protective film upon contact with steel. Under usual service conditions, an increase in the acidity of a solution generally tends to increase its corrosivity.

Alkalis—For most ferrous materials, an increase in the alkalinity of a solution generally will tend to reduce the total amount of corrosion, although it may increase the intensity of attack at local areas. Very strong caustic solutions, particularly at elevated temperatures, or molten caustic materials also may be corrosive to a serious extent on account of the amphoteric nature of iron.

Oxygen and Oxidizing Compounds—Free oxygen and many oxidizing compounds have a complex effect on the corrosion of steel. In aqueous solutions, they stimulate the total amount of corrosion but tend to restrict the area which is attacked. On the other hand, if sufficient oxygen or oxidizing compound is present in the solution, attack may be prevented entirely. This inhibiting action of oxygen and oxidizing compounds is of most importance in the case of stainless steels, while the accelerating action of dissolved oxygen is of great importance in the corrosion of unalloyed steels by natural waters and many chemical solutions.

The behavior of free oxygen and oxidizing compounds in general can be described in electrochemical terms. These materials stimulate the cathodic reaction by depolarization, but they tend to retard the anodic reaction by forming films on the surface of the anode. Thus, their behavior is complex.

In gaseous exposures at elevated temperatures, the presence of oxygen in the atmosphere generally results in increased rates of scaling or oxidation.

Sulphur Compounds—Sulphur compounds, either in solutions or in gas atmospheres, generally accelerate the corrosion of ferrous materials. Practically, such compounds give the most trouble in gaseous exposures at elevated temperatures. In the petroleum industry alone, corrosion of ferrous materials resulting from the presence of sulphur compounds in the products being handled, annually causes millions of dollars worth of damage. Apparently the sulphur compounds render the scale less protective, thus permitting increased rates of attack.

High Temperatures—In general, the higher the temperature of the exposure, the faster corrosion will proceed. There are many exceptions, since change in temperature can affect simultaneously several factors which all may influence corrosion rates. For example, raising the temperature of an aqueous solution exposed to air may either increase or decrease the rate of attack on metallic surfaces contacting the solution. Some of the effects of raising the temperature of a solution can be described in electrochemical terms. Increase in temperature increases the conductivity of the solution and also tends to decrease cathodic polarization. Both of these factors tend to stimulate corrosion. However, raising the temperature may decrease the concentration of oxygen dissolved in the solution but may cause more continuous films to be formed on anodic areas. Both of these factors tend to reduce corrosion rates. In practice, increase in the temperature of solutions freely exposed to the air

usually results first in an increase in the corrosion rate, but as temperatures above about 180° F are exceeded, the corrosion rate may decrease until the boiling point is reached.

Increase in temperature generally increases corrosion by gases, although here also special effects may come into play so that for some regions of temperature variation, relatively small increases in temperature may actually reduce corrosion rates. One of the most obvious examples of this is where the gas contains water vapor. At temperatures below the dew point, liquid water condenses from the gas and corrosion may be rapid. At somewhat more elevated temperatures, the humidity is less than 100 per cent, so liquid water does not form and the corrosion rate is much lower.

Galvanic Action—When dissimilar metals are placed in electrical contact and exposed to a conducting solution, generally corrosion of one member of the combination is accelerated while that of the other member is retarded. The metal of the combination which has the most active solution potential under the particular conditions of exposure is anodic and sends electric current through the solution to the cathodic metal. The direction of the current flow determines the member of the couple which will suffer accelerated or **galvanic corrosion.** The magnitude of the current determines the corrosion rate. The electromotive force series indicates roughly which metal of the combination will be anodic and thus suffer special attack. However, since the potentials of the different metals vary with respect to different solutions, the electromotive force series is only a very rough guide.

For example, in sea water, steel is anodic to tin. Thus, contact with tin will accelerate corrosion of steel in sea water. However, when exposed to fruit juices under food container conditions, tin is anodic to steel and will tend to protect steel when in electrical contact with it.

The solution potentials of different alloys of the same base metal may be quite different in specific exposures. Thus, galvanic corrosion can be caused by contact between two different alloys of the same metal. In general, contact between any two metals or any two alloys in any conducting solutions should be suspected of resulting in galvanic corrosion unless there is definite evidence to the contrary.

In some cases, different metallurgical structures of the same metal or alloy have different solution potentials. Thus, corrosion cells are set up. This cause of corrosion should be suspected in welded structures unless they have been heat treated after welding.

Stray Currents—Stray direct-current electricity is a common cause of corrosion of underground steel pipe lines and other buried steel structures. It is also encountered in harbor structures of steel, steel-hulled vessels while tied up at docks, and in lake or river structures. In some cases, it has caused severe corrosion in chemical plants or other plants where large amounts of electrically conducting liquids are handled. Stray current causes more rapid attack than almost any other commonly encountered cause of corrosion. In fact, wherever very rapid attack of a metallic structure buried in the ground, immersed in water or exposed to conducting liquids is encountered, stray currents should be investigated as one of the most likely causes.

Alternating current electricity is much less likely to cause severe corrosion of ferrous structures unless it is of very low frequency (say one cycle per second).

Concentration Cells—When one portion of a metal surface is exposed to an electrolytically conducting medium which differs in any way from the electrolytically conducting medium which contacts another portion of the same metal surface, selective corrosion of the portion of the surface contacting one of the two types of media is likely to occur.[8] For example, suppose a steel tank is partially filled with a salt solution. If, for any reason, the concentration of salt is different in the layers of solution near the bottom of the tank than it is toward the top of the tank, comparatively more severe corrosion of the steel contacting either the more dilute or the more concentrated solution is likely to occur. This is true even though no corrosion would occur if the tank were full of solution having a uniform concentration from top to bottom. Corrosion in this case is caused by **concentration cell action.**

A special type of concentration cell action is caused by local differences in oxygen concentration of the liquid. For example, let us suppose that liquid saturated with oxygen is circulating freely in contact with most of the inside surfaces of a steel vessel. However, there is a narrow channel or fissure in some part of the surface where stagnant liquid is trapped. The oxygen content of this stagnant liquid will generally be less than that of the freely circulating liquid in contact with it. Thus, an oxygen concentration cell is set up which causes more severe corrosion of the metal surface in contact with the portion of the liquid having the *lower* oxygen content.

Oxygen concentration cells are a very common cause of corrosion under service conditions. The severe localized corrosion at joints and crevices, and on surfaces in contact with wet insulating materials, is largely the result of oxygen concentration cells.

Stress—Applied or residual stresses, either static or dynamic, can greatly accelerate corrosion.[1] Generally speaking, the acceleration of corrosion by static stress is greatest in environments which do not cause appreciable general corrosion. In fact, stress corrosion often occurs under conditions which would cause almost negligible attack in the absence of stress. A particularly dangerous form of stress corrosion is **stress corrosion cracking.** Under some specific sets of conditions, a stressed part of almost any metal or alloy may suddenly crack, although there may have been no appreciable corrosive attack evident prior to the sudden development of the stress corrosion crack. Stress corrosion cracks rarely occur when metallic parts are stressed appreciably below the yield strength. Since design stresses for most stressed assemblies are normally kept well below the yield strength, it is normally not the stresses for which the structure was designed which cause stress corrosion cracking. Instead, it is

normally the residual or so called "internal" stresses which cause this type of failure. These residual stresses are induced during the fabrication of the structure, by bending, welding and other fabricating procedures. The magnitudes of such stresses are frequently not known to the design engineer and are consequently not considered by him in designing the structure.

Cyclic stresses also frequently accelerate corrosion. In cases where the frequency of the alternation in cyclic stresses is high, failures accompanied by corrosion are said to be caused by **corrosion fatigue.** Cyclic stresses, especially if of high frequency, normally cause more rapid failures when accompanied by corrosion than do static stresses of the same magnitude.

Abrasion, Erosion and Cavitation—Surface effects such as abrasion or wear, erosion, impingement of liquid at high velocity, or cavitation effects caused by the collapse of gas or vapor bubbles at the metal surface can all contribute to intensified corrosion damage in specific cases.

Other Surface Effects—Practically any local difference at the metal surface can cause corrosion under suitable conditions. Thus, a scratch in the metal surface can form a weak point at which localized attack may occur. Local differences in temperature, velocity of liquid flow, degree of surface roughness and even amount of illumination can all cause localized corrosion in specific cases. In fact, any heterogeneity in environment, metal surface or, as will be indicated subsequently, in the metal itself, can cause localized attack.

Metallurgical Factors—As mentioned just above, any heterogeneities in the metal or alloy itself can give rise to localized corrosion. For most commercial metals or alloys these "internal" effects are normally a minor factor in influencing corrosion under service conditions. Generally, environmental factors are of much greater importance. This is very fortunate since it is impossible to avoid internal heterogeneities in commercial metals and alloys. All such commercial materials contain inclusions or minor segregations. Whenever localized attack develops in service, it is common practice to put the blame on these small particles of different phases. Actually, as has been shown by the work of Homer[6], Mears[7] and others, very careful control of the uniformity of the corroding environment and of the metal surface is normally required to reveal the effect of inclusions on corrosion. In special cases, with specific metals or alloys, metallurgical factors may be important. For example, in the case of 18 per cent chromium-8 per cent nickel stainless steels, it is well known that slow cooling from the austenitizing temperature or reheating in a critical temperature zone for an appropriate time can cause the precipitation of carbides at grain boundaries, thus sensitizing the alloy to intergranular attack by certain media. In this case, the metallurgical condition is of great importance in controlling corrosion behavior. However, the fact remains that, in general, the metallurgical condition of most commercial materials is not of great importance in affecting corrosion rates.

---

(8) References are at end of chapter.

METHODS OF PREVENTING CORROSION

A knowledge of the factors which accelerate corrosion is of value to most people only as it aids them to understand and to guard against corrosion failures in service. A knowledge of appropriate methods of preventing corrosion is important for the same reason.

Material Selection—The most obvious method of preventing corrosion is to build the structure of a material which is unaffected by the service. Unfortunately, it is not always feasible to do this. The most inert materials may be too expensive or otherwise unsuited for the article to be built. Generally, the engineer must make a compromise. He cannot afford to use the most corrosion-resistant material but instead must compromise on a material which has the lowest combined initial cost plus maintenance costs for some selected period of time. The more accurately the engineer knows the corrosion behavior of the various competitive materials under the desired service conditions, the more accurately can he select the most economical material to use. As a guide to proper selection, nothing has yet replaced previous service use. Since small variations in service conditions can sometimes affect corrosion rates greatly, even previous service use is not infallible. Nevertheless, it is the most trustworthy criterion available.

If it is desired to select material for equipment required for some new process or chemical, there will be no previous background of experience. In such a case, the engineer must be guided by knowledge of the behavior of various materials when used as equipment for similar processes. Better yet, a pilot plant or small-scale service test can be made using a material or materials of construction deemed likely to be satisfactory. The selection of materials for these small-scale tests can be based on laboratory tests or published information. In conducting the laboratory tests, it should be kept in mind that the closer these tests can be designed to simulate actual practice, the more accurately can the results be used to predict satisfactory performance.

Selection of a suitable material of construction may eliminate the need of using any other form of corrosion prevention. However, it is frequently more economical to use some less resistant but cheaper material and to employ one or even several protective measures. In most cases it is not economical to use the most resistant material of construction, but instead to use the cheapest material which will do a satisfactory job.

Appropriate Design—It is frequently overlooked that small changes in design may make it possible to use cheaper materials of construction.[9] For instance, it might be feasible to use carbon-steel pipe as a vapor line for handling gaseous chemicals if the line were insulated to prevent condensation. If the insulation is omitted, such severe corrosion of the steel might occur that it would be necessary to employ stainless steel or non-ferrous pipe in order to reduce corrosion to a tolerable value.[4]

Similarly, the design of a processing tank might be such that liquids could lodge in crevices, pockets, joints or other dead spaces. Severe corrosion is likely to occur in such areas as a result of concentration cell formation. By altering the design to eliminate these regions, the same material of construction can be used with greatly reduced corrosion damage. In the case of tanks or processing vessels for chemicals, the most severe corrosion often occurs on the *outside* of the vessel, not on the inside as might be anticipated. Such equipment should be designed so that moisture will not be trapped in external joints between the vessel wall and the supporting members, between the bottom of the vessel and the supporting wood or concrete base, or in absorptive thermal insulation which contacts the external surfaces of the vessel. Moisture in these locations, even condensed moisture or tap water, can cause severe corrosion. To prevent corrosion, the design may be as important as the selection of the material of construction.

Protective Coatings[5]—There are a large number of different types of protective coatings. They can be classified in different ways. Based on their characteristics, it is convenient to classify them as:

1. Anodic coatings
2. Cathodic coatings
3. Inert coatings
4. Inhibitive coatings

When a coated metal article is exposed to an electrolyte, if there are discontinuities in the coating, several possibilities present themselves. An electric current may flow from the coating through the solution (electrolyte) to the base metal. If this happens, the coating is **anodic** to the base metal. Furthermore, if the current density at the exposed area (or areas) of the base metal is of the correct magnitude, corrosion of the base metal will be prevented. Thus, anodic coatings tend to prevent corrosion of exposed areas of the base metal by sending electric current to them through any contacting film or layer of an electrolytically conducting medium.

In contrast to this, **cathodic** coatings tend to stimulate corrosion at exposed areas of the base metal under similar conditions of exposure.

Coatings showing the most pronounced anodic or cathodic behavior are the metallic coatings. Non-metallic coatings, especially oxide or sulphide coatings under some conditions of exposure, act as cathodic coatings. However, there is no definite evidence of non-metallic coatings acting as anodic coatings. It should also be pointed out that the same metallic coating on the same base metal can behave as an anodic coating under one set of exposure conditions, as a cathodic coating under other conditions, and as an inert coating or even as an inhibitive coating under still different conditions.

Tin coatings on steel form a good example of this variation in behavior under different environmental conditions. When exposed outdoors, in sea water, in most natural water, or even to many food products in the presence of air, tin is cathodic to exposed areas of the steel base. However, when exposed to nearly air-free food products, tin is generally definitely anodic to steel. Presumably, if the exposure were to food products containing some critical amount of oxygen, tin would be neither anodic nor cathodic to steel. That is, it might then be classed as an inert coating. Again under different conditions, the accumulation of dissolved tin compounds from the coating in the food product might reduce greatly the corrosiveness of the product to steel. In this last case, the tin compounds would be serving as corrosion inhibitors; therefore, the tin coating could be classed as an inhibitive coating.

It should also be pointed out that, although cathodic coatings *tend* to stimulate corrosion of exposed areas of the base metal, this does not always mean that increased attack of these areas will in fact occur. For example, if the cathodic coating is thick and if the exposed areas of base metal are small, attack may be stifled by plugging of the small pores in the coating with corrosion products from the base metal.

Inorganic coatings are sometimes inert, sometimes cathodic and sometimes inhibitive. Organic coatings are generally either inert or inhibitive. Either inorganic or organic coatings which contain water-soluble chromates generally function as inhibitive coatings in most natural environments. It is obvious that the inhibitive value of such coatings is greatest when there is only limited opportunity for leaching of the soluble inhibitor to occur. For example, it would be expected that the inhibitive action of a coating containing a soluble chromate would be more in evidence if the coating were on the interior of a tank which contained only a small amount of stagnant water than if it were on the interior of a pipe through which unrecirculated water was passing continually.

Organic coatings can also function in a manner which does not permit their classification in one of the four simple groups mentioned above. For example, in special cases, organic coatings when exposed to liquid media can serve as semipermeable membranes. Then, by osmosis, dialysis or electro-dialysis, liquid can be transferred through the organic coating to the metal-coating interface. The composition of the liquid which collects at the interface may differ markedly from that of the liquid on the outside of the coating. It may be either more or less corrosive to the base metal than the parent liquid. This behavior is still obscure but it is known to exist.

Treatment of Environment—Corrosion can sometimes be prevented either by adding something to the corrosive medium or by removing some corrosive agent from the medium.[3, 10] For example, a certain tap water may be highly corrosive to the steel tank in which it is stored. By adding a corrosion inhibitor, such as sodium chromate, to the water the attack may be prevented. Alternatively, by removing dissolved oxygen from the water, the corrosion rate may be greatly reduced.

Corrosion prevention by treating the environment is normally employed when there is only a limited amount of the corrosive material. Thus, it is more widely used for waters which are recirculated than for waters which are flowing continuously from the source without recirculation.

Chromates are by far the most versatile corrosion inhibitors, although phosphates, silicates and various complex organic compounds are also used. The mechanism of inhibitor action differs for the various inhibitors and types of uses. In some cases, inhibitors function simply by forming a protective film or layer on the metal surface. In others, they retard one or more of the electrolytic processes necessary for corrosion to occur.

Inhibitors can be classified according to their behavior as "safe" or "dangerous." A safe inhibitor is one which will not cause intensified attack at local areas, even when added in insufficient amounts to prevent attack completely. A dangerous inhibitor will stimulate attack at a few local areas while reducing attack at most of the exposed areas. Unfortunately, most of the inhibitors at present used in other than mineral acid media are dangerous.

Inhibitors can also be classified as "expansive" or "contractive." As the terms imply, expansive inhibitors increase the area of the metal which is attacked, while contractive inhibitors reduce the attacked area.

Thus, a specific inhibitor may be classified as "safe, expansive," "dangerous, contractive" or "safe, contractive."

Cathodic Protection[2]—It has already been mentioned that anodic or active coatings have the property of sending an electric current through an electrolyte to exposed areas of cathodic metals. This current flow tends to prevent corrosion of the cathodic metal. Protection in this manner by current flow from any source is termed **cathodic protection,** since the metal being protected is made the cathode of an electrolytic cell.

Sometimes a coating metal is used to provide cathodic protection. Cathodic current from pieces of an anodic metal in electrical contact with the article to be protected and also exposed to the electrolyte can be used. These are termed "galvanic anodes." Alternatively, direct current from a storage battery or from a generator, or rectified alternating current from a power line, can be used. The only essential is that a sufficient cathodic current density must be maintained at all areas of the protected article which contact the corrosive solution.

Determining the magnitude of the current density just sufficient to prevent corrosion under various types of service conditions is a difficult problem. Fortunately, for most ferrous structures, it is not necessary to know the limiting current density with great accuracy. *Any* cathodic current density which is applied to a given area will reduce corrosion. Furthermore, if the limiting current density is exceeded, no harm is done to the structure. This means, simply, that protection is costing more than necessary because some of the current is being wasted.

Cathodic protection is a very effective way of preventing corrosion by most types of electrically conducting media. Also it is relatively safe, since as long as all the current flows to the structure, corrosion will be reduced even if protection is not complete. It is relatively easy to apply cathodic protection to small, geometrically simple structures. However, skilled electrochemical engineers are required to develop efficient cathodic protection for large or geometrically complicated structures.

At the present time, cathodic protection is applied widely to the steel hulls of marine vessels, to the interiors of small and large steel water tanks, to the exteriors of buried steel pipe lines and to a variety of types of chemical equipment. It should also be mentioned again that the usefulness of tin plate for food containers and of galvanized sheet for roofing, siding and the like depends upon cathodic protection of the steel base by the coating metal.

Periodic Cleaning—It is frequently overlooked that periodic cleaning may greatly reduce corrosion damage. The fundamental reason why cleaning is beneficial is that it removes moist layers of solid matter from the metal surface. Corrosion products may be hygroscopic and generally are water sorptive. Thus, a metal surface coated with a heavy layer of corrosion products and exposed to the atmosphere will be wet for a

considerably greater proportion of the time than will a similar clean surface. In like manner, layers of dust or soot of many types stimulate corrosion. Some materials hold moisture, others contain soluble products which in themselves are highly corrosive. It is only rarely that clinging debris is protective.

Coatings Combining Decorative and Protective Properties—Coatings may be not only protective but also decorative and, in fact, more often than not the feature of appearance is of prime importance. For example, galvanized sheets have often been required to exhibit a pleasing spangled surface. The presence of this spangle or bright appearance has been associated with the highest quality product although tests have shown no longer actual service life than that of galvanized sheets of duller luster with equivalent weight of coating. Thus, dependent on the required appearance of the ultimate product, a variety of bright or dull coatings may be manufactured. In the field of organic coatings, a variety of hues may be obtained by a variation of the pigments or stains used in the coating mixture.

SECTION 3

PREPARATION OF STEEL SURFACES FOR PROTECTIVE COATINGS

Importance—Correct surface preparation is the primary and most important requirement for satisfactory application of protective coatings for steel. Without a properly cleaned surface, even the most expensive coatings will fail to adhere or to prevent rusting of the steel base. It is axiomatic that coating performance is proportional to the degree of surface preparation. However, the economics of the particular coating requirement must be considered. For painting, for example, complete descaling by blast cleaning or pickling, followed by a suitable pretreatment, is best. Because maximum paint life is obtained when paint is applied to rust-free and scale-free surfaces, such thorough cleaning, while expensive, is most economical when painted surfaces are exposed in severely corrosive environments. For withstanding corrosion in mild atmospheres, wire brushing of steel surfaces before painting is adequate and economical, since intact mill scale in the absence of electrolytes is a good base for paint. When lesser degrees of surface cleaning are warranted, the protective coating must be capable of developing good adhesion to the prepared surface. Good adhesion is the primary requisite of a protective coating, and good adhesion is obtained only by proper surface preparation. A comprehensive discussion of and specifications for mechanical and chemical surface preparation is given in the "Steel Structures Painting Manual," Volumes I and II.[12]

Mill Scale—Mill scale is a relatively thick layer of iron oxide that is easily broken and does not adhere well to steel. It is cathodic to the underlying metal and must be removed to prevent failure of coatings that are exposed in severe environments.

Rust—Rust is perhaps the worst surface contaminant: it prevents satisfactory adhesion of the protec-

tive coating with the metal during application and, if covered over, leads to premature failure of the coating in service. Depending upon the history of its formation, rust may contain chemical constituents that may accelerate corrosion.

Blue Oxides—Thin blue oxides are formed on hot, clean steel such as steam-blued steel or hot-rolled strip of lighter gages that is not excessively exposed to high temperatures and oxygen. These oxides may be quite beneficial to the performance of some protective coatings such as paints or drum linings, because they improve adhesion of the coating and reduce the tendency of the surface to corrode.

Oil, Grease, Soil—These must be removed because they prevent satisfactory wetting of the surface by almost all protective coatings and lead to poor adhesion.

Solvent Cleaning—Solvents clean metal surfaces by dissolving and diluting foreign matter such as oil, grease, soil, and drawing and cutting compounds. Oil or grease may be removed by wiping or scrubbing the surface with rags or brushes wetted with a solvent, with a final wiping with clean solvent and clean rags or brushes. The steel also may be completely immersed in the solvent, or solvent sprays may be used, or the steel may be subjected to vapor degreasing in equipment in which vaporized solvent condenses on the surfaces to be cleaned. Solvents used include mineral spirits, naphthas, and some chlorinated hydrocarbons.

Alkaline Cleaning—This method is used where mineral and animal fats and oils must be removed. Mere dipping in solutions of various compositions, concentrations and temperatures are often satisfactory. The use of electrolytic cleaning may be advisable for large-scale production or where this method yields a cleaner product. Caustic soda, soda ash, alkaline silicates, and phosphates are common alkaline cleaning agents. Sometimes the addition of wetting agents to the cleaning bath will facilitate cleaning.

Hand- or Power-Tool Cleaning—These methods include brushing (wire or bristle), scraping, chipping, sanding, impact-tool cleaning, and grinding. They are used widely on larger items in the shop or in the field, particularly such items as tanks and bridges. They do not completely remove rust or mill scale, and may be used in combination with solvent cleaning to remove oil and grease. Therefore, these methods are limited in their effectiveness and must be used with protective coatings that will be adequate for surfaces prepared by these means.

Flame Cleaning—Special oxy-acetylene torches are used to partially remove scale and rust from the surfaces of heavy steel sections. The surface immediately after cleaning is warm and, therefore, in good condition for painting, but only partial removal of rust and scale is accomplished.

Blast Cleaning—Abrasives such as sand, steel or iron grit (crushed shot), or shot are impinged at high velocity against the surfaces to be cleaned, either by compressed air in nozzle-type blast-cleaning apparatus or by centrifugal force in rotary-type blast-cleaning machines. The surface is roughened by these cleaning methods, and the degree of roughness must be regulated by selection of the proper type, size shape or speed of abrasive so that the anchor-pattern profile of the surface is satisfactory for the intended protective coating. The degree of cleanliness achieved ranges from (1) white-metal blast cleaning, in which no visible residues remain on the surface and the surface is uniform in color; (2) near-white blast cleaning, which permits traces of scale and rust to remain on the cleaned surface; (3) commercial blast cleaning, which is done at a considerably faster rate than (1) and (2) and, consequently, leaves considerably more scale and rust on the surface than (2); to (4) brush-off cleaning, which is a very fast cleaning that removes any loose material from the surface and abrades it only slightly.

Pickling—In large-scale operations, pickling in a hot solution of sulphuric acid (H_2SO_4) is a common method for removing scale and rust. The time of pickling, and concentration and temperature of the solution, will be varied depending upon the type of scale to be removed or the type of steel being pickled.

In continuous pickling of strip and in other operations where the size and shape of the material being pickled does not vary greatly, electrolytic pickling may be employed at room temperature. The article to be pickled is made the anode if some actual solution of the steel is required, or the cathode where only the blast action of hydrogen evolved at the cathode is necessary. Cold muriatic (hydrochloric) acid (HCl) will pickle steel very efficiently, although this acid is more expensive than sulphuric acid. Other acids are not used as commonly as sulphuric and hydrochloric acids, although the use of phosphoric acid (H_3PO_4) is increasing in those cleaning operations where a slight phosphate coating is desired on the cleaned steel.

Special Methods—Many protective coatings require scrupulously clean surfaces or special surface-preparation procedures for their successful application. A series of cleaning procedures may be necessary; for example, preparation of steel for electrolytic tinning, hot-dip galvanizing, aluminum coating, terne coating, and porcelain enameling require detailed procedures, many of which are covered elsewhere in this book. Metallizing requires blast cleaning to the white-metal condition and a rough surface. Thick coatings such as hot bituminous melts are applied advantageously to rough surfaces. Decorative finishes such as the coatings used in the automotive industry and electroplated finishes for appliances require smooth surfaces.

Protective coatings are often applied as pretreatments after cleaning to protect the cleaned surfaces until the product receives its final coating: some pretreatment coatings must be removed by degreasing or other means before the steel is subjected to the final coating operation.

SECTION 4

METALLIC PROTECTIVE COATINGS

The most commonly used metallic coatings for steel include tin, zinc, terne metal (lead plus tin), nickel, chromium, cadmium, copper, aluminum, bronze, brass, silver, gold, and lead. As mentioned previously, a metallic coating may be anodic or cathodic to the metal to which it is applied. If anodic, it is "sacrificial" or less noble than the base. If cathodic, it is more noble than the base and its protective value is due to its own relative chemical inactivity in the environment to which it is exposed.

A rough indication of the activity of the metals may be obtained from the "electrochemical" or "electromotive" series, a classification of metals in the order of electrode potential referred to the standard hydrogen electrode at a temperature of 25° C (see Table 33—I). This table is often used mistakenly as if the order of metals were invariable, each metal displacing from solution or protecting from corrosion those below it. That this is often not true is shown in the second column of the table, where the values of potential in a normal salt solution are given. From the "electrochemical" series it would be anticipated that the corrosion of zinc would be retarded by contact with aluminum, while the potential measurements in salt solution indicate that the zinc should protect aluminum. In sea water and many natural waters, this protection of aluminum by zinc actually occurs. The electrochemical series is useful since metals near the top are generally protective to those near the bottom of the table. When, however, two metals differ little in potential, i.e., are close together in the first column of Table 33—I, one cannot predict which will protect the other, without actual tests. In many instances, the results of potential measurements in a salt solution (second column of Table 33—I) are a better guide as to the ability of one metal to protect the other under natural conditions of exposure than is the electromotive series. Many factors, such as the environment to which exposed, the magnitude of current generated, the relative area of metals exposed, the texture of metal surface and the inherent tendency of the metal to form an insoluble protective film notably affect the corrosion of metals themselves or their corrosion rate when used as coatings for steel.

Table 33—I. Comparison of the Electromotive Series and Solution Potentials in Sodium-Chloride Solution of The Common Metals and a Few Alloys

Metals or Alloys	From emf Series (Normal hydrogen scale)*	In 1 N (5.85%) NaCl containing 0.3% H_2O_2 (0.1 N) Calomel Scale**
Magnesium, Mg	+2.37[b]	+1.73[a]
Aluminum, Al	+1.66[b]	+0.85[a]
Zinc, Zn	+0.76[b]	+1.00[a]
Chromium, Cr++	+0.74[b]	....
Iron, Fe++	+0.44[b]	+0.63[a]
Cadmium, Cd	+0.40[b]	+0.82[a]
Cobalt, Co	+0.28[b]	....
Nickel, Ni	+0.25[b]	+0.07[a]
Tin, Sn++	+0.14[b]	+0.49[a]
Lead, Pb++	+0.13[b]	+0.55[a]
Hydrogen, H_2	0.00	....
Copper, Cu++	−0.34[b]	+0.20[a]
Silver, Ag	−0.80[b]	+0.08[a]
Gold, Au+++	−1.50[b]	....
Brass (60–40)	....	+0.28[a]
Stainless Steel (18–8)	....	+0.15[a]
Monel Metal	....	+0.10[a]
Inconel	....	+0.40[a]

*In some handbooks the sign of potential is reversed from that given.
** These values vary somewhat, depending on the particular lot of material investigated and on surface preparation employed.
[a] Mears and Brown; Causes of Corrosion Currents. Industrial and Engineering Chemistry, Vol. 33, Page 1008, Table XII.
Note—The sign of potential is the reverse from that given here.
[b] W. M. Latimer, Oxidation Potentials. Prentice Hall, Inc. New York (1952).

Table 33—II illustrates the variable effect of environment or exposure conditions on the solution potentials of several common metals. It will be noted that the relative potentials of these metals vary when they are exposed to different solutions. Thus, no one table of solution potential values can indicate the electrochemical behavior of the different metals under all conditions of use. Actual tests under conditions similar to those of service are required before it is

possible to make accurate predictions. The electrochemical behavior of metallic coatings on steel under conditions of atmospheric corrosion is now fairly well

Table 33—II. Solution Potentials of Several Metals in Various Solutions (all 1 molar in concentration). Referred to a 0.1 N calomel half-cell*

Metal	Sodium Chloride	Sodium Chromate	Nitric Acid	Sodium Hydroxide
Magnesium	+1.72	+0.96	+1.49	+1.47
Aluminum	+0.86	+0.71	+0.49	+1.50
Zinc	+1.15	+0.67	+1.06	+1.51
Iron	+0.72	+0.16	+0.58	+0.22

* From: Light Metals for the Cathodic Protection of Steel Structures, by R. B. Mears and C. D. Brown; Corrosion, Vol. 1, No. 2, September, 1945. National Association of Corrosion Engineers. (Sign of potential reversed.)

established. Zinc is anodic to steel under most exposure conditions and will prevent corrosion even at small discontinuities in the coating. The behavior of aluminum coatings is more complex. In some environments, they tend to protect exposed steel areas but in others there is no evidence of electrochemical protection. Tin, terne metal, nickel, copper, silver, gold and lead are all cathodic to steel under most conditions of atmospheric exposure and, if used as coatings for steel, will tend to accelerate corrosion at pores, scratches, and pinholes. In some cases, the corrosion products formed in the areas where steel is exposed, will stifle corrosion. This is particularly true for heavy coatings of lead, tin, terne metal and aluminum.

From the above it will be concluded that protection against corrosion is not a simple problem, but an extremely complex one.

METHODS OF APPLYING METALLIC COATINGS

Metallic coatings are applied to steel surfaces by the following methods:

Hot Dip Processes—The steel article to be coated is immersed, after thorough cleaning, in a molten bath of the metal forming the coating. Zinc, tin, terne metal, aluminum, and lead are applied commercially in this manner and are discussed fully elsewhere in this book (see especially Chapters 34, 35 and 36).

Metal Spraying—This method, introduced about 1910, may be used with most of the common metals including aluminum, copper, lead, nickel, tin and zinc and alloys such as brass, bronze, babbitt metal, monel metal and stainless steel. The coating metal usually is drawn into wire and fed into a specially constructed spray gun. This gun is operated with compressed air and a fuel gas. It is small and compact although it contains an air-gas mixing chamber, a special nozzle for burning the mixture and melting the wire, an outer compressed-air nozzle concentric with the inner nozzle, and an air turbine driving knurled rolls which draw the wire from its spool and feed it through the inner nozzle. The gases at the nozzle are ignited, the wire is melted as it is fed to the nozzle and is projected against the surface to be coated at a speed of over 500 feet per second. Although the particles of molten metal are cooled instantly to a temperature of about 80° F, the impact causes them to adhere firmly to the steel surface, provided it has been cleaned thoroughly, as by machining or by sand or shot blasting. Metal spraying is used for building up surfaces and sometimes for the application of thin coatings as a protection against corrosion.

Metal Cementation—The metals zinc, chromium, aluminum and silicon are successfully applied in this manner, in which the protecting metal is alloyed into the surface layers of the steel.

In *sherardizing*, practiced since about 1900, the parts to be coated, usually small articles such as nails, are thoroughly cleaned by pickling or sand blasting; packed in metal drums with fine zinc dust, usually containing 5 to 8 per cent of zinc oxide; and heated for several hours at between 650° and 750° F, the drums being slowly rotated in the furnace during the heating. The coating is thin and consists of intermetallic compounds of iron and zinc, ranging from an iron-rich alloy next to the steel base to almost pure zinc at the surface, but it affords good protection against atmospheric corrosion. The process was invented by Sherard Cowper-Coles.

Chromizing is a cementation process analogous to sherardizing. The parts to be treated are packed in a container with a mixture of 55 parts of chromium or ferrochromium powder and 45 parts of alumina by weight. They are then heated "in vacuo" or in a protective atmosphere (preferably hydrogen) at 2370° to 2560° F for three or four hours, although a shorter time and lower temperature may be used when less penetration is desired. Chromizing can also be accomplished by a gaseous method in which the part to be treated is enclosed in a hydrogen atmosphere with chromium or ferrochromium powder and an ammonium halide. A gaseous chromium halide is formed at elevated temperatures. This reacts with the steel and releases chromium that diffuses into the steel surface. The halide carrier then recombines with chromium from the chromium or ferrochromium powder and the process is repeated. Coatings formed by this process are generally about 0.004 inch thick, and may contain about 40 per cent of chromium at the surface.

In *calorizing*, developed by General Electric Company about 1925 to 1930, the thoroughly cleaned steel articles are packed in steel drums containing a mixture of aluminum, aluminum oxide, and a small amount of ammonium chloride. A reducing gas is passed into the drum, which is rotated in the furnace and heated for about 5 hours at between 1730° and 1750° F. The resulting coating is said to be a solid solution of aluminum in iron, richest in aluminum at the outer surface, and is used principally to protect the steel from oxidation at elevated temperatures, as in pyrometer tubes, superheater tubes and oil-refinery equipment.

Ihrigizing is a special type of siliconizing, or impregnation of the surface of low-carbon steels with silicon. In this process, the surface of low-carbon steel, freed of sand and heavy scale, is packed with silicon carbide or ferrosilicon mixed with mill scale (iron oxide), heated to a temperature of 1300° F or higher and exposed to the action of chlorine for two hours or more depending on the temperature used and depth of case desired. At this temperature the chlorine reacts with the carbon or the iron of the silicon-bearing substance, leaving the silicon in nascent form to combine with the iron in the steel. The siliconized layer, usually 0.005 to 0.1 inch thick as desired, is very hard and resistant to corrosion by nonoxidizing acids, such as hydrochloric and sulphuric acids, to wear and oxidation at temperatures up to 1600° F, and is capable of absorbing and retaining substantial amounts of oil. In usual practice, the silicon content of the case remains practically constant for the first 0.040 inch, varying from about 14 per cent at the surface to 12 per cent at 0.050 inch below, then decreases gradually in the next 0.020 to 0.025 inch to the silicon content of the core. The process was developed in 1935-1938 by H. K. Ihrig (U. S. Patent Reissue 20719).

In *corronizing*, developed about 1938 by Standard Steel Spring Company of Coraopolis, Pennsylvania, the steel is electroplated with nickel and subsequently with zinc or nickel-zinc alloy (U. S. Patent No. 2,419,231). The plated steel may be heated to about 750° F to form a nickel-zinc alloy, if zinc is the final coating.

Metal Cladding—*Copper cladding* processes give bi-metal products. Usually those containing steel consist of an inner steel core covered with a heavy layer of copper. In the usual process, the steel core, with a clean surface, is mounted in a covered mold and heated out of contact with air to a temperature slightly above the melting point of the copper, which then is cast about it. Other methods consist of dipping the solid steel core into a bath of molten copper, or of depositing the copper electrolytically. Starting material for copper-clad steel wire is made by forcing a steel rod into a closely fitting copper tube. Semi-finished products prepared by any of these methods may be heated to around 1700° F and hot rolled, then finished by cold rolling or drawing, as in forming copper-clad wire. The wire is used widely for electrical conductors, combining the strength of steel with the high conductivity of copper. Bundy-weld steel tubing is hydrogen-welded, copper-coated, rolled steel tubing. It is used for gasoline and oil lines in automobiles and for refrigerator coils. Copper-clad sheet steel was produced during World War II for the fabrication of copper-jacketed bullets.

Aluminum cladding is accomplished best by rolling flat steel almost to gage, cleaning it thoroughly and either placing it between two sheets of aluminum and cold rolling, or heating to between 600° and 750° and rolling. The latter method results in a better bonding of the aluminum with the steel. Subsequent annealing above 1000° F causes the aluminum to unite with the iron forming the very brittle $FeAl_3$. With basic Bessemer steel or open-hearth steel containing above 0.25 per cent silicon, the temperature of this reaction is raised above that for regular open-hearth steel so that the coated strip or sheet may be annealed at a somewhat higher temperature after cold rolling without becoming brittle.

Stainless cladding may be accomplished by (1) electro-welding stainless steel onto the carbon steel (2) casting the stainless steel around a solid carbon-

Table 33—III. Electroplating Baths

Kind of Coating	Type of Coat	Typical Composition of Baths Water to make 1 Gallon	Operating Conditions			
			pH	Temperature (°F)	Amperes per Sq. Ft.	Volts
Nickel	Matte or Dull	40 oz. nickel sulphate, (1) 8 oz. nickel chloride, (2) 5 oz. boric acid.	1.5–2.5	110–125	40	4–6
	Bright	40 oz. nickel sulphate, (1) 6 oz. nickel chloride, (2) 4½ oz. boric acid and 1 to 2 per cent of addition agents.	2 to 5	125–140	10	2–3
	Hard	24 oz. nickel sulphate, (1) 3.3 oz. ammonium chloride, 4.0 oz. boric acid.	5.6–5.9	120–140	25–50	4–6
Chromium	Bright	33–55 oz. chromic acid, 0.35–0.55 oz. sulphuric acid. (3)	. . . . .	110–120	150–300	8–12
	Hard	35–55 oz. chromic acid, 0.2–0.7 oz. sulphuric acid. (3)	. . . . .	140–150	200–300	8–12
Zinc	Acid	32 oz. zinc sulphate, (4) 2 oz. sodium acetate, 4 oz. aluminum sulphate, (5) plus 0.13 oz. addition agent (licorice).	3.5–5.0	75–120	25	4–6
	Cyanide	8 oz. zinc cyanide, 3 oz. sodium cyanide, 7 oz. sodium hydroxide, plus brighteners (mercuric salts) 1/16 oz.	12–12.2	105–120	10–20	4–10
Cadmium	. . . . . .	3 oz. cadmium oxide 14.5 oz. sodium cyanide, plus brighteners.	13.0	70–95	25	4–6
Tin	Alkaline	16 oz. sodium stannate, 1 oz. sodium hydroxide, 2 oz. sodium acetate, 1/16 oz. hydrogen peroxide.	. . . . .	160–200	10–60	4–6
	Acid	8 oz. stannous sulphate, 9 oz. sulphuric acid, (3) 13 oz. phenol sulphonic acid, plus addition agent.	. . . . .	70	25–500	1–18
Copper	Cyanide	3 oz. copper cyanide, 4.5 oz. sodium cyanide, 2 oz. sodium carbonate. (7)	11.8–12.2	75–120	15	1.5–2
	Acid	28 oz. copper sulphate, (6) 6.5 oz. sulphuric acid. (3)	. . . . .	70–80	30	4–6
Brass	. . . . . .	3.6 oz. copper cyanide, 1.2 oz. zinc cyanide, 7.5 oz. sodium cyanide, 4 oz. sodium carbonate. (7)	11	75–100	3–5	2–3

(1) $NiSO_4 \cdot 7H_2O$ (3) H_2SO_4—100%   (5) $Al_2(SO_4)_3 \cdot 18H_2O$ (7) Na_2CO_3 (anhydrous)
(2) $NiCl_2 \cdot 6H_2O$ (4) $ZnSO_4 \cdot 7H_2O$ (6) $CuSO_4 \cdot 5H_2O$

steel slab or (3) placing a slab of carbon steel between two plates of stainless steel, and hot rolling them. In the last mentioned method, fluxes or metals have been used to facilitate bonding but are not necessary if both steels are cleaned thoroughly before making the "sandwich." Welding is usually done around the perimeter of the slab. Considerable care is necessary in the preparation of such duplex material to avoid formation of blisters.

Fusion Welding of Coatings may be accomplished in different ways, as by depositing weld metal under a slag covering by the electric-arc method, or by fusing the surfaces of two bodies of metal in contact by passing a current of sufficiently high density. These initial steps are followed by heating and forming operations carried out in the usual manner, as by rolling. Similarly, weld metal may be deposited upon metal of another kind to afford greater resistance to abrasion, such as manganese-nickel steel welding rod used to face excavating and similar tools.

Electroplating[11]—This process is an old art, practiced not only to protect the base metal from corrosion but also for decorative purposes and, more recently to protect the base metal from wear by friction or abrasion. Metals used for coatings include cadmium, chromium, copper, gold, tin, lead, nickel, silver and zinc, and alloys such as brass, bronze and lead-tins as well as cobalt-tungsten, tungsten-nickel and cadmium-tin alloys. It will be noted that with the exception of zinc, which is anodic to steel, i.e., protects by sacrificing itself, nearly all electroplated coatings are cathodic to steel and provide protection through surface coverage. The decorative coatings commonly used vary in thickness, according to the life required. Durability usually depends upon the properties of the coating, especially adhesion and porosity. The severity of conditions of exposure, particularly with reference to acidic gases in the atmosphere, also affect the service

life. In plating, the preparation of the base metal is very important, not only in that a clean surface is necessary to obtain good adherence but also because surface preparation has much to do with the final appearance, since the intermediate or final coating is frequently buffed to a high lustre. Therefore, the base metal should be smooth if polishing and buffing costs are to be kept to a minimum. The decorative coatings most commonly applied are nickel, cadmium, nickel followed by chromium, or copper followed by nickel or by nickel and chromium. To protect hard steel and iron surfaces from wear or abrasion, coatings of chromium or alloy coatings of tungsten and cobalt or nickel and tungsten are sometimes used although some of these may not always be applied by electroplating. A few typical plating baths with operating data as commonly used by job platers are shown in Table 36—III.

Miscellaneous Metallic Coatings—(1) *Cathode Sputtering.* When relatively high voltage is applied between two electrodes in a partial vacuum, inducing a glow discharge, the cathode disintegrates and the metal thus removed can be deposited in a thin film on near-by objects within the chamber. In suitably designed chambers, objects may be arranged with respect to the cathode so that they will receive a uniform, thin coating of metal. The process is particularly suitable for the metallization of electrically non-conducting materials such as fabrics and phonographic recording waxes.

(2) *Evaporation or Condensation.* This process, closely related to cathode sputtering, is of more recent origin in practical application. The metal vapor is produced by thermal instead of electrical means. A coiled filament of platinum or tungsten in a higher vacuum than for cathode sputtering is a convenient heat source. The process is usually confined to the deposition of pure metals.

SECTION 5

SURFACE CONVERSION COATING

Steel is often treated in various ways by heating to form a uniform blue or black coating of oxide which, although not thoroughly protective, is pleasing in appearance and, especially if coated with oil, wax or other clear protective coating, is much more resistant to corrosion than steel not so treated. "Blue-annealed" plate now produced on continuous plate mills is one example of this finish. **Steam-blued** and **air-blued** finish on thin sheets used for common stove-pipe stock are others and the **gun metal** finish applied to gun barrels is another. Strip steel is satisfactorily colored by passing through heated sand. From three to ten minutes treatment at 650° F will produce a rich blue color. Highly polished steel may be blued by placing it in a bed of hot charcoal about two feet deep. The lower part of the charcoal is in a state of incandescence whereas the upper layers are lower in temperature and suitable for the development of oxide colors. After development of the desired shade of blue, the article

is rubbed vigorously with waste or cloth dipped in raw sperm oil.

The **gun-metal** or **carbonia** finish used on rifles, shotguns and revolvers, as well as on many other metal parts, is obtained by placing the steel loosely in a retort with a small amount of charred bone and heating to 700 to 800° F. After the articles are thoroughly oxidized, the temperature is dropped to about 650° F and a mixture of bone and carbonia oil are added, after which heating is continued for several hours. On removal, the articles are dipped in sperm oil or tumbled in oily cork to develop a uniform, black finish. If a lower temperature is necessary to prevent excessive softening of the steel, a longer time is usually required and the color obtained is less permanent than at the higher temperatures. Articles which have been first nitrided, when treated by the gun-metal or carbonia process, take a pleasing, rust-resistant finish and retain their surface hardness since coloring temperatures do not temper nitrided articles.

Barffing is a process somewhat analogous to steam bluing of sheets and black plate. The steel articles are cleaned, placed in air-tight ovens and they then are heated to a dull red heat. Super-heated steam at 60 to 100 lb. per sq. in. pressure is introduced and a slate-blue coating is obtained consisting largely of magnetic oxide of iron. The coating is of considerable depth and is quite durable especially when oil or wax coatings are used as the final application. The **Bower-Barff process** is similar except that, after the steam treatment, the steel articles are cooled to 300° F, dipped in hot linseed oil and kept at 300° F until the oil becomes oxidized. Later, the process was modified by introducing benzene with the steam, thus shortening the treatment and producing a heavier coating.

SECTION 6

CHEMICAL TREATMENT OF STEEL SURFACES

Black, blue or brown finishes on steel also may be produced in various shades by a wide variety of chemical treatments. Molten-salt baths produce effective colors on clean, polished steel, but often the temperature is so high that a change in hardness and other mechanical properties may result. The method may be high in cost because of drag-out salt adhering to the metal on removal from the molten-salt bath.

Niter Baths—Molten mixtures of sodium and potassium nitrates are effective bluing agents in the absence of rust. Manganese dioxide is generally added to the extent of about 2 per cent by volume and seems to aid in the production of good colors. Potassium nitrate is used when a bath operating at low temperature is employed, although the sodium nitrate alone may be used without affecting the quality of the work. The temperatures used vary from 600° to 1000° F. If a lower temperature is necessary, a black color may be obtained by using a 40 per cent aqueous solution of sodium hydroxide to which about 5 per cent each of sodium and potassium nitrates are added. This solution operates at 250 to 285° F. The colored articles are usually finished by immersing in hot oil followed by wiping and polishing.

Polished steel is **oil blackened** by packing in a carburizing box with spent carburizing compound, excluding air, and heating to 1200° F for about one and one-half hours, and then quenching in oil. Variations of this process at lower temperatures may be effected by heating the articles rapidly to 1000° to 1200° F in air, and quenching in oil. Small parts are colored by introducing them into a rotary furnace retort operating at about 750° F. A small amount of linseed or fish oil is added to the charge and the parts rotated for three to ten minutes after this addition, after which parts are cooled in air and dipped in a rust-retarding oil.

Articles which have been quenched in oil may be placed, without removal of oil, in a rotary, unperforated-drum retort and heated to 500° to 650° F, maintained for proper tempering time according to color desired. The longer the time the deeper and more desirable will the black color be. The retort is allowed to cool to 500° F, then articles are removed and tumbled in slightly-oiled granular cork to brighten. This method gives a combination tempering and oil-blackening treatment.

Browning of steel is accomplished by a wide variety of processes. The thoroughly cleaned steel is coated by spraying, brushing or dipping with two coats of a browning solution which generally consists of a mixture of metallic salts, acids, alcohol or water. The coating is allowed to dry, heated to 140° to 175° F, and then placed in a humidity room or chamber at the same temperature as that used for preheating, where it is allowed to rust. It is then washed in boiling water for 15 minutes, dried and cleaned with a wire brush or fiber wheel to remove loose particles of rust. Three more rustings with intermediate cleanings are applied after which the browned surfaces are coated with a rust-preventive oil.

Solutions for the coloring of steel by chemicals are very numerous and often contain lead, iron, mercury, antimony or copper salts in combination with sulphur or selenium compounds. Usually the colors obtained by the relatively-cold chemical methods are not as brilliant as those from heat tinting in air or steam, or the product from salt baths. Nevertheless, certain new chemical treatments have been widely adopted, not because of their superior appearance, but because they are beneficial in bonding paints and lacquers, especially when these are baked. Such coatings have a very durable, final finish and one in which corrosion due to porosity of or imperfections in the paint film is minimized. The most important of these are the phosphate treatments, whereby a thin adherent coating consisting largely of iron and zinc phosphate is applied to the steel. Also, thicker coatings of zinc phosphate are frequently used to aid in deep drawing operations. There are in addition a number of proprietary or commercial coatings that may be used for the above purpose.

SECTION 7

CHEMICAL TREATMENT OF METALLIC COATINGS

Metallic coatings such as zinc, tin and aluminum may be subjected to chemical treatments to increase their durability or facilitate the application and adherence of enamels, paints and the like.

Zinc-coated (galvanized) steel is usually treated to retard the formation of white corrosion products that are very detrimental to the appearance of the galvanized sheet. Treatments applied for this purpose by the producer of galvanized products are usually washes with dilute water solutions of water glass (sodium silicate) and sodium dichromate, chromic acid, and mixtures of phosphoric and chromic acids. These treatments do not significantly alter the bright appearance of the galvanized sheet. If paint adherence is of primary importance, then proprietary phosphate treatments such as "Bonderite" may be used. Many other proprietary treatments may be used for special purposes.

Surface treatments commonly used for tin plate are described elsewhere in this book (see Chapter 34). In general, these are usually rapid electrochemical treatments in dilute chromate or phosphate-chromate solutions, which have the dual function of stabilizing the surface against oxidation and/or discoloration and of imparting good lacquer and enamel adherence.

Aluminum-coated steel may, if desired, be treated by methods much similar to those discussed above. There are, of course, many patents describing treatments for aluminum that may also be applicable to the treatment of aluminum-coated steel.

SECTION 8

VITREOUS-ENAMEL COATINGS

These coatings consist of a layer of glass fused to the properly prepared steel base and thus are quite different from enamels of organic origin which will be discussed later. To adjust the properties of the finished articles to the ultimate uses, wide variations in the composition of this glass are required but, in general, it must adhere well to the steel base and possess a coefficient of expansion adjusted to that of the base metal. Good adherence is achieved by incorporating in the enamel certain oxides, usually cobalt oxide. Adjustment of coefficient of expansion is accomplished by a variety of compositions which are compounded by fusing together quartz and feldspar, with fluxes such as borax, fluorspar, cryolite, soda ash, sodium nitrate and litharge. Opacifiers such as oxides of titanium are usually added when the glass is ground to a fine powder. This is generally accomplished in a pebble or ball mill.

Ground coat application is made to the thoroughly cleaned sheet steel article by immersing in a water suspension or "slip" of pulverized enamel ingredients. The prior cleaning may consist of degreasing, pickling in acid, rinsing in a neutralizing bath, sometimes followed by a nickel-solution dip to improve enamel adherence and behavior during firing, after which the articles are washed and dried. After application, the slip is allowed to drain, dried, heated (**fired** or **burned**) at as high a temperature as 1500° to 1600° F for 1 to 4 minutes and cooled to room temperature. This fired ground coat offers sufficient protection to the steel base and may be used alone. However, since the "slip" usually contains cobalt oxide, the resulting coating is dark blue and may not be suitable for all purposes, so that a finish coat may be applied.

Finish Coats are applied when a light color or additional protection such as acid resistance is desired. The fired ground-coated article is sprayed with a slip of the required finish-coat composition, dried, fired for 1 to 3 minutes and cooled. The operation may be repeated several times using the same or different slips and many attractive color combinations can be obtained if desired.

Single-Finish Coats—Much experimental work has been directed toward the development of a suitable sheet steel on which the finish enamel coat can be applied directly. This work has led to the production of sheet steels of very low carbon content that are suitable for this purpose. These steels are being used in commercial production with satisfactory results and, because of the economics associated with single-coat enameling, are expected to find increasing use.

Low-temperature vitreous enamels—To provide a coating where the high gloss or decorative enamels are not required, ceramic coatings have been developed which can be applied by spraying and firing at a temperature of as low as 1000° F. These have found a limited field of use. The composition is said to consist of an alkaline aluminum silicate.

SECTION 9

MISCELLANEOUS INORGANIC COATINGS

Cements—These coatings differ from vitreous enamel in that they are not always fused to the steel, although the constituents consist largely of finely ground, vitrified products. Cracking vessels in the oil industry are sometimes protected by a mixture of furnace cement and sand to which short fiber asbestos and water glass are added. In this instance, curing is facilitated by heating to about 900° F. The interior of cast-iron or steel pipe and steel tanks may be coated with cement to resist corrosive waters, salt solutions, oil having a high sulphur content and the like. Concrete coatings are used on the exterior of pipe when it is buried in extremely moist or corrosive soils. This concrete is a rich mixture approximating two parts sand and one part Portland cement and may be two to four inches in thickness. The alkalinity of cements usually inhibits corrosive attack of the steel to which they are applied.

Core Plate—These coatings, which are discussed in greater detail under silicon or electrical-steel sheets

(Chapter 44), may sometimes be inorganic in nature and are usually applied to silicon-steel sheets used for transformer laminations to improve the insulating properties. Other core plates used for a similar purpose or for insulating motor laminations are organic-varnish coatings.

Metal Powders in Inorganic Vehicles—Metal powders may be incorporated with inorganic silicates or phosphates to produce a protective coating. For example, zinc dust is used in inorganic zinc-rich silicate paints that can provide sacrificial protection to steel surfaces.

SECTION 10
ORGANIC COATINGS

Steel requires an abundance of both oxygen and water to rust; organic coatings can prevent corrosion by: (1) interposing a barrier between the steel and corrosive media; (2) inhibitive action; or (3) preventing flow of galvanic currents. They also may serve as decorative or functional coatings to obtain color, reflectivity, anti-skid properties, or fire retardancy. Painting, for the sake of protection only, cannot be considered economically warranted under mild conditions represented by low humidity and absence of corrosive media, but painting is often justified under such conditions on the basis of good appearance. Where protective organic coatings must be applied to combat corrosive influences, a coating may be selected that will provide good appearance as well as protection without adding materially to the cost.

Important factors that can be controlled to improve the performance of organic coatings are:

(a) Designing to minimize corrosion and paint failure and to facilitate painting.
(b) Using a degree of surface preparation compatible with the intended service and paint scheme.
(c) Applying paint in a manner ensuring maximum life, commensurate with practical difficulties.
(d) Using paints properly formulated and capable of performing the required service.

Painting should be considered as a complete system that includes surface preparation, pretreatment, primer, intermediate coat or coats, finish paint, and method of application.

The type of organic coating or painting system used obviously depends upon the steel product and its intended use. The painting of steel structures with suitable specifications for surface preparations, pretreatments, paint application and paints is fully covered in the Steel Products Manual.[12] Production-line procedures generally used in product finishing on sheet or strip products differ radically from those for structural steel: production finishing procedures are adequately described in the literature.[13, 14, 15] Different metallic substrate require special coatings or pretreatments. Galvanized steel requires zinc-dust paints, cement-in-oil paints, wash primers or bonderizing pretreatments for satisfactory adhesion to be achieved.[16] Terne-coated steel has a film of residual oil which must be removed; otherwise, the selected coating must be capable of wetting the steel surface through the residual oil. Aluminum-coated steel requires pretreatment to achieve good paint adhesion. A wide variety of inks, varnishes, lacquers, and pigmented organic coatings are used on tin plate for caps, closures, cans, and lithography; these coatings must be compatible with the surface conditions imposed by the chemical treatments used on tin plate.

Organic coatings are commonly known as paints, varnishes, enamels, and lacquers. The pigments for organic coatings are generally of inorganic nature, but organic pigments are becoming more widely used. Paints are mixtures of pigments with drying oils, usually linseed or tung oils (which dry by oxidation), or with varnish vehicles. Varnishes are solutions of resinous materials in oils or volatile liquids which dry by evaporation or oxidation. Enamels can be called varnishes to which some pigment has been added. Lacquers comprise solutions of shellac, resins, cellulose derivatives or polymerization products in suitable solvents, all of which dry by evaporation.

The subject of organic coatings is too extensive and complex for a complete discussion here. The importance of such coatings in the protection of steel is, however, too great to dismiss without a brief discussion of some of the types of coatings that have been developed. This field is in a constant state of flux or change, due to the rapid adoption of newly developed materials.

Synthetic Resins—The introduction of the synthetic alkyd resins a comparatively few years ago led to drastic changes in organic-coating technology. While paints mixed with drying oils continue to be used in large quantities with satisfactory performance, most organic coatings include synthetic-resin vehicles. Alkyd resins are used in many of the maintenance paints and in product finishes because of their hardness, gloss, and color retention. Phenolic resins are used in combination with oils in varnishes and paints, especially to withstand immersion in water, high humidity, and condensation: these resins are used extensively in linings and tin-plate coatings. Production finishes utilize resins that require baking, such as the ureas and melamines (usually blended with other synthetics), to achieve high levels of hardness, abrasion resistance, and durability in service. Vinyl resins, usually copolymers designed to have specific properties, serve well in wet or corrosive environments; they possess resistance to many chemicals and may be applied as solution coatings, plastisol, or organic dispersions, and some are being used as latices in water-base coatings. Epoxy resins cured with amine or polyamide "catalysts," or baked, resist many chemicals and are widely used in maintenance paints and product finishes; these resins, like the vinyls, alone or combined with other resins, are used as chemical-resistant drum and tank linings and for tin-plate containers and closures. A new development is the combination of epoxy resins with coal tar to form epoxy coatings of good chemical resistance and high film build (productive of thick films) at moderate cost. Acrylic resin coatings are beginning to be used as lacquers and thermosetting finishes on automobiles, appliances, and siding; the acrylics have good weather durability and make good clear coatings for outdoor use.

Pigments—Pigments impart color, hiding power, reflectance, rust inhibition, abrasion resistance, antiskid characteristics, and fire resistance, and reduce water-vapor transmission and prolong coating life by screening out ultraviolet rays from sunlight. Red-lead and zinc-chromate continue to be used in rust-preventive paints; basic lead silico-chromate is a new pigment with good rust-inhibiting characteristics.

Zinc dust performs well in rust-preventing paints when incorporated with zinc oxide; these paints are particularly useful for painting galvanized steel. Zinc-dust pigment provides sacrificial protection to steel when the pigment is used in zinc-rich paints (paints heavily loaded with zinc dust). Inert pigments, such as those containing titanium dioxide or iron oxides, are used for intermediate and finish coats, or for primers when rust inhibition is not required or is provided by other pigments. Extenders are low cost pigments that are used to increase the pigment volume content of a paint at moderate cost.

Bituminous Coatings—These are based upon bituminous resins—coal tars, asphalts, or asphaltums. The resins are applied as solution coatings of low build (productive of relatively thin films), as mastics that have increased viscosity and high build (productive of thick films) due to incorporation of fillers, or as hot melts called enamels. Water-emulsion dispersions of these resins are also used. The bituminous resins perform well underground and in contact with water; they do not have good weather durability when exposed to sunlight.

Application and Drying of Organic Finishes— Since the bond between metal and coating is the weak point in most paint systems for metal, the proper application is extremely important. Prior to application of a coating, thorough cleaning of the surface is necessary. Since no paint system is entirely impermeable to moisture, coating durability is increased by pretreatment of the steel base with inhibitive washes, many of which are proprietary in nature (such as "Bonderizing"). The application of such treatments prior to painting is practiced extensively in fabricating steel articles.

The older and more common methods of applications of finishes by brushing or dipping are still widely used, but, in factories the installation of conveyor systems has increased the use of roller-coating methods for flat products and spraying for more complicated or formed shapes. These operations are usually performed mechanically and are often followed by a closely controlled baking treatment. Banks of electric infra-red lamps, or gas-fired or electrically heated ovens, may be used for the baking operation. In some instances, the heat from baking merely serves to drive off excess solvents. In other cases, oxidation of the coating required to produce a durable finish is also accomplished: here, the composition of the oven atmosphere is important. Baked coatings are usually harder, tougher, and often more durable than those that are air-dried, and quite often the coating mixture for an air-dry coating is different than one that requires baking. With the more general use of continuous coating methods, continuous baking is a common practice in quantity production.

A new industry to coat steel products in coils has grown because of the demand for prepainted strip steel in coils to make such articles as roofing and siding. A typical "strip-coating line" will receive a coil of steel at one end of the line, uncoil it, pass the strip through a five-stage cleaner and pretreater, dry the strip, apply one or two coats of paint to top and bottom of the strip by roller coater, bake the coated strip in long, catenary-loop ovens, cool, and recoil the coated product; all in one continuous operation.

Temporary Organic Coatings—For temporary protection in shipment or storage, steel is usually coated with oils known as slushing oils. Most often, mineral oils are mixed with inhibiting or polar compounds which deter rust formation. Mineral oils alone are sometimes used where corrosive conditions are not severe. Slushing oils are generally removed subsequent to fabrication and prior to application of a permanent organic coating. Generally, unless the temporary protective film is removed, troubles are encountered due to its incompatibility with the permanent organic coating. For severe conditions such as outdoor storage or overseas shipment, rustproofing compositions such as heavy greases or waxes compounded with inhibitors are applied. When conditions are unusually severe and the value of the steel product justifies the cost, plastic films are applied that can be removed by stripping. This latter expedient may be used for overseas transportation and storage of expensive equipment.

Bibliography

1. Am. Soc. for Testing Materials, Symposium on stress-corrosion cracking of metals. Phila., The Society, 1945.
2. Electrochemical Society and the Natl. Association of Corrosion Engineers, Symposium on cathodic protection, Pittsburgh, 1947. Houston, Texas, Natl. Association of Corrosion Engineers, 1949.
3. Evans, U. R., Inhibitors—safe and dangerous. Electrochemical Society Trans. **69**, 213–227; Discussion, 227–231 (1936)
4. Friend, W. Z. and F. L. LaQue, Some case histories of corrosion problems in chemical process equipment. Am. Inst. of Chemical Engineers Trans. **42**, 849–862 (1946)
5. Hudson, J. C. and T. A. Banfield, Protection of iron and steel by metallic coatings. Iron and Steel Inst. Journal **154**, 229–264 (1946); Discussion **157**, 349–368 (1947)
6. Iron and Steel Institute, Second report of the Corrosion Committee (Special report no. 5) 1934. Homer, C. E., p. 232.
7. Iron and Steel Institute, Third report of the Corrosion Committee (Special report no. 8) 1935. Mears, R. B., p. 116.

8. Mears, R. B. and R. H. Brown, Causes of corrosion currents. Industrial and Engrg. Chemistry **33,** 1001–1010 (1941)

9. Mears, R. B. and R. H. Brown, Designing to prevent corrosion. Corrosion **3,** 97–118; discussion 119–120 (March) and 299–300 (June 1947)

10. Symposium on corrosion inhibitors; abstracts and discussion. Chemistry and Industry, 537–539 (May 30, 1953)

11. Gray, A. G., Modern electroplating, New York, John Wiley and Sons, Inc., 1953.

12. Bigos, J., Steel structures painting manual, Vol. 1, Good painting practice; Vol. 2, Systems and specifications, Steel Structures Painting Council, 4400 Fifth Ave., Pittsburgh 13, Pa.

13. Burns, R. M., and W. W. Bradley, Protective coatings for metals, New York, Reinhold Publishing Co., 1955.

14. Mattiello, J. J., Protective and decorative coatings, New York, John Wiley and Sons, Inc., 1941.

15. Payne, H. F., Organic coating technology, New York, John Wiley and Sons, Inc., 1954.

16. Bigos, J., H. H. Greene and G. R. Hoover, Results of the AISI research project on the paintability of galvanized steel using trade-sales paints, Am. Iron and Steel Inst., New York, Contribution to the metallurgy of steel.

GENERAL

Burns, R. M. and W. W. Bradley, Protective coatings for metals; 2 ed. N. Y., Reinhold, 1955.

Champion, F. A., Corrosion Testing Procedures, N. Y., John Wiley & Sons, Inc., 1952.

Evans, U. R., The corrosion and oxidation of metals; London, Edward Arnold, Ltd., 1960.

Hudson, J. C., Corrosion of iron and steel. N. Y., Van Nostrand, 1940.

Romanoff, M., Underground Corrosion, U. S. Bureau of Standards Circular 579, 1957.

McKay, R. J. and R. Worthington, Corrosion resistance of metals and alloys. (Am. Chemical Society monograph series no. 71) N. Y., Reinhold, 1936.

Mears, R. B. and C. D. Brown, Light metals for the cathodic protection of steel structures. Corrosion **1,** 113–118 (1945)

Speller, F. N., Corrosion: causes and prevention; 3 ed. N. Y., McGraw-Hill, 1951.

Uhlig, H. H. (Ed.), Corrosion Handbook, N. Y., John Wiley & Sons, Inc., 1948.

CHAPTER 34

The Manufacture of Tin Plate

SECTION 1

TIN-MILL PRODUCT TERMINOLOGY

Tin-mill products originate with flat-rolled, mild (low-carbon) steel in relatively thin gages. They comprise **black plate, tin plate,** and **short terne plate.** Of these, tin plate is the most important commercially, accounting for about 90 per cent of the combined tonnage of all tin-mill products. Black plate accounts for most of the balance. Short terne plate, at one time produced in quantity, is now a relatively minor factor in tin-mill production, and is discussed in Chapter 35.

Black Plate—Although originally designating thin steel plates produced by hand hammering, the term "black plate" has persisted and now defines the product of the cold-reduction method in gages No. 29 and lighter (thicknesses 0.0141 inch and under). Some of the details of rolling and heat treating such light-gage product were discussed in Chapter 32.

"Black" plate does not have a black appearance. Present methods of manufacture generally result in a flat-rolled product having the typical appearance of clean steel. The appearance of black plate may be affected, however, by modifications of annealing practice, or of processing methods that affect the roughness of the surface texture.

Black plate as such is produced in the form of either cut sheets or coils, and is used for fabricating a variety of items including containers, trays and toys. When coated with suitable organic coatings, it exhibits considerable resistance to corrosion whereas uncoated black plate is extremely susceptible to rusting and precautions to prevent condensation of moisture must be taken during shipment and warehousing. Some manufacturers are equipped to apply thin films of protective oils to minimize rusting. Other mills are equipped to produce chemically treated steel (CTS), which is black plate given a protective chemical treatment to enhance rust resistance and adhesion of organic coatings. Such treated plate usually requires a protective organic coating applied by the user. Precautions to prevent condensation of moisture are necessary during shipment and warehousing of both oiled and CTS black plate.

The most important use of black plate is in the manufacture of tinplate, as described hereafter.

Tin Plate—Tin plate may be described as full-finish black plate additionally processed and coated on both sides with commercially pure tin. The widespread use of this major steel-mill product arises from its combination of the strength of steel with the protective properties and solderability of tin. When coated by the hot-dip process (see Section 5 of this chapter), the tin plate is termed **coke tin plate** or **charcoal tin plate.** These terms are defined under "Hot-Dipped Tin Plate," immediately following this paragraph. When coated by the electrolytic process (see Section 6 of this chapter), it is termed **electrolytic tin plate.** In the United States at the time this is written, more than 97 per cent of the tin plate tonnage produced represents electrolytic tin plate and the remaining tin plate is made by the hot-dip process.

Hot-Dipped Tin Plate—Tin plate formerly was produced by the hot-dip tinning of thin plates that had been hammered or rolled from bars of puddled iron. The pig iron used in puddling might have been made in blast furnaces using charcoal or coke as fuel. Plates made from "charcoal iron" were considered a more ductile and higher grade product; hence, tin plate made by coating charcoal-iron plates with tin (charcoal tin plate) was regarded as a product of higher quality than tin plate with a coke-iron base (coke tin plate). At present, the designation "charcoal tin plate" merely indicates plate with a relatively heavy tin coating as compared with "coke tin plate" as described below, and has no significance so far as quality of the steel base is concerned.

Various grades of hot-dipped tin plate are produced at present, the terminology indicating in a general way the weight of tin coating or, more exactly, the amount of tin used to produce the given unit or base box of plate. Coke tin plate has always designated the plate produced with the lowest amount of tin and formerly was called **Cokes** or **Common Cokes.** Currently, in ascending weight of coating, the various grades are **Common Cokes, Standard Cokes, Best Cokes, Kanners Special. Charcoal tin plate** carries still heavier coatings including 1A and 2A.

Electrolytic tin plate is available in both melted and matte (unmelted) finish. Electrolytic tin plate with a melted finish has bright luster and is similar in appearance to hot-dipped tin plate; whereas matte finish tin plate is lacking in luster. Until recently, electrolytic tin plate was produced only from black plate that had been annealed and temper-rolled, but the even-increasing trend toward stronger, lighter-weight tin plate has resulted in the development of two new types of double-reduced tin plate, one of which is cold-reduced after electrolytic tinning and one of which is produced from black plate that has been cold-reduced immediately prior to tinning (see Section 4 of this chapter).

Theoretically, electrolytic tin plate can be produced in any coating weight. The commercial grades of electrolytic tin plate available at present include coating weights of 0.10, 0.25, 0.50, 0.75, and 1.00 pound of tin per base box, identified by the numerals 10, 25, 50, 75, and 100 respectively. In addition, differentially coated tin plate that has different tin coating weights on opposite surfaces is available in coating weights of 0.50–0.25, 0.75–0.25, 1.00–0.25, 1.35–0.25, and 1.00–0.50. These are also identified by numerals as, for example, 50–25. Electrolytic tin plate can be produced as coils or cut sheets.

The differentially coated tin plate was developed to conserve tin and to lower container costs, with the heavier-coated surface being employed as the inside surface of the container where greater protection is required. The lighter-coated surface was formerly identified by making it less lustrous than the heavier-coated surface either by roughening the steel surface during temper rolling or by anodizing the plated surface in a suitable electrolyte just before melting. At present, however, identification is accomplished by the use of chemicals to print prescribed patterns on one or the other surface.

Symbols and Definition of Base Box—Tin plate is sold on a weight per unit area basis rather than on a thickness basis. The unit of area is the **base box**, equal to the area of 112 sheets, 14 by 20 inches, or 31,360 square inches (217.78 sq. ft.).

In the early eighteenth century in England, 14 by 20-inch plates were packaged in lots of 112 sheets to make one hundred-weight (112 lb.). When the plate was lighter or heavier, it was identified by suitable symbols as discussed in Chapter 48 under "The Tin Plate Gage." A **package** of tin plate still consists of 112 sheets.

The use of symbols to designate gage now has been displaced by the use of **base weights** (or **basis weights**), expressed in pounds per base box, that also indicate the approximate thickness of tin plate or black plate. Table 34—I shows the common nominal weights of tin plate, in pounds per base box that have been produced. Hot-dipped tin plate in sheet form has been

produced in the range of basis weights shown in the table. Present continuous strip-plating lines for electrolytic tin plate normally are designed to produce the lighter basis weights, up to about 135 pounds per base box.

Table 34—I. Nominal Weights and Thicknesses of Tin Plate Commonly Produced

Weight (lb. per base box)	Equivalent Weight (lb. per sq. ft.)	Equivalent Thickness (inch)
45	0.2066	0.00495
50	0.2296	0.00550
55	0.2526	0.00605
60	0.2755	0.00660
65	0.2985	0.00715
70	0.3214	0.00770
75	0.3444	0.00825
80	0.3673	0.00880
85	0.3903	0.00935
90	0.4133	0.00990
95	0.4362	0.01045
100	0.4592	0.01100
107	0.4913	0.01177
112	0.5143	0.01232
118	0.5418	0.01298
128	0.5878	0.01408
135	0.6197	0.01485
139	0.6383	0.01529
148	0.6796	0.01628
155	0.7117	0.01705
168	0.7714	0.01848
175	0.8036	0.01925
180	0.8265	0.01980
188	0.8633	0.02068
196	0.8954	0.02156
208	0.9551	0.02288
210	0.9643	0.02310
215	0.9872	0.02365
228	1.0469	0.02508
235	1.0791	0.02585
240	1.1020	0.02640
248	1.1388	0.02728
255	1.1709	0.02805
268	1.2306	0.02948
270	1.2398	0.02970
275	1.2628	0.03025

SECTION 2

OCCURRENCE, MINING, AND REFINING OF TIN

Tin, though one of the common metals, is the most sparsely distributed metal in common use. The deposits that produce probably 85 per cent of the world's supply are in Malaysia, Indonesia, Bolivia, Thailand, China, Republic of the Congo, and Nigeria. The large portion of the remaining 15 per cent is accounted for by the deposits in Australia, the centuries-old mines in Cornwall, the Union of South Africa and India.

The most abundant source of tin is the oxide, **cassiterite,** or **tin stone,** and the greater portion of the

world's supply from workable deposits is derived from alluvial deposits in river beds. The cassiterite originally occurred in veins and lodes in highly acid igneous rocks. The ore may be found also as primary veins in metamorphosed sedimentary rocks. Cassiterite has a relatively high specific gravity (6.4 to 7.1).

Alluvial deposits of tin stone occur associated with gravel, which may be bonded with clay and covered with more or less overburden consisting of soil, clay, etc. This type of deposit, found in Malaysia, Indonesia, Thailand, China and Nigeria, is worked by various types of hydraulic mining. Washing of the deposit with running water causes a breaking up of the gravel and a carrying away of the lighter pebbles while the heavier tin stone is retained and recovered. The concentrates are hand picked to remove non-stanniferous metals, and may be rewashed in small sluice boxes and concentrated by hand jigging.

Tin ore in Bolivia and Cornwall is practically all vein tin. Here the tin ore is found in lodes and beds, in older rocks such as granite, gneiss and mica schist, associated with a large proportion, perhaps 95-99 per cent, of gangue consisting principally of silica and siliceous minerals, metallic minerals like the sulphides of iron, copper, lead and zinc, iron oxides and wolframite (a tungstate of iron and manganese). The ore first is crushed to pass approximately a twenty-mesh screen, the tin-bearing minerals of the ore are separated by washing and recovered in settling tanks, or on slime tables.

Regardless of which method is used to concentrate the ore, the concentrates then are roasted to remove sulphur and arsenic. This operation in turn is followed by a second washing, although in some cases the roasted ore is treated in magnetic separators to remove iron oxide and wolframite prior to washing. The tin stone is then ready for the smelter. Reduction of the tin ore is accomplished either by the use of a reverberatory furnace or a blast furnace. The crude tin thus obtained is refined by a liquating operation in which advantage is taken of the low melting point of tin. The impure metal is heated on the inclined bed of a furnace to a temperature just above its melting point. Comparatively pure tin trickles down to a basin below, leaving the higher melting point impurities on the bed of the furnace. The low melting point impurities, lead and bismuth, are removed by either or both of two oxidizing methods. The first of these is an operation called **boiling**, in which sticks of green wood are immersed in the molten metal and undergo destructive distillation to produce bubbling by the steam and gases generated to agitate the molten metal bath. Different portions of the metal thus are exposed to air and are oxidized. The oxidized impurities float on top of the molten metal to form **dross** that is skimmed from the surface of the bath. Similarly, pouring ladlefuls of molten metal from a height into the bath permits the oxidation of impurities. This latter operation is called **tossing**. Drosses may be resmelted to recover the tin they contain.

In more modern extraction methods, ore concentrates are calcined with or without additions intended to facilitate further processing. The iron and other impurities then are removed by leaching the ores in solutions of hot hydrochloric acid. Leaching is followed by filtering of the chloride solution. After washing with dilute acid, the residues are of such purity that subsequent treatment in reverberatory furnaces will yield a metal containing at least 99.80 per cent tin. It is possible to obtain metal of 99.98 per cent tin content through refinement by electrolytic means.

Properties and Uses of Tin—Tin has a silver color with a slight bluish tinge, a brilliant luster, a structure which is distinctly crystalline, and is soft and malleable at ordinary temperatures. Other physical properties of tin are:

Atomic Weight: 118.7 (isotopes with masses 112 to 124)

Atomic Number: 50

Density: 7.30 gm. per cc. at 59° F (15° C)

Specific volume: 0.1395 at 68° F (20° C)

Hardness on Mohs' scale: 1.8

Tensile Strength: about 2200 lb. per sq. in. with elongation of 86 per cent

Melting Point: 449.4° F (231.9° C)

Boiling Point: 4120° F (2270° C)

Tin is alloyed with other metals to make bronze, Britannia metal, pewter, solder, or white bearing metal. Pure tin or lead-tin alloy, rolled very thin, is known as tin foil. Tin amalgam is used in making mirrors, and tin condenser tubes are used in laboratory stills. Tin, in conjunction with an acid, is used as a reducing agent.

Stannic oxide is used as a polishing powder, and as an opacifying agent in glasses, glazes and enamels. The chlorides are used as mordants in weighting silk and in dyeing. The largest use of tin at the present time is in the manufacture of tin plate.

SECTION 3

USES AND IMPORTANCE OF TIN PLATE

Tin plate represents one of the major items produced by the steel industry in the United States. In normal years, the tonnage has represented approximately 7 per cent of the total steel production. Statistics compiled by the American Metal Market show that production increased steadily from about 340,000 tons in 1900 to about 2,750,000 tons in 1940. By 1948, new facilities had increased production to about 4,000,000 tons and, by 1961, it reached a level of about 5,600,000 tons. This increase has kept pace with the growths of the population and the food industry.

The importance of tin plate to the food industry is well recognized and its widespread utilization attests to the unique properties of this product in which are combined the strength of steel and the corrosion resistance of tin. Tin plate is fabricated and soldered readily on high-speed forming equipment. It has a pleasing appearance. It is relatively inexpensive and is non-toxic. Because of these and other properties, tin plate has been found to be the ideal material for fabricating food or other containers (tin cans), crown caps and other bottle caps or closures, for kitchen utensils such as baking pans, for various drawn or fabricated parts in radios, and for such articles as electrical equipment, and toys.

The largest use of tin plate is for containers, and many of the improvements in its manufacture have been the result of research directed toward meeting the requirements of the container-manufacturing industry.

Tin cans are used not only for food, but also for paints, oils, tobacco, detergents, insecticides, proprietary drugs and beverages.

SECTION 4

PROCESSING OF STEEL FOR TIN PLATE

Types of Steel Used—Most of the steel used for the production of tin plate is made by the basic open-hearth and oxygen processes. Depending on the stiffness required for the various applications, the phosphorus content may vary from residual to as high as 0.15 per cent. Acid-Bessemer steel, because of its relatively higher phosphorus content, is stiffer than average basic open-hearth steel, and has a distinct advantage where greater stiffness is desirable.

The steels utilized for tin-plate production commonly are classified as "dead-soft" carbon steels having a maximum carbon content of 0.15 per cent. The great preponderance of tin-plate steels are produced as either rimmed or mechanically capped steels. The rimmed steels are utilized in general for the softer and deep-drawing tin-plate requirements, whereas the capped steels are used for those applications which require a harder tin plate or are less critical with regard to stamping or forming. The capped steels for tin plate have the definite advantage of being relatively more uniform throughout in grain size, cleanliness, and chemical composition than rimmed steels.

Of special importance in the manufacture of tin plate is the selection of a steel base of the proper composition for the job. Virtually all tin plate is made from steel having a composition (of the metal in the ladle) falling within the following composition ranges:

Element	Per Cent
Carbon	0.03 to 0.15
Manganese	0.20 to 0.60
Phosphorus	0.15 max.
Sulphur	0.050 max.
Silicon	0.020 max.
Copper	0.20 max.

For particular applications, as determined by temper requirements and pack corrosivity, the desired composition ranges will be selected. The acid fruit products represent in general the most corrosive media. For these applications the phosphorus, silicon, copper, and "tramp" elements in the steel are held to low limits, and nitrogen is added to impart additional strength, if required.

EQUIPMENT AND PRACTICE

The sequence of operations in the manufacture of tin plate is as follows: slabs are heated and hot-rolled to coil form on the hot-strip mill. The coils are continuously pickled and taken to the cold-reduction mills where they are reduced to the desired final tin-plate gages or to gages which may be as much as twice that required for the finished products. The cold-reduced material is cleaned, annealed, and then either temper-rolled (up to about 2 per cent extension) or cold-reduced (up to 50 per cent) in coil form in preparation for the tinning operations described in Sections 5 and 6 of this chapter.

As preceding sections of this book discuss and describe in detail the equipment and operation of the continuous hot-strip mill, the continuous pickler, the cold-reduction mills, and all other equipment necessary for the processing of black plate up to the actual coating operation, the following explanations will be limited to general control measures designed to produce the most suitable product.

Continuous Hot Rolling—In continuous hot-rolling, the slabs of steel, ranging from 4 to 7 inches in original thickness, are hot-rolled at an elevated temperature to a single continuous length which is coiled. This coiled product may be as thin as 0.065 inch or as thick as 0.125 inch, depending upon the end use of the product and the desired thickness of the product after cold reduction; it will generally be between 0.070 and 0.090 inch for the bulk of the tin plate produced in this country. Factors such as type of hot-rolled surface desired, ease with which oxide can be removed prior to the cold-reduction operation, desired hardness of the hot-rolled product and resultant mechanical properties, grain size and corrosion resistance of the final product, all must be considered in establishing an optimum hot-rolling practice. In general, the 0.070- to 0.090-inch thick hot-rolled product will have a temperature between 1500° and 1600° F at the exit side of the last finishing stand. Similarly, this product going into the coiler generally will be in the range of temperature between 1100° and 1250° F.

Continuous Pickling—For the production of tin plate, it is sufficient to say that the primary functions of the continuous pickler are to remove uniformly all of the scale and oxide from the surface of the hot-rolled steel and subsequently to oil the pickled product. These operations are necessary prior to taking the very heavy cold reductions necessary to obtain the light gages required for tin plate and to ensure the clean surface finally necessary for the tinning operation.

Cold Reduction—The importance of the cold-reduction operation to the over-all quality of tin plate cannot be over-emphasized. To a great extent, this operation determines the gage uniformity and the surface quality and flatness of the final tin plate product. These three properties require particularly close control because of the demands of the very sensitive container-lacquering operations and the high-speed automatic can-making operations. To attain the 80 to 90 per cent cold reduction used on the steels for tin plate manufacture, nearly all plants in this country use five-stand or six-stand four-high tandem cold-reduction mills with delivery speeds of 2000 to 6000 feet per minute. The design and operation of these mills are described in Chapter 32. It should be mentioned here that the mills used are generally from 42 to 56 inches wide to produce the usual 24 to 36-inch widths. The cold-reduction operation is accomplished with the aid of a suitable lubricant which must be removed from the strip before annealing so that a bright clean strip will be available for tinning. Depending upon the type of annealing utilized, cleaning may be a separate operation or in line with the annealing furnace. Electrolytic cleaning in alkaline solutions is employed, with the strip polarity and current density being varied as required.

Annealing—The cold-reduced product is quite hard, having a Rockwell (30-T scale) hardness of approximately 80 to 85, and must be softened by annealing. Both batch-type (box-annealing) and continuous-annealing furnaces are used, and the trend is toward further use of continuous-annealing furnaces. In the **box-annealing process,** coils of steel for tin plate are annealed in a protective atmosphere within the steel-temperature range of 1150 to 1250° F, for periods of 4 to 12 hours. While the heating cycle in relation to the metalloid content of the steel largely determines grain size of the finished product and exerts a strong influence on the mechanical properties of the finished tin plate, the cooling cycle plays an important part as regards surface. A clear, bright, steel surface, substantially free of oxides, can be obtained if a reducing atmosphere is maintained around the coils of steel until the steel temperature drops below approximately 250° F. In the **continuous-annnealing process,** the steel is heated in protective atmospheres to about 1200° F in a fraction of a minute at strip speeds up to 1500 feet per minute in existing furnaces and at projected speeds of 2000 feet per minute in newer furnaces. Continuously annealed strip is inherently harder and stiffer than box-annealed strip, but possesses good formability; thus, continuous annealing offers a method for obtaining tin plate of higher hardness without change in steel composition.

Temper Rolling—The function of the temper mills in the manufacture of tin plate is three fold: to impart the desired surface finish to the product, to improve its flatness and to obtain the desired metallurgical properties such as temper and freedom from fluting tendencies.

The surface finish is controlled largely by the smoothness of the exit work rolls. Smooth-ground rolls impart a bright, dense surface finish whereas rough-ground or shot-blasted rolls impart a rougher finish. All grades except matte finish (No. 5 finish) are finished with smooth-ground rolls.

Flatness is obtained by proper adjustment of such factors as roll contour, finish, pressure and strip tension.

For the softest tempers, temper rolling (also called **skin rolling**) is done on a conventional four-high single-stand coil temper mill although, with care, these tempers can be produced on two-stand tandem temper mills. The objective here is to flatten the strip and impart the proper surface finish in one pass with a minimum of hardening effect due to cold working of the product, the thickness reduction being held to less than one per cent. For the harder tempers, a two-stand four-high tandem temper mill is employed, or the strip is given two passes through single-stand mills. On such material, temper rolling has the added function of increasing the steel hardness, and thickness reductions of about two per cent are common. As an aid to temper rolling, the work-roll surface of the first mill stand is relatively rough, being rough-ground or shot blasted, and the work rolls of the second stand or finishing mill are ground smooth. Thus, superficial hardening, arising from second-stand smoothing of the rough strip surface imparted in the first stand, is added to the full-section hardening of the strip under rolling pressures and reel tension. Modifications of temper mills for tin plate include means for applying high strip tensions and for developing heavier drafts in the first stand, as mentioned in the section on finishing.

For double-reduced tin plate, the temper-rolling step is replaced by a cold-rolling operation in which the annealed black-plate coils for tin plate coils are reduced 30 to 50 per cent on a four-high tandem cold-reduction mill of either two or three stands. The resultant product has high hardness, yield strength and tensile strength but possesses sufficient formability for a wide range of container applications.

After temper-rolling or cold-rolling, the coils of black plate may be handled in one of several ways. They may be side-trimmed and packaged or side-trimmed, sheared and packaged for shipment. However, black-plate coils for electrolytic tinning are taken to a side-trimming and recoiling line for preparation. Temper-rolled black plate for hot-dip tinning is sheared into sheets.

SECTION 5

HOT-DIPPED TIN PLATE

Shearing Practice—At the flying shears, the coils for conversion to hot-dipped tin plate are side trimmed and cut to sheets. A micrometer, operating continuously, rejects off-gage sheets which are diverted automatically into an off-weight piler and thus separated from product of correct thickness. Perforated sheets are detected with an "electric eye" and are rejected automatically.

White-Pickling Practice—Pickling to remove all surface contaminants, such as light oxides resulting

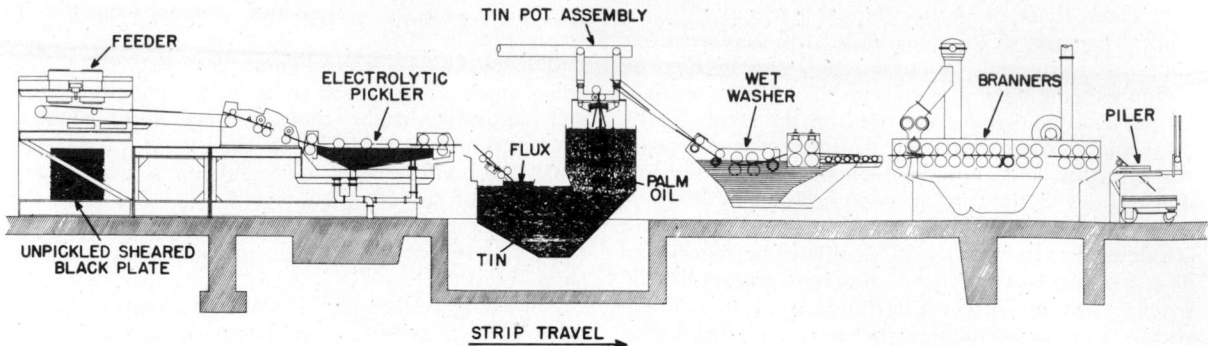

FIG. 34—1. Schematic arrangement of equipment comprising a tinning stack.

from the annealing treatment before tinning, is commonly termed **white pickling** to differentiate from other pickling processes. A clean, uniformly pickled surface is a requisite for successful hot tinning. The temper-rolled product is pickled in sulphuric acid of 2 to 6 per cent concentration at 150° to 180° F for 2 to 4 minutes, followed by rinsing in cold water. Pickling inhibitors frequently are used to prevent over-pickling or etching of the plate. The pickled steel is stored in a "bosh" or steel storage tank containing a 0.10 per cent hydrochloric-acid solution until ready for tinning.

Electrolytic pickling has supplanted white pickling in many plants. Sheared plate is fed automatically into the electrolytic pickler and thence into the tin pot (Figure 34—1). Various feeding devices may be employed and common acids (normally sulphuric) are used in such a unit.

The Hot-Dip Tinning Operation—A typical hot-dip tinning shop or **tin house** normally consists of a long, rectangular building with the **tin stacks** arranged side-by-side in a straight line. The individual tin stacks usually are hooded completely to draw off all fumes from the flux, palm-oil and tin baths and to minimize as much as possible the escape of loose bran particles from the branning unit to the surrounding air. A tinning stack consists of an assembly of equipment arranged to perform a number of operations in a con-

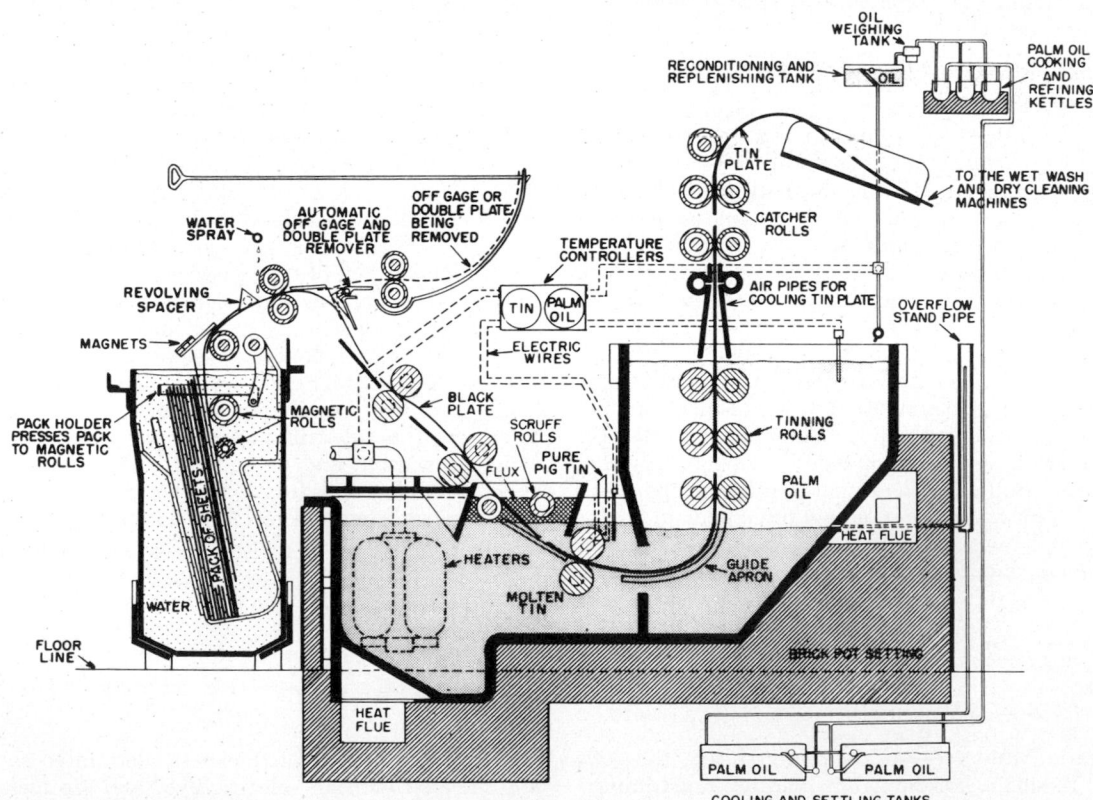

FIG. 34—2. Schematic diagram of a tin pot and tinning machine. The feeding unit at the left is known as a Poole feeder. The brushes on the tinning rolls have been omitted.

tinuous manner (Figure 34—1). The integral parts of this assembly, in the order in which they perform their function on the sheet being coated are as follows:

1. The feeder
2. The electrolytic pickler
3. The tin pot and tinning machine
4. The wet washing machine
5. The branner
6. The piler

Modern hot-dip tinning machines are commonly of two sizes; 64-inch and 75-inch. These designate the length of the roll bodies in the machines. The 64-inch machine normally operates as a two-way unit (two sheets of tin plate pass side-by-side through the molten tin bath) whereas the wider 75-inch machine may be used as a three-way machine on narrow product.

The **feeding mechanism** varies in design from plant to plant. Feeding may be done manually or by automatic-feeding machines. The **Poole feeder** (Figure 34—2) is a common automatic type, in which individual sheets are lifted by a magnetized roller from the feeder tank to the supplementary tinning-machine equipment.

The **tinning machine** consists of a series of guides and rolls to convey and guide the sheets being coated from the feeding mechanism downward through the molten flux and tin baths, then upward out of the molten tin and through a bath of hot oil onto the conveyor, as shown in Figure 34—2. The axis of each set of rolls lie in the same horizontal plane. Three pairs of rolls are positioned in the hot oil so that the lowest pair is slightly above the molten-tin level and the top pair is just below the top level of the oil. The **tinning machine rolls** normally range from 3½ to 4 inches in diameter and are of high-carbon steel heat treated to high hardness. Their surfaces are very accurately finished by machining and grinding.

The **tin pot**, which holds from 8,000 to 17,000 lb. of commercially pure molten tin at about 620° F, is filled to a point approximately 4 inches from the top of the entry side. The pot is made of plate steel, enclosed in a brick chamber, and generally is heated by gas or oil burners or by an immersion heater. The **flux box** is a long narrow box with its sides converging downward but without any top or bottom. It is located on the entry side of the tin pot and the lower edges extend downward into the molten tin bath. The flux bath, approximately 3 to 4 inches in depth, floats on the surface of the molten-tin bath. The space between the bottom of the flux box and the opening in the partition is equipped with top and bottom guides. In addition, either an apron or guides are provided in the tin-bath chamber to control the path of the plate from the flux box into the nip of the bottom rolls in the tinning machine (see Figure 34—2). The flux in common usage is essentially a water solution of zinc chloride which may contain some ammonium chloride.

The tinning rolls in the palm oil are equipped with **wipers** or **brushes** (soapstone or asbestos) to aid in the control of the weight and distribution of the tin coating. The **palm-oil bath** (temperature about 465° F) on the exit side of the tin bath not only protects the molten tin from oxidation but also keeps the tin coat-

ing on the sheet in a molten condition to permit control of tin-coating weight and distribution.

The **catcher rolls** feed the coated and oily sheets past a jet of cooling air to a conveyor from whence the plate travels through a **wet-washing machine** (Figure 34—1). The purpose of this unit is to remove the excess of palm oil from the surface of the coated sheet. The washer contains a hot water solution of soda ash or trisodium phosphate at a concentration of 0.10 to 0.15 per cent total alkalinity. The solution in most plants is circulated from a central storage tank that supplies the entire tinning shop. The inflow of solution is controlled automatically. The overflow is collected in a drainage system or sump: the palm oil in the overflow is removed at this point for disposition.

The washed sheet is relatively free from oil. Since the sheets are unsatisfactory for ultimate use without some oil being present, the sheet is next passed into a **branner** where a light oil film is distributed across the sheet surface. The branner unit consists of tandem sets of cleaning rolls composed of thousands of canton-flannel discs, about 4 inches in diameter, tightly compressed on a long, square, steel mandrel. **Bran** or **middlings** (from the milling of wheat and/or rye) are fed into the first set of rolls to absorb the moisture, and distribute uniformly the oil that remains on the plate surface from the washer. The last rolls of the machine, together with a combination of vacuum and pressure hoods, are used to minimize the presence of bran on the sheets. From these hoods the product passes down the conveyor to the **piler,** which automatically stacks the plate in neat piles without scratching or otherwise marring the tinned surface.

COKE TIN PLATE

Tinning-Roll Practice—The most commonly supplied grades of hot-dipped tin plate are Standard and Common Cokes. On Standard Cokes the mills aim for an average tin-coating weight of 1.35 pounds per base box of plate and for Common Cokes the aim is an average tin-coating weight of 1.10 pounds per base box. In order to obtain the best possible uniformity of coating, the middle and top sets of tinning-machine rolls in the exit side of the pot may be grooved spirally. The depth of grooving varies with the results desired for a given tin-house practice, but in general the grooves on the top set of rolls are shallower than on the middle set. The heavier the coating desired, the deeper is the grooving.

CHARCOAL TIN PLATE

In order to produce the heavier coated charcoal plate, it is necessary to modify the tinning equipment in such manner that the tinning rolls carry more metal. This is accomplished in a conventional machine by replacing the brushes on the top or top-and-middle rolls with pans. Tin is supplied to these pans by ladling or pumping molten metal into them; the bottom of the rolls revolving in the tin. These rolls have grooves up to 0.008 inch deep.

ASSORTING OF HOT-DIPPED TIN PLATE

After the tinning operation, the coated sheets must be inspected and classified. Individual standards for a given grade and application may vary somewhat, but the general classifications are (1) **primes**, (2) **seconds**, (3) **menders**, and (4) **waste-waste.** These classifications are defined as follows:

1. Primes are tin plates free from defects readily observed by the unaided eye.
2. Seconds are tin plates having imperfections in moderate degree or extent.
3. Menders are those tin plates having imperfections in coating, which product, upon recoating, will produce either a "prime" or "second" quality sheet.
4. Waste-waste are tin plates which, either through imperfections of coating or base metal cannot be recoated to produce a "prime" or "second" quality sheet.

HOT-DIPPED TIN-PLATE COATING WEIGHTS

In the manufacture of hot-dipped tin plate, the tin coating weight on the product is determined on the basis of **pot yield**; that is, the yield of tin plate for the amount of tin utilized in the tin pot. Because of the tinning method used, the tin coating will vary across a sheet and from sheet to sheet. Typical tin-coating-weight distribution data are contained in the Report of Industry Survey of Coating Weights of Hot-Dipped Tin Plate, Contributions to the Metallurgy of Steel, No. 39, April 1952, published by the American Iron and Steel Institute.

The minimum average tin coating-weight test val-

ues that may be expected on the standard grades of hot-dipped tin plate when tested in accordance with the procedure recommended in the American Iron and Steel Institute Steel Products Manual, "Tin Mill Products," November 1960, are shown in Table 34—II. Experience has shown that the average tin-coating weight is substantially higher than these values. For example, production records indicate that the average tin coating weights on Common Cokes and Standard Cokes will approach 1.10 and 1.35 lb. per base box, respectively. However, individual test values as much as 0.25 lb. per base box below the values shown in Table 34—II may occasionally be found.

Table 34—II. Tin Coating Weights of Standard Grades of Hot-Dipped Tin Plate

Class Designation	Minimum Average Tin-Coating-Weight-Test Value (Pounds per base box)
Common Cokes*	0.85
Standard Cokes	1.05
Best Cokes	1.19
Kanners Special Cokes	1.40
1A Charcoal*	1.80
2A Charcoal	2.30

*The terms "coke" and "charcoal" stem from the old practice of making hot-dipped tin plate from coke iron and charcoal iron. Today, they merely refer to different tin-coating-weight levels.

SECTION 6

ELECTROLYTIC TIN PLATE

Introduction—Prior to 1937, all tin plate produced commercially was manufactured by the hot-dipping process. While the electrodeposition of tin on steel had been a known process for many years, its application to the production of tin-plated sheets could not be made to compete economically with the hot-dipping process due to much higher equipment and labor costs. However, with the introduction to the sheet and tin plate industry of continuous cold-reduction mills in the early 1930's, the possibility of continuous high-speed electrotinning became obvious. As early as 1935, small experimental units were designed and constructed capable of continuously electroplating tin on steel strip moving at relatively high speeds. From the results of these studies, electrolytic tin plate appeared on the market as a commercial item in 1937.

The early development of electrolytic tin plate was given a major impetus by the requirements of the dry package market for a light-coated product which could not be produced by the hot-dip process. The precipitous necessity to conserve vital tin during World War II resulted in a phenomenal expansion of this development so that by 1948, over half of the tin plate produced was electrolytic tinplate and by 1963 it was over 97 per cent.

The superiority in tin-coating uniformity which electrolytic tin plate exhibits as compared to hot-dipped tin plate, together with the close control of

tin-coating weight which is obtained, has resulted in large savings of tin.

Basic Principles of Electrotinning—To the English scientist, Michael Faraday, belongs the credit for placing electrochemistry on a quantitative and orderly basis. In 1833, he postulated certain laws which to-day bear his name and which can be summarized as follows:

1. In any electrolysis, the quantities of materials liberated at the electrodes bear a direct relationship to the quantity of electricity passed through the system.

2. An equal number of equivalents of substances are set free by the same quantity of electricity.

It can be seen from a study of these laws that tin plating can be controlled when the electrode reactions are known. Electrotinning can be accomplished with acid or alkaline electrolytes.

In the **acid processes** the anode reaction consists of direct oxidation from metallic tin to the bivalent stannous ion with the liberation of two electrons as follows:

$$Sn^\circ = Sn^{++} + 2e$$

The reaction is usually 100 per cent efficient, thus making the quantity of tin driven into solution directly proportional to the electrical energy used. The reverse reaction takes place at the cathode,

$$Sn^{++} + 2e = Sn^\circ$$

Fig. 34—5. Side-trimming unit that prepares cold - reduced, annealed and temper-rolled coils of flat steel for electrolytic tinning by removing excess material from side edges to produce strip of exact desired width. An air-operated shear following the side trimmer cuts off the crop ends of coils preparatory to seam welding of successive coils together to form larger single coils weighing up to 30,000 lb.

in design but require considerably larger plating units. This difference in design is necessary because of the low current-density limit of the alkaline bath, which is usually a solution of sodium stannate and sodium hydroxide. The alkaline electrolytes in general operate at current densities up to 60 amperes per square foot.

The third common type of electrotinning line makes use of an acid-halogen electrolyte in plating units arranged on two levels. The strip travels through the lower plating unit in a substantially horizontal passline in the direction of the exit end of the line and leaves this lower level unit over a deflector roll which passes it upwardly to the second level where a second deflector roll causes it to travel horizontally toward the entry end of the line through the upper level plating unit. At the end of the latter are a second set of deflector rolls for reversing the direction of travel so that the plated strip will again move horizontally toward the exit end of the line. The lower and upper plating units are each comprised of a number of individual plating cells arranged in tandem. A conductor roll at the end of each cell rides the top surface of the strip to establish it as the cathode; the anodes are bars of tin disposed in the bottoms of each cell. The strip is supported by conveyor rolls, one such roll being disposed immediately below each conductor roll so as to maintain the strip barely submerged in the plating solution. The net effect of the foregoing arrangement is that only the undersides of the strip at each level is plated.

Regardless of the type of plating unit used, the steel strip for manufacturing electrolytic tin plate is similarly prepared. The strip itself is manufactured as described elsewhere: that is, it is hot rolled from slabs, continuously pickled, cold reduced, electrolytically cleaned, box or continuously annealed, and either temper rolled or cold reduced. In annealing, a protective reducing atmosphere is used to insure a uniform, bright surface and the temper rolling operation is carefully controlled to maintain this condition. At this point in the processing, strip for electrotinning takes a different course than that for hot-dipped tin plate as the retention of a long, uninterrupted unit of strip is

needed for the success of the electrotinning operation. Accordingly, the coiled temper-rolled or cold-reduced strip is usually delivered to the side trimming units (Figure 34—5) where it is uncoiled, run through pairs of rotary knives and recoiled. The rotary knives are adjustable in such a manner that the strip can be very accurately side trimmed to the ordered width. It is general practice to adjust the slab-selection and hot-rolling practice to obtain about one inch protective over-width on the process strip which is removed at these slitters. In some instances, this side trimming of strip is done after tinning in a separate shearing operation. In many plants where the strip is trimmed before coating, lap-welding equipment is included in the side trimmers to permit welding several coil units together and thus provide a continuous section of steel strip for plating, up to six or seven miles long. In other plants, the side-trimming operation is performed in the electrolytic tinning unit itself.

ENTRY-END EQUIPMENT

The entry end of an electrolytic line is usually so designed as to provide two **uncoilers** in line (Figure 34—6). This permits the operator to "pay off" from one uncoiler while charging a coil into the other. Electrolytic tinning units do not require any special type of unreeling equipment and either the conventional cone or expanding types may be used. All of the auxiliary uncoiler equipment such as brakes, forward and reversing drives, hydraulic lifts, and strippers are usually to be found on all units.

In preparing a coil for processing, the lead edge of the strip is manually engaged in a set of small **pinch rolls** which can be opened and closed by air pressure and which are usually motor driven. The function of these rolls is to permit the operator to advance the lead edge of a new coil into the welding assembly. This **welding assembly** consists primarily of an up-cut shear, a lap welder, and a set of large pinch rolls.

It is desirable to maintain a high strip speed in the plating baths, so facilities are provided to join fresh coils to the strip without reducing line speed. As the coil in process is being unrolled, the operator takes

Fig. 34—6. Entry end of an electrolytic tinning line, with one uncoated coil being paid off into the line and another in reserve position. The trailing end of the coil being fed will be welded to the leading end of the reserve coil (after squaring in the shear) to provide a continuous feed to the line.

care that the maximum amount of strip is contained in the **looper** located just after the **entry bridle** (Figure 34—3). When the last several wraps of the coil unwind from the uncoiler in use, the operator stops the entry bridle, "trues-up" the tail end of the coil with the **shear,** moves this tail end into welding position with the head end of the new coil, welds the two together and starts the entry bridle. All this must be done before the strip previously stored in the looping unit has been completely used. The entry bridle is then run at some speed greater than line operating speed to refill the loop, at which point automatic electrical devices slow these rolls back to synchronism with the rest of the unit. Since these looping units are usually designed to accumulate 300 to 500 feet of strip, it is obvious that the welder op-rator must act rapidly in order to keep a line operating at speeds no less than 400 to 600 ft. per min. These loopers may be of the "tower" type or of the "pit" type. A **tower-type looper,** as its name indicates, is constructed predominantly above ground and usually consists of fixed and movable sets of rolls over which the strip is passed. The top set of rolls moves down or up, depending on whether strip is being expended from or accumulated in the equipment. The **pit-type looper** consists of a deep pit in which hangs a long catenary of strip.

MAIN PROCESS SECTION

From the looper the strip enters the main process section of the line. In the acid lines, the process section usually consists of a dynamic tension device (often called a **drag bridle** or **tension bridle**), an alkaline **electrolytic cleaner,** a rinsing unit, a **pickler,** another **rinsing unit,** a **plating unit,** a third **rinsing unit,** a **fusion unit,** a **quench tank,** a **chemical-treating unit,**

a fourth **rinsing unit,** a **drying unit,** an **oiling unit, a drive** or **pull-through bridle,** and finally a set of **re-coilers** or a **shear** or both. The alkaline lines have the same sequence of units except that the alkaline cleaner is usually not part of such lines inasmuch as the alkaline plating bath itself does sufficient cleaning.

Tension Bridle—The function of the **tension bridle** is to produce sufficient drag on the strip to maintain a positive strip tension throughout the line. It consists of a series of rolls, some of which may be pinch rolls, through which the strip passes out of the looper. These rolls are usually geared together and to a generator. By controlling the field voltage on this generator and "shorting out" the armature through a resistance, a controllable drag can be applied to the strip through the geared rolls.

Cleaning and Pickling Units—In the acid-electro-lyte units, the strip passes from the drag bridle to the alkaline **electrolytic cleaners.** In some lines these cleaners are of conventional design, with horizontal electrodes as described in the section on the electro-cleaning of cold-reduced strip. In other lines, vertical units are used. Current densities in these units vary from 50 to 300 amperes per square foot. The hot cleaning solutions are alkaline detergents. Strip polarity may be either anodic or cathodic since it is found that both conditions yield good cleaning performance.

The strip passes from the alkaline cleaner into a **rinsing unit.** Its function is to remove all alkali from the strip in preparation for the pickling operation. This rinsing unit is usually comprised of water sprays playing on both sides of the strip and of rotary bristle brushes which rotate vigorously against the strip. There is a trend toward the use of high-pressure water sprays and the elimination of brushes in such units.

The **strip-pickling units,** which are used on all

electrolytic tinning lines, may be of the hot immersion type or of the cold electrolytic type. The immersion type usually consists of a large rubber- or brick-lined tank through which the strip passes vertically or horizontally. These tanks are filled with hot sulphuric acid of a strength varying up to 12 per cent and the pickling time is regulated by the operating strip speed. The electrolytic picklers are usually small units, as the control of pickling is maintained by regulation of the electric current. These units generally are built similar to the alkaline cleaning tanks and the electrical circuits are also similar. In some electrolytic picklers, however, the strip may be alternately anodic and cathodic. After pickling, the strip is again rinsed in a unit similar to the one used after the alkaline cleaner and enters the plating tank.

Plating Tanks—As explained earlier, the main difference in the various electrolytic tinning units lies in the type of electrolyte used. The unit used in **phenolsulphonic-acid lines** is designed for operation at high current densities and consists of at least four vertical compartments in each of which the strip passes over metal contact rolls and down into the electrolyte between banks of tin anodes. (A fifth com-

partment in line with the four plating tanks and identical in appearance plays no part in the plating operation but merely collects the solution dragged out of the plating system.) Thus, the current can be considered to pass from the tin anodes through the solution to the strip and up the strip to the metal deflector rolls which act as the negative contact of the system. By such a circuit, the tin is deposited from the solution onto the strip and is also equally driven into solution from the anodes. The anodes consist of tin bars which, for example, may be 3 inches by 2 inches in cross section and approximately six feet long, weighing close to 200 pounds each (Figure 34—7). The life of the individual anode depends on the quantity of electric current passing through it. The electrolyte is constantly recirculated through the plating tanks after passing through a settling tank and several heat exchangers. The temperature of the bath is generally maintained at about 100° to 120° F. All of this equipment must of necessity be constructed of corrosion-resistant materials and care must be taken to provide sufficient insulation in the system to prevent electric-current leakage. Generating equipment capable of developing 45,000 amperes at 8 volts has been a typi-

FIG. 34—7. Tin anode being placed in the plating tank of an electrolytic tinning line, with other anodes lined up awaiting placement.

cal installation. The total amperage required is of course dependent upon strip speed and tin-coating weight desired.

Alkaline-type plating tanks, while essentially of the same basic design, require much greater floor space than the acid type. Inasmuch as alkaline stannate baths are operated at temperatures in excess of 200° F, no recirculation of the electrolyte for cooling is necessary. These plating tanks are fabricated as a single large unit with contact rolls placed at the top of the tanks and rubber deflector rolls placed in the bottom. The tin anodes used in the alkaline units are usually very large slabs of tin hanging under and between the contact rolls. These slabs are large enough to allow several weeks of operation before replacement is necessary. Alkaline lines have been provided with up to 90,000 amperes at 10 volts, with current densities of up to 60 amperes per square foot permitting strip speed up to 600 feet per minute on half-pound per base box coatings. As indicated earlier, strip speed and tin-coating weight requirements will dictate the amperage requirements.

The third type of unit, employing a **halogen-type** electrolyte, consists of a series of small cells, each with its own circulation system, contact roll and anode bank. These tanks are so designed that the strip is barely immersed in the electrolyte and is plated on the bottom side only. After passing through a number of these units, the strip is deflected upward and backward so that the original top of the strip now becomes the bottom. It then passes through another series of similar plating cells until an equal amount of tin is deposited on this side of the strip. The halogen-type electrolyte used exclusively in these units is constantly recirculated through the cells, cooled and filtered during its circulation. The tin anodes used in the individual cells resemble regular pigs of tin and rest on side supports just under the strip pass line. Halogen lines have been designed for strip speeds greater than 2000 feet per minute. Generator capacity exceeds 100,000 amperes at a voltage of from 8 to 10 volts. The current density used is approximately 300 amperes per square foot.

Drag-Out Control—The plated strip, regardless of plating process, is now freed from the dragout and rinsed in pure water or condensate. The electrolyte which is dragged into this wash water is all or in part returned to the plating tank. To accomplish this, dragout recovery systems varying from complex recirculation and evaporation systems to simple counter-rinsing with partial recovery are used. Too much emphasis cannot be placed on the necessity for efficiently recovering the dragged-out electrolyte since solution losses from this source can be enormous at high speeds, reaching as much as 30 gallons per minute.

Fusion Units—The tin coating, as it emerges from the plating bath, is gray-white and semi-lustrous. It does not in appearance resemble tin plate as it is commonly known. While some attempts have been made to plate bright tin coatings, no commercially successful developments of this type are at present practiced. Instead, it is universal practice to melt and quench the electrodeposited tin which gives it the brilliant luster typical of hot-dipped plate (Figure

34—8). There are three types of units in which this tin fusion is accomplished. They vary only in the source of heat and not in basic construction.

One of these melting units makes use of **electrical resistance heating.** The strip is run in a vertical loop between two contact rolls, the second of which is immersed in water. These two contact rolls form the terminals of an alternating-current circuit in which the strip is the closing resistance. Thus, by regulation of the current flow through the strip (or applied voltage) it is possible to bring the plated strip up to 450° to 455° F just prior to passage into the water. The maximum temperature to which this strip can be heated falls in a very narrow range because heating to too high a temperature causes discoloration of the product and/or the formation of an excessively thick iron-tin alloy layer, whereas insufficient heating naturally results in failure to melt.

A second type of melting unit utilizes **electrical high-frequency induction heating** for melting. In this unit, the strip passes down and through a water-cooled copper coil on which is impressed a high-frequency voltage. The induced eddy currents in the tinplate strip cause it to heat up with resulting fusion of the tin coating. Control is again exercised by voltage variations on the induction-coil terminals.

The third type of melting unit in commercial use is gas-heated. It employs the principle of **radiant heating** and is equipped with special ceramic burners that radiate controlled amounts of heat to the strip. Control on such units is exercised by lateral movement of the burner banks, closer to or farther away from the strip, depending on whether more or less heat is required. Further limited control is available by regulation of the gas supply to the unit. As in the other units, the strip is quenched directly after fusion of the tin is accomplished.

The fused and quenched coating is now given a **filming treatment** which may be either chemical or electrochemical, as described later in this section. After such treatment, the tinned strip is **rinsed** with clean water and is dried either by blasts of hot air or high-pressure steam.

Oil-Film Application—Unlike hot-dipped tin plate, the electrolytic plate is not oily as it emerges from the coating operation; hence, it is necessary to deposit a controlled film of lubricant on the product in order to improve its handling properties in succeeding operations as well as to protect the tin surface against oxidation. The lubricant used is usually either cottonseed oil or di (2-ethylhexyl) sebacate, (commonly referred to as dioctyl sebacate or DOS), which is applied in several ways. Two oiling methods now widely used on electrolytic tinning units are the **emulsion** and **electrostatic processes.** The first of these consists of passing the strip through a bath or a spray of an oil emulsion. Control of the resulting oil film is exercised by emulsion composition and operating temperature. After exposure to the emulsion the strip passes through wringer rolls, is dried, and passes into the pull-through bridle ready for recoiling or shearing. The electrostatic method of oiling strip makes use of a high potential between the strip and a fixed electrode which creates a powerful electrostatic field around

FIG. 34—8. General view of an electrolytic tinning line, looking toward the entry end and showing the melting tower in the center foreground.

the moving strip. Into this electrostatic field is allowed to rise a mist of cottonseed oil, or DOS which is deflected onto the strip by the proper adjustment of strip polarity. Despite the relative complexity of the equipment, these oiling units operate very satisfactorily and economically.

Pull-Through or Drive Bridle—The strip next enters the unit which supplies tractive power to the strip to pull it entirely through the electrolytic line. This piece of equipment is called the "pull-through" or drive bridle. It actually does the pulling of the strip through the process section and is the basic unit with which the plating current and both entry and delivery ends are synchronized. The equipment itself is usually quite similar to the tension bridle described elsewhere in this section. However, instead of a drag generator being geared to the rolls, they are coupled with a powerful motor which is sufficiently large to pull the strip through the whole process section at high speeds. A tachometer generator attached to this motor provides the impulse to regulate the plating and melting currents in required relation to strip speed.

DELIVERY-END EQUIPMENT

Alkaline tinning lines are provided with large **loopers** and a single recoiler at the delivery end into which the strip passes from the drive bridle. Such an assembly performs in a manner similar to that of the entry end previously described in that the looper acts

as a strip accumulator. Acid lines are provided with two recoilers, a special shear and guides and belt wrappers which make it possible to cut the strip and wind it on the second recoiler at high speeds. A number of electrolytic plating lines are provided with both quick-change coilers and flying shears. However, the coil of coated product may be sent to the conventional **shearing units** where it is sheared to size, oiled (if not so treated in the electrolytic-plating line), assorted, counted, and piled.

In those units where **flying shears** only are included in the equipment assembly, no loopers are necessary. Instead, a very small catenary is maintained immediately in front of the shear in order that perfect guiding into the shear knives can be accomplished. Failure to guide properly into a shear results in miscutting and "out-of-square" sheets. The flying shears themselves are conventional units for light-gage-strip shearing, as described elsewhere in this chapter. There are some modifications, however, which should be mentioned. The most important ones concern the adaptation of these units for careful inspection, classification and counting of the product (Figure **34**—9).

The flying shears are equipped with four piling stations and a system of conveyor belts which allows the deposition of sheets in any of these pilers at the will of the operator.

In lines containing four **pilers,** all sheets containing perforations are accumulated in the first piler. Sheets containing bad surface defects and product which is

FIG. 34—9. Discharge end of an electrolytic tinning line, showing sheared-plate pliers (left) and inspector.

outside the accepted gage tolerances are accumulated in the second piler. The third piler is used to receive sheets while the fourth piler is changed to pile a new bundle. The accumulated sheets in the third piler are assorted on an auxiliary unit and the prime sheets are applied on the order. The fourth or end piler is the so-called **prime piler**. As the **sheet counter** is located between the third and this prime piler, the product delivered into it is usually counted into ten-, twelve-, or fifteen-package bundles (1120, 1344 or 1680 sheets) ready for packaging and shipping.

The methods of inspection and classification of electrolytic tin plate on these flying shears are rather ingenious. Located somewhere after the melting unit is a noncontacting **thickness gage**. When the strip is too thick or too thin to meet specifications, the gage actuates an electronic memory device which rejects those particulary heavy or light sheets at the second piler. Likewise, a device sometimes called a **pin-hole detector** utilizes a photoelectric cell to continuously scan the coated strip and cause sheets with perforations to be deflected into the first piler.

Trained inspectors are located at the pull-through bridle and the shear, respectively; they operate contact buttons which allow them to deflect at will any defective product they detect into the second or third piler (depending on product classification) and pass prime product into the fourth piler where the attendant sees that it is properly counted and that the shear operator is kept advised of the product flatness.

Laboratory determinations are made regularly to determine the tin-coating and oil-film weights on the finished product. The lacquerability of the tin plate is judged by specialists. Various laboratory controls of cleaning, pickling and plating solution characteristics are necessary.

SECTION 7

METALLURGICAL ASPECTS

General—A fuller appreciation of the metallurgical aspects of tin plate may be had by considering it as a nine-layer sandwich (Figure 34—10), the layers of which consist of:

1. Oil layer
2. Tin oxide
3. Free tin
4. Tin-iron alloy
5. Steel base
6. Tin-iron alloy
7. Free tin
8. Tin oxide
9. Oil layer

Adaptability for a specific purpose may depend on the properties of a given layer. To illustrate for a pressed part, such as a toy, the drawing characteristics of the steel base may be the controlling factor. In the case of electrolytic tin plate, the chemical or electrochemical filming treatment gives an oxide layer found beneficial for adhesion of lacquers and enamels. Similarly, tin plate must have an oil film adequate both to promote good "feeding" in automatic equipment and to prevent scratching during fabrication and yet not so heavy as to cause difficulty during roller coating with lacquers or printing inks. Thus, each layer requires adequate control for some of the applications. Generally, since the manufacture of tin plate is on a mass production basis, it is most economical to standardize on the optimum quality of each layer for total tin-mill production.

The Steel Base—The metallurgical controls of the steel base are similar to those employed for the production of sheet and strip and, hence, will not be elaborated on further. It is sufficient to point out that mechanical properties of the finished tin plate depend on the composition of the steel, the heat treatments and the rolling operations. Inasmuch as the steel used is a low-carbon mild steel and as the usual hardening agents are looked upon with disfavor be-

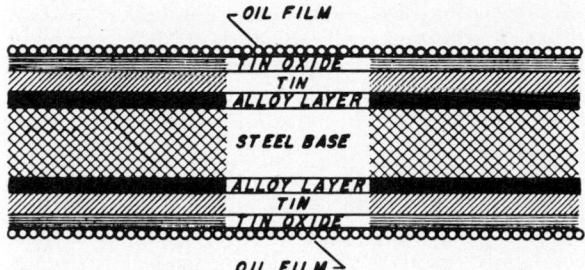

FIG. 34—10. Schematic enlarged cross-section of a sheet of tin plate, showing approximate relative thicknesses of the various "layers." The approximate thickness in inches of the individual layers is as follows:

Layer	Thickness (In.)
Oil film	10^{-7} (0.0000001)
Tin oxide	10^{-7} (0.0000001)
Alloy layer	10^{-4} (0.0001)
Tin	10^{-5} (0.00001)
Steel base	10^{-2} (0.01)

cause of their detrimental effect on corrosion resistance, as well as cost, strengthening by variations in composition is limited to addition or control with respect to phosphorus and nitrogen. Phosphorus has been used in amounts up to 0.15 per cent but its use is limited to tin plates employed for noncorrosive food and nonfood containers. Nitrogen content is not critical from the corrosion-resistance standpoint.

Strength, or **temper,** is further controlled by regulating the amount of temper rolling or cold rolling prior to plating. The tin-plate industry has adopted

the Superficial Rockwell Hardness test as a control measure of the temper of the strip. This test is described elsewhere.

As the major portion of tin plate is used for containers, the requirements of this application dictate most of the metallurgical considerations in the processing of the steel base. As will be pointed out more fully in a later paragraph, the corrosion resistance of tin plate to food products is an important consideration—and in this respect the production of steel sheet for tin plate differs from the production of sheets for other applications. Many factors affect the corrosion resistance of tin plate, but quality of the steel base is probably the most important. Besides the composition, the various processes, such as hot-strip rolling, cold reduction and annealing, are subjected to even closer control than would be necessary from the standpoint of mechanical properties alone.

The various cleaning and pickling operations, previously described, are also closely controlled so as to prepare a suitable surface for subsequent coating with tin.

The Tin-Iron Alloy Layer—When a clean steel surface comes in contact with molten tin, a reaction takes place with the formation of a tin-iron alloy layer intimately bound to the steel surface. This alloy layer is quite thin (about 25 to 5 millionths of an inch), in electrolytic tin plate.

The metallurgy of tin-iron alloy has received considerable attention by various investigators. The phase diagram for the iron-tin system in Figure 34—11 reveals that there are probably at least three compounds of tin and iron, as follows:

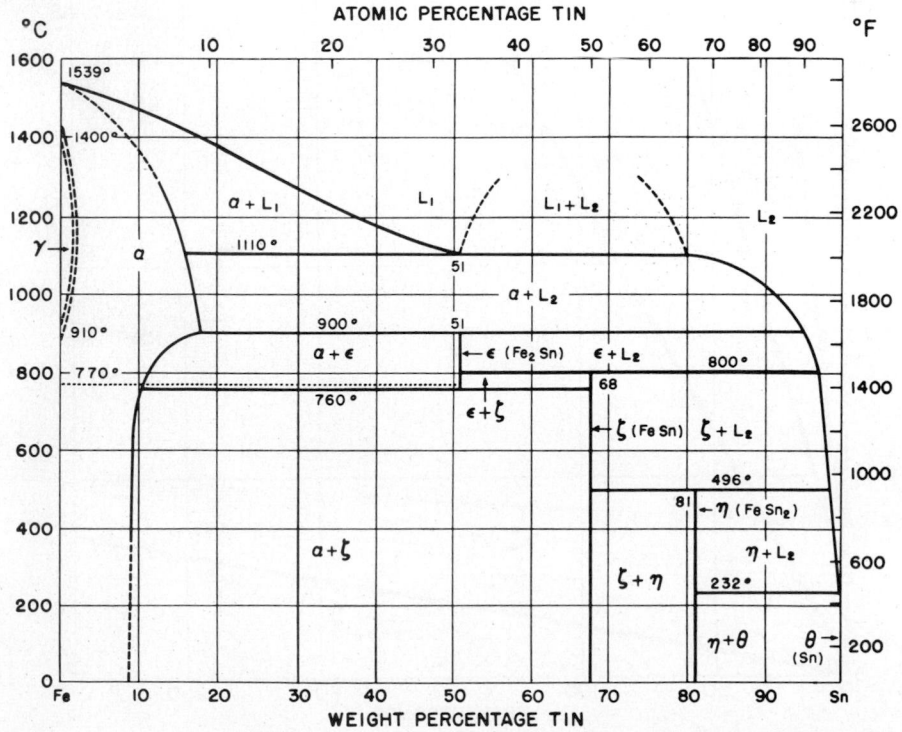

FIG. 34—11. Equilibrium diagram for the iron-tin system.

1. Fe_2Sn, referred to as the epsilon (ε) phase, which is stable between 1400° F (760° C) and 1652° F (900° C) but can, in the presence of sufficient tin, react at 1472° F (800° C) to form FeSn or zeta (ζ) phase.
2. FeSn, or zeta (ζ) phase which is stable at all temperatures below 1472° F (800° C) but which reacts with excess tin below 925° F (469° C) to form the compound $FeSn_2$, known as the eta (η) phase.
3. $FeSn_2$, or the eta (η) phase, which is stable below 925° F (496° C) and does not further react with tin.

Inasmuch as tinning operations are always carried out at temperatures considerably below 925° F (496° C), it follows that the alloy layer should contain both eta ($FeSn_2$) and zeta (FeSn) phases. The results of X-ray diffraction studies and chemical analyses indicate that the compound $FeSn_2$ predominates.

It has been demonstrated that the amount of tin-iron alloy formed is a function of time and temperature. The initial formation is extremely rapid (Figure 34—12). Although it is not obvious for the short period covered in Figure 34—12, the overall mechanism for alloy formation over a more extended period obeys a parabolic rate law which is indicative of a diffusion mechanism. The data shown in Figure 34—

12 are plotted according to the parabolic rate law, w^2 vs. t, where w is the quantity of alloy formed at time t. Linear plots are observed, but they do not go through the origin as might be expected if the parabolic rate law was obeyed from the beginning of the reaction ($t = 0$).

The thickness of alloy can be determined by electrostripping, by chemical stripping, by magnetic testing, or by metallographic cross-sectioning. The most commonly used is the electrochemical stripping method. A 4-square inch sample is attached to a suitable holder and immersed in a 1 N solution of hydrochloric acid containing a carbon electrode and a silver—silver-chloride reference electrode. The tin coating is stripped anodically at a constant predetermined stripping current. The potential difference between the specimen and the reference electrode is continuously measured by a potentiometer recorder during the stripping operation. The slope of this potential-time curve will change as the stripping proceeds from the surface, to the alloy layer, to the base metal. With proper cathode-anode geometry, the changes in slope occurring when the potential changes at the several interfaces are clearly discernible. The distances between the so-called end points, or points where the slope changes (measured parallel to the

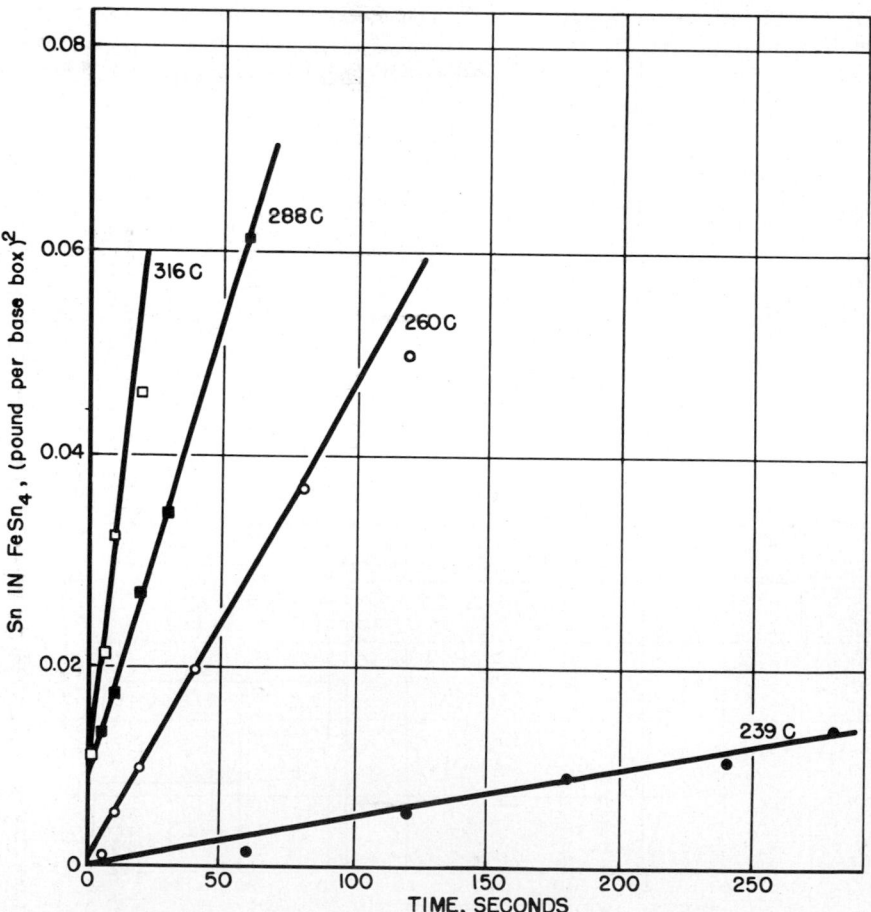

FIG. 34—12. Rate of growth of $FeSn_2$ at temperatures above the melting point of tin.

time axis), are measures of the thickness of the free tin and alloy layers.

The alloy layer on tin plate has a very definite pattern according to the manufacturing practice. Hot-dipped tin plate produced with the use of a zinc-chloride flux has a distinctive mottle shown in Figure 34—13. This pattern is the result of variation in thickness and crystal size of the alloy, the dark areas being thinner and finer grained than the light areas (Figures 34—14 and 34—15). Electrolytic tin plate (melted) has a smooth fine-grained alloy layer similar to the dark areas in coke tin plate alloy layers (Figures 34—16 and 34—17). Matte finish (unmelted) electrolytic tin plate does not have an alloy layer detectable by ordinary metallographic or chemical procedures. Heating matte finish plate at temperatures below the melting point of tin will result in formation of tin-iron alloy, the amount formed being dependent on the time and temperature.

The thickness and continuity of the tin-iron alloy layer are important with respect to tin-plate quality. An increase of thickness of the alloy layer in 0.25 lb. per base box electrolytic tin plate results in a decrease of thickness of the tin layer and may result in soldering difficulties. The continuity of the alloy layer is important from the corrosion standpoint in that the alloy layer acts as a barrier between the steel and the tin coating as discussed in Section 8.

Physically, the compound $FeSn_2$ is very hard and brittle and of itself cannot stand much bending. In commercial tin plate the alloy layer is very thin and is covered with a much thicker layer of ductile tin so that even sharp bending does not expose much of the steel base because the tin will bridge gaps in the alloy layer. With thick layers of $FeSn_2$, bending will cause breaks through the tin.

$FeSn_2$ crystals are also formed in the tin stacks for hot-dip tinning by reaction of the molten tin with the equipment. This accumulation is known as **tin dross** which is periodically cleaned out of the pots. The tin dross is heavier than the molten tin and settles to the bottom but, because of the agitation by sheets passing through, small particles may become imbedded in the tin coating, resulting in coating defects known as **scruff.**

The Tin Layer—As seen in the photomicrographs, the tin layer is considerably thicker than the alloy layer. It is customary to estimate the thickness of the tin layer in terms of weight of tin per unit of area, rather than in terms of thickness measurements. Thus,

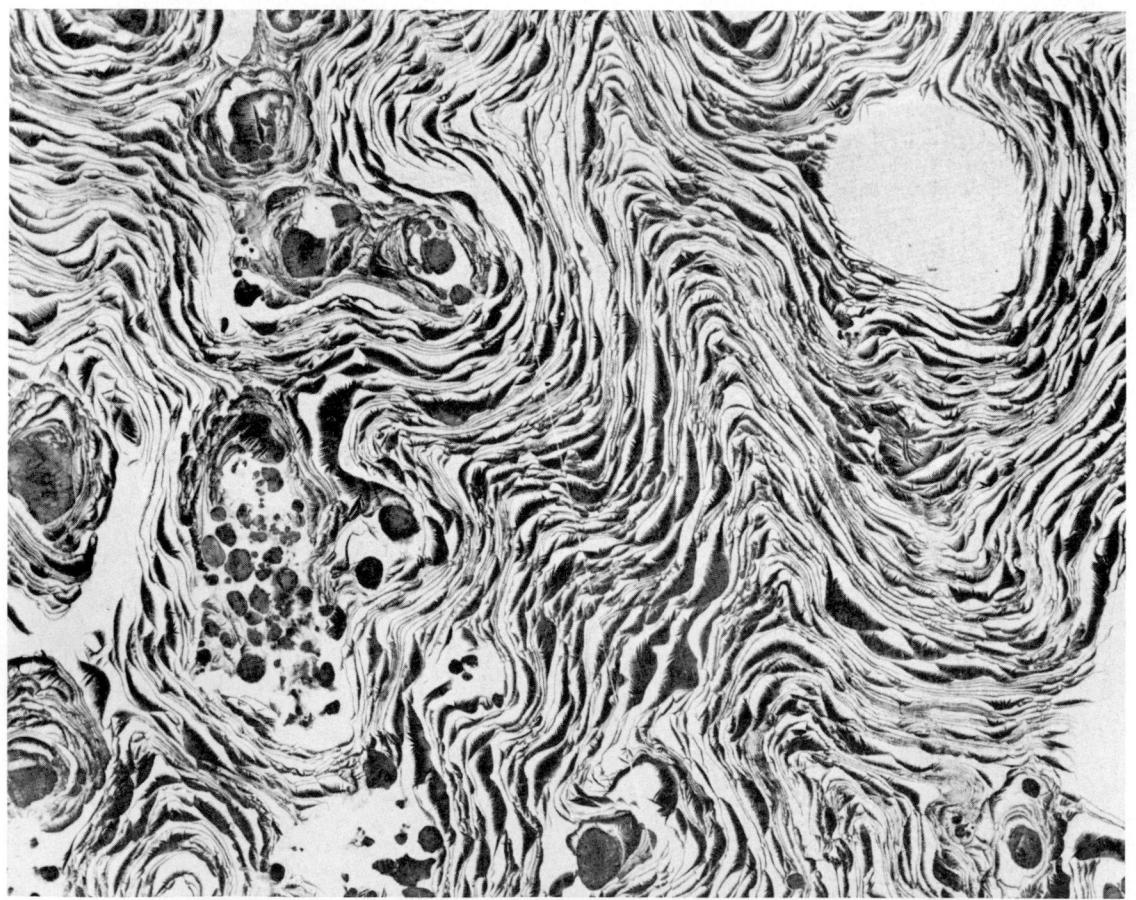

FIG. 34—13. Flux pattern on the surface of the steel base (interface of iron-tin alloy and steel) of commercial coke tin plate having a coating weight of 1.49 lb. per base box, after removal of both the tin and the iron-tin alloy. Magnification: 3X.

coke tin plate will have on the average of 1.0 to 1.5 lb of tin per base box, equivalent to 1.0 to 1.5 lb spread over both surfaces of 31,360 square inches of steel. From the specific gravity of tin it is readily calculated that 1.0 lb per base box of tin represents an average thickness of 60 millionths of an inch on a surface. The actual thickness at specific areas may vary considerably from the average.

The weight of coating is usually estimated chemically by dissolving samples of known area in hydrochloric acid under non-oxidizing conditions and titrating the stannous tin to stannic tin with standard iodine or iodate solutions. Analytical textbooks give details of the procedure. Gravimetric stripping methods are also used but to lesser extent. Recent testing methods incorporate electrolytic methods for dissolving the tin followed by standard volumetric titrations. The use of X-ray or beta-ray gages for continuous determination of tin-coating weight has also

gained favor and a number of electrolytic-tinning lines are equipped with such gages for control purposes. Generally speaking, the tin plate from each producing unit is sampled periodically for tin-coating weight. Methods for determining tin-coating weights are presented in "Methods For Determination of Coating Weights of Tinplate" published by the American Iron and Steel Institute as part of "Contributions to the Metallurgy of Steel," December 1959.

Electrolytic tin plates are produced to much closer tolerances with respect to tin-coating weight than are possible for the hot-dipped tin plates and the spread in tin-coating weight is usually within 10 per cent of the average. Electrolytic coatings are capable of fairly precise control, variations being due to fluctuations in current flow or variations in distance of the strip (cathode) from the individual tin anodes.

Tin plate usually has a bright, lustrous, mirror-like surface. The **luster** varies somewhat with the surface

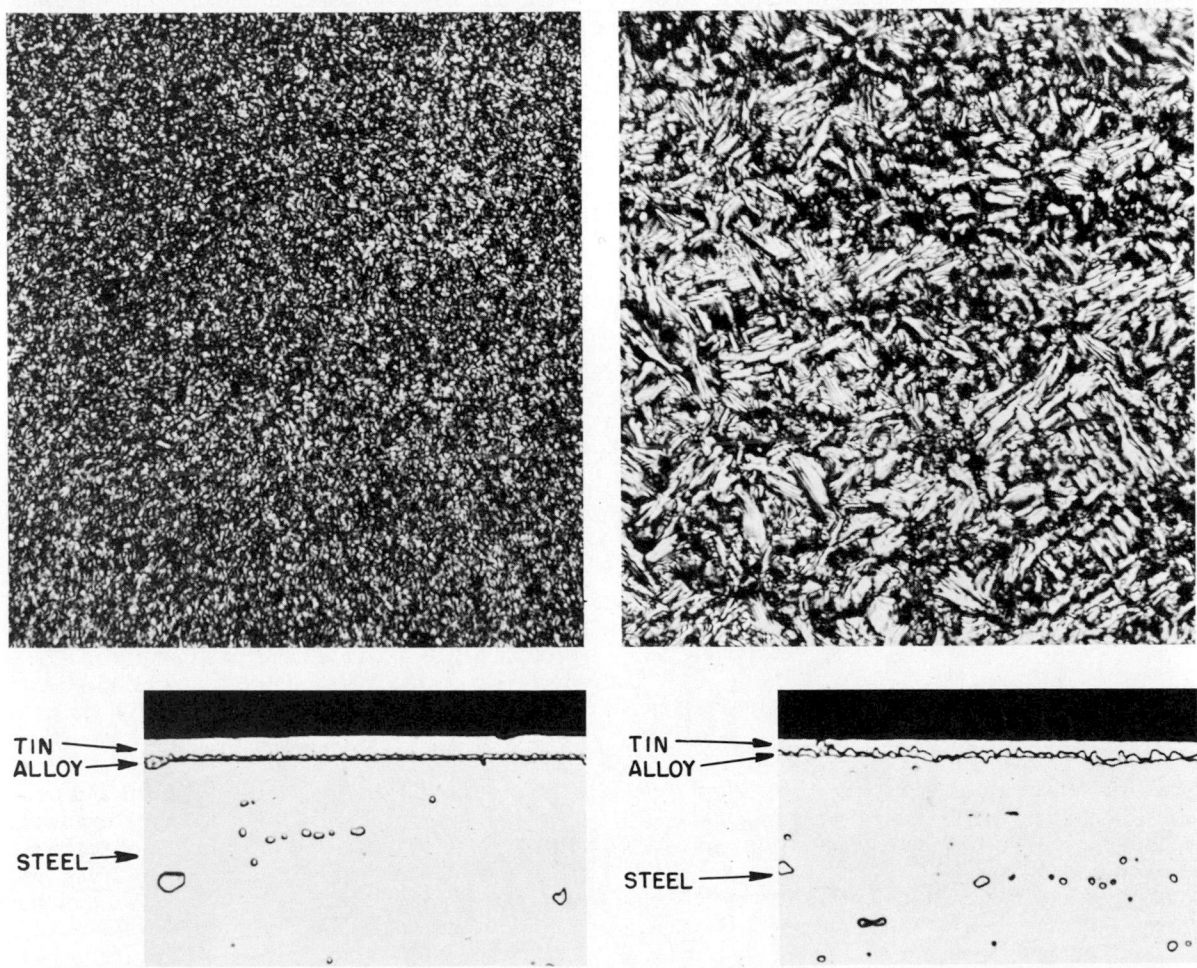

FIG. 34—14. (Above) Representative surface of iron-tin alloy layer on tin plate in dark areas, representing the interface between the iron-tin alloy and the tin of the coating, after removal of the tin portion of the coating. (Below) Representative cross-section through a dark area similar to that shown above, etched to show the tin coating and the iron-tin alloy layer. Magnification of both photomicrographs: 1000X.

FIG. 34—15. (Above) Representative surface of iron-tin alloy layer on tin plate in light areas, representing the interface between the iron-tin alloy and the tin of the coating, after removal of the tin portion of the coating. (Below) Representative cross-section through a light area similar to that shown above, etched to show the tin coating and the iron-tin alloy layer. Magnification of both photomicrographs: 1000X.

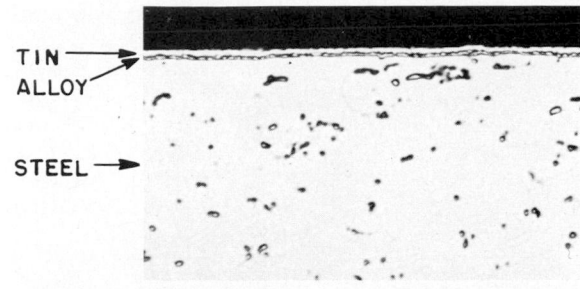

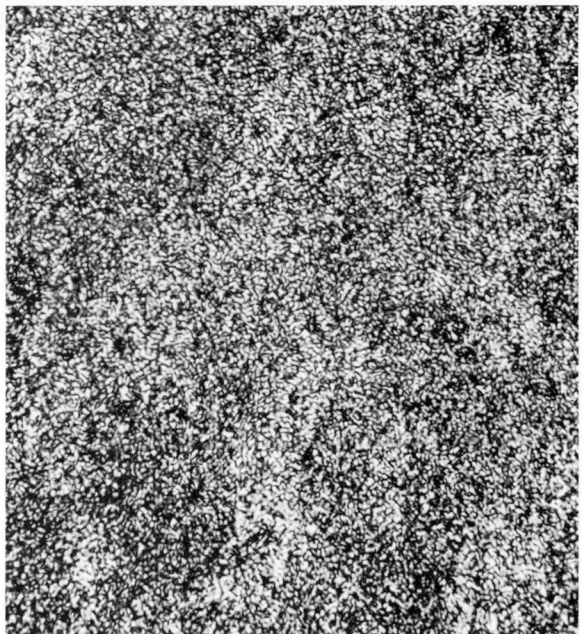

Fig. 34—16. (Above) Cross-section representative of commercial melted electrolytic tin plate (coating weight, 0.56 lb. per base box), etched to show iron-tin alloy layer. (Below) Unetched surface of iron-tin alloy layer (interface between iron-tin alloy layer and tin coating) after removal of the tin portion of the coating shown above. The surface of the iron-tin alloy has a pebbly appearance, indicating that it is not of uniform thickness. Magnification: 1000X for both photomicrographs.

finish of the steel base. Rough base finish will result in poorer luster than smooth base finish. The luster is also affected by the thickness of the tin coating. Heavy tin coatings, as on charcoal tin plates, have bright luster irrespective of base-metal roughness. The smoothness of the tin deposit on electrolytic plate also affects the luster.

Mild etching of the tin coating reveals the tin-crystal pattern which may take a variety of shapes. This pattern is evident on the interior of all non-lacquered cans which have contained fruits or vegetables and can also be seen on unetched surfaces when viewed under polarized light. The size of the tin crystal can only be partially controlled by the rate of quenching. Slow cooling such as is present in hot dip tinning produces a massive crystal whereas rapid cooling, as by water quenching in the electrolytic plating lines produces smaller crystals. This is illus-

trated in Figure 34—18. By control of the temperature of the quench water larger crystals can be obtained on electrolytic tin plate. Cleanliness of the steel strip surface prior to electrotinning affects the tin crystal size with larger tin crystals resulting from cleaner strip. Electrolytic tin plate with large tin crystals tends to show better internal corrosion resistance particularly when packed with the mildly acid fruits.

The tin coating, even when as heavy as 6 lb. per base box, is not continuous and microscopic areas of steel and alloy are exposed through the tin. The areas where steel is exposed are known as **pores.** The porosity of tin plate has been the subject of considerable research and a number of methods for indicating the degree of porosity have been developed: details of the procedures are summarized in International Tin Research Institute Bulletin, Series A, No. 7.

W. E. Hoare reports that the total area of iron exposed in pores is only about 0.7 sq. mm. per square meter of surface. The satisfactory commercial service of tin plate for fruit containers shows that despite these minute pores, the tin coating has excellent protective properties. This will be discussed more fully under resistance to corrosion.

The Tin Oxide Layer—An extremely thin oxide film is formed on tin plate upon contact with air, and although the film exerts some protective action, it can grow to the point where it becomes visible as a result of the development of interference colors beginning with yellow, then blue, and purple under very severe conditions of exposure. (The oxide formed on pure tin at temperatures as low as 167° F has been identified by electron diffraction patterns as alpha stannous oxide.) The growth of the oxide film may be expedited by lacquer-baking operations or by warehouse storage in areas of high temperature and humidity. The Gulf Coast and West Coast are among the most critical storage areas.

The visible oxide film (yellow discoloration) is objectionable not only from the appearance standpoint but also because it can cause poor adhesion of lacquer and lithographing ink and adversely affect solderability. Thus, it is necessary that the tin-plate surface be stabilized to inhibit oxide-film growth. Stabilization of tin-plate surfaces by chemical and electrochemical treatments in solutions of various chemicals has been studied extensively, and as a result a number of treatments have been developed. The protective treatment utilized must be readily applied and controlled, and compatible with the lacquers involved, without being visible or affecting container performance or solderability. Because of these broad restrictions, no individual treatment is satisfactory for all applications.

The commercial solutions most commonly used for the treatment of tin-plate surfaces contain chromic acid, chromates, or dichromates. One of the most convenient is the chromic-acid treatment which was developed during the early days of the substitution of electrolytic tin plate for hot-dipped tin plate and is still in use today. The treatment involves the immersion of the tin plate in a hot (180° F) solution of chromic acid. Chromic-acid-treated tin plate pos-

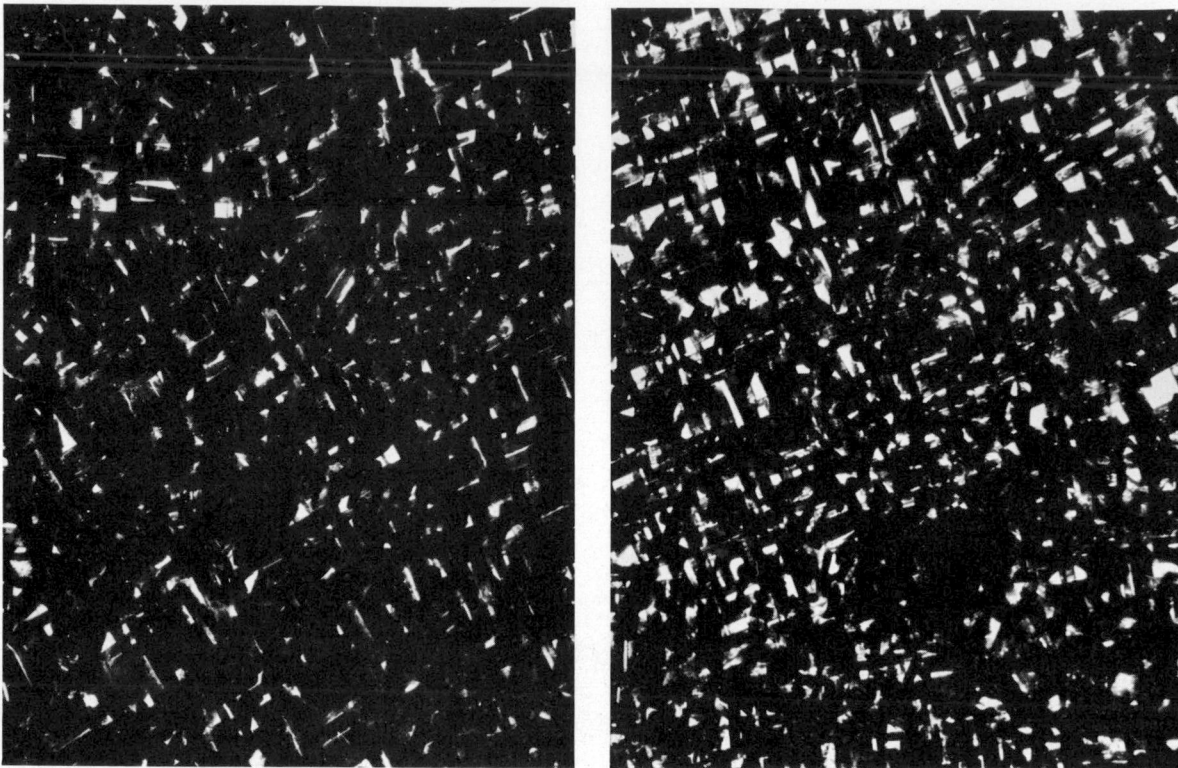

FIG. 34—17. Electron micrographs showing distribution of alloy-layer particles isolated from electrolytic tin plate. Tin removed electrolytically with NaOH; steel base removed with 1 M citric acid. Magnification: 10,000 ×, reduced ½ in reproduction.

sesses satisfactory lacquerability and exhibits improved resistance to discoloration over untreated tin plate but may not be suitable for prolonged storage. Electrochemical treatments in dichromate-phosphate solutions in which the tin plate is successively the cathode and the anode are also utilized. Such treatments yield lacquerability and storage-stability properties similar to those obtained with the chromic-acid treatment.

Electrochemical treatments in solutions containing only dichromate effectively inhibit oxide growth on tin plate for long storage periods and generally exhibit satisfactory lacquerability. Furthermore, they possess improved resistance to sulphide staining. A cathodic-anodic treatment in the dichromate solution yields storage stability and sulphide-stain resistance slightly superior to that obtained with a cathodic treatment but the latter is more satisfactory from the lacquering standpoint.

The Oil Film and Its Application—It has been

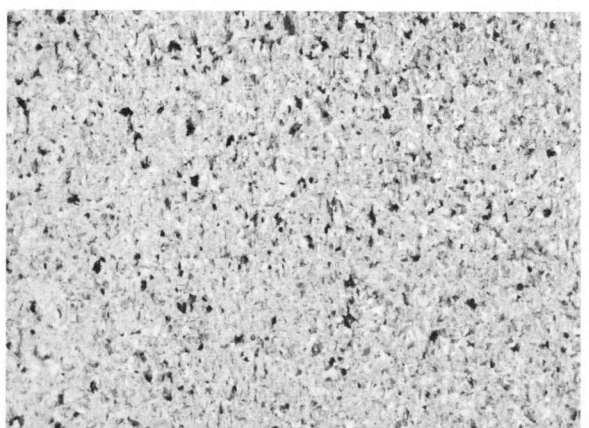 

FIG. 34—18. Effect of cooling rate on the comparative size of spangles produced on tin plate. Small-grain spangle at left resulted from rapid cooling (water quenching); larger spangle at right resulted from cooling at a slower rate (quenching in oil).

found necessary for tin plate to have a thin film of oil to permit feeding of sheets to fabricating equipment and to prevent scratching and abrasion during fabrication on automatic equipment. Too much oil, however, causes trouble if the tin plate is to be lacquered, because globules of oil immiscible in the lacquer film produce thin spots and uncoated areas. The oil, of course, must be edible since it comes in contact with food products. Cottonseed oil and di (2-ethylhexyl) sebacate (DOS) are normally used. Satisfactory oil films usually are about 0.10 to 0.30 gram per base box in weight. This means an oil film less than ten molecular layers in thickness. To illustrate the minute thickness of this oil film, imagine spreading one teaspoon

of salad oil uniformly over a wall 10 feet high and 2000 feet long. That is the equivalent of 0.10 gram per base box.

In the hot-dipping method, the tin plate is initially covered with oil which is later mostly removed in the wet washer. The final oil film thickness on the sheets is controlled by the branner. The oil content of the wheat bran used as a polishing medium is maintained at the desired level by periodic addition of **oil mids**, which is bran to which has been added fresh palm or cottonseed oil.

As mentioned earlier, both emulsion and electrostatic methods are used to apply oil to electrolytic tin plate.

SECTION 8

CORROSION RESISTANCE

To a large degree, the successful application of tin plate for containers depends on its corrosion resistance. Food products react with the tin coating and the base metal but the rate of reaction is generally sufficiently slow to permit fairly long storage or shelf life. The type of corrosion that takes place depends on the nature of the corrosive media. Thus, the corrosion problem can be divided into:

A. Atmospheric corrosion—rusting.
B. Discoloration of the interior of the container, as by etching due to food acids, or blackening by food sulphides.
C. Hydrogen-producing corrosion by contents of cans giving rise to **swells** or **hydrogen springers** in which the pressure of the evolved gas bulges the ends of the cans, thereby making them unmerchantable. In some cases, the cans may perforate.

Atmospheric Corrosion—Tin plate is very durable in dry air but all tin plate will rust eventually in the atmosphere, especially when moisture is present. The amount of external rusting depends, in large measure, on the porosity of the tin coating and the resulting area of steel base exposed. Under conditions involving moisture and oxygen, the exposed iron behaves as an anode and the tin as a cathode (see that part of Chapter 33 dealing with "Theory of Corrosion"). Increasing the thickness of the tin coating reduces the rusting, by reducing porosity. Rust resistance of tin plate can be somewhat controlled also by the nature of the tin-oxide film and the presence of oil. The composition of the steel base also has some bearing on rust resistance under certain conditions.

Discoloration of the Interior of Cans—When foods rich in sulphur-containing proteins are packed in plain tin cans (that is, without lacquer), it is generally noted that the inside of the can is stained purple, brown or black. This stain is tin sulphide and is in no way harmful. The usual method of preventing this type of corrosion is by lacquering, especially with zinc-oxide-impregnated lacquers. The sulphur reacts with the zinc oxide to form zinc sulphide which is white and not noticed in the can. Sulphide blackening

may also be prevented by a surface-filming treatment as mentioned under the section discussing the tin-oxide layer in an earlier part of this chapter.

In some mildly corrosive foods such as evaporated milk, localized detinning or dark staining may occur if the tin-oxide film is not soluble in the food product. This localized detinning may be prevented by electrochemically treating the tin plate in a solution of sodium carbonate.

The etching of the tin plate by food products is no indication of spoilage. All food products react with tin, some very slowly and others more rapidly. Spinach and other greens, rhubarb and squash are rapid detinners. These products are frequently packed in lacquered containers.

Hydrogen-Producing Corrosion—The usefulness of tin plate for food-container manufacture depends largely on its resistance toward the formation of hydrogen "swells" or perforations.

The corrosion of tin-plate containers by food products is a complex problem and the state of our knowledge is still largely empirical. There are many factors affecting the rate at which tin plate corrodes. Major factors include:

1. Type of food product.
2. Packing procedure used in canning.
   a. The initial vacuum.
   b. The headspace volume.
   c. Use of inhibitors.
3. The storage conditions.

1. Food Product—Food can be roughly divided into three classes with respect to corrosiveness:

Most Corrosive—This group includes the highly colored fruits and berries. They are generally packed in lacquered containers because tin has a reducing action on the anthocyanin pigments which results in bleaching of the color. The acidity and pH (intensity of acidity) of the food product is no criterion of its corrosivity. In fact, corrosivity can often be reduced by adding an organic acid, as by adding lemon juice to dried prunes in syrup. Sulphur in very small amounts markedly accelerates corrosion of tin cans by certain products. Spray residue on the fruit or contaminated sugar have been found to be the source of sulphur responsible for rapid corrosion failures in some instances.

Mildly Corrosive—This group includes the bland fruits such as peaches, pears, apricots and the citrus juices from grapefruit and oranges. The mildly corrosive fruits are generally packed in plain (not lacquered) tin cans.

Slightly Corrosive—This group includes the vegetables and meat products which normally do not produce hydrogen springers in the time required to merchandise the products.

2. *Food-Packaging Procedure*—The canning procedure is carefully controlled to provide maximum shelf life. Cans are sealed under a sufficient vacuum to assure maximum exclusion of oxygen because the presence of oxygen within the can markedly accelerates corrosion. The vacuum is obtained either thermally or mechanically. In the former procedure the cans are sealed at as high a temperature as feasible, normally above 165° F. At this temperature, water has an appreciable vapor pressure so that the atmosphere immediately above the liquid level of the can is largely water vapor which displaces the air that would normally be present. Upon cooling the can, the water vapor condenses, the contents shrink, increasing the headspace volume somewhat and a vacuum is produced within the can. Mechanical methods of vacuumizing involve evacuating the chamber of the seal-

ing machine in which the cans are sealed by a vacuum pump or sucking the air out of the headspace of the filled can with a jet of steam passing over the end of the container at the moment of attaching the lid. Mechanical vacuumizing eliminates preheating of the contents.

The headspace volume also affects the rate of corrosion by acting as a hydrogen reservoir. Overfilled cans require much less hydrogen to dissipate the vacuum and build up a pressure within the can than do cans with normal headspace. Underfilled cans, however, are prohibited by Federal statutes.

3. *Storage Conditions*—The temperature of storage of packed cans profoundly affects the corrosion rate as, indeed, temperature affects the rate of most chemical reactions. The higher the storage temperature the shorter is the pack life. Cans of fruit which would normally last four years at 70° F might last only a year or less at 100° F sustained storage temperature.

Characteristics of Tin Plate Affecting Its Corrosion —The resistance of tin plate to corrosion by food varies considerably according to the methods of manufacture.

Fundamentally, the corrosion of a tin can is the corrosion of the steel-tin couple as modified by the tin-iron alloy layer. In the region of the pores in the tin coating, local electrolytic cells are formed when the tin plate is in contact with an electrolyte. Depending upon the environment, either the steel exposed

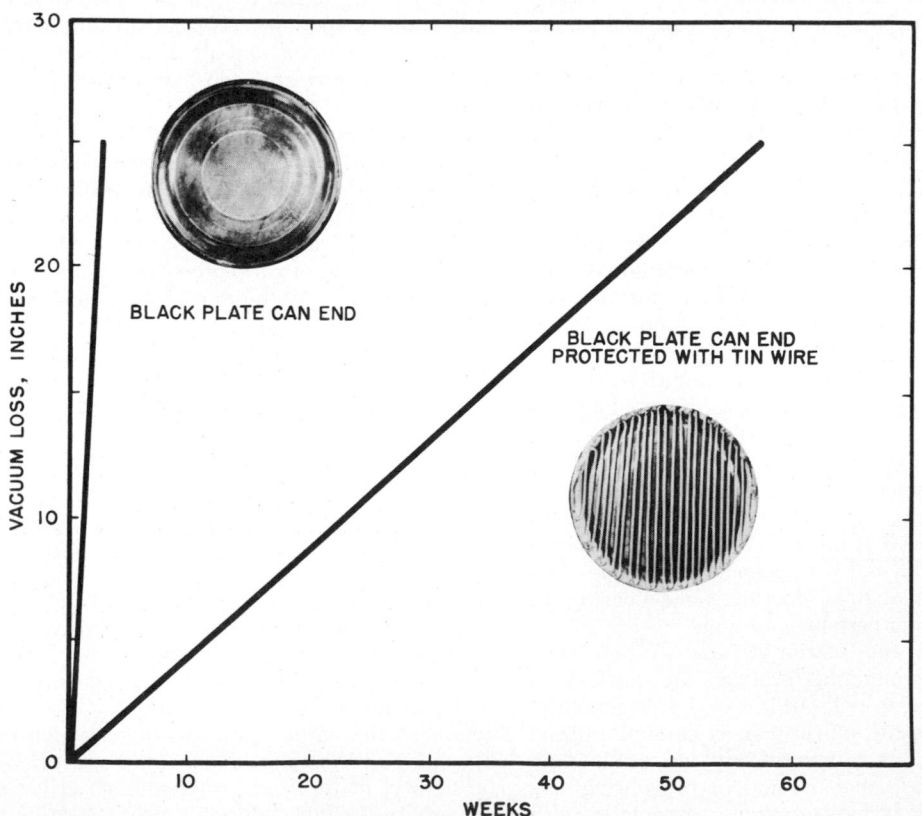

FIG. 34—19. Chart comparing results of prune-pack test on (upper left) can with black-plate end, and (lower right) similar can with black-plate end protected with tin wire, illustrating cathodic protection of steel by tin under the conditions of the test.

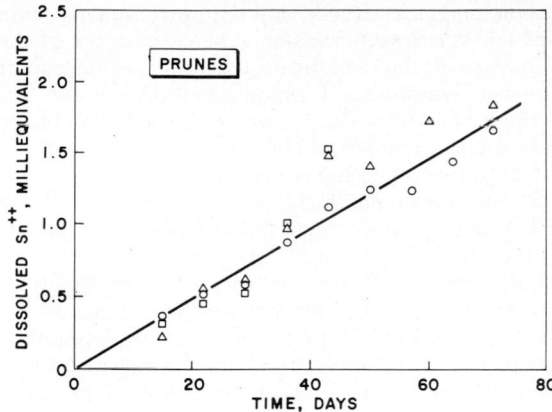

FIG. 34—20. Tin-dissolution curves for various tin plates represented by containers packed with prunes.

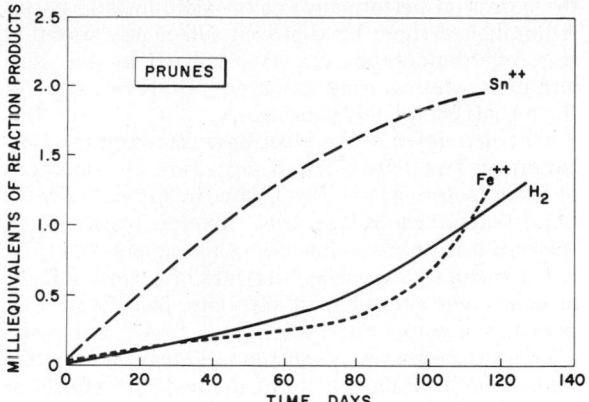

FIG. 34—22. Reaction products for corrosion of tin-plate containers packed with prunes.

through the pores in the tin coating or the surrounding tin may behave as the anode. Generally speaking, tin is anodic to steel under the normal conditions existing in a can closed so as to have a minimum amount of oxygen present, and the protection afforded the steel by the tin as affected by the tin-iron alloy layer is responsible for the excellent performance of tin-plate containers. The amount of protection that the tin provides to steel is illustrated by Figure 34—19, which compares the prune-pack performance of cans with plain black-plate can ends with black-plate ends protected with tin wire.

Extensive study by numerous investigators has helped to clarify the mechanism by which various foods corrode tin plate. Much of the work had involved accelerated-corrosion tests with prunes in water as the test medium but more recently attention has been given to accelerated tests with grapefruit juice. This work has been concerned with the role of the steel base, the tin-iron alloy layer, and the tin coating, as well as with evolution and diffusion of hydrogen in tin-plate containers. Obviously, the nature of the food product packed in tin-plate containers is quite important.

In acid food products such as prunes or prune juice which contain depolarizers, all tin plates detin at

about the same rate, and increased corrosion resistance can be obtained in unlacquered cans by increased tin-coating weights (see Figure 34—20). Hydrogen is not evolved in these cans until insufficient tin remains to cathodically protect the steel base. In other acid food products such as grapefruit juice, it has been observed that the rate of tin solution is a function of the particular lot of tin plate involved and that as tin goes into solution hydrogen is evolved (see Figure 34—21). Thus, in these instances, increasing the tin-coating weight beyond a certain limit will not result in improved corrosion resistance. The relationships between tin, evolved hydrogen, and iron in prunes and in grapefruit juice are shown in Figures 34—22, and 34—23.

Analyses of various food products stored in unlacquered cans show as much as 120 parts per million of tin after about a year's storage at room temperature. Tin pickup from lacquered cans is very much lower, averaging 10 to 30 parts per million according to Hirst and Adam (see "Bibliography" at end of chapter). The iron content of food in cans which have a good vacuum even after prolonged storage is invariably low, less than 20 parts per million.

Considerable attention has been given to the development of accelerated tests to aid in predicting

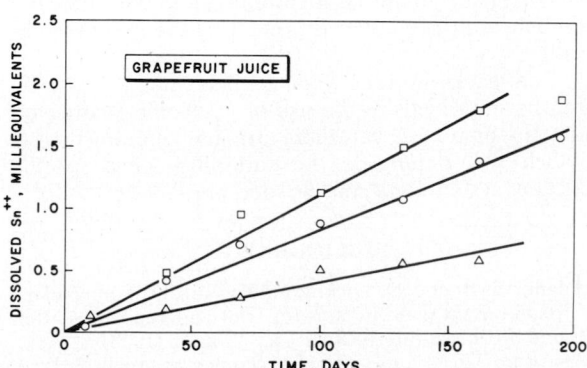

FIG. 34—21. Tin-dissolution curves for various tin plates represented by containers packed with grapefruit juice.

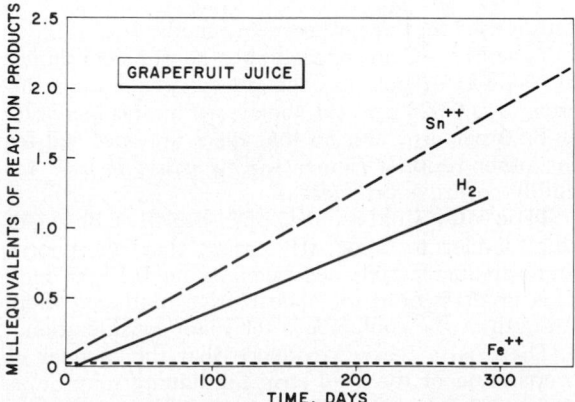

FIG. 34—23. Reaction products for corrosion of tin-plate containers packed with grapefruit juice.

the corrosion performance of tin plate in food packs. A number of these have proved sufficiently useful in this regard that they are now utilized by the steel and can-manufacturing industries. However, none of the tests is completely satisfactory.

Characteristics of the Steel Base Affecting the Corrosion of Tin Plate—The composition and methods of manufacture of the steel base are probably more important in controlling the corrosion resistance of the resulting tin plate than any other factors.

Hartwell, by experimental packs of corrosive fruits in cans from many lots of tin plate, has shown that phosphorus, copper and silicon may have pronounced effects on corrosion resistance, whereas, within the limits usually found in tin-plate steel, the effects of carbon and sulphur are not of commercial significance. Phosphorus and copper have a profound effect on the service life of enameled (lacquered) cans whereas silicon has a significant effect with plain cans. Increasing amounts of phosphorus and silicon are detrimental to the service life of containers, while copper increases or decreases the corrosion resistance, depending on the product packed. The detrimental effects of copper usually appear more serious than the benefits derived from its presence. Therefore, tin plate made from a steel base low in phosphorus (0.015 per cent maximum), copper (0.06 per cent maximum) and silicon (residual) is desirable for containers for the strongly corrosive products.

Container manufacturers order tin plate according to the type of food product packed. The following steel grades are in general use:

Type L—Cold-reduced open-hearth steel containing:

Element	Per Cent (Max.)
Carbon	0.12
Manganese	0.60
Phosphorus	0.015
Sulphur	0.050
Silicon	0.010
Copper	0.06
Chromium	0.06
Nickel	0.04
Molybdenum	0.05

This is used for the most corrosive foods.

Type MR—Cold-reduced open-hearth steel similar to Type L except that the phosphorus limit is increased to 0.020 per cent, the copper limit is increased to 0.20 per cent and no tolerances are specified for the other residual elements. This grade is used for mildly corrosive products.

Type MC—Cold-reduced open-hearth or Bessemer steel similar to Type MR except that phosphorus limits are increased to between 0.04 and 0.15 per cent. This grade is used for noncorrosive products where strength of the container is the main consideration.

There is increasing evidence that the manner of preparation of the steel strip for tinning may be as significant in controlling ultimate corrosion resistance as composition of the steel. Fairly rapid cooling after hot rolling and thorough annealing in dry, low-carbon and low-oxygen content atmosphere favor the highest corrosion resistance.

In essence, the metallurgical problem of improving corrosion resistance of tin plate resolves itself into methods of slowing down the attack on the steel base. This can be accomplished by:

1. Improved quality of steel base.
2. Heavier tin coatings.
3. Coating with proper type of lacquer in certain cases.

Lacquered Tin Plate—Lacquered cans are normally fabricated from tin plate that has been lacquered in sheet form. In the United States, the trade refers to the lacquers as enamels. The lacquers vary in composition but are either organic solutions of resins or mixtures of resins and vegetable oils, the resins being either naturally occurring or synthetic. They may be clear or pigmented.

Lacquered cans are normally used to prevent the bleaching of highly colored fruits or to prevent the sulphide staining caused by sulphur-bearing foods. Considerable success in the reduction of hydrogen swells has, however, attended the use of lacquered cans for certain food products. During World War II, considerable quantities of 0.50 lb. per base box electrolytic tin plate, and even black plate, protected by lacquers, gave satisfactory service life for meat and vegetable products. The use of lacquered 0.25 lb. per base box electrolytic tin plate has increased substantially, so that currently it accounts for a major portion of cans.

The corrosion process in lacquered cans is considerably more complex than in plain cans. The type of lacquer and methods of application may be as important as the quality of the tin plate used. Generally, improved service life may be obtained by more continuous coverage, as by spray or flush lacquering the fabricated cans.

Cracks in the lacquer coating expose minute areas of tin and iron. At these areas the tin tends to protect the iron, but because of the limited amount of tin exposed, it is soon used up and corrosion of the tin plate may be found in areas which have no apparent discontinuities in the lacquer film. Indeed, lacquered cans of fruit, which have abnormally long service life frequently show pronounced etching of the tin beneath the lacquer indicating that lacquer films may be acting as semiporous membranes and the corroding tin beneath the lacquer is protecting the iron cathodically.

Trial packs are used to determine whether pack life can be improved by the use of a specific lacquer on the tin plate. As yet there are no laboratory tests which will determine the suitability of a specific lacquer system for a specific food product.

BIBLIOGRAPHY

Adam, W. B. and D. Dickinson, The substitution of black plate for tin plate in cans for fruit and vegetables. Iron and Steel Institute Journal 152: 195-205 (1945).

Am. Can Co. Canned food reference manual; 3rd ed. N. Y. The Company, 1949.

Am. Iron and Steel Institute, Steel products manual: tin mill products. N. Y., The Institute, 1960.

Am. Society for Metals, Metals handbook 8th ed. Cleveland, The Society, 1961.

Brighton, K. W. and Pearce, W. E. Progress on Metal Containers. Presented at Fourth International Congress on Canned Foods, Berlin, Germany, May 1961.

Britton, S. C. Corrosion resistance of tin and tin alloys. Middlesex, England. Tin Research Institute, 1952.

Boggs, W. E., Trozo, P. S. and Pellisier, G. E. Oxidation of Tin, Part II, Journal of the Electrochemical Society, Vol. 108, No. 1, pages 13 to 23, January 1961.

Cooper, W., Electrolytic tinplating. Assn. of Iron and Steel Engineers, Yearly proceedings, 1943, p. 172-176.

Corrosion of Iron and Tin, A Symposium, Corrosion, Vol. 17, No. 2, pages 93 to 124, February 1961.

   Contents:

   Carter, P. R. and Butler, T. J. Accelerated Corrosion Test for Tinplate in Grapefruit and Other Juices.

   Kamm, G. G., and Willey, A. R. Corrosion Resistance of Electrolytic Tinplate, Part I.

   Kamm, G. G., Willey, A. R., Beese, R. E., and Krickle, J. L. Corrosion Resistance of Electrolytic Tinplate, Part II.

   Koehler, E. L. Coupling Shift and Hydrogen Overvoltage in the Protection of Steel by Tin.

   Button, S. C., and Bright, K. Influence of Area of the Steel Component On Behavior of a Tin-Steel Couple.

Donelson, J. G., Oxide films; their effect on tinplate. National Lithographer 58: 36-37, 83-86 (Aug. 1951)

Factors influencing shelf life of canned foods. Proc. of the technical sessions at the 48th annual convention of the National Canners Assn., Feb. 19-23, 1955; Information Letter, Convention Issue (no. 1526) Feb. 28, 1955. 15pp.

Frankenthal, R. P. and Loginow, A. W., Kinetics of the Formation of the Iron-Tin Alloy FeSn₂. Journal of the Electrochemical Society, Vol. 107, No. 11, pgs. 920 to 923, November 1960.

Frankenthal, R. P., Carter, P. R., and Laubscher, A. N. The Mechanism of Corrosion of Tinplate by Various Food Products. Agricultural and Food Chemistry, Vol. 7, No. 6, pages 441 to 442, June 1959.

Hartwell, R. R., Certain aspects of internal corrosion in tinplate containers. Advances in food research, vol. III, p. 327-383. N. Y., Academic Press, 1951.

Hartwell, R. R., Corrosion resistance of tinplate—influence of steel base composition on service life of tinplate containers. Am. Society for Metals, Surface treatment of metals, p. 69-107. Cleveland, The Society, 1941.

Hirst, F. and W. B. Adam, Hydrogen swells in canned fruits. (Monograph no. 1) Campden, England, Univ. of Bristol Research Station 1937.

Hoare, W. E. and E. S. Hedges, Tinplate. London, Edward Arnold, 1945.

Hoare, W. E. Tinplate Handbook. Tin Research Institute, 3rd Ed. 1958.

Hopper, J. H., Electrical equipment for continuous electrolytic tinplating. Assn. of Iron and Steel Engineers, Yearly proceedings, 1943, p. 128-140.

International Congress on Canned Foods, 2nd Paris, Oct. 1951, Texts of papers presented, summary of discussions and resolutions. Paris. Permanent International Committee on Canned Foods (mimeographed).

Johnston, S. S. and G. C. Jenison, Electro Tinplating of wide steel strip at high speed. Am. Electroplaters' Society Proc., 1946, p. 102-115.

Lippert, T. W., Food in cans. Iron Age 149: 29-44 (April 20, 1942).

Mantell, C. L., Tin: its mining production technology and applications; 2nd ed. N. Y., Reinhold, 1949.

McArthur, D. A. Electrolytic Tinplate, Second Ed., 1959, The Wean Engineering Company, Inc.

Neish, R. A. and Donelson, J. G. The Stabilizing of Tinplate Surfaces. Food Technology, Vol. XIV, No. 1, pages 37-42, January 1960.

Pellissier, G. E., and Wicker, E. E., X-Ray Tin Coating Gage. Electrical Manufacturing, May 1952.

Pilling, N. B. and R. E. Bedworth, The oxidation of metals at high temperatures. Journal Institute of Metals 29, 1923, p. 529.

Romig, O. E. Constitution of the iron-tin alloys. Metal Progress 42: 899-904 (1942).

Romig, O. E. and D. H. Rowland, Metallography of tin and tin coatings on steel. Metals and Alloys 13: 436-443 (1941).

Serra, G. and Perfetti, G. A. The Diffusion of Hydrogen Through Tinplate Containers Packed With Grapefruit Juice. Presented at Institute of Food Technologists. National Meeting, June 1962.

Stoll, P. E. Electron Microscopy of Tinplate. Special Technical Publication No. 262, American Society for Testing Materials, pages 73 to 76, (1959).

Stoltz, G. E., J. A. Hutcheson and R. M. Baker, Electric fusion of tinplate. Assn. of Iron and Steel Engineers, Yearly proceedings, 1943, p. 141-149.

Stone, M. D. The Rolling of Very Thin Tinplate. Special Report No. 67, British Iron and Steel Institute (London), 1960.

Symposium on tinplate for food containers (11th annual meetings, Institute of Food Technologists, June 18, 1951, N. Y.) Food Technology 5:385-413 (1951).

   Contents: Meneilly, R. B., Progress in the tinplate industry; Martin, E. D., Significance of continuous production methods in the manufacture of tinplate; Hartwell, R. R. Corrosion factors related to the use of tinplate for food containers; Stevenson, A. E., Effect of progress in tinplate manufacture on the use of tinplate for cans for foods.

Vaurio, V. W., Some aspects of corrosion of tinplate by prunes. Corrosion 6: 260-267 (1950).

CHAPTER 35

Long Terne Sheets And Terne Plate

Long Terne Sheets—Long terne sheets, or **long ternes,** are steel sheets that have been coated by immersion in a bath of terne metal, which is an alloy of lead and tin. Sheets coated with terne metal are duller in appearance than sheets coated with tin alone, and it is this feature of the product that gave rise to the name "terne"—meaning "dull." Long terne sheets fall within the dimensional ranges covered by the uncoated sheet commodities. In commercial practice, they seldom are manufactured thinner than 0.014 inch, thicker than 0.125 inch, or wider than 48 inches. Long ternes occupy a relatively minor position tonnage-wise in the sheet business, but offer a combination of properties that make them very suitable for such applications as air cleaners and fuel tanks. Long ternes are produced both in the form of single sheets and in continuous coils.

Long Terne Coatings—The composition and weight of long terne coatings were drastically restricted in 1941, when the normal supplies of tin were cut off by World War II. Prior to that period, it was customary to coat with terne metal containing approximately 80 per cent lead and 20 per cent tin, although this composition was not mandatory and could be varied for specific applications. Since the object of terne coating is to apply to the steel base an inexpensive, corrosion-resistant coating of lead, the percentage of tin used need only be sufficient to obtain a smooth, continuous coating. Lead alone does not alloy with iron, so that it is necessary to incorporate a certain amount of another element, in this case tin, which alloys readily with the steel base and forms a solid solution with the lead. It was formerly thought impractical to coat with terne metal compositions containing much less than 15 per cent tin but experience gained during the war period proved otherwise, for during this time, when government restrictions limited the amount of tin in long terne metal to 10 per cent maximum, terne coatings of entirely satisfactory quality were produced. It is to be noted, however, that decreasing the amount of tin in the coating alloy necessitates higher pot temperatures and lessens the alloying or "wetting" properties of the terne metal.

Prior to 1946, the coating weights of long terne sheets were designated by pounds per double base box, a term used in the tin plate and short terne industry, and never logically applicable to long ternes. With the exception of roofing long terne sheets, which are still produced to coating weights of 20, 30, or 40 pounds per double base box in specific gages and sizes, this designation is no longer used. Long terne sheets are now ordered to a coating weight specified in ounces per square foot, with weights ranging from "commercial" (no minimum amount) to 0.55 ounces per square foot. The designation of terne coating weights in terms of ounces per square foot follows the practice used in designating coating weights of galvanized sheet, as long ternes are commonly made on equipment located in galvanizing shops. Table 35—I lists the various weights of coating commonly available and the applicable sheet gage numbers. Commercial coating is furnished unless a special coating weight is ordered. Long terne sheets with commercial coating are well-coated sheets but are not subject to any minimum coating test.

The thickness and nature of the coating are the most important factors governing the corrosion resistance of long terne sheets. Both lead and tin are highly corrosion resistant, and their combinations as used on long terne coatings also resist corrosion well. However, both lead and tin are cathodic to iron under most conditions of exposure, so that terne metal will actually accelerate corrosive action on the steel base when any portion of the steel surface becomes exposed to attack. Since a light coating has a greater tendency to form pinholes or other discontinuities than does a heavier coating, exposure of the base metal is minimized and corrosion resistance is increased as the thickness of the coating increases. However, even the most heavily coated ternes should be well-painted when maximum protection against corrosion is desired.

Table 35—I. Ordered Coating and Minimum Coating Weight Limits for Long Terne Sheets.

Weight (Oz. Per Sq. Ft.)			Applicable Sheet Gage Numbers	Nominal Coating, Lb. Per Double Base Box
	Minimum Coating			
Ordered Coating	By Sheet Weight Test	By Triple Spot Test		
Commercial	No Min.	No Min.	10 to 30	Commercial
0.35	0.30	0.26	16 to 30	9.00
0.45	0.38	0.34	18 to 30	12.00
0.55	0.47	0.41	20 to 30	15.00

Composition and Preparation of Steel Base—The steel base of long ternes may be provided on either a "commercial quality" or a "drawing quality" basis. In the former case, rimmed, capped, or semi-killed steel is generally used; in the latter, specially selected rimmed or aluminum-killed steels are provided, because of their superior ductility. All of these steels usually fall within the following composition limits:

Carbon (%)	Manganese (%)	Phosphorus (%)	Sulphur (%)	Silicon (%)
0.03-0.10	0.25-0.50	0.025 max.	0.050 max.	0.020 max.

Selection of the composition and treatment of the steel to be used for the base of long terne sheets is governed by the end use of the products to be fabricated from them and hence must take into consideration a number of factors, important among which are the customers' fabricating practices. Factors normally considered in addition to the usual requirements for flatness, finish, and weight of coating, are such forming hazards as breakage in deep drawing operations, fluting, stretcher strains, and the conditions under which the material is to be used. In this latter connection, for example, a copper content of 0.20 per cent minimum is usually recommended for applications involving corrosion hazards, such as in roofing.

The treatment accorded the steel base used in manufacture of long terne sheets depends upon the desired combination of gage, surface finish, and physical properties. It is basically identical with the treatment which would be given a cold rolled product manufactured for the same type of customers' fabricating operations. This material is rolled on continuous cold-reduction mills.

The continuous cold reduction process involves the use of lubricating solutions containing oil, the removal of which from the surface of the steel prior to annealing is of vital importance in producing a base metal which is to be terne coated. Any oil which remains upon the sheet or strip will decompose when heated to the annealing temperature. The relatively inert, carbonaceous residue which results can interfere seriously with the application of a smooth, continuous coating of terne metal, since these residues are not attacked to any appreciable degree by the pickling solutions commonly employed for descaling and cleaning the steel prior to terne coating. As a result, they prevent the terne metal from "wetting" or alloying with the steel base, causing rough coating or entirely bare areas where the film is particularly heavy. Some manufacturers make use of an electrolytic cleaning operation prior to annealing in order to prevent the formation of the "carbon smudge"; others cold reduce the base metal in thin mixtures of volatile water-soluble oil.

Cold-reduced product is usually box annealed since it is more economical than normalizing and the sheets or coils may be kept scale-free by using a deoxidizing atmosphere, thereby reducing the iron loss due to pickling. A temper rolling operation may be performed after annealing, but may be omitted on certain gages and applications wherein it is known that the customer's fabrication involves a deep-drawing opera-tion in which fluting or straining of the base metal is not objectionable. Final preparation of the base metal prior to coating may involve shearing coil product to sheet form on a flying shear unit, with or without surface inspection, and in these operations it is important that the sheets be kept free of oil or grease, for the reasons previously stated.

The cold-reduced and box-annealed (and perhaps temper rolled) material is pickled prior to coating. Hydrogen embrittlement of the base metal is a hazard and close control of the pickling operation is required to avoid deleterious effects.

All long ternes produced by United States Steel Corporation plants are manufactured by continuous processes and, where product in sheet form is required, the continuously coated coils are sheared into the required cut lengths. The coating of individual sheets is still practiced by some manufacturers: consequently, both the single-sheet and continuous processes will be discussed.

SINGLE-SHEET COATING PROCESSES

There are two methods generally used for applying terne metal to single sheets in the manufacture of long ternes. The chief objective of both of these methods is to bring the properly prepared surface of the steel base into contact with the molten terne metal, and to remove the coated sheets from the pot, under conditions that will assure a uniform distribution of the coating. In both methods the aim is to produce a continuous coating of terne metal as free of discontinuities as possible.

The **flux process**, as the name indicates, employs a flux of molten (or a water solution of) zinc chloride, or a solution of zinc chloride in hydrochloric acid, to remove any oxides of iron that may be present and also effect a rapid drying of the sheets. This latter feature makes it possible to use a coating machine similar to that used in the tin plate industry. In fact, the flux process is quite similar to the methods used in tinning, with the exception that the temperature of the terne pot is higher than that of the tin pot because of the higher melting points of the terne metal compositions. The terne pot temperatures commonly employed range from 620° to 680° F. The process is carried out in a "rigging" or machine which carries the sheet through the several steps of the process as follows: The pickled sheets are fed from water boshes or piles into rubber pinch rolls, which conduct them through a hydrochloric acid wash tank. The object of this acid dip is to remove the iron hydroxide which may have formed on the sheets subsequent to pickling. Another set of rubber pinch rolls squeezes excess acid from the sheet, and the entry rolls of the coating rigging carry the sheet into the flux box, where it is cleaned and dried. The sheet then passes downward through the molten terne metal, where the coating is applied, then upward through a bath of oil (palm oil, fish oils, mineral oils, or combinations thereof) floating on top of the metal, being conveyed through the oil by the oil rolls. The oil bath on the exit side of the metal bath, in addition to protecting the surface of the molten metal bath from oxidation, tends to keep the coating on the sheet in a molten condition and thus allows the oil rolls to control the distribution and thickness of the coating. As the coated sheets leave the oil bath they are conducted to the conveying system of the cooling and cleaning train.

In the **combination process**, a coating machine using the flux process is followed by another machine of the same type but with oil substituted for the zinc chloride. This type of arrangement permits complete control over the coating conditions within the entire range of coating weights commonly available. Since most long ternes are ordered in the lighter coating weights, the bulk of the material produced is coated on a single unit by the flux process.

After the coating operation, the freshly coated sheets must be cooled sufficiently to permit cleaning without injury to the soft coating. Terne plate, because of a heavier steel base and higher temperature of the coating bath, requires more time than tin plate to cool to the proper temperature for cleaning, therefore special equipment is needed. In general, this equipment consists of a hooded conveyor against which blasts of cool air are directed from a distributor pipe. Control of the volume of air through the distributor main and branch tubes is effected by varying the speed of the blower and regulating the flow through the individual tubes by a system of dampers. The conveyor system carries the sheets in a horizontal position with both surfaces exposed to the cooling action of the air blast. This conveyor consists of a series of deeply hollowed rolls, sometimes referred to as double-cone sets, because each roll is so deeply concave that it resembles two cones mounted on a shaft with their apexes abutting. When a sheet passes over the conveyor only its edges are in contact with the rolls; and with the air distributors suitably arranged, both surfaces are equally exposed to the cooling action of the air blast.

Regardless of the coating process used, the terne plate emerges from the coating operation covered with oil. Part of this oil drips from the sheets as they pass over the cooling conveyor and is collected in a grease pan located under the conveyor, but the remainder must be removed with special cleaning equipment. Long terne sheets are produced with a "dry" or "bright" finish, and an "oil" finish. Sheets leaving the cleaning equipment practically free of oil are designated as dry finish, but if they carry an appreciable amount of oil, or are subsequently coated with oil, they are designated as oil finish.

The residual oil present on the surfaces of long terne sheets after coating is usually removed by a branner similar to that used on hot-dipped tin plate. Contrary to tin plate practice, however, the long terne branner is preceded by a pair of cloth squeezer rolls, which remove much of the heavy oil film before the sheet enters the regular branning operation. Middlings or sawdust may be used in the branner. Steel rolls thinly wound with flannel may be used at the exit end of the branner to exert a smoothing action on the surface when a bright finish is desired. For best results in cleaning, two branners are normally employed, one following the other. When oil finish is specified, oiling rolls may be inserted in the line to apply the desired amount of oil on the surface, or it may be accomplished as a separate operation in a regular oiling machine. Upon completion of cleaning, the sheets are ready for inspection by the inspectors stationed at the end of the line.

CONTINUOUS-STRIP PRODUCTION OF LONG TERNES

Continuous lines for the coating of strip steel with terne metal may be of the semi-continuous or the fully-continuous type. The semi-continuous line has only one payoff reel and one tension reel, which necessitates threading each individual coil through the line. The fully-continuous line is equipped with double payoff reels, welder, and looping towers or pits, which permit a continuous flow of strip through the coating unit.

The base metal for coating on continuous lines usually consists of cold reduced, box annealed and temper rolled coils. The treatment of the base metal prior to coating is identical to that given sheet product, with the exception that all the operations are accomplished in coil form. The pickling operation is performed in the line prior to the actual terne coating operation.

The equipment contained in a continuous coating line may vary from shop to shop, depending on numerous operating conditions and the preference of the manufacturers concerned. Essentially, the equipment and process involved are as follows: A coil holder, followed by a payoff reel, feeds the strip into a pinch-roll unit, which in turn is followed by a squaring shear and a welder if the process is fully continuous. The strip then enters an acid pickling tank, which may consist of a single-dip tank, wherein normal chemical pickling is effected, or which may be an electrolytic pickling unit; if the latter, it may be followed by a short non-electrolytic hydrochloric dip. In either case, the object of the operation is to provide a chemically clean surface for the effective application of the terne coating. If desired, provision may be made for an alkaline cleaner unit equipped with suitable rinsing and scrubbing facilities just ahead of the pickling tank. From the pickling unit the strip then enters a pinch roll unit which conveys it into the terne coating pot. Upon emerging from the pot, the strip is cooled and conveyed to the branner (vertical in modern installations) which removes the residual oil. At this point in a continuous line, provision may be made for shearing the strip into cut lengths, using a gage table, shear, and piler or, if the material is to be shipped in coil form, a shear for cutting out the weld and a tension reel are available to recoil the strip.

The process of continuous terne coating has several unique advantages. The first of these is the elimination of the intermittent operation characteristic of sheet pots, whereby a space of from 1 to 3 feet is left between each sheet as it passes through the line. The next distinct advantage is the uniformity of the coating that can be realized by having a continuous flow of the base metal through the coating rigging with no break in the operation. As has been indicated, the single-sheet method results in a heavier coating on the front and back ends, "entry" and "list" ends respectively, so that continuous coating makes more efficient use of a given quantity of coating metal. A disadvantage of the continuous process lies in the fact that it is less adaptable to producing small, varied types of orders since it is most efficient when used to produce coils of one coating weight. The operation of a continuous coil terne line is quite similar to a sheet unit and the principles of the coating technique are identical. Since it is not possible to make use of the sheet weight test as a routine check on coating weights on coils, the operator must rely on a determination made by electrical or chemical means. The final product may be shipped to the customer in coil form or may be sheared to sheets.

Recent developments in continuous terne coating have pointed toward the elimination of oil as a part of the coating operation. The use of oil entails a number of operating disadvantages, among which is the necessity of including a cleaning apparatus to remove excess oil from the coated strip. This operation can apparently be avoided by dispensing with oil finishing rolls and substituting partially submerged exit rolls, using a molten zinc chloride flux with ammonium bromide or ammonium chloride dissolved in it. The zinc chloride acts as a solvent for the ammonium bromide or ammonium chloride to prevent its dissipation by volatilization and makes the entire process quite similar to conventional galvanizing.

INSPECTION AND TESTING OF LONG TERNE SHEETS

The inspection of long terne sheets coated in single-sheet form normally takes place when they have completed their travel along the conveyor system, through the branners, and are being removed for piling into lifts. All but a small percentage of the sheets coated are **primes,** i.e., sheets free from any injurious defects recognized as such in the trade. However, even with the best practice and control of processing variables, a certain percentage of the sheets from the terne pots have defects which are of such a nature or magnitude that they are classified as **rejects. Recoats** are sheets containing defective areas which may be reconditioned to prime grade by rerunning them through the terne pot a second time. **Scrap sheets,** which are those totally unsuitable for reconditioning or salvaging, are normally the result of cobbles in the rigging of the terne pot itself or in the branners. The terne coating from scrap sheets is reclaimed by placing them in palm oil, heating to the proper temperature, and allowing sufficient time for most of the coating to run off and collect in the bottom of the container.

The defects of long terne sheets may be classified into three general types, depending on the basic origin of the defect. These types are as follows:

(1) Those due to an imperfection in the steel base.
(2) Those due to faulty processing of the material prior to the coating operation.
(3) Those due to faulty coating practice.

The major defects encountered in category (1) are blisters and seams, the latter sometimes being designated as "skin laminations" or "slivers." As in galvanized sheet production, the blister defect occurs most frequently. The basic causes and the method of formation of blisters and seams, as discussed in the chapter on galvanized sheets, apply also in the case of long terne sheets.

Defects which may be classified in category (2) include rolled-in scale, pits, gouges, scratches, underpickled areas, and other imperfections of a minor nature which may be eliminated by making corrections in preceding processing operations. Another defect falling into this category is the previously mentioned "rough coating," which results when the terne metal fails to "wet" or alloy with the steel base because of a film of reduced iron or carbonaceous residue which has not been satisfactorily removed in pickling. In this connection, it is to be noted that the cleanliness of the base metal is much more critical in the coating of long ternes than in the case of hot-dip zinc coatings.

Defects comprehended in category (3) include such items as bent corners, uncoated areas, oil stains, branner marks, and other minor items which may be controlled by the pot operators. In addition to the inspection for the above enumerated defects, the sheets are also checked for gage, size and flatness by the pot inspectors and are stamped with the appropriate identification marks.

The tests to which long terne sheets are subjected after completion of the coating operation may be classed as chemical, microscopic and mechanical. To determine the amount of coating being applied on single sheets, the **sheet weight test** is made on a lot of from one to ten sheets, depending on the gage. The test lots are weighed after the pickling, washing and drying operations, and then weighed again after coating. The weight of coating in ounces per square foot is calculated by dividing the difference in weight so obtained by the total area comprising the test lot. Using this test at each coating unit, an adequate control of the coating weight may be maintained and adjustments made to the coating machine as the occasion arises. For accurate determination of the weight of terne coating on the sheet and to determine conformance to specifications it is customary to use the **triple spot test method.** Where the product is coated in sheet form, three specimens exactly 2.25 inches square, or discs of equivalent area, are cut from each test sheet, one being cut from the center and the other two from diagonally opposite corners. The end spot tests are cut not closer than 4 inches from the ends and 2 inches from the sides, in order to avoid the heavier coating on these areas. In testing product made by the continuous-strip coating process, since the coating-weight difference for the back and front of the test sheet do not exist, it is acceptable to take all three spot tests across the width of the sheet. After each specimen has been weighed on an analytical balance the coating is dissolved by immersion in an appropriate solution. The specimen is then washed, dried and reweighed, the difference in weight in grams being numerically equal to the weight of coating in ounces per square foot. From time to time, and particularly when certain specifications governing the composition of the terne coating must be met, the coating on a test sample is chemically analyzed to determine the percentages of tin and lead present.

A **microscopic examination** of a properly polished and etched cross-section is made to determine the ferrite grain size of the steel base. Since the adherence of the coating to the base metal is never a problem in the production of long terne sheets, adherence testing is not required as it is for galvanized sheets. **Mechanical property tests** are used primarily as a guide in determining the ductility of the coated sheet and its suitability for the intended application. These mechanical tests include Rockwell hardness, Olsen cup, bend, fluting and tension test. Hardness tests are normally made on the base metal after the coating has been removed since the soft coating would give erroneous values if the hardness impression were made through it. Besides providing a measure of the ductility, the Olsen test is a valuable tool for detecting hydrogen embrittlement of the base metal. In the Olsen cup test the material normally "necks" at the periphery of the base of the cup, but when absorbed hydrogen has embrittled the base metal, a ragged fracture will occur on the side of the cup or, in extreme cases, at the base of the cup. Fluting tests are made by forming a suitable test piece into a cylinder and observing the presence or absence of flutes or creases.

APPLICATIONS OF LONG TERNE SHEETS

The major portion of the long terne sheet production is used in the manufacture of gasoline tanks for the tractor, truck and automotive industries. Automotive gas tanks are usually drawn in two halves, top and bottom, and seam welded around the perimeter. Truck and tractor tanks are sometimes drawn in the same manner, but are also fabricated by forming the sheets into cylinders by using bending rolls and then lockseaming or soldering the ends. The use of long ternes for these applications is dictated by the resistance of the coating to corrosion by gasoline, water and air. Other automotive parts manufactured from long ternes include water distributor tubes, radiator parts, mufflers, oil pans and air cleaners. The latter use is considered a minor corrosion hazard but manufacturers of this item prefer to draw the shapes involved from long ternes because of the lubricating value of the coating in deep drawing operations. Other uses are

for roofing, hand fire extinguishers, outboard-motor gasoline tanks and burial caskets. The latter application involves hand rubbing and polishing to a high luster for a pleasing appearance. An important wartime use was the manufacture of expendable gasoline tanks for aircraft.

Terne Plate—Terne plate, a tin mill product of relatively minor importance, is black plate that has been pickled and coated with terne metal. Known occasionally as **short ternes**, this commodity is made on hot-dip manufacturing equipment. Its approximate sheet thickness is expressed as basis weight and its coating weights are expressed in terms of pounds per double base box. The terne metal used for terne plate generally contains approximately 15 per cent tin; the balance of the coating is lead.

Roofing Ternes are no longer produced, but formerly were commonly ordered in the standard sizes, 20 by 28 inches or 14 by 20 inches, the standard basis weights of 107 lb. and 135 lb., and the standard coating weights of 8 pounds, 20 pounds, and 40 pounds per double base box. The base metal was copper-bearing steel.

Firedoor Ternes (no longer produced) were ordered in the standard size 20 by 28 inches with a basis weight of 107 lb. or heavier and a coating of 20 pounds per double base box.

Manufacturing ternes are short ternes of any tin-mill size produced by using approximately 6 pounds of terne metal per double base box. **Heavy-coated manufacturing ternes** are short ternes produced in coating weights of 8, 15, 20 and 40 pounds per double base box. **Special-coated manufacturing ternes** are short ternes customarily produced with no specified amount of coating but carrying the lightest practical coating consistent with thorough coverage of the plate.

Bibliography

Steel Products Manual, "Carbon Steel Sheets" American Iron and Steel Institute, New York.

CHAPTER 36

Production Of
Galvanized Sheet and Strip

SECTION 1

GENERAL

Production and Uses of Galvanized Sheet and Strip
—The importance of providing protection against corrosion for steel articles having a light section is obvious, and coating the steel with zinc is a very effective and economical means of accomplishing this end. Zinc coatings are commonly applied by dipping or passing the article to be coated through a molten bath of the metal. This operation is termed "galvanizing," "hot galvanizing" or "hot-dip galvanizing" to distinguish it from zinc electroplating processes which are termed "cold" or "electro-galvanizing."

The present discussion is limited (1) to **hot-dip sheet galvanizing** which is the hot-dip galvanizing of cut-length sheets by passing them one by one and in close succession through the molten zinc, and (2) **continuous (strip) hot-dip galvanizing,** in which material in coiled form from the rolling mills is uncoiled and passed continuously through the galvanizing equipment, continuity of operation being achieved by joining the trailing end of one coil to the leading end of the next.

The word "strip," as used in this chapter, denotes the *physical form* of the material in process; i.e., a continuous strand of steel of sheet gage and width. Commercially, the meaning of the term "strip" has the limitations outlined in Chapter 31.

Of all the common metals used for protective coatings, zinc enjoys the lowest cost per pound. With the single exception of tin, it is used to protect a greater area of steel than any other coating metal. In 1961, 368,773 tons of slab zinc were consumed by the galvanizing industry. Of this amount, 209,606 tons were used for the galvanizing of sheet and strip. The balance of the zinc was used largely in wire galvanizing, pipe galvanizing, and in the hot-dip galvanizing of prefabricated articles such as range boilers, wash tubs, garbage cans, pails, etc. The reported shipments of galvanized sheet and strip in the United States during 1961 amounted to over 3.3 million tons, practically all of which was produced by hot-dipping (less than 250,000 tons were produced by electrolytic processes).

Of the galvanized-sheet production in 1961, about 37.4 per cent was supplied to the construction and contractors'-products industries, and about 30.1 per cent was supplied to warehouses for miscellaneous applications. Galvanized sheets were also supplied to the automotive (9.4 per cent); appliance, utensil and cutlery (5.0 per cent); agricultural (6.1 per cent); commercial-equipment (2.6 per cent); electrical-machinery and electrical-equipment (1.8 per cent); machinery, industrial-equipment and tool (1.2 per cent); container, packaging and shipping-materials (1.4 per cent); and transportation (0.5 per cent) industries. The export trade used about 2.2 per cent.

Specific uses for galvanized sheets include: such automotive parts as rocker panels, underbody parts, mufflers, and head- and tail-light parts; roofing and siding; eave troughs; conductor pipe; air ducts; heating furnaces; air-conditioning equipment; metal lath; corner beading; switch boxes; chimney flues; metal awnings; railroad-car roofs; garbage cans; oil cans; ash cans; pails; tubs; coal hods; refrigerators; deep-freeze units; kitchen equipment; laundry tubs; automatic washers and dryers; minnow buckets; storage tanks; beverage coolers; well casings; culverts; poultry equipment; manure spreaders; hay loaders; tractors; and wagons.

FACTORS INFLUENCING EFFECTIVENESS OF GALVANIZED COATINGS

The amount of zinc on a galvanized sheet is stated in terms of ounces per square foot of sheet; since the sheet is coated on both sides, the stated weight of coating is twice the average weight of coating per square foot of either side.

The effectiveness of a protective coating depends to a considerable extent upon the character of the environment in which it is used. In general, galvanized coatings are subjected to atmospheric and liquid corrosion and, less frequently, to soil corrosion. Their effectiveness in the atmosphere depends mainly upon the amount of acidic contaminants present. Thus, in the relatively pure air of rural districts, the life of zinc coatings is four to ten times that of the same coatings in industrial areas.

For any specific set of exposure conditions, the thickness of a zinc coating is the most important factor in determining its effectiveness. Coatings applied to sheets by the hot-dip process range, in general, from 0.6 to 2.5 oz. per sq. ft. of sheet, and the 2.5 oz. per sq. ft. coating can be expected to have approximately four times the life of the 0.6 oz. per sq. ft. coating under similar exposure conditions. For this reason, uniformity of coating is also an important consideration. As a practical matter a completely uniform coating is not produced in a commercial hot-dipping operation; however, no area or spot of a hot-dipped sheet should carry a lesser weight of coating than the trade-accepted minimum for the grade. These minimums vary with the grade or class ordered and are considerably less than the nominal weight of coating, i.e., coating class, specified; see "Coating Weight Requirements" below.

One of the advantages of zinc as a protective coating is its anodic relationship to iron in the electromotive series. Due to this relationship, the protection afforded is extended to small areas of coating discontinuity adjacent to areas actually coated. Thus, lack of coating at a sheared edge or minor damage to the coating during fabrication or use of a galvanized article does not seriously impair its service life, provided, of course, the uncoated areas are not too large.

COATING WEIGHT AND GAGE REQUIREMENTS

Galvanized sheets are manufactured to several general specifications, the requirements of which have been found by usage and test to be the most suitable for the applications involved.

The so-called **Commercial Coatings** generally include those that are produced on sheets for direct weather-exposure applications. Galvanized Formed Roofing and Siding, and Galvanized Flat Sheets for Roofing and Siding, are produced to ASTM Specification "Steel Roofing Sheets" A361-59T with a 1.25 oz. per sq. ft. coating class, 0.90 oz. per sq. ft. check limit by triple-spot test, or 0.80 oz. per sq. ft. check limit by single-spot test. (Tests for galvanized sheets are described in Section 5 of this chapter.) Galvanized Flat Sheets for other than roofing and siding products, but for an intended equivalent corrosion hazard, may be produced to ASTM Specification "Steel Sheets, Coil and Cut Lengths" A93-59T with a similar 1.25 oz. per sq. ft. coating class.

For applications in which the above Commercial Coatings might cause some difficulty in forming because of their thickness, or in which extreme corrosion resistance is not a consideration, galvanized sheets may be produced to ASTM Specification A93-59T, Light Commercial, with no minimum check limits specified.

Heavier than Commercial Coatings are supplied when required for specific applications. The American Zinc Institute "Seal of Quality" roofing sheet is specified as 2.00 to 2.25 coating class with a minimum 1.80 oz. per sq. ft. check limit by triple-spot test and a minimum 1.50 oz. per sq. ft. check limit by single-spot test (see Section 5). Culvert sheets are required to carry a minimum 2.00 oz. per sq. ft. coating when tested by the triple-spot-test method.

Galvanized sheets are produced to weights per unit of sheet area. The Galvanized Sheet Gage, established by custom, is based on the United States Standard

Table 36—I. Galvanized Sheet Gage Numbers with Equivalent Unit Weights

Galvanized Sheet Gage Number	Ounces Per Square Foot	Pounds Per Square Foot	Pounds Per Square Inch	Thickness Equivalents (Inches)
8	112.5	7.03125	0.048828	0.1681
9	102.5	6.40625	0.044488	0.1532
10	92.5	5.78125	0.040148	0.1382
11	82.5	5.15625	0.035807	0.1233
12	72.5	4.53125	0.031467	0.1084
13	62.5	3.90625	0.027127	0.0934
14	52.5	3.28125	0.022786	0.0785
15	47.5	2.96875	0.020616	0.0710
16	42.5	2.65625	0.018446	0.0635
17	38.5	2.40625	0.016710	0.0575
18	34.5	2.15625	0.014974	0.0516
19	30.5	1.90625	0.013238	0.0456
20	26.5	1.65625	0.011502	0.0396
21	24.5	1.53125	0.010634	0.0366
22	22.5	1.40625	0.0097656	0.0336
23	20.5	1.28125	0.0088976	0.0306
24	18.5	1.15625	0.0080295	0.0276
25	16.5	1.03125	0.0071615	0.0247
26	14.5	0.90625	0.0062934	0.0217
27	13.5	0.84375	0.0058594	0.0202
28	12.5	0.78125	0.0054253	0.0187
29	11.5	0.71875	0.0049913	0.0172
30	10.5	0.65625	0.0045573	0.0157
31	9.5	0.59375	0.0041233	0.0142
32	9.0	0.56250	0.0039062	0.0134

Gage, each Galvanized Sheet Gage weight being 2.5 ounces per square foot heavier than the gage weight of the same United States Standard Gage number, regardless of the coating weights. For example, the equivalent unit weight of a 20-gage galvanized sheet is 26.5 ounces per square foot regardless of the weight of coating. Adjustments are made in the weight of the base metal to compensate for heavier or lighter weights of coating. Galvanized sheet gage numbers and their weight equivalents are given in Table 36—I. Thickness equivalents are also shown in this table. Table 36—II shows the coating class in ounces per square foot and the minimum coating check limits for coatings heavier than Commercial Galvanized Coatings.

Table 36—II. Coating Class and Minimum Coating Check Limits for Galvanized Sheets
(Oz. Per Sq. Ft.)

Coating Class	Minimum Check Limit by Triple-Spot Test*	Minimum Check Limit by Single-Spot Test*
2.75	2.35	2.00
2.50	2.10	1.80
2.25	1.85	1.60
2.00	1.65	1.40
1.75	1.40	1.20
1.50	1.15	1.00
1.25 (Commercial)	0.90	0.80
Light Commercial	—	—

* Test procedures are described in Section 5 of this chapter.

GENERAL QUALITY DESIGNATIONS

Sheets of "Commercial Quality" are suitable for bending and moderate forming requirements. They must be capable of withstanding standard bend tests. The adherence of the coating must be sufficient to withstand bending without flaking when tested in accordance with ASTM Specification A-93.

The production of "Drawing Quality" steel involves the exercise of close control in the selection of steel and processing to assure performance of the material within the limits specified by the producer. Trade usage has established no general standard of coating adherence for drawing operations and the matter is normally negotiated by the producer and user in each individual case. Drawing Quality sheets are made from rimmed steel.

For critical forming requirements, "Drawing Qual-

ity—Special Killed Steel" should be specified. The limitations described above for "Drawing Quality" also apply to this grade of material.

Temper rolling may be employed to produce an "Extra Smooth" sheet for applications involving critical end uses when galvanized sheets are required to have one surface of a higher degree of smoothness than is normal for regular commercial quality, or drawing quality product. Examples are for sign and panel work.

To obtain satisfactory performance in lock-forming operations, "Lock-Forming Quality" sheets should be employed.

For superior resistance of base metal to atmospheric corrosion, copper-bearing steel should be employed.

SPECIALTY PRODUCTS

Roofing and siding are produced either flat or in the form of "Corrugated Sheets," "V-Crimped Roofing," "Corrugated Roll Roofing," or regular "Roll Roofing."

Standard 2½-inch corrugated sheets have 10 corrugations to a sheet of siding and 10½ corrugations for a sheet of roofing for a covering width of 24 inches. The width of each corrugation is actually 2.66 inches and the depth is ½ inch. In siding, both edge corrugations are turned the same way and the overall width of the formed sheet is 26 inches. In roofing, the edge corrugations are turned in opposite directions and the total sheet width is about 27½ inches. Lengths of 5, 6, 7, 8, 9, 10, 11, and 12 feet are commonly available, but special lengths are sometimes supplied. Galvanized roofing and siding sheets are produced from 29-gage and heavier sheets.

The standard 1¼-inch corrugated sheets have 20½ corrugations, ¼ inch deep, to a sheet. With one edge each way, they have a formed width of 26 inches and a covering width of 24 inches. Stock lengths are the same as those for the 2½-inch corrugated stock and the gages supplied are similar.

V-crimped roofing is produced by forming 2, 3 or 5 longitudinal inverted "V" crimps in the sides or in the sides and centers of sheets. V-crimped sheets are supplied with the 24-inch covering width and the 5- to 12-foot lengths used for the corrugated material. Various modifications of the standard "V" crimped are used for roofing and siding sheets.

Various accessory fittings for use in assembling a corrugated roof usually are supplied by galvanized-sheet producers. Included in these are ridge roll, ridge cap, gambrel joint, side-wall flashing, end-wall flashing, lean-to filler, and overhang section.

SECTION 2

METALLURGICAL FEATURES OF THE HOT-DIP GALVANIZING PROCESSES

Hot-dip coatings are produced on steel objects by passing the properly prepared base metal through a bath of molten coating metal. Tin, zinc and lead are the common coating metals used. As in all coating processes, the surface of the base metal must be clean

to insure satisfactory coating continuity. In addition, successful hot-dipping requires the surface of the molten bath to be kept clean, particularly at the entrance to the bath, since oxide films of the coating metal at this point will be picked up by the surface of the entering base metal to interfere with the wetting of the latter by the molten coating metal.

In the hot-dip galvanizing of steel, the cleanliness of the base metal is somewhat less critical than in electroplating operations since molten zinc is highly reducing to iron oxide and possesses a strong tendency to form intermetallic compounds with iron. Excessive contamination of the surface with any material, of course, cannot be tolerated and must be removed by acid pickling, alkaline cleaning or other preparatory treatment prior to introduction in the zinc bath. Satisfactory cleanliness of the steel and zinc is maintained by (1) the use of suitable fluxes either carried on the surface of the bath or applied to the surface of the steel just prior to entry into the bath, or (2) in the case of continuous operations which include an annealing or other heat-treating step immediately ahead of the galvanizing pot, by keeping the heated strip under the protection of the furnace atmosphere, preferably a reducing atmosphere, until it passes below the surface of the molten zinc.

For many years, galvanized sheets were produced by passing single sheets of steel in close succession through a coating pot; the operations are described in detail in Section 3 of this chapter. However, with the development of wide strip mills capable of rolling to sheet gages, there has been a gradual shift to processing sheet products in strip form. In such operations, the steel is unwound from coils and passes as a continuous strand through the processing equipment. The product may then be recoiled or cut into individual sheets as desired. Processing in strip form is sometimes referred to as "continuous processing" to distinguish it from similar operations involving the treatment of individual sheets. Continuous processing permits many operations formerly conducted on separate pieces of equipment to be combined into one continuous processing line. In addition, certain problems inherent to operations on individual sheets disappear when the steel is processed in strip form. For example, in the hot-dip coating of sheets the necessary gap between successive sheets causes a considerable variation in the weight of coating applied to the leading and trailing ends of the sheet. The absence of this gap in operations on material in strip form therefore results in a more uniform coating and consequently affords better utilization of a given quantity of zinc. Continuous-type operations, however, require a very high investment in equipment. A detailed description of the application of continuous practices in hot-dip galvanizing of steel is given in Section 4 of this chapter.

At and above its melting point, zinc readily forms intermetallic compounds with iron. In hot-dip galvanizing, these alloys form at the interface between base metal and coating metal and ultimately constitute an appreciable portion of the finished coating. After solidification, the coating consists of an outer layer approaching the metal of the coating bath in composition, and several inner layers, generally termed "alloy layer," consisting of intermetallic phases of iron and zinc, the latter becoming successively richer in iron with depth.

The outer layer of a hot-dip galvanized coating solidifies as a cast crystalline structure starting at scattered nuclei and developing into a more or less regular "frost-flower" or "spangled" pattern (Figures 36—1 and 36—2). The size of the spangles is influenced by the composition and prior treatment of the base metal, by the duration of the solidification period, and by the composition of the coating bath. The shape and general pattern of the spangles are largely influenced by the latter.

The alloy layer has been the subject of considerable investigation. It has been considered to be the bond between the outer layer of relatively pure zinc and the

Fig. 36—1. Typical spangles on a "Tight-Coat" sheet galvanized with aluminum-free spelter. Average coating weight: 1.10 oz. per sq. ft. Actual size, unetched.

FIG. 36—2. Typical spangles on a sheet continuously galvanized with aluminum-bearing (nominal 0.15 per cent Al) spelter. Average coating weight: 1.32 oz. per sq. ft. Actual size, unetched.

steel base; but, paradoxically, many of the failures of galvanized coatings by flaking during fabrication have also been attributed to its presence. Actually the exact role of the layer in adherence of the coating has not been clearly established.

It has been known for a number of years that the addition of aluminum in small amounts (0.10 to 0.25 per cent) to the zinc bath suppresses the alloy formation and produces coatings of increased tightness. However, upon metallographic examination, coated samples made with a nominal 0.15 aluminum spelter sometimes show a relatively thick alloy layer and yet pass severe forming tests. Moreover, although the presence of a heavy alloy layer on steel sheets galvanized with aluminum-free spelter generally portends bad flaking, sheets galvanized in the same manner but galvannealed, i.e., the coating converted entirely to alloy, will exhibit excellent adherence. Thus there are indications that the composition of the layer may be significant and that the thickness of the layer is a factor; however, any generalizations must be accepted with reservation.

The equilibrium relationship between iron and zinc at different temperatures has been studied by various investigators. The constitution diagram as developed by J. Schramm (1938) is shown in Figure 36—3. The composition and lattice structure of each phase indicated on the diagram are shown in Table 36—III.

Intermetallic compounds present in hot-dipped galvanized coatings produced under a variety of conditions are indicated in Figures 36—4 through 36—7. This series of illustrations shows that the clarity of definition and the relative amounts of the various constituents of the alloy layer can be varied by varying time and temperature of immersion. The composition of the steel also, particularly the silicon content, can have a noticeable influence on the layer. The presence of tin, antimony and cadmium in the usual amounts found or used in spelter have been reported to have very little effect on the character of the layer; however, aluminum in excess of 0.10 per cent has a decided effect. Figure 36—8 is a photomicrograph at 1000 diameters showing the cross-section of a sheet galvanized coating of aluminum-free spelter.

Table 36—III. Phases in the Iron-Zinc Constitution Diagram

Phases	X-Ray Formula	Limits of Composition, (Per Cent Fe)		Space Lattice
		Atomic	Wt.	
Alpha (α) Fe	FeZn		80-100	Body-Centered Cubic
Gamma (γ) Fe	FeZn		55-100	Face-Centered Cubic
Capital Gamma (Γ)	Fe_5Zn_{21} or Fe_3Zn_{10}	23.2-31.3	20.5-28	Body-Centered Cubic
Delta$_1$ (δ_1)	$FeZn_7$ (?)	8.1-13.2	7-11.5	Hexagonal (?)
Delta (δ)	$FeZn_7$ (?)	8.1-11.5	7-10	Monoclinic
Zeta (ζ)	$FeZn_{13}$	7.2-7.4	6-6.2	Hexagonal
Eta (η)	Zn		Max. 0.003	Close Packed

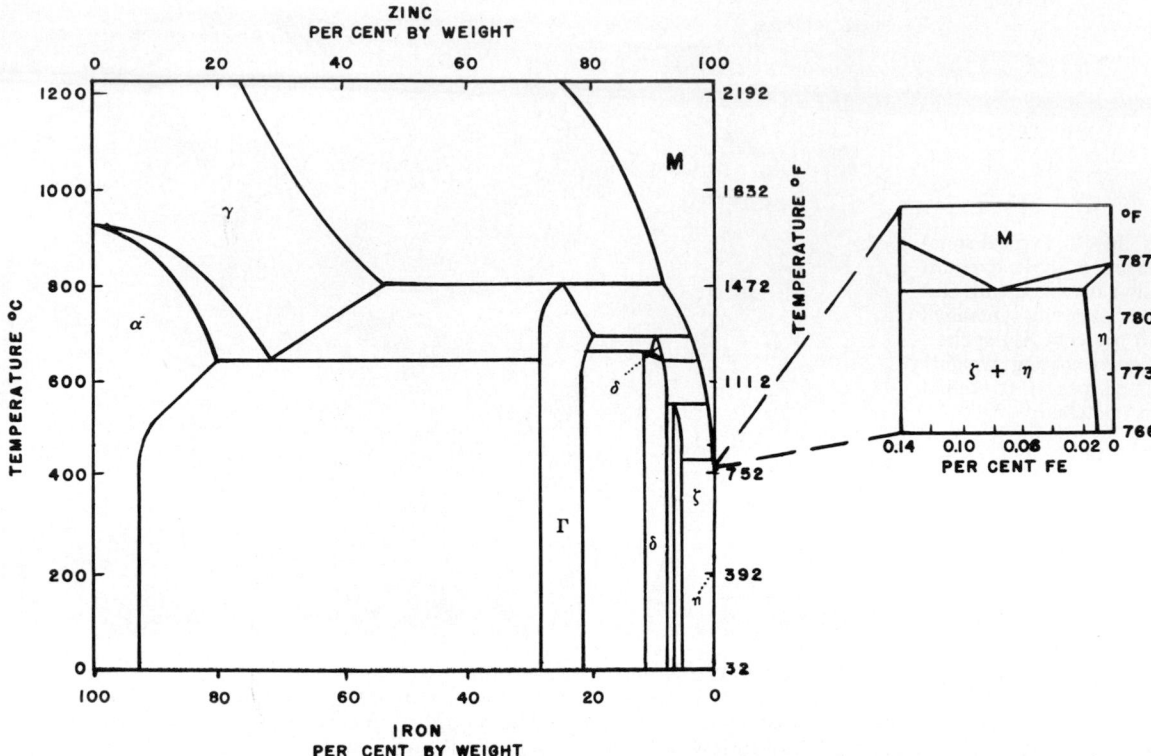

Fig. 36—3. The iron-zinc constitution diagram, according to J. Schramm.

Figure 36—9 is a similar photomicrograph of a strip galvanized coating of aluminum-bearing (nominal 0.15 per cent Al) spelter. It will also be noted that almost all the coating in the latter instance consists of the eta phase.

COATING METAL USED IN HOT-DIP GALVANIZING

There are a number of commercial grades of zinc or **spelter** available for hot-dip galvanizing. A list of the different grades is given in Table 36—IV.

In either sheet or continuous-strip galvanizing, it is the general practice to add small quantities of other metals to the coating bath to control the appearance and properties of coatings. The general effects of elements that are either found in or are added to molten commercial grades of zinc are discussed in the following paragraphs:

Lead, in certain percentages, is necessary for the production of a spangled finish. If present in amounts exceeding its solubility in zinc (around 1.00 per cent at coating temperatures), the excess lead settles to the bottom of the coating pot and serves as a cushion to support a bed of zinc-iron alloy or **dross** that forms during the coating operation.

Antimony is not present in commercial spelter grades and it may be added, if desired, either as an alloy of zinc or as the metal itself. In small amounts it assists in producing an attractive low-relief spangle.

Cadmium, which is present in most virgin spelters, assists in producing a frosty low-relief spangle finish.

Tin additions of from 0.3 to 1.50 per cent have been used for many years to produce a frosty spangle finish in conventional galvanized coatings.

Aluminum additions of between 0.10 and 0.25 per cent increase the adherence of galvanized coatings. The addition cannot be used in conjunction with practices utilizing any of the common chloride fluxes floating on the surface of the zinc, since the aluminum is rapidly removed from the bath by the flux as $AlCl_3$ which is highly volatile at galvanizing temperatures.

A small amount of iron is always present in a hot-dip galvanizing bath. The excess above its low solubility limit gradually settles to the bottom of the pot as dross.

Table 36—IV. Composition of the Different Grades of Zinc and Spelter

Grade	Composition, Maximum Per Cent of			
	Pb	Fe	Cd	Pb + Fe + Cd
Special High Grade...	0.010	0.005	0.005	0.01
High Grade...	0.07	0.03	0.07	0.10
Intermediate .	0.20	0.03	0.50	0.50
Brass Special..	0.60	0.03	0.50	1.00
Prime Western.	1.60	0.08	....	....

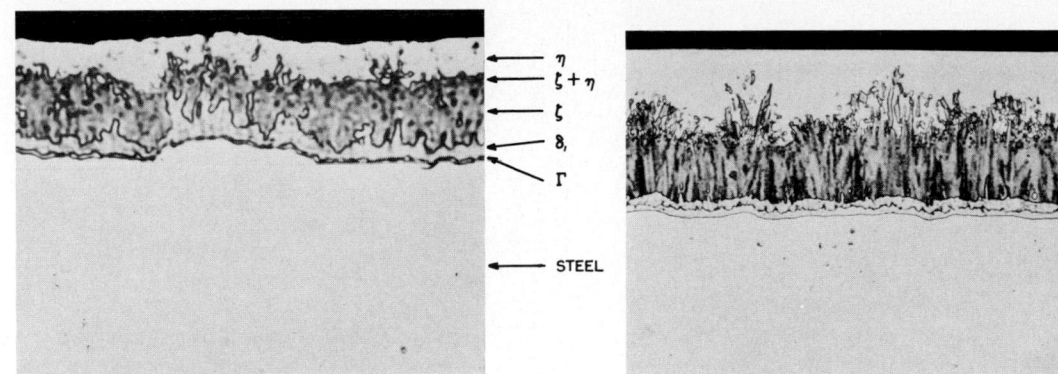

FIG. 36—4. Photomicrograph of commercial sheet galvanized coating. Average coating weight, 0.63 oz. per sq. ft. Magnification: 1000X.

FIG. 36—5. Photomicrograph of experimental galvanized coating formed by immersing sheet steel for one minute in molten zinc at 840°F (450°C). Magnification: 500X.

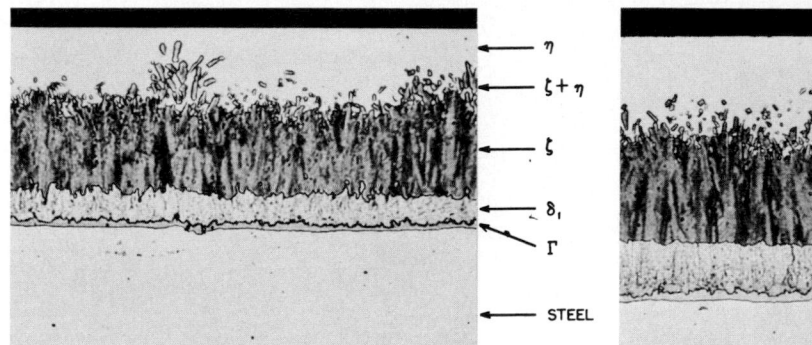
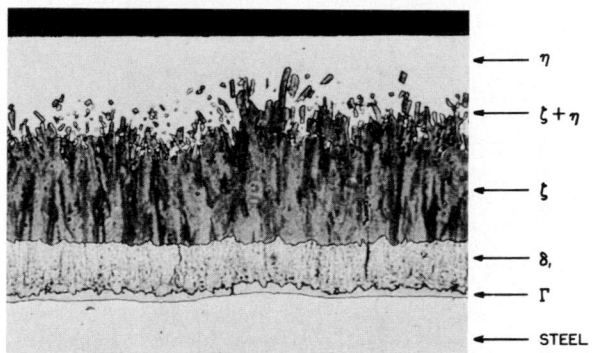

FIG. 36—6. Photomicrograph of experimental galvanized coating formed by immersing sheet steel for five minutes in molten zinc at 840°F (450°C). Magnification: 500X.

FIG. 36—7. Photomicrograph of experimental galvanized coating formed by immersing sheet steel for ten minutes in molten zinc at 840°F (450°C). Magnification: 500X.

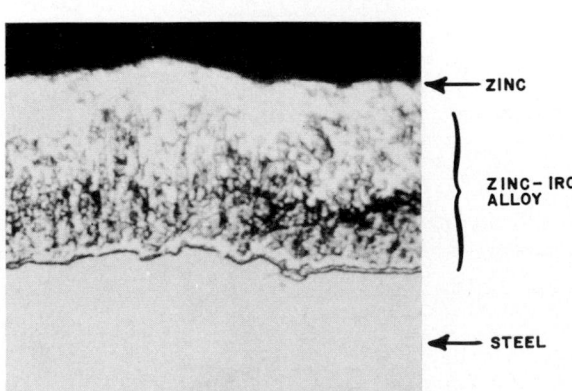
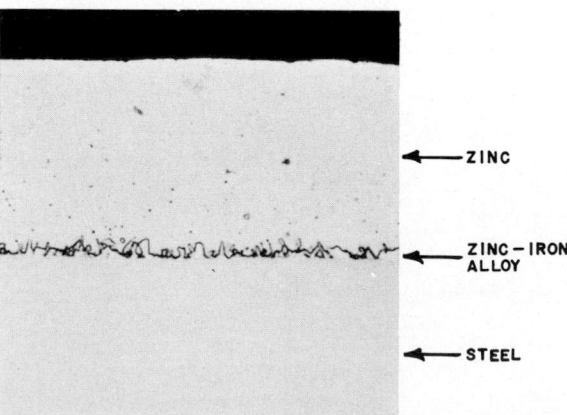

FIG. 36—8. Photomicrograph showing thickness of the alloy layer in the coating on a sheet galvanized with aluminum-free spelter. Average coating weight, 1.13 oz. per sq. ft. Magnification: 1000X.

FIG. 36—9. Photomicrograph showing thickness of the alloy layer in the coating on a sheet galvanized with aluminum-bearing spelter (nominal 0.15 per cent A1). Average coating weight, 1.17 oz. per sq. ft. Magnification: 1000X.

Table 36—V. Chemical Composition of Sheet and Strip Galvanizing Steels

Grade	Carbon (%)	Manganese (%)	Phosphorus (%)	Sulphur (%)	Silicon (%)	Copper (%)	Comments
Regular Rimmed	0.05-0.10	0.25-0.50	0.030 Max.*	0.050 Max.	Residual	Residual	Any of these Steels May Be Supplied with Copper Content of 0.20% Min.
Mechanically Capped	0.05-0.10	0.25-0.50	0.030 Max.*	0.050 Max.	Residual	Residual	
Aluminum Killed	0.05-0.10	0.25-0.50	0.030 Max.*	0.050 Max.	Residual	Residual	
Silicon Killed	0.05-0.10	0.25-0.50	0.030 Max.*	0.050 Max.	0.15-0.25	Residual	
High Strength	0.05-0.20	0.30-1.30	0.030 to 0.11	0.050 Max.	Residual to 0.80	Residual to 0.60	Nickel Residual to 1.00 / Chromium Residual to 1.00
Pure Iron, Copper Bearing (Culverts)	L.A.P.**	L.A.P.**	0.015 Max.	0.040 Max.	Residual	0.20 Min.	Sum of 1st Five Elements—0.10 Max.
Copper Iron (Culverts)	. . . .	. . . .	0.015 Max.	0.040 Max.	Residual	0.20 Min.	Sum of 1st Five Elements—0.25 Max.
Steel, Copper Bearing (Culverts)	0.05-0.10	0.25-0.40	0.030 Max.	0.050 Max.	Residual	0.20 Min.	Sum of 1st Five Elements—0.70 Max.

* Phosphorus contents may be varied up to 0.10 per cent maximum to facilitate pack rolling or to improve the adherence of the zinc coating.
** L.A.P. = Low as possible.

STEELS USED FOR HOT-DIP GALVANIZING

Hot-dip galvanized coatings may be successfully applied to a variety of ferrous metals, ranging from cast iron to low-carbon and alloy steels. In the coating of sheet, the bulk of the production is from low-carbon basic open-hearth steel. The following is a general classification of the grades used in galvanizing:

A. Rimmed Steel
    1. Regular low-carbon
    2. Pure iron, copper-bearing
B. Capped Steel
    1. Mechanically capped
C. Killed Steel
    1. Aluminum killed
D. High-Strength Steel
    1. High-strength low-alloy

Copper may be added, if desired, to any of the above grades to improve atmospheric corrosion resistance. Steels containing between 0.20 per cent and 0.30 per cent copper are designated as "copper bearing."

Chemical requirements for the various steel grades, as specified by a majority of the producers, are shown in Table 36—V.

MILL TREATMENT OF STEEL PRIOR TO HOT-DIP GALVANIZING

Sheets used for sheet galvanizing may be processed by hand-mill rolling operations (now practically obsolete) or by continuous rolling processes. Hand-mill sheets are hot rolled, box annealed, cold rolled, and pickled to prepare them for hot-dipping. Continuous-hot-rolled sheets may be either hot rolled in strip form or hot rolled and pickled in strip form before shearing to cut lengths and pickling for the galvanizing operation. Shot blasting after shearing is sometimes used to facilitate the production of heavy coatings on heavy-gage material. Cold-reduced sheets are either hot-rolled, pickled, cold-reduced, and recoiled, or they are hot rolled, pickled, cold reduced, recoiled, and sheared to cut-length sheets before box annealing. Alkaline cleaning is often used after cold reduction to remove rolling lubricants. Material that is box annealed in coils is temper rolled and sheared before pickling for galvanizing, and material that is box annealed in sheet form is temper rolled before pickling for galvanizing.

Coils for continuous galvanizing may be prepared in a number of ways. Thus, they may be hot rolled and pickled; hot rolled, pickled and cold reduced; or hot rolled, pickled, cold reduced, box annealed and temper rolled before processing. Again, alkaline cleaning may be used after cold reduction to remove rolling lubricants. Because of the inherent properties of the base metal, coated sheets made from cold-reduced coils have been found to possess ductility superior to that of coated sheets made from hand-mill products.

SPECIAL FINISHES

In addition to the regular spangled finish produced in sheet or strip galvanizing, provision may be made in the processing facilities to accommodate the production of special finishes. **Galvannealed sheets** may be produced by passing the material, after it leaves the coating pot, through a heated chamber that maintains the coating metal molten until it alloys completely with the base metal. Galvannealed coatings possess a silvery matte finish of relatively low reflectivity. They have good paint-adherence properties without additional surface preparation and are capable of withstanding moderate forming.

A **bonderized finish** may be produced by processing in line or as a separate supplementary processing operation. In the bonderizing process, a thin film composed largely of zinc phosphate is formed on the sheet surfaces. Bonderized sheets are outstanding with regard to their paint-adherence properties.

Extra-smooth finishes may be applied after galvanizing, galvannealing, or bonderizing, by temper rolling with shot-blasted or with smooth rolls. On bonderized material, the extra-smooth finish may, in some instances, be applied before bonderizing.

Metal sheets shipped and stored in piles or coils are subject to white or variously colored stains when water is allowed to remain in contact with surfaces in the interiors of piles and coils for any appreciable period of time. This condition is usually designated as "wet storage stains." Common sources of moisture may be rain water, melted snow, or condensation, the latter resulting from sudden temperature changes. Various chemical films and oil films have been found to be effective in retarding the appearance of the discoloration, but, even with filming treatments, wet storage stain is a hazard when sheets or coils get wet.

Good packaging, handling and adequate warehousing facilities have been found to be essential requirements for preserving the original finish until the material is used.

SECTION 3

HOT-DIP SHEET GALVANIZING

Pickling for Sheet Galvanizing—Pickling for sheet galvanizing is usually conducted as a batch operation in stationary tubs provided with an agitating means. This operation may sometimes be conducted as a continuous process in equipment provided with a sheet conveyor and means for electrolytic acceleration.

Very light pickling requiring only a short-time exposure to the pickling solution has been found suitable for products, such as roofing and siding, that require little mechanical deformation. Deep etching of the base metal has generally been found to be necessary when forming requirements are severe.

Following the pickling operation, a thorough water rinse, with or without an alkaline neutralizing dip, is employed to remove iron salts and residual acid. A prolonged immersion in boiling water may be used,

FIG. 36—10. A sheet galvanizing line in operation, showing the hooded setting which contains the galvanizing machine immersed in the pot containing molten zinc, the spangle conveyor, and control station.

when necessary, to minimize hydrogen embrittlement.

Equipment for Sheet Galvanizing—The equipment used for sheet galvanizing (Figure 36—10) consists of mechanical facilities for transporting cut-length sheets successively through acid washing, fluxing, hot-dipping, and cooling operations. The coating bath itself is contained in a heated low-carbon steel vessel or **pot**. A framework or **rigging** with suitable **entry feed rolls, sheet guides,** driven **bottom pinch rolls,** and driven **exit rolls,** is suspended in the bath in such a manner as to completely submerge all but the entry rolls, part of the exit rolls, and part of the supporting framework. A baffled section or **flux box** at the entry end contains a floating fused-chloride **flux** prepared from sal ammoniac and the zinc of the bath.

General Arrangement and Operation of a Sheet-Galvanizing Line—A typical sheet-galvanizing line consists of a **feeding table,** a muriatic (hydrochloric) **acid tank,** a coating **pot,** a **spangle and cooling conveyor,** a **water rinse tank,** a **dryer,** a **roller leveler** and an **inspection table** (see Figure 36—11). In operating the line, pickled sheets are either fed dry from a feeding table or wet from water boshes directly into a set of driven rubber pinch rolls. The sheets pass forward through a shallow muriatic-acid bath and a second set

of rubber pinch rolls into steel intake rolls that force them downward into the flux box of the coating pot. The sheets then pass into the coating bath downward to the driven bottom rolls, and upward through exit rolls, the latter being located at the bath surface. As they emerge from the exit rolls the sheets may have blasts of air, sulphur-dioxide fumes, or powdered sal ammoniac directed against their edges to produce the surface finish desired. To control the amount of coating applied, the level of the bath may be adjusted or the pressure against the exit rolls may be regulated.

Endless belts for conveying coated sheets away from a galvanizing pot are generally made of coarse woven-wire netting. The meshes of the netting contact the sheet in such a manner as to cause rapid solidification at regularly distributed points. These provide nuclei for crystallization and serve, to some extent, as a means for spangle control. A cooling runout conveyor, usually provided with air blasts, follows the spangle conveyor in a typical installation. Cooled sheets from the conveyor are roller leveled in line before inspecting and piling. In some coating lines, a water-rinsing and drying operation precedes the leveler. At the delivery end of the coating line the sheets are inspected, counted, stenciled, and stacked into

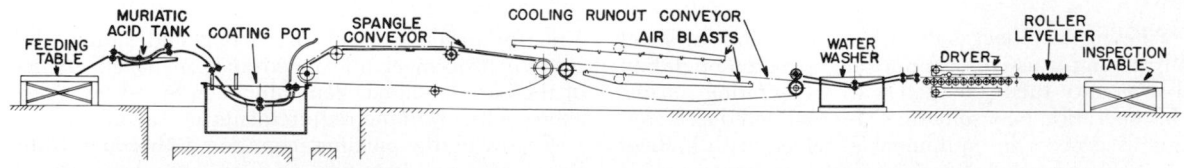

FIG. 36—11. Schematic side elevation of a conventional sheet galvanizing line.

lifts, after which they may be branded and bundled or otherwise prepared for shipment.

If a special finish, such as a bonderized finish, is to be applied to the galvanized sheets, they may be delivered from the galvanizing line to further processing units before shipment.

SECTION 4

CONTINUOUS (STRIP) HOT-DIP GALVANIZING

General Arrangement and Operation of Continuous Galvanizing Lines—The processing of steel in the form of continuous lengths unwound from coils requires more elaborate equipment than the processing of cut-length sheets, but the grouping of several manufacturing steps in one operation makes possible certain economies in production and an overall improvement in control of product quality.

Several designs of continuous hot-dip galvanizing lines are in commercial use. In the simplest arrangement a continuous strip of box annealed and temper rolled steel is passed from an uncoiler through a long muriatic (hydrochloric) acid pickling tank into a galvanizing pot. The strip enters the pot through a layer of flux and regular spelter is used. The coated strip is cooled and sheared on the line to cut-length sheets. It is then inspected and prepared for shipment.

A more elaborate design utilizes the so-called "dry-fluxing" practice. In this modification a thin film of flux in aqueous solution is applied to the strip after it leaves the cleaner and the strip then passes through a drying furnace into the zinc pot. The cleaning, if necessary, can be acid or alkaline. The furnace is operated to deliver heated strip to the coating pot and thus supplies a portion of the heat required to maintain the bath at temperature. Aluminum-bearing spelter is used as the coating metal. The coated product may be re-coiled, or it may be sheared to cut-length sheets.

Another line is characterized by a continuous anneal during which the strip is exposed to a complex gas containing hydrogen chloride. The strip passes through the annealing furnace, a cooling compartment, and a muriatic (hydrochloric) acid bath before entering the flux box of a conventional galvanizing pot. Asbestos wipes are normally used instead of exit rolls on the discharge end of the coating pot. Coatings produced are very thin but are extremely adherent. Regular spelter is used.

A fourth type of line includes controlled oxidizing and reducing steps prior to coating. The cold-reduced strip passes from the uncoilers through an open-flame oxidizing furnace, which also serves as a flame-degreaser, into a reducing furnace where it is annealed or normalized and the oxide film formed in the first furnace is reduced. The strip is cooled in the rearward zones of the reducing furnace to about the temperature of the coating bath and then passes into the zinc pot through a conduit extending from the end of the furnace to slightly below the surface of the coating bath. Cracked ammonia, introduced into this conduit to flow counter-current to strip movement, provides the necessary reducing atmosphere of the furnace. The degree of oxidation is said to be critical and must be controlled to achieve a uniform film ranging from pale yellow to blue or grey in color. Aluminum-bearing spelter is used.

In the continuous-galvanizing installations at the several United States Steel mills, strip material is alkaline cleaned, rinsed and dried, bright annealed, cooled to slightly above pot temperature and introduced into the coating bath while still protected by the furnace atmosphere. Between 0.12 and 0.18 per cent aluminum is maintained in the coating bath. Figure 36—12 is a schematic side-elevation of a line of this type designed to process 0.0157 to 0.050 in. thick light-gage material at speeds up to 300 ft. per min. When coating 28-inch wide 29-gage strip at a speed of 250 ft. per min., the line can produce about 12.5 tons of galvanized sheets per hour. Figure 36—13 is a photograph of the input portion of a line designed primarily for coating heavy-gage material. Operational details are discussed below.

The starting material, which may be, for example, 5,000 to 50,000-lb. coils of full-hard cold-reduced strip steel, is fed from an uncoiler either of the single-mandrel or of the double-mandrel type, directly through pinch rolls to a squaring shear. A leveler may be used to flatten the head end of the strip prior to shearing. From the shear, the strip advances to a welder where the tail end of the coil being processed is attached to the head end of the new coil. Lap, butt or mash welders are used for this operation.

Following the welder, the strip enters the cleaning unit where residual cold-mill lubricant and any mill dirt picked up by the surfaces of this strip in prior processing or storage is removed. Dipping and scrubbing with a hot alkaline solution is used for this purpose on some of the lines; electrolytic alkaline cleaning on the others. Polarity of the strip during electrolytic cleaning, the nature and concentration of the cleaning agent and other cleaning conditions vary. Cleaning is followed by rinsing and drying. The strip is moved through the foregoing equipment by the drive bridle, at the end of the cleaning station, which feeds the clean, dry strip into a slack accumulator. A looping pit, 30 to 90 feet deep, as shown in Figure 36—12 is usually provided for this purpose; where excavation is impractical a tower-type or a horizontal car-looper is used. The speed of the drive bridle is automatically controlled to maintain a desired length of loop in the pit and the slack so stored permits the input end of the line to be stopped for the joining operations without affecting the operation of the other sections of the line.

Strip is pulled out of the looper by a tension bridle and passes into the annealing furnace. The latter is heated either by gas or electrically and is divided into several independently controlled zones that can be

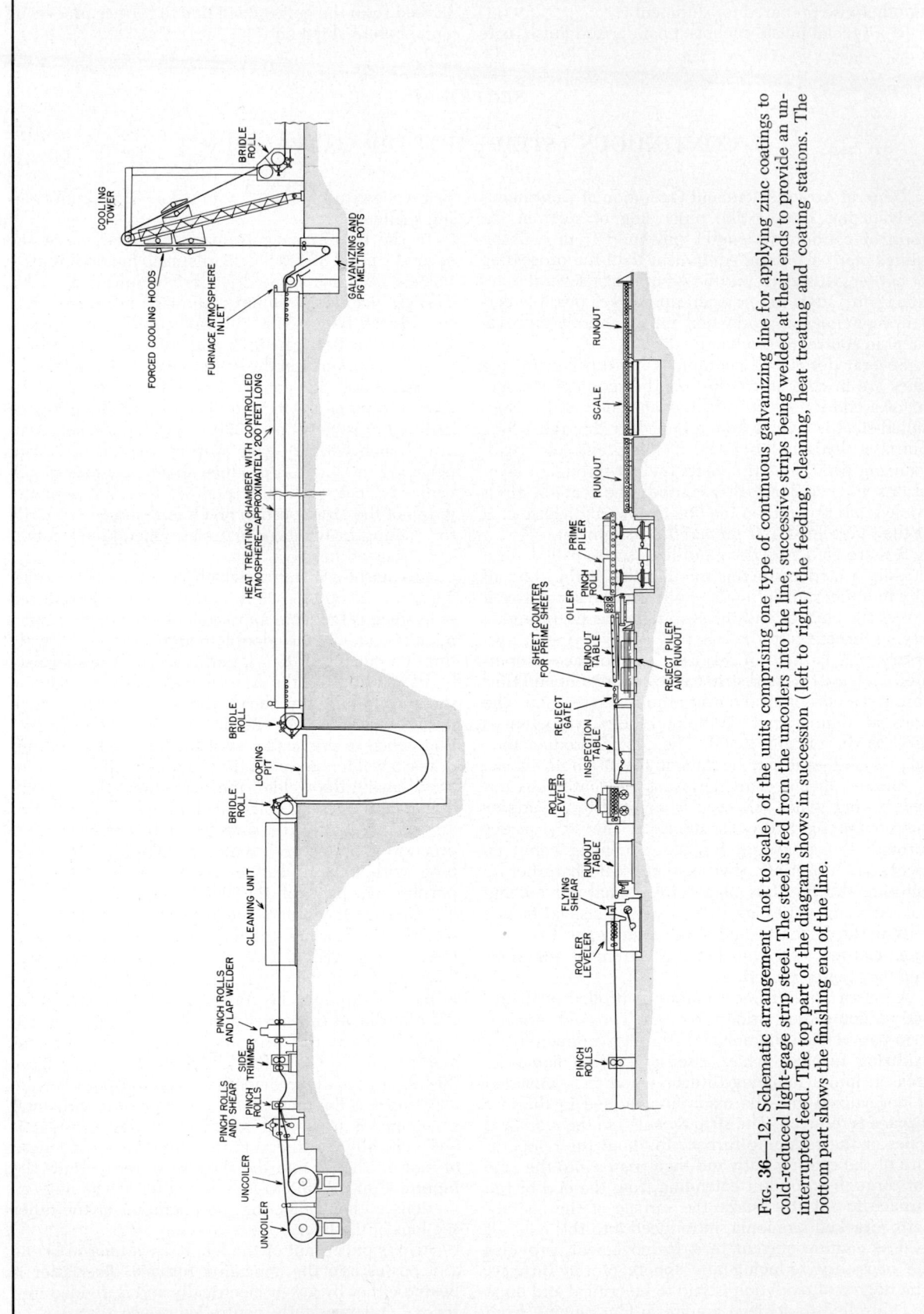

FIG. 36—12. Schematic arrangement (not to scale) of the units comprising one type of continuous galvanizing line for applying zinc coatings to cold-reduced light-gage strip steel. The steel is fed from the uncoilers into the line, successive strips being welded at their ends to provide an uninterrupted feed. The top part of the diagram shows in succession (left to right) the feeding, cleaning, heat treating and coating stations. The bottom part shows the finishing end of the line.

FIG. 36—13. A continuous galvanizing line for applying zinc coatings to cold-reduced strip steel in coil form. This particular line was designed to handle heavy-gage material.

operated in such a manner as to permit the strip to attain the desired annealing temperature in the furnace and yet enter the coating metal at but slightly above bath temperature (thus maintaining the coating bath at operating temperature). A mixture of cracked ammonia and NX gas is maintained within both heating and cooling sections of the furnace to prevent oxidation of the strip in process. The discharge end of the furnace extends below the surface of the molten zinc and the gases, which may be introduced at several points along the length of the furnace, flow counter to strip movement to escape at the entry end of the furnace. Furnace atmosphere is maintained at a positive pressure of ½ to 1 inch of water. A considerable portion of the gas is introduced near the end of the last cooling zone to aid in cooling the strip and to insure a non-oxidizing environment for the strip and zinc at their point of initial contact.

When starting operation, the metal in the coating pot is melted either with gas or electric heat. As stated earlier, the pot is kept at operating temperature by heat that is carried into the bath of molten metal by the strip.

The coating pot contains a sinker roll for submerging the strip in the bath, as well as exit rolls for controlling the thickness and distribution of the coating. The exit rolls are driven and are mounted to operate about half-submerged in the zinc. As in sheet practice, weight of coating is controlled by adjusting the pressure between the rolls and the relative position of the rolls with respect to the level of zinc in the pot.

From the exit rolls, the strip passes vertically upward to a large-diameter roll mounted at the top of a cooling tower. Forced-air blasts are directed against the strip to assist in solidifying the coating before it reaches the tower roll. Air blasts may also be used on the downward pass.

The coated strip, after returning downward from the tower, passes through a drive-bridle assembly that furnishes the necessary tension to pull the material through the annealing and coating units. Space is usually provided immediately ahead of this drive unit for any special treating facilities, provision being made to by-pass or withdraw such apparatus when not in use.

At the finishing end of a continuous galvanizing line, operations are usually of such a nature as to require occasional interruption. For this reason, looping facilities similar to those described for the entry portion of the line generally are provided. For producing coiled galvanized strip, a roller leveler and recoiler may follow the looper. For producing cut-length sheets, a flying shear equipped with suitable pinch-roll and leveling equipment is used after the looper. At the discharge end of the line, a sheet leveler may be used to flatten the sheets before preparing them for shipment.

Various automatic devices are installed in the finishing section to facilitate handling and assorting; these include automatic reject and prime pilers following the inspection table.

SECTION 5

TESTING GALVANIZED SHEETS

The **weight of coating** on a galvanized sheet is determined by weighing a 2¼-inch square test piece or a 2.539-inch diameter circular-disc test piece, dissolving the coating in hydrochloric acid containing antimony chloride as an inhibitor, and reweighing the washed and dried test piece. The weight loss in grams is numerically equal to the coating weight in ounces per square foot of sheet. Triple-spot tests selected from the center of the sheet and from two diagonally opposed corners may be used for sheet material, and edge-center-edge spot tests may be used for the continuous product. It is customary to obtain edge spot tests two inches inward from the actual edge of the sheet or strip.

Bend tests are sometimes used for determining coating adherence and base-metal formability, especially in heavy-gage galvanized sheets. The bend, which may be made in a vise or punch press, is generally a full angle of 180° around a specified number of sheet thicknesses of the same gage as the test piece.

The **beading test** is commonly used for testing coating adherence in light-gage material. The width, depth, and radii of the beads vary somewhat depending upon the beading machine employed in making the test, although it is normal for the individual operator to have established definite standards for his

testing operation. In conducting the bead-testing operation, the impressions may be made to cross each other or run straight along the edge of the test piece, depending upon the severity of the test desired.

The **lockseam test** is used quite extensively in the sheet-galvanizing industry for testing coating adherence. For sheets that are to be used for seaming, the test also serves as a check on the formability of the base metal.

Tensile properties of the base metal are determined by the standard tension test using an 11/16-in. by 8-in. specimen machined in the center to a 0.5-in. width. In this test the yield point, ultimate strength and percentage of elongation in a 2-in. gage length are measured.

The **Rockwell "B" hardness** of the base metal is determined by subjecting a stripped sheet to the standard Rockwell testing procedure.

The **Olsen cup test** can be used to obtain an indication of the drawing properties of the base metal as well as the adherence of the coating.

Ferritic grain size can be determined by polishing and etching a longitudinal section of the base metal and comparing the microscopic grain structure with that of the proper standard grain-size chart.

Selected Bibliography

Historical Interest

Bablik, H., Bending conditions of galvanizing. Iron Age **125**, 1452–54 (1930)

Bablik, H., Formation of zinc and alloy layers during galvanizing process. Iron Age **125**, 1528–31 (1930)

Cherry, R. M., Electrically heated galvanizing furnace. Iron Age **129**, 334–338 (1932)

Cowper-Coles, S., Method of hot-dip coating metallic objects. U.S. Patent 979,931 (1910)

Daniels, E. J., The attack on mild steel in hot galvanizing. Institute of Metals Journal **56**, 81–96 (1931)

Daniels, E. J., Some reactions occurring in "hot-dipping" processes. Institute of Metals Journal **59**, 169–185 (1932)

Finkeldey, W. H., The adherence of zinc coatings. Metals and Alloys **2**, 266–271 (1931)

Imhoff, Wallace G., Pickling of iron and steel. Cleveland, Penton Publishing Co., 1929.

Richards, J. W., Use of aluminum in galvanizing. U.S. Patent 456,204 (1891)

Wolf, F. L. and W. E. Renwick, Galvanized coatings. Iron Age **143**, 30–35 (Jan. 19, 1939)

General Interest

Am. Iron and Steel Institute, 1961 Annual Statistical Report. N. Y., The Institute, 1961.

Am. Zinc Institute, A survey of roofing on farm buildings. N. Y., The Institute, 1944.

Edwards, H., Technique of sheet galvanising by hot dip process. Sheet Metal Industries **22**, 1546–52, 1725–30, 1914–22, 2096–2103 (1945)

Imhoff, W. G., Cause of gray sheets in hot-dip galvanizing. Blast Furnace & Steel Plant **29**, 1124–26, 1148–49 (1941)

Marks, E., Works practice in pickling of steel. Sheet Metal Industries **22**, 1179–83 (1945)

Marshall, W. E., Process of coating metal articles with molten metal and of preparing metal articles for hot coating. U.S. Patent 2,310,451 (1943)

Pollak, F. E. and E. F. Pellowe, Chemical control of hot-dip galvanising process. Sheet Metal Industries **22**, 1349–55 (1945)

U.S. Natl. Bureau of Standards, Surface treatment of steel prior to painting (BMS 44) Wash., Gov't. Printing Office, 1940.

Special Technical Interest

Am. Iron and Steel Institute, Steel products manual: carbon steel sheets. N. Y., The Institute, 1944.

Am. Society for Metals, Metals handbook; 1948 ed. Cleveland, The Society, 1948.

Am. Society for Testing Materials, Tentative specifications for 1.25 oz. class coating (pot yield) zinc-coated (galvanized) iron or steel roofing sheets (A 361-59T). ASTM Standards, 1961, Part I, Ferrous metals, p. 1251–1254.

Am. Society for Testing Materials, Tentative specifications for zinc-coated (galvanized) iron or steel sheets, coils and cut lengths (A 93-59T). ASTM Standards, 1961, Part I, Ferrous metals, p. 1201–1206.

Bablik, H., Attack of molten zinc on steel in hot-dip galvanising. Metal Treatment **14**, 29–35 (Spring 1947)

Bablik, H., Galvanizing (hot-dip). London, E. & F. N. Spon, 1950.

Brachmann, W., Galvanized sheet and strip. Stahl und Eisen **72**, 830–33 (1952)

Burns, R. M. and W. W. Bradley, Protective coatings for metals; 2nd ed., N. Y., Reinhold, 1955.

Lynn, H. W., Continuous galvanizing of strip steel. Iron Age **164**, 96–100 (July 21, 1949)

Mauger, A. J. and A. H. Ward, Metallic coating alloy. U.S. Patent 2,360,784 (1944)

Oganowski, K., Continuous galvanizing by the Sendzimir process. Metal Finishing **48**, 63–68 (Oct. 1950)

Redmond, J. P. and R. W. Hodil, Surface treatment of metals. U.S. Patent 2,199,418 (1940)

Rodriguez, A. O., Metallic coating process. U.S. Patent 2,046,036 (1936)

Rowland, D. H., Metallography of hot-dipped galvanized coatings. Am. Society for Metals Trans. **40**, 983–1011 (1948)

Sendzimir, T., Apparatus for coating metallic objects with layers of other metals. U.S. Patent 2,136,597 (1938)

Sendzimir, T., Coating iron and steel with molten metals such as zinc. U.S. Patent 2,110,893 (1938)

Sendzimir, T., Process for galvanizing sheet metal. U.S. Patent 2,197,622 (1940)

Ward, A. H., Continuous galvanizing—a development program. Iron Age **164**, 74–79, 154 (Oct. 13, 1949)

Ward, A. H., Continuous processing ferrous strip or sheet material. U.S. Patent 2,588,439 (1952)

White, F. G., Developments in galvanizing. Products Finishing 14, 48, 50, 52, 56 (May 1950)

CHAPTER 37

Manufacture of Heavy Press Forgings

This chapter will be confined to discussion of the production of steel forgings of large size in hydraulic presses utilizing open dies, and will be based generally on the practices employed at the Homestead District Works of United States Steel Corporation. Capacities of the hydraulic forging presses at this plant are 12,-000, 10,000, 3,000 and 2,000 tons. Auxiliary equipment includes furnaces of ample capacity for heating and reheating ingots and forgings, complete heat-treating facilities, and machine tools designed to handle the massive forgings that are produced.

The principle of operation of the hydraulic press was outlined in Section 5 of Chapter 19, along with a comparison of forging with other methods for the hot-working of steel. Although steel can be hot-worked in

various ways, perhaps no other method of hot-working can surpass the forging process for producing shapes that so closely approach those required in the finished steel product.

Open-die forging may be defined as the hot-working of steel between flat or contoured dies. This hot-work produces the following advantageous effects: refinement of the relatively coarse crystal structure inherent in the as-cast ingot; performance of sufficient work on the ingot to obtain the desired mechanical and metallurgical properties; and production of a sound, homogeneous mass of steel of the desired size and shape. Typical large forgings produced by the methods to be described are used for generator shafts, steam-turbine rotors, water wheels, anvil bases for

Fig. 37—1. Overhead crane removing a 77-inch diameter fluted ingot from the hearth of a car-bottom heating furnace after a 70-hour heating cycle to prepare it for forging.

994

large forging hammers, marine propulsion shafting, rolls and roll sleeves, die blocks and crankshafts. Heavy forgings used in the construction of nuclear reactors and as components for such specialized research equipment as cyclotrons, shock tubes, wave superheaters, bubble chambers, particle accelerators and stellarators are also produced. Forged billets, blooms, and slabs for further working in customers' plants are other products.

HEATING FOR FORGING

Rate of Heating—At Homestead District Works, the majority of large forgings are produced from ingots from 52 to 130 inches in diameter and weighing up to 600,000 lb. Such large masses of steel require careful control of heating practices that must be varied according to the chemical composition, size, and prior thermal history of the ingots. These same factors govern the several reheating operations usually involved in the production of forgings of large section. The general aims in the control of heating operations are: the attainment of a uniform temperature throughout the ingot or reheated forging, and establishment

of heating rates that will achieve proper degree and uniformity of temperature in the shortest practical time. Practical considerations related to time and rate of heating are the minimizing of the amount of scaling and decarburization of the steel surfaces.

Furnaces of the direct-fired car-bottom type (Figure 37—1) are popular for heating large ingots and forgings. Any furnace employed for this work should be equipped with suitable instrumentation for the accurate measurement, control, and recording of temperature.

Only general rules can be prescribed for heating large sections. Large ingots or forgings should be heated slowly and uniformly. The rate of heating fairly well establishes the length of time necessary for the steel to attain forging temperature throughout its mass, and a rate should be selected that avoids excessive temperature differentials between the inside and outside of the mass. The temperature of the interior lags behind that of the exterior during a large part of the heating cycle, and a period of time near the end of the cycle must elapse after the exterior has attained forging temperature for sufficient heat to be con-

FIG. 37—2. Hydraulic press in operation, forging a massive rectangular ingot supported on a porter bar which, in conjunction with the link-chain sling and turning gear suspended from an overhead crane, permits manipulation of the ingot as desired.

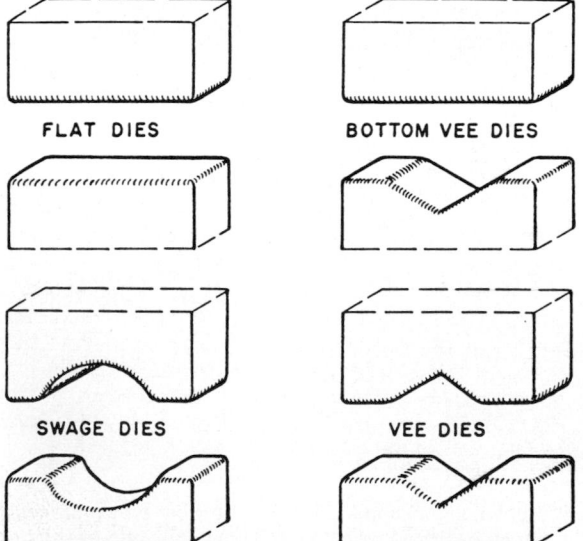

Fig. 37—3. Heavy-duty manipulator holding an ingot in position while a 10,000-ton press squeezes the hot steel into the rough shape of the finished product.

ducted into the interior to raise it to the proper temperature. The slower the heating rate, the shorter will be the time for such temperature equalization to take place. **Step heating** may be employed: that is, the

FLAT DIES

BOTTOM VEE DIES

SWAGE DIES

VEE DIES

Fig. 37—4. Basic shapes of dies for open-die forging.

steel may be held at one or more temperature levels below forging temperature and allowed to equalize before proceeding to a higher temperature level. It has been found that after its temperature has been equalized at a point slightly above the upper critical temperature (about 1475° F), steel can be heated at a rate of 40° to 60° F per hour until forging temperature is attained. This cycle results in heating times corresponding to approximately ¾ to 1 hour per inch of diameter or thickness of the ingot or forging. In general, carbon steels containing over 0.50 per cent of carbon and alloy steels require slower rates of heating than carbon steels of lower than 0.50 per cent of carbon content.

Forging Temperature—Forging temperature is selected to provide the best condition for hot-working a given steel. Although the final properties of a finished forging are established largely by heat treatments applied subsequent to hot-working, the temperature at which hot-working is completed influences, to varying degrees depending on grade, what heat treatments are necessary as well as the final mechanical properties of the steel. In general, lower finishing temperatures result in a finer-grained microstructure when forging is completed. The finer-grained structures respond better to heat treatment than do coarser-grained structures. However, the finishing

FIG. 37—5. Large corrugated ingot in the process of being "cogged" or reduced to an octagonal shape during the first stage of forging.

temperature must be kept high enough to prevent the occurrence of forging bursts (internal ruptures) that may result from severe stresses induced by working large masses of steel at too low a temperature.

Caution must be exercised to avoid **overheating** and **burning** of the steel. The safe upper limit of the hot-working range is a suitable temperature interval below the melting point of the lowest-melting constituent of a steel. **Burning** consists of heating a steel to a high temperature in an oxidizing atmosphere so that actual fusion and oxidation occur at the austenite grain boundaries, causing hot shortness that results in badly torn surfaces and internal ruptures during hot working. Burned steel cannot be salvaged. **Overheating** has less obvious effects, caused by heating to a high temperature but not sufficiently high as to cause burning. The effects of slight overheating can be removed by subsequent hot working, but more severe overheating can cause low ductility in forgings tested after final heat treatment.

HANDLING EQUIPMENT

Special equipment is required for handling the heavy masses of steel represented by forging ingots and the forgings themselves.

Electric overhead traveling cranes with special lifting devices are employed in charging ingots and forgings onto and from the hearths of car-bottom heating furnaces, and for transporting them to and from the forging presses (Figure 37—1).

An electric crane at the forging press carries a **turning gear** suspended from the main hoist. The turning gear consists of a frame carrying a drum that can be rotated by an electric motor through gearing. An endless chain called a **sling**, constructed of flat links and pins, passes over the drum and moves with it (Figure 37—2).

A device called a **porter bar** has a hollow end shaped to fit the sinkhead of the ingot being forged. The load represented by the ingot and porter bar is balanced by placing the sling at the center of gravity

FIG. 37—6. Straight-down forging of a 250-ton bloom between flat dies on a hydraulic forging press.

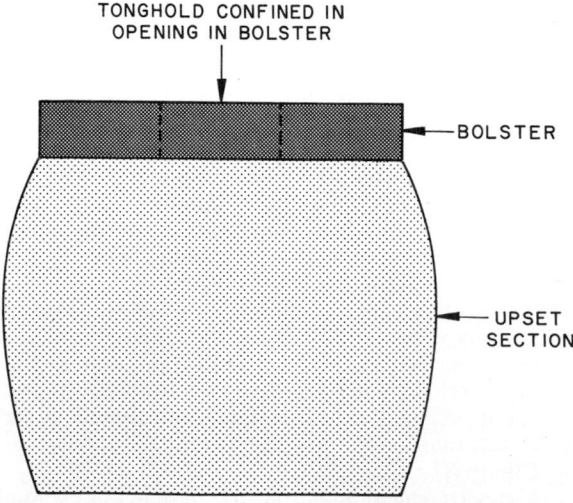

TONGHOLD CONFINED IN
OPENING IN BOLSTER

BOLSTER

UPSET
SECTION

FIG. 37—7. Schematic representation of the use of a bolster to maintain a previously forged tonghold on a piece during upsetting.

of the combined load (Figure 37—2): the sling has to be moved from time to time to preserve balance as the dimensions of the forging are changed.

Faster and more accurate handling of the hot steel during forging is accomplished by the use of machines called **manipulators**. These machines are equipped with powerful tongs at the end of a horizontal arm that can be moved from side to side, raised or lowered, and rotated about its longitudinal axis. The manipulator shown in Figure 37—3 operates on tracks in the floor in front of a 10,000-ton hydraulic press, and has a capacity for handling pieces weighing up to 75 tons. Smaller manipulators are designed to operate on wheels that have resilient or solid tires.

OPEN DIES FOR FORGING

The dies used in open-die forging are of three basic types, shown schematically in Figure 37—4. They are known as **flat dies, V dies,** and **swage dies.** For hollow forgings or ring forgings, a **mandrel** or **expanding bar** is inserted in a hole in the piece to be

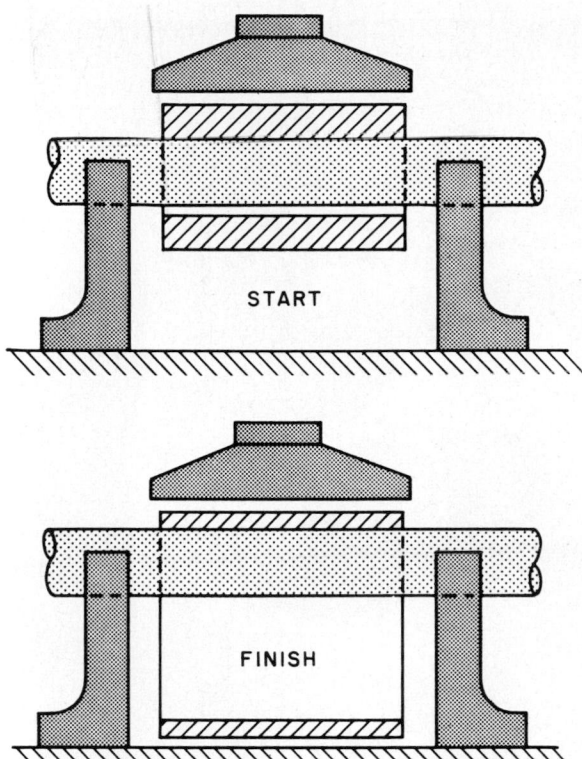

START

FINISH

FIG. 37—8. Sectional diagrammatic representation of the expanding operation for simultaneously increasing the inside and outside diameters of a hollow cylindrical forging while reducing wall thickness. The expanding bar acts as a bottom die.

forged, and forging is carried out by utilizing the mandrel or bar as the bottom die.

PRINCIPAL FORGING OPERATIONS

Superior quality, toughness and strength characteristics have gained for forgings their reputation for dependability under the most severe service conditions. The consecutive operations employed in producing heavy press forgings by open-die forging are carefully planned and executed in proper order so as to arrive at the final contour (in which the sections may vary greatly) while at the same time achieving the proper degree of grain refinement and internal soundness.

Initial working of an ingot is usually referred to as **cogging** (Figure 37—5), and removes the flutes, ripples or corrugations that were formed on the ingot as it solidified in a contoured mold and which are intended to prevent cracking of the ingot surface during solidification and cooling. Light drafts (small reductions) are taken all over the ingot until the surface irregularities are smoothed. Heavier drafts are then taken and working continues, usually to convert the cross-section of an originally round ingot to an octagon shape, then to a square, back to an octagon, and so on. Rectangular ingots usually are forged so as to retain a rectangular cross-section throughout forging. This **straight-down** or **setting-down** type of forging (exemplified by Figure 37—6),

also called **drawing out** and **forging solid,** is used on products such as blooms, rounds, and shafting having constant or variable section size, in which the work flows in a longitudinal direction. For variable section sizes or step-downs, **marking knives** or **veeing tools** are used to mark off the necessary volume of metal for any particular section (see Figure 37—11).

Upsetting is employed for forgings made into wheels, discs and gears that rotate in use. The benefit derived from such **pancaking** results from the circumferential flow that induces the best condition for parts subjected to either tangential or radial stresses, or both. Upsetting is sometimes also employed as an intermediate operation in the production of steam-turbine rotors. In this instance, the ingot is forged to a bloom of predetermined size, usually octagonal in shape, and a slug of sufficient length is sheared. The slug is upended and forged to reduce its length between 20 and 30 per cent. Further forging consists of reworking along the length, marking, and contouring. Benefits derived from this sequence of operations include working in all directions to enhance soundness and reduce the directionality of properties. In upsetting, it is necessary to keep the length of the slug within certain limits (usually not more than $2\frac{1}{2}$ times the octagon size) to prevent kinking or bending during upsetting. In some types of upsetting operations, hollow, cylindrical die-like tools called **bolsters** may be employed to retain part of the slug and prevent change in its dimensions while the upsetting force is applied to deform the rest of the slug. A simple application of a bolster is shown schematically in Figure 37—7.

Piercing and **punching** are performed by forcing a solid punch into hot steel to form a cavity. Piercing is employed to make a blind cavity by displacement without removal of metal. Punching produces a hole that extends through the entire section and both displaces and removes metal in the form of a slug. Sometimes a hollow punch is used to remove some of the central metal as a core: this operation is generally termed **hot trepanning** or **hot trephining.**

Expanding is a special process for increasing the diameter of hollow forgings. It can be used for finishing hollow forgings or to increase the size of the hole prior to finish forging on a mandrel. It is also employed in the forging of rings. For expanding a forging of considerable length, a top tool with a narrow face parallel to the expanding bar is used (Figure 37—8), to keep the lengthwise elongation of the piece to a minimum while reducing the thickness. As shown in Figure 37—8, the bottom die is replaced by an **expanding bar** or mandrel that passes through the opening in the forging and rests on supports beyond the forging. When pressure is applied, the thickness of the material between the top tool and the bar is reduced, displacement of the metal resulting in an increase in the circumference of the forging. By successive incremental movement of the work piece followed by pressing, the wall thickness can be reduced uniformly while attaining the desired inside and outside diameters. Uniformity of temperature throughout the piece is important for successful control of expanding, and a bar of sufficient strength to

FIG. 37—9. Forging a large steel ring in a hydraulic press, using an expanding bar.

withstand the bending moment is essential. Figure 37—9 illustrates the forging of a large ring on an expanding bar.

The process of **hollow forging on a mandrel** differs somewhat from the expanding process, in that the mandrel establishes the inside diameter as the piece is forged with pressure from opposed top and bottom tools. As shown in Figure 37—10, the hollow work piece is fitted to a mandrel of the desired size that is supported on both ends to position the work between the top and bottom dies. Narrow-faced tools are used in this type of work to cause the metal to flow lengthwise of the piece. The mandrel is usually tapered slightly to facilitate its removal from the finished forging.

Closing in is an operation on a hollow forging, using flat, tapered, curved, or formed dies, to partially close the end, or reduce some other portion of a forging; as, for example, in forming the hemispherical ends of a boiler drum. One or more local reheatings of the part of the forging being worked are usually involved.

Slabbing consists of forging an ingot to a large, heavy slab or plate section that is beyond the capabilities of rolling facilities.

EXAMPLES OF FORGING PROCEDURE

Figures 37—8, 37—9 and 37—10 have shown the principles employed in making hollow forgings such as cylinders and rings. These expanding and elongating principles are used singly or in combination to forge boiler drums, chemical reactors, pressure vessels, roll sleeves and many other products.

Figure 37—11 shows the steps in producing a sleeve for a cold-reduction mill back-up roll. Such sleeves generally are made from a high-carbon (0.50 to 0.65 per cent) nickel-chromium of chromium-molybdenum steel. This particular sleeve has a 42⅝-inch outside diameter, a 28-inch inside diameter, and a 42⅞-inch body length. Three sleeves of this size are produced from a 48-inch diameter ingot weighing 72,800 lb. The round, corrugated ingot is first forged to a 44-inch octagon, then sheared into three pieces, each 42 inches in length. The pieces are reheated and each is upset forged to 36 inches in length, after which a 16½-inch diameter hole is punched through the longitudinal axis of each. After reheating, each piece is forged on a 16-inch diameter expanding bar to increase the hole to 20-inch diameter. Each expanded piece is again reheated and forged on a 19½-inch diameter bar to a 39¼-inch octagon and the hole

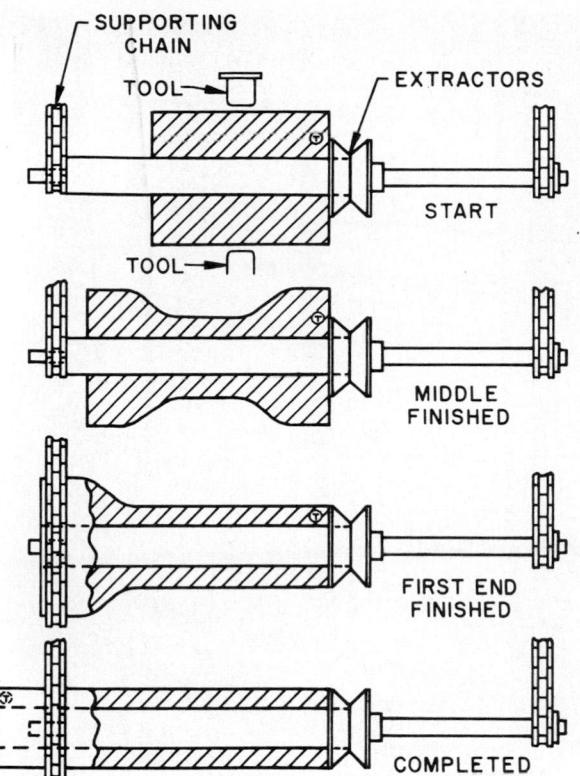

FIG. 37—10. Schematic diagram showing steps involved in forging a hollow cylinder on a mandrel. The mandrel establishes the inside diameter of the forging as pressure is applied by the top and bottom tools.

is enlarged to 21 inches. Another reheating is followed by forging the ends of each piece to a level contour. After a final reheating, the sleeves are each forged on a 19-inch diameter bar to 26 inches in inside diameter, 44⅝ inches in outside diameter, and approximately 53 inches in length. After this final forging operation, the sleeves are slowly cooled, then heat treated to secure the proper microstructure for subsequent hardening by water quenching and tempering, following rough machining.

A typical Ni-Mo-V generator-rotor shaft with a forge weight of 75 to 80 tons and a rough-machined weight of 55 to 60 tons, would be forged in three heats from a 170-ton, 95-inch diameter ingot. On the first forge heat, the corrugated ingot body is forged to approximately a 55-inch octagon, the sinkhead is sheared off, and a chuckhold forged on the top end. On the second heat, the ingot is further reduced to approximately a 47-inch octagon, marked and "veed" to define the body and journal steps, and at this stage the bottom discard is sheared off. On the third and final heat, the various steps from body to journals are forged to size, a final forge pass made on the body, and the top chuckhold sheared off. The appropriate slow cooling, heat treating, and machining operations are carried out before the shaft is shipped.

COOLING AFTER FORGING

It is important that large forgings be cooled after hot-working is finished in a manner that will prevent

the formation of thermal **bursts** or **ruptures** caused by internal stresses related to differences in rate of cooling of different parts of the forging, or **flakes** that are attributed to gases (particularly hydrogen) absorbed by the liquid metal during steelmaking. As described in Chapter 18, vacuum stream degassing of molten

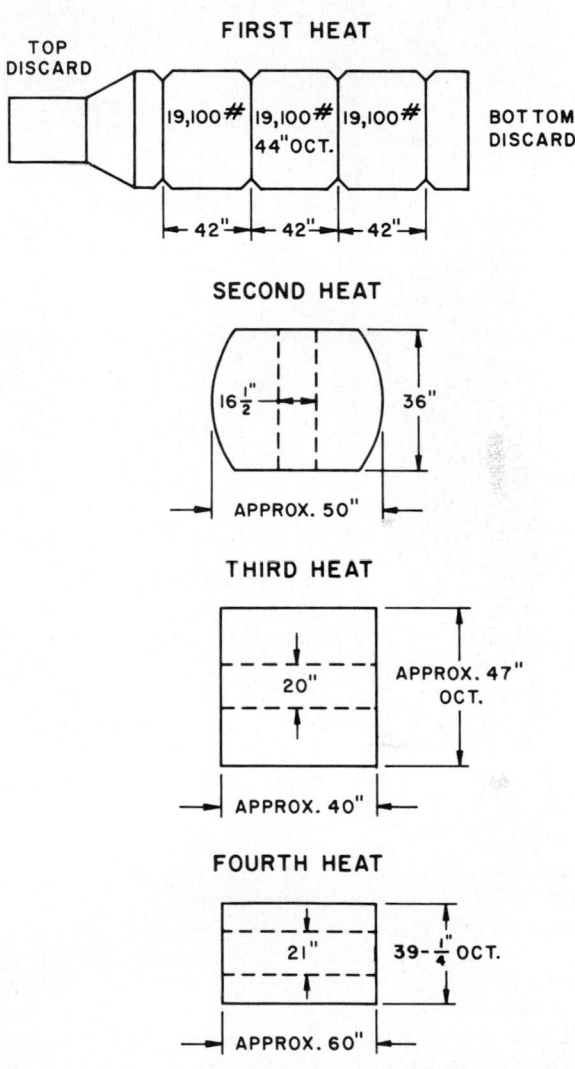

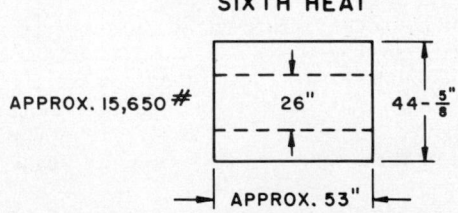

FIG. 37—11. Steps involved in forging a sleeve for a back-up roll for a cold-reduction mill.

FIG 37—12. Forging positioned over one of a battery of four pit-type heat-treating furnaces (see also Figure 37—13).

FIG. 37—13. General view of battery of pit-type furnaces (right) and vertical quench chamber (left) for the heat treatment of large forgings. Generator-shaft forging is shown rotating about its vertical axis within the quench chamber, the doors of which normally are closed during operation but which were left open for this photograph.

FIG. 37—14. Generator-shaft forging being lowered onto holding fixture on rotating base of quench chamber. Structure at floor level in left foreground is an upending cradle that raises long forgings from a horizontal position to a vertical position to facilitate handling by crane. Sliding vertical doors close front of chamber during quenching.

steel to lower the hydrogen content to safe limits will effectively prevent formation of flakes, even in very large ingots, and consumable-electrode melting and vacuum melting (see Chapter 17) can achieve the same end in smaller ingots. However, prevention of damaging internal stresses can only be achieved through closely controlled cooling. For applications where minimum residual stresses are necessary, very slow cooling rates and long tempering times are advisable.

HEAT TREATMENT OF FORGINGS

Few heavy forgings are shipped without some form of heat treatment. At Homestead District Works, horizontal car-bottom furnaces and vertical pit-type furnaces are used, depending upon the shape and weight of the forgings undergoing heat treatment.

Typical heat-treating operations include:

1. Annealing (various cycles)
2. Normalizing (with optional accelerated air-cooling) and tempering.
3. Water or oil quenching followed by tempering, utilizing tanks for quenching.
4. Water-spray quenching, followed by tempering.
5. Stress relieving.
6. Various combinations of the above.

Car-Bottom Furnaces—The plant has thirteen car-bottom furnaces for the heat treatment of forgings. These are direct top-and-bottom fired, using natural gas as fuel, and have a maximum operating temperature of 1940° F. Heating chambers of these large furnaces are of two sizes: 216 in. wide by 140 in. high by 540 in. long, and 108 in. wide by 84 in. high by 912 in. long.

Vertical Furnaces—Ten vertical pit-type furnaces are available for heat treating large and lengthy shafting, steam-turbine rotors, generator shafts, and similar types of forgings.

Three of these furnaces can accommodate forgings up to 5 feet in diameter and 30 feet long. The other seven furnaces can handle forgings approximately 6 feet in diameter and 50 feet long, with a maximum weight of 100 tons. The principal use of these furnaces is for grain-refinement treatments and stress relieving of rotors and shafts. The tops of the three furnaces that can handle 30-foot forgings are at ground level, the furnaces proper being below ground level. Only part of the other seven furnaces is below ground, as shown in Figures 37—12 and 37—13. All ten of the furnaces are charged from the top by an overhead crane. Work rests on a special hearth casting at the bottom of each furnace and is stabilized by pins inserted through sides of the furnace to contact the forging, except in one furnace that has a rotating hearth that revolves the charge about its longitudinal axis throughout the heating cycle. Natural-gas-fired burners fire tangentially into the heating chambers to prevent flames from impinging directly on the charges and to circulate the products of combustion in a manner that promotes temperature uniformity in the furnaces.

A typical heating cycle consists of a heat-up period at a controlled rate of temperature rise, a soak period, another heating at a controlled rate to a higher temperature, another soak period, and then a controlled cooling period. Because of the slow cooling rates involved, it is usually necessary to provide a small amount of heat to maintain the desired rate of cooling. When the natural cooling rate is slower than that desired, the gas is shut off and the proportioning controller operates the air valve only, thus increasing the cooling rate. A complete heat-treating cycle can last from one to eight days.

Quenching Facilities—Some forgings to be quenched in liquid media (water or oil) require a more rapid cooling rate than air-cooling in the furnaces can provide. For this purpose, a vertical quench chamber (Figure 37—14) is located near a battery of the pit-type furnaces. Forgings are positioned vertically and held securely in the base that can be rotated continuously during the quenching operation. A variety of cooling media can be employed, such as water spray, fog spray, a combination fog-and-air spray, or an air quench.

For liquid-media quenching, the plant has water and oil tanks of ample dimensions, equipped for forced circulation of the quenchants.

CHAPTER 38

Castings - Steel And Iron

SECTION 1

STEEL CASTINGS

Casting Compared with Other Forms of Shaping Steel—The process of making steel castings consists simply of pouring metal into a mold which is of the desired shape, dimensionally accurate and of sufficient stability to permit the metal to solidify in the exact shape of the mold cavity. Intricate and complicated castings of practically any desired shape or size, and for almost any particular application, can be made in this manner. The versatility of the foundry trade commands recognition throughout the industrial world, and design engineers in every field of endeavor have come to rely upon the utility of steel castings.

Mechanically, steel castings are considered inferior to wrought-steel products, and it is true that wrought steels do exhibit higher mechanical properties than cast steels, especially when the former are tested in the direction of rolling or forging. Moreover, cast structures, unless designed in strict conformity with the natural characteristics of metal solidification, sometimes contain internal defects or surface imperfections which may seriously affect serviceability and otherwise render them less dependable than a wrought-steel product. However, the casting of steel is the most direct method of producing a given shape and, for this reason, the method provides the basis for a key industry.

Tonnagewise, the steel-casting or steel-foundry industry would appear to be of minor importance, approximately two per cent of the total steel production per year being in the form of castings. However, few industries enjoy so prominent a role in the industrial and domestic development of the world as the foundry industry. Many articles, especially turbine shells, valve bodies, and machine parts are made by casting, not by choice, but because they cannot be made as readily by other processes. For example, valve bodies, exhaust manifolds, pump casings, and turbine diaphragms could be fabricated by other processes or from wrought products only with extreme difficulty and at a serious economic disadvantage. Also, cast structures are generally considered to be more rigid than their wrought counterparts.

Steel castings vary in weight from a few ounces to hundreds of tons and cover a multitude of designs and services. Latch castings for airplane cowls weigh less than four ounces, while one of the largest castings ever produced was a 240-ton casting for an armor press of 35,000 tons capacity. Castings for steel-mill service alone cover a very large field and include housings, gears, charging boxes, guides, blast-furnace bells, hoppers and cinder pots. Rolls for certain types of rolling mills are made of cast steel; because of the specialized foundry techniques employed in roll casting, the manufacture of rolling-mill rolls by casting is discussed separately and at length in Chapter 20. The transportation industry relies upon castings for railroad and marine use, such as couplings, journal boxes, bolsters, frames, brake shoes, cylinders, housings, valves, crankshafts, engine beds and steam chests. These are but a few of the examples in everyday use and hundreds of other applications could be mentioned serving the chemical, petroleum, mining, excavating, agricultural, ceramic and construction industries.

Composition and Mechanical Properties of Cast Steels—The development of the mechanical properties of cast steels depends almost wholly upon heat treatment, and since the depth of hardening in carbon steels is limited, it follows that alloys in varying proportions must be added when high strength is required. This is especially true of castings with heavy metal sections. Nickel, chromium, manganese, molybdenum, and vanadium are alloys commonly added to cast steels. These are added according to the manufacturers' past experiences and heat-treating facilities. Table 38—I shows typical compositions and results of tension tests for some heat-treated cast steels.

MAKING STEEL FOR CASTINGS

Five types of furnaces are or have been employed by foundries for melting steel. These are: (1) the direct-arc electric furnace; (2) the open-hearth furnace; (3) the pneumatic converter; (4) the electric-induction furnace; and (5) the crucible furnace. The pneumatic-converter and the crucible processes, formerly of importance, have now been supplanted almost entirely by electric-furnace melting. The size and type of castings being made dictate the type of furnace. Foundries making small castings weighing from 1 to 500 pounds favor the electric process. Producers of large castings weighing from 500 pounds up to 25 tons or more use open-hearth furnaces.

Electric furnaces in foundries vary in size and the normal weight of charge runs from 250 pounds to 25 tons. Open-hearth furnaces in foundry practice usually

Table 38—I. Compositions and Mechanical Properties of Some Cast Steels.

COMPOSITIONS

Type of Steel	C (%)	Mn (%)	Si (%)	Ni (%)	Cr (%)	V (%)	Mo (%)	Cu (%)
Low-Carbon	0.12	0.32	0.25					
	0.19	0.60	0.44					
	0.19	0.60	0.44					
	0.11	0.60	0.30					
	0.17	0.67	0.23					
Medium-Carbon	0.21	0.55	0.45					
	0.25	0.57	0.41					
	0.28	0.63	0.47					
	0.28	0.62	0.40		0.10*			
	0.27	0.69	0.26					
	0.31	0.75	0.42					
	0.31	0.75	0.42					
	0.42	0.69	0.43					
	0.46	0.73	0.28					
High-Carbon	0.50	0.59	0.54					
	0.56	0.62	0.47					
	0.84	0.73	0.44					
2% Nickel	0.15–0.35	0.60–1.00		2.00				
3% Nickel	0.20–0.45	0.50–0.80		2.50–3.50				
Nickel-Manganese	0.20–0.40	0.90–1.50		0.75–1.50				
Nickel-Vanadium	0.20–0.35	0.60–1.10		1.40–1.75		0.80–0.15		
Nickel-Molybdenum	0.20–0.35	0.60–1.00		1.25–2.00			0.25–0.40	
Nickel-Chromium-Molybdenum	0.30–0.50	0.60–0.90		1.50–3.00	0.45–1.00		0.20–0.40	
Medium-Manganese	0.30–0.40	1.35–1.55	0.25–0.50					
Manganese-Molybdenum	0.20–0.40	1.10–1.50	0.25–0.50				0.25–0.50	
Low-Chromium	0.25–0.40	0.65–0.85			0.60–0.90			
2%-3% Chromium	0.25–0.40	0.65–0.85			2.00–3.00			
4%-6% Chromium	0.10–0.30	0.60–1.00			4.00–6.00			
Chromium-Molybdenum	0.25–0.50	0.65–0.85			0.50–1.50		0.20–0.50	
Carbon-Molybdenum	0.25–0.40	0.60–0.80					0.30–0.50	
Vanadium	0.25–0.40	0.65–0.90	0.30–0.50			0.15–0.25		
Copper	0.15–0.40	0.70–1.00	0.30–0.50					1.00–2.00
Hadfield Manganese	1.00–1.40	10.00–14.00	0.30–1.00					

*Residual element.

Table 38—I (Continued)

MECHANICAL PROPERTIES (Corresponding to compositions given in first part of table)

Type of Steel	Heat Treatment	Tensile Strength (Lb./Sq. In.)	Yield Strength (Lb./Sq. In.)	Elongation (%)	Reduction of Area (%)	Brinell Hardness Number	Impact** Properties (Ft.—Lb.)	Source
Low-Carbon	Annealed	51,000	26,000	36.2	66.3	...	...	Korber & Pomp
	Annealed	71,500	46,500	34.0	58.0	139	24[a]	Lorig
	Normalized	74,500	48,000	32.0	55.1	142	26[a]	Lorig
	Water quenched and tempered at 1250°F.	62,500	35,500	36.5	59.6	...	...	Korber & Pomp
	Annealed	64,000	35,000	28.5	40.2	...	...	
	Annealed	77,100	40,900	27.0	42.5	...	...	
	Annealed	77,950	40,600	32.0	51.9	...	...	
	Annealed	80,450	42,950	29.0	42.9	...	...	
Medium-Carbon	Water quenched and tempered at 1050°F.	101,250	84,350	18.0	43.7	207	...	Phillips
	Normalized	76,000	41,500	28.0	44.8	156	14[a]	Lorig
	Annealed	77,000	43,500	28.7	44.5	134	20[a]	Lorig
	Normalized	83,500	53,000	29.3	51.9	146	...	Hall–Nissen–Taylor
	Annealed	77,000	...	22.0	25.0	...	...	Melmouth
	Annealed	93,000	...	22.0	33.6	...	...	Hall–Nissen–Taylor
	Annealed	84,000	...	19.8	24.5	...	...	
High-Carbon	Annealed	91,250	56,300	16.0	21.0	...	...	
	Annealed	114,750	60,150	8.0	12.7	...	...	
2% Nickel	Normalized and tempered	80,500	50,000	28.0	59.0	...	...	
	tempered	97,100	60,700	26.0	53.0	...	56[b]	Internat'l. Nickel Co.
3% Nickel	Fully annealed	85,500	53,500	29.0	55.0	...	...	
	Normalized and tempered	100,000	63,500	23.5	46.5	...	...	Internat'l. Nickel Co.
Nickel-Manganese	Normalized and tempered	89,600	56,150	26.5	51.5	...	...	
	Normalized and tempered	96,500	69,800	26.0	55.0	...	47[b]	Internat'l. Nickel Co.
Nickel-Vanadium	Normalized and tempered	105,000	79,000	26.0	51.0	...	...	Internat'l. Nickel Co.
Nickel-Molybdenum	Normalized and tempered	83,500	57,500	27.0	52.0	...	...	
	Normalized and tempered	88,000	55,000	25.0	48.0	...	55[b]	Internat'l. Nickel Co.
	Water quenched and tempered	104,000	81,300	21.0	46.5	...	...	
Nickel-Chromium-Molybdenum	Normalized and tempered	149,000	135,000	12.0	32.0	...	...	Internat'l. Nickel Co.
Medium-Manganese	Normalized and tempered	88,850	51,200	27.5	58.1	187	15[b]	Industry
	Normalized and tempered	98,800	61,450	22.0	44.0	202	...	
Manganese-Molybdenum	Quenched and tempered	85,550	56,600	29.0	56.4	196	40[b]	Industry
	Normalized and tempered	119,400	95,050	21.0	51.4	235	...	
Low-Chromium	Normalized and tempered	84,000	51,000	33.0	63.0	187	26[b]	Industry
	Normalized and tempered	99,500	58,400	16.0	29.0	220	...	Critchett
2%–3% Chromium	Normalized and tempered	118,000	94,000	23.0	51.0	...	...	Industry
4%–6% Chromium	Normalized and tempered	122,500	97,500	15.0	38.0	...	...	
Chromium-Molybdenum	Normalized and tempered	86,300	53,850	23.4	39.8	...	...	Industry
	tempered	120,000	79,000	19.0	35.6	241	...	
Carbon-Molybdenum	Normalized and tempered	77,500	48,000	30.0	56.2	168	...	Industry
Vanadium	Normalized and tempered	90,000	60,000	20.5	33.3	...	...	Industry
	Normalized and tempered	92,400	46,250	28.0	55.0	...	...	
Copper	Normalized and tempered	79,000	58,600	23.5	42.4	119	47[b]	Industry
	Normalized and tempered	67,000	49,500	32.5	53.9	183	...	
Hadfield Manganese	Quenched	96,250	61,750	22.0	35.0	...	...	Greenridge-Lorig
	Quenched	125,000	35,000	50.0	40.0	...	...	

*Residual element.　**At room temperature.　(a)Charpy.　(b)Izod.

have capacities between 10 tons and 100 tons. The present trend in melting equipment seems to be in favor of the electric process and many of the open-hearth foundries are converting to electric-furnace practice. The reason for this is the greater flexibility of the electric furnace over the open hearth, as well as various economic considerations.

In general, furnace charges consist of purchased scrap in the form of billets, shearings, flashings, punchings, plates and turnings; also, scrap from the foundry itself in the form of gates, heads, and scrapped castings. High-grade pig iron, low in phosphorus and sulphur, is used in the open-hearth furnace charges, and frequently in the electric-furnace charges when a high-carbon melt is required. Ferro-alloys and slag-making materials are used in about the same proportions in the melt as for steel-ingot production. However, the casting-from-melt yield is considerably lower than that generally experienced with ingots. For every ton of steel castings produced, at least three tons of raw materials are consumed, including scrap steel, pig iron, fuel oil, limestone, sand, organic and clay binders, and miscellaneous materials. This includes the mold-making materials.

Fifty per cent of the steel-casting tonnage is melted in open-hearth furnaces, approximately half being made in basic-lined furnaces. The basic furnace offers one distinct advantage in permitting partial removal of sulphur and phosphorus, thereby making possible the use of less costly scrap. However, in localities where scrap low in sulphur and phosphorus is abundant, the acid open-hearth process commonly is used for various reasons, some of which are largely a matter of beliefs.

The most important advantage of the acid open hearth is that the rate of carbon drop can be closely controlled; if no ore is added, the heat will remain at a given carbon level. This characteristic permits close control of composition of the finished steel, and permits a heat to be held in the furnace for as long as 30 minutes if molds are not available.

Another advantage of an acid furnace is that the bottom and banks are not harmed by the sand that often adheres to the heads and gates that are part of each furnace charge. This sand would be extremely erosive to a basic furnace bottom.

Hydrogen content of acid open-hearth steel is lower than that of basic open-hearth steel by about two or three parts per million, and the recoveries of ferro-alloys are higher and more consistent for acid open-hearth steel.

Much has been written concerning the operation of open-hearth furnaces, and elsewhere in this book the subject is treated in some detail. Suffice it to say that the melting process in foundry practice is very similar to that practiced in the steel mills, the chief difference being that greater amounts of deoxidizers are required in foundry practice to produce sound castings, free from porosity. It is necessary to add silicon and manganese in amounts in excess of 0.35 and 0.60 per cent, respectively. The 0.35 per cent minimum silicon content is necessary to assure castings free from blowholes (dead-killed steels) and the 0.60 per cent of manganese is necessary to keep "hot tearing" to a mini-

mum. Also, aluminum and alloys of calcium, manganese, silicon and zirconium commonly are added to insure complete deoxidation, removal of dissolved gases such as hydrogen and nitrogen, and, finally, for grain-size control.

Electric furnaces offer several distinct advantages over the open-hearth furnaces in the foundry. The modern arc furnace, with its top-charge mechanism, improved switchgear and automatic control, is an extremely flexible unit and rapidly is replacing the open-hearth furnace in the foundry. Electric furnaces permit a wider range of scrap selection than the open hearth, can be charged quickly and without the aid of a charging machine, operation requires fewer men, and the power costs are less than fuel costs in many localities. The furnaces can be shut down and allowed to cool to room temperature with less damage. The types of steels that can be produced in electric furnaces are unlimited. Highly-alloyed steels can be made as well as the plain carbon steels and electric furnaces are more flexible in the size and type of heats. This facilitates foundry planning and affects customer relations by the ability to make quicker deliveries.

Electric furnaces are lined with acid or basic refractories as available scrap or product characteristics may warrant. High-manganese steels are always melted in basic-lined furnaces because the slag from such steels is very destructive to acid refractories. Where low-sulphur and low-phosphorus scrap is not available, basic slags must be used to remove these elements, hence basic-lined furnaces are used. However, the major part of the electric-steel-casting tonnage is made by the acid-electric-furnace process.

The generally accepted method for making steel in **acid** electric furnaces is to melt hot, then by the application of either iron ore or oxygen, bring the bath to a violent boil or "blow," following which the heat is tapped before the action subsides completely. The metal generally is deoxidized in the ladle by the addition of relatively large amounts of deoxidizers.

There is greater variation in the melting operation of **basic** furnaces than acid furnaces. However, the three principal methods employed in the basic furnace are: (1) the **dead-melt process,** in which a reducing slag is made up as quickly as possible and maintained throughout the heat; (2) the **double-slag process** in which the first oxidizing slag is removed and replaced with a white, lime finishing slag; and (3) the **single-slag method** with an oxidizing slag which may or may not be made reducing before tapping. Each method has its own specific advantages, depending upon the type of steel being made.

MOLDING FOR CASTING STEEL

Patterns and Molds for Steel Castings—The construction of the **pattern** is perhaps the most important single factor in the production of a casting. Not only must the pattern be dimensionally accurate, but full consideration must be given to making it meet the requirements of the foundry equipment and technique. The patterns for steel castings are usually made ³⁄₁₆ to ¼ of an inch per foot larger than the dimensions shown on the drawing to compensate for metal shrinkage, because steel castings cooling from the liquid state to room temperature contract approximately ¼ inch per foot, depending upon the chemical composition of the steel and the size and design of the casting. It follows, therefore, that to make dimensionally accurate castings provision must be made for metal shrinkage. Patternmakers make such adjustments by **shrink rules** or **patternmakers' rules** which are graduated to compensate for the necessary shrink allowance. Other details of pattern construction, such as allowance for **draft** to facilitate removal of the pattern from the molding sand, **padding** for feed purposes, avoidance of sharp changes in metal sections, and elimination of sharp edges, corners and reentrant angles, all require full consideration.

There are several types or classes of patterns, each fulfilling a specific need. Patterns may be made of wood or metal, as required, and used in conjunction with hand-molding or machine-molding methods, depending upon the number of castings to be made and the degree of precision required. Descriptions of patterns and molding machines and procedures will be found in the books listed at the end of this chapter.

The materials used for making molds vary to a great extent, not only from foundry to foundry, but within the same foundry. The size and type of castings, the composition and temperature of the metal, pouring methods and foundry technique, sand mixing and reclaiming facilities, and location of the foundry exercise a profound influence upon the type of molding material. Some foundries prefer to make molds of crude or **bank sand.** For special work **calcined ganister** or **chamotte** is sometimes favored.

Patents have been issued for many molding media, such as those used in the **Fischer process** (calcined aluminous-clay grog), or in the **Randupson process** (sand and cement). Highly refractory **silica sands** of known particle size, mixed with weighed or measured quantities of various types of **clays, resins, dextrins, vegetable oils,** and water to develop desired molding characteristics are used. **Plaster, plastic** and **wax patterns** have been used for special purposes, such as making an experimental casting. Wax patterns are used extensively for castings weighing a few ounces and a special operation known as the "lost wax" or "precision casting" process is based upon the use of such patterns; this process is described in more detail later in this chapter.

Other molding materials include **mold and core washes** which are sprayed, or swabbed, on the mold surfaces to make a smooth mold and resist metal penetration, **gaggers** or reinforcing rods which are placed around the pattern in the sand to add strength to the mold, and **chills** of various types are used to promote directional solidification and reduce the effect of severe temperature gradients caused by sharp changes in metal sections of the casting. **External chills** are placed directly on the pattern and the chill is flush with the mold wall when the pattern is removed from the sand. **Internal chills** are placed in the mold after the pattern has been removed. Internal chills are often more effective than external chills, but they must be positioned with the utmost discretion. **Chaplets** and **stem anchors** are used within the mold cavity to support an internal core. **Nails** frequently are inserted in the mold surface to prevent metal penetration and sand erosion. Rolled-steel, cast-steel or wooden frames, commonly called **flasks,** are used to hold the molding sand around the pattern.

Flasks are made in two sections—the lower half is called the **drag** section; the upper half is called the **cope** section. Occasionally, there is need for a third section which is placed between the cope and the drag. This is known as the **cheek** section. The bottom of the flask is termed the **bottom board** or **bottom plate.** It is important that the cope and drag sections match properly. With small or medium flasks, this is accomplished by hardened pins placed on the outside of the drag section: with larger flasks, this matching is performed with guides, peep-sights, match blocks and many other ingenious devices. The flask sections and the bottom board are held together by "C" clamps or wooden or steel wedges. Figure 38—1 shows patterns, cope and drag sections of two different molds, and accessories required for one of the molds, and the finished castings produced with this equipment.

Making the Mold—The size and shape of the casting are the controlling factors in deciding how the molten steel should be introduced into the mold and where to locate **gates, risers** and **vents.** A flask is selected which is sufficiently larger than the pattern to provide room between the pattern and the flask wall to accommodate at least several inches of sand and the gate system. The flask also must be sufficiently large to permit placement of the **feedheads** or **risers** which are attached to the pattern and leave spaces in the finished mold to serve as reservoirs for molten metal that supply extra metal to feed the voids formed by shrinkage as the metal cools and passes from the liquid to the solid state.

In preparing the mold for a typical steel casting of relatively small size, the bottom board or bottom plate is clamped securely to the flange of the drag section of the mold as shown in Figure 38—1. The pattern is set on the bottom plate in such a position that sand may be rammed over the top of the pattern. The amount of sand must be sufficient to prevent metal runout, to develop the required strength to resist ferrostatic pressure, and to permit handling of the mold. **Facing sand** is riddled or sifted over the surface of the pattern to a depth of one inch and packed in any pockets and around the corners of the pattern. **Heap sand,** which is nothing more than used facing and core sands, sometimes re-bonded, is rammed into the flask to a depth of four inches. Pneumatic air hammers may be used for this purpose, and many foundries use sandslingers. More heap sand is added to a depth of six to eight inches, or until the flask is full and, after ramming, the excess sand is removed by a straight-edge. This operation is known as **striking off.** A bottom plate is clamped over the top of the flask and the entire flask section is rotated or turned 180°. The first bottom board is now removed and the cope section of the pattern is placed on the drag section. The two parts of the pattern are matched properly by dowel pins fitted into holes located in the face of the **parting line,** joint line, or split sections of the pattern. The cope section of the flask, which is reinforced with cross bars, is set on the drag section and fitted properly, as described. The

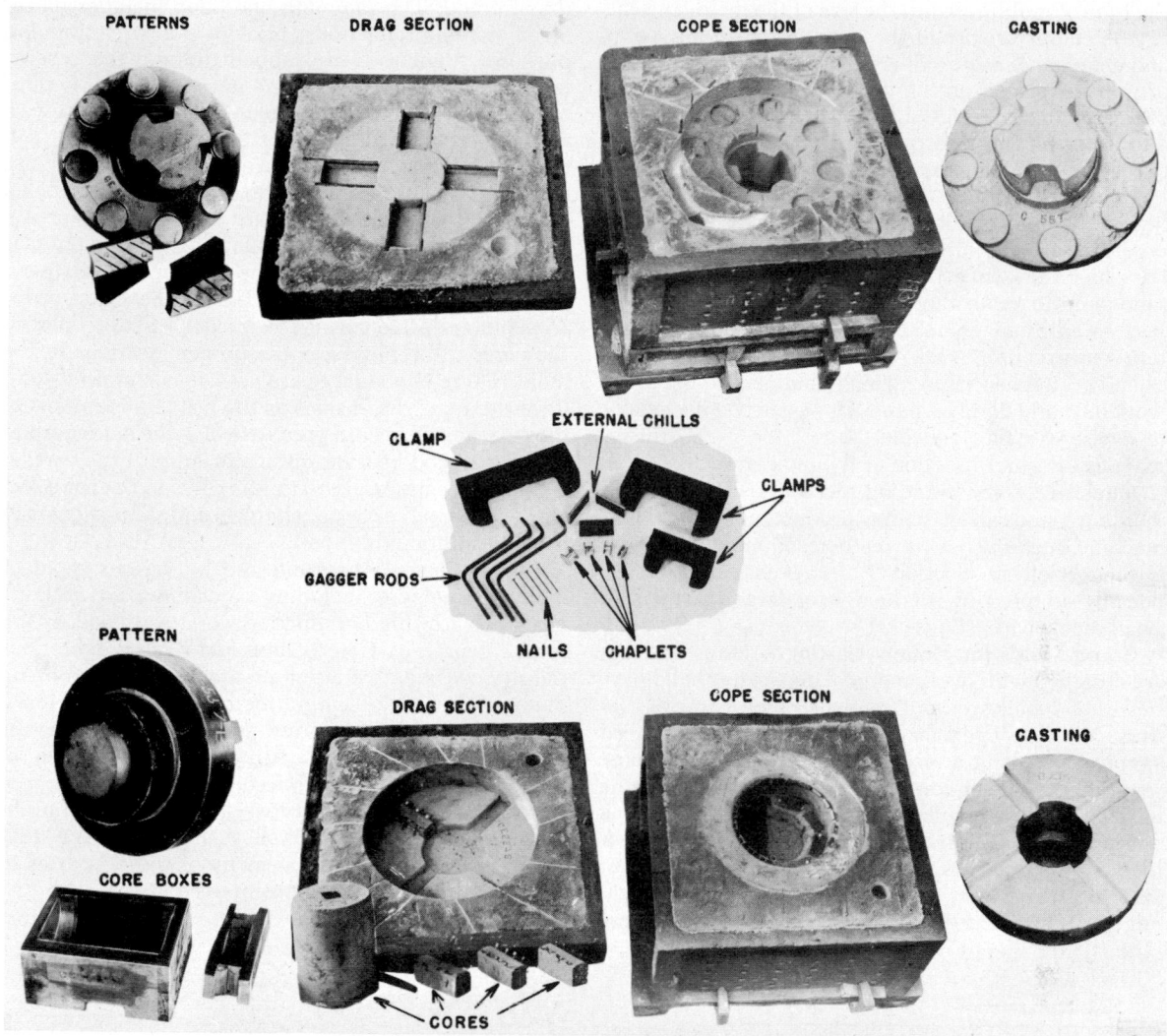

Fig. 38-1. Parts and accessories for preparing typical molds for two relatively small ferrous castings.

cross bars in the cope section also serve to support gagger rods which reinforce the sand, thereby preventing possible distortion of the mold cavity by pressure of the metal entering the mold.

A finely ground sand, known as **parting sand**, is dusted on the face of the drag section to prevent cohesion of the sand in the cope section with the sand in the drag section. **Riser patterns** are placed at the desired locations on the casting pattern and a **sprue stick** or **gate tile** is placed upright on the sand surface of the drag near the point where the metal is to enter the mold cavity. Facing sand is then riddled over the pattern and packed firmly by hand. The gagger rods are placed and heap sand rammed into the flask in the same manner as described for the drag section. After ramming is complete, the riser patterns and sprue stick, if used, are removed. The cope section is removed from the drag and the cope and drag patterns **drawn** from the sand by **lifting screws**. Pneumatic **vibrators** are sometimes attached to the patterns for the purpose of freeing the pattern from the sand. The mold is smoothed off and patched, and rough corners

and edges are rounded. The gate is cut in the drag section from the base of the sprue stick to the mold cavity. **Cores**, and chaplets, if required, are properly placed as shown by core prints and markings on the pattern. Provision for elimination of mold and core gases is made by jabbing a rod through the mold wall or by scratching **vents** across the drag section of the mold at the parting line. Internal chills, if required, are placed at this time. External chills are placed on the pattern surface prior to adding the facing sand.

If the casting is to be what is known as a **green sand casting**, the cope section of the mold is placed on the drag section and clamped securely to the bottom board. A runner cup, a sand mold having an internal shape similar to a funnel, is placed directly over the gate, and the mold is ready to pour.

If the casting is to be what is known as a **dry sand casting**, the mold cavity is sprayed or swabbed with a mold wash, and placed in a mold oven before the cores are set. Operating temperatures of **mold drying ovens** vary from 300–800° F and the time of drying may vary from 4 hours to 72 hours, depending upon the type of molding sand, the size of the mold, and the drying characteristics of the oven. After drying, cores and chaplets, if required, are placed and asbestos rope or putty is placed on the joint surface for a seal. The cope section then is fitted properly on the drag section and, after placing the runner cup, the mold is ready to receive the molten metal.

Machine Molding—Fundamentally, machine molding methods differ little from the process previously described for the manual or floor molding operation, the chief difference being that the ramming of the sand and the removal of the pattern from the sand are performed by machine. Also, there are details of pattern construction, such as integral gates and, frequently, attached risers, which eliminate some of the work formerly done by hand. However, the placement of cores, patching and finishing of the mold still remain as the chief function of the molder.

A relatively new molding method known as "shell molding" lends itself to the production of molds by machine methods. This method of molding is described briefly in Section 2 of this chapter. It is especially adapted to production of large numbers of small repetitive castings.

Cored Molds for Hollow Castings—Many castings are designed with overhanging flanges, ribs, bolt holes, bosses and hollowed-out sections. Such castings, because of their irregular shape, cannot be produced simply by making a mold, and the foundryman must resort to the use of cores to meet the demands of the design. A core is nothing more than a solid shape made of sand. Sand is rammed either by hand or machine, or blown into a **core box.** When the core box is filled with sand and the excess sand "struck off" with a straight edge, it is turned over and the box lifted from the core

thus formed. The ramming operation includes placement of reinforcing rods, or wire, for strengthening purposes. Vent rods are jabbed through the core to permit escape of gases. Sometimes wax wire is rammed in with the sand and, upon baking, the wax wire melts, thereby forming a passageway through which mold gases escape. As soon as the core is vented and sprayed with core wash, it is placed in an oven to bake. The baked core should be hard, strong, and smooth, but it should be sufficiently collapsible at high temperature in order not to cause the casting to "hot tear," i.e., pull apart due to contraction as the metal cools. Appendages attached to the molder's pattern permit the cores to be placed at the proper locations in the mold. These appendages are known as **coreprints** and have the same dimensions as the inside dimensions of the core box. The core prints are of sufficient length to provide a good bearing surface to support the core. It is sometimes necessary to tie the cores in the cope section of the mold or to use chaplets and stem anchors to provide additional support.

Cores are made by hand and by various types of molding machines, including sandslinger and rollover machines. For high production work, core blowers are used extensively. Core baking and drying operations require considerable attention and much use is being made of dielectric heating methods, as well as automatically controlled oil- and gas-fired ovens. Perhaps one of the greatest problems in the foundry is the selection and development of core sands to fill the specific needs of the various types of castings. Such problems are so varied and of such importance that specialists are employed in many of the foundries to study sands and sand compositions.

Gates, Risers and Vents—The gate, as mentioned

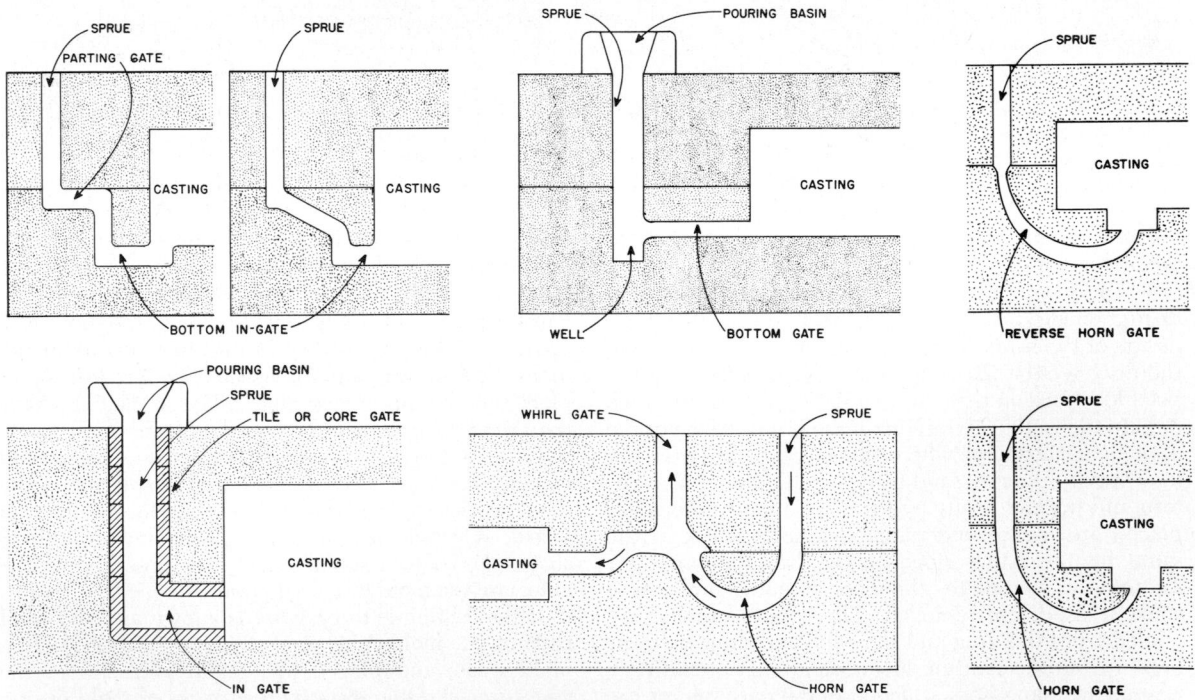

Fig. 38—2. Schematic vertical sections through various molds, illustrating types of gates frequently employed (After Briggs).

previously, is the channel or passageway through which the metal flows in filling the mold. The height, the cross-sectional area, and the shape of the gate, as well as the point at which it enters the mold cavity, are all important factors in any gate system. Many defects in steel castings, such as imbedded sand, cracks, shrinkage cavities, core failures, and misrun castings are attributed directly to poor gating practice. A gate, in order to function properly, must permit the flow of the metal into the mold with the least amount of turbulence. It must carry sufficient volume of metal with enough pressure to fill the mold quickly, and must be arranged to permit proper distribution of temperature gradients.

There are four general types of gates, (1) the **bottom gate**, (2) the **parting gate**, (3) the **top gate**, and (4) the **step gate** which is a combination of the three aforementioned types. The bottom gate is used most commonly for large floor-molded castings. The parting gate is favored for smaller work and is used on practically all machine-molded castings. There are many modifications of each of the four types, such as **horn gates, pencil** or **finger gates, swirl** or **whirl gates, skimmer gates, shower gates, ring gates** and **strainer gates.** Figure 38—2 shows types frequently used.

There are two types of risers; (1) the **open riser,** and (2) the **blind riser.** Open risers are attached to the surface of the casting at some location on the cope side and extend through the sand to the surface of the mold. The size of the riser depends upon the size of the section to be fed and upon the design of the casting. In general, the cross section of the neck of the riser should be equal to the section thickness of the casting at the point of attachment. The body of the riser should be slightly larger than the neck and the height at least 1.5 times its diameter or width (see Figure 38—3).

Blind risers usually are attached to the drag side of the casting and are covered completely with sand. The neck thickness should be 1½ to 2 times the sectional

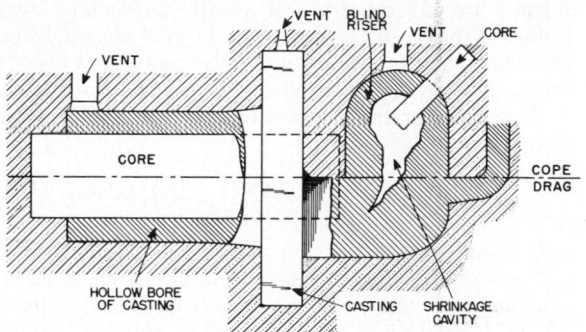

FIG. 38—4. Vertical section of a mold employing a Williams core in conjunction with a blind riser. (After Briggs).

thickness of the casting at the point of attachment. The diameter of the riser body should be 2 to 2½ times the sectional thickness at the point of attachment. The height of the riser should be about 1.5 times the diameter and the topmost surface rounded off or dome shaped. In order to insure proper feeding action of blind risers, a sand core or carbon rod should be inserted in the top section. Also a vent or **pop riser** should extend from the top of the riser to the surface of the mold. The use of the core in blind risers is patented and is known as the **Williams method.** The core serves to admit atmospheric pressure, thereby increasing feed efficiently. Figure 38—4 is a sketch of a Williams core on a blind riser.

Risers placed on steel castings present a serious problem to foundrymen from the standpoint of cleaning, because all risers must be removed prior to shipment. For this reason the **Washburn core** or **necked-down riser** is finding considerable use in conjunction with both open risers and blind risers. The necking core is nothing more than a core through which a small opening connects the riser to the casting. The thickness of the core and the size of the opening depend upon the size of the riser required. The necking core has the advantage that risers can be removed easily by sledge hammers, whereas oxyacetylene torches are necessary to remove conventional risers. Figure 38—5 illustrates use of a necking core with a blind riser.

During the teeming process many mold gases are formed by volatilization and burning of sand binders and by the expansion of the cool air within the mold cavity. Provision for the exhaust of such gases is made by jabbing wires through the mold to the surface or by the use of very small risers. The small holes thus

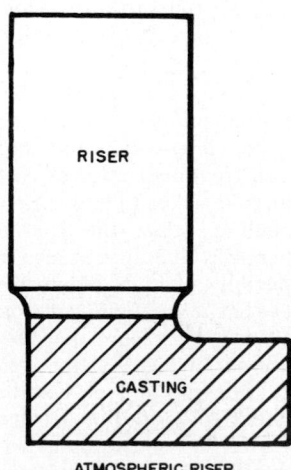

FIG. 38—3. Schematic representation of an open or atmospheric type feedhead or riser. (After Briggs).

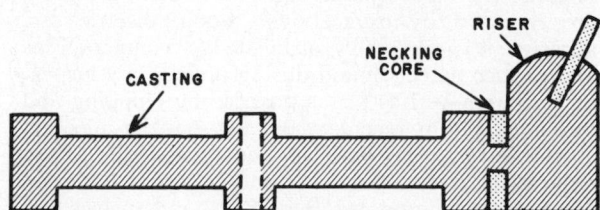

FIG. 38—5. Washburn necking core used to neck down the riser to facilitate removal, applied to a blind riser using a Williams core. (After Briggs).

formed are called vents and usually are located over points of the mold cavity where trapped gas might be expected, such as pockets and high points, or at flanges where a blind riser is used in place of an open riser. The vent rod preferably should be flat in shape rather than round.

STEEL CASTING AND FINISHING OPERATIONS

Casting—There are two classes of castings, **static castings,** and **centrifugal castings.** The discussion, so far, has dealt only with static castings, i.e., castings which depend upon proper molding practice, atmospheric pressure and gravity to form castings free from internal shrinkage cavities and other defects. The second class, centrifugal castings, as the name implies, makes use of centrifugal action to perform the function of gravity in static casting. There are two types of centrifugal castings—the horizontal type and the vertical type. In the horizontal type, the mold rotates on a horizontal axis. This method is used principally for making long, concentric, hollow castings with uniform wall thickness, where risers are not required. Tubing, pipe, gun barrels, bushings, sleeves, etc., are typical castings made by this process. The vertical method, employing rotation about a vertical axis, is essentially a pressure-casting method and depends, in part at least, on gravity, atmospheric pressure, and proper location of riser or risers to produce sound castings. Gears, piston rings, impellers, propellers, turbine diaphragms, etc., with sections too thin to be cast by static methods or where exceptional feeding problems arise which cannot be surmounted in any other way, are made by the vertical centrifugal process. There are several advantages to be gained from centrifugal casting methods: (1) castings are said to be sounder and have fewer inclusions, (2) fewer cleaning problems, and (3) a 10 to 30 per cent increase in yield.

Shaking Out, Cleaning, Finishing and Testing— After the castings have been poured and sufficient time allowed for solidification and cooling, they are **shaken out,** i.e., the castings are removed from the flask and sand. This operation is performed by placing the entire flask on a vibrating grid called a **shakeout machine.** The clamps are removed from the flask sections and the vibration of the machine causes the sand to fall loose and free of the castings. The castings are then removed to the cleaning room where they are subjected to blast cleaning or put through a tumbling barrel, where the abrasive action of sand particles or metallic shot impinging upon the walls of the castings loosens and removes adhering sand. Risers and gates are removed by oxyacetylene torch, electric arc, abrasive or friction saws, or by sledge hammers. Fins and surface defects found during preliminary inspection are removed as far as possible by chipping and burning. Within recent years, the powder-injection acetylene torch has been applied successfully to the removal of burnt-on sand. Another recent improvement in removing gates, fins, risers, and surface imperfections is by the carbon-arc—air process. This method employs a copper-clad electrode with which an arc is struck against the casting, while a stream of compressed air directed behind the arc flushes away the slag created by the "burning" or oxidation of the metal of the casting liquefied by the heat of the arc. This process offers several advantages over conventional chipping and grinding practice, particularly on carbon-steel castings, and permits removal of risers and gates to the pattern line. The riser necks, gate stubs, and slight surface imperfections are dressed by grinding wheels of various types and sizes. Repairs by welding also are performed sometimes, depending upon the carbon and alloy content of the steel. Castings containing more than 0.30 per cent carbon or of equivalent hardness that require repairing by welding are welded prior to heat treatment. After heat treatment, the castings are subjected to final surface-finishing operations—chipping, grinding, or sand blasting—as required. Finally, they are inspected for surface defects and dimensional accuracy. This inspection may include examinations utilizing X-ray, gamma-ray, magnetic-particle, fluorescent-penetrant, or ultrasonic methods.

HEAT TREATMENT OF STEEL CASTINGS

In the "as cast" or "green" state, steel castings are relatively brittle and possess poor mechanical properties. It follows, therefore, that in order to render them serviceable they must be subjected to a heat treatment which will refine the grain and break up the dendritic structure, relieve internal stresses, and develop the desired physical and mechanical properties. The heat treatment applied to steel castings depends upon the chemical composition, section size, design, grain size, and the desired mechanical properties. Because of the variations in size, section and design of castings, their heat treatment requires considerable care. However, steel castings respond to heat treatment similarly to wrought steel products and, for all practical purposes, the same rules apply, with care being exercised in placing castings in the furnace in such a way that there is minimum of danger of warpage, distortion or cracks which may cause them to be unfit for service. The common heat treatments applied to steel castings are as follows:

Annealing—The castings are placed in a furnace and heated slowly to a temperature slightly above the Ac_3 point, usually 1650° F for carbon steels. The castings are held at that temperature 1 hour per inch of thickness of the heaviest section and cooled slowly in the furnace. Such treatment relieves casting stresses, refines the grain, and serves to eliminate the dendritic structure. Annealing raises the tensile and yield strength and increases ductility. It also improves machinability, especially of high-carbon steels.

Normalizing—The normalizing treatment is similar to the annealing process, except that the castings are removed from the furnace at the end of the soaking or holding time and allowed to cool in still air. The normalizing treatment produces a harder steel with higher yield and tensile strength than the annealed product, with ductility value approximately the same. However, internal stresses are not removed to the same extent as in the annealing process. Double normalizing is often employed to produce a more uniform grain structure and such treatment improves the ductility. To remove internal stresses or to reduce the hardness of normalized steels, a **draw** or **tempering** treatment is used frequently, i.e., heating the casting to a temperature below the critical range and allowing it to cool in the furnace. Tempering temperatures for steel castings range from 500 to 1250° F.

Quenching and Tempering—The quenching and tempering treatment is confined principally to high-carbon and alloy-steel castings where high strength and resistance to impact and/or abrasion is required. The general practice is to anneal or normalize the castings, reheat and quench. The tempering treatment should follow immediately, because internal stresses set up by the quench may cause the castings to crack. Sometimes, it is necessary to use a time quench to eliminate cracking, in which case the casting is immersed in the quenching bath for a predetermined time interval, removed, and subjected to the tempering treatment immediately. Such procedure must be controlled closely; otherwise, wide variations in hardness values may result. The end-quench hardenability test is of great value in determining quenching and tempering procedure for steel castings.

Some alloy steels, particularly straight manganese steel in the range of 1.00 per cent up to 2.00 per cent, are susceptible to temper brittleness. Such steels have low impact and ductility values when cooled slowly from the tempering temperature. To avoid this, it is sometimes necessary to cool quickly from the tempering temperature by quenching or air cooling.

Flame Hardening—It is sometimes desirable that castings be differentially hardened, i.e., parts of the casting subject to extreme wear or abrasion should be harder than another part of the same casting which requires a machine operation. A pinion gear, for example, should have hard, wear-resistant teeth with a machinable bore. In such cases, the castings first are annealed or normalized and then only the surfaces to be hardened are heated to the hardening temperature by a torch or induction-heating apparatus. The heated parts are quenched in water. A time quench often is employed to prevent critical internal stresses. Sections can be hardened up to ¼-inch in depth by the flame hardening process.

HEAT- AND CORROSION-RESISTANT STEEL CASTINGS

Highly Alloyed Steels—Normally, high-alloy steel castings contain at least 12.0 per cent of alloying elements, such as chromium, nickel, cobalt, copper, molybdenum and tungsten, although 4 to 6 per cent chromium steel is generally considered in this class. Various alloy combinations have been developed by consumers and manufacturers for specific applications where conditions of heat and corrosion are critical. There is no clear line of demarcation between heat-resistant castings and corrosion-resistant castings since corrosive media, in the form of fumes and exhaust vapors, usually accompany high temperatures. Moreover, the so-called stainless or corrosion-resistant castings possess excellent mechanical properties at high temperatures. It is not uncommon, therefore, to see castings of a composition designed to resist corrosion being used for heat-resistant applications, and vice versa.

Typical Applications—Heat- and corrosion-resistant castings serve a very broad field. Mine pumps, impellers, fans, valves, valve trim, tubing, sleeve nuts, return bends, agitators, retorts, stills, vessels, digesters, thimbles, nozzles, and centrifuges, are but a few of the castings being used in chemical plants for corrosive applications. The explosives manufacturers, oil and petroleum refineries, paper mill plants, nylon and fabric manufacturers, food and medicinal producers, and the mining and ore-concentrating industries use many corrosion-resistant castings. Heat-resisting alloy castings are used in practically every installation where temperatures exceed 1200° F or where alternate heating and cooling cycles are employed; typical examples are chain conveyors, blower tubes, carburizing trays, recuperators, heat exchangers, hearth plates, grate bars, dampers, retorts, rolls, furnace doors, skid bars, carrier blades, muffles, safety sleeves, fractionating towers, normalizing shafts, guides, piercer points, and tube supports.

In the past, the optimum chemical compositions were determined largely by trial and error methods, but in recent years scientific studies and tests conducted by the Alloy Casting Institute and other interested parties have done much toward the standardization and proper use of the various grades of high-alloy steels. Table 38—II shows the compositions of some of the important grades of heat- and corrosion-resistant steels used for castings.

Melting—Steels for heat- and corrosion-resistant castings are melted in arc-type electric furnaces and high-frequency electric induction furnaces. The direct-arc electric furnace is used more extensively, but modern developments in induction melting equipment make it an extremely desirable unit for melting alloy steels for metallurgical, as well as operating, reasons. Furnace linings may be acid or basic and, in the case of the induction furnace, the lining may be neutral. The basic-lined furnace has the advantage of greater alloy efficiency and makes possible the use of chrome ore and nickel oxide for chromium and nickel additions. Also, it is possible to oxidize and reduce heats containing alloy scrap without serious loss of expensive alloys. On the other hand, acid furnaces require less skill to operate, they are faster, and the refractory costs are lower. Melting costs of induction furnaces compare favorably with acid- or basic-lined arc furnaces, and chemical composition and metal temperatures can be controlled within closer limits. Moreover, alloy recoveries are said to be higher. The induction furnace is limited to the dead-melt process but with present developments in flushing inert gases, such as argon and nitrogen, through the bath to remove dissolved gases, this does not pose a serious disadvantage.

Regardless of the type of melting unit, strict metallurgical control is necessary to produce high-alloy steels. Care must be exercised in the purchase of ferro-alloys and other raw materials, and scrap must be segregated according to composition and used with utmost discretion. Because most furnaces used for melting alloy steels for foundry use are small, seldom ex-

Table 38—II. Standard Designations and Chemical Composition Ranges of Heat- and Corrosion-Resistant Steels for Castings (Per cent)*

CORROSION RESISTANT

Alloy Casting Institute Type	C (Max.)	Mn (Max.)	Si (Max.)	P (Max.)	S (Max.)	Cr	Ni	Other
CA-15	0.15	1.00	1.50	0.04	0.04	11.5–14.0	1 max.	Mo: 0.5 max.
CA-40	0.20–0.40	1.00	1.50	0.04	0.04	11.5–14.0	1 max.	Mo: 0.5 max.
CB-30	0.30	1.00	1.00	0.04	0.04	18.0–22.0	2 max.	0.90–1.20 Cu optional
CC-50	0.50	1.00	1.00	0.04	0.04	26.0–30.0	4 max.	. . . .
CE-30	0.30	1.50	2.00	0.04	0.04	26.0–30.0	8.0–11.0	. . . .
CF-8	0.08	1.50	2.00	0.04	0.04	18.0–21.0	8.0–11.0	. . . .
CF-20	0.20	1.50	2.00	0.04	0.04	18.0–21.0	8.0–11.0	. . . .
CF-8M	0.08	1.50	1.50	0.04	0.04	18.0–21.0	9.0–12.0	Mo: 2.0–3.0
CF-12M	0.12	1.50	1.50	0.04	0.04	18.0–21.0	9.0–12.0	Mo: 2.0–3.0
CF-8C	0.08	1.50	2.00	0.04	0.04	18.0–21.0	9.0–12.0	Co: 8xC Min., 1.00 max.
CF-16F	0.16	1.50	2.00	(a)	(a)	18.0–21.0	9.0–12.0	(a)
CG-12	0.12	1.50	2.00	0.04	0.04	20.0–23.0	10.0–13.0	. . . .
CH-10	0.10	1.50	2.00	0.04	0.04	22.0–26.0	12.0–15.0	. . . .
CH-20	0.20	1.50	2.00	0.04	0.04	22.0–26.0	12.0–15.0	. . . .
CK-20	0.20	1.50	2.00	0.04	0.04	23.0–27.0	19.0–22.0	. . . .
CN-7M Cu	0.07	1.50	(b)	0.04	0.04	18.0–22.0	21.0–31.0	May contain Mo and Cu.

HEAT RESISTANT

Alloy Casting Institute Type	C	Mn (Max.)	Si (Max.)	P (Max.)	S (Max.)	Cr	Ni	Mo (Max.)
HC	0.50 max.	1.00	2.00	0.04	0.04	26.0–30.0	4.0 max.	0.5
HD	0.50 max.	1.50	2.00	0.04	0.04	26.0–30.0	4.0– 7.0	0.5
HE	0.20–0.50	2.00	2.00	0.04	0.04	26.0–30.0	8.0–11.0	0.5
HF	0.20–0.40	2.00	2.00	0.04	0.04	18.0–23.0	8.0–12.0	0.5
HH	0.20–0.50	2.00	2.00	0.04	0.04	24.0–28.0	11.0–14.0	0.5
HI	0.20–0.50	2.00	2.00	0.04	0.04	26.0–30.0	14.0–18.0	0.5
HK	0.20–0.60	2.00	3.00	0.04	0.04	24.0–28.0	18.0–22.0	0.5
HL	0.20–0.60	2.00	3.00	0.04	0.04	28.0–32.0	18.0–22.0	0.5
HT	0.35–0.75	2.00	2.50	0.04	0.04	13.0–17.0	33.0–37.0	0.5
HU	0.35–0.75	2.00	2.50	0.04	0.04	17.0–21.0	37.0–41.0	0.5
HW	0.35–0.75	2.00	2.50	0.04	0.04	10.0–14.0	58.0–62.0	0.5
HX	0.35–0.75	2.00	2.50	0.04	0.04	15.0–19.0	64.0–68.0	0.5

* Based on: "Steel Castings Handbook," Steel Founders' Society of America (1950).
(a) For free-machining properties, suitable combinations of Se, P, Mo and S may be used.
(b) Silicon content varies for different proprietary alloys.

ceeding three tons' capacity, heats are made rapidly and time is not available to run control analyses. For this reason, complete control of furnace operation and all raw materials and scrap is necessary.

Casting—High-alloy castings are made in static molds and centrifugal molds of the horizontal or vertical type. By far the greater tonnage is produced in static molds by conventional molding methods. However, a large number of horizontal centrifugal castings are made in the form of tubing, retorts, rolls and rollers. For work of this type, the centrifugal method is of great advantage since casting yield approaches 90 per cent, no cores are required, and the molds may be made of sand or, in some instances, cast iron sprayed with a highly refractory material. The vertical centrifugal method of casting is used only when static

methods fail and the castings cannot be made any other way. Impellers containing thin vanes, for example, or castings designed in such a manner that they cannot be properly fed, are made by the vertical centrifugal method.

Molding—Fundamentally, the molding procedure for high-alloy castings is the same as that employed for carbon-steel castings. However, greater skill and more precision is required on the part of the molder because excess stock on castings necessitates expensive machining operations. Every effort must be expended to produce clean, smooth, sound castings. The molding sand must be rigidly controlled and the particle size and bonding must be such that details of the pattern are reproduced accurately. The risers and gates should be located so as to avoid internal defects and center-line shrinkage, for such defects in castings exposed to high temperatures or corrosive media cause premature failures. The use of internal chills should be avoided, but if the casting problem cannot be surmounted in any other way, the chill material should be of the same chemical composition as the metal in the casting. Likewise, stem anchors and chaplets should be used sparingly and with care. Chill nails should never be used on high-alloy castings because contamination of the surface of the casting by the steel nail head may initiate corrosion and ultimately cause failure.

Finishing Operations—Cleaning and finishing operations for high-alloy steel castings differ but slightly from ordinary steel castings. Shot blasts or other abrasive cleaning devices must contain high-alloy shot or what is called high-alloy sand, since steel shot causes the castings to corrode. Risers and gates are removed by burning with an electric arc, although abrasive or friction saws are sometimes used for this purpose. The riser and gate pads are removed completely by grinding and all surface imperfections must be smoothed off by grinding. Frequently, alloy castings are ground to template. Casting repair by welding is limited strictly to minor defects and when welding is permitted, a rod of the same chemical composition as the casting generally is used. Heat treatments vary according to compositions, and range from carbide-solution treatments for corrosion-resistant castings such as 18 Cr–8 Ni, to precipitation-hardening treatments for the high-chromium, low-nickel-molybdenum steels. Steels containing 11.5 to 14.0 per cent chromium respond to the conventional hardening and tempering treatments. Heat-resistant alloys, such as 24 Cr–12 Ni, are sometimes treated to improve machinability,

in which case they are heated to approximately 1600° F and slowly cooled. The purpose of the treatment is to precipitate carbides.

Before shipment, castings are checked thoroughly for dimensional inaccuracies and surface imperfections and finally are cleaned in a sand blast or similar equipment.

Methods of Sampling and Testing—Sampling and preparation of samples for chemical tests have become standardized fairly well in all foundries. In general, test specimens for chemical analyses are poured from the ladle at about the mid-point of the teeming operation so that the sample is representative of the entire heat. The sample is cleaned and drilled; the first ¼ inch of drillings is thrown away as insurance against contamination. The chemical composition is then determined from subsequent drillings according to proven analytical procedures. Heat numbers are stamped on the castings and test specimens, thereby making possible the identification of the chemical composition of the castings. Most foundry laboratories are equipped to determine completely and accurately the compositions of steels, ferroalloys, sands, and various raw materials.

Mechanical properties of cast steels are determined from **test coupons** or **test lugs** cast integrally with the castings. At times it is necessary, by reason of the size or design of the casting, to make separate test coupons which are identified properly with the castings they represent by heat numbers stamped on the castings and coupons. The test bars always are heat treated with the castings, machined and tested in accordance with standard mechanical-testing procedure. Test specimens cut from castings sometimes show inferior mechanical properties when compared to stand-

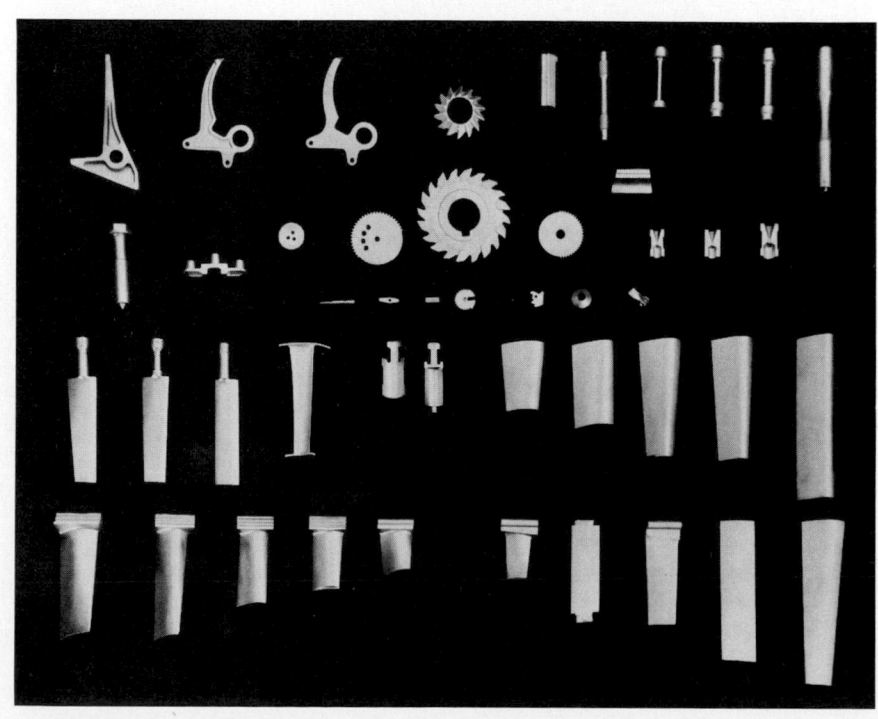

FIG. 38—6. Typical products produced by the lost wax or investment molding process for precision castings of materials not readily machinable that cannot be formed by hot or cold working. (Courtesy, Westinghouse Electric Corporation.)

ard coupon specimens. This is due principally to the mass effect, although in some instances it may be attributed to improper foundry technique, such as inadequate feeding action. Generally, results of mechanical tests as performed in the foundries may be considered indicative of the quality of the castings, but it should be recognized that excellent mechanical properties shown by tests do not preclude the possibility of poor mechanical properties in a casting.

Many foundries make use of modern non-destructive testing equipment, such as X-ray and gamma-ray apparatus. Also, an ultrasonic method for detecting internal defects and magnetic particle testing for detecting surface imperfections, such as cracks and small sand inclusions, is used extensively. In the case of high-alloy steels of the austenitic type which are non-magnetic, a method which makes use of a fluorescent penetrant and black light, is used to indicate cracks. Destructive tests in which castings are machined to complete destruction are employed frequently to determine the internal soundness of castings. Such tests are used as control measures and serve to establish foundry technique for subsequent castings. The microscope has been used in foundries for many years as a control tool to establish heat-treating practices and for other related metallurgical investigations.

PRECISION STEEL CASTINGS

The **lost wax** or **investment molding** process of making castings is often referred to as "precision casting."

Castings weighing one pound or less can be made to tolerances of 0.005 to 0.010 inch: considerably larger castings have been made successfully by this method. The process is restricted largely to high-alloy steel parts which cannot be machined readily and which cannot be formed by hot or cold working methods. Such parts include valve parts; turbine blades, buckets and nozzles; molds and dies for the plastic and ceramic industries; small gears for timers; hobs, milling cutters, magnets, jewelry, surgical and dental tools, etc. Figure 38—6 shows some typical precision castings.

The process consists of making a pattern of free-machining steel, around which a mold is formed of an alloy of low melting point. The mold thus formed is used for making wax patterns. The wax patterns are then used to make up molds similar to those used in the conventional molding process, except that risers are not required and the molding sand is bonded with an ethyl silicate, making a very hard and highly refractory mold when dried. The wax patterns within the mold are not lifted out of the sand but are removed by melting with steam or hot air; hence, the name "lost wax." The molds then are inverted over small induction furnaces containing the metal to be cast and clamped to the furnace. The furnace is rotated 180 degrees and the molten metal forced into the molds by air pressure, by centrifugal force, or by vacuum. The castings finally are cleaned and finished just as in conventional casting practice.

SECTION 2

IRON CASTINGS

Pig Iron for Castings—Iron castings are of innumerable kinds and uses, roughly grouped as **chilled-iron castings, gray-iron castings, alloyed-iron castings, malleable castings** and **nodular-iron castings.** In general, castings are made by mixing and melting together different grades of pig iron; different grades of pig iron and foundry scrap; different grades of pig iron, foundry scrap and steel scrap; or different grades of pig iron, foundry scrap, steel scrap and ferroalloys or other metals. In rare instances, molten iron direct from the blast furnace is run to a mixer, then to an electric furnace in which its composition is adjusted. In all remelting operations, the pig iron undergoes some change. Hence, physical properties of the pig iron itself are held subordinate to chemical composition in iron for remelting. However, by selecting iron of different grades and controlling the rate of cooling, the widest variations in mechanical properties may be obtained, from extreme hardness and brittleness with low impact resistance to extreme softness with, however, considerable strength and enhanced toughness. Thus, without the use of alloys and by selecting different malleable and foundry pig irons and controlling the rate of cooling, the following ranges in properties may be obtained:

Brinell Hardness Number . . . . 100 to 500
Tensile Strength
    (Lbs. per sq. in.) . . . . 10,000 to 60,000
Deflection
    (Transverse, In.) . . . . 0.04 to 0.36
Modulus of Elasticity
    (Lbs. per sq. in.) . . . . 12,000,000 to 29,000,000
Other important properties in iron for castings are:
a. **Fluidity,** at time of casting, which depends upon composition and temperature. The melting and freezing points of pig iron and cast irons of eutectic and hypoeutectic composition, for a given phosphorus content, vary inversely with the carbon and silicon, from 1990° F (1088° C) with 4.40 per cent carbon and 0.6 per cent silicon to 2280° F (1250° C) with 3.56 per cent carbon and 2.40 per cent silicon, the melting point varying inversely with the combined carbon for a given low (under one per cent) silicon content.
b. **Shrinkage,** which is the net result of contractions and expansions in cooling to atmospheric temperature, i.e., through the point where solidification begins, through the solidification range, and in cooling from this range to atmospheric temperature. Shrinkage depends upon the temperature of the

iron as it enters the mold, the composition of the iron, the rate of cooling, and subsequent heat treatments, and it varies from $\frac{1}{32}$ to $\frac{1}{8}$ in. per ft.

The net volume change on cooling from the liquid state is incurred stepwise and is complicated by structural and other changes that take place, somewhat in the following sequence and at the indicated approximate temperatures.

1. Contraction in the liquid state—Tapping temperature to solidification (say 2200° F, corresponding to 1205° C).
2. Contraction, liquid-to-solid, solidification—Temperature nearly constant at freezing, largest change.
3. Contraction of austenite and ledeburite—2200° F (1205° C) to 2050° F (1120° C).
4. Expansion due to graphitization—2050° F (1120° C) to 1950° F (1065° C)—large.
5. Contraction due to cooling—1950° F (1065° C) to 1325° F (720° C).
6. Expansion—austenite to pearlite, gamma to alpha iron—1325° F (720° C).
7. Contraction due to cooling—1325° F (720° C) to room temperature.

c. **Growth** is the tendency of castings to increase in volume after repeated heatings to temperatures between 850 and 1650° F (455 and 900° C) in the absence of stress. It is usually measured in linear units and expressed in per cent. It varies from essentially zero to several per cent (there is an example of a reported extreme of 50 per cent) according to the time of heating or number of heating cycles and type of iron. For ordinary castings, 5 per cent is extreme, while a growth of 0.002 inch per linear inch is common, and depends upon composition and prior heat treatment. The causes of growth are believed to be (1) graphitization and (2) penetration of active gases into the discontinuities of the coarser-grained irons.

d. **Creep** is the tendency to increase in length under stress (tension) at elevated temperatures above 700° F; the stress being but a fraction of that required to break a specimen of the material in a short-time tension test at room temperature. As it is expressed in different ways, one example is cited for an ordinary gray iron. In short-time tension tests, the breaking loads were 34,200 lb. per sq. in. at 70° F, and 35,100 lb. per sq. in. at 700° F; at a testing temperature of 700° F the test broke in 9 days under a load of 18,000 lb. per sq. in., and in 90 days under a load of 9,000 lb. per sq. in. Creep is lessened by certain alloy additions.

e. **Porosity, density, and closeness of grain** are designations referring primarily to macroscopic structure, particularly of heavier sections, as revealed by fractured surfaces. A porous structure is conducive to weakness, and is indicative of a condition bordering on **unsoundness**, which term is applied when the structure shows more clearly visible blowholes or gas pockets, or small cavities due to bleeding or shrinkage. The term "density" is sometimes used loosely to designate grain size rather than mass per unit weight; thus, iron showing a fine-grained fracture is said to be a "dense" iron.

Porosity may be due to segregation of low-melting constituents, to minute slaglike inclusions, or oxides that react with carbon to form gas while the casting is solidifying.

f. **Machinability** (the capability of being machined) may be viewed from various standpoints. Most frequently it is considered to be the characteristic (of the metal being machined) which causes more or less wear on the cutting tool; less frequently the definition involves the power required for the machining operation; often it refers to the degree of smoothness obtainable on the machined surface. With due precautions to keep the casting free of sand or dirt, machinability is controlled through the composition and rate of cooling, but often must be sacrificed for some more essential property, such as strength or toughness.

g. **Graphitization,** a phenomenon common to pig iron and cast iron, refers to the decomposition of iron carbide or, in any event, the rejection of elemental carbon in a casting after solidification has taken place, the carbon being liberated in the form of graphite which is usually found existing as minute, flaky particles disseminated throughout the casting. This property is controlled basically through composition of the iron, and is very important in castings, particularly malleable castings in which, upon reheating, carbon is rejected as nodules. As will be shown later, the formation of graphite is promoted by slow cooling, hindered or prevented by rapid cooling, and, if suppressed, can be brought about by subsequent heat treatment.

The effects of the different elements upon the properties of pig iron and cast iron will now be discussed.

IRON COMPOSITION vs. PROPERTIES

Forms of Carbon in Pig Iron—The factors influencing the carbon content of pig iron were discussed in Chapter 14. In considering the effect of temperature on molten iron, it is necessary to keep in mind that the effective temperatures are inevitably above a certain minimum of about 2085° F (1140° C), marking the freezing point of the iron-carbon eutectic. Referring to the iron-carbon diagram (see Index) and Figure 38—7, it will be observed that iron at 2370° F (1300° C) may absorb about 5.0 per cent carbon. Being a saturated solution, **cementite** (Fe_3C, 93.33 per cent Fe and 6.67 per cent C) crystallizes and separates as the liquid cools to 2065° to 2085° F (1130° to 1140° C), at which temperature we have the eutectic (lowest freezing) liquid, called **ledeburite,** containing 4.3 per cent carbon. Upon freezing, this eutectic liquid becomes a two-phase solid, one phase of which is composed of primary austenite (47.7 per cent) containing 1.7 per cent carbon in solution (equivalent to 12.1 per cent Fe_3C) and the other (52.3 per cent) of cementite. In the freezing of the eutectic, no drop in temperature occurs until heat equivalent to the heat of fusion of this eutectic is abstracted. Then, if the cooling is extremely rapid, practically all the carbon remains in these combined forms and the metal is extremely hard and brittle. But the saturated liquid solution may, in rapid cooling, produce a supersaturated solid solution. As another complication, the iron changes its allotropic form at about 1310° F (710° C) losing its power to hold carbon in solution, and if then the cooling is slow, some of the already formed cementite breaks down, or decomposes, to precipitate free carbon, which assumes the graphitic form, and usually is distributed as tiny flakes throughout the metal. The remainder of the carbon remains as combined carbon, part of which may be present as free or "proeutectoid" cementite, and some as **pearlite,** a fine lamellar aggregate of iron and cementite (so-called from its resemblance to mother-of-pearl). This last component is a microscopically laminated structure composed of alternate layers of nearly pure iron, called **ferrite,** and cementite, in the proportion of about 7 parts ferrite to 1 part of cementite (about 0.80 per cent carbon). The proportion is by no means constant. The presence of pearlite in cast iron usually strengthens it without producing too great an embrittling effect.

Influence of Silicon—The silicon content of the iron is second only to its carbon content in regard to its effectiveness as a means of controlling the properties of the castings. As it is increased above 3.5 per cent, it makes the iron matrix more and more brittle, forming silvery iron, so that it is generally held to amounts between 0.5 and 3.0 per cent. Since it tends to throw carbon out of solution, as explained in the discussion of carbon in pig iron in Chapter 14, it is used as a "softener" in gray-iron castings, as a graphitizing agent in malleable castings or castings to be heat treated, and to regulate depth of chill in chill castings. With sulphur under 0.05 per cent, even one per cent silicon makes it difficult to obtain a **chill** (an external zone of hard cementitic iron without appreciable graphite). Below one per cent, the chilling properties are roughly inversely proportional to the silicon present. Its effect in increasing the rate of graphitizing the combined carbon in white iron for malleable castings is remarkable. In a certain casting, for example, raising the silicon from 0.7 per cent to 1.0 per cent shortens the annealing cycle from 180 hours to 72 hours. Silicon above 2 per cent hardens the matrix of iron solid solution to such an extent that machinability is adversely affected. Silicon added to white iron until

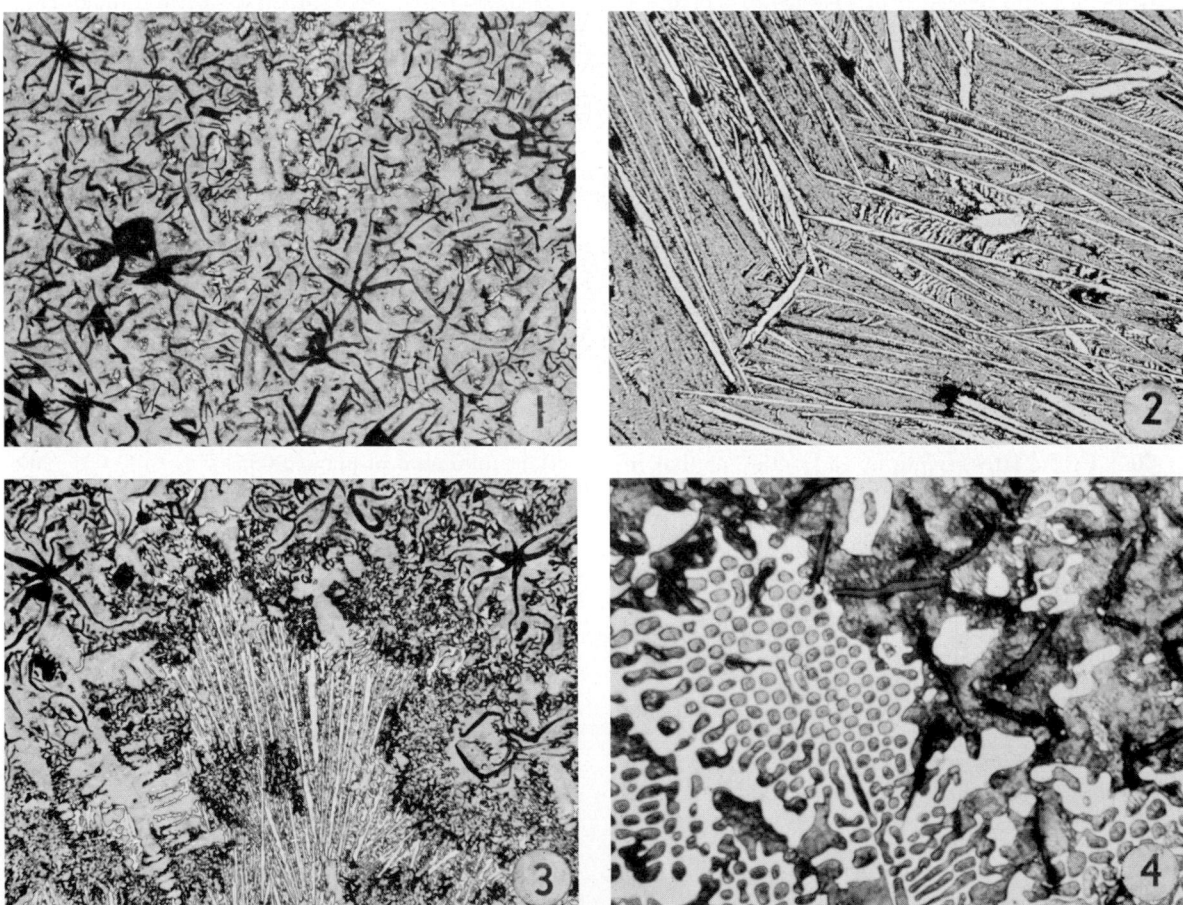

FIG. 38—7. Photomicrographs of typical microstructural constituents of cast iron as influenced by heat treatment and cooling rate. Sample 1: annealed specimen, showing graphite flakes in a fine pearlite matrix. Sample 2: "Chilled" sample showing ledeburite containing long needles and irregularly shaped areas of iron carbide (cementite; Fe₃C). Sample 3: Annealed specimen; region near chilled surface, showing areas of "chilled" ledeburite and graphite in a fine pearlite matrix. Sample 4: Annealed specimen; showing ledeburite and graphite flakes in a fine pearlite matrix. White constituent is cementite. All samples etched with picral. Magnifications: Samples 1, 2 and 3, 100×; Sample 4, 1000×.

it just turns gray increases the toughness by changing massive Fe_3C to pearlite and graphite, but more weakens it by forcing the pearlite ratio below 0.80 per cent carbon and increasing the graphite. Silicon tends to decrease shrinkage, to prevent blowholes, but increases the tendency to growth; silicon is oxidized in the cupola or air furnace and excessive amounts thus may favor a dirty casting, due to the entrapment of silicate-type inclusions. Silicon, from 1.5 up to 4.5 per cent, increases the resistance of the iron to atmospheric and acid corrosion, and more than 10 per cent greatly protects the metal from all forms of oxidation and from chemical attack.

Effects of Manganese—As to whether high manganese content has an overall good or a bad effect on cast iron, there is much difference of opinion, some considering it almost as a cure for all troubles and others condemning it as a source of much trouble, especially in chilled castings. While it tends to hold carbon in solution, iron in which chill is produced by increasing the manganese content alone is "soft" and tends to spall. In *moderate* amounts, it is said to prevent cracking of the surface and also spalling to some extent, especially in chilled rolls, and it may harden the chill, if other conditions are right. It does tend to decrease blowholes, increase fluidity, and to neutralize the effect of the sulphur present. The amount used in castings varies from 0.1 to 2.0 per cent, 0.5 to 0.7 per cent being most common. In malleable castings, it is added in proportion to the sulphur, and according to the formula, $Mn = 2S + 0.15$. Held to these proportions, it will be found ultimately as MnS and in the cementite, and will not prevent graphitization of the cementite while larger amounts of manganese tend to stabilize cementite and increase growth. In high-grade gray-iron castings, the per cent manganese is held between 5 and 7 times the sulphur.

Influence of Sulphur—Sulphur in pig iron is considered now to be less injurious than was thought formerly. As sulphur, except for special purposes (e.g., enhanced machinability), is undesirable in steel, and as the blast furnace affords the only positive and economical means of reducing it, pig iron containing less than 0.05 per cent is preferable for making steel by all the fusion processes. In castings, it is varied from about 0.04 per cent to 0.20 per cent, though in irons for foundries it will seldom exceed 0.1 per cent. Iron melted in cupolas always takes on sulphur from the coke, the percentage sometimes being doubled. Sulphur with iron forms sulphide, which is soluble in the liquid metal and has a melting point that is lower than the other constituents of the iron. This sulphide in iron used for castings has a three-fold influence. First, it tends to hold the carbon in combined condition, hence, can be used to increase the depth of chill in chilled castings, but in malleable castings and other castings that are to be heat treated, it thus retards graphitization, if it is not fully neutralized with manganese, and may be very undesirable. Chill produced with sulphur may be very brittle; low-silicon iron containing between 0.2 and 0.4 per cent sulphur often cracks when cooled rapidly. Second, its low melting point causes it to segregate as the iron solidifies, thereby causing the condition in castings known as

bleeding. Third, it increases the shrinkage of the iron to a marked degree, thus increasing the difficulty of making accurate castings and increasing the tendency to form cracks, which are a result of the high shrinkage.

Influence of Phosphorus—Since compounds of phosphorus present in the materials charged into the blast furnace are completely reduced, all the phosphorus in the raw materials is ultimately found in the metal. Therefore, its content must be regulated by proper selection of raw materials. High phosphorus content causes a slight brittleness in pig iron and markedly reduces the total carbon content. **Ferrophosphorus** containing about 24 per cent phosphorus is almost carbonless and melts between 2245 and 2310° F (1230 and 1265° C). The melting point range for the 17 to 19 per cent grade is 2426 to 2498° F (1330 to 1370° C). Lesser amounts permit a proportionate increase of carbon, so that the total carbon in an iron containing 0.20 per cent phosphorus may be as high as 4.25 per cent. In this respect its action is not selective, since the ratio of combined to graphitic carbon is not affected. Phosphorus is known to form a compound, Fe_3P, with iron, containing 15.6 per cent phosphorus, but it apparently is able to combine or alloy with it in any proportion up to 25 per cent.

In pig iron and cast iron, Stead found that phosphorus forms a ternary eutectic solution containing 91.19 per cent iron, 6.89 per cent phosphorus, and 1.92 per cent carbon, to which Sauveur gave the name **steadite**. The amount formed in pig iron depends upon the phosphorus present, and since steadite has a low fusion point, the influence of phosphorus is to lower the freezing *range* of the iron. Another effect is to decrease the pearlite, so that more than one per cent phosphorus decreases the strength of the casting rapidly, the maximum strength being obtained with 0.25 to 0.40 per cent. For uniformly thin castings, such as stove plate and sanitary ware that is to be enameled, from 0.55 to 0.75 per cent is used with marked benefit to obtain the necessary fluidity and good mechanical properties. But in castings with thin and thick parts, such as engine blocks, these percentages of phosphorus make the thick portions porous, so that not more than 0.30 per cent can be permitted. High phosphorus also increases the shrinkage, particularly of the heavier parts, and increases the harmful stress-producing shrinkage (called "draw" shrinkage) and those making highest type castings generally agree that phosphorus above 0.30 per cent tends to produce unsound, porous, and brittle castings. Since the required fluidity can be had by raising the temperature, better results are obtained by lowering the phosphorus to 0.12 to 0.20 per cent and increasing the temperature. Castings thus made have a closer grain and machine better than those made with higher phosphorus content. Therefore, this range is recommended as the best for general work, including machinery castings of various kinds. In general, the resistance of unalloyed cast iron to corrosion decreases as the phosphorus content is increased above 0.05 per cent.

Effects of Chromium—Chromium occurs only occasionally, and in traces, in pig iron made from ordinary iron ore, but it now is added commonly to iron for high-grade castings in amounts from 0.1 to 3.5 per cent. It is a carbide-forming element, hence it holds the carbon in the combined state, opposes graphitization, decreases the tendency for growth, and increases the hardness of the matrix. In moderate amounts of 0.1 to 0.5 per cent, it increases the strength, but greater additions are made with some increase of brittleness. In high-grade castings, it is used mainly to increase the resistance to wear. It is used also with other elements, particularly nickel and copper, to obtain resistance to corrosion and growth. Additions of chromium are made to the iron in the ladle, as solid or preferably molten ferrochromium. Its effects were early studied and reported by Hadfield in 1892 (see: Iron and Steel Institute, Vol. II, 1892).

Influence of Nickel—Nickel, like chromium, is rare in pig iron made from ordinary iron ores; but its use in high-grade castings is common, the amount added to gray-iron castings varying from 0.10 to 2.50 per cent, and to special alloy castings from 5 to 15 per cent. Nickel dissolves in the iron, and, like silicon, promotes graphitization; but, unlike silicon, it does not graphitize eutectoid cementite (that is, the portion of cementite that goes to make up pearlite) and it causes a reduction in the size of the graphite plates, giving a "closer grain." Therefore, in the smaller percentages, it is added to toughen the iron, prevent formation of massive carbides, and increase machinability. For example, one per cent added to gray iron, with carbon reduced from 3.50 to 3.00 per cent and silicon from 1.50 to 1.00 per cent, doubles the tensile strength and increases the Brinell hardness from 175 to 225, and gives an iron that is readily machinable. From 5 to 6 per cent nickel hardens the iron and may result in a martensitic matrix, the Brinell hardness being 250 to 280. A maximum of about 360 Brinell is obtained with 10 to 12 per cent nickel; while larger amounts, about 12 to 16 per cent, produce a distinct type wholly austenitic (except for cementite or graphite) and much softer, the Brinell hardness being as low as 130 with 18 per cent nickel. In these larger amounts, it is used in conjunction with chromium, with copper and chromium, or with silicon and chromium, to produce various special corrosion- and heat-resistant irons. In cupola practice, nickel is added in the form of shot to the metal in the ladle; in air- or electric-furnace practice, it may be added as pig nickel to the charge in the furnace, or in the form of shot in the ladle. Commercial forms of nickel used for this purpose contain some carbon, which should be considered if it is added in large amounts.

Influence of Copper—Copper may occur in pig iron, if it is present in the charge. Usually, it is absent. It is added to castings in various proportions from 0.10 to 2.00 per cent in gray-iron castings and up to 7.00 per cent in special alloy-iron castings. In the smaller amounts, its effects are similar to nickel, decreasing slightly the combined carbon, increasing the strength, preventing formation of massive carbides, improving machinability, and in addition, increasing the fluidity and decreasing the shrinkage slightly. Its solublity in iron is limited, but is increased by nickel, in conjunction with which it is used up to 6.5 to 7.0

per cent to produce corrosion- and heat-resistant castings. As to its influence on graphitization, one per cent copper is equivalent to 0.1 to 0.2 per cent silicon. In malleabilizing, it may be, therefore, both a hindrance and a help, tending to make the iron mottled in casting but shortening the annealing time. The strength of malleable iron containing about one per cent copper can be increased 2000 to 8000 lbs. per sq. in. by precipitation hardening, a treatment usually carried out by heating for one hour at 1380° F and reheating for 3 hours at 930° F.

Effects of Molybdenum—Molybdenum is rarely found in pig iron, but is added in the ladle as **ferromolybdenum** in cupola practice, or in the furnace as ferromolybdenum or **calcium molybdate** in air- and electric-furnace practice. It strengthens and toughens the metal, and is added in amounts of 0.30 to 1.25 per cent to increase strength, hardness, and resistance to shock. It is credited also with preventing cracking. It does not decrease the shrinkage on solidification, but does decrease slightly the contraction following solidification. Its effect upon graphitization is slight, and it appears not to affect the amount of combined carbon, but does increase the depth of chill when added in amounts of 0.25 to 0.60 per cent. It increases resistance to wear, hinders graphitization somewhat, has little effect on growth, improves the properties at high service temperatures, and promotes uniformity in mechanical properties as between large and small sections.

Effects of Titanium and Aluminum—Both of these elements have been added to cast iron, but only titanium is used regularly. Both are reported to promote graphitization, titanium decreasing the size of the graphite flakes. A little titanium, 0.05 to 0.10 per cent, is common in pig iron, and its effect appears to be generally beneficial. The addition of titanium to cast iron is reported to impart greater tenacity and resistance to wear.

Influence of Vanadium—Vanadium has been added to cast iron in amounts of 0.10 to 0.15 per cent. It is an expensive addition, and its chief effect seems to be that of opposing graphitization.

Effects of Special Additives—Various chemical elements other than those discussed above are added to iron for casting to effect changes in microstructure, improve mechanical properties, and so on. Such elements may be added singly or in various combinations. A notable instance is that of adding magnesium or cerium alloys to iron to produce what is designated as "nodular iron;" this practice will be described later in this chapter under the heading of "Kinds and Uses of Iron Castings."

IRON-FOUNDRY MELTING METHODS

The chapter on pig iron describes the manufacture of iron used in the production of iron castings. The pig iron for castings may be melted in one of several types of furnaces, the cupola, the air furnace or the electric furnace, though the cupola is the principal source of molten metal for iron castings. In the case of certain alloy and high-test iron castings, the metal is frequently duplexed; i.e., melted in a cupola and further processed in an electric furnace. The open-hearth furnace also has been used for melting iron for castings, but its use for this purpose is limited.

The Cupola—The cupola resembles a miniature blast furnace. It differs primarily in that pig iron and steel scrap replace iron ore in the charge. The cupola is lined with fireclay or firestone refractories. Since, in most installations, no water cooling is utilized in the melting zone, the lining has to be repaired with plastic-fireclay patching between periods of operations. In the few installations where water-cooling of the melting zone is employed, such frequent repair of the lining is not required. The charging door is located on the side of the cupola near the top. The cupola is supported by legs, permitting the use of a drop bottom which facilitates the removal of the remaining burden after the last charge has been tapped. Intermittent operation is the general rule, but continuous operation is possible.

The charge is composed of coke, steel scrap, iron scrap and pig iron in alternate layers of metal and coke. Sufficient limestone is added to flux the ash from the coke and form the slag. The ratio of coke to metallics varies, depending on the melting point of the metallic charge. Ordinarily, the coke will be about 8 to 10 per cent of the weight of the metallic charge. It is kept as low as possible for the sake of economy and to exclude sulphur and some phosphorus absorption by the metal.

During melting, the coke burns as air is introduced at a 10 to 20 ounce pressure through the tuyeres. This melts the metallic charge and some of the manganese combines with the sulphur, forming manganese sulphide which goes into the slag. Some manganese and silicon are oxidized by the blast and the loss is proportional to the amount initially present. Carbon may be increased or reduced, depending on the initial amount present in the metallic charge. It may be increased by absorption from the coke or oxidized by the blast. Phosphorus is little affected, but sulphur is absorbed from the coke. Prior to casting, the slag is removed from the slag-off hole which is located just below the tuyeres. The molten metal is then tapped through a hole located at the bottom level of the furnace. The depth between these two tapping holes and the inside diameter of the furnace governs the capacity of the cupola.

The Air Furnace is a type of reverberatory furnace somewhat similar to the puddling furnace described in Chapter 1. It has a fireplace at one end, the stack at the other end, and between them a hearth covered by a roof sloping toward the stack. A cross, or "bridge," wall near the stack (the flue bridge) and another next to the fireplace (the fire bridge), together with the lining (usually of silica sand) form a rectangular basin which holds the charge. A removable-bung type of roof is used to permit charging large pieces through the top with a crane. Coal, fuel oil or gas are used as fuel, the liquid or gaseous fuels being preferred. When coal is used, the fireplace is constructed and manipulated to serve as a crude producer. About 15 per cent of the carbon, 30 per cent of the silicon, 45 per cent of the manganese, and 1 to 2 per cent of the iron of a pig-iron charge are oxidized in the air furnace, the exact amounts varying with the composition of the charge and the oxidizing conditions of the flame.

The Electric Furnace—A description of the arc-type electric furnace, which is used to a limited extent for melting iron for iron castings, is given in Chapter 17.

KINDS AND USES OF IRON CASTINGS

One of the principal reasons for using iron castings in applications at elevated temperatures is the fact that cast iron is resistant to warping and cracking in the presence of heat. At ordinary temperatures, cast iron—through proper control of composition and molding and casting methods—can be made to exhibit such valuable properties as: high hardness and wear resistance, good damping capacity and corrosion resistance, while lending itself to the design of castings characterized by intricacy of shape and/or massiveness. The various kinds of iron castings are: **chilled-iron castings, malleable castings, alloyed-iron castings, gray-iron castings,** and **nodular-iron castings.** Among the innumerable uses may be mentioned pipe, rolls, permanent molds, ingot molds and stools, sanitary ware, engine blocks and all kinds of machinery parts. A few of the various kinds of iron castings, with their compositions, properties and uses, are given in Table 38—III. Further details may be found in "Cast Metals Handbook" published by the American Foundrymens' Association.

Chilled-Iron Castings are extremely hard on the surface. They are made by melting iron of certain compositions, and casting the molten metal in such a way that the parts to be hardened will be solidified on contact with a metal or graphite block capable of abstracting heat rapidly and thus causing quick cooling. Chilled-iron castings are made of ordinary low-silicon iron and of irons alloyed, usually, with nickel and chromium. The chilled surface is very hard, and when fractured, shows white for a distance beneath the chilled surface varying with the rate of cooling and the composition of the iron; hence, such irons are commonly spoken of as chilled iron. The hardness and the white fracture are due to the fact that all the carbon, in the clear chill at least, is in combined form, the rapid cooling preventing the separation of graphite. In heavy sections, the clear chill will extend only a short distance, $\frac{1}{8}$ inch to 2 inches from the surface, where it merges into mottled, then into a gray appearance, all these structures being the result of varying the rate of cooling. Such castings are used for rolls and various other articles which require a hard, wear-resisting surface. All three types of furnaces are used for melting, depending upon the kind of iron and other factors.

Malleable Castings, while not strictly malleable, are soft and can be bent without breaking. They are of two kinds, known as **white heart,** or European, and **black heart,** or American, these terms indicating differences in the process and the products and countries of origin. As an initial step in making malleable castings, a charge consisting of malleable grades of pig iron (10 to 15 per cent), steel scrap (35 to 40 per cent), and cast-iron scrap (45 to 55 per cent), consisting of feeders, runners, sprues, and defective castings, may

Table 38—III. Some Varieties of Iron Castings, Their Composition Ranges, Properties and Uses

	Composition—Range (%)												Mechanical Properties			
	Si	S	P	Mn	T.C.*	G.C.*	C.C.*	Cu	Ni	Cr	Mo	Other Elements	Brinell Hard. No.	Tensile Strength p.s.i.	Transverse Load-Lbs.	Deflection In.
Gray Iron—Ordinary	2.00 / 2.40	.12 max.	.20 max.	.60 / .70	3.00 / 3.35								187 / 235	30,000-45,000	1800	.14-.16
Cast Iron Pipe	As required	.10 max.	.90 max.	.40 / .60			about 3.00							20,000-25,000		
Automotive Cylinder Blocks	2.00 / 2.20	.09 / .12	.14 / .18	.70 / .85	3.25 / 3.40	2.60 / 2.75	.55 / .65		.75 / .85	.25 / .35			187 / 196	33,000-36,000	3,600-3,900	.12-.14
Cylinder Blocks	2.35 / 2.40 max.	.15 max.	.18 max.	.55 / .75	3.25 / 3.40		.50 / .65	.75 / 1.00		.20 / .30			192 / 220	38,000-42,000	4,000-5,000	.17-.20
Cylinder Blocks	2.10 / 2.50	.10 max.	.20 max.	.50 / .90	3.00 / 3.40		.60 / .80			.20 / .40			187 / 240	35,000-45,000	3,500-4,500	.11-.17
Cylinder Blocks	1.80 / 2.00	.12 / .15	.16 / .20	.70 / .90	3.20 / 3.40	2.60 / 2.80	.60 / .80			.15 / .20	.15 / .20		212 / 231	38,000-41,000	4,600-5,000	.14-.16
Crank Cases	1.90 / 2.10	.09 / .12	.14 / .18	.70 / .85	3.20 / 3.40	2.70 / 2.80	.50 / .60		1.00 / 1.10				240 / 270		3,800-4,000	.12-.15
Crank Shafts	2.20 / 2.40 max.	.15 max.	.18 max.	.65 / .90	3.20 / 3.40		.70 / .90		.40 max.	.80 / .90	.40 / .50		263 / 300	48,000-52,000	4,800-5,000	.17-.20
Crank Shafts	2.20 / 2.50	.08 max.	.08 max.	.90 / 1.00	2.60 / 2.80		.60 / .75		.75 / 1.00	.10 / .20	.70 / 1.25		220 / 240	60,000-80,000	6,000-7,000	.18-.22
Pistons—Diesel	1.65 / 1.80	.07 max.	.15 max.	.50 / .70	2.50 / 2.70	1.80 / 2.15	.50 / .70		1.25 / 1.70		.55 / .65	<0.12	229 / 241	63,000-68,500		
Piston Rings	1.90 / 2.25	.10 max.	.35 / .75	.50 / .70	3.40 / 3.60	2.70 / 3.10	.45 / .75		.90 / 1.10		.20 / .30		297 / 311			
Piston Rings	2.50 / 3.10	.10 max.	.30 / .80	.50 / .80	3.50 / 3.75	2.70 / 3.20	.50 / .80					<0.10 / 0.25				
Dies—Forming	1.40 / 1.50	.10 max.	.18 max.	.60 / .80	3.20 / 3.50				.90 / 1.00	.60 / .70	.80 / .90		200 / 220			
Dies—Forming & Bending	2.00 / 2.40	.10 max.	.20 max.	.55 / .70	2.60 / 2.90	1.90 / 2.10	.65 / .80		1.40 / 1.70	.35 / .50	.40 / .60			55,000-65,000	3,200-3,600	.22-.29
High Alloy Irons Ni-Resist—Typical	1.10 / 2.00	.06	.04 / .30	.60 / 1.50	2.40 / 2.90	1.60 / 1.80	.60 / .75	5.00 / 7.30	14.50 / 16.50	1.50 / 4.00			120 / 170	20,000-35,000	2,000-4,000	.20-.30
Silal—Typical	5.70	.06	.30	.70	2.40	2.30	.08							33,000	2,400	.11-.20
Nicor-Silal	4.50 / 5.90	.04	.04	.60 / .70	1.80	1.50	.30		17.70 / 18.70	2.10 / 2.60				23,000	2,000	.40-.60

*T.C. = Total carbon content; G.C. = Graphitic carbon content; C.C. = Combined carbon content

be melted to give metal containing 2.25 to 3.00 per cent carbon, 0.3 to 0.50 per cent manganese, 0.05 to 0.08 per cent phosphorus, 0.06 to 0.11 per cent sulphur, and 0.60 to 1.15 per cent silicon, the exact composition, particularly in regard to silicon, being varied according to the thickness of the section being made. If the carbon is under 2 per cent, graphitization in annealing is slow and if the carbon is near 4 per cent, graphite may be formed in casting. To prevent the latter occurrence, the silicon is lowered as the carbon is increased in a given casting, if the iron must be white all the way through after casting, with all the carbon in the combined form. When the iron has melted, it is tapped and cast in well-prepared green-sand molds, made about ¼ inch per foot oversize to allow for total shrinkage, or liquid-to-solid contraction. When cool, the castings are removed from the molds and, unless finish is of no consideration, cleaned by tumbling, sand blasting, pickling, or hand scouring. The castings next are packed carefully in annealing boxes or pots with an oxidizing agent, such as roll scale or crushed furnace slag for white-heart castings, or with nonoxidizing materials such as blast-furnace slag, fine sand, etc., for black-heart castings. The packed castings then are placed in an annealing furnace and heated gradually to about 900° C (1650° F) for white-heart castings or to near 871° C (1600° F) for black-heart castings. The former are held at this temperature 3 to 5 days, during which time the iron carbide is eliminated almost completely by a process of migration and surface oxidation of the carbon to CO or CO_2, leaving a metal similar to soft steel but of much coarser grain and less ductile. Since the migration of the carbon is very slow, only thin castings can be decarburized successfully or "malleableized" by this process. Black-heart castings are treated by an "annealing cycle," requiring about 30 hours for heating to temperature, about 45 hours holding at temperature, 30 to 35 hours for cooling to and holding at 650° C (1205° F) and 5 hours for cooling to handling temperature. In this cycle, the combined carbon is completely graphitized, causing the casting to grow slightly and leaving the iron as ferrite. But instead of forming plates, the graphite is dispersed in a very finely divided form known as temper carbon, which, under the microscope, is seen as black spots distributed in haphazard fashion throughout the metal except near the surface of the casting where the metal may be partly or wholly decarburized. Thoroughly malleableized castings have a yield point of about 27,000 lbs. per square inch, and a tensile strength of about 45,000 lbs. per square inch. Some standard specifications require a yield point of more than 32,000 lbs. per square inch (32,500 and 35,000 minimum for two grades), and a tensile strength of more than 50,000 lbs. per square inch (50,000 to 53,000 minimum for two grades). The modulus of elasticity is about 25,000,000 lbs. As to ductility, standard specifications require a minimum elongation of 10 to 18 per cent in 2 inches. Castings that have been malleableized are immune to growth.

Alloyed Castings—Alloyed irons are used most extensively for applications where resistance to wear, to heat (including growth), and to corrosion, along with the high strength of the alloyed iron, rigidity, "damping" of vibrations and amenability to heat treatment are of prime importance. They are produced and used extensively by the steel industry but are used most widely by the automotive industry for purposes where the above properties are a requirement. The alloying elements used are silicon, nickel, chromium, molybdenum, copper and titanium, in amounts varying from a few tenths to 20 per cent or more. They may be classed as: (1) low-alloyed gray-iron castings, (2) high-alloyed gray-iron castings, and (3) austenitic alloy castings, the latter containing sufficient alloying elements to hold the iron in the austenitic condition. These are used for resistance to corrosion, both atmospheric and chemical; for resistance to heat, including oxidation and growth; and for their high thermal coefficient of expansion. Many of these irons are patented compositions and are sold under various trade names, such as Ni-resist, Causal metal, Silal, Nicrosilal, etc.

Gray-Iron Castings—Gray-iron castings are made of pig iron, of mixtures of pig iron and steel, or of mixtures of pig iron, steel and other metals in smaller amounts, and have been referred to as semi-steel, high-test iron, and alloy iron. They are frequently sold under trade names, such as Meehanite, Gunite, Ermalite, Ferrosteel, Gun-iron, etc. Chemically, gray-iron castings include a large number of metals covering a wide range in composition, with carbon varying from 2 to 4 per cent, and silicon from 0.5 to 3 per cent, with small amounts of Ni, Cr, Mo, and Cu frequently added. Grouped according to uses, they include (1) pipe-foundry castings, (2) sanitary ware, (3) automotive castings, (4) locomotive castings, (5) light machinery, (6) heavy machinery, (7) miscellaneous shapes.

Mention has been made of the use of cast iron for ingot molds and stools. If available, molten iron direct from the blast furnace may be used instead of cupola iron because of its lower cost and high percentage of graphitic carbon. In some cases where iron direct from the blast furnace is not available, cupola iron is used for this purpose; however, studies invariably indicate that blast-furnace iron produces a mold with longer life than those produced with more refined cupola iron. The composition of the iron, pouring temperature and their relation to ingot-mold and stool life require considerable study; however, the consensus of mold makers in this country indicates that the composition should be about as follows:

Silicon	1.25 to 1.75%	
Phosphorus	0.120 to 0.140%	
Sulphur	0.035 to 0.050%	
Manganese	1.00 to 1.40%	

A casting temperature of 2300° F to 2350° F is desirable.

Pipe-foundry castings include cast-iron pipe and fittings. A great part of cast-iron pipe now is cast centrifugally from ordinary iron containing less than 0.1 per cent sulphur, under 0.9 per cent phosphorus, with carbon and silicon controlled to give the required mechanical properties. When not centrifugally cast, the molten metal is poured into cored dry-sand molds supported in a vertical position, those 18 inches or more in diameter being cast with the hub end down.

Nodular-Iron Castings—Nodular iron, also called ductile iron and spheroidal graphite iron, is a relatively new grade introduced around 1948; it has been used for castings having sections from ⅛ inch up to 40 inches thick. It is produced by treating molten iron that normally would produce a soft, weak, gray iron casting with cerium or magnesium alloys. The addition of these special alloys results in castings which have the carbon present in spheroidal form. Castings so made have relatively high strength and better ductility than ordinary gray iron. Pearlitic nodular irons have a tensile strength in excess of 80,000 lb. per sq. in., with an elongation of at least 3 per cent, while ferritic grades, having tensile strengths of over 60,000 lb. per sq. in., will show an elongation of from 10 per cent to 25 per cent. For economy, iron having a sulphur content below about 0.15 per cent is required for the process. Several types of matrix structures can be developed by alloying or heat treatment; the pearlitic and ferritic matrices were mentioned above. As this type of iron has been discussed extensively in recent literature, no further details will be given here.

IRON-FOUNDRY MOLDING AND CASTING PRACTICE

Molding practice for iron castings is somewhat similar to that already described for steel castings in Section 1 of this chapter, the chief differences being in the preparation and types of sand and the placement and size of gates and risers, the latter being modified by reason of the lower shrinkage in cast iron.

The scope of this book does not permit more than a brief description of the casting of iron castings. The metal is cast in one of five types of molds: namely, (1) **green-sand molds,** made of moist sand which is rammed about a pattern (usually of wood) in a "flask" of wood or iron, and the metal is poured with the mold in the condition as rammed; (2) **dry-sand molds,** made up like green-sand molds, but dried before they receive the metal; (3) **loam molds,** made up of loam (a kind of low-grade sand) which, for heavy castings, is backed with brick and faced with other more refractory material; (4) **permanent molds** or **semi-permanent molds,** which have become more and more popular for certain applications; and (5) **shell molds** which are a recent development.

The permanent mold is a cast-iron or graphite mold into which the molten iron is poured. The semi-permanent mold is built up of cast iron and sand, the latter having to be replaced after use. In both the latter cases, the molds are prepared with a graphite coating and warmed to 150 to 200° F before the hot metal is poured into the mold. Shell-molding techniques are described in numerous recently published articles and papers and will not be discussed in detail here; briefly, shell molds are made by applying a coating of sand mixed with a synthetic resin or other suitable binder to a prepared pattern and then "curing" the coating by heating to form a solid shell that can then be stripped from the pattern. Shell molds are used in the production of steel and nonferrous castings, as well as iron castings.

TESTING OF CAST IRON

The tests most commonly employed for gray cast iron are the tension test, transverse load and deflection (measured bend) test, and hardness (Brinell and file) tests. In making tension tests, standard test specimens are machined from a standard cast test bar, and "pulled" in a tensile-testing machine until the piece breaks, the load calculated to pounds per square inch being taken as the tensile strength. In short-time tension tests, most grades of cast iron show no point corresponding to the yield point of steel and very little, if any, elongation or reduction of area. The form of specimen used for making tensile tests is somewhat different from that used for testing steel. There are three standard sizes; viz., 0.505 inch, 0.750 inch, and 1.25 inches in diameter (at the center), the diameter being varied with the thickness (and design) of the castings they represent. As standard specifications do not require the measurement of elongation but only the tensile strength, specifications covering the lengths of specimens merely state that the affected test length shall not be less than the diameter. The tensile strength varies: (a) with the diameter of the test bar, being higher for bars of smaller diameter and lower for bars of greater diameter; (b) with the temperature above 250° F, being almost constant up to 600° F and decreasing rapidly above 800° F; and (c) with the time after casting, most castings increasing in strength with age. This change is attributed to relief of casting strains, which may be relieved also by tumbling and by heat treatment. The relief of strain by aging is called **seasoning.**

Transverse testing consists of placing a standard bar upon supports 12, 18, or 24 inches apart, then either applying a specified load and noting the deflection, which is measured in inches, or of loading until deflection occurs and then gradually increasing the load till the specimen breaks. With the latter procedure, the **modulus of rupture** is found from the equation $M R = \dfrac{2.546\, L S}{D^3}$ where $M R$ = modulus of rupture, L = distance between supports in inches, S = the breaking load, and D = the diameter of the test bar.

In the Brinell hardness test, a special machine is used to apply a load of 3,000 kg. to a steel ball 10 mm. in diameter, resting on a filed-smooth surface of the iron to be tested. The Brinell number is taken as the quotient of the load divided by the area of the impression made by the ball. Thus, small numbers up to 100 indicate softness, while high numbers (400 to 600) indicate great hardness.

Bibliography

American Foundrymen's Association, Cast Metals Handbook (1944 Edition).

American Society for Metals, Metal Progress, Vol. 66, No. 1-A, July 15, 1954. (Nodular Cast Iron, page 49; Design of Ferrous Castings, page 112.)

C. W. Briggs, The Metallurgy of Steel Castings, McGraw-Hill Book Co., New York (1946).

Steel Founders' Society of America, Steel Castings Handbook (1950 Edition).

CHAPTER 39

Principles of Heat Treatment of Steel

SECTION 1

METALLOGRAPHY

The Importance of Heat Treatment—The outstanding advantage of steel as an engineering material is its versatility. This is illustrated by the wide variety of products already described and remaining to be described in this book. The reader has seen and will see that through heat treatment one or another of the characteristics of steel may be enhanced, and it is generally true that much of the versatility of steel arises from the fact that its properties can be controlled and changed at will by heat treatment. Thus, if steel is to be formed into some intricate shape, it can be made very soft and ductile by heat treatment; if, on the other hand, it is to resist wear, it can be heat treated to a very hard, wear-resisting condition.

This important faculty which steel possesses of being amenable to control of its properties by heat treatment arises largely from the fact that these properties, in turn, reflect primarily the **constitution** of the steel, that is, the nature, distribution, and amounts of its **metallographic constituents,** as distinct from its chemical composition. It is these factors which are controlled and changed by heat treatment, and it thus becomes apparent that steel's versatility reflects largely the very wide range of constitutional changes which can be brought about by heat treatment.

The Science of Heat Treatment—The science of heat treatment, then, deals with the factors and mechanisms involved in the control of the constitution of steel by heating and cooling and the relationships between the constitution and properties of steel. Many, although by no means all, of these constitutional changes can be followed by microstructural studies, or a broader type of study known as **metallography,** and many of the known relationships between constitution and properties are in terms of microscopic structures, which, with the advent of the electron microscope, are fine indeed. However, although the microscope has certainly been the most important single tool used in the development of the science of heat treatment, many other methods and techniques have been utilized, including dilatometric studies, magnetic measurements, thermal analyses, X-ray diffraction and, more recently, electron diffraction.

THE CONSTITUENTS OF STEEL

The two constituents of steel, the amount and distribution of which primarily control the properties, are iron (**ferrite**) and iron carbide (**cementite**). True

enough; most plain carbon steels will also contain manganese, silicon, phosphorus, sulphur, oxygen and traces of nitrogen, hydrogen and other chemical elements such as aluminum and copper. These elements, however, as will be shown later, may modify to a certain extent the major effects of the constitution in respect to ferrite and cementite but the cementite is always the predominating influence. This is largely true even of medium-alloy steels, which may contain considerable percentages of such elements as nickel, chromium, molybdenum, vanadium or titanium. The properties of such steels are still dependent primarily upon the distribution and amount of the constituents ferrite and cementite, and the major effects of the alloying elements is to help in the control of this distribution, although the properties may be modified somewhat by solution of the alloying element in the ferrite or by its combination with the carbide phase.

Ferrite—Pure iron without any impurities whatsoever has so far defied manufacture and its properties are therefore unknown. The properties of some of the purer forms of iron, however, are given in Table 39—I. Still purer iron has recently been prepared by the application of a process known as **zone refining.** In this process, a bar of relatively high purity iron is locally heated by induction in a vacuum so that a narrow zone along the length of the bar becomes molten. The bar (or the local heating source) is then moved slowly so that the molten zone progressively moves along the length of the bar. The impurities are concentrated in the moving molten zone, and the purity of the iron as it resolidifies behind the moving zone is increased. Iron containing less than two parts per million (0.0002 per cent) of oxygen, nitrogen, hydrogen and carbon has been prepared by this process. Yield strengths as low as 7000 lb. per sq. in. and tensile strengths of 24,000 lb. per sq. in. have been measured on samples of this higher purity iron.

The metallographic name for iron in steel is ferrite and its microstructural appearance in a low-carbon steel in which it is the predominant constituent is shown in Figure 39—1. It appears as polyhedral grains, distinguishable from one another by the boundaries which have been etched out by the etching reagent and by differences in orientation which cause different etching behaviors. The reagent most commonly used to bring out the ferrite grain boundaries is a dilute solution of nitric acid in ethyl alcohol. Figure

Table 39—I. Properties of Relatively Pure Iron

Sample Description	Chemical Composition (%)								
	C	Mn	P	S	Si	Cu	Ni	O₂	N₂
Armco Ingot Iron...	0.012	0.017	0.005	0.025	trace	......	......	....	.....
Electrolytic........	0.006	....	0.005	0.004	0.005	......	......	....	.....
H₂ purified.........	0.005	0.028	0.004	0.003	0.0012	......	......	0.003	0.0001

Allotropic Forms	Crystallographic Form	Unit Cube Edge (Angstrom Units)	Temperature Range
Alpha	Body Centered Cubic	2.86 (70° F)	Up to 910° C (1670° F)
Gamma	Face Centered Cubic	3.65 (1800° F)	910-1403° C (1670°-2557° F)
Delta	Body Centered Cubic	2.93 (2650° F)	1403-1535° C (2557°-2795° F)

Density, 7.868 grams per cu. cm.   Melting Point, 1535° C (2795° F)   Boiling Point, 3000° C (5432° F)

Mechanical Properties

Property	Hot Rolled	Annealed	Cold Worked	Water Quenched
Compression				
Proportional Limit (Lb. per Sq. In.)....		19,200		
Yield Strength (Lb. per Sq. In.).......		20,600		
Tensile*				
Yield Strength (Lb. per Sq. In.).......	26,000-32,000			30,300
Tensile Strength (Lb. per Sq. In.)......	42,000-48,000		100,000	47,000
Elongation (%).....................	22-28 (in 8″)			36 (in 2″)
Reduction of Area (%)...............	65-78			70
Hardness				
Brinell............................	82-100			
Rockwell B........................	39-55			
Fatigue Strength (Lb. per Sq. In.)				
(Reversed Bend)....................		26,000		
Impact				
Izod (Ft.-lb.).....................	(Long.) 90 (Trans.) 56			

Tensile Strength** 200° C (392° F), 65,600   Limiting Creep Stress for 0.010 inches, 25 days**
Tensile Strength** 400° C (752° F), 44,800   200° C (392° F), 60,000
Tensile Strength** 600° C (1112° F), 15,200   300° C (572° F), 45,000
Tensile Strength** 700° C (1292° F), 9,200   400° C (752° F), 25,000

*At room temperature.
**At indicated temperatures.
Data from National Metals Handbook, American Society for Metals, 1948. [See also: 1961 (Eighth) Edition of Metals Handbook published by American Society for Metals, Vol. I, pages 1206-1212.]

39—2 shows the appearance of ferrite in a slowly-cooled steel of somewhat higher carbon content in which the ferrite appears as a white or light-etching network surrounding bodies of "pearlite," another very common metallographic constituent to be described shortly.

In pure iron-carbon alloys, the ferrite consists of iron with a trace of carbon in solution, but in steels it may also have considerable amounts of alloying elements such as manganese, silicon or nickel dissolved in it.

The atomic arrangement in crystals of the two allotropic forms of iron is shown in Figure 39—3.

Cementite—Cementite is the metallographic term for iron carbide in steel. This is the form in which carbon occurs in steels and the proportions of iron and carbon correspond to the chemical formula Fe_3C. Cementite thus consists of 6.67 per cent carbon and

93.33 per cent iron. Little is known about its properties except that it is very hard and brittle. It is the hardest constituent of plain carbon steel and will scratch glass and feldspar but not quartz. It has about two-thirds the induction of pure iron in a strong magnetic field. The atomic structure of cementite is illustrated in Figure 39—4.

Its metallographic appearance in the grain boundaries of a slowly-cooled, relatively high carbon steel is shown in Figure 39—5. In this case, the cementite appears as a brilliant white network around the pearlite colonies or as needles interspersed with the pearlite. Figure 39—6 shows the metallographic appearance of cementite in a steel which has been heated to a temperature just below that at which austenite (to be described shortly) first forms. This heating has caused the cementite to coalesce into spheroidal particles and

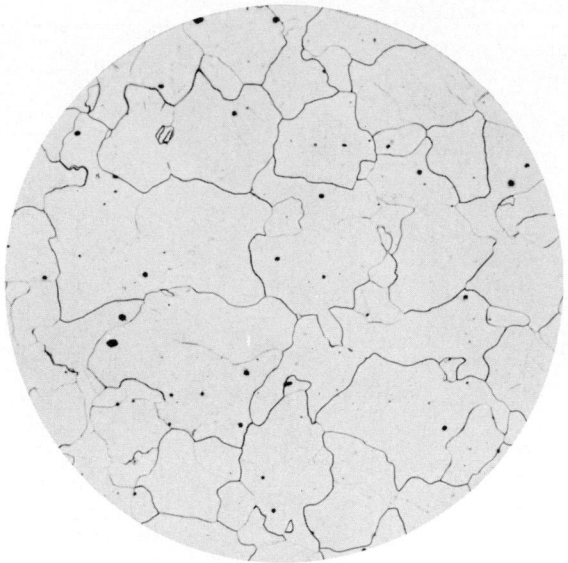

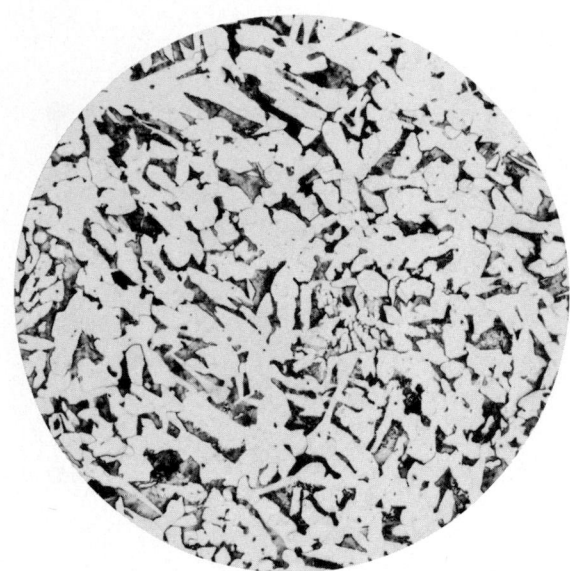

FIG. 39—1. The microstructure of ferrite. Magnification: 100X. (This sample has a coarse grain size.)

FIG. 39—2. The microstructure of slowly cooled hypo-eutectoid steel showing ferrite and pearlite. Magnification: 100X.

the illustration shows these spheroidal particles in a matrix of ferrite. This form of cementite is known as **spheroidized cementite,** or the whole structure as "spheroidite."

Austenite—Although austenite is not ordinarily a constituent of steel after it has been cooled, it seems appropriate to describe it at this point since it is the important high-temperature phase, the decomposition of which on cooling forms the room-temperature constituents which are being discussed. It is a homogeneous phase, consisting of a solid solution of carbon in the gamma form of iron. It is formed when steel is heated

to a relatively high temperature, say above 1450° F, (788° C). The limiting temperatures for the formation of austenite vary with composition and will be discussed in connection with the iron-carbon diagram. The metallographic appearance of austenite is shown in Figure 39—7, which represents a sample of an alloy steel which has been very rapidly cooled from the temperature range at which the austenite is stable, the steel being high enough in alloy content to make possible the retention of austenite structure at room temperature.

The atomic structure of austenite is that of gamma

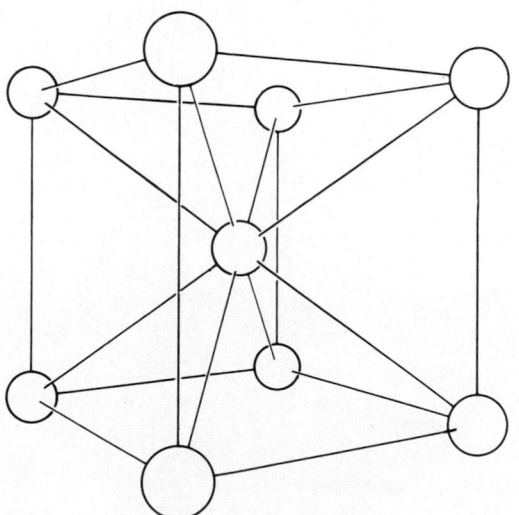

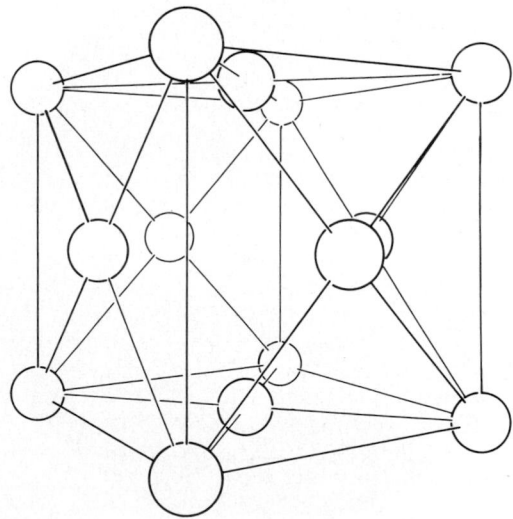

FIG. 39—3. Crystalline structure of the allotropic forms of iron. Each white sphere represents the relative position of an atom in a "unit cube" of: (left) alpha and delta iron, which have the body-centered cubic form, and (right) gamma iron, which possesses the face-centered cubic form.

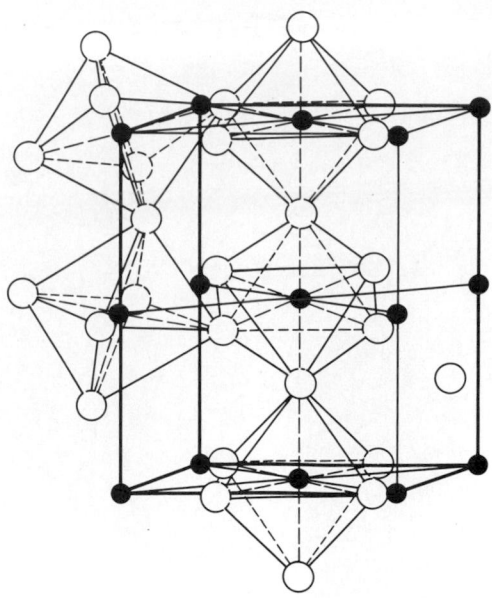

Fig. 39—4. The atomic structure of cementite. Positions of carbon atoms are indicated by solid circles; positions of iron atoms by open circles. (Hendricks, S. B.: Zeitschrift fur Kristallographie, Vol. 74 (1930), 534–545.)

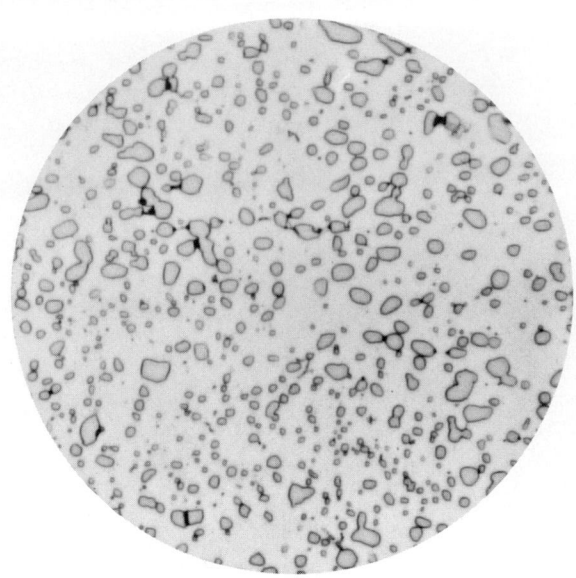

Fig. 39—6. Micrograph showing spheroidized cementite in matrix of ferrite. Magnification: 1000X.

iron—face-centered cubic—and the atomic spacing varies with the carbon content.

Pearlite—When a plain carbon steel of approximately 0.80 per cent carbon is cooled slowly from the temperature range at which austenite is stable, all of the ferrite and cementite precipitate together in a characteristic lamellar structure known as pearlite. This structure is illustrated in Figure 39—8. It is generally similar in its characteristics to an eutectic structure but since it is formed from a solid solution rather than from a liquid phase, it is known as an **eutectoid structure**.

At carbon contents above and below 0.80 per **cent**, pearlite of about 0.80 per cent carbon is likewise formed on slow cooling, but the excess ferrite or cementite first precipitates usually as a grain boundary network, but occasionally also along cleavage planes of the austenite. This excess ferrite or cementite re-

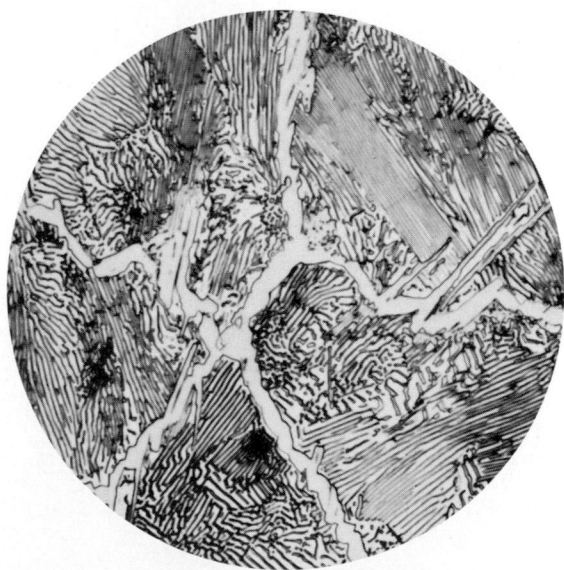

Fig. 39—5. The microstructure of slowly cooled, high-carbon steel showing pearlite with cementite in the grain boundaries. Magnification: 1000X.

Fig. 39—7. The microstructure of austenite. Magnification: 500X.

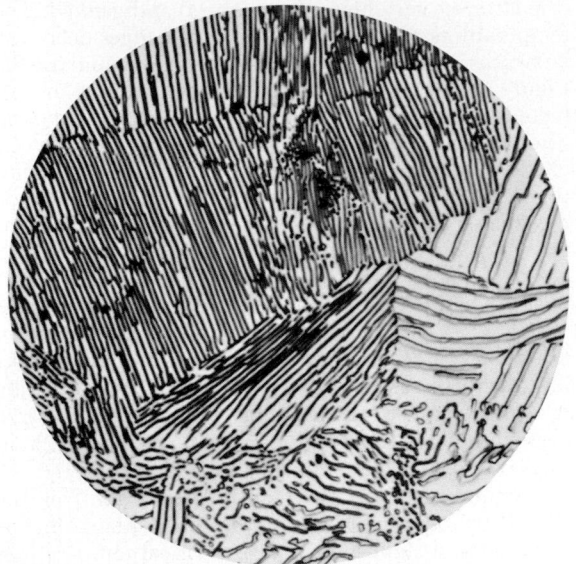

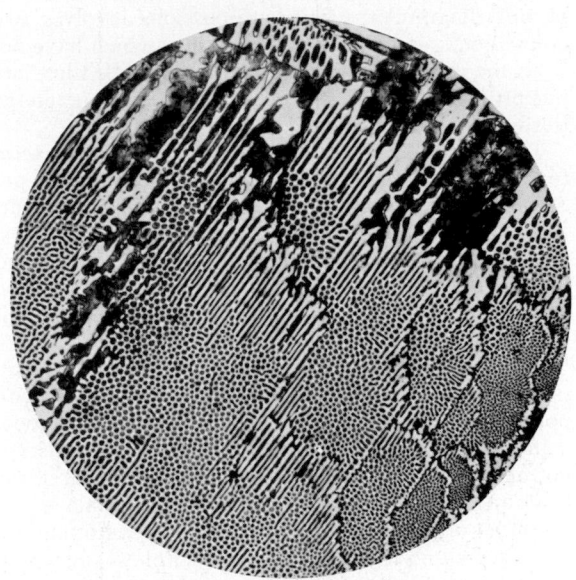

FIG. 39—8. The microstructure of pearlite. Magnification: 1000X.

FIG. 39—10. The microstructure of ledeburite. Magnification: 150X.

jected by the cooling austenite is known as a **proeutectoid** constituent. The carbon content of a slowly-cooled steel can be estimated from the relative amounts of the pearlite and proeutectoid constituents in the microstructure.

The Iron-Carbon Equilibrium Diagram—The iron-carbon equilibrium diagram furnishes a "map" showing the ranges of compositions and temperatures within which the various phases are stable and the boundaries at which phase changes occur. Although heat treatment is largely concerned with a controlled

departure from equilibrium, this diagram represents the limiting conditions and is basic to an understanding of heat-treating principles.

The iron-carbon phase-equilibrium diagram that appeared earlier in this book as Figure 12—41 in Chapter 12 is repeated for convenience in Figure 39—9. This diagram, covering the temperature range from 600° C (1112° F) to the melting point of iron and carbon contents of from 0 to 5 per cent, represents the equilibrium conditions for the entire range of steels and cast irons in both the liquid and solid states. Use

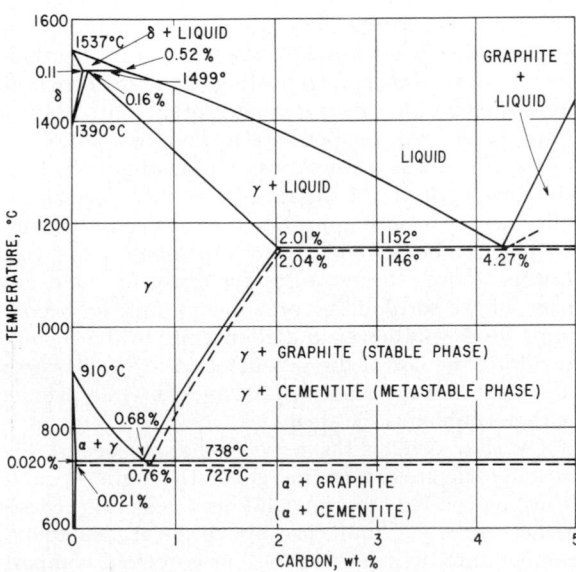

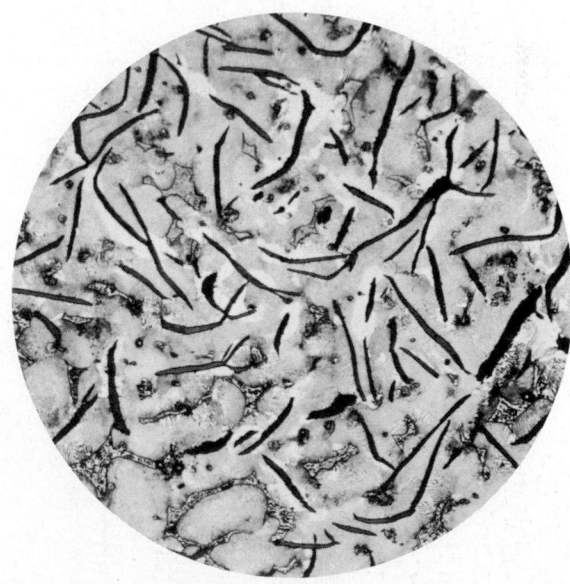

FIG. 39—9. The iron-carbon equilibrium diagram, for carbon contents up to 5 per cent.

FIG. 39—11. The microstructure of gray cast iron showing graphite flakes. Magnification: 100X.

of this diagram in ensuing discussions involves two constituents, **ledeburite** and **graphite,** which have not been mentioned up to this point. Although these are not ordinarily constituents of steels, their characteristics will be briefly discussed at this point.

Ledeburite—Ledeburite is the metallographic term for the iron-iron carbide eutectic, containing 4.27 per cent carbon. This eutectic is a constituent of iron-carbon alloys containing more than 2.01 per cent carbon and for this reason the dividing line between steels and cast iron is customarily set at 2.0 per cent carbon. The metallographic appearance of ledeburite in cast iron is shown in Figure 39—10.

Graphite—Cementite is unstable over certain ranges of composition and temperature and decomposes into iron and graphite. Thus, in most slowly-cooled cast irons, graphite is an equilibrium constituent at room temperature. The gray appearance of the fracture of such slowly-cooled cast irons reflects the presence of the graphite and the metallographic appearance of graphite in gray cast iron is shown in Figure 39—11. Graphite may, under certain conditions, be a constituent of steels and the metallographic appearance of graphite in a low-carbon steel which has been subjected to a prolonged heating at a temperature below that at which austenite is formed is illustrated in Figure 39—12.

The Iron-Iron Carbide Equilibrium Diagram for Steels—The portion of the iron-iron carbide diagram of concern in connection with the heat treatment of steel is that part extending from 0 to 2.01 per cent carbon. The general features of this diagram (Figure 39—9) will be discussed and its application to heat treatment will be illustrated by considering the changes occurring on heating and cooling steels of selected carbon contents as depicted by the diagram.

Critical Temperatures—In Table 39—I, iron is listed as occurring in two allotropic forms, alpha or delta

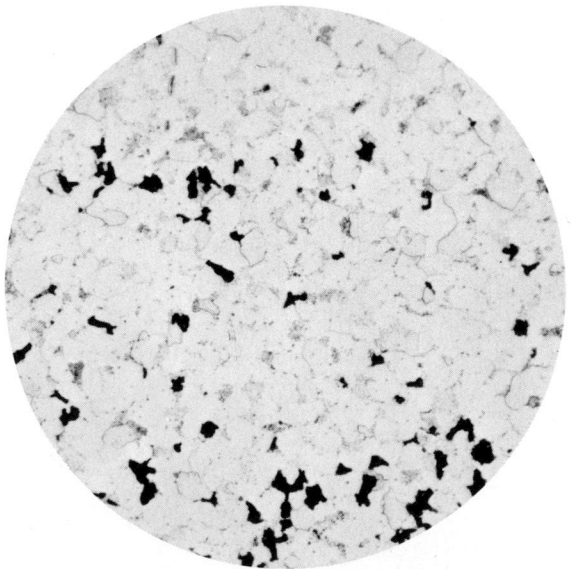

Fig. 39—12. Micrograph showing graphite particles in low-carbon steel. Magnification: 100X.

(the latter at very high temperature) and gamma. The temperatures at which these phase changes occur are known as critical temperatures and the boundaries in Figure 39—9 show how these temperatures are affected by composition. For pure iron, these temperatures are 1670° F (910° C) for the alpha-gamma phase change and 2534° F (1390° C) for the gamma-delta phase change. The critical temperatures on heating are designated as A_c (from the French "chauffage," meaning "heating") temperatures, while those on cooling are designated as A_r (from the French "refroidissement," meaning "cooling") temperatures. Although, in principle, the transformations A_c and A_r result from the same temperature of equilibrium, in practice, the A_r temperatures are lower than the corresponding A_c temperatures, falling as the cooling is more rapid; even with very slow heating or cooling these temperatures do not coincide and, therefore, the subscript "e" (for equilibrium) is used in the designation of the critical temperatures in the equilibrium diagram. The meaning and significance of the critical temperatures will be clarified in the following discussion of the changes occurring on heating and cooling iron-carbon alloys as depicted by the equilibrium diagram.

Changes Occurring on Heating and Cooling Pure Iron—The only changes occurring on heating or cooling pure iron are the reversible changes, (1) at about 1670° F (910° C) from body-centered alpha iron to face-centered gamma iron and (2) from the face-centered gamma iron to body-centered delta iron at about 2534° F (1390° C).

Changes Occurring on Heating and Cooling Hypoeutectoid Steels—Hypoeutectoid steels are those which contain less than the eutectoid percentage of carbon (0.80 per cent). The diagram shows the equilibrium constituents are ferrite and pearlite, the relative amounts of each depending upon the carbon content. The diagram also shows that at 1112° F (600° C) the ferrite may hold in stable solution about 0.007 per cent carbon. Up to 1340° F (727° C), the solubility of carbon in the ferrite increases until at this temperature, the ferrite contains about 0.025 per cent carbon. The first phase change on heating (if the steel contains above 0.025 per cent carbon) occurs at 1340° F (727° C) and this temperature is therefore designated as the A_1 critical temperature. On heating just above this temperature, the pearlite (ferrite and cementite) all changes to austenite. Some proeutectoid ferrite, however, remains unchanged. As temperature rises farther above A_1, the austenite dissolves more and more of the surrounding proeutectoid ferrite, becoming lower and lower in carbon, until at the A_3 temperature, the last of the proeutectoid ferrite has been absorbed into the austenite having the same average carbon content as the steel.

On slow cooling the reverse changes occur. The austenite first rejects ferrite (generally at grain boundaries) on cooling below A_3 and becomes progressively richer in carbon, until, just above the A_1 (eutectoid) temperature, it is substantially of eutectoid composition. On cooling below A_1, this eutectoid austenite changes to pearlite so that the final product after cooling below A_1 is a mixture of ferrite and pearlite, the relative proportions of each constituent depending upon the carbon content.

Changes Occurring on Heating and Cooling Eutectoid Steels—Since no excess ferrite or cementite is present in eutectoid steel, the only change occurring on slow cooling or heating is the reversible change from pearlite to austenite at the eutectoid temperature. Thus, in the case of eutectoid steels, the A_3 and A_1 temperatures coincide and this eutectoid composition and temperature is designated as the A_{3-1} point.

Changes Occurring on Heating and Cooling Hypereutectoid Steels—The behavior on heating and cooling **hypereutectoid steels** (steels containing more than 0.80 per cent carbon) is similar to that of hypoeutectoid steels except that the excess constituent is cementite rather than ferrite, so that on heating above A_1, the austenite gradually dissolves the excess cementite until at the A_{cm} temperature all of the proeutectoid cementite has been dissolved and austenite of the same carbon content as the steel is formed. Similarly, on cooling below A_3, cementite precipitates and the carbon content of the austenite approaches the eutectoid composition. On cooling below A_1, this eutectoid austenite changes to pearlite and the room temperature constitution is, therefore, pearlite and proeutectoid cementite.

The A_2 Formerly Designated Critical Temperature—Early iron-carbon equilibrium diagrams indicated a critical temperature at about 1414° F (768° C). It has since been found that the behavior at this temperature differs from those at A_1 and A_3 in that it does not involve a phase change. In the neighborhood of 1414° F (768° C) and up to about 1454° F (790° C) there is a gradual magnetic change, ferrite being ferromagnetic below this temperature range, and paramagnetic above. The change is also accompanied by a heat effect. This A_2 change is of little or no significance in regard to the heat treatment of steel.

The Effect of Alloys on the Equilibrium Diagram—The iron-carbon diagram may, of course, be profoundly altered by alloying elements, and, therefore,

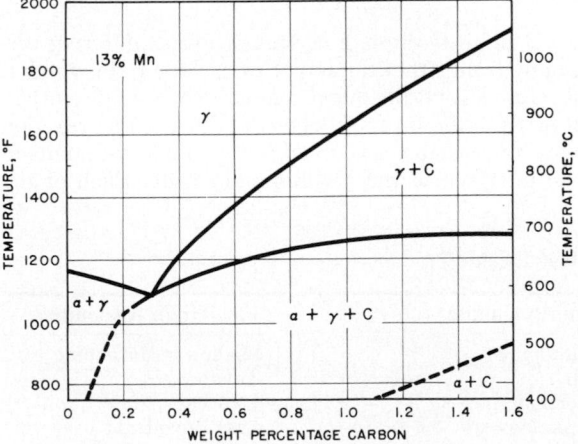

FIG. 39—13. Section of the Fe-C-Mn equilibrium diagram at 13 per cent manganese content. From "Metals Handbook" (American Society for Metals), 1948 Edition; page 1252.

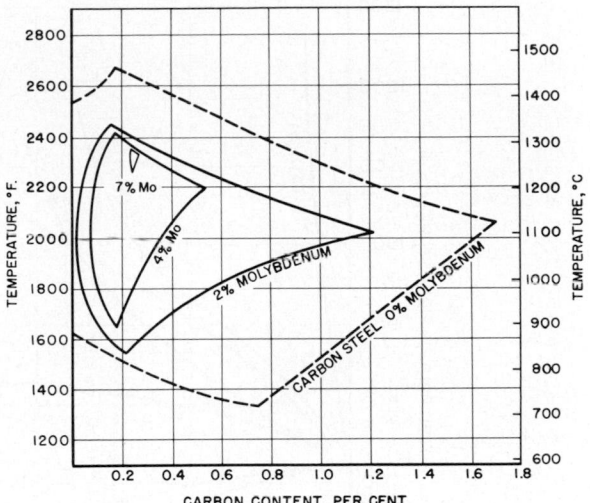

FIG. 39—14. The effect of molybdenum on the composition and temperature range over which austenite is stable. (After Bain.)

its application should be limited to plain carbon and low-alloy steels. The most important general effects of the alloying elements may be listed as follows:

1. The number of phases which may be in equilibrium is no longer limited to two as in the iron-carbon diagram.

2. The temperature and composition range, with respect to carbon, over which austenite is stable may be increased or reduced.

3. The eutectoid temperature and composition may be changed.

The alloying elements may be divided generally into two classes in respect to the second effect: those which enlarge the austenite field and those which reduce it. The elements which enlarge this field include manganese, nickel, cobalt, copper, carbon and nitrogen. Because of this characteristic, elements of this type are descriptively known as **austenite formers.** Figure 39—13, which shows the 13 per cent manganese section of the iron-carbon-manganese equilibrium diagram, is illustrative of the effect of elements of this type. The large field in which austenite is stable, the lowering of the eutectoid temperature and carbon content, and the three-phase field in which alpha iron, austenite and carbides exist in equilibrium should be noted.

The commoner elements which decrease the "size" of the austenite field include chromium, silicon, molybdenum, tungsten, vanadium, tin, columbium, phosphorus, aluminum and titanium. Such elements are known as **ferrite formers.** Figure 39—14 showing the effect of molybdenum on the composition and temperature range over which austenite is stable will serve to illustrate the effect of alloys of this type. These steels will likewise have the three-phase zone in which austenite, ferrite and carbides will be in equilibrium at temperatures below the austenite field.

The effect of the elements on the eutectoid temperature and composition is summarized in Figure 39—15. It will be noted that manganese and nickel lower

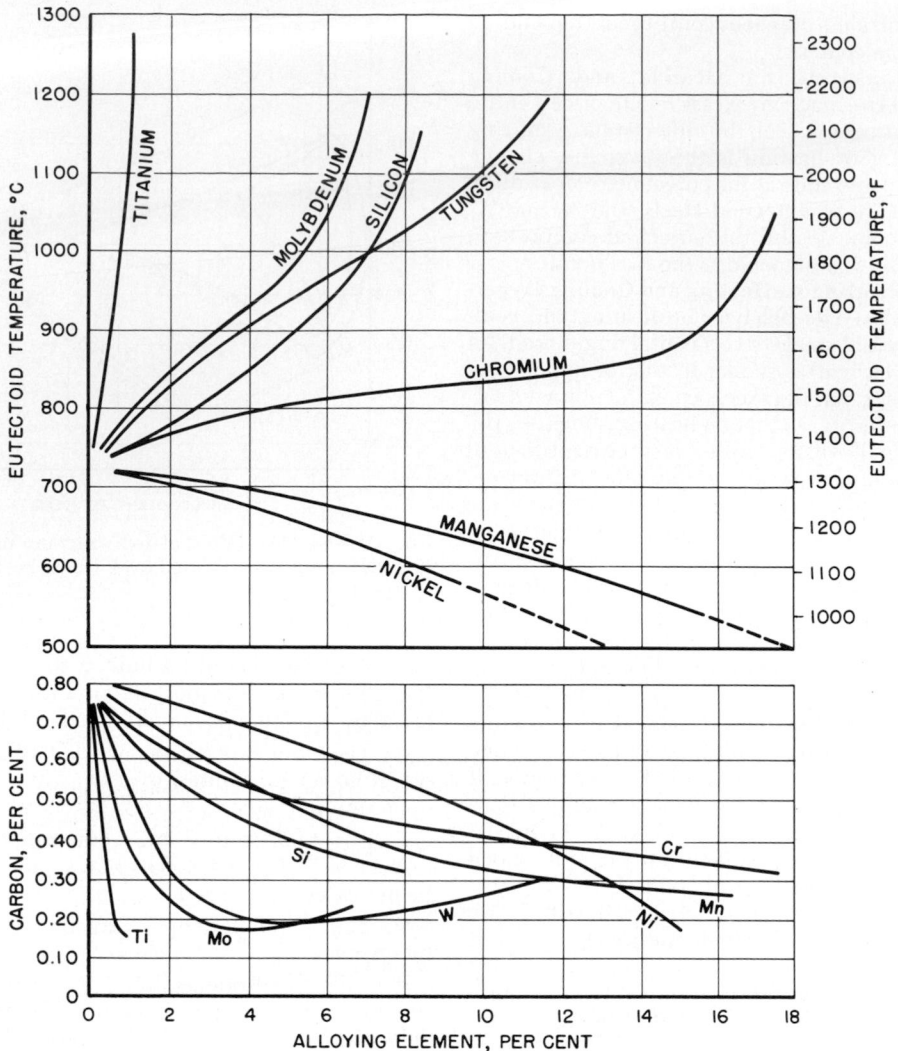

FIG. 39—15. Eutectoid composition and temperature as influenced by several alloying elements. (After Bain.)

the eutectoid temperature while the other elements generally raise it. All of the elements seem to lower the eutectoid carbon content.

Grain Size—As described above, when a piece of steel is heated above the critical temperature, the ferrite and carbide react with one another to form austen-ite. The austenite is a crystalline phase differing distinctly from either the ferrite or carbide from which it is formed. Like any metal composed of a solid solution, it exists in the form of polyhedral grains. The reaction which forms austenite begins at a number of points in the interface of the carbide and ferrite. Each of the

Table 39—II. Trends in Heat-Treated Products

Property	Coarse-Grain Austenite	Fine-Grain Austenite
Hardenability	Deeper Hardening	Shallower Hardening
Toughness	Less Tough	Tougher
Distortion	More Distortion	Less Distortion
Quench Cracking	More Prevalent	Less Prevalent
Internal Stress	Higher	Lower
For Annealed or Normalized Products		
Machinability (Rough)	Better	Inferior
Machinability (Fine Finish)	Inferior	Better

little islands of austenite grows until finally it reaches its similarly growing neighbors. As the temperature above the critical increases, further grain growth occurs, presumably by encroachment of a grain into adjacent grains. The final austenite grain size is, therefore, a function of the temperature above the critical to which it is heated. This grain growth may, however, be inhibited by carbides which dissolve slowly or remain undissolved in the austenite or by a suitable dispersion of non-metallic inclusions. Hot working refines the coarse grain size formed by heating to the relatively high temperature used in forging or rolling and the grain size of hot-worked products is determined largely by the finishing temperature, that is, the temperature at which the final stage of the hot-working process is carried out.

Grain Size and Properties—The coarseness of the ferritic and pearlitic "grains" in the cooled steel reflects the grain size of the austenite prior to its transformation and the properties of the product are profoundly influenced by its grain size. The general effects of the austenite grain size are summarized in Table 39—II.

Determination of Microscopic Grain Size—The microscopic grain size of steel is customarily determined by preparing a polished plane section, prepared in such a way as to delineate the grain boundaries, and then applying one of three basic procedures for estimating the grain size. These three procedures are described in ASTM Designation E-112, and are known as the **comparison procedure,** the **intercept** (or **Heyn**) **procedure,** and the **planimetric** (or **Jeffries'**) **procedure.**

For specimens consisting of equiaxed grains, the method of comparing the specimen with a standard chart (the comparison procedure) is the most convenient and of sufficient accuracy for commercial purposes: it is the method used by the steel industry for specification testing. Standard charts (and transparencies of the same) are published by the American Society for Testing and Materials (ASTM) for estimating the grain size of metallic materials. Each chart represents a series of structures of different grain sizes, each structure in the series being identified with a number (see Table 39—III). The estimation of micro-grain size is made by comparing a projected image or a photomicrograph of a representative field of the test specimen with the photomicrographs of the appropriate standard grain size series, or with suitable reproductions or transparencies of them, and selecting the photomicrograph that most nearly matches the image of the test specimen or interpolating between two standards. This estimated grain size is reported to the nearest appropriate unit listed in Table 39—III. The comparison procedure can be used, as an example, for estimating the austenitic grain size of ferritic steel after a McQuaid-Ehn test, or after the austenite grains have been revealed by any other means. Two of the three most common methods of delineating the austenite grain boundaries are too cool the steel from its austenitizing temperature in such a way that the shape of the original austenite grains is outlined by (1) a grain-boundary network of ferrite in the case of hypoeutectoid steels, or (2) a grain-boundary network of cementite in the case of hyper-

eutectoid steels. In the third method (3) the steel is quenched to full hardness and a special reagent is used to disclose orientation differences in the martensite grains formed from austenite on quenching. Other methods can be used but cannot be discussed here.

With the intercept (or Heyn) procedure, the grain size is estimated by counting, on the ground-glass screen of the metallurgical microscope, on a representative photomicrograph of the specimen, or on the specimen itself, the number of grains intercepted by one or more straight lines sufficiently long to yield at least 50 intercepts. Grains touched by the end of the line count only as half grains. The length of the line in millimeters divided by the average number of grains intersected by it gives the average intercept length (Table 39—III). For equiaxed structures, counts should be made on at least three fields to assure a reasonable average. For non-equiaxed structures, measurements should be made on longitudinal and transverse sections along lines that lie in all three principal directions of the specimen. ASTM Designation E-112 gives details for calculating the number of grains per cubic millimeter in the specimen from these observations on a non-equiaxed structure and for converting counts to ASTM grain-size numbers.

In the planimetric (or Jeffries') procedure, a circle or rectangle of known area (usually 5000 sq. mm.) is inscribed on a photomicrograph or on the ground-glass screen of the metallurgical microscope. A magnification is selected that will give at least 50 grains in the field to be counted. The sum of all the grains included completely within the known area plus one half the number of grains intersected by the circumference of the area gives the number of equivalent whole grains (measured at the magnification used) within the area. If this number is multiplied by a factor, f, known as Jeffries' multiplier, that varies in value according to the magnification used, the product will be the number of grains per sq. mm. A minimum of three fields should be counted to assure a reasonable average. The foregoing applies to use of the planimetric method for determining the grain size of equiaxed structures. When the grains are not equiaxed, a grain count is made on three mutually perpendicular planes determined by the longitudinal, transverse, and normal directions. ASTM Designation E-112 tells how to convert the number of grains per sq. mm. determined for these planes to grains per cu. mm.

The grain size, as estimated by any of the foregoing methods, may be expressed in terms such as "diameter" of average grain in millimeters (reciprocal of the square root of the number of grains per sq. mm.), number of grains per unit area, grains per unit volume, or ASTM micro-grain-size number (Table 39—III).

Fine- and Coarse-Grain Steels—As was mentioned previously, austenitic-grain growth may be inhibited by undissolved carbides or by a suitable distribution of non-metallic inclusions. Steels of this type are commonly referred to as inherently fine-grained or simply as fine-grained steels, while steels which are free from these grain growth inhibitors are known as coarse-grained steels.

The general pattern of grain coarsening in steels of the coarse- and fine-grained types on heating above

Table 39—III. Micro-Grain Size Relationships.

ASTM Micro-Grain Size Number	Calculated "Diameter" of Average Grain		Average Intercept Distance[b]		Calculated Area of Average Grain Section		Average Number of Grains per cu mm	Nominal Grains per sq mm at 1×	Nominal Grains per sq in. at 100×
	mm	in.	mm	in.	sq mm	sq in.			
		×10⁻³		×10⁻³	×10⁻³	×10⁻⁶			
00[a]	0.508	20.0	0.451	17.8	258	400	7.63	3.88	0.250
0	0.359	14.1	0.319	12.6	129	200	21.6	7.75	0.50
0.5	0.302	11.9	0.268	10.6	91.2	141	36.3	11.0	0.707
1.0	0.254	10.0	0.226	8.88	64.5	100	61.0	15.5	1.0
...	0.250	9.84	0.222	8.74	62.5	96.9	64.0	16.0	1.03
1.5	0.214	8.41	0.190	7.47	45.6	70.7	103	21.9	1.41
...	0.200	7.87	0.178	6.99	40.0	62.0	125	25.0	1.61
...	0.180	7.09	0.160	6.29	32.4	50.2	171	30.9	1.99
2.0	0.180	7.07	0.160	6.28	32.3	50.0	172.3	31.0	2.0
2.5	0.151	5.95	0.134	5.30	22.8	35.4	290	43.8	2.83
...	0.150	5.91	0.133	5.24	22.5	34.9	296	44.4	2.87
3.0	0.127	5.00	0.113	4.44	16.1	25.0	488	62.0	4.0
...	0.120	4.72	0.107	4.20	14.4	22.3	578.9	69.4	4.48
3.5	0.107	4.20	0.0948	3.73	11.4	17.7	821	87.7	5.66
...	0.900	3.54	0.0799	3.15	8.10	12.6	1 370	123	7.97
4.0	0.0898	3.54	0.0797	3.14	8.06	12.5	1 380	124	8.0
4.5	0.076	2.97	0.0671	2.64	5.70	8.84	2 320	175	11.3
...	0.070	2.76	0.0622	2.45	4.90	7.59	2 920	204	13.2
5.0	0.064	2.50	0.0564	2.22	4.03	6.25	3 910	248	16.0
...	0.060	2.36	0.0533	2.10	3.60	5.58	4 630	278	17.9
5.5	0.0534	2.10	0.0474	1.87	2.85	4.42	6 570	351	22.6
...	0.050	1.97	0.0444	1.75	2.50	3.88	8 000	400	25.8
6.0	0.045	1.77	0.0399	1.57	2.02	3.13	11 000	496	32.0
...	0.040	1.58	0.0355	1.40	1.60	2.48	15 600	625	40.3
6.5	0.038	1.49	0.0335	1.32	1.43	2.21	18 600	701	45.3
...	0.035	1.38	0.0311	1.22	1.23	1.90	23 000	816	52.7
7.0	0.032	1.25	0.0282	1.11	1.01	1.56	31 000	992	64.0
...	0.030	1.18	0.0267	1.05	0.90	1.40	37 000	1 110	71.7
7.5	0.027	1.05	0.0237	0.933	0.713	1.10	52 500	1 400	90.5
...	0.025	0.984	0.0222	0.874	0.625	0.969	64 000	1 600	103
8.0	0.0224	0.884	0.0199	0.785	0.504	0.781	88 400	1 980	128
...	0.0200	0.787	0.0178	0.699	0.40	0.620	125 000	2 500	161
8.5	0.0189	0.743	0.0168	0.660	0.356	0.552	149 000	2 810	181
9.0	0.0159	0.625	0.0141	0.555	0.252	0.391	250 000	3 970	256
...	0.0150	0.591	0.0133	0.524	0.225	0.349	296 000	4 440	287
9.5	0.0134	0.526	0.0119	0.467	0.178	0.276	420 000	5 610	362
10.0	0.0112	0.442	0.00997	0.392	0.126	0.195	707 000	7 940	512
...	0.0100	0.394	0.00888	0.350	0.10	0.155	1.00×10^6	10 000	645
10.5	0.00944	0.372	0.00838	0.330	0.089	0.138	1.19×10^6	11 200	724
...	0.00900	0.354	0.00799	0.315	0.081	0.126	1.37×10^6	12 300	797
...	0.00800	0.315	0.00710	0.280	0.064	0.0992	1.95×10^6	15 600	1 010
11.0	0.00794	0.313	0.00705	0.278	0.063	0.0977	2.00×10^6	15 900	1 020
...	0.00700	0.276	0.00622	0.245	0.049	0.0760	2.92×10^6	20 400	1 320
11.5	0.00667	0.263	0.00593	0.233	0.045	0.0691	3.36×10^6	22 400	1 450
...	0.00600	0.236	0.00533	0.210	0.036	0.0558	4.63×10^6	27 800	1 790
12.0	0.00561	0.221	0.00498	0.196	0.031	0.0488	5.66×10^6	31 700	2 050
...	0.00500	0.197	0.00444	0.175	0.025	0.0388	8.00×10^6	40 000	2 580
12.5	0.00472	0.186	0.00419	0.165	0.022	0.0345	9.51×10^6	44 900	2 900
...	0.00400	0.158	0.00355	0.140	0.0160	0.0248	15.62×10^6	62 500	4 030
13.0	0.00397	0.156	0.00352	0.139	0.0158	0.0244	16.0×10^6	63 500	4 100
13.5	0.00334	0.131	0.00296	0.117	0.011	0.0173	26.9×10^6	89 800	5 800
...	0.00300	0.118	0.00266	0.105	0.009	0.0140	37.0×10^6	111 000	7 170
14.0	0.00281	0.111	0.00249	0.0981	0.0079	0.0122	45.2×10^6	127 000	8 200
...	0.00250	0.098	0.00222	0.0874	0.00625	0.00969	64.0×10^6	160 000	10 300

[a]The use of 00 is recommended instead of "−1" or "minus 1" to avoid confusion.

[b]Value of Heyn intercept for equiaxed grains.

[c]From: Designation E-112, ASTM Standards, 1961, Part 3—Metal Test Methods; published by American Society for Testing and Materials, Philadelphia, Pa.

the critical temperature is illustrated in Figures 39—16 and 39—17. It will be noted that the coarse-grained steel coarsens gradually and consistently as the temperature is increased, while the fine-grained steel coarsens only slightly, if at all, until a certain temperature is reached, above which an abrupt coarsening occurs. This temperature is known as the **coarsening temperature**. It should further be noted that either type of steel may be heat treated so as to be either fine or coarse grained, and as a matter of fact, at temperatures above its coarsening temperature, the fine-grained steel will usually exhibit a coarser grain size than the coarse-grained steel at the same temperature.

The usual method of making steels which remain fine grained at 1700° F (ASTM E19-46) involves the judicious use of aluminum deoxidation. The inhibiting agent in such steels is generally conjectured to be a submicroscopic dispersion of aluminum nitride, or, perhaps at times, aluminum oxide.

THE TRANSFORMATION OF AUSTENITE

Thus far, this chapter has largely been concerned with equilibrium conditions. Under equilibrium conditions, that is, with very slow cooling, it has been shown that austenite transforms to pearlite when it is cooled below the A_1 critical temperature, and at a temperature only a little below the Ae_1 temperature. When more rapidly cooled, however, this transformation is depressed and does not occur until a lower temperature is reached. The faster the cooling rate, the lower is the temperature at which transformation occurs. Furthermore, the nature of the ferrite-carbide aggregate formed when the austenite transforms varies markedly with the temperature of transformation and the properties are found to vary correspondingly. Thus, heat treatment is seen to involve a controlled supercooling of austenite, and in order to take full advantage of the wide range of structures and properties which this permits, a knowledge of the transformation behavior of austenite and the properties of the resulting aggregates is essential.

Isothermal Transformation Diagrams—The transformation behavior of austenite can best be studied by a technique developed at the United States Steel Corporation Fundamental Research Laboratory in 1930. This involves studying the transformation behavior at a series of temperatures below A_1, by quenching small samples to the desired temperature in

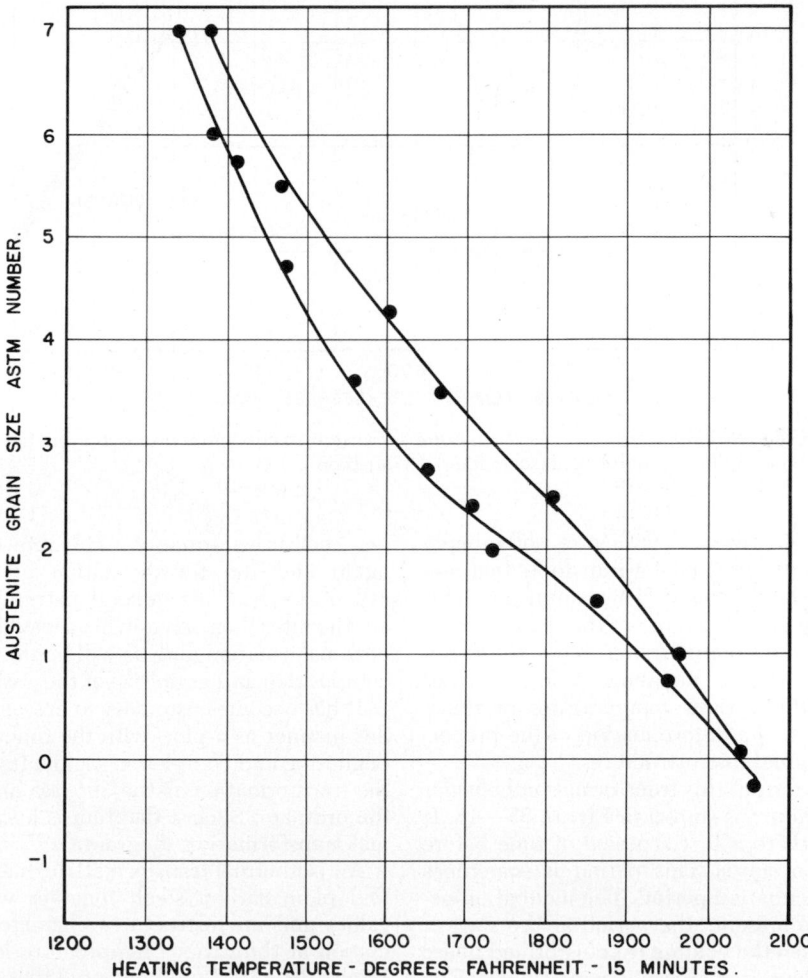

FIG. 39—16. Grain size as a function of austenitizing temperature for inherently coarse-grained steels. (After Bain.)

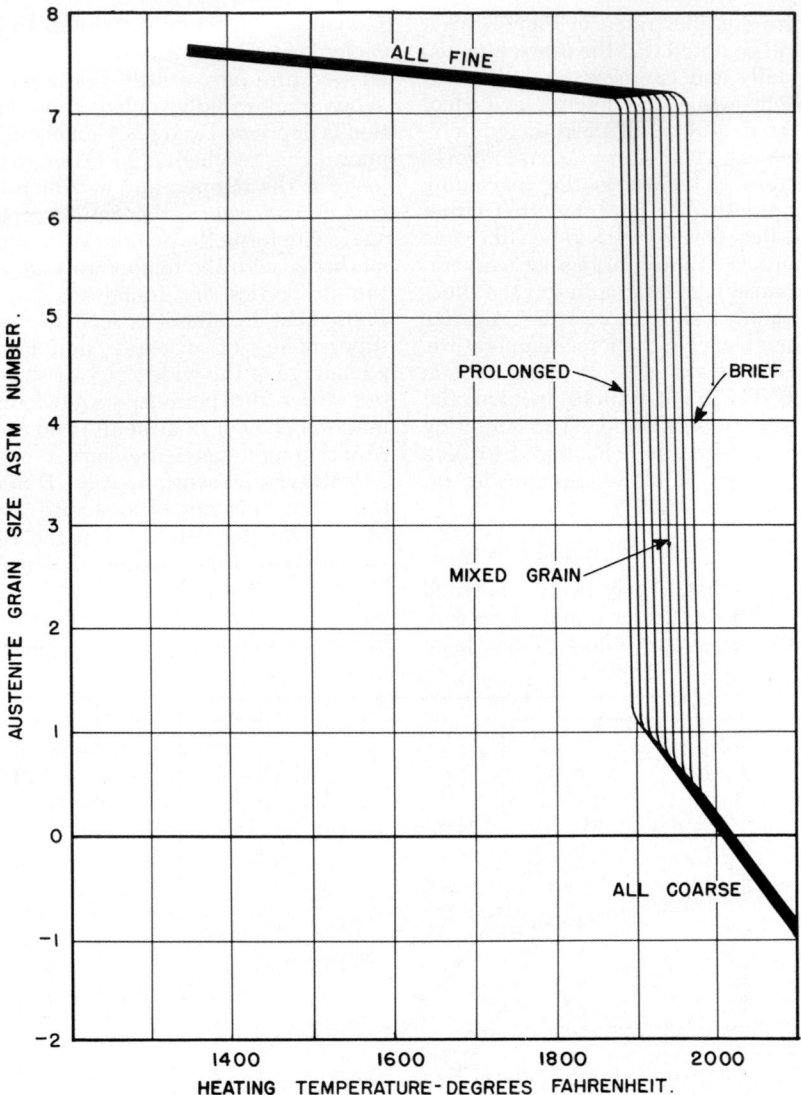

Fig. 39—17. Grain size as a function of austenitizing temperature for an inherently fine-grained steel (schematic). (After Bain.)

a liquid bath, allowing them to transform isothermally and following the progress of the transformation metallographically or by dilatometric measurements. This procedure not only gives a picture of the rates of transformation at the various temperatures, but also furnishes information as to the metallographic structures characteristic of the various temperatures of transformation and permits a determination of the properties of these individual microstructures.

The general pattern of this transformation behavior at a single temperature is shown in Figure 39—18. It will be seen that there is first a period of time before any transformation starts. This period is sometimes spoken of as an **incubation period.** The incubation period presumably represents the period at the start of transformation when the volume of transformed phase around each nucleus is increasing very slowly. The transformation accelerates as it progresses so that the fastest transformation rate corresponds to about 50

per cent transformation. The rate then slows down again and the transformation goes to completion rather slowly. This general pattern is characteristic, but the rates themselves will vary with the temperature of transformation and, as will be shown later, with the composition and grain size of the austenite.

It has become customary to present data obtained in this manner as a plot, with the times required for the beginning and completion (and a few other stages) of the transformation as the abscissa and temperature as the ordinate. Such a diagram is known as an **isothermal transformation diagram.**

An isothermal transformation diagram for a eutectoid plain carbon steel, together with the hardness values and microstructures characteristic of transformation at the various temperature levels, is shown in Figure 39—19. It will be noted that the diagram has a **nose** or temperature of most rapid transformation at about 1000° F. The transformation rate at tempera-

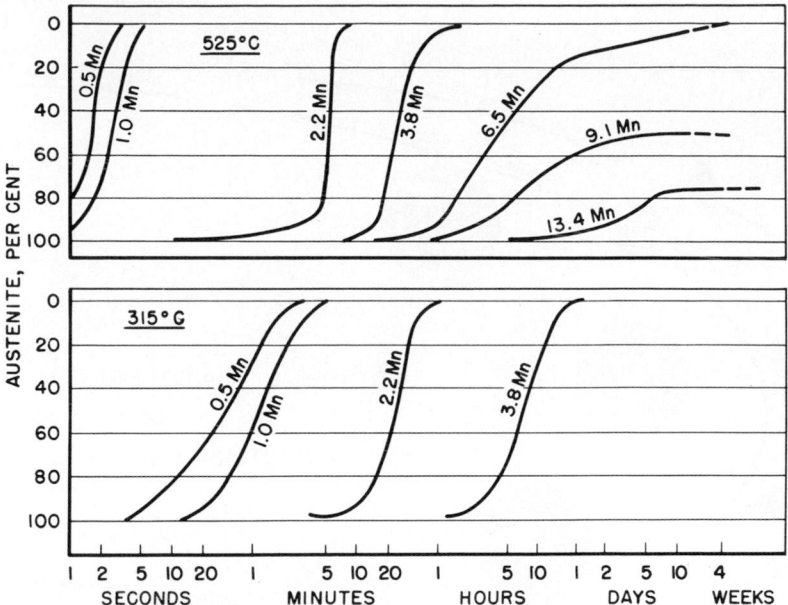

FIG. 39—18. Transformation behavior at a single temperature in a series of manganese steels of about 0.55% carbon content. (After Bain.)

tures near the A_1 is very slow and it is likewise relatively slow at a lower temperature range.

Transformation to Pearlite—Transformation over the temperature range of about 1300° to 1000° F (in carbon and low-alloy steels) forms pearlitic microstructures and the characteristic lamellar appearance of these structures is apparent in the photomicrographs. It will also be noted that as the transformation temperature decreases, the lamellae become more closely spaced, so that as transformed at 1000° F they can hardly be resolved by the light microscope. The much greater resolving power of the electron microscope does, however, permit resolution of the closely spaced lamellae of fine pearlite, as illustrated in the electron micrograph of Figure 39—20a, showing the microstructure of fine pearlite formed at 1100° F. The hardness is also seen to increase as the lamellar spacing becomes smaller.

Transformation to Bainite—Transformation to bainite occurs over the temperature range of about 1000° to 450° F. The bainitic microstructures differ markedly from pearlitic in that they are acicular in nature. Here again, the hardness increases as the transformation temperature decreases, though the bainite formed at the highest possible temperature is often softer than pearlite formed at a still higher temperature. The details of the bainitic microstructures forming in this temperature range are, as with fine pearlite, generally irresolvable with the light microscope, but are readily resolved with the electron microscope. Electron micrographs of the bainitic microstructures formed on complete transformation of a eutectoid steel at 850, 700, and 500° F are shown in Figures 39—20b, 39—20c, 39—20d.

Transformation to Martensite—Transformation to martensite, which in this steel occurs at temperatures below 450° F, differs from transformation to pearlite or bainite in that it is not time dependent, but occurs almost instantly during cooling and the percentage of transformation is dependent only on the temperature to which it is cooled. Thus, in this steel, transformation to martensite will start on cooling to 450° F (designated as the M_s temperature), will be 50 per cent complete on cooling to about 300° F, and will be essentially completed at about 200° F (designated as the M_f temperature). The microstructure of martensite is likewise acicular but it is generally lighter etching than bainite. It is the hardest of the transformation products of austenite. It is possible to form a little martensite at, say, 425° F and then to cause bainite to form thereafter isothermally.

MICROSTRUCTURAL AND MECHANICAL PROPERTIES

The dependence of the properties of steel upon its constitution has been emphasized in this chapter and, as would be expected, the properties of steel vary with the temperature at which the austenite transforms in accordance with the corresponding microstructural changes.

The microstructures discussed above fall into three general classes: pearlite, bainite, and martensite. In discussing the relationships between microstructure and properties, a fourth class of microstructure, tempered martensite, must also be considered. This is the structure formed when martensite is reheated to a subcritical temperature after quenching. Its microscopic appearance is illustrated in the electron micrograph of Figure 39—21. The general effect of tempering martensite is to precipitate and coagulate the carbide particles, so that tempered martensite microstructures consist of carbide particles dispersed in a ferrite matrix. The steel in this illustration has been tempered at a relatively high temperature and some tendency for

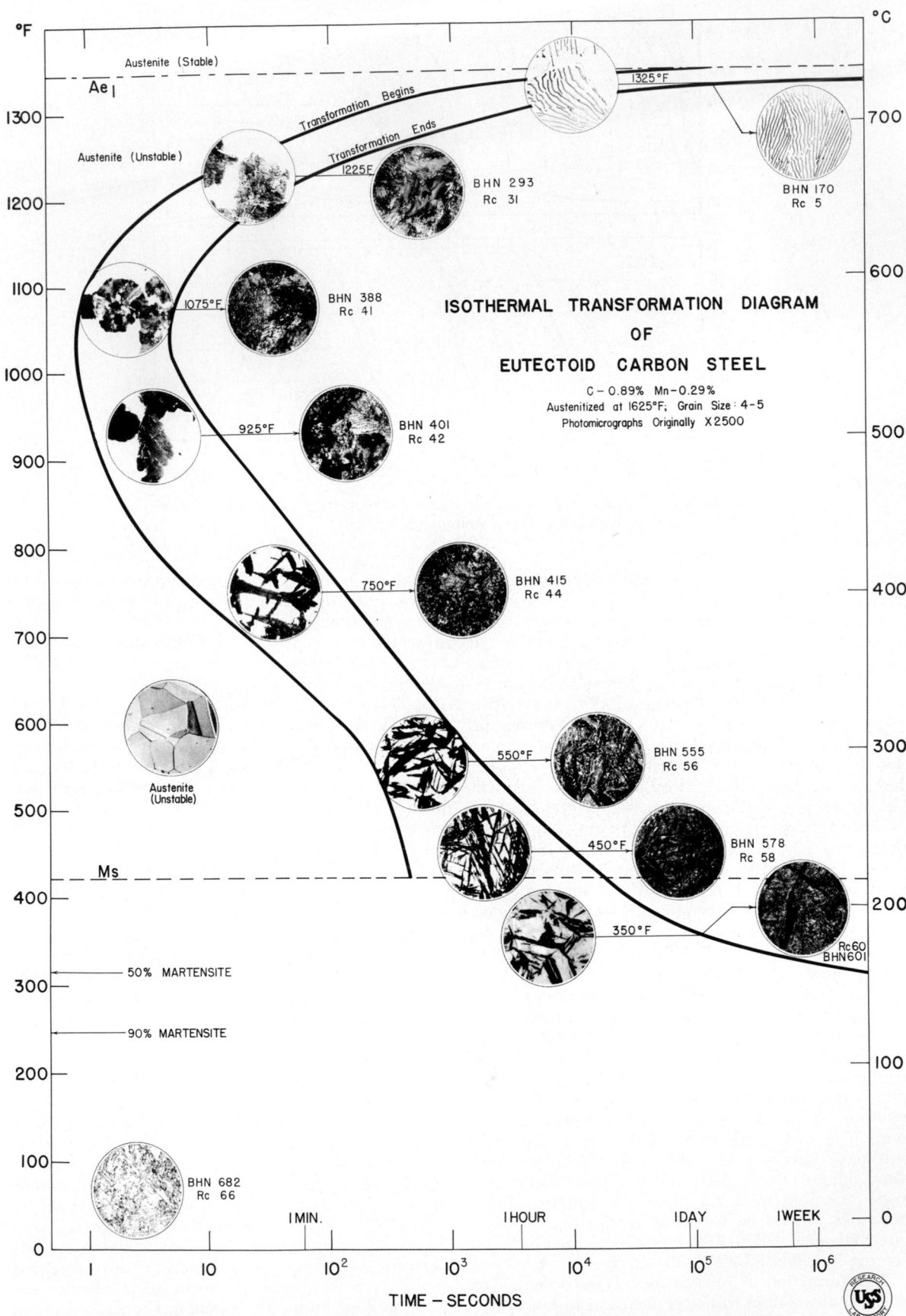

FIG. 39—19. Isothermal transformation diagram for a plain carbon eutectoid steel.

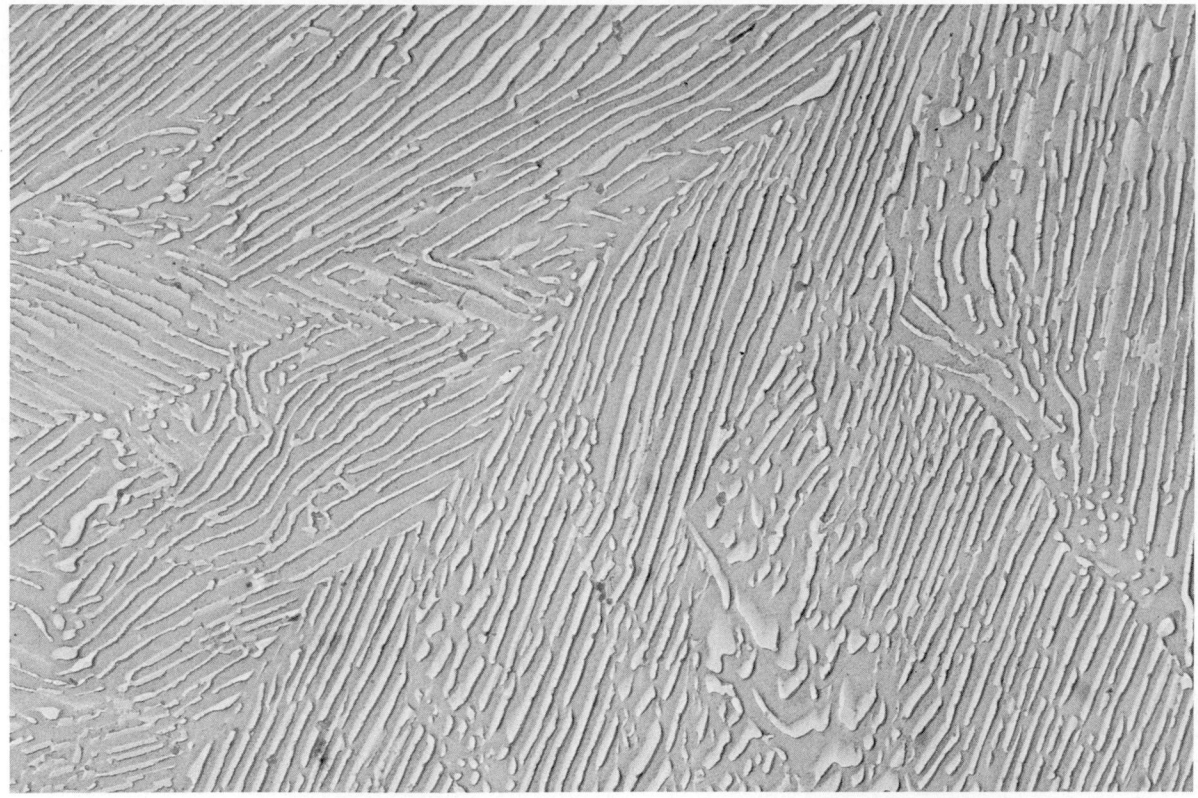

FIG. 39—20a. Electron micrograph showing microstructure of fine pearlite formed at 1100° F. Magnification: 15,000X.

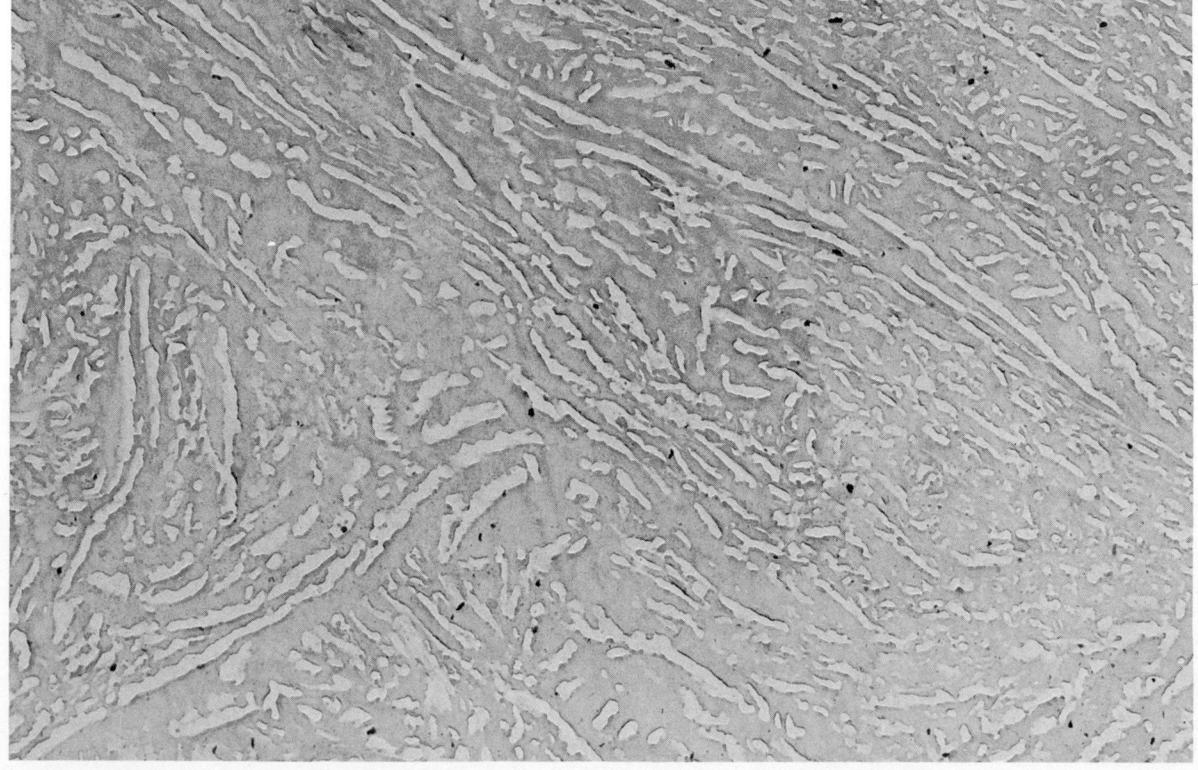

FIG. 39—20b. Electron micrograph of bainitic microstructure formed on complete transformation of a eutectoid steel at 850° F. Magnification: 15,000X.

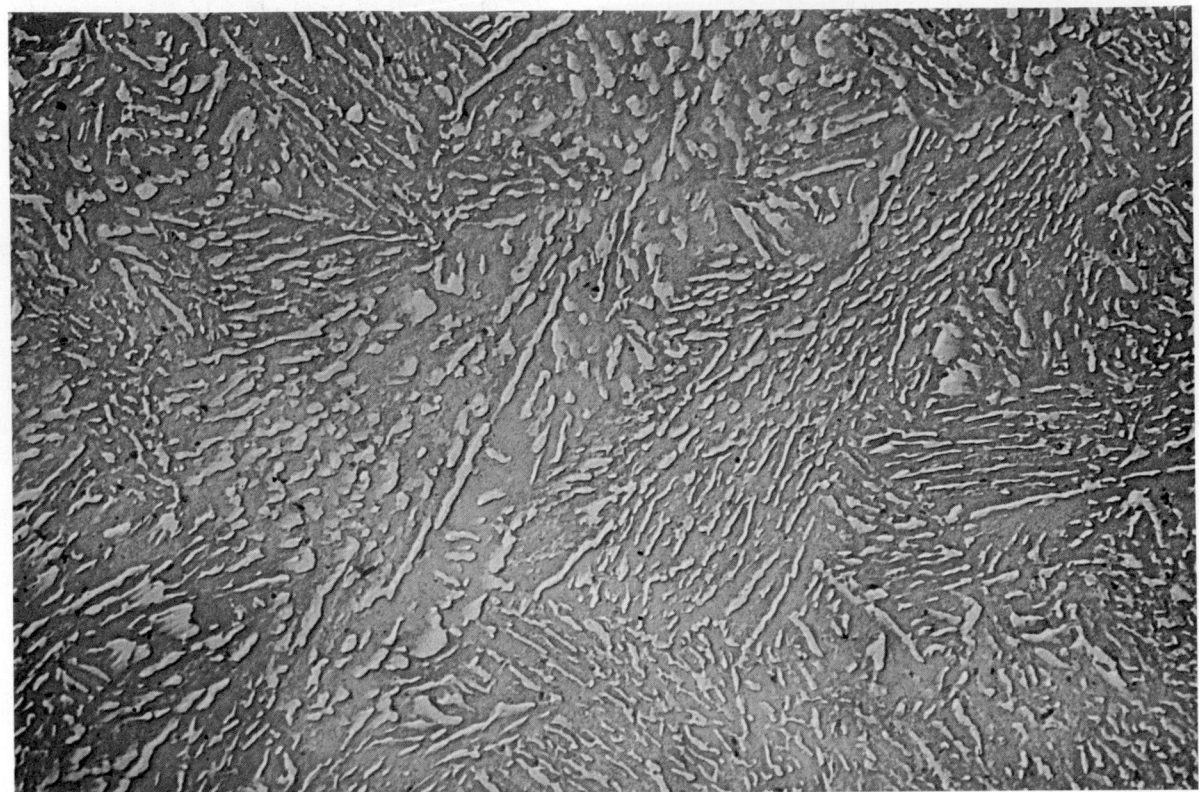

FIG. 39—20c. Electron micrograph of bainitic microstructure formed on complete transformation of a eutectoid steel at 700° F. Magnification: 15,000X.

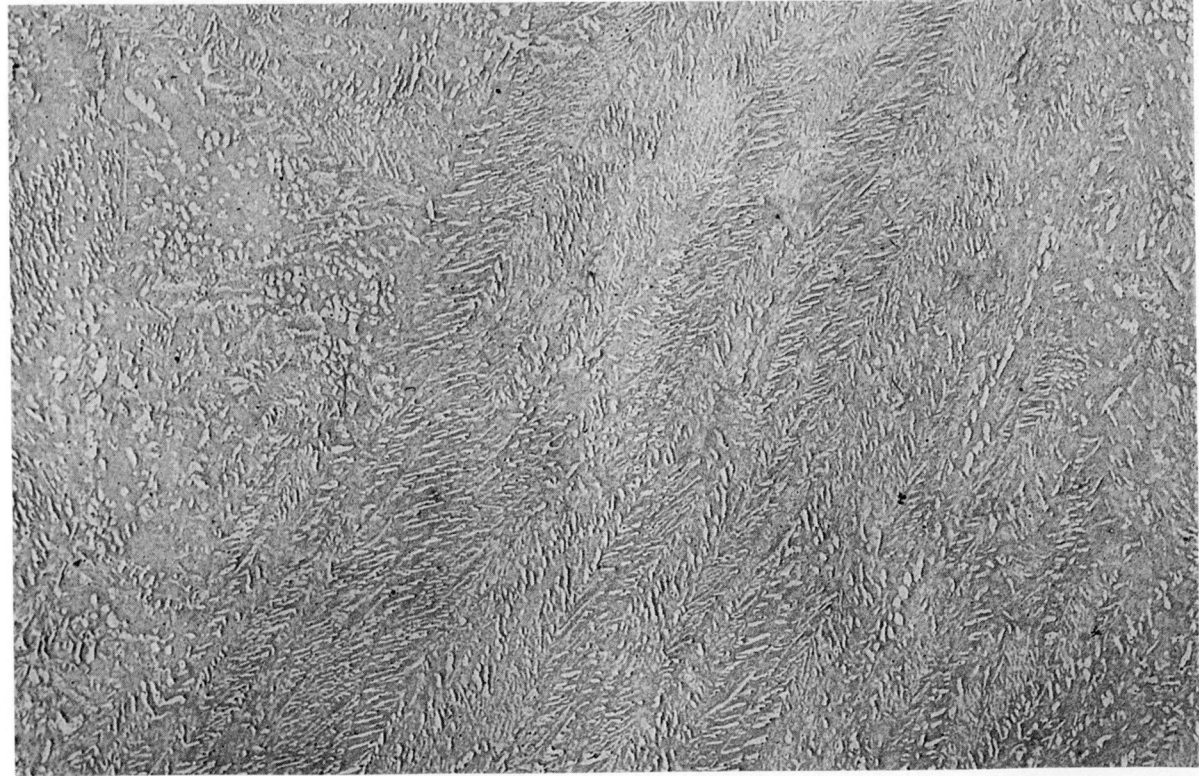

FIG. 39—20d. Electron micrograph of bainitic microstructure formed on complete transformation of a eutectoid steel at 500° F. Magnification: 15,000X.

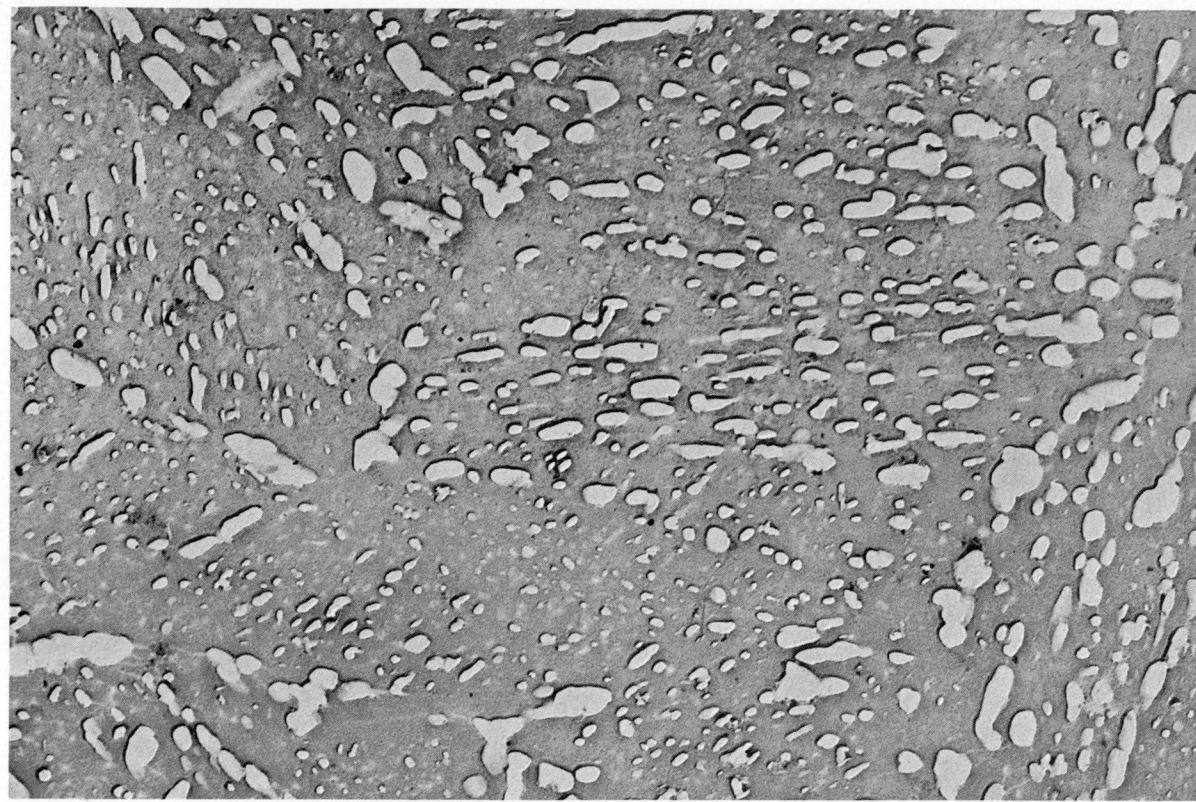

Fig. 39—21. Electron micrograph of the structure of tempered martensite. Tempering temperature, 1100° F (594° C). Magnification: 15,000X.

the particles to assume a spheroidal form can be noted. This microstructure, consisting of spheroidized or partially spheroidized carbides in a ferrite matrix is, as might be expected, a very favorable one in respect to ductility.

Each of these types of microstructures has characteristic properties typical of the class but the properties of pearlite and bainite also each vary quite widely with transformation temperature.

Properties of Pearlite—In any steel, the pearlites

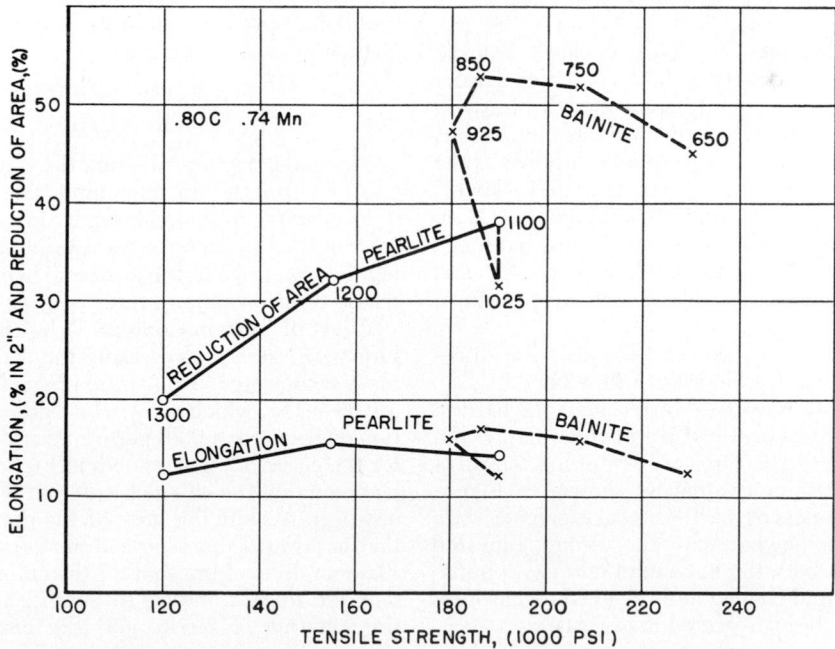

Fig. 39—22. The properties of pearlite and bainite in a eutectoid steel.

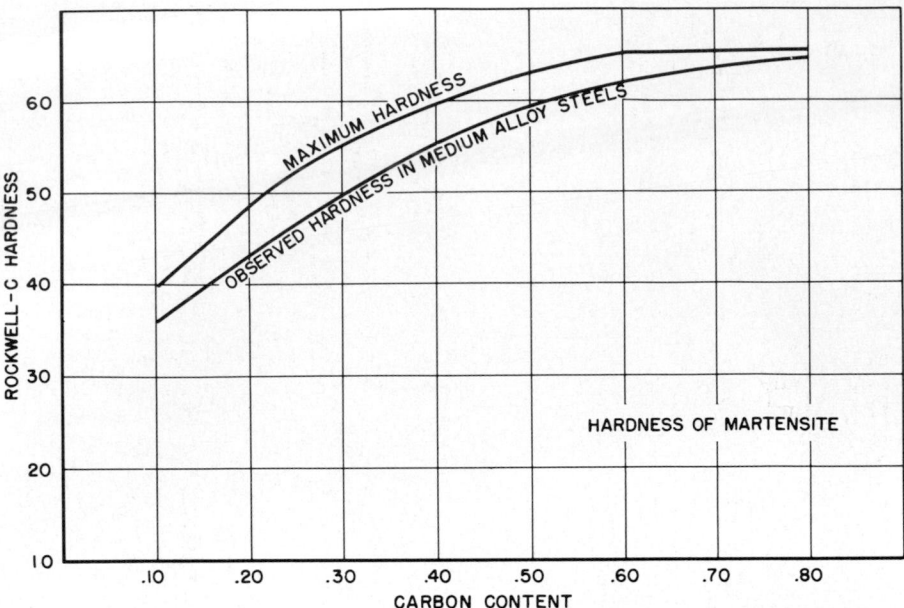

FIG. 39—23. The hardness of martensite as a function of carbon content.

are, as a class, softer than the bainites or martensites. In general, even though softer, they are less ductile than the lower temperature bainites and for a given hardness they will be far less ductile than tempered martensite. As the transformation temperature decreases within the pearlite range, the inter-lamellar spacing decreases, as was described above, and these "fine" pearlites, formed near the nose of the isothermal diagram, are both harder and more ductile than the "coarse" pearlites formed at higher temperatures. Thus, although, as a class, pearlite tends to be soft and not exceedingly ductile, its hardness and toughness both increase markedly with decreasing transformation temperatures.

Properties of Bainite—In a given steel, bainitic microstructures will generally be found both harder and tougher than pearlite, although the hardness will be lower than that of martensite. Within the class, as with pearlite, the properties generally improve as the transformation temperature decreases and "lower" bainite will compare favorably with, or exceed in toughness, tempered martensite at the same hardness. "Upper" bainite, on the other hand, may be somewhat deficient in toughness as compared with fine pearlite at the same hardness.

The properties of pearlite and bainite in a eutectoid steel are summarized in Figure 39—22.

Properties of Martensite—Martensite is the hardest and likewise the most brittle of the microstructures obtainable in a given steel. The hardness of martensite as a function of carbon content is shown in Figure 39—23. The hardness of martensite, at a given carbon content, varies somewhat with the cooling rate and this figure shows both the maximum hardness obtainable with very rapid cooling and the average hardness values which might be expected in practice.

Although, for some applications, particularly those involving wear resistance, the high hardness of mar-

tensite is desirable in spite of the accompanying brittleness, the principal importance of this microstructure is as the starting material for tempered martensite structures, which latter have definitely superior properties.

Properties of Tempered Martensite—Tempered martensitic structures are, as a class, characterized by relatively high toughness at any strength level. Their properties are illustrated in Figure 39—24. This chart designates, within plus or minus 10 per cent, the usual mechanical properties of any steel with this microstructure, regardless of composition. Because of its high ductility at a given hardness, this is the structure that is aimed for in heat treating for toughness by quenching and tempering.

FACTORS AFFECTING TRANSFORMATION RATES

The major factors affecting the rates of transformation of austenite are its composition, grain size, and homogeneity. In general, increasing carbon and alloy content tend to decrease transformation rates. Increasing the grain size of the austenite likewise tends to decrease transformation rates.

Effect of Carbon Content—The effect on the transformation rates of decreasing the carbon content of a plain carbon steel is illustrated by comparision of Figure 39—25a, which shows the isothermal transformation diagram for a 0.35 per cent carbon steel, with that for the eutectoid steel shown in Figure 39—19. It will be noted that the effect of lowering the carbon content has been to shift the lines of the diagram to the left, that is, toward more rapid transformation rates. This diagram differs from that for the eutectoid steel also in that the transformation to pearlite is preceded by a precipitation of ferrite and the diagram, therefore, shows a line designating the time for the initiation of this ferrite precipitation at the temperature levels

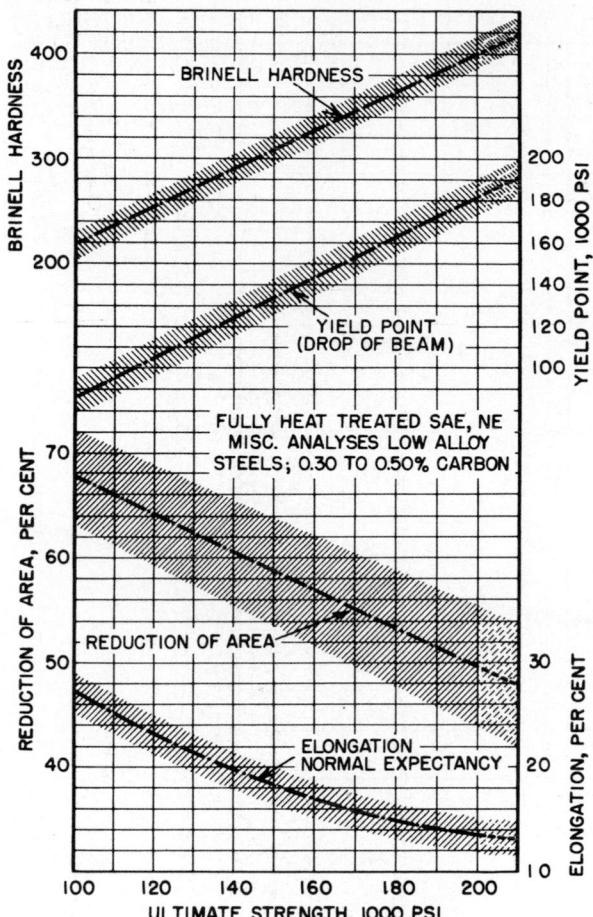

FIG. 39—24. The properties of tempered martensite.

wherein this separation precedes the formation of pearlite.

Effects of Alloys—Figure 39—25b shows an isothermal transformation diagram for a 0.35 per cent carbon, 1.85 per cent manganese steel. Comparing this with the lower manganese steel (Figure 39—25a), it will be noted that the entire curve has been displaced to the right; that is, transformation at all temperature levels starts later and is slower to go to completion. This is characteristic of the effect of alloys in solution in the austenite; in general, increased alloy content delays the start of transformation and increases the time for its completion.

Although alloy additions tend in general to delay the start of transformation and to increase the time for its completion, they differ greatly, nevertheless, in both the magnitude and the nature of their effects. Figure 39—26 represents the isothermal transformation diagram for a 0.33 per cent carbon, 0.45 per cent manganese, 1.97 per cent chromium steel. By comparison with the plain carbon steel (Figure 39—25a), it will be noted that the effect of the chromium has been, not only to move the curve to the right, but also to change the shape of the curve. The time for beginning of transformation in the pearlite region has been greatly increased, while that for the beginning in the bainite region has been only moderately increased. Thus the

diagram now has two "noses" (or time minima), one in the temperature region of transformation to pearlite and the other in the bainite region.

Figure 39—27 represents the isothermal transformation diagram for a more-complex alloy steel. This steel (SAE 4340) contains 0.42 per cent carbon, 0.78 per cent manganese, 1.79 per cent nickel, 0.80 per cent chromium and 0.33 per cent molybdenum. It will be noted that the effect of the addition of moderate amounts of these several alloying elements has been to displace the curve even farther to the right than that of the 2 per cent chromium steel (Figure 39—26). This is characteristic of the effect of alloys; relatively small amounts of several alloying elements are more effective in decreasing transformation rates than are larger amounts of a single alloy, i.e., more retarding than if they were merely additive.

Summarizing the effects of alloying elements on transformation behavior, it can be seen that the general effect of increasing the alloy content is to delay both the start and the completion of transformation and that the effect of alloy additions is cumulative. The effects of alloying elements, however, differ greatly both in magnitude and in specific effects on transformation in different temperature regions, so that a precise prediction of the effect of a given alloy combination is not yet quite possible.

Effect of Grain Size—The effect of increasing the grain size of the austenite is similar to that of alloys; it delays both the start and completion of the transformation. This is illustrated by Figure 39—28, which shows the isothermal transformation diagrams for the same alloy steel with both fine- and coarse-grained austenite.

Effect of Homogeneity of Austenite—The general effect of inhomogeneous austenite will be to speed up the start of transformation. This occurs because the initial transformation will occur in the portions of the austenite which are "leaner" in alloy. In addition, undissolved carbides may act as nuclei for transformation, thereby hastening the start of transformation.

TRANSFORMATION ON CONTINUOUS COOLING

The preceding section has described the manner in which the microstructure and, therefore, the properties of steel vary with the temperature of transformation, and has shown how the isothermal transformation behavior governing these microstructural changes can be studied and depicted as isothermal transformation diagrams. The factors affecting transformation characteristics have been enumerated and the nature of their effects described. The composition of the steel, particularly in respect to the alloying elements, has been shown to be the major factor, and the effects of austenite grain size and homogeneity have also been described. Thus, the basic information about the transformation behavior of a steel is fully described by the isothermal transformation diagram.

This basic information tells what structure is formed at each reaction temperature, if the cooling is interrupted so that the reaction goes to completion at that temperature. The information is equally useful for interpreting behaviors when the cooling proceeds di-

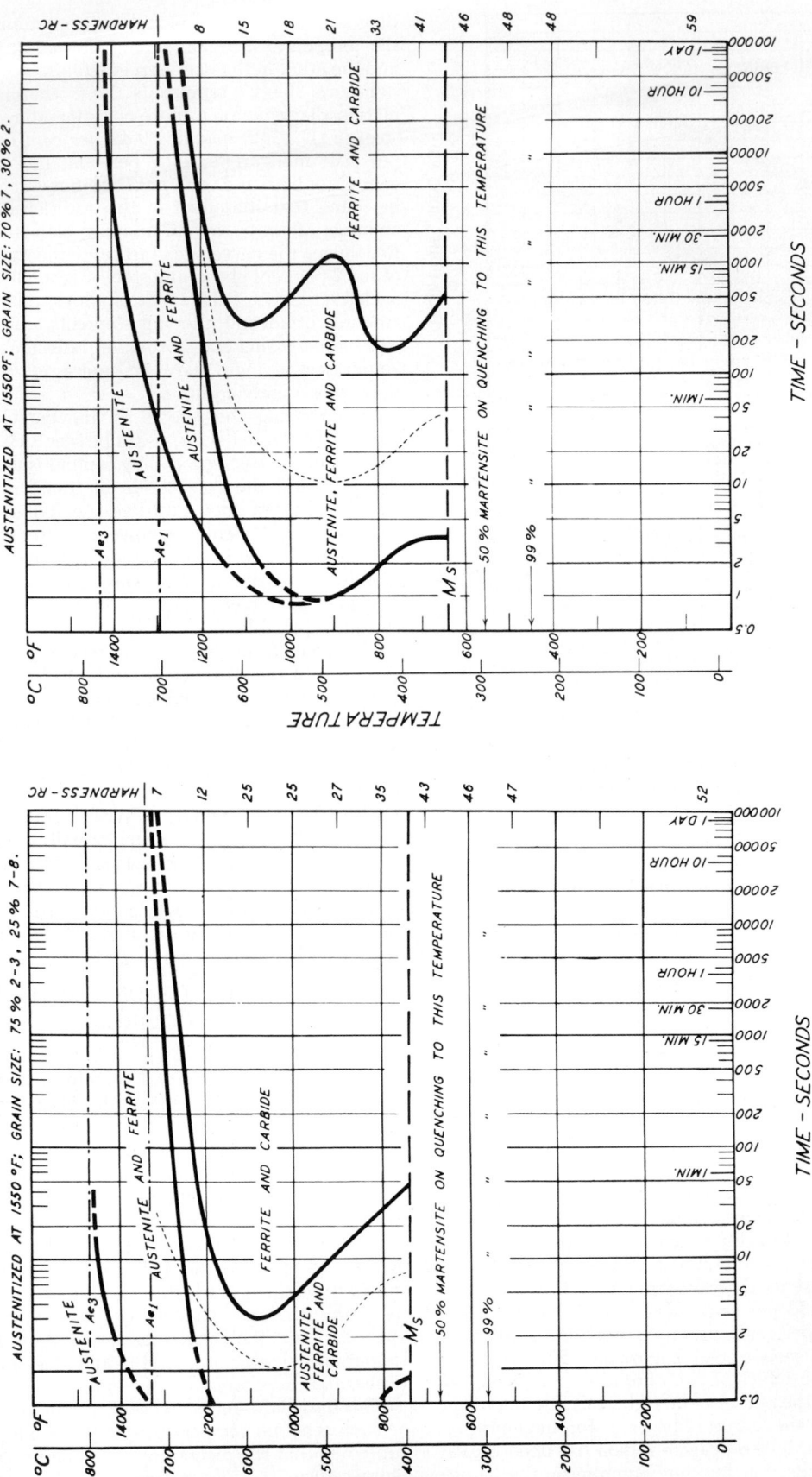

Fig. 39—25b. Isothermal transformation diagram for a 0.35% carbon, 1.85% manganese steel.

Fig. 39—25a. Isothermal transformation diagram for a 0.35% carbon, 0.37% manganese, plain carbon steel.

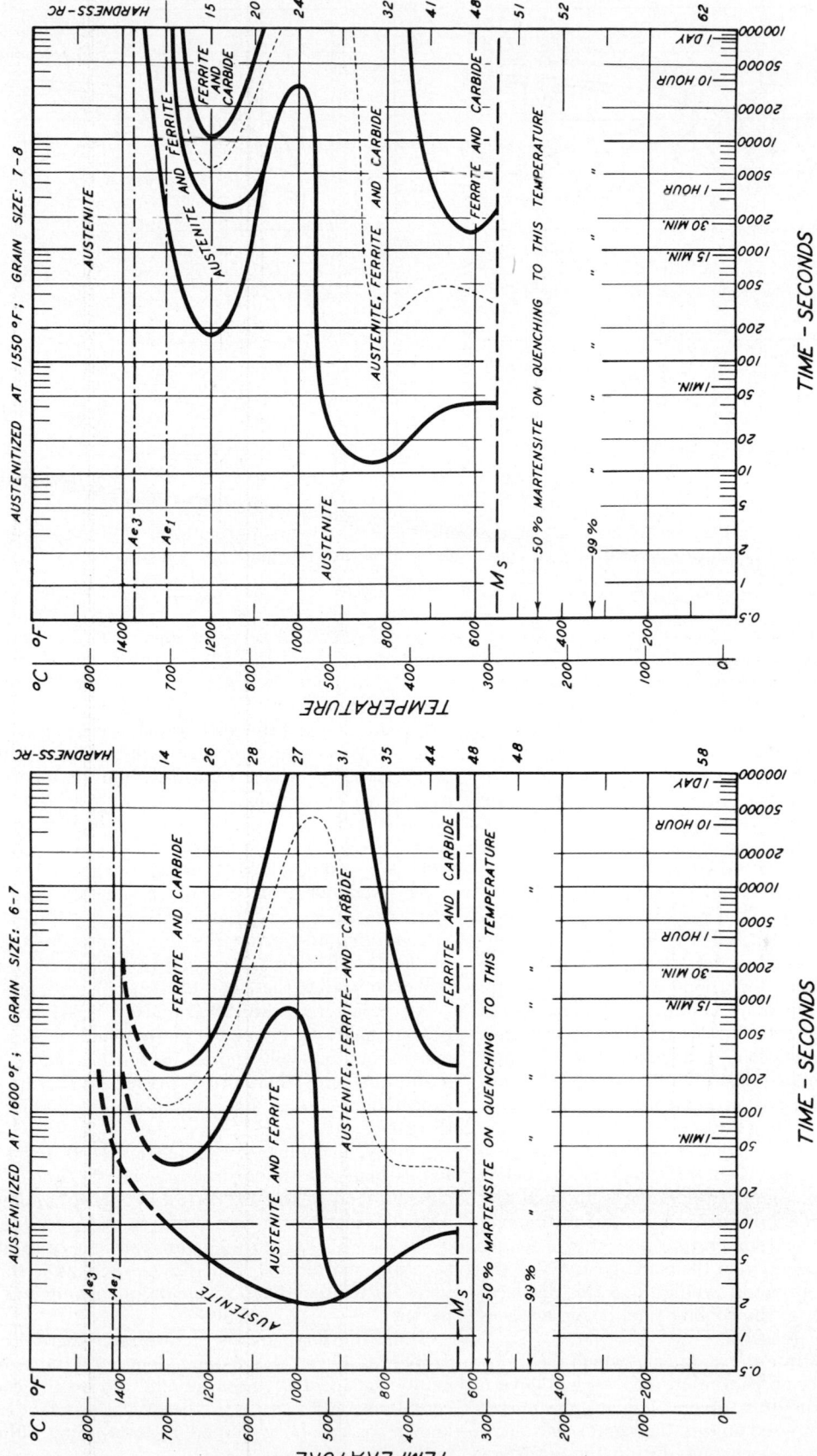

Fig. 39—27. Isothermal transformation diagram for an SAE 4340 steel, containing 0.42% carbon, 0.78% manganese, 1.79% nickel, 0.80% chromium and 0.33% molybdenum.

Fig. 39—26. Isothermal transformation diagram for a 0.33% carbon, 0.45% manganese, 1.97% chromium steel.

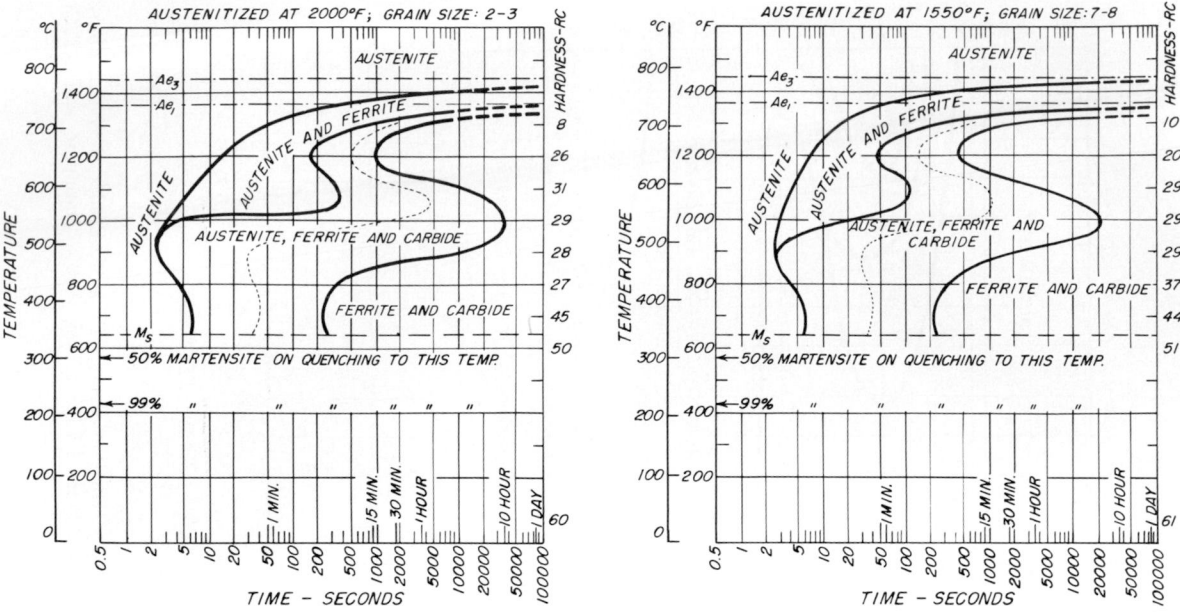

FIG. 39—28. Comparison of the effect of grain size on the isothermal transformation of an SAE 4140 alloy steel, containing 0.37% carbon, 0.77% manganese, 0.98% chromium and 0.21% molybdenum.

rectly without interruption, as is the case in the industrial processes of annealing, normalizing and quenching. In these industrial processes, the time at a single temperature is generally insufficient for the reactions to go to completion at such a single temperature; instead, the end structure consists of an association of microstructures which individually were formed at successively lower temperatures as the piece cooled. But the tendency to form the several structures is still explained by the isothermal diagram.

The final microstructure after continuous cooling will obviously depend upon the times spent at the various transformation temperature ranges through which the piece is cooled. The transformation behavior on continuous cooling thus represents an integration of these times and this integration can be carried out by the method developed by Grange and Kiefer at the U. S. Steel Fundamental Research Laboratory. By this method, a continuous-cooling diagram generally similar to the isothermal transformation diagram, but depicting the transformation behavior on cooling at a series of constant cooling rates, can be constructed.

Such a diagram for an alloy steel is shown in Figure 39—29. This continuous-cooling diagram lies below and to the right of the corresponding isothermal diagram. That is, transformation on continuous cooling will start at a lower temperature and after a longer time than the intersection of the cooling curve and the isothermal diagram would predict, and this displacement is a function of the cooling rate, being larger as the cooling rate increases.

In order to illustrate the manner in which the transformation behavior on continuous cooling will govern the final microstructures, several cooling-rate curves have been superimposed on this diagram. A consideration of the changes occurring during these various

cooling cycles will serve to illustrate the manner in which diagrams of this nature can be correlated with heat-treating practice and used to predict the resulting microstructure.

Considering first the relatively slow cooling rate (less than 40° F per hour), the steel will be cooled through the regions in which transformation to ferrite and pearlite will occur and these constituents, ferrite and pearlite, will, therefore, make up the final microstructure. This cooling rate corresponds to a slow furnace cool, such as might be used in annealing.

At a somewhat faster cooling rate (40° to 150° F per hour), such as might be obtained on normalizing a large forging, the ferrite, pearlite, bainite, and martensite fields will all be traversed and final microstructure will contain all of these constituents.

At cooling rates of 150° to 2100° F per hour, the pearlite field will be missed entirely and the resulting microstructures will consist of ferrite, bainite, and martensite. This, therefore, is the microstructure to be expected on normalizing small or moderate sections of this steel.

Finally, on cooling at rates of from 2100° to 54,000° F per hour, the microstructure will be free of proeutectoid ferrite and will consist largely of bainite with a small amount of martensite present. A cooling rate of at least 54,000° F per hour is necessary to obtain the fully martensitic structure desired as a starting point for tempered martensite on quenching and tempering.

Thus, the final microstructure, and therefore, the properties of a steel, are dependent upon the transformation behavior of the austenite and on the cooling conditions, and can be predicted if these factors are known, or can be governed by controlling either or both of these factors.

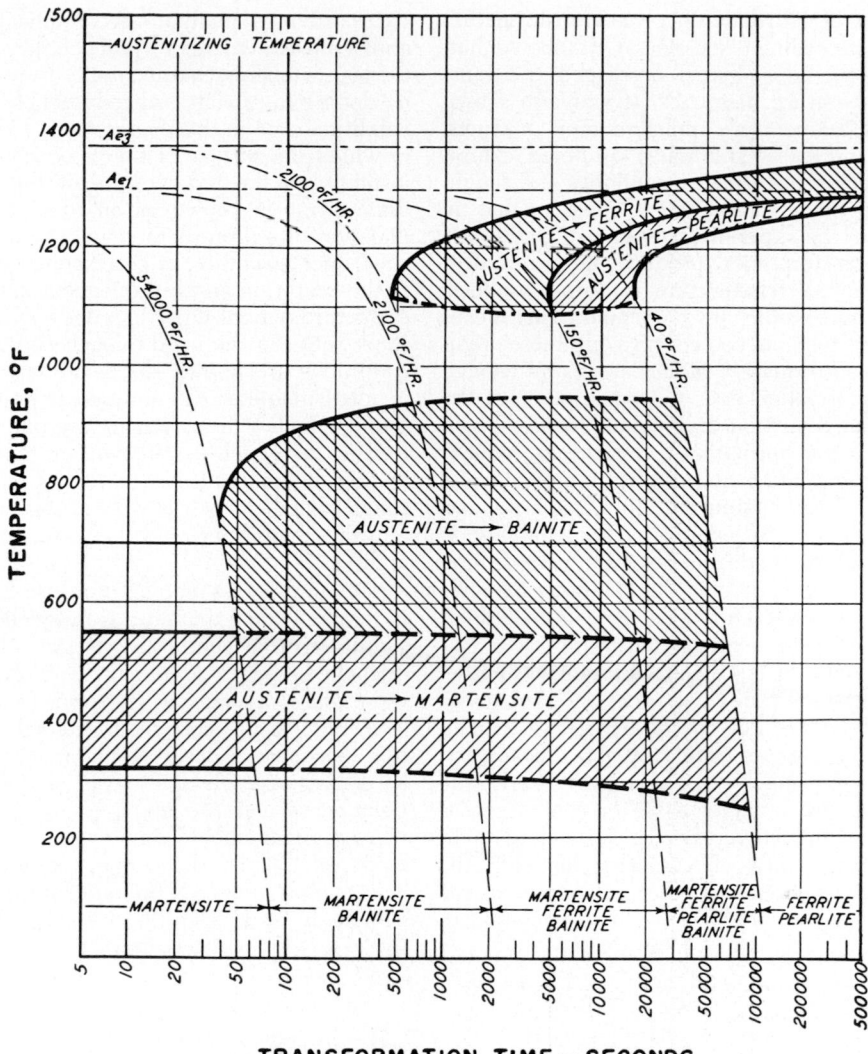

FIG. 39—29. Continuous-cooling transformation diagram for a 4340-type alloy steel, with superimposed cooling curves illustrating the manner in which transformation behavior during continuous cooling governs final microstructures.

SECTION 2

HARDENABILITY

The one attribute of a steel which is certainly of the greatest significance to the heat treater is its capacity for hardening, commonly referred to as its **hardenability.** This attribute has a two-fold significance; it is important, not only in relation to the attainment of a higher hardness or strength level by heat treatment, but also in relation to the attainment of a high degree of toughness through heat treatment to a desirable microstructure, usually tempered martensite or lower bainite. As a matter of fact, the attainment of toughness is the most important, since the attainment of a certain high strength level may often have little significance

unless accompanied by a sufficient toughness to meet service requirements.

It should be clearly understood that hardenability refers to the **depth of hardening** or to the size of piece which can be hardened under given cooling conditions and not to the maximum hardness that can be obtained in a given steel. This maximum hardness, as previously described, is dependent almost entirely upon the carbon content (Figure 39—23), while the hardenability (depth of hardening) is, in general, far more dependent upon the alloy content and grain size of the austenite than upon the carbon content.

Relationship of Hardenability to Transformation Rates—In the preceding discussion, it was shown that, in general, the hardness of steel increases as the transformation temperature decreases. It was also shown that the lower-temperature transformation products, lower bainite and martensite, when tempered, exhibit superior properties in respect to ductility and toughness at a given strength level. It is apparent that, in order to realize the superior properties of these low-temperature transformation products, prior transformation at a higher temperature to softer products must, insofar as possible, be prevented. This means that the steel must be cooled through these high-temperature transformation ranges at a rapid enough rate that transformation does not occur, even at the nose of the transformation diagram. This rate, which will just permit transformation to martensite without any prior transformation at a higher temperature is known as the **critical cooling rate** for martensite, and furnishes one method for expressing hardenability. It can be readily ascertained from the continuous cooling diagram. For example, in the steel of Figure 39—29, the critical cooling rate for martensite is 54,000° F per hour or 15° F per second.

How Hardenability Is Expressed and Measured—Although the critical cooling rate can be used to express hardenability, it has the disadvantage that, in practice, cooling rates are ordinarily not constant, but vary during the cooling cycle. This is particularly true of liquid quenching, in which case, the cooling rate is always slower as the temperature of the cooling medium is approached, and is also greatly affected by the presence of a vapor phase in the earlier part of the quenching cycle. Furthermore, as already mentioned, hardenability refers to depth of hardening.

In order to facilitate the application of hardenability measurements to practice, it is, therefore, customary to express hardenability in terms of depth of hardening in a standardized quench. The quenching condition used in this expression is a hypothetical one, in which the surface of the piece is assumed to come instantly to the temperature of the quenching medium. This is known as an ideal quench, and the diameter of a round which will just quench to the desired microstructure, or corresponding hardness value at the center, in an ideal quench is known as the **ideal diameter** (symbol D_I). Since the cooling rate relationships between the ideal quench and other quenching conditions are known, hardenability values in terms of ideal diameter can be used to predict the size of round which will harden in any quench, the characteristics of which are known, or similarly, if the diameter which will just harden to the center in a standardized quench is known, this can be converted into the ideal diameter value used to express hardenability.

The most direct method of measuring hardenability in terms of ideal diameter is by quenching a cylinder series. In this method, a series of bar sizes are quenched under identical conditions. These bars should have a length at least four times the diameter. They are then sectioned, etched, and cross-section hardness measurements made. The depth of hardening of each of the bars is determined by the point at which the etching characteristics change, which corresponds to a microstructure of 50 per cent martensite, or by the corresponding hardness value. This microstructure of 50 per cent martensite is a very commonly used criterion of hardenability because of the ease with which it may be located. The diameter

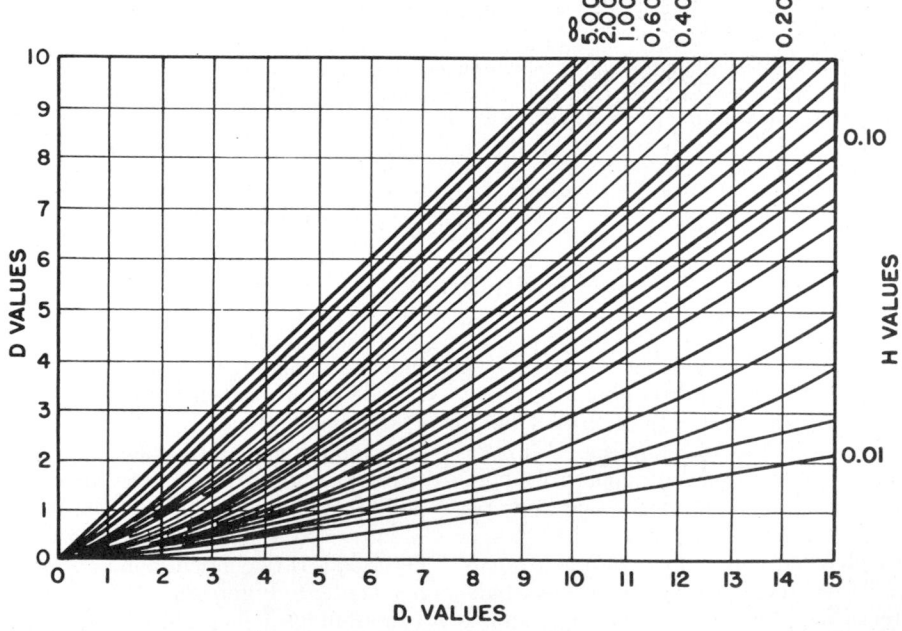

FIG. 39—30. Relationships among ideal diameter, critical diameter and severity of quench. See also Figure 39—31.

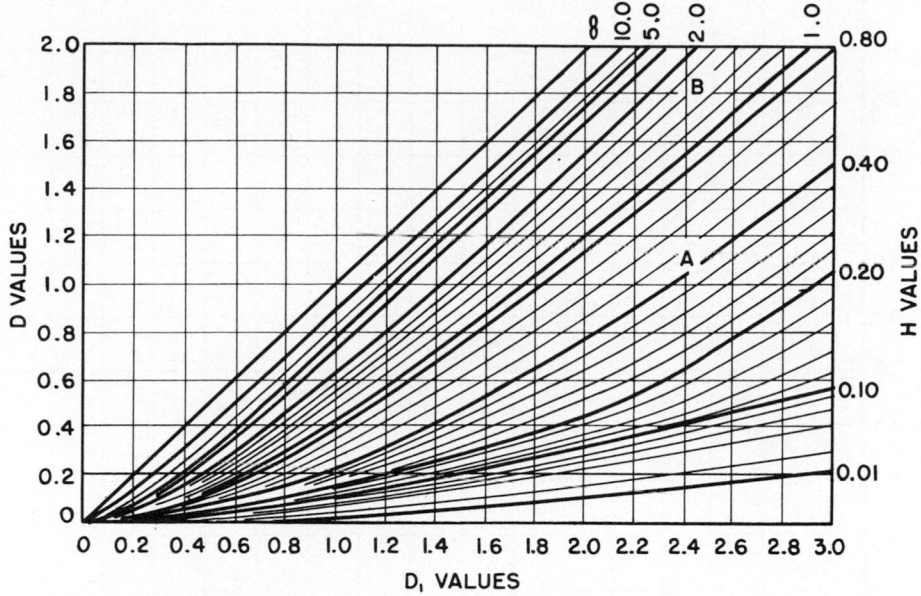

FIG. 39—31. Enlargement of the portion of Figure 39—30 for D values between 0 and 2.1, and D_I values from 0 to 3.0.

of the bar in this series which just hardens to the center is noted and this is known as the **critical diameter** (D) for the series.

As mentioned above, this critical diameter value can be translated into the fundamental terms of ideal diameter (D_I) by the charts of Figures 39—30 and 39—31. In order to make this conversion, however, it is necessary to evaluate the factor expressing the **severity of the quench** (H factor). Typical values of this H coefficient are tabulated in Table 39—IV.

The cylinder series method, just described, is the most direct method of measuring hardenability, but because of numerous advantages, the **end-quench test**, developed by Jominy and Boegehold, is the hardenability test which is now by far the most generally accepted and used. In this test, a cylindrical specimen one inch in diameter and four inches long is heated to the desired hardening temperature and quenched in a fixture by a stream of water impinging upon only one end. The bar is then ground on two opposite sides to a depth of 0.015 inch below the surface and hardness measurements made at $\frac{1}{16}$-inch intervals along the length of the specimen. The harden-

ability is expressed as a curve of hardness versus distance from the quenched end of the specimen. Figure 39—32 illustrates the type of quenching fixture used for this test and a typical end-quench hardenability curve is shown in Figure 39—33. Standard procedures for this test have been established by the American Society for Testing and Materials and the Society of Automotive Engineers and the reader is referred to the publications of these societies for the details of the testing procedures.

This test furnishes a method of applying a contin-

Table 39—IV. Typical Values of the H Coefficient Designating Severity of Quench (H Value)

Agitation	Oil	Water	Brine
None	0.25–0.30	0.9–1.0	2
Mild	0.30–0.35	1.0–1.1	2.0–2.2
Moderate	0.35–0.40	1.2–1.3	
Good	0.40–0.50	1.4–1.5	
Strong	0.50–0.80	1.6–2.0	
Violent	0.80–1.1	4.0	5.0

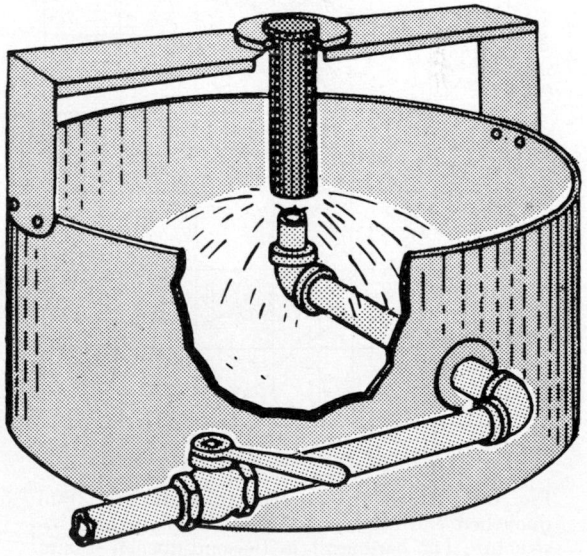

FIG. 39—32. Quenching fixture for end-quench test.

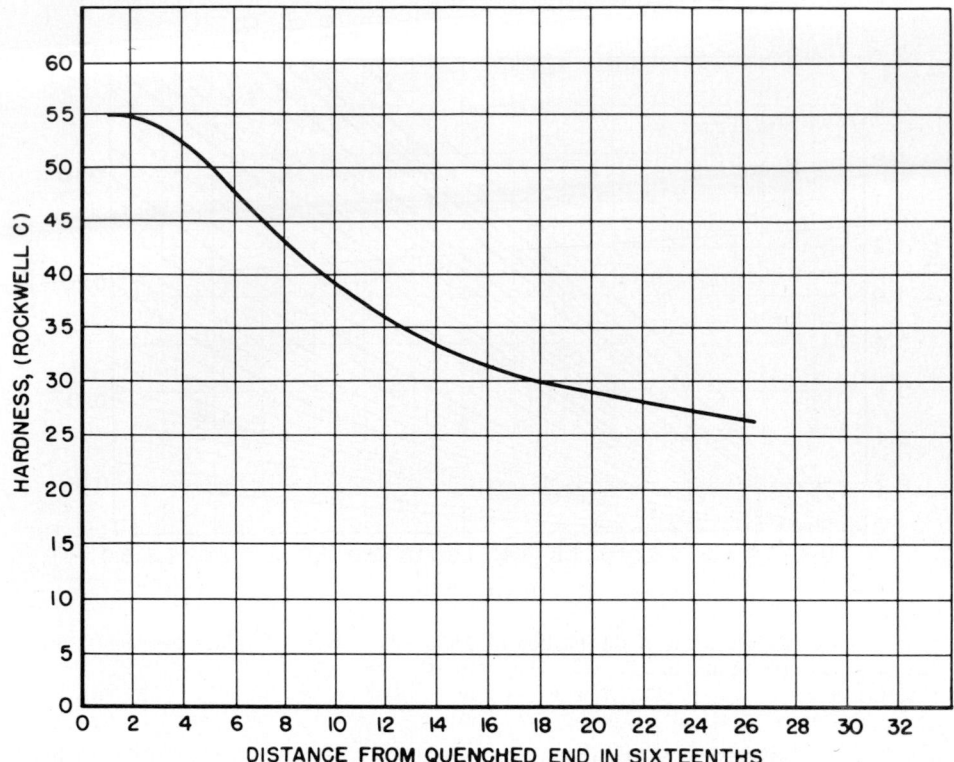

FIG. 39—33. Typical end-quench hardenability curve.

uous series of varying cooling rates to a single specimen, and, since these rates are known the results can be converted to hardenability values in terms of ideal

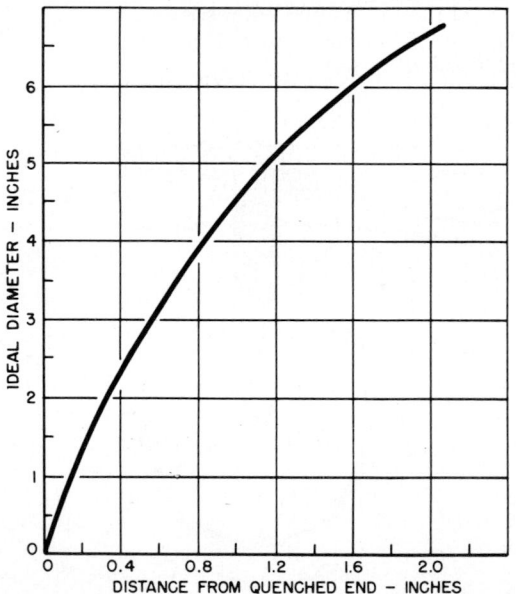

FIG. 39—34. Curve for converting distance from quenched end corresponding to the desired microstructure (or hardness) in the end-quench test to hardenability values in terms of ideal diameter. (After Carney)

diameter. The curve used for this conversion is shown in Figure 39—34. To use this curve, the distance along the end-quench bar to the desired microstructure, or corresponding hardness value, is noted and the ideal diameter corresponding to this distance is read from the curve. This ideal diameter value may then be converted into terms of bar size which can be hardened under any given quenching conditions, by the methods described above.

Hardenability and Heat Treatment—It has been emphasized in the preceding sections of this chapter that the most desirable microstructural constituents from the standpoint of strength and toughness, are those involving transformation at the lower temperature levels,—lower bainite and tempered martensite. In order to obtain these desirable structures, the transformation rates must be slow enough, or in other words, the hardenability must be high enough, to prevent prior transformation at a high temperature during the cooling cycle. The results of hardenability measurements serve to establish the limiting conditions in terms of cooling rates or quenching practices necessary to meet this requirement. Similarly, if the heat-treating practice and cooling conditions have been established and evaluated, the hardenability necessary to obtain the desired microstructure may be determined by the methods described above.

Thus, it is seen that, in general, the suitability of a steel for a given heat treatment practice or the suitability of a heat treatment practice for a given steel is determined largely by its hardenability.

HEAT-TREATMENT PROCEDURES

QUENCHING AND TEMPERING

The desirable properties of tempered martensitic microstructures have been emphasized in this chapter. Quenching and tempering is the heat treatment commonly used to obtain such microstructures and, therefore, represents the final heat treatment ordinarily used to obtain optimum properties in heat-treated materials.

This method is depicted diagrammatically in Figure 39—35. It involves a continuous cooling from the austenitizing temperature through the martensite transformation temperature range at a rate rapid enough to prevent any transformation at temperatures above the M_s temperature, followed by tempering to the desired hardness or strength level.

Heating—The first step in this heat treatment, as in most of the heat treatments to be described, is the heating of the material to a temperature at which austenite is formed. The actual austenitizing temperature should, in general, be such that all carbides are in solution in order that full advantage may be taken of the hardenability effects of the alloying elements, although in some cases, particularly in tool steels, it may be desirable to leave some undissolved carbides. The temperature should not, however, be so high that pronounced grain growth occurs. The piece should be held at the austenitizing temperature long enough to dissolve carbides but, again, not long enough for excessive growth to occur.

Too rapid a heating rate may set up high stresses, particularly if irregular sections are involved, and is, therefore, generally undesirable. A heating time of one hour per inch of section is commonly employed, and this is a safe rule. In numerous cases, however, much more rapid heating rates may be employed. In such cases, the safety of the practice must generally be determined by experiment. The available heating rate will, of course, be determined by the mass of the material being heated and the rate at which it can absorb heat, the temperature to which it is desired to heat, and the temperature and heat-transfer characteristics of the heating medium. In general, heating rates will be faster the higher the temperature, and the times will vary with the square of the thickness or diameter. Salt or liquid baths will have generally higher heat-transfer coefficients and, therefore, will heat more rapidly than furnaces in which the heating is in air. Since the heating rate is a function of the difference in temperature between the piece and the heating medium, rapid heating may be obtained by using a heating medium at a temperature well above the desired austenitizing temperature and removing the piece when this temperature is reached. Advantage is taken of this principle in continuous-furnace practice in which the temperature of the furnace is kept well above the desired temperature and the passage through the furnace regulated so that the piece being treated will reach the desired temperature at the outgoing end of the furnace. Temperature control is, however, uncertain in such treatment. Flame hardening, in which rapid heating is obtained by the actual impingement of a high-temperature flame on the surface of the piece being treated is also based on this principle. These rapid heating practices are the exception, however, and the usual and safe practice is a relatively slow and uniform heating to the austenitizing temperature, followed by a holding period at that temperature long enough to insure that the piece is at a uniform temperature throughout.

Unless special precautions are taken, heating will usually result in a certain amount of oxidation or **scaling** and may also result in **decarburization**. Both scaling and decarburization are usually undesirable. Scaling represents a loss of metal, mars the surface finish and may prevent rapid extraction of heat in quenching. Decarburization results in a soft surface and may seriously affect the fatigue life. The processes do not however, necessarily proceed together. For this reason, a slightly oxidizing atmosphere is often desirable when freedom from decarburization is important. Since the amount of scaling is largely determined by the time and temperature of the heating operation, austenitizing temperatures and times should be as low as is consistent with the principles described above in order to minimize scaling. Scaling is materially reduced by the presence of 4 per cent or more of carbon monoxide in the furnace atmosphere.

Special measures are necessary if complete freedom from scaling or decarburization is necessary. These measures include heating in a muffle containing reducing gases such as carbon monoxide or methane and hydrogen mixtures, packing in cast-iron chips or in a mixture of charcoal and sodium carbonate or heating

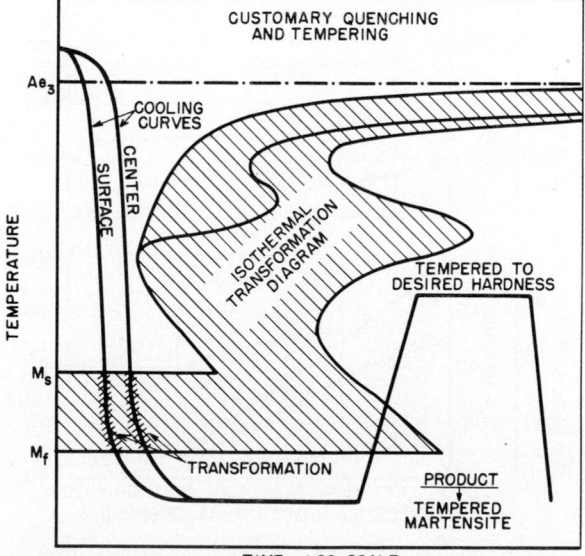

FIG. 39—35. Schematic transformation diagram for quenching and tempering.

in neutral salt or lead baths. All of these methods, however, have limitations and disadvantages and require special precautions to insure their success. The composition of the gases used in controlled atmosphere heating varies with the temperature, and the composition of the steel, and must be carefully balanced so that neither carburization nor decarburization occurs. At the higher temperatures packing mixtures such as charcoal and sodium carbonate may also lead to carburization and their use is frequently very inconvenient. Salt or lead baths may become contaminated with oxides through contact with the atmosphere and these may accelerate decarburization.

Quenching—The primary purpose of quenching is, as described above, to cool the piece rapidly enough that no transformation occurs at temperatures above the martensite range. The first requisite of a quenching medium is, therefore, a sufficient cooling rate to accomplish this result. The necessary cooling rate is, in turn, determined by the size and hardenability of the piece being quenched, so that the choice of a quenching medium is primarily determined by these factors. The temperature gradient set up by the quenching operation results in relatively high thermal and transformation stresses which are usually, although not always, undesirable since they may lead to cracking or distortion. In order to minimize these stresses, the quenching rate should not be much in excess of that dictated by the size and hardenability of the piece.

The quenching media most commonly used are water, oils, or brine. The relative severity of quench of these media is indicated in Table 39—IV of this chapter. As indicated by this table, brine quenching is the most severe, although when thoroughly agitated, as by a submerged pressure-spray, water approaches it in severity. Oil is considerably less drastic, although its cooling rate may likewise be markedly increased by a proper and sufficient agitation.

Agitation of the quenching medium is important both because of acceleration of the cooling rate and because of the more uniform cooling obtained. Such agitation may be obtained from judiciously placed propellers, from pumps or from pressure sprays.

The severity of water quenching varies with the temperature of the quenching bath, hot water being quite markedly slower than cold water. This is presumably because of the large amounts of steam which are formed in quenching into hot water and which cling to the work and surround it with "gas pockets." The cooling rate in hot water is, however, not only slower, but less uniform and this lack of uniformity may lead to distortion or even cracking. The increased cooling rate in brine is also presumably due to its increased boiling point which diminishes the chance of gas envelopes forming around the work. The cooling rate of oil quenches tends to increase somewhat with a moderate increase in temperature, presumably because of the decreased viscosity at the higher temperature.

Tempering—The martensite formed by quenching is very hard and very brittle and, as described above, its formation leaves high residual stresses. The purpose of tempering is to relieve these stresses and to improve the ductility, which it does at the expense of

strength or hardness. The opening at temperatures below the _____ ature (A_1). The stress relief a____ are brought about through pr____ from the supersaturated unst____ solution (martensite) and th____ coalescence of the carbide as the____ proceeds.

The effect of tempering on th____ illustrated by Figure 39—36. It ____ considerable stress relief has occu____ at 300° F and that tempering at ____ the stresses to a quite low value.

A typical illustration of the effe____ notch toughness measured by the ____ shown in Figure 39—37. It will ____ toughness first increases on temperin____ up to 400° F, then decreases on tem____ atures between 400° and 600° F, an____ rapidly in tempering at temperature____ above. This is a characteristic behavio____ the temperature range 450° to 60____ avoided in tempering.

In order to minimize cracking, the ____ eration should immediately follow the ____ ing fully-quenched pieces to stand ov____ tempering is liable to result in a large____ cracked work.

The tempering of martensite results ____ tion and if the heating is not uniform, s____ set up by this unequal contraction whi____ distortion or even cracking. Similarly, ____ heating for tempering may be dangerou____ the sharp temperature gradient set up ____ surface and interior of the piece. Rec____

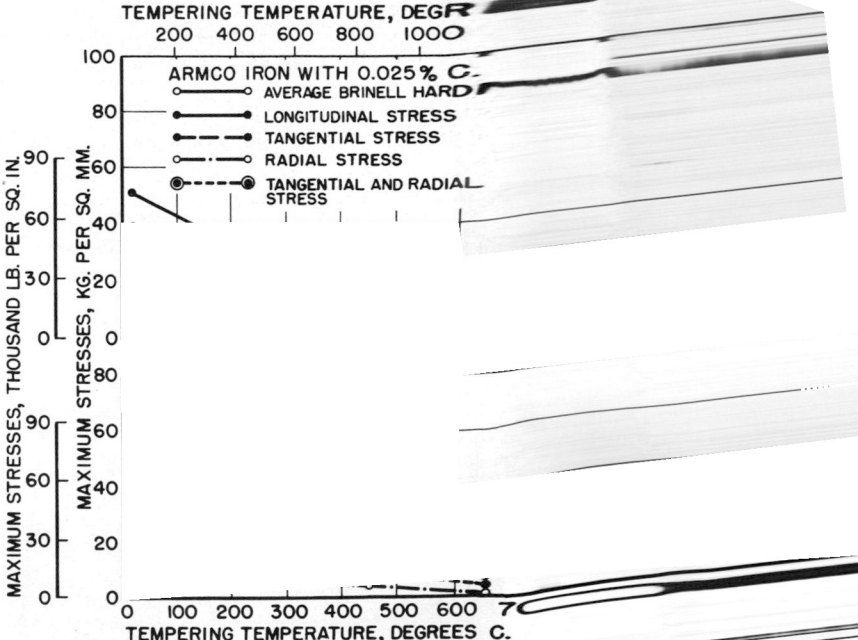

FIG. 39—36. The effect of tempering on residual st____ in quenched cylinders. (Buhler, Buchholtz and S____ Archiv fur das Eisenhuttenwesen, Vol. 5, 1932; ____ 413–418.)

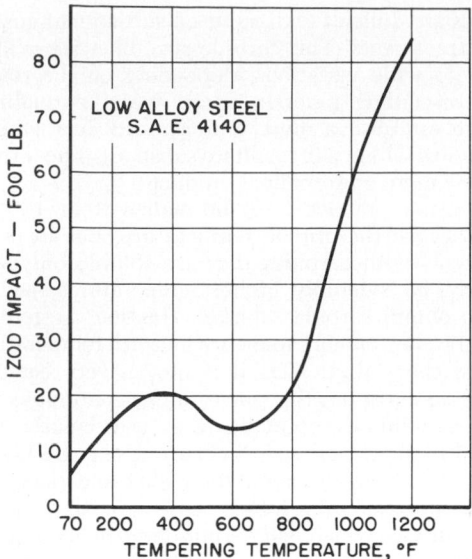

Fig. 39—37. The effect of tempering temperature on notch toughness of low-alloy steel.

furnaces are ideal for obtaining the uniform heating desired for tempering and are very commonly employed for this purpose. Oil or salt baths are very commonly used for low-temperature tempering and are generally safe, in spite of their rapid heating rate, since the temperature differential is low. Lead or salt baths may be used for higher tempering temperatures if the pieces to be tempered are not too large or irregular so that the heating stresses may be kept at a safe level.

Some steels exhibit a loss of toughness on slow cooling from temperatures of about 1000° F and above (the phenomenon known as "temper brittleness" which will be discussed further in another chapter) and therefore, a rapid cooling after tempering is generally desirable in these cases.

MARTEMPERING

As discussed above, the transformation to martensite, occurring during the rapid cooling through the martensite temperature range with the accompanying sharp temperature gradient, results in high stresses. A modified quenching procedure, known as martempering, which was developed by B. F. Shepherd, is helpful in lowering these stresses after quenching. This method is illustrated diagrammatically in Figure 39—38. In practice, it is ordinarily carried out by quenching the piece into a molten-salt bath at a temperature just above the M_s temperature, holding in this bath long enough to permit the piece to acquire the temperature throughout, and then air cooling to room temperature. Transformation to martensite then occurs during the relatively slow air cooling and, since the temperature gradient characteristic of the conventional quench is absent, the stresses set up by the transformation are much lower than in conventional quenching and tempering. Along with these lower stresses goes, of course, a much greater freedom from distortion and cracking. After martempering, the piece

may be tempered to the desired strength level. Martempering has been applied to the heat treatment of tools, bearings, dies, etc. in which difficulty was encountered with quench cracking or distortion when heat treated by conventional quenching and tempering.

AUSTEMPERING

As discussed above, the properties of lower bainite are generally similar in respect to strength and somewhat superior in ductility to those of tempered martensite. Austempering, which is an isothermal heat treatment to lower bainite, therefore, offers an alternative method of heat treatment for obtaining optimum strength and ductility.

The austempering treatment is illustrated diagrammatically in Figure 39—39. It involves quenching to the desired temperature in the lower bainite region, usually in molten salt, and holding at this temperature until transformation is complete. It is the usual practice to hold for a time twice as long as that indicated by the isothermal transformation diagram to insure complete transformation of segregated areas. The piece may be quenched or air cooled to room temperature after transformation is complete and may be tempered to a lower hardness level if desired.

Austempering has the tremendous advantage over conventional quenching and tempering that the bainite transformation takes place isothermally at a relatively high temperature so that the transformation stresses are very low, with a resultant absolute minimum of distortion and a practically complete assurance that quench cracking will not occur.

Austempering, on the other hand, has the disadvantage, which it shares with martempering, that, because of the slower cooling rates of the molten salt baths as compared with the usual water or oil quenches a higher hardenability steel is required to prevent high temperature transformation during the

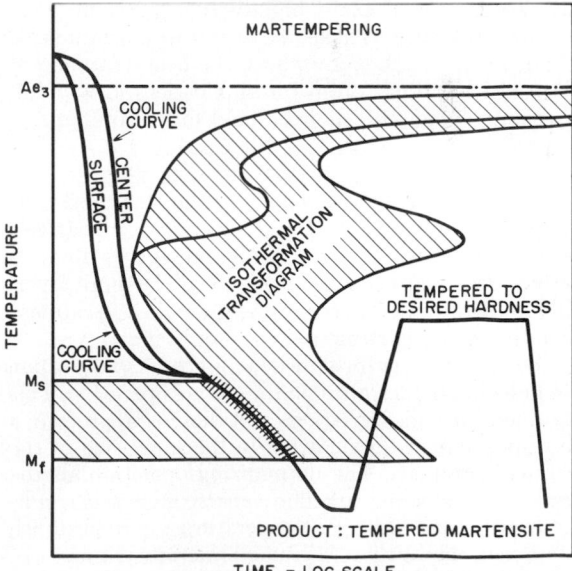

Fig. 39—38. Schematic transformation diagram for martempering.

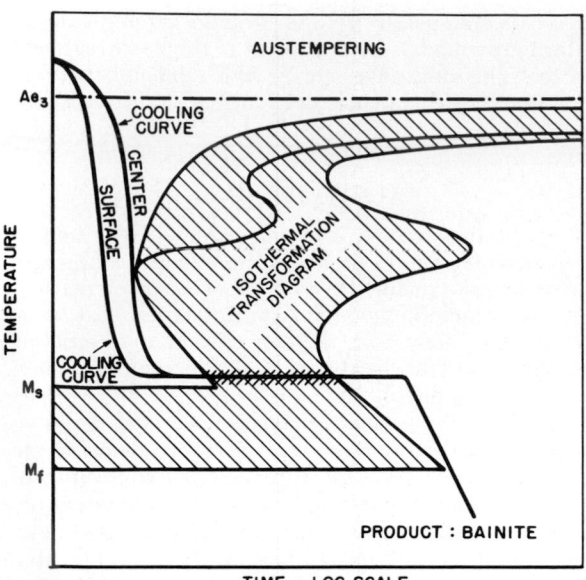

FIG. 39—39. Schematic transformation diagram for austempering.

cooling to the bainite temperature. Along with these higher hardenabilities also go longer times for complete transformation to bainite so that austempering may be considerably more time consuming than martempering or conventional quenching and tempering.

This hardenability limitation may be overcome to a certain extent by the introduction of a prequench in water or oil to a temperature just below the M_s temperature, so that some martensite transformation occurs prior to the final holding at the bainite transformation. The final product is then a mixture of tempered martensite and bainite and steel with this microstructure has good properties.

Largely because of this hardenability limitation, austempering has found its widest application in the heat treatment of plain high-carbon steels in small section sizes, such as sheet, strip and wire products. It is, however, also, being used for the heat treatment of alloy steels and cast irons for applications in which it is essential that distortion be held to a minimum.

NORMALIZING

Normalizing involves reheating the steel above its critical temperature (Ac_3) and air cooling. It has two primary purposes: to refine the grain, and to obtain a carbide size and distribution which will be more favorable for carbide solution on subsequent heat treatment than the as-rolled structure.

The as-rolled grain size depends principally upon the finishing temperature in the rolling operation. This is subject to wide variations and there is, therefore, a corresponding wide variation in the grain size of the as-rolled products. The normalizing operation, as the name implies, serves to refine a coarse grain size resulting from a high finishing temperature and to establish a uniform, relatively fine-grained microstructure.

In alloy steels, particularly if they have been slow cooled after rolling, the carbides in the as-rolled condition tend to be rather large and massive. These large carbides are difficult to dissolve on subsequent austenitizing treatments. This carbide size, likewise, will be subject to wide variations, depending on the rolling and slow-cooling practice. Here again, normalizing tends to establish a more uniform and finer carbide particle size which will facilitate subsequent heat treatment to a more uniform final product.

The usual practice is to normalize from 100° to 150° F above the critical temperature, but for some alloy steels with carbides that are soluble only with difficulty, considerably higher temperatures may be used to obtain carbide solution. Heating, in general, should be slow enough to insure uniform temperatures and low thermal stresses. It is now a very common practice to carry out this operation in continuous furnaces. Continuous normalizing is particularly well adapted to sheet and strip because it may be heated quickly, but it is also used for plates and bars. The heating operation may, however, be carried out in any type of furnace which will permit uniform heating and accurate temperature control.

ANNEALING

The principal purposes of annealing are to relieve cooling stresses induced by cold or hot working, and to soften the steel so as to improve its machinability or formability. It may involve only a subcritical heating to relieve stresses, to recrystallize cold-worked material, or to spheroidize the carbides or it may involve heating above the critical temperature with subsequent transformation to pearlite or directly to a spheroidized structure on cooling.

Full Anneal—As discussed above, the most favorable microstructure for machinability in the low- or medium-carbon steels is coarse pearlite. The customary heat treatment to develop this microstructure is a full anneal, illustrated diagrammatically in Figure 39—40. It consists of austenitizing at a relatively high temperature so that full carbide solution is obtained,

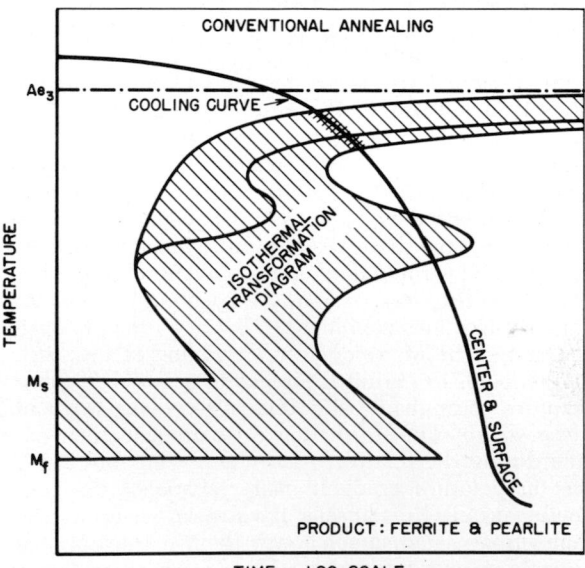

FIG. 39—40. Schematic transformation diagram for full annealing.

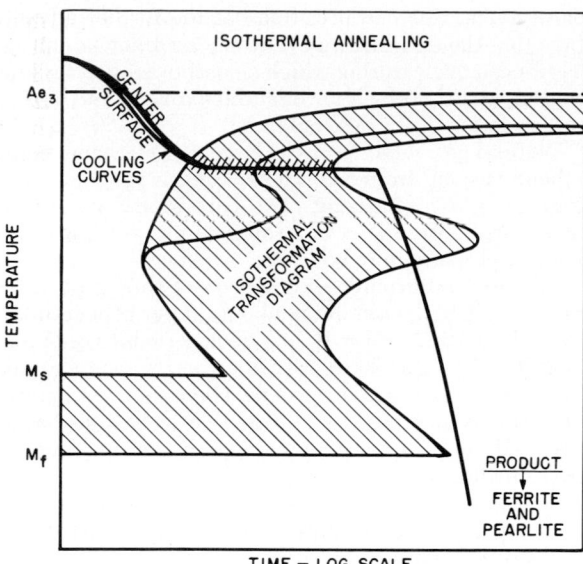

ISOTHERMAL ANNEALING

TIME – LOG SCALE

FIG. 39—41. Schematic transformation diagram for isothermal annealing.

followed by a slow cooling so that transformation occurs only and completely in the high-temperature end of the pearlite range. This is a simple heat treatment and is reliable for most steels. It is, however, rather time consuming since it involves a slow cooling over the entire temperature range from the austenitizing temperature to a temperature well below that at which transformation is complete.

Isothermal Annealing—This annealing to coarse pearlite can, of course, be carried out isothermally by cooling to the proper temperature for transformation to coarse pearlite, and holding at this temperature until transformation is complete in a manner similar to the austempering procedure. This method is illustrated diagrammatically in Figure 39—41. Such an isothermal-annealing cycle may make possible a very considerable time saving over the conventional full-annealing treatment described above. Neither the time from the austenitizing temperature to the transformation temperature, or from the transformation temperature to room temperature is critical and these may be speeded up as much as is desired or is practical. Furthermore, if the extreme softness of the coarsest pearlite is not necessary, the transformation may be carried out at the "nose" of the curve where the transformation goes to completion most rapidly and the operation thereby further expedited; the pearlite is much finer and the hardness is higher.

Isothermal annealing is most practical for applications in which full advantage may be taken of the rapid cooling to the transformation temperature and from this temperature down to room temperature. Thus for small parts which can be conveniently handled in salt or lead baths, this isothermal annealing makes possible large time savings as compared with the conventional slow furnace cooling. It is also very conveniently adapted to continuous heat treatment, and continuous annealing by this method is commonly referred to as "cycle annealing." This is usually carried

out in an especially designed furnace, incorporating an air-blast chamber in order to cool rapidly from the high-heat stages for austenitizing down to the lower-temperature stages in which the transformation to pearlite occurs. This permits an accelerated cooling down to the transformation temperature. On the other hand, the method offers no particular advantage for applications such as the batch annealing of large furnace loads in which the rate of cooling to the center of the load may be so slow as to preclude any rapid cooling to the transformation temperature. For such applications, the conventional full-annealing method usually offers a better assurance of obtaining the desired microstructure and properties.

Spheroidize Annealing—Coarse pearlite microstructures are too hard for optimum machinability in the higher carbon steels, and such steels are, therefore, customarily annealed to develop spheroidized microstructures. This may be accomplished by tempering the as-rolled, slow-cooled or normalized materials at a temperature just below the lower critical temperature. Such an operation is known as "sub-critical annealing." Full spheroidization of the carbides by this method may require long holding times at the sub-critical temperature and the method may, therefore, be slow, but it is a simple heat treatment and may frequently be more convenient than annealing above the critical temperature.

It has been found, however, that the procedures described above for annealing to produce pearlite, can, with some modifications, be applied to annealing methods that will result in spheroidized microstructures. If free carbide remains after the austenitizing treatment, transformation (in the temperature range at which coarse pearlite would ordinarily form) will proceed to spheroidized rather than to pearlitic microstructures. Thus, heat treatment to form spheroidized microstructures can be carried out in a manner completely analogous to heat treatment to form pearlite, except for the use of lower austenitizing temperatures. Spheroidize annealing may thus involve a slow cooling similar to the full-annealing treatment to produce pearlite or it may be an isothermal heat treatment similar to the isothermal annealing to form pearlite. An austenitizing temperature not more than 100° F above the lower critical temperature is customarily used for this super-critical annealing to produce spheroidized microstructures.

Process Annealing—Process annealing is the term used to describe the sub-critical annealing of cold-worked materials. It customarily involves heating at a temperature high enough to cause recrystallization of the cold-worked structure and to soften the steel.

The most important example of process annealing is the box annealing of cold-rolled low-carbon sheet steel; the sheets are packed in a large box which is sealed to protect them from oxidation. This annealing is usually carried out at temperatures of from about 1100° to 1300° F. The heating and holding at temperature usually takes about 24 hours after which the charge is slowly cooled in the box, the entire process taking about 40 hours.

The process and equipment are described in detail in Chapter 32.

CARBURIZING

In carburizing, a high-carbon surface layer is imparted to low-carbon steel by heating it in contact with carbonaceous materials. On quenching after carburizing, the high-carbon "case" becomes very hard, while the low-carbon core remains comparatively soft. The result is a very wear-resistant exterior combined with an interior possessing great toughness, particularly suitable for gears, camshafts, etc.

Carburizing is most commonly carried out by packing the steel in boxes with carbonaceous solids, sealing to exclude the atmosphere and heating to about 1700° F for a period of time depending upon the case depth desired. This process is known as **pack carburizing**. Carburizing may also be carried out by heating the steel in direct contact with carburizing gases, in which case the process is known as **gas carburizing**; or, least commonly, in liquid baths of carburizing salts, in which case it is known as **liquid carburizing**.

Pack Carburizing—Although in pack carburizing, as described above, the parts are packed in a solid compound, the actual carburizing medium is carbon-monoxide gas. The **carburizing compound** usually consists of charcoal, coke and an **energizer** such as barium or sodium carbonate. The energizer is supposed to break down in the presence of carbon, forming carbon monoxide as follows:

$$BaCO_3 = BaO + CO_2$$
$$CO_2 + C = 2CO$$

but the precise behavior of the energizer is not exactly known. The CO then carburizes the steel:

$$3Fe + 2CO = Fe_3C + CO_2$$

The usual carburizing temperature is 1700° F, and a case depth of about $\frac{1}{16}$ inch is ordinarily obtained on carburizing 8 hours at this temperature. Where speed is a primary consideration, temperatures up to 1750° F may be used. The higher temperatures, however, require more careful control to assure uniform results. For some steels, especially the higher-nickel alloy steels, lower temperatures of 1625° to 1650° F are used, and these lower temperatures have the advantage of decreasing warpage.

The carbon content at the surface should ordinarily not be over 1.15 per cent and the gradation toward the core should be uniform. This can be controlled to a considerable extent by the composition of the carburizing compound; for example, reducing the amount of energizer and increasing the charcoal or coke content will lower the surface carbon. In general, the maximum surface carbon will increase as the carburizing temperature decreases because of the low diffusion rate of the carbon at the lower temperature.

Gas Carburizing—The principal carburizing agents in gas carburizing are methane and carbon monoxide; the reactions may be represented as follows:

$$CH_4 + 3Fe = Fe_3C + 2H_2$$
$$2CO + 3Fe = Fe_3C + CO_2$$

The most common practice is to lead the gas into a heated retort in which the work is continuously tumbled by rotating the retort. Such carburizing is faster than pack carburizing since the time of heating the carburizer is saved, and the case depth can be held to close limits. Gas carburization has the further advantage that the carburizing cycle may be followed up by a diffusion cycle during which no carburizing gas is admitted, and thereby a lower surface carbon and a better gradation of the case obtained.

Natural gas, which consists largely of methane, with ethane varying from 5 to 10 per cent, is very satisfactory for gas carburizing. The carburizing gas may, however, be produced in a separate gas generator, or bottled propane may be used.

Liquid Carburizing—Immersion of steel parts in a molten-salt bath containing about 30 per cent sodium cyanide at 1600° F for ½ to 1 hour periods to obtain a light (0.010 inch) hard case for wear resistance has been practiced for many years. The case is a mixture of carbides and nitrides and its relatively high hardness reflects to a considerable extent the presence of iron nitride.

The above cyaniding process is now, however, largely being replaced by liquid carburizing in activated baths which employ a floating slag of calcium cyanide as the active agent and which produce deeper cases which are lower in nitrogen and higher in carbon than those obtained with the simple sodium-cyanide bath. A typical composition of an activated bath is as follows:

Calcium Cyanamide	$CaCN_2$	2–5%
Calcium Cyanide	$Ca(CN)_2$	43–48%
Sodium Chloride	NaCl	30–35%
Calcium Oxide	CaO	14–16%
Carbon	C	4–5%

The comparative case depths as a function of time and temperature in activated and cyanide baths are shown in Figure 39—42. The cases obtained with activated baths range from 0.70 to 1.00 per cent carbon with about 0.2 per cent nitrogen concentrated mainly at the surface of the steel parts.

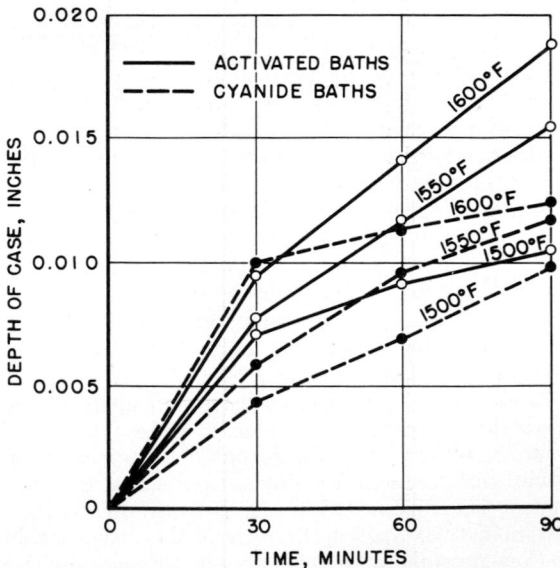

FIG. 39—42. Comparative case depths as a function of time and temperature in activated and cyanide baths. From "Metals Handbook," 1939 Edition (page 1061). Published by American Society for Metals.

Heat Treatment of Carburized Parts—Since carburized articles have a high-carbon case and a low-carbon core, the proper heat-treating temperature for the case will be too low for the core, and vice versa. Thus a double treatment is desirable to obtain optimum properties of both case and core; the piece is first heated to above the critical temperature corresponding to the low-carbon core and suitably cooled to refine its structure. It is then reheated to just above the critical temperature of the case and quenched to harden the case. However, when the carburizing temperature is not too high, refining of the core may not be essential, and after cooling from the carburizing temperature, a single reheating and quench from above the critical temperature of the case is sufficient. Quenching directly from the carburizing temperature is sometimes employed, although this may lead to undue warpage.

Nitriding—The nitrogen case-hardening process which is termed "nitriding" consists in subjecting machined and preferably heat-treated parts to the action of a nitrogenous medium, commonly ammonia gas, under certain conditions whereby surface hardness is imparted to the material without necessitating any further treatment. Wear resistance, retention of hardness at elevated temperatures, and resistance to certain types of corrosion are other properties imparted to the steel by nitriding.

It has been found that chromium and aluminum are desirable in steels for nitriding and compositions especially adapted for nitriding have been developed. A typical composition is as follows:

Carbon	0.20–0.30%
Manganese	0.40–0.60%
Aluminum	0.90–1.40%
Chromium	0.90–1.40%
Molybdenum	0.15–0.25%

Usual conditions for the nitriding process consist of subjecting the articles to the action of ammonia gas at temperatures ranging from 930° to 1220° F. The range most commonly used is 950° to 1000° F. Nitrided cases are ordinarily light, case depth of 0.010 to 0.015 inch being obtained in 48 hours at 975° F. The surface hardness is, however, very high (900 to 1200 Vickers), and this hardness is retained even after reheating to temperatures up to 900° F.

SECTION 5

HEAT-TREATING FURNACES

General Design Requirements—Heat-treating furnaces are grouped into either batch or continuous furnaces. There are many different types in each group, and only general design features can be discussed here: furnaces for specific applications are described in other chapters that deal with the manufacture of such steel products as bars, plates, flat-rolled material, heavy forgings, wire, etc.

The simplest furnaces are the direct-fired batch type with manual controls. The more elaborate installations used for large production lines are continuous furnaces with automatic program control. In a number of installations, special facilities for controlling the atmosphere in the working chamber are provided to obtain the desired surface condition. The most common heat treatments performed in furnaces are annealing, normalizing, spheroidizing, hardening, tempering, carburizing and stress relieving. Heat-treating furnaces seldom are designed for temperatures in excess of 2000° F, and generally are operated in the 800° F to 1600° F range. They are usually well insulated and built tight to prevent air infiltration or a loss of special atmosphere gas. Attention in design is directed toward procuring uniform temperature distribution in the working chamber of the furnace. The position and method of heat application, and the circulation of gases in the furnace, are of major consequence in this. In annealing furnaces, means for controlling both the rate of heating and cooling of the stock usually are provided. Since the required heating and cooling rates of different types of steel vary, it is necessary to provide flexible means for controlling these functions. Insulating firebrick is used generally in heat-treating furnace construction, due to its low heat-storage capacity, to permit heating and cooling the furnace quickly. For intermittent furnace operation this is particularly vital. Attention is directed in design to spacing the charge in order to attain the most efficient flow of heat around the stock. In coil-annealing furnaces, and in furnaces for heat treating other material, special facilities often are provided to improve the circulation of special atmosphere gases during heating and cooling. In all heat-treating layouts, special consideration is given to providing sufficient furnace capacity to maintain the desired time-temperature relation of the treatment. Furnaces forced beyond their normal capacity usually yield an erratic and non-uniform product.

For handling batch loads of material to be heated, quenched, and tempered, quench tanks and cranes should be located in such a way that little time is lost in getting the material from the furnace into the quenching medium. Furnaces also must be arranged so that, after quenching, a second furnace is available for taking the charge promptly for further treatment. Usually three furnaces are provided for operations of this type: two for heating and one for tempering.

In large-scale heat-treating operations, the layout of facilities is very important. The furnaces must be arranged to suit an orderly flow of material through the shop. Adequate space for temporary storage and handling is necessary for both the raw and the finished material. A sufficient number of cranes or other stock-handling facilities of the proper capacity must be provided to eliminate bottlenecks or interference with prescribed furnace cycles. A central station for the preparation of atmosphere gas generally is provided in the larger furnace layouts where particular attention to steel surface is required.

In heat-treating furnaces, many furnace parts, such

as conveyors or rollers in continuous furnaces, radiant tubes for indirect firing and covers in coil and pack-annealing furnaces, are of metallic construction since the temperature seldom exceeds the 800° to 1600° F range. Special alloy materials are utilized to reduce the maintenance of these parts to a minimum. In selecting the furnaces for a heat-treating plant, careful consideration must be given to the type of product to be heated, to the kind of treatment to be performed, and to the production rate required. The ensuing sections explain pertinent factors in design and describe the application of various furnace types.

Method of Heat Application—The character of the material to be heated and the type of treatment to be performed have an important bearing on the choice of method of heat application. Heat-transfer laws govern the flow of heat to the steel in heat-treating as in other heating furnaces. The surface of the material absorbs heat transmitted to it by radiation or by convection or both, and this heat is transferred though the body of the material by conduction. In heat-treating furnaces, the transfer of heat by convection is relatively more significant than in furnaces operated at a higher temperature level. In heat treating steel, the rate of heat transfer to the surface is usually low in order that each individual piece, as well as all pieces in the furnace, may be brought up uniformly to the required temperature level. However, in some furnaces which utilize induction heating or radiant-type open-flame burners, uniform heating can be accomplished rapidly with high heat-transfer rates.

Gaseous fuel and electric power are the two main sources of heat used in heat-treating furnaces. In some cases, fuel oil has been substituted for gas due to a shortage of the latter or for economic reasons. In gas heating, a number of variations in method of firing are used. These variations may be separated into two general classes, **direct** and **indirect firing**. Direct firing is used more generally. This method permits the products of combustion of the fuel to circulate about the material to be heated. In direct-fired furnaces, open burners may be used either in the furnace proper or they may be installed outside the work-heating chamber in the path of an external fan which circulates large volumes of hot gases through the furnace. Temperatures attainable in this type of furnace are limited by the materials of which the fan is constructed. The latter modification is used in **convection-type** furnaces. In indirect-fired furnaces the products of combustion do not enter the work-heating chamber. Indirect firing is used in **muffle** furnaces, an example of which is shown in Figure 39—43.

Another common application of indirect firing is obtained with radiant tubes, an example of which is shown in the furnace in Figure 39—44. Furnaces using direct firing are relatively lower in operating cost and original capital investment. Furnaces using indirect firing generally are selected where the control of furnace atmosphere is of particular importance.

Electric power is used as a source of heat in many heat-treating furnaces due to the ease it affords for controlling temperature, to its suitability for use with protective-gas atmospheres, and to its cleanliness. Resistance-type heating elements, which either are im-

bedded in the furnace refractory lining or suspended from heat-resisting hangers, radiate heat to the furnace charge. The resistance units are positioned in the furnace to permit uniform heating. Furnaces with zone heating sometimes use electrical resistance units because of their easy adaptation to the control of temperature levels. Another method for heating electrically is by induction. Induction heating is done by passing a high-frequency alternating current through a coil surrounding the material to be heated. The coils are shaped to suit the material to be heated. The rapidly alternating electrical field, in which the material to be heated is held, causes the steel to heat very rapidly, due to eddy currents and hysteresis. Due to the rapidity of the process, the duration of heating is very critical, necessitating precise control.

Atmosphere Control—The effect of a heat-treating operation on the surface condition of the work pieces is influenced by the time of heating, the temperature level maintained, and the atmosphere surrounding the material. Figure 39—45 shows graphically the relative amount of scale formed in a batch reheating furnace for variations of these conditions. While the temperature level in heat-treating furnaces is somewhat lower than that shown in the figure, the time is generally longer. By using the proper atmosphere in the working chamber, a clean scale-free surface is obtained. Such a surface is required for most sheet and strip material

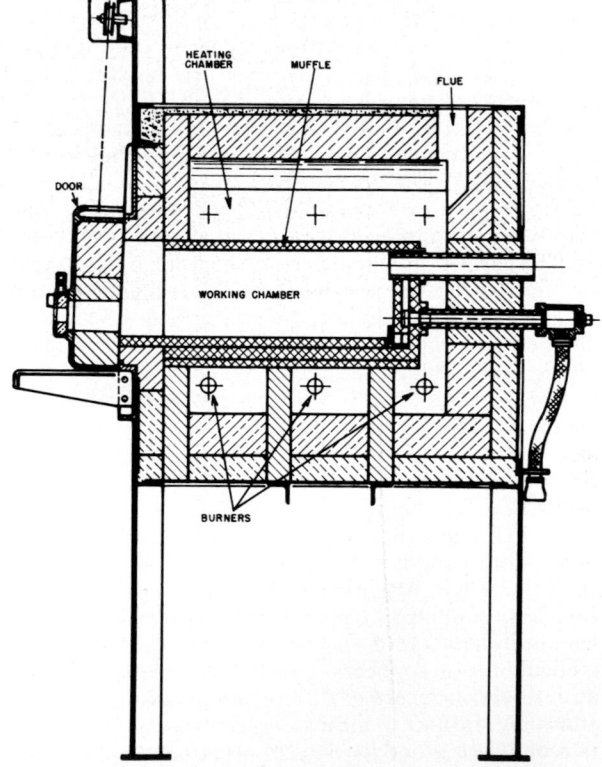

Fig. 39—43. Diagrammatic cross-section of an indirect-fired muffle type furnace equipped for use of a controlled atmosphere in the muffle. Openings in rear provide for insertion of control thermocouple and entrance of prepared atmosphere gas. (Courtesy, Surface Combustion Corporation.)

Fig. 39—44. Radiant-tube fired cover-type furnace employed in heat treating coils of flat rolled products enclosed in inner covers under which controlled-atmosphere gas is circulated. (Courtesy, Surface Combustion Corporation.)

and other important steel products, such as wire and tubes. The three gases most injurious to surface condition are oxygen, carbon dioxide, and water vapor. The effect of each of these, as well as effects from other gases, follows:

Oxygen reacts with the iron of the steel to produce iron oxide. For this reason it must be excluded entirely for bright annealing. It also reacts with the carbon in steel to lower the carbon content of its surface; that is, it decarburizes the steel. In some types of controlled annealing, oxygen of the air may be caused to scale the steel faster than it decarburizes it. This results in a product having a decarburized surface layer of minimum thickness and the scale, being flaky, is easily removed.

Nitrogen, in the molecular state, is entirely passive to iron and is entirely satisfactory for bright annealing low-carbon steels. If pure and very dry, it will be passive to high-carbon steel, but the presence of even slight traces of moisture will cause decarburization.

Carbon dioxide and carbon monoxide are considered together since the ratio of their concentration in the atmosphere plays an important part in their action on the steel surface. As an example, if the ratio of carbon dioxide to carbon monoxide is 0.6 or higher at 1500° F, the atmosphere will scale steel readily. If the ratio is reduced to 0.4, or lower, the atmosphere will no longer scale steel but will remain decarburizing to a 1 per cent carbon steel. For low-carbon steels, a ratio of carbon monoxide to carbon dioxide on the order of about two to one will be in equilibrium with the steel, and a gas of this composition is used to advantage for producing bright-annealed sheets. A higher carbon-monoxide content actually will carburize the steel.

Hydrogen is highly reducing to iron oxide, and, therefore, opposes the formation of a heavy, flaky scale and when present in the products of combustion, promotes formation of a tight scale that is hard to remove. At certain temperatures it is absorbed by the steel and is likely to result in embrittlement, more particularly

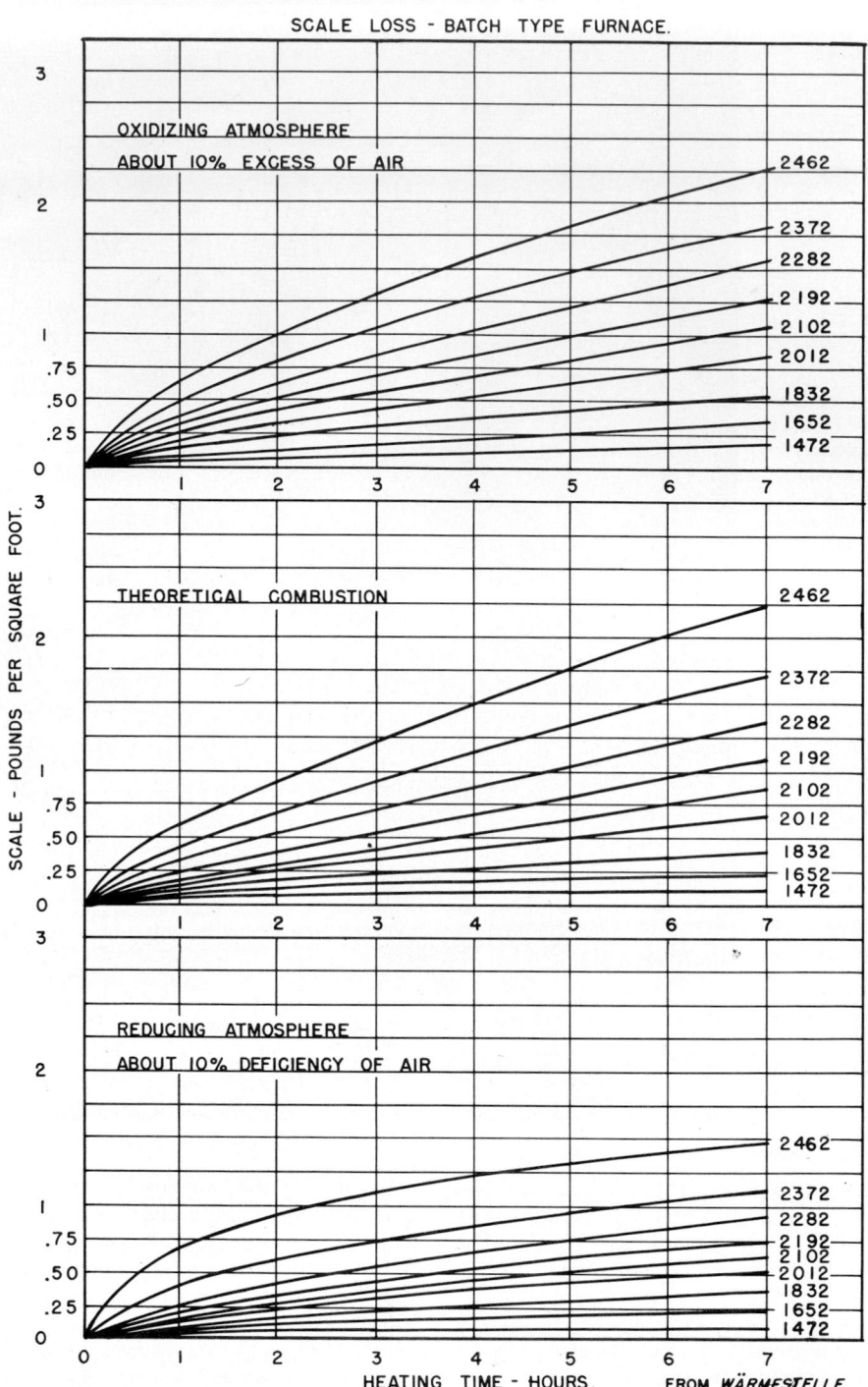

SCALE LOSS - BATCH TYPE FURNACE.

Fig. 39—45. Graphical representation of relative amounts of scale formed on steel heated in a batch-type reheating furnace with variations in time of heating, temperature level, and heating-chamber atmosphere. (From "Warmestelle.")

in high-carbon steel. If the hydrogen is dry, it has no scaling effect on high-carbon steel at elevated temperatures, but it does cause considerable decarburization. A common prepared atmosphere which is used for bright-annealing work is composed of 75 per cent hydrogen and 25 per cent nitrogen. It is formed by cracking anhydrous ammonia. Hydrogen is highly ex-

plosive if mixed with air and particular precaution must be exercised to prevent air infiltration into furnaces in which it is employed.

Water vapor is oxidizing to iron and combines with carbon of steel to form carbon monoxide and hydrogen within the temperature range of the "water-gas reaction." It is reactive to a steel surface at temperatures even as low as 400 to 700° F, and is thus often the cause of formation of a blue oxide during the cooling cycle.

Hydrocarbons, more specifically methane, are carburizing gases. They are subject to thermal decomposition at annealing temperature, liberating hydrogen and depositing soot on the steel.

The most commonly prepared gases for control of atmosphere are formed by the partial combustion of hydrocarbon gases, contained in such fuels as coke-oven gas, natural gas, propane, or butane. Manufacturers of converters for the preparation of gases describe the various kinds under trade names, such as "DX" gas, "Drycolene," etc. The first step in making such a gas is to burn a mixture of the fuel gas with air. This provides a gas high in nitrogen, but containing other undesirable gases including water vapor, which must be removed. Other atmosphere gases are prepared by (1) cracking a non-combustible mixture of air and gas with a catalyst at high temperature, (2) by cracking anhydrous ammonia at high temperature, and (3) by passing air through a heated retort filled with charcoal.

Furnaces using controlled atmosphere have a number of construction features not incorporated in ordinary furnaces. These features are essential to prevent loss of gas and to minimize the entrance of air into the furnace which would upset the control established. Casings for furnaces with controlled atmosphere are welded gas-tight. Batch-type furnaces are provided with sand seals. Continuous furnaces charged and discharged from the ends sometimes have flame curtains to burn out the oxygen from any possible air infiltration, or the furnace may be operated under sufficient pressure to prevent air infiltration. In the latter case, a small loss of the prepared atmosphere usually occurs through the small unavoidable openings in the furnace. Doors, where required, are fitted snugly by sloping fronts with ground surfaces or by wedging devices or clamps. Modern continuous pusher-type furnaces for special heat treatment of bar and wire coils utilize a vestibule and inner-door arrangement at the charge and discharge ends of the furnace. This permits complete purging of air as material is charged and discharged from the furnace.

Batch-Type Furnaces—The five principal general types of batch furnaces are described below:

1. **Box furnaces** are constructed with a solid hearth. They are shaped, as their name implies, similar to a box and are charged through door openings by tongs or some mechanical charger. The furnace hearth may vary from a few square feet in area to over 30 square feet. Heating may be done by direct or indirect fuel firing or by electricity. Muffle and semimuffle type construction often is employed when control of atmosphere is required. This type of furnace is used frequently for individual-piece or small-lot heat treating, for laboratory test and shop work, and for general production work on a small scale. Box furnaces have been constructed for convection heating either with a fan underneath the roof or with one external to the furnace for recirculation. Furnaces of this type are used for annealing, normalizing, tempering and carburizing.

2. **The car-bottom furnace** consists of a furnace shell equipped with burners or heating units with the hearth built upon a separate car which runs in and out of the furnace shell to charge and unload the furnace. The car usually is moved into and out of the furnace by a toothed rack attached to the bottom of the car and a stationary pinion actuated by an electric motor, the car itself resting on rollers or wheels that move over a two-rail track. The doors of the furnace are of the vertically lifting type, full width of the furnace, and are hydraulically or electrically operated. In order that the entire surface of the charge may be exposed to heat of the same intensity and to aid circulation, the charge is supported above the floor of the car bottom by heat-resisting alloy castings or on refractory piers. The car bottom is made to fit the furnace closely and the escape of hot gases around it is prevented by sand seals. Car-bottom furnaces have been constructed to process charges from a few tons to several hundred tons. They are used for heat treating of axles, bars, heavy plates, castings and miscellaneous shapes.

For operations involving heating, quenching and tempering, it is desirable that the quenching tank be located in proximity to the furnace to enable the charge to be placed in the tank in the shortest possible time. In some installations, less than a minute is required to transfer the charge from a closed furnace to the quenching tank. Car-bottom furnaces may be direct or indirect fired, and various designs have been developed to improve heat distribution in the working chamber. Electric heating also is employed in some car-bottom furnaces. Car-bottom furnaces sometimes are constructed of two chambers side by side, with a common division wall to facilitate annealing and tempering operations. In some installations, an auxiliary cooling system employing blowers is provided to accelerate cooling. Some car-bottom furnaces are known as **elevator furnaces** where the car is rolled under the furnace shell and then raised into the furnace by a motor-driven lifting mechanism. Those in which the shell is lowered over the car, as shown in Figure 39—46, are used to provide a more complete sand or water seal than is obtainable with the conventional car-bottom furnaces.

3. **The bell-type furnace** has a removable shell or cover. The furnace usually is used for processing material which requires special surface protection from oxidation or decarburization. The furnace shell is removed by a crane and set aside while the hearth of the furnace is charged. The shell is then replaced, as was shown in Figure 39—44. Furnaces of this type, used for annealing sheet, strip, rod and wire, usually are called **box annealing, pack annealing, coil annealing,** or **cover annealing furnaces.** In these, the material is stacked on a permanent base or **stand,** a light **inner cover** is placed over the stack, sealed with sand at the bottom and provided with a constant supply of prepared gas atmosphere, and then the portable heating unit is lowered over the assembly. The heating covers are square, rectangular or cylindrically shaped. Loads vary from 35 to 400 tons per charge, distributed on one to eight stands per base. In most instances, a number of bases and inner covers are provided with one or more covers for heating. After heating of each charge

Fɪɢ. 39—46. Charge of mixed sizes of steel bars, supported above hearth by cast-alloy fixtures, ready to be rolled under bell-type furnace body, which then will be lowered over charge. Toothed rack above floor at lower left is driven by a pinion to move car. (Courtesy, Surface Combustion Corporation.)

is completed on a base, the heating cover is moved to another base, leaving the charge protected by the atmosphere under the inner cover which is left in place. The covers may be direct fired or equipped with radiant tubes for indirect firing, or they may be heated by electrical resistance units. The heating elements are attached to the inside of the heating cover, which is built of steel and lined with a refractory insulating material and braced substantially in order that it can be moved from base to base with an overhead crane. Many inner covers are made of heat-resisting alloys. All are sealed to the base at their bottom edges with a powdered refractory. The heating time in a cover annealing furnace for coils of sheet or tin plate range from 24 to 44 hours for the larger sized furnaces, depending upon the length of soaking period required. The soaking period usually is about 4 to 12 hours. In furnaces of 150 to 300 tons capacity, the average production is about 5.5 tons per hour, the fuel consumption about 1,000,000 Btu per ton, the maximum fuel-burning capacity about 12,000,000 Btu per hour, and the atmosphere-gas consumption about 1,200 cu. ft. per hour. In pack or box annealing furnaces, natural gas or some inert gas is used to surround the charge; the circulation of gases inside the inner cover is by natural or forced convection. In cover furnaces for annealing coils, separators are placed between each coil to aid in distribution of the gas inside the inner cover. The circulation of this gas in a number of modern installations is forced. The fan is located in the base below each stand. The trend in annealing sheet and tin plate has been towards the greater use of coils and heating by forced convection rather than by the former pack method of annealing, in order to obtain higher production and improved uniformity of heating.

4. **Pit furnaces** are furnaces of cylindrical or rectangular shape in which the material is charged and withdrawn through an opening in the furnace top. The larger furnaces are installed usually with at least part of their work chambers below floor level, while many of the smaller and shallower furnaces rest on the working floor, for convenience in handling material. The material to be processed can be suspended by a fixture, loaded into a basket and set into the working chamber, or, as in the case of large forgings, be supported on a suitable base in the furnace. Pit furnaces employ either direct firing or electrical heating, in either case with natural or forced circulation. They may or may not be equipped with special facilities for atmosphere control. Pit furnaces are used for normalizing, hardening, annealing, tempering, and carburizing.

5. **A salt-bath or lead-bath furnace** is another type of heat-treating furnace. It is designed to hold a bath of molten salt or lead in which the material is immersed for treatment. These furnaces are usually small pot-like affairs used in batch operations, but some large furnaces have been constructed of rectangular shape with depths of 15 feet to suit the shape and size of the material to be handled, with conveyors or other means for carrying out continuous operations.

They are equipped usually with a hinged cover or a ventilating hood for minimizing fumes. Such furnaces are used to obtain uniform temperature distribution and close temperature control of the work piece. The bath is heated and maintained at proper temperature either by electrical resistance or by combustion of a fuel. Furnaces with a molten bath for heat treating are called **pot furnaces** when the bath is contained in a pot or crucible constructed of a heat and corrosion-resistant metal, usually externally heated by suitable burners. Other bath-type furnaces may be heated by electric current passing through the (salt) bath between immersed electrodes, or by immersed resistance coils or fuel-fired tubes.

Continuous Furnaces—In continuous furnaces, the material moves through the furnace, and two basic types of these are recognized. In one, the furnace is circular with a rotating hearth which carries the charge. The walls and roof are stationary, and the furnace enclosure is made by contacting the walls with the periphery of the moving hearth through a sand or liquid seal. In the other type, the furnace is composed of a single, long straight chamber, or series of chambers, through which the material is moved. Differentiation of continuous furnace types may be made according to the way the material is moved, such as the **rotary-hearth**, the **roller-hearth**, the **pusher**, the **conveyor**, the **walking-beam**, the **tunnel**, the **continuous-strand** and the **monorail** types. Modern production methods, dealing with ever increasing tonnages of material of identical size and treatment, favor the continuous-furnace type best suited to the nature of material to be heat treated.

Continuous furnaces are designed with and without auxiliary equipment for atmosphere control. Heat may be applied by direct or indirect firing or electrically. They are especially suited for zone heating and cooling. A brief description of continuous furnace types and their application is given below.

1. **Rotary-hearth furnaces** are used generally for heating pieces that are to be handled individually. Typical applications are the heating of gears, shells, cylinders, billets, etc., that are to be fixture-quenched or handled individually for scale-free hardening without decarburization, for normalizing or drawing. This furnace type is used also for heating smaller parts loaded in lightweight trays, and for pack carburizing. Charging and discharging are accomplished at the same location. Rotary-hearth furnaces are built in a wide range of hearth sizes, to heat from a few hundred pounds up to 60 tons per hour. A typical rotary-hearth furnace for heat treating steel is shown in Figure 39—47.

2. **Roller-hearth furnaces** are high production, continuous-type units, especially suited for uniform treatment of large orders of identical material. This type of furnace is used widely for bright annealing of tubes, stampings, drawn parts, etc.; for normalizing, annealing, hardening and tempering steel bars; for annealing malleable iron, small steel and iron castings, and forgings; and for normalizing flat-rolled products. Roller-hearth furnaces are constructed as a single furnace or as a line of furnaces for zone heating and cooling, and sometimes have an intermediate section with a tank for quenching.

In some modern furnaces used for continuously treating short lengths of sheet, disc rollers made of heat-resisting alloys with polished surfaces are utilized to reduce the cooling effect of full contact with the ordinary type of roller and to avoid scratching of the piece. The discs are staggered and mounted upon water-cooled shafts, which are driven by variable-speed motors either through a chain and sprocket system or shafts and gears. A gas-fired normalizing furnace with automatic pyrometric control is shown in Figure 39—48. Furnaces of this type are built up to 100 inches in width and vary from 120 to 200 feet in length, the larger ones having capacities for normalizing up to 300

FIG. 39—47. Rotary-hearth furnace for heat-treating steel. Hearth is rotated by a chain-and-sprocket drive, seen in the foreground. (Courtesy, Surface Combustion Corporation.)

Fig. 39—48. Continuous disc-roller-hearth type of normalizing furnace, divided lengthwise into zones each having individual automatic temperature control.

tons per 24-hour day. Sheets undergoing treatment in roller-hearth furnaces may be protected further from contact with rollers of whatever type by the use of **rider sheets,** which are placed on the rollers and support the work. **Cover sheets** on top of the work also may be used to further increase protection. Rider and cover sheets may be used repeatedly before they must be scrapped, since they generally are made of alloy steel.

3. **Pusher-type furnaces** are of two general types. In one type the parts are pushed against each other, as in the continuous reheating furnace. In the other type, the parts are loaded in trays or other types of carriers which are pushed through the furnace.

4. **Conveyor-type furnaces** are constructed similarly to roller-hearth furnaces except that belt conveyors are used to carry the material through the furnace. They are suitable for accurately heat treating small miscellaneous pieces which would not ride properly on a roller hearth. Belt conveyors are made of alloy material of sufficient strength to carry the load and are resistant to heat, oxidation, corrosion and abrasion. A number of different designs of conveyors are utilized to satisfactorily meet the requirements. Some conveyors consist of several individual chains held on constant centers by spacer bars provided with suitable projecting lugs upon which the load, such as sheet or plate cut to length, rests. Many other belts are constructed of open mesh or woven chain to permit free circulation of hot furnace gases or protective atmosphere, while another construction utilizes pans or trays connected to a roller chain to carry the material. The production rate or heating cycle in this furnace type is controlled both by the temperature setting and by varying the speed of the conveyor.

5. **Walking-beam furnaces** employ a special mechanism within the furnace, known as a "walking beam" to move the material through the furnace. The walking beam consists of a number of alloy supports or beams which are arranged in rows of two or more beams to the row, throughout the length of the furnace. The beams are staggered with the one immediately ahead, and are placed in longitudinal slots in the furnace hearth. They are attached from below to toggles or cams that intermittently raise the beams, move them

forward, and then lower them, thus depositing the material on the beams ahead. By this step action the material is moved through the furnace at the desired rate. This furnace type is used commonly for tubes, bars, structural shapes or similar material.

6. In **tunnel-type furnaces,** the stock to be heated is placed upon cars which then are pushed or pulled slowly through the furnace. This furnace type was used at one time for continuous box annealing of sheets. Furnaces used for this purpose sometimes reached 300 feet in length and were built in the form of a long tunnel, not necessarily straight, nor with a level bottom. The sheets were piled upon a base and sealed in a box for annealing. The box then was placed upon a small car which was pushed into the furnace. As the furnace was full of these cars, one car was removed as each car entered the furnace.

7. **Continuous strand-type furnaces** have been developed to reduce the extra handling and the long heating and cooling periods required in annealing sheet and tin plate in coil form. Heat treating uncoiled strip provides greater possibilities for the control of the time-temperature requirements for the entire piece and therefore, a more uniform product. A coil can be processed in a matter of minutes or a few hours compared to the long cycle required in a batch furnace. Another special advantage of this furnace type is that other operations, such as cleaning or coating, may be combined with the heat-treating process to avoid extra handling and the expense of duplicated handling equipment for separate lines. Continuous strand-type furnaces are constructed either as horizontal or vertical units. Furnaces of the latter type of construction are sometimes referred to as **tower-type furnaces** and are used primarily to conserve floor space. Furnaces of this type utilize either electric or radiant-tube heating or both.

Figure 39—49 shows a modern tower-type furnace for annealing cold-reduced material at one stage in the manufacture of tin plate.

The horizontal type of continuous-strand furnace sometimes utilizes catenary suspension of the uncoiled strip, where neither rolls nor any other type of support are used throughout the heating zone. The heating zone of these furnaces may be from 20 to 50 feet in

FIG. 39—49. Tower-type furnace in a continuous annealing line in a tin mill. The furnace proper, surrounded by structural-steel operating platforms, is 64 feet in height, and is heated by a combination of gas-fired and electric heating units.

length. The preheating and cooling zones usually are constructed shorter than in the conveyor type and for some kinds of work are omitted entirely.

8. In **overhead monorail furnaces,** the material undergoing heating is suspended from rods that serve as hangers or even may be welded to the suspension rods. The suspension rods are attached at their upper ends to the carriers that operate on the monorail. If the rods are welded to the work pieces, they are removed after the assembly leaves the heating furnace.

Bibliography

"Functions of the Alloying Elements in Steel," by E. C. Bain. Published by American Society for Metals, 1939, (Second edition by E. C. Bain and Harold W. Paxton, 1961.)

"Metals Handbook," 1961 (Eighth) Edition. Published by American Society for Metals.

"Principles of Heat Treatment," by M. A. Grossmann. Published by American Society for Metals, 1953 edition.

"Elements of Hardenability," by M. A. Grossmann. Published by American Society for Metals, 1952.

"Atlas of Isothermal Transformation Diagrams (1951)," and Supplement (1953). Published by United States Steel Corporation.

"Another Look at Quenchants, Cooling Rates and Hardenability," by I. J. Carney. Trans. ASM, **46,** 1954; pages 882–927.

ASTM Designation E112-61T, published by American Society for Testing and Materials.

CHAPTER 40

Carbon Steels

SECTION 1

CLASSIFICATION AND APPLICATION

The plain carbon steels undoubtedly represent the most important group of engineering materials known. They represent by far the major percentage of steel production and the widest diversity of application of any of the engineering materials. These applications are so diversified that anything like a complete listing, or even a classification on the basis of application, is impossible. Some of the more important classes of application have, however, been discussed in this book. These include castings, forgings, tubular products, plates, sheet and strip, wire and wire products, structural shapes, bars, tools, and such railway materials as rails, wheels and axles.

Although a classification by application is impossible, plain carbon steels may be described by their method of manufacture as basic open hearth, basic oxygen, acid open hearth or acid Bessemer steels. The basic open hearth steels, of course, represent the preponderance of the tonnage. This classification may be extended to include the method of deoxidation used. For example, the basic open hearth steels may be rimmed, semi-killed or fully killed.

In recent years, considerable quantities of plain carbon steel ingots have been produced in plants equipped with basic electric-arc furnaces. At the present time, the basic oxygen steelmaking process is being employed to produce ever-increasing quantities of plain carbon steel ingots. Steels made by either the electric-arc or basic oxygen processes in general are made to the same specifications as basic open-hearth steels for the plain carbon grades.

The plain carbon steels may also be classified on the basis of carbon content as hypoeutectoid or hypereutectoid steels; the hypoeutectoid steels are those in which the carbon content is below the eutectoid value of about 0.80 per cent, and the hypereutectoid steels those with carbon contents above this value.

The composition ranges for the plain carbon steels have been published by the American Iron and Steel Institute and these composition ranges are listed in Tables 40—I, 40—II, 40—III and 40—IV. Concerning these four tables, it should be noted that the prefix letters "B" and "C" are used to designate the two principal steel-making processes for carbon steels as follows: "B" denotes acid Bessemer carbon steel, "C" denotes basic open hearth steel.

SECTION 2

FACTORS AFFECTING CARBON-STEEL PROPERTIES

The principal factors affecting the properties of the plain carbon steels are the carbon content and the microstructure. The general relationships between microstructure and properties, and the factors governing microstructure, have been discussed in the preceding chapter on heat treatment, and need not be repeated here. Most of the plain carbon steels are, however, used without a final heat treatment and the factors affecting the microstructure and thereby the properties in such as-rolled or as-forged products will be emphasized in this chapter. Standard mechanical-property specifications of plain carbon steels in these classes are summarized in Table 40—V.

In addition to the predominant effects of carbon content and microstructure, the properties of plain carbon steels may be modified by the effects of residual elements other than the carbon, manganese, silicon, phosphorus and sulphur which are always present, or the properties of carbon steel may also be affected by the presence of gases, especially oxygen, nitrogen and hydrogen and their reaction products. These incidental elements are usually picked up from the scrap, from the deoxidizers, or from the furnace atmosphere. The gas content is largely dependent upon the melting, deoxidizing and pouring practice so that the final properties of the plain carbon steels

Table 40—I. Standard A.I.S.I. Composition Ranges of Basic Open Hearth Carbon Steels[1] [2]

A.I.S.I. Number	Chemical Composition Limits, Per Cent				Corresp. SAE No.
	C	Mn	P (Max.)	S (Max.)	
C1005	0.06 Max.	0.35 Max.	0.040	0.050	—
C1006	0.08 Max.	0.25–0.40	0.040	0.050	1006
C1008	0.10 Max.	0.25–0.50	0.040	0.050	1008
C1010	0.08–0.13	0.30–0.60	0.040	0.050	1010
C1011	0.08–0.13	0.60–0.90	0.040	0.050	—
C1012	0.10–0.15	0.30–0.60	0.040	0.050	1012
C1013	0.11–0.16	0.50–0.80	0.040	0.050	—
C1015	0.13–0.18	0.30–0.60	0.040	0.050	1015
C1016	0.13–0.18	0.60–0.90	0.040	0.050	1016
C1017	0.15–0.20	0.30–0.60	0.040	0.050	1017
C1018	0.15–0.20	0.60–0.90	0.040	0.050	1018
C1019	0.15–0.20	0.70–1.00	0.040	0.050	1019
C1020	0.18–0.23	0.30–0.60	0.040	0.050	1020
C1021	0.18–0.23	0.60–0.90	0.040	0.050	1021
C1022	0.18–0.23	0.70–1.00	0.040	0.050	1022
C1023	0.20–0.25	0.30–0.60	0.040	0.050	—
C1024	0.19–0.25	1.35–1.65	0.040	0.050	1024
C1025	0.22–0.28	0.30–0.60	0.040	0.050	1025
C1026	0.22–0.28	0.60–0.90	0.040	0.050	1026
C1027	0.22–0.29	1.20–1.50	0.040	0.050	1027
C1029	0.25–0.31	0.60–0.90	0.040	0.050	—
C1030	0.28–0.34	0.60–0.90	0.040	0.050	1030
C1031	0.28–0.34	0.30–0.60	0.040	0.050	—
C1032	0.30–0.36	0.60–0.90	0.040	0.050	—
C1033	0.30–0.36	0.70–1.00	0.040	0.050	1033
C1034	0.32–0.38	0.50–0.80	0.040	0.050	—
C1035	0.32–0.38	0.60–0.90	0.040	0.050	1035
C1036	0.30–0.37	1.20–1.50	0.040	0.050	1036
C1037	0.32–0.38	0.70–1.00	0.040	0.050	—
C1038	0.35–0.42	0.60–0.90	0.040	0.050	1038
C1039	0.37–0.44	0.70–1.00	0.040	0.050	1039
C1040	0.37–0.44	0.60–0.90	0.040	0.050	1040
C1041	0.36–0.44	1.35–1.65	0.040	0.050	1041
C1042	0.40–0.47	0.60–0.90	0.040	0.050	1042
C1043	0.40–0.47	0.70–1.00	0.040	0.050	1043
C1044	0.43–0.50	0.30–0.60	0.040	0.050	—
C1045	0.43–0.50	0.60–0.90	0.040	0.050	1045
C1046	0.43–0.50	0.70–1.00	0.040	0.050	1046
C1048	0.44–0.52	1.10–1.40	0.040	0.050	1048
C1049	0.46–0.53	0.60–0.90	0.040	0.050	1049
C1050	0.48–0.55	0.60–0.90	0.040	0.050	1050
C1051	0.45–0.56	0.85–1.15	0.040	0.050	—
C1052	0.47–0.55	1.20–1.50	0.040	0.050	1052
C1053	0.48–0.55	0.70–1.00	0.040	0.050	—
C1054	0.50–0.60	0.50–0.80	0.040	0.050	—
C1055	0.50–0.60	0.60–0.90	0.040	0.050	1055
C1060	0.55–0.65	0.60–0.90	0.040	0.050	1060
C1065	0.60–0.70	0.60–0.90	0.040	0.050	1065
C1069	0.65–0.75	0.40–0.70	0.040	0.050	—
C1070	0.65–0.75	0.60–0.90	0.040	0.050	1070
C1075	0.70–0.80	0.40–0.70	0.040	0.050	—
C1078	0.72–0.85	0.30–0.60	0.040	0.050	1078
C1080	0.75–0.88	0.60–0.90	0.040	0.050	1080
C1084	0.80–0.93	0.60–0.90	0.040	0.050	—
C1085	0.80–0.93	0.70–1.00	0.040	0.050	1085
C1086	0.82–0.95	0.30–0.50	0.040	0.050	1086
C1090	0.85–0.98	0.60–0.90	0.040	0.050	1090
C1095	0.90–1.03	0.30–0.50	0.040	0.050	1095

SILICON.—When silicon is required, the following ranges and limits are common for standard basic open-hearth steel grades: up to and excluding C 1015, silicon limit is 0.10 max.; C 1015 up to and including C 1025, silicon content may be 0.10 max., 0.10/0.20, or 0.15/0.30; over C 1025, silicon ranges may be 0.10/0.20 or 0.15/0.30.

COPPER AND LEAD.—When required, copper and lead are specified as added elements to a standard steel.

[1] Hot-rolled carbon-steel bars and semifinished products not exceeding 200 square inches cross-sectional area.
[2] From: Steel Products Manuals, American Iron and Steel Institute; "Carbon-Steel—Semifinished for Forging," "Hot-Rolled and Cold-Finished Carbon-Steel Bars," and "Wire and Rods, Carbon Steel."

are, to a very considerable extent, dependent upon the steelmaking practice used in their production.

Thus, the factors governing the properties of a plain carbon steel are primarily its carbon content and microstructure, with the microstructure being determined largely by the composition and the final rolling, forging or heat-treating operation, and secondarily by the residual alloy, non-metallic and gas content of the steel which, in turn, depend upon the steelmaking practice.

Carbon Content and Properties—The average mechanical properties of as-rolled one-inch bars of carbon steels, as a function of carbon content, are shown in Figure 40—1. These values are based on statistical analyses made by several investigators and plotted by Sisco. This figure is illustrative of the general effect of carbon content when the microstructure and grain size are held reasonably constant. It will be seen that the hardness, tensile strength and yield strength increase with increasing carbon content, while the elongation, reduction of area, and Charpy impact values decrease sharply.

Effect of Microstructure and Grain Size—The general relationships between microstructure and properties have been discussed in Chapter 39 on heat treatment. The carbon steels, being of relatively low

hardenability, are predominantly pearlitic in the cast, rolled or forged conditions. The constituents of the hypoeutectoid steels are, therefore, ferrite and pearlite, and of the hypereutectoid steels, cementite and pearlite. As described in the previous chapter, the properties of such pearlitic steels are dependent primarily upon the interlamellar spacing of the pearlite and the grain size. Both the hardness and the ductility increase as the interlamellar spacing or the pearlite-transformation temperature decreases, and the ductility increases with decreasing grain size. The effect of grain size was discussed in some detail in the preceding chapter. The effect of the interlamellar spacing of the pearlite was also discussed and illustrated for a eutectoid steel. The effect of this variable on tensile strength is further illustrated in Figure 40—2, which shows the approximate relationship between tensile strength and carbon content for a series of plain carbon steels isothermally transformed to fine and coarse pearlitic microstructures. The line for the 1200° F transformation product in this illustration is generally similar to, although slightly above, the tensile strength line for as-rolled bars in Figure 40—1, indicating that these as-rolled bars have transformed during cooling at temperatures in the vicinity of 1200° F.

Table 40—II. Standard A.I.S.I. Composition Ranges of Basic Open Hearth Resulphurized Carbon Steels[1]

| A.I.S.I. No. | Chemical Composition Limits, Per Cent | | | | Corresponding SAE No. |
	C	Mn	P (Max.)	S (Max.)	
C1108	0.08/0.13	0.50/0.80	0.040	0.08/0.13	1108
C1109	0.08/0.13	0.60/0.90	0.040	0.08/0.13	1109
C1110	0.08/0.13	0.30/0.60	0.040	0.08/0.13	—
C1113	0.10/0.16	1.00/1.30	0.040	0.24/0.33	—
C1115	0.13/0.18	0.60/0.90	0.040	0.08/0.13	1115
C1116	0.14/0.20	1.10/1.40	0.040	0.16/0.23	—
C1117	0.14/0.20	1.00/1.30	0.040	0.08/0.13	1117
C1118	0.14/0.20	1.30/1.60	0.040	0.08/0.13	1118
C1119	0.14/0.20	1.00/1.30	0.040	0.24/0.33	1119
C1120	0.18/0.23	0.70/1.00	0.040	0.08/0.13	1120
C1125	0.22/0.28	0.60/0.90	0.040	0.08/0.13	—
C1126	0.23/0.29	0.70/1.00	0.040	0.08/0.13	1126
C1132	0.27/0.34	1.35/1.65	0.040	0.08/0.13	1132
C1137	0.32/0.39	1.35/1.65	0.040	0.08/0.13	1137
C1138	0.34/0.40	0.70/1.00	0.040	0.08/0.13	1138
C1139	0.35/0.43	1.35/1.65	0.040	0.12/0.20	1139
C1140	0.37/0.44	0.70/1.00	0.040	0.08/0.13	1140
C1141	0.37/0.45	1.35/1.65	0.040	0.08/0.13	1141
C1144	0.40/0.48	1.35/1.65	0.040	0.24/0.33	1144
C1145	0.42/0.49	0.70/1.00	0.040	0.04/0.07	1145
C1146	0.42/0.49	0.70/1.00	0.040	0.08/0.13	1146
C1151	0.48/0.55	0.70/1.00	0.040	0.08/0.13	1151

SILICON.—When silicon is required, the following ranges and limits are common for basic open-hearth steel grades:

Standard Steel Designations	Silicon Ranges or Limits
Up to C 1113 Excl.	0.10 Max.
C 1113 and Over	0.10 Max., 0.10/0.20, or 0.15/0.30

LEAD.—When required, lead is specified as an added element to a standard steel.

[1] See Footnote (1), Table 40—I.

Table 40—III. Standard A.I.S.I. Composition Ranges of Basic Open Hearth Rephosphorized and Resulphurized Carbon Steels[1]

A.I.S.I. Number	Chemical Composition Limits, Per Cent					Corresp. SAE No.
	C	Mn	P	S	Pb	
C1211	0.13 Max.	0.60/0.90	0.07/0.12	0.08/0.15	—	—
C1212	0.13 Max.	0.70/1.00	0.07/0.12	0.16/0.23	—	—
C1213	0.13 Max.	0.70/1.00	0.07/0.12	0.24/0.33	—	—
C12L14	0.15 Max.	0.80/1.20	0.04/0.09	0.25/0.35	0.15/0.35	—

SILICON.—Because of the technological nature of the process basic open hearth rephosphorized and resulphurized steels are not furnished to specified limits for silicon.
LEAD.—When required, lead is specified as an added element to a standard steel.

[1] See Fcotnote (1), Table 40—I.

Table 40—IV. Standard A.I.S.I. Composition Ranges of Acid Bessemer Resulphurized Carbon Steels[1]

A.I.S.I. No.	Chemical Composition Limits, Per Cent				Corresponding SAE No.
	C	Mn	P	S	
B1111	0.13 Max.	0.60/0.90	0.07/0.12	0.08/0.15	1111
B1112	0.13 Max.	0.70/1.00	0.07/0.12	0.16/0.23	1112
B1113	0.13 Max.	0.70/1.00	0.07/0.12	0.24/0.33	1113

SILICON.—Because of the technological nature of the process, acid Bessemer steels are not furnished with specified silicon content.
LEAD.—When required, lead is specified as an added element to a standard steel.

[1] See Footnote (1), Table 40—I.

Table 40—V. Standard Mechanical Property Specifications [1]

Tensile Ranges (Lb. per Sq. In.)	American Society for Testing and Materials Specifications		
	Title	Designation	Grade
45,000/55,000	Structural—General	A-306	45
45,000/55,000	Boiler Rivet Steel	A-31	A
48,000/58,000	Structural for Locomotives & Cars	A-113	C
50,000/60,000	Structural—General	A-306	50
50,000/62,000	Structural—Locomotives & Cars	A-113	B
52,000/62,000	Structural Rivet Steel	A-141	—
55,000/65,000	Structural—General	A-306	55
55,000/65,000	Structural for Ships	A-131	Rivet
58,000/68,000	Boiler Rivet Steel	A-31	B
58,000/71,000	Structural for Ships	A-131	Struct.
60,000/72,000	Structural—General	A-306	60
60,000/72,000*	Structural—Bridges and Buildings	A-7	—
60,000/72,000*	Structural—Locomotives and Cars	A-113	A
65,000/77,000	Structural—General	A-306	65
68,000/82,000	High Strength Rivet Steel	A-195	—
70,000/85,000	Structural—General	A-306	70
75,000/90,000	Structural—General	A-306	75
80,000 min.	Structural—General	A-306	80
60,000/80,000	Structural—Bridges and Buildings	A-36	—

* 60,000/75,000 lb. per sq. in. permitted for thickness or diameter over 1½ in.
[1] From Steel Products Manual of American Iron and Steel Institute entitled: "Carbon Steel: Semifinished for Forging, Hot Rolled and Cold Finished Bars, and Hot Rolled Deformed Concrete Reinforcing Bars," with data on Designation A-36 added.

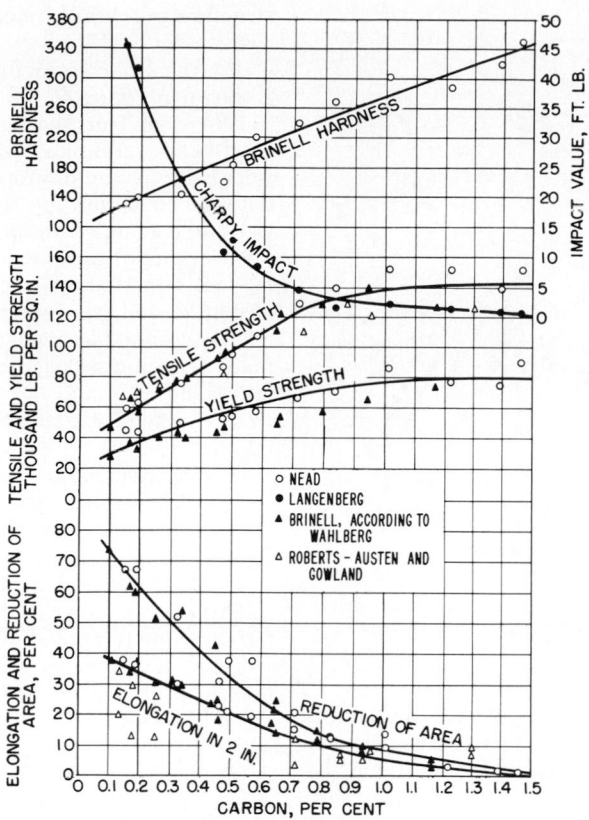

FIG. 40—1. Variations in average mechanical properties of as-rolled, one-inch diameter bars of plain carbon steels, as a function of carbon content. (After Sisco.)

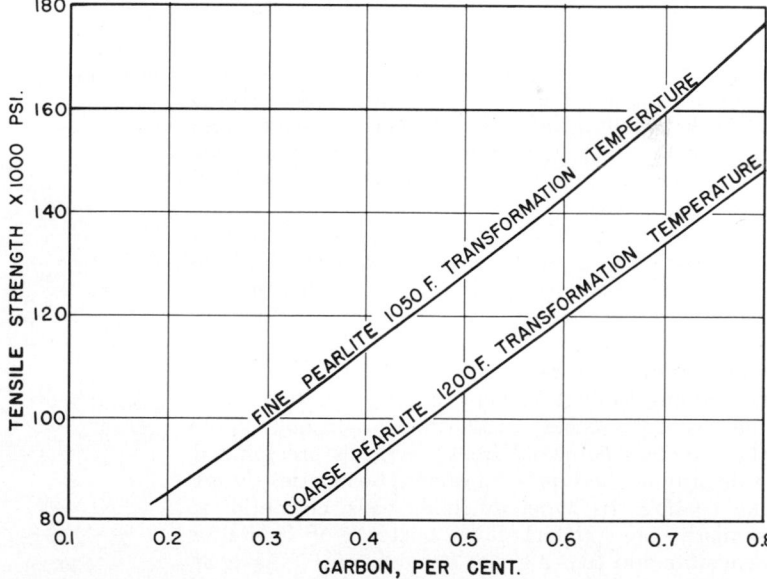

FIG. 40—2. Relationship between tensile strength and carbon content of a series of plain carbon steels isothermally transformed to fine and coarse pearlitic microstructures.

SECTION 3

FACTORS AFFECTING MICROSTRUCTURE AND GRAIN SIZE

Composition—As explained in Chapter 39 on heat treatment, the microstructure of steel is determined by the temperature range in which transformation of the austenite takes place on cooling. This, in turn, is determined by the cooling rate employed and the transformation rate of the steel. This latter factor is

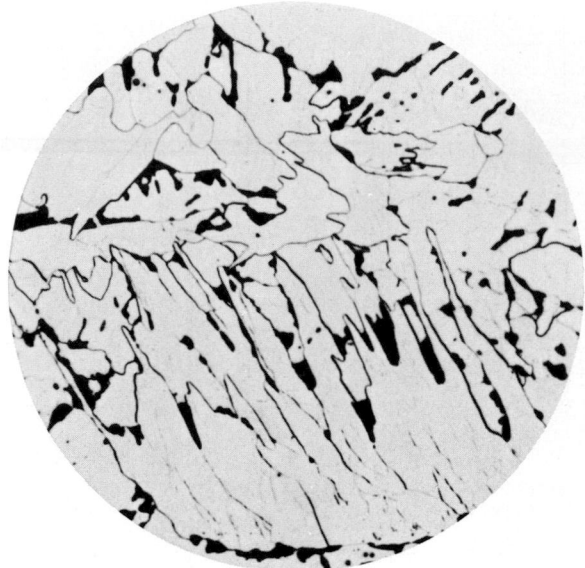

FIG. 40—3. As-cast microstructure of 0.20 per cent carbon steel. Nital etch; magnification: 200X.

dependent largely upon the composition; thus, for a given cooling rate after rolling, for instance, the resulting microstructure is largely dependent upon the composition. The composition will, of course, similarly control the microstructure for given cooling conditions in cast, as-rolled, or heat-treated carbon steels.

The austenite-transformation behavior in carbon steel is determined almost entirely by the carbon and manganese content; the effects of phosphorus and sulphur are almost negligible, and the silicon contents are normally so low that they are likewise ineffective. The carbon content is ordinarily chosen in accordance with the strength level desired and the manganese content then selected in order to produce suitable microstructure and properties at this carbon level under the given cooling conditions.

Microstructure of Cast Steels—The microstructure of as-cast steels is, of course, determined by the composition and cooling conditions in the same manner as in wrought steels. Cast steels are usually very coarse grained since the austenite forms at a high temperature, and the pearlite is usually coarse since the cooling through the critical range, particularly if the casting is cooled in the mold, is usually quite slow. In hypoeutectoid steels, ferrite is precipitated ordinarily at the original austenite boundaries during the cooling. In hypereutectoid steels, cementite is similarly precipitated. Such mixtures of ferrite or cementite and coarse-grained coarse pearlite have, as would be expected, poor properties both in respect to strength and ductility, and heat treatment is usually necessary to obtain suitable microstructures and properties in cast steels.

The dendritic segregation occurring during the solidification of steel castings also results in an irregular microstructure and correspondingly poor properties, and the homogenization of this segregated

structure is another function of the heat treatment of cast steels.

A typical microstructure of an as-cast carbon steel is shown in Figure 40—3.

Effects of Hot Working—Many carbon steels are used in the form of as-rolled finished sections and the microstructure and properties of these sections are determined largely by the composition, rolling practice and cooling conditions after rolling. The rolling or hot working of these sections is ordinarily carried out in the temperature range at which the steel is austenitic and has four major effects, as follows:

1. Considerable homogenization that tends to eliminate dendritic segregation occurs during the heating for rolling.

2. The dendritic structure is broken up during rolling.

3. Recrystallization occurs during rolling so that the final austenitic grain size is determined by the temperature at which the last passes are made (the finishing temperature).

4. Dendrites and inclusions are reoriented in the rolling direction so that the final ductility in the rolling direction is markedly improved.

Thus, homogeneity and grain size of the austenite is largely determined by the rolling practice. It should be pointed out, however, that, as discussed in earlier chapters, the recrystallization characteristics of the austenite and, therefore, the austenite-grain size characteristic of a given finishing temperature may be markedly affected by the steelmaking practice, particularly in respect to the deoxidation practice used.

The distribution of the ferrite or cementite and the nature of the pearlite is, however, as has been explained earlier, determined by the cooling rate after rolling. Since the usual practice is air cooling, the final microstructure and, therefore, the properties of

FIG. 40—4. Microstructure of full-hard cold-reduced black plate (85 per cent reduction). Nital etch; magnification: 200X.

these as-rolled sections will be principally dependent on the composition and section size.

Effects of Cold Working—The manufacture of wire, sheet and strip, and tubular products often involves a cold-working operation and the general effects of cold working will, therefore, be discussed in this chapter. The effects of this cold working may often be destroyed by a suitable annealing operation but some products, particularly wire, are used in the cold-worked condition.

A typical microstructure of a heavily cold-worked steel is shown in Figure **40—4**. The elongation of the ferrite and pearlite grains and the generally distorted microstructure are characteristic. The most pro-

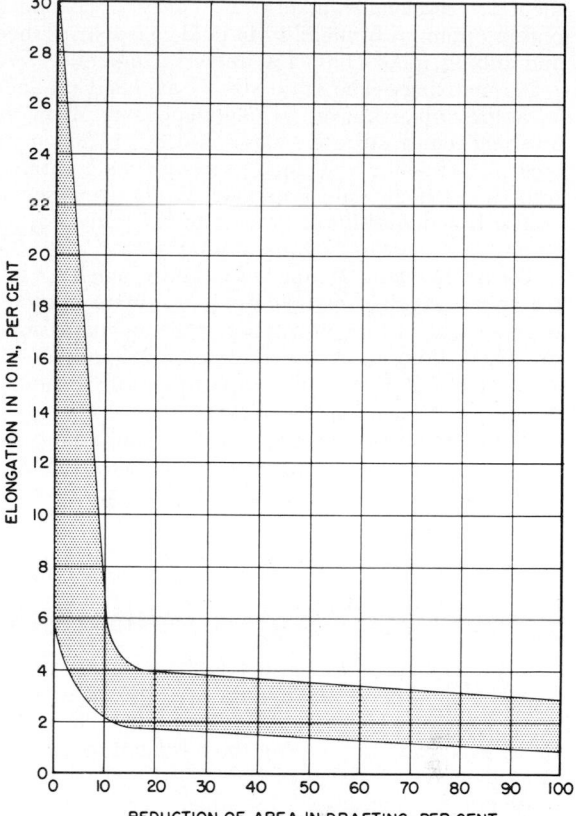

Fig. 40—6. Effect of cold working on the ductility of plain carbon steel.

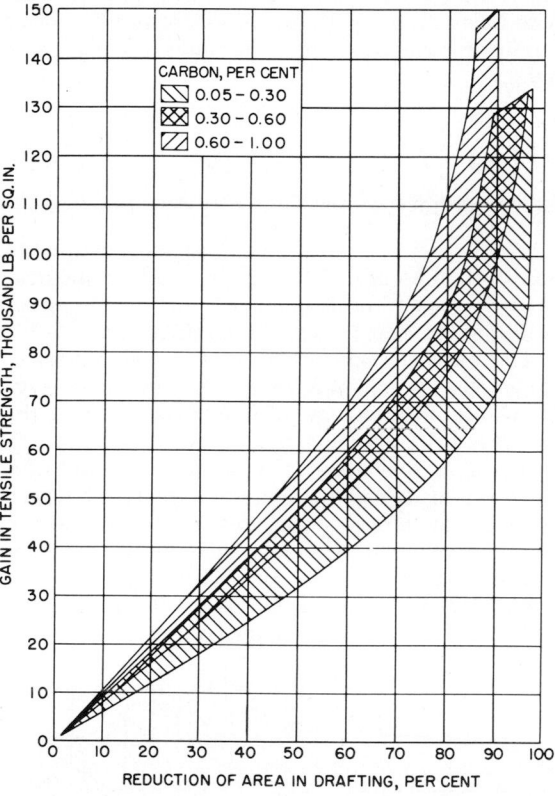

Fig. **40—5**. Increase of tensile strength of plain carbon steel with increasing amounts of cold working.

nounced effect of this cold work is an increase in strength and hardness and a decrease in ductility as represented by elongation and reduction of area. The effects of cold working on tensile strength and elongation are shown in Figures **40—5** and **40—6**. Upon reheating cold-worked steel to the recrystallization temperature (750° F) or above, depending upon composition, amount of cold work and other variables, the original microstructure and properties may be restored. The annealing of cold-worked steels (process annealing) has been discussed in the chapter on heat treatment.

SECTION 4

HEAT TREATMENT OF CARBON STEELS

Although the majority of carbon steels are used without a final heat treatment, heat treatment may be employed to improve the microstructure and properties for specific applications. The principles of these heat treatments have been discussed in Chapter 39 and many of the heat-treating practices have been described in detail in the chapters of the various carbon-steel products. As mentioned earlier, the heat treatment of *cast* carbon steels improves the properties of the material by breaking up the dendritic structure and refining the grain size and micro-

structure. These treatments usually involve normalizing the castings at a high temperature to homogenize the dendritic structure, followed by annealing at a lower temperature for grain refinement. The heat treatment employed in processing *wrought* steel products are described in the following paragraphs.

Annealing—Annealing is practiced for applications requiring better machinability or formability than would be obtained with the as-rolled microstructure. This is usually a full anneal to form coarse pearlite, although a sub-critical anneal or spheroidizing treatment is occasionally practiced. Process annealing to obtain optimum formability in cold-rolled strip, sheet and tubing is, of course, a universal practice.

Normalizing—The grain size of as-rolled products is, as described above, largely dependent upon the finishing temperature in rolling and this is difficult to control. Therefore, a final normalizing treatment from a relatively low temperature may be used to establish a fine uniform grain size for critical applications in respect to ductility or toughness.

Quenching and Tempering—The quenching and tempering of plain carbon steels to obtain optimum microstructures and properties is being increasingly practiced. Because of the relatively low hardenability of these steels, this type of treatment falls generally into two classifications, as follows:

1. Heat treatment to produce essentially tempered martensite for optimum properties. Hardenability restrictions limit the application of this type of treat-

ment to section sizes of not more than ⅜ to ½ inch. It is, however, commonly practiced for small tools, sheet and strip, etc., which fall within this size limitation.

2. Heat treatment to form fine pearlite. Quite large sections of plain carbon steels may be quenched and tempered to produce fine pearlite microstructures, thereby making available the greatly improved strength and ductility associated with this microstructure as compared with the properties of the coarse pearlite of the usual as-rolled or normalized products.

Austempering—Thin sections (0.2-inch and below) of carbon steels are particularly suitable for austempering, since the times for transformation to bainite are relatively short, and this heat treatment is likewise being increasingly practiced for applications requiring toughness at high hardness in such section sizes.

SECTION 5

AGING IN CARBON STEELS

Aging in steel is manifested as a spontaneous increase in hardness at room temperature, the process being accelerated by raising the temperature slightly. It is generally assumed to be caused by the disintegration of a supersaturated solid solution. In a system in which the solid solubility of the solute decreases sharply with temperature, the solute may be retained in supersaturated solid solution on rapid cooling, but it will tend to precipitate out on standing. Such incipient or complete precipitation is considered to be the cause of aging in steels. This precipitation is accelerated by straining, and straining frequently plays an important part in the aging of steel. To separate the effects of straining from the effects of precipita-

tion in the absence of strain, aging in the absence of strain is referred to as **quench aging**, and aging after or during straining is known as **strain aging**.

The elements in carbon steel which seem most likely to cause aging are carbon, nitrogen and oxygen. Curves for the change of solubility of these three elements in ferrite as a function of temperature, are shown in Figure **40—7**. These curves are all of the type that can lead to aging. Probably all three of these elements play a part in the aging of steel, but it is very difficult to isolate their individual effects.

The general nature of the hardness increase from quench aging is shown in Figure **40—8**. It will be noted that aging above room temperature results in

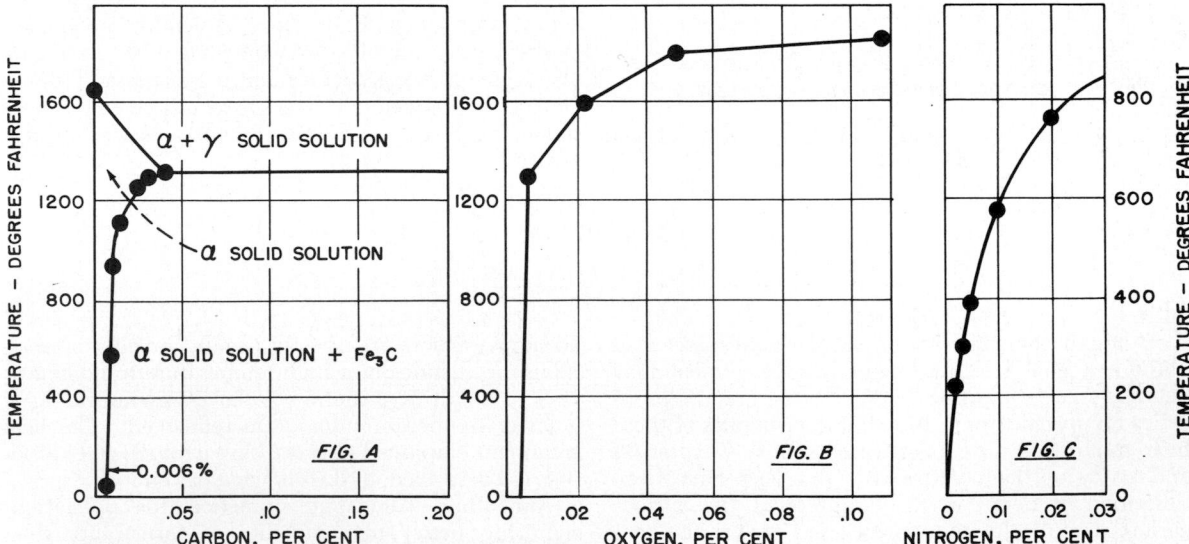

FIG. 40—7. Effect of temperature upon the solubilities of carbon, oxygen, and nitrogen in ferrite. (From "Metals Handbook," 1948 Edition; American Society for Metals.)

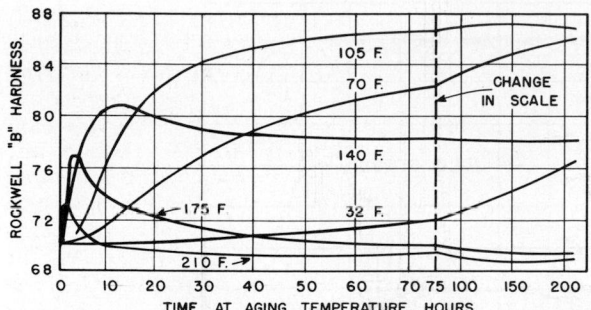

FIG. 40—8. Changes in hardness of 0.06 per cent carbon steel quenched from 1325° F after aging at indicated temperatures. (From "Metals Handbook," 1948 Edition; American Society for Metals.)

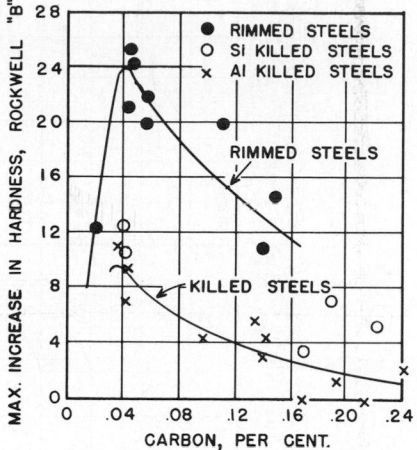

FIG. 40—9. Effect of deoxidation practice on quench-aging characteristics of carbon steels. (From "Metals Handbook," 1948 Edition; American Society for Metals.)

a more rapid hardness increase, but that the maximum hardness attained is lower than in steel aged at room temperature. Aging for times beyond that corresponding to the maximum hardness results in a decrease in hardness. This is sometimes called **overaging.**

It has been found that steels which are drastically deoxidized with aluminum or aluminum and titanium are essentially non-aging and that the rimmed and Bessemer steels are the most susceptible to aging. This effect is illustrated by Figure 40—9, which shows the increase in hardness resulting from quench aging in steels with three different deoxidation practices as a function of carbon content. It is perhaps significant that the maximum aging effect was found at 0.04 per cent carbon, which is approximately the maximum solid solubility of carbon in ferrite. In

general, the changes in hardness on strain aging are somewhat less than those from quench aging, but there is some indication that strain aging may be more embrittling than quench aging.

The effects of strain aging on the impact properties of steels with different manufacturing practices are shown in Figure 40—10. The Izett steel is a strongly deoxidized "non-aging" steel. Since these tests were made immediately after straining, the embrittlement represents a combination of the effect of cold working and of precipitation occurring during the straining. Further embrittlement would result from aging,

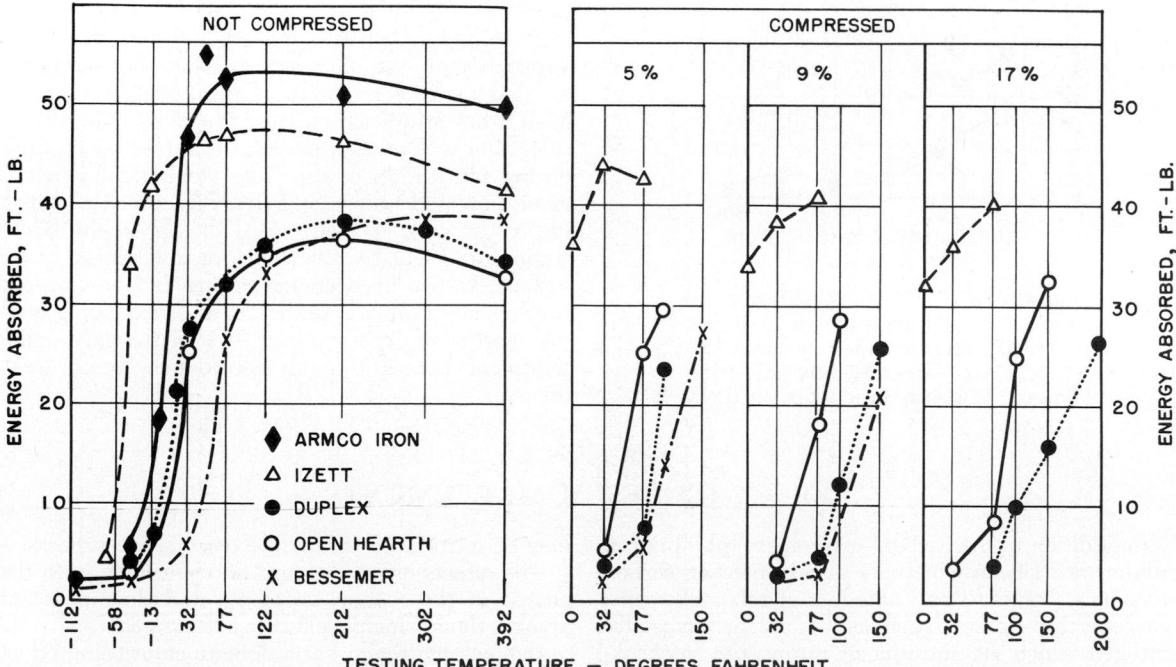

FIG. 40—10. Effect of cold work on impact resistance of aging and non-aging steels. Izett is the only non-aging steel in this series. (From "Metals Handbook," 1948 Edition; American Society for Metals.)

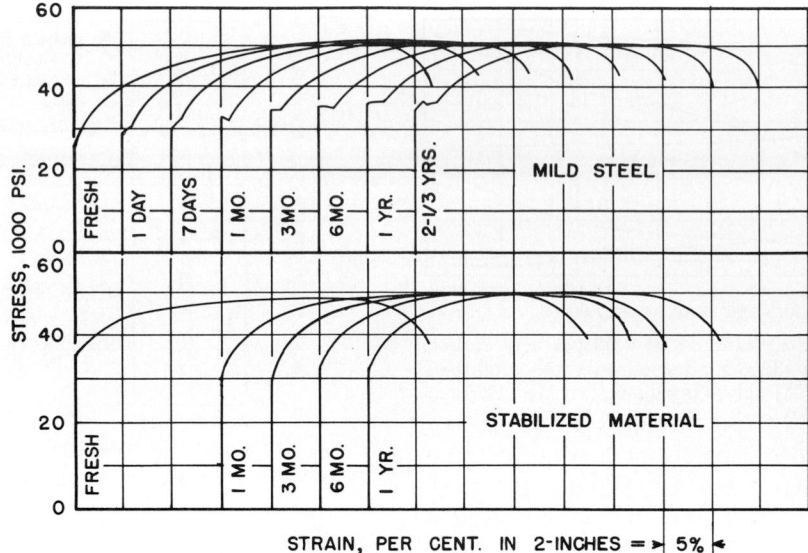

FIG. 40—11. Effects of strain aging on the characteristics of the stress-strain curves obtained by tension testing of plain carbon steels. (From "Metals Handbook," 1948 Edition; American Society for Metals.)

particularly accelerated aging, and a maximum embrittlement has been found in heating about ½ hour at 500° F.

The effect of aging is also reflected in the characteristics of the stress-strain curve. Most as-rolled carbon steels show a jog in the stress-strain curve or a drop of the beam at the yield point in tension testing. This

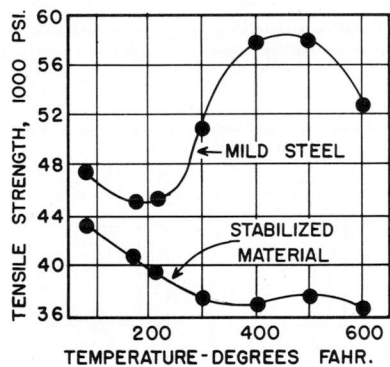

FIG. 40—12. Effect of testing temperature on the tensile strength of ordinary mild steel compared to stabilized steel. (From "Metals Handbook," 1948 Edition; American Society for Metals.)

jog or drop of the beam disappears if the specimen has been subjected to a previous strain, but again reappears upon aging after this straining. This phenomenon does not occur, however, in a strongly deoxidized "non-aging" steel. This effect on the stress-strain curves is illustrated in Figure 40—11.

Still another manifestation of the strain aging phenomenon is the increased hardness and decreased ductility of steels at 400° to 500° F, as shown by tension tests at this temperature. This phenomenon is illustrated in Figure 40—12 and the distinction between the stabilized and aging type of steel is apparent.

These aging phenomena are of importance for applications of carbon steels in which formability or toughness are of importance, and possible embrittlement from strain aging must be given careful consideration whenever a material is subjected to strain during fabrication or use. The yield point phenomenon discussed above is of importance in the stamping or drawing of sheet, since the jog in the stress-strain curve will be reflected in a roughening of the surface, known as **stretcher strains.** Galvanizing embrittlement is also a reflection of strain aging with the short time exposure at 850° F of the galvanizing treatment constituting an accelerated aging treatment.

SECTION 6

EFFECT OF RESIDUAL ELEMENTS

In addition to the carbon, manganese, phosphorus, sulphur and silicon which are always present, carbon steels may contain small amounts of other elements. These include gases, such as hydrogen, oxygen or nitrogen which are introduced during the steelmaking process, nickel, copper, molybdenum, chromium and tin which may be present in the scrap, and aluminum, titanium, vanadium or zirconium which

may be introduced during the deoxidation process.

The effects of oxygen and nitrogen have been discussed in the section on aging, and their effect on aging is their principal effect in carbon steel.

In steel, hydrogen has a definite embrittling effect, the mechanism of which is not well understood. Although hydrogen may diffuse out of steel at room temperature if the section is small enough and sufficient time is allowed, tension tests on carbon steels will show low ductility if made soon after rolling and the ductility will increase on aging at room temperature or after shorter times at slightly elevated temperatures. This effect is, of course, more pronounced in larger section sizes because of the longer time required for the diffusion of hydrogen to the surface. Hydrogen contents of more than about 0.0005 per cent will give rise to this effect and such contents are common in as-rolled steels that have been cast into ingots in the conventional way. It is possible to reduce the content of hydrogen (and other gases) in steel ingots by employing the vacuum degassing process (described in Chapter 18) for teeming.

Hydrogen, in excess of about five parts per million (0.0005 per cent), also plays an important role in the phenomenon known as **flaking** which is manifested as internal cracks or bursts, usually occurring during the cooling from rolling or forging. The phenomenon is more pronounced in heavy sections and in the higher carbon steels. In carbon steels, flaking may be prevented by slow cooling after rolling or forging. This slow-cooling operation presumably permits the hydrogen to diffuse out of the steel and thereby minimizes the susceptibility to flaking. Such a controlled slow-cooling operation after rolling is now standard practice in the manufacture of rails, and this practice has practically eliminated the occurrence of flaking and resultant occasional "transverse fissure" failures.

The alloying elements, such as nickel, chromium, molybdenum and copper, which may be introduced in the scrap will, of course, increase the hardenability of carbon steels, although, since the percentages are ordinarily low, this effect will usually not be large. It may, however, change the heat-treating characteristics and for applications in which ductility is important, such as steels for deep drawing, the increased hardness from these residual elements may be serious.

Tin in relatively low amounts is harmful in steels for deep drawing, but for most applications the effect of tin in the amounts ordinarily present is negligible.

Aluminum, as described above, is generally desirable since it acts as a grain refiner and tends to decrease the susceptibility to strain aging. It has the disadvantage, however, that it tends to promote graphitization and is, therefore, undesirable in steels to be used for high-temperature applications. The other elements which may be introduced as deoxidizers, titanium, vanadium or zirconium, are, unless intentionally added, ordinarily present in such small amounts as to be generally ineffective.

Bibliography

"Alloys of Iron and Carbon: Vol. II—Properties," Frank T. Sisco. Published for The Engineering Foundation by McGraw-Hill Book Co., Inc., New York (1937).

"Metals Handbook." 1948 and 1961 (Eighth) Editions. American Society for Metals, Cleveland, Ohio.

CHAPTER 41

Alloy Steels

Introductory—Alloy steels may be defined as those steels which owe their enhanced properties to the presence of one or more special elements or to the presence of larger proportions of elements such as manganese and silicon than are ordinarily present in carbon steel. The major classifications of steels containing alloying elements are as follows:

1. High-strength low-alloy steels
2. AISI alloy steels
3. Alloy tool steels
4. Stainless steels
5. Heat-resisting steels
6. Electrical steels (silicon steels)

The high-strength low-alloy steels, stainless steels, heat-resisting steels, and electrical steels are discussed in other chapters. This chapter covers the AISI alloy steels, often referred to commonly as "constructional alloy steels," with an introductory discussion of the functions of the alloying elements. Alloy tool steels are discussed in Chapter 42.

SECTION 1

FUNCTIONS OF THE ALLOYING ELEMENTS

As stated above, alloying elements are added to steel to enhance its properties. In the broadest sense, alloy steels may contain up to approximately 50 per cent of alloying elements, and the enhancement of properties may be a specific and direct function of the alloying elements, as in the instances of the increased corrosion resistance of the high-chromium steels and the enhanced electrical properties of the silicon steels. In the narrower and more technical sense, however, the term "alloy steels" refers to the heat-treatable alloy constructional and automotive steels which contain from about one to three or four per cent alloying elements. The American Iron and Steel Institute definition of alloy steel is as follows: "By common custom steel is considered to be alloy steel when the maximum of the range given for the content of alloying elements exceeds one or more of the following limits: manganese, 1.65 per cent; silicon, 0.60 per cent; copper, 0.60 per cent; or in which a definite range or a definite minimum quantity of any of the following elements is specified or required within the limits of the recognized field of constructional alloy steels: aluminum, boron, chromium up to 3.99 per cent, cobalt, columbium, molybdenum, nickel, titanium, tungsten, vanadium, zirconium, or any other alloying element added to obtain a desired alloying effect." It may be noted that steels that contain 4.00 or more per cent of chromium are included by convention among the special types of alloy steels known as stainless steels (Chapter 45).

Such steels have been standardized and classified jointly by the American Iron and Steel Institute and the Society of Automotive Engineers, and represent by far the largest tonnage of alloy steels. Alloy steels of this type are generally known as "AISI alloy steels" and will be so designated in this chapter. As previously stated, they are also commonly referred to as "constructional alloy steels." The composition of these steels is shown in Table 41—I. Small quantities of certain elements are present in alloy steels which are not specified or required. These elements are considered as incidental and may be present to the following maximum amounts: copper, 0.35 per cent; nickel, 0.25 per cent; chromium, 0.20 per cent; and molybdenum, 0.06 per cent.

As was emphasized in the chapter on heat treatment, the mechanical properties of steel are dependent upon its microstructure. In the AISI alloy steels the effect of the alloying is indirect; i.e., through their influence on the microstructure of the material. The AISI alloy steels make it possible to attain desirable microstructures and corresponding desirable properties over a very much wider range of sizes and sections than is possible with the carbon steels.

Hardenability—The mechanism by which the alloying elements affect the microstructure obtained with a given heat treatment is discussed in the chapter on heat treatment. It is shown that the alloying elements in general decrease the rates of transformation of austenite at sub-critical temperatures, thereby facilitating the attainment of low-temperature transformation to martensite or lower bainite when these are the end products desired, without prior transformation to unwanted higher temperature products. It was pointed out that this function of the alloying elements could be evaluated and expressed in terms of the property known as hardenability. Alloying elements thus control microstructure through their effect on hardenability, and this hardenability effect is by far their most important function.

Table 41—I. Chemical Compositions of Open-Hearth and Electric-Furnace Steels
(Bars, Billets, Blooms and Slabs).[a]

AISI Number[b]	C	Mn	Ni	Cr	Mo	V (Min.)
1330	0.28–0.33	1.60–1.90	—	—	—	—
1335	0.33–0.38	1.60–1.90	—	—	—	—
1340	0.38–0.43	1.60–1.90	—	—	—	—
1345	0.43–0.48	1.60–1.90	—	—	—	—
3140	0.38–0.43	0.70–0.90	1.10–1.40	0.55–0.75	—	—
E 3310	0.08–0.13	0.45–0.60	3.25–3.75	1.40–1.75	—	—
4012	0.09–0.14	0.75–1.00	—	—	0.15–0.25	—
4023	0.20–0.25	0.70–0.90	—	—	0.20–0.30	—
4024[c]	0.20–0.25	0.70–0.90	—	—	0.20–0.30	—
4027	0.25–0.30	0.70–0.90	—	—	0.20–0.30	—
4028[c]	0.25–0.30	0.70–0.90	—	—	0.20–0.30	—
4037	0.35–0.40	0.70–0.90	—	—	0.20–0.30	—
4042	0.40–0.45	0.70–0.90	—	—	0.20–0.30	—
4047	0.45–0.50	0.70–0.90	—	—	0.20–0.30	—
4063	0.60–0.67	0.75–1.00	—	—	0.20–0.30	—
4118	0.18–0.23	0.70–0.90	—	0.40–0.60	0.08–0.15	—
4130	0.28–0.33	0.40–0.60	—	0.80–1.10	0.15–0.25	—
4135	0.33–0.38	0.70–0.90	—	0.80–1.10	0.15–0.25	—
4137	0.35–0.40	0.70–0.90	—	0.80–1.10	0.15–0.25	—
4140	0.38–0.43	0.75–1.00	—	0.80–1.10	0.15–0.25	—
TS 4140	0.38–0.43	0.80–1.05	—	0.90–1.20	0.08–0.15	—
4142	0.40–0.45	0.75–1.00	—	0.80–1.10	0.15–0.25	—
4145	0.43–0.48	0.75–1.00	—	0.80–1.10	0.15–0.25	—
4147	0.45–0.50	0.75–1.00	—	0.80–1.10	0.15–0.25	—
4150	0.48–0.53	0.75–1.00	—	0.80–1.10	0.15–0.25	—
TS 4150	0.48–0.53	0.80–1.05	—	0.90–1.20	0.08–0.15	—
4320	0.17–0.22	0.45–0.65	1.65–2.00	0.40–0.60	0.20–0.30	—
4337	0.35–0.40	0.60–0.80	1.65–2.00	0.70–0.90	0.20–0.30	—
E 4337	0.35–0.40	0.65–0.85	1.65–2.00	0.70–0.90	0.20–0.30	—
4340	0.38–0.43	0.60–0.80	1.65–2.00	0.70–0.90	0.20–0.30	—
E 4340	0.38–0.43	0.65–0.85	1.65–2.00	0.70–0.90	0.20–0.30	—

(Continued on page 1082)

[a] The ranges and limits apply only to material not exceeding 200 sq. in. cross-sectional area.
Where minimum and maximum sulphur content is shown it is indicative of resulphurized steels.
The phosphorus and sulphur limitations for each process is as follows except for resulphurized steels:
    Basic electric furnace—0.025 per cent max.
    Basic open hearth   —0.040 per cent max.
    Acid electric furnace —0.050 per cent max.
    Acid open hearth   —0.050 per cent max.
Unless otherwise indicated the silicon range is 0.20–0.35 per cent.
E indicates electric furnace manufacture only: TS indicates tentative standard steels.
[b] In general, numerals of SAE numbers correspond to AISI-number numerals.
[c] Sulphur is 0.035–0.050 per cent.

It was also shown in the chapter on heat treatment that the properties of tempered martensite, which represents the most desirable microstructure in respect to strength and toughness, were characteristic of the microstructure rather than of the composition. Thus, alloy steels of equal hardenabilities, but utilizing different combinations of alloying elements, are generally interchangeable for heat treatment to produce this microstructure. This principle permits an intelligent choice of alloy combinations which, for reasons of economy or availability, are best suited for particular applications. This principle was widely used during World War II to develop substitute compositions utilizing the alloying elements most available at the time, thereby conserving the scarcer alloying elements.

Effects of the Alloying Elements on Hardenability —The Multiplying Factor Principle—The effects of the alloys on grain size or hardenability may be quantitatively evaluated by hardenability measurements on a series of steels in which a single alloying element is the only variable. This method is illustrated by Figure 41—1 which shows the hardenabilities of two series of steels in terms of ideal diameter for a microstructure of 50 per cent martensite. These series were

Table 41—I (Continued)

AISI Number[b]	C	Mn	Ni	Cr	Mo	V (Min.)
4422	0.20–0.25	0.70–0.90	—	—	0.35–0.45	—
4427	0.24–0.29	0.70–0.90	—	—	0.35–0.45	—
4520	0.18–0.23	0.45–0.65	—	—	0.45–0.60	—
4615	0.13–0.18	0.45–0.65	1.65–2.00	—	0.20–0.30	—
4617	0.15–0.20	0.45–0.65	1.65–2.00	—	0.20–0.30	—
4620	0.17–0.22	0.45–0.65	1.65–2.00	—	0.20–0.30	—
4621	0.18–0.23	0.70–0.90	1.65–2.00	—	0.20–0.30	—
4718	0.16–0.21	0.70–0.90	0.90–1.20	0.35–0.55	0.30–0.40	—
4720	0.17–0.22	0.50–0.70	0.90–1.20	0.35–0.55	0.15–0.25	—
4815	0.13–0.18	0.40–0.60	3.25–3.75	—	0.20–0.30	—
4817	0.15–0.20	0.40–0.60	3.25–3.75	—	0.20–0.30	—
4820	0.18–0.23	0.50–0.70	3.25–3.75	—	0.20–0.30	—
5015	0.12–0.17	0.30–0.50	—	0.30–0.50	—	—
5046	0.43–0.50	0.75–1.00	—	0.20–0.35	—	—
5115	0.13–0.18	0.70–0.90	—	0.70–0.90	—	—
5120	0.17–0.22	0.70–0.90	—	0.70–0.90	—	—
5130	0.28–0.33	0.70–0.90	—	0.80–1.10	—	—
5132	0.30–0.35	0.60–0.80	—	0.75–1.00	—	—
5135	0.33–0.38	0.60–0.80	—	0.80–1.05	—	—
5140	0.38–0.43	0.70–0.90	—	0.70–0.90	—	—
5145	0.43–0.48	0.70–0.90	—	0.70–0.90	—	—
5147	0.45–0.52	0.70–0.95	—	0.85–1.15	—	—
5150	0.48–0.53	0.70–0.90	—	0.70–0.90	—	—
5155	0.50–0.60	0.70–0.90	—	0.70–0.90	—	—
5160	0.55–0.65	0.75–1.00	—	0.70–0.90	—	—
E 50100	0.95–1.10	0.25–0.45	—	0.40–0.60	—	—
E 51100	0.95–1.10	0.25–0.45	—	0.90–1.15	—	—
E 52100	0.95–1.10	0.25–0.45	—	1.30–1.60	—	—
6118	0.16–0.21	0.50–0.70	—	0.50–0.70	—	0.10–0.15
6120	0.17–0.22	0.70–0.90	—	0.70–0.90	—	0.10 min.
6150	0.48–0.53	0.70–0.90	—	0.80–1.10	—	0.15 min.
8115	0.13–0.18	0.70–0.90	0.20–0.40	0.30–0.50	0.08–0.15	—
8615	0.13–0.18	0.70–0.90	0.40–0.70	0.40–0.60	0.15–0.25	—
8617	0.15–0.20	0.70–0.90	0.40–0.70	0.40–0.60	0.15–0.25	—
8620	0.18–0.23	0.70–0.90	0.40–0.70	0.40–0.60	0.15–0.25	—
8622	0.20–0.25	0.70–0.90	0.40–0.70	0.40–0.60	0.15–0.25	—
8625	0.23–0.28	0.70–0.90	0.40–0.70	0.40–0.60	0.15–0.25	—
8627	0.25–0.30	0.70–0.90	0.40–0.70	0.40–0.60	0.15–0.25	—
8630	0.28–0.33	0.70–0.90	0.40–0.70	0.40–0.60	0.15–0.25	—
8637	0.35–0.40	0.75–1.00	0.40–0.70	0.40–0.60	0.15–0.25	—
8640	0.38–0.43	0.75–1.00	0.40–0.70	0.40–0.60	0.15–0.25	—

(Continued on facing page)

made by additions of phosphorus to successive ingots so that in each series the composition was constant except for the phosphorus. It will be noted that the hardenability increases regularly with increasing phosphorus content, and that the rate of increase is more rapid for the steel of the higher base hardenability. In order to obtain a numerical evaluation of the effect of phosphorus on hardenability, the hardenabilities of the steels containing phosphorus may be divided by the base hardenability of the steel containing no phosphorus. This value expressing the effect of the element on hardenability is known as a **multiplying factor,** and the multiplying factors for phosphorus, derived from the series in Figure 41—1, are plotted in Figure 41—2. It will be seen that a steel with 0.020 per cent phosphorus will have 1.05 times the hardenability of a steel with no phosphorus, while a steel with 0.100 per cent phosphorus would have roughly one and one

Table 41—I (Continued)

AISI Number[b]	C	Mn	Ni	Cr	Mo	V (Min.)
8642	0.40–0.45	0.75–1.00	0.40–0.70	0.40–0.60	0.15–0.25	—
8645	0.43–0.48	0.75–1.00	0.40–0.70	0.40–0.60	0.15–0.25	—
8650	0.48–0.53	0.75–1.00	0.40–0.70	0.40–0.60	0.15–0.25	—
8655	0.50–0.60	0.75–1.00	0.40–0.70	0.40–0.60	0.15–0.25	—
8660	0.55–0.65	0.75–1.00	0.40–0.70	0.40–0.60	0.15–0.25	—
8720	0.18–0.23	0.70–0.90	0.40–0.70	0.40–0.60	0.20–0.30	—
8735	0.33–0.38	0.75–1.00	0.40–0.70	0.40–0.60	0.20–0.30	—
8740	0.38–0.43	0.75–1.00	0.40–0.70	0.40–0.60	0.20–0.30	—
8742	0.40–0.45	0.75–1.00	0.40–0.70	0.40–0.60	0.20–0.30	—
8822	0.20–0.25	0.75–1.00	0.40–0.70	0.40–0.60	0.30–0.40	—
9255[d]	0.50–0.60	0.70–0.95	—	—	—	—
9260[d]	0.55–0.65	0.70–1.00	—	—	—	—
9262[d]	0.55–0.65	0.75–1.00	—	0.25–0.40	—	—
E 9310	0.08–0.13	0.45–0.65	3.00–3.50	1.00–1.40	0.08–0.15	—
9840	0.38–0.43	0.70–0.90	0.85–1.15	0.70–0.90	0.20–0.30	—
9850	0.48–0.53	0.70–0.90	0.85–1.15	0.70–0.90	0.20–0.30	—
Standard Nitriding Steel[e]	0.38–0.43	0.50–0.70	—	1.40–1.80	0.30–0.40	—
BORON STEELS[f]						
TS 14B35	0.33–0.38	0.75–1.00	—	—	—	—
50B40	0.38–0.43	0.75–1.00	—	0.40–0.60	—	—
50B44	0.43–0.48	0.75–1.00	—	0.40–0.60	—	—
50B46	0.43–0.50	0.75–1.00	—	0.20–0.35	—	—
50B50	0.48–0.53	0.75–1.00	—	0.40–0.60	—	—
50B60	0.55–0.65	0.75–1.00	—	0.40–0.60	—	—
51B60	0.55–0.65	0.75–1.00	—	0.70–0.90	—	—
81B45	0.43–0.48	0.75–1.00	0.20–0.40	0.35–0.55	0.08–0.15	—
86B45	0.43–0.48	0.75–1.00	0.40–0.70	0.40–0.60	0.15–0.25	—
94B15	0.13–0.18	0.75–1.00	0.30–0.60	0.30–0.50	0.08–0.15	—
94B17	0.15–0.20	0.75–1.00	0.30–0.60	0.30–0.50	0.08–0.15	—
94B30	0.28–0.33	0.75–1.00	0.30–0.60	0.30–0.50	0.08–0.15	—
94B40	0.38–0.43	0.75–1.00	0.30–0.60	0.30–0.50	0.08–0.15	—

[d] Silicon content, 1.80–2.20 per cent.
[e] Silicon content, 0.20–0.40 per cent: aluminum content, 0.95–1.30 per cent.
[f] These steels can be expected to have 0.0005 per cent minimum boron content.

NOTE: These tables are subject to change from time to time, with new steels sometimes added, other steels eliminated, and compositions of retained steels occasionally altered. The reader is referred to publications of the American Iron and Steel Institute and the Society of Automotive Engineers for information published later than 1961.

quarter times the base hardenability. Also, with this information, the effect of increasing the phosphorus content from 0.020 to 0.100 per cent can be evaluated by multiplying the hardenability of the 0.020 per cent phosphorus steel by $\frac{1.27}{1.05}$ or 1.21.

The pioneer work of this nature was done by Grossmann in 1941. Hardenability factors for many of the common alloying elements, as well as hardenability values for pure iron-carbon alloys and the effect of grain size, were evaluated at that time. These factors have, in some cases, been modified by the work of other investigators and the values as published by the American Iron and Steel Institute are shown for alloying elements in Figure 41—3, and for grain size in Figure 41—4.

Grossmann and his associates further found that the cumulative effects of alloying elements on hardenability could be evaluated by multiplying the base hardenability of the iron-carbon alloy progressively by

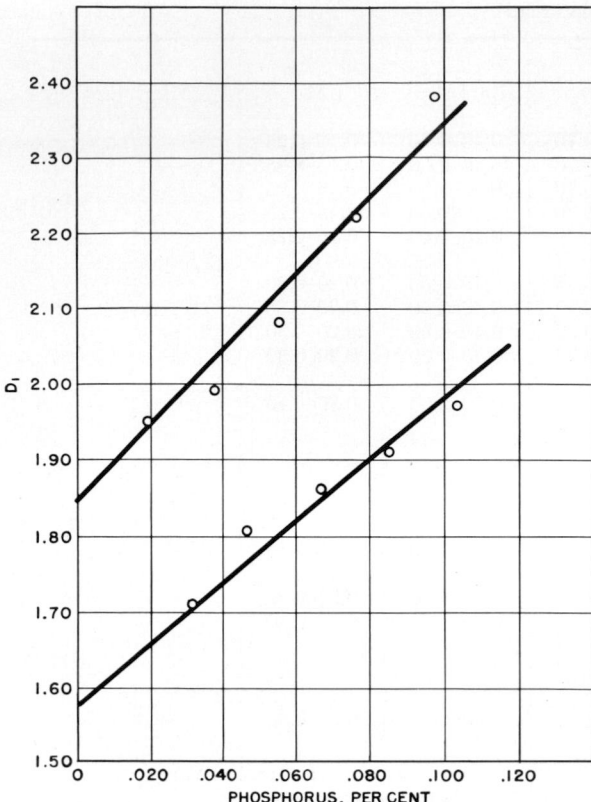

FIG. 41—1. Hardenability as a function of phosphorus content in two series of steels.

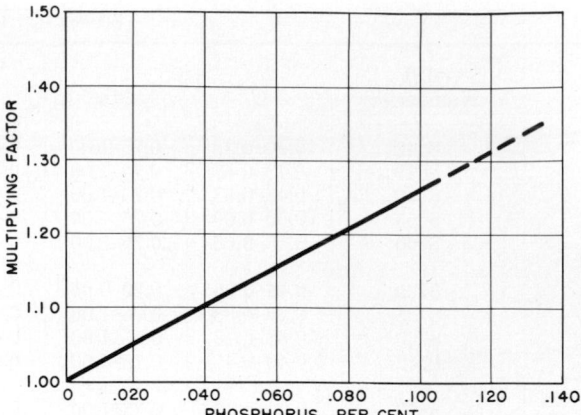

FIG. 41—2. Multiplying factors for phosphorus.

ing elements since additions over a certain optimum amount produce no further increase in hardenability. Experience has shown that the optimum content is 0.0005 to 0.004 per cent boron. The multiplying factor for boron depends not on boron content, but on carbon content and varies from approximately 2.00 for 0.20 per cent carbon steels to nearly zero for 0.90 per cent carbon.

The multiplying factor principle is of importance not only as a means of predicting the approximate hardenability of a steel from its composition, but also since it shows that, in general, the addition of relatively small amounts of several alloying elements is more effective in increasing hardenability than a relatively large amount of a single element. This principle was also widely applied during World War II to the development of substitute compositions which would utilize to the fullest extent the hardenability effects of the alloying elements most available.

Effects of the Alloys in Tempering—While the martensitic microstructure is the product of proper

the multiplying factors for the elements. Thus the chart of Figure 41—3 enables one to calculate the hardenability in terms of 50 per cent martensite microstructures of a given alloy combination.

The element boron increases the hardenability of steel but its effect differs from that of the other alloy-

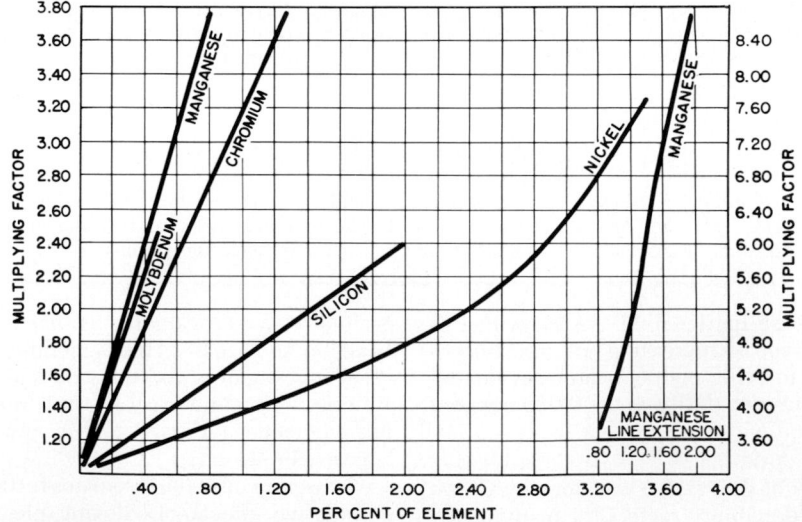

FIG. 41—3. Multiplying factors for a variety of alloying elements (American Iron and Steel Institute).

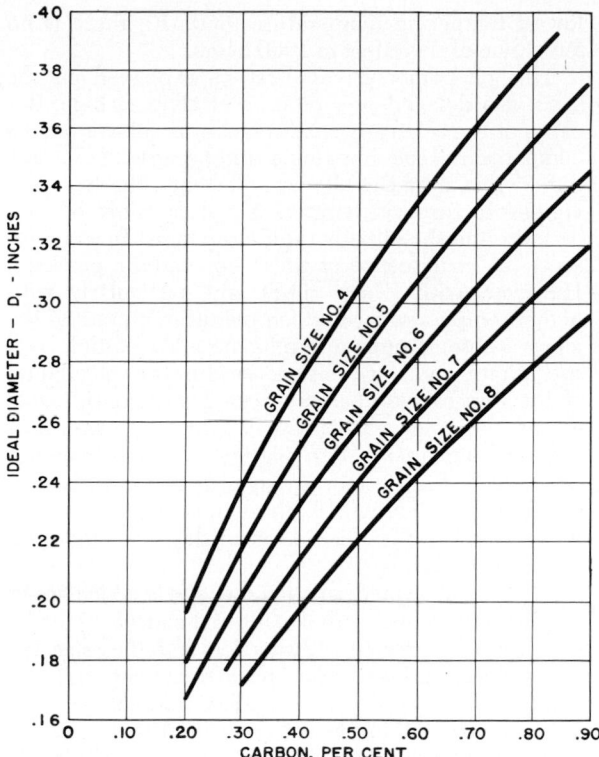

Fig. 41—4. Effect of grain size on the hardenability of pure iron-carbon alloys, expressed as ideal critical diameter, D_I.

quenching, it must be realized that martensite itself is very brittle, and that in order to realize the properties generally sought in machine parts, this martensite must be reheated or tempered. It is essential to an understanding of alloy steels, therefore, to consider the roles played by the alloying elements in this tempering process, and the manner in which they will affect the behavior on tempering.

The primary purpose of tempering is to impart a degree of plasticity or toughness to the steel to alleviate the brittleness of the martensite. Although this process may, and usually does, soften the steel, this softening is only incidental to the very important increase in toughness. This increase in toughness after tempering reflects two effects of tempering: (1) the relief of internal stresses set up by the quenching operation; and (2) a crystallization, coalescence and spheroidization of iron and alloy carbides, resulting in a microstructure of greater plasticity.

The addition of alloying elements which increase hardenability may be very helpful in decreasing the magnitude of the internal stresses resulting from the quench, since they will permit the attainment of a martensitic microstructure with a less drastic quench. For this reason, the use of an alloy steel and a mild quench for an application requiring high hardness, and, therefore, a low tempering temperature with an accompanying relatively low degree of stress relief, may be very advantageous. It should be noted, however, that this is only secondarily an effect of alloys in

tempering; here again the primary function of the alloying elements is to increase hardenability.

The alloying elements will, however, have a direct and significant effect upon the second behavior, that of crystallization and coalescence of the carbides. In general, the effect of alloying elements will be to slow up the processes of crystallization and coalescence. This means that an alloy steel will customarily require higher tempering temperatures, or longer times at temperature, to obtain a given hardness.

The effects of some of the individual alloying elements on the tempering rate are illustrated in Figure 41—5 for silicon, Figure 41—6 for chromium, Figure 41—7 for molybdenum and Figure 41—8 for vanadium. These charts show the hardness of tempered martensite in these steels after tempering one hour at the indicated tempering temperature.

The effects of nickel and manganese, as in the case of silicon, while they are significant, are quite moderate, and the hardness changes are nearly a direct function of the tempering temperature. This type of behavior is characteristic of alloys which dissolve largely in the ferrite phase, and do not tend to form carbides.

Boron in the amount used to increase hardenability has no perceptible effect on hardness changes during tempering.

The **carbide-forming elements**, such as chromium, molybdenum or vanadium, however, have very

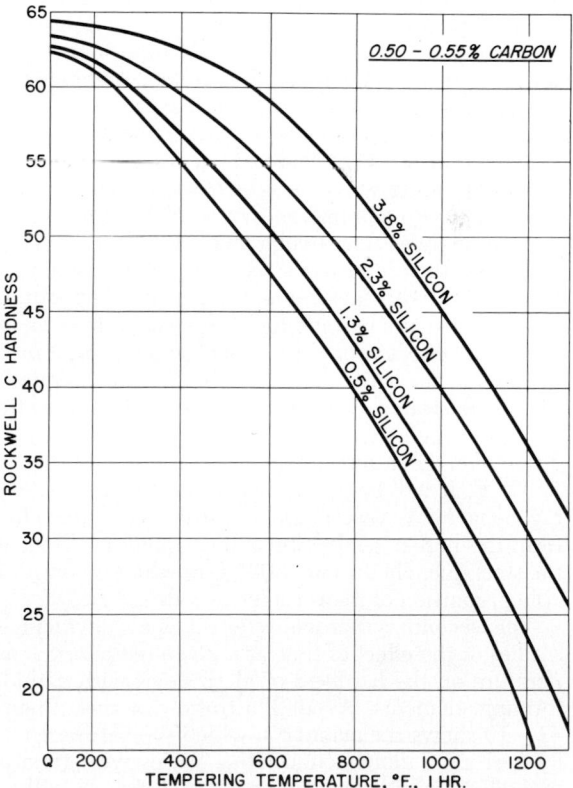

Fig. 41—5. The effect of silicon on tempering rate of 0.50-0.55% carbon steel, tempered for 1 hour at indicated temperatures.

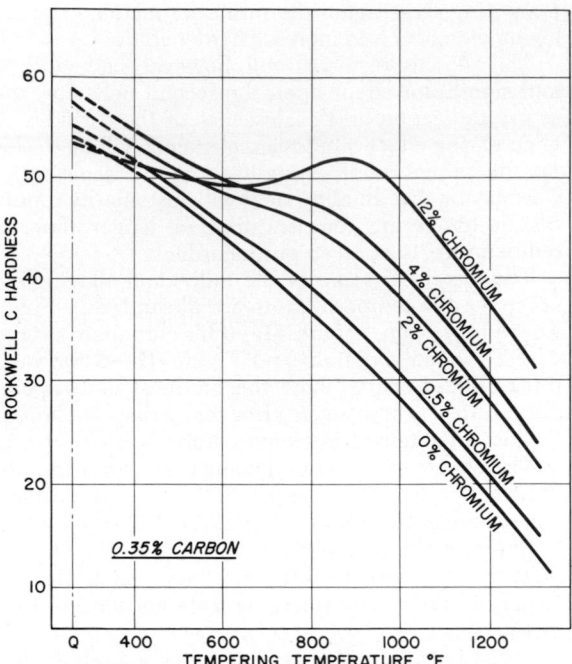

FIG. 41—6. The effect of chromium on tempering rate of 0.35% carbon steel, tempered for 1 hour at indicated temperatures.

lowest tempering temperature (660° F), there is no indication of this effect in 1000 hours.

This phenomenon can best be explained on the basis of a delayed precipitation of alloy carbide. Because of the relatively small number of alloy atoms in comparison to the iron atoms, and because of the slow diffusion rate of the alloying elements, the first precipitate to form on tempering will certainly be iron carbide, and the initially rapid drop in hardness represents the coalescence of these iron-carbide particles. However, with longer times and particularly with higher temperatures at which the diffusion rate of the alloys becomes more rapid, some alloy carbide will precipitate, and since this occurs after the coagulation of the iron carbide has progressed to a considerable extent, these fine particles will result in a reversal of the softening action. With relatively low alloy content, this may be manifested as only a decrease in the rate of softening while with high alloy content, an actual increase in hardness may occur as this secondary precipitation proceeds.

In the case of modern alloy tool steels which are of such a composition as to consist of a matrix of considerable plasticity with a dispersion of rather sizeable undissolved carbides after heat treatment, full advantage is taken of this secondary hardening effect. The composition and heat treatment of these steels is such that, although a number of the alloy carbides remain undissolved, enough are taken into solution to bring about a marked resistance to softening at temperatures up to 1100° F. Such tools can then be used for high-speed machining at relatively high operating temperature without softening.

marked effects on the tempering behavior. Elements of this type not only raise the tempering temperature to obtain a given hardness, but with the higher percentages of these elements, the rate of softening is no longer a continuous function of the tempering temperature. In steels of this type, such as the 0.5 per cent molybdenum steel of Figure 41—7, there is a tempering temperature range in which the softening is retarded or, with still higher alloy content as in the 2.0 per cent molybdenum steel, in which the hardness first decreases, then increases somewhat before continuing the decline with increasing tempering temperature.

In order that a carbide forming element may manifest its full effect upon the tempering behavior, it must dissolve in the austenite at the heating temperature. This is illustrated by Figure 41—9, which shows the tempering behavior of a chrome-molybdenum-vanadium steel after quenching from 1500°, 1800° and 2100° F. It will be noted that the secondary hardening behavior is very marked in the steels quenched from the higher temperature, but is almost absent in the steel quenched from 1500° F in which a considerable proportion of the carbides is undissolved.

This secondary hardening effect is also evident in studies of the effect of time at a given tempering temperature on the hardness of alloy steels with carbide forming elements. As an illustration of this, Figure 41—10 shows the manner in which the hardness of a 2.0 per cent molybdenum steel varies with time at several different tempering temperatures. It will be noted that at the highest tempering temperature (1200° F), the secondary hardening effect occurs at times of from 10 seconds to 10 minutes, while at the

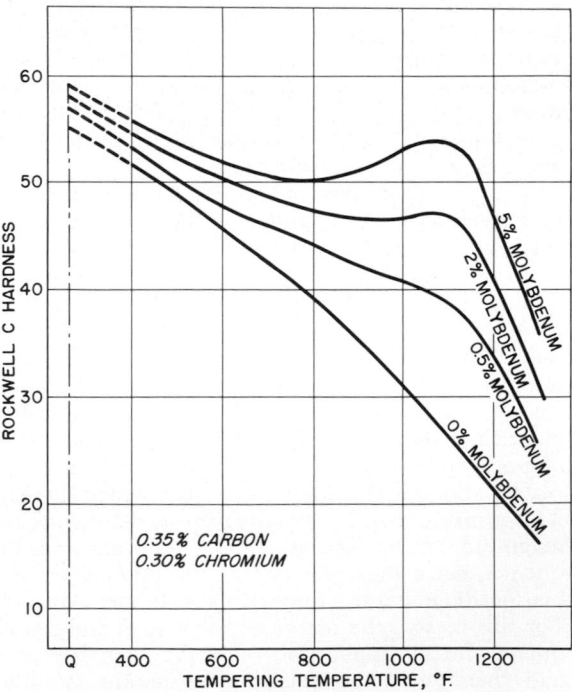

FIG. 41—7. The effect of molybdenum on tempering rate of 0.35% carbon, 0.30% chromium steel, tempered for 1 hour at the indicated temperatures.

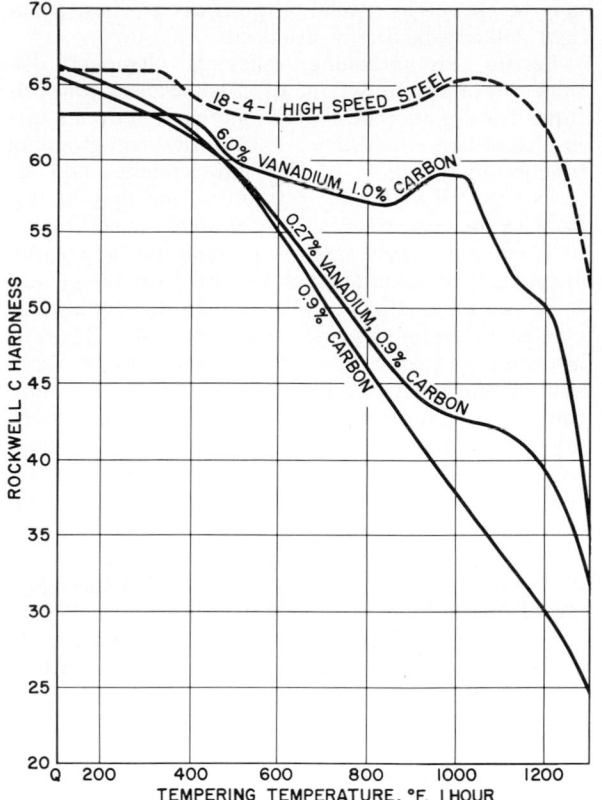

FIG. 41—8. The effect of vanadium on tempering rate of steels tempered for 1 hour at the indicated temperatures.

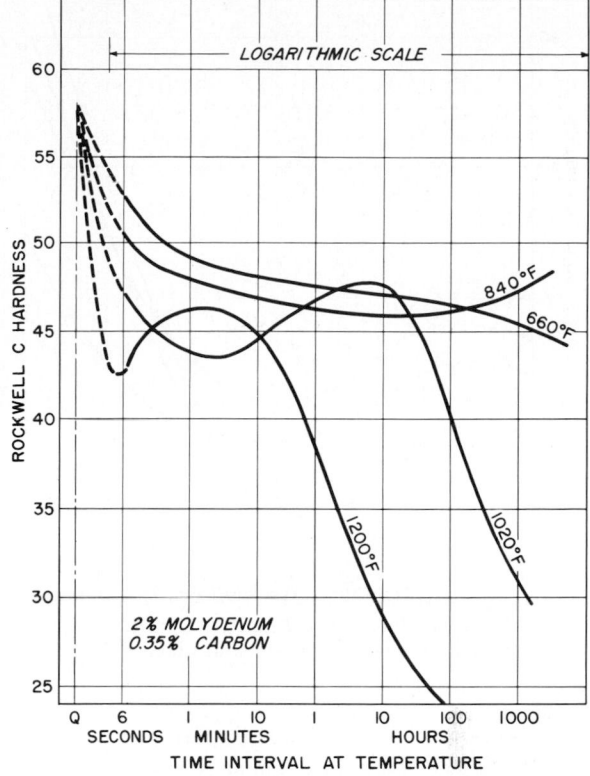

FIG. 41—10. The effect of time of tempering on the secondary hardening behavior in tempering.

It might further be mentioned that this effect of the alloying elements, and particularly the carbide-forming elements, on tempering may be reflected in an increased toughness of high-alloy steels. We have seen that the toughness of tempered martensite results from both the relief of internal stresses, and the forma-

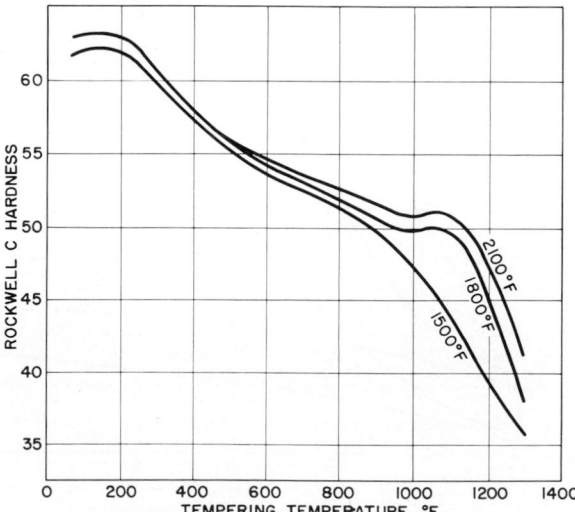

FIG. 41—9. The effect of carbide solution on tempering rate of a Cr-Mo-V steel quenched from 2100°, 1800° and 1500° F.

tion of a desirable carbide dispersion. The higher tempering temperatures for a given strength level, characteristic of these high-alloy steels, will permit a greater degree of stress relief with an accompanying increase in toughness. Furthermore, as we have seen, a given hardness level in the tempered alloy steels reflects not only the state of dispersion and coagulation of the iron carbides, but also that of the alloy carbides, and thus coagulation and spheroidization of the iron carbides must progress further for a given hardness to offset the secondary hardening effect of the alloy carbides. This more completely spheroidized microstructure would also favor plasticity, particularly at hardness levels at which a moderate coalescence of the alloy-carbide dispersion has taken place.

The increase in plasticity on tempering has so far been considered as though it were a continuous effect, that is, as if the steel softened and became more ductile continuously as the tempering temperature is increased. However, this is not altogether true, as many steels exhibit a minimum toughness on tempering at temperatures of 500°-600° F. This behavior is illustrated in Figure 41—11, which shows the impact values of several alloy steels as a function of tempering temperature. This phenomenon is not fully understood, nor can the effects of the alloying elements on this behavior be evaluated. However, it should be realized that, in general, tempering temperatures in this range (500°-600° F) should be avoided wherever possible.

Temper brittleness in alloy steels is another com-

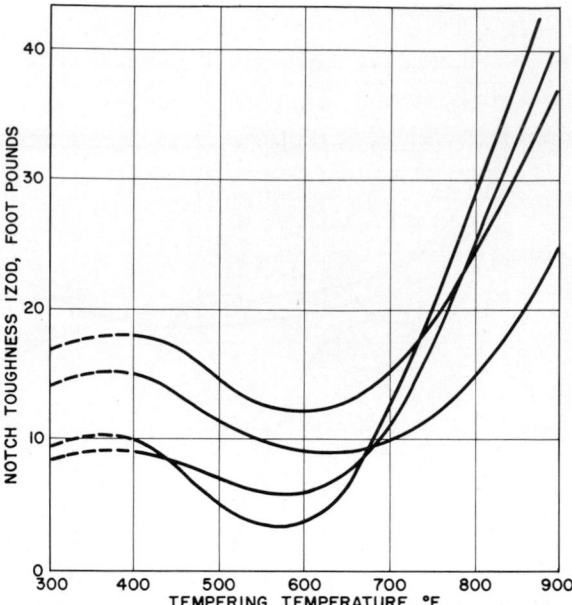

FIG. 41—11. The loss of notch toughness in the Izod test in several alloy steels on tempering at about 600° F.

may be classed as special purpose steels. These functions will now be briefly discussed.

Ferrite Strengthening—Alloying elements dissolved in pure iron will increase its hardness, and this furnishes a method of increasing the strength of steels in the unhardened state. This ferrite-strengthening function of the alloys is, thus, independent of the effect of the alloys on microstructure, and may be utilized to increase the strength of steels which essentially receive no heat treatment, except for the cooling after the hot-working operation. This hardening effect is, of course, small as compared with that obtainable by changes in the dispersion of the carbide. This is illustrated by Figure 41—12, which shows the hardness of chromium steels as a function of chromium content in a series of steels which have been very slowly cooled, in which the ferrite-strengthening effect will be predominant, as compared with a rapidly cooled series in which the effects of microstructural changes will be predominant. Each of the alloying elements will exert its individual effect in ferrite strengthening. The relative effectiveness of the alloying elements in this respect is indicated by Figure 41—13. The order of increasing effectiveness of these elements appears to be as follows: chromium, tungsten, vanadium, molybdenum, nickel, manganese, sili-

mon example of a discontinuous increase in plasticity on tempering. This phenomenon is manifested as a loss of toughness on slow cooling after tempering at temperatures of 1100° F or above, or on tempering in the temperature range of approximately 850° to 1100° F. Thus, a steel which is susceptible to this type of embrittlement may lose much of its ductility as indicated by a notched-bar impact test on slow cooling from a tempering temperature of 1150° F, although the same steel will be very tough if it is quenched from the same tempering temperature, and this expedient of quenching from the tempering temperature is a common practice to insure freedom from this embrittlement. However, in such steels, embrittlement will also occur on tempering at 850°-1050° F, particularly if the tempering times are protracted and quenching from the tempering temperature will, in such cases, never completely restore the toughness. This phenomenon also is not completely understood, although the behavior suggests that something which dissolves at temperatures of 1100° F and above precipitates in a damaging form at the lower temperatures, either during slow cooling or on reheating to these temperatures. High manganese, phosphorus and chromium contents appear to accentuate this behavior, and molybdenum seems to have a definite retarding effect.

OTHER FUNCTIONS OF THE ALLOYING ELEMENTS

The primary function of the alloying elements in alloy steels has been seen to be that of enhancing the properties through control of the microstructure, particularly in conjunction with suitable heat treatments, and this function has been discussed in considerable detail. However, the alloying elements may exert other useful influences, particularly in steels which

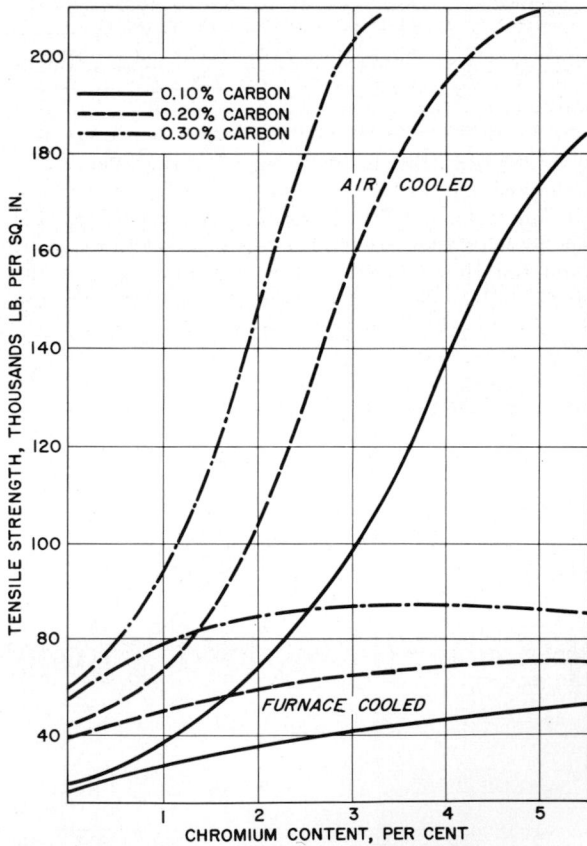

FIG. 41—12. The minor effect of chromium in furnace-cooled steels compared with its strong effect as a strengthener through its influence upon structure in air-cooled steels.

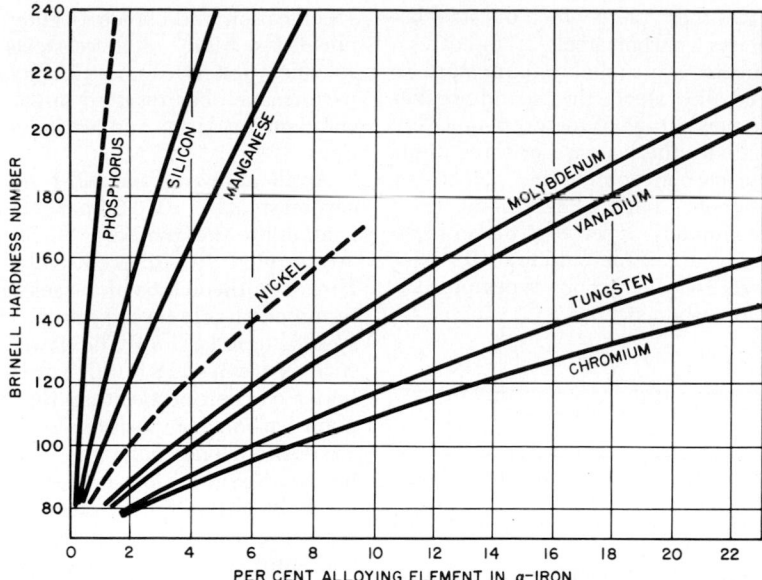

FIG. **41**—13. The relative effectiveness of the alloying elements as ferrite strengtheners.

con, phosphorus. Significant increases in strength may be obtained by the use of several elements in a single composition. In general, the higher strength levels obtained by this method of ferrite strengthening will be accompanied by a relatively small loss in plasticity, as compared with the considerable loss in ductility accompanying the hardness increases resulting from microstructural changes.

As discussed in the chapter on the low-alloy high-strength steels, these ferrite-strengthening effects have been utilized to their fullest extent in such steels.

Corrosion Resistance—Another function of some of the alloying elements in steel is to increase its resistance to corrosive attack. This function is also utilized in the low-alloy high-strength steels, in which chromium, copper, and phosphorus have been found very effective in increasing resistance to atmospheric corrosion, thereby permitting the use of the lighter sections made possible by their higher strengths, without decreased life from corrosion.

Chromium in high percentages imparts an extraordinary corrosion resistance to steel, and the stainless steels are largely based on this effect of chromium. This effect is discussed in detail in Chapter 45 on the stainless steels and need not be elaborated on here.

Abrasion Resistance—The compositions of alloy tool steels are such that at the heat-treating temperature many of the alloy carbides remain undissolved in the austenite. These hard carbide particles serve to increase the abrasion resistance of the steel, and this represents another function of the alloying elements. The elements commonly used for this purpose are tungsten, molybdenum, vanadium, titanium and chromium.

The Hadfield manganese steels represent another class of abrasion-resistant steels in which the function of the element is to stabilize austenite in order to produce austenitic steels which harden on cold working.

Magnetic (Electrical) Characteristics—The addition of alloying elements may greatly modify the characteristics of steel used for electrical equipment. Improved electrical characteristics for a desired application may be obtained by utilizing these effects (see Chapter 44).

One example of this function of the alloying elements is represented by the silicon steels used for transformer cores. These steels, containing silicon up to 5 per cent, have a greatly increased electrical resistivity and, as annealed, high permeability. When used as transformer cores, these properties result in greatly reduced core losses.

The magnet steels, for permanent magnets, are another example of alloy electrical steels. The outstanding property of these steels is their retentivity or ability to retain magnetism. Cobalt, chromium, and tungsten are the alloying elements commonly used to enhance this characteristic.

SECTION 2

THE AISI ALLOY STEELS

Classification and Standardization of the AISI Steels—The alloy steels most commonly used for heat-treated parts have been classified by the American Iron and Steel Institute and the Society of Automotive Engineers. The composition ranges of these steels have been listed in Table **41**—I.

These steels are identified by a numerical index system that is partially descriptive of the composition.

The first digit indicates the type to which the steel belongs; thus "1" indicates a carbon steel; "2" indicates a nickel steel; "3" indicates a nickel-chromium steel. In the case of the simple alloy steels, the second number usually indicates the percentage of the predominating alloying element. Usually the last two or three digits indicate the average carbon content in "points," or hundredths of a per cent. Thus, "2340" indicates a nickel steel of approximately 3 per cent nickel (3.25 to 3.75) and 0.40 per cent carbon (0.35 to 0.45).

The basic numerals for the various types of AISI steels (including plain-carbon steels) are:

Series Designation	Types
10xx	Nonresulphurized basic open hearth and acid bessemer carbon steel grades
11xx	Resulphurized basic open hearth and acid bessemer carbon steel grades
12xx	Rephosphorized and resulphurized basic open hearth carbon steel grades
13xx	Manganese 1.75 per cent
23xx	Nickel 3.50 per cent
25xx	Nickel 5.00 per cent
31xx	Nickel 1.25 per cent—Chromium 0.65 per cent
33xx	Nickel 3.50 per cent—Chromium 1.55 per cent
40xx	Molybdenum 0.25 per cent
41xx	Chromium 0.50 or 0.95 per cent—Molybdenum 0.12 or 0.20 per cent
43xx	Nickel 1.80 per cent—Chromium 0.50 or 0.80 per cent—Molybdenum 0.25 per cent
46xx	Nickel 1.55 or 1.80 per cent—Molybdenum 0.20 or 0.25 per cent
47xx	Nickel 1.05 per cent—Chromium 0.45 per cent—Molybdenum 0.20 per cent
48xx	Nickel 3.50 per cent—Molybdenum 0.25 per cent
50xx	Chromium 0.28 or 0.40 per cent
51xx	Chromium 0.80, 0.90, 0.95, 1.00 or 1.05 per cent
5xxxx	Carbon 1.00 per cent—Chromium 0.50, 1.00 or 1.45 per cent
61xx	Chromium 0.80 or 0.95 per cent—Vanadium 0.10 per cent or 0.15 per cent min.
86xx	Nickel 0.55 per cent—Chromium 0.50 or 0.65 per cent—Molybdenum 0.20 per cent
87xx	Nickel 0.55 per cent—Chromium 0.50 per cent—Molybdenum 0.25 per cent
92xx	Manganese 0.85 per cent—Silicon 2.00 per cent
93xx	Nickel 3.25 per cent—Chromium 1.20 per cent—Molybdenum 0.12 per cent
98xx	Nickel 1.00 per cent—Chromium 0.80 per cent—Molybdenum 0.25 per cent
TS	denotes Tentative Standard Steel, as in TS 4130 and others.
B	denotes Boron Steel, as in 46B12 and others.
BV	denotes Boron Vanadium Steel, as in TS 43BV12 and TS 43BV14.

Needless to say, this list, representing as it does, a standardization and simplification of thousands of alloy-steel compositions, is a very valuable aid to the specification and choice of alloy steels for various applications. Many of these steels were developed for specific applications, and their continued satisfactory performance has resulted in a considerable degree of standardization of application among these compositions.

Applications of the AISI Alloy Steels—The low-carbon steels (0.10–0.25 per cent carbon) in this classification are designated as carburizing steels and they are applied almost exclusively to carburized parts. However, the choice of a steel within this group is determined largely by the core properties desired for the specific application. The lower alloy combinations, such as 4023, 4118 or 5015 are used where somewhat better core properties than those obtainable with the plain carbon compositions such as C1018 or C1117 are desired. They have the further advantage of being hardenable in oil in moderate sections, and therefore can be heat treated with less distortion than the types requiring water quenching. The higher manganese and sulphur steels are used where superior machinability is required. Typical applications of these low-alloy carburizing grades would be for the production of cam shafts, wrist pins, clutch fingers, and other automotive parts in which high strength and optimum core properties are not required.

The higher alloy carburizing steels, such as 3120, 3310, 4320, 4620, 4815, 5120, 6120, 8620, 9310 or 94B17 are used where superior case hardness or core properties are desired. The choice of steels within this group is determined primarily by the hardenability necessary to obtain the desired core properties under the given conditions of section size and heat treatment. The low nickel-chromium (3120), nickel-molybdenum (4620), plain chromium (5120), chromium-vanadium (6120) or low nickel-chromium-molybdenum (8620) steels are customarily used for such applications as automotive gears, universal joints, small hand tools, piston pins, and similar parts of moderate section for relatively severe service. The higher alloy steels 3310, 4815, 9310 or 94B17 are used for severe service applications or heavy sections. Typical applications of these steels are aircraft-engine parts, truck transmissions and differentials, rotary rock-bit cutters and large antifriction bearings.

Similarly, the choice of the higher carbon alloy steels is based largely on the hardenability requirements of the specific applications. This will, of course, be a function of the heat treatment and section size. Intricate sections or higher carbon materials (over 0.40 per cent carbon) which must be oil quenched to prevent danger of quench cracking may frequently require higher alloy compositions than the simpler sections or low-carbon materials which can be safely heat treated under more drastic quenching conditions.

As with the carburizing steels, the lower alloy higher carbon steels, such as the manganese (1330-45), plain molybdenum (4037-47), plain chromium (5130-50), or the low nickel-chromium-molybdenum (8630-50), are used for applications involving relatively small sections, but which are subject to severe service conditions, or in larger sections which may not necessitate optimum properties, but in which advantage is taken of the weight saving derived from the higher strength of the alloy steels. Typical applications are the use of the manganese steels for automotive axles and high-strength bolts, molybdenum steels and chromium steels for automotive steering parts and low nickel-chromium-molybdenum steels for small machinery axles and shafts. These lower alloy steels are also widely used for high-quality small tools.

The higher alloy AISI steels, such as the 4337-40, 9840-50 or 86B45 compositions are used for heavy sections or for parts subject to particularly severe service conditions or for which very mild quenches must be used to prevent distortion. Typical uses would be for relatively heavy aircraft or truck parts or for ordnance materials.

In addition to the more or less general uses described above, some of the AISI steels have quite specialized applications. Thus the 52100 steels are used almost exclusively for ball- and roller-bearing applications, and the chromium steels (5155 and 5160) were developed for and are used almost entirely for spring-steel applications.

Hardenabilities of the AISI Alloy Steels—Hardenability has been stressed as the most important function of the alloying elements in these steels, and the above discussion of their applications has shown that the choice of the alloy steel to be used for a given application is largely based on its hardenability. Realizing the importance of hardenability, the American Iron and Steel Institute, together with the American Society of Automotive Engineers, have established minimum and maximum end-quench hardenability curves, known as **hardenability bands**, for most of these alloy steels. These bands or hardenability limits, typified by Figure **41**—14, are based on the analysis of data collected from hundreds of heats of each grade of steel. Such information permits these steels to be sold on the basis of this most important property, hardenability, and steels sold to such a hardenability specification are known as "H" steels.

Since, for application purposes, the minimum hardenability values for a given steel are usually the most pertinent, the minimum hardenability limits for numerous "H" steels are shown in Figures **41**—15 and

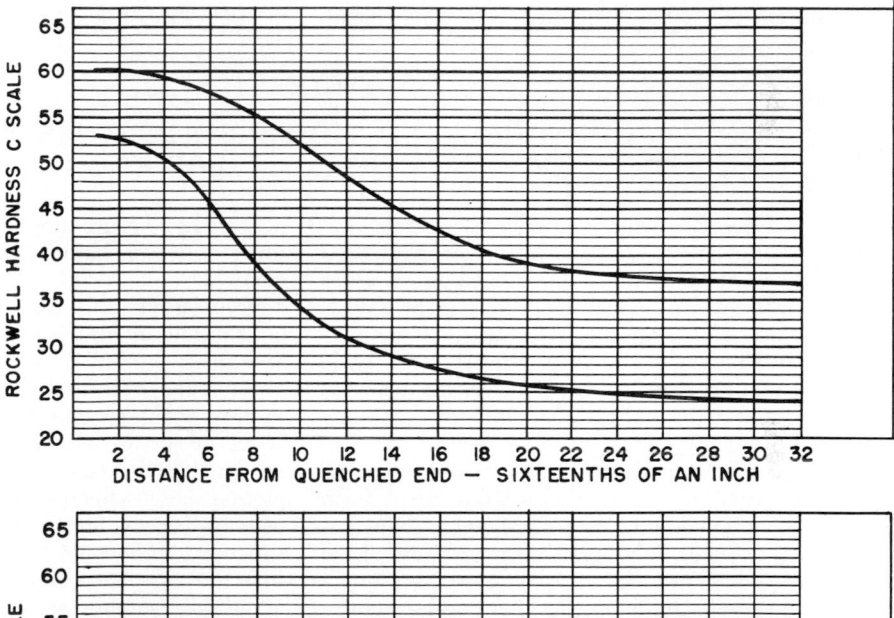

Fɪɢ. **41**—14. Typical hardenability band (41-40H steel).

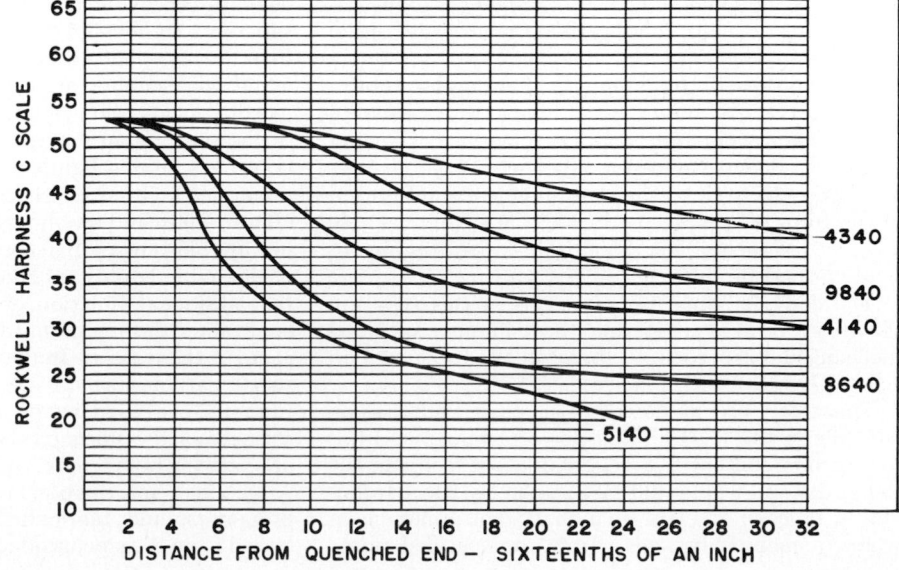

Fɪɢ. **41**—15. Minimum hardenability limits for 4140H, 4340H, 5140H, 8640H and 9840H, comparing minimum hardenabilities for steels of different alloy content but of the same carbon content.

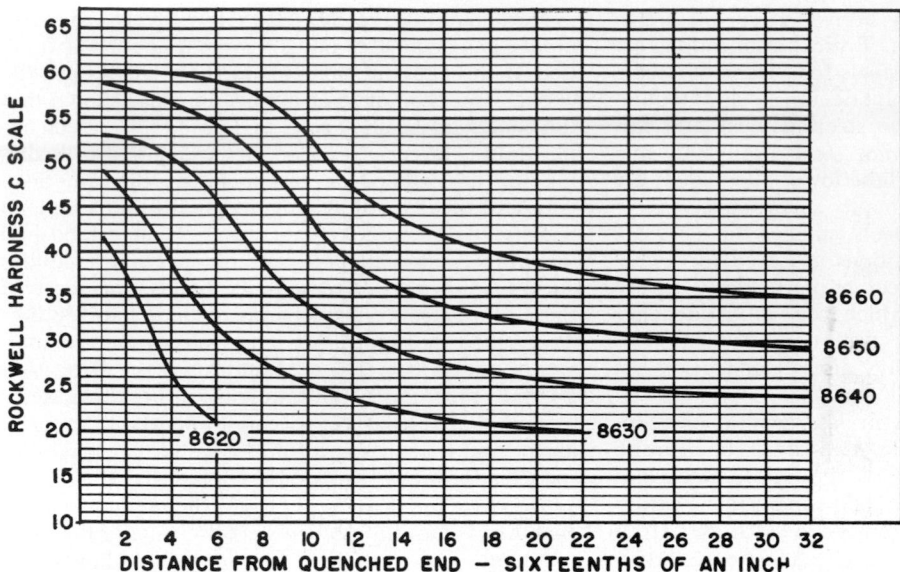

Fig. 41—16. Minimum hardenability limits of a group of steels of the 8600 (nickel-chromium-molybdenum) series, showing the increase in minimum hardenability with increasing carbon content.

41—16. Figure 41—15 also compares the minimum hardenability limits for a group of steels of different alloy content but having essentially the same carbon content. Figure 41—16 shows the effect on the minimum hardenability limit of increasing carbon content in 8600 series (nickel-chromium-molybdenum) steels.

SECTION 3

QUENCHED AND TEMPERED LOW-CARBON CONSTRUCTIONAL ALLOY STEELS

A class of quenched and tempered low-carbon constructional alloy steels has been very extensively used in a wide variety of applications such as pressure vessels, earth-moving and mining equipment and as major members of large steel structures. Their outstanding attributes and their usefulness for a wide variety of applications warrant their consideration as a separate and important class of constructional alloy steels.

As a general class, these steels are referred to as **low-carbon martensites,** to differentiate them from those constructional alloy steels of higher carbon content that develop high-carbon martensite upon quenching. They are characterized by a relatively high strength, with minimum yield strengths of 100,-000 lb. per sq. in., toughness at temperatures down to −50° F, and weldability, with welded joints showing full joint efficiency when welded with suitable low-hydrogen electrodes. They are most commonly used in the form of a plate product but are also available as sheet products, bars, structural shapes, forgings or semi-finished products.

The compositions of some steels of this type are shown in Table 41—II, and the minimum specified mechanical properties of these steels are shown in Table 41—III.

The steels are all low-carbon steels with carbon contents in the 0.10 to 0.20 per cent range, and this low carbon content is a very important factor in the toughness and weldability of these steels. The hardenability of each steel is such that transformation on water quenching in sizes within the specified thickness range occurs predominantly at low temperatures to lower bainite or martensite. The alloying elements used to impart this requisite hardenability have been chosen with economy in mind so that the outstanding attributes of these steels can be realized at a relatively low cost. The very significant hardenability effect of a small percentage of boron is utilized in some of these steels and also, in some instances, different grades are available, with the alloy content and hardenability being varied in accordance with the section size in which it is to be applied. Thus, advantage can often be taken of the higher strength and superior toughness of these alloy steels at a lower cost than that for plain carbon steels which would be used in heavier sections at their lower strengths. The atmospheric-corrosion resistance of these alloy steels is, furthermore, from two to four times that of plain carbon steels, so that lighter sections can be used without a sacrifice in atmospheric corrosion life. Although the high strength and toughness of these steels reflects primarily their low carbon content and their efficient use of the hardenability function of the alloying elements, the additional function of the alloying elements of controlling the tempering behavior is also utilized in some of these steels. In these steels, small additions of strong carbide-forming elements such as vanadium or titanium are used to permit retention of the high strength of the steels on tempering or stress relieving at relatively high temperatures.

Detailed information in regard to availability, properties, and fabrication procedures can be obtained from the steel producers.

Table 41—II. Composition Ranges of Quenched and Tempered Constructional Alloy Steels (Per Cent)

Designation	Producer	C	Mn	Si	Ni	Cr	Mo	V	Ti	B	Zr	Cu
"T-1"	U. S. Steel	0.10/0.20	0.60/1.00	0.15/0.35	0.70/1.00	0.40/0.80	0.40/0.60	0.03/0.08	—	0.002/0.006	—	0.15/0.50
"T-1" type A	U. S. Steel	0.12/0.21	0.70/1.00	0.20/0.35	—	0.40/0.65	0.15/0.25	0.03/0.08	0.01/0.03	0.0005/0.005	—	—
N-A-XTRA 100	Great Lakes Steel	0.15	0.80	0.70	—	0.60	0.15	—	—	—	0.07	—
JALLOY S 100	Jones and Laughlin	0.10/0.20	1.10/1.50	0.15/0.30	—	—	0.20/0.30	—	—	—	—	—
Super Strength 100	Armco	0.12/0.20	0.40/0.70	0.20/0.35	—	1.40/2.00	0.40/0.60	—	0.04/0.10	0.0015/0.005	—	0.20/0.40

Table 41—III. Mechanical Properties of Quenched and Tempered Constructional Alloy Steels*

Designation	Minimum Yield Strength (lb. per sq. in.)	Tensile Strength (lb. per sq. in.)	Minimum Elongation (%)	Minimum Reduction of Area (%)	Impact Resistance** at −50° F (ft.-lb.)
"T-1"	100,000	115,000/135,000	18.0	50.0	15
"T-1" type A	100,000	115,000/135,000	16.0	50.0	15
N-A-XTRA 100	100,000	Not specified	Not specified	Not specified	Not specified
JALLOY S 100	100,000	115,000/135,000	Not specified	Not specified	Not specified
Super Strength 100	100,000	115,000/135,000	17.0	Not specified	15

* For 1-inch thick plates. Properties vary with thickness and compositions are selected from ranges in Table 39—II to give desired properties for a given thickness.
** Charpy keyhole specimens.

SECTION 4

MARAGING STEELS

A specific group of high-nickel martensitic steels called **maraging steels** (also not included in the AISI classification of constructional alloy steels), has been developed by The International Nickel Company. These high-nickel alloy steels contain so little carbon that they are referred to as carbon-free, iron-nickel martensites.

Iron-carbon martensite is hard and brittle in the as-quenched condition and becomes softer and more ductile when tempered. Carbon-free iron-nickel martensite, on the other hand, is relatively soft and ductile and becomes hard, strong and tough when aged. Thus, maraging steels can be fabricated while they are in a comparatively ductile martensitic condition and later strengthened by a simple aging treatment.

The first iron-nickel martensitic alloys contained about 0.01 per cent of carbon, either 20 or 25 per cent of nickel, and 1.5 to 2.5 per cent of aluminum and titanium. Later, an 18 per cent nickel steel containing cobalt, molybdenum and titanium was developed, and, still more recently, a series of 12 per cent nickel steels containing chromium and molybdenum.

18 Per Cent Nickel Steels—The 18 per cent nickel maraging steels contain 7 to 9½ per cent of cobalt, 3 to 5 per cent of molybdenum, and 0.1 to 0.8 per cent of titanium. By adjusting the percentages of these elements, yield strengths in the range of 200,000 to 300,000 lb. per sq. in. can be obtained. Since molybdenum has an adverse effect on toughness, more cobalt rather than more molybdenum is used to achieve the highest strength levels.

Heat treatment of the maraging steels is quite simple. They are annealed at 1500° F for one hour, air cooled to room temperature, and finally aged at 900° F for 3 hours. The aging treatment can be varied to obtain different strength levels. Because the 18 per cent nickel alloy transforms to martensite during air cooling from 1500° F, it can be maraged directly after hot rolling without going through the annealing step, although this step may be included to insure uniformity of starting structure. Additional strength can be obtained by cold working the martensitic structure before aging.

Strengthening of the 18 per cent nickel maraging steels during aging is believed to be achieved mainly by the precipitation of extremely fine particles of the intermetallic compounds Ni_3Mo and Ni_3Ti on dislocation sites.

Table **41**—IV shows some properties of nominally 18 per cent nickel steels with compositions adjusted to produce yield strengths of 200,000 and 300,000 lb. per sq. in. The "200" steels contain 17 to 19 per cent of nickel, 8 to 9 per cent of cobalt, 3 to 3.5 per cent

of molybdenum, 0.15 to 0.25 per cent of titanium, and 0.1 per cent of aluminum. The "300" steels contain 18 to 19 per cent of nickel, 8.5 to 9.5 per cent of cobalt, 4.7 to 5.2 per cent of molybdenum, 0.5 to 0.7 per cent of titanium, and 0.1 per cent of aluminum.

In addition to these properties, the 18 per cent nickel steels have a resistance to stress-corrosion cracking that is superior to that of any known alloy steel of comparable strength.

Table 41—IV. Properties of 18 Per Cent Nickel Bar Steels after Maraging.

Property	200 Steel[a]	300 Steel[b]
Yield Strength, Lb. per Sq. In.	200,000	300,000
Ultimate Strength, Lb. per Sq. In.	210,000	305,000
Reduction of Area, Per Cent	64	60
Elongation in 2 In., Per Cent	15	12
Notch Tensile Strength, Lb. per Sq. In. ($K_t = 12$, root diameter 0.212 in.)	340,000	440,000
Notch Tensile Strength to Tensile Strength Ratio	1.6	1.5
Charpy Impact, Ft.-Lb., at room temperature	50	22
Charpy Impact, Ft.-Lb., at −320°F	30	14

[a] Annealed at 1500° F for 1 hr., air cooled and then maraged at 900° F for 3 hr.

[b] Maraged at 900° F for 3 hr. directly after hot rolling, omitting the annealing step.

12 Per Cent Nickel Steels—Another series of maraging steels is represented by the 12 per cent Ni-Cr-Mo steels. These steels, which after solution annealing and aging develop yield strengths in the range 150,000 to 200,000 lb. per sq. in. or more, are characterized by nickel contents of 10 to 12 per cent, chromium contents of 3 to 5 per cent, molybdenum contents of about 3 per cent, and titanium and aluminum contents suitably adjusted to develop yield strengths in the aforementioned range. At these yield strengths, the 12 per cent nickel maraging steels generally exhibit notch toughness significantly higher than that observed for alloy steels quenched and tempered to these strength levels.

Bibliography

"Functions of the Alloying Elements in Steel," by E. C. Bain. Published by American Society for Metals, 1939. (Second edition, by E. C. Bain and Harold W. Paxton, 1961).

"Metals Handbook," 1961 (Eighth) Edition. Published by American Society for Metals.

CHAPTER 42

Alloy Tool Steels

Compositions and Applications—The principal functions of the alloying elements in tool steels are to increase hardenability, to form hard, wear-resisting alloy carbides, and to increase resistance to softening on tempering. The alloy tool steels may be roughly classified according to the extent of their utilization of these three functions. On this basis, the three classes would be as follows:

1. **Relatively low-alloy tool steels.** These are of higher hardenability than the plain carbon tool steels in order that they may be hardened in heavier sections or with less drastic quenches and thereby less distortion.

2. **Intermediate alloy tool steels.** These steels usually contain elements such as tungsten, molybdenum or vanadium, which form hard, wear-resisting carbides. They are employed in the manufacture of fast-finishing tools in which the retention of a smooth cutting edge is of particular importance.

3. **High-speed tool steels.** These contain large amounts of the carbide-forming elements which serve not only to furnish wear-resisting carbides but also to promote secondary hardening and thereby to increase resistance to softening at elevated temperature.

Table 42—I. Compositions of Some Tool Steels (Per Cent)

Class	Type	C	Mn	Si	Ni	Cr	Mo	W	V	Co
1	Non-Deforming ...	0.90	1.60	...	......	....	....	....	...	...
1	Chromium	0.90–1.10	0.25	0.25	......	1.0–2.0	....	....	...	...
1	Chromium-Vanadium	0.50–1.10	0.25	0.25	......	0.75–1.50	....	....	0.20	...
1	Chromium-Nickel .	0.40–0.75	0.40	0.25	1.0–2.0	0.75–2.25	....	....	...	...
1	Chromium-Molybdenum ...	0.40–0.75	0.40	0.25	......	0.75–1.50	0.20–0.50	....	...	...
1	Nickel-Chromium-Molybdenum ...	0.40–0.75	0.40	0.25	1.0–2.0	0.75–1.50	0.20–0.50	....	...	...
2	Tungsten Finishing	1.35	0.25	0.25	......	....	....	3.0–4.0	...	...
2	Tungsten Finishing	1.35	0.25	0.25	......	0.50–1.00	....	3.0–4.0	...	...
2	Tungsten Finishing	1.35	0.25	0.25	......	....	0.50–1.00	3.0–4.0	...	...
2	Tungsten Chisel...	0.50	0.25	0.25	......	1.50	....	2.10	0.25	...
3	18-4-1 High Speed.	0.50–0.80	0.25	0.25	......	4.00	....	18.00	1.00	...
3	18-4-3 High Speed.	0.95	0.25	0.25	......	4.00	....	18.00	3.00	...
3	Tungsten Cobalt ..	0.75	0.25	0.25	......	4.00		18.00	1.00	5.00
3	Molybdenum High Speed..........	0.75	0.25	0.25	......	4.00	8.50	1.50	1.00	...
3	Tungsten-Molybdenum High Speed.....	0.80	0.25	0.25	......	4.00	4.75	5.75	1.50	...

Typical compositions of these three classes of tool steels are given in Table 42—I. More detailed information on types of tool steels, their composition, treatments and applications, may be found in the 1961 (Eighth) Edition of the American Society for Metals' Handbook, pages 637-659, and in "Tool Steels" by Gill, Rose, Roberts, Johnstin and George, published by the American Society for Metals.

Table 42—I is illustrative of the types of compositions used for alloy tool steels, of which there are hundreds of variations. The uses of tool steels are so diversified and the compositions and types that may be used for a single application overlap to such an extent that a satisfactory general classification on this basis is impossible. However, the high-speed steels obviously are used for applications requiring long life at relatively high operating temperatures such as for heavy cuts or high-speed machining, the intermediate alloy types are used for finishing operations in which extreme wear resistance and the ability to retain a smooth cutting edge on light cuts is necessary, and the first class of steels are general purpose tool steels, the choice of which is based primarily on section size, permissible distortion, intricacy of design, and the hardness and toughness requirements of the application; all of which are, to a considerable extent, functions of the hardenability. The higher hardenability steels are used in cases where a low "movement" (change of dimension) in hardening is required, since relatively slow oil or even air quenches may be used. These steels are also designed to be capable of hardening from relatively low quenching temperatures which also tends to decrease distortion and danger of quench cracking. Within this class, the higher carbon steels are used for applications requiring high resistance to wear or abrasion and the lower carbon steels for applications in which resistance to shock or impact is of particular importance.

HEAT TREATMENT OF ALLOY TOOL STEELS

General—The general principles of heat treatment, as described in Chapter 39, naturally apply to the heat treatment of the alloy tool steels. The alloy tool steels are generally high carbon, and many of them are relatively high-alloy steels so that their heat treatment necessarily involves special precautions to avoid distortion, cracking, and decarburization. The heating operation must be conducted at a slow rate to minimize thermal stresses, and relatively low austenitizing temperatures are usual to minimize distortion and cracking. It is a common practice to carry out the heating in two stages: a preliminary preheat to an intermediate temperature preceding the heating to the final temperatures. Decarburization is usually particularly harmful in tool steels, and the practices mentioned in the chapter on heat treatment, such as use of controlled atmospheres, packing in cast-iron chips, or heating in neutral liquid baths, are very commonly employed.

Because of their sensitivity to cracking and the dangers of distortion, relatively mild quenches are commonly used in the heat treatment of alloy tool steels, and many of them are of high enough hardenability to permit air quenching.

Since the residual stresses are high in these high-carbon steels after quenching, the stress-relieving function of the tempering operation is of particular importance. Tempering to relieve these stresses and toughen the steels is therefore an essential part of the heat-treating operation and should immediately follow the quench. Since high hardness is usually desired, the tempering temperatures are generally low (250° to 450° F), although in cases such as some of the die applications, in which resistance to shock and impact are important, higher temperatures may be used. Tempering in the temperature range of 500° F to 600° F should generally be avoided.

High-Speed Steel—As mentioned above, the high-speed steels, typified by the 18 per cent tungsten, 4 per cent chromium, 1 per cent vanadium composition, differ from the lower alloy tool steels, not only in the presence of higher percentages of carbide-forming elements, but also in the fact that the secondary hardening effects of these elements are much more fully realized and a high resistance to softening at elevated temperature is obtained. These steels require a special heat treatment in order that their unique properties may be fully realized. In outline, this procedure consists of heating to a high temperature (2150° to 2400° F) to obtain solution of a substantial percentage of the alloy carbides, quenching to room temperature, at which stage a considerable amount of austenite is retained, tempering at 1000° to 1150° F, and again cooling to room temperature. During the tempering operation, alloy carbides are precipitated, resulting in a marked secondary hardening and in a reduction of alloy content in the retained austenite, which then transforms to martensite on cooling to room temperature and results in a still greater hardness increase. It is often desirable to temper a second time to temper the martensite formed on cooling from the original tempering.

In order to prevent excessive grain growth and decarburization, the steels are held at the high quenching temperature for only a few minutes before quenching. Steels are customarily preheated to between 1400° and 1600° F before transferring to the high-heat furnace. This serves the dual purpose of eliminating the severe thermal shock of placing the cold tool into the high-temperature furnace, and of decreasing the decarburization because of the shorter time of exposure to the high temperature. The use of controlled-atmosphere furnaces, or of neutral liquid baths for the high-heat treatment is also very desirable, and in many cases essential, to minimize decarburization. The time in the high-heat furnace will, of course, vary with the heating rate and size and shape of the piece. Typical hardening temperatures are 2250° to 2350° F for the tungsten types, 2150° to 2250° F for the molybdenum types, and 2325° to 2400° F for the cobalt types.

Quenching may be in air, oil, or in liquid baths. Air cooling has the disadvantage of the formation of a tightly adherent scale during cooling. Oil quenching, while it facilitates the removal of this scale, results in higher stresses. These may be minimized, however, by removing the piece from the oil at the flash point and then air cooling. By this method, the tools will be air cooled through the temperature range in which transformation to martensite occurs. The third method, which is very commonly practiced to insure low quenching stresses, is to quench into a liquid bath at 1000° F, hold until equalized, and then slowly air cool to between 200° and 300° F and immediately temper. This procedure is particularly applicable to the hardening without undue distortion or cracking of intricate tools.

Tempering may be carried out in salt baths, lead baths, or circulating-air furnaces. The latter are particularly desirable because of their adaptability to close control of temperature and uniformity of heating the work. The rapid heating of high-speed tool steels immersed in lead baths is undesirable since it may set up stresses which would lead to cracking. The maximum hardness will usually be developed at temperatures of 1000° to 1100° F, and the holding times in this temperature range usually are from 1 to 4 hours. The specific time and temperature will vary with the hardness and toughness desired.

As mentioned above, a second tempering at a relatively low temperature (600° to 650° F) will temper the martensite formed in cooling from the first tempering operation and will serve to increase the toughness of these steels without causing appreciable softening.

Bibliography

"Functions of the Alloying Elements in Steel," by E. C. Bain. Published by American Society for Metals, 1939 (Revised by E. C. Bain and Harold W. Paxton, 1961.)

"High-Speed Steels," by M. A. Grossmann and E. C. Bain. Published by John Wiley & Sons, Inc., 1931.

"Tool Steels," by J. P. Gill, R. S. Rose, G. A. Roberts, H. G. Johnstin, R. B. George. Published by American Society for Metals, 1944.

"Metals Handbook," 1961 (Eighth) Edition. Published by American Society for Metals.

CHAPTER 43

High-Strength Low-Alloy Steels

Introduction—The steels that are the subject of this chapter have been variously termed "high-tensile steels" and "low-alloy steels," but the formal name "high-strength low-alloy steels" is generally accepted as the proper designation.

High-strength low-alloy steels are categorized on the basis of their mechanical properties, particularly the yield point; for example, within certain thickness limitations, they have minimum yield points ranging from 45,000 to 65,000 lb. per sq. in., as compared with 33,000 to 36,000 lb. per sq. in. for structural carbon steel. This method of classifying is in contrast to the usual method, in which steels are classified as "plain carbon" or "structural carbon" steels, "alloy" steels, and "stainless" steels on the basis of the presence (or absence) of added alloying elements in the particular steel.

Because enhanced mechanical properties can be obtained by the addition to steel of several different single alloying elements and combinations of these elements (other than carbon), high-strength low-alloy steels may have different chemical compositions, but each steel in the group must meet essentially the same minimum mechanical-property requirements. The high-strength low-alloy steels are available as sheet, strip, bar, plate, and shapes. They are intended for general structural applications and are not, therefore, to be considered as special-purpose steels or as steels requiring, or adapted for, heat treatment.

Historical Background—Although a steel containing chromium was specified for certain members of the Eads Bridge, erected at St. Louis between 1867 and 1874, the most widely used steel for construction used before 1900 was mild carbon steel having an ultimate tensile strength of about 60,000 lb. per sq. in. In 1902, the design engineers of the Queensboro Bridge, that was to span the East River in New York City, requested a stronger steel so that the number and size of supporting members could be reduced. Carnegie Steel Company, now part of the United States Steel Corporation, supplied 3.25 per cent nickel steel for this application. This steel was also used in the stiffening trusses of the Manhattan Bridge in 1906. Although it was satisfactory for riveted structures from the standpoint of strength, this material was relatively expensive and economical only for structures in which reduction in weight or size of members was a necessity. Another steel, offering higher strength than mild carbon steel and containing about 1.00 per cent silicon and 0.25 per cent carbon, was used for hull plates in the S. S. Mauretania in 1907. Although this latter steel was less expensive than the nickel steel mentioned above, its use was ultimately discontinued because of many difficulties that were encountered in its application. Another steel, stronger than mild carbon steel, that contained only a nominal amount of silicon and depended for its strength mostly on its high carbon content (usually over 0.30 per cent), was first used in 1915 in a bridge spanning the Ohio River at Metropolis, Illinois. This grade, under the designation "silicon structural steel," until recently has been one of the most widely used materials for riveted structures.

In 1927, the American Bridge Company, now a Division of United States Steel Corporation, used a 1.60 per cent manganese steel for the lower chord members of the Kill van Kull Bridge connecting Staten Island with the mainland at Bayonne, New Jersey.

Similar developments had taken place in other countries. Engineers in Great Britain, attempting through weight reduction to effect economies in ocean freights and handling charges, had used carbon steels containing generous amounts of silicon and manganese. On the Continent similar steels were used, and early in 1933 the Germans completed "The Flying Dutchman," the first light-weight streamlined train built of a high-strength low-alloy steel (ST. 52) that contained additions of silicon, manganese, and copper.

The earliest of the present-day high-strength low-alloy steels was "COR-TEN" brand which was introduced by United States Steel in 1933. This steel has been continuously improved to meet the increasingly severe demands of fabricators—an experience common with most new steels. Since COR-TEN steel was introduced, many other steel-producing companies have developed their own grades, so that there are at present a considerable number of high-strength low-alloy steels on the market. These steels have found wide acceptance in the metal-working industry for many applications.

FUNDAMENTAL CHARACTERISTICS

To be of interest as construction materials, high-strength low-alloy steels must have characteristics and properties that result in economies to the user when the steels are properly applied. They should be considerably stronger, and in many instances tougher, than structural carbon steel. Also, they must have sufficient ductility, formability, and weldability to be successfully fabricated by customary shop methods. In addition, improved resistance to corrosion is often required so that equal service life in a thinner section or longer life in the same section is obtained in com-

Table 43—I. Important Characteristics of an All-Purpose High-Strength Steel

Property	Method of Determination
High strength......	Yield point in tension test.
Good corrosion resistance........	Atmospheric-corrosion resistance judged from weight loss in exposure-rack test, and useful life judged from service performance.
Good formability...	Bend test, tensile elongation and fabrication performance.
Good weldability...	Weldment performance judged by various weld-bending tests.
Good toughness under adverse conditions.......	Temperature of transition from tough to brittle behavior in notched-bar impact test.
Good resistance to repeated loading..........	Endurance tests on simple specimens or on built-up structures.
Good abrasion resistance........	Service performance.

parison to that of a structural carbon steel member. The combination of important characteristics that an all-purpose high-strength low-alloy steel should possess, and the methods by which these characteristics are commonly determined, are shown in Table 43—I. The first property, high strength, is common to all of these steels. The other properties, singly or in combination, may or may not be exhibited by any particular steel, depending on its composition.

Strength—A comparison of the tensile properties of a typical high-strength low-alloy steel with those of structural carbon steels is shown in Table 43—II. The yield point of a constructional member determines the stress to which a structure may be subjected without permanent deformation. Therefore, the unit working stresses of each structure are based upon this

Table 43—II. Comparative Tensile Properties for A Typical High-Strength Low-Alloy Steel and for Structural Carbon Steels.

Property	Typical High-Strength Low-Alloy Steel	Structural Carbon Steels	
		ASTM A-7 Steel	ASTM A-36 Steel
Yield Point, Minimum (Lb. per Sq. In.)	50,000	33,000	36,000
Tensile Strength, Minimum (Lb. per Sq. In.)	70,000	60,000 to 72,000	58,000 to 80,000
Elongation, Minimum (Per Cent in 8 In.)	19	21	20

important property. The minimum yield point of a typical structural carbon steel (ASTM A 7 steel) is 33,000 lb. per sq. in.; that of a typical high-strength low-alloy steel is 50,000 lb. per sq. in. Hence, on the basis of the proportionality of their yield points, the unit working stress employed with the high-strength low-alloy steels may be increased to 1½ times that used with the structural carbon steel. The use of higher unit working stresses generally permits reduction in the thickness of section in the structure and this results in a decrease in weight. Frequently, high-strength low-alloy steels are substituted for structural carbon steel without change in section, the sole purpose being to produce a stronger and more durable structure with no increase in weight. Savings in weight are of utmost importance in mobile structures when it permits these structures to carry greater payload.

Corrosion Resistance—When high-strength low-alloy steels are employed to save weight, it is desirable to make the maximum reduction in section. The engineer, however, must consider the structure not only at the time it is built but also as it will exist perhaps twenty years later when the members have been thinned by corrosion. Since the structural members are already relatively thin by virtue of the desired weight-saving, it is necessary that further thinning from the ravages of corrosion be prevented, at least in so far as possible, else the structure will become too weak to serve its intended purpose. Similarly, when high-strength low-alloy steels are employed to obtain increased service life, corrosive attack must be retarded. Thus, it may be said that improved corrosion resistance is equal in importance to higher strength and that the corrosion resistance of the high-strength low-alloy steels should be as high as is economically feasible without, at the same time, adversely affecting the other properties and characteristics to a marked extent. Unfortunately, the corrosion resistance of a material cannot be expressed quantitatively (as the yield point is described, for instance) because it is only a relative term. Furthermore, no material is equally resistant to all the corrosive conditions to which it might conceivably be exposed. Its performance can only be compared with that of other materials under similar conditions. A large number of corrosion tests under many conditions of exposure, particularly atmospheric rack tests, have been conducted for the purpose of determining these relative values. Such tests differentiate between the performances of various steels and permit a close evaluation of the trends in weight loss due to corrosion. The atmospheric-corrosion resistance of high-strength low-alloy steels varies with the combination and content of those alloying elements most effective in building up this resistance. Several steels of this type possess four to six times the atmospheric-corrosion resistance of structural carbon steel having a low copper content. The superior atmospheric corrosion resistance which most of the high-strength low-alloy steels have shown in rack tests has been confirmed by their performances in many different kinds of service. This superiority is particularly evident in those applications in which the materials are subjected principally to atmospheric

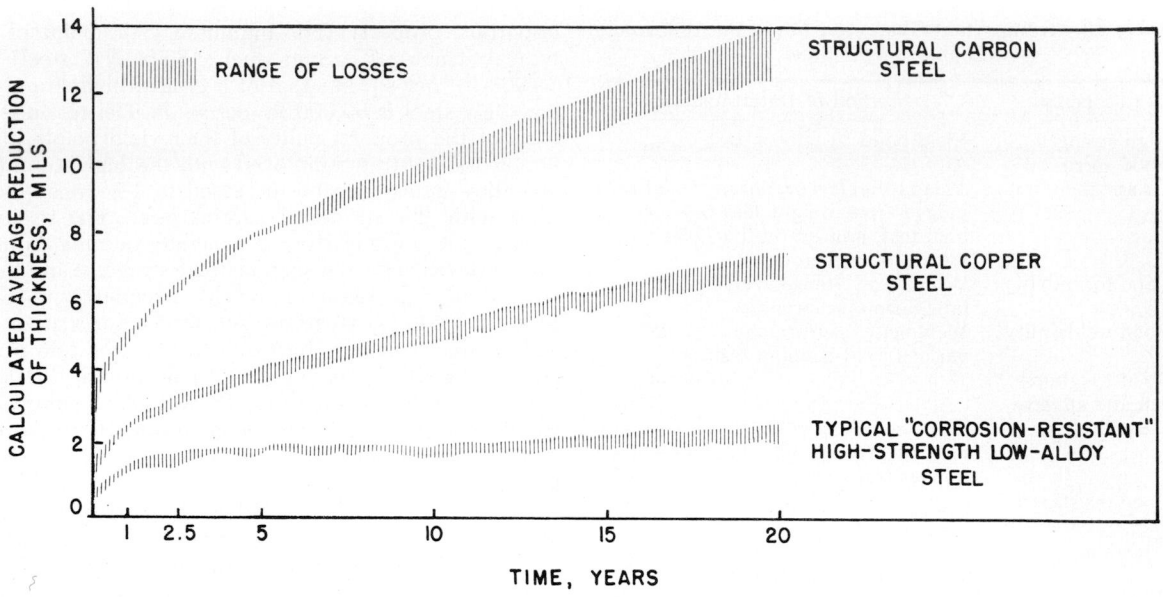

FIG. 43—1. Comparative corrosion of steel specimens exposed to an industrial atmosphere.

corrosion. Much has been written concerning the details and results of corrosion tests and a number of references are included in the bibliography for the use of those who wish to pursue the subject further. Figure 43—1 shows time-corrosion curves for structural carbon steel, structural copper steel, and a typical corrosion-resistant high-strength low-alloy steel exposed to an industrial atmosphere.

In other exposure tests, it has been shown that paint coatings applied to the corrosion-resistant high-strength low-alloy steels exhibit a longer service life than when applied to structural carbon steels. Figure 43—2 illustrates an instance of superior paint life on COR-TEN high-strength low-alloy steel as compared to that on carbon steel containing copper.

Formability—High-strength low-alloy steels must have suitable properties so that they may be hot or cold worked readily and economically into various commodities for engineering structures. These operations, and others such as shearing, punching, and machining, can generally be performed on high-strength low-alloy steels with almost as much ease as on structural carbon steels. Despite their high yield points, high-strength low-alloy steels can be satisfactorily formed in the same press brakes, draw benches, presses, and other equipment used for cold forming structural carbon steels, even when these forming operations are quite severe.

There are some inherent differences between the cold-forming characteristics of high-strength low-alloy steels and those of structural carbon steels. First, more force is required to produce a given amount of permanent set in a high-strength low-alloy steel section than in a structural carbon steel section of the same thickness. Second, a somewhat greater allowance for springback should be provided when forming the high-strength low-alloy steels. In bending operations, the amount of elastic deformation is increased consid-

FIG. 43—2. Appearance, after 12 years of service, of painted hopper side sheets on opposite sides of the same railroad car. Note the deterioration of paint on the copper-steel side sheet in the top illustration. Light markings on the painted COR-TEN steel side sheet in the bottom illustration were made by hammer blows to loosen the lading.

erably by reductions in section thickness. Therefore, even when lighter sections of high-strength low-alloy steel are used, more springback is obtained, although the force to produce the part is little or no greater than that required for the original part of structural carbon steel.

Experience has shown that more liberal radii of bend must be used with high-strength low-alloy steel than with structural carbon steel for successful cold forming. This again is ascribed to the greater strength of the high-strength low-alloy steel.

Weldability—Since welding is often employed in fabricating structural steel, it is important that high-strength low-alloy steels for these applications be readily weldable by metal-arc welding and by gas welding in plate thicknesses and by all the resistance-welding processes in sheet and strip thicknesses. It is equally important that the welds in fabricated structures have the required strength and ductility to withstand the most adverse conditions anticipated in the contemplated service. The development of the present-day high-strength low-alloy steels has paralleled the growth of the various welding processes, and particular care was exercised to make certain that these steels possessed suitable welding characteristics. Most of these steels are considered to be readily weldable by conventional processes.

For metal-arc welding of high-strength low-alloy steels, ordinary covered E-60 group electrodes are generally satisfactory (E-70 may be required for higher joint efficiency). However, for heavier sections and for grades that have higher carbon or manganese contents, preheating and/or low-hydrogen electrodes such as E-7015 or 7016 may be required.

Notch Toughness—As measured in a notched-bar impact test, high-strength low-alloy steels generally exhibit toughness superior to that of structural carbon steels. This superiority is shown both when the notch toughness is expressed in terms of the amount of energy absorbed in breaking a specimen at room temperature and in terms of the low temperatures to which high-strength low-alloy steels preserve their toughness.

Fatigue Resistance—The resistance to repeated loading, or the fatigue resistance, of materials is generally determined by testing polished specimens. The fatigue limit determined by this method of testing, therefore, is considered to have little bearing on the fatigue resistance of full-sized structures since failures of structural members, subject to alternating or pulsating stresses, generally originate at some surface notch or discontinuity acting as a stress raiser. Laboratory tests of polished specimens do, however, indicate that the high-strength low-alloy steels are superior to structural carbon steels. The ratio of fatigue limit to tensile strength is greater for high-strength low-alloy steels than for structural carbon steel.

Abrasion Resistance—There is general agreement that the resistance of various steels to abrasive action increases with strength or hardness and, to some extent, with carbon content. Service tests have demonstrated that the abrasion resistance of the high-strength low-alloy steels, with their inherently greater strength, is somewhat higher than that of structural carbon steels containing 0.15 to 0.20 per cent carbon.

EFFECT OF CHEMICAL COMPOSITION ON PROPERTIES AND CHARACTERISTICS

In the development of chemical compositions to obtain the desired properties in high-strength low-alloy steels, it was, of course, imperative that strength be given first consideration. Since increased strength can be obtained with various combinations of alloying elements, a number of different compositions have been produced which offer interesting combinations of other properties and characteristics in addition to the required minimum strength. The compositions of a representative group of current high-strength low-alloy steels are shown in Table 43—III.

Table 43—III. Composition Ranges of Some Representative High-Strength Low-Alloy Steels.

Brand	Chemical Composition (Per Cent)								
	C	Mn	P	S (max.)	Si	Cu	Ni	Cr	Other
COR-TEN*	0.12 max.	0.20–0.50	0.07–0.15	0.05	0.25–0.75	0.25–0.55	0.65 max.	0.30–1.25	—
COR-TEN**	0.10–0.19	0.90–1.25	0.04 max.	0.05	0.15–0.30	0.25–0.40	—	0.40–0.65	V: 0.02–0.10
TRI-TEN	0.22 max.	1.25 max.	0.04 max.	0.05	0.30 max.	0.20 min.	—	—	V: 0.02 min.
MAN-TEN	0.28 max.	1.10–1.60	0.04 max.	0.05	0.30 max.	0.20 min.	—	—	—
EX-TEN 50***	0.22 max.	1.25 max.	0.04 max.	0.05	—	—	—	—	Cb or V: 0.01 min.
GLX-50-W	0.20 max.	1.00 max.	0.04 max.	0.05	0.10 max.	—	—	—	Cb: 0.20 min.
Dynalloy	0.15 max.	0.60–1.00	0.05–0.10	0.05	0.30 max.	0.30–0.60	0.40–0.70	—	Mo: 0.05–0.15
Mayari "R"	0.12 max.	0.50–1.00	0.12 max.	0.05	0.20–0.90	0.50 max.	1.00 max.	0.40–1.00	Zr: 0.10 max.
NAX High Tensile	0.18 max.	0.50–0.90	0.04 max.	0.05	0.60–0.90	—	—	0.40–0.70	Mo: 0.20 max., Zr: 0.03–0.13
Yoloy "E" HSX	0.18 max.	0.90 max.	0.08 max.	0.05	—	0.20–0.50	0.40–1.00	0.20–0.35	—
Jalten #1	0.15 max.	1.30 max.	0.04 max.	0.05	0.10 max.	0.30 min.	—	—	V: 0.035–0.065
Yoloy "E" ACR	0.10 max.	0.60 max.	0.05 max.	0.05	—	0.25–0.50	0.60 max.	0.35 max.	—

*½-inch and under in thickness.
**Over ½-inch in thickness.
***In addition to EX-TEN 50 steel (50,000 lb. per sq. in. minimum yield point), EX-TEN steels are also available with minimum yield points of 45,000, 55,000, 60,000, and 65,000 lb. per sq. in.

Carbon—Carbon is one of the more potent and more economical strengthening elements. As a generalization, an increase in yield point of about 500 lb. per sq. in. can be realized for each 0.01 per cent increase in carbon content. However, because the increase in strength obtained by this means is accompanied by a marked impairment in ductility, notch toughness and weldability, the carbon content of high-strength low-alloy steels is generally kept below some maximum value that depends upon the over-all chemical composition and the intended application.

For welding applications, these steels are often required to meet ASTM Specifications A 242, A 441, A 374, or A 375, which limit the carbon content, by check analyses, to 0.26 per cent. In contrast, ASTM Specification A 440 permits carbon contents as high as 0.32 per cent in a high-strength low-alloy steel intended for bolted and riveted applications.

It is generally desirable to keep the carbon content below certain maximum values when metal-arc welding is involved to avoid embrittlement of the heat-affected zone adjacent to the weld. Increased carbon content increases hardenability so that the tendency for hard, brittle martensite to form in the heat-affected zone is increased. Also, the higher the carbon content, the more brittle the martensitic-type structure will be in the event that it does form. For structural carbon steels with manganese contents below about 0.60 per cent, the upper limit of carbon content should be about 0.30 per cent for metal-arc welding unless a pre-heat and/or low-hydrogen electrodes are used. With high-strength low-alloy steels that have increased hardenability due to the presence of other alloying elements, this upper limit for carbon content may be reduced to considerably lower values, depending upon the particular composition involved. Appreciably lower carbon contents are required for spot welding than can be tolerated for metal-arc welding.

The addition of carbon improves the fatigue limit in direct proportion to the amount it raises the tensile strength. Variations in carbon content or thermal history have little or no effect on the atmospheric-corrosion properties of high-strength low-alloy steels.

Manganese—High-strength low-alloy steels generally have higher manganese contents than structural carbon steels. The effect of this element on strength and fatigue limit is similar to that of carbon but to a milder degree. Manganese has been shown to improve notch toughness and is often added to high-strength low-alloy steels to counteract an impairment of this property caused by some other strengthening element that is present. In steels for welding applications, this element should be kept below some maximum value that depends on the over-all composition but mainly on the carbon content. For example, ASTM specifications for weldable high-strength low-alloy steels (A 242 and A 441) limit the manganese content to 1.30 per cent by check analyses, whereas the specification for non-welding steels (A 440) allows content as high as 1.65 per cent. A small beneficial effect on atmospheric-corrosion resistance is attributed to manganese.

Phosphorus—Many of the present-day high-strength low-alloy steels have phosphorus contents in the range of 0.04 to 0.15 per cent. Additions of phosphorus markedly increase the strength properties of steel, but this increase is accompanied by a decrease in ductility. Phosphorus was formerly considered to cause embrittlement in steels when present in amounts exceeding about 0.10 per cent. It has been found, however, that the embrittling effect of phosphorus is influenced markedly by the carbon content and that this effect is not so pronounced in the low range of carbon contents generally employed in the manufacture of high-strength low-alloy steels. It has also been noted that additions of aluminum, such as are used in silicon-aluminum deoxidation practice, improve the notch toughness of phosphorus-bearing steels.

With respect to metal-arc welding, the effect of phosphorus is similar to, but somewhat greater than, that of manganese. Since the heat-affected parent metal is of principal concern when a steel is welded, the carbon content must be kept low enough so that the phosphorus that is present will not increase the hardenability of the steel by an amount sufficient to produce martensite. Addition of phosphorus, as in the case of carbon and manganese, increases the fatigue limit in approximately direct proportion to the increase in the tensile strength. The atmospheric-corrosion resistance of steel is considerably increased by the addition of phosphorus. Also, when small amounts of copper are present in the steel, the effect of phosphorus is greatly enhanced so that a given amount of phosphorus and copper together provide a greater beneficial effect than that produced by the corresponding amount of either of the individual elements.

Copper—Copper in limited quantities is beneficial to steels of the high-strength low-alloy type. Many present-day high-strength low-alloy steels contain copper in amounts ranging from 0.20 to 1.30 per cent. Copper increases the strength properties and the hardness of low- and medium-carbon steels with only a slight accompanying decrease in ductility. The fatigue limit is improved by the addition of copper, in proportion to the increase produced in the tensile strength. Copper up to at least 0.75 per cent is considered to have little effect on notched-bar toughness or welding performance. Steels containing over about 0.60 per cent copper are susceptible to precipitation hardening. Steels containing about 0.50 per cent or more of copper frequently exhibit "hot shortness" during hot working, so that cracks or extremely roughened surfaces, sometimes referred to as "checking," may develop during hot deformation at too high a temperature or during hot working after overheating. The occurrence of these undesirable surface conditions can be minimized by careful control of oxidation during heating and taking care not to overheat for hot working. Also, the addition of nickel in an amount equal to at least one-half the copper content is very beneficial to the surface quality of steels containing copper. Copper, in the concentrations used, is by far the most potent of all the common alloying elements in improving atmospheric-corrosion resistance. Copper is especially effective in amounts up to about 0.35 per cent in regular carbon steel. Continued improvement may be obtained up to about 1.00 per cent copper, but the effect is not nearly so marked as with additions up to about 0.35 per cent copper.

Vanadium—Vanadium is a widely used strengthening agent in high-strength low-alloy steels. In fact, a separate ASTM specification (A 441) has been developed for high-strength low-alloy steels with a minimum vanadium content of 0.01 per cent by check analyses. This element, in amounts up to about 0.12 per cent, provides increased strength without impairing the weldability or notch toughness of high-strength low-alloy steels. For this reason, the vanadium-bearing high-strength low-alloy steels are especially suited for welding applications where notch toughness is an important factor.

Columbium (Niobium)—The use of columbium as a strengthening agent in high-strength low-alloy steels became commercially important several years ago when the economic availability of this element was markedly increased. Small additions of this element provide significant increases in the yield point and, to a lesser extent, in the tensile strength of carbon steel. For example, the addition of 0.02 per cent of columbium has been found to provide an increase of 10,000 to 15,000 lb. per sq. in. in yield point in medium-carbon steel. However, the increased strength is accompanied by a marked impairment of notch toughness in heavier sections. Therefore, columbium-bearing high-strength low-alloy steels are generally limited to lighter thicknesses. Columbium, in the small amounts added, also does not impair weldability. Columbium-bearing high-strength low-alloy steels are usually produced as low-cost steels for maximum economy and do not generally contain additional alloying elements for such attributes as enhanced resistance to corrosion.

Other Elements—Examination of Table 43—III discloses that elements other than those discussed above are added to various high-strength low-alloy steels. Space does not permit a full discussion of the effect of the individual elements, but the amount of each element present in these steels has been added to obtain a desired improvement in one or more of the essential characteristics and properties. Generally, some sacrifice has been made in weldability, and even occasionally in formability, in order to obtain the desired higher strength and increased resistance to atmospheric corrosion, along with higher fatigue limit and greater abrasion resistance. The specific combinations of elements employed in the individual steels have resulted in various compromises of the properties and characteristics previously discussed.

Many articles and papers have been published that deal with the properties, characteristics, and fabrication of the steels of various compositions that are termed high-strength low-alloy steels, and a number of references that cover the subject in greater detail will be found at the end of this chapter.

APPLICATIONS

High-strength low-alloy steel can be used advantageously in any structural application where its greater strength can be utilized either to decrease the weight or increase the durability of the structure. Although these steels find application in all recognized market classifications, the largest single field of application has been in the construction of transportation equipment. From 1934 to 1959, one of the leading grades of high-strength low-alloy steel had been used in the construction of 275,000 railroad freight cars and 7,000 railroad passenger cars. If all the prominent grades were considered, the number of freight cars in service constructed partly of high-strength low-alloy steels would doubtless have exceeded 400,000 or 25 per cent of the current car ownership of American Class I railroads.

Previously, the main emphasis in railroad freight-car usage was on the savings in operating costs obtained by using high-strength low-alloy steels in somewhat reduced thicknesses to decrease the dead weight of cars or to increase their capacity without increasing the dead weight. In recent years, however, the emphasis has shifted in many applications from weight reduction to the obtaining of stronger, more durable equipment with little or no increase in weight. Similar benefits have also been obtained with other mobile equipment, such as various types of trucks, trailers, and buses.

In bridges, designers are giving increased recognition to the importance of reducing dead weight. One solution has been the use of high-strength low-alloy steels, particularly for bridges involving long spans in which a reduction of weight at the center permits additional savings in the weight of supporting members. High-strength low-alloy steels also lend themselves to economical tower construction, where the properties permit the use of sections smaller than would be required in structural carbon steel. This advantage is important in tall television towers, where forces resulting from wind resistance are lessened by use of smaller sections, and in transmission towers where lighter weight is a substantial advantage in reducing freight and handling costs.

A recent new use of high-strength low-alloy steels has been for columns in high-rise buildings. Judicious use of high-strength low-alloy steels in place of, and in combination with, structural carbon steel can result in substantial cost savings and an increase in usable floor area. High-strength low-alloy steels are also being used to advantage in the framing members of industrial and farm buildings.

COR-TEN steel has been used for exposed members of buildings because the architects desired the appearance of the tightly adherent oxide coating that forms on this steel. Also, because of the superior atmospheric-corrosion resistance of this steel, it is being used in the "bare" condition for towers and similar structures to eliminate the cost of maintenance painting.

The weight of portable containers for liquified petroleum gas, such as used to supply gas for domestic and other low-capacity heating requirements, has been reduced appreciably by the use of high-strength low-alloy steel, making them easier and less costly to handle and ship. Almost all such portable containers are now made of high-strength low-alloy steel.

A few of the many applications for high-strength low-alloy steels include: the inner bottoms, floors, tanks, and hatch covers of ore boats; hulls and other structural members of small tankers, barges, tugs, launches, and river boats; coal bunkers; street-lighting poles; portable oil-drilling rigs; jet-blast fences;

cable reels; automobile bumpers; pole-line hardware; air-conditioning equipment; oil-storage tanks; stokers; agricultural-machinery parts; earth-moving equipment; military and domestic shipping containers; and air-preheater tubes.

Bibliography

Am. Chemical Society, Corrosion resistance of metals and alloys; 2nd ed., Monograph series no. 158, N. Y., Reinhold (1963).

Am. Society for Metals, Corrosion of metals, Cleveland, Ohio, The Society (1946).

Am. Society for Metals, Metals handbook; 8th ed. Vol. 1, Cleveland, Ohio, The Society (1961), (High-strength structural steels of 40,000 to 100,000 psi minimum yield strength, 87–94).

Am. Society for Testing and Materials, 1964 book of ASTM Standards; part 4, Philadelphia, Pa., The Society, (1964), (Designations A 242–63T, A 440–63T, and A 441–63T).

Am. Welding Society, Welding handbook; section 4, 4th ed., N. Y., The Society, (1960), (Chapter 63: Low-alloy steels, 63.1–63.30).

Architectural Record (Editors), The steel that will weather naturally, 132, 148–150 (1962).

Austin, J. B., Trends in the metallurgy of low-alloy high-yield-strength steels. Amer. Society for Testing and Materials, 1963 Gillett Memorial lecture.

Bain, E. C., Functions of the alloying elements in steel. Published by American Society for Metals, Cleveland, Ohio (1939).

Bain, E. C. and Llewellyn, F. T., Low alloy structural steels (Part of structural application of steel and light-weight alloys: a symposium) Am. Society of Civil Engineers, Trans. 102, 1240–1256 (1937).

Clapp, H. E. and Lore, S. C., High-performance steels in modern railroad freight and passenger-car construction. Am. Society of Mechanical Engineers, Paper no. 63-WA-221 (1963) (to be published in Technical Digest).

Coburn, S. K., Gilliland, G. W., and Pohlman, J. C., Bare steel structures—a new concept. Electrical Engineering 82, 666–672 (1963).

Copson, H. R. and Larrabee, C. P., Extra durability of paint on low-alloy steels. ASTM Bull. no. 242, 68-74 (1959).

Fenwick, F. and Johnston, J., Steels resistant to scaling and corrosion. Industrial and Engineering Chemistry 28, 1374–1379 (1936).

Frost, R. W., The static and dynamic behaviour of hybrid steel beams. Society of Automotive Engineers, Paper 769A, October 1963.

Haaijer, G., Economy of high strength steel structural members. Am. Society of Civil Engineers, Transactions 128; part 2, 820–847 (1963).

Kelly, B. J., Corrosion of railroad hopper car body sheets. Corrosion 7, 196–201 (1951).

LaQue, F. L. and Boylan, J. A., Effect of composition of steel on performance of organic coatings in atmospheric exposure. Corrosion 9, 237–241 (1953).

Larrabee, C. P., Corrosion resistant steels for marine application. Corrosion 14, 501t–504t (1958).

Larrabee, C. P., Mechanism of atmospheric corrosion of ferrous metals. Corrosion 15, 526t–529t (1959).

Larrabee, C. P., Corrosion resistance of high-strength low-alloy steels as influenced by composition and environment. Corrosion 9, 259–271, (1953).

Pohlman, J. C., Higher strength steels provide design flexibility. Inst. of Electrical and Electronics Engineers, Conference paper 61–1173, October 16–20 (1961).

Priest, H. M., Design manual for high-strength steels. Pgh., U. S. Steel Corp., (1954).

CHAPTER 44

Silicon-Steel Electrical Sheets

Introductory—When an alternating electric current is passed through a wire coiled around an iron bar, a magnetic field is induced in the bar, or core as it is commonly called. This magnetic field will, in turn, induce an electric current in a second wire coiled around the same bar or core, but not connected to the first wire. During this process, some of the electrical energy is converted to heat which is wastefully dissipated. If the core is constructed of thin laminations insulated from each other, the amount of energy lost as heat will be considerably reduced because the stray magnetic fields that cause part of the energy loss cannot flow as freely in a laminated structure as they do in a solid bar. An additional, and far greater, reduction in energy loss can be obtained, however, by replacing the iron in the core with silicon steel. The relatively high permeability, high electrical resistance, and low hysteresis loss of the silicon steels, which contain ½ per cent to 5 per cent silicon, account for the beneficial reduction in energy loss.

The silicon steels (first patented by Sir Robert Hadfield about 1900) have made possible the development of more efficient and more powerful electrical equipment and have played an important role in the rapid growth of the electrical power industry. It has been estimated that this industry uses approximately 650,000 tons of silicon steel sheets annually.

In this chapter, reference is made only to steels produced in sheet form for the magnetic cores of electrical equipment and containing up to approximately 5 per cent silicon, which is the upper limit for commercial materials. Such products are referred to in the industry as electrical sheets.

CLASSIFICATION AND USES OF ELECTRICAL SHEETS

Silicon-steel electrical sheets may be divided into two general classifications, (1) grain-oriented steels, and (2) non-oriented steels. The grain-oriented steels, containing about 3¼ per cent silicon, are used in the highest-efficiency distribution and power transformers and in large turbine-generators. The non-oriented steels may be further subdivided into three classes on the basis of composition and application.

1. **Low-silicon steels** containing about ½ per cent to 1½ per cent silicon. These steels are used principally in the rotors and stators of motors and generators. Steels containing about 1 per cent are also used for reactors, relays, and small intermittent-duty transformers.

2. **Intermediate-silicon steels** containing about 2½ per cent to 3½ per cent silicon. These steels are used in motors and generators of average to high efficiency and in small to medium-sized intermittent-duty transformers, reactors, and motors.

3. **High-silicon steels** containing about 3¾ per cent to 5 per cent silicon. This class is used in power transformers and the highest-efficiency motors, generators, transformers, and in communications equipment.

There are a number of grades of electrical sheets in each of the above classifications. Specifically, there are three grain-oriented grades, typified by USS Transformer 73, 66 and 60, and eight non-oriented grades, USS Armature, USS Electrical (low-silicon), USS Motor, USS Dynamo (intermediate-silicon), USS Transformer 72, 65, 58, and 52 (high-silicon). The sheets are "graded" on the basis of a maximum specified core loss* at an induction of either 10 or 15 kilogausses. Specified maximum values for the grain-oriented grades have been established only at 15 kilogausses. Core loss values are expressed as watts per pound at 60 cycles and vary for each grade and thickness as shown in Table 44—I. It can be seen that the core loss of the non-oriented grades decreases (improves) as silicon content increases and thickness decreases.

PROCESSING OF ELECTRICAL SHEETS

Grain-Oriented—These grades are made from open hearth steel containing about 3¼ per cent silicon. The selection of the charge for the heats, and the melting and refining are under very close controls to insure the cleanest and purest steel possible. Otherwise, the furnace practice is similar to that used for other low-carbon steels. The alloying addition of silicon in the form of ferrosilicon is made to the steel in the ladle. Pouring practices are much like those used for other fully-killed steels and the ingots are rolled to slabs by common practices.

The slabs are next hot rolled and coiled in continuous hot strip mills. After rolling, the coils are pickled in continuous, single-strand picklers to remove the surface oxides formed during hot rolling. Subsequent steps in the processing may vary some-

---

* Definitions for core loss and other magnetic terms are given at the end of this chapter.

1105

Table 44—I. Maximum Core Losses for Electrical Sheets, Based on Epstein Test, A.S.T.M. Standard Method A-34.
(Watts per Pound at 60 Cycles and 10 Kilogausses)*

Electrical Sheet Gage No.		29	26	24	23	22
Gage Thickness (In.)		0.014	0.0185	0.025	0.0280	0.031
USS Grade	AISI Type No.					
USS Armature	M-43	—	1.47	1.83	2.05	2.30
USS Electrical	M-36	1.06	1.23	1.48	1.70	1.92
USS Motor	M-27	0.89	1.02	1.25	1.40	1.60
USS Dynamo	M-22	0.80	0.91	1.10	—	—
USS Transformer 72	M-19	0.72	0.83	0.97	—	—
USS Transformer 65	M-17	0.65	0.75	—	—	—
USS Transformer 58	M-15	0.58	0.68	—	—	—
USS Transformer 52	M-14	0.52	—	—	—	—
(Watts per Pound at 60 Cycles and 15 Kilogausses)						
USS Armature	M-43	—	3.45	4.20	4.70	5.30
USS Electrical	M-36	2.57	2.93	3.45	3.90	4.40
USS Motor	M-27	2.20	2.45	2.85	3.13	3.50
USS Dynamo	M-22	2.00	2.20	2.55	—	—
USS Transformer 72	M-19	1.75	2.00	2.35	—	—
USS Transformer 65	M-17	1.60	1.85	—	—	—
USS Transformer 58	M-15	1.45	1.70	—	—	—
USS Transformer 52	M-14	1.30	—	—	—	—
USS Transformer 73	M-7**	0.73	—	—	—	—
USS Transformer 66	M-6**	0.66	—	—	—	—
USS Transformer 60	M-5**	0.60	—	—	—	—

* Samples of Fully Processed Quality in as-sheared condition, unless otherwise indicated.
** Graded on the basis of a stress-relief annealed all-length Epstein Sample.

what among the various manufacturers, but generally they consist of two cold reductions, each followed by a suitable continuous anneal, and a final high-temperature box anneal. The steel may be used directly from the coil after box annealing for wound-core distribution transformers in spite of curvature ("coil-set") caused by annealing in coil form. If the steel is to be used for laminations in power transformers or turbine-generators, where this curvature is undesirable, the coil-set must be removed by continuous annealing.

Non-Oriented—Non-oriented electrical sheets are produced in two qualities: fully-processed and semi-processed. The fully-processed material has its desired magnetic properties developed prior to shipment from the mill. Semi-processed material, as shipped from the mill, requires annealing by the customer—usually after stamping—to develop the desired magnetic properties. The following descriptions apply to the production of fully-processed non-oriented electrical sheets.

Two general processing methods are used in the production of non-oriented electrical sheets. The older method consists of hot rolling the sheets on hand mills; it is being supplanted by the newer continuous cold-reduction method. The inherent brittleness of silicon steel at room temperature, however, normally limits the grades that can be cold reduced to those containing less than 3½ per cent silicon. Thus, it appears that production of high-silicon sheets in the hand mills will be continued until such an operation becomes uneconomical, or these grades can be made by the cold-reduction method.

The same grades of steel, with the exception noted above and also with some minor adjustments in composition, are used in both the hot-rolling and the cold-reduction methods. The practices for steelmaking, pouring, slabbing and rolling on a hot-strip mill are practically the same for both methods and are similar to those previously described for the grain-oriented grades. Beyond the hot-strip-mill rolling stage, however, the hot-rolling method and the cold-reduction method differ materially.

Hot-rolled strip coils intended for processing into sheets by the hot-rolling method are uncoiled and sheared into suitable lengths. The sheared pieces are doubled, reheated, and hot rolled in packs on hand-mills to a predetermined length. The length is such that the thickness of the individual sheets comprising the pack is reduced to the ordered thickness during the hot-rolling. After rolling, the packs are sheared to the ordered length and width and the sheets in the packs are separated from each other. Subsequent processing of the sheets may vary somewhat, depending on the magnetic quality desired, but generally the treatments will include pickling, cold-rolling to flatten (no substantial reduction in thickness), and box annealing at a suitable temperature to develop the required magnetic properties.

The hot-rolled coils that are to be processed by the cold-reduction method are pickled (continuous) and then cold-reduced to the desired thickness. The cold-reduction operation is accomplished in tandem mills or in single-stand reversing mills. The processing includes suitable box-annealing and continuous-annealing treatments to develop the required magnetic properties and suitable flatness.

The processing of grain-oriented and non-oriented electrical sheets described above may be followed by core plating if this is desired by the customer. The core plating operation is discussed in the following paragraphs.

CORE PLATING

The cores of transformers and other electrical structures are constructed of laminations to restrict the flow of eddy currents and hereby reduce this component of the core loss. For this to be successful, however, it is necessary that each lamination be insulated from the others so that the eddy currents will not flow readily from one lamination to another. The normal surface oxide on fully-annealed silicon-steel sheets provides a certain amount of this necessary insulation or interlamination resistance, but in many cases it must be supplemented. The additional insulation is supplied by coating the sheets or laminations with a thin coating of varnish or core plate, which has good electrical resistance and which is capable of maintaining this resistance under normal operating conditions of temperature and pressure. When used in oil-immersed transformer cores, the core plate must not react with the oil because the products of this reaction would interfere with the circulation of the oil and thus cause excessive heating of the transformer.

There are two main types of core plate in common use, organic and inorganic, although there are many different classes of these two types. The usual method of applying either type is to pass the sheets or laminations through rolls coated with the core plate, and then through a combination flashing and baking oven. The thickness of the coating must be controlled, since the heavier the coating the greater will be the insulating properties. The coating cannot be too thick, however, because this will in effect reduce the amount of steel in a core of a specific height. Baking temperatures differ, depending on the composition and type of coating used. In general, the organic varnishes require more care in baking, since it is essential to volatilize off most of the vehicle and thus obtain a coating free from tackiness. Under-baking results in a soft, tacky coating which will not have satisfactory insulating properties at the pressure present in the core after assembling. Care also must be taken to prevent over-baking because the varnish will become carbonized and the insulation characteristics of the coating will be thereby impaired.

The inorganic type core plates are free of volatile oils and organic matter. One of the requisites of an inorganic core plate is that it must be capable of withstanding annealing temperature up to about 1500° F. Transformer manufacturers specify this type of core plate when they anneal the laminations before assembling the core.

FACTORS AFFECTING MAGNETIC PROPERTIES

Among the many factors that affect the magnetic properties of silicon-steel electrical sheets, the most important are (1) composition, (2) internal stress, and (3) grain orientation.

Composition—Electrical sheets composed of pure silicon ferrite, if obtainable, would be superior to the best commercial grades of silicon steel manufactured today. Practically all elements other than silicon and aluminum, when added to iron, adversely affect the magnetic properties desired in these "soft" magnetic materials. The absolute influence of each element is masked by the effects of other elements, but it is generally agreed that carbon is the most detrimental, followed in order by sulphur, oxygen, and nitrogen. Manganese and phosphorus apparently have little effect on magnetic properties, at least in the quantities normally present in commercial silicon steels. Consideration must be given to the state or form in which the impurity is present, however, as this may greatly alter its effect on magnetic properties. For example, widely-dispersed, fine particles of an impurity are more harmful than an agglomeration of the same impurity into a few relatively large particles.

Internal Stress—Three of the more important magnetic properties, permeability, coercive force, and hysteresis loss, are adversely affected by internal stress. For that reason, every effort is made in the processing of electrical sheets to produce a stress-free product. There are two main sources of internal stresses, (1) impurities that cause dislocations in the crystal lattice, and (2) mechanical stresses introduced during the rolling operations that are not completely removed during subsequent annealing or that are introduced by cooling too rapidly from the annealing temperature. Precautions are taken throughout the processing to reduce impurities such as carbon, sulphur, nitrogen, and oxygen to the lowest possible level to avoid internal stresses from this source. Mechanical stresses are minimized by annealing at high temperatures to completely remove the stresses introduced during working and by cooling very slowly from the annealing temperature.

Grain Orientation—Most magnetic properties are markedly affected by crystal orientation. That is, such properties are better in one of the three principal crystallographic directions of the unit cubes than they are in the other two directions. This directionality of magnetic properties is undesirable in many applications such as in rotating machinery, but it has definite advantages in other applications. The cores of distribution and power transformers can be wound or constructed from laminations cut from the sheets to take advantage of such directionality. Consequently, the manufacturers of grain-oriented electrical sheets strive to develop this characteristic to a high degree. The processing of grain-oriented sheets was described in an earlier section of this chapter.

After completion of this processing, most of the grains are so arranged that edges of the unit cubes comprising each grain are aligned parallel to the rolling direction and face diagonals are aligned in the transverse direction. Because each cube is most easily

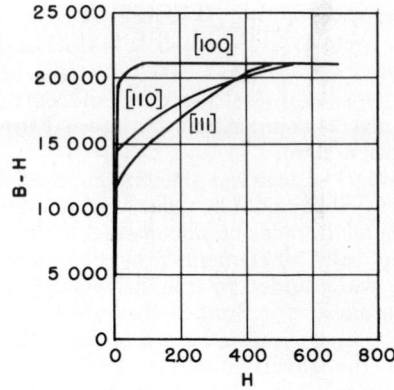

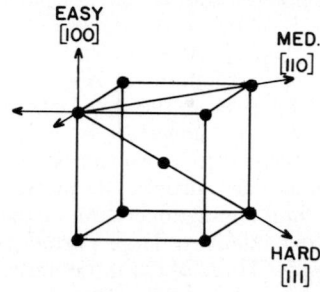

FIG. 44—1. Effect of orientation on the magnetic properties of a crystal, showing relative ease with which the cubes comprising the iron-silicon space lattice can be magnetized in different directions.

magnetized along its edge, the [100] direction, the magnetic properties of grain-oriented sheets are best in the rolling direction. As shown in Figure 44—1, the face diagonal, [110] direction, of each cube is more difficult to magnetize than the cube edge, and the cube diagonal, [111] direction, is the most difficult to magnetize. The magnitude of these differences is also illustrated in Figure 44—1. Thus, the magnetic properties of grain-oriented sheets are best in the rolling direction, poorer at 90 degrees to the rolling direction, and poorest at 55 degrees.

Consumers of grain-oriented sheets take advantage of this directionality effect by constructing magnetic cores in such a manner that the main flux path is in the rolling direction. As examples of the extent of the directional effect, the core loss and permeability at 15 kilogausses in the rolling direction may be as much as 2½ and 50 times better, respectively, than the same properties in the transverse direction.

EFFECTS OF SILICON ON IRON-CARBON ALLOYS

In addition to improving magnetic properties by decreasing eddy-current and hysteresis losses and by increasing permeability, silicon also has the following effects on metallographic, physical, and mechanical characteristics:

1. Alloys of iron and silicon form a metallographic gamma loop which is closed at a silicon content of about 2¼ per cent. In the complete absence of carbon, only alpha iron (or delta iron at high temperatures) is present in alloys containing more than 2¼ per cent silicon. The addition of even as little as 0.05 per cent carbon, however, causes some gamma iron (austenite) to be present up to at least 5 per cent silicon, as shown in Figure 44—2.

2. The magnetic transformation (A_2) is depressed about 9° C (16° F) for each per cent of silicon up to about 4 per cent silicon. At a silicon content of about 4 per cent, the magnetic transformation (A_2) occurs at approximately 730° C (1346° F).

3. Silicon increases the electrical resistivity of iron 11.4 microhms per cubic centimeter for each added per cent of silicon.

4. The addition of silicon to iron reduces the density of the resulting alloy.

5. The addition of silicon to a low-carbon steel decreases the tendency for the material to age (impairment of magnetic properties with increased time and temperature), provided other factors are normal and properly controlled.

6. Brittleness, or lack of ductility, increases as the percentage of silicon increases.

MECHANICAL PROPERTIES

Although no appreciable drawing operations are involved in fabricating articles from silicon-steel sheets, the material must have good punching and shearing qualities and must be reasonably flat so that motor, generator, and transformer laminations may be punched or sheared therefrom without difficulty. Typical mechanical properties of the various silicon-steel grades are listed in Table 44—II.

In general, as the silicon content increases, elongation, Erichsen ductility, and Amsler bend values decrease, and hardness, yield point, and tensile strength increase. In the transformer grades, however, differences in processing treatments may alter these trends to some extent.

DEFINITIONS OF TERMS AND METHODS OF TESTING

The practical value of electrical sheets is determined principally by their magnetic characteristics. The most important characteristics that are used to evaluate this product are defined as follows:

Magnetic Aging is defined as the deterioration of magnetic properties of a material with increased time and temperature. Thus, as a material ages magnetically, its core loss increases and its permeability decreases. The American Society for Testing and Materials Standard Aging Test consists of measuring the magnetic properties of a sample before and after heating it to 100° C for 600 hours and then determining the change in properties.

Core Loss is defined as the energy expended in magnetizing a material with an alternating electric current. The core loss of a low-loss material such as

Table 44-II. Typical Mechanical Properties of Fully Processed Electrical Sheets

Grade*	Thickness (In.)	Approximate Si Content (Per Cent)	Approximate Resistivity (Microhms per cm³)	Yield Point Longitudinal (Lb. per Sq. In.)	Tensile Strength Longitudinal (Lb. per Sq. In.)	Per Cent Elongation in 2 In. Longitudinal	Rockwell Hardness B	Erichsen Cup (mm.)	Amsler Bends
USS Electrical (CR)	0.025	1.60	31	37,000	56,000	28	72	—	21
USS Motor (CR)	0.025	2.80	45	51,000	68,000	24	80	7.0	10
USS Dynamo (CR)	0.0185	3.25	50	55,000	69,000	16	82	5.4	10
USS Transformer 72 (CR)	0.0185	3.25	50	59,000	68,000	16	84	5.2	9
USS Transformer 65 (HR)	0.014	4.00	58	59,000	66,000	12	70	4.0	7
USS Transformer 58 (HR)	0.014	4.25	61	60,000	61,600	4	75	3.5	5
USS Transformer 52 (HR)	0.014	4.50	64	60,000	69,500	2	74	2.7	3
Grain-Oriented									
USS Transformer 60 (CR)	0.014	3.25	50	48,200	55,500	10	77	—	—

*(CR) indicates cold-reduced product; (HR) indicates hot-rolled product.

grain-oriented steel is composed of hysteresis, eddy-current and residual losses. Only the hysteresis and eddy-current losses are present in higher-loss material.

Core loss is measured on 3 by 28 centimeter specimens assembled with lap joints in the standard Epstein testing apparatus. The resulting values are expressed as watts per pound at a given flux density (usually 10 or 15 kilogausses) at a frequency of 60 cycles per second.

Eddy-Current Loss is that portion of the core loss caused by the circulation of stray magnetic currents in the magnetic material. These stray or eddy currents are generated in the core by the oscillation of the magnetic field in phase with the alternating electric current in the coil surrounding the core.

Eddy-current loss can be calculated from Maxwell's equation, or it can be determined by "separating" core loss into its components by the graphical method.

Hysteresis Loss is the power expended in a magnetic material, as a result of magnetic hystersis, when the magnetic induction is cyclic. Hysteresis loss is proportional to the area of the hysteresis loop and can be determined by measuring the area of a hysteresis loop plotted from data obtained in a permeameter.

Permeability is a measure of the ease with which the magnetic lines of force can pass through a substance magnetized with a given magnetizing force. Quantitatively, it is expressed as the ratio between the magnetic flux density (B) produced and the magnetizing force (H) producing this flux density. The Greek letter μ (mu) is used to designate this ratio. Thus,

$$\text{Permeability, } \mu = \frac{B}{H}$$

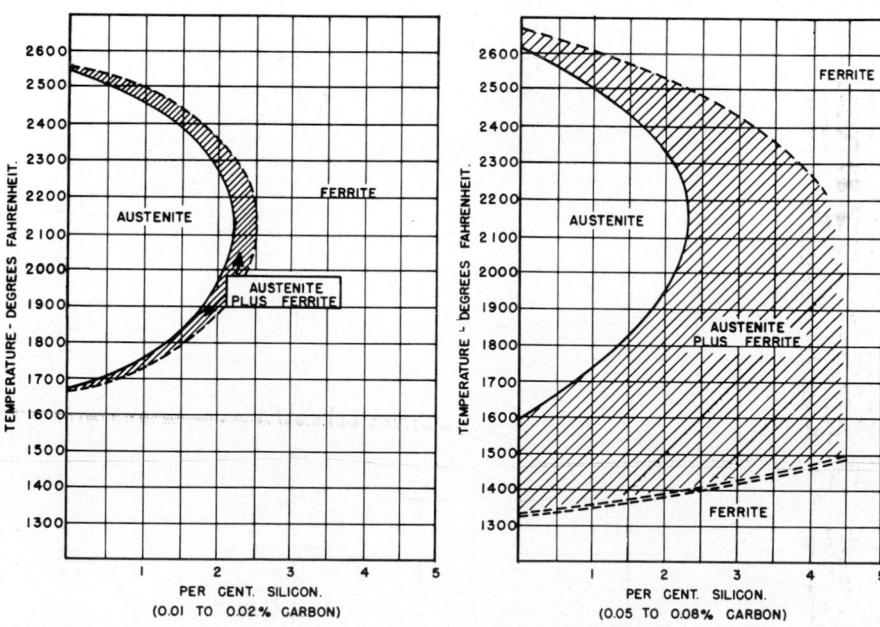

FIG. 44—2. (Left) Section of the ternary iron-silicon-carbon diagram at the 0.01 to 0.02 per cent carbon level; (right) same at the 0.05 to 0.08 per cent carbon level.

Alternating-current permeability is measured in the Epstein apparatus on 3 by 28 centimeter specimens assembled with lap joints. Direct-current permeability is measured in a permeameter, such as the Fahy Simplex Permeameter in which the specimen size is 3 by 25 centimeters or longer.

Magnetic Flux Density, or Induction is the number of lines of magnetic flux per unit area at right angles to the direction of the flux.

When a magnetic core having a closed magnetic circuit is magnetized by current flowing in the windings of the coil which enclose the core, magnetic lines of force are generated which are designated as magnetic flux. The total magnetic flux in the core, designated as Φ (phi), divided by the cross-sectional area of the core in square centimeters, gives the flux density (B), in lines per square centimeter, or gausses.

Magnetomotive Force is defined as the force which tends to produce a magnetic field. This force, when generated by an electric current flowing through a coil of wire, is proportional to the current and to the number of turns of wire in the coil. The term is not commonly used except in defining magnetizing force.

Magnetizing Force is defined as the magnetomotive force per unit of core length and is designated by the letter H. When the length of the core is expressed in centimeters, the unit of magnetizing force is the oersted. Another unit of magnetizing force sometimes used is ampere turns per inch which is 2.02 times greater than an oersted.

Saturation is the maximum flux density that can be obtained in a magnetic material. Further increases in magnetic force over that necessary to achieve this saturation flux density will not cause the generation of any additional flux within the material. Saturation occurs at a flux density of about 21,500 gausses in low-silicon steels and about 19,500 gausses in high-silicon steels.

Interlamination Resistance is the term applied to the electrical resistance measured perpendicular to the lamination plane in a stack of laminations under pressure. It indicates the effectiveness of surface oxides or core-plate coatings on the laminations in reducing interlamination (eddy-current) losses. Interlamination resistance values are generally expressed as ohms per square centimeter per strip at a given pressure in pounds per square inch.

Lamination Factor or Space Factor is the ratio of the volume of a stack of laminations under a given pressure to that of the solid material of the same mass, assuming a definite density based on the chemical composition. Thus, the factor indicates the deficiency of effective steel volume due to the surface roughness and lack of flatness of the laminations, or to the presence of oxides and core-plate coatings on the surface of the laminations. Space factor values are generally expressed as a percentage which is obtained by multiplying the volume ratio by 100.

Bibliography

T. Spooner, Properties and Testing of Magnetic Materials, McGraw-Hill Book Company, Inc., New York (1933).

E. S. Greiner, J. S. Marsh and B. Stoughton, Alloys of Iron and Silicon, McGraw-Hill Book Company, Inc., New York (1933).

C. S. Barrett, Structure of Metals, McGraw-Hill Book Company, Inc., New York (1943).

American Iron and Steel Institute, New York, New York, Steel Products Manual: "Flat Rolled Electrical Steel."

H. F. Shannon, Cold-Rolled Electrical Strip, Electrical Manufacturing, August, 1950.

R. M. Bozorth, Ferromagnetism, D. Van Nostrand Company, Inc., New York (1951).

United States Steel Corporation, Electrical Steel Sheets, Engineering Manual, Fourth Edition (1955).

CHAPTER 45

Stainless Steels

General—As the name implies, stainless steels are more resistant to rusting and staining than are plain carbon and lower alloy steels. This superior corrosion resistance is brought about by addition of the element chromium to alloys of iron and carbon. Although other elements, such as copper, aluminum, and silicon, nickel and molybdenum, also increase the corrosion resistance of steel, they are limited in their usefulness, and the discussion in this chapter will be confined to the iron-chromium and iron-chromium-nickel steels in which chromium is the major element for conferring corrosion resistance.

The minimum amount of chromium necessary to confer this superior corrosion resistance depends upon the corroding agent. The American Iron and Steel Institute has chosen 4 per cent chromium as the dividing line between "alloy" steel and "stainless" steel and for this discussion, the AISI views will be adopted. The standard types of stainless steels listed by the American Iron and Steel Institute in the Steel Products Manual entitled "Stainless and Heat Resisting Steels" (June, 1957) as amended by a Supplementary Information circular dated September 1959 are shown in Table **45**—I. (The information in these manuals is revised from time to time.) Most of these types are available in the main product forms such as plates, bars, shapes, sheet, strip, and tubes. A detailed list of the products and sizes available for each type of stainless steel is given in the AISI Steel Products Manual referred to above. [1]

As is true of all scientific developments, no single nation can claim credit for the stainless steels; Germany, England, and the United States shared alike in the development of these materials.

In 1912 Harry Brearley, head of the Brown-Firth Research Laboratory in England, while attempting to develop steels to resist the fouling and corrosion encountered in gun barrels, reported that a composition of 12.8 per cent chromium and 0.24 per cent carbon was quite resistant to corrosion. Brearley suggested that this composition be used for cutlery. In fact, our present cutlery steel, AISI Type 420 (12 to 14 per cent chromium, over 0.15 per cent carbon), is similar to the steel suggested by Brearley.

The development of the higher chromium-iron alloys was due to the work of F. M. Becket in the United States who, from 1903 on, was continuously attacking the problem of producing low-carbon ferrochromium from chromium ores. While investigating the effect of chromium on oxidation resistance

[1] References are at end of chapter.

at 2000° F (1095° C), Becket noted a marked increase in resistance as the chromium content was raised above 20 per cent. It is significant that even now and with steels containing appreciable quantities of nickel, 20 per cent seems to be the minimum amount of chromium necessary for oxidation resistance at 2000° F (1095° C).

The austenitic iron-chromium-nickel alloys were developed in Germany during the years 1909-1912 by Benno Strauss and Edward Maurer while searching for materials for use in pyrometer tubes. Further work by Strauss and others ultimately led to the versatile 18 per cent chromium, 8 per cent nickel steels (popularly called 18-8) which are used so widely today.

CONSTITUTION

As mentioned above, the corrosion resistance or "stainlessness" of the stainless steels is primarily a function of their chromium content. Therefore, in order to understand the structures, heat treatments, and properties of the present commercial steels, a working knowledge is needed of the iron-chromium, the iron-chromium-nickel, and iron-chromium-carbon diagrams.

Iron-Chromium System—At the present time, the iron-chromium diagram is known only on a semiquantitative basis. The diagram illustrated by Figure **45**—1 is a compromise diagram based on the work of many investigators. [2, 7] The difficulties of establishing a precise equilibrium diagram are due primarily to two causes:

1. The difficulty of preparing pure alloys of iron and chromium (nitrogen and carbon seem to be the chief impurities).
2. The sluggishness of the iron-chromium alloys to respond to heat treatment.

The first difficulty is relatively unimportant because melting practices have improved and purer alloys may be expected. However, the second difficulty often may be overlooked and thus lead to false conclusions.

The high-temperature portion of the diagram is based on the data of Adcock reported in 1931. [3] Adcock's data were accepted because of the high purity of his alloys and the techniques he employed.

The existence of the gamma loop was discovered in 1926 by Bain, [4] who also showed the effect of higher carbon contents on enlarging the austenite field. The intermetallic compound, sigma phase, was discovered in 1927 by Bain and Griffiths. [5]

These two regions were extensively studied by

Table 45—I. American Iron and Steel Institute Standard Type Numbers, Chemical Composition Limits and Ranges for Stainless Steels.

Type Number	C	Mn Max.	Si Max.	P Max.	S Max.	Cr	Ni	Other Elements
						Chemical Composition, Per Cent		
201	0.15 Max.	5.50-7.50	1.00	0.060	0.030	16.00-18.00	3.50-5.50	N: 0.25 Max.
202	0.15 Max.	7.50-10.00	1.00	0.060	0.030	17.00-19.00	4.00-6.00	N: 0.25 Max.
301	0.15 Max.	2.00	1.00	0.045	0.030	16.00-18.00	6.00-8.00	
302	0.15 Max.	2.00	1.00	0.045	0.030	17.00-19.00	8.00-10.00	
302B	0.15 Max.	2.00	2.00-3.00	0.045	0.030	17.00-19.00	8.00-10.00	
303	0.15 Max.	2.00	1.00	0.20	0.15 Min.	17.00-19.00	8.00-10.00	Mo: 0.60 Max.*
303 Se	0.15 Max.	2.00	1.00	0.20	0.06	17.00-19.00	8.00-10.00	Se: 0.15 Min.
304	0.08 Max.	2.00	1.00	0.045	0.030	18.00-20.00	8.00-12.00	
304L	0.03 Max.	2.00	1.00	0.045	0.030	18.00-20.00	8.00-12.00	
305	0.12 Max.	2.00	1.00	0.045	0.030	17.00-19.00	10.00-13.00	
308	0.08 Max.	2.00	1.00	0.045	0.030	19.00-21.00	10.00-12.00	
309	0.20 Max.	2.00	1.00	0.045	0.030	22.00-24.00	12.00-15.00	
309S	0.08 Max.	2.00	1.00	0.045	0.030	22.00-24.00	12.00-15.00	
310	0.25 Max.	2.00	1.50	0.045	0.030	24.00-26.00	19.00-22.00	
310S	0.08 Max.	2.00	1.50	0.045	0.030	24.00-26.00	19.00-22.00	
314	0.25 Max.	2.00	1.50-3.00	0.045	0.030	23.00-26.00	19.00-22.00	
316	0.08 Max.	2.00	1.00	0.045	0.030	16.00-18.00	10.00-14.00	Mo: 2.00-3.00
316L	0.03 Max.	2.00	1.00	0.045	0.030	16.00-18.00	10.00-14.00	Mo: 2.00-3.00
317	0.08 Max.	2.00	1.00	0.045	0.030	18.00-20.00	11.00-15.00	Mo: 3.00-4.00
321	0.08 Max.	2.00	1.00	0.045	0.030	17.00-19.00	9.00-12.00	Ti: 5 x C, Min.
347	0.08 Max.	2.00	1.00	0.045	0.030	17.00-19.00	9.00-13.00	Cb-Ta: 10 x C, Min.†
348	0.08 Max.	2.00	1.00	0.045	0.030	17.00-19.00	9.00-13.00	Cb-Ta: 10 x C, Min., Ta: 0.10 Max., Co: 0.20 Max.†
403	0.15 Max.	1.00	0.50	0.040	0.030	11.50-13.00		
405	0.08 Max.	1.00	1.00	0.040	0.030	11.50-14.50		Al: 0.10-0.30
410	0.15 Max.	1.00	1.00	0.040	0.030	11.50-13.50		
414	0.15 Max.	1.00	1.00	0.040	0.030	11.50-13.50	1.25-2.50	
416	0.15 Max.	1.25	1.00	0.06	0.15 Min.	12.00-14.00		Mo: 0.60 Max.*
416 Se	0.15 Max.	1.25	1.00	0.06	0.06	12.00-14.00		Se: 0.15 Min.
420	Over 0.15	1.00	1.00	0.040	0.030	12.00-14.00		
430	0.12 Max.	1.00	1.00	0.040	0.030	14.00-18.00		
430F	0.12 Max.	1.25	1.00	0.06	0.15 Min.	14.00-18.00		Mo: 0.60 Max.*
430F Se	0.12 Max.	1.25	1.00	0.06	0.06	14.00-18.00		Se: 0.15 Min.
431	0.20 Max.	1.00	1.00	0.040	0.030	15.00-17.00	1.25-2.50	
440A	0.60-0.75	1.00	1.00	0.040	0.030	16.00-18.00		Mo: 0.75 Max.
440B	0.75-0.95	1.00	1.00	0.040	0.030	16.00-18.00		Mo: 0.75 Max.
440C	0.95-1.20	1.00	1.00	0.040	0.030	16.00-18.00		Mo: 0.75 Max.
446	0.20 Max.	1.50	1.00	0.040	0.030	23.00-27.00		N: 0.25 Max.
501	Over 0.10	1.00	1.00	0.040	0.030	4.00-6.00		Mo: 0.40-0.65
502	0.10 Max.	1.00	1.00	0.040	0.030	4.00-6.00		Mo: 0.40-0.65

*At producer's option; reported only when intentionally added.   †Columbium is also called niobium.

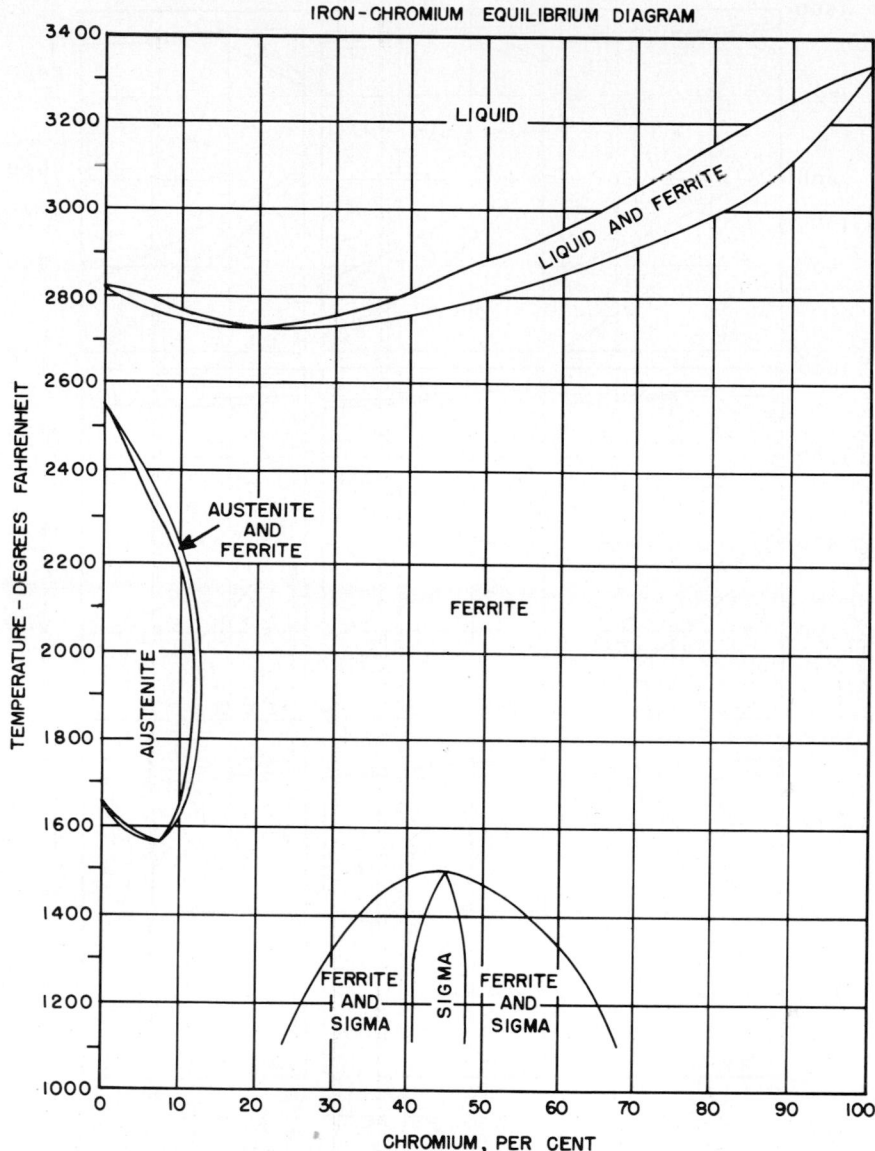

IRON-CHROMIUM EQUILIBRIUM DIAGRAM

Fig. 45—1. The iron-chromium equilibrium diagram. (Adapted from American Society for Metals Handbook, 1948 Edition.)

other investigators and their data differed widely. This difference was especially marked for the sigma region. The most careful investigation, that of Adcock, who used the purest alloys of all, failed to detect the phase and Adcock came to the conclusion that the phase did not exist.

However, the evidence of other investigators was overwhelmingly in favor of the existence of sigma phase. In 1936, Jette and Foote,[6] using alloys similar in purity to those of Adcock, were able to produce and identify sigma phase. Surprisingly enough, when they used treatments similar to those of Adcock, no sigma phase was formed. They concluded that Adcock's alloys were too pure and too well annealed for transformation to take place in the time allowed.

Finally, the entire matter was conclusively settled in 1943 by Cook and Jones[7] who, using Adcock's original alloys and longer transformation times, reported the sigma limit as shown. The boundary lines as shown by Cook and Jones are based on X-ray data but may still be questioned because equilibrium may not have been attained and longer annealing times may widen the ferrite + sigma region. An excellent bibliography pertaining to more recent studies of sigma phase in stainless steels has been published by Smith.[22]

The diagram itself shows that as the chromium content increases, the austenite region is decreased until, above 12.5 per cent chromium, austenite no longer exists. After normal heat treatment, alloys above this

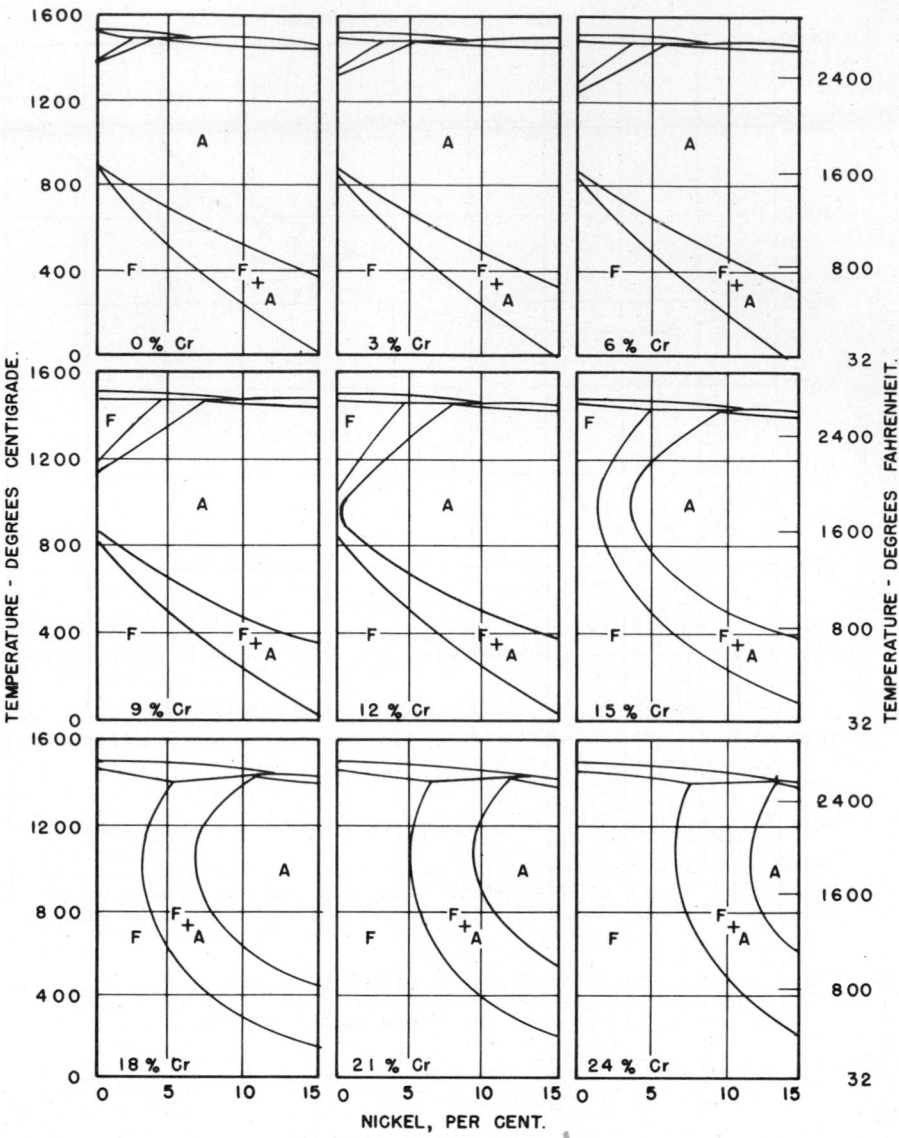

FIG. 45—2. The iron-chromium-nickel diagram at constant chromium content.[9] The symbols "A" and "F" stand for austenite and ferrite, respectively.

chromium content consist entirely of a single phase—alpha, but as shown, sigma phase is stable and will form after long times at temperatures as low as 900° F (480° C) and below the upper limit.

Very little is known quantitatively about the effect of impurities upon this diagram. Bain[4] has reported on the effect of carbon on the austenite region. Andersen and Jette[8] reported that silicon increases the sigma region. Bain and Aborn[9] reported that nickel also increases the sigma region. Aluminum, molybdenum, titanium, and columbium (niobium) probably increase it.

Iron-Chromium-Nickel System—Like the iron-chromium system, the iron-chromium-nickel system is known only semi-quantitatively but the existing diagrams are useful for interpretation of what otherwise would be mysterious behavior. The investigation of this system also has been hampered by slow reaction

rates. The first investigation of the iron-chromium-nickel system was conducted in 1909–1912 by Strauss[10] who studied the iron-rich corner. He found that the alloy having 20 per cent chromium and 7 per cent nickel contained free carbide which could be dissolved at 2280° F (1250° C) and retained in solution at room temperature by rapid cooling. He also noted a grain boundary precipitation at 1290° F (700° C).

The first comprehensive study was the heretofore mentioned investigation of Bain and Griffiths.[5] These investigators were the first to report sigma phase and they noted that nickel raised the upper temperature limit of this phase.

Bain and Aborn[9] made a comprehensive review of the iron-chromium-nickel system, which is summarized in Figure 45—2.

The work of the British in this field has been very extensive. Figure 45—3 shows an isothermal section

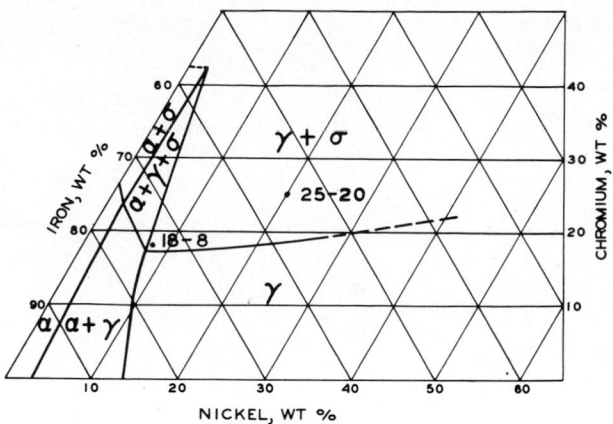

FIG. 45—3. The iron-chromium-nickel diagram. Isothermal section at 1200° F.[11] α, γ and σ represent alpha (ferrite), gamma (austenite), and sigma phases, respectively.

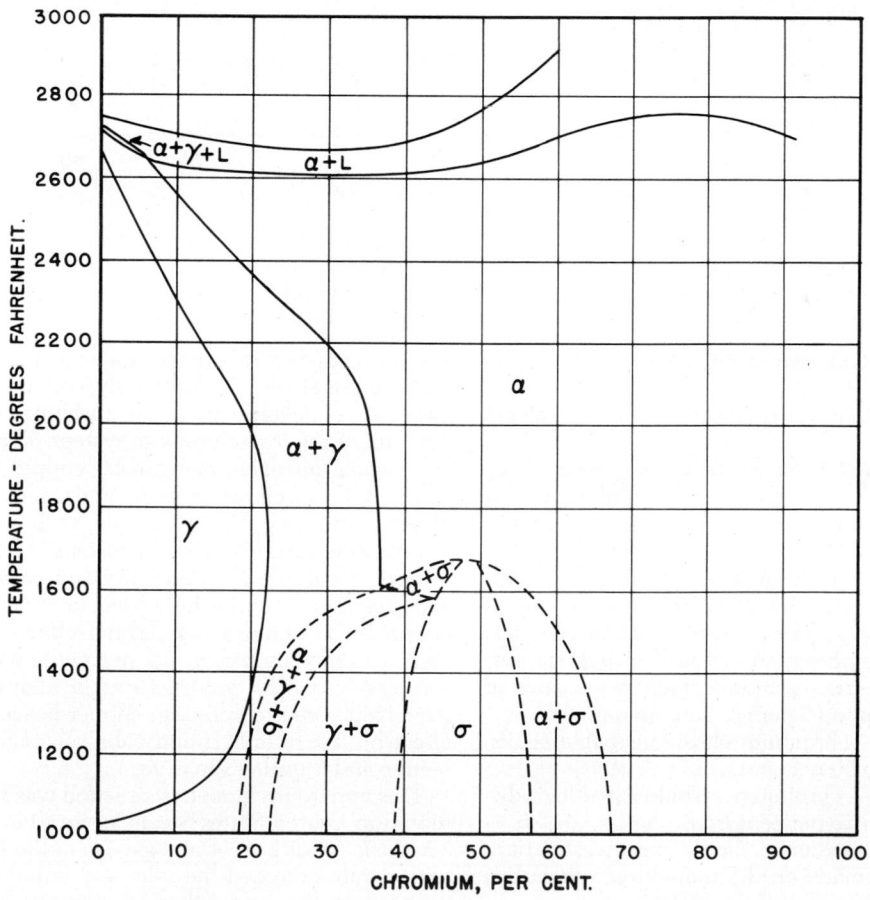

FIG. 45—4. The iron-chromium-nickel diagram. Section at 8 per cent nickel.[15] α, γ and σ represent alpha (ferrite), gamma (austenite), and sigma phases respectively. L signifies liquid.

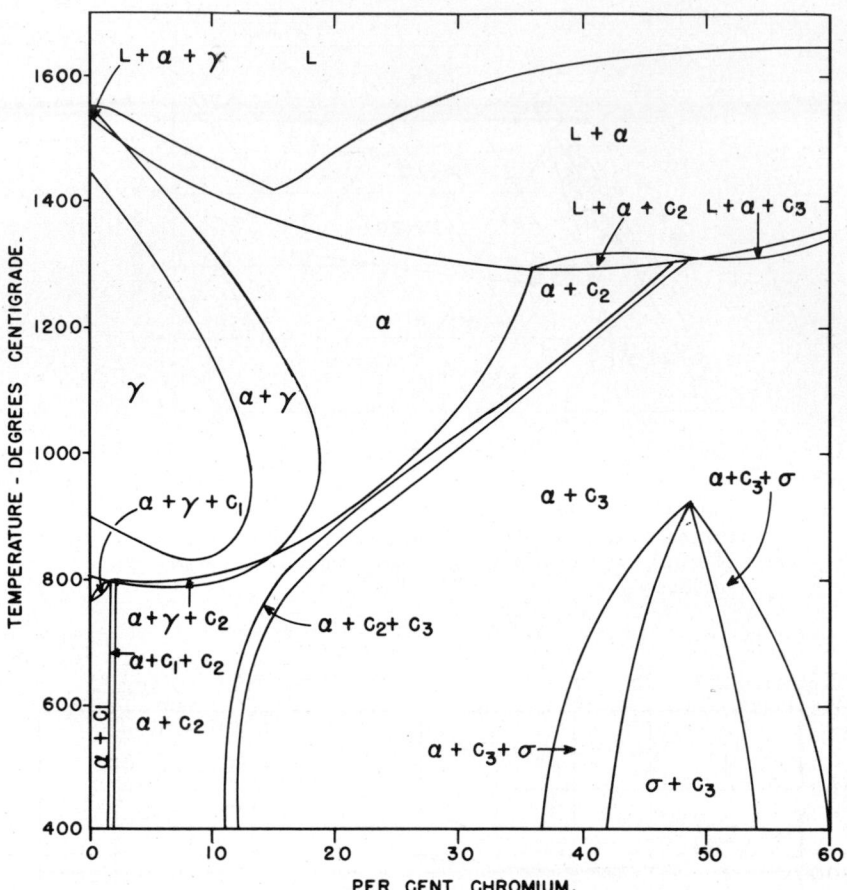

FIG. 45—5. The iron-chromium-carbon diagram. Section at 0.10 per cent carbon.[12] α, γ and σ represent alpha (ferrite), gamma (austenite), and sigma phases, respectively. $C_1 = (Fe, Cr)_3C$. $C_2 = (Cr, Fe)_7C_3$. $C_3 = (Cr, Fe)_{23}C_6$.

at 1202° F (650° C) based on the data of Rees, Burns and Cook.[11]

Figure 45—4 shows a diagram at constant nickel content.

Iron-Chromium-Carbon System—The most complete information on the iron-chromium-carbon system has been supplied by Tofaute and his co-workers.[12, 13]

Figure 45—5[12] shows a section through the iron-chromium-carbon diagram at 0.10 per cent carbon and, as may be seen, the diagram is quite complex. The three carbide phases shown in this diagram are:

1. $(Fe, Cr)_3C$—iron carbide (cementite) capable of dissolving up to 15 per cent chromium.
2. $(Cr, Fe)_7C_3$—chromium carbide capable of dissolving up to 50 per cent iron.
3. $(Cr, Fe)_{23}C_6$—chromium carbide capable of dissolving up to 25 per cent iron.

An excellent discussion of the various investigations which have been made on the iron-chromium-carbon alloys is given by Kinzel and Crafts.[2]

Iron-Chromium-Manganese-Nitrogen System—The scarcity of nickel that occurred during World War II and again during the Korean conflict prompted a considerable amount of research in both the United States

and Germany on substitutes for nickel in the austenitic stainless steels. Unfortunately, only a few elements (other than nickel) expand the austenite region in the diagram of the iron-chromium system. These elements are carbon, nitrogen, manganese, copper, and cobalt. None of these elements as a single addition is completely satisfactory. For example, carbon in amounts necessary to form completely austenitic structures has a detrimental effect on ductility and corrosion resistance; nitrogen cannot be added in sufficiently large quantities to achieve the desired effect; manganese, even in amounts above 25 per cent, will not form completely austenitic structures in alloys containing over 15 per cent chromium; copper has a detrimental effect on hot ductility; and cobalt is only slightly effective and is quite expensive.

This apparently hopeless situation was solved by research in United States Steel Corporation which indicated that additions of manganese to the iron-chromium system increased the solid and liquid solubility of nitrogen to the extent that additions of nitrogen sufficient to make completely austenitic structures were possible. These results are summarized in Figures 45—6, 45—7, 45—8, and 45—9, which are so-called structure diagrams.[25] These diagrams show the in-

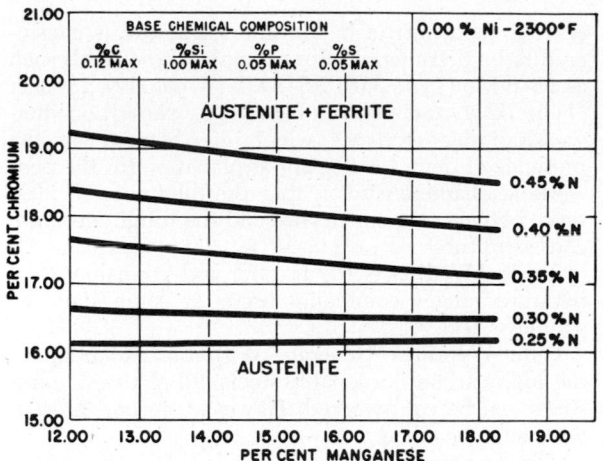

Fig. 45—6. Structure diagram for 0.00 per cent nickel, 0.25–0.45 per cent nitrogen steels after heating for one hour at 2300° F and water quenching.[25]

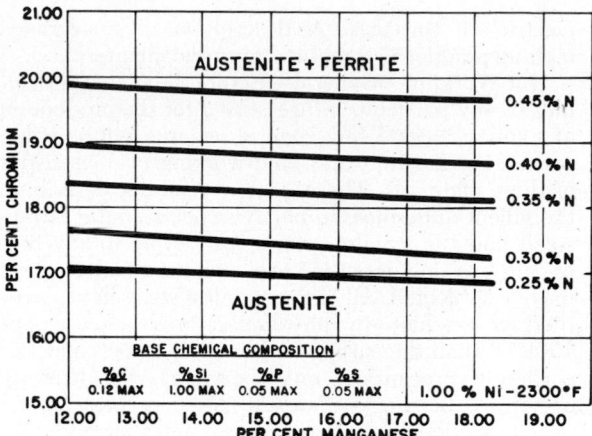

Fig. 45—7. Structure diagram for 1.00 per cent nickel, 0.25–0.45 per cent nitrogen steels after heating for one hour at 2300° F and water quenching.[25]

fluence of chromium, manganese, and nitrogen on the austenite—austenite-plus-ferrite boundary at 2300° F and at nickel-content levels of zero, 1, 2, and 3 per cent.

A temperature of 2300° F was chosen because this would represent a maximum hot-working temperature and the austenite formed at this temperature will not transform on cooling to room temperature.

MANUFACTURE AND FABRICATION

For the purpose of general discussion, the stainless steels are grouped into three classes:

1. **Martensitic—**Those iron-chromium alloys that lie within the gamma loop and thus are hardenable by heat treatment. Include Types 403, 410, 414, 416, 420, 431, 440A, 440B, 440C, 501 and 502.

2. **Ferritic—**Those iron-chromium alloys that are largely ferritic and not hardenable by heat treatment (ignoring the 885° F embrittlement). Include Types 405, 430, 430F and 446.

3. **Austenitic—**The iron-chromium-nickel alloys not hardenable by heat treatment and predominantly austenitic as commercially heat treated. Include Types 301, 302, 302B, 303, 304, 304L, 305, 308, 309, 310, 314, 316, 316L, 317, 321 and 347. Other austenitic stainless steels include those recently developed in which all or part of the nickel of the iron-chromium-nickel type of steel is replaced by manganese and nitrogen in proper amounts, such as USS TENELON and AISI grades 201 and 202.

Melting—All of the stainless steels are melted in either the electric-arc or high-frequency induction furnace, the largest tonnages by far being melted in

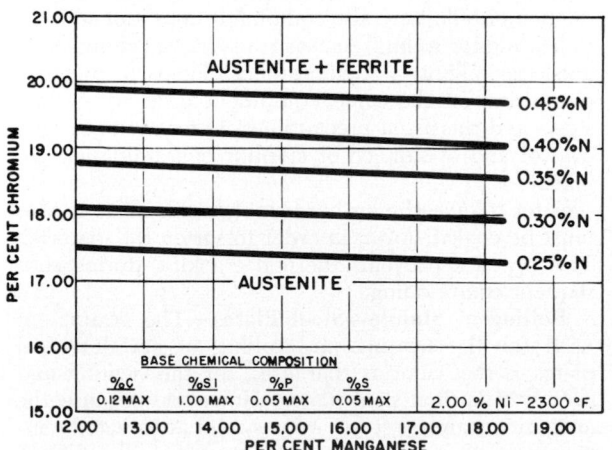

Fig. 45—8. Structure diagram for 2.00 per cent nickel, 0.25–0.45 per cent nitrogen steels after heating for one hour at 2300° F and water quenching.[25]

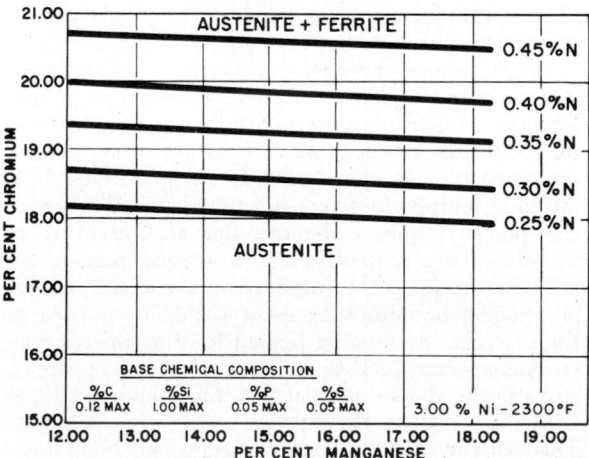

Fig. 45—9. Structure diagram for 3.00 per cent nickel, 0.25–0.45 per cent nitrogen steels after heating for one hour at 2300° F and water quenching.[25]

electric-arc furnaces. A description of arc-furnace melting practice is contained in earlier chapters.

Hot Working—General—Before discussing the details of any particular process used for the production of stainless steel, a few general remarks will be made concerning the hot- and cold-working characteristics of these materials. These general remarks, describing the salient differences in behavior between the carbon steels and the stainless steels, will apply to any hot- or cold-working operation to which the stainless steels may be subjected. All of the stainless steels have lower thermal conductivity at temperatures below about 1500° F than the carbon and low-alloy steels and, accordingly, precautions must be taken when heating, or surface burning will result. Also, for most of the stainless grades, the temperature ranges for optimum hot-working characteristics are narrower than those for the carbon steels and, hence, closer temperature control is necessary when hot working the stainless steels.

For all grades of stainless steel, optimum hot workability is obtained when the structure of the steel at the hot-working temperature consists essentially of a single phase. Small amounts of ferrite in the structure of the austenitic and martensitic steels and small amounts of austenite in the structure of the ferritic steels can be tolerated, but must be kept within proper limits either by proper adjustment of the chemical composition of the steel or by adjustment of the hot-working temperature.

The martensitic stainless steels can be forged, pierced and rolled. However, because these steels are air hardening, they must be slow cooled after rolling before any subsequent operation such as conditioning or cold working. Their "as-rolled" hardness also makes for brittleness which must be taken into account when handling the hot-rolled product.

The ferritic stainless steels also can be forged, pierced and rolled. These steels are very soft when hot, thus they are easily marked by guides or rolls, and spread considerably during hot rolling. Over-heating these grades causes excessive grain growth, which makes the material susceptible to tears and cracks. Additions of nitrogen have helped somewhat in preventing grain growth. To refine the grain size, finishing temperatures are kept as low as possible.

The austenitic stainless steels are generally stronger than ferritic steels at rolling temperature and, consequently, require more power for deformation. Like the ferritic steels, the austenitic steels are susceptible to grain growth and overheating should be avoided. Low finishing temperatures are not practicable because of the power required. During the heating of these nickel-bearing austenitic steels, special precautions are taken to keep the sulphur content of the furnace or soaking pit atmospheres at a minimum because these steels, after being heated in atmospheres containing sulphur, tend to tear and crack during rolling. Apparently, the sulphur in the atmosphere combines with the nickel in the steel to form nickel sulphide. This reaction usually occurs at the grain boundaries of the metal and, because the nickel sulphide is liquid at the rolling temperatures, the steels so attacked are weak and easily break apart during rolling. The presence of delta ferrite in the microstructure is considered to be detrimental. For example, those steels such as 18–8 Mo (Type 316), 18–8 Cb (Type 347), 18–8 Ti (Type 321), and 25–12 (Type 309), show poor hot-working characteristics which are blamed on the presence of delta ferrite. The explanation for the poor working characteristics is that the difference in plasticity between the soft ferrite and the tough austenite causes ruptures.

Table 45—II lists the forging and annealing temperature ranges commonly used for some standard stainless steels.

Cold Working—General—With the exception of the high-carbon hardenable steels, all of the stainless steels can be cold worked. However, certain precautions must be taken.

The ferritic stainless steels, especially those containing over 20 per cent chromium, are extremely notch sensitive at room temperature and care must be taken to avoid notches, otherwise considerable breakage will result. However, between 400° F (205° C) and 600° F (315° C) the steels are tough, and difficult cold-working operations are successfully accomplished by working the material in this temperature range.

Cold work causes some austenitic stainless steels to transform partially to a low-carbon martensite. This transformation, plus the effect of the strain hardening caused by the cold work itself, causes such austenitic steels to have a high rate of work hardening. More power is required to work these steels.

The Rolling of Stainless-Steel Ingots to Blooms and Slabs—Figure 45—10 shows flow diagrams illustrating the various steps involved in the manufacture of stainless-steel products. The equipment used for the heating and rolling of stainless-steel ingots is the same as that used for carbon-steel ingots. However, as previously mentioned, close temperature control and avoidance of sulphur contamination are precautions which should be followed when heating the stainless steels. Also, the stainless steels require more conditioning than the carbon steels. The bloom and slab products are completely conditioned.

Rolling of Billets—The blooms used for the production of billets are also completely conditioned prior to heating for rolling. As was true for the rolling of ingots, the rolling of stainless-steel blooms to billets is performed on the same equipment used for carbon steels and the usual precautions of close temperature control and avoidance of sulphur contamination are taken.

After rolling, the air-hardenable martensitic grades must be cooled slowly in order to soften the material. This practice prevents thermal cracking during subsequent conditioning.

Rolling of Stainless-Steel Plates—The equipment used for the heating and rolling of stainless-steel plates is the same as that used for the heating and rolling of carbon-steel plates. However, because the austenitic stainless steels are very stiff at elevated temperatures, they require more power for rolling. Consequently, the amount of reduction per pass is smaller for the austenitic grades. Also, these steels spread less than do the ordinary steels and due allowances are

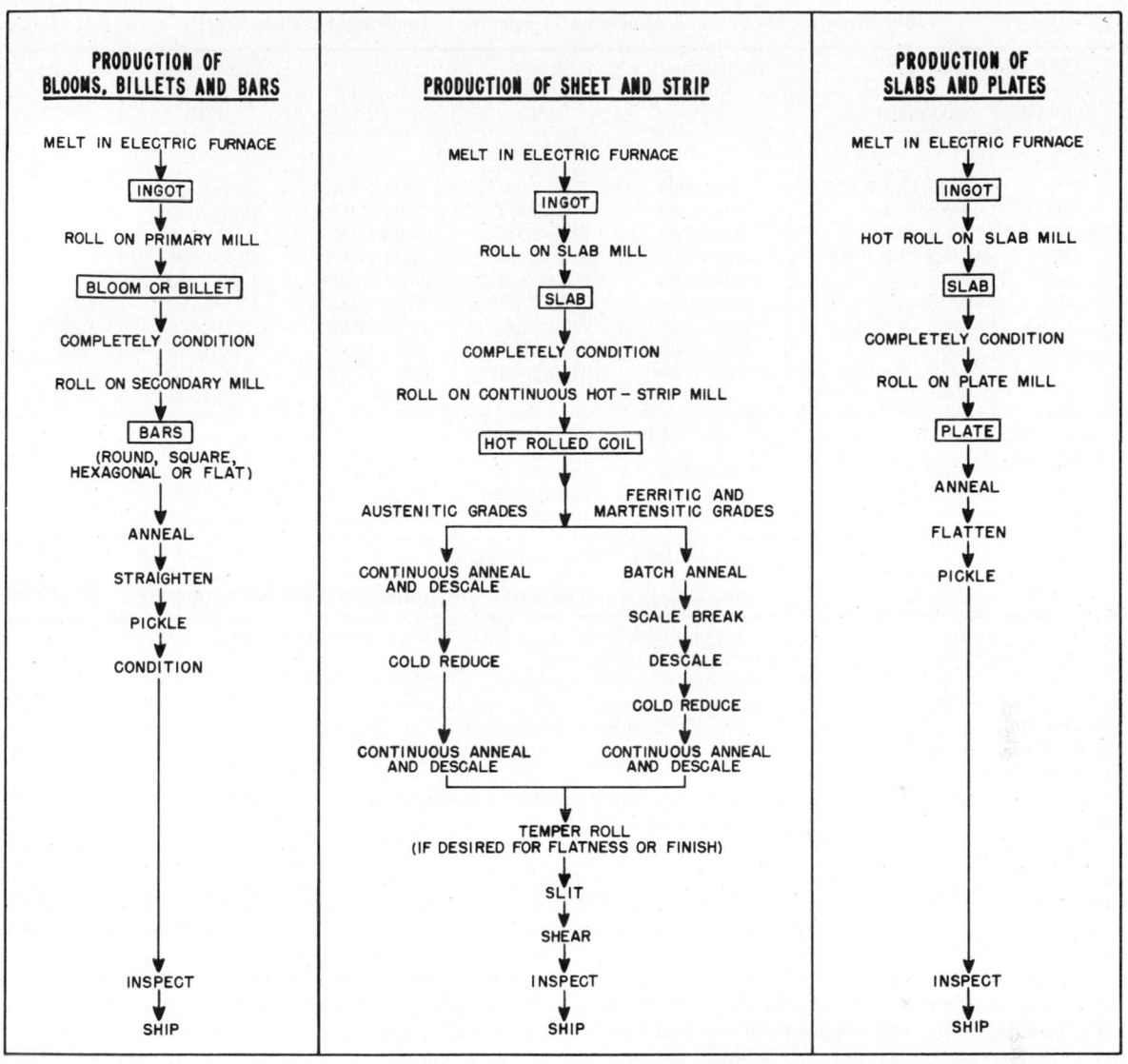

FIG. 45—10. Flow sheets indicating general principal steps in the production of stainless-steel products.

made for this lack of spread in order that the resulting plate widths will satisfy dimensional requirements.

After rolling, the stainless-steel plates are annealed and pickled. As might be expected, the annealing temperatures employed depend upon the composition of the material, and the specific annealing temperatures used for the standard AISI grades are listed in Table 45—II. The pickling procedure used for stainless steel varies from plant to plant. One installation consists of a 10 per cent sulphuric acid bath operated at 140° to 160° F (60° to 70° C) and a 10 per cent nitric acid, 4 per cent hydrofluoric acid bath operated at 130° to 150° F (50° to 70° C). The first bath softens and loosens the scale but will not remove it completely; the second solution will remove the scale loosened by the first solution.

Most recent of the developments in the pickling of stainless steels is the use of molten salts consisting of sodium hydroxide to which is added some agent such as sodium hydride. These molten-salt descaling processes are rapid and efficient and have replaced many acid pickling installations.

After annealing and pickling, the stainless plates are sheared to size, and are then suitable for shipment.

Rolling of Stainless-Steel Bars—The billets used for the rolling of stainless-steel bars are conditioned as the surface requires it. Martensitic steels must not exceed 275 Brinell hardness prior to conditioning, and if this hardness is exceeded, the billet must be annealed before swing grinding in order to prevent thermal cracking which might occur during the grinding operation or during heating for rolling. Prior to heating for rolling, the ends of the billets are pointed by a scarfing torch to prevent the splitting of the ends of the bar and also to decrease slippage when entering the mill.

During the rolling of the ferritic grades, spread control is important and is accomplished by providing a

Table 45—II. Forging and Annealing Temperatures for Some Stainless Steels.

AISI Type Number	USS Grade Designation	Preheating[a] Range (°F)	Begin Forging (°F)	Finish Forging (°F)	Annealing Range (°F)	Rate of Cooling
			AUSTENITIC GRADES			
201	USS 17-4-6	1500-1600	2100-2300	1600-1700[c]	1900-2000	Rapid
202	USS 18-5-8	1500-1600	2100-2300	1600-1700[c]	1900-2000	Rapid
302, 304	USS 18-8	1500-1600	2100-2300	1600-1700[c]	1900-2000	Rapid
303	USS 18-8 FM[b]	1500-1600	2100-2300	1600-1700[c]	1900-2000	Rapid
309	USS 25-12	1500-1600	2000-2250	1700-1800[c]	2000-2100	Rapid
310	USS 25-20	1500-1600	2000-2250	1700-1800[c]	2000-2100	Rapid
316	USS 18-8 Mo	1500-1600	2100-2300	1600-1700[c]	1950-2050	Rapid
321	USS 18-8 Ti	1500-1600	2100-2300	1600-1700[c]	1750-2050[d]	Air
347	USS 18-8 Cb	1500-1600	2100-2300	1600-1700[c]	1850-2050[d]	Air
—	USS TENELON	1800	2100	(e)	1900-2000	Rapid[f]
			FERRITIC GRADES			
405	USS 12 (Al)	1400-1500	1950-2050	Under 1500	1350-1450	Air
430	USS 17	1400-1500	1950-2050[g]	Under 1500	1400-1500	Air
446	USS 27	1400-1500	1950-2050[g]	Under 1450	1550-1650	Rapid
			MARTENSITIC GRADES			
403, 410	USS 12	1400-1500	2000-2200	Under 1500	1550-1600[h]	Slow

(a) Allow preheating time about twice that required for plain carbon steel of equivalent section.
(b) Not recommended for extremely severe forging operations.
(c) Do not form below 1800° F. Finish below this temperature only with light blows in the final sizing.
(d) Annealing on low side of range provides maximum carbide stability with some sacrifice in optimum mechanical properties. Annealing on high side of range provides optimum mechanical properties with some loss in stability.
(e) No definite temperature.
(f) Water quench.
(g) Avoid long soaking at forging temperatures to guard against excessive growth.
(h) Cool 50° per hour maximum at 1100° F and air cool.

billet size slightly less in cross-section than that which would be used for carbon or alloy steels. This smaller size permits lighter initial drafting.

On delivery from the rolling mill, the austenitic and ferritic stainless-steel bars are rapidly (air) cooled, while cooling of the martensitic stainless-steel bars is deliberately retarded. Sections of the latter two inches and over are cooled slowly in covered pits, while those under about two inches have cooling retarded by packing on the hot bed.

After annealing and pickling, stainless-steel bars are straightened on standard equipment and may be shipped in this condition or finished by centerless grinding or cold drawing.

Rolling of Stainless-Steel Sheet and Strip—In this section, the discussion of the rolling of stainless-steel sheet and strip will be confined to the continuous method by which the largest tonnage of stainless steels is produced. However, recognition should be given to hand-mill methods which, although being gradually replaced by the continuous method, find importance for the production of those grades of stainless steel that are difficult to roll and also for the production of small lots not conveniently produced by the continuous method and widths exceeding the limits of continuous rolls. Figure 45—10 presents a flow chart indicating typical steps in the processing of stainless-steel sheet and strip.

The slab or billet used for the production of stainless-steel sheet or strip is completely conditioned.

As is true for the other products, stainless-steel sheet and strip is rolled on the same equipment as that used for carbon-steel sheet and strip.

After rolling and annealing, all of the stainless steels are descaled, usually by pickling in acids. For the straight-chromium grades of stainless steel containing up to about 21 per cent chromium, the hot-rolled sheet or strip, in coil form, is batch annealed at subcritical temperatures. On the other hand, the straight-chromium grades containing over about 21 per cent chromium, and the austenitic grades, are annealed on a continuous unit and quenched from the annealing temperature. Often, for the austenitic steels, this annealing is performed in an oxidizing atmosphere which, by producing a heavy scale, "burns off" the defects and thus reduces the amount of conditioning necessary at some later stage. The quenching practice used depends upon the thickness of the material. For thick materials, high-pressure water sprays are used, but for thin materials, cooling in air is sufficient. All of the stainless steels are descaled on continuous units, usually arranged in tandem with a continuous annealing unit.

A typical continuous descaling or pickling installation (see Figure 45—11) consists of two 35-foot long tanks containing approximately 15 per cent hydrochloric acid (HCl) at 160° F followed by a tank of similar size containing about 4 per cent hydrofluoric acid (HF) and 10 per cent nitric acid (HNO_3) at 150° F to 170°F. In some installations, electrolytic-pickling

Fig. 45—11. Stainless-steel strip entering a continuous pickling line.

facilities using either cold sulphuric acid (H_2SO_4) or nitric acid (HNO_3) are substituted for the first two tanks.

Molten-salt descaling processes are now being used commercially. Normally a light acid pickle, usually hot nitric acid, follows the descaling treatment. These processes provide scale removal on all grades of stainless steel without metal loss and result in a smoother surface than is obtainable from acid pickling. The method requires more heat input than pickling, and care must be taken to prevent the introduction of any water.

If, after the first annealing and pickling operation, some of the surface defects produced during hot rolling are still present, the material may be reannealed (and pickled) to "burn off" these defects or the defects can be removed in a continuous coil-grinding operation.

To obtain lighter gages and improvements in surface, grain size and mechanical properties, the material is cold rolled in coil form. Usually, the cold rolling of stainless-steel sheet and strip is performed on a reversing mill, although a tandem mill may be used. Depending upon the final thickness desired, an intermediate anneal may or may not be used. This anneal, like the first anneal, may be performed on a continuous annealing and pickling line or it may be performed in a continuous bright-annealing furnace. For best results, stainless steel is bright annealed in pure hydrogen having a dew point of $-100°$ F or lower. Generally, the surface of the bright-annealed product is smoother (and brighter) than that of the conventionally annealed and pickled product.

After annealing and pickling, the surface of the cold-rolled material has what is called a No. 2-D (dull, cold-rolled) finish for sheet or a No. 1 cold-rolled finish for strip. In this condition, the material either may be sheared to desired lengths and shipped, or may remain in coil form and be subjected to further processing. If a brighter finish is desired, the material is rolled on a temper mill; the finish resulting from this process is called a No. 2-B (bright, cold-rolled) finish for sheet or a No. 2 cold-rolled finish for strip. As previously mentioned, bright-annealed material has a higher finish (brighter surface) than material that has been conventionally annealed and pickled. Even higher finishes are obtained by mechanical polishing either as sheets or as coils. Flattening, or leveling, is accomplished on standard units used for this purpose.

Of special interest is the work-hardening characteristic of the austenitic stainless steels which permits these grades to be produced to tensile strengths as high as 200,000 pounds per square inch. The composition best suited for the production of these high strengths is AISI Type 301 (17 per cent chromium, 7 per cent nickel). Usually, this grade is supplied to four standard minimum tensile strength levels of 125,000, 150,000, 175,000 and 185,000 pounds per square inch. Materials having these respective tensile strengths are designated commercially as having ¼, ½, ¾ and full-hard temper. The amount of cold reduction necessary to produce these strengths depends upon the composition of the material.

HEAT TREATMENT

Heat Treatment of Iron-Chromium Stainless Steels —Knowing the phase diagrams of the stainless steels, an understanding of the philosophy of the commercial heat treatments employed for the various grades becomes possible.

From 5 per cent chromium to 12 per cent chromium, using 0.15 per cent carbon as a base, the steels are hardenable by the austenite-to-martensite transformation. As would be expected from the high chromium contents, the hardenability of these steels is good and increases with increasing chromium and carbon.

However, most of the applications for the 5 to 9 per cent chromium steels require the metal to be in the most ductile condition, and the "softening" practice employed consists of normalizing and tempering or one of the various annealing cycles. Ductility is required because these steels, before they are placed into service, are subjected to various cold-fabrication practices. Because these steels are air hardening, welding must be performed with the necessary precautions such as pre-heating and post-heating. Often in field welding, these precautions cannot be taken and, when this situation is anticipated, stabilization with titanium or columbium (niobium) may be employed. Titanium and columbium form stable carbides and the material behaves like a low-carbon stainless steel and has lower hardness than material without stabilizing elements.

Depending upon the intended application, the 12 per cent chromium steels are used in the fully-hardened and tempered as well as the annealed condition. These materials may be either air-cooled or oil-quenched from the hardening temperature. Oil quenching produces slightly higher hardnesses but air cooling is employed in order to minimize the danger of cracking or warping. Figure 45—12 shows the effect of tempering temperature on the hardness and tensile properties of hardened Type 410 (12 per cent

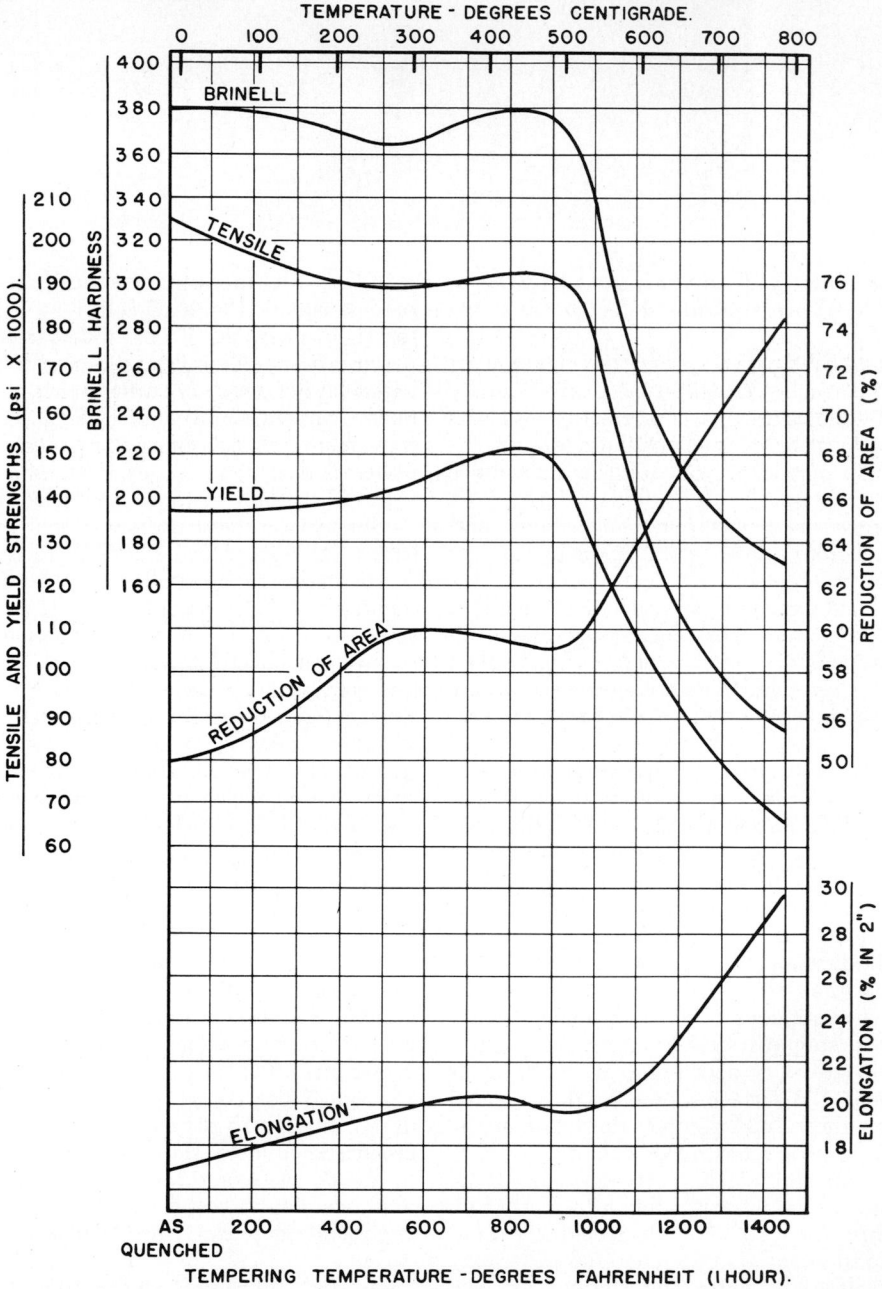

Fig. 45—12. The effect of tempering for one hour on the hardness and tensile properties of hardened Type 410 (12% Cr-0.10% C) stainless steel.

chromium, 0.10 per cent carbon). The impact strength decreases in the temperature range 750° to 950° F; also maximum corrosion resistance is not obtained in the range 750° to 1000° F, hence, the range 750° to 1000° F is to be avoided. Heating this type of steel below 750° F is commonly called "stress relieving" while heating above 1000° F is called "tempering." Annealing is usually accomplished by heating above the lower critical temperature and slow cooling, but also may be accomplished by sub-critical annealing. As is true for the lower chromium steels, the 12 per cent chromium steels must be welded with caution because of air-hardening. Unlike the lower chromium steels, the hardening capacity of the 12 per cent chromium steels is lowered by small additions of aluminum. These small amounts of aluminum (0.3 per cent) are sufficient to minimize austenite formation and make the steel essentially ferritic at all temperatures so that little phase transformation, and consequently no hardening, occurs.

A group of steels containing about 0.10 per cent of carbon and between 15 and 21 per cent of chromium deserves special mention. Such steels, when air cooled from about 1500° F, can contain up to 50 per cent of martensite and, in this sense, they can be considered as martensitic stainless steels. However, because the steels are used almost exclusively for their corrosion-resistant properties in applications that require optimum formability, an annealed (or soft) microstructure is desired. This microstructure is achieved by an annealing treatment that consists of heating in the range 1400 to 1500° F for a sufficiently long time to spheroidize the carbide phase and then slow cooling to room temperature.

The higher chromium steels (over about 21 per cent chromium) are completely ferritic. Annealing would then seem to be a simple process of heating at a recommended temperature for a reasonable time and slow cooling. However, two difficulties arise. First, the alloys are single phase except for carbide, hence, no grain refinement by a phase transformation

is possible. A large grain size once formed will be retained on cooling to room temperature. Only by cold work and recrystallization can the grain size be reduced. The fact that the high-chromium steels are inherently notch sensitive makes the effect of grain coarsening even worse. Additions of nitrogen have been used to obtain a finer grain size. The nitrogen forms small pools of austenite which inhibit grain growth.

The second difficulty is that embrittlement occurs when the steels are heated in or slowly cooled through the temperature range of 800° to 1400° F. The embrittlement, which is actually an age-hardening phenomenon, is caused by the precipitation of a body-centered cubic phase of iron and chromium containing 70 to 80 per cent chromium.[23]

Keeping in mind grain growth and embrittlement, the high-chromium steels are annealed by heating in the temperature range 1400° to 1700° F and cooling rapidly.

Iron-Chromium-Nickel Stainless Steels—The austenitic stainless steels also are considered to be single phase although this belief is erroneous for two reasons.

First, in ordinary 18–8, austenite is not thermodynamically stable at room temperature. By the means of plastic deformation at or below room temperature, meta-stable austenite can be transformed, at least partially, to martensite. Furthermore, additions of aluminum and titanium in sufficient quantities cause the 18–8 steel to transform to a low-carbon martensite without benefit of cold work. This effect has been used advantageously in developing Stainless W, an age-hardening ferritic 17 per cent chromium, 7 per cent nickel steel.[14]

Second, the carbide phase, unfortunately, cannot be ignored. In Figure **45—13**[15] it will be noted that the carbide solubility changes abruptly with temperature. Therefore, during slow cooling a carbide precipitation occurs and these carbides, rich in chromium, precipitate at the grain boundaries. At the temperature

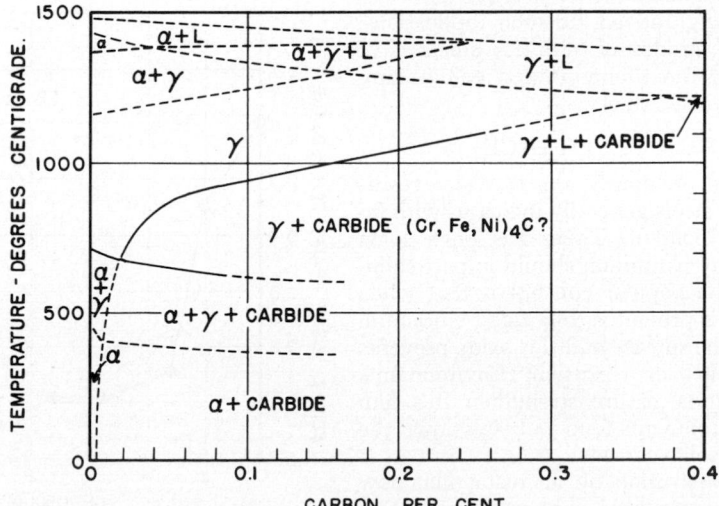

Fig. **45—13**. The effect of carbon on the constitution of stainless steels containing 18 per cent chromium and 8 per cent nickel.[15]

where the precipitation occurs, chromium diffusion from the matrix is not rapid enough to replenish the chromium taken out of the immediate vicinity of the carbide and, consequently, this region is low in chromium. Because chromium is the element largely responsible for the excellent corrosion resistance, the region adjacent to the carbide becomes lower in corrosion resistance and the material is susceptible to intergranular corrosion.

The austenitic steels are, therefore, heat treated by an anneal at a temperature high enough to effect carbide solution but low enough to minimize grain growth, and then cooled to room temperature rapidly enough to keep the carbides in solution.

Such a treatment is not always possible, especially where these steels are welded in the field, and modifications of the austenitic grades have been developed. These modified steels contain titanium or columbium (niobium) which combine with the carbon and eliminate intergranular carbide precipitation and susceptibility to intergranular corrosion. Titanium in amounts of five times the carbon and columbium in amounts of ten times the carbon are considered to be sufficient, although the actual amounts necessarily depend upon the grain size and composition (other than carbon content) of the material (see also "Intergranular Corrosion").

The relationship of these variables to the amount of titanium required has been quantitatively evaluated, and a suitable formula developed.[16]

The titanium or columbium grades are sometimes given a stabilizing treatment at 1600° F to insure complete chemical combination of carbon with titanium or columbium.

Another solution to the problems encountered in field welding and/or stress relieving is the use of austenitic stainless steels containing 0.03 per cent maximum of carbon, such as Types 304L and 316L. Although these steels are not "completely" immune to susceptibility to intergranular corrosion in the sense that they cannot be heated for prolonged periods of time in the sensitizing temperature range, they are satisfactory for almost all applications requiring welding and stress relieving. Indeed, for such applications, these so-called "L" grades of stainless steels have completely replaced the titanium- and columbium-bearing grades of stainless steel.

CORROSION RESISTANCE

As was mentioned previously, the corrosion resistance of the stainless steels generally increases with increasing chromium content. There has been some speculation as to why chromium should impart stainlessness to steel. The popular concept is that when sufficient chromium is present, a thin, tight, chromium oxide is formed on the surface and this oxide prevents any further oxidation or corrosion. Environments which are oxidizing in nature strengthen this film while reducing environments tend to break down the film and cause the steel to corrode.

This theory of passivation by an oxide film now has considerable experimental support. Films were first stripped by Evans[17] and his co-workers. Later, Rhodin[24] and his associates isolated films to determine their structure and chemical composition. Rhodin's results show the films to be "gel-like" substances having no well-defined crystalline structure. A chemical composition corresponding to the approximate formula is:

$$4M_3O_4 \cdot SiO_2 \cdot nH_2O$$

where:

$12M = 7 Fe + 2 Ni + 3 Cr$, n is approximately 9.

Voluminous data have been published on the corrosion resistance of specific grades of stainless steel in specific environments. The data in the literature represent both controlled laboratory tests and actual service records. To discuss these corrosion data, the subject of corrosion is divided into four separate parts: atmospheric, elevated-temperature, intergranular, and pitting corrosion.

Atmospheric Corrosion—The most common type of corrosion encountered in steel is ordinary rusting. Recent investigations of the atmospheric corrosion of stainless steels have disclosed that ferritic steels above 12 per cent chromium are partially resistant, and above 18 per cent chromium are fully resistant to rusting. Figure 45—14[20] shows graphically the effect of chromium content on the atmospheric corrosion of stainless steels. Noteworthy are the breaks in the curve at 3 per cent and 12 per cent chromium. Some variations from this behavior may be expected in different atmospheres and when the metal is in different conditions of heat treatment.

The austenitic steels also are very resistant to atmospheric corrosion. A report made by a task group on inspection of corrosion-resistant steels in architectural and structural applications and published in the 1961 Proceedings of the American Society for Testing and Materials concludes that stainless steels are entirely adequate for architectural applications. These steels retain their metallic luster and appearance beneath urban dirt and grime. With even limited cleaning, there is no deterioration of the metal. In industrial buildings where appearance is not a big factor, stainless steel has practically an indefinite life, even with-

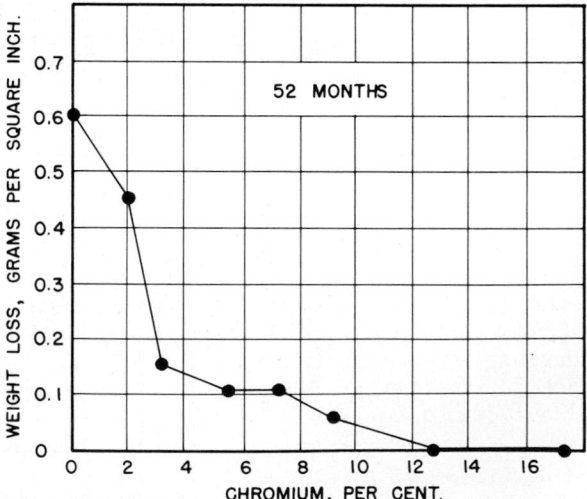

FIG. 45—14. The influence of chromium on the atmospheric corrosion of low-carbon steel.[20]

out cleaning. Moreover, after long periods of neglect or abuse, stainless steel can be returned to a pleasing appearance by cleaning. In industrial environments that contain chlorides, and in seacoast areas, Type 316 stainless steel is the preferred grade.

The effect of surface was also studied and it was reported that the smoother the surface, the better the corrosion resistance.

The amount of work which has been done on the corrosion of stainless steels in various reagents is voluminous but, unfortunately, the data never have been properly organized. The effect of chromium on the resistance of steel to corrosion by these various reagents is similar to its effect on the resistance to atmospheric corrosion, although nickel and molybdenum enhance the resistance to corrosion by certain chemicals.

Elevated-Temperature Corrosion — Corrosion at elevated temperatures is usually one of three types: oxidation, carburization, and sulphidation.

As was true for atmospheric corrosion, the resistance of the stainless steels to oxidation is primarily a function of the chromium content. This effect of chromium on oxidation resistance is discussed in Chapter 46, entitled "Steels for Elevated-Temperature Service."

The chromium content also determines the rate of carburization. In general, ferritic steels are more resistant to carburization than austenitic steels. Addition of 2 per cent silicon improves resistance of 18–8 and 25–20 to carburization, but the effect of titanium, columbium (niobium) and molybdenum is negligible.

Usually, carburization rates are not appreciable below 1500° F in steels containing 18 per cent or more chromium. However, under special conditions, especially cyclic oxidation and carburization, 18–8 has been known to carburize at 1400° F.

The austenitic stainless steels, because of their nickel content, are susceptible to attack by reducing sulphurous gases, notably hydrogen sulphide. The ferritic stainless steels are more resistant.

Oxidizing sulphurous gases slightly increase the corrosion of the austenitic and the ferritic stainless steels.

These three types of elevated-temperature attack are very important but too often neglected when recommending materials. In many installations, elevated-temperature corrosion by oxygen, carbon, or sulphur causes more failures than stresses. Consequently, many of the steels such as 18–8, although possessing adequate strength, will not meet service requirements because of excessive oxidizing, carburizing or sulphidizing conditions.

Intergranular Corrosion—Bain, Aborn, and Rutherford[21] have ascribed intergranular corrosion to chromium impoverishment at the grain boundaries, caused by the grain boundary precipitation of chromium-rich carbides. There are two possible remedies for this difficulty. First, the carbon may be immunized, either by precipitating the carbide at a temperature where chromium diffusion will be rapid enough to restore passivity to the grain-boundary area, or by forming a stable carbide of some element other than chromium. Second, the steel may be made with less than 0.03 per cent carbon.

Probably the first method to be used commercially was that of forming a stable carbide of some element other than chromium. Bain, Rutherford and Aborn suggested the addition of titanium in amounts of four to five times the carbon content. By heating the titanium-bearing 18–8 at 1600° F, they obtained the complete fixing of carbon by titanium to form titanium carbide, and the steel was said to be **stabilized**. Concurrent with this development, the Union Carbide and Carbon Corporation developed a columbium-bearing (niobium-bearing) steel having a columbium content of eight times the carbon content. The columbium, like titanium, formed a stable carbide and thus prevented the formation of chromium carbide at elevated temperatures.

During World War II, United States Steel Corporation developed a method for producing 18–8 and 18–8 containing molybdenum, both containing 0.03 per cent maximum carbon. These "new" steels are more resistant to carbide precipitation and the resultant susceptibility to intergranular corrosion than regular grades of these steels, because of their lower carbon contents. These new grades, designated as Types 304L and 316L have been accepted commercially as replacements for the columbium- and titanium-bearing grades for service at temperatures below about 800° F.

Pitting Corrosion—Pitting usually occurs during continuous exposure to relatively-weak corroding media, such as chlorides, to which the steels are otherwise substantially resistant. Very little is known about the cause of this type of corrosion except that it probably occurs in certain vulnerable spots where the passivity is continuously destroyed. Pitting manifests itself by small holes distributed at random over the surface of the steel, or it may develop at points where the steel is in contact with other materials, such as leather, glass, and grease. The formation of an electrolytic cell may be the cause. The mechanism probably involves a lack of oxygen on the surface of the metal that is corroded.

Pitting may be inhibited somewhat by treating the environments with some strong oxidizing agents such as some chromates or phosphates. Molybdenum additions to 18–8 also inhibit pitting.

MECHANICAL PROPERTIES

Low-Temperature Properties—At extremely low temperatures, the ferritic and martensitic steels are quite brittle, having impact strengths on the order of one foot pound. However, the austenitic stainless steels have impact strengths well above 15 foot pounds at minus 423° F and are the best materials for use at the extremely low temperatures.

Room Temperature Properties—The range of room-temperature mechanical properties of each grade of stainless steel is given in the AISI Steel Products Manual entitled "Stainless and Heat Resisting Steels."[1] Table 45—III shows typical properties of Type 301 (17–7), Type 410 (12 per cent chromium), and Type 430 (17 per cent chromium).

As was mentioned, the martensitic grades are hard-

Table 45—III.   Representative Mechanical Properties of Some Grades of Stainless Steel*

Type	Form and Treatment	Tensile Strength (Lb. per Sq. In.)	Yield Strength (Offset: 0.2 Per Cent) (Lb. per Sq. In.)	Elongation in 2 In. (Per Cent)	Reduction of Area (Per Cent)	Impact-Resistance, Ft.-Lb. Charpy	Impact-Resistance, Ft.-Lb. Izod	Brinell (3000-kg. Load 10-mm. Ball)	Rockwell	Endurance Limit (Fatigue) (Lb. per Sq. In.)	Cold Bend (Degrees)	Erichsen Value (mm.)	Olsen Value (In.)
301	Sheet and Strip Annealed:	110,000	40,000	60					B-85	35,000	180	10 to 14	0.4 to 0.5
	¼ Hard	125,000	75,000	25					C-25	80,000			
	to	to	to	to					to	(Full Hard)			
	Full Hard:	185,000	140,000	9					C-41				
	Plate Annealed:	105,000	40,000	55	70		110	165		39,000			
410	Sheet and Strip Annealed:	65,000	35,000	25					B-80		180	7 to 8	0.3 to 0.4
	Wire Annealed Temper:	75,000	40,000	30	70				B-82				
	Tempered and Cold Drawn:	95,000	80,000	15	60				B-92				
	Heat Treated:	135,000	105,000	10	50				C-29				
	Plate Annealed:	70,000	35,000	30				150			180		
	Bars Annealed:	75,000	40,000	35	70		90	155	B-82	40,000			
	Tempered:	110,000	85,000	23	65		75	225	B-97	55,000			
	Tempered and Cold Drawn:	100,000	85,000	17	60		70 to 90	205	B-94	53,000			
430	Sheet and Strip Annealed:	75,000	45,000	25					B-80		180	7 to 9	0.3 to 0.4
	Wire Annealed Temper:	70,000	40,000	35	70				B-82				
	Soft Temper:	85,000	70,000	15	70				B-90				
	Plate Annealed:	75,000	40,000	30				160			180		
	Bars Annealed:	75,000	45,000	30	65			155		40,000			
	Annealed and Cold Drawn:	85,000	70,000	20	65			185		46,000			

*Ranges from individual data in American Iron and Steel Institute's Steel Products Manual entitled "Stainless and Heat Resisting Steels" (June 1957 and Supplement dated Sept. 1959).

enable, and by proper selection of composition and heat treatment, their tensile properties can be made similar to those of the low-alloy steels. Ductility values and impact strengths are somewhat inferior to those of the low-alloy steels.

Table **45**—III shows typical properties of 17 per cent chromium, Type 430. The ferritic steels, particularly those containing over 21 per cent of chromium, are extremely notch sensitive. The notch sensitivity, or rather the transition temperature from brittle to ductile behavior, increases with chromium content, the 27 per cent chromium steel having a Charpy impact strength of only two foot pounds at room temperature. This notch sensitivity is undesirable, and when fabricating these steels, special precautions must be taken. Because of the notch sensitivity, aggravated by large grain size and 885° F embrittlement, both of which may result from welding, the ferritic steels have not found as wide usage at room temperatures as have the austenitic steels. However, in many environments, the ferritic steels have as good corrosion resistance as the austenitic steels.

The austenitic steels are not hardenable by heat treatment but they can be hardened by cold work which for some grades transforms the austenite (metastable at room temperature) to a low-carbon martensite. This transformation hardening by cold work is additive to the strain hardening and the result is that an extremely wide range of tensile properties may be produced. As an example, Table **45**—III shows typical properties of Type 301 (17–7). As would be expected, the degree of hardening obtained by cold work is a function of the composition, and extensive investigations have been made on the effect of various elements on the work hardenability of 17–7.[15]

The disadvantage of the austenitic stainless steels is that the work hardening is confined to those shapes which can be rolled (cold worked). For example, an article such as a valve cannot be hardened economically by cold working. This disadvantage was overcome

by the development of an age-hardening stainless steel designated as Stainless W.[14]

Stainless W is essentially a 17 per cent chromium, 7 per cent nickel steel containing titanium and aluminum. As would be expected, this is an "unbalanced" composition. At high temperature, its structure consists of austenite and delta ferrite. On cooling, the austenite transforms at about 200° F (93° C) to low-carbon martensite, so that the room-temperature structure of this alloy consists of martensite plus delta ferrite and some retained austenite. The age hardening occurs in the martensite and in the ferrite but not in the austenite. Aging is accomplished by heating in the temperature range 900° to 1050° F. Table **45**—IV shows the typical properties of Stainless W in the annealed and aged conditions.

Elevated-Temperature Properties—In Figure **45**—15 is shown the creep strength of many of the commercial stainless steels, compared with that of carbon steel. Note that the austenitic stainless steels have higher strength than the ferritic stainless steels and that additions of chromium and silicon have little effect on the creep strength. On the other hand, the effect of molybdenum, columbium (niobium), and tungsten are marked. This phase of the subject is discussed in detail in Chapter 46.

APPLICATIONS

Martensitic Grades—The most widely used of the martensitic grades is Type 410 containing under 0.15 per cent carbon and 11.50 to 13.50 per cent chromium. In the annealed condition, this grade may be drawn or formed. As it is an air-hardening steel, a wide range of mechanical properties may be obtained by heat treatment. In sheet or strip form, Type 410 is used extensively in the oil industry for ballast trays and liners. It is also used for furnace parts where the operating temperature is not over 1200° F and for blades and buckets in steam turbines. Type 420, with about 0.35 per cent carbon and resultant greater hard-

Table 45—IV. Typical Ranges of Mechanical Properties of Stainless W, as Solution Annealed and as Aged at the Temperatures Indicated.

Item No.	Treatment	Yield Strength 0.2% Offset (1000 Lb. per Sq. In.)	Tensile Strength (1000 Lb. per Sq. In.)	*Elongation (% in 2 In.)		Rockwell Hardness "C" Scale
				½ In. and Less	Over ½ In.	
1	Solution Annealed at 1850 to 1950° F, Air Cooled.	75–115	120–150	8–14	10–15	22–28
2	No. 1 plus Aged at 950° F, ½ hour, Air Cooled.	180–210	195–225	8–14	10–15	39–47
3	No. 1 plus Aged at 1000° F, ½ hour, Air Cooled.	170–210	190–220	8–14	10–15	38–46
4	No. 1 plus Aged at 1050° F, ½ hour, Air Cooled.	150–185	170–210	8–15	10–16	35–43

*For thicknesses of plates and bars indicated.

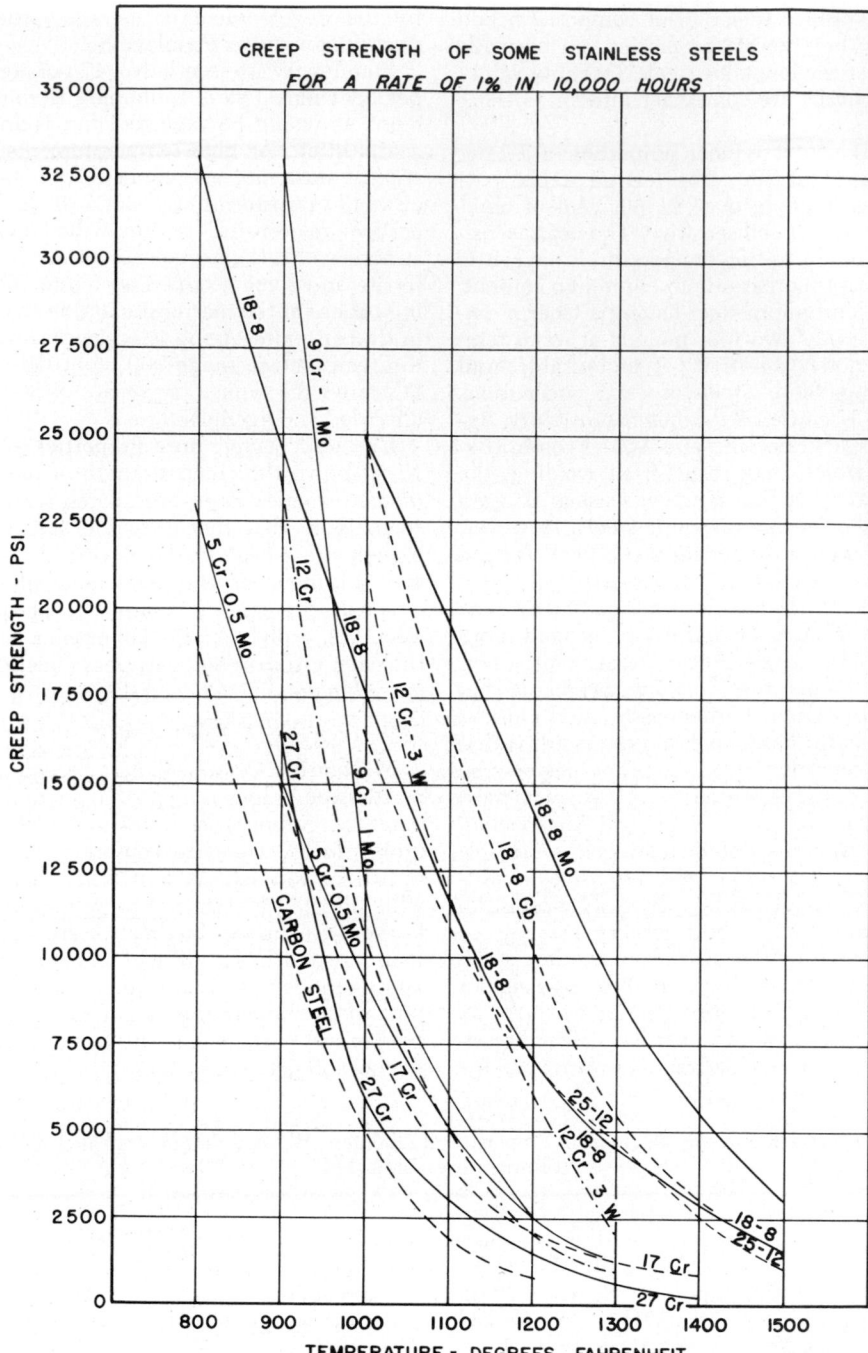

FIG. 45—15. The creep strength of some stainless steels.

ness, is used for cutlery. In bar form it is used for valves, valve stems, valve seats, and shafting where resistance to corrosion and wear are needed. Type 440 may be employed for such applications as surgical instruments, especially those requiring a durable cutting edge. The necessary hardness for different applications can be obtained by selecting Grade A, B, or C, which have increasingly greater carbon contents, in that order.

Other martensitic grades are Types 501 and 502,

the former having carbon over 0.10 per cent and the latter having under 0.10 per cent carbon, but both containing 4 to 6 per cent chromium. These grades are also air-hardening, but do not have the corrosion-resisting properties of the 12 per cent chromium grades. These grades have wide application in the oil industry for such uses as hot-oil lines, bubble towers, valves, plates, and so on.

Ferritic Grades—The most common and widely used of the ferritic grades is Type 430 containing 0.12

per cent carbon or under and 14 to 18 per cent chromium. The higher chromium content of Type 430 makes its corrosion resistance superior to that of the martensitic grades and, in addition, this material may be drawn, formed and, with proper techniques, welded. It is widely used for automotive and architectural trim. Its resistance to nitric acid makes it useful in the manufacture and handling of this acid. Type 430 does not have a high creep strength, but it is suitable for some types of service up to 1500° F and thus finds application for such parts as combustion chambers for domestic heating furnaces.

The high chromium content of Type 446 (23 to 27 per cent chromium) gives this grade excellent heat-resistant characteristics although its elevated-temperature strength is only slightly better than that of carbon steel. Type 446 is used in sheet or strip form at temperatures up to 2100° F. This grade does not have the good drawing characteristics of Type 430, but it may be formed. Accordingly, it is used widely for furnace parts such as muffles, burner sleeves and annealing baskets. Its resistance to nitric and other oxidizing acids makes it suitable for much chemical-processing equipment, and tubular products of Type 446 were widely used during World War II by the synthetic-rubber industry for the processing of butane.

Austenitic Grades—The basic and most widely used grade of the austenitic types is "18–8"—Type 302, with 0.15 per cent maximum carbon, 8 to 10 per cent nickel and 17 to 19 per cent chromium. It has excellent corrosion resistance and, because of its austenitic structure, possesses very good ductility. It may be deep drawn and can be very severely formed. It can be welded readily, but, as described in the general section on iron-chromium-nickel alloys, the heat of welding may cause carbides to precipitate in the weld and in the metal adjacent to the weld if a sufficiently rapid rate of cooling is not obtained, thus rendering these zones susceptible to intergranular corrosion. This may be corrected by annealing the welded part above 1900° F to redissolve the carbides, followed by rapid cooling to retain them in solution. Where such a treatment is not feasible, Types 321, 347, or 18–8 with 0.03 per cent maximum carbon may be used.

The applications of Type 302 are wide and varied, including kitchen equipment and utensils; dairy installations; transportation equipment; oil-, chemical-, paper- and food-processing machinery.

Type 301 contains a maximum of 0.15 per cent carbon, 6 to 8 per cent nickel and 16 to 18 per cent chromium. Its lower nickel content causes it to work harden more rapidly than Type 302 (18–8) because of reduced austenite stability. Accordingly, while Type 301 can be drawn successfully, it does not have quite as good drawing properties as Type 302, but for the same reason, this grade (Type 301) can be cold rolled to very high strength levels for use in applications where a high strength-to-weight ratio is desired.

Type 304 contains less carbon and more chromium and nickel than Type 301. Because of its lower carbon content it is not so prone to give trouble after welding due to carbide precipitation and resultant corrosion. In addition, the somewhat higher chromium content makes it slightly more resistant to general corrosion. It is well suited for those applications which require resistance to severe forms of corrosion such as are encountered in the paper and chemical industries. The austenitic grades have good elevated-temperature strength and these grades are widely used for elevated-temperature service.

Types 321 and 347, with carbide-forming additions of titanium and columbium (niobium), respectively, are widely used in those applications involving welding and where high-temperature service under corrosive conditions is required. Type 304L, the 0.03 per cent maximum carbon grade, may be used as an alternative for Types 321 and 347 in those applications involving welding and stress relieving for service below about 800° F.

The addition of 2 to 4 per cent molybdenum to the basic 18–8 composition produces Types 316 and 317 which have improved corrosion resistance. These grades are used in applications in the textile, paper and chemical industries where strong sulphates, chlorides and phosphates and such reducing acids as sulphuric, sulphurous, acetic and hydrochloric acids are used in such concentrations as to make the use of a more highly corrosion-resistant alloy mandatory. Types 316 and 317 have the highest creep and rupture strengths of the commercial stainless steels.

The austenitic stainless grades most resistant to oxidation are Types 309 (22 to 24 per cent chromium, 12 to 15 per cent nickel) and Type 310 (24 to 26 per cent chromium, 19 to 22 per cent nickel). Because of their high nickel and chromium contents these steels resist scaling at temperatures up to 2000 and 2100° F and, consequently, are ideal for furnace parts and heat exchangers. They are somewhat harder and not as ductile as the 18–8 types, but they may be drawn and formed. They can be readily welded and are finding increasing use in the manufacture of jet-propulsion motors and industrial-furnace equipment.

For applications requiring good machinability, Type 303 containing sulphur or selenium may be used.

SUMMARY

For some years, the stainless steels have been alloys of iron and chromium or iron, chromium, and nickel. Occasionally, small amounts of certain other elements are added in order to enhance corrosion resistance and mechanical properties or to immunize the steels to the action of certain harmful impurities. Recently, new grades of stainless steels have been developed in which the nickel content of steels of the iron-chromium-nickel type has been replaced wholly or in part by combinations of nitrogen and manganese (for example, AISI types 201 and 202, and USS TENELON). The inherently slow reaction rates of the stainless steels have hampered the establishment of precise equilibrium diagrams; however, the diagrams now in existence permit at least qualitative conclusions to be drawn regarding the structure of these steels. In regard to corrosion resistance, the chromium content seems to be the controlling variable and the effect of chromium may be enhanced by additions of molybdenum, nickel, and other elements. The mechanical properties of the stainless steels, like those of the plain carbon and lower alloy steels, are functions of the structure and composition of the material. Thus, the austenitic steels possess the best impact properties at low temperatures and the best strength at elevated temperatures while the martensitic steels possess the highest hardness at room temperature. Therefore, the stainless steels, by being available in a variety of structures, exhibit a range of mechanical properties which, combined with their excellent corrosion resistance, makes these steels highly versatile from the standpoint of design.

Bibliography

1. Am. Iron and Steel Institute, Steel products manual: Stainless and heat resisting steels (June 1957 and Supplementary Information circular dated September 1959). N.Y., The Institute, 1957.
2. Kinzel, A. B. and W. Crafts, Alloys of iron and chromium: vol. I, Low-chromium alloys. N.Y., McGraw-Hill, 1937.
3. Adcock, F., Alloys of iron research: Part X, The chromium-iron constitutional diagram. Iron and Steel Institute Journal 124: 99–149 (1931)
4. Bain, E. C., Nature of the alloys of iron and chromium. Am. Society for Steel Treating Trans. 9: 9–32 (1926)
5. Bain, E. C. and W. E. Griffiths, Introduction to the iron-chromium-nickel alloys. Am. Institute of Mining and Metallurgical Engineers Trans. 75: 166–213 (1927)
6. Jette, E. R. and F. Foote, The Fe-Cr alloy system; the brittle non-magnetic phase. Metals and Alloys 7: 207–210 (1936)
7. Cooke, A. J. and F. W. Jones, Brittle constituent of the iron-chromium system (sigma phase): I, A survey of the limits of the sigma phase in the binary system. Iron and Steel Institute Journal 148: 217–226 (1943)
8. Andersen, A. G. H. and E. R. Jette, X-ray investigation of the iron-chromium-silicon phase diagram. Am. Society for Metals Trans. 24: 375–419 (1936)
9. Bain, E. C. and R. H. Aborn, The iron-nickel-chromium system. Am. Society for Metals, Metals handbook, 1939 ed., pp. 418–422. Cleveland, The Society, 1939.
10. Strauss, B., Non-rusting chromium-nickel steels. Am. Society for Testing Materials Proc. 24 (Part II): 208–216 (1924)
11. Rees, W. P., B. D. Burns and A. J. Cook, Constitution of iron-nickel-chromium alloys at 650° to 800° C. Iron and Steel Institute Journal 162: 325–336 (1949)
12. Tofaute, W., A. Sponheuer and H. Bennek, Transformation, hardening and tempering phenomena in steels with 1% carbon and up to 12% chromium content. Archiv fur das Eisenhuttenwesen 8: 499–506 (1935)
13. Tofaute, W., C. Kuttner and A. Buttinghaus, Iron-chromium-chromium carbide systems, Cr_7C_3 cementite. Archiv fur das Eisenhuttenwesen 9: 607–617 (1936)
14. Smith, R., E. H. Wyche and W. W. Gorr, Precipitation-hardening stainless steel of the 18 per cent chromium, 8 per cent nickel type. Am. Institute of Mining and Metallurgical Engineers Trans. 167: 313–345 (1946)
15. Kinzel, A. B. and R. Franks, Alloys of iron and chromium: vol. II, High-chromium alloys. N.Y., McGraw-Hill, 1940.
16. Phillips, F. J., Quantitative evaluation of intergranular corrosion of 18–8 Ti. Am. Society for Metals Trans. 39: 891–914 (1947)
17. Evans, U. R. and J. Stockdale, The passivity of metals: Part III, The quantity and distribution of the superficial oxide. Chemical Society of London Journal, 1929, Article 335, p. 2651–2660.
18. Uhlig, H. H. and J. Wulff, Nature of passivity in stainless steel and other alloys, I and II. Am. Institute of Mining and Metallurgical Engineers Trans. 135: 494–534 (1939)
19. Fontana, M. G. and F. H. Beck, Nature and mechanism of passivity of 18–8S stainless steel. Metal Progress 51: 939–944 (1947)
20. Binder, W. O. and C. M. Brown, Atmospheric corrosion tests on high-chromium steels. Am. Society for Testing Materials Proc. 46: 593–609 (1946)
21. Bain, E. C., R. H. Aborn and J. J. B. Rutherford, Nature and prevention of intergranular corrosion in austenitic stainless steels. Am. Society for Steel Treating Trans. 21: 481–509 (1933)
22. Smith, G. V., Sigma phase in stainless: what, when and why. Iron Age 166: 63–68 (Nov. 30, 1950); 127–132 (Dec. 7, 1950)
23. Fisher, R. M., E. J. Dulis and K. G. Carroll, Identification of the precipitate accompanying 885° F embrittlement in chromium steels. Am. Institute of Mining and Metallurgical Engineers Trans. 197: 690–695 (1953)
24. Rhodin, T. N., Oxide films composition studies. Annals of the N.Y. Academy of Sciences 58: 855–872 (1954)
25. Carney, D. J., Nickel-free and low-nickel austenitic stainless steels. Regional technical meetings, Am. Iron and Steel Institute, 1955. N.Y., The Institute.

CHAPTER 46

Steels For Elevated-Temperature Service

SECTION 1

CLASSES OF STEEL

The designation "elevated-temperature service" is an inclusive one, involving many types of operations in numerous industries. Some of the more conventional examples of equipment operated at high temperature are steam boilers and turbines, gas turbines, stills for cracking petroleum, tar stills, vessels for hydrogenating oils, heat-treating furnaces, and fittings for diesel and other internal-combustion engines. Numerous steels are available from which to select the proper one for each of the foregoing applications. Where unusual conditions occur, some modification of the chemical composition may be made to better adapt an existing steel grade to service conditions. In some cases, however, entirely new alloy combinations must be developed to meet service requirements. For example, the aircraft and missile industries have encountered design problems of increased complexity, requiring metals of greater strength at higher temperatures for both power plants and structures, and new steels have been and are being developed to meet these requirements.

Valve steels, hot-work die steels and some alloy tool steels are used at elevated temperature, but these form special categories and, with the exception of the alloy tool steels described in Chapter 42, will not be discussed in this book.

The steels under consideration in this chapter are those used in large tonnages for construction of equipment to operate under stress at elevated temperature, where creep is involved. (Creep and creep rupture testing are discussed in detail in Section 6 of Chapter 47.) In spite of the fact that plain carbon steel has lower creep strength than the alloy steels used for elevated-temperature applications, it is widely used in such applications up to 1000° F, where rapid oxidation commences and a chromium-bearing steel must be employed. Low-alloy steels containing small amounts of chromium and molybdenum have higher creep strength than carbon steel and are employed where materials with higher strength are needed. Above about 1000° F, the amount of chromium required to impart adequate oxidation resistance increases rapidly. The 2 per cent chromium steels, with added molybdenum, are useful up to about 1150° F, and steels containing 10 to 14 per cent of chromium may be employed up to about 1300–1400° F. Above this temperature, the austenitic 18 per cent chromium, 8 per cent nickel stainless steels are used customarily, and their oxidation resistance is considered adequate up to about 1500° F. For service in the temperature range between about 1500° F and 2000° F, steels containing 25 per cent of chromium and 20 per cent of nickel, or 27 per cent of chromium, are used.

SECTION 2

FACTORS AFFECTING HIGH-TEMPERATURE PROPERTIES

Composition—The creep and rupture strength of steel can be greatly improved by the addition of alloying elements. It has been found that creep strength may be increased by use of those elements such as molybdenum which increase the recrystallization temperature and form stable carbides or intermetallic compounds. The effect of molybdenum is shown in Figure 46—1 and the effect of chromium is shown in Figure 46—2. Small additions of chromium do not appear to improve the creep strength of 0.5 per cent and 1.0 per cent molybdenum steels and high additions actually decrease the strength. However, above 1000° F, chromium is needed for oxidation resistance.

Carbon itself is beneficial in amounts to about 0.15 or 0.20 per cent; above this amount, an increase of the carbon content may result in a decrease of creep strength. Tungsten and vanadium act in a manner similar to molybdenum and are useful in improving high-temperature strength although they are not widely used in this country. Titanium and columbium (niobium) are moderately beneficial and a slight increase in phosphorus has been found desirable. The influence of manganese, nickel, copper and silicon is mild, and aluminum decreases creep strength. It has been found that the face-centered cubic structure of austenite is more creep resistant than the body-cen-

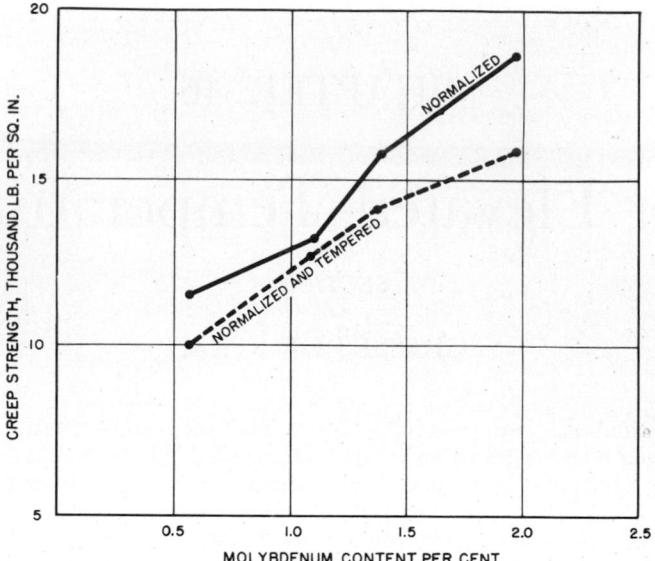

Fig. 46—1. Effect of molybdenum content on creep strength (stress per creep rate of 1 per cent per 10,000 hours) of molybdenum steel at 1000° F.

tered cubic structure of ferrite, and the austenitic chromium-nickel steels have excellent creep strength, i.e., when used as a means of changing the lattice structure, nickel is very beneficial, and carbon, manganese and nitrogen in certain combinations may act in a similar manner.

The effect of the alloying additions on creep strength is summarized in Figure 46—3, which shows the decrease of strength with increase of temperature. For the sake of simplicity and comparison, this chart is based on average properties.

Heat Treatment (Microstructure)—The strength of steel at elevated temperatures can be affected by its microstructure, and hence by the heat treatment employed for the material. Carbon and molybdenum steels are used in the as-rolled, normalized, or annealed conditions, while the air-hardening chromium-molybdenum steels are normalized and tempered or annealed. Steels for bolts are quenched and tempered. Stainless steels are annealed or annealed and stabilized. Steels are purchased to specifications having room-temperature mechanical strength and hardness requirements. Because these properties may be produced by several of the above heat treatments, few of the various types of steel are used in only one condition of heat treatment, accounting for part of the spread in the high-temperature data that appear in the literature for a given grade of steel.

The temperature at which the steel is used in service may serve as a heat-treating temperature and bring about internal changes in the material which will cause a change of its properties. Sometimes the strength and hardness are found to increase, at least temporarily, but more often lack of structural stability causes a progressive loss of strength. There are several forms in which structural instability makes itself

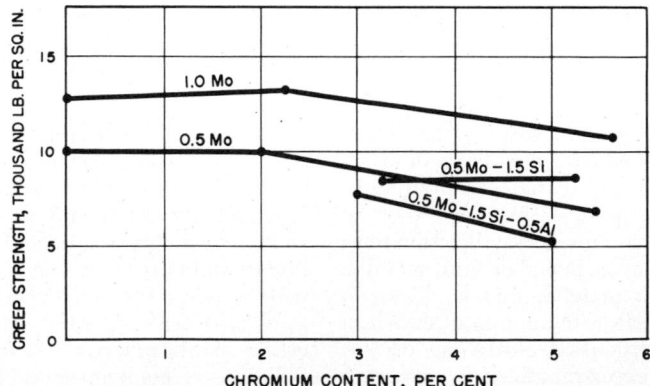

Fig. 46—2. Effect of chromium content on creep strength (stress for creep rate of 1 per cent per 10,000 hours) in chromium-molybdenum steel at 1000° F.

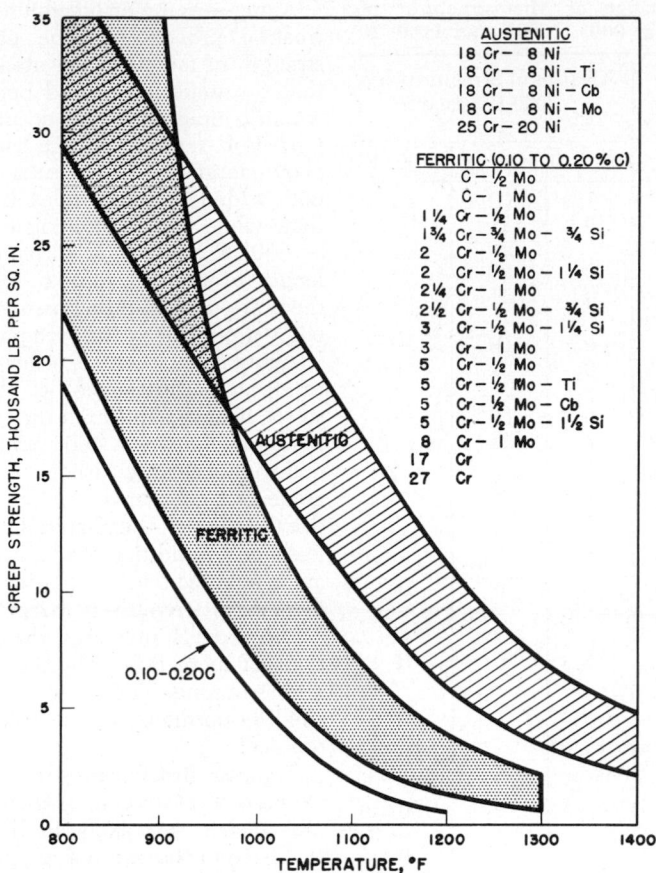

AUSTENITIC
18 Cr — 8 Ni
18 Cr — 8 Ni — Ti
18 Cr — 8 Ni — Cb
18 Cr — 8 Ni — Mo
25 Cr — 20 Ni

FERRITIC (0.10 TO 0.20% C)

C — ½ Mo	
C — 1 Mo	
1¼ Cr — ½ Mo	
1¾ Cr — ¾ Mo — ¾ Si	
2 Cr — ½ Mo	
2 Cr — ½ Mo — 1¼ Si	
2¼ Cr — 1 Mo	
2½ Cr — ½ Mo — ¾ Si	
3 Cr — ½ Mo — 1¼ Si	
3 Cr — 1 Mo	
5 Cr — ½ Mo	
5 Cr — ½ Mo — Ti	
5 Cr — ½ Mo — Cb	
5 Cr — ½ Mo — 1½ Si	
8 Cr — 1 Mo	
17 Cr	
27 Cr	

FIG. 46—3. Creep strength (stress for creep rate of 1 per cent per 10,000 hours) of various steels at temperatures between 800° and 1400° F.

manifest: these include spheroidization, graphitization, precipitation hardening or aging embrittlement, and carbide precipitation. These will be discussed in the section entitled "Behavior of Steels at Elevated Temperature."

Grain Size—Generally, the creep strength is increased by a coarsening of the grain size. However, it is not possible to coarsen the grains unduly without injuring other properties such as impact strength.

SECTION 3

BEHAVIOR OF STEELS AT ELEVATED TEMPERATURE

A. INTERNAL STABILITY

Carbide Instability—Steels in service at elevated temperature do not usually show any significant change of grain size or shape, but important microstructural changes may occur within or between the grains. Such changes include the formation of new phases, spheroidization and agglomeration of carbides and nitrides, and graphitization.

In carbon and molybdenum steels, spheroidization occurs at temperatures above 1000° F; as shown in Figure 46—4, graphitization, particularly in fine-grained aluminum-killed steel, may also occur. The addition of chromium tends to stabilize the carbides, thus lessening or eliminating graphitization and delaying spheroidization. The relative stability of 24 steels

at 900°, 1000°, and 1100° F, is shown in Table 46—I.

A form of carbide instability occurs in the austenitic chromium-nickel steels in the temperature range between 800° and 1600° F. In this temperature range, chromium carbides form and precipitate at the grain boundaries, depleting these regions in chromium and hence lowering the resistance of the grain boundaries to corrosion. This form of carbide precipitation has not been found to lower the tensile, creep or room-temperature impact strength of the material, which has been successfully used for oil-cracking still tubes in this temperature range. Carbide precipitation can be retarded by lowering the carbon content below 0.02 per cent or alloying with such carbide stabilizers as titanium or columbium (niobium).

Table 46—I. Relative Change of Microstructure* of Alloys During 3000 Hours at 900°, 1000°, and 1100° F.

Nominal Composition	Heat Treatment**	Change in Structure† in 3000 Hours at		
		900° F	1000° F	1100° F
C-0.5 Mo	1650 AC	I	III	III
C-0.5 Mo	1650 AC, 1300 AC	0	II	III
C-1 Mo	1650 AC	0	III	—
C-1 Mo	1650 AC, 1300 AC	0	II	—
C-1.5 Mo	1650 AC	0	III	—
C-1.5 Mo	1650 AC, 1300 AC	0	II	—
C-2 Mo	1650 AC	0	III	—
C-2 Mo	1650 AC, 1300 AC	—	II	—
C-Mo-Mn	1650 AC, 1300 AC	0	II	—
2 Cr-0.5 Mo	1650 AC, 1380 FC	—	I	—
2.25 Cr-1 Mo	1650 AC, 1380 FC	—	0	II
2.25 Cr-1 Mo	1650 FC	—	I	—
1.2 Cr-0.5 Mo-0.7 Si	1650 AC, 1380 FC	—	0	II
1.7 Cr-0.7 Mo-0.7 Si	1750 AC, 1375 FC	—	I	—
3 Cr-0.5 Mo-1.5 Si	1600 FC	—	0	0
3 Cr-Mo-Si-Al	1550 AC	—	0	0
5 Cr-0.5 Mo	1600 FC	—	0	0
5 Cr-0.5 Mo	1600 AC, 1380 AC	—	0	I
5 Cr-1 Mo	1650 AC, 1380 AC	—	0	I
5 Cr-1 Mo	1650 FC	—	0	—
5 Cr-0.5 Mo-1.5 Si	1600 FC	—	0	0
5 Cr-Mo-Si-Al	1550 AC	—	0	0
5 Cr-Mo-Ti	1380 AC	—	I	—
5 Cr-Mo-Ti	1850 AC	—	0	—
5 Cr-Mo-Cb	1380 AC	—	I	—
5 Cr-Mo-Cb	1850 AC	—	0	—
5 Cr-Mo-Si-Cb	1750 AC, 1380 FC	—	0	—
8 Cr-1 Mo	1700 FC	—	0	0
8 Cr-1 Mo-Cb	1700 FC	—	0	0
9 Cr-1 Mo	1700 FC	—	0	0
18-8	1900 WQ	—	—	II
18-8 Ti	1900 AC	—	—	I
18-8 Ti	1900 AC, 1600 AC	—	—	0
18-8 Cb	1900 AC	—	—	I
18-8 Cb	1900 AC, 1600 AC	—	—	I

*It may be assumed that steels showing a change of microstructure at 1000° F would do so at a higher temperature, and that steels which remained unchanged at 1000 or 1100° F would do likewise at a lower temperature.

**AC = Air Cool FC = Furnace Cool WQ = Water Quench

†0 —no change.
I —slight change.
II —moderate change.
III—marked change.

Aging—Aging or precipitation hardening as a heat-treating process may be utilized to increase the strength of metals at elevated temperature providing that the material is used below the temperature at which overaging would occur during the life of the part. For example, in age-hardened Stainless W, an alloy containing 17 per cent chromium, 7 per nickel with added titanium, relaxation measurements show that, while some softening occurs in about a week at 800° F, very little softening occurs in the same length of time at 600° F. Below this temperature, therefore, it should be possible to utilize the strengthening produced by the precipitation hardening.

Aging can, of course, occur during service and may result in embrittlement of the material. In carbon steels, it has been found that aging occurring at temperatures between 400° and 600° F is more pronounced in ferritic carbon steels having high nitrogen contents, and that it is greater the less thorough the deoxidation of the material. The aging tendency is lessened by addition of titanium and aluminum. If this aging or precipitation hardening resulted only in an increase of strength, no harm would result. However, as the strength increases, the ductility decreases, particularly as measured by the notched-bar impact test after straining. The sensitivity to strain-aging is lessened by normalizing and by thorough deoxidation of the steel.

Temper Brittleness—Steels with even moderate amounts of chromium or manganese, and such steels plus nickel, are likely to become brittle if cooled slowly from the tempering operation after quenching—hence the name, "temper brittleness." Steels with 1 to 2 per cent manganese, and even plain 3 to 5 per cent nickel steels, may show it. The addition of 0.30 to 0.50 per cent of molybdenum lessens the embrittlement. Vanadium has also been found to minimize the effect of this embrittlement. The higher the nickel and chromium content, the greater the amount of molybdenum required to increase freedom from embrittlement, and an increase in the nickel content decreases the resistance to embrittlement of steels containing chromium and molybdenum. The brittleness resulting from heating at about 840° F can be eliminated by heating to between 930° and 1110° F. Embrittlement can occur under no load, but stress has been found to accelerate the embrittlement.

Temper brittleness is found in bolts, studs, and other quenched and tempered parts used in high-temperature steam lines at temperatures in the vicinity of 800° to 900° F. The embrittled material may retain its full original toughness at the service temperature, and yet be brittle to a notch test at room temperature. There is no measurable difference between the tough and the embrittled forms of the steel observable in tension, bend or fatigue tests, provided that the test pieces are not notched.

Embrittlement of Ferritic Chromium Steels—Plain chromium steels containing more than 12 to 15 per cent chromium have been found to become embrittled during prolonged heating in the vicinity of 900° F. This embrittlement is due to the formation of a body-centered-cubic iron-chromium compound containing 70 to 80 per cent chromium. The embrittlement dur-

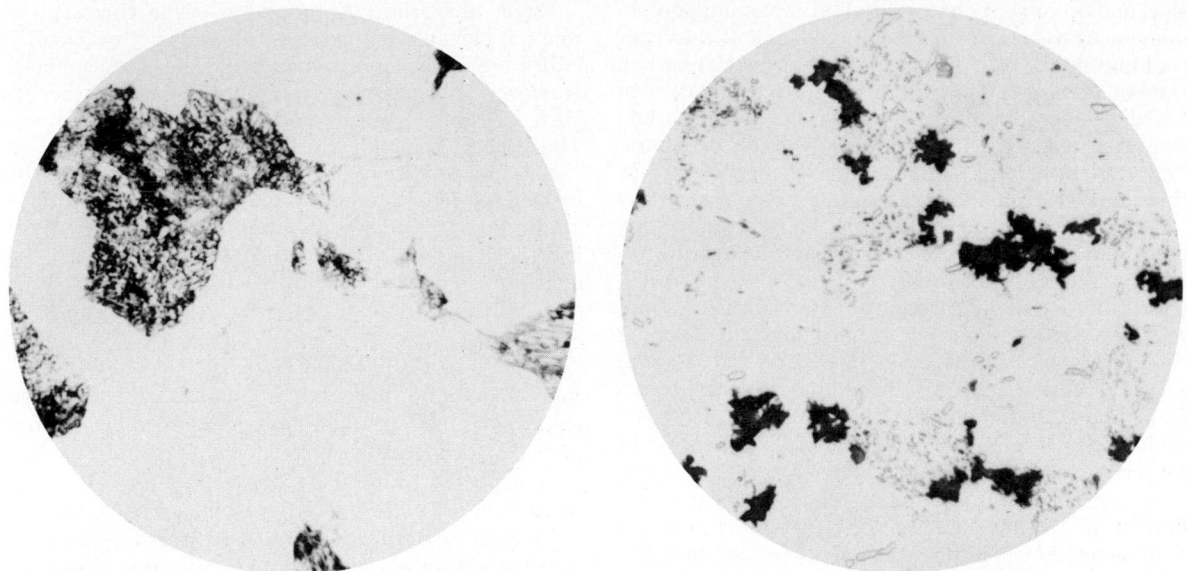

FIG. 46—4. (Left) Spheroidized annealed molybdenum steel. (Right) Same steel exhibiting graphitization after heating at 1100° F for 1000 hours. Magnification (both photomicrographs): 1000X.

ing heating at higher temperature (1120° to 1470° F) is due to the precipitation of this intermetallic compound, designated as sigma phase. The ductility and impact properties of alloys containing over 20 per cent chromium may be seriously impaired even by slow cooling in the range 1100° to 700° F.

B. EXTERNAL OR SURFACE STABILITY

Scaling and Corrosion Resistance—The property of surface stability or corrosion resistance is considered to be of primary importance, since the metal must not deteriorate excessively during service at elevated temperature. One of the simplest forms of corrosion, and one frequently encountered, is oxidation of the metal. Oxidation occurs by a process of diffusion of oxygen inward and of alloying elements outward through the scale layer already formed. In plain carbon steel, the amount of oxidation in air is negligible below about 1000° F. Above this temperature, the rate of oxidation

of carbon steel increases rapidly. For a given period of exposure, the amount of oxidation varies exponentially with respect to the reciprocal of the absolute temperatures.

The most important element for increasing the oxidation resistance of carbon steel above 1000° F is chromium. This element appears to oxidize preferentially to iron, and to form a tightly adherent layer of chromium-iron oxide on the surface of the metal, retarding the inward diffusion of oxygen and inhibiting further oxidation. Other elements such as silicon and aluminum also increase the oxidation resistance, particularly when added to a steel containing chromium. These elements have a greater affinity for oxygen than does iron, and are also preferentially oxidized.

The rate of oxidation decreases as the oxide layer becomes thicker and additional protective layers are formed. The nature of the progress of oxidation with time at 1100° F is shown in Figure 46—5 for carbon

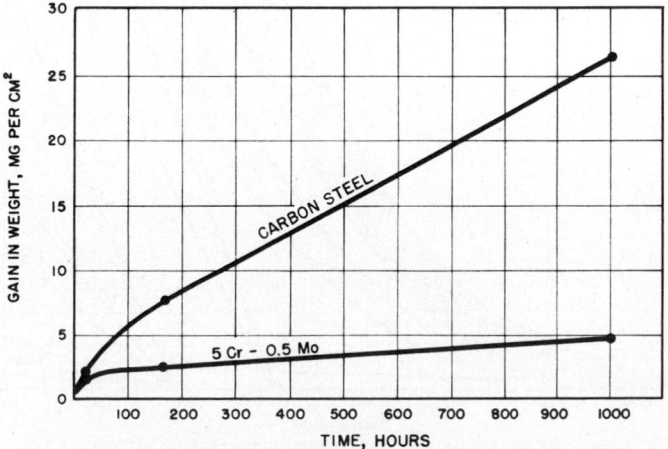

FIG. 46—5. Oxidation of plain carbon and 5 per cent chromium —0.5 per cent molybdenum steel at 1100° F.

steel and 5 per cent chromium steel containing molybdenum. At the start, the rate of oxidation of the 5 per cent chromium steel is as rapid as that of the carbon steel or perhaps more so, but the rate of oxidation of the alloy steel soon decreases while that of the carbon steel continues at a rapid rate. The results of laboratory oxidation tests are shown in Figure 46—6. In these tests, the amount of oxidation was measured by the gain in weight in 1000 hours. Several interesting points immediately become apparent. As the temperature is increased above 1000° F, the amount of oxidation in the plain carbon and molybdenum steels increases rapidly. Increase of chromium to 2.25 per cent improves the oxidation resistance up to about 1150° F. The 5 per cent chromium steels are somewhat better, but their oxidation resistance decreases rapidly above 1200° F. Additions of 9 per cent or 12 per cent chromium considerably improve the oxidation resistance, these materials showing little oxidation in 1000 hours below 1400° F. The increase in scaling resistance in going from 5 per cent to 9 per cent chromium is noticeable. The very large increase in oxidation resistance produced in 3 per cent chromium or 5 per cent chromium steel by addition of 1.5 per cent silicon is also striking.

A survey of the available data indicates that the chromium content for freedom from oxidation increases almost linearly with an increase in temperature, as shown in Figure 46—7. While this diagram indicates the maximum chromium content for freedom from oxidation, it should be noted that addition of 1.25 to 1.50 per cent silicon greatly improves oxidation resistance, decreasing the amount of chromium needed for protection at a given temperature.

Effect of Various Atmospheres—The corrosion of steels at elevated temperatures in air is not necessarily indicative of their performance in other atmospheres. However, it is generally true that the corrosion resistance of steel increases with its chromium content. The precise behavior must, however, be established under the conditions in which the material will be used in service. Based on service experience in various atmospheres, as well as on laboratory tests, the American Society for Testing and Materials has listed the maximum temperature which various stainless steels can withstand without excessive scaling (Table 46—II).

In 3000 and 7000 hour tests in steam at 1100° F, Van Duzer and McCutchan found that the silicon content of the chromium-molybdenum steels did not increase their resistance to steam corrosion, as had been expected from laboratory tests in air. They also found that the corrosion of the plain carbon steels proceeded at a constant rate, but that as little as 1 to 2 per cent chromium lessened materially the amount of corrosion. In the 12 per cent chromium stainless steels, the high-sulphur free-machining steel was as good as the standard grades, but addition of 2 per cent manganese lowered the corrosion resistance.

Rohrig, Van Duzer and Fellows tested various carbon and alloy steels in steam at 925° and 1100° F. In periods up to 15,000 hours at 925° F, the steels formed a thin, dense, tightly adherent layer of scale. The amount of scaling was very light and there was little difference between the various types of steels. At 1100° F, scaling of the carbon steels increased continuously, but that of the alloy steels decreased after

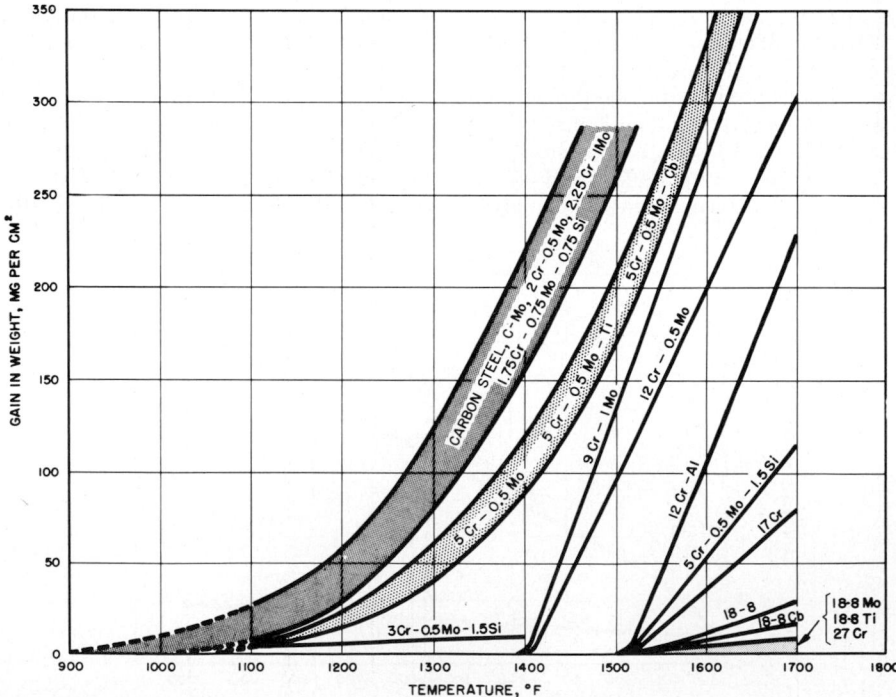

Fig. 46—6. Amount of oxidation (scaling) of carbon, low-alloy, and stainless steels in 1000 hours in air at temperatures from 1100° to 1700° F.

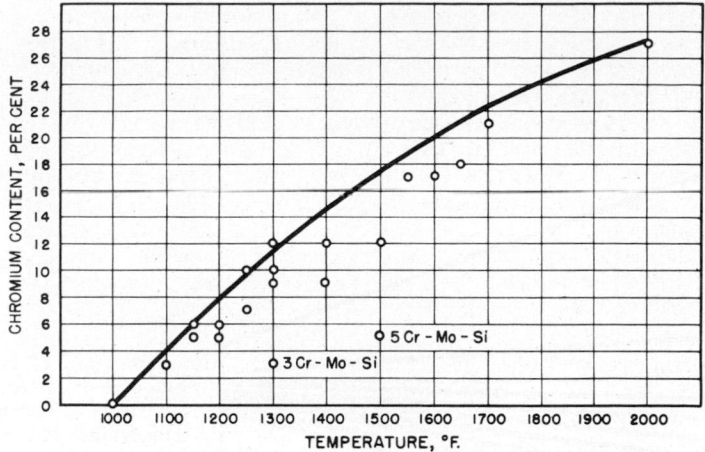

Fig. 46—7. Maximum amount of chromium necessary for freedom from scaling at temperatures from 1000° to 2000° F.

a period of time. In general, the same trends are shown by these tests in steam as by the tests in air.

Corrosion tests in carbon dioxide show about the same results as corrosion tests in air.

In flue gases, Oertel and Landt found that the rate of corrosion in 10 per cent chromium steels at temperatures between 1300° and 2000° F was three times as rapid as in air. Gases that are chemically reducing in nature increase the corrosion rate over that obtained in air.

Chromium is particularly effective in increasing the resistance of steel to corrosion by sulphur compounds at elevated temperature, a condition frequently encountered in oil refining. Service experience with oil-cracking still tubes and evaporators has shown that

Table 46—II. Maximum Temperature Without Excessive Scaling

Alloy Nominal Composition (%)	Steel Type No.	Maximum Temperature Withstood Without Excessive Scaling (°F)
4-6 Cr-Mo	502	1150
8-10 Cr	—	1200
10-14 Cr	410	1250
12-14 Cr	420	1200
14-18 Cr	440	1400
14-18 Cr	430	1550
23-30 Cr	446	2000
18-8	302	1650
18-8	303	1600
18-8	304	1650
25-12	309	2000
25-20	310	2000
18-8 Mo	316	1650
18-8 Ti	321	1650
18-8 Cb	347	1650

From: "Tables of Data on Chemical Compositions, Physical and Mechanical Properties of Wrought Corrosion-Resisting and Heat-Resisting Chromium-Nickel Steels," American Society for Testing and Materials, Dec., 1942.

under these conditions small additions of chromium are effective; 2 per cent chromium was found to reduce the amount of corrosion to ⅕ that encountered in plain carbon steel.

In ammonia synthesis, Schiffler and Berlecken showed that the conditions at high temperatures and pressures lead to reactions between the hydrogen of the gas and the carbon of the steel to form methane (CH_4) and other hydrocarbons. At 390° and 750° F, at 50 and 75 atmospheres pressure, respectively, carbon steel and 1 per cent chromium steel with molybdenum showed loss of impact strength after service, while 5 per cent chromium steel with molybdenum was unaffected. The improvement of the resistance of steels to hydrogen must be accomplished by using lower carbon content, minimizing inclusions, and alloying with chromium, preferably above 3 per cent, in connection with such carbide stabilizers as tungsten, molybdenum, titanium, vanadium, tantalum, and columbium. The elements that resist hydrogen are also good nitride formers, so the formation of a brittle nitride layer is possible when these elements are used. All high-chromium and chromium-nickel steels show excellent resistance to hydrogen. Chromium steels are resistant to hydrogen sulphide (H_2S) and sulphur dioxide (SO_2) gases, while nickel steels are sensitive to these gases. A chromium-silicon-aluminum steel was found to be useful where gases containing H_2S had to be handled at 1830° F.

Caustic Embrittlement of Boiler Plates—Caustic embrittlement or "caustic cracking" of boiler plates sometimes occurs when alkalies are present in the boiler feedwater. The caustic cracking is intergranular and results from a combination of stress, exposure to alkaline solutions at temperatures of 212° F or above, and the opportunity for concentration of the solution in capillary spaces. Both hydrogen (H_2) and the deposit of iron oxide (FeO) formed by the reaction enter into the process, but the full explanation of the phenomenon is lacking. Common methods of protection when using alkaline water are to maintain a ratio of sulphate to alkali above a certain value which depends on the working pressure, or to distill the water.

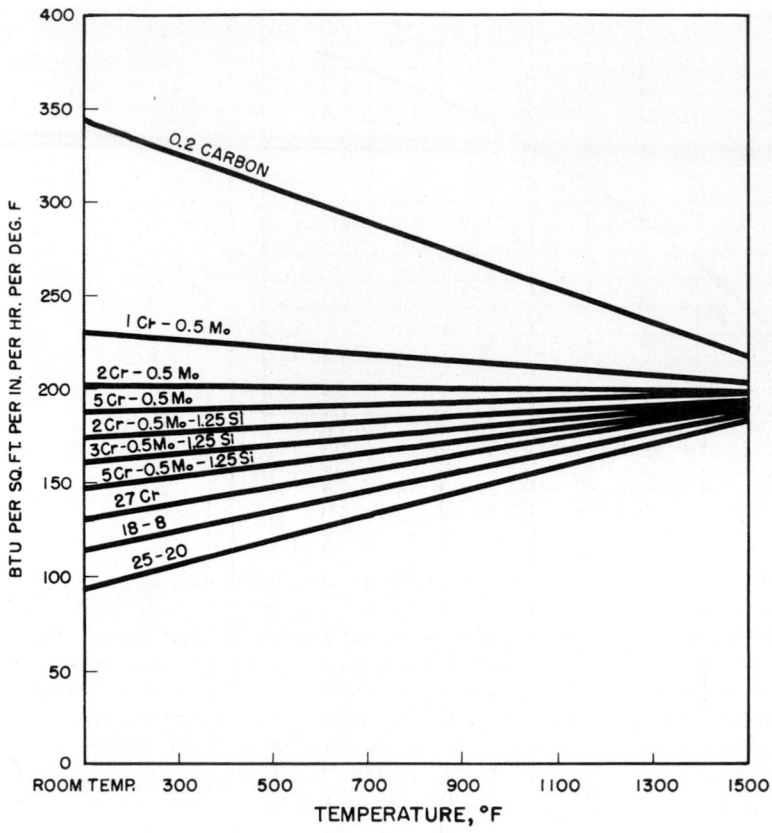

FIG. 46—8. Thermal conductivity of various steels at temperatures between room temperature and 1500° F.

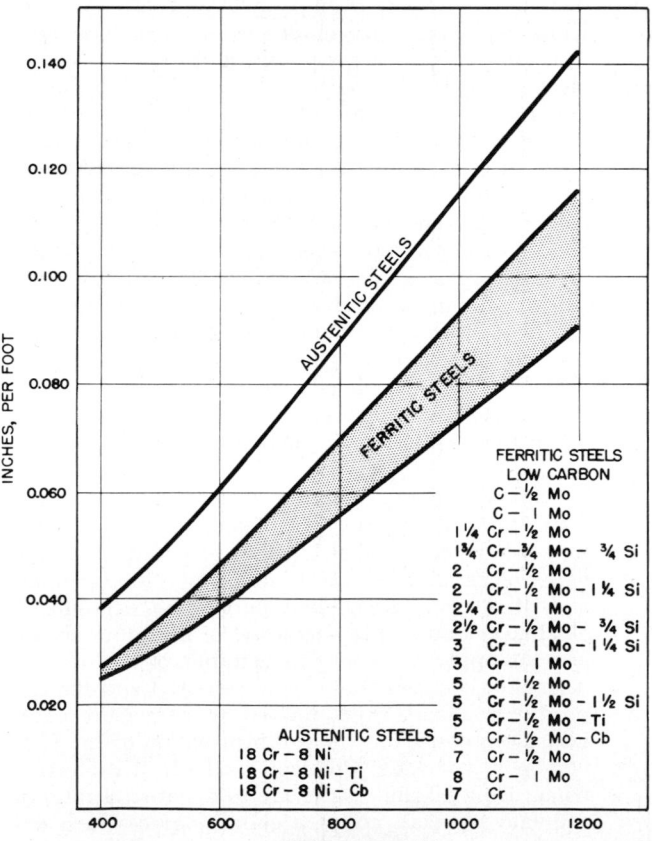

FIG. 46—9. Influence of temperature on linear thermal expansion. The diagram shows the change of length, in inches per foot, occurring in carbon, low-alloy, and stainless steels as they are heated from room temperature to any temperature between 400° and 1200° F. For the ferritic steels, the thermal expansion decreases with increasing chromium content, following the order of the steels as listed on the diagram. In the austenitic steels the thermal expansion is larger than in the carbon steel.

SPECIAL PROPERTIES

In addition to strength, stability and corrosion resistance, other properties occasionally have to be considered in designing for elevated-temperature service: some of these properties are thermal conductivity, thermal expansion, and modulus of elasticity.

Thermal Conductivity—Of importance at elevated temperature is the thermal conductivity of the material. Average data for various steels are shown in Figure 46—8. It will be noted that the addition of alloying elements decreases the thermal conductivity of carbon steel, and that the difference between the thermal conductivities of the various steels decreases with increasing temperature. The thermal conductivities of the austenitic 18 per cent chromium, 8 per cent nickel steels and of the 25 per cent chromium, 20 per cent nickel steels, are the two lowest on the chart.

Thermal Expansion—In designing apparatus for use at elevated temperature, allowance must be made for the thermal coefficient of expansion of the component materials.

The linear thermal expansion (increase in length) in inches per foot in going from room temperature to any elevated temperature up to 1200° F is shown in Figure 46—9.

The steels are listed in the order in which they occur on these bands. It is seen that the austenitic stainless steels have a higher coefficient of expansion than the ferritic steels.

Modulus of Elasticity—Elastic moduli are often needed for design for service at elevated temperatures. The temperature dependence of Young's modulus (tensile modulus, E) for a number of ferrous materials that might be used in service at elevated temperatures is shown in Figure 46—10. The rela-

tively low spread in values which encompasses all the ferritic or austenitic steels should be noted, since it indicates that this property is relatively independent of composition and microstructure.

Bibliography

S. H. Weaver, The Effect of Carbide Spheroidization Upon Creep Strength of Carbon-Molybdenum Steel, Proc. ASTM, 1941, Vol. 41, pp. 608–627.

American Society for Testing Materials, Dec., 1942, Tables of Data on Chemical Compositions, Physical and Mechanical Properties of Wrought Corrosion Resisting and Heat Resisting Chromium-Nickel Steels.

R. M. Van Duzer, Jr., and A. McCutchan, High-Temperature-Steam Experience at Detroit, Trans. ASME, 1939, July, Vol. 61, pp. 383–398.

I. A. Rohrig, R. M. Van Duzer and C. H. Fellows, High-Temperature-Steam Corrosion Studies at Detroit, Trans. ASME, Vol. 66, May, 1944, pp. 277–290.

Oertel and Landt, Influence of Carbon Content on the Scaling of Chromium Iron, Stahl und Eisen, July 8, 1937.

H. J. Schiffler and E. Berlecken, Corrosion by Gas Due to the Special Conditions of Chemical Synthesis, Chem. Fabrik, Vol. 11, August 17, 1938, pp. 385–390.

F. Garofalo, P. R. Malenock and G. V. Smith, The Influence of Temperature on the Elastic Constants of Some Commercial Steels; ASTM, Spec. Tech. Publication No. 129, pp. 10–30, 1952.

R. Michel, Elastic Constants and Coefficients of Thermal Expansion of Piping Materials Proposed for 1954 Code for Pressure Piping, ASME Paper No. 53–A–52, 1953.

P. A. Haythorne, Sheet Metals for High Temperature Service, Iron Age 162, September 23, 1948.

Frances H. Clark. Metals at High Temperatures. Reinhold Publishing Corp., New York, 1950.

George V. Smith. Properties of Metals at Elevated Temperatures. McGraw-Hill Book Co., Inc., New York, 1950.

E. R. Parker, N. J. Grant, H. J. Grover, H. C. Cross, Carl Wagner and J. J. B. Rutherford. High Temperature Properties of Metals. Published by American Society for Metals, 1951.

American Society for Testing and Materials. Selected reports issued under auspices of the ASTM-ASME Joint Committee on Effect of Temperature on the Properties of Metals and published by ASTM, Philadelphia, Pa.

Special Technical Publication No. 100, Report on the Strength of Wrought Steels at Elevated Temperatures, prepared by R. F. Miller and J. J. Heger, 1950.

Special Technical Publication No. 124, Report on the Elevated-Temperature Properties of Stainless Steels, prepared by Ward F. Simmons and Howard C. Cross, 1952.

Special Technical Publication No. 151, Report on the Elevated-Temperature Properties of Chromium-Molybdenum Steels, prepared by Ward F. Simmons and Howard C. Cross, 1953.

Special Technical Publication No. 160, Report on the Elevated-Temperature Properties of Selected Super-Strength Alloys, prepared by Ward F. Simmons and Howard C. Cross, 1954.

Special Technical Publication No. 171, Symposium on Basic Effects of Environment on the Strength, Scaling and Embrittlement of Metals at High Temperatures, 1955.

Special Technical Publication No. 180, Elevated-Temperature Properties of Carbon Steels, prepared by Ward F. Simmons and Howard C. Cross, 1955.

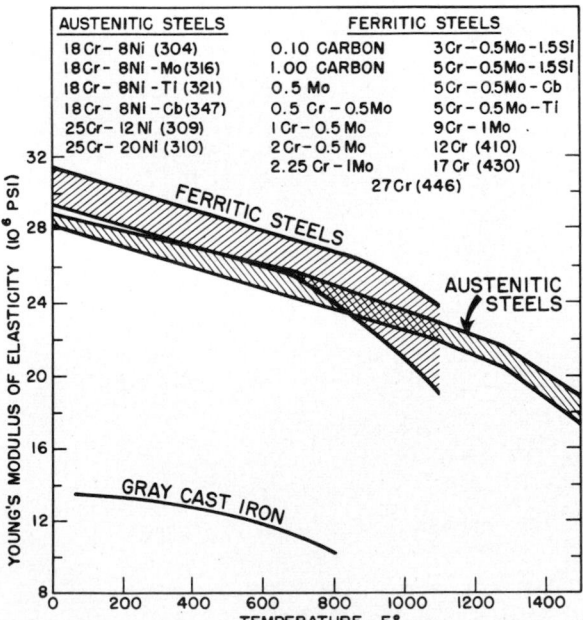

AUSTENITIC STEELS	FERRITIC STEELS	
18 Cr - 8 Ni (304)	0.10 CARBON	3 Cr - 0.5 Mo - 1.5 Si
18 Cr - 8 Ni - Mo (316)	1.00 CARBON	5 Cr - 0.5 Mo - 1.5 Si
18 Cr - 8 Ni - Ti (321)	0.5 Mo	5 Cr - 0.5 Mo - Cb
18 Cr - 8 Ni - Cb (347)	0.5 Cr - 0.5 Mo	5 Cr - 0.5 Mo - Ti
25 Cr - 12 Ni (309)	1 Cr - 0.5 Mo	9 Cr - 1 Mo
25 Cr - 20 Ni (310)	2 Cr - 0.5 Mo	12 Cr (410)
	2.25 Cr - 1 Mo	17 Cr (430)
	27 Cr (446)	

FIG. 46—10. Young's modulus, E, of various ferrous materials, as affected by temperature.

Special Technical Publication No. 187, Relaxation Properties of Steels and Super-Strength Alloys at Elevated Temperatures, prepared by James W. Freeman and Howard R. Voorhees, 1956.

Special Technical Publication No. 199, Report on Elevated-Temperature Properties of Wrought Medium-Carbon Alloy Steels, prepared by Ward F. Simmons and Howard C. Cross, 1956.

Special Technical Publication No. 226, The Elevated-Temperature Properties of Weld-Deposited Metals and Weldments, prepared by Howard R. Voorhees and James W. Freeman, 1958.

Special Technical Publication No. 228, Report on Elevated-Temperature Properties of Chromium Steels (12-27 Per Cent), prepared by Ward F. Simmons and Howard C. Cross, 1958.

Special Technical Publication No. 296, Report on Physical Properties of Metals and Alloys from Cryogenic to Elevated Temperatures, prepared by E. A. Eldridge and H. W. Deem, 1961.

CHAPTER 47

Mechanical Testing

SECTION 1

INTRODUCTION

The manner in which metals react to applied forces is important in almost all practical applications. Steels, for example, are used in a multitude of applications involving their ability to withstand service loadings without permanently deforming or rupturing. Of equal importance, on the other hand, is the ability of steel to undergo large permanent deformations, thus permitting the formation of useful shapes under the application of the proper forces. Even though the final service application of a metal part may not in any way involve load-carrying ability, it is almost certain that at some stage in fabrication the manner of reaction of the metal to applied forces has come into play. **Mechanical properties** are the characteristic response of a material to applied forces; the **methods of measurement** of these properties and of evaluating their significance form the subject matter of this chapter.

It is both logical and useful to think of mechanical properties as falling into two broad categories: strength and ductility. **Strength** properties are related to the ability of the material to resist applied forces, while **ductility** is a measure of the ability to undergo permanent changes of shape without rupturing. Many mechanical characteristics or behaviors depend on both strength and ductility, frequently in a complex manner, as illustrated so well by that characteristic of materials known as **toughness,** or the ability to absorb energy. Even such complex behavior can be better understood, however, by considering it in terms of the separate contributions of strength and ductility.

The mechanical reactions of metals to applied forces are extremely diversified, depending upon the exact nature of the forces and the conditions under which they are applied. It is essential that cognizance be taken of this fact in attempting to devise or select tests which will permit a prediction of service performance. The final answer to the question of suitability for service can, in general, only be found in an actual service test. In most cases, however, actual service tests are impractical and simpler tests must be found, especially where frequent inspection of material is essential. In devising simpler tests, it is important that the type of forces involved in the particular service application of interest be known, i.e., whether the loading is tension, compression, bending, twisting, shear, etc. It is also important to know whether the loading is static or dynamic, and if dynamic, it is important to know the nature of the rate of application and variation of the loading. The temperature at which the loading is applied also may be of critical importance. If these features of the service conditions are known, one can be guided in the selection of tests most likely to provide a reliable evaluation of the suitability of a material for a particular application. One criterion of test validity with respect to service would be, then, the extent to which the test simulates the actual application. For example suppose that a large structural member is required to carry a certain compressive load at a temperature of 500° F. A test of the actual member is out of question because of the large size. An alternate course of action is to select from the material in question a small specimen suited to available testing equipment and to make a compression test at 500° F. The type of loading and the service temperature are thereby duplicated, and it is likely that the test results will be a reliable guide in selecting a material suitable for the application.

Another criterion by which a test may be selected depends on whether or not the test measures the same ultimate fundamental property on which successful performance in service depends. For example, in bending, the minimum bend radius obtainable with a particular material depends on the ability of the material to elongate over very short gage lengths on the tension fibers of the bend. Since the reduction of area in the tension test may be interpreted also as a measure of ability to elongate over very short gage lengths, it has been possible in some instances to relate minimum bend radii to reduction of area. The test is thus measuring a property which is directly responsible for the behavior in the application.

There exist a great many applications of metals, however, which are characterized by such complex conditions of loading that a directly applicable test may not be readily found. Because of this circumstance, the selection of mechanical tests for a particular instance is based primarily on experience. It may be known that, over a period of years, many lots of a certain grade of steel having properties falling within a certain range have performed satisfactorily in service. It can be expected, then, that new lots of this grade of steel having the same mechanical properties will perform satisfactorily in the same application.

A good example of a test selected on the basis of experience is offered by the extensive use of hardness testing in the inspection of deep-drawing sheets. It is known from experience that, in order for a sheet to be formed satisfactorily into a particular part, its hardness must lie within a certain range. Although hardness in itself can hardly be considered the property which controls the performance, it reflects the critical properties to a degree which makes it extremely useful as a control test, particularly in view of the ease with which hardness tests can be made. Testing on this basis, however, should only be considered as a means of increasing the probability of selecting satisfactory material. Unless the actual characteristics which determine the performance are known and are actually being tested for, an arbitrary test, even though backed by considerable experience, may at some time fail to discriminate between good and poor material.

In the field of the mechanical behavior of metals, there is a strong trend away from arbitrary tests and toward a more exact evaluation of the fundamental properties which are actually called upon in particular service applications. The new methods of experimental stress analysis, particularly the wire-resistance strain-gage techniques, have permitted great advances to be made in more thorough evaluation of service requirements. Once the mechanics of an application have been analyzed and the critical fundamental material characteristics have been ascertained, the task of selecting a suitable test is greatly simplified.

Many steel products are sold to mechanical property specifications and much of the testing carried out by the steel producer is for the purpose of ascertaining whether or not a given specification is being met. If the product is a widely used one, a standard specification may be set up by a body such as the American Society for Testing and Materials in order to assist the user in specifying material for a certain application. Such specifications may provide fundamental design figures for the engineer, or in many cases may be based on previous experience which indicates that, if a material has certain properties, it will serve a particular purpose satisfactorily.

As already indicated, mechanical testing may be carried out as a means of quality control, even though the product may not be sold to a mechanical-property specification. In such instances, the experience of the producer dictates the test most suitable for the purpose. The particular test chosen may depend to a great extent upon the ease with which it can be made if frequent inspection or extensive sampling is needed.

Another important function of mechanical testing is to determine the causes for failure in service. If the material is shown to be at fault, a substitution of another material or the elimination of the deficiency of the first material can be guided by judicious mechanical tests. If no fault can be found with the material, a change in design may be indicated.

Still another function of mechanical testing results from its great usefulness in the development of new and improved products. Even in applications so complex in nature that a final test in service may be required, it is usually possible, by judicious mechanical tests, to establish trends and select the materials most likely to perform satisfactorily.

In the subsequent sections of this chapter, the mechanical tests most generally applied to steel will be discussed. Attention will be focused primarily upon the tension test, the hardness test, the notched-bar impact test, the fatigue test, and the creep and rupture tests. In addition, certain miscellaneous tests sometimes made on steel will be briefly described. Emphasis will be placed on the significance of the various mechanical properties to be discussed, as well as on the precautions necessary to obtain reliable test results. Test procedures approved and recommended by the American Society for Testing and Materials will be indicated for those tests for which standards or tentative standards have been established.

SECTION 2

THE TENSION TEST

Because of the large amount of information which can be derived from it, the tension test is undoubtedly the most generally useful of all the mechanical tests applied to steel. The versatility of the tension test lies in the fact that it permits both strength and ductility properties to be measured. The strength properties measured in the tension test are directly useful in design, whereas the ductility properties provide some indication of the extent to which changes in shape can be brought about by plastic forming, or an indication as to whether sufficient ductility is present for the intended service. Since the tension test is used quite extensively in the steel industry, a rather complete description of the test and of the properties measured will be presented.

Testing Machines—The machines employed in tension testing consist essentially of a load-producing mechanism and a load-measuring mechanism. The most elementary method of producing a tensile load simply involves the suspension of dead weights from the specimen to be loaded. This procedure is in general not practicable, however, because of the inconvenience of handling the large weights which would be required. Dead-weight loading, sometimes with the force multiplied by a lever, is used in certain instances, however, where it is desired to subject a specimen to a fixed load for a period of considerable duration. Creep and rupture testing, which is discussed in a later section, is perhaps the best example of the use of dead-weight loading for testing purposes.

The more commonly used testing machines employ either a mechanical system of loading actuated by screws or a hydraulic system in which the load is applied through a hydraulic ram. In both types of machines, there is a fixed crosshead and a moving crosshead through which the tensile force is applied. The moving crosshead in the screw machine is motivated either by threaded columns (screws) rotating in stationary nuts or by rotating nuts, depending upon the design of the machine. Various speeds of crosshead movement are available through changes of the gear combination in the drive and, in the newer machines, by variable-speed drives. In the hydraulic machine, the moving crosshead is powered by a hydraulic ram. A continuous variation in the rate of crosshead movement from extremely slow up to the limit set by the capacity of the hydraulic pump is obtainable; however, the slow rate can usually be adjusted to a rate slower than most mechanical machines with variable-speed drive.

The mechanical or screw type of testing machine used to be characterized by the load-measuring mechanism generally employed. The older machines use a mechanism in which the load is transmitted through a system of levers acting on fulcrums of hardened steel to a beam carrying a movable weight or poise. The lever system is arranged so that the force exerted by the poise on the beam has a great mechanical advantage and can balance the force being applied to the tensile specimen. The poise can be moved outward along the beam, thereby increasing its lever arm and providing by its position a means of load indication. The movement of the poise is effected by manually rotating a screw during the test so that the beam is kept in balance. Because of the characteristic load-measuring mechanism, this type of machine is generally referred to as a "beam-and-poise" or "lever" machine. One of the greatest objections to the lever machine lies in the manual operation of the weighing mechanism and the attendant human factor introduced into the test. To circumvent this objection, some machines have been developed in which a pendulum counteracts the machine force and the movement of which provides a continuous and automatic indication of load on a dial.

Hydraulic testing machines are of two main types: the lapped-ram type and the packed-ram type. In the lapped-ram type, the piston and cylinder are lapped to an extremely close fit so that an almost frictionless movement is possible. Because of the extremely low friction, the oil pressure in the cylinder can be used directly as a measure of load on the machine. One load-measuring device used rather widely is the pendulum weighing mechanism. A small piston is acted upon by the same hydraulic pressure acting on the main ram, thus producing a force proportional to that acting on the main ram. The small piston is arranged in such a way as to displace a pendulum, the magnitude of the displacement providing an indication of the test load. Another method employs electronic indication methods for the direct measurement of the oil pressure.

In the packed-ram type of hydraulic testing machine, the piston and cylinder are not fitted as closely as in the lapped-ram type, and a packing is necessary to prevent leakage of oil from the system. Since friction between the packing and the ram is variable, depending upon the applied hydraulic pressure, the possibility of a direct pressure measurement being used to provide an accurate indication of load is precluded. One device used to circumvent this difficulty is the so-called Tate-Emery load indicator, which utilizes a hydraulic capsule. The load on the machine acts on the capsule which is part of a closed hydraulic system. The capsule is a very rigid assembly containing an oil layer of only about 0.030-inch thickness. As the load is applied, a pressure is developed in the capsule and transmitted to a Bourdon tube. The actual load indication is provided by a measurement of the force which is necessary to hold the tip of the Bourdon tube in its equilibrium position. This force is measured by the displacement of the free end of a helical spring attached to the tip of the Bourdon tube. The spring is made from an alloy of the Elinvar type, so that the spring constant is unaffected by minor temperature fluctuations. Since the tip of the Bourdon tube is not required to move more than a very small amount, the usual objections to a Bourdon tube, such as hysteresis effects, are eliminated, and the weighing system is practically free of inertia. A hydraulic testing machine provided with a weighing system of the type just described is shown in Figure 47—1.

Electronic devices are employed for load measurement in some mechanical and hydraulic machines of recent design. One method uses wire resistance strain gages to measure the changes in dimensions of an elastic member through which the load is applied. The system is calibrated so that the changes in resistance of the strain gages provide an indication of the load. Another method uses linearly variable differential transformers to sense elastic motion of torque bars caused by the applied load. Different load ranges can be obtained by appropriate selection of the dimensions of the elastic members.

Generally, a number of load-measuring ranges are provided so that the most sensitive and accurate range can be chosen for a particular test, that is, the range having its top limit just above the maximum load expected in the test. It is important to know the accuracy of the load-measuring mechanism, and frequent calibration should be carried out to insure that the accuracy remains within the desired limits. With modern load-weighing mechanisms, accuracies of one-half of one per cent of the indicated load over all but the lowest 10 per cent of the range is usually guaranteed. For most purposes, one per cent accuracy is considered satisfactory, but even at this level of accuracy, frequent calibration is desirable. (ASTM Standard E4 recommends that machines in constant use be verified at intervals of twelve months.) If the errors are found to exceed the desired limits, the load-measuring mechanism should be adjusted until further calibration indicates the accuracy to be within the desired range.

In the ASTM Standard E4, three methods for the verification of testing machines are described. These include: (a) verification by standard weights (only applicable in the case of machines weighing a downward force), (b) verification by standardized proving levers, and (c) verification by elastic calibration devices. The first two of these methods make use of standard weights, in one case applying the weights directly to the machine, and in the other case making

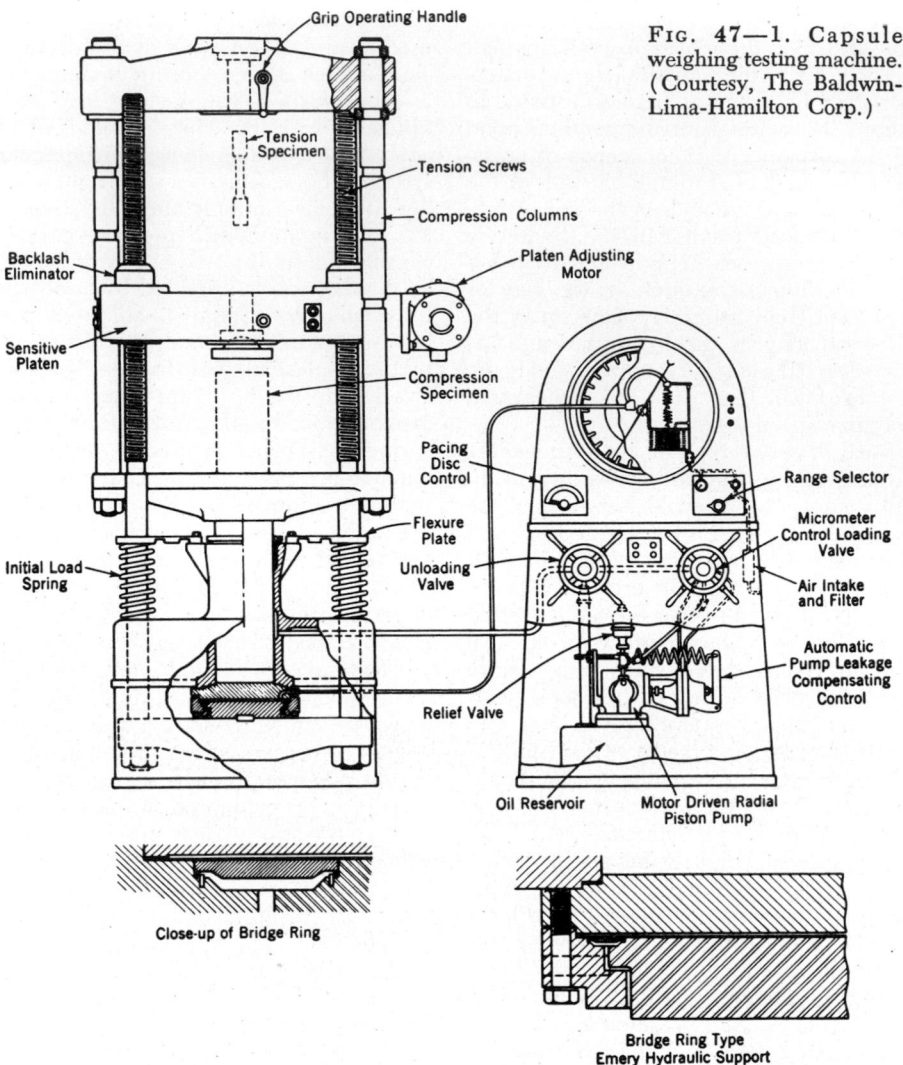

FIG. 47—1. Capsule weighing testing machine. (Courtesy, The Baldwin-Lima-Hamilton Corp.)

Close-up of Bridge Ring

Bridge Ring Type
Emery Hydraulic Support

use of levers to multiply the forces that can be applied by the standard weights. Although both methods are quite accurate, they are obviously very inconvenient, and the feasible range of load capacities which can be covered does not encompass the larger machines.

The most widely used method of calibration makes use of elastic calibration devices. The most frequently employed device of this type is the so-called proving ring, shown in Figure 47—2. Such a ring is subjected to a series of loads in the machine to be calibrated, and the deflection of the ring is measured by a micrometer which is an integral part of the proving ring. Proving rings are available in a variety of ranges up to 300,000 lb. and are calibrated and certified by the National Bureau of Standards.

Extensometers—Certain aspects of tension testing require the use of some device for the measurement of the extension of the specimen; such a device is called an extensometer. There are a very large number of types of extensometers available and no attempt will be made here to describe the features and specific applications of all the various types. The characteristics of a few of the more widely used types will be dis-

cussed briefly in order to illustrate the general nature of commercially available extensometers.

Extensometers can be considered to fall into two main groups, depending on the range of extensions which can be covered. On the one hand, there are the very accurate, high-sensitivity extensometers used for the measurement of minute extensions. These extensometers are characterized by very small ranges; i.e., the total extension which can be measured is quite small. On the other hand, there are the long-range extensometers designed to measure extensions up to the instant of rupture of the specimen. It is evident that, if long range is desired, sensitivity must be sacrificed; while it is equally true that sensitivity can be gained only at the expense of range. Extensometers can be either of the direct-reading (indicating) or recording type. The indicating extensometers make use of a dial gage to measure the movement of some element of the extensometer. A great many combinations of range and sensitivity can be obtained in dial-gage extensometers, the choice depending on the strain range over which observations are to be made.

The optical types of extensometers provide a high

FIG. 47—2. Morehouse proving ring, compression type. (Courtesy, Morehouse Machine Company.)

degree of sensitivity and accuracy for extremely small extensions and are of the indicating type. These extensometers are used in elastic-strain measurements and for very precise indications of the beginning of plastic yielding. Such an extensometer is the Tuckerman extensometer. This extensometer is attached to the specimen so that a fixed knife edge and a movable knife edge are in contact with the specimen. The movable knife edge consists of a lozenge, one face of which is polished to a mirror finish. A light beam is focused on the lozenge, and as the lozenge rotates as a result of extension of the specimen, the reflected beam is displaced relative to the incident beam. A specially calibrated collimator provides the light source and measures the deflection of the reflected beam. Extensions as small as two millionths (0.000002) of an inch per inch can be measured on a gage length of two inches.

Generally, the great sensitivity of the optical extensometers is not required and other more convenient types of low-range extensometers are employed.

Bonded wire resistance strain gages are sometimes used in the determination of stress-strain curves, although their main application is in experimental stress analysis. Essentially, this type of gage consists of a grid of fine wire which is suitably bonded to the specimen, usually by cementing. As the specimen is strained, the wires of the grid undergo similar strains which produce a change in the cross-section of the wire. This change in cross-section results in a change in electrical resistance that is proportional to the amount of strain and can be readily measured. The range of strain of most wire resistance gages is about one per cent, but special gages having considerably higher ranges have recently become available. When suitable techniques are employed, the sensitivity and accuracy of wire resistance gages is at least as good as the best optical strain gages.

Recording extensometers are now in wide use and offer the advantage of an automatically plotted stress-strain curve from which determinations of various material characteristics can be made, as well as the advantage of a permanent record of the test. High-sensitivity short-range recording extensometers can be obtained with an accuracy of better than 0.0001 inches per inch of indicated strain (see ASTM Standard E83), and with a range of up to 0.02 inch to 0.04 inch. Extensometers with sensitivities up to 0.00002 inch can be obtained.

One of the currently popular types of recording extensometers is the LVDT or linearly variable differential transformer type that operates on a magnetic principle. In this extensometer, the lever system is arranged in such a way that extension of the specimen results in a movement of an iron core in a small magnetic coil, thus changing the inductance of the coil. A similar magnetic coil is contained in the recorder, and is automatically kept in balance with the extensometer coil by a servomotor that also actuates the recorder. The movement in the stress-strain recorder can be calibrated to indicate the extension directly. By a different arrangement of the lever system in this type of recording extensometer, the range can be greatly extended, and such extensometers, known as total-elongation extensometers, are commercially available.

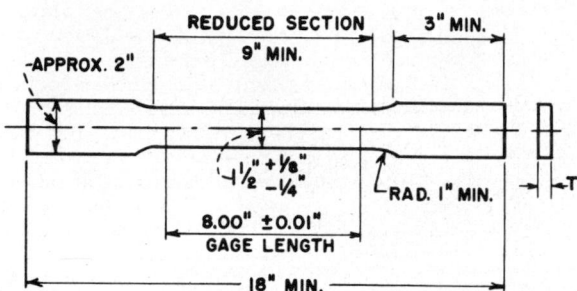

FIG. 47—3A. Standard rectangular tension test specimen with 8-in. gage length. (Based on "ASTM Standards, 1961.")

NOTE 1.—Punch marks for measuring elongation after fracture shall be made on the flat or on the edge of the specimen and within the reduced section. Either a set of nine or more punch marks 1 in. apart, or one or more pairs of punch marks 8 in. apart may be used.

NOTE 2.—When necessary a narrower specimen may be used. In such case the width should be as great as the width of the material being tested permits. If the width is 1½ in. or less the sides may be parallel throughout the length of the specimen.

NOTE 3.—The ends of the reduced section shall not differ in width by more than 0.004 in. There may be a gradual taper in width from the ends to the center, but the width at either end shall not be more than 0.015 in. greater than the width at the center.

NOTE 4.—The dimension "T" is the thickness of the test specimen as provided for in the applicable material specifications.

NOTE 5.—A ½ in. minimum radius at the ends of the reduced section is permitted for steel specimens under 100,000 psi in tensile strength when a profile cutter is used to machine the reduced section.

NOTE 6.—It is desirable, if possible, to make the length of the grip section great enough to allow the specimen to extend into the grips a distance equal to two thirds or more of the length of the grips.

NOTE 7.—The ends of the specimen shall be symmetrical with the center line of the reduced section within 0.10 in.

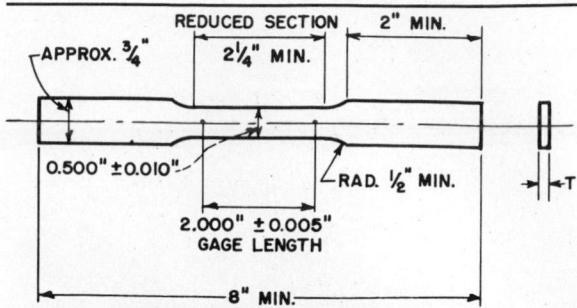

FIG. 47—3B. Standard rectangular tension test specimen with 2-in. gage length. (Based on "ASTM Standards, 1961.")

NOTE 1.—When necessary a narrower specimen may be used. In such case the width should be as great as the width of the material being tested permits. If the width is ½ in. or less the sides may be parallel throughout the length of the specimen.

NOTE 2.—The ends of the reduced section shall not differ in width by more than 0.002 in. There may be a gradual taper in width from the ends to the center, but the width at either end shall not be more than 0.005 in. greater than the width at the center.

NOTE 3.—The dimension "T" is the thickness of the test specimen as provided for in the applicable material specifications.

NOTE 4.—It is desirable, if possible, to make the length of the grip section great enough to allow the specimen to extend into the grips a distance equal to two thirds or more of the length of the grips. If the thickness of the specimen is over ⅜ in., longer grips and correspondingly longer grip sections of the specimen may be necessary to prevent failure in the grip section.

NOTE 5.—The ends of the specimen shall be symmetrical with the center line of the reduced section within 0.01 in. However, for steel if the ends are symmetrical within 0.05 in. a specimen may be considered satisfactory for all but referee testing.

The magnification ranges of this extensometer vary from 5 to 20 as compared to 250 to 1000 for the more sensitive, short-range extensometer.

Another type of long-range recording extensometer which has seen considerable application is the wedge type. In this extensometer, a wedge of known taper is pulled through a slot in the extensometer which opens as the specimen elongates. The movement of the wedge is used to rotate the recorder drum and since the taper of the wedge is known, the strain can be calculated. The magnification obtainable with this extensometer depends upon the degree of the taper in the wedge.

One of the first successful types of high-magnification recording extensometers operates on a micrometer-screw principle. A small electric motor, known as a Selsyn motor, rotates a screw which makes electrical contact with an element of the extensometer actuated by the extension of the specimen. The movement of the screw results in a corresponding movement in the stress-strain recorder, which can be calibrated to indicate the extension directly. The load-elongation curves drawn by this instrument are characterized by steps. The ranges and sensitivities avail-

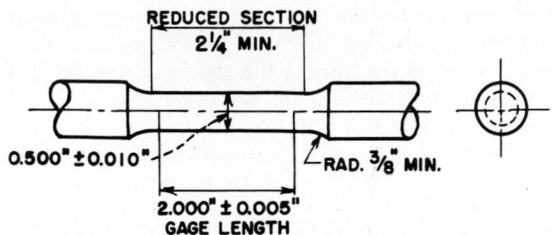

FIG. 47—3C. Standard round tension test specimen with 2-in. gage length. (Based on "ASTM Standards, 1961.")

NOTE 1.—The reduced section may have a gradual taper from the ends toward the center, with the ends not more than 0.005 in. larger in diameter than the center.

NOTE 2.—The gage length and fillets shall be as shown, but the ends may be of any form to fit the holders of the testing machine in such a way that the load shall be axial. If the ends are to be held in grips it is desirable, if possible, to make the length of the grip section great enough to allow the specimen to extend into the grips a distance equal to two thirds or more of the length of the grips.

able are comparable to those available in the LVDT type.

For strain measurements in and just beyond the elastic range, it is desirable to use extensometers which incorporate an averaging mechanism. Unless extreme precautions are taken, axiality of loading will not be obtained and a non-uniform strain distribution will result. By averaging the extension along two opposite fibers of the specimen, a closer approximation to the extension which would have occurred had the loading been axial can be obtained.

Specimens—Certain standard tension specimens have been adopted and are recommended by the American Society for Testing and Materials. The shapes and dimensions of the most frequently used specimens are shown in Figures 47—3A, B, C and D. Figure 47—3A shows the rectangular cross-section specimen with 8-inch gage length used for tests of plates and structural sections. The rectangular cross-section specimen with 2-inch gage length generally used in sheet-metal testing is shown in Figure 47—3B. The standard circular cross-section specimen with 2-inch gage length is shown in Figure 47—3C. The details of the ends of this type of specimen will vary widely, depending on the types of grips employed. If the section from which the specimen is to be taken is too small to permit the procurement of a full-size specimen, smaller specimens can be used if the dimensions are kept in geometric proportion. It is especially important that the gage length for measuring elongation be proportioned to the nominal diameter of the specimen. One-inch and 1.4-inch gage-length specimens are frequently used and have diameters of 0.252 inch and 0.357 inch respectively. The nominal diameters of 0.252, 0.357 and 0.505 inch for the specimens having gage lengths of 1 inch, 1.4 inches, and 2 inches, respectively, were selected to simplify calculation of loads in pounds per square inch from actual loads. These diameters provide specimens having respective cross-sectional areas of very nearly 0.05, 0.1, and 0.2

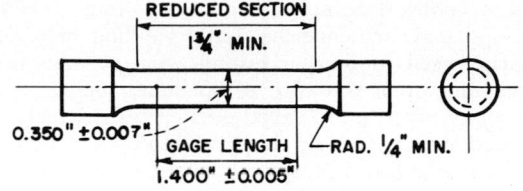

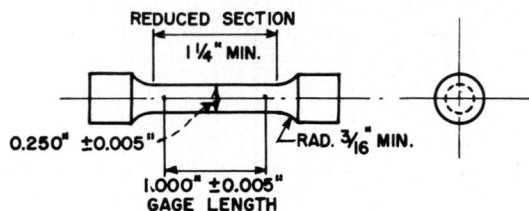

FIG. 47—3D. Example of small size specimens proportional to standard 2-in. gage specimen. (Based on "ASTM Standards, 1961.")

NOTE 1.—The reduced section may have a gradual taper from the ends toward the center, with the ends not more than 0.003 in. larger in diameter than the center.

NOTE 2.—If desired, the length of the reduced section may be increased to accommodate an extensometer. However, reference marks for the measurement of elongation should nevertheless be spaced at the indicated gage length.

NOTE 3.—The gage length and fillets shall be as shown, but the ends may be of any form to fit the holders of the testing machine in such a way that the load shall be axial. If the ends are to be held in grips it is desirable, if possible, to make the length of the grip section great enough to allow the specimen to extend into the grips a distance equal to two thirds or more of the length of the grips.

sq. in. Other specimens for special products can be found in the ASTM Standards. For certain types of products, such as small bars, tests may be made on the full section, in which case the only preparation necessary is the cutting of the specimen to length.

A number of general precautions should be observed in the procurement and preparation of tension-test specimens. It is important that heating and cold working of the specimen be kept to a minimum during procurement and preparation if reliable results are to be obtained. When specimen blanks are flame cut from plates, for example, allowance should be made for machining off all metal affected by the heat introduced during flame cutting. Cold shearing or punching of specimen blanks should be performed with care, since specimens improperly prepared in this manner may become cold worked and thus not be representative of the material being sampled. Care should also be taken to insure that the test specimen is straight and flat. An initial bow or curvature in a tension specimen will result in distortion of the elastic loading line and may affect the stress level at which initial plastic yielding occurs. In machining tension-test specimens, precautions should be taken to insure that the various portions of the specimen are symmetrical with respect to the loading axis of the specimen. If such precautions are not observed, the specimen will be loaded eccentrically, and bending stresses will be set up. Such eccentric loading will affect the elastic loading line and may influence the initial yielding behavior.

Grips used in tension testing vary considerably, depending upon the type of specimen being used. For many tests, the so-called wedge grips, which are serrated and simply grip the specimen by a transverse pressure which builds up as the specimen is loaded, are satisfactory. However, if the specimen is rather short, eccentric loading may become serious, necessitating the use of machined specimen ends and of grips with spherical bearings, an arrangement which to some extent provides self-alignment. Eccentric loading of plate or sheet-type specimens may be caused by the method used in preparing the test specimen; for example, shear or punch drag, or beads of metal deposited on the edges of the grip ends when burning out the specimen. A sketch of typical spherical seated grips is shown in Figure 47—4. For extremely accu-

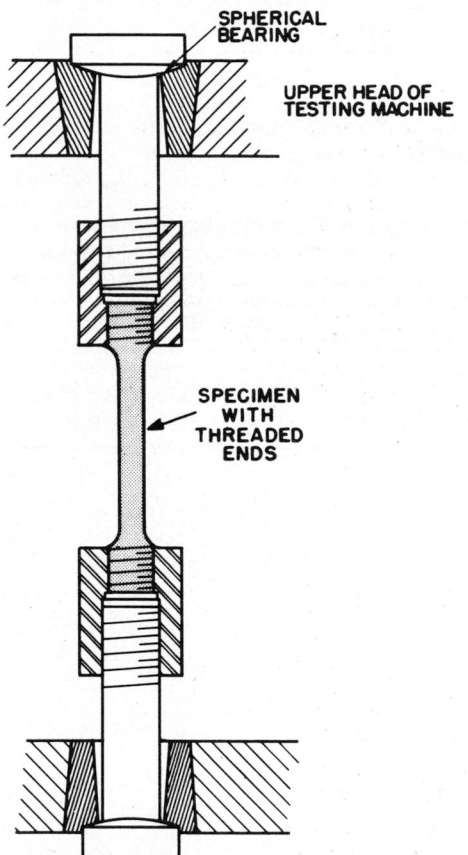

FIG. 47—4. Sketch of self-aligning tension grips. (From "ASTM Standards, 1961.")

rate work, adjustable grips may be used in which the load is transmitted through a small hardened-steel ball and which permit a shift of the specimen with respect to the load application points in order to obtain a very high degree of axiality.

The Tension Test and the Properties which are Determined—In conducting a tension test, the specimen is introduced into the machine in such a manner that a load can be applied along the specimen axis,

and the applied load is then gradually increased until the specimen breaks. An important factor which is generally controlled within certain predetermined limits in tension testing is the speed of testing. Some of the tensile properties are markedly affected by rate of straining, and it is important to specify and control the speed of testing within certain definite limits. These limits should be chosen in such a way as to prevent more than a certain percentage variation in the property being measured from arising as a result of variations in the speed of testing. Speed of testing may be specified in terms of rate of stressing the specimen, rate of crosshead movement, or rate of straining of the specimen. The most reliable of the three methods of specifying speed of testing is the rate of straining of the specimen, since any variations in properties as a result of variations of speed of testing arise directly from variations of strain rate in the specimen itself. In some instances the rate of crosshead movement may be closely enough related to rate of strain in the specimen that it can be used satisfactorily for control purposes.

Before considering the determination of specific properties in the tension test, it is necessary to define stress and strain, since these concepts are used in the definitions of the various tensile properties. The definitions of stress and strain proposed by the American Society for Testing and Materials are as follows:

Stress—The intensity at a point in a body of the internal forces or components of force which act on a given plane through the point. Stress is measured in force per unit area (pounds per square inch, kilograms per square millimeter, etc.).

Strain—A measure of the change in size or shape of a body, due to force, referred to its original size or shape. Strain is a non-dimensional quantity, but it is sometimes expressed in inches per inch, etc.

In discussing the various properties which are determined in tension tests, these properties will be classified according to whether some aspect of strength or ductility is being measured. Further details of testing procedure will be mentioned as they apply to the measurement of specific properties.

A. STRENGTH PROPERTIES

Modulus of Elasticity (Young's Modulus)—When a metal is subjected to load, there is an initial range of loading in which no permanent deformation of the specimen occurs; i.e., if the load is removed at any value within this range, the specimen will return completely to its original dimensions. Furthermore, within this range of loading, which is designated as the **elastic range**, the strain produced is directly proportional to the applied stress; i.e., the strain produced by 20,000 lb. per sq. in. stress will be twice that produced by 10,000 lb. per sq. in. The law of proportionality between stress and strain in the elastic range is known as **Hooke's Law**. The **modulus of elasticity** is simply the proportionality constant between stress and strain and can be obtained from the slope of a plot of stress against strain within the elastic range. The modulus for ordinary steels is usually taken as 30,000,000 lb. per sq. in. in design work. Since the modulus does not vary much from steel to steel, it is not determined except in special instances where a more accurate value may be needed, or for example, where the effect of temperature on the modulus must be ascertained. Very great accuracy of load measurement and strain measurement is necessary for reliable modulus determinations. Furthermore, special precautions must be exercised to procure specimens free from residual stress and to insure very accurate specimen alignment.

Elastic Limit—In practice, the elastic limit is determined by subjecting a specimen carrying a strain-measuring device (extensometer) to a series of loading steps in which the maximum load applied is gradually increased, the load being released completely at each step. A load will finally be reached upon release of which the specimen will fail to return to its original length: this load is the elastic limit. The size of the load increments used and the sensitivity of the extensometer used will, of course, affect the value obtained, and, consequently, this property is seldom determined.

Proportional Limit—The proportional limit represents an aspect of elastic behavior similar to the elastic limit, the principal difference lying in the method of determination. The straight-line proportionality between stress and strain in the elastic range has already been discussed. It is the upper limit of the range of proportionality that defines the proportional limit. In other words, the proportional limit is the greatest stress which a material is capable of developing without a deviation from the law of proportionality (Hooke's Law).

In practice, the proportional limit is determined from a plot of stress against strain, being taken as the stress at the first visible departure from the straight line drawn through the points in the elastic range. Since the departure from linearity is in general quite gradual, the determined value will depend on the accuracy and sensitivity of the strain-measuring device employed in the test. The experimentally determined value for a given material will be found to decrease as the sensitivity of extensometer used is increased, that is, as the ability to detect smaller and smaller strain increments is increased. As a reference, see R. L. Templin paper listed in the bibliography at the end of this chapter. Because of these uncertainties, proportional limit is very seldom employed in specifications.

Yield Strength—As the tensile load on a specimen is increased through the elastic range, a stress will be reached at which the specimen will begin to deform in a plastic manner; i.e., it will undergo a permanent set which is not recoverable upon release of load. In the design of structural members to be subjected to static loads, it is generally necessary to design so that the service loads do not cause large deformations, since the usefulness of the structure would thereby be destroyed. It is for this reason that the portion of the tension test concerned with the onset of plastic yielding is of extreme importance. It has already been shown that in many materials the very first stages of plastic yielding are very difficult to detect, and that the stresses corresponding to the apparent beginning of yielding depend on the sensitivity of the strain measuring instrument used. It has become customary, therefore, to refer to the stress at which a material

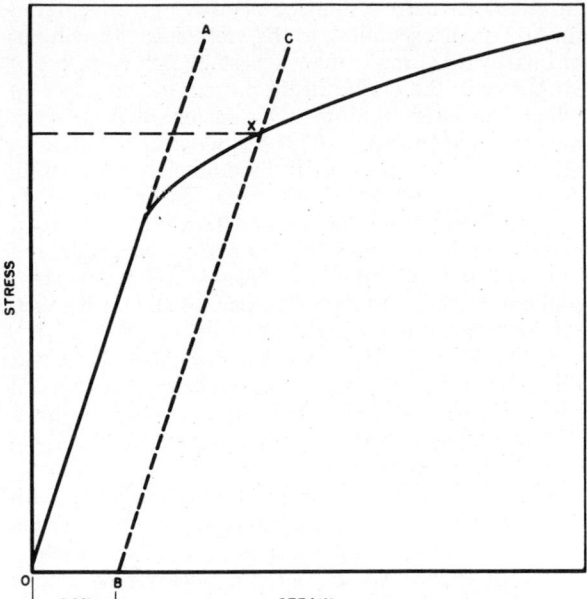

FIG. 47—5. Diagram illustrating offset method for determining yield strength.

exhibits a specified limiting permanent set as the yield strength. The choice of the limiting amount of offset is to some extent arbitrary, but insofar as possible should be based on that amount of plastic yielding that would be considered damaging in a statically loaded member of a structure. Generally, yield strength is based on a 0.2 per cent permanent set.

Assuming that a 0.2 per cent permanent set has been chosen, the following example will illustrate the so-called **offset method** which is commonly used in determinations of yield strength. In Figure **47—5**, the early portion of a stress-strain diagram extended up to about one per cent elongation is shown. Let the origin be designated as O and the elastic line and its extension as OA. Now, on the strain axis, lay off OB = 0.2 per cent, and construct BC parallel to OA. The stress corresponding to the point at which BC intersects the stress-strain curve represents the 0.2 per cent offset yield strength. The offset method is based on the observed fact that if the load is released at X, the specimen will recover along BX until at zero load, the permanent set OB remains. The procedure for any other amount of offset is identical with the exception that the offset OB will correspond to the new amount of permanent set chosen as the basis of the yield strength. The amount of offset used should always be reported with yield-strength values.

If a large number of tests, as for example in production control testing, are to be made on a material for which the stress-strain characteristics are known from experience, a shortened procedure for determination of yield strength may be used, which is known as the **extension-under-load method**. This method is based on the fact that the total extension, i.e., the sum of the elastic and plastic extensions, corresponding to the amount of permanent set chosen as a basis for the yield strength determination will be known within certain fairly narrow limits. Since for a given material the stress corresponding to the yield strength will not ordinarily vary more than a certain percentage, say 10 per cent, the elastic strain present at the offset on which the yield strength is based also will not vary more than 10 per cent. This 10 per cent variation in elastic strain will be a small fraction of the total strain at 0.2 per cent offset. For this reason, the yield strength can satisfactorily be determined at a total extension which is based on the permanent set chosen plus a mean expected value of elastic strain. An extensometer reading to 0.0001 in. per in. should be used for the total-strain method.

It should be pointed out that the elastic limit and the proportional limit can be considered as special cases of yield strength, the permanent set or offset corresponding to the least permanent strain detectable with the instruments used.

Yield Point—It is only for those materials that with increasing stress show a gradual departure from elastic behavior and thus exhibit a stress-strain curve such as shown in Figure 47—5 that it is necessary to define the onset of plastic yielding in terms of yield strength. Many steels exhibit a rather abrupt yielding and may show an initial increase of strain without any appreciable increase of stress when yielding occurs. Such materials are said to exhibit a yield point, the yield point being defined as "the stress in a material at which there occurs a marked increase in strain without an increase in stress." This definition of yield point is that presented in the ASTM Standards and forms the basis for yield-point specifications. As will be pointed out, the definition does not provide a complete description of the yield-point behavior.

Since the yield-point phenomenon is complex, an understanding of its general features is essential for the proper planning and execution of yield-point determinations. The degree to which the yield point is manifested varies widely, depending upon the grade of steel being tested and upon the thermal and mechanical history of the steel. In some steels, the yield point may appear as little more than a "jog" in the stress-strain curve, while in low-carbon deep-drawing steel whose final treatment has been box annealing, the yield-point behavior may extend over elongations of several per cent.

The yield-point behavior can most easily be pictured by a description of the sequence of events during the yielding of a steel which shows a very pronounced yield point. If such a steel is stressed in tension, the load rises as the specimen is strained in the elastic region, and suddenly falls when the first yielding occurs. After this initial drop, with continuing elongation, the load fluctuates about some fairly constant value for a time and then begins to rise again. The maximum stress before the sudden drop is known as the **upper yield point,** and the average value of the relatively constant stress level that follows is known as the **lower yield point.** The amount of extension which occurs before the load begins to rise steadily again is called the **yield-point elongation.** The yielding process just described is very heterogeneous, different portions of the specimen successively under-going yielding. After the first drop in load, locally depressed

areas can be seen to form and to grow over the entire specimen as straining proceeds. These locally deformed areas are usually visible in the form of surface irregularities or strain markings which are referred to by a variety of terms including Lüders' lines, Hartmann lines, stretcher strains, "worms," and others. The formation of such strain markings has also been referred to as the Piobert effect, since the Frenchman Piobert was one of the first to observe the phenomenon. As the specimen is strained through the yield-point elongation range, which may amount to about 10 per cent, the strain markings continue to grow and gradually merge until the entire specimen has yielded. From this point on, the specimen deforms in a homogeneous manner, as opposed to the highly localized mode of deformation occurring during the yield-point elongation. Aggregate features of the yielding behavior just described are well illustrated by the stress-strain curve shown in Figure 47—6 for an annealed-last, rimmed, deep-drawing steel. Generally, the heterogeneous yielding process will be much less pronounced as, for example, is illustrated by the stress-strain curve shown in Figure 47—7 for a quenched and tempered bar of AISI 4340 steel.

Heterogeneous yielding is associated with the presence of carbon and nitrogen in solid solution in ferrite. The carbon and nitrogen atoms are so situated that they exert an anchoring effect against the onset of plastic flow. When a sufficiently high stress is reached, the anchoring effect is suddenly overcome, and a yield point is observed.

One of the outstanding features of the yield-point behavior is the extreme sensitivity of the upper yield point to specimen preparation and testing conditions. Initial yielding can be greatly affected by non-axial loading, sharp fillets in the specimen, cold working of the specimen during procurement or preparation, or the presence of residual stresses in the specimen. Any of these factors may be sufficiently effective to obscure the upper yield point entirely, and if the material being tested does not exhibit appreciable yield-point

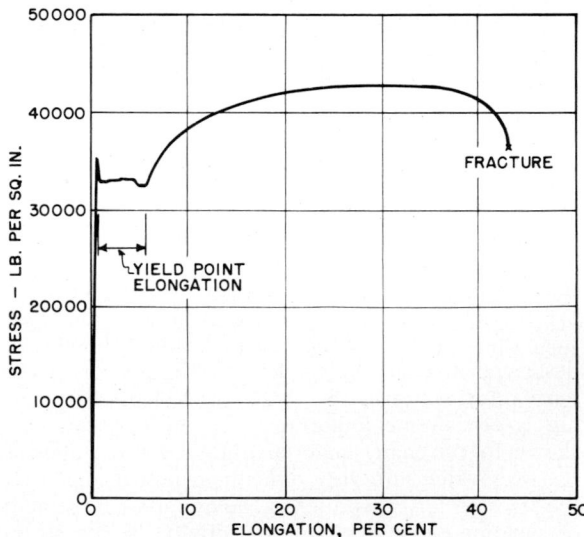

FIG. 47—6. Stress-strain curve for box-annealed rimmed deep-drawing steel.

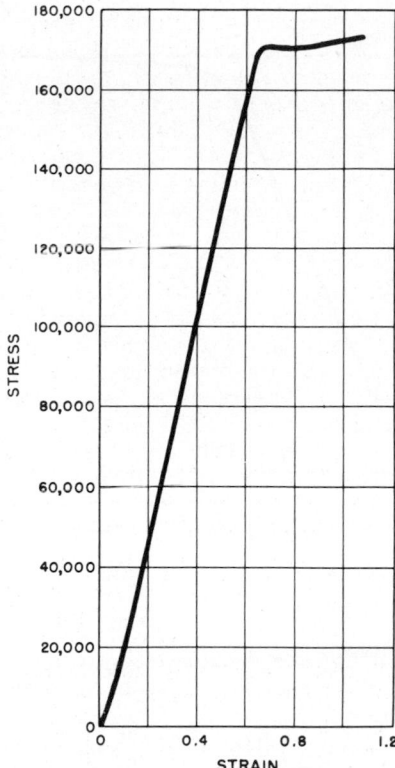

FIG. 47—7. Stress-strain curve for AISI 4340 steel, quenched and tempered at 900° F.

elongation, the influence of the aforementioned factors may eliminate all evidence of the yield point.

A number of methods of determining the yield point are recognized by the American Society for Testing and Materials and are discussed in ASTM A-370. These include the drop-of-the-beam or halt-of-the-pointer (halt-in-gage) and autographic-diagram methods for material having a sharp-kneed stress-strain diagram; and the divider method and total-extension-under-load (total-strain) method for materials that do not exhibit a well-defined proportionate deformation that characterizes a yield point as measured by the drop-of-the-beam, halt-of-the-pointer or autographic-diagram methods. The foregoing methods for the determination of yield point are described in the following quotations from ASTM A-370:

"Drop of the Beam or Halt of the Pointer Method. —In this method an increasing load is applied to the specimen at a uniform rate. When a lever and poise machine is used, the operator keeps the beam in balance by running out the poise at approximately a steady rate. When the yield point of the material is reached, the increase of the load stops, but the operator runs the poise a trifle beyond the balance position, and the beam of the machine drops for a brief but appreciable interval of time. When a machine equipped with a load-indicating dial is used there is a halt or hesitation of the load-indicating pointer corresponding to the drop of the beam. The load at the 'drop of

the beam' or the 'halt of the pointer' is noted and the corresponding stress is recorded as the yield point.

"Autographic Diagram Method.—When a sharp-kneed stress-strain diagram is obtained by an autographic recording device, the stress corresponding to the top of the knee or the point at which the curve drops is to be taken as the yield point (see Figure 47—8a).

"Divider Method.—In this method the operator, with a pair of dividers or similar device, notes detectable elongation between two gage marks on the specimen. When detectable elongation occurs, the load at that instant is noted, and the stress corresponding to the load recorded as the yield point. The gage marks selected for this determination shall not be more than 2 in. apart, even on specimens of longer gage lengths.

"Total Extension Under Load Method.—A class C extensometer (Ed. note: An extensometer having maximum error of indicated strain of 0.001 in.) is attached to the specimen. When the load producing a specified extension is reached the stress corresponding to the load is recorded as the yield point, and the extensometer is removed (Figure **47**—8b)." ASTM A-370 states that, for steels with a yield point specified not over 80,000 lb. per sq. in., an appropriate value for the specified extension under load is 0.005 in. per inch of gage length and that for values above 80,000, this method is not valid unless the limiting total extension is increased: for these latter materials yield strength should preferably be specified. Automatic devices are available that determine the load at the specified total extension without plotting a stress-strain curve and, according to ASTM A-370, may be used if their accuracy has been demonstrated.

Tensile Strength—As the specimen is strained past the yield point, the load rises. For ductile materials, the load passes through a maximum and fracture eventually occurs, as shown in the schematic load-extension diagram of Figure **47**—9. Some less-ductile materials may fracture while the load is still increasing, that is, without passing through a maximum. The tensile strength, according to the ASTM, "shall be calculated by dividing the maximum load carried by the specimen during a tension test by the original cross-sectional area of the specimen."

As already mentioned, speed of testing can affect the tension properties of a material. Considerable research has been conducted on the effects of speed of testing, and it has been generally concluded that the yield point is affected to a much greater extent than the tensile strength. It has been shown that a tenfold increase in rate of pulling increased the yield point of a 0.12 per cent carbon steel by about 7200 lb. per sq. in. in a two-inch gage length specimen. The effect on tensile strength in the range of speeds investigated was considered to be negligible. These observations have the practical significance that, in general, the control of the speed of testing is more critical in the region of the yield point than in the later stages of the test.

B. DUCTILITY PROPERTIES

Elongation—One aspect of the ductility of a material which is generally determined in the tension

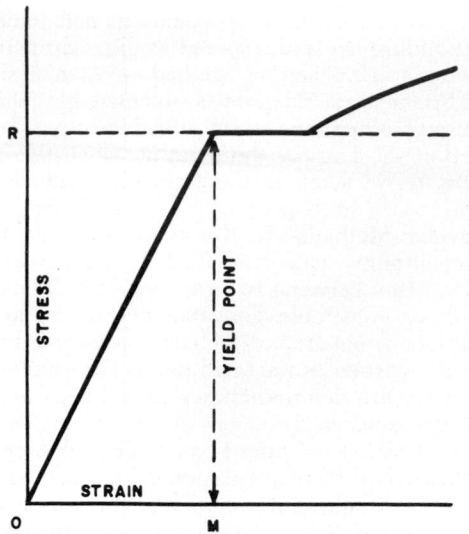

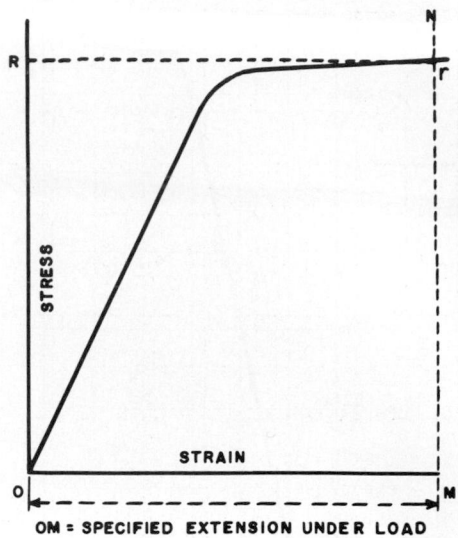

FIG. 47—8. (a) Stress-strain curve showing yield point corresponding with top of knee. (b) Stress-strain diagram showing yield point by extension under load method.

test is the elongation which the material is capable of undergoing before the occurrence of fracture. The elongation is measured over some arbitrarily chosen gage length which is laid out on the specimen prior to the test. The gage length chosen depends upon the specimen being tested, but is usually two inches or eight inches. After the specimen is broken, the two fractured portions are fitted together and the new distance measured, usually to the nearest 0.01 inch. The percentage elongation is then calculated in the following manner:

Per Cent Elongation =

$$\frac{\text{New length} - \text{Original length}}{\text{Original Length}} \times 100$$

The original length refers to the initial gage length

chosen and the new length refers to the length to which the initial gage length has been extended during the test.

The elongation at fracture of a ductile metal is not distributed uniformly along the length of the specimen. This nonuniform distribution is a consequence of **necking down**, the local elongation being greatest in the necked down region of the specimen. This behavior is illustrated in Figure 47—10, which shows the distribution of elongation over one-inch gage lengths along a fractured specimen. Up to the maximum load, the specimen elongates in a uniform manner; at maximum load, however, the strain becomes localized and the specimen necks down. The portions of the specimen sufficiently removed from the necking zone then cease to elongate. It can be seen, therefore, that the total elongation measured at fracture over some arbitrary gage length is a sum of two components: the elongation up to maximum load (uniform elongation) and the elongation after maximum load (local elongation). The elongation will obviously vary, therefore, with the gage length over which it is measured, being greater the smaller the gage length. This variation of elongation with initial gage length is illustrated in Figure 47—11 for the same specimen represented in Figure 47—10.

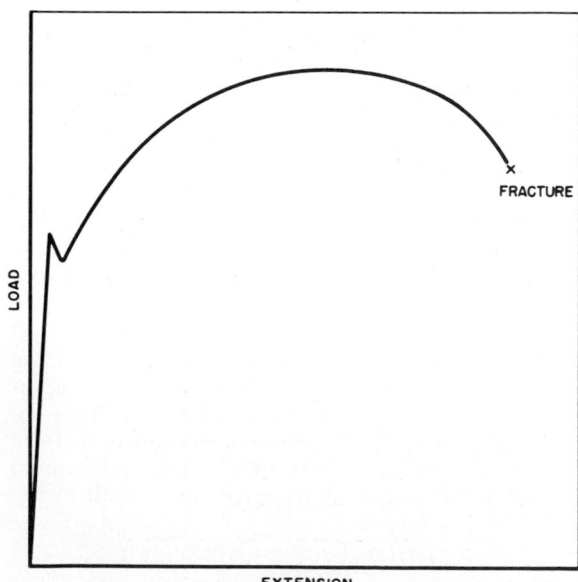

FIG. 47—9. Typical load-extension diagram.

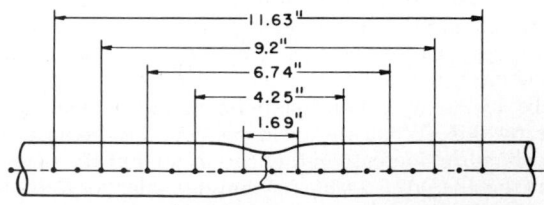

FIG. 47—10. Distribution of elongation along fractured tension specimen. (Original spacing between gage marks, ½ inch.) (From "The Mechanical Testing of Metals and Alloys," by P. Field Foster, page 76. Published by Sir Isaac Pitman & Sons, Ltd., London, 1948.)

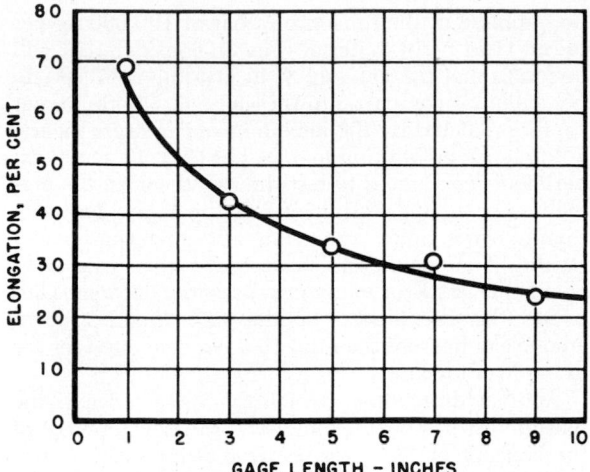

FIG. 47—11. Per cent elongation as function of gage length for fractured tension specimen. (From "The Mechanical Testing of Metals and Alloys," by P. Field Foster, page 77. Published by Sir Isaac Pitman & Sons, Ltd., London, 1948.)

When comparing elongations obtained from different sizes of specimens, it is essential that geometric similarity be observed in the comparison. In other words, the ratio of gage length to cross sectional dimensions must be held constant if comparable results are to be obtained. **Barba's Law of Similarity** states that for tension tests on different sizes of specimens from the same material, the same elongation values are to be expected only if the gage lengths are maintained in proportion to the square root of the cross-sectional area of the specimens.

Reduction of Area—The reduction of area provides a measure of the ultimate local ductility of a material up to the instant of rupture. In determining the reduction of area, the fractured tensile specimen is fitted together, and the dimensions at the minimum cross-section are measured. From the original and final areas, the percentage reduction of area is calculated in the following manner:

Per Cent Reduction of Area =

$$\frac{\text{Original Area} - \text{Final Area}}{\text{Original Area}} \times 100$$

Per cent reduction of area is most accurately determined from round specimens. Since considerable restraint to plastic flow occurs at the corners of rectangular specimens, the outline of the fractured surface is not rectangular and, hence the final area is more difficult to determine.

C. SIGNIFICANCE OF THE TENSION TEST

In addition to providing engineering design data, the tension test is used to a very great extent as an empirical test for evaluating the suitability of materials for particular mechanical applications. The test is interpreted in such instances on the basis of a wealth of practical experience, which permits an engineering opinion of the probable performance of a material to be drawn according to the tensile properties of materials known to have performed satisfactorily in the

past. Many tensile-property specifications are drawn up in this manner and may not be used directly for actual design purposes.

Traditionally tensile strength has been used widely as a basis for design. At present, there is a marked trend to base the engineering design of structures to be subjected to static loads upon yield point or yield strength, with the application of safety factors based on engineering judgment. The use of the yield point or yield strength as a basis for design is, of course, based on the premise that any appreciable over-all yielding of the structure will destroy its usefulness. Tensile ductility specifications are almost universally based on practical experience as to what amount of ductility in the tension test has accompanied adequate ductility in service.

With regard to the use of the tensile yield strength or yield point in design, the question may well be raised as to how such a property, determined in a simple unidirectional tensile loading, can be used in the design of structures which are to be subjected to complex loads and complex states of stress. Any state of combined stresses can always be broken up into three so-called principal normal stresses which act in three mutually perpendicular directions. These three principal stresses can be designated as S_1, S_2, and S_3, the subscripts indicating the order of algebraic magnitude; i.e., S_1 is the algebraically greatest principal stress. Some examples of simple stress combination

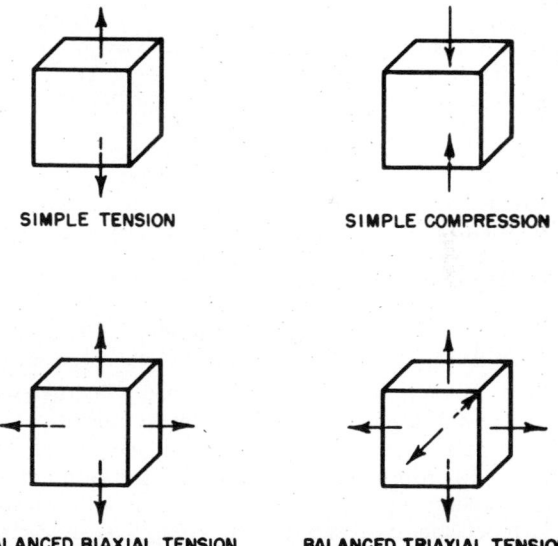

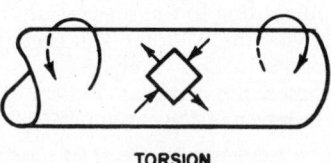

FIG. 47—12. Illustration of simple states of stress.

are listed below and are illustrated in Figure **47—12**. Tensile stresses are ordinarily designated as positive, while compressive stresses are designated as negative.

Simple tension: S_1 positive; $S_2 = S_3 = 0$
Simple compression: $S_1 = S_2 = 0$; S_3 negative
Balanced biaxial tension: $S_1 = S_2$, both being positive; $S_3 = 0$
Balanced triaxial tension: $S_1 = S_2 = S_3$, all positive
Torsion or twisting: $S_1 = -S_3$, S_1 positive and S_3 negative; $S_2 = 0$

Two principal theories of initial yielding are used in predicting the strength under combined stresses; the **critical shear stress theory** and the **critical shear strain energy theory**. Shear stresses are those stresses which tend to cause one part of a body to slip over another part, as opposed to normal stresses which act in such a way as to tend to separate the body along a plane normal to the stress direction. It is recognized that shear stresses are the important stresses in controlling plastic flow. The maximum shear stress theory of yielding states that plastic action will begin when the maximum shear stress reaches some critical value characteristic of the material, the maximum shear stress being given by half the difference between the greatest and the least principal normal stresses. If the yield point in the tension test is designated as S_0, the maximum shear stress yielding criterion can be stated as:

$$\text{Critical shear stress} = \frac{S_1 - S_3}{2} = \frac{S_0}{2}$$

As an example of the use of this relationship, the value of the greatest principal stress at yielding will be calculated for torsion, where the state of stress is: $S_1 = -S_3$; $S_2 = 0$. For purposes of illustration, it is assumed that the yield point in simple tension, S_0, is 100,000 lb. per sq. in. It is then found that:

$$\frac{S_1 - S_3}{2} = \frac{100,000}{2}$$

$$S_1 - (-S_1) = 100,000$$

$$S_1 = 50,000$$

This solution indicates that a bar which is twisted will yield at half the value of the greatest principal stress, S_1, at which a bar pulled in tension will yield.

The other important theory of yielding is the shear strain energy theory. As a body is loaded in the elastic range, elastic strain energy is stored up, just as when a spring is stretched. The total elastic energy stored in a body consists of two parts: that resulting from a change in volume of the body and that resulting from a change in shape of the body. The latter portion is known as the distortion energy or the shear strain energy. According to the shear strain energy criterion for initial yielding, yielding will occur when the shear strain energy reaches a critical value, which is dependent upon the material. This criterion can be expressed in terms of the three principal stresses as follows:

$$(S_1 - S_2)^2 + (S_2 - S_3)^2 + (S_3 - S_1)^2 = 2S_0^2,$$

where S_0 is again the yield point in simple tension. If the problem of the torsion of a bar of 100,000 lb. per sq. in. yield point material is again considered, it will be found that the value of S_1 at yielding is 57,700 lb. per sq. in. as compared to the value of 50,000 lb. per sq. in. predicted by the maximum shear stress theory, a difference amounting to 15.4 per cent. In actual experiments conducted to test the two theories, the predictions of the shear strain energy theory are generally found to be in better agreement with the experimental results. The maximum shear stress theory is sufficiently accurate for many purposes, the difference between the predictions of the two theories never amounting to more than the 15.4 per cent cited for the example of torsion.

Another direction in which the significance of the tension test has been extended is the development of the concept of the so-called **true stress-strain curve**. Ludwik, a German investigator who was one of the outstanding figures in the development of better understanding of the mechanical behavior of materials, pointed out around 1910 that the definitions of stress and strain, as commonly used in materials testing and in defining engineering properties, are in some respects lacking in fundamental significance. Only in relatively recent years, however, have the concepts of Ludwik come to be widely used in this country. The principal criticism of the customary treatment of tensile data lies in the definitions of stress and strain, these quantities generally being referred to the initial dimensions of the specimen throughout a test. Such a procedure is obviously in error and has no real physical significance except at the very beginning of the test.

As a tensile specimen is stretched, its cross-sectional area diminishes progressively. Only at the beginning of the test, therefore, can stress be based on the original area without introducing appreciable, and, indeed, serious error. **True stress,** then, is defined as the instantaneous stress acting on the specimen and is computed by dividing the instantaneous load by the actual cross-sectional area at the instant that particular load is acting.

Since the area will have changed a negligible amount at initial yielding, the usual definitions of yield point and yield strength are satisfactory. Since the change in cross-sectional area at the maximum load is considerable, however, it must be concluded that the tensile strength is not a real stress and has no fundamental physical significance. Its principal use is for relative comparison purposes and in testing for uniformity of product.

The usual definition of strain, in which strain is referred to initial dimensions, is likewise in error. The inaccuracy of referring elongation increments to an original gage length can be visualized in the following manner. If a bar ten inches long is stretched one inch, the elongation expressed as a percentage is 10 per cent. Now suppose that the bar, initially ten inches long, has been stretched to a length of 100 inches and is then stretched one inch further. The last inch of stretch referred to the original length would represent an elongation of 10 per cent. If, however, we base the elongation produced by the last one inch increment of stretch on the length of the specimen just prior to that increment, the elongation would be considered to be 1 per cent. Obviously, the latter procedure provides a truer physical description of the stretching process than referring the strains to the initial dimensions. "True strain" has been defined, therefore, in the following manner:

$$\text{True strain} = \int_{l_0}^{l} \frac{dl}{l}$$

$$= \log_e \frac{l}{l_0}$$

where l_0 is the original length between two gage marks, l is the instantaneous length between these marks as the specimen is stretched, and e is the base of Naperian or natural logarithms. Log_e is usually expressed simply as $\ln$, so that the above expression may be written: $\text{True strain} = \ln \frac{l}{l_0}$. According to this definition, true strain is simply a summation of strain increments in which each increment is referred to the instantaneous specimen dimensions. A comparison of true strain to ordinary or nominal strain can be seen in Figure 47—13. This relationship is valid as long as the elongation is uniform within the gage length being for the ordinary strain measurement.

A stress-strain curve making use of true stresses and true strains provides a more fundamental description of the plastic behavior of a material than the ordinary nominal stress-strain curve and can, therefore, be expected to be of greater general significance. In practice, the method of determining true stress depends to some extent upon the shape of the specimen. For a cylindrical specimen, a convenient method is based on simultaneous measurements of load and minimum specimen diameter. The true strain can be calculated

from area changes as well as from length changes, since the volume of the specimen does not change by a significant amount during plastic deformation. Therefore,

$$A_0 l_0 = A l$$
$$\text{and}$$
$$\frac{A_0}{A} = \frac{l}{l_0}$$

where A_0 and l_0 are the original cross-sectional area and length, A and l are the instantaneous area and length, respectively. Since true strain was defined as $\log_e \frac{l}{l_0}$, it follows that $\log_e \frac{A_0}{A}$ also represents true strain. Pointed micrometers should be used in the diameter measurements for the determination of true strain, especially after maximum load when the local constriction produced by necking down has become appreciable.

With thin sheet specimens, where area measurements are difficult to make, an extensometer can be used up to maximum load; i.e., during the period of uniform elongation, for obtaining length measurements to be used in calculating true strain. In order to obtain instantaneous area values for the calculation of true stress, the constancy of volume condition is used, thus permitting a computation of area changes from length changes. This procedure must not be used after maximum load because of the nonuniformity of the elongation along the gage length which arises as a result of necking down.

An example of a true stress-strain curve is shown in Figure 47—14 along with an ordinary or nominal stress-strain curve obtained from a single test on a 0.357-in.-diameter specimen. The true stress-strain data were obtained from instantaneous diameter measurements, while the ordinary stress-strain data were obtained from a load-elongation diagram (the

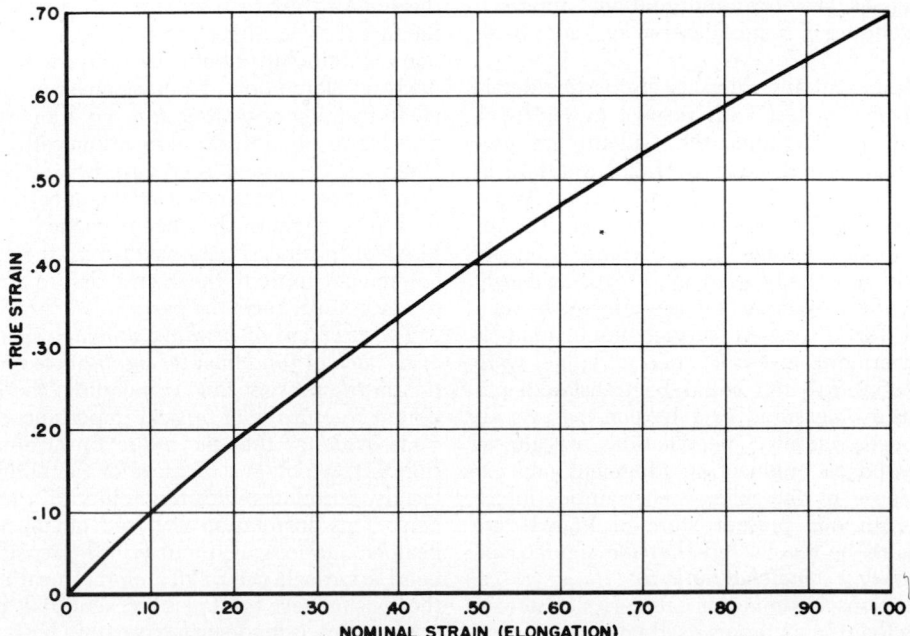

FIG. 47—13. Comparison of nominal and true strains.

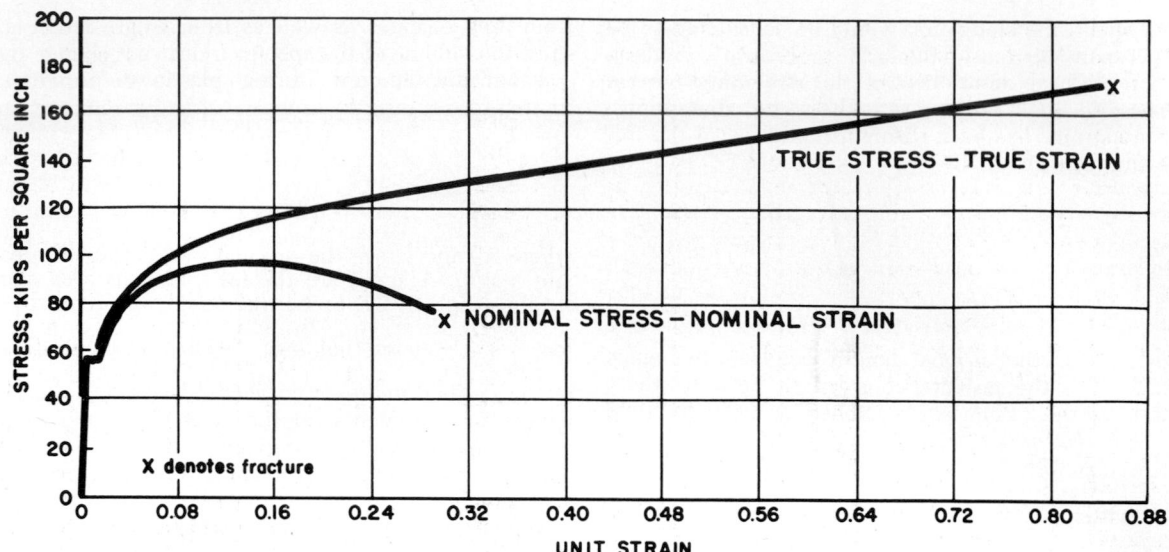

FIG. 47—14. True stress-true strain curve and nominal stress-nominal strain curve. (Prepared from data in "TRUE Stress Vs. Elongation Recorder" by D. E. Driscoll and T. S. DeSisto: Watertown Arsenal Report No. WAL 111/23, PR131104; July 15, 1955.)

elongation was measured over a 1.4-inch gage length). It can be seen that the true stress rises continuously with increasing true strain. This is a consequence of strain hardening which is active during the entire test up to the instant of fracture. It is apparent that the ordinary load-extension diagram does not provide a clear-cut description of strain hardening. The strain-hardening characteristics of a material are of especial importance in sheet metal forming operations where the ability of the sheet to work harden and thereby pass the deformation along from element to element is critical. This is only one example of many problems where the true stress-strain curve, which is based on actual physically existent stresses and strains rather than fictitious ones, provides a more rational approach to the understanding of material behavior under loading.

The significance of the ductility properties determined in the tension test with respect to service is much more difficult to interpret. Gillette has presented a very capable discussion of this question in the American Society for Testing and Materials "Symposium on The Significance of the Tension Test of Metals in Relation to Design" (see reference). Tensile ductility values are rarely used in design, primarily because it is indeed seldom that the amount of ductility needed for a certain service application is known. Furthermore, even if such a value were known, it is doubtful if it could be translated into terms of ductility measured in a tension test. As already mentioned, ductility specifications are almost universally based on engineering judgment and experience. Because of the many uncertainties in interpretation with our present state of knowledge, however, it must be recognized that *the significance of tensile ductility is somewhat limited.*

Gillette mentions a number of categories of service which require that the materials used possess a certain amount of ductility. The first example is that of plastic forming, especially where operations such as bending or deep drawing are involved, and the deformations may be sufficiently large to substantially exhaust the capacity of the material to deform. In attempting to apply tension-test ductility data to analyses of formability, it is important that care be taken to interpret the ductility data in the proper manner. Many attempts have been made to correlate the percentage elongation in 2 inches in the tension test with formability, and the general lack of success is well known. The total elongation in the tension test can only be considered as a rough indication of relative ductility to be expected in actual drawing operations. One obvious reason for the failure of the total elongation in the tension test to correlate with drawability lies in the fact that, as already pointed out, the total elongation value includes both the uniform and the local or necking elongation. In a stretching type of sheet metal forming operation, it is more logical to expect a correlation of uniform elongation with performance. Once a pronounced necking down or localization of deformation occurs in a forming operation, the useful limit of elongation has been reached, since the material at positions removed from the neck can no longer contribute to the overall deformation necessary to successfully form the part.

The problem of bending provides another example of the lack of fundamental significance of total elongation in the tension test. In bending, the local elongation at fracture is of critical importance, and there is some evidence that the reduction of area in the tension test, which is a measure of the ability to deform locally, correlates with the ability of a material to be bent. This correlation is based on the fact that the peak elongations at fracture in the tension fibers of a bend approach the values of the local elongation in the tension test for the same material, provided the comparision is made on a true strain basis.

The second example of service cited by Gillette,

which involves ductility, is that in which the normal service calls for plastic extension. In many structural applications, a small amount of local plastic extension may be very important in relieving local stress concentrations, thereby possibly preventing rupture. Readjustment of local stresses by local plastic flow may also occur in cyclic loading applications. Although the availability of sufficient ductility to permit these readjustments is very important, it is extremely difficult to predict just what amount of ductility is adequate and how it should be measured; i.e., by elongation over some definite gage length or by reduction of area. Again, the engineer must call upon his past experience and best judgment.

Ductility is sometimes demanded as an "insurance factor," that is, extra protection in the event of accidents or overloads. The ability to deform, locally, especially as expressed by test values for the reduction of area, and the ability to absorb overloads without rupture may be desired, although again the necessary amount of ductility may be unpredictable. Actually, what is required in this class of application is the ability to absorb energy, or toughness, an attribute which depends not only on ductility but on strength as well. Toughness will be discussed in more detail in a subsequent section dealing with impact testing and notch toughness.

In considering the significance of ductility, it is important to recognize that ductility in the tension test, especially as measured by elongation or by reduction of area, is strongly dependent upon microstructure and is considered, therefore, to be a "structure sensitive" property. The tensile and yield strength, on the other hand, are less structure-sensitive. Tensile ductility, therefore, may provide a useful means of detecting the presence of undesired microstructures, particularly in heat-treated steels, which could result in inferior mechanical performance.

In summary, it can be said that the tension test, if properly conducted and interpreted, is an informative and versatile test, providing information on both the strength and ductility properties of materials. In addition to the direct application of some of the tensile properties in design, practical experience built up around the tension test makes it useful in specifying materials for particular applications as well as in the control of the uniformity of material supplied for those applications.

SECTION 3

HARDNESS TESTING

Hardness is a material characteristic which can perhaps best be defined in terms of resistance to deformation. The degree of hardness of a material can be manifested in a number of different ways depending upon the conditions to which the material is subjected. In metals, the most commonly used measure of hardness depends upon the resistance to penetration by a much harder body. Hardness may also be manifested as a resistance to abrasion or wear, as a resistance to cutting, as a resistance to crushing, as a resistance to deformation as in tension or compression, as a manifestation of resilience, i.e., rebound hardness, and others. In this discussion, attention will be focused on the types of hardness tests which measure the resistance to penetration under certain specified conditions, since these are by far the most widely used.

The extremely wide use of hardness tests, especially in conjunction with the making, shaping, and treating of steel, can be attributed not only to the extreme simplicity of sample preparation and test procedure, but also to the close relationship between hardness and other mechanical properties. The best example of the correlation between hardness and other mechanical properties is provided by quenched and tempered steels, where a hardness measurement permits a good estimate of most of the other mechanical properties. Hardness tests are especially well adapted to checks of uniformity of product, because of the great ease with which they can be made. If a process or treatment passes out of control, the departure from uniformity can frequently be detected in hardness changes in the product. It is primarily because of this usefulness in control of uniformity that hardness testing is used so extensively in the steel industry.

The two hardness tests used most widely are the Brinell test and the Rockwell test, each of these tests having been standardized by the American Society for Testing and Materials. Because of their universal usage, these two tests will be described in considerable detail. Other types of hardness tests which have certain specialized applications will also be discussed briefly.

THE BRINELL HARDNESS TEST

In the Brinell hardness test, which was proposed by Dr. J. A. Brinell of Sweden around 1900, a spherical ball, usually made of hardened steel, is forced into the specimen under a definite static load. The size of the resulting indentation provides a measurement of hardness as it is manifested under the particular conditions of the Brinell test.

A **Brinell hardness tester** consists of a device for applying a predetermined static load to the specimen through the indenter. One of the most commonly used types of Brinell machines is shown in Figure **47—15**. In this machine, the load is applied hydraulically, and a weighted yoke is provided to prevent the maximum load desired from being exceeded. The yoke, which carries weights proportional to the desired load, acts on a small piston in the hydraulic system. As the pressure is increased by pumping, the load on the indenter and on the yoke piston will gradually increase until the yoke and weights float, indicating that the desired load has been attained. As long as the weights float, the load will remain constant. A Bourdon tube is usually provided for the purpose of giving an indication of the rate of loading and the approach to the desired testing load. If the parts of the hydraulic system are well made and the pistons accurately lapped, this type of machine will provide a very accurate load application and is much to be preferred to the use of a Bourdon gage alone.

The standard indenter for the Brinell test used in this country is a 10-millimeter spherical ball which is usually made of hardened steel. For tests on extremely hard materials, cemented carbide balls may be employed. According to the ASTM Standard for the Brinell test (A 370 and E 10), a ball must not exhibit a permanent change in diameter greater than 0.01 mm. (0.0004 in.) when pressed with a force of 3000 kg. against the test specimen.

Once an indentation has been made, either its diameter or depth must be measured in order to obtain the Brinell hardness number. The diameter is the usual measurement and is determined by a special measuring microscope that is fitted with a glass scale graduated in tenths of a millimeter. The depth of indentation can be measured by a special device attached to the indenter. Although measurements of indentation depth can be made very rapidly, it has been found that, in general, hardness values determined on the basis of depth measurements are less reliable than those determined from diameter meas-

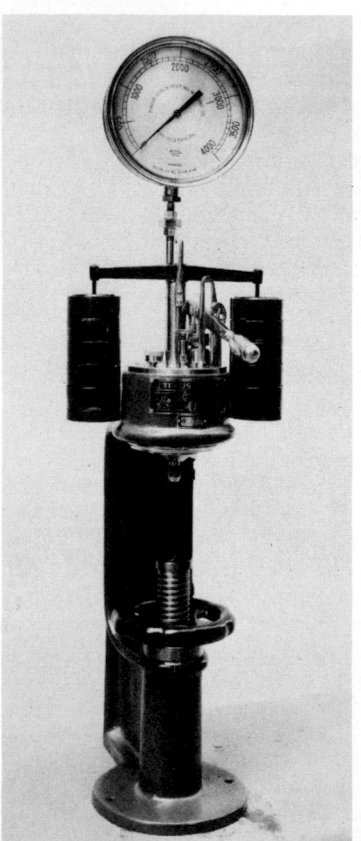

FIG. 47—15. Brinell hardness testing machine. (Courtesy, Tinius Olsen Testing Machine Company.)

urements. For this reason, measurement of depth of indentation has never been approved by ASTM as a standard method. Unless great speed is desired, therefore, the diameter of the indentation should be used in determining the Brinell hardness number.

Brinell-Testing Technique—In selecting and preparing the specimen for use in the Brinell test, a number of precautions should be observed. First of all, the specimen must be thick enough that no **anvil effect** is encountered. After a test, the side of the specimen opposite the impression must show no effect from the loading such as a local bulging. In order to avoid such effects, which may lead to fictitious hardness values, the thickness of the specimen should never be less than ten times the depth of the impression. Care should also be taken that an indentation is not made too near the edge of the specimen. A distance from the specimen edge of not less than 2.5 times the diameter of the indentation should prove sufficient to eliminate **edge effects.** The specimen should be flat, and its surface should be sufficiently smooth that the periphery of the indentation appears sharply defined under the measuring microscope. Another precaution which should be observed is concerned with spacing of multiple indentations. A spacing of at least two indentation diameters should be used in order to avoid testing metal which has been disturbed by a previous indentation.

In the United States, the load for the Brinell test on iron and steel has been standardized as 3000 kilograms; for softer materials, a load of 500 kilograms may be used. In conducting the test, the prepared specimen is placed on the anvil, which is raised until the specimen is in contact with the penetrator ball, and the load applied as smoothly as possible. The load is held for at least 10 seconds in the case of ferrous materials and for at least 30 seconds for softer metals. In order to be acceptable by ASTM Standard E 10, the load-measuring device should indicate actual loads within two per cent tolerance.

In measuring the diameter of the indentation, most satisfactory results may be obtained by measuring in at least two directions and using the average in determining the hardness number. If the indentation is not circular, a directional variation in hardness may be present in the material being tested. On the other hand, out of roundness of the indentation may also indicate deformation of the indenting ball. The ASTM Standard requires that if a ball is used in testing a specimen of greater than 500 Brinell hardness number, it should be checked for permanent set after each indentation.

The Brinell hardness number is given by the quotient of the applied load and the surface area of the indentation, i.e.,

$$\text{Brinell Hardness Number (BHN)} = \frac{P}{A},$$

where P is the applied load in kilograms, and A is the area of the surface of the indentation expressed in square millimeters. It is important to note that the area referred to is the actual surface area and not the projected area of the indentation. If "D" is the diameter of the ball indenter, and "d" is the diameter of the indentation as measured with the Brinell microscope, the Brinell hardness number will be given by the relationship

$$BHN = \frac{P}{\frac{\pi D}{2}\left(D - \sqrt{D^2 - d^2}\right)}$$

where "P" is expressed in kilograms and "D" and "d" are expressed in millimeters. Tables have been calculated from this equation for the standard test conditions of 500-kilogram and 3000-kilogram loads and the 10-millimeter ball. Hardness numbers are tabulated for a wide range of impression diameters, so that it is merely necessary to locate in the table the diameter measured in the test and to read the corresponding number.

It may sometimes be desirable to obtain Brinell hardness values on very small specimens or thin specimens in which the standard loads and indenter would be too large to obtain a satisfactory test from the point of view of anvil or edge effects. In such instances, it is possible to obtain an approximate Brinell hardness number by reducing the size of the ball indenter, and at the same time reducing the applied load in proportion to the square of the reduction in diameter of the ball. In other words, comparable test results should be obtained with different sizes of indenting balls, provided the applied loads are in the same ratios as the squares of the diameters of the indenting balls. For iron and steel, where the standard conditions call for a 3000-kilogram load and a 10-millimeter ball, the load "P" which should be used for a ball diameter "D" will be given by the equation:

$$\frac{P}{3000} = \frac{D^2}{10^2}$$

or

$$P = 30D^2$$

A test carried out under other than the standard conditions is not considered as standard by the ASTM, but is merely recommended as an alternate if the specimen size prohibits a standard test. From Table 47—I, however, it can be seen that it is possible to obtain consistent results under a wide range of test conditions.

In considering the Brinell test, it should be remembered that the deformation of the indenter under load, in addition to a certain amount of recovery of the indented metal, prevents a perfectly spherical surface from being formed. When the indenting ball is pressed into the specimen, it tends to flatten to an extent which depends on the magnitude of the applied

Table 47—I. Results of Brinell Hardness Determinations Using Various Loads and Sizes of Indenters

Diameter of Ball, mm.	Load, kg.	Diameter of Impression, mm.	Brinell Hardness Number
10.00	3,000.0	6.300	85
7.00	1,470.0	4.400	85
5.00	750.0	3.130	87
1.19	42.5	0.748	86

load, and thus creates a larger diameter of indentation than would have resulted had no deformation of the indenter occurred. This circumstance, of course, causes some error in the hardness tables, particularly at higher hardness levels. One of the principal reasons for standardizing on the size and characteristics of the indenting ball and on the magnitude of the applied load has been to circumvent this difficulty; in reality, an attempt has been made to standardize the error. In the hardness-conversion tables for steel presented in the ASTM Standards for Methods of Testing of Metals (E 140), the effect of varying amounts of indenter deformation can be seen. Brinell hardness numbers are shown for standard steel balls, Hultgren balls (a cold-worked steel ball), and carbide balls for a 3000-kilogram load. Up to 433 Brinell hardness, the values agree for all three balls. Above 433 BHN, the carbide ball deforms least and indicates the greatest hardness of any of the indenters. When the indicated hardness with the carbide ball is 517, it is only 505 with a standard steel ball. Above 505 BHN no hardness values are given for the standard steel ball since in tests on harder materials it no longer conforms to the requirements for permanent set. However, a comparison of the Hultgren ball with the carbide ball is given at a considerably higher hardness level. When the carbide ball indicates 656 BHN, the Hultgren ball results in a value of only 615. Undoubtedly, if a material such as diamond were used as an indenter, a still higher hardness would have been indicated. In attempting to compare results of tests above 433 BHN, therefore, it is important to take into account the characteristics of the balls used in making the indentations. The type of ball used in tests at high hardness levels should always be designated in reporting test results.

For testing articles too large or unwieldy to be tested in the type of Brinell testing machine just discussed, and for testing parts of structures or for testing under conditions where the indenting force must be applied in a direction other than vertical, portable Brinell testing units have been devised that are discussed later under "Portable Hardness-Testing Units."

THE ROCKWELL HARDNESS TEST

The Rockwell hardness test, like the Brinell test, measures that aspect of hardness which manifests itself as a resistance to penetration. Because of its simplicity, accuracy, and extreme versatility, the Rockwell test is more widely used today than any other type of hardness test. A wide variety of testing conditions is available, which permits testing over a wide range of hardnesses and also permits testing of very thin materials. In the Rockwell test, in contrast to the Brinell test, the hardness numbers do not bear a mathematical relation to diameter of indentation but are dial divisions, which indicate the depth of impression. Much of the inaccuracy associated with a measurement of total indentation depth is eliminated by the use of a differential depth measurement. The indenter is first seated by a minor load, after which a standardized major load is applied. It is the increment in indentation depth produced by the major load over that produced by the minor load which provides the basis of the Rockwell hardness. In this manner, the effects

Fig. 47—16. Rockwell hardness testing machine. (Courtesy, Wilson Mechanical Instrument Div., American Chain and Cable Co., Inc.)

of small surface irregularities and surface disturbances caused by the indentation itself are eliminated and a very reproducible measurement is made possible.

The Rockwell hardness machine which is shown in Figure 47—16 is a precision-built apparatus which permits the application of accurate, predetermined loads to standardized indenters, as well as a device for measuring the depth indentation produced. The load is applied through a system of weights and levers, and the rate of loading is controlled by a dashpot mechanism which provides a smooth, steady application of load. A dial gage which indicates depth directly during the test is provided for measurement of indentation depth, thus eliminating a separate operation such as required in the Brinell test. On the normal Rockwell machine, one dial division is equivalent to 0.002 millimeter penetration.

(Portable units for carrying out the Rockwell-type test have been developed for testing articles or structures that cannot be handled on the ordinary stationary Rockwell machine: these are discussed later under "Portable Hardness-Testing Units.")

The penetrators which are most frequently used are the spheroconical diamond penetrator and the 1/16-inch spherical steel ball, which are designated as the C-scale and B-scale penetrators respectively. The C-scale penetrator consists of a conical portion with a spherical tip lapped tangent to the cone. The angle of the cone is 120 degrees, and the radius of the spherical tip is 0.200 millimeter.

Specimen preparation for the Rockwell test is somewhat more critical than for the Brinell test, since the size of the indentation is much smaller. The surface of the specimen should be smooth, clean, and dry, and if a high degree of accuracy is desired, polishing through 2/0 or 3/0 metallographic paper is advisable. The surface to be tested should be free of scale and other foreign particles. The bottom surface should be reasonably flat, parallel to the test surface, and should

also be free of scale or other matter which would tend to crush under the applied load. Pitted surfaces should be avoided. The presence of oil on the test surface will also tend to cause a low reading. The thickness of the specimen should be sufficient to prevent any anvil effect. It is desirable that no effect of the indentation be evident on the back side of the specimen, although if any such effect is not too pronounced, the hardness reading may not be greatly affected. It has been found in tests on specimens of commercially pure iron of Rockwell hardness B-35 that the readings were not affected by thickness down to a thickness of 0.040 inch, although the impressions showed through the specimen at 0.060-inch thickness. ASTM has established tables of limiting thicknesses of various hardness levels for selected Rockwell scales using the 1/16-inch diameter ball and the diamond cone indenters. Nevertheless some products such as tin plate are tested with anvil effect.

When the specimen has been prepared, it is placed on the anvil of the machine ready for testing. The anvil is raised slowly until the indenter is contacted, and continued to be raised until the minor load is applied. The small pointer on the machine dial shown in Figure 47—17 indicates the application of the minor load. When the minor load has been applied, the hardness dial is set to zero on the scale being used, and the major load is applied. The rate of application of major load, which can be controlled by adjustment of the dashpot mechanism, is very important and should be checked periodically. The ASTM recommends that the travel of the operating handle of the machine be completed in four to five seconds, with a major load of 100 kilograms and with no specimen in the machine. The duration of major load application is also important, and should be controlled according to the procedures described in ASTM Specification E 18.

Fig. 47—17. Indicating dial on Rockwell hardness testing machine. (Courtesy, Wilson Mechanical Instrument Div., American Chain and Cable Co., Inc.)

When the major load is removed, and with the minor load still on, the hardness is read directly from the dial which is an integral part of the Rockwell machine. The scale of this dial is calibrated to read Rockwell hardness number directly, as already indicated. The dial is divided into 100 equal divisions on each of two scales, the "B" and "C" scales. In order to avoid confusion, the B-scale is printed in red, while the C-scale is printed in black. The B-scale also differs in that the zero is shifted counterclockwise 30 hardness points so that the marking for hardness of B-30 corresponds to that of C-0. In using other Rockwell scales on the standard machine, the red scale is always used with a ball penetrator and the black scale with the C-scale penetrator. The scale of the dial is numbered in such a way that low numbers correspond to deep impressions and relatively soft material, whereas a high hardness is indicated for a shallow indentation in harder material. The dial scale can be rotated manually and can always be set exactly on zero just prior to application of the major load. This arrangement permits a direct reading of the increment of penetration produced by the application of the major load over that produced by the minor load.

The principle of operation of the Rockwell testing machine can be seen from the series of sketches shown in Figure 47—18, which indicates the sequence of steps in a test in which the B-scale is employed. The operation is identical for other scales, with the exception of variations in major load and indenter.

In Table 47—II, the various standard Rockwell scales are listed. As already indicated, the "B" and "C" scales are most widely used. The B-scale is used in what might be considered a medium hardness range, and is especially useful in testing low carbon and medium-carbon steels in the annealed condition. The 1/16-inch diameter hardened steel ball, used as the penetrator in the B-scale test, is carried in a special chuck which permits rapid change of balls. The ball must not differ by over ±0.0001 inch from its nominal diameter, and must not show a variation of over ±0.00002 inch in diameter within itself.

The C-scale is the scale used most frequently for hardness above C-20. There is some overlapping in a number of the Rockwell scales, and for the sake of accuracy, it is desirable to select a scale such that the test value will fall in the middle of the scale range. In making B-scale tests, the steel ball tends to flatten at hardnesses of 100 and above, while at very low hardness near B-0, the impression is so deep that the cap holding the ball may contact the specimen surface and affect the reading. Likewise, in using the C-scale indenter at hardnesses below C-20, the impression is so deep that inaccuracies which may exist in the upper portion of the cone may affect the readings.

Rockwell Superficial Hardness Tests—It is frequently necessary to obtain a hardness value under conditions which prohibit the use of other than an extremely shallow indentation. The Rockwell superficial hardness tester has been developed for such applications. This test operates on the same principle as the regular Rockwell test, but utilizes much lighter loads and a more sensitive dial gage. The superficial test is

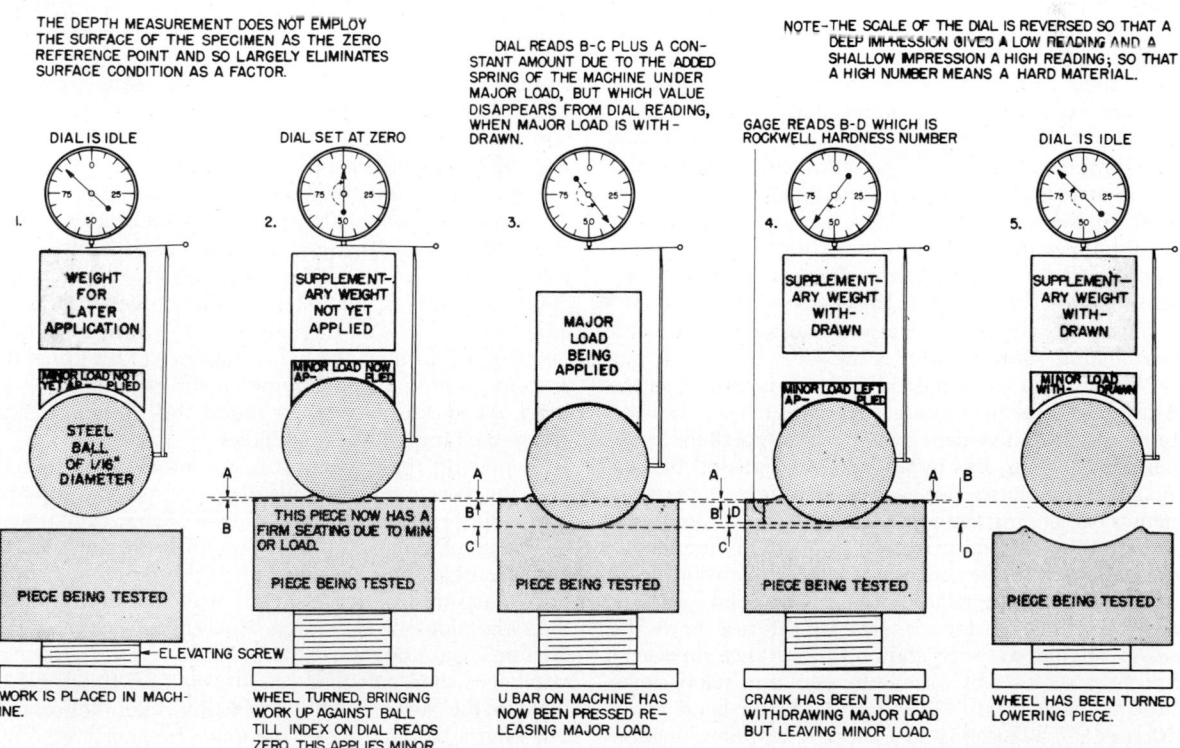

FIG. 47—18. Sketches illustrating principle of operation of Rockwell hardness testing machine. (Courtesy, Wilson Mechanical Instrument Div., American Chain and Cable Co., Inc.)

Table 47—II. Rockwell Hardness Scales

Scale Symbol	Penetrator	Major Load, kg.	Dial Figures
Group One			
B.........	1/16-in. ball	100	Red
C.........	Sphero-conical diamond	150	Black
Group Two			
A.........	Sphero-conical diamond	60	Black
D.........	Sphero-conical diamond	100	Black
E.........	1/8-in. ball	100	Red
F.........	1/16-in. ball	60	Red
G.........	1/16-in. ball	150	Red
H.........	1/8-in. ball	60	Red
K.........	1/8-in. ball	150	Red
Group Three			
L.........	1/4-in. ball	60	Red
M.........	1/4-in. ball	100	Red
P.........	1/4-in. ball	150	Red
R.........	1/2-in. ball	60	Red
S.........	1/2-in. ball	100	Red
V.........	1/2-in. ball	150	Red

Table 47—III. Rockwell Superficial Hardness Scales

Major Load, kg.	Prefix Symbols				
	N Scale, Diamond	T Scale, 1/16-in. Ball	W Scale, 1/8-in. Ball	X Scale, 1/4-in. Ball	Y Scale, 1/2-in. Ball
15.........	15 N	15 T	15 W	15 X	15 Y
30.........	30 N	30 T	30 W	30 X	30 Y
45.........	45 N	45 T	45 W	45 X	45 Y

Specimen preparation for the superficial test is very critical, and polished surfaces are advisable. Specimens should be flat and free from dirt and foreign matter on both upper and lower surfaces. Test blocks are available for standardization as for the regular Rockwell test.

Superficial hardness numbers are prefixed by a number indicating the major load used and a letter designating the indenter. For example, if a reading of 42 were obtained in a test using the N-diamond and a 30-kilogram major load, the hardness would be designated by Rockwell 30N-42. If the 1/16-inch ball had been used, on the other hand, the hardness would be indicated as Rockwell 30T-42.

THE VICKERS OR DIAMOND PYRAMID HARDNESS TEST

The Vickers hardness test is another of the class of tests which measures resistance to penetration. It is similar in principle to the Brinell test, but utilizes a different indenter and different magnitudes of loads. The indenter used in the Vickers test is a square-based diamond pyramid, and the hardness value obtained when using this penetrator is frequently referred to as the diamond pyramid hardness. The angle between opposite faces of the pyramid is 136 degrees, which was chosen so that the Vickers hardness scale would correspond approximately to the Brinell scale. This choice is based on the fact that it is recommended that loads be used in the Brinell test which result in indentations having diameters in the range of 0.25 to 0.50 times the ball diameter. The average of this range is 0.375 times the ball diameter, and if tangents are constructed to an impression of this size at the specimen surface, it will be found that the angle between the tangents is 136 degrees.

In making the Vickers test, the indenter is forced into the specimen and the diagonals of the square impression measured and averaged. From the known geometry of the indenter, the surface area of the indentation can be calculated once the diagonals have been measured. The diagonals are measured rather than the sides of the impression in order to obtain greater accuracy. The diamond pyramid hardness number is then calculated as the ratio of the applied load to the surface area of the impression. For the 136-degree square-based pyramid, the hardness can be calculated from the formula:

$$\text{Diamond pyramid hardness} = 1.854\,\frac{P}{D^2}$$

particularly useful in hardness determinations on very thin strip, on nitrided or lightly carburized surfaces, and on very small parts or parts shaped in such a manner that they would collapse under the heavy load used in the standard test. The small indentation is also frequently useful in obtaining hardness readings very close to the edge of an object where an edge effect would affect the reading in a regular test. ASTM requirements for Rockwell superficial hardness tests are also found in the ASTM E 18 specification.

Two types of indenters are used in superficial hardness testing. One indenter is the same 1/16-inch diameter ball used in the standard test, and is used in superficial tests on the softer metals, such as brasses, bronzes, and unhardened steel. The superficial hardness scales using this indenter are designated by "T." In superficial tests on harder materials, a diamond penetrator having the same configuration as the standard C-scale penetrator is used, the only difference being a more accurate finishing to final dimensions. This penetrator is designated as the "N diamond," and the corresponding hardness scales are referred to as "N" scales. Table **47—III** shows the various superficial hardness scales, with the indenters and major loads used in each. It will be noted that major loads of 15, 30, and 45 kilograms are used. The minor load in every instance is 3 kilograms. Each scale division on the hardness dial represents 0.001 millimeter penetration, as compared to 0.002 mm. on the regular dial.

where "P" is the load in kilograms applied in making the indentation, and "D" is the average of the measured diagonals of the indentation expressed in millimeters.

The principal advantage of the diamond pyramid type of test is that geometrically similar indentations are always obtained regardless of the load applied. This useful characteristic of the impression geometry is not obtained with the spherical indenter, since the ratio of impression diameter to depth varies with the actual depth of the impression. In the discussion of the Brinell test, it was shown that, in order to make tests on thin material, it is not possible merely to decrease the load, but that it is also necessary to decrease the diameter of the indenter in proportion to the square root of the change in load in order to obtain a comparable hardness value. Since geometrically similar indentations are always obtained with the pyramidal indenter, decrease in load permits a satisfactory test on thin material, thus permitting the test to be applied over a wide range of thicknesses and over a wide range of hardnesses.

Specimen surface preparation is very important for the Vickers test, and for very light loads should approach a metallographic polish. It is also recommended that the thickness of the specimen be at least 1.5 times the diagonal of the indentation. The Vickers test is especially useful at high hardness levels because the diamond indenter deforms very little as compared to the balls used in the Brinell test. Up to about 300 Brinell hardness, Vickers numbers and Brinell numbers are practically identical. Above 300, the Vickers number becomes appreciably higher, partially because of the deformation of the Brinell ball and partially because of the shallowness of the Brinell impressions, which causes the 136-degree conical impression to be no longer comparable to the spherical impression.

For certain types of research work where especially reliable hardness values are desired, the Vickers test has seen considerable use and has been standardized by ASTM in Specification E 92 (see also ASTM E 110 for specification covering portable diamond pyramid tester and the description of the Penetrascope under "Portable Hardness-Testing Units" below).

MICROHARDNESS TESTERS

Although the applications of microhardness testing are highly specialized, more and more applications are being found, and many special problems can be studied with this type of test. One of the primary uses of a microhardness tester is in fundamental studies of the hardness of various phases in the microstructure of a metal. By the use of very light loads, extremely small indentations can be placed in different phases in the microstructure and their differences in hardness determined. Extremely small scale variations in hardness such as variations across the diameter of very fine wire or across the thickness of very thin sheet can also be measured.

Several microhardness testers are on the market, but perhaps the most widely used of these is the Tukon tester. The indenter provided with this machine is known as the Knoop indenter, a pyramidal

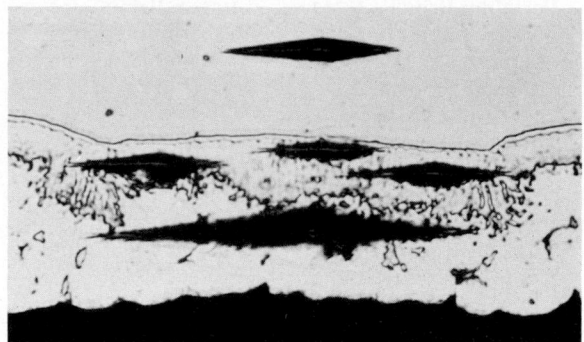

FIG. 47—19. Microhardness tests of various layers in galvanized sheet steel (Knoop indenter).

type of indenter which was developed by the National Bureau of Standards. The indentation produced is a long, narrow, diamond-shaped impression. It is claimed that the advantage of this indenter lies in the fact that elastic recovery along the long axis of the indentation is very small, thus reducing variation from this source, which could be especially troublesome at very low loads. Hardness numbers are based on the long dimension of the indentation and are calculated as the ratio of the indenting load to the projected area of the indentation. An application of the Knoop indenter to a study of the variation of hardness in the various layers of a galvanized steel sheet is shown in Figure 47—19. The Tukon tester can also be fitted with the Vickers type of diamond pyramid, so that ordinary diamond pyramid hardness numbers can be obtained.

Another principle of microhardness measurement is utilized in the **microcharacter.** The microcharacter is a small, cubically pointed diamond mounted under a very light load. A scratch is produced on a polished specimen by drawing the specimen under the diamond, and the width of the scratch is measured under a microscope. Variations in scratch width indicate variations in hardness, the narrower the scratch the higher the hardness.

PORTABLE HARDNESS-TESTING UNITS

Portable hardness testers are used principally for testing articles that are too large or unwieldy to be tested in the usual types of testing machines, for testing parts of fixed structures, or for testing under any conditions which require that the indenting force be applied in a direction other than vertical. There are two general types of portable hardness testers: (1) those that employ the indentation principle, and (2) the Scleroscope that operates on the rebound principle. Among the first type are portable Brinell testers, Rockwell-type testers and diamond-pyramid testers, which are provided with various means for holding the indenter in contact with the surface to be tested: some of these means include chain clamps, "C"-clamps and magnets. However the tester is held to the piece being tested, there shall be no relative motion between the tester and the piece when the load is applied, and the tester must be mounted so that the axis of the indenter is normal to the surface of the test piece.

Portable Brinell Testers—Portable Brinell testers generally apply the load by a hydraulic cylinder equipped with both a presssure gage and a spring-loaded relief valve. With this arrangement it is not possible to maintain the load at the point where the relief valve opens for any appreciable time. It is therefore necessary to bring up the load several times to the point where the pressure is released: for steel, when testing with a 3000-kg. load, three load applications are equivalent to holding the load for 15 seconds as required in the standard method.

Portable Rockwell-Type Testers—Portable Rockwell-type testers generally apply the load through a calibrated spring by a screw and are generally equipped with two indicators, one a dial gage that measures deflection of the spring to indicate the load, and the other a dial gage or micrometer screw to indicate the depth of penetration. The minor load is first applied as shown by the load indicator. The index on the depth indicator is set to the proper point. Then the major load is applied. The loading screw is then turned in the opposite direction until the minor load is again indicated on the load dial. The hardness is then read on the depth indicator as the difference between the readings at the minor load before and after application of the major load.

Portable Diamond-Pyramid Tester—An instrument designated as the Penetrascope is a portable hardness tester which is similar in principle to the Vickers test in that a square-based 136-degree pyramidal diamond is utilized as an indenter. In operation, a load is applied on the specimen through the indenter and the diagonals of the resulting square indentation are measured. The load is applied through a hydraulic thrust unit and can be varied through a range up to 40 kilograms. The diagonals are measured and averaged in the same manner as is done in the Vickers test.

The Shore Scleroscope Test—This test, which operates on the rebound principle, was introduced commercially about 1907, shortly after the advent of the Brinell test. It was used to a considerable extent for many years as a supplement to the Brinell test. The advantages claimed for the scleroscope are its portability and the small size of indentation made. The portability feature permitted the testing of massive objects which otherwise could not be readily tested. A small smooth spot was prepared, the scleroscope placed over it and a reading taken. The small impression made by the tester also made it suitable for testing finished articles on which a large indentation would have been undesirable.

The scleroscope itself consists of a small diamond-tipped hammer enclosed in a glass tube which is provided with a suction bulb whereby the hammer may be raised to the top of the tube and dropped from a fixed and predetermined height. When the hammer is dropped on the object being tested, it rebounds to a height which is considered as a measure of hardness. If the impact were perfectly elastic, the hammer would rebound to its original height. A slight amount of energy will be dissipated in deforming the specimen, however, and this energy is not available for the rebound. A scale is provided on the instrument for measuring the height of the rebound, the units of the

scale being obtained by dividing the average rebound from quenched high carbon steel into one hundred equal parts. In one model the height of rebound is determined by careful observation, while another model is equipped with an indicating dial.

In making the test, precautions must be taken that the specimen is solidly supported, the sound of the impact providing some indication of the solidity. The specimen surface must, of course, be smooth and flat. The tube of the scleroscope must be vertical and the surface being tested must be horizontal so that true vertical impact and rebound can be obtained.

The scleroscope is not used as much as in the past, because the advantages once held over the standard Brinell test do not hold over newer types of tests. Furthermore, the nature of rebound hardness is not as well understood as indentation hardness. Perhaps the principal use of the scleroscope test has been in testing the surface hardness of rolls for rolling mills.

It is of interest to note that the rebound principle has also been utilized in establishing a go–no go gage for the hardness of steel balls. Balls are allowed to fall from an incline onto a hardened steel anvil. The balls rebound into two bins, one placed above the other, so that hard balls rebound into the top bin and softer balls rebound into the lower bin.

MISCELLANEOUS HARDNESS TESTS

File Hardness—Hardness testing with a file is an old and crude method of measuring relative hardness, but one which can be useful in the hands of an experienced operator. A standard file is rubbed against the surface to be tested. If the file does not bite, the piece is designated as **file hard.** The test is, of course, greatly dependent upon the human factor and can only be considered useful where relatively large differences in hardness are of interest.

The Monotron Hardness Test—In this test, the load required to produce an indentation of fixed depth is measured. The standard penetrator is a hemispherical diamond of 0.75-millimeter diameter which is forced into the specimen to a depth of 0.045 millimeter. The hardness is read in Brinell units directly from a dial on the machine while the load is on the specimen. The test can be made on a surface which has had no special preparation by using a preloading arrangement which seats the indenter. The basic principle of the Monotron test is that the same size of indentation is always obtained so that the strain distribution in the specimen is always the same. The contribution of work hardening to the measured hardness is thereby controlled to some degree.

The Cloudburst Tester—The principal use of the cloudburst tester is in determining the uniformity of hardness over a relatively large area of surface. Essentially, the cloudburst process is simply a shot-peening process in which the intensity of peening can be adjusted. The surface of the object being tested is subjected to a rain of small balls 1/8 inch in diameter. The force of impact is adjusted to a point so the impact just fails to indent material of the desired hardness. Softer areas will then be delineated by peening marks. The original cloudburst machine was also used as a shot peener for the purpose of surface hardening.

Table 47—IV. Hardness Conversion Numbers for Steel (see Notes Below).

Rockwell C Hardness Number	Diamond Pyramid Hardness Number	Brinell Hardness Number* 10-mm Standard Ball 3000-kg Load	Brinell Hardness Number* 10-mm Hultgren Ball 3000-kg Load	Brinell Hardness Number* 10-mm Carbide Ball 3000-kg Load	Rockwell A Scale, 60-kg Load, Diamond-Cone Penetrator	Rockwell D Scale, 100-kg Load, Diamond-Cone Penetrator	15-N Scale, 15-kg Load, Superficial Diamond-Cone Penetrator	30-N Scale, 30-kg Load, Superficial Diamond-Cone Penetrator	45-N Scale, 45-kg Load, Superficial Diamond-Cone Penetrator	Scleroscope Hardness Number	Approx. Tensile Strength, 1000 psi	Rockwell C Hardness Number
68	940	**	...	...	85.6	76.9	93.2	84.4	75.4	97	...	68
67	900	**	...	...	85.0	76.1	92.9	83.6	74.2	95	...	67
66	865	**	...	...	84.5	75.4	92.5	82.8	73.3	92	...	66
65	832	**	...	**739**	83.9	74.5	92.2	81.9	72.0	91	...	65
64	800	**	...	**722**	83.4	73.8	91.8	81.1	71.0	88	...	64
63	772	**	...	**705**	82.8	73.0	91.4	80.1	69.9	87	...	63
62	746	**	...	**688**	82.3	72.2	91.1	79.3	68.8	85	...	62
61	720	**	...	**670**	81.8	71.5	90.7	78.4	67.7	83	...	61
60	697	**	**613**	**654**	81.2	70.7	90.2	77.5	66.6	81	...	60
59	674	**	**599**	**634**	80.7	69.9	89.8	76.6	65.5	80	326	59
58	653	**	**587**	**615**	80.1	69.2	89.3	75.7	64.3	78	315	58
57	633	**	**575**	595	79.6	68.5	88.9	74.8	63.2	76	305	57
56	613	**	**561**	577	79.0	67.7	88.3	73.9	62.0	75	295	56
55	595	**	**546**	560	78.5	66.9	87.9	73.0	60.9	74	287	55
54	577	**	**534**	543	78.0	66.1	87.4	72.0	59.8	72	278	54
53	560	**500**	**519**	525	77.4	65.4	86.9	71.2	58.6	71	269	53
52	544	**487**	**508**	512	76.8	64.6	86.4	70.2	57.4	69	262	52
51	528	**475**	494	496	76.3	63.8	85.9	69.4	56.1	68	253	51
50	513	464	481	481	75.9	63.1	85.5	68.5	55.0	67	245	50
49	498	451	469	469	75.2	62.1	85.0	67.6	53.8	66	239	49
48	484	442	455	455	74.7	61.4	84.5	66.7	52.5	64	232	48
47	471	432	443	443	74.1	60.8	83.9	65.8	51.4	63	225	47
46	458	421	432	432	73.6	60.0	83.5	64.8	50.3	62	219	46
45	446	409	421	421	73.1	59.2	83.0	64.0	49.0	60	212	45
44	434	400	409	409	72.5	58.5	82.5	63.1	47.8	58	206	44
43	423	390	400	400	72.0	57.7	82.0	62.2	46.7	57	201	43
42	412	381	390	390	71.5	56.9	81.5	61.3	45.5	56	196	42
41	402	371	381	381	70.9	56.2	80.9	60.4	44.3	55	191	41
40	392	362	371	371	70.4	55.4	80.4	59.5	43.1	54	186	40
39	382	353	362	362	69.9	54.6	79.9	58.6	41.9	52	181	39
38	372	344	353	353	69.4	53.8	79.4	57.7	40.8	51	176	38
37	363	336	344	344	68.9	53.1	78.8	56.8	39.6	50	172	37
36	354	327	336	336	68.4	52.3	78.3	55.9	38.4	49	168	36
35	345	319	327	327	67.9	51.5	77.7	55.0	37.2	48	163	35
34	336	311	319	319	67.4	50.8	77.2	54.2	36.1	47	159	34
33	327	301	311	311	66.8	50.0	76.6	53.3	34.9	46	154	33
32	318	294	301	301	66.3	49.2	76.1	52.1	33.7	44	150	32
31	310	286	294	294	65.8	48.4	75.6	51.3	32.5	43	146	31
30	302	279	286	286	65.3	47.7	75.0	50.4	31.3	42	142	30
29	294	271	279	279	64.7	47.0	74.5	49.5	30.1	41	138	29
28	286	264	271	271	64.3	46.1	73.9	48.6	28.9	41	134	28
27	279	258	264	264	63.8	45.2	73.3	47.7	27.8	40	131	27
26	272	253	258	258	63.3	44.6	72.8	46.8	26.7	38	127	26
25	266	247	253	253	62.8	43.8	72.2	45.9	25.5	38	124	25
24	260	243	247	247	62.4	43.1	71.6	45.0	24.3	37	121	24
23	254	237	243	243	62.0	42.1	71.0	44.0	23.1	36	118	23
22	248	231	237	237	61.5	41.6	70.5	43.2	22.0	35	115	22
21	243	226	231	231	61.0	40.9	69.9	42.3	20.7	35	113	21
20	238	221	226	226	60.5	40.1	69.4	41.5	19.6	34	110	20

*The Brinell hardness numbers in bold-face are outside the range recommended in Method of Test for Brinell Hardness of Metallic Materials (ASTM Designation E 10).

**For the 10-mm standard steel ball, no values of Brinell hardness are given higher than 500 Bhn. This is in conformance with the limitations established by the Standard Method of Test for Brinell Hardness of Metallic Materials (ASTM Designation E 10).

The values of scleroscope hardness number and approximate tensile strength are from the 1955 SAE Handbook. All other values are from ASTM Standard E 140.

The Telebrineller (or Brinell Meter)—This instrument is a portable hardness tester consisting of a rubber anvil containing a 10-mm. Brinell ball that protrudes through the base of the anvil, and a ½-inch square steel bar, of known hardness, that is inserted into the anvil to back up the Brinell ball. To obtain a hardness number the tester is held in such a way that the ball is between the bar of known hardness and the specimen. The anvil is struck a sharp blow with a hammer and the diameters of the indentations made in the bar and the specimen are measured.

The Brinell hardness number of the specimen is then determined by mutiplying the ratio of the diameter of impression in the test bar to the diameter of the impression in the specimen by the Brinell hardness number of the test bar. This calculation is done on a hardness calculator furnished with the instrument.

The instrument is used in determining the hardness of large castings, railroad rails, pipe, etc.

Hardness Conversion Tables—It is evident from the descriptions of the various methods of hardness testing, that each test possesses certain inherent advantages. The choice of test for a particular hardness determination will depend on a number of factors, including the size of specimen and the hardness level. Frequently it may be desirable to convert a hardness reading obtained on one scale, say Rockwell "C," to some other scale, say Brinell hardness, for purposes of comparison with other data. Hardness conversion tables have been prepared for this purpose. The Society of Automotive Engineers, American Society for Metals, and American Society for Testing and Materials have jointly prepared a set of conversion data for steels harder than 220 BHN, which is presented in Table 47—IV. Considerable discretion must be exercised in making hardness conversions, and particular care must be taken with regard to testing details if reliable conversions are to be made. Hardness con-

version tables for other metals, including austenitic stainless steels, can be found in the ASM Handbook.

Significance and General Utility of Hardness Tests—It has been seen that the most widely used hardness tests measure resistance to penetration under certain arbitrarily chosen conditions. In forcing a penetrator into a metal specimen, the metal in the vicinity of the penetration is plastically deformed, in order that the penetrator can be accommodated. The factors controlling the amount of distribution of this plastic deformation are very complex and no exact quantitative analysis of the penetration of a metal by any shape of indenter has been developed. Qualitatively, however, it can be seen that resistance to penetration is a measure of resistance to plastic flow and should be related in some manner to the stress-strain curve of the material being tested, i.e., to the strength and strain-hardening properties of the material. In general for steels, a good correlation has been found to exist between hardness and tensile strength. A particularly close correlation exists in quenched and tempered steels where, in addition, yield strength and ductility can also be predicted reasonably well from hardness measurements. For this reason, the hardness test is of particular value in the field of heat-treatable steels.

In the making, shaping, and treating of steel products, the most extensive use of the hardness test is for inspection and control of uniformity. A good example of such use is provided by the extensive use of hardness tests in the production of deep-drawing sheets. It is usually known from experience that the hardness must be within a certain range if the sheet is to successfully form a certain part. Because of the great ease of making hardness tests on sheet products, very frequent tests can be made to assure that all the product is within the desired hardness range. Most uses of hardness tests are of a similar nature, depending upon a combination of ease of testing and correlation with other properties.

SECTION 4

NOTCHED-BAR IMPACT TESTS

The notched-bar impact test is, as the name implies, a test in which a bar containing a notch is supported as a beam and subjected to the impact from a moving mass having sufficient kinetic energy to break the bar. The energy absorbed by the specimen is measured by the loss in kinetic energy of the moving mass. Notched-bar impact tests were originally conceived with the idea of providing an indication of the ability of a material to absorb punishment under very severe service conditions. Notches or stress concentrations of one kind or another are present in most structures and, generally, are the origin of structural failures. It was suggested that the capacity of a material to absorb energy in the notched-bar impact test should indicate the ability of the material to absorb energy in the event of overloading in a structural member and the ability to resist failure at local stress concentrations. In recent years, the notched-bar impact test has taken on a more general significance, in

that attention has come to be focused on the variation of energy absorption with temperature, rather than on the absolute level of energy absorption at a single testing temperature. Many steels exhibit a rapid drop-off in the level of energy absorption in some critical temperature interval as the testing temperature is lowered. As will be discussed in more detail in a subsequent section, the temperature range in which this abrupt decrease in energy absorption occurs provides much more information about the notch-toughness characteristics of a steel than the energy absorption at a single temperature.

Impact-Testing Methods—The details of impact-testing procedures are described in a tentative ASTM specification designated as E 23. The most generally used impact testing machines are of the pendulum type such as shown in Figure 47—20. In this type of machine, the impact energy is furnished by the swing of a weighted pendulum. The available energy de-

FIG. 47—20. Sonntag pendulum impact testing machine. (Courtesy, The Baldwin-Lima-Hamilton Corp.)

pends, therefore, on the effective mass of the pendulum and its velocity at impact. The point of impact usually is situated at the bottom of the swing, at which point the pendulum has attained its maximum velocity. The available kinetic energy at this point is equivalent to the potential energy just before the start of the swing. If the pendulum were allowed to swing through its arc freely without striking a specimen, it would rise to the height from which it had been released, neglecting the effects of friction and air resistance. If a specimen is struck, the pendulum loses the amount of energy required to break the specimen and will not swing to the full height from which released. The amount by which the pendulum fails to reach its original height provides an easy method for the measurement of the energy absorbed by the specimen.

The principal type of notched-bar impact test is the **Charpy** type: the method of supporting and striking the specimen is shown in Figure 47—21. There is another type of impact test called the **Izod** test, in which the specimen is supported as a cantilever beam; this test, however, is difficult to conduct at other than room temperature. Hence, the Charpy-type test is generally used. In the Charpy-type test, it is a simple matter to transfer the specimen from a controlled-temperature bath to the anvil support and break it

in a sufficiently short time that no appreciable temperature change occurs.

The types of specimens used in the Charpy-type test are shown in Figure 47—22. The **keyhole-notch specimen** is a very widely used impact specimen and that upon which most impact specifications have been based in the past. The **V-notch specimen** is coming into wider usage, however, and its use is now required in many materials specifications. The details of impact-test specimen preparation are of considerable importance, in that, in some temperature regions of testing, the degree of scatter of test results may be increased by improper attention to specimen preparation. One of the most critical parts of the specimen is the root of the notch, and it is especially important that the finish of the notch surface be free of pronounced machining marks and excessive cold work from the machining operation. The base of the notch should be accurately parallel to the back face of the specimen, and the specimen should be square, so that fracture will not start at a corner of the notch surface. In notching the keyhole specimen, a hole is drilled at the proper location and a slot sawed or milled to the hole. Special care should be exercised that the saw or cutter does not accidentally bite the bottom of the notch, since the notch contour will be drastically altered. In the U-notch also shown in Figure 47—22, special attention should also be given to machining marks, since such marks will be disposed parallel to the notch axis and thus are more effective as stress raisers.

In an actual impact test, the pendulum is raised to its release position, the specimen placed in the testing position, the pendulum released, and the energy ab-

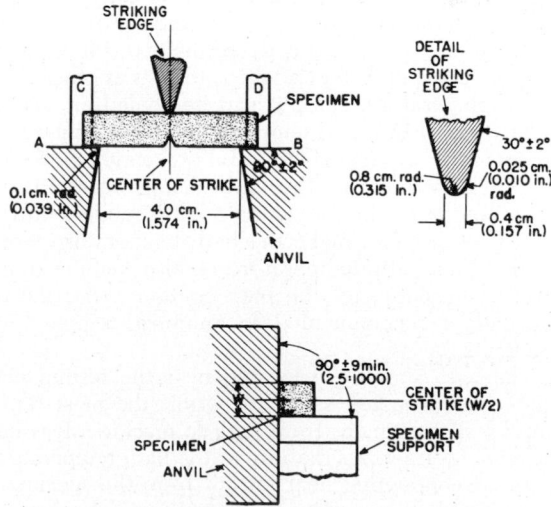

ALL DIMENSIONAL TOLERANCES SHALL BE ±0.005 cm. (0.002 in.) UNLESS OTHERWISE SPECIFIED.

NOTES:
1. A SHALL BE PARALLEL TO B WITHIN 2.0:1000 AND COPLANAR WITH B WITHIN 0.005 cm. (0.002 in.)
2. C SHALL BE PARALLEL TO D WITHIN 2.0:1000 AND COPLANAR WITH D WITHIN 0.0125 cm. (0.005 in.)
3. FINISH ON UNMARKED PARTS SHALL BE 4 MICRONS (125 MICROINCH RMS).

FIG. 47—21. Method of striking and supporting Charpy (simple beam) impact specimens. (Based on information in ASTM Specification E 23.)

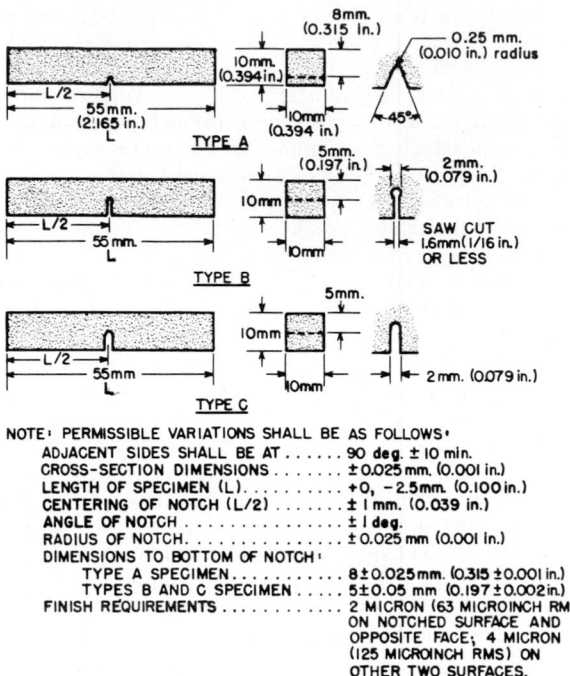

NOTE: PERMISSIBLE VARIATIONS SHALL BE AS FOLLOWS:
ADJACENT SIDES SHALL BE AT . . . . . . 90 deg. ± 10 min.
CROSS-SECTION DIMENSIONS . . . . . . ±0.025 mm. (0.001 in.)
LENGTH OF SPECIMEN (L) . . . . +0, −2.5mm. (0.100 in.)
CENTERING OF NOTCH (L/2) . . . . . . ± 1 mm. (0.039 in.)
ANGLE OF NOTCH . . . . ± 1 deg.
RADIUS OF NOTCH . . . . ± 0.025 mm (0.001 in.)
DIMENSIONS TO BOTTOM OF NOTCH:
TYPE A SPECIMEN . . . . 8±0.025mm. (0.315 ±0.001 in.)
TYPES B AND C SPECIMEN . . . . . 5±0.05 mm (0.197 ±0.002in.)
FINISH REQUIREMENTS . . . . 2 MICRON (63 MICROINCH RMS)
ON NOTCHED SURFACE AND
OPPOSITE FACE; 4 MICRON
(125 MICROINCH RMS) ON
OTHER TWO SURFACES.

Fig. 47—22. Types of specimens for Charpy (simple beam) impact tests. (Based on information in ASTM Specification E 23.)

sorption noted. Details of machine calibration and precautions to be exercised in the use of pendulum impact machines can be found in the ASTM specification E 23 already mentioned.

Since a great deal of impact testing is conducted at low temperatures, it is important to consider some of the methods employed in obtaining controlled testing temperatures. As already mentioned, the Charpy type of specimen is best adapted to tests at other than room temperature, since it can be cooled or heated in a bath of the desired temperature and readily transferred to the impact machine and broken within 5 seconds. The volume of the bath should be relatively large compared to the volume of specimens introduced, in order to make the bath temperature more stable. The bath temperature is also stabilized by efficient insulation of the bath container. Stirring of the bath is recommended to minimize temperature gradients.

The bath should be located near the testing machine and arranged so as to permit the most rapid transfer of specimens from bath to machine. It is imperative to use tongs that are at the bath temperature to avoid conducting heat into or from the specimen. It is possible to complete the test in less than three to five seconds from the time of removal of the specimen from the bath, in which time the specimen temperature will have changed only very slightly. In tests at liquid nitrogen temperatures, the evaporation of the liquid on the specimen carried out of the bath may actually lower the surface temperature of the specimen to a slight extent.

Interpretation of Notched-Bar Impact Test Results —Before attempting to evaluate the significance of any notched-bar test, it is of the utmost importance to

recognize that the behavior of a metal in such a test is strongly dependent on the geometry of test piece, rate of loading, and temperature of testing chosen as the basis of the test. Because of the extremely complex interrelationships among these variables, results obtained in some particular test cannot be translated directly, at least in our present state of knowledge, to a service application in which the conditions of loading are altogether different. Even if the energy-absorbing capacity needed in structures for safe performance could be estimated, which is rarely the case, the energy absorption in a notched-bar impact test could not be used directly as a design figure because of the lack of similarity of geometry and loading conditions. Impact specifications are, therefore, usually based on experience or engineering estimates, as has been seen to be the case in so many other mechanical-property specifications. Most impact-strength specifications are written in such a way as to specify the minimum energy absorption required, as, for example, 15 foot-pounds in the keyhole-notch Charpy test, at the minimum service temperature to be encountered. Although a steel passing such a specification would probably perform better in service than one which did not pass, it must be recognized that passing does not necessarily assure the desired service performance. The converse also holds true, that is, a steel that is notch-brittle as measured by an impact test may perform satisfactorily in service, as discussed later.

The concept of "transition temperature" does much to provide a general basis of interpretation, not only for notched-bar impact tests, but for all other toughness tests. If a series of notched-bar impact tests is made on a ferritic steel at successively lower temperatures, it will be found that the energy absorption decreases to very low values over a range of temperature called the **transition temperature range.** The temperature at which some specified change in notch toughness takes place, as evidenced by various criteria, such as energy absorption or per cent cleavage fracture, is called a transition temperature. The transition temperature is not constant for a particular steel, but varies with the specimen geometry and with the criterion selected for evaluation. Transition temperature behavior is now considered the crux of all notched-bar testing. A transition temperature provides the least uncertain basis for the comparison of the notch-toughness characteristics of different steels. Two steels that would be considered alike in room temperature tests might be found to be markedly different if compared on the basis of transition temperature, as can be seen in Figure 47—23. If tests are made at any single temperature above or below the transition range of both steels, it could only be concluded that the two steels are alike.

The transition temperature is markedly dependent upon the degree of restraint or state of stress imposed on the material. Sharper notches tend to raise this temperature. Since extremely sharp notches and high degrees of restraint exist in many structures, particularly in welded structures having a high degree of continuity, the transition temperature of an actual structure may be higher than that indicated by keyhole-notch Charpy tests on the material of construc-

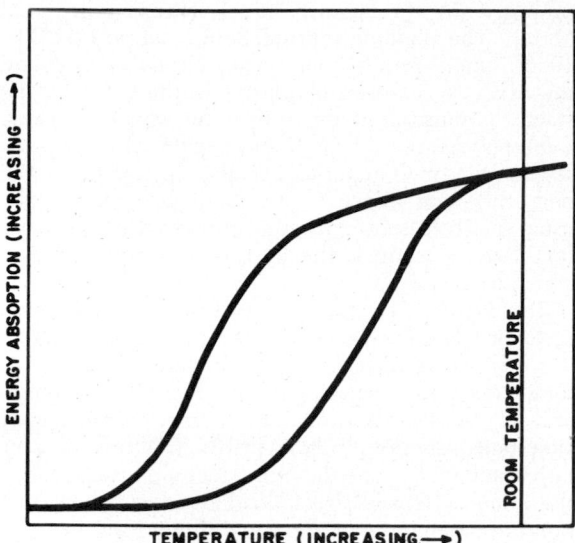

Fig. 47—23. Schematic transition curves for two steels having same energy absorption at room temperature.

tion. It follows that tough behavior at a certain temperature in a keyhole Charpy test does not necessarily insure tough behavior at the same temperature in service. Because of the greater notch severity, the V-notch Charpy impact test shows a higher transition temperature and therefore seems to correlate more closely with actual service. The V-notch Charpy test is being used more widely, and may well replace the keyhole notch test in many specifications.

In attempts to correlate notched-bar tests with service as well as with one another, it is essential to recognize that at least two distinctly different transition temperatures exist; one, a ductility transition temperature that indicates the crack-initiating tendencies, and the other, a fracture transition temperature that assesses the fracture-propagation tendencies.

The ductility transformation temperature may be defined as the highest temperature at which fracture is likely to initiate if the local stresses do not greatly exceed the yield point at the root of the notch (that is, if initiation is not forced by excessive local deformation). The fracture transition temperature, which occurs at a higher temperature, may be defined as the highest temperature at which a cleavage type of crack will continue to propagate once it has been started. In keeping with these concepts, the ductility transition temperature is usually selected at some low level on the performance curve for a particular test specimen where the fracture is predominantly cleavage, and the fracture transition temperature is selected at some intermediate level such as 50 per cent cleavage fracture appearance.

The cleavage mode of fracture is characterized by separation along definite crystallographic planes. The separation of layers of mica or the cleavage of ordinary rock salt are examples of this type of fracture. A cleavage fracture in a ferritic steel exhibits a shiny, crystalline appearance because the fracture occurs essentially along a single plane in each ferrite grain, thus exposing a series of bright crystalline facets.

The shear type of fracture, on the other hand, occurs by a sliding action; i.e., two portions of the grain separate by sliding over one another. The shear fracture is generally associated with greater amounts of plastic deformation than the cleavage fracture. This results in a dull, fibrous appearance in the shear fracture. In general, therefore, the fibrous fracture can be interpreted as denoting a high energy absorption during crack propagation, whereas the granular or crystalline type of fracture is associated with a very low energy absorption. For this reason, the latter type of fracture can propagate over great distances at extremely high velocities of about 5000 ft. per sec.

A typical set of keyhole-notch Charpy impact data is shown in Figure 47—24. A procedure that is sometimes used to determine the ductility-transition temperature involves drawing an envelope about the results, as shown in Figure 47—24, and selecting a temperature near the middle of the envelope. More specifically, a smooth curve may be drawn through the average energy value for each testing temperature, and a transition temperature may be selected where this curve crosses the energy level at the middle of the ductility-transition temperature range, or at an arbitrarily selected energy value such as 15 foot-pounds, as shown in Figure 47—24. The width of the ductility transition temperature range will depend on the number of tests and the intervals between testing temperatures, but the position of the middle of the range will be less sensitive to these factors.

As shown in Figure 47—25, the results of V-notch Charpy impact tests are somewhat different in character than those of the keyhole test. The ductility-transition temperature is usually selected as the temperature at which a curve drawn through the average energy-absorption values reaches some selected low energy level. The energy level selected is based on service experience or correlation with other tests. For semikilled medium-carbon steels, a level of 10 to 15 foot-pounds appears to provide a good correlation. Other levels may be required for other steels.

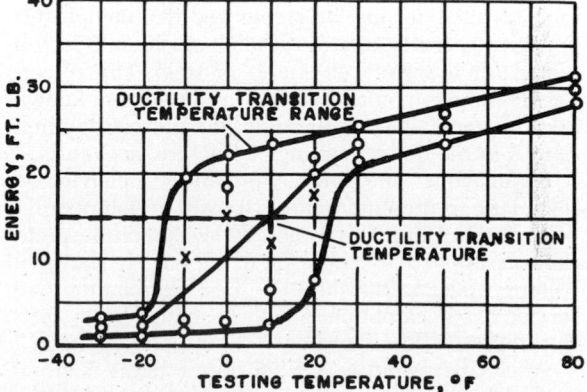

Fig. 47—24. Typical transition curve for Charpy keyhole-notch impact tests on a mild steel. Open circles represent actual test valves, X's are points representing calculated average impact values. Large cross represents intercept of smooth curve through average values with 15 ft.-lb. line. (After R. W. Vanderbeck and M. Gensamer; "The Welding Journal Research Supplement." January, 1950.)

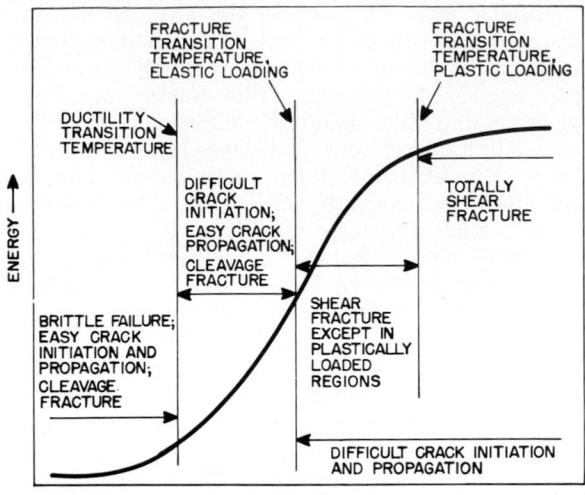

FIG. 47—25. Schematic representation of notch toughness behavior with respect to a V-notch Charpy performance curve. This idealized curve could be derived from a plot of actual test data that would show a scatter of points in the transition range similar to that shown for the Charpy keyhole test specimens in Figure 47—24, although the range of the scatter would be different. (After Lightner and Vanderbeck.)

A typical relationship between the transition curves for keyhole and V-notch Charpy tests is shown in Figure 47—26. Since the V-notch Charpy specimen has a sharper notch, its ductility transition temperature at 15 ft.-lb. is higher than that of the keyhole specimen at 15 ft.-lb., usually by about 40° F, but this amount may vary appreciably with steel grade. Because of the greater breaking section of the V-notch specimen, its curve rises to about twice the energy level of that of the keyhole. The fracture transition temperature at 50 per cent shear is usually about 50° F lower in the keyhole Charpy test than in the V-notch test.

Even when comparing the same kinds of transition temperatures, it must be recognized that coincidence or rigorous correlation of results has seldom been obtained for a variety of grades of steel. The reasons for seemingly anomalous behavior are seldom known, and the anomalies simply underline present-day limitations in the understanding of fracture mechanics.

Significance of Notch Toughness Behavior—A schematic representation of transition temperature behavior and the most generally accepted interpretation, as applied to behavior in service, is shown in Figure 47—25. Because the best correlation with service has been obtained with V-notch Charpy tests, this representation is shown super-imposed upon a V-notch Charpy curve. Truly brittle fracture is visualized as occurring only below the ductility transition temperature and at low energy levels on the Charpy curve. Above this temperature, even though the fracture may be of the cleavage type, the behavior is not considered to be brittle because an appreciable amount of energy is required to initiate failure. The use of two fracture transition temperatures has been

proposed (W. S. Pellini, "Notch Ductility of Weld Metal," **The Welding Journal**, 35(5), pages 217s-233s; 1956). One refers to material in elastic loading and the other to material in plastic loading. Above the fracture transition temperature for elastic loading, fractures are not likely to propagate even through severely deformed material, because the fracture is 100 per cent shear. Since elastic loading represents the usual service case, the fracture transition temperature for elastic loading is the one to which reference is generally made.

The factors that can lead to brittle fracture, that is, to cleavage fracture with little plastic deformation are: (1) stress raisers, (2) steel which lacks notch toughness at the operating temperatures encountered, and (3) tensile stress. All three factors must exist simultaneously to produce brittle fracture. A very important feature of the third factor is the level of the nominal tensile stress (load divided by net section area, without consideration of any local increase in stress at a notch) required to bring about failure. Even in the presence of an extremely sharp crack (such as a fatigue crack), it has been found that brittle fracture will occur only when the nominal tensile stress reaches the yield-point value unless residual tensile stresses are present. This feature alone serves to protect many structures that contain notches and are built of notch-brittle steel, because failure is not likely to take place at the relatively low nominal stress (well below yield point) for which structures are usually designed.

For brittle fracture to take place at a low stress level, studies indicate that local tensile residual stresses, such as produced by welding, are necessary in addition to sharp notches. As the constraint in a joint increases, the residual stress will increase, and the nominal applied stress necessary to initiate brittle failure in the presence of a sharp crack will decrease. For example, there are many known instances of brittle fracture occuring in a welded joint from residual stress alone. Welding is not the only factor that can bring about failure at a low stress level, although it usually is responsible. A notched area that has been plastically strained in compression can fail at a low

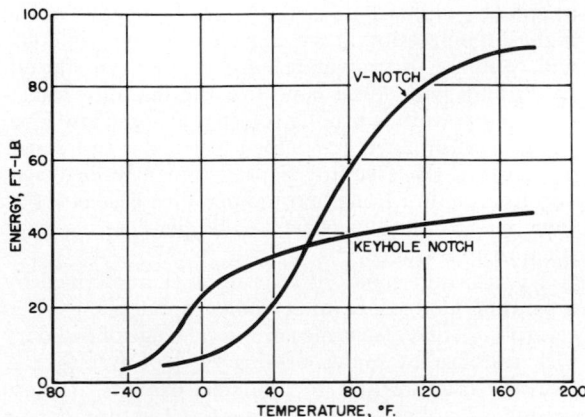

FIG. 47—26. General relationship of typical V-notch and keyhole-notch Charpy impact curves.

stress level when subsequently subjected to tensile loading; as with welding, residual tensile stresses are again involved in this type of low-stress failure.

The brittle-fracture problem has been accentuated by the increasing size of structures and by the more extensive use of welding. It must still be recognized, however, that in many applications notch toughness is not pertinent to satisfactory service performance.

In thin sections, like sheets, notch toughness formerly was not considered important and, in many cases, this is still true. However, with the development of sheet steels having tensile strengths in the range of 200,000 to 300,000 lb. per sq. in. for severe service in missile and aircraft applications, the notch toughness of these thin sections is a factor influencing material selection, design and fabrication procedures.

In heavier sections, many structures such as bridges, rails, and machine and automotive parts, have operated remarkably well at even the lowest ambient temperatures despite their apparent deficiencies in toughness according to the usual tests. Such behavior points up the fact that correlation of test results with service behavior is often a necessity for reliable assessment of notch-toughness needs. Without service experience, notch-toughness requirements are bound to become a matter of judgment.

In conclusion, it can be said that the importance of the notched-bar impact test lies in its ability to discriminate between steels of varying susceptibility to brittle fracture, providing the results are interpreted on the basis of the temperature of transition. The test is an extremely useful tool in the development of new and improved products with greater notch toughness, because of the possibility of detecting differences in materials that are not manifested in other tests, such as the tension test. Of particular value is the ability of the test to reflect differences in notch toughness caused by differences in steelmaking practices, as for example, differences in deoxidation practices. Furthermore, on the basis of empirical correlations of V-notch Charpy impact-test results with service performance, it is possible to evaluate with better reliability the suitability of steels for service in which a brittle-fracture hazard exists.

SECTION 5

FATIGUE TESTING

In a great many types of service applications, steel parts are required to withstand repeated or cyclic stressing; moving parts of machinery such as shafts, connecting rods, gears, etc., are examples of such applications. It has long been recognized that failures can occur in a machine part under repeated stress application at stresses well below those which the part is capable of withstanding under static load application. The failures which occur under repeated or cyclic stressing are referred to as **fatigue failures.** The importance of fatigue failures is well attested by the large percentage of failures in machine elements which are attributable to fatigue. It has been estimated that over 80 per cent of the failures in machines are a direct result of fatigue action.

Fatigue failures are progressive in nature, in that a crack is formed at some local spot or nucleus on the surface of the part after a certain number of load reversals, and is gradually propagated across the part. Finally, the remaining section becomes so small that it can no longer carry the applied load and complete failure ensues. A fatigue fracture generally appears brittle, even in metal which would be considered quite ductile in an ordinary tension test; the bright facets of the fracture led to the erroneous concept that the metal had "crystallized." The extremely localized nature of the fatigue failure is one of its most distinguishing characteristics and one which must be constantly kept in mind in considering the danger of fatigue.

Fatigue failures can almost always be traced to a nucleus which is situated at some surface irregularity, such as a notch, a scratch, a flaw, or an abrupt change in section. It is evident, therefore, that the specific details of design and loading are of paramount importance in establishing the fatigue life of a particular part. The environment of the part is another aspect of the service conditions which is of great importance in establishing fatigue life in service. If the environment is at all corrosive, the fatigue resistance can be greatly impaired. It is obvious that the fatigue problem provides an excellent example of the importance of evaluating the actual service conditions to which a material is to be subjected, as discussed in the introduction to this chapter. Considerable data have now been accumulated which indicate that, if the actual loading conditions in the critical area of a part are accurately determined, the fatigue life of a particular material in that part can be predicted from simple laboratory tests. This conclusion has been reached on the basis of a comparison of results of both full-scale fatigue tests on actual parts, and service performance, with results on simple laboratory specimens.

The types of fatigue tests which are to be discussed here are those small-scale laboratory tests which are employed primarily to study materials, as opposed to tests of actual parts. Applicability of the results to service performance will be subject to the considerations of the relationship between test and service conditions mentioned above. It will be assumed that the tests to be discussed are at least capable of rating the relative fatigue properties of materials, and that, by properly taking into account particular service conditions, they may in many cases be directly applicable for design purposes. Since so many of the applications to which steels are subjected involve repetitive loads, fatigue testing is considered of great importance since it is the only reliable method for evaluating the suitability of steels for this type of service.

Types of Fatigue Tests— The most commonly used type of fatigue test is the rotating-beam test, in which

FIG. 47—27. R. R. Moore fatigue-testing machine. (Courtesy, The Baldwin-Lima-Hamilton Corp.)

the specimen is subjected to a bending moment while being rotated. Any given fibre of the specimen is thus subjected alternately to compression and tension stresses of equal magnitude. One widely used machine of this type is the R. R. Moore machine shown in Figure 47—27. A schematic diagram of the loading arrangement is shown in Figure 47—28A, from which it is evident that a uniform bending moment is applied over the length of the specimen. Another type of rotating bending test utilizes a cantilever loading arrangement shown schematically in Figure 47—28B.

Another important type of fatigue test is the repeated bending or direct flexure test, in which the specimen is bent back and forth but not rotated. This

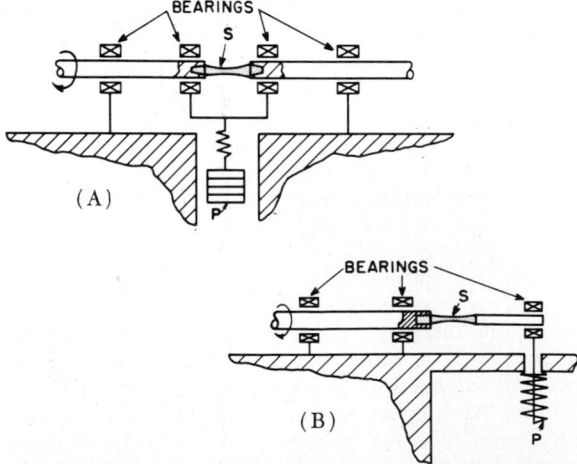

FIG. 47—28. Schematic loading arrangements for: (A) R. R. Moore and (B) cantilever-type of fatigue-testing machines. "S" indicates specimen and "P" indicates load, in both cases. (From STP 91, "Manual on Fatigue Testing," published by American Society for Testing and Materials, 1949.)

type of test is particularly useful in the testing of specimens of flat rolled products. The direct flexure test has the further advantage that surface preparation of the specimen is not necessary, thus permitting the test to be made on specimens having the actual surface to be exposed in service. The mechanical type of machine shown in Figure 47—29 introduces the load into the specimen, which is fixed at one end, through an adjustable crank.

Direct flexure tests may also be of the resonant frequency type, in which the specimen is vibrated at its fundamental frequency by some oscillating applied force. Because of the characteristics of resonant vibrations, very small forces applied at or near the resonance frequency of the specimen are capable of producing large amplitudes of vibration and correspondingly high stresses. Some resonant frequency machines make use of an oscillating magnetic field tunable to the resonant frequency of the specimen. The specimen is supported at the nodes and vibrates as a free-free beam. By taking advantage of resonance vibration in this manner, specimens of relatively large cross-section can be tested which would require very large machines if direct mechanical loading were employed. Other resonant frequency machines make use of mechanical rather than magnetic oscillators.

For certain types of fatigue, it may be desirable to conduct tests under direct, or axial loading conditions, i.e., the load is applied directly along the axis of the specimen. One of the major considerations in the design of axis-load fatigue machines is the provision of a loading arrangement which will insure the application of a truly axial load. Eccentricity of loading introduces bending moments in the specimen and may have a very pronounced effect on the observed fatigue properties. Most axial-load machines are designed so that tests can be conducted in which the mean stress is not zero, i.e., in which the stress is not completely

FIG. 47—29. Krouse direct flexure fatigue-testing machine. (Courtesy, Krouse Testing Machine Company.)

reversed. In many service applications, a part may not be subjected to alternate compressive and tensile stresses of equal magnitude, as is the case in the rotating beam type of test. For example, the stress may vary from zero to a maximum of 10,000 lb. per sq. in. tensile stress, in which case the fatigue properties are quite different than if the loading produced a range of stresses from 10,000 lb. per sq. in. in compression to 10,000 lb. per sq. in. in tension. It should be pointed out that the direct flexure test also affords some possibility of variation in mean stress. In some types of direct-flexure machines, it is possible to bend the specimen back and forth about an average position different from its equilibrium position, thus arriving at an average stress other than zero.

Fatigue results obtained from tests in which the specimens are bent should not be compared with results obtained from tests in which the specimens were axially loaded even if the mean stress in both cases was zero. This is illustrated in Figure 47—30. This figure also shows the effect of variation of the mean stress on fatigue results.

As already indicated, the environment to which a part is subjected can exert a profound influence on the observed fatigue behavior. If corrosive conditions are involved in a cyclic loading application, it is necessary to conduct the fatigue test under the same corrosive conditions. Usually, the standard types of machines and specimens are used in corrosion-fatigue testing, it merely being necessary to provide a jacket about the specimen suitable for carrying the corrosive medium. In the planning of corrosion fatigue tests, it is important to consider the relationship of testing frequency and rate of corrosion and to maintain a similar relationship to that existing in service.

Fatigue-Testing Specimen Preparation—The most critical aspect of fatigue testing is the preparation of the test specimen. As already pointed out, fatigue behavior is very sensitive to surface conditions, and unless extreme care is taken in surface preparation, large scatter and unreliable results can be expected.

Table 47—V gives some indication of the effects of surface finish on observed endurance limit for a steel. In the preparation of cylindrical specimens for use in rotating bending tests, the specimen is first rough machined, great care being taken to obtain a concentric test section in order that the stresses can be calculated accurately. Following the rough machining operation, a finish machining cut is taken. This finishing operation should be made with a sharp tool and a light feed in order to prevent bending, overheating, or

Table 47—V. Effect of Surface Condition on Endurance Limit

Moore & Kommers, rotating beam	
0.49% C quenched and tempered, 197 Brinell steel	
Finish	Endurance Limit, (Lb. per Sq. In.)
High polish (long.).........	51,000
00 Emery.................	48,000
Ground...................	45,000
Smooth turned............	43,000
Rough turned.............	42,000

Thomas, rotating cantilever	
0.33% C steel	
Finish	Endurance Limit, (Lb. per Sq. In.)
High polish (long.).........	41,500
FF Emery.................	40,500
No. 1 Emery..............	40,000
Coarse emery.............	39,000
Smooth file...............	38,500
Turned...................	36,500
Bastard file..............	35,500
Coarse file...............	33,000–34,000

excessive cold working of the specimen. For steels harder than about Rockwell C-40, grinding should be used for the finishing operation. The finishing cut should allow about 0.003 inch to 0.005 inch on the diameter for polishing, which is the next step in the specimen preparation. In order to carry out this operation successfully, it is important to recognize that this polishing is actually a cutting and not a buffing operation. Buffing may cold work the surface layers of the specimen sufficiently to affect the test results. A wide variety of polishing procedures are employed in different laboratories, but, in general, fatigue specimens are polished by a series of alternate circumferential and longitudinal polishing operations in which successively finer abrasives are employed. In each stage, the scratches from the previous operation are completely removed, the final polishing being carried out in the longitudinal direction of the specimen, since longitudinal scratches are less harmful than those in the circumferential direction. The specimen is generally rotated slowly in a lathe during polishing, about five stages being used in the polishing operation. One criterion of satisfactory polish, recommended by some laboratories, is that the surface produced should be satisfactory for metallographic examination at 100 magnifications. One of the types of specimens commonly used in rotating-beam tests is shown in Figure 47—31. In fatigue tests on notched specimens, great precautions must be taken in preparation of the root of the notch. The root of the notch should be very carefully lapped with a rotating, abrasive-bearing wire of

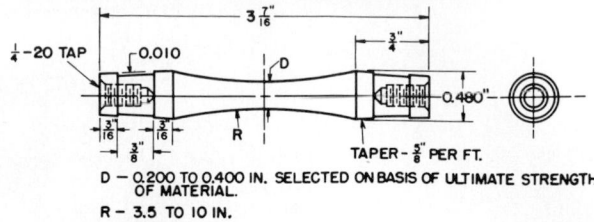

FIG. 47—31. Sketch illustrating rotating-beam fatigue specimen (R. R. Moore type). (From "Manual on Fatigue Testing," published by American Society for Testing and Materials, 1949.)

the same radius as the notch root. Lapping should be continued until all circumferential scratches left by the machining operation have been removed.

In testing specimens of flat-rolled products, it is generally desired to include the actual surface of the manfactured product in the test, especially if this is the surface to be exposed in service. If such is the case, no extensive surface preparation is needed. It is desirable, however, to remove burrs from the edges of the specimen and to produce a very slight chamfer or radius of about 0.005 inch on the corners. Such a procedure will usually eliminate spurious edge effects which could affect the final results.

Presentation of Fatigue-Test Data—Data on the fatigue strength of metals are generally presented in the form of so-called "S-N" diagrams, in which fatigue life is plotted as a function of the applied stress. Such

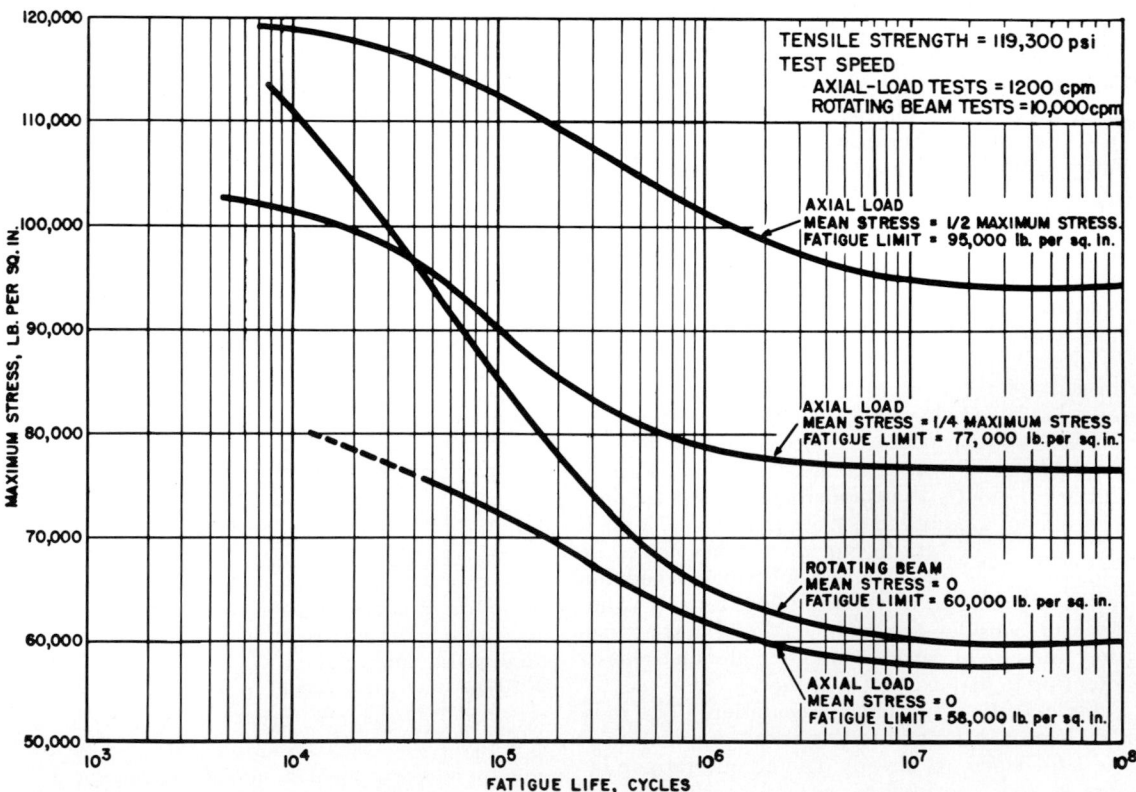

FIG. 47—30. Composite results of fatigue tests made on specimens of "T-1" steel under conditions indicated on the individual curves.

a diagram has already been shown in Figure **47—30**. Test results are shown as open circles. It is convenient to use a logarithmic scale in plotting the number of cycles, since the duration of tests at low stress levels may extend to hundreds of millions of cycles. The stress axis is usually an arithmetical scale although occasionally a logarithmic scale is used. Most steels exhibit what is known as a **fatigue limit,** i.e., a limiting stress below which an infinite number of stress cycles can be endured. The value of the endurance limit is the fatigue characteristic most frequently reported for steels. In some applications, such as aircraft parts, however, steels may be used at stresses above their fatigue limit in order to permit savings in weight. Such parts are removed from service after some period of use based on some selected number of stress cycles. It is important to know, therefore, the highest value of stress which the material can withstand without failure for a given number of cycles. This value of stress is known as the **fatigue strength,** and is used not only for steels above the fatigue limit but also in describing the fatigue characteristics of materials which do not show a true fatigue limit, such as austenitic stainless steels. Another fatigue characteristic sometimes reported is the fatigue life at some given stress level. For example, a part may be required to operate at a certain stress level. It then becomes necessary to select a material which can endure this stress for the greatest number of cycles.

In experimental determination of the fatigue limit, it is customary to make the first test at a stress level well above the fatigue limit, and to gradually lower the stress level in subsequent tests until the fatigue limit is reached. If the approximate value of the fatigue limit is not known beforehand, a tension test can be made, and the first fatigue test made at a stress level corresponding to about two-thirds of the tensile strength. It is obviously important to make the first tests at high stress levels, since initial tests at stresses below the fatigue limit are of very little value, because the proximity of a selected stress to the value of the endurance limit cannot be ascertained.

The S-N diagram for most steels consists of a sloping portion and a horizontal portion corresponding to the fatigue limit. For steels in a medium range of hardness, the knee of the curve will generally occur somewhere between one million and ten million cycles, so that a fatigue limit value based on ten million cycles is usually satisfactory. Fifty million cycles may be somewhat more reliable, however, and judgment based on experience with the shapes of S-N diagrams for various materials should be used in selecting the maximum number of cycles for the series of tests to determine the fatigue limit.

Significance of Small-Scale Fatigue Tests—There has been much discussion in recent years of the applicability of fatigue data derived from tests on small, highly polished bars to the prediction of fatigue life in service. One extreme point of view has been that such data are practically worthless and may even rate materials in the wrong order with respect to their service performance. This appears to be an unduly pessimistic attitude, especially in view of certain recent researches which indicate that if the service conditions are properly analyzed and if the state of stress at the critical point of a part is known, the fatigue limit of the part can be related to that determined in a simple polished-bar test. Fatigue tests on full-sized automobile parts have provided the basis for this conclusion. It should not be inferred from these remarks, however, that results of polished-bar tests should be applied indiscriminately to predictions of service behavior. Frequently, the service conditions will be so complex as to preclude the possibility of accurate analysis. In this event, the only alternative is a simulated service test.

In general, the fatigue limits of structural steels vary in a fairly regular way with tensile strength. An outstanding exception is provided by certain steels such as Bessemer steel or some of the high-strength low-alloy, phosphorus-bearing steels, in which the ratio of yield strength to tensile strength is higher than that normally found in most steels. In these steels, the fatigue limit is relatively high for a given tensile strength, which may indicate that fatigue limit is more closely related to the yield point than to tensile strength. The **fatigue ratio** is defined as the ratio of the fatigue limit to the static tensile strength and is in the neighborhood of 0.50 for most steels. Figure **47—32** is a schematic diagram for ordinary steels indicating the general relationship between fatigue limit and tensile strength for polished specimens, severely notched specimens, and corroding specimens.

In considering the effect of notches on fatigue, it is customary to use as a measure of the notch effect the **fatigue strength reduction factor,** which is usually designated as K_f, and is defined as the ratio of the fatigue strength of a member or specimen with no stress concentration to the fatigue strength in the presence of stress concentration. It is obvious that the strength reduction factor has no meaning except in terms of a specific notch geometry. A concept of notch sensitivity originated by Peterson relates the strength reduction factor K_f to the theoretical stress concentration factor K_t resulting from the notch. K_t is the ratio of the maximum stress in a notched section to the nominal or average stress across the entire section computed from mathematical analyses or determined experimentally. Peterson defines notch sensitivity by a "q" factor which depends on the relative values of K_f and K_t in the following way:

$$q = \frac{K_f - 1}{K_t - 1}$$

Notch sensitivity according to this definition varies from zero (where $K_f = 1$) to unity (where $K_f = K_t$). This concept is useful in describing the reaction of a material to notches of varying degrees of severity. Since most actual parts subjected to cyclic loading actually contain stress concentrations of some type, it is important that the effect of notches on fatigue properties be considered.

In summary, it can be said that small-scale tests are very useful in comparing the behavior of different materials under repeated stress and can be used in studies of the effects of metallurgical variables on fatigue characteristics. Such tests not only form a useful guide in the development of new materials of improved fatigue strength, but also permit the evaluation of various surface treatments such as carburizing, nitriding, shot peening, cold rolling, etc. The effect of different environments on fatigue behavior also can be studied conveniently in laboratory tests.

Some aspects of statistical analysis of these data may be found in "A Guide for Fatigue Testing and the Statistical Analysis of Fatigue Data," ASTM STP (Special Technical Publication) 91A (1958).

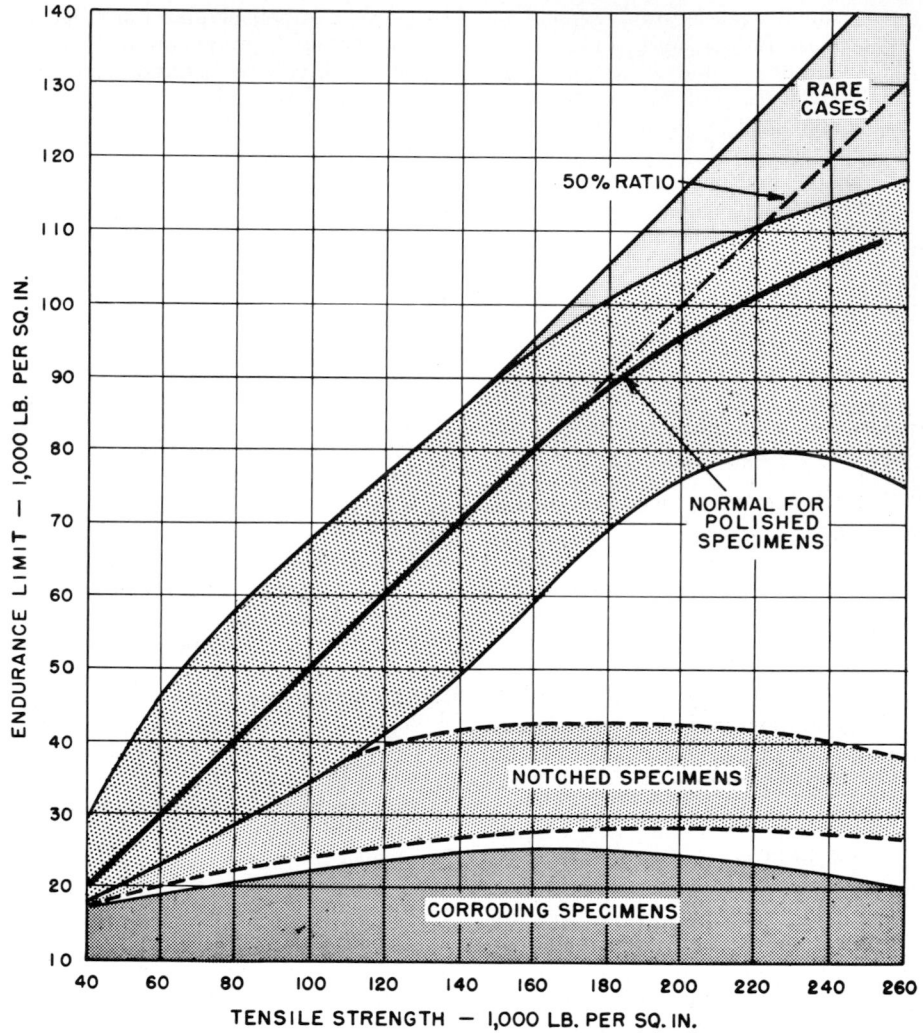

FIG. 47—32. Fatigue limit as a function of tensile strength for polished, notched and corroding specimens. (From "Prevention of Fatigue of Metals," by the staff of Battelle Memorial Institute. Published by John Wiley & Sons, Inc., New York, 1941.)

SECTION 6

HIGH-TEMPERATURE TENSION, CREEP, RUPTURE AND HARDNESS TESTING

The design of load-bearing structures for service at atmospheric temperature is generally based on the yield strength—or for some applications, on the tensile strength—determined in the ordinary room-temperature tension test. In service at ordinary temperature with a design stress determined in such a way, the metal behaves essentially in an elastic manner, that is, the structure undergoes an elastic deformation immediately upon load application and no further deformation occurs with time; when the load is removed the structure returns to its original dimensions.

At elevated temperature the behavior is different. A structure designed according to the principles employed for atmospheric temperature service continues to deform with time after load application, even though the design data may have been based on tension tests at the temperature of interest. This deformation with time is called creep, since at the design stresses at which it was first recognized it occurred at a relatively slow rate. A somewhat similar, though not exactly analogous, phenomenon is the flow of tar under its own weight on a warm day. A detailed discussion of the subject of creep has been presented by G. V. Smith (see reference).

When creep was originally encountered—the subject first received experimental attention only several decades ago—it was logical to decrease the stress to a sufficiently low value that creep would not occur. Much of the early work was devoted to such an effort. It was discovered, however, that such a limiting creep stress was lower the greater the sensitivity of the measuring apparatus and that quite low stresses would have to be employed to preclude the occurrence of measurable creep. In fact, the required stresses were so low and the section size correspondingly so large that the application of metals to high-temperature service was appreciably retarded. Accordingly, a new and more rational technique of design was developed and is now employed. This recognizes the existence of creep and is concerned not with avoiding its occurrence, but with limiting it to tolerable values within the contemplated service life of the structural member.

The rate of creep depends, for a given material, upon the stress, temperature and history of the material. Accordingly, the function of the creep-testing laboratory is to determine the dependence of creep upon such variables.

The possibility that creep may continue until fracture occurs raises another limitation in addition to that of the allowable deformation. In the use of metals at elevated temperature, not only must the design stress be chosen so that the deformation shall not exceed a limiting amount for the contemplated service life, but also it must be such that fracture will not occur. This latter characteristic is empirically related to the former. The variation of time for fracture or, as it is more commonly called, rupture, is determined in the so-called rupture test.

THE HIGH-TEMPERATURE TENSION TEST

The most common method for measuring the strength of metals is the tension test, which provides useful information up to the temperature at which creep in encountered. The special techniques involved in performing the tension test at elevated temperature are covered by ASTM Specification E 21 and E 151. Elevated-temperature tension tests may be made in conventional testing machines. A typical arrangement used in a conventional machine is shown in Figure 47—33; the temperature controls are also shown. With this arrangement, the specimen is heated by a furnace supported on one column of the machine, the furnace being free to swing into and out of the axial position.

Tests may be made on either bar or thin, flat stock. For bar tests, a 0.505-in. diameter specimen with threaded ends is usually used, although other sizes may be used. Threaded-end specimens are customarily gripped within the furnace. For sheet tests, a regular ½-in. wide specimen is used. If sufficient material is available, the specimen may be gripped outside the furnace; however, it is customary to grip the specimen within the furnace by use of pins or wedges or a combination of both.

The specimen extension is usually recorded autographically, although various types of indicating extensometers are available.

Tensile strength, yield strength, reduction of area, and elongation obtained from short-time tension tests

FIG. 47—33. Elevated-temperature tension-test equipment showing specimen ready for testing in hydraulic tension test machine. Temperature control equipment at left.

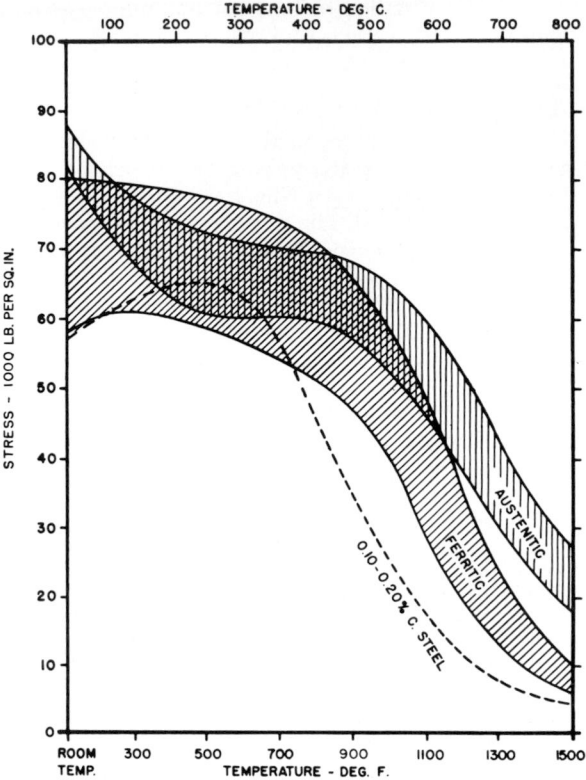

FIG. 47—34. Tensile strength of various steels as measured at temperatures between room temperature and 1500° F.

at temperatures above about 800° F are usually not used in design; for applications above this temperature, more reliable design information is obtained from creep or creep-rupture tests. At temperatures above 1500° F, data obtained from short-time tests are often useful as a guide for hot-working operations or for studying structural changes within the material.

The results of a series of elevated temperature tension tests on carbon steel and a wide variety of alloy steels are summarized in Figure 47—34. The strength of metals usually decreases with increase of temperature, but it will be seen from Figure 47—34 that the strength of plain carbon steel actually increases as the temperature of test is raised from room temperature to about 500° F. This increase of strength and the accompanying decrease of ductility in certain steels is called "blue brittleness," because in this temperature range, the oxide film which forms on the steel has a bluish tinge. With further increase of temperature, the strength of the material decreases, until at about 700° F, the strength is approximately the same as that at room temperature, after which the strength continues to decrease with increasing temperature. The increase of strength at 400° F to 600° F is believed to be due to a selective segregation of carbon and nitrogen atoms during the progress of the tension test, and is usually called "strain-aging." The segregation, which may result in a typical type of precipitate, is so small in amount that it cannot be detected under the electron microscope. The chemical composition of the precipitate is unknown.

THE CREEP TEST AND RUPTURE TEST

Creep Test—Since strain hardening by cold working is progressive in steel stressed at temperatures below 700° to 800° F, and since creep is small and occurs at a decreasing rate at these moderately elevated temperatures, the tension test suffices for determination of strength values for design purposes in a temperature range from room temperature up to about 800° F. Above this temperature, steel will flow continuously under the applied load and design cannot be based on the yield strength or proportional limit as measured by the tension test. The rate of flow or creep rate is related to the stress, and the purpose of the creep test is to determine the stress which will result in a given creep rate.

The method of measuring creep resistance is simple enough in principle, but in practice it requires considerable laboratory apparatus, and great care and precision in its operation. Disregarding for the moment the exact type of apparatus, the following fundamental steps are almost universally employed. The specimen is held at a constant temperature in an electric furnace, and is subjected to a static tensile load. The load causes the specimen to elongate gradually, and the amount of elongation is measured periodically. The total elapsed time of each test may be a matter of hours, weeks or months. Some creep tests have been run for more than ten years. In this country, the customary testing time is from 1000 to 3000 hours. The general method for creep testing is covered by ASTM Specification E 139.

The temperature of the specimen should be held within ± 1° F over the gage length and from day to day during the 3000-hour (4½-month) test period, since a change of as much as 2° F may cause enough thermal expansion or contraction to introduce an error into the readings. Such accuracy is necessary, since the amount of flow which can be tolerated in commercial parts operating at elevated temperature is very small —from a fraction of 1 per cent up to 1 per cent in 10 or 15 years—and accurate measurements of creep rates of 0.1 per cent or 0.01 per cent per 1000 hours must be made within the test period.

When the change of length taking place in the specimen from day to day is plotted against the elapsed time, a creep curve is obtained, whose typical form is shown in Figure 47—35. When the load is first applied, an immediate elastic extension (A) occurs. Then the specimen stretches gradually, at a decreasing rate, during the "first stage" of creep (B). The rate then becomes constant for a period of time during the "second stage" of creep (C). The slope of the creep curve in this second stage is the creep rate commonly used for design purposes. Finally, if the load or temperature is high enough, or the time long enough, the creep rate increases in the "third stage" (D), leading to fracture of the specimen. At the end of the testing period, if fracture has not occurred, the load is removed and elastic contraction (E) occurs, corresponding approximately to the elastic extension found upon application of the load at the start of the test. Thus, it is apparent that metals creeping under stress at high temperature can and do show both plastic and elastic

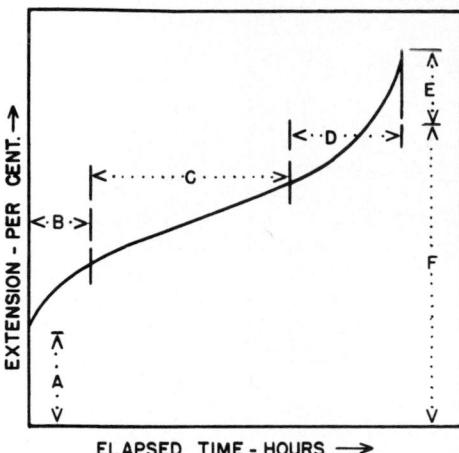

FIG. 47—35. Schematic creep curve. Extension plotted against elapsed time. (A) Elastic extension; (B) creep at decreasing rate; (C) creep at approximately constant rate; (D) creep at increasing rate; (E) elastic contraction; (F) permanent change of length.

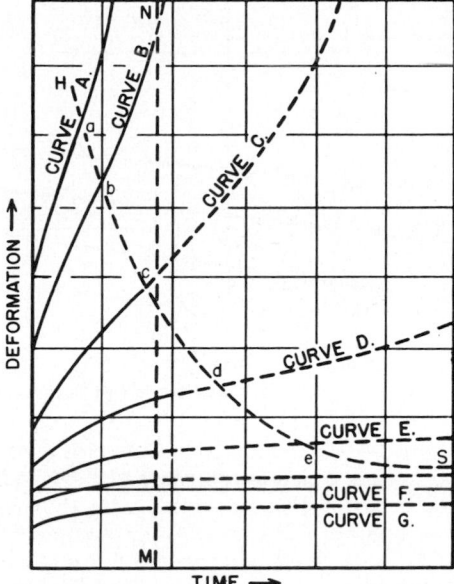

FIG. 47—37. Schematic plot of typical creep curves for seven specimens of the same steel; each specimen tested under a different stress ranging from a very high stress, curve A, to a very low stress, curve G, at a constant temperature. (Taken from "The Interpretation of Creep Tests" by P. G. McVetty, Proc. ASTM, Vol. 34, Part 2, 1934; pp. 105-116.)

properties simultaneously. The amount of permanent deformation is represented by (F).

The exact shape of an individual creep curve depends on the stress employed and upon the temperature, as well as upon the composition and structure of the metal. While elastic extension is always found at the beginning and elastic contraction is always found at the end of the creep test, it is rare in any one test to find periods of decreasing, constant, and increasing creep rate. An actual creep curve for a steel at 1000° F under a tensile load of 10,000 lb per sq. in. is shown in Figure 47—36.

Two standards of creep strength are commonly used in this country: (a) the stress producing a creep rate of 0.0001 per cent per hour, often expressed as 1 per cent per 10,000 hours (a little over a year); or (b) the stress for a creep rate of 0.00001 per cent per hour or 1 per cent per 100,000 hours (about 11 years). The second standard is used in designing moving parts such as steam turbines, in which the total creep must be very small, for example, a fraction of 1 per cent in 20 years.

The stress for a selected creep rate for the material in question must be ascertained by experiment. This is done in the following manner: several creep tests are run under different stresses at a single temperature and the creep curves plotted on the same chart. A family of curves is shown in Figure 47—37. Three or four tests on any given material are usually sufficient to indicate its behavior at a given temperature. The creep rate during the second stage of creep is measured and plotted against the applied stress. On log-log coordinates, the points are found to lie approximately on a straight line as shown in Figure 47—38. The stress for a creep rate of 0.0001 per cent per hour or 0.00001 per cent per hour may then be obtained by interpolation or extrapolation.

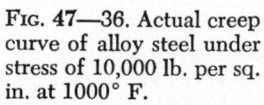

FIG. 47—36. Actual creep curve of alloy steel under stress of 10,000 lb. per sq. in. at 1000° F.

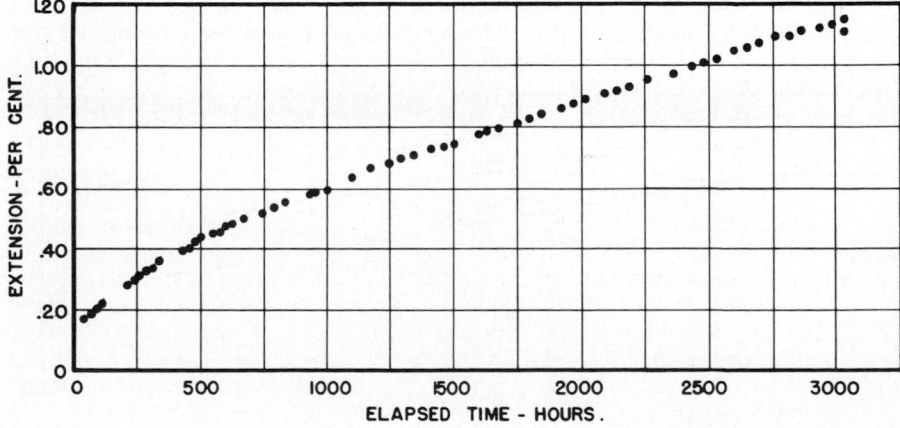

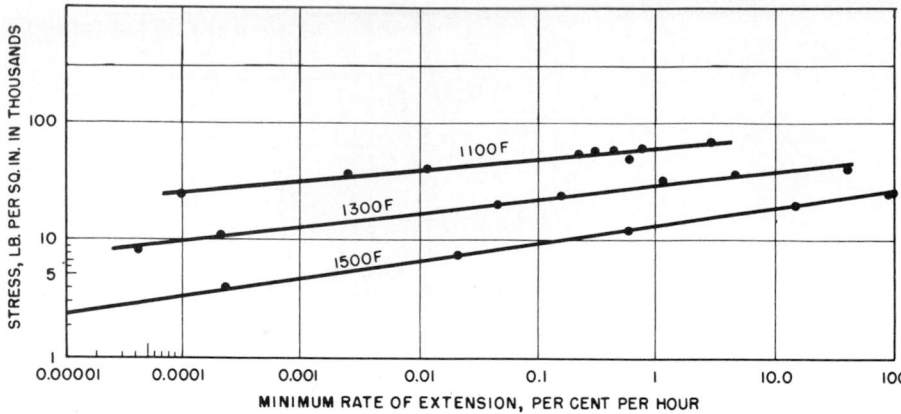

Fig. 47—38. Effect of stress on creep rate of 18-8 Mo (Type 316) steel at various temperatures.

In Figure 47—37 the line MN represents the end of a testing period which is too short to show the true long-time behavior of the material, since the later increase of creep rate in curve D, for example, would not have been detected, and the useful strength of the material would have been overestimated. For accurate determination of long-time creep strength, standard testing periods of from 1000 to 3000 hours are now generally employed to overcome this difficulty. Short-time creep tests may tell us that some materials are relatively stronger than others over the period of the test, but they tell little that is not revealed by a high-temperature tension test. Short-time creep tests obviously cannot show the effect of a structural change which would not occur at the test temperature until several weeks after application of the load. Extrapolation from such short-time creep tests generally results in an over-estimate of the creep strength of the material under investigation.

The Rupture Test—The rupture test (sometimes called the stress-rupture or creep-rupture test) is identical with the creep test, except that the loads and consequently the creep rates are higher, and the test is carried to failure of the material. The apparatus for carrying out the rupture test is usually the same as that employed for the creep test, except that a different instrument is used for measurement of the elongation. In the creep test, the rate and corresponding stress during the second stage of creep are plotted on a log-log diagram, and extrapolation to a lower creep rate, such as the standard 1 per cent per 10,000 hours, will give a fair prediction of the creep behavior of the material (Figure 47—38).

In reporting rupture data, it is customary to plot the applied stress against the time for failure on log-log coordinates as shown in Figure 47—39. It has been found that after a certain time, the type of fracture changes from predominantly transgranular to predominantly intergranular, that is, from rupture primarily through the grains to separation primarily along the grain boundaries. Although this change is frequently associated with the increase in the downward slope of the log stress-log rupture time curve, convincing proof of such relationship is still lacking. Because of the change in slope, however, it is desirable to carry the rupture tests out to a considerable time period. Rupture tests lasting as long as 40,000 hours (about 4½ years) are now considered to be desirable. Rupture values are usually reported as the stress for fracture in 100, 1000, 10,000 or 100,000 hours.

In recent years, it has become desirable to conduct creep- and creep-rupture tests on metallic materials under conditions of rapid heating and short-time periods. Tests of this nature are covered by ASTM specification E 150.

CREEP- AND RUPTURE-TEST EQUIPMENT

The facilities of United States Steel Corporation for research and development testing of steels for elevated temperature service can be taken to exemplify the types of equipment in current use. The design of this equipment varies to permit: (a) lever-type loading, (b) direct loading, (c) testing with constant stress, and (d) testing in vacuum or inert atmosphere. Figures 47—40 and 47—41, respectively, represent equipment for carrying out tests of types (c) and (d).

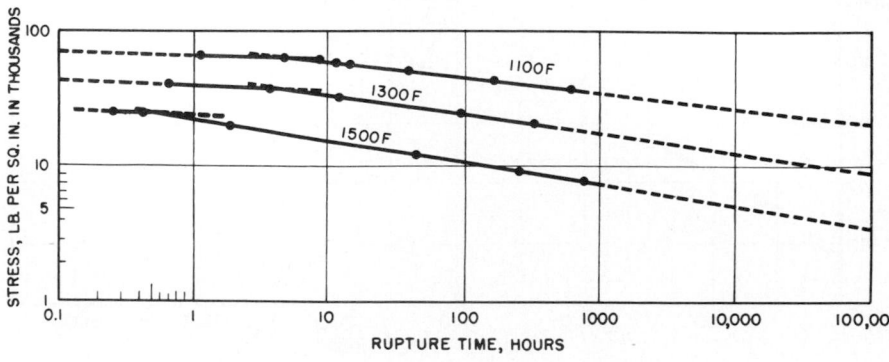

Fig. 47—39. Effect of stress on time for rupture of 18-8 Mo (Type 316) steel at various temperatures.

FIG. 47—40. Rupture-test equipment for constant-load testing up to 2200° F at the Applied Research Laboratory of United States Steel's Research Center at Monroeville, Pa.

FIG. 47—41. Apparatus for rupture testing in controlled atmospheric environment in the Edgar C. Bain Laboratory for Fundamental Research of United States Steel's Research Center at Monroeville, Pa.

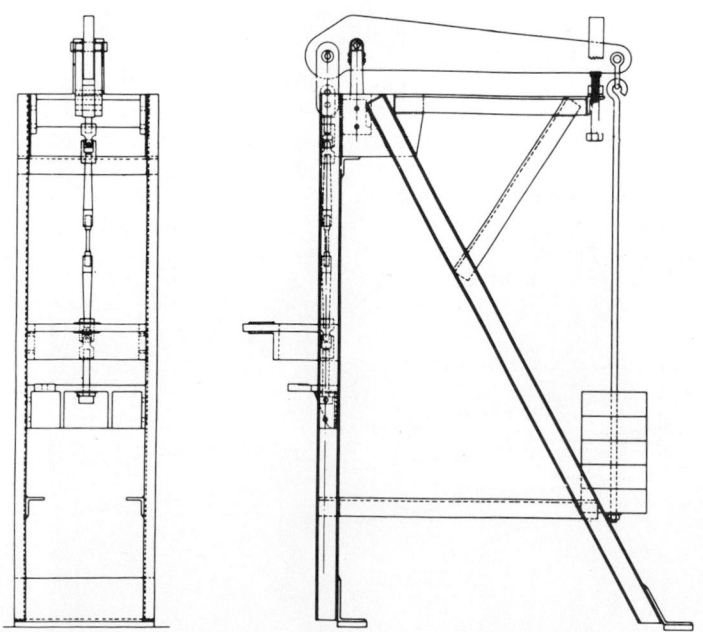

FIG. 47—42. Diagrammatic representation of creep and rupture test stand.

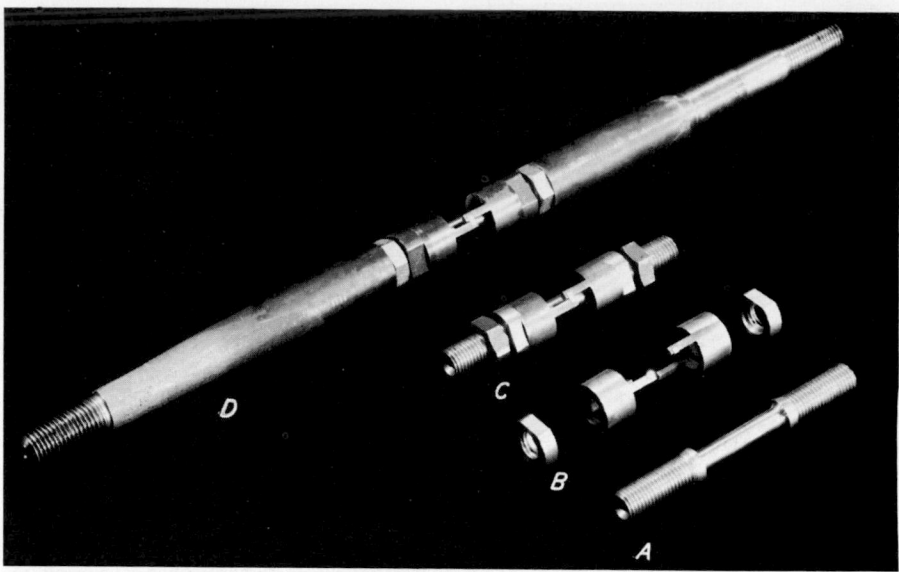

FIG. 47—43. Creep specimen (bottom) and assembly used at the Edgar C. Bain Laboratory for Fundamental Research at the United States Steel Research Center, Monroeville, Pa.

FIG. 47—44. Creep test microscope in position for making measurements through window in wall of furnace at the Edgar C. Bain Laboratory for Fundamental Research at the United States Steel Research Center, Monroeville, Pa.

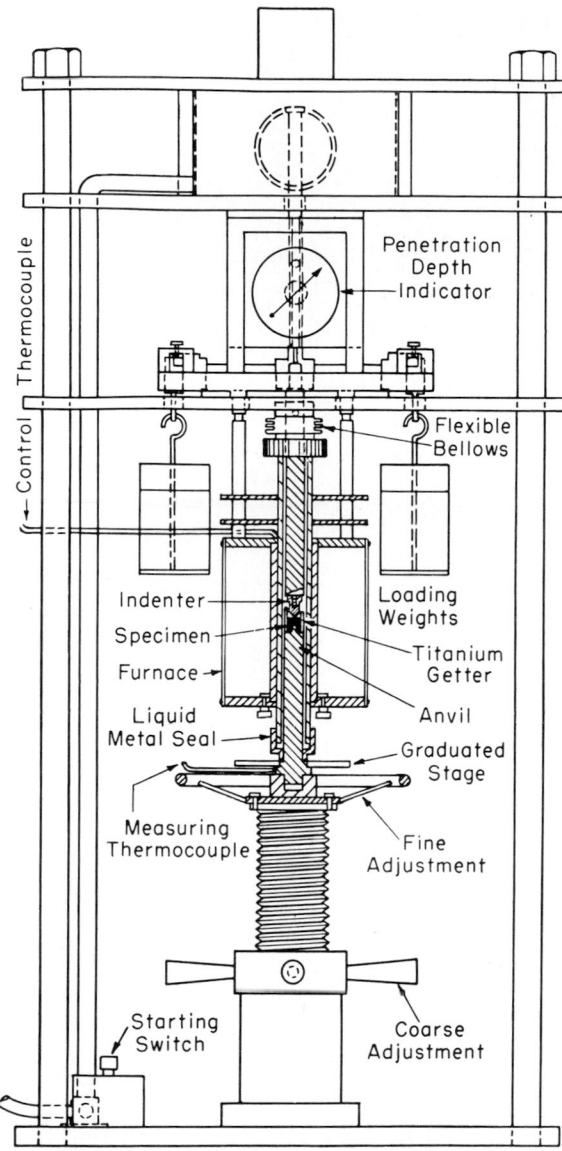

FIG. 47—45. Schematic sketch of high-temperature-hardness tester used at the Edgar C. Bain Laboratory for Fundamental Research at the Research Center of the United States Steel Corporation.

As has been outlined above, a specimen in either the creep or rupture test, enclosed within an electric-resistance heating furnace, normally is subjected to a tensile load imposed by dead weights and a lever. A diagrammatic sketch of a creep-test stand employing this principle is shown in Figure 47—42. As has been stated above, creep and rupture tests differ only in the magnitude of the stresses employed; in the rupture test greater stresses are used and the test is continued to fracture of the specimen to determine the relation between the stress and the time to fracture. In either test, the progressive variation of extension with time is observed and correlated with the imposed stress, thus permitting an estimation of the creep rate that may be expected during elevated-temperature service.

The extension that is of interest in the creep test is generally quite small, the rate being about 0.0001 per cent per hour (1 per cent per 10,000 hours) down to 0.00001 per cent per hour (1 per cent per 100,000 hours) with the total elongation not exceeding 1 to 2 per cent. The extension occurring in the rupture test is much greater, ranging up to 100 per cent per hour, with the total elongation ranging up to 100 per cent or more. Accordingly, different means are employed in the two types of test for measuring the extension. In creep tests conducted at the Edgar C. Bain Laboratory for Fundamental Research, the required high sensitivity is achieved by measuring the movement of reference marks engraved on polished platinum beads on arms extending from cylinders seated against the shoulders of the specimen (Figure 47—43). The measurement is made by a microscope, magnifying 100 times, sighted through a window in the furnace wall (Figure 47—44).

In the creep tests conducted at the Applied Research Laboratory, the creep extension is measured with mechanical extensometers that are clamped to the shoulders of the test specimens. The extension is recorded automatically in microinches on a strip-type recorder.

The extension during the rupture test, which is of much greater magnitude than in the creep test, is measured from the motion of the long arm of the lever (Figure 47—42) which falls as the specimen elongates. This motion is recorded autographically by attaching a flexible linkage to the lever at a location corresponding to a magnification of 10 to 1.

THE HIGH-TEMPERATURE HARDNESS TEST

The high-temperature hardness test is one of various elevated-temperature mechanical tests which has not been widely used, but which promises to be valuable as a tool in determining the high-temperature behavior of metals. Two test methods have been developed for

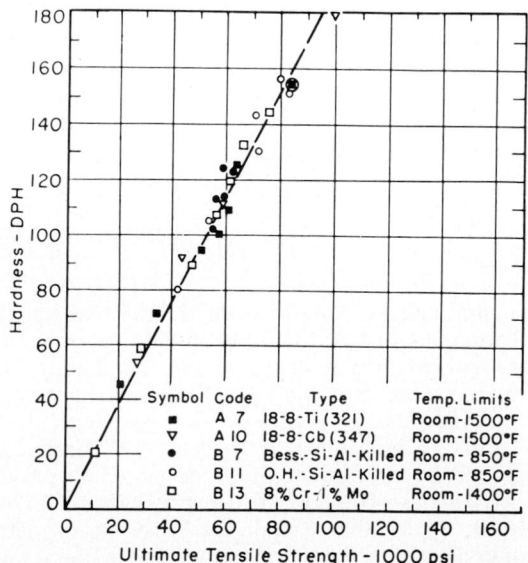

Symbol	Code	Type	Temp. Limits
■	A 7	18-8-Ti (321)	Room-1500°F
▽	A 10	18-8-Cb (347)	Room-1500°F
●	B 7	Bess.-Si-Al-Killed	Room- 850°F
○	B 11	O.H.-Si-Al-Killed	Room- 850°F
□	B 13	8% Cr-1% Mo	Room-1400°F

FIG. 47—46. Relation between hot hardness and ultimate tensile strength for several ferritic and austenitic steels.

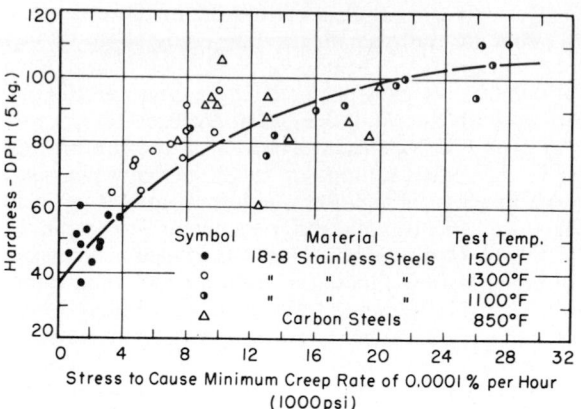

FIG. 47—47. Relation between hot hardness and creep strength of 18 Cr-8 Ni stainless and carbon steels.

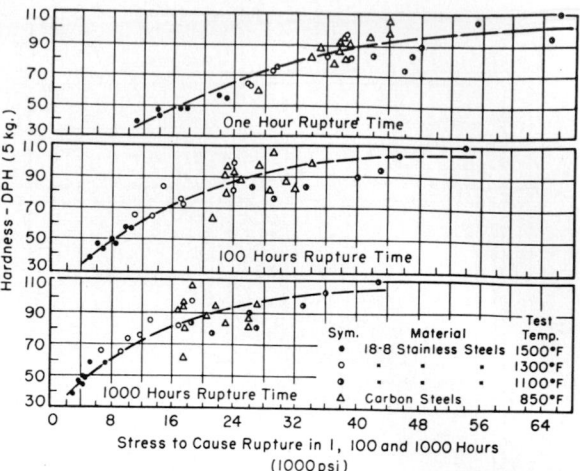

FIG. 47—48. Relation between hot hardness and creep-rupture strength for 18 Cr-8 Ni stainless and carbon steels.

determining the hardness at elevated temperatures, one employing static loading and the second employing dynamic loading. A certain degree of standardization of test equipment employing static loading has been in evidence recently; in addition, refinements in testing techniques have made it possible to determine high-temperature hardness with the same accuracy and degree of reproducibility as in room-temperature hardness testing. Little attempt has been made to standardize dynamic loading apparatus or techniques. Little correlation is found between static and dynamic results. This lack of correlation is related primarily to the strong dependency of mechanical behavior at elevated temperatures on rate of deformation.

The design of hot-hardness apparatus employing static loading has been based essentially on standard room-temperature equipment, including Vickers and Rockwell testers. Inert atmosphere, or a vacuum, have been employed in the test chamber to minimize oxidation. In all instances, small samples are used and a considerable number of hardness impressions are made on each sample at constant temperature or at different temperatures up to at least 1500° F. In hot-hardness apparatus based on the Vickers tester, the diagonals of the impressions are measured after cooling the specimen to room temperature.

A schematic sketch of the equipment used at the Edgar C. Bain Laboratory for Fundamental Research at the Research Center of the United States Steel Corporation is shown in Figure 47—45. In this apparatus the specimen, whose test surface is given a metallographic polish, and a Vickers-type indenter are heated to the desired temperature in a virtually inert atmosphere. The measuring thermocouple is spot-welded on the surface of the specimen. A dead-weight load ranging between 3 and 10 kg. is automatically applied to the indenter while in contact with the specimen. Following a loading cycle of one minute, the load is removed automatically and the sample rotated about its axis, which is offset from the indenter axis, in preparation for making a new impression at the same or at a different temperature. This apparatus has been employed in studying solid-state reactions such as strain-aging, phase changes during tempering and recovery and recrystallization phenomena. Other studies have shown that hardness results on steel at elevated temperatures are closely related to the tensile strength as shown in Figure 47—46, and approximately related to the creep strength as shown in Figure 47—47 and the creep-rupture strength as shown in Figure 47—48.

SECTION 7
USE OF HIGH-TEMPERATURE DATA IN DESIGN

In studying the flow of metals under stress at elevated temperature, it should be noted that, to a much more marked degree than at room temperature, the lower the strain rate, the lower the apparent strength of material. The relation between the strength of carbon steel as determined from the short-time tension test, and the strength of the same material as determined from creep and rupture tests is shown in Figure 47—49. At the lowest strain rates, permanent deformation occurs at high temperature under stresses less than the yield strength or proportional limit as determined from short-time tension tests. In fact, continu-

ous flow occurs under even the smallest applied stresses and design must be based on a dynamic rather than a static concept of the strength of materials.

Another important effect of the decrease of strain rate is the change in the type of fracture from transgranular to intergranular as the rate is decreased. The change in type of fracture is accompanied by a decrease in the amount of elongation. The exact amount of elongation accompanying creep failure is usually unknown, since failure under creep conditions does not usually occur for many years. Extrapolation indi-

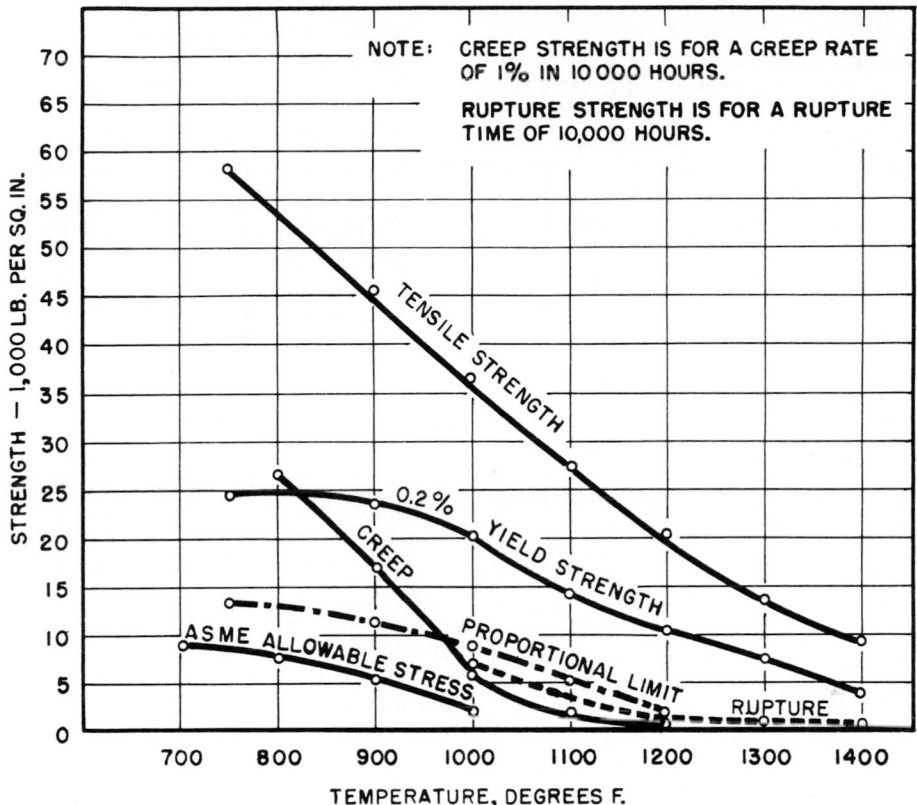

NOTE: CREEP STRENGTH IS FOR A CREEP RATE OF 1% IN 10 000 HOURS.

RUPTURE STRENGTH IS FOR A RUPTURE TIME OF 10,000 HOURS.

FIG. 47—49. The effect of temperature on the strength of killed, 0.10 to 0.20 per cent carbon steel as indicated by tension, creep, and rupture tests.

cates that, in molybdenum steel (0.15 per cent carbon, 0.56 per cent molybdenum), the amount of elongation at 1100° F decreases from about 38 per cent in a short-time tension test carried out at a strain rate of about 7.5 inches per inch per hour to less than 10 per cent under creep conditions.

A clearer picture of the effect of strain rate on the strength of material is obtained when strain rates are plotted against the applied stress, as shown in Figure 47—50. In this study, a series of controlled strain-rate tests were carried out on spheroidized and pearlitic molybdenum steels at 1100° F. The most rapid test was conducted at a rate of about 7.5 inches per inch per hour. Tests were also carried out at 1, 0.1 0.01, and 0.001 inches per inch per hour. Slower strain-rate data from stress-rupture and creep tests of these

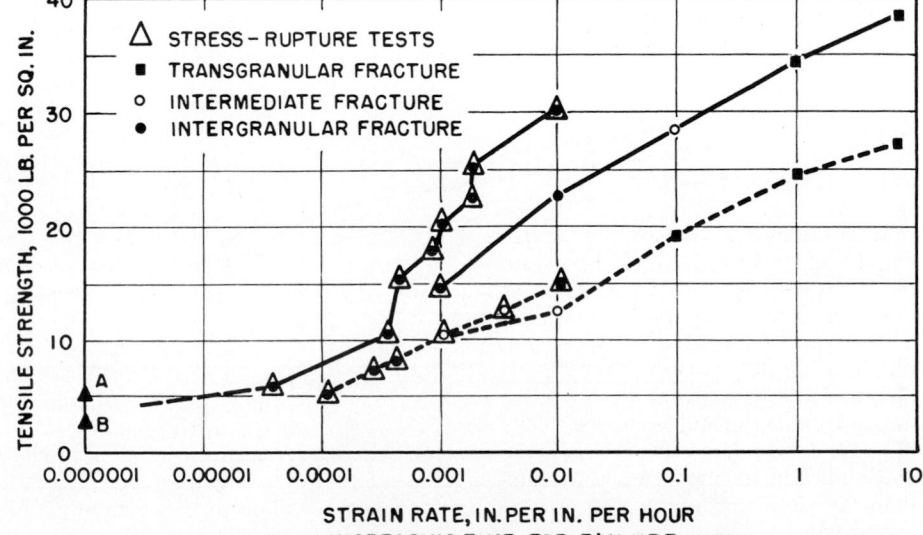

FIG. 47—50. The effect of strain rate on the apparent strength of pearlitic (solid line) and spheroidized (dashed line) molybdenum steel (0.15% C, 0.56% Mo) at 1100° F. A and B indicate reported stresses for creep rate of 1 per cent per 10,000 hours in molybdenum steel at 1100° F.

materials are also represented and show the same trend of decrease of strength. In fact, at a strain rate of 0.000001 inches per inch per hour, about 1 ten-millionth of the strain rate employed in the short-time tension test, the apparent strength of molybdenum steel at 1100° F, has decreased from 37,000 to 2,500 lb. per sq. in. This clearly illustrates the necessity of determining the strength of materials in the creep range from creep and rupture tests rather than from short-time tension tests. High-temperature design stresses, as set by the American Society of Mechanical Engineers, are established on the basis of long-time creep and rupture strength, and the limiting temperature is determined by the scaling resistance of the material. Below 700° to 800° F, the stresses are obtained from short-time tension data. Service experience and the behavior of similar materials are also taken into consideration. Allowable working stresses for the standard ferrous alloys may be found in Sections I and VIII of the ASME Boiler Construction Code and in the API-ASME code for Unfired Pressure Vessels.

ELASTIC PROPERTIES

Under certain conditions of design at elevated temperature the permissible strain is of the order of magnitude of the elastic strain. It is necessary in such a case to compute working stresses on the basis of elastic properties of the material. In general, the design of structural members on this basis requires values of three constants of elasticity, the elastic modulus in tension and compression (Young's modulus), the shear modulus and Poisson's ratio. Of equal importance is the fact that these·elastic constants are also needed in computing the magnitude of thermal stresses.

The elastic moduli can be measured under conditions of static or dynamic loading. Under static load-

ing, Young's modulus can be determined from a simple tension or a bend test and the shear modulus can be determined from a torsion test. Poisson's ratio (μ) is then computed from the following relationship:

$$\mu = \frac{E}{2G} - 1$$

where E is Young's modulus and G is the shear modulus (modulus of rigidity). By subjecting a small cantilever beam to simultaneous bending and twisting by application of a single load it is possible to determine both E and G from a single test. Such a method has been employed to determine the variation of the elastic moduli under static loading for a number of commercial, ferritic and austenitic stainless steels up to 1500° F. Average curves for the results obtained are shown in Figure 47—51.

Under dynamic loading, high-frequency cyclic tests of relatively low stress amplitude are generally used. Both E and G can be determined from the measured velocity of longitudinal and transverse waves produced by high-frequency pulses. Dynamic tests on steels have been made up to 1600° F.

Theoretically it is predicted that the variation of the elastic constants, E and G, is linear with temperatures up to nearly the melting point of metals; however, deviations from linearity are caused by various phase and crystallographic lattice changes, magnetic changes and grain-boundary gliding in polycrystalline metals. Because of the low stresses encountered, the dynamic results are not affected by grain-boundary gliding. At temperatures where gliding at the grain boundaries is nil, below 700° F for plain carbon, 900° F for alloyed ferritic, and 1300° F for austenitic stainless steels, the static and dynamic results agree very well.

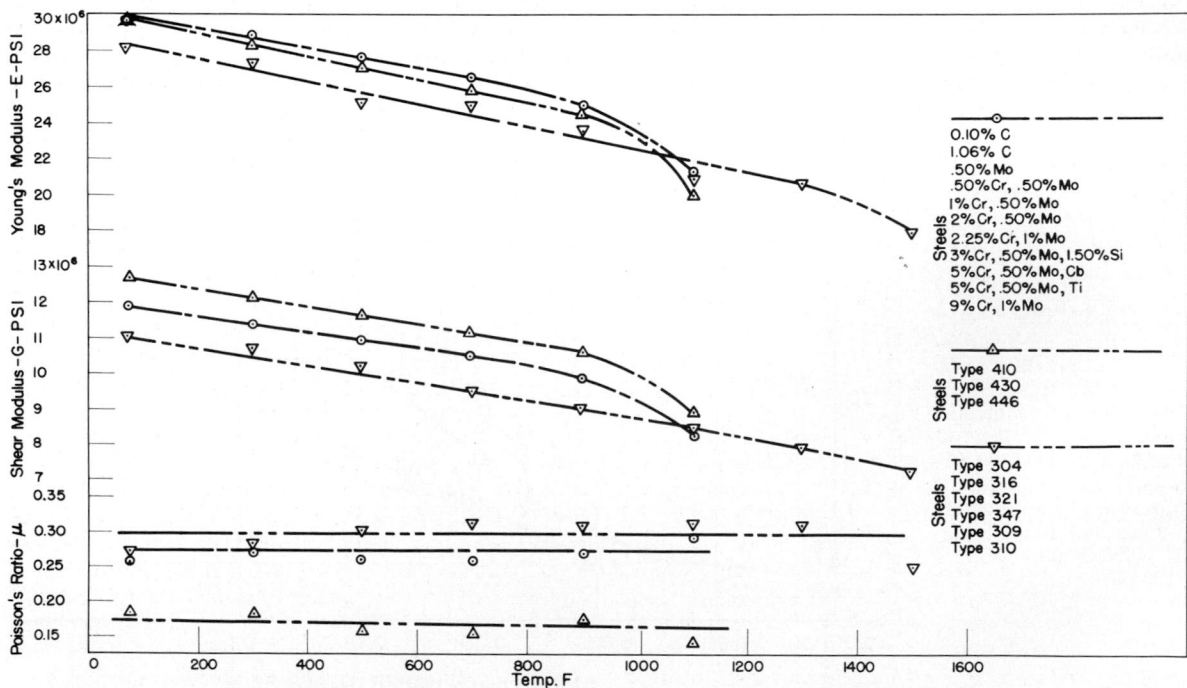

Fig. 47—51. Variation of elastic moduli with temperature for various ferritic and austenitic stainless steels.

SECTION 8

MISCELLANEOUS MECHANICAL TESTS

Metals are subjected to a great variety of applications which may involve mechanical properties not directly measured in the more common mechanical tests already described. For this reason, a great many specialized tests have been developed which are usually aimed at a closer approximation to some important aspect of the actual service condition than the ordinary tests provide. A few of the more important miscellaneous mechanical tests are briefly described in this section, in order to provide some indication of the types of tests which have been developed.

A. Compression Testing—Frequently, in the design of structural members which are to be subjected to compressive working stresses, it is desirable to design on the basis of compressive yield strength rather than tensile yield strength, particularly if there is reason to believe that the compression properties of the material under consideration differ from the tension properties. The data obtainable from a compression test may include the proportional limit, the elastic limit, the yield strength or yield point, and in some cases "compressive strength." The term compressive strength has been defined by the American Society for Testing and Materials as the maximum compressive stress which a material is capable of developing. This strength figure has a definite value only for a material which fractures in compression. For other materials, arbitrary compression strength values are sometimes reported which are based on some degree of distortion which is regarded as indicating complete failure of the material.

An ASTM tentative specification for the compression testing of metallic material in other than sheet form has been drawn up and is designated as E9. It is recommended that standard specimens be in the form of circular cylinders, the important feature in specimen preparation being parallelism of the ends and perpendicularity of the planes of the ends to the specimen axis. As in the case of tension testing, axial loading is of great importance. In some instances, a special subpress is used in conjunction with the regular testing machine in order to facilitate truly axial application of the compression load.

Compression members are frequently fabricated from sheet material, particularly for use in aircraft. In the design of such members, it is necessary to use the compression properties of the sheet material. Obviously, edgewise compression tests are not simple on thin sheets because of buckling difficulties. Several methods of testing sheet specimens in compression have been proposed. One of these is the "pack" method, in which a composite specimen is built up of several layers of sheets. In this way, a specimen of sufficient thickness to avoid buckling is provided. Another type of test provides support against buckling by special jigs. One such jig consists of a number of rollers which rest against the faces of the specimen. Another type of fixture which was developed at the National Bureau of Standards simply uses flat tool-steel blocks lubricated with a high-pressure lubricant to support the specimen (Figure 47—52). The speci-

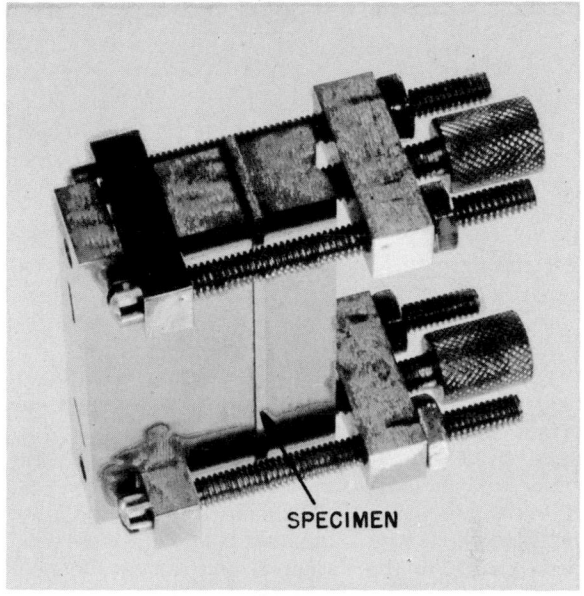

SPECIMEN

FIG. 47—52. National Bureau of Standards jig for compression tests on sheet metals. (Courtesy, U. S. Department of Commerce, National Bureau of Standards.)

men is allowed to overhang the supports slightly for loading and attachment of extensometers. Still another type of sheet metal compression test is the cylinder method, in which the flat specimen is formed, by bending rolls, into a cylinder about one and one-half inches in diameter and soldered along the longitudinal joint. This cylinder is very resistant to buckling and the ends can be accurately machined to insure axial loading. Another advantage of this method is the accessibility of the specimen for strain measurement. The principal disadvantage of the cylinder method is that a small amount of cold work is unavoidably introduced in forming the cylinder.

B. Bend Testing—The bend test, as the name implies, is intended to evaluate the ability of a material to undergo bending during forming operations to which it may be subjected. Generally, the bend test is conducted as a "go-no go" test; i.e., either the specimen meets the desired bend requirement or fails by cracking. In some instances, however, a ductility value is derived from the bend test by placing gage marks on the outside or tension side of the bend and measuring the elongation after completing the bend. This procedure is covered by ASTM Designation E16 and was developed primarily for testing of welds.

Ordinarily the bend test is much simpler, merely involving a determination of whether or not a specified bend can be made satisfactorily. A typical method of stating a bend-test specification for a plate material, for example, is as follows: "The bend-test specimens shall stand being bent cold through 180 degrees without cracking on the outside of the bent portion to an inside diameter which shall have the following relation

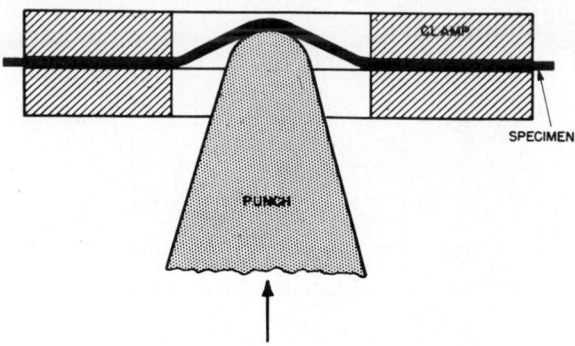

Fig. 47—53. Schematic representation of cupping test for sheet metals.

to thickness or gage of material." A set of bend diameters is then specified for various thickness ranges, the bend diameters increasing with increasing plate thickness. Edge conditions are very important and generally sufficient edge preparation is permitted to avoid an initial edge fracture. The method of bending is not specified and a large number of bending devices have been designed, the design usually being aimed at convenience so that large numbers of tests can be run in a relatively short time.

C. Cupping Tests—A number of so-called "cupping" tests have been developed for the purpose of measuring the ductility of sheet metal under conditions where the sheet is stretched in all directions simultaneously. Cupping tests are made on different machines, or testers, known as the Erichsen, the Olsen, the Guillery, the Wazau, etc., of which the first two are the most commonly used. While they differ in many respects, the Erichsen and the Olsen testers are similar in the manner of applying the test. In both, the specimen of sheet or strip is clamped between two rings or dies, and a smooth ball, mounted upon or attached to a plunger, is forced against the flat surface of the specimen enclosed within the area of the ring, as shown in Figure 47—53, thus stretching it into the form of a cup, and continuing until the material is fractured. In the Olsen type of machine, the depth of the cup causing fracture is measured in thousandths of an inch by a recording or measuring device, the indicator of which is actuated directly from the surface of the sample. The end point of the test is indicated by a pressure gage, the pointer of which drops back upon fracture of the specimen. In the Erichsen tester, the plunger is somewhat cone-shaped with a smooth spherical end; the fracture of the specimen is detected visually by a mirror attachment, and the depth of the cup is measured in millimeters.

In a great many actual sheet-metal forming operations, the blank is required to stretch in all directions. It would be expected, therefore, that a cupping test would prove a better criterion of the behavior to be expected in such forming operations than would a simple tension test in which the material is stretched in only one direction. Actually, the correlation between cupping tests and actual performance has in general been disappointing, except in cases where

large differences in formability exist. Cupping tests are widely used for inspection purposes, however, since they provide a quick indication of ductility and some indication of the surface condition to be expected after drawing by the degree of roughness or coarseness developed on the cup during the cupping test.

D. Strain-Sensitivity and Strain-Aging Sensitivity Tests—Steel products are very frequently subjected to cold-forming operations prior to or during fabrication for their final use and may go into service in the cold-worked condition. As discussed in the chapter on plain carbon steels, the properties of cold-worked steel may change progressively with time, this change being known as strain-aging. The question arises, therefore, as to how the changes in properties brought about by cold working and strain-aging will affect the performance of the material in service.

It is well known that straining and strain-aging exert a profound influence on the notch toughness characteristics of certain steels, tending to increase the susceptibility of these steels to brittle fracture. One of the most informative methods of evaluating the effect of straining and strain-aging on notch toughness is the determination of the shift in transition temperature in the notched-bar impact test. The interpretation of the relationship between test results and service behavior is, of course, subject to the same limitations as emphasized earlier in the general discussion of notched-bar impact tests. It is possible, however, to obtain extremely useful comparisons among different steels and to provide relative measures of the extent to which the notch toughness is impaired by straining and strain-aging.

One testing procedure which has proved convenient and useful involves the cold rolling of oversize blanks for Charpy-type specimens. The degree of oversize is based on the desired amount of cold working; for example, if ten per cent reduction is desired, the blank is made about 0.0394 inch oversize and reduced to the standard dimension of 0.394 inch. Two sets of specimens sufficient for the determination of transition temperatures are prepared in this manner. One set is tested as soon as possible after rolling and notching, while the other set is artificially aged for one hour at 550° F. This treatment is believed to produce the maximum effect of strain aging on notch toughness. The shifts of transition temperature caused first by straining, and second by straining and aging give an indication of the extent to which the ability to resist brittle fracture has been impaired. Examples of the types of transition behavior which may be obtained are shown in Figure 47—54.

Another test which is sometimes used to indicate the effects of straining and strain-aging on notch toughness is the Graham tapered-bar test. Varying amounts of cold work are produced by drawing a tapered circular bar through a die so as to produce a uniform cross section. The bar is then notched at various points along its length which correspond to various amounts of cold work and is broken as a cantilever specimen at each notch. The maximum amount of cold work is usually ten per cent. The cold-drawn bar can also be aged before testing. Although

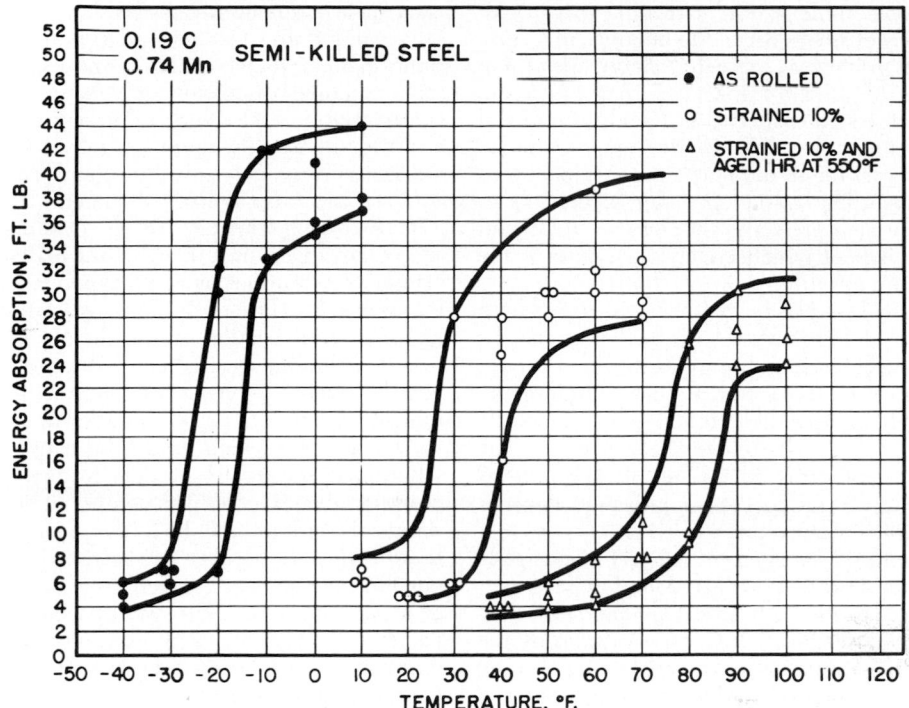

FIG. 47—54. Effect of strain aging on transition temperature in the Charpy impact test.

this test is relatively fast and simple, it has the disadvantage of not permitting the determination of transition temperatures, and is thus subject to the uncertainties which arise in impact testing at a single temperature.

Steels which exhibit pronounced strain aging show an increase in tensile strength when tested at temperatures in the neighborhood of 400° F over that obtained in room-temperature tests. This increase in tensile strength is sometimes used as a measure of the effects of strain aging, but should not be substituted for a notch toughness test unless a correlation has been established.

Another aspect of strain aging, which is of great practical importance, is the return of the yield point in temper-rolled sheets intended for deep-drawing operations. Such sheets are normally temper rolled after annealing in order to eliminate the yield-point elongation and the accompanying tendency for the formation of stretcher strains or fluting during forming. In steels which are susceptible to strain aging, however, the yield-point elongation and stretcher-strain tendency will return with time. Accelerated aging, in which the temper-rolled material is held at an elevated temperature such as 400° F for some predetermined length of time, is frequently applied in order to indicate the aging tendency. The extent to which the yield point elongation returns in a tension test provides some indication of the manner in which the material can be expected to behave in a drawing operation after a considerable lapse of time at atmospheric temperature.

E. Torsion Testing—In the torsion test, a specimen is subjected to twisting or torsional loads analogous to those encountered in drive shafts, crank shafts, etc. In-

formation on the strength in torsion, particularly the yield point or yield strength, is important in designing for such applications. Torsion tests are not extensively used, since a satisfactory estimate of the yield point in torsion can generally be made from the yield point in tension. In some instances, however, a direct measurement of torsion properties may be desirable and occasionally may be specified.

Torsion data are usually obtained in the form of a torque-twist curve, in which the applied torque is plotted against the angle of twist. Torsion produces a state of stress known as pure shear, and the shear stress at yielding can be calculated from the torque at yielding and the specimen dimensions. Actually, the stress varies from a maximum at the surface of the specimen to zero at the axis. In the elastic range, the variation is linear, and the maximum stress for a cylindrical specimen can be readily calculated from the following relation:

$$S = \frac{16T}{\pi d^3}$$

where: S = maximum shear stress (lb. per sq. in.)
         T = torque in inch-pounds
         d = diameter of specimen.

In the plastic range, the calculation of the maximum shear stress is more complicated and the reader is referred to the method developed by A. Nadai, which considers the twisting of a cylindrical bar in the plastic range.

In the elastic range, the shear strain is proportional to the shear stress, the constant of proportionality being known as the **shear modulus** (modulus of rigidity). The shear modulus for steel is about 10,000,000 lb. per sq. in.

Impact tests utilizing dynamic torsional loads are

used to a considerable extent in testing brittle materials such as tool steels. Since the ductility in torsion is greater than in tension, a greater energy absorption is obtained in the torsion impact test than in a beam type of impact test. Sensitivity is thereby improved making separations possible in the torsion impact which are not possible in the notched-bar impact test. The energy absorbed by the specimen in the torsion impact test is measured by the loss in rotational energy of a flywheel which engages one end of the specimen and breaks it.

F. Shear Testing—The term "shear testing" as used here refers to determinations of the resistance of metals to shearing in dies, i.e., cutting by shearing. "Shear test" is sometimes also used to refer to the torsion test, which, as indicated above, measures the resistance to deformation under shear stresses. The sense in which the terms "shear" or "shear strength" are used should always be clearly indicated in order to avoid any misinterpretation.

If a load-penetration diagram is determined while shearing a metal in dies, it will be found to be similar in general shape to the load-extension diagram in tension testing. The maximum load observed during the shearing operation divided by the area being sheared is taken as the shearing strength or shearing resistance of a material. It is necessary to state the exact testing conditions in reporting shearing resistance, since the value obtained will depend markedly on the die arrangement. The clearances, shear angles, and sharpness of the cutting edges will all affect the observed value of shearing resistance. The degree of penetration of the punch into the metal when the fracture begins is also usually reported. It has been generally observed that the shearing resistance of medium carbon steels is from two-thirds to three-fourths of the ultimate tensile strength.

G. Wear Testing—H. W. Gillette has defined the wear of a metal part as "its undesired gradual change in dimensions in service under frictional pressure." Wear generally involves two stages, in the first of which deformation occurs, and in the second of which removal of material may occur. Wear of metals may involve the contact of metal on metal, as in shafts and bearings, brakes and wheels, valves and seats; or it may involve the contact of non-metals on metals, as in the case of coke chutes, or in shovel buckets, etc. The phenomenon of wear is so complex that it is extremely difficult to interpret, and is one kind of service for which suitability can be reliably evaluated only in terms of actual service tests. Various wear tests have been used for specific purposes, but are only valid if the test method produces wear in the same manner in which it is produced in service. A more detailed discussion of wear and wear testing can be found in ASTM STP 30, entitled "Symposium on Wear of Metals," published in 1937, and in the publications by Haworth, Rowe and Gardner that are listed in the bibliography at the end of this chapter.

H. Damping Capacity Tests—Damping capacity is a measure of the rate at which a material dissipates energy of vibration, or in other words, a measure of the ability to damp out vibrations. Damping depends upon internal friction in the metal, which is manifested at stresses well below those at which gross yielding occurs. Internal friction probably arises from minute amounts of plastic flow on a submicroscopic scale, a process which results in heating and a loss of vibrational energy. The ability to damp vibrations is of importance in certain structures subjected to vibrations, where there may be a danger of resonant vibrations arising. Resonance can lead to large amplitudes of vibrations and excessively high stresses. A choice of a material with relatively high damping capacity, which can also satisfy the ordinary mechanical requirements, may be of some benefit in avoiding resonance conditions. High damping capacity materials are also of value in supports for moving machinery, in that the transmission of vibrations to the supporting structure may be reduced.

A commonly used method of measuring damping capacity involves the measurement of the rate of decrease of amplitude of torsional vibrations. One end of a cylindrical specimen is clamped in a rigid base with the specimen in a vertical position. On the other end of the specimen, a heavy inertia bar is clamped. This inertia bar is rotated through an angle corresponding to the desired stress level in the specimen, usually by means of magnets, and then released. The specimen is thus set in torsional vibration, and the rate of decrease of vibration amplitude is measured by some suitable method. In a recently developed machine, a light beam is focused on a mirror on the inertia bar, and the beam is reflected onto a rotating drum carrying a strip of sensitive photographic paper. Measurements of the rate of decrease of vibration amplitude from the photographic record permit a calculation of the damping capacity. Damping capacity is usually expressed in terms of **specific damping capacity,** which is defined as the ratio of the energy loss per cycle to the elastic potential energy at the maximum amplitude of the cycle.

SECTION 9

NONDESTRUCTIVE TESTS

Certain nondestructive tests, although not providing a direct measurement of mechanical properties, are extremely valuable in locating and isolating material defects which could greatly impair the mechanical performance if permitted to remain in a machine element or structural member placed in service. Since the part or article inspected by nondestructive methods is in no way altered or affected, it is possible to inspect the entire article. Furthermore, in many cases, it is feasible to carry out 100 per cent inspection of all product intended for applications which demand especially high quality. In this way, uncertainties as to whether representative sampling has been attained are eliminated. It should also be pointed out than an extremely important function of nondestructive tests is in the examination of parts which have been in service, such examination frequently being possible without removing the part from service. Incipient failures can oftentimes be detected in this manner, thus permitting removal of the part from service before serious damage is done. Since nondestructive testing provides such an important supplement to the conventional mechanical test procedures in evaluating suitability for mechanical service, it is appropriate that a few of the more important nondestructive testing methods be briefly described in this chapter on mechanical testing.

Radiography—Radiography is one of the oldest and most widely used methods of nondestructive testing. Its use is based upon the great penetrating power of X-rays or gamma rays, which, depending on their initial intensity, are capable of penetrating several inches of steel. X-ray tubes operating at voltages as high as three million volts are now in use capable of producing an X-ray beam which can penetrate six to seven inches of steel. Gamma rays, which are given off spontaneously by certain radioactive materials such as radium and by synthetically produced isotopes such as Co^{60}, Ir^{192} and Cs^{137}, are capable of penetrating greater thicknesses than X-rays, and have the important advantage that the equipment required is entirely portable and requires no maintenance. The sensitivity of gamma rays to defects in thinner sections, however, is considerably inferior to that of X-rays, and X-rays are, therefore, more commonly used for radiographic work.

As a beam of X-rays or gamma rays passes through an object, it is absorbed to a degree depending upon the thickness of the object and upon the specific absorbing capacity of the material. Metals are characteristically strong absorbers of X-rays. If a cavity in the object being radiographed lies in the path of the beam, the effective thickness which must be traversed by the beam is decreased and the intensity of the emitted beam is greater in the vicinity of a point opposite the cavity. In this way, an image of the cavity is formed, which can be considered as an X-ray shadow picture. Any large cavity or inclusion which differs in absorbing capacity from the bulk of the test object will act in such a manner as to produce variations in intensity from point to point of the beam as it passes through the object. These variations in intensity or X-ray shadows, so to speak, are generally recorded on photographic film, but may also be observed visually by a fluorescent screen which is activated by the X-ray beam.

Considerable experience is necessary for the expert interpretation of radiographs, particularly in identifying the source of an indication and in judging how harmful the defect may be. A background of practical experience is usually built up by sectioning objects on which certain radiographic indications have been obtained, in order to positively correlate the indication with its source. The principal fields of application of radiography are in testing castings and welds. In castings, defects such as pipe, shrinkage, hot tears, blowholes, and sand or slag inclusions may be detected by radiographic inspection. In welds, detection of hot tears, shrinkage cracks, blowholes, slag inclusions, lack of fusion, and lack of penetration is possible. One of the principal shortcomings of radiography is its inability to detect very thin defects, unless the plane of such defects lies parallel to the beam. A crack in which the surfaces are very close together is an example of such a defect. Since this type of defect can be very harmful in service, some other method of detection such as magnetic or sonic methods must be adopted.

Magnetic Methods—The magnetic methods of nondestructive testing to be described here are not aimed primarily at an evaluation of actual magnetic properties of a given steel specimen, as carried out for electrical or magnetic steels, but are employed for the measurement of some other characteristic of interest which is reflected by variations in magnetic behavior. The magnetic tests of primary interest here are those which are used in detecting physical discontinuities in steel. These methods depend upon establishing a uniform magnetic field around the steel part or test object, either by a magnetizing coil or by passing an electrical current through the part. Any physical discontinuity in the metal creates a magnetic flux leakage which can be detected by the use of magnetic powders or by a pick-up coil.

Magnaflux and Magnaglo are two widely used magnetic powders which are particularly useful in detecting fine surface and subsurface cracks. The Magnaglo powder differs only in that the magnetic particles are coated with a fluorescent material which glows under ultraviolet light. In this way, the contrast of the magnetic powder indication can sometimes be improved. In use, the powders are applied wet or dry to a magnetized part. If cracks are present, the leakage flux causes a local concentration of magnetic particles in the vicinity of the discontinuity.

The well known Sperry rail tester is an example of a magnetic flaw detector utilizing a pick-up coil. In using this device, a heavy direct current is passed through a rail section from a testing car as the car moves along. A uniform magnetic field is thus set up around the rail. If a transverse fissure is present in the rail the magnetic field is disturbed. A small coil moving along just above the track surface detects this disturbance by variations in induced current, which are recorded and used to indicate the location of the defect.

Ultrasonic Methods—Sonic methods have long been used in the detection of flaws or defects in steel. The clearness of the ring given off when an object is struck is well known to give an indication of soundness or freedom from gross discontinuities. The recent development of the ultrasonic testing techniques represents the culmination of much research to improve the sensitivity of sonic methods.

The ultrasonic method of flaw detection depends on the fact that when a beam of ultrasonic waves is projected into the metal object, a small physical discontinuity in the path of the beam acts as an obstacle to the beam. The reflection method, which is the most useful of the various ultrasonic techniques for flaw detection, makes use of the fact that a portion of the incident beam may be reflected from a discontinuity lying in the path of the beam. By timing the interval between the generation of the initial pulse and the reception of the reflected pulse, the location of the defect can be determined. The ultrasonic waves are generated by a quartz crystal, making use of the piezoelectric effect, which causes the crystal to expand or contract when subjected to an electric charge. By using a rapidly oscillating electric field, the crystal is made to vibrate at the same frequency as the oscillation of the field. This effect is reversible, permitting the same crystal to be employed as a detector, in which case an oscillating electric charge is set up in the crystal as it is subjected to mechanical vibration. Measurement of this oscillating charge provides a method of detecting ultrasonic waves.

The reflection method of ultrasonic inspection has been successful in detecting a large number of types of defects such as pipe, shrinkage, cracks, flakes, fatigue cracks, concentrations of inclusions, segregations, and laminations. The method is rapid and is useful in production line work. As in the case of any nondestructive test, a background of experience must be built up in the interpretation of the indications with respect to the nature of the defect producing a particular type of indication.

Bibliography

Am. Society for Metals, Metals handbook; 1948 ed. Cleveland, The Society, 1948.
>   Sections on mechanical testing.

Am. Society for Testing Materials, Manual on fatigue testing (Special technical publication no. 91). Phila., The Society, 1949.

Am. Society for Testing Materials, A tentative guide for fatigue testing and the statistical analysis of fatigue data (Special technical publication no. 91A). Phila., The Society, 1958.

Am. Society for Testing and Materials, 1961 Book of ASTM Standards, Part I, Ferrous metals. Phila., The Society, 1961.
>   Section on testing methods.

Am. Society for Testing Materials, Symposium on wear of metals (Special technical publication no. 30). Phila., The Society, 1937.

Correlation of short- and long-time elevated temperature test methods (Project no. 25); Appendix II of Report of Joint Research Committee on Effect of temperature on properties of metals. Am. Society for Testing Materials Proc. 44: 186–215 (1944).

Foster, P. F., Mechanical testing of metals and alloys; 4th rev. ed. N. Y., Pitman, 1948.

Gardner, D., These machines grind, scratch, gouge to measure abrasive wear. Prod. Eng., Nov. 9, 1959.

Garofalo, F. and G. V. Smith, Effect of time and temperature on various mechanical properties during strain aging of normalized low carbon steels. Am. Society for Metals Trans. 47: 957–983 (1955).

Garofalo, F., P. R. Malenock and G. V. Smith, Hardness of various steels at elevated temperatures. Am. Society for Metals Trans. 45: 377–396 (1953)

Garofalo, F., P. R. Malenock and G. V. Smith, Influence of temperature on elastic constants of some commercial steels. Am. Society for Testing Materials, Symposium on determination of elastic constants (Special Technical Publication 129) Phila., The Society, 1952.

Haworth, R. D., The abrasion resistance of metals. Am. Society for Metals Trans. 41: 819–869 (1949).

Kula, E. B., and Fahey, N. H., Effect of specimen geometry on determination of elongation in sheet tension specimens. Materials and Research Standards, August, 1961; pages 631–636.

Lysaght, V. E., Indentation hardness testing. N. Y., Reinhold, 1949.

McVetty, P. G., The interpretation of creep tests. Am. Society for Testing Materials Proc. 34 (Part 2): 105–116 (1934)

Miller, R. F., G. V. Smith and G. L. Kehl, Influence of strain rate on strength and type of failure of carbon-molybdenum steel at 850, 1000 and 1100 degrees Fahrenheit. Am. Society for Metals Trans. 31: 817–848 (1943)

Nadai, A., Plasticity. N. Y., McGraw-Hill, 1931.

Smith, G. V., Properties of metals at elevated temperatures. N. Y., McGraw-Hill, 1950.

Symposium on significance of the tension test of metals in relation to design. Am. Society for Testing Materials Proc. 40: 501–609 (1940)

Templin, R. L., The determination and significance of the proportional limit in the testing of metals. Am. Society for Testing Materials Proc. 29 (Part 2): 523–553 (1929).

CHAPTER 48

Gage Numbers

In the metal industries, the word gage is used in various systems, or scales, for expressing the thickness or weight per unit area of thin plates, sheets, and strips, or the diameters of rods and wires. Specific diameters, thicknesses, or weights per square foot are denoted in gage systems by certain numerals prefixed to the word gage; for example, No. 12 gage, No. 20 gage, No. 30 gage, or simply 12 gage, 20 gage, and 30 gage. Gage numbers are used only in connection with thin materials; that is, usually when the thickness is not more than one-quarter inch or the weight per square foot is not more than 10 pounds, although most gage tables actually begin at about one-half inch, or 20 pounds per square foot, and one table begins at double these quantities. Heavier and thicker materials are always indicated by weight per unit area or length, or by thickness in English or metric units.

It is advisable, at this point to emphasize the danger of confusion in the use of gage numbers to indicate thicknesses and diameters. This danger is present in domestic as well as in foreign trade, and can be avoided by specifying thickness or diameter in inches, centimeters, or millimeters, or in weights per square foot or per square meter, or by giving other equivalents, in absolute units, of the gage desired. The relations and equivalents of the principal gages are shown in the several tables in this chapter.

Origin of Gages—This custom of indicating thickness and diameter by gage numbers originated in the early days of the metal industries, and the gage numbers were probably first employed to designate the different sizes that could be most readily produced by different stages, or steps, in the processes of manufacture. Inasmuch as these manufacturing processes sometimes varied considerably, not only for different commodities but often among different manufacturers of the same product, and as an individual system of measurement was often considered a trade advantage, a great number of gage systems came into existence. It has been said that at one time there were in use in this country and in England more than fifty different wire gages and several distinct gages for sheets. This condition alone would give rise to considerable confusion, but, as if confusion were to be sought rather than avoided, different names were often applied to the same or practically the same gage system. Also, the same names or symbols were frequently employed to designate different gage systems. All these systems were not only dissimilar with respect to each other in actual thickness denoted by the gage numbers, but the different numbers in the same table seldom bore any mathematical relation to each other.

Relation of Gage Number to Thickness—These gage systems had but one characteristic in common, namely, that the higher the gage number the thinner was the material. This relation of gage numbers to actual thicknesses has always been maintained, and the association of high gage number with thin material or with small diameter has become fixed, by long custom, in the minds of people associated with the metal industries. With but few exceptions, this relation of gage number to thickness or diameter persists to the present time. The exceptions are the Sheet Zinc Gage, Belgian Zinc Gage, Paris (French) Gage, and Music Wire Gage, in which the gage numbers increase with the thickness of the sheet or the diameter of the wire.

British Gages—Chief among the early gage systems were the Birmingham gages, one for sheets and another for wire, and the Stubs' gages. As Stubs was from Warrington, his most popular gage was often called the Warrington Wire Gage, but was also known as Peter Stubs' Gage. In this country, Peter Stubs' Gage and the Birmingham Wire Gage are considered to be identical. The first attempt at reform in gages was to list the equivalent of the gage numbers in decimals of an inch. This was done first individually by Stubs, and later by organized action of the British Board of Trade, in 1883. In that year, a gage was prepared which was intended as a standard for both wire and sheets but was later found to be unsuitable for sheets. This gage became the legal British standard gage on March 1, 1884, and became known as the British Imperial Standard Wire Gage, designated in the British Empire by the initials W.G. or B.W.G., and in the United States by the initials I.S.W.G. or S.W.G. When this gage was found to be unsuitable for sheets, a new gage, called the Birmingham Sheet and Hoop Iron Gage, was prepared by revising the old sheet gage. The new gage has since been used in England, merely by common consent until 1914, at which time it was established legally as the British Standard Gage for Iron and Steel Sheets and Hoops, represented by the symbols B.G. Custom gages for galvanized sheets now usually have B.G. suffixed to the gage numbers, but the weights have no systematic relation to the weights of the British Standard Gage (B.G.) for uncoated sheets. The earlier English gages, Birmingham Wire Gage and Stubs' Warrington Wire Gage, are no longer in common use except for telephone and telegraph wire. The relationships between the more common gages mentioned above and some others are given in Table 48—I.

United States Sheet Gages—The next attempt at

Table 48—I. Relationship of Gage Numbers in Common Use.

	WEIGHT GAGES							THICKNESS GAGES				
Name of Gage	United States Standard Gage, U.S.S.G.		Galvanized Sheet Gage, G.S.G.		Tin Plate Gage, T.P.G.			Steel Wire Gage Washburn & Moen or W. & M. Wire G. U.S. Steel W.G.	Music Wire Gage, M.W.G.	Brown & Sharpe Gage, B. & S.G. A.W.G.	Stubs' Iron Wire Gage, W.W.G. B.W.G.	Name of Gage
Principal Use	Uncoated Carbon Steel Sheets and Light Plates		Galvanized Sheet Steel		Tin Plate			Steel Wire, except Music Wire	Steel Music Wire	Non-ferrous Sheets and Wire	Flats, Plates and Wire	Principal Use
Gage No.	Equivalent Thickness, Inch	Lb. per Sq. Ft.	Lb. per Sq. Ft.	Oz. per Sq. Ft.	Lb. per Sq. Ft.	Lb. per Base Box	Symbol	Thickness, Inch	Thickness, Inch	Thickness, Inch	Thickness, Inch	Gage No.
7/0's	0.4902	20.0000						0.4900	0.004	0.5800		7/0's
6/0's	.4596	18.7500						.4615	.005	.5165		6/0's
5/0's	.4289	17.5000						.4305	.006	.4600	0.500	5/0's
4/0's	.3983	16.2500						.3938	.007	.4096	.454	4/0's
3/0's	.3676	15.0000						.3625	.008	.3648	.425	3/0's
2/0's	.3370	13.7500						.3310	.009	.3249	.380	2/0's
0	.3064	12.5000						.3065	.010	.2893	.340	0
1	.2757	11.2500						.2830	.011	.2576	.300	1
2	.2604	10.6250						.2625	.012	.2294	.284	2
3	.2451	10.0000						.2437	.013	.2043	.259	3
4	.2298	9.3750						.2253	.014	.1819	.238	4
5	.2145	8.7500						.2070*	.016	.1620	.220	5
6	.1991	8.1250						.1920*	.018	.1443	.203	6
7	.1838	7.5000						.1770*	.020	.1285	.180	7
8	.1685	6.8750	7.0312	112.5				.1620*	.022	.1144	.165	8
9	.1532	6.2500	6.4062	102.5				.1483*	.024	.1019	.148	9
10	.1379	5.6250	5.7812	92.5				.1350*	.026	.0907	.134	10
11	.1225	5.0000	5.1562	82.5				.1205*	.029	.0808	.120	11
12	.1072	4.3750	4.5312	72.5				.1055*	.031	.0720	.109	12
13	.0919	3.7500	3.9062	62.5				.0915*	.033	.0641	.095	13
14	.0766	3.1250	3.2812	52.5				.0800*	.035	.0571	.083	14
15	.0689	2.8125	2.9687	47.5				.0720*	.037	.0508	.072	15
16	.0613	2.5000	2.6562	42.5				.0625*	.039	.0453	.065	16
17	.0551	2.2500	2.4062	38.5				.0540*	.041	.0403	.058	17
18	.0490	2.0000	2.1562	34.5				.0475*	.043	.0359	.049	18
19	.0429	1.7500	1.9062	30.5				.0410*	.045	.0320	.042	19
20	.0368	1.5000	1.6562	26.5				.0348	.047	.0285	.035	20
21	.0337	1.3750	1.5312	24.5				.0317	.049	.0253	.032	21
22	.0306	1.2500	1.4062	22.5				.0286	.051	.0226	.028	22
23	.0276	1.1250	1.2812	20.5	1.1250			.0258			.025	23
					1.079	235	6X					
					1.047	228	6XL					
24	.0245	1.0000	1.1562	18.5	1.0000			.0230	.055	.0201	.022	24
					.987	215	5X					
					.964	210	D2X					
					.955	208	5XL					
					.895	195	4X					

Gage No.					Symbol							Gage No.
25	.020	.0179	.059	.0204			.8750	16.5	1.0312	.8750	.0214	25
26	.018	.0159	.063	.0181	4XL DX 3X 3XL	188 180 175 138	.863 .827 .804 .771	14.5	.9062	.7500	.0184	26
27	.016	.0142	.067	.0173	2X	163 155	.7500 .748 .712	13.5	.8437	.6875	.0169	27
28	.014	.0126	.071	.0162	2XL DC	148 143 139	.6875 .680 .657 .638	12.5	.7812	.6250	.0153	28
29	.013	.0113	.075	.0150	IX IXL	135 128 125 123	.6250 .620 .588 .574 .565	11.5	.7187	.5625	.0138	29
30	.012	.0100	.080	.0140		118 112 110	.5625 .542 .514 .505	10.5	.6562	.5000	.0123	30
31	.010	.0089	.085	.0132	IC ICL	107 100	.5000 .491 .459	9.5	.5937	.4375	.0107	31
32	.009	.0080	.090	.0128		95 90	.4375 .436 .413	9.0	.5625	.4062	.0100	32
33	.008	.0071	.095	.0118		85	.4062 .390	8.5	.5312	.3750	.0092	33
34	.007	.0063	.100	.0104		80 75 70	.3750 .367 .3437 .321	8.0	.5000	.3437	.0084	34
35	.005	.0056	.106	.0095		65	.3125 .298			.3125	.0077	35
36	.004	.0050	.112	.0090		60	.2812 .276			.2812	.0069	36
37		.0045	.118	.0085		55	.2656 .253			.2656	.0065	37
38		.0040	.124	.0080		50	.2500			.2500	.0061	38
39		.0035	.130	.0075			.2343 .2295			.2344	.0057	39
40		.0031	.138	.0070		45	.2187			.2187	.0054	40
41		.0028	.146	.0066			.2109 .2066			.2109	.0052	41
42		.0025	.154	.0062			.2031			.2031	.0050	42
43		.0022	.162	.0060			.1953			.1953	.0048	43
44		.0020	.170	.0058		40	.1875 .1836			.1875	.0046	44

*Three intermediate fractional gages sometimes used are omitted in this table.

Table above is based on the theoretical weight, which makes the weight of a plate one foot square and one inch thick 40.8 pounds. Sheets and light plates are gaged on the edge, and the spring in the rolls causes the centers to be slightly thicker than the edges. To have the estimated weights of sheets and light plates equal the actual weight, the average weight of a square foot one inch thick is taken as 41.82 pounds.

standardizing gages was made in the United States, in 1892. On March 3rd of that year, the United States Standard Gage for Sheet and Plate Iron and Steel (Table 48—I) was established by an Act of Congress as the only standard gage for these materials after July 1, 1893. This gage is a weight gage based upon weights per square foot in pounds avoirdupois. The gage table as established by Congress began with 20 lbs. per square foot, No. 7/0's gage, and ended with 0.25 lb. per square foot, No. 38 gage, but the light side of the table has been extended by custom to 0.1875 lb. per square foot, or No. 44 gage. In this country the gage is standard for all uncoated iron and steel sheet and plate, and is also used for tin plate in the lighter gages.

Galvanized and Long Terne Sheets have individual gages based on the U.S. Standard Gage with allowances made for the thickness of the coating in each table. Thus, for the same gage number the weight shown in the Galvanized Sheet Gage regardless of coating weight, is 0.1562 pounds per square foot heavier than the weight shown in the U.S. Standard Gage (uncoated product). In the Long Terne Sheet Gage, each gage number may have various weights depending upon the coating weight. With a commercial coating (6 pounds per double base box) each gage number is 0.016 pounds per square foot heavier than

the weight shown for the corresponding U.S. Standard Gage number (see Table 48—II).

As stated in the preceding paragraph, the U.S. Standard Gage is based on weights per square foot in pounds avoirdupois. Table 48—I shows the approximate thickness for each gage number adopted by the originators of the gage, who based these thicknesses on the density of wrought iron, which is 480 pounds per cubic foot or 0.2778 pound per cubic inch. Since the adopted standard density for steel is about 2 per cent heavier than that of wrought iron (489.6 vs. 480 pounds per cubic foot), the thickness equivalents for steel are slightly less than those listed in the U.S. Standard Gage. Although this change is legal because the governing factors in the gage schedule are weights and not thicknesses, much confusion occurs in converting from weight to thickness for steel sheets. Consequently, the manufacturers of steel sheets in this country have adopted a new gage, known as the Manufacturers' Standard Gage for Sheet Steel (Table 48—III). The gage numbers and corresponding weights in this gage are identical to those contained in the U.S. Standard Gage, but the equivalent thicknesses are less since they are based on the density of steel, not that of wrought iron. The conversion factor used in determining these thicknesses is actually greater than the density of steel by an amount necessary to allow for

Table 48—II. Gage Weights for Long Terne Sheets of Various Coating Weights

Long Terne Gage No.	Gage Weights in Ounces and Pounds per Square Foot, for the Gages and Coatings Given													
	Commercial		0.35 Ounce		0.45 Ounce		0.55 Ounce		0.75 Ounce		1.10 Ounce		1.45 Ounce	
	Oz. per Sq. Ft.	Lb. per Sq. Ft.	Oz. per Sq. Ft.	Lb. per Sq. Ft.	Oz. per Sq. Ft.	Lb. per Sq. Ft.	Oz. per Sq. Ft.	Lb. per Sq. Ft.	Oz. per Sq. Ft.	Lb. per Sq. Ft.	Oz. per Sq. Ft.	Lb. per Sq. Ft.	Oz. per Sq. Ft.	Lb. per Sq. Ft.
10	90.25	5.641												
11	80.25	5.016												
12	70.25	4.391												
13	60.25	3.766												
14	50.25	3.141												
15	45.25	2.828												
16	40.25	2.516	40.35	2.522										
17	36.25	2.266	36.35	2.272										
18	32.25	2.016	32.35	2.022	32.45	2.028								
19	28.25	1.766	28.35	1.772	28.45	1.778								
20	24.25	1.516	24.35	1.522	24.45	1.528	24.55	1.534	24.75	1.547				
21	22.25	1.391	22.35	1.397	22.45	1.403	22.55	1.409	22.75	1.422				
22	20.25	1.266	20.35	1.272	20.45	1.278	20.55	1.284	20.75	1.297	21.10	1.319	21.45	1.341
23	18.25	1.141	18.35	1.147	18.45	1.153	18.55	1.159	18.75	1.172	19.10	1.194	19.45	1.216
24	16.25	1.016	16.35	1.022	16.45	1.028	16.55	1.034	16.75	1.047	17.10	1.069	17.45	1.091
25	14.25	0.892	14.35	0.897	14.45	0.903	14.55	0.909	14.75	0.922	15.10	0.944	15.45	0.966
26	12.25	0.766	12.35	0.722	12.45	0.778	12.55	0.784	12.75	0.797	13.10	0.819	13.45	0.841
27	11.25	0.703	11.35	0.709	11.45	0.716	11.55	0.722	11.75	0.734	12.10	0.756	12.45	0.778
28	10.25	0.641	10.35	0.647	10.45	0.653	10.55	0.659	10.75	0.672	11.10	0.694	11.45	0.716
29	9.25	0.578	9.35	0.584	9.45	0.591	9.55	0.597	9.75	0.609	10.10	0.631	10.45	0.653
30	8.25	0.516	8.35	0.522	8.45	0.528	8.55	0.534	8.75	0.547	9.10	0.569	9.45	0.591

Nominal Coating Weights, pounds per double base box						
6	9	12	15	20	30	40

the facts that sheet weights are calculated on the basis of ordered width and length with shearing tolerances on the over side, and that sheets are thicker in the center than they are at the edges where thickness is commonly and most conveniently measured.

The factor commonly used in converting from weight to thickness of steel *sheets* is 41.82 pounds per square foot per inch thick (see Footnote, Table 48—I).

Density of Iron and Steel—In the foregoing discussion, the density of steel was given as 489.6 pounds per cubic foot or 40.8 pounds per square foot per inch of thickness, which figure has been adopted as the standard density of steel of the grades and kinds generally used in *plates*. The actual density of steel varies slightly with composition and treatment, and thus

Table 48—III. Manufacturers' Standard Gage for Sheet Steel

Gage thickness equivalents are based on 0.0014945 in. per oz. per sq. ft.; 0.023912 in. per lb. per sq. ft. (reciprocal of 41.820 lb. per sq. ft. per in. thick); 3.443329 in. per lb. per sq. in.

Manu-facturers' Standard Gage No.	Ounces per Square Foot	Pounds per Square Inch	Pounds per Square Foot	Inch Equivalent for Steel Sheet Thickness	Manu-facturers' Standard Gage No.
3	160	0.069444	10.0000	0.2391	3
4	150	.065104	9.3750	.2242	4
5	140	.060764	8.7500	.2092	5
6	130	.056424	8.1250	.1943	6
7	120	.052083	7.5000	.1793	7
8	110	.047743	6.8750	.1644	8
9	100	.043403	6.2500	.1495	9
10	90	.039062	5.6250	.1345	10
11	80	.034722	5.0000	.1196	11
12	70	.030382	4.3750	.1046	12
13	60	.026042	3.7500	.0897	13
14	50	.021701	3.1250	.0747	14
15	45	.019531	2.8125	.0673	15
16	40	.017361	2.5000	.0598	16
17	36	.015625	2.2500	.0538	17
18	32	.013889	2.0000	.0478	18
19	28	.012153	1.7500	.0418	19
20	24	.010417	1.5000	.0359	20
21	22	.0095486	1.3750	.0329	21
22	20	.0086806	1.2500	.0299	22
23	18	.0078125	1.1250	.0269	23
24	16	.0069444	1.0000	.0239	24
25	14	.0060764	0.87500	.0209	25
26	12	.0052083	.75000	.0179	26
27	11	.0047743	.68750	.0164	27
28	10	.0043403	.62500	.0149	28
29	9	.0039062	.56250	.0135	29
30	8	.0034722	.50000	.0120	30
31	7	.0030382	.43750	.0105	31
32	6.5	.0028212	.40625	.0097	32
33	6	.0026042	.37500	.0090	33
34	5.5	.0023872	.34375	.0082	34
35	5	.0021701	.31250	.0075	35
36	4.5	.0019531	.28125	.0067	36
37	4.25	.0018446	.26562	.0064	37
38	4	.0017361	.25000	.0060	38

Table 48—IV. Approximate Densities of Different Varieties of Iron and Steel.

Material (In Wrought Form)	Density (at 60° F.)		
	Grams per cc.	Lb. per Cu. In.	Lb. per Cu. Ft.
Pure Iron (99.9% Fe)	7.86	0.284	491
Soft Steel (0.06% C)	7.87	0.284	491
Carbon Steel (0.40% C)	7.84	0.283	489
Tool Steel (0.90% C)	7.82	0.282	487
Wrought Iron	7.40-7.90	0.267-0.285	461-493
Stainless Steel (18% Cr, 8% Ni)	8.03	0.29	501
Stainless Steel (17% Cr, 0.12% C)	7.75	0.28	484
Stainless Steel (27% Cr, 0.35% C)	7.47	0.27	467
High Speed Tool Steel (18% W)	8.75	0.316	546

may be at variance with the adopted standard density as can be seen from Table 48—IV, which presents data collected from various sources.

From these values, it is evident that the weight gage thickness equivalents cannot be applied with accuracy to many of the high alloy steels.

The Tin Plate Gage—The commonly accepted types of tin-mill products are tin plate, short terne plate and black plate. For these products long custom has established the use of the Tin Plate Gage, which is practically the same for this country and England. This gage is expressed in pounds per base box, rather than in gage numbers. By base box is meant 112 sheets, each 14 by 20 inches, or other combinations of number and size of sheets that will cover an area of 31,360 square inches. The gages of tin plate were formerly designated by symbols and names, as IC (Common), IX (X or Extra), DC (Double Common), 2X (two-X), ICL (Light), corresponding respectively to 107 lb., 135 lb., 139 lb., 155 lb., and 100 lb. per base box. In these symbols, each X represents a specific additional weight and each L a specific decrease in weight. These symbols are falling into disuse, giving way to the more logical method of designation of pounds per base box. Tin plate and black plate of 60-lb. basis weight and lighter are usually referred to as "light basis weight plate" and are produced by the double cold-reduction method; that is, a second cold reduction is given the plate after annealing, either prior to or after coating.

U. S. Wire Gages—The wire gages in general use have never been legally standardized in the United States; the practice had been for each of the steel wire manufacturers to adopt his own gage. Chief among the historical gages were the gage of the American Steel and Wire Company, now part of United States Steel, which adopted the Washburn and Moen gage, and the nearly identical Roebling gage. Therefore, upon recommendation of the Bureau of Standards, these manufacturers' gages were merged into one gage designated as the Steel Wire Gage (Stl. W.G.), or the United States Steel Wire Gage (U.S. Stl. W.G.), which was accepted as the standard gage for all steel wire other than music wire. This is now the most commonly used steel-wire gage in this country. For all sheets and wire made of metals other than iron and steel, the Brown and Sharpe Gage (B. & S. G.), or American Wire Gage (A.W.G.), is recognized as the standard gage in the United States. It was prepared by Messrs. Brown and Sharpe of Providence, R. I., at the request of leading manufacturers of nonferrous wire in this country. Another gage, known as the Edison or Circular Mil gage, is used by electrical engineers to simplify their calculations. This gage is based on the circular mil which is the area of a circle with a diameter of one mil (0.001 inch). Other gages in use are the Trenton Iron Company's gages, and Stubs' Steel Wire Gage. None of the wire gages mentioned above, however, has any legal authorization in this country. The only wire gage recognized in Acts of Congress is the Birmingham Wire Gage (B.W.G.), also known as Stubs' Iron Wire Gage, although it is not used to any extent by the wire manufacturers in the United States, except for telephone and telegraph wire (See ASTM A-111-52). This gage is sometimes used in designating the thickness of hoop and other strip steel products, but the tendency in these fields is to abandon the use of gages entirely and specify all thicknesses in thousandths of an inch.

INDEX

INDEX